Holt Mathematics COURSE 1

Features Quicklist

COMPREHENSIVE DIFFERENTIATED INSTRUCTION	SEE PAGE(S)
• Reaching All Learners includes strategies for adapting the material for all types of learners.	TE 75
• English Language Learners identifies strategies particularly effective with this group of students.	TE 58
• Hands-on Labs involve visual and kinesthetic learners in activities using manipulatives	66-67
• Reteach, Practice, Challenge, Reading Strategies, and Problem Solving reduced images make selecting worksheets quick and easy.	TE 64-65
• Teaching Tips provide suggestions for addressing various learning styles. (Teaching Tip)	TE 75
• Additional Examples offer more classroom review for struggling students.	TE 75
• Assignment Guide recommends homework assignments based on student ability.	TE 72
• Power Presentations are editable PowerPoint® presentations for every lesson as well as extra examples and quizzes.	TE 70

BUILT-IN ASSESSMENT AND INTERVENTION	SEE PAGE(S)
• Are You Ready? at the beginning of each chapter assesses students' prerequisite skills.. (ARE YOU READY?)	51
• Ready to Go On? diagnoses students' skill development within the chapter.	68
• Ongoing Assessment and Intervention identifies specific resources to monitor student comprehension	TE 57
• Common Error Alert helps teachers anticipate potential pitfalls for students. (COMMON ERROR ALERT)	TE 71
• Lesson Quiz gives teachers a chance to check for understanding with every lesson.	TE 73
• Chapter Test assesses students' mastery of concepts and skills.	97

READING AND WRITING MATH FOR COMPREHENSION	SEE PAGE(S)
• Reading and Writing Math lessons help students develop strong communication skills as they master math concepts.	53
• Reading Math and Writing Math hints appear throughout each chapter to help students use the language of math.	70, 55
• Write About It exercises require students to explain a math concept or procedure.	80
• Journal suggestions encourage students to write about math.	TE 73
• Think and Discuss questions in every lesson extend and enrich student knowledge.	86
• Glossary contains definitions and illustrations of key mathematical terms in English and Spanish.	789-815

PROVEN INSTRUCTIONAL DESIGN	SEE PAGE(S)
• Consistent lesson format of **Example, Solution, Check It Out** provides a logical instructional approach.	54-55
• Step-by-step examples and color-coded explanations help students become independent learners.	62-63
• Exercises matched to examples mean no homework surprises!	64

ENGAGING CONNECTIONS AND APPLICATIONS	SEE PAGE(S)
• Links spark student interest by giving them the opportunity to apply math skills to other disciplines and the real world. (LINK)	57, 61,84
• Focus on Problem Solving addresses a specific step in the problem-solving process.	123
• Game Time gives students a fun way to practice and apply skills	92
• It's in the Bag are creative, hands-on chapter review activities	93
• Problem Solving Project at the start of each chapter connects the chapter concepts to a career.	TE 102
• Problem Solving on Location uses word problems set in Georgia to develop problem solving skills.	100-101

INTEGRATED CRCT PREP	SEE PAGE(S)
• Countdown to CRCT prepares students for state tests with daily practice questions.	GA4-GA27
• CRCT Prep. GPS Support, and Spiral Review provide daily practice of new and previously taught skills in standardized test format.	77
• Test Prep Doctor addresses specific test-taking strategies related to the lesson. (TEST PREP DOCTOR)	TE 57
• Multi-Step Test Prep uses real-world scenarios to develop higher order thinking skills.	89
• Test Tackler targets specific test-taking strategies to help students become savvy test-takers.	156-157
• CRCT Prep provides cumulative assessment in standardized test format.	98-99

STUDENT SUPPORT	SEE PAGE(S)
• Study Guide: Preview prepares students for the concepts they will learn in the chapter and connects the concepts to the real world.	52
• Extra Practice directs students to additional, immediate practice of lesson concepts.	80,83,87
• Homework Help Online provides stepped-out solutions and additional practice for students as they work independently. (go.hrw.com Homework Help Online KEYWORD: MA7 2-5)	60
• Study Guide: Review highlights each lesson's vocabulary and key skills and offers additional examples and practice exercises.	94-96

GEORGIA TEACHER'S EDITION

Mathematics

Course 1

Jennie M. Bennett

Edward B. Burger

David J. Chard

Audrey L. Jackson

Paul A. Kennedy

Freddie L. Renfro

Janet K. Scheer

Bert K. Waits

HOLT, RINEHART AND WINSTON

A Harcourt Education Company

Orlando • Austin • New York • San Diego • London

Course 1 Georgia Student Edition

Contents in Brief

Student Handbook

Printed in the United States of America

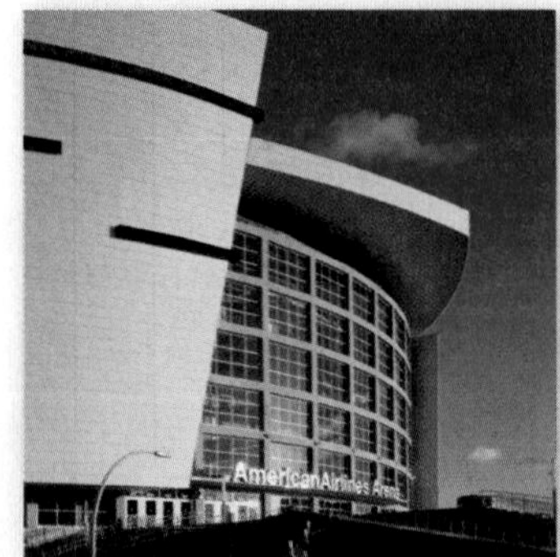

Cover photo: American Airlines Arena Miami Exterior © Arcaid/Alamy

ISBN 0-03-092019-1

1 2 3 4 5 048 09 08 07 06

Course 1 Georgia Teacher's Edition

Contents in Brief

Chapter Teacher Material

Student Handbook

Contributing Authors

Linda Antinone
Fort Worth, TX

Ms. Antinone teaches mathematics at R. L. Paschal High School in Fort Worth, Texas. She has received the Presidential Award for Excellence in Teaching Mathematics and the National Radio Shack Teacher award. She has coauthored several books for Texas Instruments on the use of technology in mathematics.

Carmen Whitman
Pflugerville, TX

Ms. Whitman travels nationally helping districts improve mathematics education. She has been a program coordinator on the mathematics team at the Charles A. Dana Center, and has served as a secondary math specialist for the Austin Independent School District.

Reviewers

Marilyn Adams
Mathematics Department Chair
Eanes ISD
Austin, TX

Thomas J. Altonjy
Assistant Principal
Robert R. Lazar Middle School
Montville, NY

Jane Bash, M.A.
Math Education
Eisenhower Middle School
San Antonio, TX

Charlie Bialowas
District Math Coordinator
Anaheim Union High School District
Anaheim, CA

Lynn Bodet
Math Teacher
Eisenhower Middle School
San Antonio, TX

Chandra Budd
Mathematics Teacher
Amarillo ISD
Amarillo, TX

Terry Bustillos
Mathematics Teacher
El Paso ISD
El Paso, TX

Louis D'Angelo, Jr.
Math Teacher
Archmere Academy
Claymont, DE

Troy Deckebach
Math Teacher
Tredyffrin-Easttown Middle School
Berwyn, PA

Linda Foster
Mathematics Department Chair
Abilene ISD
Abilene, TX

Mary Gorman
Math Teacher
Sarasota, FL

Brian Griffith
Supervisor of Mathematics, K-12
Mechanicsburg Area School District
Mechanicsburg, PA

Ruth Harbin-Miles
District Math Coordinator
Instructional Resource Center
Olathe, KS

Jo Ann Hawkins
Mathematics Department Chair
Lake Travis ISD
Austin, TX

Kim Hayden
Math Teacher
Milford Jr. High School
Milford, OH

Susan Howe
Math Teacher
Lime Kiln Middle School
Fulton, MD

Emily Hyatt
Mathematics Teacher, retired
Klein ISD
Klein, TX

Paula Jenniges
Austin, TX

Ronald J. Labrocca
District Mathematics Coordinator
Manhasset Public Schools
Plainview, NY

Victor R. Lopez
Math Teacher
Washington School
Union City, NJ

George Maguschak
Math Teacher/Building Chairperson
Wilkes-Barre Area
Wilkes-Barre, PA

Dianne McIntire
Math Teacher
Garfield School
Kearny, NJ

Kenneth McIntire
Math Teacher
Lincoln School
Kearny, NJ

Francisco Pacheco
Math Teacher
IS 125
Bronx, NY

Vivian Perry
Edwards, IL

Vicki Perryman Petty
Math Teacher
Central Middle School
Murfreesbro, TN

Teresa Roy
Mathematics Curriculum Specialist
Round Rock ISD
Round Rock, TX

Jennifer Sawyer
Math Teacher
Shawboro, NC

Russell Sayler
Math Teacher
Longfellow Middle School
Wauwatosa, WI

Raymond Scacalossi
Math Chairperson
Hauppauge Schools
Hauppauge, NY

Richard Seavey
Math Teacher–Retired
Metcalf Jr. High
Eagan, MN

Sherry Shaffer
Math Teacher
Honeoye Falls, NY

Dianne Shaver
Mathematics Department Chair
Round Rock ISD
Round Rock, TX

Gail M. Sigmund
Math Teacher
Charles A. Mooney Preparatory School
Cleveland, OH

Jonathan Simmons
Math Teacher
Manor Middle School
Killeen, TX

Jeffrey L. Slagel
Math Department Chair
South Eastern Middle School
Fawn Grove, PA

Karen Smith, Ph.D.
Math Teacher
East Middle School
Braintree, MA

Melba Smithwick
Mathematics Department Chair
Corpus Christi ISD
Corpus Christi, TX

Bonnie Thompson
Math Teacher
Tower Heights Middle School
Dayton, OH

Mary Thoreen
Mathematics Subject Area Leader
Wilson Middle School
Tampa, FL

Paul Turney
Math Teacher
Ladue School District
St. Louis, MO

Lori Van Houten
Mathematics Teacher
Abilene ISD
Abilene, TX

Pam Walker
Curriculum Teacher Specialist
Nacogdoches ISD
Nacogdoches, TX

Georgia
The Peach State

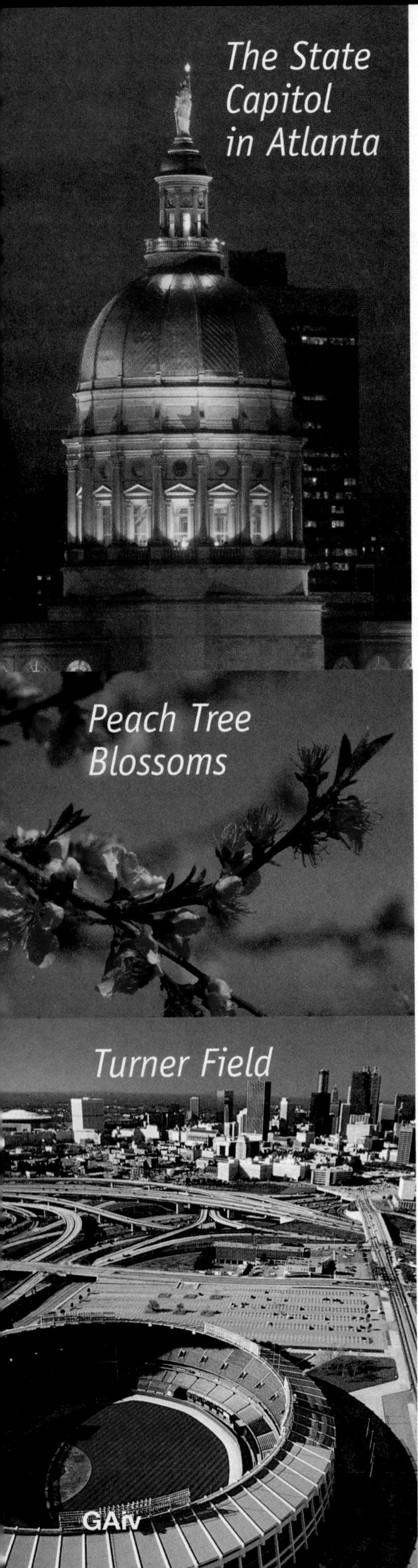

Explanation of Correlation

The following document is a correlation of Holt Middle School Mathematics Course 1 to the Georgia Mathematics Performance Standards for Grade 6. The format for this correlation follows the same basic format established by the GPS, modified to accommodate the addition of page references. The correlation provides a cross-reference between the curriculum in the GPS and representative page numbers where the curriculum is taught or assessed. The references contained in this correlation reflect Holt, Rinehart and Winston's interpretation of the mathematics objectives outlined in the Georgia curriculum.

KEY TO REFERENCES

Prefix	Explanation
SE	*Student Edition*

The Cherokee Rose is the state flower

The state bird is the Brown Thrasher

Numbers and Operations

Students will understand the meaning of the four arithmetic operations as they relate to positive rational numbers and will apply these concepts and associated skills in real world situations.

(M6N1) Students will understand the meaning of the four arithmetic operations as related to positive rational numbers and will use these concepts to solve problems.

(a)	Apply factors and multiples.	SE	168, 169–172, 756
(b)	Decompose numbers into their prime factorization (Fundamental Theorem of Arithmetic).	SE	169–172, 173–176
(c)	Determine the greatest common factor (GCF) and the least common multiple (LCM) for a set of numbers.	SE	173–176, 177, 228–231
(d)	Add and subtract fractions and mixed numbers with unlike denominators.	SE	232–233, 234–237, 238–241, 242–243, 244–247, 248–251
(e)	Multiply and divide fractions and mixed numbers.	SE	254–257, 258–259, 260–263, 264–267, 268–269, 270–273, 274–277
(f)	Use fractions, decimals, and percents interchangeably.	SE	180, 181–184, 381–384, 385–388, 389, 668–671
(g)	Solve problems involving fractions, decimals, and percents.	SE	108–111, 112–115, 116–117, 118–121, 124–127, 128–129, 130–133, 134–136, 137–140, 141–143, 144–147, 186–189, 192–195, 198–201, 202–205, 206–209, 234–237, 238–241, 244–247, 248–251, 254–257, 258–259, 268–269, 260–263, 264–267, 270–273, 274–277, 381–384, 385–388, 390–393, 394–397, 400–401, 504–507, 558–561, 758, 763

Measurement

Students will understand how to determine the volume and surface area of solid figures. They will understand and use the customary and metric systems of measurement to measure quantities efficiently and to represent volume and surface area appropriately.

(M6M1) Students will convert from one unit to another within one system of measurement (customary or metric) by using proportional relationships.

		SE 496–499, 500–503, 504–507

(M6M2) Students will use appropriate units of measure for finding length, perimeter, area, and volume and will express each quantity using the appropriate unit.

(a)	Measure length to the nearest half, fourth, eighth, and sixteenth of an inch.	**SE** 190–191, 457–458, 486–487, 554–556, 760
(b)	Select and use units of appropriate size and type to measure length, perimeter, area, and volume.	**SE** 436, 486–487, 488–491, 492–495, 518–519
(c)	Compare and contrast units of measure for perimeter, area, and volume.	**SE** 573, 770

(M6M3) Students will determine the volume of fundamental solid figures (right rectangular prisms, cylinders, pyramids, and cones).

(a)	Determine the formula for finding the volume of fundamental solid figures.	**SE** 570–571
(b)	Compute the volumes of fundamental solid figures, using appropriate units of measure.	**SE** 570–571, 576–579, 771
(c)	Estimate the volumes of simple geometric solids.	**SE** 570–571
(d)	Solve application problems involving the volume of fundamental solid figures.	**SE** 572–575, 576–579

(M6M4) Students will determine the surface area of solid figures (right rectangular prisms and cylinders).

(a)	Find the surface area of right rectangular prisms and cylinders using manipulatives and constructing nets.	SE	582–585
(b)	Compute the surface area of right rectangular prisms and cylin.ders using formuls	SE	582–585
(c)	Estimate the surface areas of simple geometric solids.	SE	582–585
(d)	Solve application problems involving surface area of right rectangular prisms and cylinders.	SE	584–585

Geometry

Students will further develop their understanding of plane and solid geometric figures, incorporating the use of appropriate technology and using this knowledge to solve authentic problems.

(M6G1) Students will further develop their understanding of plane figures.

(a)	Determine and use lines of symmetry.	SE	464–467
(b)	Investigate rotational symmetry, including degree of rotation.	SE	767
(c)	Use the concepts of ratio, proportion, and scale factor to demonstrate the relationships between similar plane figures.	SE	366–369, 370–372, 374–377
(d)	Interpret and sketch simple scale drawings.	SE	373
(e)	Solve problems involving scale drawings.	SE	374–377

(M6G2) Students will further develop their understanding of solid figures.

(a)	Compare and contrast right prisms and pyramids.	SE	567
(b)	Compare and contrast cylinders and cones.	SE	568–569
(c)	Interpret and sketch front, back, top, bottom, and side views of solid figures.	SE	564–565, 580–581
(d)	Construct nets for prisms, cylinders, pyramids, and cones.	SE	580–581

Algebra

Students will investigate relationships between two quantities. They will write and solve proportions and simple one-step equations that result from problem situations.

(M6A1) Students will understand the concept of ratio and use it to represent quantitative relationships.

		SE 352–355, 356–359, 360–361

(M6A2) Students will consider relationships between varying quantities.

(a)	Analyze and describe patterns arising from mathematical rules, tables, and graphs.	**SE** 33–36, 37, 356–359, 190–191, 446–449, 518–519, 640–643, 644–645, 646–649, 652–653
(b)	Use manipulatives or draw pictures to solve problems involving proportional relationships.	**SE** 360–361
(c)	Use proportions (a/b = c/d) to describe relationships and solve problems, including percent problems.	**SE** 362–365, 366–369, 370–372, 374–377, 390–393
(d)	Describe proportional relationships mathematically using y = kx, where k is the constant of proportionality.	**SE** 652–653
(e)	Graph proportional relationships in the form y = kx and describe characteristics of the graphs.	**SE** 652–653
(f)	In a proportional relationship expressed as y = kx, solve for one quantity given values of the other two. Given quantities may be whole numbers, decimals, or fractions. Solve problems using the relationship y = kx.	**SE** 652–653
(g)	Use proportional reasoning (a/b = c/d and y = kx) to solve problems.	**SE** 362–365, 366–369, 370–372, 374–377, 390–393, 694–697

(M6A3) Students will evaluate algebraic expressions, including those with exponents, and solve simple one-step equations using each of the four basic operations.

SE	54–57, 58–61, 62–65, 66–67, 70–73, 74–77, 78–80, 81–84, 85–87, 130–133, 134–136, 144–147, 202–205, 274–277, 248–251, 254–257, 260–263, 400–401, 424–427, 437–440, 514–517, 520–523, 542–545, 546–549, 551–553, 554–556, 557, 558–561, 570–571, 572–575, 576–579, 646–649, 617–620, 622–624, 625–627, 628–631, 634–635, 636–639, 640–643, 756, 762, 772

Marta Rapid Transit

Data Analysis and Probability

Students will demonstrate understanding of data analysis by posing questions to be answered by collecting data. They will represent, investigate, and use data to answer those questions. Students will understand experimental and theoretical probability.

(M6D1) Students will pose questions, collect data, represent and analyze the data, and interpret results.

(a)	Formulate questions that can be answered by data. Students should collect data by using samples from a larger population (surveys), or by conducting experiments.	**SE** 312–313. 318, 524–525
(b)	Using data, construct frequency distributions, frequency tables, and graphs.	**SE** 308–311, 312–313, 314–317, 318, 322–325, 765-766
(c)	Choose appropriate graphs to be consistent with the nature of the data (categorical or numerical). Graphs should include pictographs, histograms, bar graphs, line graphs, circle graphs, and line plots.	**SE** 309, 315, 323, 333–335
(d)	Use tables and graphs to examine variation that occurs within a group and variation that occurs between groups.	**SE** 310–311
(e)	Relate the data analysis to the context of the questions posed.	**SE** 302–305

(M6D2) Students will use experimental and simple theoretical probability and will understand the nature of sampling. They will also make predictions from investigations.

(a)	Predict the probability of a given event through trials/simulations (experimental probability), and represent the probability as a ratio.	**SE** 672–675, 676–677
(b)	Determine, and use a ratio to represent, the theoretical probability of a given event.	**SE** 668–671, 682–685, 688–691, 694–697, 700–701
(c)	Discover that experimental probability approaches theoretical probability when the number of trials is large.	**SE** 674–675

Process Standards

Each topic studied in this course should be developed with careful thought toward helping every student achieve the following process standards.

(M6P1) Students will solve problems (using appropriate technology).

(a)	Build new mathematical knowledge through problem solving.	SE	10–13, 20–21, 308–311, 383–384, 364–365, 418–419, 452–453, 466–467, 544–545, 574–575, 506–507, 612–613, 630–631, 648–649, 668–671, 689, 696–697
(b)	Solve problems that arise in mathematics and in other contexts.	SE	10–13, 58–61, 72–73, 74–77, 83–84, 85–87, 108–111, 112–115, 118–121, 126–127, 130–133, 134–136, 142–143, 164–167, 192–195, 202–205, 206–209, 228–231, 244–247, 254–257, 266–267, 316–317, 320, 324–325, 326–329, 330–332, 333–335, 370–372, 376–377, 381–384, 387–388, 396–397, 424–427, 428–431, 456–458, 461–462, 464–467, 488–491, 492–495, 500–503, 504–507, 510–513, 514–517, 520–523, 542–545, 548–549, 551–553, 555–556, 568–569, 584–585, 608–609, 612–613, 623–624, 625–627, 638–639, 652–653, 672–675, 678–680, 682–685, 688–691, 700–701
(c)	Apply and adapt a variety of appropriate strategies to solve problems.	SE	14–17, 20–21, 26–29, 30–32, 35–36, 58–61, 81–84, 100–101, 112–115, 135–136, 137–140, 177, 222–223, 230–231, 234–237, 261, 274–277, 294–296, 300–301, 308–311, 334, 346–347, 366–369, 389, 439–440, 441, 446–449, 461–462, 463, 480–481, 496–499, 522–523, 544–545, 550, 552, 559, 572–575, 578–579, 596–597, 606–609, 640–643, 678–680, 694–697, 710–711
(d)	Monitor and reflect on the process of mathematical problem solving.	SE	14–17, 63, 75, 78–80, 81–84, 85–87, 86, 119, 135, 137–140, 141–143, 145, 245, 249, 271, 274–277, 334, 308–311, 353, 395, 357, 366–369, 386, 391, 421, 425, 446–449, 451, 496–499, 511, 521, 606–609, 611, 618, 623, 626, 636–639, 640–643, 647, 552, 559, 572–575, 678–680, 694–697

(M6P2) Students will reason and evaluate mathematical arguments.		
(a) Recognize reasoning and proof as fundamental aspects of mathematics.	SE	432–435, 436, 439–440, 441, 468–469, 550, 652–653
(b) Make and investigate mathematical conjectures.	SE	299, 432–435, 436, 439–440, 441, 550, 652–653, 673, 676–677
(c) Develop and evaluate mathematical arguments and proofs.	SE	23, 75, 79, 82, 86, 109, 119, 125, 131, 145, 182, 187, 193, 203, 229, 235, 255, 261, 265, 275, 295, 303, 310–311, 323, 326–329, 373, 386, 417, 465, 429, 438, 442–445, 448–449, 456–458, 468–469, 490–491, 493, 494–495, 502–503, 521, 543, 555, 559, 560–561, 574–575, 603, 607, 616, 621, 647, 652–653, 676–677, 695
(d) Select and use various types of reasoning and methods of proof.	SE	436, 442–445, 448–449, 450–453

Palmyra Plantation at Melon Bluff in Midway

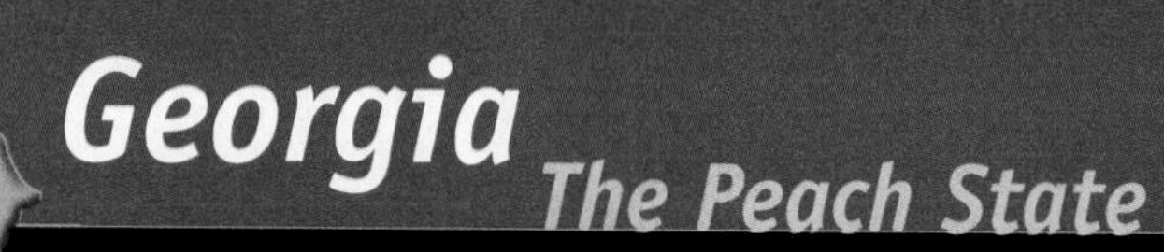

(M6P3) Students will communicate mathematically.		
(a) Organize and consolidate their mathematical thinking through communication.	**SE**	11, 16–1727, 31–32, 34, 35–36, 56–57, 60–61, 64–65, 72–73, 76–77, 83–84, 86–87, 110–111, 113, 114–115, 120–121, 135–136, 139–140, 142–143, 146–147, 165–167, 171–172, 175–176, 183–184, 188–189, 194–195, 200–201, 204–205, 208–209, 230–231, 240–241, 246–247, 250–251, 256–257, 262–263, 266–267, 272–273, 276–277, 295–296, 303, 304–305, 316–317, 320–321, 324–325, 328–329, 334–335, 354–355, 358–359, 364–365, 368–369, 371–372, 376–377, 383–384, 387–388, 392–393, 396–397, 418–419, 422–423, 426–427, 430–431, 444–445, 448–449, 452–453, 457–458, 461–462, 466–467, 490–491, 494–495, 498–499, 502–503, 506–507, 512–513, 516–517, 522–523, 544–545, 548–549, 552–553, 555–556, 560–561, 568–569, 574–575, 577, 578–579, 584–585, 604–605, 608–609, 612–613, 619–620, 626–627, 629, 630–631, 638–639, 642–643, 668–671, 674–675, 679–680, 682–685, 690–691, 696–697
(b) Communicate their mathematical thinking coherently and clearly to peers, teachers, and others.	**SE**	7, 11, 27, 31, 34, 55, 59, 71, 125, 138, 142, 165, 170, 174, 182, 187, 193, 199, 203, 207, 229, 235, 239, 245, 265, 271, 295, 299, 309, 315, 320, 323, 327, 331, 353, 357, 363, 367, 371, 375, 382, 386, 391, 395, 417, 421, 425, 429, 438, 443, 447, 451, 457, 460, 489, 497, 501, 505, 515, 555, 567, 573, 577, 583, 603, 607, 612, 618, 623, 637, 641, 669, 673, 679, 683, 689, 695
(c) Analyze and evaluate the mathematical thinking and strategies of others.	**SE**	8–9, 24–25, 28–29, 56–57, 79–80, 126–127, 132–133, 139–140, 146–147, 165–167, 171–172, 175–176, 183–184, 204–205, 236–237, 239, 246–247, 272–273, 304–305, 331–332, 396–397, 358–359, 364–365, 368–369, 392–393, 418–419, 422–423, 430–431, 444–445, 448–449, 494–495, 498–499, 502–503, 506–507, 512–513, 516–517, 547, 568–569, 608–609, 623–624, 626–627, 642–643, 682–685, 690–691, 696–697

(d)	Use the language of mathematics to express mathematical ideas precisely.	SE	7, 12–13, 15, 55, 63, 170, 320–321, 363, 416–419, 420–423, 424–427, 428–431, 442–445, 446–449, 459–462, 468–469, 560–561, 613

(M6P4) Students will make connections among mathematical ideas and to other disciplines.

(a)	Recognize and use connections among mathematical ideas.	SE	26–29, 124–127, 180, 181–184, 352–355, 356–359, 362–365, 385–388, 390–393, 394–397, 416–419, 420–423, 463, 518–519, 543, 547, 610–613, 644–645, 668–671
(b)	Understand how mathematical ideas interconnect and build on one another to produce a coherent whole.	SE	124–127, 181–184, 352–355, 356–359, 362–365, 385–388, 390–393, 394–397, 416–419, 420–423, 463, 518–519, 610–613, 644–645, 668–671

Jekyll Island, Georgia

(c)	Recognize and apply mathematics in contexts outside of mathematics.	SE	6–9, 12–13, 16–17, 22–25, 28–29, 30–32, 31–32, 60–61, 64–65, 70–73, 76–77, 79–80, 86–87, 100–101, 110–111, 114–115, 120–121, 124–127, 132–133, 141–143, 144–147, 188–189, 194–195, 200–201, 208–209, 222–223, 234–237, 238–241, 248–251, 256–257, 262–263, 276–277, 294–296, 298–301, 302–305, 312–313, 314–317, 319–321, 322–325, 328–329, 331–332, 334–335, 346–347, 352–355, 367, 371–372, 374–377, 382, 385–388, 394–397, 420–423, 428–431, 437–440, 450–453, 456–458, 460, 465, 466–467, 480–481, 488–491, 492–495, 498–499, 500–503, 512–513, 514–517, 520–523, 546–549, 552–553, 555–556, 558–561, 578–579, 596–597, 604–605, 619–620, 626–627, 628–631, 638–639, 640–643, 648–649, 668–671, 672–675, 679–680, 682–685, 690–691, 696–697, 700–701, 710–711

High Museum of Art, Atlanta

(M6P5) Students will represent mathematics in multiple ways.		
(a) Create and use representations to organize, record, and communicate mathematical ideas.	SE	6–9, 54–57, 62–65, 66–67, 90–91, 106–107, 108–111, 116–117, 118–121, 130–133, 128–129, 185, 198–201, 206–209, 212–213, 232–233, 242–243, 294–296, 300–301, 310–311, 314–317, 322–325, 330–332, 354–355, 380, 381–384, 432–435, 422–423, 437–440, 459–462, 490–491, 557, 564–565, 580–581, 582–585, 602–605, 606–609, 610–613, 616, 617–620, 621, 622–624, 634–635, 646–649, 692–693
(b) Select, apply, and translate among mathematical representations to solve problems.	SE	6–9, 58–61, 62–65, 66–67, 70–73, 74–77, 78–80, 90–91, 108–111, 116–117, 128–129, 144–147, 185, 192–195, 198–201, 202–205, 206–209, 212–213, 232–233, 242–243, 244–247, 258–259, 297, 298–301, 308–311, 314–317, 322–325, 330–332, 333–335, 354–355, 356–359, 360–361, 368–369, 380, 426–427, 430–431, 459–462, 564–565, 582–585, 602–605, 606–609, 616, 617–620, 621, 622–624, 634–635642–643, 644–645, 646–649, 678–680, 688–691, 692–693
(c) Use representations to model and interpret physical, social, and mathematical phenomena.	SE	54–57, 70–73, 74–77, 106–107, 118–121, 141–143, 168, 181–184, 192–195, 198–201, 212–213, 228–231, 255, 260–263, 270–273, 297, 298–301, 333–335, 376–377, 360–361, 362–365, 380, 381–384, 387–388, 392–393, 516–517, 557, 564–565, 566–569, 580–581, 602–605, 616, 617–620, 621, 622–624, 634–635, 636–639, 668–671, 682–685, 692–693

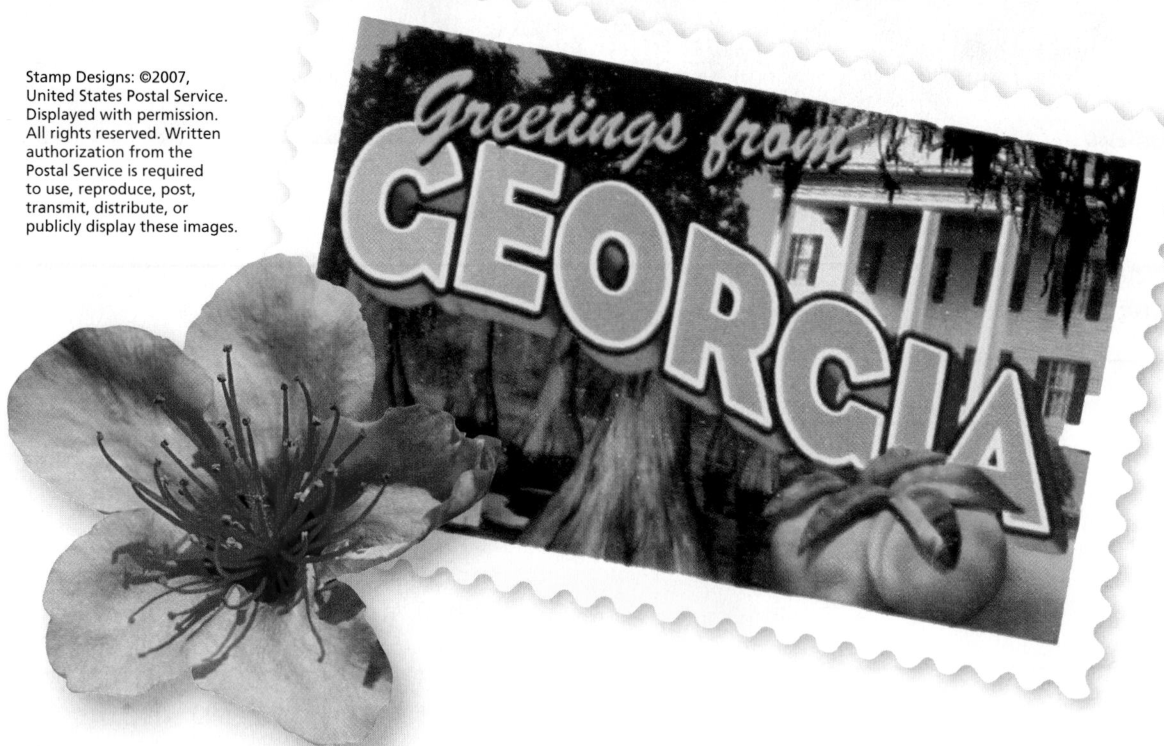

PREPARING FOR CRCT

Holt Mathematics provides many opportunities for you to prepare for CRCT.

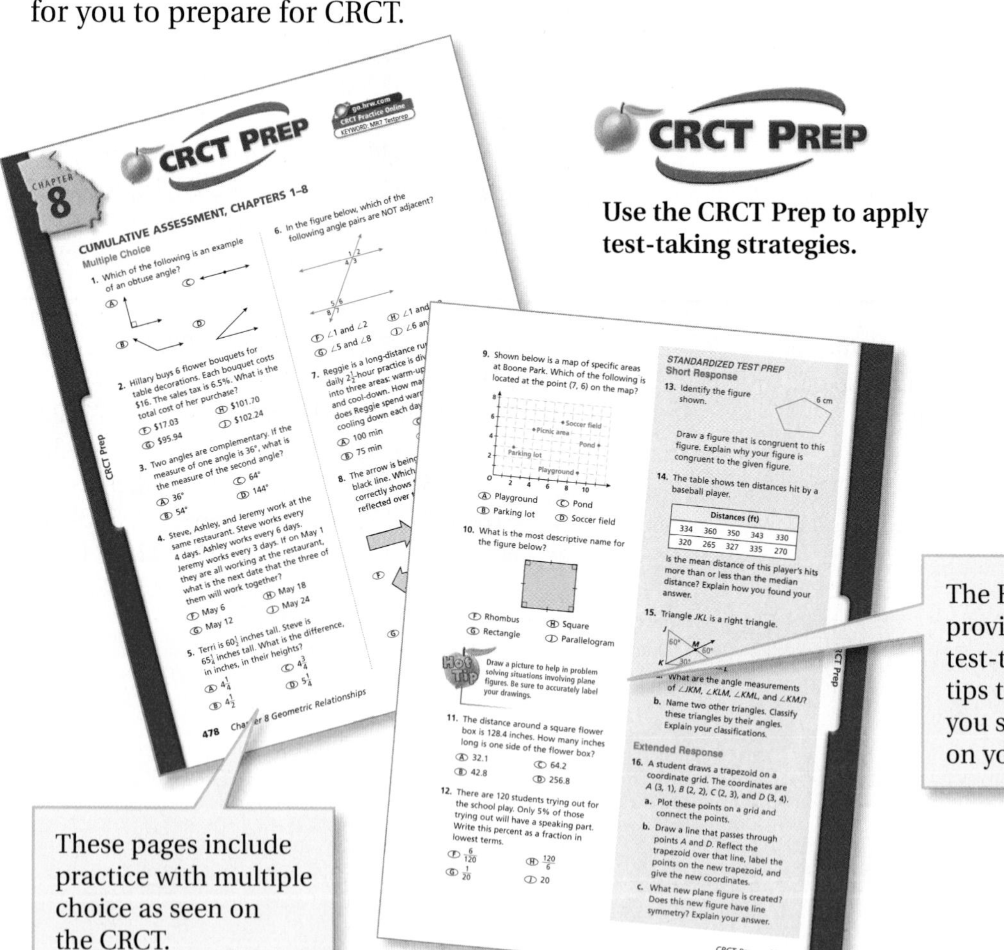

CHAPTER 8

CRCT PREP

go.hrw.com
CRCT Practice Online
KEYWORD: MK7 Testprep

CUMULATIVE ASSESSMENT, CHAPTERS 1–8

Multiple Choice

1. Which of the following is an example of an obtuse angle?

2. Hillary buys 6 flower bouquets for table decorations. Each bouquet costs $16. The sales tax is 6.5%. What is the total cost of her purchase?
Ⓕ $17.03 Ⓗ $101.70
Ⓖ $95.94 Ⓙ $102.24

3. Two angles are complementary. If the measure of one angle is 36°, what is the measure of the second angle?
Ⓐ 36° Ⓒ 64°
Ⓑ 54° Ⓓ 144°

4. Steve, Ashley, and Jeremy work at the same restaurant. Steve works every 4 days. Ashley works every 6 days. Jeremy works every 3 days. If on May 1 they are all working at the restaurant, what is the next date that the three of them will work together?
Ⓕ May 6 Ⓗ May 18
Ⓖ May 12 Ⓙ May 24

5. Terri is $60\frac{1}{4}$ inches tall. Steve is $65\frac{1}{2}$ inches tall. What is the difference, in inches, in their heights?
Ⓐ $4\frac{1}{4}$ Ⓒ $4\frac{3}{4}$
Ⓑ $4\frac{1}{2}$ Ⓓ $5\frac{1}{4}$

6. In the figure below, which of the following angle pairs are NOT adjacent?

7. Reggie is a long-distance ru… daily $2\frac{1}{2}$-hour practice is div… into three areas: warm-up… and cool-down. How ma… does Reggie spend warm… cooling down each day…
Ⓐ 100 min
Ⓑ 75 min

8. The arrow is being… black line. Which… correctly shows… reflected over…

478 Chapter 8 Geometric Relationships

9. Shown below is a map of specific areas at Boone Park. Which of the following is located at the point (7, 6) on the map?
Ⓐ Playground Ⓒ Pond
Ⓑ Parking lot Ⓓ Soccer field

10. What is the most descriptive name for the figure below?
Ⓕ Rhombus Ⓗ Square
Ⓖ Rectangle Ⓙ Parallelogram

Hot Tip! Draw a picture to help in problem solving situations involving plane figures. Be sure to accurately label your drawings.

11. The distance around a square flower box is 128.4 inches. How many inches long is one side of the flower box?
Ⓐ 32.1 Ⓒ 64.2
Ⓑ 42.8 Ⓓ 256.8

12. There are 120 students trying out for the school play. Only 5% of those trying out will have a speaking part. Write this percent as a fraction in lowest terms.
Ⓕ $\frac{6}{120}$ Ⓗ $\frac{120}{6}$
Ⓖ $\frac{1}{20}$ Ⓙ 20

STANDARDIZED TEST PREP

Short Response

13. Identify the figure shown.
Draw a figure that is congruent to this figure. Explain why your figure is congruent to the given figure.

14. The table shows ten distances hit by a baseball player.

Distances (ft)				
334	360	350	343	330
320	265	327	335	270

Is the mean distance of this player's hits more than or less than the median distance? Explain how you found your answer.

15. Triangle *JKL* is a right triangle.
a. What are the angle measurements of ∠*JKM*, ∠*KLM*, ∠*KML*, and ∠*KMJ*?
b. Name two other triangles. Classify these triangles by their angles. Explain your classifications.

Extended Response

16. A student draws a trapezoid on a coordinate grid. The coordinates are *A* (3, 1), *B* (2, 2), *C* (2, 3), and *D* (3, 4).
a. Plot these points on a grid and connect the points.
b. Draw a line that passes through points *A* and *D*. Reflect the trapezoid over that line, label the points on the new trapezoid, and give the new coordinates.
c. What new plane figure is created? Does this new figure have line symmetry? Explain your answer.

CRCT Prep 479

CRCT PREP

Use the CRCT Prep to apply test-taking strategies.

These pages include practice with multiple choice as seen on the CRCT.

The Hot Tip provides test-taking tips to help you succeed on your tests.

Countdown to CRCT

Use the Countdown to CRCT to practice for your state test every day.

There are 24 pages of practice for your state test. Each page is designed to be used in a week so that all practice will be completed before your state test is given.

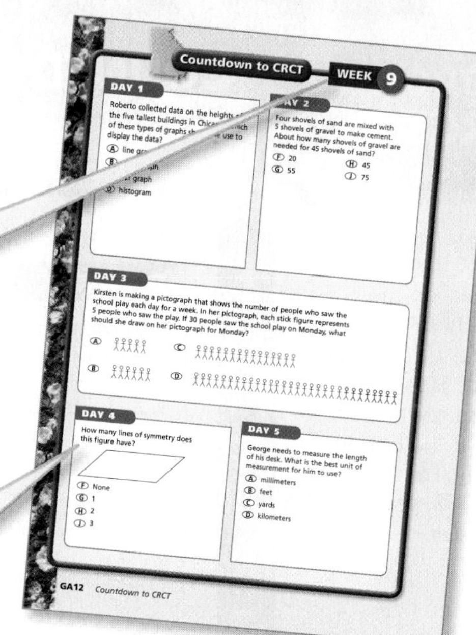

Each week's page has five practice test items, one for each day of the week.

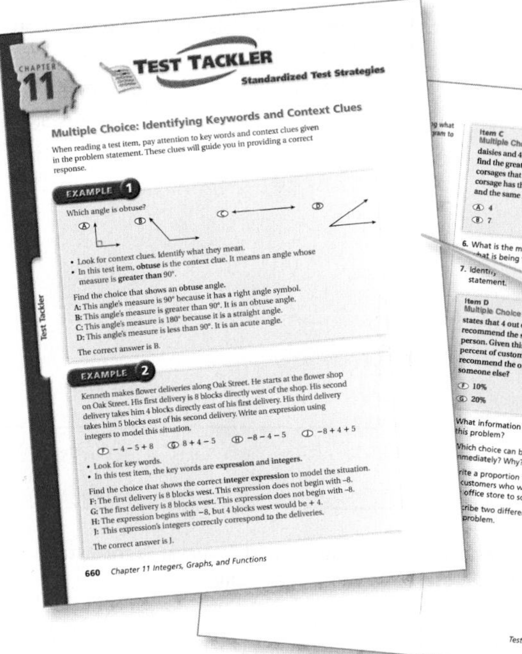

Use the Test Tackler to become familiar with and practice test-taking strategies.

The first page of this feature explains and shows an example of a test-taking strategy.

The second page guides you through applications of the test-taking strategy.

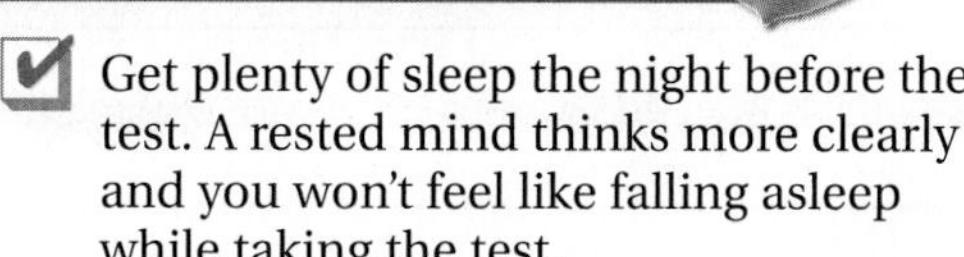

- Get plenty of sleep the night before the test. A rested mind thinks more clearly and you won't feel like falling asleep while taking the test.
- Draw a figure when one is not provided with the problem. If a figure is given, write any details from the problem on the figure.
- Read each problem carefully. As you finish each problem, read it again to make sure your answer is reasonable.
- Review the formula sheet that will be supplied with the test. Make sure you know when to use each formula.
- First answer problems that you know how to solve. If you do not know how to solve a problem, skip it and come back to it when you have finished the others.
- Use other test-taking strategies that can be found throughout this book, such as working backward and eliminating answer choices.

Countdown to CRCT

Each problem on the *Countdown to CRCT* is correlated to the Georgia Performance Standards (GPS). These correlations are shown at the bottom of each page. For the full text of the GPS, see pp. GAv–GAxvii.

Countdown to CRCT

WEEK 1

DAY 1

Suki created the following pattern. What is the next number in Suki's pattern?

12	15	14	17	16	19	18	?

(A) 13
(B) 17
(C) 20
(D) 21

DAY 2

The expression $12x + 3$ gives the cost of buying x DVDs from Movie Mania. How much does it cost to buy 3 DVDs from Movie Mania?

(F) \$18
(G) \$36
(H) \$39
(J) \$45

DAY 3

What numbers complete the factor tree for the prime factorization of 160?

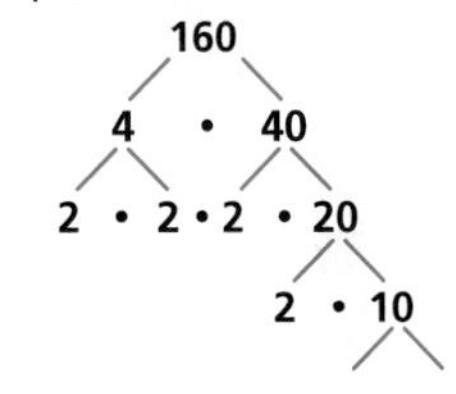

(A) 4, 5
(B) 2, 10
(C) 2, 5
(D) 2^2, 5

DAY 4

What is the solution of the equation $\frac{m}{4} = 12$?

(F) $m = 3$
(G) $m = 15$
(H) $m = 16$
(J) $m = 48$

DAY 5

Tom swims one lap every 5 minutes. Rob swims one lap every 4 minutes. If they start together, in how many minutes will they start a lap together again?

(A) 9
(B) 10
(C) 20
(D) 40

Day	CRCT GPS Grade 6
1	M6A2.a
2	M6A3
3	M6N1.b
4	M6A3
5	M6N1.a

Countdown to CRCT WEEK 2

DAY 1

What is the greatest common factor (GCF) of 24 and 36?

Ⓐ 2
Ⓑ 6
Ⓒ 12
Ⓓ 18

DAY 2

For every 3 scarves that Kendall knits, Rhonda can knit 4 hats. When Kendall has knit 15 scarves, how many hats will Rhonda have knit?

Kendall	3	6	9	12
Rhonda	4	8		

Ⓕ 20
Ⓖ 24
Ⓗ 30
Ⓙ 60

DAY 3

Kris has four pet turtles. Last week he measured each turtle. What is the order of the turtles from shortest to longest?

Ⓐ Carly, Patty, Bennie, Charley
Ⓑ Patty, Bennie, Charley, Carly
Ⓒ Patty, Carly, Bennie, Charley
Ⓓ Bennie, Patty, Carly, Charley

Turtle	Length (in.)
Bennie	5.67
Charley	5.75
Patty	5.07
Carly	5.5

DAY 4

Peter has $\frac{4}{5}$ yard of fabric. Robert has $\frac{3}{7}$ yard of fabric. How much more fabric does Peter have?

Ⓕ $\frac{1}{35}$ yard
Ⓖ $\frac{7}{35}$ yard
Ⓗ $\frac{13}{35}$ yard
Ⓙ $\frac{1}{2}$ yard

DAY 5

What is the prime factorization of 84?

Ⓐ $3 \times 4 \times 7$
Ⓑ $2 \times 3^2 \times 7$
Ⓒ $2^2 \times 3 \times 7$
Ⓓ $2^3 \times 3 \times 7$

Day	CRCT GPS Grade 6
1	M6N1.c
2	M6A2.a
3	M6N1.g
4	M6N1.d
5	M6N1.b

Countdown to CRCT

Countdown to CRCT — WEEK 3

DAY 1

Which expression best represents the value of y?

x	2	4	6	8	10
y	1	2	3	4	5

(A) $x - 1$

(B) $2x$

(C) $\frac{x}{2}$

(D) $x + 1$

DAY 2

What is the least common multiple (LCM) of 2, 3, and 5?

(F) 20

(G) 30

(H) 60

(J) 120

DAY 3

Jack ate $\frac{1}{2}$ of a pizza. Andy ate $\frac{1}{4}$ of a pizza. Which picture correctly models how much pizza the boys ate in all?

(A)

(B) 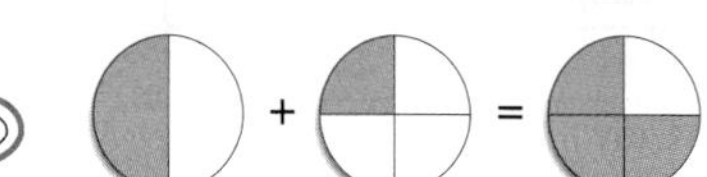

(C) 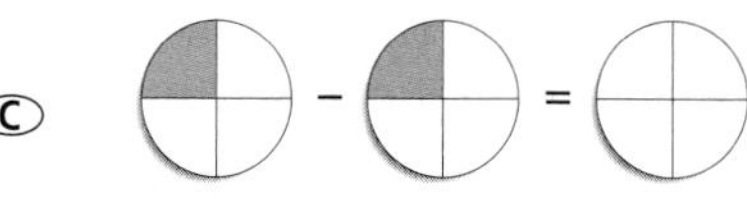

(D) 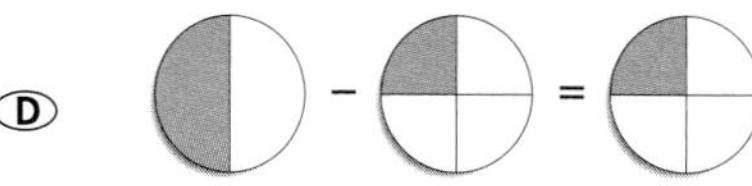

DAY 4

Lauren waters her plants every 6 days. She gives them fertilizer every 10 days. If she does both jobs today, how long will it be until the next time she does both jobs on the same day?

(F) 10 days

(G) 16 days

(H) 30 days

(J) 60 days

DAY 5

What is the equivalent decimal form of $\frac{12}{15}$?

(A) 0.008

(B) 0.08

(C) 0.8

(D) 12.15

Day	CRCT GPS Grade 6
1	M6A2.a
2	M6N1.c
3	M6N1.d
4	M6N1.a
5	M6N1.f

DAY 1

What is the solution of the equation $15 = x - 12$?

Ⓐ $x = 3$

Ⓑ $x = 12$

Ⓒ $x = 17$

Ⓓ $x = 27$

DAY 2

Tomas has $8\frac{5}{10}$ feet of fishing line and Mike has $2\frac{8}{16}$ feet of fishing line. How many feet of fishing line do they have together?

Ⓕ 6

Ⓖ 10

Ⓗ $10\frac{1}{2}$

Ⓙ 11

DAY 3

Eric's science class grew plants from bean seeds. The table shows how much each student's plant grew in two weeks. Put the plants in order from least change to greatest change.

Student	Miguel	Eric	Jane	Trisha	Cindy
Plant Heights (in.)	$\frac{1}{2}$	$\frac{5}{12}$	$\frac{3}{16}$	$\frac{1}{8}$	$\frac{4}{5}$

Ⓐ $\frac{1}{2}, \frac{5}{12}, \frac{3}{16}, \frac{1}{8}, \frac{4}{5}$

Ⓑ $\frac{1}{8}, \frac{3}{16}, \frac{5}{12}, \frac{1}{2}, \frac{4}{5}$

Ⓒ $\frac{1}{2}, \frac{4}{5}, \frac{1}{8}, \frac{5}{12}, \frac{3}{16}$

Ⓓ $\frac{1}{2}, \frac{1}{8}, \frac{3}{16}, \frac{4}{5}, \frac{5}{12}$

DAY 4

What are the factors of 26?

Ⓕ 1, 2, 3, 6, 13, 26

Ⓖ 1, 2, 26

Ⓗ 1, 2, 13, 26

Ⓙ 1, 2, 4, 6, 13, 26

DAY 5

Cheryl bought 3 books for $5.25 each. She also bought a pack of construction paper for $3.99. How much did Cheryl spend in all?

Ⓐ $9.24

Ⓑ $15.75

Ⓒ $19.74

Ⓓ $27.72

Day	CRCT GPS Grade 6
1	M6A3
2	M6N1.d
3	M6N1.g
4	M6N1.a
5	M6N1.g

Countdown to CRCT WEEK 5

DAY 1

What is the product of $\frac{3}{8}$ and $\frac{2}{9}$?

(A) $\frac{1}{12}$

(B) $\frac{5}{17}$

(C) $\frac{43}{72}$

(D) $1\frac{11}{16}$

DAY 2

What is the prime factorization of 90?

(F) $2 \times 3 \times 5$

(G) $2^2 \times 3 \times 5$

(H) $2 \times 3^2 \times 5$

(J) $2 \times 6 \times 3 \times 5$

DAY 3

Cara has $\frac{5}{8}$ yard of fabric. She used $\frac{1}{2}$ yard of the fabric to make a doll's dress. Which picture correctly models how much fabric Cara has left?

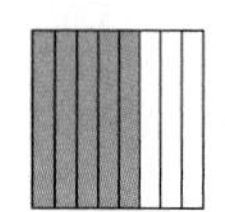
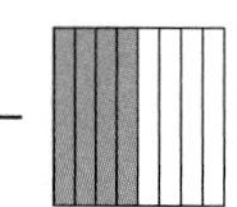
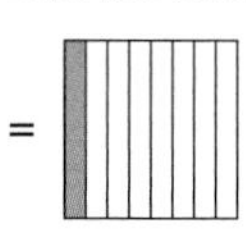
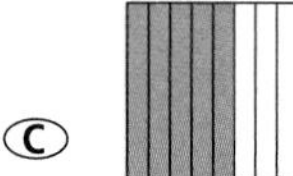
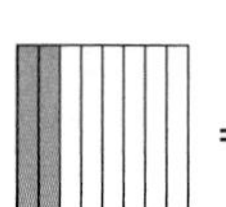
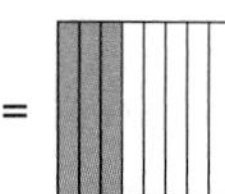

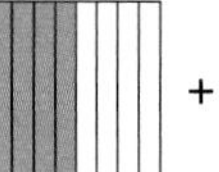
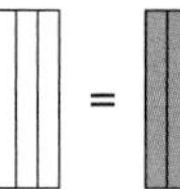

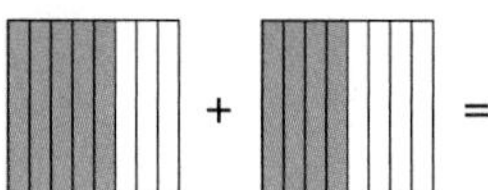

DAY 4

What is the equivalent decimal form of $\frac{1}{25}$?

(F) 0.04

(G) 0.25

(H) 0.4

(J) 1.25

DAY 5

The expression $n^2 - 3$ gives the number of tiles in row n of a pattern. How many tiles are in row 7?

(A) 4

(B) 12

(C) 16

(D) 46

Day	CRCT GPS Grade 6
1	M6N1.e
2	M6N1.b
3	M6N1.d
4	M6N1.f
5	M6A3

DAY 1

Nora wants to display data about the amount of time it took each runner to complete a race. What type of graph should she use?

(A) bar graph
(B) line graph
(C) histogram
(D) frequency table

DAY 2

Willy is 25 inches tall. His brother Carlos is $2\frac{1}{4}$ times as tall. Which is the best estimate of Carlos's height?

(F) 23 inches
(G) 50 inches
(H) 25 inches
(J) 56 inches

DAY 3

What is the ratio of the number of stars to the total number of shapes?

(A) 2 to 5
(B) 1 to 2
(C) 2 to 3
(D) 5 to 2

DAY 4

What is the greatest common factor (GCF) of 12, 36, and 20?

(F) 2
(G) 4
(H) 6
(J) 12

DAY 5

In Mrs. Kendall's class, $\frac{12}{15}$ of the students prefer tennis to basketball. Which decimal shows the part of the class that prefers tennis to basketball?

(A) 0.08
(B) 0.8
(C) 1.25
(D) 8.0

Day	CRCT GPS Grade 6
1	M6D1.c
2	M6N1.e
3	M6A1
4	M6N1.c
5	M6N1.f

Countdown to CRCT

Countdown to CRCT WEEK 7

DAY 1

Jerome has a ribbon that is $10\frac{1}{2}$ ft long. He cuts the ribbon into pieces that are each $\frac{3}{4}$ ft long. How many pieces does he have?

Ⓐ 5

Ⓑ 7

Ⓒ 12

Ⓓ 14

DAY 2

The shadow of a 4-foot-tall mailbox is 2 feet long. If the shadow of a tree is 16 feet long, what is the height of the tree?

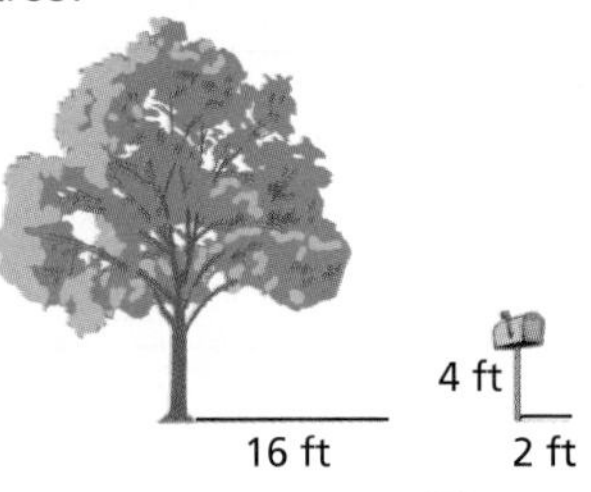

Ⓕ 18 feet

Ⓖ 24 feet

Ⓗ 32 feet

Ⓙ 64 feet

DAY 3

Miranda surveyed her classmates to find out how many brothers and sisters each student has. Which question CANNOT be answered based on the data she collected?

Ⓐ What percentage of students have fewer than 3 brothers and sisters?

Ⓑ How many students have no brothers or sisters?

Ⓒ What is the average number of brothers and sisters?

Ⓓ How many students have an older brother or sister?

DAY 4

What is the value of n?

2	3	4	5	6
30	45	60	75	n

Ⓕ 80

Ⓖ 85

Ⓗ 90

Ⓙ 95

DAY 5

What is the missing number in this proportion?

$\frac{5}{8} = \frac{■}{48}$

Ⓐ 6

Ⓑ 30

Ⓒ 35

Ⓓ 40

Day	CRCT GPS Grade 6
1	M6N1.e
2	M6A2.g
3	M6D1.a
4	M6A2.a
5	M6A2.g

DAY 1

Paul used tiles to make the pattern shown here. What is the ratio of black tiles to white tiles?

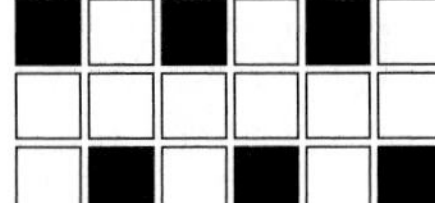

(A) 1:4
(B) 1:3
(C) 1:2
(D) 1:1

DAY 2

This rectangle is enlarged by a scale factor of 3. What is the new length in centimeters?

(F) 9 centimeters
(G) 10 centimeters
(H) 20 centimeters
(J) 21 centimeters

DAY 3

It takes Ari 40 minutes to walk 2 miles. How long will it take him to walk 4 miles?

(A) 60 minutes
(B) 70 minutes
(C) 80 minutes
(D) 90 minutes.

DAY 4

What is the equivalent of $\frac{1}{50}$ in decimal form?

(F) 0.02
(G) 0.05
(H) 0.2
(J) 5.0

DAY 5

Julie converted $\frac{2}{5}$ to a percent by first writing the proportion $\frac{2}{5} = \frac{x}{100}$. Then she solved the proportion correctly. What value did she get for x?

(A) 20
(B) 40
(C) 50
(D) 80

Day	CRCT GPS Grade 6
1	M6A1
2	M6G1.c
3	M6A2.g
4	M6N1.f
5	M6A2.c

Countdown to CRCT WEEK 9

DAY 1

Roberto collected data on the heights of the five tallest buildings in Chicago. Which of these types of graphs should he use to display the data?

Ⓐ line graph
Ⓑ circle graph
Ⓒ bar graph
Ⓓ histogram

DAY 2

Four shovels of sand are mixed with 5 shovels of gravel to make cement. About how many shovels of gravel are needed for 45 shovels of sand?

Ⓕ 20 Ⓗ 45
Ⓖ 55 Ⓙ 75

DAY 3

Kirsten is making a pictograph that shows the number of people who saw the school play each day for a week. In her pictograph, each stick figure represents 5 people who saw the play. If 30 people saw the school play on Monday, what should she draw on her pictograph for Monday?

Ⓐ 5 stick figures
Ⓑ 6 stick figures
Ⓒ 15 stick figures
Ⓓ 30 stick figures

DAY 4

How many lines of symmetry does this figure have?

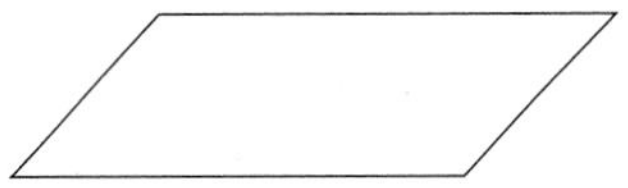

Ⓕ None
Ⓖ 1
Ⓗ 2
Ⓙ 3

DAY 5

George needs to measure the length of his desk. What is the best unit of measurement for him to use?

Ⓐ millimeters
Ⓑ feet
Ⓒ yards
Ⓓ kilometers

Day	CRCT GPS Grade 6
1	M6D1.c
2	M6A2.g
3	M6D1.b
4	M6G1.a
5	M6M2.b

DAY 1

In Derek's class, 18 of the 25 students belong to an after-school club. Which of the following describes the ratio of students not in an after-school club to students in an after-school club?

(A) $\frac{7}{18}$
(B) 18 to 25
(C) 25:18
(D) $\frac{7}{25}$

DAY 2

Jimmy ran 0.82 miles. What distance in feet did he run?

(F) 0.0001 feet
(G) 433 feet
(H) 4,329.6 feet
(J) 6,439 feet

DAY 3

In which month were the savings greatest?

(A) June
(B) July
(C) August
(D) September

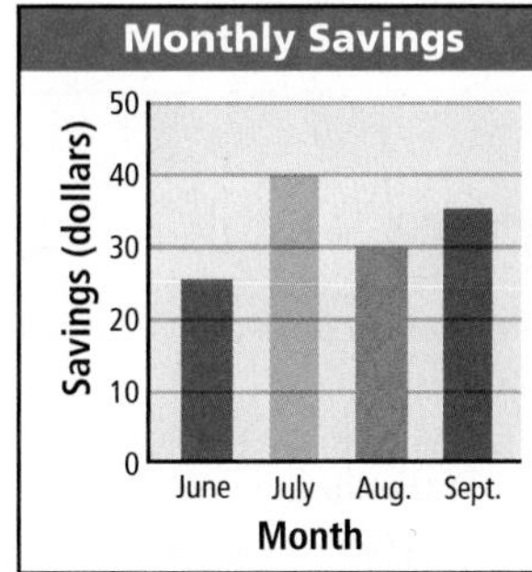

DAY 4

What is the length of the line to the nearest $\frac{1}{4}$ inch?

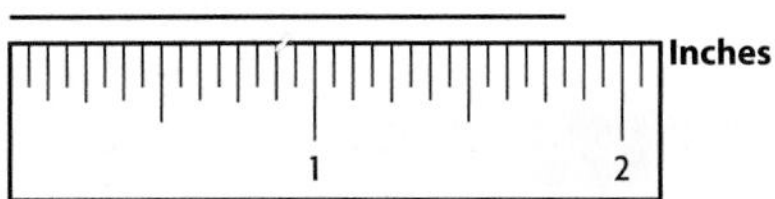

(F) $1\frac{1}{4}$ in.
(G) $1\frac{1}{2}$ in.
(H) $1\frac{3}{4}$ in.
(J) 2 in.

DAY 5

How many lines of symmetry does a square have?

(A) None
(B) 1
(C) 2
(D) 4

Day	CRCT GPS Grade 6
1	M6A1
2	M6M1
3	M6D1.d
4	M6M2.a
5	M6G1.a

Countdown to CRCT WEEK 11

DAY 1

The picture shows a scale model of a snake. What is the length, in feet, of the actual snake?

Ⓐ 2 feet
Ⓑ 4 feet
Ⓒ 6 feet
Ⓓ 8 feet

DAY 2

What is the length of the line to the nearest $\frac{1}{8}$ inch?

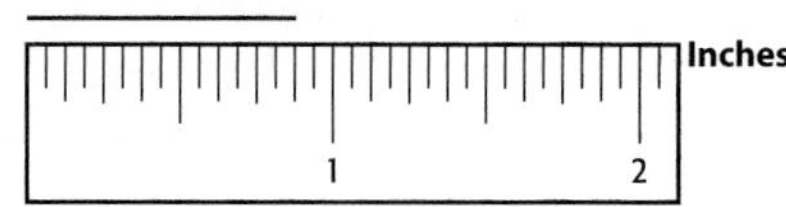

Ⓕ $\frac{1}{2}$ in.
Ⓖ $\frac{5}{8}$ in.
Ⓗ $\frac{3}{4}$ in.
Ⓙ $\frac{7}{8}$ in.

DAY 3

What information does the circle graph not tell you about Chris?

Ⓐ Chris spends more time at soccer practice than at the library.
Ⓑ Chris spends the most amount of time doing his chores.
Ⓒ Chris spends less time at guitar practice than at soccer practice.
Ⓓ Chris spends more time doing chores than at the library.

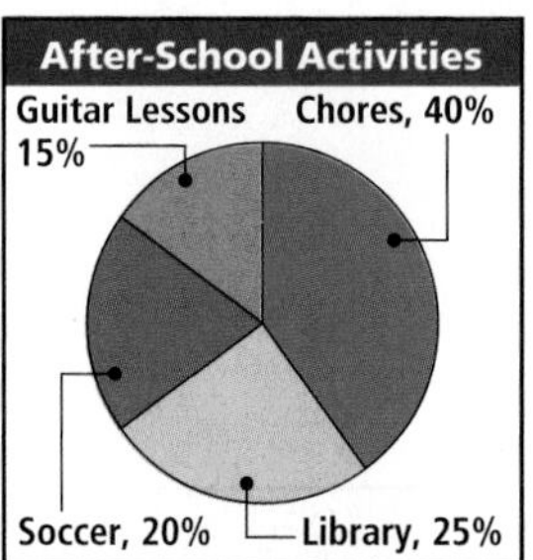

DAY 4

Which of these is equivalent to 12 feet?

Ⓕ 1 inch
Ⓖ 4 yards
Ⓗ 36 yards
Ⓙ 36 inches

DAY 5

Sara is measuring the length of a postage stamp. Which unit is most appropriate?

Ⓐ centimeters
Ⓑ meters
Ⓒ feet
Ⓓ kilometers

Day	CRCT GPS Grade 6
1	M6G1.e
2	M6M2.a
3	M6D1.d
4	M6M1
5	M6M2.b

DAY 1

If 30 buses can carry 1,500 people, how many people can 5 buses carry?

(A) 200
(B) 250
(C) 500
(D) 750

DAY 2

What are the factors of 24?

(F) 1, 2, 4, 6, 12, 24
(G) 1, 2, 3, 4, 6, 8, 12, 24
(H) 1, 2, 3, 8, 12, 24
(J) 1, 2, 3, 4, 6, 12, 24

DAY 3

Jeff drew this model of an airplane. He is using a scale of 1 inch:5 feet. What is the actual length of the wing?

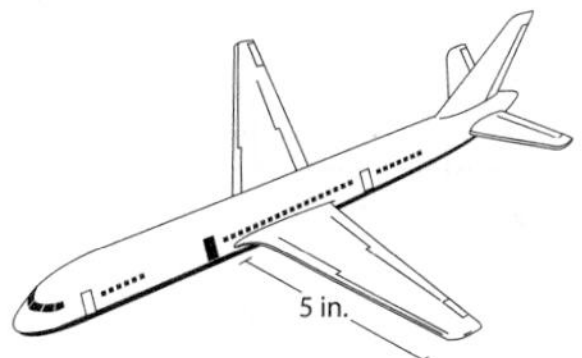

(A) 5 feet
(B) 10 feet
(C) 25 feet
(D) 30 feet

DAY 4

Bryan collected data about the average price of a movie ticket in various years. Which of the following types of graphs should he use to display the data?

(F) circle graph
(G) line graph
(H) histogram
(J) pictograph

DAY 5

Which of these figures has exactly three lines of symmetry?

(A) square
(B) parallelogram
(C) equilateral triangle
(D) pentagon

Day	CRCT GPS Grade 6
1	M6A2.c
2	M6N1.a
3	M6G1.e
4	M6D1.c
5	M6G1.a

DAY 1

Nick uses the Internet to find a table that lists the 50 states and the population of each state. Which question CANNOT be answered based on this data?

(A) Which state has the greatest population?

(B) What is the average population of the states?

(C) Which state has grown the fastest in the past 10 years?

(D) How many states have more than 10 million residents?

DAY 2

The table shows the results of a survey of 40 people who were asked to choose their favorite fruit. Which fraction shows the number of people who named strawberry?

Fruit	Number of People
Apple	18
Orange	10
Strawberry	12

(F) $\frac{1}{4}$

(G) $\frac{3}{10}$

(H) $\frac{9}{20}$

(J) $\frac{11}{20}$

DAY 3

Which figure has 90° rotational symmetry?

(A) 

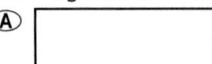

(B) 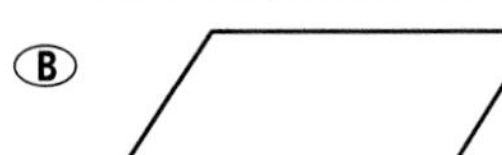

(C) 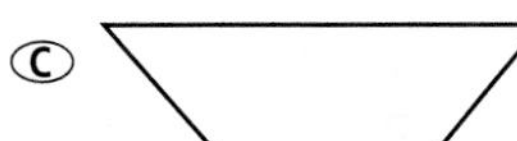

(D) 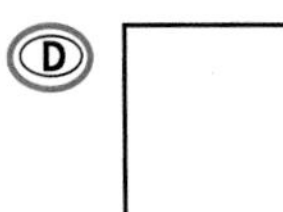

DAY 4

The scale factor for a map is 1 centimeter: 200 kilometers. On the map, Boston is about 1.5 centimeters from New York. How far is Boston from New York?

(F) 150 kilometers

(G) 200 kilometers

(H) 300 kilometers

(J) 350 kilometers

DAY 5

Which of these is equivalent to 4 meters?

(A) 40 millimeters

(B) 400 centimeters

(C) 400 millimeters

(D) 4000 kilometers

Day	CRCT GPS Grade 6
1	M6D1.a
2	M6A1
3	M6G1.b
4	M6G1.e
5	M6M1

DAY 1

If the two rectangles are similar, what is the length of the smaller rectangle?

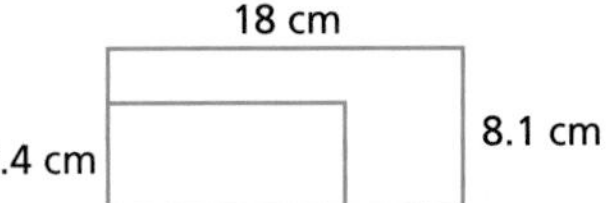

Ⓐ 6.7 centimeters
Ⓑ 12 centimeters
Ⓒ 14.1 centimeters
Ⓓ 15 centimeters

DAY 5

Ivy's Fresh Eggs transports its eggs in crates. How many crates will 8 trucks carry?

Trucks	2	3	4	5
Crates	80	120	160	200

Ⓕ 220
Ⓖ 280
Ⓗ 320
Ⓙ 360

DAY 3

Philip created this table for the data in the graph. What mistake did he make?

Plant	A	B	C	D
Height (in.)	$1\frac{1}{2}$	3	1	$2\frac{1}{4}$

Ⓐ He confused the data for plants A and C.
Ⓑ He misread the data for plant C.
Ⓒ He rounded the data to the nearest $\frac{1}{4}$ inch.
Ⓓ He misread the data for plant D.

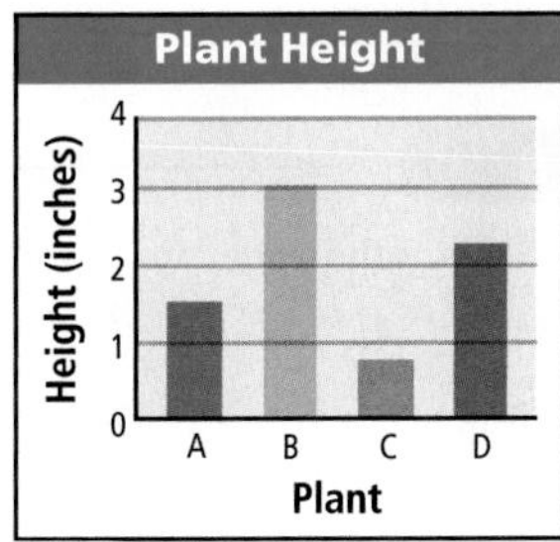

DAY 4

Diana needs to know the area of a wall in her house. Which of these units are best for describing the area of the wall?

Ⓕ meters
Ⓖ square feet
Ⓗ cubic yards
Ⓙ kilometers

DAY 5

Which figure has 120° rotational symmetry?

Ⓐ equilateral triangle
Ⓑ square
Ⓒ rectangle
Ⓓ pentagon

Day	CRCT GPS Grade 6
1	M6G1.c
2	M6A2.c
3	M6D1.c
4	M6M2.c
5	M6G1.b

COUNTDOWN TO CRCT

Countdown to CRCT WEEK 15

DAY 1

The Great Pyramid in Giza, Egypt, is a rectangular pyramid. Which formula could you use to determine the volume of the pyramid?

Ⓐ $V = \frac{1}{2}Bh$
Ⓑ $V = \frac{1}{3}Bh$
Ⓒ $V = Bh$
Ⓓ $V = \frac{4}{3}\pi r^3$

DAY 2

If $\triangle ACE$ is similar to $\triangle BCD$, what is the length of AC?

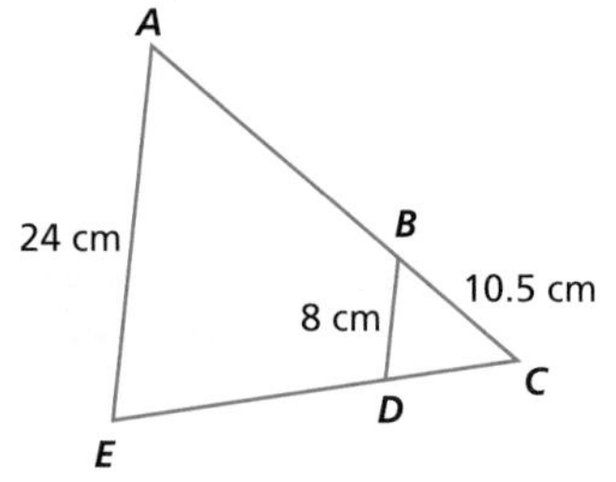

Ⓕ 5.5 centimeters
Ⓖ 13.5 centimeters
Ⓗ 21.5 centimeters
Ⓙ 31.5 centimeters

DAY 3

What is the length of the line to the nearest half inch?

Ⓐ 1 in.
Ⓑ $1\frac{1}{4}$ in.
Ⓒ $1\frac{1}{2}$
Ⓓ 2 in.

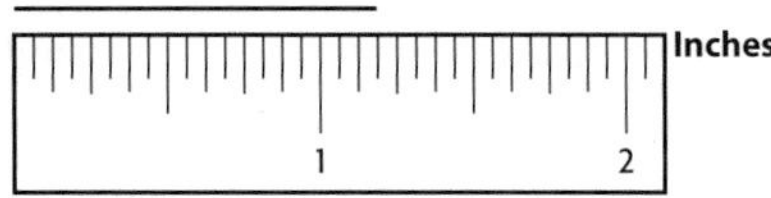

DAY 4

Sandra needs to fill a window box with dirt. If she measures the sides of the box in centimeters, what is the unit of capacity Sandra should use?

Ⓕ cubic millimeters
Ⓖ centimeters
Ⓗ square centimeters
Ⓙ cubic centimeters

DAY 5

Sandy bought 2.75 liters of cranberry juice, 3.5 liters of pineapple juice, and 4.2 liters of orange juice for punch for a party. How many liters of punch will this make?

Ⓐ 3.52 liters
Ⓑ 9.45 liters
Ⓒ 7.7 liters
Ⓓ 10.45 liters

Day	CRCT GPS Grade 6
1	M6M3.a
2	M6G1.c
3	M6M2.a
4	M6M2.c
5	M6N1.g

DAY 1

Ted wants to make a small fountain in his garden. The diagram shows the dimensions of the fountain. How much water will Ted need to fill the fountain?

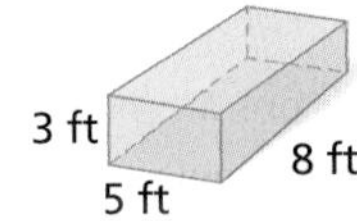

Ⓐ 18 cubic feet
Ⓑ 40 cubic feet
Ⓒ 80 cubic feet
Ⓓ 120 cubic feet

DAY 2

The equation $y = 2.4x$ gives the cost in dollars, y, of buying x gallons of gasoline. How many gallons of gasoline can you buy for $12?

Ⓕ 5
Ⓖ 9.6
Ⓗ 16
Ⓙ 28.8

DAY 3

Which equation describes the relationship in the table?

x	0	2	5	7
y	0	10	25	35

Ⓐ $y = \frac{x}{5}$
Ⓑ $y = x + 8$
Ⓒ $y = 5x$
Ⓓ $y = 20 + x$

DAY 4

Gil wants to fill his fish tank with water. Which is the best estimate of the volume of water he needs?

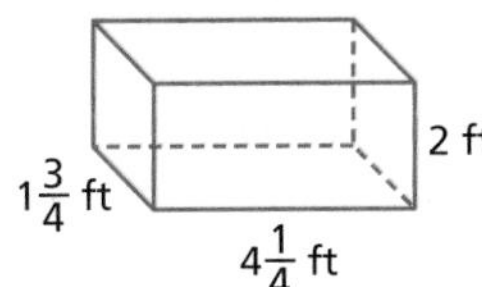

Ⓕ 8 cubic feet
Ⓖ 16 cubic feet
Ⓗ 24 cubic feet
Ⓙ 32 cubic feet

DAY 5

Which solid has exactly two triangular faces?

Ⓐ rectangular prism
Ⓑ triangular prism
Ⓒ square pyramid
Ⓓ none of the above

Day	CRCT GPS Grade 6
1	M6M3.b
2	M6A2.f
3	M6A2.d
4	M6M3.c
5	M6G2.a

Countdown to CRCT WEEK 17

DAY 1

The window box measures $4\frac{6}{8}$ inches × $4\frac{6}{8}$ inches × $10\frac{1}{4}$ inches. Which is the best estimate for the amount of soil that will fill the window box?

Ⓐ 100 cubic inches
Ⓑ 150 cubic inches
Ⓒ 250 cubic inches
Ⓓ 350 cubic inches

DAY 2

For which of the following shapes could you **not** use the formula $V = Bh$ to find the volume?

Ⓕ hexagonal prism
Ⓖ cylinder
Ⓗ rectangular prism
Ⓙ triangular pyramid

DAY 3

Zack cuts out and folds the net shown here. What type of solid does he make?

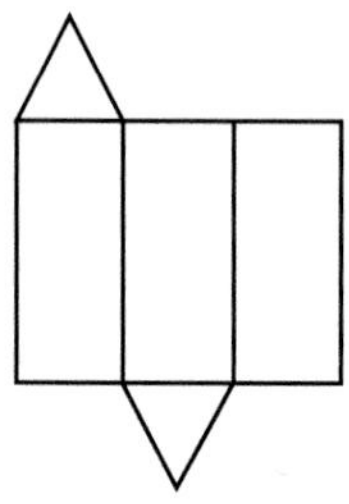

Ⓐ rectangular prism
Ⓑ pyramid
Ⓒ triangular prism
Ⓓ cone

DAY 4

Which of the following is the best estimate for the surface area of the rectangular prism?

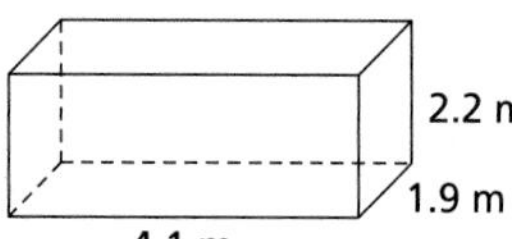

Ⓕ 16 m^2
Ⓖ 32 m^2
Ⓗ 40 m^2
Ⓙ 48 m^2

DAY 5

Mei drives on the highway at 55 mi/h. The equation $d = 55t$ gives the distance in miles, d, that she travels in t hours. If Mei drives 247.5 miles on the highway, how long does the trip take?

Ⓐ 4 hours
Ⓑ 4.5 hours
Ⓒ 5 hours
Ⓓ 5.5 hours

Day	CRCT GPS Grade 6
1	M6M3.c
2	M6M3.a
3	M6G2.d
4	M6M4.c
5	M6A2.f

Countdown to CRCT WEEK 18

DAY 1

Isaac had to draw four different pyramids for math class. He drew the figures below. Which figure is not a pyramid?

Ⓐ 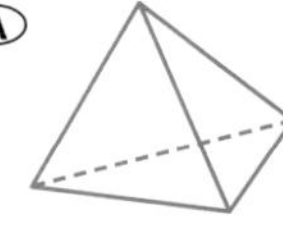

Ⓒ 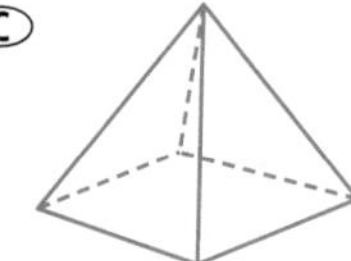

(B) 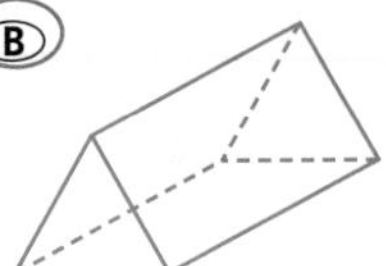

Ⓓ 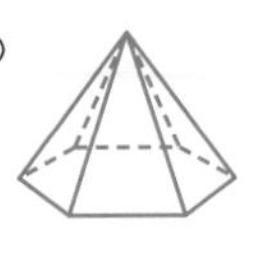

DAY 2

What object is represented by this net?

(F) cone
Ⓖ sphere
Ⓗ cylinder
Ⓙ prism

DAY 3

A bag contains 4 red marbles and 6 blue marbles. Michelle reaches into the bag and chooses one of the marbles at random. What is the probability that she chooses a blue marble?

Ⓐ $\frac{1}{6}$

Ⓑ $\frac{2}{5}$

(C) $\frac{3}{5}$

Ⓓ $\frac{2}{3}$

DAY 4

There are 12 inches in 1 foot, 24 inches in 2 feet, 36 inches in 3 feet, and so on. Which equation describes the relationship between the number of inches, x, and the number of feet, y?

Ⓕ $y = 12x$
(G) $y = \frac{1}{12}x$
Ⓗ $y = x + 12$
Ⓙ $y = 12 - x$

DAY 5

Which of the following could be measured using square meters?

Ⓐ perimeter
Ⓑ volume
Ⓒ length
(D) area

Day	CRCT GPS Grade 6
1	M6G2.a
2	M6G2.d
3	M6D2.b
4	M6A2.d
5	M6M2.c

COUNTDOWN TO CRCT

Countdown to CRCT WEEK 19

DAY 1

Martin is filling a trough with water. If the pail he is using can hold 9 cubic feet of water, how many times will he need to empty his pail into the trough in order to fill the trough completely?

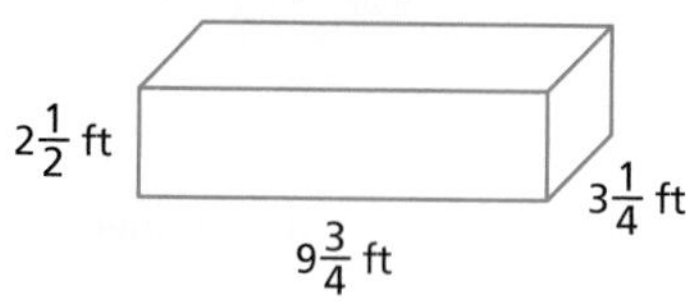

(A) 6
(B) 7
(C) 8
(D) 9

DAY 2

Janelle has a plastic cube that contains paper clips. Each edge of a cube is 4 inches long. What is the surface area of the cube?

(F) 32 in^2
(G) 48 in^2
(H) 64 in^2
(J) 96 in^2

DAY 3

Mark spins the spinner shown here. What is the probability that the spinner lands on a number that is greater than 6?

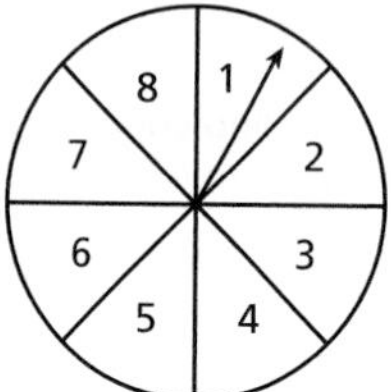

(A) $\frac{1}{4}$
(B) $\frac{3}{8}$
(C) $\frac{1}{2}$
(D) $\frac{3}{4}$

DAY 4

Which statement is true for both cylinders and cones?

(F) It has a vertex.
(G) It has at least one circular base.
(H) You can find the volume using the formula $V = Bh$.
(J) It has a triangular face.

DAY 5

What is the pattern in the following table?

Input x	5	10	15	20
Output y	25	50	75	100

(A) $y = x^2$
(B) $y = 3x$
(C) $y = 5x$
(D) $y = 2x$

Day	CRCT GPS Grade 6
1	M6M3.d
2	M6M4.b
3	M6D2.b
4	M6G2.b
5	M6A2.d

DAY 1

As you perform more and more trials of an experiment, which of the following is true?

(A) The experimental probability gets close to 1.

(B) The experimental probability does not change.

(C) The experimental probability gets close to the theoretical probability.

(D) The experimental probability gets close to 0.

DAY 2

Which is the best estimate for the surface area of the cylinder?

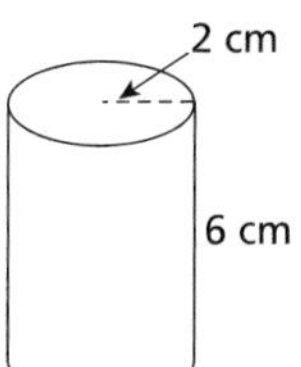

(F) 50 cm^2

(G) 75 cm^2

(H) 100 cm^2

(J) 125 cm^2

DAY 3

Which figure shows the top view of the solid?

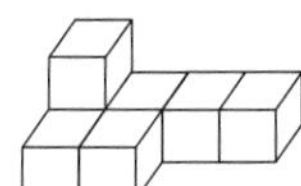

(A) 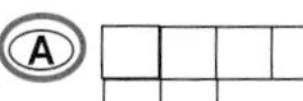

(B) 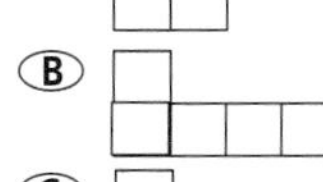

(C)

(D) 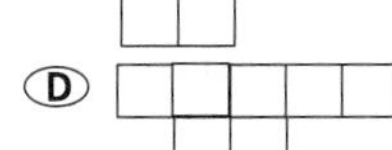

DAY 4

Latrell flips a coin 40 times. The coin lands heads up 24 times. Based on this, what is the experimental probability that the coin lands heads up?

(F) 0.4

(G) 0.5

(H) 0.6

(J) 0.8

DAY 5

Paula has a stick that is $2\frac{3}{4}$ feet long. She cuts it into pieces that are each $\frac{1}{4}$ feet long. How many pieces does she have?

(A) 3

(B) 5

(C) 8

(D) 11

Day	CRCT GPS Grade 6
1	M6D2.c
2	M6M4.c
3	M6G2.c
4	M6D2.a
5	M6N1.e

Countdown to CRCT WEEK 21

DAY 1

Estimate the volume of the figure below.

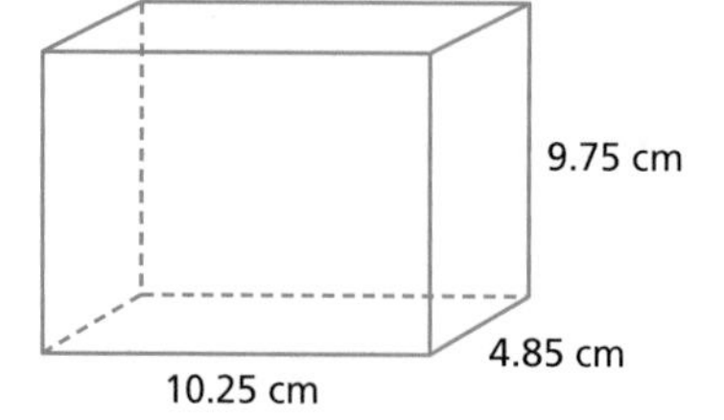

(A) 300 cubic centimeters
(B) 450 cubic centimeters
(C) 500 cubic centimeters
(D) 650 cubic centimeters

DAY 2

Rose is painting this cylindrical support beam in her house. She only needs to paint the lateral surface of the beam. What is the area that will be painted?

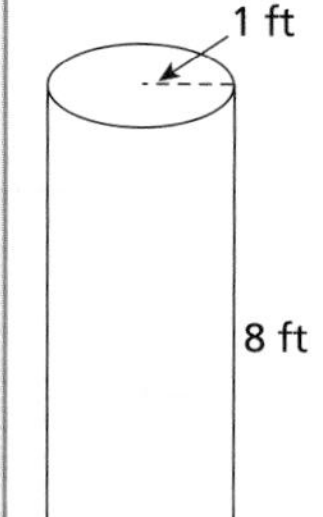

(F) 25.1 ft^2
(G) 50.3 ft^2
(H) 64.0 ft^2
(J) 100.6 ft^2

DAY 3

Which type of solid figure has the front, top, and side views shown here?

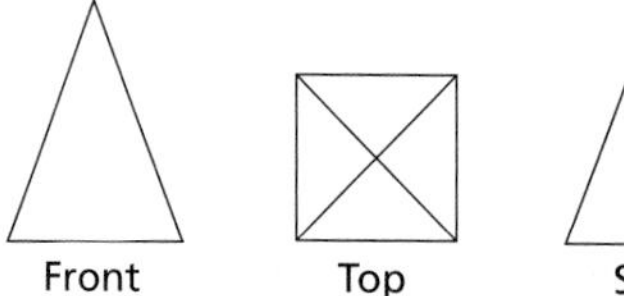

(A) pyramid
(B) cone
(C) cylinder
(D) prism

DAY 4

Jake rolls a number cube. What is the probability that he will roll a number less than 3?

(F) $\frac{1}{6}$
(G) $\frac{1}{4}$
(H) $\frac{1}{3}$
(J) $\frac{1}{2}$

DAY 5

The equation $y = 6.2x$ gives the number of hours, y, that a candle will burn if the candle is x inches tall. How long will a 4-inch candle burn?

(A) 1.55 hours
(B) 6.8 hours
(C) 10.2 hours
(D) 24.8 hours

Day	CRCT GPS Grade 6
1	M6M3.c
2	M6M4.d
3	M6G2.c
4	M6D2.b
5	M6A2.f

Countdown to CRCT WEEK 22

DAY 1

Which equation is shown in the graph?

(A) $y = x$
(B) $y = 2x$
(C) $y = \frac{1}{2}x$
(D) $y = x + 2$

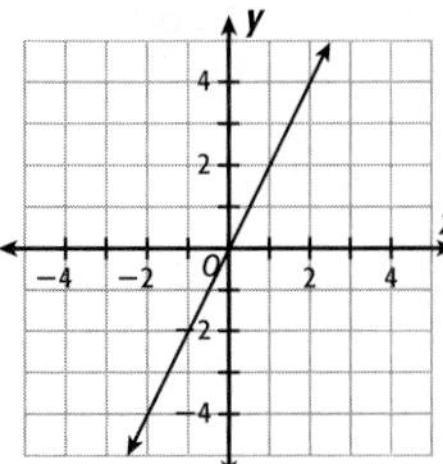

DAY 2

Which solid can be made by cutting out and folding this net?

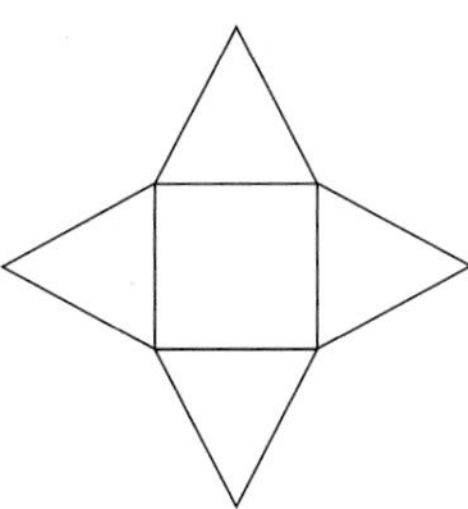

(F) cone
(G) triangular prism
(H) rectangular prism
(J) pyramid

DAY 3

Bryan wants to measure the volume of a large fish tank in his classroom. Which of the following units would be most appropriate?

(A) square feet
(B) centimeters
(C) cubic meters
(D) yards

DAY 4

Which figure does NOT have rotational symmetry?

(F) 
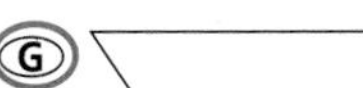
(H) 
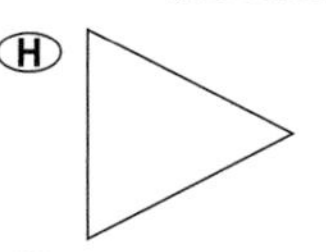
(J)

DAY 5

In a frog-jumping contest, Ben's frog jumped 20.75 centimeters in one hop. Billy's frog jumped 24.09 centimeters in one hop. How much farther did Billy's frog jump than Ben's frog?

(A) 2.34 centimeters
(B) 3.34 centimeters
(C) 3.35 centimeters
(D) 4.66 centimeters

Day	CRCT GPS Grade 6
1	M6A2.a
2	M6G2.d
3	M6M2.b
4	M6G1.b
5	M6N1.g

Countdown to CRCT WEEK 23

DAY 1

Doug surveyed 100 students to find out whether they preferred vanilla, chocolate, or strawberry frozen yogurt. Which type of graph could he use to display the results?

Ⓐ stem-and-leaf plot
Ⓑ double-line graph
Ⓒ circle graph
Ⓓ histogram

DAY 2

In Katie's class, 65% of the students have a pet. What fraction of the class does NOT have a pet?

Ⓕ $\frac{7}{50}$
Ⓖ $\frac{7}{20}$
Ⓗ $\frac{1}{2}$
Ⓙ $\frac{13}{20}$

DAY 3

Gina is drawing a scale model of a park. If the scale factor is 1 inch = 4 feet, what is the perimeter of the actual park?

6 in.
8 in.

Ⓐ 28 feet
Ⓑ 56 feet
Ⓒ 112 feet
Ⓓ 768 feet

DAY 4

Which figure has exactly two lines of symmetry?

Ⓕ 
Ⓖ 
Ⓗ 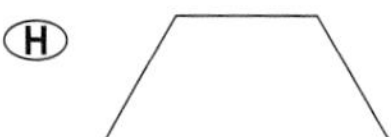
Ⓙ 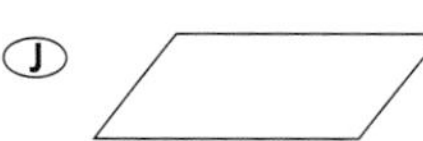

DAY 5

Which statement is true for a cylinder, but not for a cone?

Ⓐ It has two bases.
Ⓑ It has a curved surface.
Ⓒ It has a vertex.
Ⓓ It has a triangular face

Day	CRCT GPS Grade 6
1	M6D1.c
2	M6N1.f
3	M6G1.e
4	M6G1.a
5	M6G2.b

DAY 1

What equation is shown in the graph?

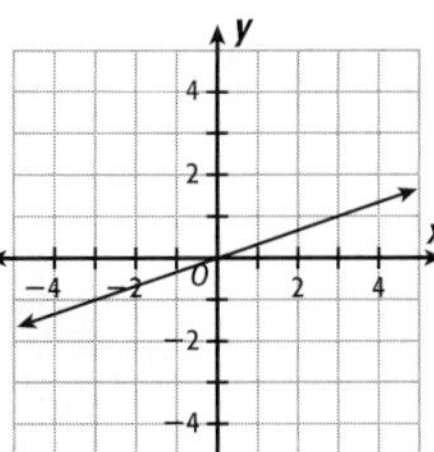

Ⓐ $y = 3x$
Ⓑ $y = \frac{1}{3}x$
Ⓒ $y = x + 3$
Ⓓ $y = x - 3$

DAY 2

Jeremy spins the spinner shown here. What is the probability that the spinner lands on a vowel?

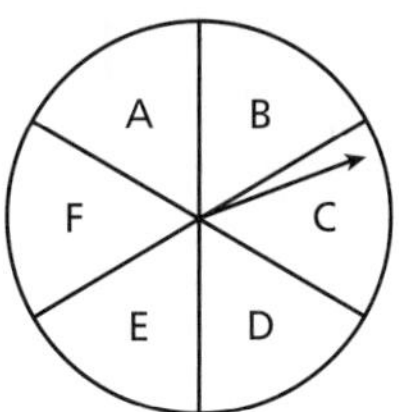

Ⓕ $\frac{1}{6}$
Ⓖ $\frac{1}{3}$
Ⓗ $\frac{1}{2}$
Ⓙ $\frac{2}{3}$

DAY 3

A model car and a real car have the given dimensions. What is the length of the real car if the scale factor is 1:30?

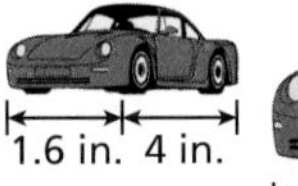

Ⓐ 8 feet
Ⓑ 9 feet
Ⓒ 10 feet
Ⓓ 12 feet

DAY 4

What is the value of x in the proportion $\frac{6}{8} = \frac{x}{20}$?

Ⓕ 12
Ⓖ 15
Ⓗ 18
Ⓙ 24

DAY 5

A solid figure has a top view that is a square. Its front and side views are rectangles. What type of figure is it?

Ⓐ cylinder
Ⓑ cone
Ⓒ pyramid
Ⓓ prism

Day	CRCT GPS Grade 6
1	M6A2.e
2	M6D2.b
3	M6G1.e
4	M6A2.c
5	M6G2.c

Georgia Mathematics Performance Standards

Georgia Mathematics Performance Standards Grade 6

By the end of grade six, students will understand the four arithmetic operations as they relate to positive rational numbers; convert between and compute with different forms of rational numbers; understand the concept of ratio and solve problems using proportional reasoning; understand and use line and rotational symmetry; determine the surface area and volume of solid figures; use variables to represent unknown quantities in formulae, algebraic expressions and equations; utilize data to make predictions; and determine the probability of a given event.

Instruction and assessment should include the use of manipulatives and appropriate technology. Topics should be represented in multiple ways including concrete/pictorial, verbal/written, numeric/data-based, graphical, and symbolic. Concepts should be introduced and used in the context of real world phenomena.

Concepts/Skills to Maintain

- Operations with decimal fractions
- Addition and subtraction of common fractions and mixed numbers with unlike denominators such as 2, 3, 4, 5, 6, 8, 10 and 12.
- Modeling multiplication of common fractions
- Modeling percent
- Graphing data
- Multiples and factors
- Perimeter, capacity and area of geometric figures
- Evaluating algebraic expressions

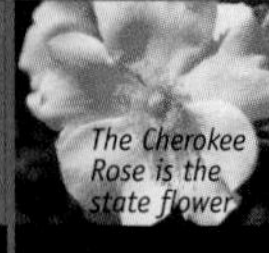

NUMBER AND OPERATIONS

Students will understand the meaning of the four arithmetic operations as related to positive rational numbers and will apply these concepts and associated skills in real world situations.

M6N1. Students will understand the meaning of the four arithmetic operations as related to positive rational numbers and will use these concepts to solve problems.

a Apply factors and multiples.

b Decompose numbers into their prime factorization (Fundamental Theorem of Arithmetic).

c Determine the greatest common factor (GCF) and the least common multiple (LCM) for a set of numbers.

d Add and subtract fractions and mixed numbers with unlike denominators.

e Multiply and divide fractions and mixed numbers.

f Use fractions, decimals, and percents interchangeably.

g Solve problems involving fractions, decimals, and percents.

MEASUREMENT

Students will understand how to determine the volume and surface area of solid figures. They will understand and use the customary and metric systems of measurement to measure quantities efficiently and to represent volume and surface area appropriately.

M6M1. Students will convert from one unit to another within one system of measurement (customary or metric) by using proportional relationships.

M6M2. Students will use appropriate units of measure for finding length, perimeter, area and volume and will express each quantity using the appropriate unit.

a Measure length to the nearest half, fourth, eighth and sixteenth of an inch.

b Select and use units of appropriate size and type to measure length, perimeter, area and volume.

c Compare and contrast units of measure for perimeter, area, and volume.

M6M3. Students will determine the volume of fundamental solid figures (right rectangular prisms, cylinders, pyramids and cones).

a Determine the formula for finding the volume of fundamental solid figures.

b Compute the volumes of fundamental solid figures, using appropriate units of measure.

c Estimate the volumes of simple geometric solids.

d Solve application problems involving the volume of fundamental solid figures.

M6M4. Students will determine the surface area of solid figures (right rectangular prisms and cylinders).

a Find the surface area of right rectangular prisms and cylinders using manipulatives and constructing nets.

b Compute the surface area of right rectangular prisms and cylinders using formulae.

c Estimate the surface areas of simple geometric solids.

d Solve application problems involving surface area of right rectangular prisms and cylinders.

GEOMETRY

Students will further develop their understanding of plane and solid geometric figures, incorporating the use of appropriate technology and using this knowledge to solve authentic problems.

M6G1. Students will further develop their understanding of plane figures.

a Determine and use lines of symmetry.

b Investigate rotational symmetry, including degree of rotation.

c Use the concepts of ratio, proportion and scale factor to demonstrate the relationships between similar plane figures.

d Interpret and sketch simple scale drawings.

e Solve problems involving scale drawings.

M6G2. Students will further develop their understanding of solid figures.

a Compare and contrast right prisms and pyramids.

b Compare and contrast cylinders and cones.

c Interpret and sketch front, back, top, bottom and side views of solid figures.

d Construct nets for prisms, cylinders, pyramids, and cones.

ALGEBRA

Students will investigate relationships between two quantities. They will write and solve proportions and simple one-step equations that result from problem situations.

M6A1. Students will understand the concept of ratio and use it to represent quantitative relationships.

M6A2. Students will consider relationships between varying quantities.

a Analyze and describe patterns arising from mathematical rules, tables, and graphs.

b Use manipulatives or draw pictures to solve problems involving proportional relationships.

c Use proportions ($\frac{a}{b} = \frac{c}{d}$) to describe relationships and solve problems, including percent problems.

d Describe proportional relationships mathematically using $y = kx$, where k is the constant of proportionality.

Chattahoochee National Forest

e Graph proportional relationships in the form $y = kx$ and describe characteristics of the graphs.

f In a proportional relationship expressed as $y = kx$, solve for one quantity given values of the other two. Given quantities may be whole numbers, decimals, or fractions. Solve problems using the relationship $y = kx$.

g Use proportional reasoning ($\frac{a}{b} = \frac{c}{d}$ and $y = kx$) to solve problems.

M6A3. Students will evaluate algebraic expressions, including those with exponents, and solve simple one-step equations using each of the four basic operations.

DATA ANALYSIS AND PROBABILITY

Students will demonstrate understanding of data analysis by posing questions to be answered by collecting data. They will represent, investigate, and use data to answer those questions. Students will understand experimental and theoretical probability.

M6D1. Students will pose questions, collect data, represent and analyze the data, and interpret results.

a Formulate questions that can be answered by data. Students should collect data by using samples from a larger population (surveys), or by conducting experiments.

b Using data, construct frequency distributions, frequency tables, and graphs.

c Choose appropriate graphs to be consistent with the nature of the data (categorical or numerical). Graphs should include pictographs, histograms, bar graphs, line graphs, circle graphs, and line plots.

d Use tables and graphs to examine variation that occurs within a group and variation that occurs between groups.

e Relate the data analysis to the context of the questions posed.

M6D2. Students will use experimental and simple theoretical probability and understand the nature of sampling. They will also make predictions from investigations.

a Predict the probability of a given event through trials/simulations (experimental probability), and represent the probability as a ratio.

b Determine, and use a ratio to represent, the theoretical probability of a given event.

c Discover that experimental probability approaches theoretical probability when the number of trials is large.

Terms/Symbols: positive rational numbers, factors, multiples, decompose, prime numbers, prime factorization, Fundamental Theorem of Arithmetic, GCF, LCM, evaluate, surface area, metric system of measurement, customary system of measurement, proportional relationships, right rectangular prism, cylinder, pyramid, cone, geometric solid, net, geometric figures, line symmetry, rotational symmetry, similar plane figures, scale factor, scale drawings, relations, varying quantities, ratio, direct proportion, proportions, proportional reasoning, frequency distributions, pictographs, histograms, bar graphs, line graphs, circle graphs, line plot, frequency table, experimental probability, theoretical probability, sampling, event, random sample, population, non-routine word problems.

Centennial Park, Atlanta

Process Standards

Each topic studied in this course should be developed with careful thought toward helping every student achieve the following process standards.

M6P1. Students will solve problems (using appropriate technology).

a Build new mathematical knowledge through problem solving.

b Solve problems that arise in mathematics and in other contexts.

c Apply and adapt a variety of appropriate strategies to solve problems.

d Monitor and reflect on the process of mathematical problem solving.

M6P2. Students will reason and evaluate mathematical arguments.

a Recognize reasoning and proof as fundamental aspects of mathematics.

b Make and investigate mathematical conjectures.

c Develop and evaluate mathematical arguments and proofs.

d Select and use various types of reasoning and methods of proof.

M6P3. Students will communicate mathematically.

a Organize and consolidate their mathematical thinking through communication.

b Communicate their mathematical thinking coherently and clearly to peers, teachers, and others.

c Analyze and evaluate the mathematical thinking and strategies of others.

d Use the language of mathematics to express mathematical ideas precisely.

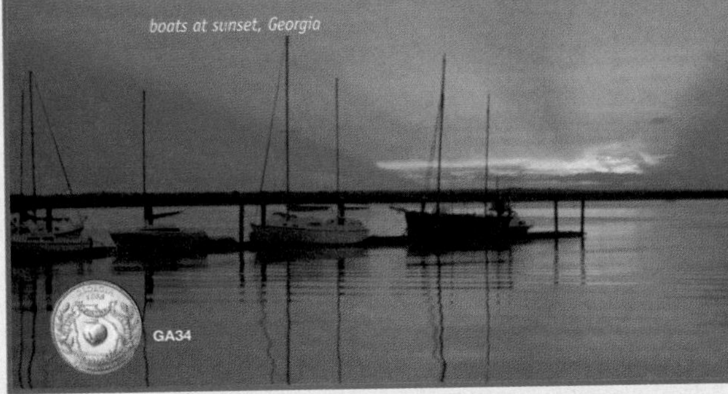

boats at sunset, Georgia

M6P4. Students will make connections among mathematical ideas and to other disciplines.

a Recognize and use connections among mathematical ideas.

b Understand how mathematical ideas interconnect and build on one another to produce a coherent whole.

c Recognize and apply mathematics in contexts outside of mathematics.

M6P5. Students will represent mathematics in multiple ways.

a Create and use representations to organize, record, and communicate mathematical ideas.

b Select, apply, and translate among mathematical representations to solve problems.

c Use representations to model and interpret physical, social, and mathematical phenomena.

Melon Bluff Nature Center

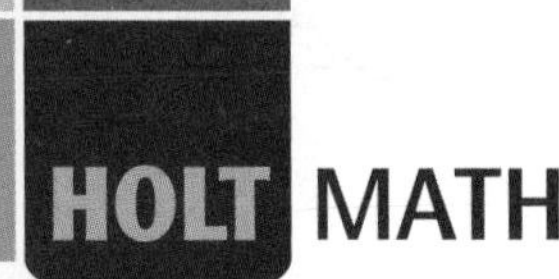

You can count on **Holt Mathematics** for

1

Built-in Assessment and Intervention. Prescribe the resources your students need when they need them in order to lead your students to success.

2

Comprehensive Differentiated Instruction. Ensure all students have the opportunity to succeed with strategies designed to reach students of all learning styles and skill levels.

3

Success on High-Stakes Tests. Prepare students for success on test day with standards-based test preparation that's embedded into daily lessons.

4

Integrated Technology that Enhances Learning. Motivate your students to excel and manage your classroom with maximum effectiveness using Holt technology.

ASSESSMENT AND INTERVENTION 1

DIFFERENTIATED INSTRUCTION 2

HIGH-STAKES TEST PREP 3

INTEGRATED TECHNOLOGY 4

GROUNDED IN RESEARCH • BUILT BY EXPERTS • PROVEN IN CLASSROOMS

Built for Student Success... from the Ground Up

Every student is unique with individual strengths and weaknesses. Starting with *Holt Mathematics* and *Pre-Algebra* for middle school through *Holt Algebra 1, Geometry,* and *Algebra 2,* Holt provides the instruction and resources you need to reach and teach every one of your students. Whether it's an alternative approach to a lesson, a modification for a visual learner, or extra practice with basic skills, Holt has what you need to help all of your students succeed.

> *"Deep and abstract ideas are challenging to all, but the challenge should be a pleasurable one that students want to conquer."*
>
> **– Dr. Edward B. Burger, Holt author**

Count on Holt Mathematics for

Built-in assessment and intervention

Holt's at-a-glance system makes it easy to keep students on track.

You need to know how well your students understand the lesson BEFORE they take the test. With *Holt Mathematics*, informal and formal assessment options are given at every stage within the chapter. Intervention resources allow you to reteach or review material without merely sending students back to previous lessons in the book.

- **Assess Prior Knowledge** to make sure all students start the chapter on solid footing.

  Intervene with alternate teaching strategies and basic skills review in **Are You Ready? Intervention and Enrichment.**

- **Formative Assessment** diagnoses skill development within the chapter.

  Intervene with **Ready to Go On?, Lesson Tutorial Videos, Homework Help Online,** and more.

- **Summative Assessment** allows students to demonstrate their mastery of the concepts.

  Intervene with **Reteach** and **Lesson Tutorial Videos**.

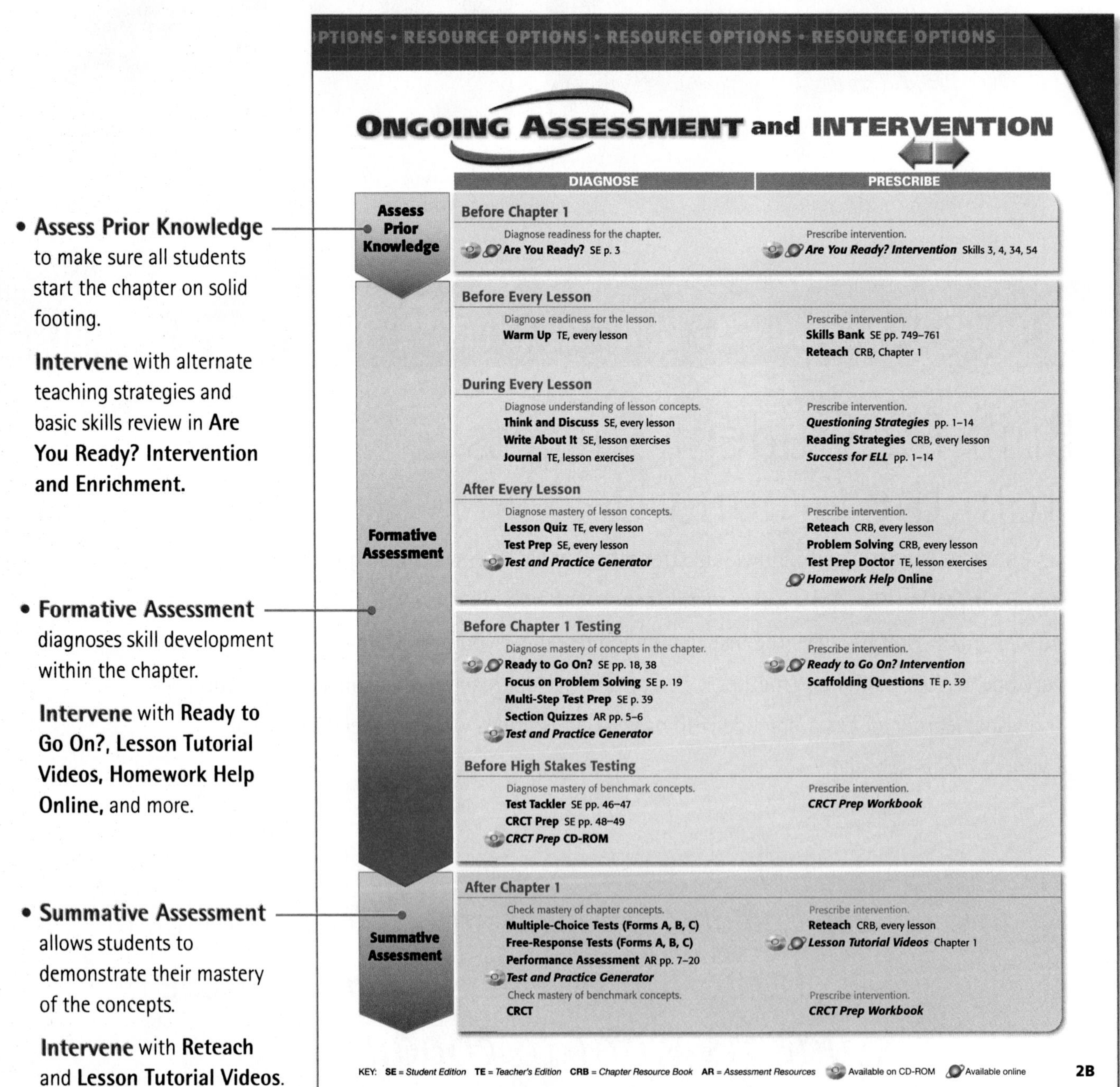

PTIONS • RESOURCE OPTIONS • RESOURCE OPTIONS • RESOURCE OPTIONS

ONGOING ASSESSMENT and INTERVENTION

		DIAGNOSE	PRESCRIBE
Assess Prior Knowledge	**Before Chapter 1**	Diagnose readiness for the chapter. ***Are You Ready?*** SE p. 3	Prescribe intervention. ***Are You Ready? Intervention*** Skills 3, 4, 34, 54
Formative Assessment	**Before Every Lesson**	Diagnose readiness for the lesson. **Warm Up** TE, every lesson	Prescribe intervention. **Skills Bank** SE pp. 749–761 **Reteach** CRB, Chapter 1
	During Every Lesson	Diagnose understanding of lesson concepts. **Think and Discuss** SE, every lesson **Write About It** SE, lesson exercises **Journal** TE, lesson exercises	Prescribe intervention. ***Questioning Strategies*** pp. 1–14 **Reading Strategies** CRB, every lesson ***Success for ELL*** pp. 1–14
	After Every Lesson	Diagnose mastery of lesson concepts. **Lesson Quiz** TE, every lesson **Test Prep** SE, every lesson ***Test and Practice Generator***	Prescribe intervention. **Reteach** CRB, every lesson **Problem Solving** CRB, every lesson **Test Prep Doctor** TE, lesson exercises ***Homework Help Online***
	Before Chapter 1 Testing	Diagnose mastery of concepts in the chapter. **Ready to Go On?** SE pp. 18, 38 **Focus on Problem Solving** SE p. 19 **Multi-Step Test Prep** SE p. 39 **Section Quizzes** AR pp. 5–6 ***Test and Practice Generator***	Prescribe intervention. ***Ready to Go On? Intervention*** **Scaffolding Questions** TE p. 39
	Before High Stakes Testing	Diagnose mastery of benchmark concepts. **Test Tackler** SE pp. 46–47 **CRCT Prep** SE pp. 48–49 ***CRCT Prep CD-ROM***	Prescribe intervention. ***CRCT Prep Workbook***
Summative Assessment	**After Chapter 1**	Check mastery of chapter concepts. **Multiple-Choice Tests (Forms A, B, C)** **Free-Response Tests (Forms A, B, C)** **Performance Assessment** AR pp. 7–20 ***Test and Practice Generator*** Check mastery of benchmark concepts. **CRCT**	Prescribe intervention. **Reteach** CRB, every lesson ***Lesson Tutorial Videos*** Chapter 1 Prescribe intervention. ***CRCT Prep Workbook***

KEY: **SE** = *Student Edition* **TE** = *Teacher's Edition* **CRB** = *Chapter Resource Book* **AR** = *Assessment Resources* Available on CD-ROM Available online

2B

HOLT MATH

When students are struggling they don't want to keep rereading the same lesson in the hope that eventually it will make sense. They need to try a new approach to the lesson. That's at the core of the assessment and intervention system in *Holt Mathematics.*

Name ______ Skill ______

Practice on Your Own **Skill 1**

Give the value of the digit 3.

BILLIONS			MILLIONS			THOUSANDS			ONES		
Hundreds	Tens	Ones ,	Hundreds	Tens	Ones ,	Hundreds	Tens	Ones ,	Hundreds	Tens	Ones
		2,	9	4	0,	6	3	5,	7	1	8

The 3 is in the thousands period.
The 3 is in the tens place.
The value of the digit 3 is 3 ten thousands or 30,000.

Give the period, the place, and the value of the digit in 2,940,635,718.

1. Digit: 7
Period ______
Place ______
Value ______

2. Digit: 0
Period ______
Place ______
Value ______

3. Digit: 2
Period ______
Place ______
Value ______

Give the value of the underlined digit.

4. 815,623,497
5. 815,623,497
6. 815,623,497
7. 1,482,700,576
8. 1,482,700,576
9. 1,482,700,576

Check

Give the value of the underlined digit.

10. 3,175,264,358
11. 3,175,264,358
12. 3,175,264,358

 16 Holt Mathematics

Are You Ready? Intervention and Enrichment

- Diagnoses mastery of prerequisite skills
- Strengthens student weaknesses with direct instruction, conceptual models, and scaffolded practice
- Enriches every chapter with critical thinking activities
- Available in print, on CD-ROM, and online

Name ______ Date ______ Class ______

LESSON 1-2 **Ready to Go On? Skills Intervention**
Exponents

Numbers may be written as a **power.** The **exponent** tells how many times the **base** is multiplied by itself.

Vocabulary
power
exponent
base

Evaluating Powers
Find each value.

A. 7^3

7^3 = ______ How many times is 7 multiplied by itself? ____
What is the base? ____ What is the exponent? ____
= ____ Find the product.

B. 2^5

2^5 = ______ How many times is 2 multiplied by itself? ____
What is the base? ____ What is the exponent? ____
= ____ Find the product.

Expressing Whole Numbers as Powers
Write the number using an exponent and the given base.

64, base 4

64 = ______ How many times must 4 be multiplied by itself to equal 64? ____
= 4– What is the exponent? ____

Earth Science Application
A radar altimeter measures the distance from a space satellite to the surface of the earth by measuring the time delay between the emission of a short microwave pulse and the echo it produces when it bounces off the earth. The microwave region between 100 MHz and 10,000 MHz is used for this measurement. Find the microwave range as a power of ten.

What is the microwave range? ______
Write each value as a product of 10.

100 = ______ 10,000 = ______
= 10– MHz = 10– MHz

The microwave region used by the radar altimeter is between ____ and ____MHz.

 3 Holt Mathematics

Only from Holt!

Ready to Go On? Intervention and Enrichment

- Diagnoses mastery of newly taught skills
- Addresses deficiencies with alternative instruction and practice
- Checks student progress with post tests
- Available in print, on CD-ROM, and online

> *"Formative assessment and targeted intervention empower the teacher to build every student's math confidence."*
>
> – Audrey Jackson, Holt author

Program Highlights

Count on Holt Mathematics for

Comprehensive differentiated instruction 2

Reach all learners in your classroom—no matter what their skill levels or learning styles are.

Not all students "get it" at the same time or in the same way. *Holt Mathematics* accommodates the students in your classroom with different skill levels and those whose learning styles benefit from different approaches.

With leveled practice and tests, content presented in a variety of media, and teaching strategies built in at point-of-use, helping all of your students succeed has never been easier.

Think and Discuss

1. Tell what value of n makes $-n + 32$ equal to zero.

2. Explain why you would or would not multiply both sides of an equation by 0 to solve it.

Teaching Tip **Visual** Students might incorrectly divide 9 by −3 instead of multiplying in Example 2. Encourage students to write the step that shows multiplying each side by the same integer.

2 Teach

Guided Instruction

In this lesson, students learn to solve one-step equations with integers. Show students that the inverse operation with the same integer is applied to each side to isolate the variable, using the properties of equality. As students look at an equation, you may want to suggest that they begin solving by asking themselves, "What has been done to the variable?" and "What is the opposite of doing that?"

Teaching Tip **Cooperative Learning** Have students work in pairs, with one student identifying the integer and the other student identifying the inverse operation needed to isolate the variable and solve the equation.

Reaching All Learners

Through Visual Cues

Suggest that students use colored pencils to circle the integer that must be moved (or operated on) in order to isolate the variable. Then students can use a different color to write the step of performing the inverse operation on each side of the equation.

Close

Summarize

Ask students which operations undo, or are inverses of, each other. Discuss why it is necessary to perform the same operation on both sides of the equation when isolating the variable.

2-5 Solving Equations Containing Integers **101**

- **Reaching All Learners** recommends alternative approaches to the lesson at point-of-use.

- **Teaching Tips** make your teaching more adaptable to the range of learning styles in your classroom.

HOLT MATHEMATICS COURSE 2

Chapter 1: Algebraic Reasoning
Lesson 1-4: Powers of Ten and Scientific Notation

KEY OBJECTIVES

- Learn to express large numbers in scientific notation.

LESSON TUTORIALS
HOLT, RINEHART AND WINSTON

Writing Numbers in Scientific Notation

Write 11,700,000 in scientific notation.

Move the decimal until the result is a number between 1 and 10.

Move 1 place	Move 2 places	Move 3 places	Move 4 places
1170000.0	117000.00	11700.000	1170.0000
> 10	> 10	> 10	> 10

Move 5 places	Move 6 places	Move 7 places	Move 8 places
117.00000	11.700000	1.1700000	0.11700000
> 10	> 10	< 10	< 1 too far!

$11{,}700{,}000 = 1.17 \times 10^7$

The exponent is equal to the number of places the decimal point is moved.

Scientific notation is a method of writing very large or very small numbers using powers of 10.

Hundreds of videos available!

Lesson Tutorial Videos

- Illustrate every example!
- Your students' personal take-home tutor
- Reach your visual and auditory learners
- Available online or on CD-ROM
- 276 videos for *Course 1*
- 294 videos for *Course 2*
- 333 videos for *Course 3*

Only from Holt!

IDEA Works! Special Education CD-ROM

- Modified tests, quizzes, and worksheets
- Adapted format for students with special needs

LESSON **1-1** **Practice A**
Variables and Expressions

Write each algebraic expression in words.

algebraic expression
a mathematical phrase that contains operations, numbers, and/or variables

1. $a + 3$ ______

2. $2x$ ______

3. $5 - y$ ______

4. $\frac{n}{4}$ ______

5. Clint runs c miles.
Brenda runs 2 miles more than Clint.
Write an expression for the number of miles Brenda runs. ______

Evaluate each expression for $a = 2$ and $b = 6$.
The first one has been started for you.

evaluate
replace the variable with a number

6. $a + b$ $2 + \quad =$ ______

7. $b - a$ ______

8. ab ______

"If they can hold it in their hand, they will hold it in their head." **– Jan Scheer, Holt author**

Program Highlights

Count on Holt Mathematics for

Success on High-Stakes Tests

3

Test prep that covers the basics AND develops higher order thinking

Integrated test prep means no surprises on test day. *Holt Mathematics* includes lesson and cumulative review in standardized test format throughout every lesson and chapter to develop student confidence in test-taking skills—without taking time away from core content.

Multi-Step Test Prep uses real-world scenarios to develop higher order thinking skills.

Test Prep and Spiral Review provide daily practice of new and previously taught skills in standardized test format.

MULTI-STEP TEST PREP

CHAPTER 1

Go for the Gold The table shows the number of medals won by the United States at four Summer Olympic Games.

1. Find the total number of medals won by the United States at each Olympics. Then order the Olympic sites from the greatest number of medals won to the least.
2. Estimate the total number of gold medals won by the United States at these four Olympics. Explain how you found your estimate.

Olympic Medals Won by U.S. Athletes				
Year	Site	Gold	Silver	Bronze
1992	Barcelona	37	34	37
1996	Atlanta	44	32	25
2000	Sydney	40	24	33
2004	Athens	35	39	29

3. To compare the performances of U.S. athletes at different Olympics, Jocelyn assigns 3 points to each gold medal, 2 points to each silver medal, and 1 point to each bronze medal. To find the total number of U.S. points for the Barcelona Olympics, she writes the expression $3 \times 37 + 2 \times 34 + 1 \times 37$. Explain how to evaluate this expression, and then find the point total.
4. In 1996, Romania won 2^2 gold medals, 7^1 silver medals, and 3^2 bronze medals. How many of each medal did Romania win? Find the difference in the number of medals won by the United States and the number of medals won by Romania in 1996.
5. The total number of medals won by the United States at each Summer Olympics since 1896 is $3^7 + 2$. About how many more medals do U.S. athletes need to win in order to have a total of 2,200?

Multi-Step Test Prep

Multi-Step Test Prep 39

HOLT MATH

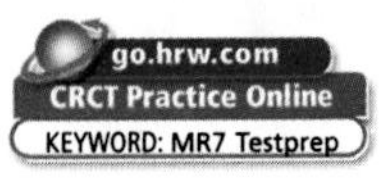

CHAPTER 1

CRCT Prep

CUMULATIVE ASSESSMENT, CHAPTER 1

Multiple Choice

1. Jonah has 31 boxes of baseball cards. If each box contains 183 cards, about how many baseball cards does Jonah have in his collection?

   (A) 3,000 cards (C) 9,000 cards
   (B) 6,000 cards (D) 12,000 cards

2. Which of the following does NOT ... a value of 27?

   (F) 3^3 (H) $3 \times 3 +$ ...
   (G) $3^2 + 3 \times 7$ (J) $9^2 \div 3$

3. What are the next two terms in t... following sequence?

   6, 3, 12, 6, 24, ...

   (A) 3, 12 (C) 12, 48
   (B) 6, 36 (D) 18, 72

4. Which of the following correctly ... the use of the Distributive Proper... find the product of 64 and 8?

   (F) $64 \times 8 = (8 \times 60) + (8 \times 4)$
   (G) $64 \times 8 = 8 \times 64$
   (H) $64 \times 8 = 8 + (60 + 4)$
   (J) $64 \times 8 = (8 \times 4) \times 60$

5. What is five billion, two hundred ... two million, six hundred thousan... three hundred eleven in standard form?

   (A) 5,252,603,011 (C) 5,252,600...
   (B) 52,526,311 (D) 5,252,060...

6. The attendance at a local library is shown in the table below. How many people visited the library last week

Last Week's Attendance	
Sunday	Closed
Monday	78

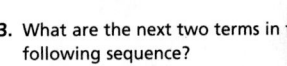

48 *Chapter 1 Whole Numbers an...*

CRCT Prep provides a cumulative assessment in standardized test format.

CHAPTER 1

Test Tackler

TEST TACKLER

Standardized Test Strategies

Multiple Choice: Eliminate Answer Choices

You can solve some math problems without doing detailed calculations. You can use mental math, estimation, or logical reasoning to help you eliminate answer choices and save time.

EXAMPLE 1

Which number is the closest estimate for 678 + 189?

(A) 700 (C) 1,000
(B) 900 (D) 5,000

You can use logical reasoning to eliminate choice A because it is too small. The estimated sum has to be greater than 700 because 678 + 189 is greater than 700.

Choice D may also be eliminated because the value is too large. The estimated sum will be less than 5,000.

Round 678 up to 700 and 189 up to 200. Then find the sum of 700 and 200: 700 + 200 = 900. You can eliminate choice C because it is greater than 900.

Choice B is the closest estimate.

EXAMPLE 2

Which of the following numbers is the standard form of four million, six hundred eight thousand, fifteen?

(F) 468,015 (H) 4,068,150
(G) 4,608,015 (J) 4,600,815,000

Logical reasoning can be used to eliminate choices. Numbers that have a place value in the millions must have at least seven but no more than nine digits. Choices F and J can be eliminated because they do not have the correct number of digits.

Both choices G and H have the correct range of digits, so narrow it down further. The number must end in 15. Choice H ends in 50, so it cannot be correct. Eliminate it.

The correct answer choice is G.

46 *Chapter 1 Whole Numbers and Patterns*

Test Tackler targets specific test-taking strategies to help students become savvy test-takers.

"Rich problem solving experiences help students succeed both inside and outside of the math classroom."

— Dr. Jennie Bennett, Holt author

Program Highlights

Count on Holt Mathematics for

Integrated Technology that enhances learning

4

Resources help you manage your classroom and motivate students to take learning one step further.

Holt Mathematics empowers you with key management and presentation tools that help you meet the needs of a broad range of students.

Interactive Answers and Solutions CD-ROM allows teachers to create a screen of selected answers and access complete solutions.

One-Stop Planner® CD-ROM with Test and Practice Generator contains everything you need to plan and manage your lessons in one place.

- All print ancillaries
- Customizable lesson plans
- Holt Calendar Planner®
- Holt PuzzlePro®
- ExamView Test and Practice Generator

Transparencies CD-ROM enhances instruction with **Daily Warm-Ups, Teaching Transparencies, Additional Examples** and more! Available in print or on CD-ROM

Power Presentations CD-ROM contains colorful, animated, editable presentations for every lesson.

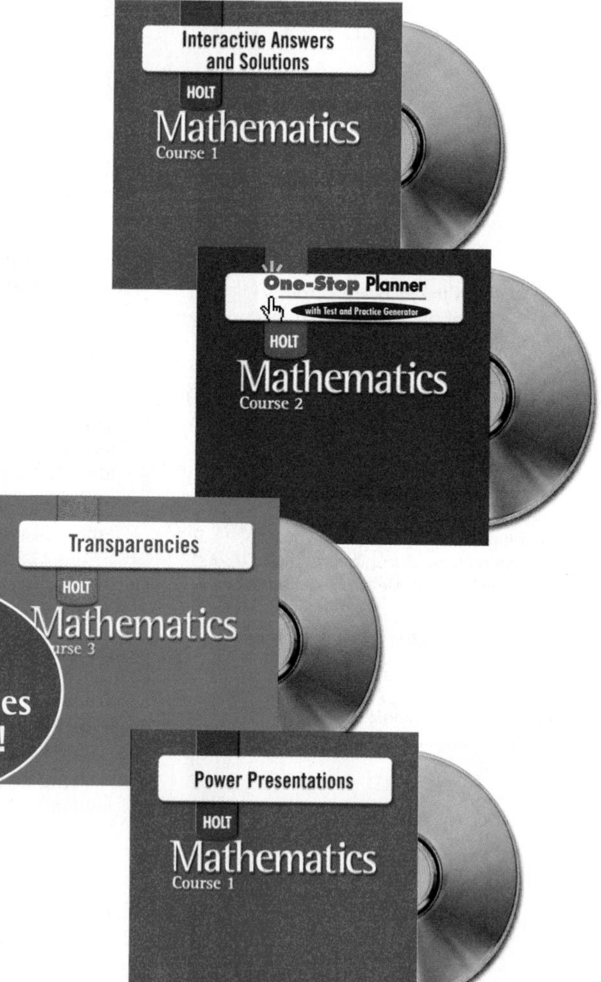

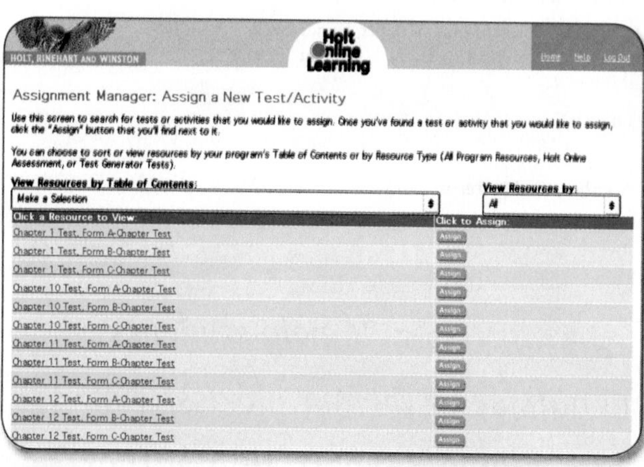

Holt Online Assessment

- Diagnoses individual student performance by standards and textbook objectives
- Automatically assigns resources to strengthen students' skills
- Tracks student progress in one easy-to-manage reporting system

INTEGRATED TECHNOLOGY

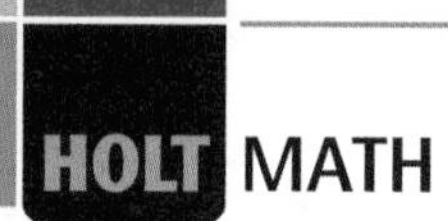

With *Holt Mathematics* technology, students get all the help they need, any time they need it. Interactive features and online tools make the math more meaningful to deepen student understanding.

Premier Online Edition makes math come alive!
- **Lesson Tutorial Videos**
- Interactive practice with feedback
- Online study tools

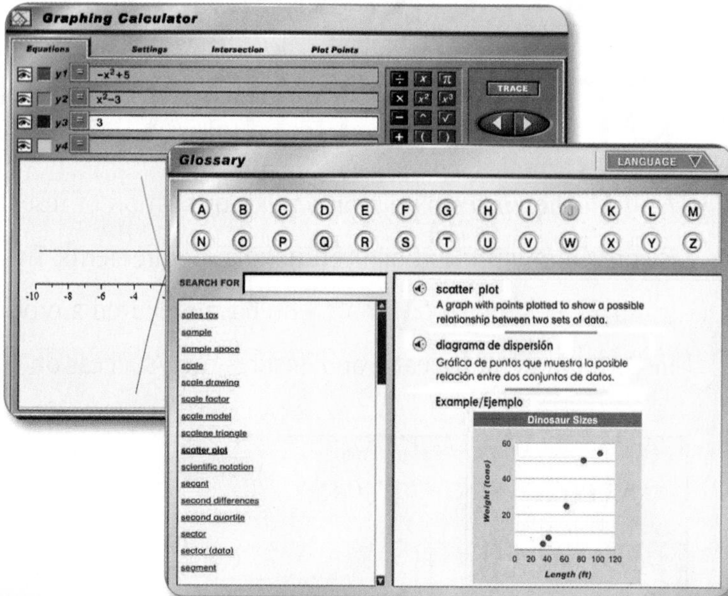

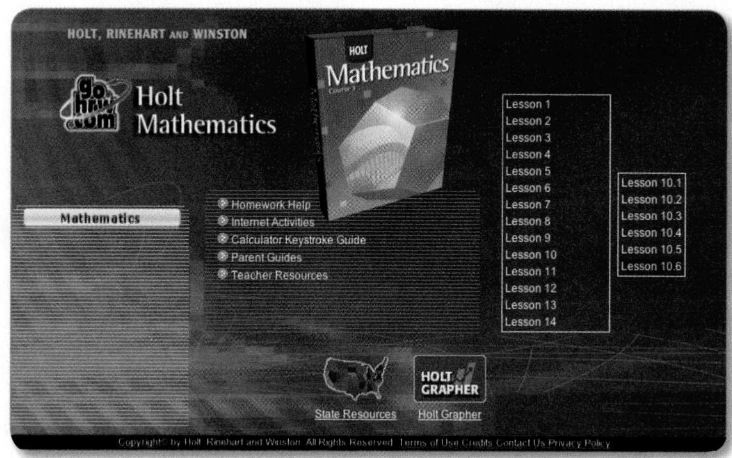

go.hrw.com gives students easy access to lesson resources.
- Homework Help Online
- **Intervention** and **Enrichment** exercises
- Online games and projects

Student One Stop CD-ROM solves the backpack problem.
- Entire *Student Edition*
- Workbooks
- **Intervention** and **Enrichment** exercises

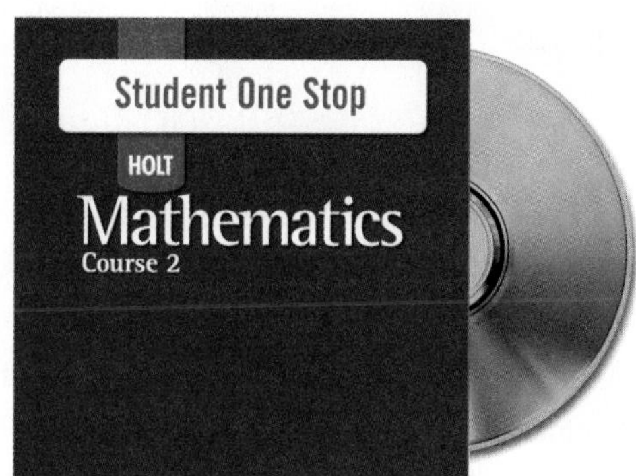

> *"Technology, when used appropriately, can improve students' mathematical understanding and problem-solving skills."*
>
> **– Dr. Bert K. Waits, Holt author**

Program Highlights

Program Research

Count on **Holt Mathematics** to be

Grounded in research, built by experts, proven in classrooms

Holt Mathematics is built on a solid foundation of research, proven to work in the classroom, and is consistent with No Child Left Behind requirements. This research is backed by the expertise of a world-class team of authors who have executed a program that makes students *want* to learn, helps them *actually* learn, and ensures their success on high-stakes tests.

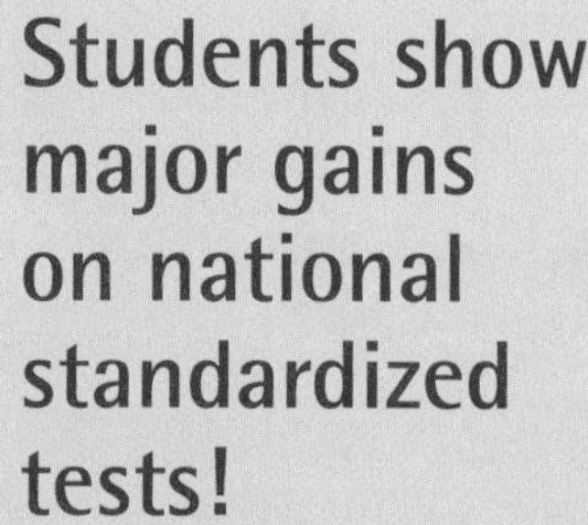

Students show major gains on national standardized tests!

Students using *Holt Middle School Math* consecutively for two years show a significant improvement in performance on the SAT 10, a national standardized test.

On average, *Holt Middle School Math* students score at least a full grade level ABOVE their peers!

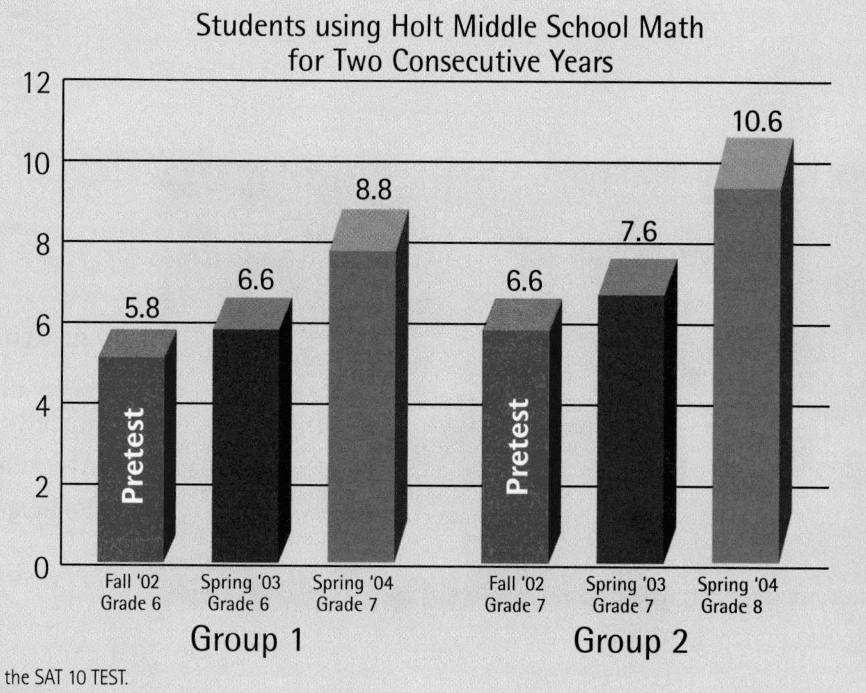

* The national norms are established by the publisher of the SAT 10 TEST.

The Research Underlying the Program

Holt established a pattern of interaction with the educational community throughout all stages of the program's development.

Needs Assessment
- Teacher Interviews
- University Faculty Interviews
- Federal, State, and Local Agencies
- Advisory Panels
- Task Forces
- Academic Conferences
- Surveys with Teachers, Sales, Administrators

Pedagogical Research
- Thorough
- Effective
- Scientifically-Based

Program Development
- Classroom Observation
- Field Testing of Prototypes
- Reviewed by Program and Field Consultants
- Reviewed by Teachers and Administrators

Program Validation
- User Surveys
- Student and Teacher Appraisals
- Field Consultant and Sales Reports

Program Effectiveness
- Post-Implementation Effectiveness Studies
- Valid and Reliable Tests

Jennie M. Bennett, Ed.D.
Mathematics Teacher, Hartman Middle School | Houston , TX

Strategic Problem-Solving

"Problem solving plays a pivotal role in mathematics learning and is an integral part of the *Holt Mathematics* program. Problem solving should strengthen and stretch students' thinking and build students' confidence in their ability to solve challenging problems.

Reading mathematics is a necessary skill for all students to master. Students who have English as a second language will face words that may be confusing to them. For example a table in mathematics can mean something different in a student's native language than in the context of mathematics. *Holt Mathematics* provides Reading and Writing Opportunities at the chapter level as well as at the lesson level."

SUPPORTING RESEARCH

Artzt, Alice F., and Shirel Yaloz-Femia. (1999). *Mathematical reasoning during small-group problem solving. In Developing mathematical reasoning in grades K-12.* **Reston, Va:** National Council of Teachers of Mathematics.

Jensen, Eric. (1998). *Teaching with the brain in mind.* **Alexandria, Va: Association for Supervision and Curriculum Development.**

Edward B. Burger, Ph.D.
Professor of Mathematics and Chair | Williams College, MA

Student Engagement

"Learning should be fun. Deep and abstract ideas are challenging to all, but the challenge should be a pleasurable one that students want to conquer. Thus we offer levity throughout the *Holt Mathematics* series– jokes for the teachers to share with their students and entertaining antics on the accompanying videos, mixing mathematical insights with laughs. There is no better student than the student who wants to learn. In this program we worked hard to make learning fun so students enjoy the journey and, as a result, attain a deeper understanding of the mathematics they explore.

The mathematics is developed in a meaningful manner with student readers in mind. Questions such as "What would resonate with real middle school students today?" were asked at every stage of the writing."

SUPPORTING RESEARCH

Ames, R., & Ames, C. (Eds.). (1984). *Research on motivation in education: Vol. 1. Student motivation.* New York: Academic Press.

Brewster, Cori, and Jennifer Fager. (2000). *Increasing Student Engagement and Motivation: From Time-on-Task to Homework.* **Portland, Ore.: Northwest Regional Educational Laboratory.**

David J. Chard, Ph.D.
Assistant Professor and Director of Graduate Studies in Special Education| University of Oregon

Reaching All Learners

“*Holt Mathematics* is designed to assist teachers in helping all their students to learn conceptual knowledge, skills, and strategies essential to understanding sophisticated mathematics.

This program was designed with instructional features that represent a coherent pedagogical approach to mathematics instruction. Each lesson begins with carefully wrought examples of all of the skills, concepts, and strategies addressed. Key to any instructional program is sufficient scaffolding to support student learning. This ensures that all students are able to understand and solve increasingly complex problems.”

SUPPORTING RESEARCH

Bransford, J. D., Brown, A. L., & Cocking, R. R. (Eds.). (2000). *How people learn: Brain, mind, experience, and school.* Washington, DC: National Research Council.

Gersten, R., Chard, D. J., Baker, S., et al. (2005). *A meta-analysis of research on mathematics instruction for students with learning disabilities.* Signal Hill, CA: Instructional Research Group.

Audrey Jackson
Program Coordinator for Leadership Development | St. Louis, MO

Learning and the Classroom Environment

“The fundamental goal of *Holt Mathematics* is to provide teachers with the necessary tools and understanding of mathematics to ensure student success at all levels.

Highly qualified teachers of mathematics establish and create cultures for learning for all students within their classroom. *Holt Mathematics* promotes successful learning by supporting numerous teaching strategies, including direct instruction and cooperative learning.”

SUPPORTING RESEARCH

National Council of Teachers of Mathematics (2000). *Principles and Standards for School Mathematics.* Reston, VA: National Council of Teachers of Mathematics.

Tomlinson, C. (1995). *How to differentiate instruction in mixed ability classrooms.* Alexander, VA: Association for Supervision and Curriculum Development.

Wiggins, G. and J. McTighe (1998). *Understanding by design.* Alexander, VA: Association for Supervision and Curriculum Development.

Paul A. Kennedy, Ph.D.
Professor, Department of Mathematics | Colorado State University

Algebraic Thinking

"When students enter the middle grades, they are beginning the preparation for the transition to more advanced mathematical topics such as algebra and geometry while enhancing their basic arithmetic knowledge. It is crucial that they develop abstract reasoning as well as symbolic manipulation skills.

In *Holt Mathematics*, content is carefully developed using methods aligned with standard best practices. The idea of "doing and undoing" is developed early in the program and carried thought the series. Additionally students need to see the relationships between the math they are learning and real-world scenarios."

SUPPORTING RESEARCH

Vygotsky, L.S. (1978). *Mind and society: The development of higher mental processes.* Cambridge, MA: Harvard University Press.

Driscoll, Mark J. (1997). *Fostering algebraic thinking.* **Portsmouth, NH.; Heinemann.**

Freddie L. Renfro
Former Director of Mathematics Instruction K–12 | Texas City Independent School District

Differentiated Instruction

"Imagine a classroom where diversity in learning is the norm, and the teacher responds to the learners' needs with flexible strategies, open dialogue, and ongoing assessment.

Every child is unique. Finding ways to tailor instruction to meet individual student needs in the classroom can be a manageable task with the right support. In the *Holt Mathematics* series, we promote differentiated instruction by including activities that address a variety of learning styles: discovery learning, the use of concrete examples, and student interaction, to name a few.

The *Teacher's Edition* offers suggestions for differentiated assessment as well so that students have the opportunity to demonstrate their understanding in a manner that reflects their learning style."

SUPPORTING RESEARCH

Tomlinson, C. (1999). *The differentiated classroom: Responding to the needs of all learners.* Alexandria, VA: Association for Supervision and Curriculum Development.

Willis, S. and Mann, Larry. (2000). *Differentiating instruction.* Alexandria, VA: Association for Supervision and Curriculum Development.

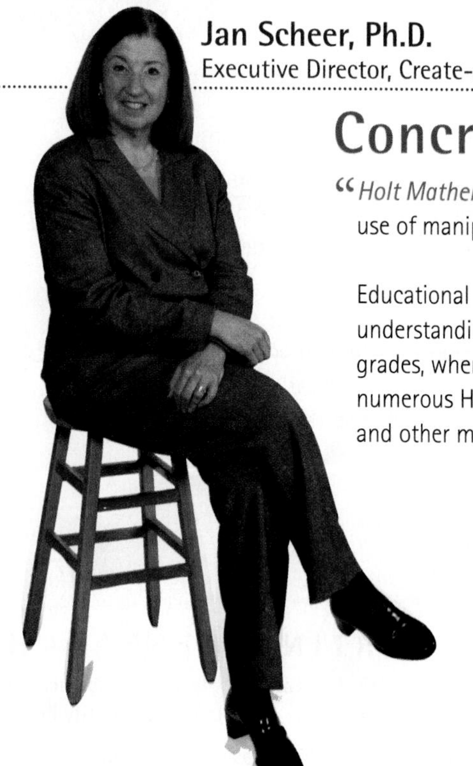

Jan Scheer, Ph.D.
Executive Director, Create-A-Vision

Concrete Understanding

"*Holt Mathematics* makes use of mathematical modeling and provides many options for the use of manipulatives to enhance student understanding of abstract concepts.

Educational research demonstrates the effectiveness of hands-on learning in supplementing understanding of mathematical ideas for students This is especially important in the middle grades, when students are exposed to increasingly abstract concepts. This program provides numerous Hands-On Labs where students use algebra tiles, pattern blocks, two-color counters, and other materials to provide opportunities for concrete methods for learning selected topics."

SUPPORTING RESEARCH

Bohan, Harry J., and Peggy Bohan Shawaker (1994). Using manipulatives effectively: A drive down rounding road. *Arithmetic Teacher 41 (5): 246-48*

Stein, Mary Kay, and Jane W. Bovalino. (2001). Manipulatives: One piece of the puzzle. *Mathematics Teaching in the Middle School, 6 (6): 356-59.*

Bert K. Waits, Ph.D.
Professor Emeritus of Mathematics | The Ohio State University

Technology to Enhance Learning

"Research has demonstrated that technology, when used appropriately, can improve students' mathematical understanding and problem-solving skills. Similarly, technological tools can help teachers challenge students to use and understand mathematics in real-world scenarios.

The *Holt Mathematics* series presents a balanced approach to learning. We stress that students must utilize all available tools, including mental and paper-and- pencil skills and technology, in the mathematics-learning process. This series uses technology not as an end in itself, but rather as a means for understanding and application. Current research supports this use of computer software including spreadsheets, dynamic geometry software, and graphing calculators. "

SUPPORTING RESEARCH

Graham, A.T., & J.O.J. Thomas. (2000). Building a versatile understanding of algebraic variables with a graphic calculator. *Educational Studies in Mathematics*, 41 (3), 265-282.

Hallar, Jeannie C., & Karen Norwood. (1999). The effects of a graphing-approach intermediate algebra curriculum on students' understanding of function. *Journal for Research in Mathematics Education*, 30 (2), 220-226.

Holt Mathematics Program Components

Georgia Student Edition
Georgia Student One Stop CD-ROM
Georgia Premier Online Edition
Georgia Teacher's Edition

Assessment and Intervention

Are You Ready? Intervention and Enrichment
Assessment Resources
Questioning Strategies
Ready to Go On? Intervention and Enrichment

Differentiated Instruction

Alternate Openers: Explorations Transparencies
Family Involvement Activities
Hands-on Lab Activities
IDEA Works! Special Education CD-ROM
Lesson Tutorial Videos
Manipulatives Kit
Multilingual Glossary
Interdisciplinary Posters
Premier Online Edition
Student One Stop CD-ROM
Success for English Language Learners
Technology Lab Activities

Workbooks

Georgia Homework and Practice Workbook
Know-It Notebook
Georgia Problem Solving Workbook
CRCT Prep Workbook

Spanish Resources

Student Edition
Are You Ready? Intervention and Enrichment
Assessment Resources
Homework and Practice Workbook
Lesson Tutorial Videos with Spanish closed captioning
Ready to Go On? Intervention and Assessment
Family Involvement Activities

High-Stakes CRCT Test Prep

Countdown to CRCT Transparencies
CRCT Prep for Middle School CD-ROM
CRCT Prep Workbook

Integrated Technology

Are You Ready? Intervention and Enrichment CD-ROM
CRCT Prep for Middle School CD-ROM
IDEA Works! Special Education CD-ROM
Interactive Answers and Solutions CD-ROM
Lesson Tutorial Videos CD-ROM
Georgia One-Stop Planner with Test and Practice Generator and State-Specific Resources CD-ROM
Power Presentations CD-ROM
Georgia Premier Online Edition
Ready to Go On? Intervention and Enrichment CD-ROM
Georgia Student One Stop CD-ROM
Technology Lab Activities
Transparencies CD-ROM

Teaching Resources

Chapter Resource Books
Interactive Answers and Solutions CD-ROM
Know-It Notebook Teacher's Guide with Transparencies
Lesson Plans
Lesson Transparencies
Georgia One-Stop Planner with Test and Practice Generator and State-Specific Resources CD-ROM
Power Presentations CD-ROM
Georgia Solutions Key
Transparencies CD-ROM

Anytime, Anyplace Professional Development: Building a Community of Learners

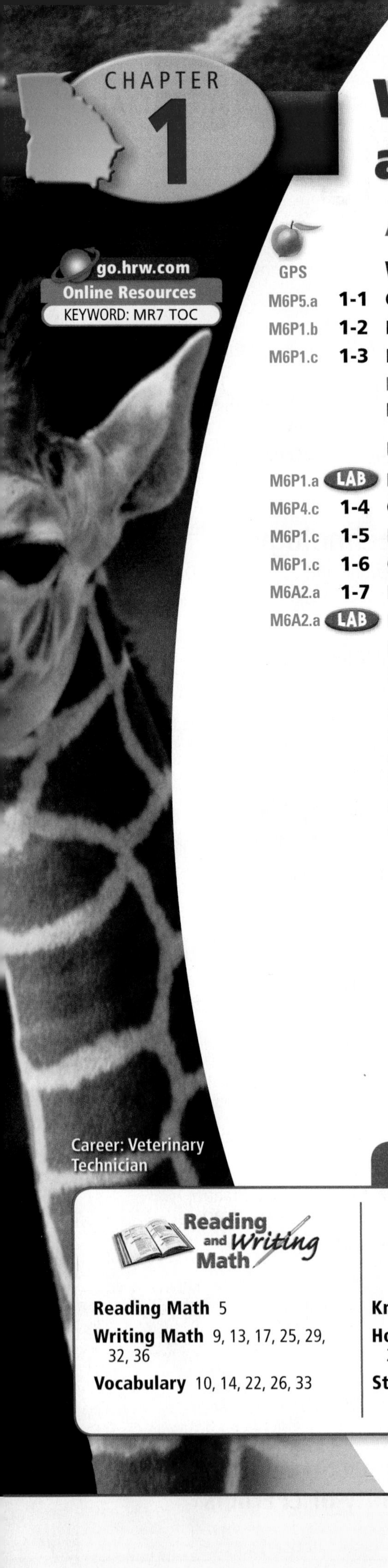

Whole Numbers and Patterns

go.hrw.com
Online Resources
KEYWORD: MR7 TOC

Career: Veterinary Technician

Tools for Success

Study Skills

Introduction to Algebra

CHAPTER 2

Career: Traffic Engineer

Table of Contents

Tools for Success

CHAPTER 3

Decimals

Career: Sports Historian

Tools for Success

Number Theory and Fractions

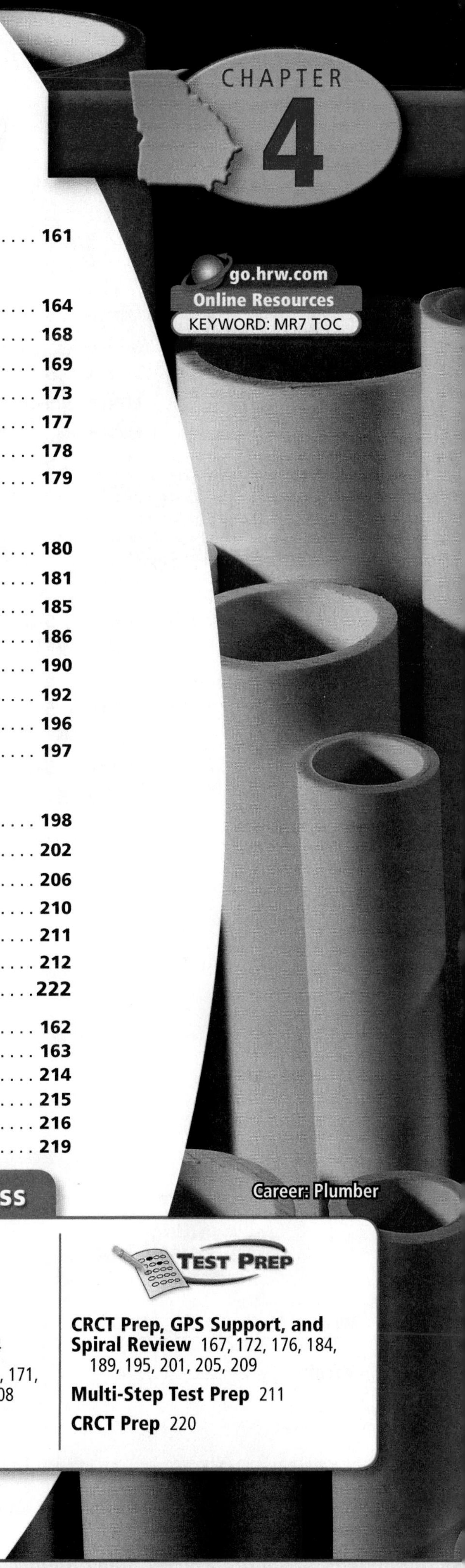

CHAPTER 4

go.hrw.com
Online Resources
KEYWORD: MR7 TOC

Career: Plumber

Tools for Success

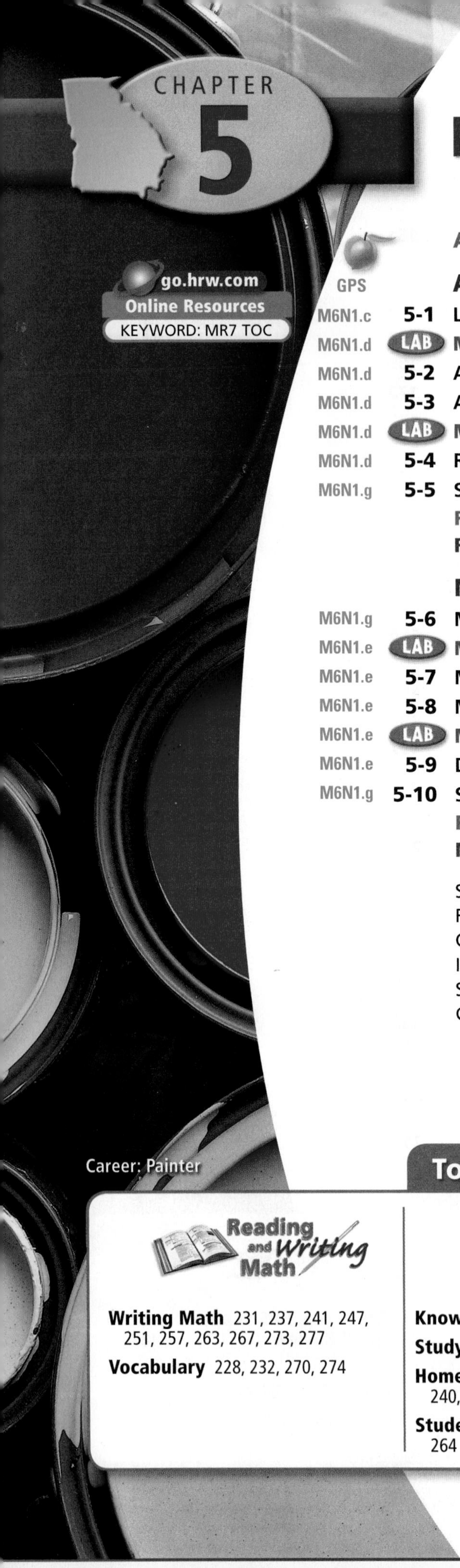

CHAPTER 5

Fraction Operations

go.hrw.com
Online Resources
KEYWORD: MR7 TOC

Career: Painter

Tools for Success

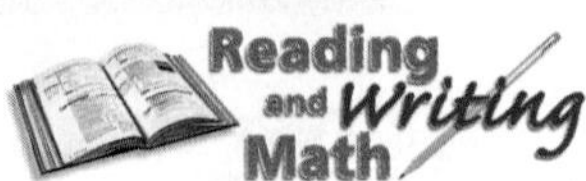

Collecting and Displaying Data

CHAPTER 6

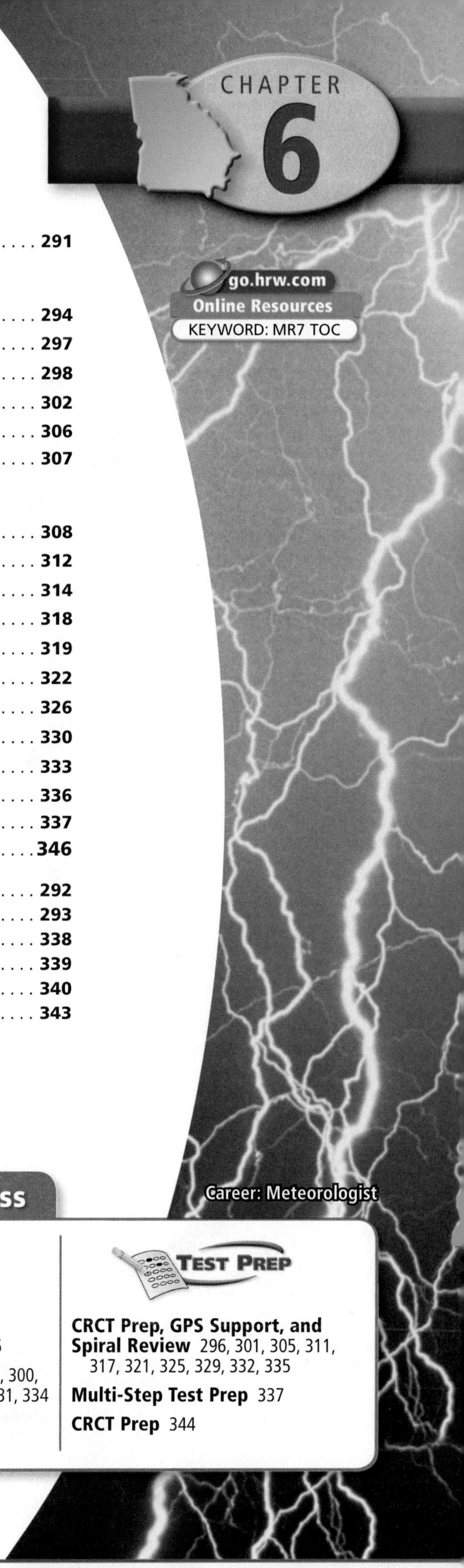

go.hrw.com
Online Resources
KEYWORD: MR7 TOC

Career: Meteorologist

Tools for Success

CHAPTER 7

Proportional Relationships

go.hrw.com
Online Resources
KEYWORD: MR7 TOC

Career: Fisheries Biologist

Tools for Success

Reading Math 352, 356, 362
Writing Math 351, 355, 359, 365, 369, 372, 377, 384, 388, 393, 397, 401
Vocabulary 362, 366, 370, 374, 381, 394, 400

Know-It Notebook Chapter 7
Homework Help Online 354, 358, 368, 371, 376, 383, 387, 392, 396
Student Help 363, 364, 367, 382, 394

CRCT Prep, GPS Support, and Spiral Review 355, 359, 365, 369, 372, 377, 384, 388, 393, 397
Multi-Step Test Prep 399
Test Tackler 408
CRCT Prep 410

Geometric Relationships

CHAPTER 8

go.hrw.com
Online Resources
KEYWORD: MR7 TOC

Career: Artist

Tools for Success

Measurement and Geometry

Career: Mathematician

Tools for Success

Measurement: Area and Volume

CHAPTER 10

go.hrw.com
Online Resources
KEYWORD: MR7 TOC

Career: Landscape Architect

Tools for Success

Integers, Graphs, and Functions

Tools for Success

Probability

CHAPTER 12

go.hrw.com
Online Resources
KEYWORD: MR7 TOC

Career: Financial Advisor

Tools for Success

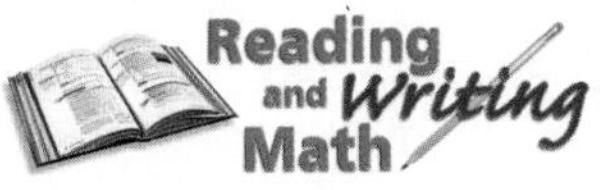

INTERDISCIPLINARY CONNECTIONS

Many fields of study require knowledge of the mathematical skills and concepts taught in *Holt Mathematics Course 1.* Examples and exercises throughout the book highlight the math you will need to understand in order to study other subjects, such as art or finance, or to pursue a career in fields such as medicine or architecture.

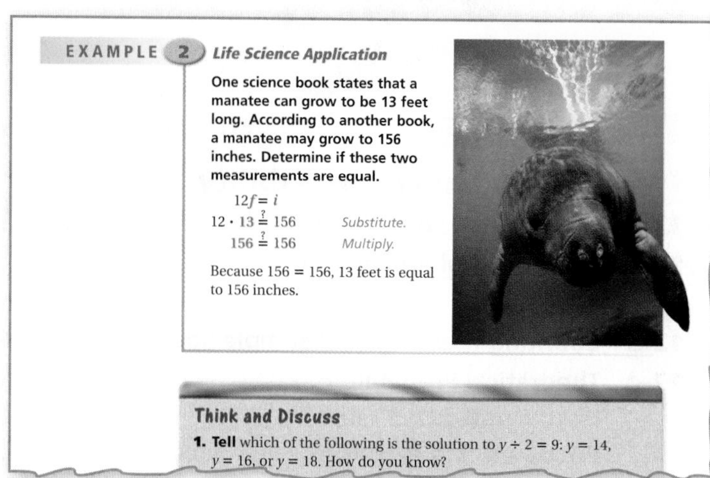
EXAMPLE 2 Life Science Application
One science book states that a manatee can grow to be 13 feet long. According to another book, a manatee may grow to 156 inches. Determine if these two measurements are equal.
12f = i
12 · 13 ≟ 156 Substitute.
156 ≟ 156 Multiply.
Because 156 = 156, 13 feet is equal to 156 inches.
Think and Discuss
1. Tell which of the following is the solution to y ÷ 2 = 9: y = 14, y = 16, or y = 18. How do you know?

Science

Language Arts

Health and Fitness

Social Studies

Economics

Fine and Performing Arts

WHY LEARN MATHEMATICS?

Throughout the text, links to interesting application topics, such as entertainment, music, and technology, will help you see how math is used in the real world. Some of these links have additional information and activities at go.hrw.com. For a complete list of all real-world problems in ***Holt Mathematics Course 1,*** see page 815 in the Index.

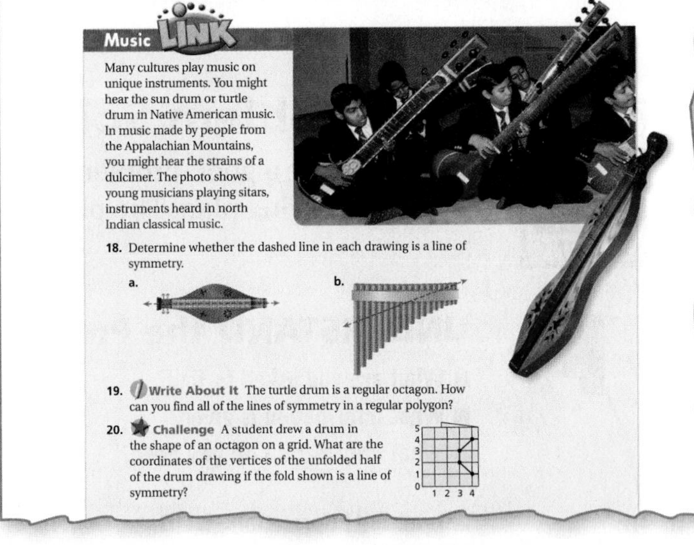

Music LINK
Many cultures play music on unique instruments. You might hear the sun drum or turtle drum in Native American music. In music made by people from the Appalachian Mountains, you might hear the strains of a dulcimer. The photo shows young musicians playing sitars, instruments heard in north Indian classical music.
18. Determine whether the dashed line in each drawing is a line of symmetry.
a.
b.
19. Write About It The turtle drum is a regular octagon. How can you find all of the lines of symmetry in a regular polygon?
20. Challenge A student drew a drum in the shape of an octagon on a grid. What are the coordinates of the vertices of the unfolded half of the drum drawing if the fold shown is a line of symmetry?

Real-World LINKS

Earth Science LINK

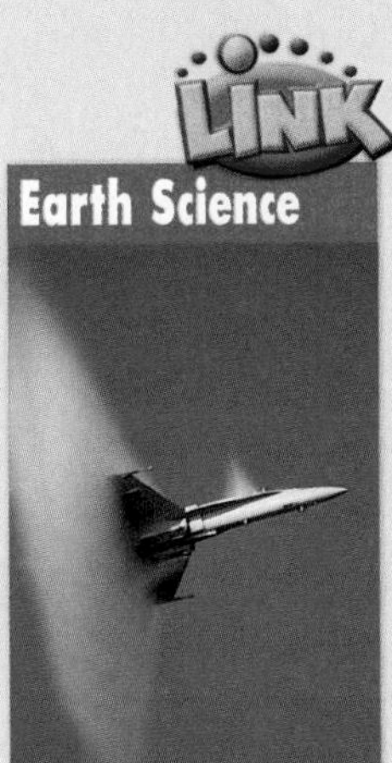

This F/A-18 Hornet makes a vapor cloud by flying at Mach 0.98, just under the speed of sound.

Georgia LINK Life Science

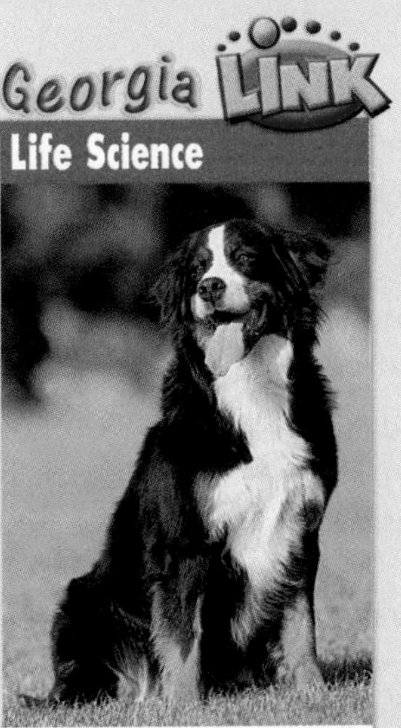

The University of Georgia College of Veterinary Medicine runs a program called Dog Doctors. Veterinary students bring Bernese Mountain dogs to schools across Georgia to educate students about pet care.

Georgia LINK Social Studies

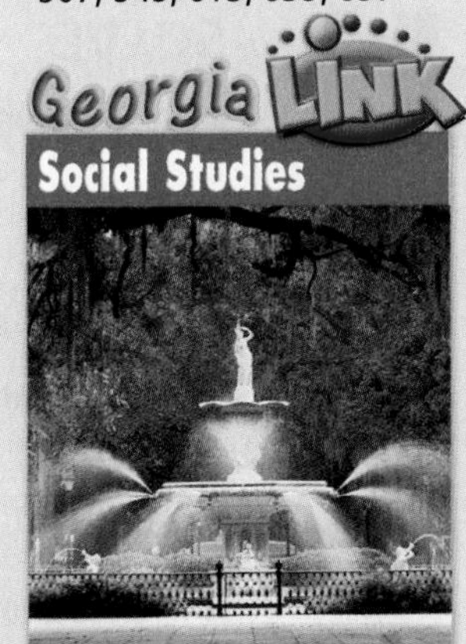

Savannah is considered to be the first planned city in the U.S. The streets are laid out in a grid with 22 public squares placed throughout the city.

Focus on Problem Solving

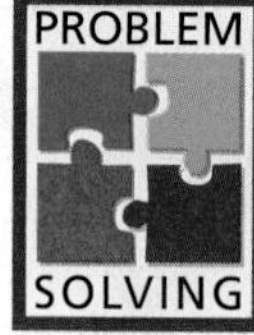

The Problem Solving Plan

In order to be a good problem solver, you first need a good problem-solving plan. The plan used in this book is detailed below.

UNDERSTAND the Problem

■ **What are you asked to find?**	Restate the question in your own words.
■ **What information is given?**	Identify the facts in the problem.
■ **What information do you need?**	Determine which facts are needed to answer the question.
■ **Is all the information given?**	Determine whether all the facts are given.
■ **Is there any information given that you will not use?**	Determine which facts, if any, are unnecessary to solve the problem.

Make a PLAN

■ **Have you ever solved a similar problem?**	Think about other problems like this that you successfully solved.
■ **What strategy or strategies can you use?**	Determine a strategy that you can use and how you will use it.

SOLVE

■ **Follow your plan.**	Show the steps in your solution. Write your answer as a complete sentence.

LOOK BACK

■ **Have you answered the question?**	Be sure that you answered the question that is being asked.
■ **Is your answer reasonable?**	Your answer should make sense in the context of the problem.
■ **Is there another strategy you could use?**	Solving the problem using another strategy is a good way to check your work.
■ **Did you learn anything while solving this problem that could help you solve similar problems in the future?**	Try to remember the problems you have solved and the strategies you used to solve them.

Using the Problem Solving Plan

During summer vacation, Nicholas will visit first his cousin and then his grandmother. He will be gone for 5 weeks and 2 days, and he will spend 9 more days with his cousin than with his grandmother. How long will he stay with each family member?

UNDERSTAND the Problem

Identify the important information.

- Nicholas's visits will total 5 weeks and 2 days.
- He will spend 9 more days with his cousin than with his grandmother.

The answer will be how long he will stay with each family member.

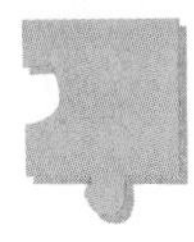

Make a PLAN

You can draw a diagram to show how long Nicholas will stay. Use boxes for the length of each stay. The length of each box will represent the length of each stay.

SOLVE

Think: There are 7 days in a week, so 5 weeks and 2 days is 37 days in all. Your diagram might look like this:

Cousin	? days	9 days	= 37 days	
Grandmother	? days			
Cousin	14 days	9 days	37 − 9 = 28	*Subtract 9 days from the total days.*
Grandmother	14 days		28 ÷ 2 = 14	*Divide this number by 2 for the 2 places he will visit.*

So Nicholas will stay with his cousin for 23 days and with his grandmother for 14 days.

LOOK BACK

Twenty-three days is 9 days longer than 14 days. The total of the two stays is 23 + 14, or 37 days, which is the same as 5 weeks and 2 days. This solution fits the description of Nicholas's trip given in the problem.

USING YOUR BOOK FOR SUCCESS

This book has many features designed to help you learn and study math. Becoming familiar with these features will prepare you for greater success on your exams.

Learn

Preview new **vocabulary** terms listed at the beginning of every lesson.

Study the **examples** to learn new math ideas and skills. The examples include step-by-step solutions.

Practice

Look back at examples from the lesson to solve the **Guided Practice** exercises.

If you get stuck, use the Internet for **Homework Help Online**.

Review

Study and review **vocabulary** from the entire chapter.

Test yourself with **practice problems** from every lesson in the chapter.

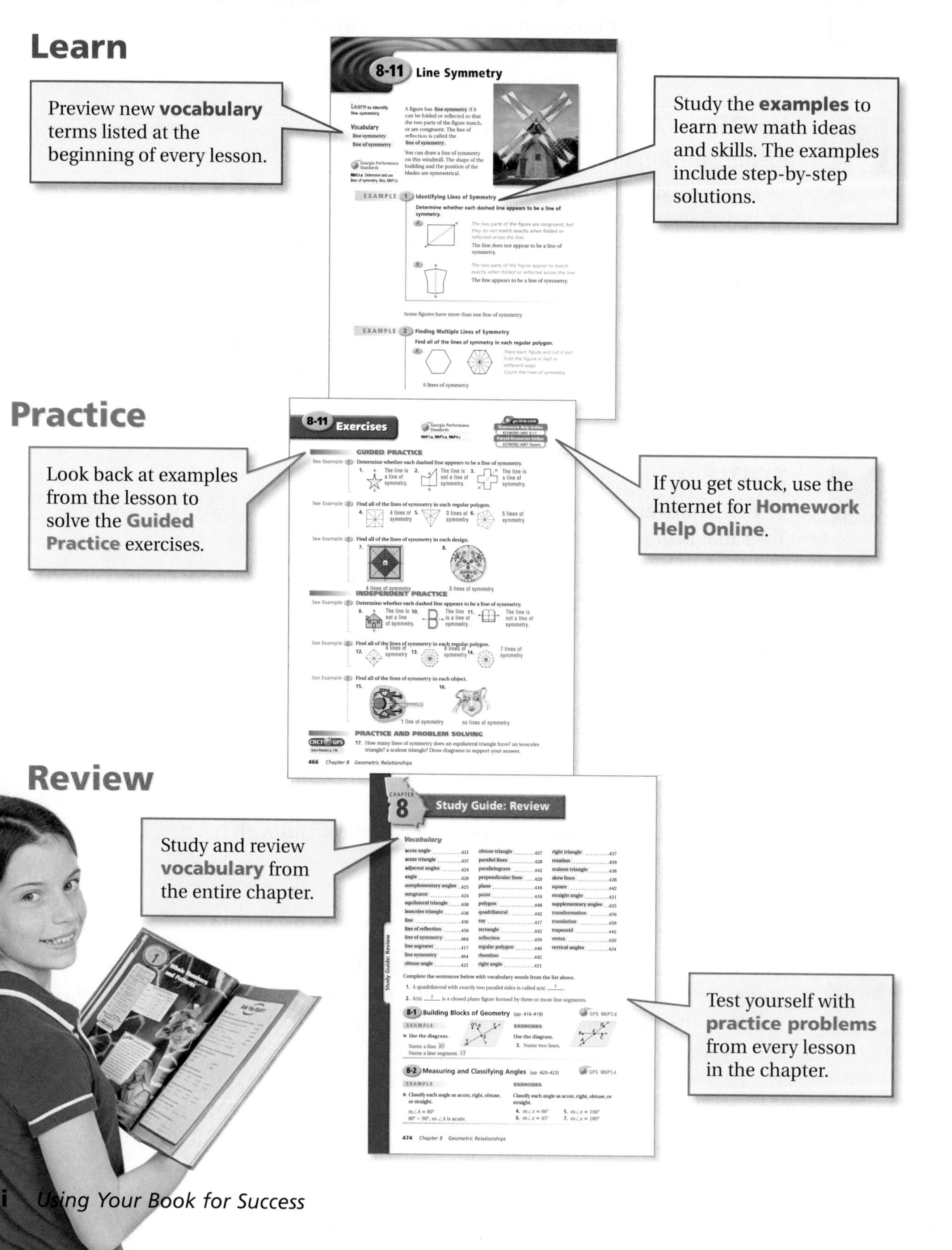

Scavenger Hunt

Use this scavenger hunt to discover a few of the many tools in the Georgia Edition of ***Holt Mathematics*** that you can use to become an independent learner. On a separate sheet of paper, write the answers to each question below. Within each answer, one letter will be in a yellow box. After you have answered every question, identify the letters that would be in yellow boxes and rearrange them to reveal the answer to the question at the bottom of the page.

1. What is the first key **vocabulary** term in the Study Guide: Preview for Chapter 6?

   BAR GRAPH

2. What are you asked to solve in Chapter 4 **Game Time**?

   RIDDLE

3. What hobby is explored in **Problem Solving on Location** in Chapter 12?

   LAKE FISHING

4. What is the last key **vocabulary** term in the Study Guide: Review for Chapter 6?

   STEM AND LEAF PLOT

5. Chapter 5's **Test Tackler** gives strategies for what kind of standardized test item?

   GRIDDED RESPONSE

6. What school subject is connected to math in the **Link** on page 419?

   GEOGRAPHY

7. What keyword would you use for Lesson 7-1 **Homework Help Online**?

   MR7 7-1

8. What **career** is spotlighted on page 412?

   ARTIST

9. What **study strategy** is described on page 485?

   USE MULTIPLE REPRESENTATIONS

Math Humor

What kind of message do you send a snake?

HISTOGRAM

Scavenger Hunt xxiii

CHAPTER 1

Whole Numbers and Patterns

Section 1A

Whole Numbers and Exponents

1-1 **Comparing and Ordering Whole Numbers**
1-2 **Estimating with Whole Numbers**
1-3 **Exponents**

Section 1B

Using Whole Numbers

1-4 **Technology Lab** Explore the Order of Operations
1-4 **Order of Operations**
1-5 **Mental Math**
1-6 **Choose the Method of Computation**
1-7 **Patterns and Sequences**
1-7 **Technology Lab** Find a Pattern in Sequences

Pacing Guide for 45-Minute Classes

Chapter 1

Countdown to Testing Weeks 1, 2

DAY 1	DAY 2	DAY 3	DAY 4	DAY 5
1-1 Lesson	1-2 Lesson	1-3 Lesson	Ready to Go On? Focus on Problem Solving 1-4 Technology Lab	1-4 Lesson
DAY 6	**DAY 7**	**DAY 8**	**DAY 9**	**DAY 10**
1-5 Lesson	1-6 Lesson	1-7 Lesson	1-7 Technology Lab Ready to Go On? Multi-Step Test Prep	Chapter 1 Review
DAY 11				
Chapter 1 Test				

Pacing Guide for 90-Minute Classes

Chapter 1

DAY 1	DAY 2	DAY 3	DAY 4	DAY 5
1-1 Lesson 1-2 Lesson	1-3 Lesson Ready to Go On? Focus on Problem Solving 1-4 Technology Lab	1-4 Lesson 1-5 Lesson	1-6 Lesson 1-7 Lesson	1-7 Technology Lab Ready to Go On? Multi-Step Test Prep Chapter 1 Review
DAY 6				
Chapter 1 Test				

ONGOING ASSESSMENT and INTERVENTION

	DIAGNOSE	PRESCRIBE
Assess Prior Knowledge	**Before Chapter 1**	
	Diagnose readiness for the chapter.  **Are You Ready?** SE p. 3	Prescribe intervention. ***Are You Ready? Intervention*** Skills 3, 4, 34, 54
Formative Assessment	**Before Every Lesson**	
	Diagnose readiness for the lesson. **Warm Up** TE, every lesson	Prescribe intervention. **Skills Bank** SE pp. 749–761 **Reteach** CRB, Chapter 1
	During Every Lesson	
	Diagnose understanding of lesson concepts. **Think and Discuss** SE, every lesson **Write About It** SE, lesson exercises **Journal** TE, lesson exercises	Prescribe intervention. ***Questioning Strategies*** pp. 1–14 **Reading Strategies** CRB, every lesson ***Success for ELL*** pp. 1–14
	After Every Lesson	
	Diagnose mastery of lesson concepts. **Lesson Quiz** TE, every lesson **Test Prep** SE, every lesson ***Test and Practice Generator***	Prescribe intervention. **Reteach** CRB, every lesson **Problem Solving** CRB, every lesson **Test Prep Doctor** TE, lesson exercises ***Homework Help* Online**
	Before Chapter 1 Testing	
	Diagnose mastery of concepts in the chapter. ***Ready to Go On?*** SE pp. 18, 38 **Focus on Problem Solving** SE p. 19 **Multi-Step Test Prep** SE p. 39 **Section Quizzes** AR pp. 5–6 ***Test and Practice Generator***	Prescribe intervention. ***Ready to Go On? Intervention*** **Scaffolding Questions** TE p. 39
	Before High Stakes Testing	
	Diagnose mastery of benchmark concepts. **Test Tackler** SE pp. 46–47 **CRCT Prep** SE pp. 48–49 ***CRCT Prep* CD-ROM**	Prescribe intervention. ***CRCT Prep Workbook***
Summative Assessment	**After Chapter 1**	
	Check mastery of chapter concepts. **Multiple-Choice Tests (Forms A, B, C)** **Free-Response Tests (Forms A, B, C)** **Performance Assessment** AR pp. 7–20 ***Test and Practice Generator*** Check mastery of benchmark concepts. **CRCT**	Prescribe intervention. **Reteach** CRB, every lesson ***Lesson Tutorial Videos*** Chapter 1 Prescribe intervention. ***CRCT Prep Workbook***

KEY: **SE** = *Student Edition* **TE** = *Teacher's Edition* **CRB** = *Chapter Resource Book* **AR** = *Assessment Resources* Available on CD-ROM 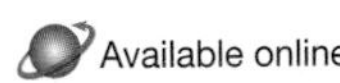 Available online

CHAPTER 1

Supporting the Teacher

Chapter 1 Resource Book

Practice A, B, C
pp. 3–5, 11–13, 20–22, 28–30, 36–38, 45–47, 53–55

Reading Strategies ELL
pp. 9, 18, 26, 34, 43, 51, 59

Puzzles, Twisters, and Teasers
pp. 10, 19, 27, 35, 44, 52, 60

Reteach
pp. 6, 14–15, 23, 31, 39–40, 48, 56

Problem Solving
pp. 8, 17, 25, 33, 42, 50, 58

Challenge
pp. 7, 16, 24, 32, 41, 49, 57

Parent Letter pp. 1–2

Transparencies

Lesson Transparencies, Volume 1 .... Chapter 1
- Teaching Tools
- Warm Ups
- Problem of the Day
- Teaching Transparencies
- Lesson Quizzes

Know-It Notebook .... Chapter 1
- Additional Examples
- Graphic Organizers
- Vocabulary
- Chapter Review
- Foldnotes
- Big Ideas

Alternate Openers: Explorations .... pp. 1–7

Countdown to CRCT .... pp. 1–4

Teacher Tools

Power Presentations®
Complete PowerPoint® presentations for Chapter 1 lessons

Lesson Tutorial Videos® SPANISH
Holt authors Ed Burger and Freddie Renfro present tutorials to support the Chapter 1 lessons.

One-Stop Planner® SPANISH
Easy access to all Chapter 1 resources and assessments, as well as software for lesson planning, test generation, and puzzle creation

IDEA Works!®
Key Chapter 1 resources and assessments modified to address special learning needs

Lesson Plans .... pp. 1–7

Questioning Strategies .... pp. 1–14

Solutions Key .... Chapter 1

Interdisciplinary Posters and Worksheets .... Chapter 1

TechKeys

Lab Resources

Project Teacher Support

Parent Resources

Workbooks

Homework and Practice Workbook SPANISH
Teacher's Edition .... pp. 1–7

Know-It Notebook
Teacher's Guide .... Chapter 1

Problem Solving Workbook SPANISH
Teacher's Guide .... pp. 1–7

CRCT Prep Workbook
Teacher's Guide

Technology Highlights for the Teacher

Power Presentations

Dynamic presentations to engage students. Complete PowerPoint® presentations for every lesson in Chapter 1.

2-1 Solving One-Step Equations

Isolate a variable by using inverse operations which "undo" operations on the variable.

An equation is like a balanced scale. To keep the balance, perform the same operation on both sides.

Inverse Operations	
Operation	**Inverse Operation**
Addition	Subtraction
Subtraction	Addition

One-Stop Planner SPANISH

Easy access to Chapter 1 resources and assessments. Includes lesson-planning, test-generation, and puzzle-creation software.

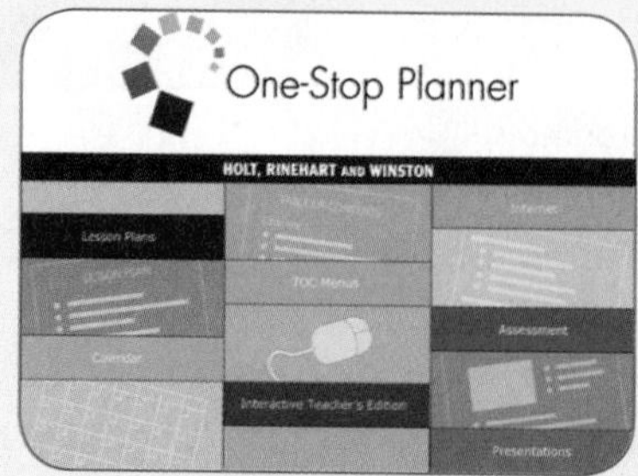

Premier Online Edition SPANISH

Chapter 1 includes Tutorial Videos, Lesson Activities, Lesson Quizzes, Homework Help, and Chapter Project.

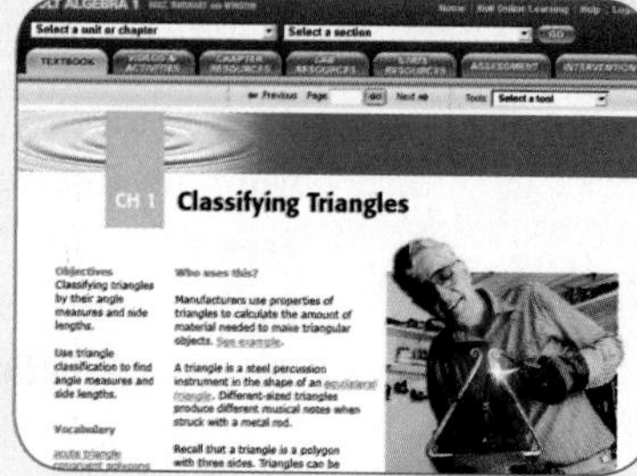

KEY: **SE** = *Student Edition* **TE** = *Teacher's Edition*  English Language Learners  Spanish version available  Available on CD-ROM

Reaching All Learners

Resources for All Learners

- *Hands-On Lab Activities* .... Chapter 1
- *Technology Lab Activities* .... Chapter 1
- *Homework and Practice Workbook* SPANISH .... pp. 1–7
- *Know-It Notebook* .... Chapter 1
- *Problem Solving Workbook* SPANISH .... pp. 1–7

DEVELOPING LEARNERS

- Practice A .... CRB, every lesson
- Reteach .... CRB, every lesson
- Inclusion .... TE p. 7
- *Questioning Strategies* .... pp. 1–14
- Modified Chapter 1 Resources .... *IDEA Works!*
- *Homework Help* Online

ON-LEVEL LEARNERS

- Practice B .... CRB, every lesson
- Puzzles, Twisters, and Teasers .... CRB, every lesson
- Multiple Representations .... TE p. 34
- Cooperative Learning .... TE pp. 23, 31

ADVANCED LEARNERS

- Practice C .... CRB, every lesson
- Challenge .... CRB, every lesson
- Extension .... TE pp. 5, 39, 40, 41
- Critical Thinking .... TE pp. 11, 13

English Language Learners

ENGLISH LANGUAGE LEARNERS

- Are You Ready? Vocabulary .... SE p. 3
- Vocabulary Connections .... SE p. 4
- Lesson Vocabulary .... SE, every lesson
- Vocabulary Review .... SE p. 42
- English Language Learners .... TE pp. 15, 26, 31
- Reading Strategies .... CRB, every lesson
- *Success for English Language Learners* .... pp. 1–14
- *Multilingual Glossary*

Reaching All Learners Through...

- Inclusion .... TE p. 7
- Diversity .... TE p. 7
- Visual Cues .... TE pp. 7, 15
- Auditory Cues .... TE p. 15
- Kinesthetic Experience .... TE p. 27
- Multiple Representations .... TE p. 34
- Cooperative Learning .... TE pp. 23, 31
- Critical Thinking .... TE pp. 11, 13
- Test Prep Doctor .... TE pp. 9, 13, 17, 25, 29, 36, 46, 48
- Common Error Alert .... TE pp. 7, 15, 23, 27, 29, 34
- Scaffolding Questions .... TE p. 39

Technology Highlights for Reaching All Learners

Lesson Tutorial Videos SPANISH

Starring Holt authors Ed Burger and Freddie Renfro! Live tutorials to support every lesson in Chapter 1.

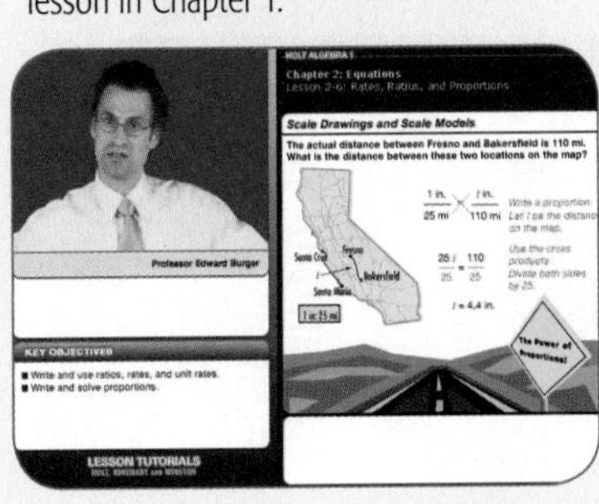

Multilingual Glossary

Searchable glossary includes definitions in English, Spanish, Vietnamese, Chinese, Hmong, Korean, and 4 other languages.

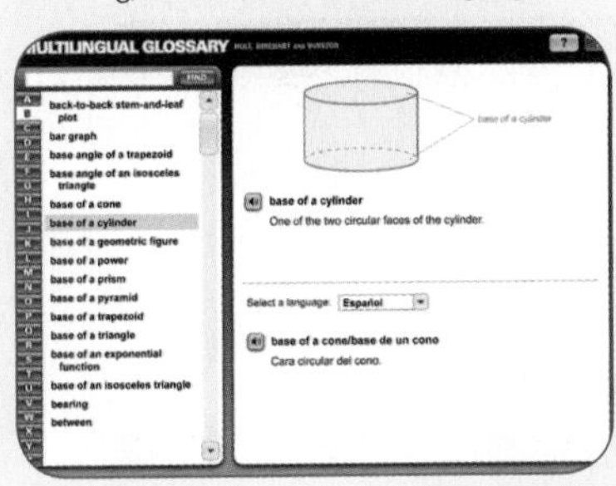

Online Interactivities

Interactive tutorials provide visually engaging alternative opportunities to learn concepts and master skills.

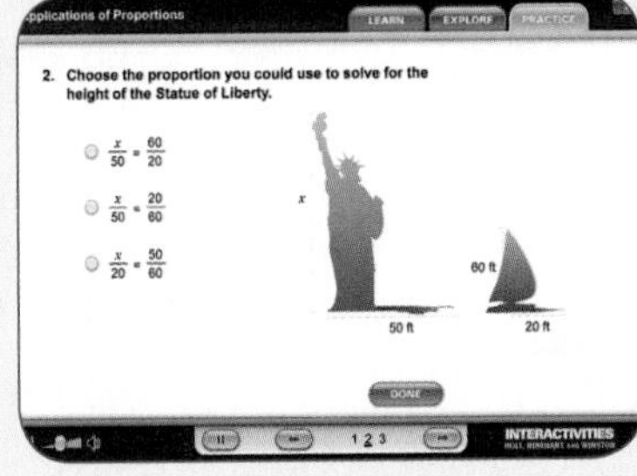

KEY: **SE** = *Student Edition* **TE** = *Teacher's Edition* **CRB** = *Chapter Resource Book* SPANISH Spanish version available  Available on CD-ROM 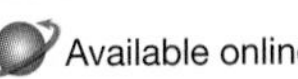 Available online

CHAPTER 1

Ongoing Assessment

Assessing Prior Knowledge

Determine whether students have the prerequisite concepts and skills for success in Chapter 1.

Are You Ready? SPANISH .... SE p. 3
Warm Up .... TE, every lesson

Test Preparation

Provide review and practice for Chapter 1 and standardized tests.

Multi-Step Test Prep .... SE p. 39
Study Guide: Review .... SE pp. 42–44
Test Tackler .... SE pp. 48–49
Standardized Test Prep .... SE pp. 46–47
Countdown to CRCT Transparencies .... pp. 1–4
CRCT Prep Workbook
***CRCT Prep* CD-ROM**
IDEA Works!

Alternative Assessment

Assess students' understanding of Chapter 1 concepts and combined problem-solving skills.

Chapter 1 Project .... SE p. 2
Performance Assessment SPANISH .... AR pp. 19–20
Portfolio Assessment SPANISH .... AR p. xxxiv

Daily Assessment

Provide formative assessment for each day of Chapter 1.

Questioning Strategies .... pp. 1–14
Think and Discuss .... SE, every lesson
Write About It .... SE, lesson exercises
Journal .... TE, lesson exercises
Lesson Quiz .... TE, every lesson
Modified Lesson Quizzes .... *IDEA Works!*

Weekly Assessment

Provide formative assessment for each week of Chapter 1.

Focus on Problem Solving .... SE p. 19
Multi-Step Test Prep .... SE p. 39
Ready to Go On? SPANISH .... SE pp. 18, 38
Cumulative Assessment .... SE pp. 46–47
Test and Practice Generator SPANISH ... *One-Stop Planner*

Formal Assessment

Provide summative assessment of Chapter 1 mastery.

Section Quizzes SPANISH .... AR pp. 5–6
Chapter 1 Test .... SE p. 45
Chapter Test (Levels A, B, C) SPANISH .... AR pp. 7–18
• Multiple Choice • Free Response
Cumulative Test SPANISH .... AR pp. 21–24
Test and Practice Generator SPANISH ... *One-Stop Planner*
Modified Chapter 1 Test .... *IDEA Works!*

Technology Highlights for Ongoing Assessment

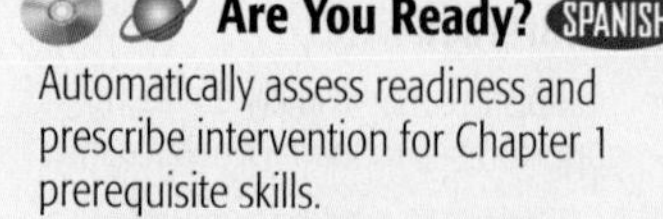

Are You Ready? SPANISH

Automatically assess readiness and prescribe intervention for Chapter 1 prerequisite skills.

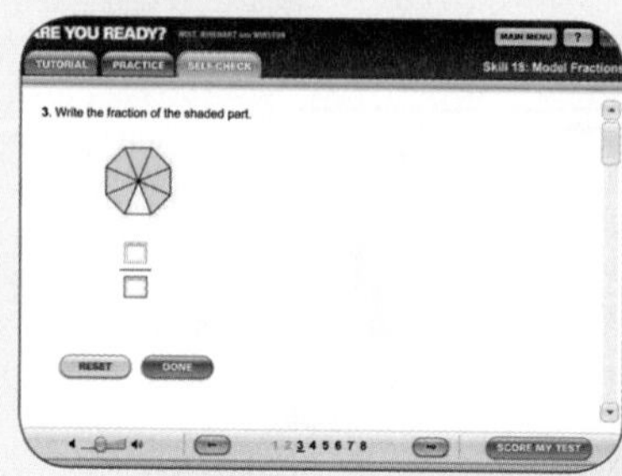

Ready to Go On? SPANISH

Automatically assess understanding of and prescribe intervention for Sections 1A and 1B.

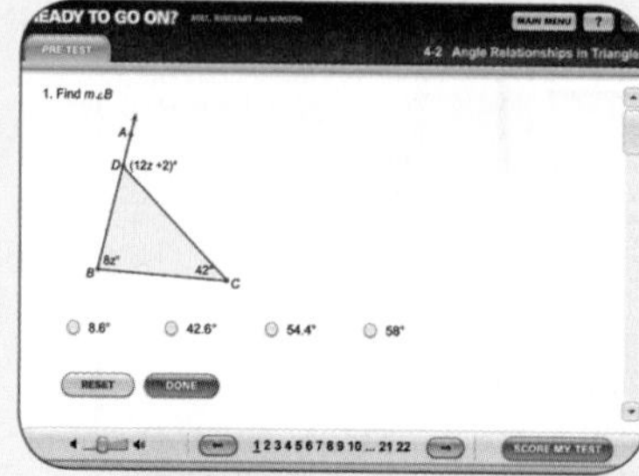

Test and Practice Generator SPANISH

Use Chapter 1 problem banks to create assessments and worksheets to print out or deliver online. Includes dynamic problems.

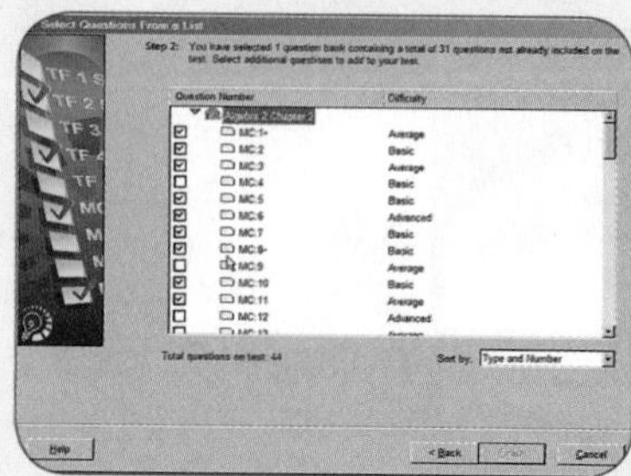

KEY: **SE** = *Student Edition* **TE** = *Teacher's Edition* **AR** = *Assessment Resources* SPANISH Spanish version available  Available on CD-ROM Available online

Formal Assessment

Three levels (A, B, C) of multiple-choice and free-response chapter tests are available in the *Assessment Resources.*

A Chapter 1 Test

C Chapter 1 Test

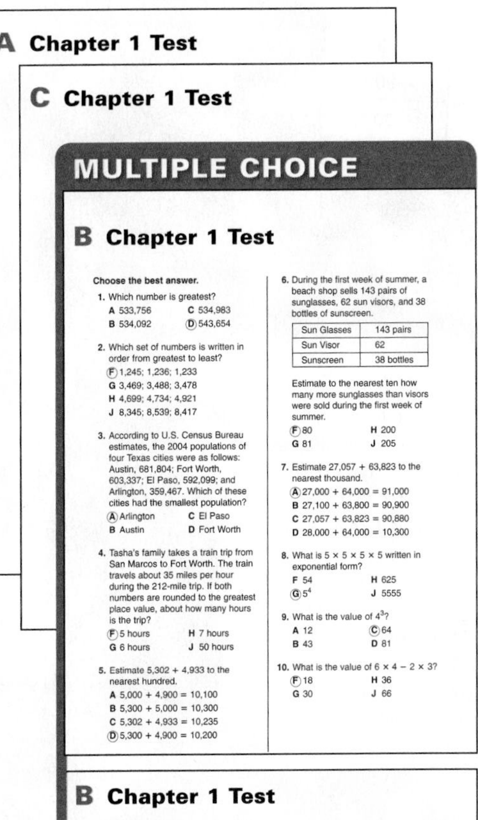

MULTIPLE CHOICE

B Chapter 1 Test

Choose the best answer.

1. Which number is greatest?
   A 533,756 C 534,983
   B 534,092 (D) 543,654
2. Which set of numbers is written in order from greatest to least?
   (F) 1,245; 1,236; 1,233
   G 3,469; 3,488; 3,478
   H 4,699; 4,734; 4,921
   J 8,345; 8,539; 8,417
3. According to U.S. Census Bureau estimates, the 2004 populations of four Texas cities were as follows: Austin, 681,804; Fort Worth, 603,337; El Paso, 592,099; and Arlington, 359,467. Which of these cities had the smallest population?
   (A) Arlington C El Paso
   B Austin D Fort Worth
4. Tasha's family takes a train trip from San Marcos to Fort Worth. The train travels about 35 miles per hour during the 212-mile trip. If both numbers are rounded to the greatest place value, about how many hours is the trip?
   (F) 5 hours H 7 hours
   G 6 hours J 50 hours
5. Estimate 5,302 + 4,933 to the nearest hundred.
   A 5,000 + 4,900 = 10,100
   B 5,300 + 5,000 = 10,300
   C 5,302 + 4,933 = 10,235
   (D) 5,300 + 4,900 = 10,200
6. During the first week of summer, a beach shop sells 143 pairs of sunglasses, 62 sun visors, and 38 bottles of sunscreen.

Sun Glasses	143 pairs
Sun Visor	62
Sunscreen	38 bottles

   Estimate to the nearest ten how many more sunglasses than visors were sold during the first week of summer.
   (F) 80 H 200
   G 81 J 205
7. Estimate 27,057 + 63,823 to the nearest thousand.
   (A) 27,000 + 64,000 = 91,000
   B 27,100 + 63,800 = 90,900
   C 27,057 + 63,823 = 90,880
   D 28,000 + 64,000 = 10,300
8. What is 5 × 5 × 5 × 5 written in exponential form?
   F 54 H 625
   (G) 5^4 J 5555
9. What is the value of 4^3?
   A 12 (C) 64
   B 43 D 81
10. What is the value of 6 × 4 − 2 × 3?
   (F) 18 H 36
   G 30 J 66

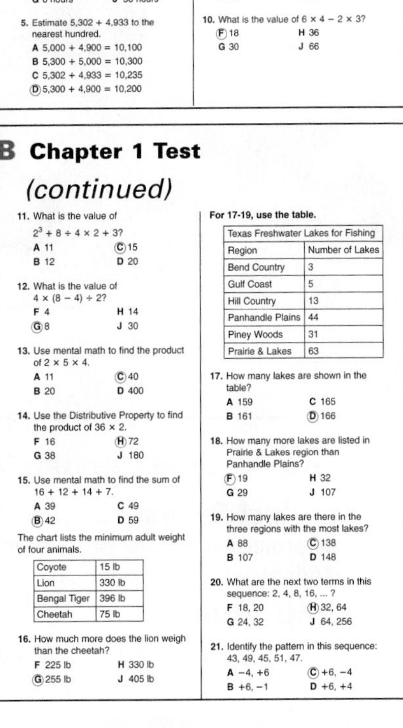

B Chapter 1 Test

(continued)

11. What is the value of $2^3 + 8 \div 4 \times 2 + 3$?
   A 11 (C) 15
   B 12 D 20
12. What is the value of 4 × (8 − 4) ÷ 2?
   F 4 H 14
   (G) 8 J 30
13. Use mental math to find the product of 2 × 5 × 4.
   A 11 (C) 40
   B 20 D 400
14. Use the Distributive Property to find the product of 36 × 2.
   F 16 (H) 72
   G 38 J 180
15. Use mental math to find the sum of 16 + 12 + 14 + 7.
   A 39 C 49
   (B) 42 D 59

The chart lists the minimum adult weight of four animals.

Coyote	15 lb
Lion	330 lb
Bengal Tiger	396 lb
Cheetah	75 lb

16. How much more does the lion weigh than the cheetah?
   F 225 lb H 330 lb
   (G) 255 lb J 405 lb

For 17–19, use the table.

Texas Freshwater Lakes for Fishing	
Region	Number of Lakes
Bend Country	3
Gulf Coast	5
Hill Country	13
Panhandle Plains	44
Piney Woods	31
Prairie & Lakes	63

17. How many lakes are shown in the table?
   A 159 C 165
   B 161 (D) 166
18. How many more lakes are listed in Prairie & Lakes region than Panhandle Plains?
   (F) 19 H 32
   G 29 J 107
19. How many lakes are there in the three regions with the most lakes?
   A 88 (C) 138
   B 107 D 148
20. What are the next two terms in this sequence: 2, 4, 8, 16, ... ?
   F 18, 20 (H) 32, 64
   G 24, 32 J 64, 256
21. Identify the pattern in this sequence: 43, 49, 45, 51, 47.
   A −4, +6 (C) +6, −4
   B +6, −1 D +6, +4

A Chapter 1 Test

C Chapter 1 Test

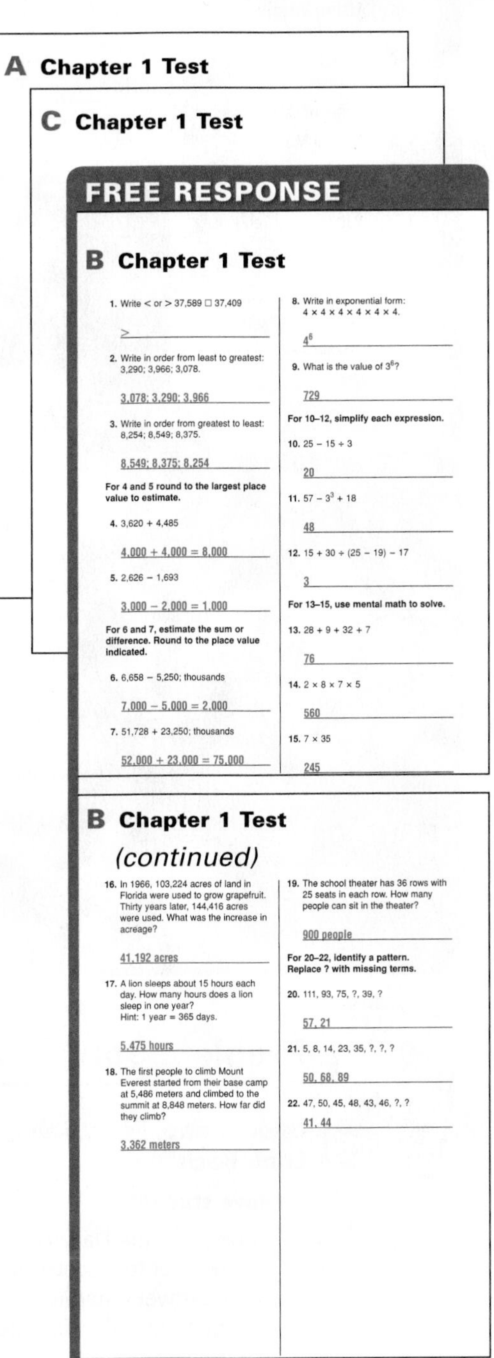

FREE RESPONSE

B Chapter 1 Test

1. Write < or > 37,589 □ 37,409
   \>
2. Write in order from least to greatest: 3,290; 3,966; 3,078.
   3,078; 3,290; 3,966
3. Write in order from greatest to least: 8,254; 8,549; 8,375.
   8,549; 8,375; 8,254

For 4 and 5 round to the largest place value to estimate.

4. 3,620 + 4,485
   4,000 + 4,000 = 8,000
5. 2,626 − 1,693
   3,000 − 2,000 = 1,000

For 6 and 7, estimate the sum or difference. Round to the place value indicated.

6. 6,658 − 5,250; thousands
   7,000 − 5,000 = 2,000
7. 51,728 + 23,250; thousands
   52,000 + 23,000 = 75,000
8. Write in exponential form: 4 × 4 × 4 × 4 × 4 × 4.
   4^6
9. What is the value of 3^6?
   729

For 10–12, simplify each expression.

10. 25 − 15 ÷ 3
   20
11. $57 - 3^3 + 18$
   48
12. 15 + 30 ÷ (25 − 19) − 17
   3

For 13–15, use mental math to solve.

13. 28 + 9 + 32 + 7
   76
14. 2 × 8 × 7 × 5
   560
15. 7 × 35
   245

B Chapter 1 Test

(continued)

16. In 1966, 103,224 acres of land in Florida were used to grow grapefruit. Thirty years later, 144,416 acres were used. What was the increase in acreage?
   41,192 acres
17. A lion sleeps about 15 hours each day. How many hours does a lion sleep in one year? Hint: 1 year = 365 days.
   5,475 hours
18. The first people to climb Mount Everest started from their base camp at 5,486 meters and climbed to the summit at 8,848 meters. How far did they climb?
   3,362 meters
19. The school theater has 36 rows with 25 seats in each row. How many people can sit in the theater?
   900 people

For 20–22, identify a pattern. Replace ? with missing terms.

20. 111, 93, 75, ?, 39, ?
   57, 21
21. 5, 8, 14, 23, 35, ?, ?, ?
   50, 68, 89
22. 47, 50, 45, 48, 43, 46, ?, ?
   41, 44

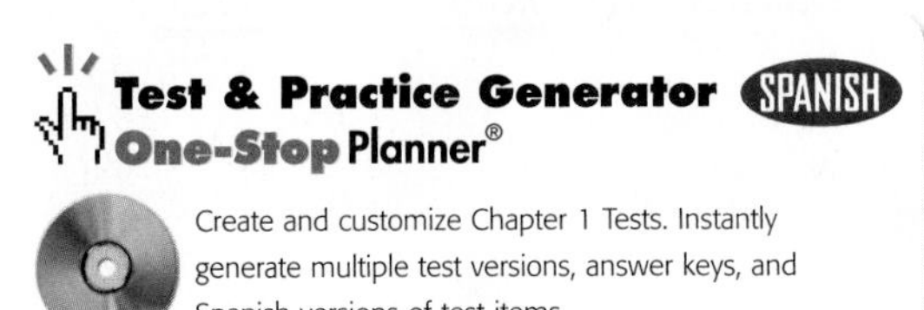

Create and customize Chapter 1 Tests. Instantly generate multiple test versions, answer keys, and Spanish versions of test items.

Why Learn This?

Remind students that mathematics and arithmetic are used in many jobs. Have students look at the table. Point out that a veterinary technician must know an animal's weight when determining how much food the animal requires.

Using Data

To begin the study of this chapter, have students:

- Order the animals from heaviest to lightest. elephant, hippopotamus, giraffe, buffalo, zebra
- Estimate the amount of food (in pounds) that a zebra eats in one month. about 900 pounds
- Find the difference in the amount of food eaten in one day by an elephant and a giraffe. 585 pounds

On page 48, students will find cumulative CRCT practice.

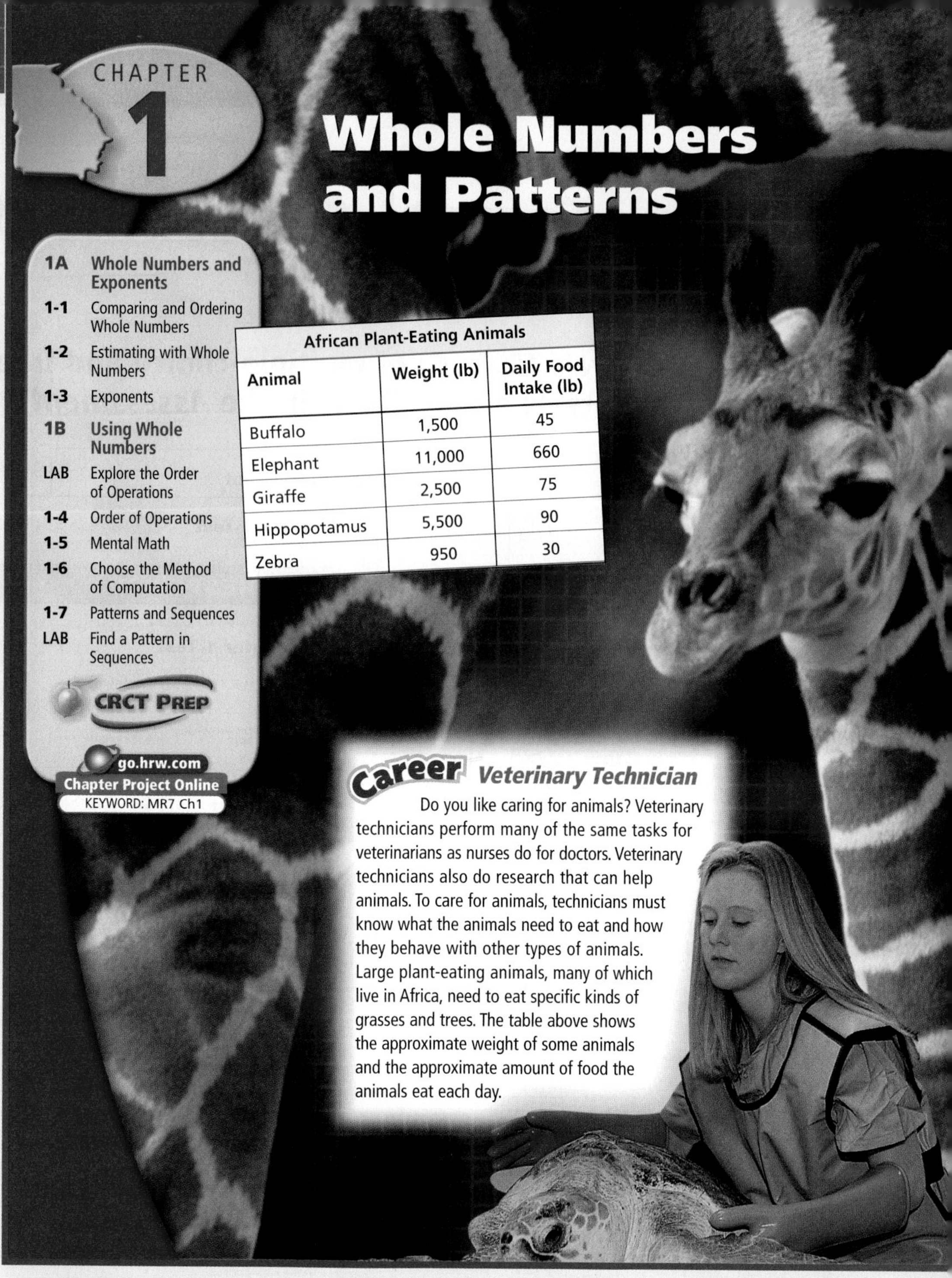

CHAPTER 1

Whole Numbers and Patterns

go.hrw.com
Chapter Project Online
KEYWORD: MR7 Ch1

African Plant-Eating Animals

Animal	Weight (lb)	Daily Food Intake (lb)
Buffalo	1,500	45
Elephant	11,000	660
Giraffe	2,500	75
Hippopotamus	5,500	90
Zebra	950	30

Career *Veterinary Technician*

Do you like caring for animals? Veterinary technicians perform many of the same tasks for veterinarians as nurses do for doctors. Veterinary technicians also do research that can help animals. To care for animals, technicians must know what the animals need to eat and how they behave with other types of animals. Large plant-eating animals, many of which live in Africa, need to eat specific kinds of grasses and trees. The table above shows the approximate weight of some animals and the approximate amount of food the animals eat each day.

Problem Solving Project

Understand, Plan, Solve, and Look Back

Have students:

- Complete the Daily Food Intake worksheet to discover the relationship between herbivore weight and amount of food required per day.
- Research the number of acres, hectares, or square miles required to sustain a family of three giraffes in the wild.
- Research hydroponics. Some of the food for herbivores in wild animal parks is grown hydroponically. Why?

Life Science Connection

Project Resources

All project resources for teachers and students are provided online.

Materials:

- Daily Food Intake worksheet

go.hrw.com
Project Teacher Support
KEYWORD: MR7 PSProject1

ARE YOU READY?

Vocabulary

Choose the best term from the list to complete each sentence.

place value
estimate
product
expanded
standard
period

1. The answer in a multiplication problem is called the __?__. product
2. 5,000 + 400 + 70 + 5 is a number written in __?__ form. expanded
3. A(n) __?__ tells about how many. estimate
4. The number 70,562 is written in __?__ form. standard
5. Ten thousands is the __?__ of the 4 in 42,801. place value

Complete these exercises to review skills you will need for this chapter.

Compare Whole Numbers

Compare. Write <, >, or =.

6. 245 ▒ 219 >
7. 5,320 ▒ 5,128 >
8. 64 ▒ 67 <
9. 784 ▒ 792 <

Round Whole Numbers

Round each number to the nearest hundred.

10. 567 600
11. 827 800
12. 1,642 1,600
13. 12,852 12,900
14. 1,237 1,200
15. 135 100
16. 15,561 15,600
17. 452,801 452,800

Round each number to the nearest thousand.

18. 4,709 5,000
19. 3,399 3,000
20. 9,825 10,000
21. 26,419 26,000
22. 12,434 12,000
23. 4,561 5,000
24. 11,784 12,000
25. 468,201 468,000

Whole Number Operations

Add, subtract, multiply, or divide.

26. 18 × 22 396
27. 135 ÷ 3 45
28. 247 + 96 343
29. 358 − 29 329

Evaluate Whole Number Expressions

Evaluate each expression.

30. 3 × 4 × 2 24
31. 20 + 100 − 40 80
32. 5 × 20 ÷ 4 25
33. 6 × 12 × 5 360

ARE YOU READY? CHAPTER 1

Organizer

Objective: Assess students' understanding of prerequisite skills.

Prerequisite Skills

Compare Whole Numbers
Round Whole Numbers
Whole Number Operations
Evaluate Whole Number Expressions

Assessing Prior Knowledge

INTERVENTION

Diagnose and Prescribe

Use this page to determine whether intervention is necessary or whether enrichment is appropriate.

Resources

***Are You Ready? Intervention and Enrichment* Worksheets**

***Are You Ready?* CD-ROM**

***Are You Ready?* Online**

my.hrw.com

ARE YOU READY?

Diagnose and Prescribe

NO INTERVENE

Prerequisite Skill	*Are You Ready? Intervention,* Chapter 1: Worksheets	CD-ROM	Online
Compare Whole Numbers	Skill 4	Activity 4	Diagnose and Prescribe Online
Round Whole Numbers	Skill 3	Activity 3	
Whole Number Operations	Skill 34	Activity 34	
Evaluate Whole Number Expressions	Skill 54	Activity 54	

***Are You Ready? Enrichment,* Chapter 1**
Worksheets
CD-ROM
Online

CHAPTER 1 Study Guide: Preview

Organizer

Objective: Help students organize the new concepts they will learn in Chapter 1.

Online Edition
Multilingual Glossary

Resources

***Multilingual Glossary* Online**

go.hrw.com
KEYWORD: MR7 Glossary

Answers to *Vocabulary Connections*

Possible answers:

1. Numerical expressions will be evaluated in this chapter.
2. The order of operations determines which operation comes next when there is more than one operation in an expression.
3. A numerical expression is made up of numbers and mathematical operations.
4. This chapter has sequences made up of numbers.

CHAPTER 1

Study Guide: Preview

Study Guide: Preview

Where You've Been

Previously, you

- compared and ordered whole numbers to the hundred thousands.
- used the order of operations without exponents.
- looked for patterns.

In This Chapter

You will study

- comparing and ordering whole numbers to the billions.
- using the order of operations, including exponents.
- how to recognize and extend sequences.
- using properties to compute whole-number operations mentally.
- representing whole numbers by using exponents.

Where You're Going

You can use the skills learned in this chapter

- to express numbers in scientific and standard notation in science classes.
- to recognize and extend geometric sequences.

Key Vocabulary/Vocabulario

Associative Property	propiedad asociativa
base	base (en la numeración)
Commutative Property	propiedad conmutativa
Distributive Property	propiedad distributiva
evaluate	evaluar
exponent	exponente
numerical expression	expresión numérica
order of operations	orden de las operaciones
sequence	sucesión
term	término (en una sucesión)

Vocabulary Connections

To become familiar with some of the vocabulary terms in the chapter, consider the following. You may refer to the chapter, the glossary, or a dictionary if you like.

1. The word *evaluate* means "to determine the value of something." What do you think you will **evaluate** in this chapter?
2. An *order* is the way things are arranged one after the other. How do you think an **order of operations** will help you solve math problems?
3. The word *numerical* means "of numbers." The word *expression* can refer to a mathematical symbol or combination of symbols. What do you think a **numerical expression** is?
4. A *sequence* is a list or arrangement that is in a particular order. What kind of **sequence** do you expect to see in this chapter?

Grade 6 CRCT GPS

M6NA2. **Students will consider relationships between varying quantities.** **a.** Analyze and describe patterns arising from mathematical rules, tables, and graphs.	M6P1. **Students will solve problems (using appropriate technology.** M6P4. **Students will make connections among mathematical ideas and to other disciplines.** M6P5. **Students will represent mathematics in multiple ways.**

******Georgia Mathematics Performance Standards* **statements are written out completely on pp. GA28–GA35.**

Reading Strategy: Use Your Book for Success

Understanding how your textbook is organized will help you locate and use helpful information.

As you read through an example problem, pay attention to the margin notes, such as Reading Math notes, Writing Math notes, Helpful Hints, and Caution notes. These notes will help you understand concepts and avoid common mistakes.

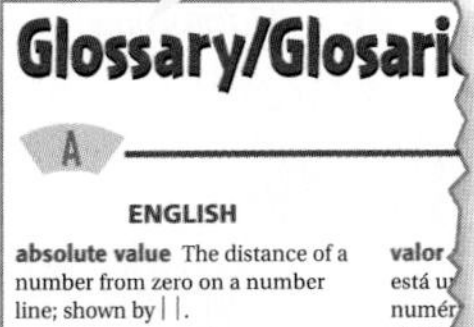

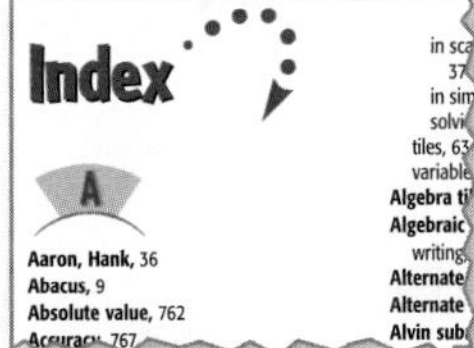

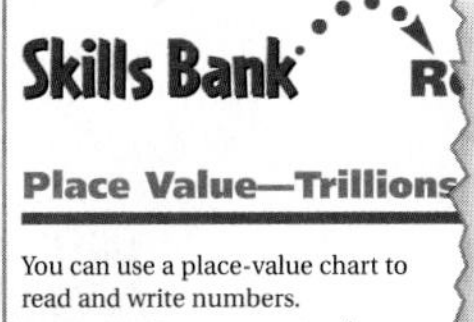

Helpful Hint
Estimating before
you add or subtra
will help you che

Caution!
When you write a
expression for dat
a table, check tha

The Glossary is found in the back of your textbook. Use it as a resource when you need the definition of an unfamiliar word or property.

The Index is located at the end of your textbook. Use it to locate the page where a particular concept is taught.

The Skills Bank is found in the back of your textbook. These pages review concepts from previous math courses, including geometry skills.

Glossary/Glosari

A

ENGLISH

absolute value The distance of a number from zero on a number line; shown by | |.

Index

A

Aaron, Hank, 36
Abacus, 9
Absolute value, 762

Skills Bank

Place Value—Trillions

You can use a place-value chart to read and write numbers.

Use your textbook.

1. Use the glossary to find the definitions of *bisect* and *factor tree.*
2. Where in the Skills Bank can you review how to round whole numbers and decimals?
3. Use the Problem Solving Handbook to list the four steps of the problem-solving plan and two different problem-solving strategies.
4. Use the index to find the pages where *angles* and *histogram* appear.

Grade 6 CRCT GPS

Standards	1-1	1-2	1-3	LAB 1-4	1-4	1-5	1-6	1-7	LAB 1-7
M6A2.a								★	★
M6P1		★	★	★		★	★		★
M6P4	★				★	★	★		
M6P5	★								

Reading and Writing Math

Organizer

Objective: Help students apply strategies to understand and retain key concepts.

Online Edition

Resources

Chapter 1 Resource Book
Reading Strategies

ENGLISH LANGUAGE LEARNERS

Reading Strategy: Use Your Book for Success

Discuss Explain the purpose and location of each element of information. Students will use their books more efficiently if they know where information is located and how it is organized.

Extend As students work through Chapter 1, have them refer to information in the glossary, Skills Bank, Problem Solving Handbook, and index at least once as part of their journal entries.

Answers to *Try This*

1. bisect—to divide into two congruent parts
   factor tree—a diagram showing how a whole number breaks down into its prime factors
2. round whole numbers—p. 750
   round decimals—p. 750
3. Understand the problem, make a plan, solve, and look back; possible answer: draw a diagram, work backward
4. angles—p. 420
   histograms—p. 315, 764

SECTION 1A Whole Numbers and Exponents

One-Minute Section Planner

Lesson	Materials	MiC and Lab Resources
Lesson 1-1 Comparing and Ordering Whole Numbers • Compare and order whole numbers using place value or a number line. ☐ CRCT ☑ SAT-10 ☐ ITBS ☑ CTBS ☑ NAEP		***Hands-On Lab Activities*** 1-1
Lesson 1-2 Estimating with Whole Numbers • Estimate with whole numbers. ☐ CRCT ☑ SAT-10 ☑ ITBS ☑ CTBS ☑ NAEP		**MiC: *Expressions and Formulas*** pp. 8–10
Lesson 1-3 Exponents • Represent numbers by using exponents. ☐ CRCT ☑ SAT-10 ☑ ITBS ☐ CTBS ☐ NAEP		***Technology Lab Activities*** 1-3

MK = *Manipulatives Kit*

Mathematics in Context

The unit ***Expressions and Formulas*** from the *Mathematics in Context* © 2006 series can be used with Section 1A. See Section Planner above for suggestions for integrating *MiC* with *Holt Mathematics*.

Section Overview

Comparing and Ordering Whole Numbers

Lesson 1-1

Comparing and ordering numbers is the beginning of developing number sense.

1,234
1,254

1,234 < 1,254

To order numbers, you can compare and order numbers by using **place value**.

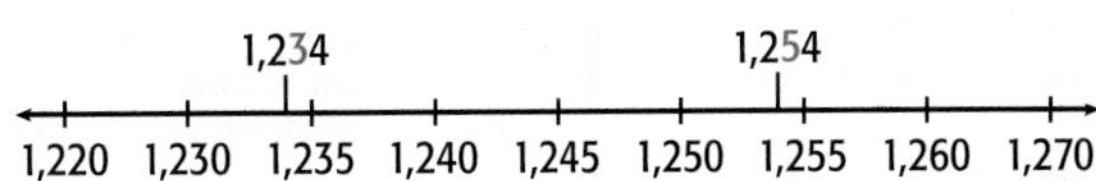

Numbers on a number line are ordered from least to greatest from left to right.

Estimating Whole Numbers

Lesson 1-2

Estimating helps you check your answers or determine whether the result of an operation is reasonable.

When rounding, look at the digit to the **right** of the place to which you are rounding.

- If that digit is 5 or greater, round up.
- If that digit is less than 5, round down.

Estimate 2**3**5 × 8**2**9 to the nearest hundred.

200 × 800 = 160,000

Estimate 8**7** ÷ 2**8** to the nearest ten.

90 ÷ 30 = 3

Compatible numbers are numbers close to the numbers in the problem that you can calculate mentally.

Estimate 3,256 + 6,930 using compatible numbers.

3,000 + **7,000** = 10,000

Representing Numbers Using Exponents

Lesson 1-3

Why? Exponents provide a shorthand method of representing numbers.

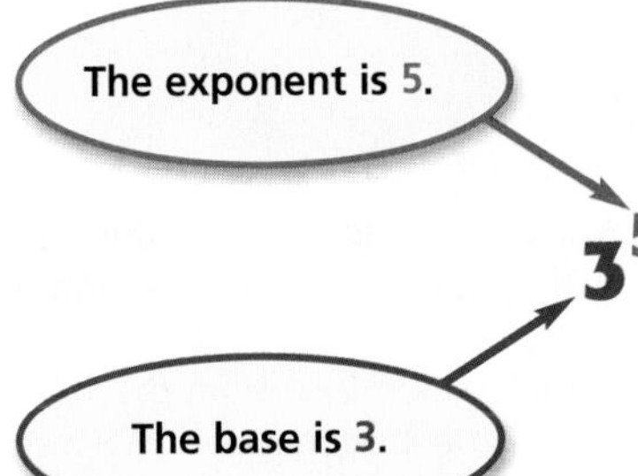

An **exponent** tells how many times the **base** is used as a factor.

$$3^5 = 3 \times 3 \times 3 \times 3 \times 3$$

3^5 is read as "three to the fifth power."

1-1 Organizer

Pacing: Traditional 1 day
Block $\frac{1}{2}$ day

Objective: Students compare and order whole numbers using place value or a number line.

Hands-On Lab
In *Hands-On Lab Activities*

Online Edition
Tutorial Videos, Interactivities

Countdown to CRCT Week 1

Power Presentations with PowerPoint®

Warm Up

Compare. Use <, >, or =.

1. 8 ▢ 9 < **2.** 27 ▢ 14 >
3. 56 ▢ 23 > **4.** 10 ▢ 15 <
5. 11 ▢ 12 < **6.** 37 ▢ 16 >

Problem of the Day

Subtract your age from your age multiplied by 100. Divide the result by 11, and then divide the quotient by 9. What number do you get?
The answer will be the student's age.

Also available on transparency

A line was injured and started to feel numb. Later, the line felt even more numb. What kind of line was it?
A "number" line

Georgia Performance Standards

M6P4.c Recognize and apply mathematics in contexts outside of mathematics.

M6P5.a Create and use representations to organize, record, and communicate mathematical ideas.

M6P5.b Select, apply, and translate among mathematical representations to solve problems.

1-1 Comparing and Ordering Whole Numbers

Learn to compare and order whole numbers using place value or a number line.

Georgia Performance Standards

M6P5.a Create and use representations to organize and communicate mathematical ideas. Also, M6P5.b, M6P4.c.

The midyear world population in 1995 was 5,694,418,460 people. The world population by midyear 2015 is projected to be 7,202,516,136 people.

You can use place value to read and understand large numbers. In the place value chart below, 1 has a value of 1 ten thousand or 1 hundred, depending on its position in the number.

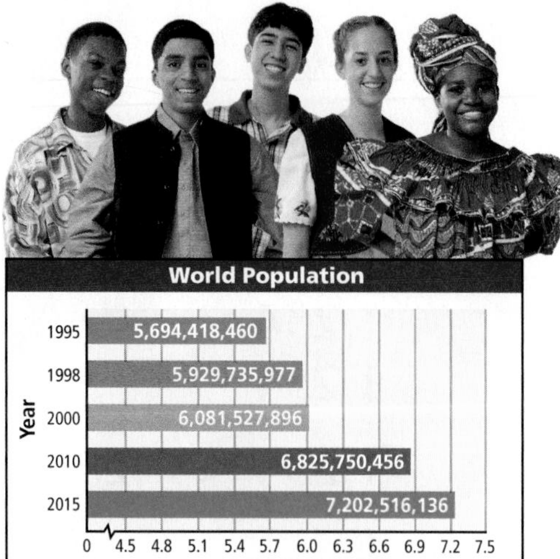

Source: U.S. Bureau of the Census, International Data Base, 2005

Place Value

Hundreds	Tens	Ones	Hundreds	Tens	Ones	Hundreds	Tens	Ones	Hundreds	Tens	Ones
		7,	2	0	2,	5	1	6,	1	3	6
Billions			Millions			Thousands			Ones		

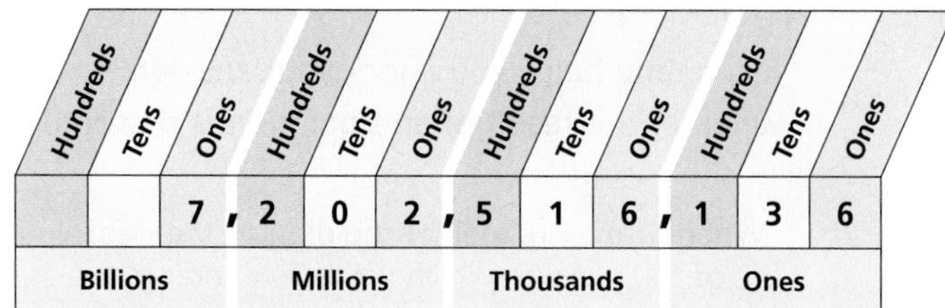

Standard form: 7,202,516,136

Expanded form: 7,000,000,000 + 200,000,000 + 2,000,000 + 500,000 + 10,000 + 6,000 + 100 + 30 + 6

Word form: seven billion, two hundred two million, five hundred sixteen thousand, one hundred thirty-six

1 Introduce

Alternate Opener

EXPLORATION

1-1 Comparing and Ordering Whole Numbers

Values **increase** as you move **right** on a number line.
Values **decrease** as you move left on a number line.

The number line below shows some large whole numbers between 1,000 and 1,100.

Compare the numbers from the number line above. Write < or >.

1. 1,024 ▢ 1,080
2. 1,024 ▢ 1,004
3. 1,064 ▢ 1,040
4. 1,004 ▢ 1,040
5. 1,040 ▢ 1,024
6. 1,064 ▢ 1,098

Think and Discuss

7. **Explain** how to use a number line to compare whole numbers.
8. **Describe** how to use place value to compare the numbers 1,004 and 1,040.

Motivate

Ask students to estimate the number of sixth-grade, seventh-grade, and eighth-grade students in your school. (You may wish to get exact numbers from the school office.) Then have students decide which grade has the most students and which has the fewest students.

Explorations and answers are provided in *Alternate Openers: Explorations Transparencies.*

EXAMPLE 1 Using Place Value to Compare Whole Numbers

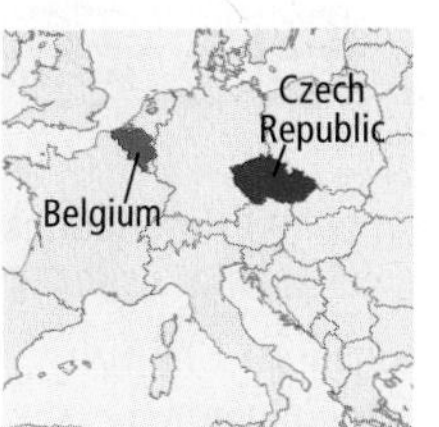

Belgium's 2005 population was 10,364,388 people. The Czech Republic's 2005 population was 10,241,138 people. Which country had more people?

Belgium: 1 0, 3 6 4, 3 8 8

Czech Republic: 1 0, 2 4 1, 1 3 8

Start at the left and compare digits in the same place value position. Look for the first place where the values are different.

200 thousand is less than 300 thousand.
10,241,138 is less than 10,364,388.
So, Belgium had more people.

To order numbers, you can compare them using place value and then write them in order from least to greatest. You can also graph the numbers on a number line. As you read the numbers from left to right, they will be ordered from least to greatest.

EXAMPLE 2 Using a Number Line to Order Whole Numbers

Order the numbers from least to greatest.
923; 835; 1,266

Graph the following numbers on a number line:
The number 923 is between 900 and 1,000.
The number 835 is between 800 and 900.
The number 1,266 is between 1,200 and 1,300.

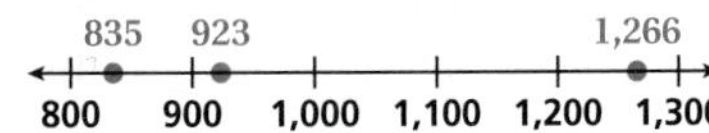

The numbers are ordered when you read the number line from left to right.

The numbers in order from least to greatest are 835, 923, and 1,266.

Remember!

< means "is less than."
3 < 5   120 < 504

> means "is greater than."
17 > 9   212 > 83

Think and Discuss

1. **Give** the place value of the digit 3 in each of the following numbers: 2,307,912; 2,370,912; 2,703,912.
2. **Read** each of the following numbers: 937,052; 3,012,480; 8,135,712,004.
3. **Look** at the bar graph at the beginning of the lesson. In which years was the population between 5,500,000,000 and 6,500,000,000?

Answers to *Think and Discuss*

1. hundred thousand; hundred thousand; thousand
2. nine hundred thirty-seven thousand, fifty-two; three million, twelve thousand, four hundred eighty; eight billion, one hundred thirty-five million, seven hundred twelve thousand, four
3. 1995, 1998, and 2000

COMMON ERROR ALERT

Remind students to start at the leftmost place value, not the right, when they are comparing and ordering numbers. Tell students that the order in which they compare digits when comparing numbers is the same order in which they read digits when reading numbers.

Power Presentations with PowerPoint®

Additional Examples

Example 

Belize's 2000 population was 249,183 people. Iceland's 2000 population was 276,365 people. Which country had more people?
Iceland had more people.

Example 

Order the numbers from least to greatest: 675; 1,044; 497
The numbers in order from least to greatest are 497, 675, and 1,044.

Also available on transparency

Teaching Tip

Visual In example 2, point out that when whole numbers with different numbers of digits are being compared, the number with more digits is the greater of the two numbers.

2 Teach

Guided Instruction

In this lesson, students learn to compare and order whole numbers using place value or a number line. Show students how to use place value to compare two numbers with equal numbers of digits. Then, have students use a number line to order three numbers with different numbers of digits. Use number lines and place value in both examples so students can see that both methods work for comparing and ordering.

Teaching Tip

Diversity Extend the examples by using numbers that the students generate, e.g., populations of nearby towns, number of boys and girls in the school, and so on.

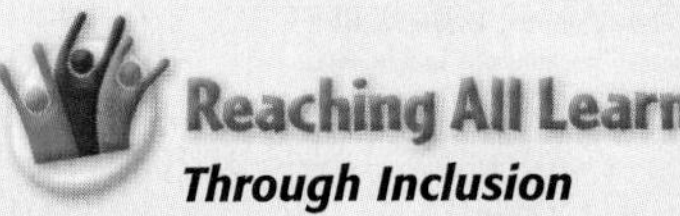

Through Inclusion

To help students with place value comparisons, have them associate place value with denominations of currency. For example, 392 would be represented as 3 hundred-dollar bills, 9 ten-dollar bills, and 2 one-dollar bills.

3 Close

Summarize

Demonstrate ordering numbers using both place value and number lines. Give students two sets of numbers; have students use place value to order one of the sets and a number line to order the other set.

1-1 Exercises

Assignment Guide

If you finished Example 1 assign:
Average 1–2, 9–11, 21–29, 38, 42–51
Advanced 1–2, 9–11, 21–29, 40, 42–51

If you finished Example 2 assign:
Average 1–39, 42–51
Advanced 3–51

Homework Quick Check

Quickly check key concepts.
Exercises: 10, 12, 22, 32

Math Background

The decimal system was developed by a Hindu mathematician before the year 1000. The system did not reach Europe until the thirteenth century. It took hundreds of years after that for the decimal system to be broadly adopted.

Comparing and ordering whole numbers is simple with the decimal system. Because only the 10 digits 0, 1, 2, 3, 4, 5, 6, 7, 8, and 9 are used, and because a digit's place indicates its value, you can read and compare any two numbers from left to right.

Georgia Performance Standards

M6P3.c Analyze and evaluate the mathematical thinking and strategies of others.

M6P4.c Recognize and apply mathematics in contexts outside of mathematics.

1-1 Exercises

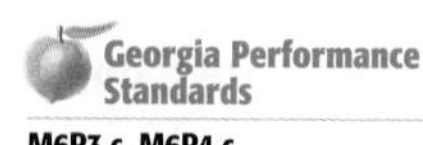

M6P3.c, M6P4.c

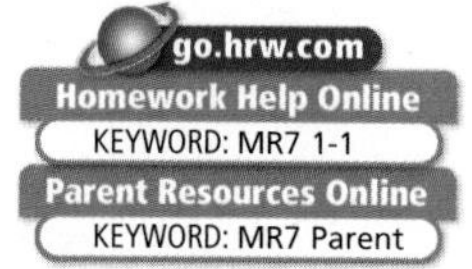

GUIDED PRACTICE

See Example 1

1. **Geography** Mount McKinley, in Alaska, is 20,320 feet tall. Mount Aconcagua, in Argentina, is 22,834 feet tall. Which mountain is taller? **Mount Aconcagua is taller.**
2. The area of the Caribbean Sea is 971,400 square miles. The area of the Mediterranean Sea is 969,100 square miles. Which sea is smaller in area? **The Mediterranean Sea is smaller.**

See Example 2

Order the numbers from least to greatest.

3. 726; 349; 642 **349; 642; 726**
4. 513; 915; 103 **103; 513; 915**
5. 497; 1,264; 809 **497; 809; 1,264**
6. 672; 1,421; 1,016 **672; 1,016; 1,421**
7. 982; 5,001; 3,255 **982; 3,255; 5,001**
8. 4,079; 9,976; 2,951 **2,951; 4,079; 9,976**

INDEPENDENT PRACTICE

See Example 1

9. The attendance in 1999 at a theme park was 17,459,000 people. The attendance in 1999 at a water park was 15,200,000 people. Which park had the higher attendance? **the theme park with 17,459,000 in attendance**
10. According to the table, which river is longer, the Missouri or the Mississippi? **The Mississippi River is longer.**
11. A New York City driving range reported 413,497 golf balls were hit by customers last year. A Philadelphia range reported customers hit 408,959 golf balls. Which range had more golf balls hit? **New York City**

River Length (mi)	
Mississippi	2,340
Missouri	2,315
Ohio	618
Red	1,290
Rio Grande	1,900

See Example 2

Order the numbers from least to greatest.

12. 367; 597; 279 **279; 367; 597**
13. 619; 126; 480 **126; 480; 619**
14. 946; 705; 810 **705; 810; 946**
15. 423; 1,046; 805 **423; 805; 1,046**
16. 1,523; 2,913; 111 **111; 1,523; 2,913**
17. 1,764; 1,359; 666 **666; 1,359; 1,764**
18. 742; 777; 711 **711; 742; 777**
19. 4,228; 1,502; 978 **978; 1,502; 4,228**
20. 6,704; 5,902; 2,792 **2,792; 5,902; 6,074**

PRACTICE AND PROBLEM SOLVING

Extra Practice p. 714

Compare. Write <, >, or =.

21. 46,495 ▇ 46,594 **<**
22. 162,648 ▇ 126,498 **>**
23. 3,654 ▇ 3,654 **=**
24. 512,105 ▇ 512,099 **>**
25. 29,448 ▇ 29,488 **<**
26. 913,203 ▇ 913,600 **<**
27. 23,172,458 ▇ 231,724 **>**
28. 21,782 ▇ 21,782 **=**
29. 1,556,982 ▇ 1,556,983 **<**

Order the numbers from greatest to least.

30. 591; 924; 341 **924; 591; 341**
31. 601; 533; 823; 149 **823; 601; 533; 149**
32. 291; 911; 439; 747 **911; 747; 439; 291**
33. 2,649; 3,461; 1,947 **3,461; 2,649; 1,947**
34. 5,349; 5,389; 5,480 **5,480; 5,389; 5,349**
35. 7,467; 7,239; 7,498 **7,498; 7,467; 7,239**
36. Americans own about 74,000,000 dogs as pets and 90,000,000 cats as pets. Do Americans own more dogs or cats? **cats**

RETEACH 1-1

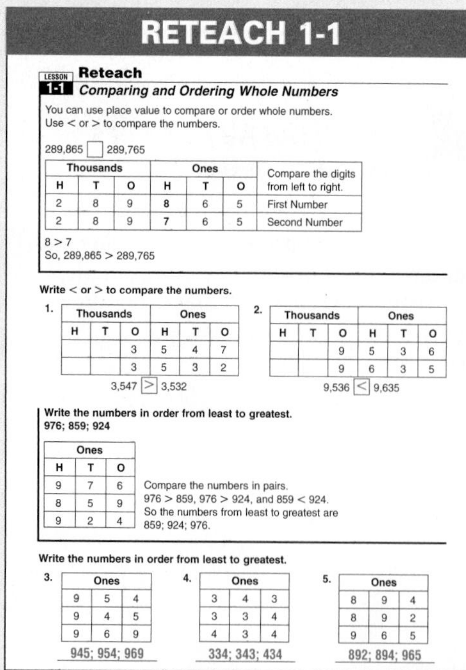

LESSON 1-1 **Reteach**
Comparing and Ordering Whole Numbers

You can use place value to compare or order whole numbers.
Use < or > to compare the numbers.

289,865 ☐ 289,765

Thousands			Ones			Compare the digits from left to right.
H	T	O	H	T	O	
2	8	9	**8**	6	5	First Number
2	8	9	**7**	6	5	Second Number

8 > 7
So, 289,865 > 289,765

Write < or > to compare the numbers.

1.

Thousands			Ones		
H	T	O	H	T	O
		3	5	4	7
		3	5	3	2

3,547 [>] 3,532

2.

Thousands			Ones		
H	T	O	H	T	O
		9	5	3	6
		9	6	3	5

9,536 [<] 9,635

Write the numbers in order from least to greatest.
976; 859; 924

Ones		
H	T	O
9	7	6
8	5	9
9	2	4

Compare the numbers in pairs.
976 > 859, 976 > 924, and 859 < 924.
So the numbers from least to greatest are 859; 924; 976.

Write the numbers in order from least to greatest.

3.

Ones		
9	5	4
9	4	5
9	6	9

945; 954; 969

4.

Ones		
3	4	3
3	3	4
4	3	4

334; 343; 434

5.

Ones		
8	9	4
8	9	2
9	6	5

892; 894; 965

PRACTICE 1-1

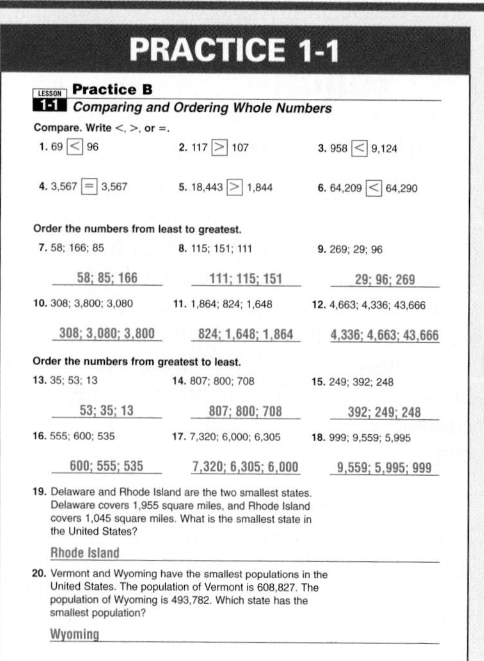

LESSON 1-1 **Practice B**
Comparing and Ordering Whole Numbers

Compare. Write <, >, or =.

1. 69 [<] 96
2. 117 [>] 107
3. 958 [<] 9,124
4. 3,567 [=] 3,567
5. 18,443 [>] 1,844
6. 64,209 [<] 64,290

Order the numbers from least to greatest.

7. 58; 166; 85 — 58; 85; 166
8. 115; 151; 111 — 111; 115; 151
9. 269; 29; 96 — 29; 96; 269
10. 308; 3,800; 3,080 — 308; 3,080; 3,800
11. 1,864; 824; 1,648 — 824; 1,648; 1,864
12. 4,663; 4,336; 43,666 — 4,336; 4,663; 43,666

Order the numbers from greatest to least.

13. 35; 53; 13 — 53; 35; 13
14. 807; 800; 708 — 807; 800; 708
15. 249; 392; 248 — 392; 249; 248
16. 555; 600; 535 — 600; 555; 535
17. 7,320; 6,000; 6,305 — 7,320; 6,305; 6,000
18. 999; 9,559; 5,995 — 9,559; 5,995; 999
19. Delaware and Rhode Island are the two smallest states. Delaware covers 1,955 square miles, and Rhode Island covers 1,045 square miles. What is the smallest state in the United States?
    Rhode Island
20. Vermont and Wyoming have the smallest populations in the United States. The population of Vermont is 608,827. The population of Wyoming is 493,782. Which state has the smallest population?
    Wyoming

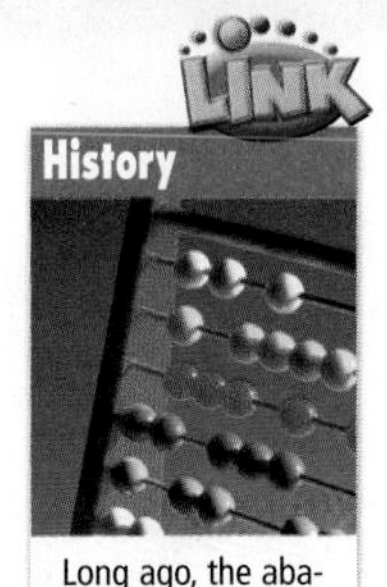

History

Long ago, the abacus was used to solve math problems. The rods represent place values, and the beads are used as counters.

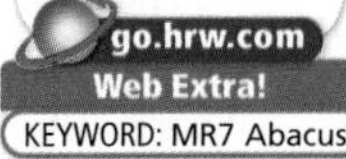

KEYWORD: MR7 Abacus

37. **Geography** The three biggest states in the continental United States are California, 159,869 square miles; Montana, 147,047 square miles; and Texas, 267,277 square miles. Write the states in order from smallest area to largest area. **Montana, California, Texas**

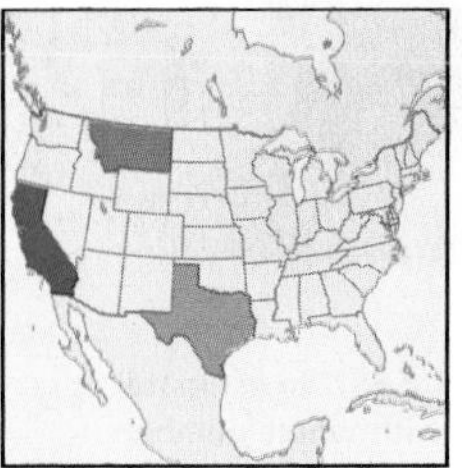

38. **History** The two drawings show another way to represent numbers. The rod on the far left of each drawing represents the hundred thousands place. The number of beads on a rod tells the value for that place. Which drawing represents the greater number? **Drawing B**

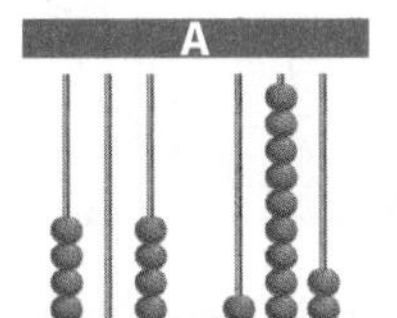

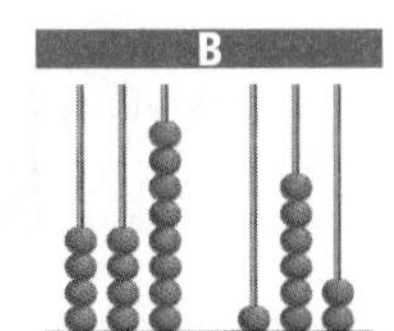

39. **What's the Error?** A student said 19,465,405 is greater than 19,465,425. Explain the error. Write the statement correctly.

40. **Write About It** Explain how you would compare 19,465,146 and 19,460,146.

41. **Challenge** In Roman numerals, letters represent numbers. For example, I = 1, V = 5, X = 10, L = 50, and C = 100. Letters in Roman numerals are written next to each other; this is how the value of the number is shown. To read the numbers below, add the values of all of the letters. What numbers do the following represent?

a. CLX **160** b. LVI **56** c. CIII **103**

CRCT Prep • GPS Support • Spiral Review

42. **Multiple Choice** Which list shows the numbers in order from least to greatest?

Ⓐ 101; 10,001; 1,001
Ⓑ 9,428; 9,454; 9,478
Ⓒ 502; 205; 5,002
Ⓓ 2,123; 2,078; 2,055

43. **Multiple Choice** The 2000 populations of four major Texas cities were as follows: Amarillo, 17,627; Brownsville, 139,722; Laredo, 176,576; and Lubbock, 199,564. Which of the cities had the greatest population?

Ⓕ Amarillo Ⓖ Brownsville Ⓗ Laredo Ⓙ Lubbock

Write each number in word form. (Previous course)

44. 1,645 45. 24,498 46. 306,927 47. 4,605,926

Write the value of the red digit in each number. (Previous course)

48. 649,809 **800** 49. 349,239 **300,000** 50. 27,463 **20,000** 51. 16,239 **6,000**

CHALLENGE 1-1

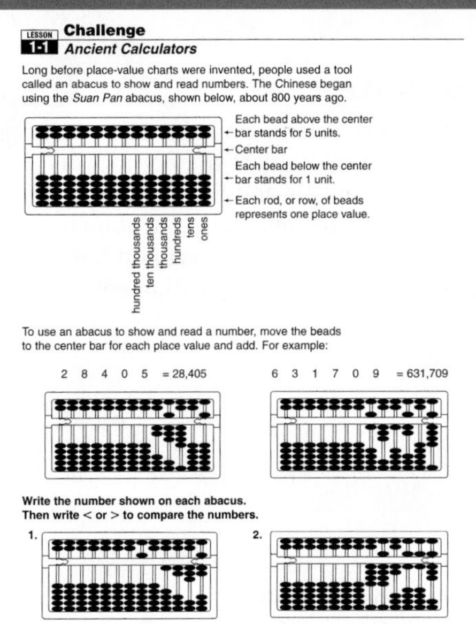
LESSON 1-1 **Challenge**
Ancient Calculators

Long before place-value charts were invented, people used a tool called an abacus to show and read numbers. The Chinese began using the *Suan Pan* abacus, shown below, about 800 years ago.

To use an abacus to show and read a number, move the beads to the center bar for each place value and add. For example:

Write the number shown on each abacus. Then write < or > to compare the numbers.

1. 2.

501, 237 > 492,668

PROBLEM SOLVING 1-1

LESSON 1-1 **Problem Solving**
Comparing and Ordering Whole Numbers

Use the tables below to answer each question.

Most Populated Countries	
Brazil	174,468,575
China	1,273,111,290
India	1,029,991,145
Indonesia	228,437,870
United States	278,058,881

Largest Countries (square mi)	
Brazil	3,265,059
Canada	3,849,646
China	3,705,408
Russia	6,592,812
United States	3,539,224

1. Which country has the greatest population? China; 1,273,111,290
2. Which countries have more than one billion people? China and India
3. Which country is the largest in the world? Russia
4. Which country's area is closest to 4,000,000 square miles? Canada
5. What is the error in the following statement? Canada is larger than the United States, but smaller than China. Canada is larger than China.
6. Based on population and size, which country do you think is more crowded, Brazil or the United States? Explain. U.S.; They are about the same size, but U.S. has more people.
7. Which country has a population less than two hundred million?
A China Ⓒ Brazil
B Indonesia D India
8. Which countries have populations greater than the United States?
F China and Brazil
Ⓖ China and India
H India and Indonesia
J Indonesia and China
9. Which list shows the countries in order by population from greatest to least?
A China, United States, India, Indonesia, Brazil
B China, India, Indonesia, Brazil, United States,
C China, India, Indonesia, United States, Brazil
Ⓓ Indonesia, United States, India, Brazil
10. Which list shows the countries in order by size from smallest to largest?
F Brazil, United States, China, Canada, Russia
G Brazil, United States, Canada, China, Russia
H Brazil, United States, Canada, Russia, China
Ⓙ Brazil, United States, Russia, China, Canada

Ongoing Assessment and Intervention

Diagnose ***Before*** **the Lesson**
1-1 Warm Up, TE p. 6

Monitor ***During*** **the Lesson**
1-1 Know-It Notebook
1-1 Questioning Strategies

Assess ***After*** **the Lesson**
1-1 Lesson Quiz, TE p. 9

Answers

39. Possible answer: The student should compare the tens place and note that 0 < 2. Correctly written, it is 19,465,405 < 19,465,425.
40. Possible answer: Compare each place value starting with ten millions. When a place value is less in one of the numbers, that number is less than the other number.
44. one thousand, six hundred forty-five
45. twenty-four thousand, four hundred ninety-eight
46. three hundred six thousand, nine hundred twenty-seven
47. four million, six hundred five thousand, nine hundred twenty-six

Test Prep Doctor In Exercise 42 and 43, because the numbers are so large, comparing the place values might be the method to use. Encourage students to align the numbers by place value and compare digits from left to right.

Journal

Have students write about when they would use place value or a number line to order numbers and why.

Power Presentations with PowerPoint®

1-1 Lesson Quiz

Order the numbers from least to greatest.

1. 698; 469; 976 **469; 698; 976**
2. 941; 914; 491 **491; 914; 941**
3. 726; 847; 221 **221; 726; 847**
4. The area of Panama is 78,200 square kilometers, and the area of Lithuania is 65,200 square kilometers. Which country is smaller in area? **Lithuania**

Also available on transparency

1-2 Organizer

Pacing: Traditional 1 day
Block $\frac{1}{2}$ day

Objective: Students estimate with whole numbers.

Online Edition
Tutorial Videos

Countdown to CRCT Week 1

Power Presentations with PowerPoint®

Warm Up

Find each sum.

1. 3,214 + 5,490 8,704
2. 9,225 + 8,652 17,877
3. 3,210 + 1,200 4,410
4. 8,774 + 2,156 10,930

Problem of the Day

Continue the number pattern below. Explain the pattern you found.

3, 6, 10, 15, ____, ____

21, 28; one possible pattern is to increase the difference between consecutive terms by one more than the difference between preceding consecutive terms.

Also available on transparency

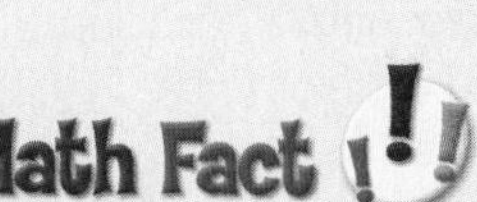

Math Fact

The estimated distance that light will travel in a year is 5,880,000,000,000 miles, or 1 light-year.

Georgia Performance Standards

M6P1.a Build new mathematical knowledge through problem solving.

M6P1.b Solve problems that arise in mathematics and in other contexts.

1-2 Estimating with Whole Numbers

Learn to estimate with whole numbers.

Vocabulary

compatible number
underestimate
overestimate

Georgia Performance Standards

M6P1.b Solve problems that arise in mathematics and in other contexts. Also, M6P1.a.

Sometimes in math you do not need an exact answer. Instead, you can use an estimate. Estimates are close to the exact answer but are usually easier and faster to find.

When estimating, you can round the numbers in the problem to *compatible numbers.* **Compatible numbers** are close to the numbers in the problem, and they can help you do math mentally.

EXAMPLE 1 Estimating a Sum or Difference by Rounding

Estimate each sum or difference by rounding to the place value indicated.

> **Remember!**
> When rounding, look at the digit to the right of the place to which you are rounding.
> - If that digit is 5 or greater, round up.
> - If that digit is less than 5, round down.

A 5,439 + 7,516; thousands

5,000	*Round 5,439 down.*
+ 8,000	*Round 7,516 up.*
13,000	

The sum is about 13,000.

B 62,167 − 47,511; ten thousands

60,000	*Round 62,167 down.*
− 50,000	*Round 47,511 up.*
10,000	

The difference is about 10,000.

An estimate that is less than the exact answer is an **underestimate**.

An estimate that is greater than the exact answer is an **overestimate**.

1 Introduce

Alternate Opener

EXPLORATION

1-2 Estimating with Whole Numbers

Harvard Middle School is collecting aluminum cans to recycle for a fund-raiser. The number of cans that each grade collected is shown in the bar graph.

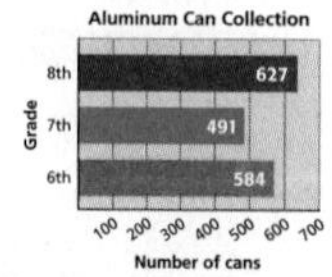

1. Estimate the total number of cans that Harvard Middle School collected.

The principal announced that nearly 2,000 cans were collected. The newspaper reported that over 1,700 cans were collected.

2. Is either of these reports correct?
3. Why are the reports different?

Think and Discuss

4. **Describe** how you reached your estimate.
5. **Identify** some words that indicate whether an amount is an estimate or approximation.

Motivate

Have students plan a party for 12 people. They'll need to estimate the number of plates and napkins and the amount of food and drink to buy. Tell them that sometimes you do not need to use exact numbers. Planning a party is one situation where an estimate is sufficient.

Explorations and answers are provided in *Alternate Openers: Explorations Transparencies.*

EXAMPLE 2 Estimating a Product by Rounding

Answers to *Think and Discuss*

1. Possible answer: Overestimate; that way you will be sure to have enough money to buy everything you need.

Ms. Escobar is planning a graduation celebration for the entire eighth grade. There are 9 eighth-grade homeroom classes of 27 students. Estimate how many cups Ms. Escobar needs to buy for the students if they all attend the celebration.

Find the number of students in the eighth grade.

$9 \times 27 \rightarrow 9 \times 30$ *Overestimate the number of students.*

$9 \times 30 = 270$ *The actual number of students is **less than** 270.*

If Ms. Escobar buys 270 cups, she will have enough for every student.

EXAMPLE 3 Estimating a Quotient Using Compatible Numbers

Georgia LINK Social Studies

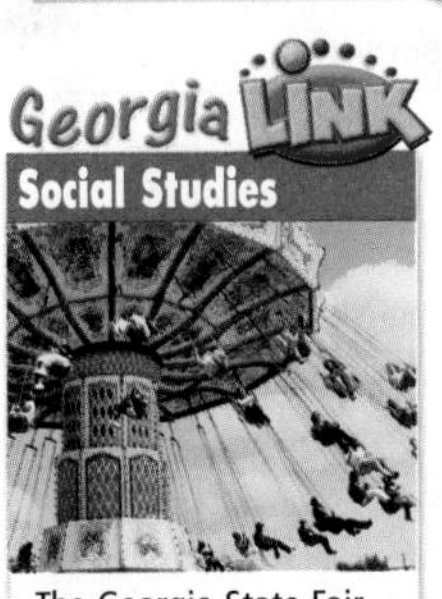

The Georgia State Fair has been held in Macon every year since 1851. The only time the fair was cancelled was during the Civil War.

Mrs. Byrd will drive 120 miles to take Becca to the state fair. She can drive 65 mi/h. About how long will the trip take?

To find how long the trip will be, divide the miles Mrs. Byrd has to travel by how many miles per hour she can drive.

miles ÷ miles per hour

$120 \div 65 \rightarrow 120 \div 60$ *120 and 60 are compatible numbers.* ***Underestimate** the speed.*

$120 \div 60 = 2$ *Because she **underestimated** the speed, the actual time will be **less than** 2 hours.*

It will take Mrs. Byrd about two hours to reach the state fair.

2. It is best to underestimate the number of miles per gallon you car can travel.
3. Possible answers: when figuring the amount of time needed to complete a project; when saving money to buy something; when deciding how much paper is needed to wrap a gift

Think and Discuss

GPS M6P3.a, M6P3.b

1. **Suppose** you are buying items for a party and you have $50. Would it be better to overestimate or underestimate the cost of the items?
2. **Suppose** your car can travel between 20 and 25 miles on a gallon of gas. You want to go on a 100-mile trip. Would it be better to overestimate or underestimate the number of miles per gallon your car can travel?
3. **Describe** situations in which you might want to estimate.

Power Presentations with PowerPoint®

Additional Examples

Example 

Estimate each sum or difference by rounding to the place value indicated.

A. 12,345 + 62,167; ten thousands
The sum is about 70,000.

B. 4,983 − 2,447; thousands
The difference is about 3,000.

Example 

Chelsea is planning the annual softball banquet for the 8 teams in the region. Each team has 18 members. Estimate how many plates she will need to buy if all the members attend
Chelsea should buy about 180.

Example 

Mr. Dehmel will drive 243 miles to the fair at 65 mi/h. About how long will his trip take? The actual time will be less than 4 hours.

Also available on transparency

Teaching Tip **Critical Thinking** In example 3, if students attempt to round 65 up to 70, remind them to look for compatible numbers when estimating quotients.

2 Teach

Guided Instruction

In this lesson, students learn to estimate with whole numbers. Show students how to round numbers to estimate sums, differences, and products and to use compatible numbers to estimate quotients. Point out that the compatible numbers used to estimate a quotient are not necessarily found by rounding.

Teaching Tip **Communicating Math** Show students how to find compatible numbers for estimating quotients. Instead of always rounding numbers, they may want to choose a pair of numbers that are easy to divide mentally. For example, use 420 ÷ 70 to estimate 435 ÷ 75.

Reaching All Learners

Through Number Sense

Have students work in pairs to rewrite each expression so that an estimate can be given. For the benefit of the class, have one pair explain what they did to find an estimate in each expression.

1. 29,502 + 24,098 30,000 + 20,000
2. 94,142 − 47,071 90,000 − 50,000
3. 23 × 2,802 20 × 3,000
4. 178,932 ÷ 6 180,000 ÷ 6

3 Close

Summarize

Emphasize that estimates should be easy enough to obtain mentally. Remind students to round to the highest place value for sums, differences, and products. Encourage them to be mathematically creative when looking for compatible numbers to estimate quotients.

1-2 Exercises

Assignment Guide

If you finished Example 1 assign:
Average 1–2, 6–9, 25–26, 32–41
Advanced 1–2, 6–9, 27–28, 32–41

If you finished Example 2 assign:
Average 1–3, 6–10, 13–18, 25–26, 32–41
Advanced 6–10, 13–18, 25–29, 32–41

If you finished Example 3 assign:
Average 1–27, 32–41
Advanced 5–41

Homework Quick Check

Quickly check key concepts.
Exercises: 6, 10, 12, 14, 20

Math Background

Another way to estimate a sum or product is to round both terms down to obtain one estimate and to round both terms up to obtain a second estimate. Together, the two estimates form a range within which the actual answer must lie. This is true only when adding or multiplying. It is not true when subtracting or dividing.

For example, 457 × 341 can be estimated by the products 400 × 300 = 120,000 and 500 × 400 = 200,000. You then can conclude that the actual product lies between 120,000 and 200,000.

Georgia Performance Standards

M6P3.d Use the language of mathematics to express mathematical ideas precisely.

M6P4.c Recognize and apply mathematics in contexts outside of mathematics.

1-2 Exercises

M6P3.d, M6P4.c

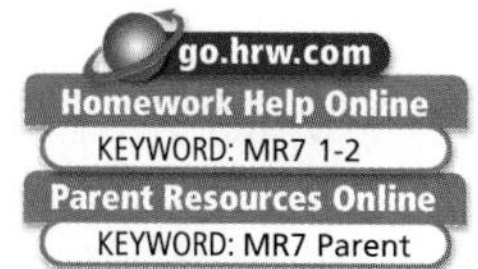

GUIDED PRACTICE

See Example 1

Estimate each sum or difference by rounding to the place value indicated.

1. 4,689 + 2,469; thousands **7,000**
2. 50,498 − 35,798; ten thousands **10,000**

See Example 2

3. The graph shows the number of bottles of water used in three bicycle races last year. If the same number of riders enter the races each year, estimate the number of bottles that will be needed for races held in May over the next five years. **1,500 bottles of water**

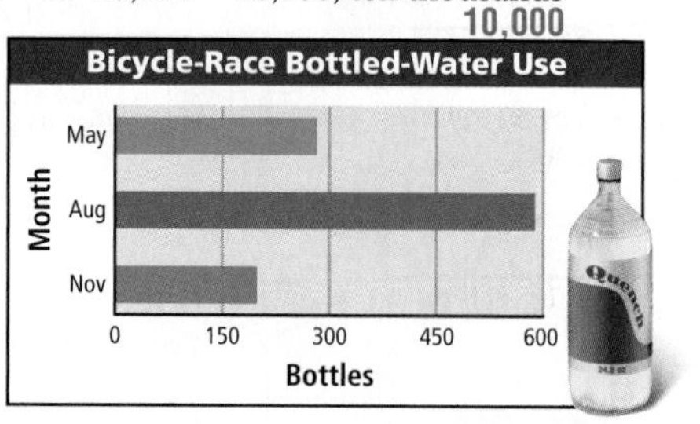

Bicycle-Race Bottled-Water Use

See Example 3

4. If a local business provided half the bottled water needed for the August bicycle race, about how many bottles did the company provide? **300 bottles**
5. Carla drives 80 miles on her scooter. If the scooter gets about 42 miles per gallon of gas, about how much gas did she use? **about 2 gallons**

INDEPENDENT PRACTICE

See Example 1

Estimate each sum or difference by rounding to the place value indicated.

6. 6,570 + 3,609; thousands **11,000**
7. 49,821 − 11,567; ten thousands **40,000**
8. 3,912 + 1,269; thousands **5,000**
9. 37,097 − 20,364; ten thousands **20,000**

See Example 2

10. The recreation center has provided softballs every year to the city league. Use the table to estimate the number of softballs the league will use in 5 years. **150 softballs**

Recreation Center Balls Supplied

Sport	Number of Balls
Basketball	21
Golf	324
Softball	28
Table tennis	95

See Example 3

11. The recreation center has a girls' golf team with 8 members. About how many golf balls will each girl on the team get? **40 golf balls**
12. If the recreation center loses about 4 table tennis balls per year, and they are not replaced, how many years will it take until the center has none left? **24 years**

PRACTICE AND PROBLEM SOLVING

CRCT GPS
Extra Practice p. 714

Estimate each sum or difference by rounding to the greatest place value.

13. 152 + 269 **500**
14. 797 − 234 **600**
15. 242 − 179 **0**
16. 6,152 − 3,195 **3,000**
17. 9,179 + 2,206 **11,000**
18. 10,982 + 4,821 **16,000**
19. 82,465 − 38,421 **40,000**
20. 38,347 + 17,039 **60,000**
21. 51,201 + 16,492 **70,000**
22. 639,069 + 283,136
23. 777,060 − 410,364
24. 998,927 − 100,724

22. 900,000
23. 400,000
24. 900,000

RETEACH 1-2

LESSON 1-2 **Reteach**
Estimating with Whole Numbers

In mathematics, you can find an estimate when an exact answer is not needed. An estimate is close to the exact answer.

You can use rounding to estimate sums and differences.

A. Estimate the sum by rounding to the hundreds.
3,478 → 3,500
+ 7,136 → + 7,100
10,600

B. Estimate the difference by rounding to the thousands.
23,848 → 24,000
− 16,132 → − 16,000
8,000

Estimate each sum or difference by rounding to the place value indicated.

1. hundreds
789 → 800
+ 453 → + 500
1,300

2. thousands
4,987 → 5,000
− 2,348 → − 2,000
3,000

3. tens
456 → 460
+ 875 → + 880
1,340

4. tens
876 → 880
− 432 → − 430
450

5. hundreds
6,898 → 6,900
+ 2,671 → + 2,700
9,600

6. thousands
1,857 → 2,000
+ 3,598 → + 4,000
6,000

7. hundreds
8,813 → 8,800
− 2,384 → − 2,400
6,400

8. thousands
9,128 → 9,000
− 4,716 → − 5,000
4,000

PRACTICE 1-2

LESSON 1-2 **Practice B**
Estimating with Whole Numbers

Estimate each sum or difference. Possible answers:

1. 67 + 14 — 80
2. 583 − 329 — 300
3. 94 − 36 — 50
4. 2,856 + 2,207 — 5,000
5. 276 + 316 — 600
6. 6,020 − 3,688 — 2,000
7. 34,465 + 19,002 — 50,000
8. 78,135 − 19,431 — 60,000
9. 216,135 + 165,800 — 400,000

Estimate each product or quotient.

10. 59 ÷ 6 — 10
11. 51 × 8 — 400
12. 83 ÷ 4 — 21
13. 9 × 27 — 270
14. 49 ÷ 6 — 8
15. 53 × 8 — 400
16. 147 ÷ 5 — 30
17. 118 ÷ 6 — 20
18. 79 × 5 — 400
19. Sailfish are the fastest fish in the world. They can swim 68 miles an hour. About how far can a sailfish swim in 3 hours?
about 210 miles
20. At a height of 3,281 feet, Angel Falls in Venezuela is the tallest waterfall in the world. Niagara Falls in the United States is only 190 feet tall. About how much taller is Angel Falls?
about 3,000 feet taller
21. Ali, a gardener, is preparing to fertilize a lawn. The lawn is 30 yards by 25 yards. One bag of fertilizer will cover an area of 100 square yards. How many bags of fertilizer does Ali need to buy?
8 bags

Social Studies LINK

Use the bar graph for Exercises 25–31.

25. On one summer day there were 2,824 sailboats on Lake Erie. Estimate the number of square miles available to each boat. **10 square miles**

26. If the areas of all the Great Lakes are rounded to the nearest thousand, which two of the lakes would be the closest in area? **Erie and Ontario**

27. About how much larger is Lake Huron than Lake Ontario? **40,000 square miles**

28. The Great Lakes are called "great" because of the huge amount of fresh water they contain. Estimate the total area of all the Great Lakes combined. **280,000 square miles**

29. **What's the Question?** Lake Erie is about 50,000 square miles smaller. What is the question?

30. **Write About It** Explain how you would estimate the areas of Lake Huron and Lake Michigan to compare their sizes.

31. **Challenge** Estimate the average area of the Great Lakes. **60,000 square miles**

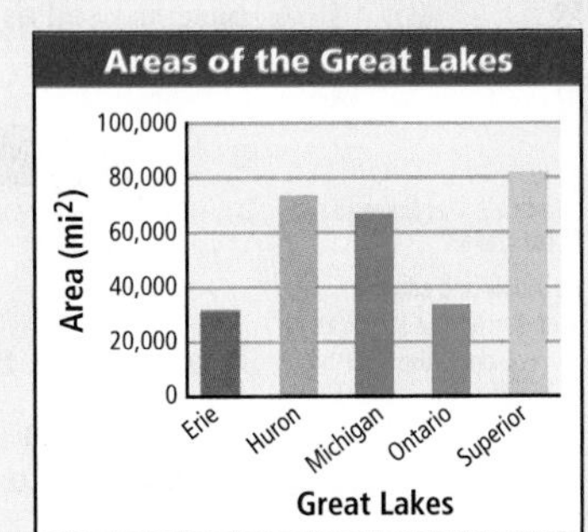

Area includes the water surface and drainage basin within the United States and Canada.

29–30. See p. A1.

CRCT Prep • GPS Support • Spiral Review

32. **Multiple Choice** Which number is the best estimate for 817 + 259?

Ⓐ 10,000 Ⓑ 2,000 Ⓒ 1,100 Ⓓ 800

33. **Short Response** The National Football League requires home teams to have 36 new footballs for outdoor games and 24 new footballs for indoor games. Estimate how many new footballs the Washington Redskins must buy for 8 outdoor games. Explain how you determined your estimate.
400; 36 rounds to 40, and 8 rounds to 10

Find each product or quotient. (Previous course)

34. 148 ÷ 4 **37** **35.** 523 × 5 **2,615** **36.** 1,054 ÷ 31 **34** **37.** 312 × 8 **2,496**

Write each number in expanded form. (Lesson 1-1) **38–41. See p. A1.**

38. 269 **39.** 1,354 **40.** 32,498 **41.** 416,703

Ongoing Assessment and Intervention

***Diagnose Before* the Lesson**
1-2 Warm Up, TE p. 10

***Monitor During* the Lesson**
1-2 Know-It Notebook
1-2 Questioning Strategies

***Assess After* the Lesson**
1-2 Lesson Quiz, TE p. 10

Interdisciplinary LINK

Social Studies

Exercises 25–31 involve the areas of the Great Lakes. U.S. geography, including the Great Lakes, is studied in middle-school social studies programs, such as Holt, Rinehart & Winston's *People, Places, and Change.*

Test Prep Doctor For Exercise 32, students should round each addend to estimate the sum. Students who answered **A** might have experienced a problem with place value. Students who answered **B** incorrectly rounded both addends, possibly rounding both up to 1,000. Students who answered **C** disregarded the second addend.

Journal

Have students write about two situations in which estimations would be helpful.

CHALLENGE 1-2

LESSON 1-2 Challenge
A Shopping Spree!

You have just won a $2,000 shopping spree at Electronics City! Use estimation and the store's advertisement below to make two different shopping lists of what you can buy without going over your spending limit.

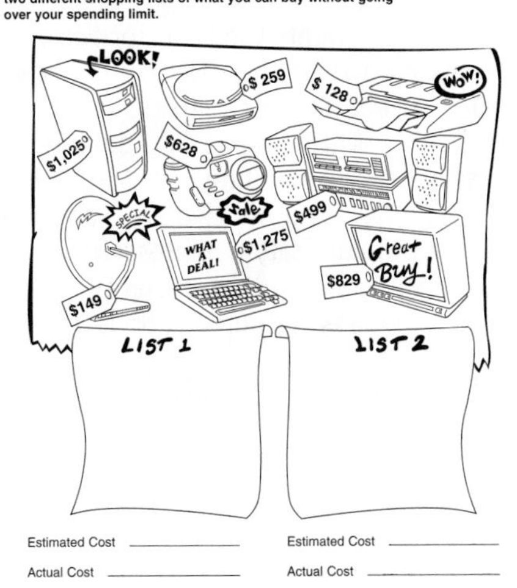

Estimated Cost ______ Estimated Cost ______

Actual Cost ______ Actual Cost ______

Answers will vary depending on students' chosen items. Check for correct estimation. All lists should total less than $2,000.

PROBLEM SOLVING 1-2

LESSON 1-2 Problem Solving
Estimating with Whole Numbers

Use the table below to answer each question.

Facts About the World's Oceans

Ocean	Area (square mi)	Greatest Depth (ft)
Arctic	5,108,132	18,456
Atlantic	33,424,006	30,246
Indian	28,351,484	24,460
Pacific	64,185,629	35,837

1. If the depths of all the oceans were rounded to the nearest ten thousand, which two oceans would have the same depth?
Arctic and Indian

2. In 1960, scientists observed sea creatures living as far down as thirty thousand feet. In which ocean(s) could these creatures have lived?
Pacific and Atlantic

3. If you wanted to compare the depths of the Pacific Ocean and the Atlantic Ocean, which place value would you use to estimate?
thousands

4. The oceans cover about three-fourths of Earth's surface. Estimate the total area of all the oceans combined by rounding to the nearest million.
about 130 million sq. mi

Choose the letter for the best answer.

5. There are 5,280 feet in a mile. About how many miles deep is the deepest point in the Pacific Ocean?
A about 0.7 mile
Ⓑ about 7 miles
C about 70 miles
D about 700 miles

6. Rounding to the greatest place value, about how much larger is the Indian Ocean than the Arctic Ocean?
F about 5 million sq. mi
G about 10 million sq. mi
H about 15 million sq. mi
Ⓙ about 25 million sq. mi

7. The Atlantic Ocean is about 40 times larger than the world's largest island, Greenland. Use this information to estimate the area of Greenland.
Ⓐ about 800,000 sq. mi
B about 8,000,000 sq. mi
C about 80,000,000 sq. mi
D about 1,200,000,000 sq. mi

8. About how much larger would the Pacific Ocean have to be to have more area than the other three oceans combined?
F about 2 hundred sq. mi
G about 2 thousand sq. mi
Ⓗ about 2 million sq. mi
J about 20 million sq. mi

Power Presentations with PowerPoint®

1-2 Lesson Quiz

Estimate each sum or difference by rounding to the place value indicated.

1. 7,420 + 3,527; thousands
11,000

2. 47,821 + 19,925; ten thousands
70,000

3. 8,254 − 5,703; thousands **2000**

4. 66,845 − 24,782; ten thousands
50,000

5. One quart of paint covers an area of 100 square feet. How many quarts are needed to paint a wall 8 feet tall and 19 feet wide? **2**

Also available on transparency

1-3 Organizer

Pacing: Traditional 1 day
Block $\frac{1}{2}$ day

Objective: Students represent numbers by using exponents.

Technology Lab
In *Technology Lab Activities*

Online Edition
Tutorial Videos, Interactivities

Countdown to CRCT Week 1

Power Presentations with PowerPoint®

Warm Up

Multiply.

1. $3 \times 3 \times 3$ 27
2. $4 \times 4 \times 4$ 64
3. $2 \times 2 \times 2 \times 2$ 16
4. $5 \times 5 \times 5 \times 5$ 625

Problem of the Day

Replace the letters *a*, *b*, and *c* with the numbers 3, 4, and 5 to make a true statement.

$\mathbf{2^a + 2^a = b^c}$ $\quad 2^5 + 2^5 = 4^3$

Also available on transparency

Math Humor

In the math Olympics, the contestant from Havana calculated the largest result. Everyone else was squarin' while he was *Cuban*.

Georgia Performance Standards

M6P1.c Apply and adapt a variety of appropriate strategies to solve problems.

M6P1.d Monitor and reflect on the process of mathematical problem solving.

1-3 Exponents

Learn to represent numbers by using exponents.

Vocabulary
exponent
base
exponential form

Georgia Performance Standards
M6P1.c Apply and adapt a variety of appropriate strategies to solve problems. Also, M6P1.d.

Since 1906, the height of Mount Vesuvius in Italy has increased by 7^3 feet. How many feet is this?

The number 7^3 is written with an exponent. An **exponent** tells how many times a number called the **base** is used as a factor.

The most recent eruption of Mount Vesuvius took place in 1944.

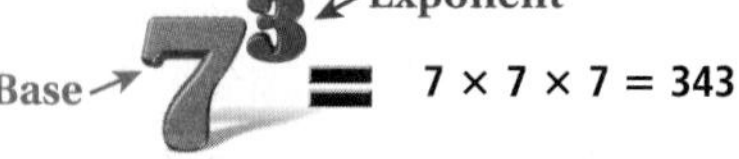

$7^3 = 7 \times 7 \times 7 = 343$

So the height of Mount Vesuvius has increased by 343 ft.

A number is in **exponential form** when it is written with a base and an exponent.

Exponential Form	Read	Multiply	Value
10^1	"10 to the 1st power"	10	10
10^2	"10 squared," or "10 to the 2nd power"	10×10	100
10^3	"10 cubed," or "10 to the 3rd power"	$10 \times 10 \times 10$	1,000
10^4	"10 to the 4th power"	$10 \times 10 \times 10 \times 10$	10,000

EXAMPLE 1 Writing Numbers in Exponential Form

Write each expression in exponential form.

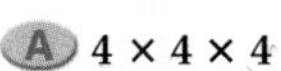

A $4 \times 4 \times 4$

4^3 *4 is a factor 3 times.*

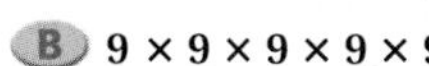

B $9 \times 9 \times 9 \times 9 \times 9$

9^5 *9 is a factor 5 times.*

EXAMPLE 2 Finding the Value of Numbers in Exponential Form

Find each value.

A 2^7

$2^7 = 2 \times 2 \times 2 \times 2 \times 2 \times 2 \times 2$
$= 128$

B 6^4

$6^4 = 6 \times 6 \times 6 \times 6$
$= 1{,}296$

1 Introduce

Alternate Opener

EXPLORATION

1-3 Exponents

1. Maria won the grand prize on a game show. She will be given \$2 the first month, \$4 the second month, \$8 the third month, and so on as her payment is doubled each month for one year.
   a. Complete the table.
   b. How much will Maria receive in the fifth month?
   c. How much will Maria receive in the eighth month?
   d. Use a calculator to determine how much Maria will receive in the last month of the year.

Month	Amount (\$)
1	2
2	4
3	8
4	
5	
6	
7	
8	

Think and Discuss

2. **Describe** the pattern in the table.
3. **Explain** how the values in the table compare with the values 2, 2^2, 2^3, 2^4, and so on.

Motivate

Review with students the term *repeated addition,* and have them give examples, e.g., $5 + 5 + 5 + 5$. Discuss with students an easier way to write a repeated addition expression, such as writing $5 + 5 + 5 + 5$ as 4×5. Have students give an example of a repeated multiplication expression, e.g., $7 \times 7 \times 7$. Explain that an easier way to write this repeated multiplication is 7^3.

Explorations and answers are provided in *Alternate Openers: Explorations Transparencies.*

EXAMPLE 3 PROBLEM SOLVING APPLICATION

If Dana's school closes, a phone tree is used to contact each student's family. The secretary calls 3 families. Then each family calls 3 other families, and so on. How many families will be notified during the 6th round of calls?

1 Understand the Problem

The **answer** will be the number of families called in the 6th round.

List the **important information:**

- The secretary calls 3 families.
- Each family calls 3 families.

2 Make a Plan

You can draw a diagram to see how many calls are in each round.

3 Solve

Notice that in each round, the number of calls is a power of 3.

1st round: 3 calls = $3 = 3^1$

2nd round: 9 calls = $3 \times 3 = 3^2$

So during the 6th round there will be 3^6 calls.

$3^6 = 3 \times 3 \times 3 \times 3 \times 3 \times 3 = 729$

During the 6th round of calls, 729 families will be notified.

4 Look Back

Drawing a diagram helps you visualize the pattern, but the numbers become too large for a diagram after the third round of calls. Solving this problem by using exponents can be easier and faster.

Answers to *Think and Discuss*

1. four to the eighth power; twelve cubed, or twelve to the third power; three squared, or three to the second power
2. 7; 169; 27

Think and Discuss
GPS M6P3.d

1. **Read** each number: 4^8, 12^3, 3^2.
2. **Give** the value of each number: 7^1, 13^2, 3^3.

Students may multiply a base by its exponent instead of using the base as a factor the number of times indicated by the exponent. Remind them that in 4 to the 3rd power ($4 \times 4 \times 4$), 4 is used as a factor 3 times.

Power Presentations with PowerPoint®

Additional Examples

Example 1

Write each expression in exponential form.

A. $5 \times 5 \times 5 \times 5$ 5^4

B. $3 \times 3 \times 3 \times 3 \times 3$ 3^5

Example 2

Find each value.

A. 2^6 64

B. 4^5 1,024

Example 3

A phone tree is used to contact families at Paul's school. The secretary calls 4 families. Then each family calls 4 other families, and so on. How many families will be notified during the fourth round of calls?

256 families will be notified.

Also available on transparency

Teaching Tip **Visual** In example 1, when writing expressions in exponential form, make sure that students count the number of times the factor appears, not the number of multiplication signs.

2 Teach

Guided Instruction

In this lesson, students learn to represent numbers by using exponents. First, teach students to write repeated multiplication expressions in exponential form using the Teaching Transparency. Then, teach students to find the values of numbers in exponential form. Show students how to apply exponents to a problem-solving situation. Remind students that numbers that are multiplied are called factors.

Teaching Tip **Auditory** Have students practice correctly pronouncing the exponential terms, such as "four to the third power."

Reaching All Learners

Through Number Sense

Have students write the repeated multiplication expression for each exponential term before computing its value until they become comfortable with exponential notations.

3 Close

Summarize

ENGLISH LANGUAGE LEARNERS

Briefly review definitions of the new vocabulary in the lesson: *exponent*, *base*, and *exponential form*. Correctly pronounce the exponential terms for the class and have them repeat your pronunciation.

1-3 Exercises

Assignment Guide

If you finished Example 1 assign:
Average 1–6, 33–37, 65–71
Advanced 13–21, 38–42, 65–71

If you finished Example 2 assign:
Average 1–12, 33–47, 65–71
Advanced 13–31, 38–52, 65–71

If you finished Example 3 assign:
Average 1–37, 48–71
Advanced 13–71

Homework Quick Check
Quickly check key concepts.
Exercises: 14, 16, 20, 24, 30

Answers

33. $16 \times 16 \times 16$
34. 22×22
35. $31 \times 31 \times 31 \times 31 \times 31 \times 31$
36. $46 \times 46 \times 46 \times 46 \times 46$
37. $50 \times 50 \times 50$
38–42. See p. A1.

Math Background

The use of the terms *squared* and *cubed* is directly related to the measurements of area and volume. The area of a square with sides 5 units long is found by multiplying 5×5, or 5^2, or five squared. The volume of a cube with sides 5 units long is found by multiplying $5 \times 5 \times 5$, or 5^3, or five cubed.

Georgia Performance Standards

M6P3.a Organize and consolidate their mathematical thinking through communication.

M6P4.c Recognize and apply mathematics in contexts outside of mathematics.

1-3 Exercises

M6P3.a, M6P4.c

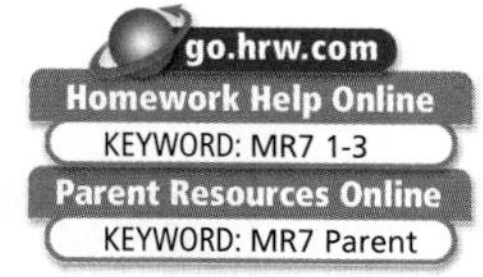

GUIDED PRACTICE

See Example 1 Write each expression in exponential form.

1. $8 \times 8 \times 8$ 8^3
2. 7×7 7^2
3. $6 \times 6 \times 6 \times 6 \times 6$ 6^5
4. $4 \times 4 \times 4 \times 4$ 4^4
5. $5 \times 5 \times 5 \times 5 \times 5$ 5^5
6. 1×1 1^2

See Example 2 Find each value.

7. 4^2 16
8. 3^3 27
9. 5^4 625
10. 8^2 64
11. 7^3 343

See Example 3

12. At Russell's school, one person will contact 4 people and each of those people will contact 4 other people, and so on. How many people will be contacted in the fifth round? 1,024 people

INDEPENDENT PRACTICE

See Example 1 Write each expression in exponential form.

13. $2 \times 2 \times 2 \times 2 \times 2 \times 2$ 2^6
14. $9 \times 9 \times 9 \times 9$ 9^4
15. 8×8 8^2
16. $1 \times 1 \times 1$ 1^3
17. $6 \times 6 \times 6 \times 6 \times 6$ 6^5
18. $5 \times 5 \times 5$ 5^3
19. $7 \times 7 \times 7 \times 7 \times 7 \times 7 \times 7$ 7^7
20. $3 \times 3 \times 3 \times 3$ 3^4
21. 4×4 4^2

See Example 2 Find each value.

22. 2^4 16
23. 3^5 243
24. 6^2 36
25. 9^2 81
26. 7^4 2,401
27. 8^3 512
28. 1^4 1
29. 16^2 256
30. 10^8 100,000,000
31. 12^2 144

See Example 3

32. To save money for a video game, you put one dollar in an envelope. Each day for 5 days you double the number of dollars in the envelope from the day before. How much have you saved after 5 days? 32 dollars

PRACTICE AND PROBLEM SOLVING

Extra Practice p. 714

Write each expression as repeated multiplication.

33. 16^3
34. 22^2
35. 31^6
36. 46^5
37. 50^3
38. 4^1
39. 1^9
40. 17^6
41. 8^5
42. 12^4

Find each value.

43. 10^6 1,000,000
44. 73^1 73
45. 9^4 6,561
46. 80^2 6,400
47. 10^5 100,000
48. 19^2 361
49. 2^9 512
50. 57^1 57
51. 5^3 125
52. 11^3 1,331

Compare. Write $<$, $>$, or $=$.

53. 6^1 ▒ 5^1 $>$
54. 9^2 ▒ 20^1 $>$
55. 10^1 ▒ $1{,}000{,}000^1$ $<$
56. 7^3 ▒ 3^7 $<$
57. 5^5 ▒ 25^1 $>$
58. 100^2 ▒ 10^4 $=$

RETEACH 1-3

CHAPTER 1-3 Reteach
Exponents

You can write a number in exponential form to show repeated multiplication. A number written in exponential form has a base and an exponent. An exponent tells you how many times a number, called the base, is used as a factor.

8^4 ← exponent
↑
base

Write the expression in exponential form.
$6 \times 6 \times 6$
6 is used as a factor 3 times.
$6 \times 6 \times 6 = 6^3$

Write each expression in exponential form.

1. $8 \times 8 \times 8 \times 8 \times 8$ 8^5
2. 3×3 3^2
3. $5 \times 5 \times 5 \times 5$ 5^4
4. $7 \times 7 \times 7$ 7^3

You can find the value of expressions in exponential form.
Find the value.
2^5

Step 1: Write the expression as repeated multiplication.
$2^5 = 2 \times 2 \times 2 \times 2 \times 2$

Step 2: Multiply.
$2 \times 2 \times 2 \times 2 \times 2 = 32$

$2^5 = 32$

Find each value.

5. 12^3 1,728
6. 6^5 7,776
7. 10^4 10,000
8. 4^6 4,096

PRACTICE 1-3

LESSON 1-3 Practice B
Exponents

Write each expression in exponential form.

1. 9×9 9^2
2. $7 \times 7 \times 7$ 7^3
3. $1 \times 1 \times 1 \times 1 \times 1$ 1^5
4. $5 \times 5 \times 5 \times 5$ 5^4
5. $2 \times 2 \times 2 \times 2 \times 2 \times 2$ 2^6
6. $10 \times 10 \times 10 \times 10$ 10^4

Find each value.

7. 6^2 36
8. 5^3 125
9. 10^3 1,000
10. 7^2 49
11. 2^5 32
12. 3^4 81
13. 25^1 25
14. 16^0 1

Compare. Write $<$, $>$, or $=$.

15. $8^0 < 7^1$
16. $10^2 < 11^2$
17. $8^2 = 4^3$
18. $3^4 > 5^2$
19. $2^5 < 9^2$
20. $6^2 > 3^3$

21. What whole number equals 25 when it is squared and 125 when it is cubed?
5

22. Use exponents to write the number 81 three different ways.
81^1; 9^2; 3^4

Life Science

You are able to grow because your body produces new cells. New cells are made when old cells divide. Single-celled bodies, like bacteria, divide by *binary fission*, which means "splitting into two parts." A cycle is the length of time a cell type needs to divide.

59. In science lab, Carol has a dish containing 4^5 cells. How many cells are represented by this number? **1,024 cells**

60. A certain colony of bacteria triples in length every 15 minutes. Its length is now 1 mm. How long will it be in 1 hour? (*Hint:* There are four cycles of 15 minutes in 1 hour.) **81 mm**

Use the bar graph for Exercises 61–64.

Cell Division Cycles

Cycle length (hr): 0, 3, 6, 9

Cell type: A, B, C

61. Determine how many times cell type A will divide in a 24-hour period. If you begin with one type A cell, how many cells will be produced in 24 hours? **8; 2^8, or 256**

62. Multi-Step If you begin with one type B cell and one type C cell, what is the difference between the number of type B cells and the number of type C cells produced in 24 hours? **8**

63. Write About It Explain how to find the number of type A cells produced in 48 hours.

64. Challenge How many hours will it take one C cell to divide into at least 100 C cells? **56 hours**

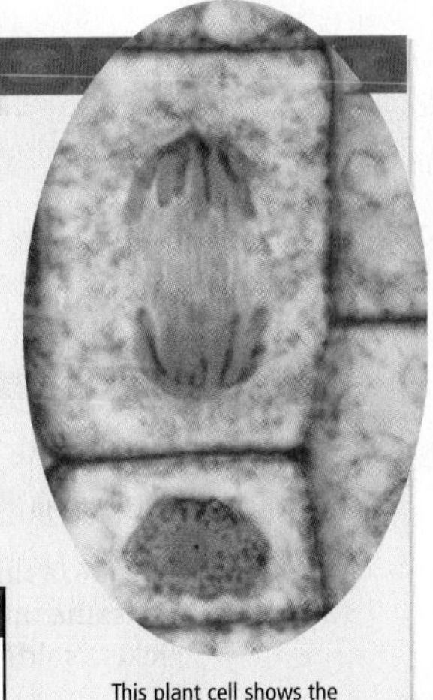

This plant cell shows the anaphase stage of mitosis. Mitosis is the process of nuclear division in complex cells called eukaryotes.

go.hrw.com
Web Extra!
KEYWORD: MR7 Cell

CRCT Prep • GPS Support • Spiral Review

65. Multiple Choice Which of the following shows the expression $4 \times 4 \times 4$ in exponential form?

Ⓐ 64 Ⓑ 444 Ⓒ 3^4 **Ⓓ 4^3**

66. Multiple Choice Which expression has the greatest value?

Ⓕ 2^5 **Ⓖ 3^4** Ⓗ 4^3 Ⓙ 5^2

Order the numbers from least to greatest. (Lesson 1-1)

67. 8,452; 8,732; 8,245 **8,245; 8,452; 8,732**

68. 991; 1,010; 984 **984; 991; 1,010**

69. 12,681; 11,901; 12,751 **11,901; 12,681; 12,751**

Estimate each sum or difference by rounding to the place value indicated. (Lesson 1-2)

70. 12,876 + 17,986; thousands **31,000**

71. 72,876 − 15,987; ten thousands **50,000**

CHALLENGE 1-3

LESSON 1-3 Challenge
Exponent Riddle

What is the greatest number that can be written with two digits?

Find the value of each expression below. Then in the box at the bottom of the page, write each expression's letter in the blank above its value. When you have found all the values, you will have solved the riddle.

E	3^3	27
H	5^2	25
I	2^4	16
N	34^0	1
O	9^2	81
P	4^3	64
R	6^2	36
T	7^2	49
W	10^2	100

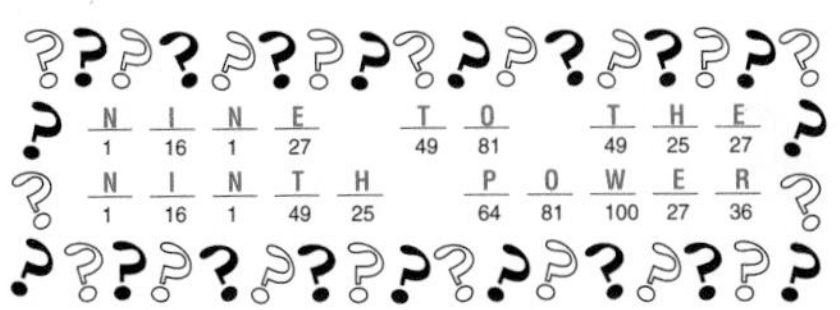

N I N E T O T H E
1 16 1 27 49 81 49 25 27

N I N T H P O W E R
1 16 1 49 25 64 81 100 27 36

PROBLEM SOLVING 1-3

LESSON 1-3 Problem Solving
Exponents

1. The Sun is the center of our solar system. The Sun is the star closest to our planet. The surface temperature of the Sun is close to 10,000°F. Write 10,000 using exponents.

10^4

2. Patty Berg has won 4^2 major women's titles in golf. Write 4^2 in standard form.

16

3. William has 3^3 baseball cards and 4^3 football cards. Write the number of baseball cards and footballs cards that William has.

27 baseball cards and 64 football cards

4. Michelle recorded the number of miles she ran each day last year. She used the following expression to represent the total number of miles: $3 \times 3 \times 3 \times 3 \times 3 \times 3 \times 3$. Write this expression using exponents. How many miles did Michelle run last year?

3^7; 2,187 miles

Choose the letter for the best answer.

5. In Tyrone's science class he is studying cells. Cell A divides every 30 minutes. If Tyrone starts with two cells, how many cells will he have in 3 hours?

A 6 cells
B 32 cells
Ⓒ 128 cells
D 512 cells

6. Tanisha's soccer team has a phone tree in case a soccer game is postponed or cancelled. The coach calls 2 families. Then each family calls 2 other families. How many families will be notified during the 4th round of calls?

F 2 families
G 4 families
H 8 families
Ⓙ 16 families

7. The Akashi-Kaiko Bridge is the longest suspension bridge in the world. It is located in Kobe-Naruto, Japan and was completed in 1998. It is about 3^8 feet long. Write the approximate length of the Akashi-Kaiko Bridge in standard form.

Ⓐ 6,561 feet
B 2,187 feet
C 512 feet
D 24 feet

8. The Strahov Stadium is the largest sports stadium in the world. It is located in Prague, Czech Republic. Its capacity is about 12^5 people. Write the capacity of the Strahov Stadium in standard form.

F 60 people
G 144 people
H 20,736 people
Ⓙ 248,832 people

Ongoing Assessment and Intervention

***Diagnose Before* the Lesson**
1-3 Warm Up, TE p. 14

***Monitor During* the Lesson**
1-3 Know-It Notebook
1-3 Questioning Strategies

***Assess After* the Lesson**
1-3 Lesson Quiz, TE p. 17

Interdisciplinary

Life Science

Exercises 59–64 pertain to a type of cell division called binary fission. Binary fission is studied in middle-school life science programs such as *Holt Science & Technology*.

Answers

63. Divide 48 hours by the length of the cell-division cycle, 3 hours; $48 \div 3 = 16$. Raise 2 to this power; $2^{16} = 65{,}536$.

Test Prep Doctor In Exercise 65, students need to understand the relationship between exponents and multiplication. students answering **A** may not have read the exercise correctly.

Journal

Have students write about how they would explain the use of exponents to a student who was absent from class.

Power Presentations with PowerPoint®

1-3 Lesson Quiz

Write each expression in exponential form.

1. $12 \times 12 \times 12$ **12^3**

2. $9 \times 9 \times 9 \times 9 \times 9 \times 9 \times 9$ **9^7**

Find each value.

3. 20^2 **400**

4. 6^4 **1,296**

5. In a phone tree, each of 3 people will call 3 people, and then each of those will call 3 more. If there are 5 levels of the tree, how many people will be called? **243**

Also available on transparency

Organizer

Objective: Assess students' mastery of concepts and skills in Lessons 1-1 through 1-3.

Resources

Assessment Resources
Section 1A Quiz

INTERVENTION 

Resources

***Ready to Go On? Intervention and Enrichment* Worksheets**

***Ready to Go On?* CD-ROM**

***Ready to Go On?* Online**

my.hrw.com

SECTION 1A

Ready to Go On?

Quiz for Lessons 1-1 Through 1-3

1-1 Comparing and Ordering Whole Numbers

Compare. Write <, >, or =.

1. 12,563,284 ▢ 12,587,802 <

2. 783,100,570 ▢ 780,223,104 >

3. In 2006, a university sold 1,981,299 tickets to its football games. In 2005, the same university sold 1,881,702 tickets. During which year were more tickets sold? 2006

Order the numbers from least to greatest.

4. 1,052; 1,803; 1,231
1,052; 1,231; 1,803

5. 4,344; 3,344; 3,444
3,344; 3,444; 4,344

6. 10,463; 14,063; 10,643
10,463; 10,643; 14,063

1-2 Estimating with Whole Numbers

Estimate each sum or difference by rounding to the place value indicated.

7. 61,582 + 13,281; ten thousands 70,000

8. 86,125 − 55,713; ten thousands 30,000

9. 7,903 + 2,654; thousands 11,000

10. 34,633 − 32,087; thousands 3,000

11. 1,896,345 + 3,567,194; hundred thousands 5,500,000

12. 56,129,482 − 37,103,758; ten millions 20,000,000

13. Marcus wants to make a stone walkway in his garden. The rectangular walkway will be 3 feet wide and 18 feet long. Each 2-foot by 3-foot stone covers an area of 6 square feet. How many stones will Marcus need? 9 stones

14. Jenna's sixth-grade class is taking a bus to the zoo. The zoo is 156 miles from the school. If the bus travels an average of 55 mi/h, about how long will it take the class to get to the zoo? about 3 hours

1-3 Exponents

Write each expression in exponential form.

15. $7 \times 7 \times 7$ 7^3

16. $5 \times 5 \times 5 \times 5$ 5^4

17. $3 \times 3 \times 3 \times 3 \times 3 \times 3$ 3^6

18. $10 \times 10 \times 10 \times 10$ 10^4

19. $1 \times 1 \times 1 \times 1 \times 1$ 1^5

20. $4 \times 4 \times 4 \times 4$ 4^4

Find each value.

21. 3^3 27

22. 2^4 16

23. 6^2 36

24. 8^3 512

25. To start reading a novel for English class, Sara reads 1 page. Each day for 4 days she reads double the number of pages she read the day before. How many pages will she have read by the end of the fourth day? 16

READY TO GO ON?
Diagnose and Prescribe

NO
INTERVENE

Ready to Go On? Intervention	*Ready to Go On?* Intervention, Section 1A		
	Worksheets	CD-ROM	Online
Lesson 1-1	1-1 Intervention	Activity 1-1	Diagnose and Prescribe Online
Lesson 1-2	1-2 Intervention	Activity 1-2	
Lesson 1-3	1-3 Intervention	Activity 1-3	

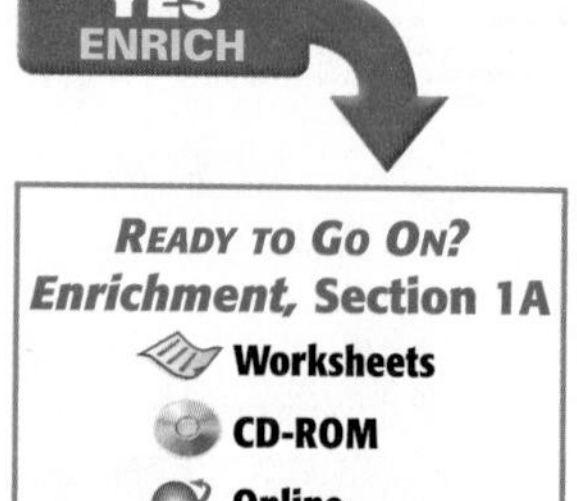

***Ready to Go On?* Enrichment, Section 1A**
Worksheets
CD-ROM
Online

Focus on Problem Solving

Solve

• **Choose the operation: addition or subtraction**

Read the whole problem before you try to solve it. Determine what action is taking place in the problem. Then decide whether you need to add or subtract in order to solve the problem.

If you need to combine or put numbers together, you need to add. If you need to take away or compare numbers, you need to subtract.

Action	Operation	Picture
Combining Putting together	Add	
Removing Taking away	Subtract	
Comparing Finding the difference	Subtract	

Read each problem. Determine the action in each problem. Choose an operation in order to solve the problem. Then solve.

Most hurricanes that occur over the Atlantic Ocean, the Caribbean Sea, or the Gulf of Mexico occur between June and November. Since 1886, a hurricane has occurred in every month except April.

Number of Out-of-Season Hurricanes Since 1886	
Month	**Number**
Jan	1
Feb	1
Mar	1
May	14
Dec	10

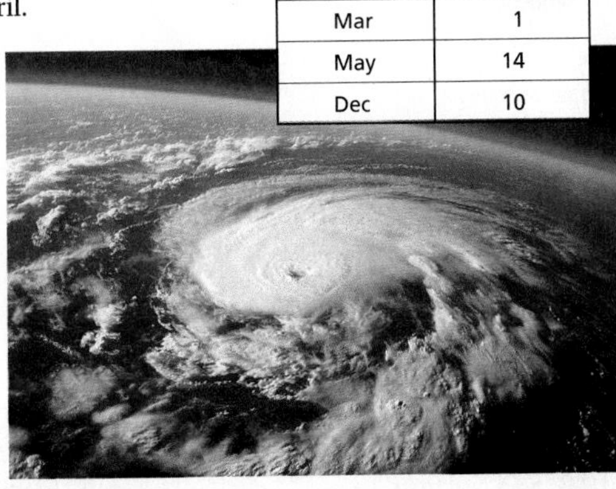

Use the table for problems 1 and 2.

1. How many out-of-season hurricanes have occurred in all?
2. How many more hurricanes have occurred in May than in December?
3. There were 14 named storms during the 2000 hurricane season. Eight of these became hurricanes, and three others became major hurricanes. How many of the named storms were not hurricanes or major hurricanes?

Focus on Problem Solving

Organizer

Objective: Focus on choosing an addition or subtraction operation.

Online Edition

Resources

Chapter 1 Resource Book
Reading Strategies

Problem Solving Process

This page focuses on the third step of the problem-solving process: **Solve**

Discuss

Have students discuss which actions take place in each problem and which operations the actions indicate.

1. combining; addition
2. finding the difference; subtraction
3. taking away; subtraction

Answers

1. 1 + 1 + 1 + 14 + 10 = 27
2. 14 − 10 = 4
3. 14 − (8 + 3) = 3

SECTION **1B**

Using Whole Numbers

One-Minute Section Planner

Lesson	Materials	MiC and Lab Resources
1-4 Technology Lab Explore the Order of Operations • Use a graphing calculator to explore the order of operations. **Lesson 1-4** Order of Operations • Use the order of operations. ☐ CRCT ☑ SAT-10 ☑ ITBS ☑ CTBS ☑ NAEP	Graphing calculators	**MiC:** ***Expressions and Formulas*** pp. 32–38, 42–44 ***Technology Lab Activities*** 1-4
Lesson 1-5 Mental Math • Use number properties to compute mentally. ☐ CRCT ☑ SAT-10 ☑ ITBS ☑ CTBS ☑ NAEP	Number cubes (MK)	**MiC:** ***Expressions and Formulas*** pp. 6–8
Lesson 1-6 Problem Solving Skill: Choose the Method of Computation • Choose an appropriate method of computation and justify the choice. ☐ CRCT ☐ SAT-10 ☑ ITBS ☑ CTBS ☐ NAEP	Calculators	**MiC:** ***Expressions and Formulas*** pp. 25–29 ***Hands-On Lab Activities*** 1-6
Lesson 1-7 Patterns and Sequences • Find patterns and recognize, describe, and extend patterns in sequences. **1-7 Technology Lab** Find a Pattern in Sequences • Use a spreadsheet to perform repeated operations that generate a sequence. ☑ CRCT ☑ SAT-10 ☑ ITBS ☑ CTBS ☑ NAEP	Spreadsheet software	**MiC:** ***Expressions and Formulas*** pp. 14–15, 16–17 ***Hands-On Lab Activities*** 1-7 ***Technology Lab Activities*** 1-7

MK = *Manipulatives Kit*

Mathematics in Context

The unit ***Expressions and Formulas*** from the *Mathematics in Context* © 2006 series can be used with Section 1B. See Section Planner above for suggestions for integrating *MiC* with *Holt Mathematics*.

Section Overview

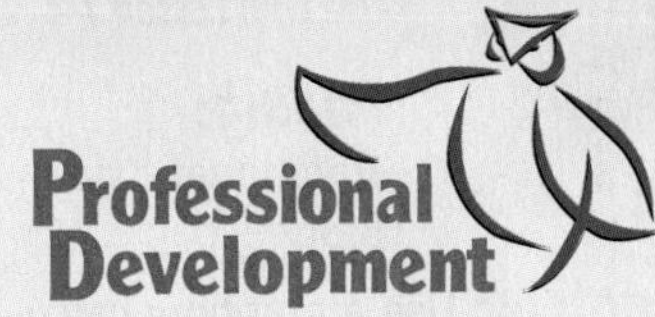

Using the Order of Operations — Lesson 1-4

Why? The order of operations ensures that everyone gets the same answer.

Order of Operations
1. Parentheses
2. Exponents
3. Multiply/Divide
4. Add/Subtract

Evaluate $9 \div (1 + 2) \times 4^2 - 5$.

$9 \div (1 + 2) \times 4^2 - 5$	*Perform operations within parentheses.*
$9 \div 3 \times 4^2 - 5$	*Find the values of numbers with exponents.*
$9 \div 3 \times 16 - 5$	*Divide.*
$3 \times 16 - 5$	*Multiply.*
$48 - 5$	*Subtract.*
43	

Using Number Properties — Lesson 1-5

Number properties can help you perform calculations mentally.

Commutative Property

Addition: $2 + 3 = 3 + 2$
Multiplication: $2 \times 3 = 3 \times 2$

Associative Property

Addition: $(3 + 5) + 4 = 3 + (5 + 4)$
Multiplication: $(3 \times 5) \times 4 = 3 \times (5 \times 4)$

Distributive Property

$4 \times (8 + 2) = (4 \times 8) + (4 \times 2)$
and
$4 \times (8 - 2) = (4 \times 8) - (4 - 2)$

Use number properties to evaluate mentally.

$14 + 22 + 16 + 28 = 14 + \mathbf{16} + \mathbf{22} + 28$ ***Commutative Property***
$= (14 + 16) + (22 + 28)$ ***Associative Property***
$= 30 + 50$
$= 80$

$7 \times 64 = 7 \times (60 + 4)$
$= (7 \times 60) + (7 \times 4)$ ***Distributive Property***
$= 420 + 28$
$= 448$

Extending Patterns in Sequences — Lessons 1-6, 1-7

By recognizing and extending number patterns, you can make predictions and solve problems involving function relationships.

A **sequence** is an ordered set of numbers.

×2 ×2 ×2 ×2

1, 2, 4, 8, 16, ...

Each number in a sequence is called a **term**.

Multiply by 2 to get the next term.
The next three terms are as follows:

$16 \times 2 = \mathbf{32}$
$36 \times 2 = \mathbf{64}$
$64 \times 2 = \mathbf{128}$

Note: Some students may find different rules or patterns for the same sequence. There will always be many rules that will give rise to a given sequence.

Organizer

Use with Lesson 1-4

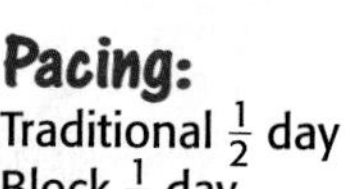

Pacing:
Traditional $\frac{1}{2}$ day
Block $\frac{1}{4}$ day

Objective: Use a graphing calculator to solve two-step equations.

Materials: Graphing calculator

Online Edition
Scientific Calculator

Countdown to CRCT Week 1

Resources

Technology Lab Activities
Lab 1-4 Recording Sheet

Teach

Discuss

Calculators that are not scientific or graphing do not have the internal programming to apply the correct order of operations to an expression.

Close

Key Concept

The student must be able to correctly apply the order of operations or know to use the kind of calculator that will give the correct result.

Assessment

Suppose you used the following keystrokes:

2  3  4 

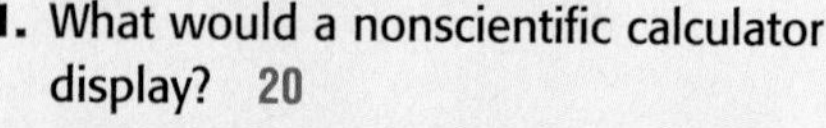

1. What would a nonscientific calculator display? 20
2. What would a scientific or graphing calculator display? 14

Georgia Performance Standards

M6P1.a Build new mathematical knowledge through problem solving.

M6P1.c Apply and adapt a variety of appropriate strategies to solve problems.

Explore the Order of Operations

Use with Lesson 1-4

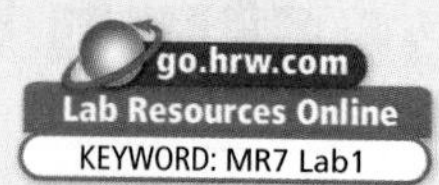

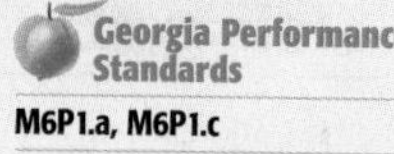

Georgia Performance Standards
M6P1.a, M6P1.c

Look at the expression 3 + 2 · 8. To evaluate this expression, decide whether to add first or multiply first. Knowing the correct *order of operations* is important. Without this knowledge, you could get an incorrect result.

Activity 1

Use pencil and paper to evaluate 3 + 2 · 8 two different ways.

Add first, and then multiply by 8.	3 + 2 = 5 5 · 8 = 40
Multiply first, and then add 3.	2 · 8 = 16 16 + 3 = 19

Now evaluate 3 + 2 · 8 using a graphing or scientific calculator.

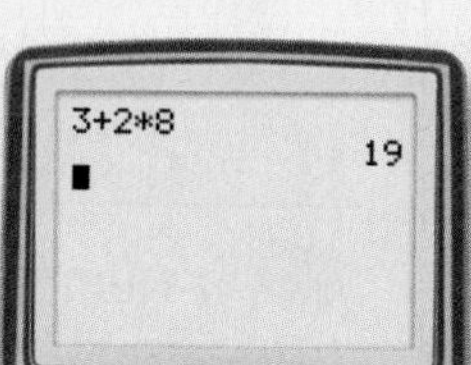

The result, 19, shows that this calculator multiplied first, even though addition came first in the expression.

If there are no parentheses, then multiplication and division are done before addition or subtraction. If the addition is to be done first, parentheses *must* be used.

When you evaluate (3 + 2) · 8 on a calculator, the result is 40. Because of the parentheses, the calculator adds before multiplying.

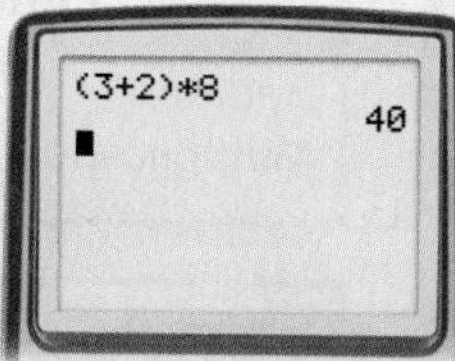

Graphing and scientific calculators follow a logical system called the algebraic order of operations. The order of operations tells you to multiply and divide before you add or subtract.

Think and Discuss

1. In 4 + 15 ÷ 5, which operation do you perform first? How do you know? Division; multiplication and division must be done before addition or subtraction.
2. Tell the order in which you would perform the operations in the expression 8 ÷ 2 + 6 · 3 − 4. division, multiplication, addition, subtraction

Try This

Evaluate each expression with pencil and paper. Check your answer with a calculator.

1. 4 · 12 − 7 41
2. 15 ÷ 3 + 10 15
3. 4 + 2 · 6 16
4. 10 − 4 ÷ 2 8

Emily Hodges
Austin, Texas

Teacher to Teacher

When graphing calculators are available in the classroom, students enjoy exploring and they can learn a lot very quickly.

After students understand the order of operations, give students numerical expressions including both parentheses and multiplication dots with any other operations. Have students predict what the resulting value will be. Encourage students to repeat the operations one at a time to see whether the same result is obtained.

Activity 2

What should you do if the same operation appears twice in an expression? Use a calculator to decide which subtraction is done first in the expression 7 – 3 – 2.

If 7 – 3 is done first, the value of the expression is 4 – 2 = 2.

If 3 – 2 is done first, the value of the expression is 7 – 1 = 6.

On the calculator, the value of 7 – 3 – 2 is 2. The subtraction on the left, 7 – 3, is done first.

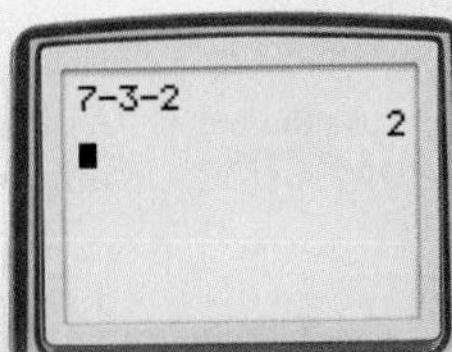

Addition and subtraction (or multiplication and division) are done from left to right.

Think and Discuss

1. In 15 + 5 + 4, does it matter which operation you perform first? Explain. No; the result is 24 whether you add 15 + 5 first or 5 + 4 first.
2. Does it matter which operation you perform first in 15 – 5 + 4? Explain. Yes; if you subtract first, the result is 14, but if you add first, the result is 6. 15–5 should be performed first since addition and subtraction are done from left to right.

Try This

Evaluate each expression. Check your answer with a calculator.

1. 8 – 6 – 1 1
2. 20 ÷ 5 ÷ 2 2
3. 3 · 6 · 2 36
4. 19 + 6 + 5 30

Activity 3

Without parentheses, the expression 8 + 2 · 10 – 3 equals 25. Insert parentheses to make the value of the expression 22.

What happens if you add first?	What happens if you subtract first?
(8 + 2) · 10 – 3	8 + 2 · (10 – 3)
10 · 10 – 3	8 + 2 · 7
100 – 3	8 + 14
97	22

8+2*(10-3)
22

For the expression to equal 22, the subtraction must be done first.

Think and Discuss

1. To evaluate 13 + 5 · 255 on a calculator, you type 13 + 5 and then press the **x** key. But before you can type in the 255, the display changes to 18!
   a. Does this calculator follow the correct order of operations? Why? No; the calculator evaluated 13 + 5 first.
   b. How could you use this calculator to evaluate 13 + 5 · 255? Possible answer: Multiply 5 · 255 first, and then add 13 to the result.

Try This

Insert parentheses to make the value of each expression 12.

1. 56 – 40 + 4 56 – (40 + 4)
2. 3 – 1 · 10 – 4 (3 – 1) · (10 – 4)
3. 18 ÷ 2 + 1 + 6 18 ÷ (2 + 1) + 6
4. 100 + 8 ÷ 2 · 2 + 5 (100 + 8) ÷ (2 · 2 + 5)

1-4 Organizer

Pacing: Traditional 1 day
Block $\frac{1}{2}$ day

Objective: Students use the order of operations.

Online Edition
Tutorial Videos

Countdown to CRCT Week 1

Power Presentations with PowerPoint®

Warm Up

Perform the operations in order from left to right.

1. 8 + 4 − 2 10
2. 9 × 3 + 1 28
3. 7 − 3 + 5 9
4. 20 ÷ 4 + 6 11

Problem of the Day

0 1 2 3 4 5 6 7 8 9 = 1

Put the appropriate plus or minus signs between the numbers so that the total equals 1.

0 + 1 − 23 + 45 + 67 − 89 = 1

Also available on transparency

Math Humor

The forgetful student never made it through medical school because he couldn't remember the order of operations.

Georgia Performance Standards

M6P4.c Recognize and apply mathematics in contexts outside of mathematics.

1-4 Order of Operations

Learn to use the order of operations.

Vocabulary
numerical expression
evaluate
order of operations

Georgia Performance Standards

M6P4.c Recognize and apply mathematics in contexts outside of mathematics.

A **numerical expression** is a mathematical phrase that includes only numbers and operation symbols.

Numerical Expressions	4 + 8 ÷ 2 × 6	371 − 203 + 2	5,006 × 19

When you **evaluate** a numerical expression, you find its value.

Erika and Jamie each evaluated 3 + 4 × 6. Their work is shown below. Whose answer is correct?

When an expression has more than one operation, you must know which operation to do first. To make sure that everyone gets the same answer, we use the **order of operations**.

Remember!

The first letters of these words can help you remember the order of operations.

Please — *Parentheses*
Excuse — *Exponents*
My — *Multiply/*
Dear — *Divide*
Aunt — *Add/*
Sally — *Subtract*

ORDER OF OPERATIONS

1. Perform operations in parentheses.
2. Find the values of numbers with exponents.
3. Multiply or divide from left to right as ordered in the problem.
4. Add or subtract from left to right as ordered in the problem.

3 + 4 × 6 — *There are no parentheses or exponents. Multiply first.*
3 + 24 — *Add.*
27 — *Erika has the correct answer.*

EXAMPLE 1 Using the Order of Operations

Evaluate each expression.

A 9 + 12 × 2

9 + 12 × 2 — *There are no parentheses or exponents.*
9 + 24 — *Multiply.*
33 — *Add.*

1 Introduce

Alternate Opener

EXPLORATION

1-4 Order of Operations

Calculators are programmed to perform operations in a certain order. Each keystroke sequence below results in 17.

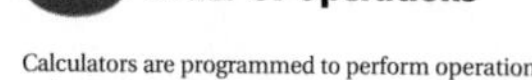

For each keystroke sequence, determine the order of operations the calculator follows.

1. (2 + 3) × 5 ENTER
2. 2 ^ 3 − 1 × 4 ENTER
3. 2 ^ (3 − 1) × 4 ENTER

Write the keystroke sequence for each expression.

4. $5 - 2^2$
5. $(2 - 3)^3 + 2$

Think and Discuss

6. **Explain** why there needs to be a rule for the order of operations.

Motivate

Have students evaluate 7 + 3 × 4. Tell them the expression represents 7 red marbles and 3 groups of 4 blue marbles. Then ask for the total number of marbles.

Explorations and answers are provided in *Alternate Openers: Explorations Transparencies.*

PEMDAS

Evaluate each expression.

B $7 + (12 \times 3) \div 6$

$7 + (12 \times 3) \div 6$	
$7 + \quad 36 \quad \div 6$	*Perform operations within parentheses.*
$7 + \quad 6$	*Divide.*
13	*Add.*

EXAMPLE 2 Using the Order of Operations with Exponents

Evaluate each expression.

A $3^3 + 8 - 16$

$3^3 + 8 - 16$	*There are no parentheses.*
$27 + 8 - 16$	*Find the values of numbers with exponents.*
$35 \quad - 16$	*Add*
19	*Subtract.*

B $8 \div (1 + 3) \times 5^2 - 2$

$8 \div (1 + 3) \times 5^2 - 2$	
$8 \div \quad 4 \quad \times 5^2 - 2$	*Perform operations within parentheses.*
$8 \div \quad 4 \quad \times 25 - 2$	*Find the values of numbers with exponents.*
$2 \quad \times 25 - 2$	*Divide.*
$50 \quad - 2$	*Multiply.*
48	*Subtract.*

EXAMPLE 3 *Consumer Application*

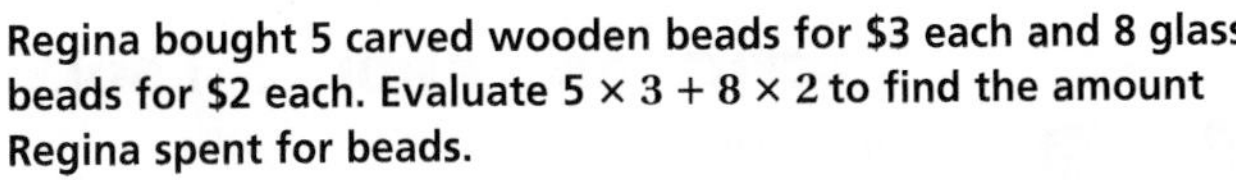

Regina bought 5 carved wooden beads for $3 each and 8 glass beads for $2 each. Evaluate $5 \times 3 + 8 \times 2$ to find the amount Regina spent for beads.

$5 \times 3 + 8 \times 2$

$15 \quad + \quad 16$

31

Regina spent $31 for beads.

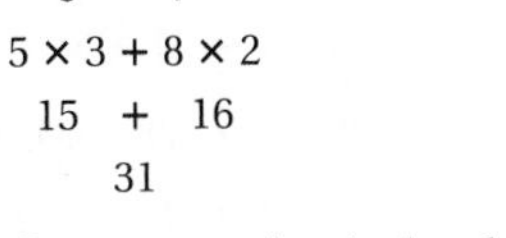

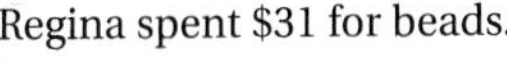

Think and Discuss

GPS M6P2.c

1. Explain why $6 + 7 \times 10 = 76$ but $(6 + 7) \times 10 = 130$.

2. Tell how you can add parentheses to the numerical expression $2^2 + 5 \times 3$ so that 27 is the correct answer.

COMMON ERROR ALERT

Students using "**P**lease **E**xcuse **M**y **D**ear **A**unt **S**ally" to remember the order of operations may think that all multiplication is done before division and all addition is done before subtraction. Stress that this is not the case, as is explained in the chart on the first page of the lesson.

Power Presentations with PowerPoint®

Additional Examples

Example 1

Evaluate each expression.

A. $15 - 10 \div 2$ 10

B. $9 + (21 \div 7) \times 5$ 24

Example 2

Evaluate each expression.

A. $2^4 + 6 \times 4$ 40

B. $24 \div (9 - 6) \times 3^2 - 10$ 62

Example 3

Mr. Kellett bought 6 used CDs for $4 each and 5 used CDs for $3 each. Evaluate the following expression to find the amount Mr. Kellett spent on CDs. $6 \times 4 + 5 \times 3$ $39

Also available on transparency

Answers to *Think and Discuss*

1. Possible answer: Using the order of operations for $6 + 7 \times 10$, you multiply 7×10 before adding 6. However, for $(6 + 7) \times 10$, you perform the operation in parentheses before multiplying by 10.
2. $(2^2 + 5) \times 3$

2 Teach

Guided Instruction

In this lesson, students learn to use the order of operations. Show students how to evaluate numerical expressions containing more than one operation. Then have students apply the order of operations to a real-world (consumer) context. You may use the Teaching Transparency to remind students of the correct order of operations.

Reaching All Learners

Through Cooperative Learning

Have students work in groups to try to stump their classmates. Each group writes several numerical expressions, with no more than three operations, for which the order of operations must be used. For each expression, the group gives its actual value and an incorrect value that can be found by not following the order of operations. Groups then switch papers and choose the correct value for each expression.

Sample expression:

$4 + (6 + 8) \times 4$

60 or 72

(correct answer: 60)

3 Close

Summarize

Review definitions of new vocabulary in the lesson: *numerical expression, evaluate,* and *order of operations*. Discuss how the terms relate to each other. Emphasize that multiplication and division have the same priority and that the same can be said of addition and subtraction.

1-4 Exercises

Assignment Guide

If you finished Example 1 assign:
Average 1–3, 8–13, 22–24, 48–58
Advanced 1–3, 8–13, 22–24, 48–58

If you finished Example 2 assign:
Average 1–6, 8–19, 22–37, 43–44, 48–58
Advanced 8–19, 22–41, 43–46, 48–58

If you finished Example 3 assign:
Average 1–37, 42–45, 48–58
Advanced 7–58

Homework Quick Check
Quickly check key concepts.
Exercises: 8, 18, 20, 26, 32

Answers

42. Julie; Jon should have multiplied 3 times 8 before adding 1.

Math Background

Without the order of operations, one person could conclude 2 + 3 × 4 = 14 and another could conclude 2 + 3 × 4 = 20, and neither would be incorrect! A fundamental idea in arithmetic is that a numerical expression has a unique value. A simple explanation of why the correct answer is 14 and not 20 is based on the fact that 3 × 4 = 4 + 4 + 4. Thus the expression 2 + 3 × 4 can be written as 2 + 4 + 4 + 4, which equals 14.

The purpose of the order of operations is to guarantee that every numerical expression has a unique value.

Georgia Performance Standards

M6P3.c Analyze and evaluate the mathematical thinking and strategies of others.

M6P4.c Recognize and apply mathematics in contexts outside of mathematics.

1-4 Exercises

M6P3.c, M6P4.c

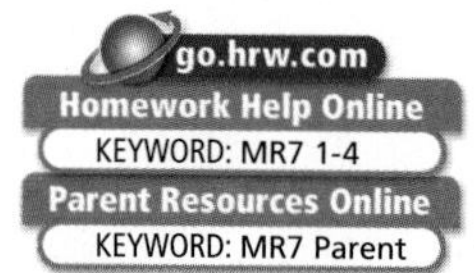

GUIDED PRACTICE

See Example 1
Evaluate each expression.

1. 36 − 18 ÷ 6 **33** **2.** 7 + 24 ÷ 6 × 2 **15** **3.** 62 − 4 × (15 ÷ 5) **50**

See Example 2
4. $11 + 2^3 \times 5$ **51** **5.** $5 \times (28 \div 7) - 4^2$ **4** **6.** $5 + 3^2 \times 6 - (10 - 9)$ **58**

See Example 3
7. Coach Milner fed the team after the game by buying 24 Chicken Deals for \$4 each and 7 Burger Deals for \$6 each. Evaluate 24 × 4 + 7 × 6 to find the cost of the food. **\$138**

INDEPENDENT PRACTICE

See Example 1
Evaluate each expression.

8. 9 + 27 ÷ 3 **18** **9.** 2 × 7 − 32 ÷ 8 **10** **10.** 45 ÷ (3 + 6) × 3 **15**

11. (6 + 2) × 4 **32** **12.** 9 ÷ 3 + 6 × 2 **15** **13.** 5 + 3 × 2 + 12 ÷ 4 **14**

See Example 2
14. $4^2 + 48 \div (10 - 4)$ **24** **15.** $100 \div 5^2 + 7 \times 3$ **25** **16.** $6 \times 2^2 + 28 - 5$ **47**

17. $6^2 - 12 \div 3 + (15 - 7)$ **40** **18.** $21 \div (3 + 4) \times 9 - 2^3$ **19** **19.** $(3^2 + 6 \div 2) \times (36 \div 6 - 4)$ **24**

See Example 3
20. The nature park has a pride of 5 adult lions and 3 cubs. The adults eat 8 lb of meat each day and the cubs eat 4 lb. Evaluate 5 × 8 + 3 × 4 to find the amount of meat consumed each day by the lions. **52 lb**

21. Angie read 4 books that were each 150 pages long and 2 books that were each 325 pages long. Evaluate 4 × 150 + 2 × 325 to find the total number of pages Angie read. **1,250 pages**

PRACTICE AND PROBLEM SOLVING

CRCT GPS
Extra Practice p. 715

Evaluate each expression.

22. 12 + 3 × 4 **24** **23.** 25 − 21 ÷ 3 **18** **24.** 1 + 7 × 2 **15**

25. $60 \div (10 + 2) \times 4^2 - 23$ **57** **26.** $10 \times (28 - 23) + 7^2 - 37$ **62** **27.** (5 − 3) ÷ 2 **1**

28. 72 ÷ 9 − 2 × 4 **0** **29.** $12 + (1 + 7^2) \div 5$ **22** **30.** $25 - 5^2$ **0**

31. $(15 - 6)^2 - 34 \div 2$ **64** **32.** $(2 \times 4)^2 - 3 \times (5 + 3)$ **40** **33.** 16 + 2 × 3 **22**

Add parentheses so that each equation is correct.

34. $2^3 + 6 - 5 \times 4 = 12$ **$2^3 + (6 - 5) \times 4 = 12$**
35. $7 + 2 \times 6 - 4 - 3 = 53$ **$(7 + 2) \times 6 - (4 - 3) = 53$**
36. $3^2 + 6 + 3 \times 3 = 36$ **$3^2 + (6 + 3) \times 3 = 36$**
37. $5^2 - 10 + 5 + 4^2 = 36$ **$5^2 - 10 + (5 + 4^2) = 36$**
38. $2 \times 8 + 5 - 3 = 23$ **$2 \times (8 + 5) - 3 = 23$**
39. $9^2 - 2 \times 15 + 16 - 8 = 11$ **$9^2 - 2 \times (15 + 16) - 8 = 11$**
40. $5 + 7 \times 2 - 3 = 21$ **$(5 + 7) \times 2 - 3 = 21$**
41. $4^2 \times 3 - 2 \div 4 = 4$ **$4^2 \times (3 - 2) \div 4 = 4$**

42. **Critical Thinking** Jon says the answer to 1 + 3 × (6 + 2) − 7 is 25. Julie says the answer is 18. Who is correct? Explain.

RETEACH 1-4

LESSON 1-4 **Reteach**
Order of Operations

A mathematical phrase that includes only numbers and operations is called a numerical expression.

9 + 8 × 3 ÷ 6 is a numerical expression.

To evaluate a numerical expression, you find its value.

You can use the order of operations to evaluate a numerical expression.

Order of Operations
1. Do all operations within parentheses.
2. Find the values of numbers with exponents.
3. Multiply and divide in order from left to right.
4. Add and subtract in order from left to right.

Evaluate the expression.

$60 \div (7 + 3) + 3^2$	
$60 \div 10 + 3^2$	Do all operation within parentheses.
$60 \div 10 + 9$	Find the values of numbers with exponents.
6 + 9	Multiply and divide in order from left to right.
15	Add or subtract in order from left to right.

Evaluate each expression.

1. 7 × (12 + 8) − 6
7 × __20__ − 6
__140__ − 6
__134__

2. 10 × (12 + 34) + 3
10 × __46__ + 3
__460__ + 3
__463__

3. 10 + (6 × 5) − 7
10 + __30__ − 7
__40__ − 7
__33__

4. $2^3 + (10 - 4)$ __14__

5. 7 + 3 × (8 + 5) __46__

6. 36 ÷ 4 + 11 × 8 __97__

7. $5^2 - (2 \times 8) + 9$ __18__

8. $3 \times (12 \div 4) - 2^2$ __5__

9. $(3^3 + 10) - 2$ __35__

PRACTICE 1-4

LESSON 1-4 **Practice B**
Order of Operations

Evaluate each expression.

1. 10 + 6 × 2 __22__
2. (15 + 39) ÷ 6 __9__
3. (20 − 15) × 2 + 1 __11__
4. $(4^2 + 6) \div 11$ __2__
5. 9 + (7 −1) × 2 __21__
6. (2 × 4) + 8 − (5 × 3) __1__
7. $5 + 18 \div 3^2 - 1$ __6__
8. 8 + 5 × 10 − 12 __46__
9. $14 + (50 - 7^2) \times 3$ __17__

Add parentheses so that each equation is correct.

10. 7 + 9 × 3 − 1 = 25 __(3 − 1)__
11. $2^3 - 7 \times 4 = 4$ __$(2^3 - 7)$__
12. 5 + 6 × 9 ÷ 3 = 23 __(9 ÷ 3)__
13. 12 ÷ 3 × 2 = 2 __(3 • 2)__
14. 8 + 3 × 6 − 4 − 1 = 13 __(6 − 4)__
15. $4 \times 3^2 + 1 = 40$ __$(3^2 + 1)$__
16. 9 × 0 + 5 − 3 = 42 __(0 + 5)__
17. $15 \times 3^2 - 2^3 = 15$ __$(3^2 - 2^3)$__
18. 14 ÷ 2 + 5 × 5 = 10 __(2 + 5)__

19. Tyler walked 2 miles a day for the first week of his exercise plan. Then he walked 3 miles a day for the next 9 days. How many miles did Tyler walk in all?

__41 miles__

20. Paulo's father bought 8 pizzas and 12 bottles of juice for the class party. Each pizza cost \$9 and each bottle of juice cost \$2. Paulo's father paid with a \$100-bill. How much change did he get back?

__\$4__

Social Studies LINK

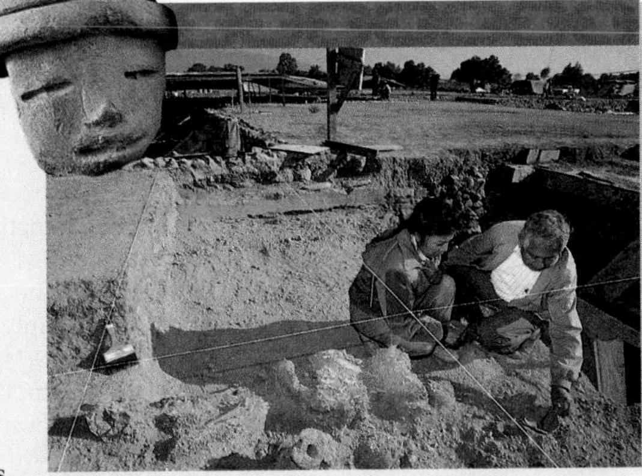

Archaeologists uncovered pieces of pottery at the La Ventilla site in Mexico.

Archaeologists study cultures of the past by uncovering items from ancient cities. An archaeologist has chosen a site in Mexico for her team's next dig. She divides the location into rectangular plots and labels each plot so that uncovered items can be identified by the plot in which they were found.

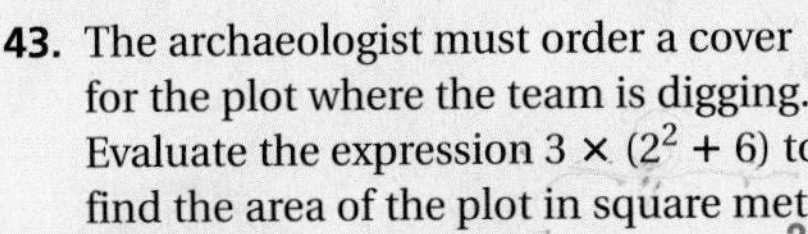

43. The archaeologist must order a cover for the plot where the team is digging. Evaluate the expression $3 \times (2^2 + 6)$ to find the area of the plot in square meters. **$30\ m^2$**

44. In the first week, the archaeology team digs down 2 meters and removes a certain amount of dirt. Evaluate the expression $3 \times (2^2 + 6) \times 2$ to find the volume of the dirt removed from the plot in the first week. **$60\ m^3$**

45. Over the next two weeks, the archaeology team digs down an additional 2^3 meters. Evaluate the expression $3 \times (2^2 + 6) \times (2 + 2^3)$ to find the total volume of dirt removed from the plot after 3 weeks. **$300\ m^3$**

46. **Write About It** Explain why the archaeologist must follow the order of operations to determine the area of each plot.

47. **Challenge** Write an expression for the volume of dirt that would be removed if the archaeologist's team were to dig down an additional 3^2 meters after the first three weeks. **$3 \times (2^2 + 6) \times (2 + 2^3 + 3^2)$**

46. If she does not follow the order of operations, she will buy the wrong size cover.

CRCT Prep • GPS Support • Spiral Review

48. Multiple Choice Which operation should you perform first when you evaluate $81 - (6 + 30 \div 2) \times 5$?

Ⓐ Addition Ⓑ Division (circled) Ⓒ Multiplication Ⓓ Subtraction

49. Multiple Choice Which expression does NOT have a value of 5?

Ⓕ $2^2 + (3 - 2)$ Ⓖ $(2^2 + 3) - 2$ Ⓗ $2^2 + 3 - 2$ Ⓙ $2^2 - (3 + 2)$ (circled)

50. Gridded Response What is the value of the expression $3^2 + (9 \div 3 - 2)$? **10**

Write each number in standard form. (Lesson 1-1)

51. $3{,}000 + 200 + 70 + 3$ **3,273** **52.** $10{,}000 + 500 + 20 + 1$ **10,521** **53.** $70{,}000 + 7$ **70,007**

Find each value. (Lesson 1-3)

54. 8^5 **32,768** **55.** 5^3 **125** **56.** 3^8 **6,561** **57.** 4^4 **256** **58.** 7^2 **49**

CHALLENGE 1-4

LESSON 1-4 **Challenge**
Crack the Expression Code

Each of these symbols stands for a different operation symbol:

♥ ♠ ♦ ♣

Each of these animals stands for a different whole number 1–4:

Use the equations below to find what each symbol and animal represents in the expression code.

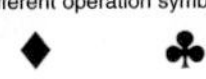

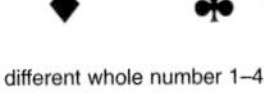

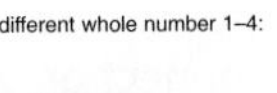

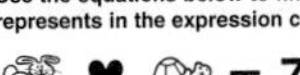

OPERATIONS

1. ♥ = +
2. ♠ = −
3. ♦ = ×
4. ♣ = ÷

NUMBERS

5. (rabbit) = 4
6. (dog) = 2
7. (cat) = 1
8. (turtle) = 3

PROBLEM SOLVING 1-4

LESSON 1-4 **Problem Solving**
Order of Operations

Evaluate each expression to complete the table.

Mammals with the Longest Tails

	Mammal	Expression	Tail Length
1.	Asian elephant	$2 + 3^2 \times 7 - (10 - 4)$	59
2.	Leopard	$5 \times 6 + 5^2$	55
3.	African elephant	$6 \times (72 \div 8) - 3$	51
4.	African buffalo	$51 + 6^2 \div 9 - 12$	43
5.	Giraffe	$4^3 - 3 \times 7$	43
6.	Red kangaroo	$11 + 48 \div 6 \times 4$	43

Choose the letter for the best answer.

7. Adam and his two brothers went to the zoo. Each ticket to enter the zoo costs $7. Adam bought two bags of peanuts for $4 each, and one of his brothers bought a lion poster for $12. Which expression shows how much money they spent at the zoo in all?
   - A $7 + 4 + 12$
   - B $7 \times 3 + 4 + 12$
   - Ⓒ $7 \times 3 + 4 \times 2 + 12$
   - D $(7 \times 3) + (4 \times 12)$

8. An elephant eats about 500 pounds of grass and leaves every day. There are 2 Africa elephants and 3 Asian elephants living in the City Zoo. How many pounds of grass and leaves do the zookeepers need to order each week to feed all the elephants?
   - F 2,500 pounds
   - Ⓖ 17,500 pounds
   - H 3,000 pounds
   - J 21,000 pounds

9. The average giraffe is 18 feet tall. Which of these expressions shows the height of a giraffe?
   - A $4^2 - 2$
   - B $3 \times 12 \div 4 + 2$
   - Ⓒ $3^3 \div 9 \times 6$
   - D $20 \div 5 + 5 - 6$

10. Some kangaroos can cover 30 feet in a single jump! If a kangaroo could jump like that 150 times in a row, how much farther would it need to go to cover a mile? (1 mile = 5,280 feet)
    - Ⓕ 780 feet
    - G 26 feet
    - H 176 feet
    - J 5,100 feet

ONGOING ASSESSMENT and INTERVENTION

Diagnose **Before the Lesson**
1-4 Warm Up, TE p. 22

Monitor **During the Lesson**
1-4 Know-It Notebook
1-4 Questioning Strategies

Assess **After the Lesson**
1-4 Lesson Quiz, TE p. 25

Interdisciplinary LINK

Social Studies

Exercises 43–47 focus on archaeological digs. The early histories of many regions are studied in middle-school social studies programs, such as Holt, Rinehart & Winston's *People, Places, and Change.* These histories are often based on remains and ruins uncovered during archaeological digs.

Answers

46. If she does not follow the order of operations, she will buy the wrong size cover.

TEST PREP DOCTOR In Exercise 48, students who answered **C** or **D** did not remember to perform operations inside parentheses first. Students who answered **A** should be reminded that division is performed before addition.

Journal

Have students write about a situation outside of solving math problems in which the order in which things are done is important.

Power Presentations with PowerPoint®

1-4 Lesson Quiz

Evaluate each expression.

1. $15 + 4 \times 2$ **23**
2. $(12 - 5)^2 - 10$ **39**
3. $3 + 9 \times 2 - 5$ **16**
4. $4^3 - 30 \div 2$ **49**
5. Chaz bought 4 football cards for $2 each and 8 baseball cards for $3 each. Evaluate the expression to find the amount Chaz spent on cards: $4 \times 2 + 8 \times 3$ **$32**

Also available on transparency

1-5 Organizer

Pacing: Traditional 1 day
Block $\frac{1}{2}$ day

Objective: Students use number properties to compute mentally.

Online Edition
Tutorial Videos

Countdown to CRCT Week 2

Warm Up

Find each sum or product.

1. 17 + 15	32	**2.** 29 + 39	68
3. 8(24)	192	**4.** 7(12)	84
5. 3(91)	273	**6.** 6(15)	90

Problem of the Day

Determine the secret number from the following clues:

- The number is a multiple of 5.
- It is divisible by 3.
- It is less than 200.
- Its tens digit equals the sum of its other two digits. 165

Also available on transparency

Math Humor

I can do mental math with fractions and decimals, but I have trouble computing with wholes in my head.

Georgia Performance Standards

M6P1.c Apply and adapt a variety of appropriate strategies to solve problems.

M6P4.a Recognize and use connections among mathematical ideas.

1-5 Mental Math

Learn to use number properties to compute mentally.

Vocabulary
Commutative Property
Associative Property
Distributive Property

Georgia Performance Standards
M6P1.c Apply and adopt a variety of appropriate strategies to solve problems. Also, M6P4.a.

Mental math means "doing math in your head." Shakuntala Devi is extremely good at mental math. When she was asked to multiply 7,686,369,774,870 by 2,465,099,745,779, she took only 28 seconds to multiply the numbers mentally and gave the correct answer of 18,947,668,177,995,426,462,773,730!

Most people cannot do calculations like that mentally. But you can learn to solve some problems very quickly in your head.

Many mental math strategies use number properties that you already know.

COMMUTATIVE PROPERTY (Ordering)

Words	Numbers
You can add or multiply numbers in any order.	$18 + 9 = 9 + 18$ $15 \times 2 = 2 \times 15$

ASSOCIATIVE PROPERTY (Grouping)

Words	Numbers
When you are only adding or only multiplying, you can group any of the numbers together.	$(17 + 2) + 9 = 17 + (2 + 9)$ $(12 \times 2) \times 4 = 12 \times (2 \times 4)$

EXAMPLE 1 Using Properties to Add and Multiply Whole Numbers

A Evaluate 12 + 4 + 18 + 46.

12 + 4 + 18 + 46	*Look for sums that are multiples of 10.*
12 + 18 + 4 + 46	*Use the Commutative Property.*
(12 + 18) + (4 + 46)	*Use the Associative Property to make*
30 + 50	*groups of compatible numbers.*
80	*Use mental math to add.*

1 Introduce

Alternate Opener

EXPLORATION

1-5 Mental Math

1. Choose one expression from each pair to evaluate using mental math.
   a. 25 · 24 (25 · 4) · 6
   b. 5 · 22 (5 · 20) + (5 · 2)
   c. 13 + 44 + 27 44 + (13 + 27)
   d. 41 + 32 + 9 + 18 (41 + 9) + (32 + 18)
2. What makes the expressions you chose easier to evaluate?
3. What makes the expressions you did not choose more difficult to evaluate?

Think and Discuss

4. **Discuss** the mental math strategies you used.
5. **Compare** the first expression with the second expression in each pair. How are they alike? How are they different?

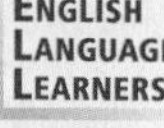

Motivate

Define *commute* (to travel back and forth), *associate* (to connect or combine), and *distribute* (to scatter or spread out). Connect the general meanings of these words to the meanings of the properties being introduced in this lesson.

Explorations and answers are provided in *Alternate Openers: Explorations Transparencies.*

B Evaluate 5 × 12 × 2.

5 × 12 × 2	*Look for products that are multiples of 10.*
12 × 5 × 2	*Use the Commutative Property.*
12 × (5 × 2)	*Use the Associative Property to group compatible numbers.*
12 × 10	
120	*Use mental math to multiply.*

DISTRIBUTIVE PROPERTY

Words	Numbers
When you multiply a number times a sum, you can • find the sum first and then multiply, or • multiply by each number in the sum and then add.	6 × (10 + 4) = 6 × 14 = 84 6 × (10 + 4) = (6 × 10) + (6 × 4) = 60 + 24 = 84

When you multiply two numbers, you can "break apart" one of the numbers into a sum and then use the Distributive Property.

EXAMPLE 2 **Using the Distributive Property to Multiply**

Use the Distributive Property to find each product.

Helpful Hint

Break the greater factor into a sum that contains a multiple of 10 and a one-digit number. You can add and multiply these numbers mentally.

A 4 × 23

4 × 23 = 4 × (20 + 3)	*"Break apart" 23 into 20 + 3.*
= (4 × 20) + (4 × 3)	*Use the Distributive Property.*
= 80 + 12	*Use mental math to multiply.*
= 92	*Use mental math to add.*

B 8 × 74

8 × 74 = 8 × (70 + 4)	*"Break apart" 74 into 70 + 4.*
= (8 × 70) + (8 × 4)	*Use the Distributive Property.*
= 560 + 32	*Use mental math to multiply.*
= 592	*Use mental math to add.*

Think and Discuss GPS M6P3.a, M6P3.b

1. **Give examples** of the Commutative Property and the Associative Property.
2. **Name** some situations in which you might use mental math.

COMMON ERROR ALERT

When using the Distributive Property, some students may multiply only one addend. Stress that all addends inside the parentheses must be multiplied by the number outside the parentheses.

Power Presentations with PowerPoint®

Additional Examples

Example 1

Evaluate.

A. 17 + 5 + 3 + 15 **40**

B. 4 × 13 × 5 **260**

Example 2

Use the Distributive Property to find each product.

A. 6 × 35 **210**

B. 9 × 87 **783**

Also available on transparency

Answers to *Think and Discuss*

1. Possible answers:
   Commutative: 2 × 17 = 17 × 2
   Associative: (4 × 9) × 10 = 4 × (9 × 10)
2. Possible answers: calculating movie expenses, planning expenses for theme park visit

2 Teach

Guided Instruction

In this lesson, students learn to use number properties to compute mentally. Show students how to use the Commutative, Associative, and Distributive Properties to find sums and products mentally. (Teaching Transparency) You may introduce other mental math strategies to students. For example, when adding two numbers, you can add to one and subtract from the other to make them easier to compute mentally: 57 + 69 = (57 + 3) + (69 − 3) = 60 + 66 = 126.

Reaching All Learners

Through Kinesthetic Experience

Have students roll number cubes and generate numbers to be used in mentally applying the Distributive Property. Example: Three rolls of the number cube yield 6, 4, and 3. Use the numbers to write the expression 6 × 43 and mentally apply the Distributive Property.

6 × 43 = (6 × 40) + (6 × 3)
= 240 + 18
= 258

3 Close

Summarize

Review the definitions of the new vocabulary in the lesson: *Commutative Property, Associative Property,* and *Distributive Property*. Discuss how the terms relate to and are different from each other.

Place emphasis on the Distributive Property, the property least familiar to the students. Remind students to "break apart" one number and to distribute the multiplication over the addends.

1-5 Exercises

Assignment Guide

If you finished Example 1 assign:
Average 1–6, 15–20, 56, 62–69
Advanced 1–6, 15–20, 58, 62–69

If you finished Example 2 assign:
Average 1–42, 62–69
Advanced 1–39, 43–50, 55–69

Homework Quick Check

Quickly check key concepts.
Exercises: 16, 22, 32, 34

Math Background

The multiplication of the term outside the parentheses gets distributed over all of the terms being added inside the parentheses. If there are more than two terms being added inside the parentheses, then all the addends get multiplied by the term outside the parentheses. For example, 4 × (2 + 3 + 5) equals (4 × 2) + (4 × 3) + (4 × 5).

Georgia Performance Standards

M6P3.c Analyze and evaluate the mathematical thinking and strategies of others.

M6P4.c Recognize and apply mathematics in contexts outside of mathematics.

1-5 Exercises

M6P3.c, M6P4.c

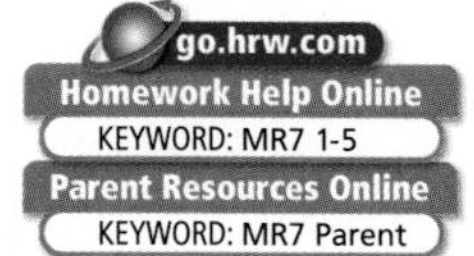

GUIDED PRACTICE

See Example 1
Evaluate.

1. 13 + 9 + 7 + 11 **40**
2. 19 + 18 + 11 + 32 **80**
3. 25 + 7 + 13 + 5 **50**
4. 5 × 14 × 4 **280**
5. 4 × 16 × 5 **320**
6. 5 × 17 × 2 **170**

See Example 2
Use the Distributive Property to find each product.

7. 5 × 24 **120**
8. 8 × 52 **416**
9. 4 × 39 **156**
10. 6 × 14 **84**
11. 3 × 33 **99**
12. 2 × 78 **156**
13. 9 × 12 **108**
14. 2 × 87 **174**

INDEPENDENT PRACTICE

See Example 1
Evaluate.

15. 15 + 17 + 3 + 5 **40**
16. 14 + 7 + 16 + 13 **50**
17. 6 + 21 + 14 + 9 **50**
18. 5 × 25 × 2 **250**
19. 2 × 32 × 10 **640**
20. 6 × 12 × 5 **360**

See Example 2
Use the Distributive Property to find each product.

21. 3 × 36 **108**
22. 4 × 42 **168**
23. 6 × 71 **426**
24. 2 × 94 **188**
25. 6 × 23 **138**
26. 5 × 25 **125**
27. 6 × 62 **372**
28. 7 × 21 **147**
29. 8 × 41 **328**
30. 2 × 94 **188**

PRACTICE AND PROBLEM SOLVING

Extra Practice p. 715

Use mental math to find each sum or product.

31. 8 + 13 + 7 + 12 **40**
32. 2 × 25 × 4 **200**
33. 4 + 22 + 16 + 18 **60**
34. 5 × 8 × 12 **480**
35. 5 + 98 + 95 **198**
36. 6 × 5 × 14 **420**
37. 11 + 75 + 25 **111**
38. 8 × 11 × 5 **440**
39. 19 + 1 + 11 + 39 **70**
40. Paul is writing a story for the school newspaper about the landscaping done by his class. The students planted 15 vines, 12 hedges, 8 trees, and 35 flowering plants. How many plants were used in the project? **70 plants**
41. **Earth Science** The temperature on Sunday was 58°F. The temperature is predicted to rise 4°F on Monday, then rise 2°F more on Tuesday, and then rise another 6°F by Saturday. What is the predicted temperature on Saturday? **70°F**
42. **Multi-Step** Janice wants to order disks for her computer. She needs to find the total cost, including shipping and handling. If Janice orders 7 disks, what will her total cost be? **$175**

Description	Number	Unit Cost with Tax	Price
Computer Disk	7	$24.00	
		Shipping & Handling	$7.00
		Total	

RETEACH 1-5

LESSON 1-5 Reteach
Mental Math

Commutative Property
Changing the order of addends does not change the sum.
21 + 13 = 13 + 21

Changing the order of factors does not change the product.
5 × 7 = 7 × 5

Associative Property
Changing the grouping of addends does not change the sum.
(3 + 8) + 4 = 3 + (8 + 4)

Changing the grouping of factors does not change the product.
2 × (7 × 4) = (2 × 7) × 4

Distributive Property
When you multiply a number by a sum, you can

- Find the sum and then multiply. 3 × (8 + 4) = 3 × 12 = 36
  or
- Multiply the number by each addend and then find the sum.
  3 × (8 + 4) = (3 × 8) + (3 × 4) = 24 + 12 = 36

Identify the property shown.

1. 3 × (2 × 6) = (3 × 2) × 6 — associative
2. 7 + 18 = 18 + 7 — commutative
3. 4 × (8 + 5) = 4 × 13 — distributive
4. 11 × 8 = 8 × 11 — commutative
5. 3 × (8 + 4) = (3 × 8) + (3 × 4) — distributive
6. (3 + 8) + 4 = 3 +(8 + 4) — associative

Identify the property shown and the missing number in each equation.

7. 9 + 16 = y + 9 — commutative; $y = 16$
8. 4 × (3 × 2) = (4 × n) × 2 — associative; $n = 3$
9. 3 × (11 + 4) = 3 × a — distributive; $a = 15$
10. 6 × (9 + 14) = b × 23 — distributive; $b = 6$

PRACTICE 1-5

LESSON 1-5 Practice B
Mental Math

Evaluate.

1. 17 + 4 × 5 — 37
2. 25 × 3 × 4 — 300
3. 28 + 39 + 11 + 22 — 100
4. 12 + 7 + 8 + 13 — 40
5. 10 + 3 × 2 — 16
6. 9 × 8 × 5 — 360
7. 97 + 4 + 3 + 26 — 130
8. 2 × 6 × 5 — 60
9. 28 + 2 × 6 — 40

Use the Distributive Property to find each product.

10. 4 × 16 — 64
11. 8 × 31 — 248
12. 3 × 62 — 186
13. 2 × 46 — 92
14. 5 × 29 — 145
15. 7 × 22 — 154
16. 9 × 21 — 189
17. 6 × 15 — 90
18. 8 × 44 — 352
19. 4 × 29 — 116
20. 7 × 31 — 217
21. 5 × 57 — 285
22. Each ticket to a play costs $27. How much will it cost to buy 4 tickets? Which property did you use to solve this problem with mental math?
    $108; Distributive Property
23. Mr. Stanley bought two cases of pencils. Each case has 20 boxes. In each box there is 10 pencils. Use mental math to find how many pencils Mr. Stanley bought.
    400 pencils
24. When you consider that cows eat grass and the water needed to grow the grass that cows eat, it takes 65 gallons of water to produce one serving of milk! Use mental math to find how many gallons of water are needed to produce 5 servings of milk.
    325 gallons

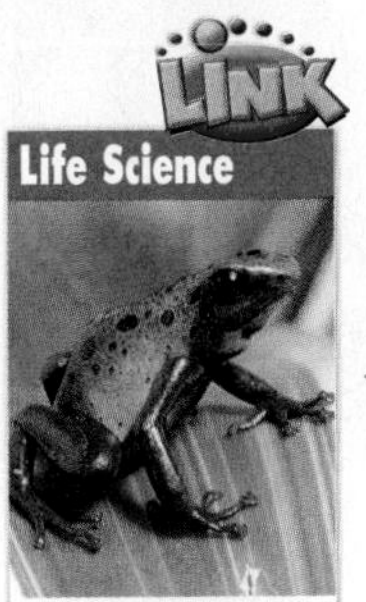

Life Science

Poison-dart frogs are members of the family Dendrobatidae, which includes about 170 species. Many are brightly colored.

Multiply using the Distributive Property.

43. 9 × 17 **153** 44. 4 × 27 **108** 45. 11 × 18 **198** 46. 7 × 51 **357**

47. 2 × 28 **56** 48. 9 × 42 **378** 49. 5 × 55 **275** 50. 3 × 78 **234**

51. 4 × 85 **340** 52. 6 × 36 **216** 53. 8 × 24 **192** 54. 11 × 51 **561**

55. **Life Science** Poison-dart frogs can breed underwater, and the females lay from 4 to 30 eggs. What would be the total number of eggs if four female poison-dart frogs each laid 27 eggs? **108 eggs**

Use the table for Exercises 56 and 57.

56. Rickie wants to buy 3 garden hoses at the home center clearance sale. How much will they cost? **$48**

57. The boys in Josh's family are saving money to buy 4 ceiling fans at the home center sale. How much will they need to save? **$208**

Home Center Clearance Sale	
Table lamp	$15
Garden hose	$16
Ceiling fan	$52

58. **Critical Thinking** Give a problem that you could simplify using the Commutative and Associative Properties. Then, show the steps to solve the problem and label the Commutative and Associative Properties.

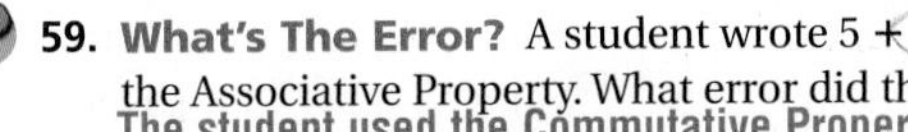

59. **What's The Error?** A student wrote 5 + 24 + 25 + 6 = 5 + 25 + 24 + 6 by the Associative Property. What error did the student make? **The student used the Commutative Property instead of the Associative Property.**

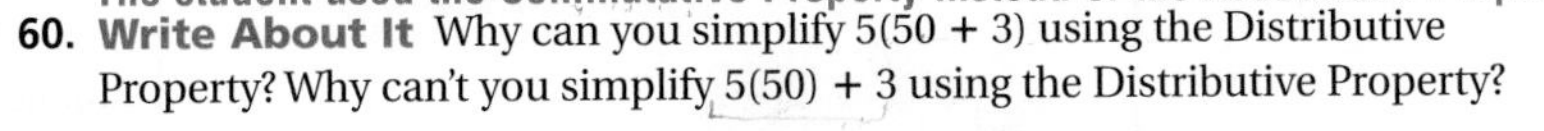

60. **Write About It** Why can you simplify 5(50 + 3) using the Distributive Property? Why can't you simplify 5(50) + 3 using the Distributive Property?

61. **Challenge** Explain how you could find the product of 5^2 × 112 using the Distributive Property. Evaluate the expression. **Possible answer: Break apart 112 as 100 + 10 + 2 and multiply by 5^2 = 25. So, 25 × 112 = (25 × 100) + (25 × 10) + (25 × 2) = 2,500 + 250 + 50 = 2,800.**

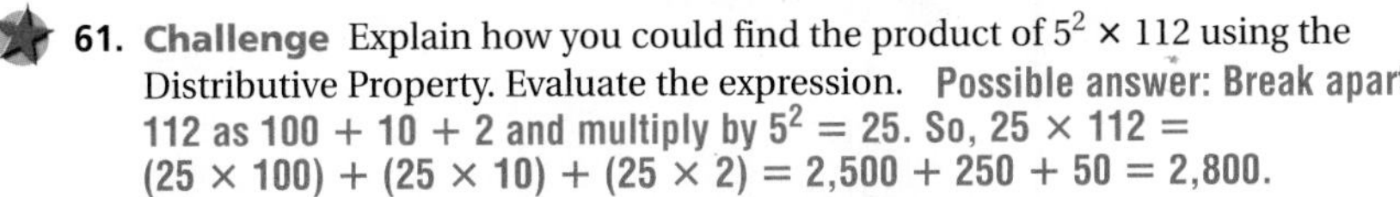

CRCT Prep • GPS Support • Spiral Review

62. **Multiple Choice** Which expression does NOT have the same value as 7 × (4 + 23)?

(A) 7 × 27 (B) (7 × 4) + (7 × 23) **(C) 7 × 4 + 23** (D) 28 + (7 × 23)

63. **Gridded Response** Michelle flew 1,240 miles from Los Angeles to Dallas, and another 718 miles from Dallas to Atlanta. From Atlanta, she flew 760 miles to New York City. How many miles did Michelle fly in all? **2,718 mi**

Estimate each sum or difference by rounding to the nearest thousandths place. (Lesson 1-2)

64. 5,237 − 1,586 **3,000** 65. 915,178 + 451,836 **1,367,000** 66. 39,187 − 24,999 **14,000**

Evaluate each expression. (Lesson 1-4)

67. 4 × 14 + 12 ÷ 2 **62** 68. 16 ÷ 4^2 + 15 − 2 **14** 69. 62 + 14 − (5 × 4) **56**

CHALLENGE 1-5

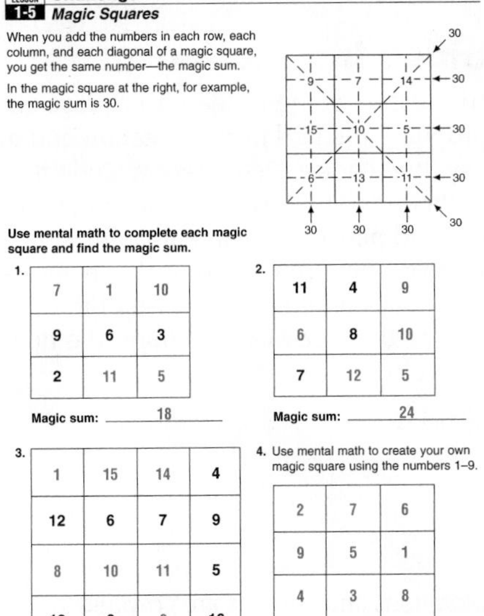

LESSON 1-5 **Challenge**
Magic Squares

When you add the numbers in each row, each column, and each diagonal of a magic square, you get the same number—the magic sum.

In the magic square at the right, for example, the magic sum is 30.

9	7	14
15	10	5
6	13	11

Use mental math to complete each magic square and find the magic sum.

1.

7	1	10
9	6	3
2	11	5

Magic sum: 18

2.

11	4	9
6	8	10
7	12	5

Magic sum: 24

3.

1	15	14	4
12	6	7	9
8	10	11	5
13	3	2	16

Magic sum: 34

4. Use mental math to create your own magic square using the numbers 1–9.

2	7	6
9	5	1
4	3	8

Magic sum: Possible answer: 15

PROBLEM SOLVING 1-5

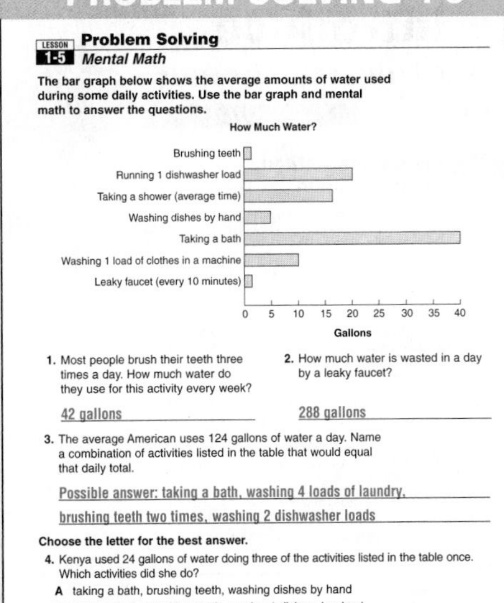

LESSON 1-5 **Problem Solving**
Mental Math

The bar graph below shows the average amounts of water used during some daily activities. Use the bar graph and mental math to answer the questions.

1. Most people brush their teeth three times a day. How much water do they use for this activity every week? 42 gallons

2. How much water is wasted in a day by a leaky faucet? 288 gallons

3. The average American uses 124 gallons of water a day. Name a combination of activities listed in the table that would equal that daily total. Possible answer: taking a bath, washing 4 loads of laundry, brushing teeth two times, washing 2 dishwasher loads

Choose the letter for the best answer.

4. Kenya used 24 gallons of water doing three of the activities listed in the table once. Which activities did she do?
   A taking a bath, brushing teeth, washing dishes by hand
   B taking a bath, brushing teeth, running 1 dishwasher load
   (C) taking a shower, brushing teeth, washing dishes by hand
   D taking a shower, brushing teeth, running 1 dishwasher load

5. If you wash two loads of dishes by hand instead of using a dishwasher, how much water do you save?
   (F) 30 gallons G 15 gallons H 10 gallons J 1 gallon

Ongoing Assessment and Intervention

***Diagnose Before* the Lesson**
1-5 Warm Up, TE p. 26

***Monitor During* the Lesson**
1-5 Know-It Notebook
1-5 Questioning Strategies

***Assess After* the Lesson**
1-5 Lesson Quiz, TE p. 29

Common Error Alert

When using the Distributive Property, students may randomly break apart one of the factors. For example, students may break 12 into 6 + 6 instead of 10 + 2. Caution them that the whole point of using the Distributive Property is to make the numbers easy to compute mentally.

Answers

58, 60. See p. A1.

Test Prep Doctor In Exercise 62, students may not realize that they do not have to solve the expressions. Students who answer **D** may not have noticed that choice **B** is the same.

Journal

Have students write about how the ability to multiply very large numbers mentally could help them in daily activities.

Power Presentations with PowerPoint®

1-5 Lesson Quiz

Evaluate.

1. 18 + 24 + 2 + 6 50
2. 10 × 5 × 3 150
3. 13 + 42 + 7 + 8 70

Use the Distributive Property to find each product.

4. 8 × 12 96 5. 6 × 15 90
6. 5 × 34 170 7. 3 × 71 213

Also available on transparency

1-6 Organizer

Pacing: Traditional 1 day
Block $\frac{1}{2}$ day

Objective: Students choose an appropriate method of computation and justify their choice.

GPS M6A2.b
Hands-On Lab
In *Hands-On Lab Activities*

Online Edition
Tutorial Videos

Countdown to CRCT Week 2

Warm Up

Use mental math to find each fraction of 80.

1. $\frac{1}{2}$ 40 **2.** $\frac{1}{10}$ 8
3. $\frac{1}{4}$ 20 **4.** $\frac{1}{5}$ 16

Problem of the Day

About 23% of 600 firefighters are not on duty on any particular day. Steven estimates that about 200 firefighters have the day off. Is his estimate too high or too low? Explain.
too high; 25% of 600 is 150

Also available on transparency

Math Fact

Historically, people who studied mathematics also studied astronomy. For example, Johannes Kepler and Sir Isaac Newton made contributions in both fields.

Georgia Performance Standards

M6P1.c Apply and adapt a variety of appropriate strategies to solve problems.

M6P4.a Recognize and use connections among mathematical ideas.

1-6 Choose the Method of Computation

Problem Solving Skill

Learn to choose an appropriate method of computation and justify your choice.

Earth has one moon. Scientists have determined that other planets in our solar system have as many as 39 moons. Mercury and Venus have no moons at all.

Georgia Performance Standards
M6P1.c Apply and adapt a variety of appropriate strategies to solve problems. Also, M6P4.c.

EXAMPLE 1 ***Astronomy Application***

Choose a solution method and solve. Explain your choice.

A How many known moons are in our solar system?

It might be hard to keep track of all of these numbers if you tried to add mentally. But the numbers themselves are small. You can use paper and pencil.

Planet	Moons
Mercury	0
Venus	0
Earth	1
Mars	2
Jupiter	63
Saturn	50
Uranus	27
Neptune	13
Pluto	1

Source: The Planetary Society, 2005

$$\begin{array}{r} 1 \\ 2 \\ 63 \\ 50 \\ 27 \\ 13 \\ +\ 1 \\ \hline 157 \end{array}$$

There are 157 known moons in our solar system.

B The average temperature on Earth is 59°F. The average temperature on Venus is 867°F. How much hotter is Venus's average temperature?

Venus temperature − **Earth temperature**
867 − 59

These numbers are small, and 59 is close to a multiple of 10. You can use mental math.

$(867 + 1) - (59 + 1)$ *Think: Add 1 to 59 to make 60. Add 1 to 867 to compensate.*
$868 - 60$
808

The average temperature on Venus is 808°F hotter than the average temperature on Earth.

1 Introduce

Alternate Opener

EXPLORATION

1-6 Choose the Method of Computation

Decide whether you would use mental math, pencil and paper, or a calculator to solve each problem. Then solve.

1. Susan makes $9.50 per hour. She worked 7 hours on Monday, 8 hours on Tuesday, 5 hours on Wednesday, and 10 hours on Friday. What is the total amount that Susan earned for the week?
2. Carlos is saving his money to buy a new bike. He earns $45 each week doing yard work, and the bike costs $189. How many weeks will he have to work to have enough money to buy the bike?
3. At a basketball game, 9,980 tickets were sold at $22 each. Find the total amount of money from ticket sales.
4. Rina counted the following numbers of books on each shelf in the storeroom: 24, 47, 26, 53, and 39. Find the total number of books.
5. A group of 12 people wants to rent a room at a pizza restaurant for a party. The room costs $75 to rent. Will $6 from each person be enough to cover the rent?

Think and Discuss

6. **Discuss** when you might choose to use mental math.
7. **Explain** how you decide whether to use pencil and paper or a calculator when you choose not to use mental math.

2 Teach

Guided Instruction

In this lesson, students learn to choose an appropriate method of computation and to justify their choice. First, present students with three different methods of computation: paper and pencil, mental math, and a calculator. Then provide some loose guidelines for making the choice: size of the numbers, the type of calculations, the number of calculations, etc.

Explorations and answers are provided in *Alternate Openers: Explorations Transparencies.*

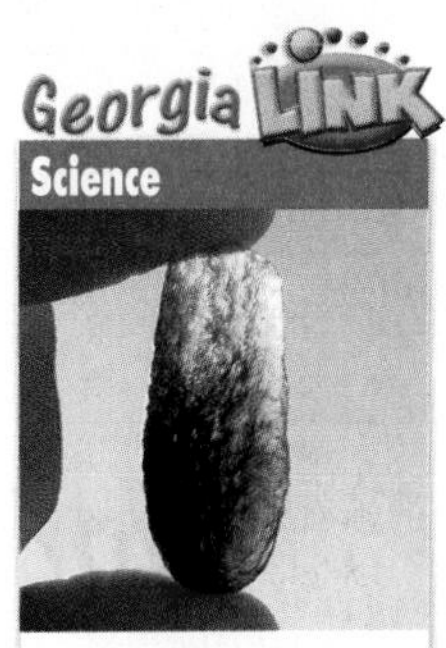

Science

Georgiaites are natural pieces of glass found in Dodge and Blakely counties. Scientists estimate they were formed after a meteor impact 35 million years ago.

Choose a solution method and solve. Explain your choice.

The cameras onboard the International Space Station take about 115 photographs of Earth each day. How many photographs do the cameras take in one year?

photos per day × days per year *Think: There are 365 days in a year.*

115 × 365

These numbers are not compatible, so mental math is not a good choice.

You could use paper and pencil. But finding a product of 3-digit numbers requires several steps. Using a calculator will probably be faster.

Carefully enter the numbers on a calculator. Record the product.

115 × 365 = 41,975

Each year, the International Space Station cameras take about 41,975 photographs of Earth.

Answers to *Think and Discuss*

2. Add 1 to 59 to make 60. Subtract 1 from 867 to compensate.
867 + 59 =
(867 − 1) +
(59 + 1) =
866 + 60 = 926

Think and Discuss GPS M6P3.a, M6P3.b

1. **Give an example** of a situation in which you would use mental math to solve a problem. When would you use paper and pencil?
2. **Tell** how you could use mental math in Example 2 if the problem were 867 + 59.

1-6 Exercises

Georgia Performance Standards
M6P3.a, M6P4.c

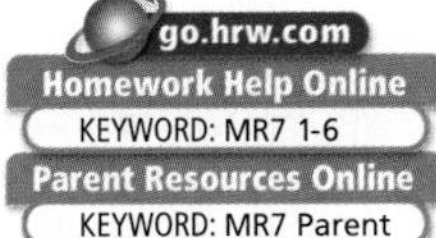

go.hrw.com
Homework Help Online
KEYWORD: MR7 1-6
Parent Resources Online
KEYWORD: MR7 Parent

GUIDED PRACTICE

See Example 1

Choose a solution method and solve. Explain your choice.

1. **Astronomy** What is the total number of astronauts who have space flight experience? paper and pencil; 364

U.S.	Germany	France	Canada	Japan	Italy	Russia
244	9	8	7	5	3	88

Student's methods and explanations may vary.

2. **Sports** In the 2004 Summer Olympic Games, 929 medals were given. The U.S. team brought home the most medals, 103. How many medals were not won by the U.S. team? mental math; 826
3. A factory produces 126 golf balls per minute. How many golf balls can be produced in 515 minutes? calculator; 64,890

Power Presentations with PowerPoint®

Additional Examples

Example 1

Evaluate the expression and state the method of computation you used.

A. 4 + 3 + 2 + 10 + 8 + 2 + 5 + 1 mental math; 35

B. 4,562 − 397. mental math; 4,165

C. 9,288 ÷ 24. calculator; 387

Also available on transparency

Answers to *Think and Discuss*

1. Possible answers: mental math: finding the combined weight of 2 packages when the weight of one is close to a mutiple of 10 paper and pencil: finding the area of a room

1-6 Exercises

Assignment Guide

If you finished Example 1 assign:
Average 1–15, 18–26
Advanced 1–6, 9–26

Homework Quick Check

Quickly check key concepts.
Exercises: 4, 6, 10, 14

ENGLISH LANGUAGE LEARNERS

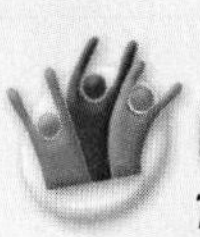

Reaching All Learners

Through Cooperative Learning

Have students work in groups to build their confidence in the areas of problem solving and mental math. Provide the groups with the "Additional Examples." Have them first understand the problem and be able to restate the problem in their own words to another group member. Then the operations should be identified and the students should arrive at a method of computation. Consider grouping more proficient students with students who require more modeling.

3 Close

Summarize

Remind the students that the choice of a method of computation depends on their understanding of the problem, the numbers involved in the problem, and the calculations needed to solve the problem. The most important factor in selecting a method of calculation is the individual student's proficiency with each method.

Georgia Performance Standards

M6P3.a Organize and consolidate their mathematical thinking through communication.

M6P4.c Recognize and apply mathematics in contexts outside of mathematics.

ONGOING ASSESSMENT and INTERVENTION 

Diagnose *Before* the Lesson
1-6 Warm Up, TE p. 30

Monitor *During* the Lesson
1-6 Know-It Notebook
1-6 Questioning Strategies

Assess *After* the Lesson
1-6 Lesson Quiz, TE p. 32

Answers

7–13, 16. Complete answers on p. A1.

Power Presentations with PowerPoint®

1-6 Lesson Quiz

Evaluate the expression and state the method of computation you used.

1. 17 + 6 + 24 + 35 + 3 + 5
90; mental math

2. 63 × 197 12,411; paper and pencil

3. It takes Jupiter approximately 4,344 days to complete one revolution around the Sun. It takes Earth 365 days to revolve around the Sun. How many more days does it take Jupiter to revolve around the Sun than Earth?
3,979 days; calculator

Also available on transparency

INDEPENDENT PRACTICE

See Example 1

Student's methods and explanations may vary.

Choose a solution method and solve. Explain your choice. For 4 and 5, use the diagram at right.

6	9	5
10	20	8
3	7	4

4. The highest score is a total of all the squares on the board. What is that score? paper and pencil; 72

5. What score is higher, the total of the squares in the middle row or middle column? mental math; middle row

6. If each store in a chain of 108 furniture stores sells 135 sofas a year, what is the total number of sofas sold? calculator; 14,580

PRACTICE AND PROBLEM SOLVING

CRCT GPS
Extra Practice p. 715

Evaluate the expression, and state the method of computation you used.

7. 5 + 24 + 7 + 1 + 64 + 2 + 8 111 **8.** 16 + 2 + 4 + 13 + 5 + 1 + 14 55

9. 828 × 623 515,844 **10.** 742 − 167 575 **11.** 41 + 169 210 **12.** 499 − 201 298 **13.** 338 + 12 350

14. A satellite travels 985,200 miles per year. How many miles will it travel if it stays in space for 12 years? 11,822,400

15. What's the Question? An astronaut has spent the following minutes training in a tank that simulates weightlessness: 2, 15, 5, 40, 10, and 55. The answer is 127. What is the question? How many total minutes has she spent in weightlessness?

16. Write About It Explain how you can decide whether to use pencil and paper, mental math, or a calculator to solve a subtraction problem.

17. Challenge A list of possible astronauts was narrowed down by two committees. The first committee selected 93 people to complete a written form. The second selected 31 of those people to come to an interview. If 837 were not asked to complete a form, how many were on the original list? 930 astronauts

CRCT PREP • GPS SUPPORT • SPIRAL REVIEW

18. Multiple Choice It takes Mars 687 days to revolve around the Sun. It takes Venus only 225 days to revolve around the Sun. How many more days does it take Mars to revolve around the Sun than it takes Venus?

Ⓐ 462 days Ⓑ 500 days Ⓒ 900 days Ⓓ 912 days

19. Short Response Hector biked 13 miles on Monday, Wednesday, and Friday of every week for 24 weeks. Find the total number of miles he biked during the 24 weeks. Explain your answer. 936, 13 · 3 = 39; 39 · 24 = 936

Evaluate each expression. (Lesson 1-4)

20. (2 + 7 − 5) ÷ 2 2 **21.** 10(6 − 3) 30 **22.** 5 + 8 × 7 − 1 60 **23.** 5 + (8 + 2) − 3 12

Identify the property illustrated by each equation. (Lesson 1-5)

24. 3 + (4 + 5) = (3 + 4) + 5 Associative Property **25.** 19(24) = 19(20) + 19(4) Distributive Property **26.** 2(13) = 13(2) Commutative Property

CHALLENGE 1-6
PROBLEM SOLVING 1-6

LESSON 1-6 Problem Solving
Choose the Method of Computation

Use the table below to answer questions 1–6. For each question, write the method of computation you should use to solve it. Then write the solution.

Bones in the Human Body

Body Part	Number of Bones
Head	28
Throat	1
Spine	26
Chest	25
Shoulders	4
Arms	6
Hands	54
Legs	10
Feet	52

1. How many bones are in an average person's arms and hands altogether?
mental math; 60 bones

2. How many more bones are in an average person's head than chest?
mental math; 3 bones

3. Which part of the body has twice as many bones as the spine?
mental math; feet

4. How many bones are in the body altogether?
paper and pencil; 206 bones

5. A newborn baby has 350 bones. How many more bones does a newborn baby have than an adult?
paper and pencil; 144 bones

6. How many bones are in each of an average person's feet, hands, legs, and arms?
paper and pencil; feet: 26 bones; hands: 27 bones; legs: 5 bones; arms: 3 bones

Choose the letter for the best answer.

7. The body's longest bones—thighbones and shinbones—are in the legs. The average thighbone is about 20 inches long, and the average shinbone is about 17 inches long. What is the total length of those four bones?
Ⓐ paper and pencil; 74 inches
B paper and pencil; 37 inches
C mental math; 20 inches
D calculator; 17 inches

8. The body has 650 muscles. Seventeen of those muscles are used to smile and 42 muscles are used to frown. How many more muscles are used to frown than to smile?
F mental math; 35 muscles
Ⓖ mental math; 25 muscles
H paper and pencil; 608 muscles
J calculator; 633 muscles

RETEACH 1-6

LESSON 1-6 Reteach
Choose the Method of Computation

Paper and pencil, mental math, and a calculator are three computation methods for solving problems.

- If there are many small numbers, use paper and pencil.
- If the numbers are small and easy, use mental math.
- If the numbers are large, use a calculator.

Before you solve a problem decide which computation method is the best.

Choose a computation method. Then solve.

At a book fair, 76 books were sold on the first day and 82 books were sold on the second day. How many books were sold during the two days?

Number of books sold on the first day + Number of books sold on the second day

76 + 82

The numbers are small and 82 is close to a multiple of 10. You can use mental math.

(76 + 2) + (82 − 2) = 78 + 80 = 158

During the two days, 158 books were sold.

Choose a computation method. Then solve.

1. Of the 248 books on display, 46 were nonfiction books. How many books were not nonfiction books?
mental math, 202 books

2. Lisa bought 2 biographies for $5.37 each, a novel for $7.95, and a bookmark for $1.19. How much money did Lisa spend?
paper and pencil, $19.88

3. Over two days, 234 students visited the book fair in groups of 18. How many groups visited the fair?
calculator, 13 groups

PRACTICE 1-6

LESSON 1-6 Practice B
Choose the Method of Computation

1. Athletes from 197 countries competed at the 1996 Summer Olympic Games held in Atlanta, Georgia. That is 25 more countries that competed at the 1992 games held in Barcelona, Spain. How many different countries competed in Barcelona?
Athletes from 172 countries competed in Barcelona.

2. At the 1996 Summer Olympic Games held in Atlanta, Georgia, 10,310 athletes competed. At the 1992 Summer Olympic Games held in Barcelona, Spain, 9,364 athletes competed. How many more athletes competed in Atlanta than in Barcelona?
946 more athletes competed in Atlanta.

3. The marathon race is one of the oldest events in the Summer Olympic Games. Marathon competitors run a total of 26 miles 385 yards. There are 5,280 feet in a mile and 3 feet in a yard. How many yards long is the entire marathon race?
The marathon is 46,145 yards long.

4. The world record for the fastest men's marathon race is 2 hours, 5 minutes, 42 seconds. The world record for the fastest women's marathon race is 2 hours, 20 minutes, 43 seconds. How much faster is the men's record marathon time?
It is 15 minutes, 1 second faster.

5. The men's outdoor world record in the high jump is 2.45 meters or 8 feet 0.5 inches. The women's outdoor world record in the high jump is 2.09 meters or 6 feet 10.25 inches. How much higher is the men's high jump record? Write the answer in meters and feet.
0.36 meter or 1 foot 2.25 inches

6. The men's world record in the 400-meter relay is 37.40 seconds, held by the U.S. If each of the four runners each ran 100 meters in the same time, how long did each runner run?
9.35 seconds

7. Athletes from 13 nations competed in the first modern Olympics in 1896. Today, athletes from nearly 200 nations compete in the Summer Olympics. About how many more nations participate in the Olympics today than in 1896?
about 187 nations

1-7 Patterns and Sequences

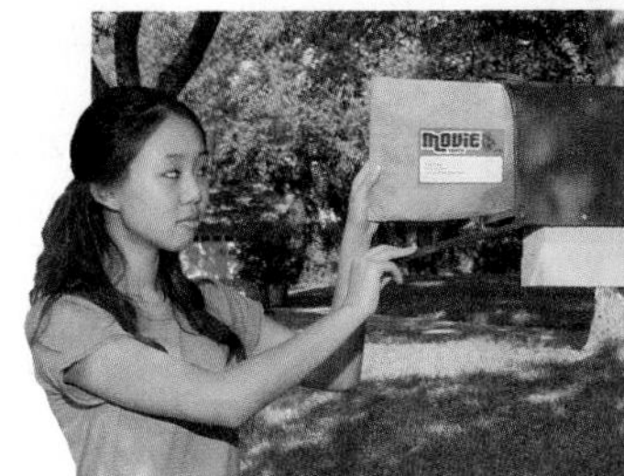

Learn to find patterns and to recognize, describe, and extend patterns in sequences.

Vocabulary
sequence
term
arithmetic sequence

Georgia Performance Standards
M6A2.a Analyze and describe patterns arising from mathematical rules, tables, and graphs.

Each month, Eva chooses 3 new DVDs from her DVD club.

Eva's DVDs	
Month	DVDs
1	3
2	6
3	9
4	12

Position ⇨ Month; DVDs ⇦ Value of Term; +3, +3, +3

The number of DVDs Eva has after each month shows a pattern: Add 3. This pattern can be written as a sequence. 3, 6, 9, 12, 15, . . .

A **sequence** is an ordered set of numbers. Each number in the sequence is called a **term**. In this sequence, the first term is 3, the second term is 6, and the third term is 9.

When the terms of a sequence change by the same amount each time, the sequence is an **arithmetic sequence**.

EXAMPLE 1 Extending Arithmetic Sequences

Helpful Hint
Look for a relationship between the 1st term and the 2nd term. Check if this relationship works between the 2nd term and the 3rd term, and so on.

Identify a pattern in each arithmetic sequence and then find the missing terms.

A 3, 15, 27, 39, ▢, ▢, . . .

Look for a pattern.
A pattern is to add 12 to each term to get the next term.

3, 15, 27, 39, ▢, ▢, . . .
+12 +12 +12 +12 +12

$39 + 12 = 51$ $51 + 12 = 63$
So 51 and 63 are the missing terms.

B 12, 21, 30, 39, ▢, ▢, . . .

Use a table to find a pattern.

Position	1	2	3	4	5	6
Value of Term	12	21	30	39	▢	▢

+ 9 + 9 + 9 + 9 + 9

A pattern is to add 9 to each term to get the next term.
$39 + 9 = 48$ $48 + 9 = 57$
So 48 and 57 are the missing terms.

Organizer 1-7

Pacing: Traditional 1 day
Block $\frac{1}{2}$ day

Objective: Students find, recognize, describe, and extend patterns in sequences.

GPS M6A2.a
Hands-On Lab
In *Hands-On Lab Activities*

Online Edition
Tutorial Videos, Interactivities

Countdown to CRCT Week 2

Power Presentations with PowerPoint®

Warm Up

Determine what could come next.

1. 3, 4, 5, 6, ____ 7
2. 10, 9, 8, 7, 6, ____ 5
3. 1, 3, 5, 7, ____ 9
4. 2, 4, 6, 8, ____ 10
5. 5, 10, 15, 20, ____ 25

Problem of the Day

How can you place the numbers 1 through 6 in the circles so that the sums along each side are equal?

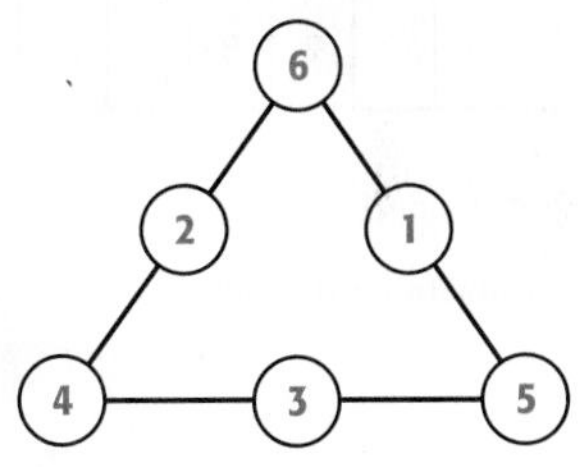

Also available on transparency

1 Introduce

Alternate Opener

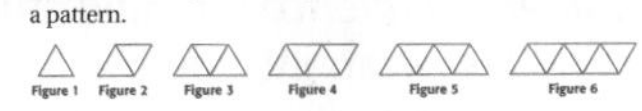

EXPLORATION

1-7 Patterns and Sequences

1. Examine the sequence of figures below and look for a pattern.

Figure 1 Figure 2 Figure 3 Figure 4 Figure 5 Figure 6

a. Sketch the next two figures in your pattern. Count the number of line segments it takes to draw each.
b. Copy and complete the table for your pattern.

Figure Number	1	2	3	4	5	6	7	8	9	10
Number of Line Segments	3	5	7							

Find the next three numbers in each sequence.

2. 1, 3, 5, 7, ___, ___, ___, . . .
3. 96, 84, 72, ___, ___, ___, . . .
4. 1, 3, 6, 10, 15, ___, ___, ___, . . .

Think and Discuss

5. **Describe** the pattern you noticed in the sequence of triangles.
6. **Explain** how you found the next three numbers in numbers 2–4.

Motivate

Give examples of sequences in math.

1, 2, 3, 4, . . .
2, 4, 6, 8, . . .
5, 10, 15, 20, . . .

Discuss with students what makes something a pattern. (A pattern is a sequence along with some explicit rule that determines the next term in the sequence.)

Explorations and answers are provided in *Alternate Openers: Explorations Transparencies.*

Georgia Performance Standards

M6A2.a Analyze and describe patterns arising from mathematical rules, tables, and graphs.

COMMON ERROR ALERT

Remind students not to assume that a pattern for a sequence can be based only on the relationship between the first two terms. The entire sequence must fit the pattern.

Power Presentations with PowerPoint®

Additional Examples

Example 1

Identify a pattern in each sequence and then find the missing terms.

A. 48, 42, 36, 30, ■, ■, ■, . . .
One pattern is to subtract 6 from each term. 24, 18, 12

B.

Position	1	2	3	4	5	6
Value of Term	9	22	35	48	■ 61	■ 74

A pattern is to add 13 to each term to get the next term.

Example 2

Identify a pattern in each sequence. Name the missing terms.

A. 24, 34, 31, 41, 38, 48, ■, ■, ■, . . .
One pattern is to add 10 to one term and subtract 3 from the next. 45, 55, 52

B.

Position	1	2	3	4	5	6	7
Value of Term	1	4	2	8	■ 4	16	■ 8

A pattern is to multiply one term by 4 and divide the next term by 2.

Also available on transparency

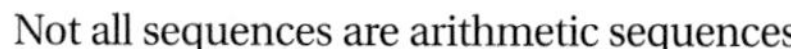

Not all sequences are arithmetic sequences.

Arithmetic Sequences		Not Arithmetic Sequences	
2, 4, 6, 8,... (+2 +2 +2)	20, 35, 50, 65,... (+15 +15 +15)	1, 3, 6, 10,... (+2 +3 +4)	2, 6, 18, 54,... (×3 ×3 ×3)

In nonarithmetic sequences, look for patterns that involve multiplication or division. Some sequences may even be combinations of different operations.

EXAMPLE 2 Completing Other Sequences

Identify a pattern in each sequence. Name the missing terms.

A 4, 15, 8, 19, 12, 23, 16, ■, ■, ■, . . .

4 15 8 19 12 23 16 ■ ■ ■
+11 −7 +11 −7 +11 −7 +11 −7 +11

A pattern is to add 11 to one term and subtract 7 from the next.

$16 + 11 = 27$ $27 - 7 = 20$ $20 + 11 = 31$

So 27, 20, and 31 are the missing terms.

B

Position	1	2	3	4	5	6	7	8	9
Value of Term	1	6	2	12	■	24	8	■	16

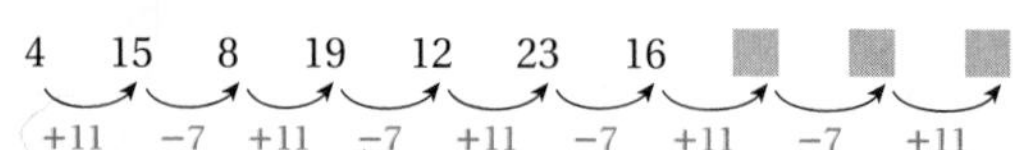

Position	1	2	3	4	5	6	7	8	9
Value of Term	1	6	2	12	■	24	8	■	16

×6 ÷3 ×6 ÷3 ×6 ÷3 ×6 ÷3

A pattern is to multiply one term by 6 and divide the next by 3.

$12 \div 3 = 4$ $8 \times 6 = 48$

So 4 and 48 are the missing terms.

Possible Answers to *Think and Discuss*

1. Determine a pattern for the sequence and check to see if 13 and 15 fit the pattern.
2. First find a relationship between the given terms. One pattern is $8 \div 2 = 4$ and $4 \div 2 = 2$; divide each term by 2 to get the next term. $2 \div 2 = 1$, so 1 is the next term.
3. A pattern of subtracting one number will not work for this sequence therefore, this is a nonarithmetic sequence.

Think and Discuss

GPS M6P3.a, M6P3.b

1. **Tell** how you could check whether the next two terms in the arithmetic sequence 5, 7, 9, 11, . . . are 13 and 15.
2. **Explain** how to find the next term in the sequence 16, 8, 4, 2, ■, ...
3. **Explain** how to determine whether 256, 128, 64, 32, . . . is an arithmetic or nonarithmetic sequence.

2 Teach

Guided Instruction

In this lesson, students learn to use the strategy "find a pattern" to recognize, describe, and extend sequences. First have students extend sequences with addition and subtraction. Then have them complete sequences with multiplication and division. Next, point out that some patterns could involve more than one operation.

Reaching All Learners

Through Multiple Representations

Triangular numbers are similar to perfect squares, except that they are represented by triangular instead of square arrays. Have students find the next three triangular numbers in the sequence by drawing. Then have the students write the number sequence generated by the drawings to discover a number pattern that will continue the sequence.

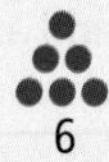

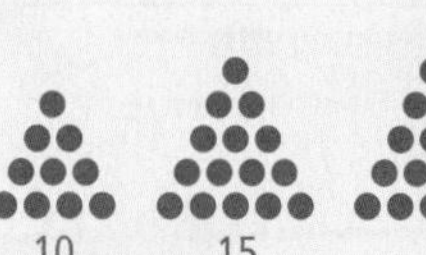

3 Close

Summarize

Give brief definitions of the new vocabulary in the lesson: *sequence*, *term*, and *arithmetic sequence*. Remind students that patterns can include the four operations or combinations of the operations. Also, a pattern that fits a sequence should not be considered the only one that could generate that sequence.

1-7 Exercises

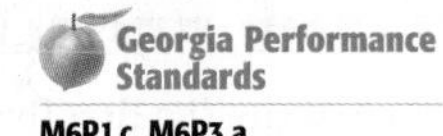
Georgia Performance Standards
M6P1.c, M6P3.a

go.hrw.com
Homework Help Online
KEYWORD: MR7 1-7
Parent Resources Online
KEYWORD: MR7 Parent

GUIDED PRACTICE

See Example 1 — Identify a pattern in each arithmetic sequence and then find the missing terms.

1. 12, 24, 36, 48, ■, ■, ■, . . .
add 12; 60; 72; 84

2. 105, 90, 75, 60, 45, ■, ■, ■, . . .
subtract 15; 30; 15; 0

3.

Position	1	2	3	4	5	6
Value of Term	7	18	29	40	■ 51	■ 62

add 11

4.

Position	1	2	3	4	5	6
Value of Term	44	38	32	26	■ 20	■ 14

subtract 6

See Example 2 — Identify a pattern in each sequence. Name the missing terms.

5. 2, 9, 7, 14, ■, ■, . . .
add 7 and subtract 2; 12; 19

6. 80, 8, 40, 4, ■, 2, 10, ■, . . .
divide by 10 and multiply by 5; 20; 1

7.

Position	1	2	3	4	5	6	7	8
Value of Term	1	6	3	18	■ 9	54	27	■ 162

multiply by 6 and divide by 2

INDEPENDENT PRACTICE

See Example 1 — Identify a pattern in each arithmetic sequence and then find the missing terms.

8. 9, 19, 29, 39, 49, ■, ■, ■, . . .
add 10; 59; 69; 79

9. 98, 84, 70, 56, 42, ■, ■, ■, . . .
subtract 14; 28; 14; 0

10.

Position	1	2	3	4	5	6
Value of Term	45	38	31	24	■ 17	■ 10

subtract 7

11.

Position	1	2	3	4	5	6
Value of Term	8	11	14	17	■ 20	■ 23

add 3

See Example 2 — Identify a pattern in each sequence. Name the missing terms.

12. 50, 40, 43, 33, ■, 26, ■, . . .
subtract 10 and add 3; 36; 29

13. 7, 28, 24, 45, ■, ■, ■, . . .
add 21 and subtract 4; 41; 62; 58

14.

Position	1	2	3	4	5	6	7
Value of Term	120	60	180	90	■ 270	■ 135	405

divide by 2 and multiply by 3

15.

Position	1	2	3	4	5	6	7
Value of Term	400	100	200	50	■ 100	■ 25	50

divide by 4 and multiply by 2

1-7 Exercises

Assignment Guide

If you finished Example 1 assign:
Average 1–4, 8–11, 16–18, 27–32
Advanced 8–11, 16–22, 27–32

If you finished Example 2 assign:
Average 1–23, 27–32
Advanced 5–32

Homework Quick Check

Quickly check key concepts.
Exercises: 8, 10, 12, 14, 18

RETEACH 1-7

LESSON 1-7 **Reteach**
Patterns and Sequences

Find the next three numbers in the sequence.

8, 12, 16, 20, 24, □, □, □, ...

Step 1: Look at pairs of numbers to find the pattern.

8, 12, 16, 20, 24, □, □, □, ...

8 + 4 = 12   12 + 4 = 16   16 + 4 = 20

The pattern is to add 4.

Step 2: Use the pattern to name the next three numbers.

24 + 4 = 28   28 + 4 = 32   32 + 4 = 36

The next three numbers are 28, 32, and 36.

Find the next three numbers in each sequence.

1. 5, 8, 6, 9, 7 □, □, □, ... 10, 8, 11
2. 90, 80, 70, 60, □, □, □, ... 50, 40, 30
3. 2, 8, 4, 16, □, □, □, ... 8, 32, 16
4. 10, 14, 18, 22, □, □, □, ... 26, 30, 34
5. 13, 21, 29, 37, □, □, □, ... 45, 53, 61
6. 24, 12, 16, 8, □, □, □, ... 12, 6, 10
7. 14, 12,10, 8, □, □, □, ... 6, 4, 2
8. 1, 7, 13, 19, □, □, □, ... 25, 31, 37
9. 1, 3, 6, 10, □, □, □, ... 15, 21, 28
10. 40, 38, 36, □, □, □, ... 34, 32, 30
11. 54, 45, 36, □, □, □, ... 27, 18, 9
12. 10, 25, 40, □, □, □, ... 55, 70, 85
13. 36, 29, 22, □, □, □, ... 15, 8, 1
14. 18, 36, 72, □, □, □, ... 144, 288, 576

PRACTICE 1-7

LESSON 1-7 **Practice B**
Patterns and Sequences

Identify a pattern in each arithmetic sequence and then find the missing terms.

1. 4, 8, 16, 32, □, □, □, ... multiply by 2; 64, 128, 256
2. 100, 95, 90, 85, □, □, □, ... subtract 5; 80; 75; 70
3. 8, 20, 32, 44, □, □, □, ... add 12; 56; 68; 80
4. 6, 12, 18, 24, □, □, □, ... add 6; 30; 36; 42
5. 9, 18, 27, 36, □, □, □, ... add 9; 45, 54, 63
6. 3, 6, 12, 24, □, □, □, ... multiply by 2; 48, 96, 192

7.

Position	1	2	3	4	5	6	7
Value of Term	5	10	20	40	80	160	320

multiply by 2

8. 300, 250, □, □, 100, □, 0, ... subtract 50; 200; 150; 50
9. 1, 15, □, 43, 57, □, 85, 99, ... add 14; 29; 71
10. 7, □, 21, 28, □, □, □, 56, ... add 7; 14; 35; 42; 49
11. 9, □, 13, □, □, □, 21, 23, ... add 2; 11; 15; 17; 19

12.

Position	1	2	3	4	5	6	7
Value of Term	5	10	20	40	80	160	320

33 inches

13. A forest ranger in Australia took measurements of a eucalyptus tree for the past 3 weeks. The tree was 12 inches tall the first week, 19 inches the second week, and 26 inches the third week. If this growth pattern continues, how tall will the tree be next week?
33 inches

14. Maria puts the same amount of money in her savings account each month. She had $450 in the account in April, $600 in May, and $750 in June. If she continues her savings pattern, how much money will she have in the account in July?
$900

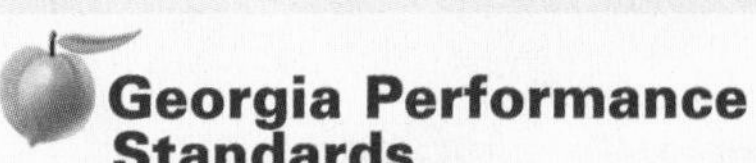
Georgia Performance Standards

M6P1.c Apply and adapt a variety of appropriate strategies to solve problems.

M6P3.a Organize and consolidate their mathematical thinking through communication.

ONGOING ASSESSMENT and INTERVENTION

Diagnose ***Before*** **the Lesson**
1-7 Warm Up, TE p. 33

Monitor ***During*** **the Lesson**
1-7 Know-It Notebook
1-7 Questioning Strategies

Assess ***After*** **the Lesson**
1-7 Lesson Quiz, TE p. 36

Answers

25. Possible answer: If terms of a sequence changes by the same amount each time, the sequence is arithmetic.

TEST PREP DOCTOR In Exercise 28, remind students to answer all five parts of the exercise. During an actual test, the students should circle each part that has to be answered.

Journal

Have students explain what could happen if the first and second terms are the only ones considered in determining a pattern.

Power Presentations with PowerPoint®

1-7 Lesson Quiz

Identify a pattern in each sequence and then find the missing terms.

1. 12, 24, 36, 48, ■, ■, ■, ...
60, 72, 84

2. 75, 71, 67, 63, ■, ■, ■, ...
59, 55, 51

Identify a pattern in each sequence. Name the missing terms.

3. 1000, 500, ■, 125, ... 250

4. 100, 50, 200, ■, 400, ■, ...
100, 200

Also available on transparency

PRACTICE AND PROBLEM SOLVING

CRCT GPS
Extra Practice p. 715

Use the pattern to write the first five terms of the sequence.

16. Start with 1; multiply by 3. 1, 3, 9, 27, 81
17. Start with 5; add 9. 5, 14, 23, 32, 41
18. Start with 100; subtract 7. 100, 93, 86, 79, 72

19. Social Studies The Chinese lunar calendar is based on a 12-year cycle, with each of the 12 years named after a different animal. The year 2006 is the year of the dog.

a. When will the next year of the dog occur? 2018
b. When was the last year of the dog? 1994
c. Will the year 2030 be a year of the dog? Explain. yes; 2006 + 2(12) = 2030

Identify whether each given sequences could be arithmetic. If not, identify the pattern of the sequence.

20. 10, 16, 22, 28, 34, . . . yes
21. 60, 56, 61, 57, 62, . . . subtract 4 and add 5
22. 111, 121, 131, 141, 151, . . . yes

23. Choose a Strategy The * shows where a piece is missing from the pattern. What piece is missing?

Ⓐ  y
Ⓑ B
Ⓒ  y
Ⓓ  Y

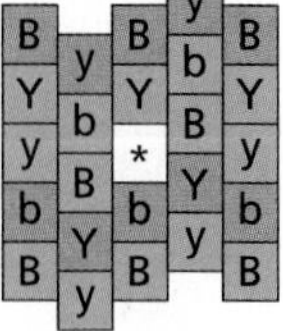

24. Whole numbers raised to the second power are called perfect squares. This is because they can be represented by objects arranged in the shape of a square. Perfect squares can be written as the sequence 1, 4, 9, 16, . . .

a. Find the next two perfect squares in the sequence. 25; 36
b. Explain how can you know whether a number is a perfect square?

25. Write About It Explain how to determine if a sequence is arithmetic.

26. Challenge Find the missing terms in the following sequence:
■, 2^3, 27, 4^3, 125, ■, 343, . . . 1, 6^3

24b. The number is a perfect square if it can be shown to be a whole number raised to the second power.

CRCT PREP • GPS SUPPORT • SPIRAL REVIEW

27. Multiple Choice Identify the pattern in the sequence 6, 11, 16, 21, 26, . . .

Ⓐ Add 5. Ⓑ Add 6. Ⓒ Multiply by 5. Ⓓ Multiply by 6.

28. Extended Response Identify the first term and a pattern for the sequence 5, 8, 11, 14, 17, . . . Is the sequence arithmetic? Explain why or why not. Find the next three terms in the sequence. 5; add 3; yes; it increases by the same amount each time; 20, 23, 26

Use mental math to find each sum or product. (Lesson 1-5)

29. 13 + 6 + 17 + 24 60
30. 4 × 11 × 5 220
31. 45 + 11 + 35 + 29 120

Choose a solution method and solve. Explain your choice. (Lesson 1-6)

32. As of 2005, Hank Aaron was Major League Baseball's career home run leader with 755 home runs. Sadaharu Oh was the career home run leader of Japanese baseball with 868 home runs. How many more home runs did Oh hit than Aaron? calculator; 113

CHALLENGE 1-7

LESSON 1-7 **Challenge**
Picture Patterns

Draw the next three figures in each pattern.

1.
2.
3.
4.
5.
6.
7.

PROBLEM SOLVING 1-7

LESSON 1-7 **Problem Solving**
Patterns and Sequences

1. A giant bamboo plant was 5 inches tall on Monday, 23 inches tall on Tuesday, 41 inches tall on Wednesday, and 59 inches tall on Thursday. Describe the pattern. If the pattern continues, how tall will the giant bamboo plant be on Friday, Saturday, and Sunday?

Each day the giant bamboo plant grew 18 inches. The giant bamboo plant will be 77 inches tall on Friday, 95 inches tall on Saturday, and 113 inches tall on Sunday.

2. A scientist was studying a cell. After the second hour there were two cells. After the third hour there were four cells. After the fourth hour there were eight cells. Describe the pattern. If the pattern continues, how many cells will there be after the fifth, sixth, and seventh hour?

The number of cells doubled every hour. After the fifth hour there will be 16 cells. After the sixth hour there will be 32 cells. After the seventh hour there will be 64 cells.

Choose the letter for the best answer.

3. The first place prize for a sweepstakes is $8,000. The third place prize is $2,000. The fourth place prize is $1,000. The fifth place prize is $500. What is the second place prize?
A $7,000 Ⓒ $4,000
B $6,000 D $3,000

4. The temperature was 59°F at 3:00 A.M., 62°F at 5:00 A.M., and 65°F at 7:00 A.M. If the pattern continues, what will the temperature be at 9:00 A.M., 11:00 A.M., and 1:00 P.M.?
F 66°F at 9:00 A.M., 67°F at 11:00 A.M., 68°F at 1:00 P.M.
G 68°F at 9:00 A.M., 70°F at 11:00 A.M., 72°F at 1:00 P.M.
Ⓗ 68°F at 9:00 A.M., 71°F at 11:00 A.M., 74°F at 1:00 P.M.
J 70°F at 9:00 A.M., 75°F at 11:00 A.M., 80°F at 1:00 P.M.

Find a Pattern in Sequences

Use with Lesson 1-7

M6A2.a, M6P1.c

Lab Resources Online
KEYWORD: MR7 Lab1

The numbers 4, 7, 10, 13, 16, 19, ... form an arithmetic sequence. To continue the sequence, identify a pattern. Here is a possible pattern:

4, 4 + 3 = 7, 7 + 3 = 10, 10 + 3 = 13,...

Activity

Use a spreadsheet to generate the first seven terms of the sequence above.

To start with 4, type **4** in cell A1.

To add 3 to the value in cell A1, type **=A1 + 3** in cell B1.

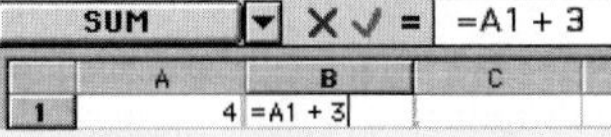

Press ENTER.

To continue the sequence, click the square in the lower right corner of cell B1, hold down the mouse button, and drag the cursor across through cell G1.

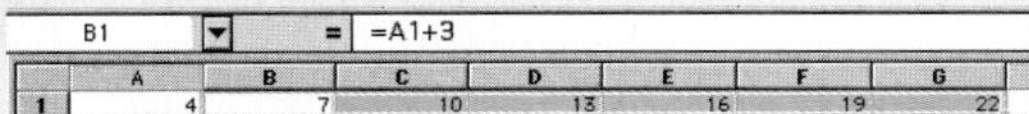

When you release the mouse button, A1 through G1 will list the first seven terms of the sequence.

	A	B	C	D	E	F	G
1	4	7	10	13	16	19	22

Think and Discuss

1. How do you use a sequence's pattern when you use your spreadsheet to generate the terms? Possible answer: Enter the formula for the pattern into one cell. Then copy the formula into as many other cells as necessary.

Try This

Identify a pattern in each sequence. Then use a spreadsheet to generate the first 12 terms.

1. 9, 14, 19, 24, 29, 34, ...
2. 7, 13, 19, 25, 31, 37, ...
3. 105, 98, 91, 84, 77, 70, ...
4. 21, 29, 37, 45, 53, 61, ...
5. 150, 174, 198, 222, 246, 270, ...
6. 600, 550, 500, 450, 400, 350, ...

Answers to *Try This*

1. 39, 44, 49, 54, 59, 64
2. 43, 49, 55, 61, 67, 73
3. 63, 56, 49, 42, 35, 28
4. 69, 77, 85, 93, 101, 109
5. 294, 318, 342, 366, 390, 414
6. 300, 250, 200, 150, 100, 50

Organizer

Use with Lesson 1-7

Pacing:
Traditional $\frac{1}{2}$ day
Block $\frac{1}{4}$ day

Objective: Use a spreadsheet to perform repeated operations that generate a sequence.

Materials: Spreadsheet Software

Online Edition

Resources

Technology Lab Activities
Lab 1-7 Recording Sheet

Teach

Discuss

This technology lab will relate to students the importance of recognizing a pattern in a sequence and how the technology uses the pattern to easily generate sequences.

Close

Key Concept

A spreadsheet program uses a pattern to generate a sequence quickly and more accurately.

Assessment

Suppose you entered 6 in cell A1, then entered =A1 + 4 in cell B1, and then pressed **ENTER**.

1. What number would appear in cell B1? 10
2. How do you use the spreadsheet to generate the next 4 terms? Click the fill handle (box in lower right corner of the cell) in cell B1, hold down, and drag through cell F1.

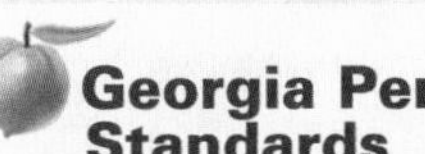

M6A2.a Analyze and describe patterns arising from mathematical rules, tables, and graphs.

M6P1.c Apply and adapt a variety of appropriate strategies to solve problems.

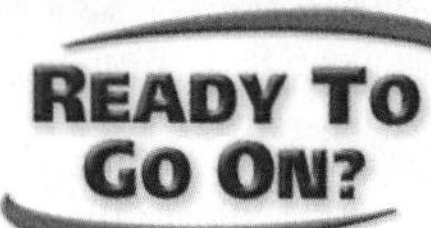

Organizer

Objective: Assess students' mastery of concepts and skills in Lessons 1-4 through 1-7.

Resources

 ***Assessment Resources***
Section 1B Quiz

INTERVENTION

Resources

 ***Ready to Go On? Intervention and Enrichment*** **Worksheets**

 ***Ready to Go On?*** **CD-ROM**

 ***Ready to Go On?*** **Online**

my.hrw.com

CHAPTER 1

SECTION 1B

Quiz for Lessons 1-4 Through 1-7

1-4 Order of Operations

Evaluate each expression.

1. $3 \times 4 \div (10 - 4)$ 2
2. $5^2 + 10 \div 2 - 1$ 29
3. $4 + (12 - 8) \times 6$ 28
4. $(2^3 + 2) \times 10$ 100
5. Mrs. Webb buys 7 cards for $2 each, 3 metallic pens for $1 each, and 1 pad of writing paper for $4. Evaluate $7 \times 2 + 3 \times 1 + 1 \times 4$ to find the total amount Mrs. Webb spends. $21

1-5 Mental Math

Evaluate.

6. $4 + 21 + 9 + 6$ 40
7. $5 \times 17 \times 2$ 170
8. $45 + 19 + 1 + 55$ 120
9. $2 \times 17 \times 10$ 340

Use the Distributive Property to find each product.

10. 5×62 310
11. 9×41 369
12. 4×23 92
13. 7×14 98
14. 5×34 170

1-6 Choose the Method of Computation

Choose a solution method and solve. Explain your choice.

15. How many Texas state parks are shown in the table? Possible answer: paper and pencil; 81
16. How many more parks are there in the Prairies and Lakes region than in the Big Bend region? Possible answer: mental math; 15

Texas State Parks

Region	Number of Parks
Big Bend	7
Gulf Coast	11
Hill Country	11
Panhandle Plains	12
Pineywoods	13
Prairies and Lakes	22
South Texas Plains	5

Ready to Go On?

1-7 Patterns and Sequences

Identify a pattern in the arithmetic sequence and then find the missing terms.

17.

Position	1	2	3	4	5	6	7
Value of Term	5	14	23	32	■	■	■
					41	50	59

Identify a pattern in each sequence. Name the missing terms.

18. 4, 20, 15, 31, ■, ■, 37, … add 16 and subtract 5; 26; 42
19. 16, 32, 8, 16, ■, 8, 2, ■, 1, … multiply by 2 and divide by 4; 4; 4
20. A concert hall has 5 seats in the front row, 9 seats in the second row, 13 seats in the third row, and 17 seats in the fourth row. If this pattern continues, how many seats are in the sixth row? 25 seats

READY TO GO ON? Diagnose and Prescribe

NO INTERVENE

Ready to Go On? Intervention	*Ready to Go On? Intervention, Section 1B* Worksheets	CD-ROM	Online
Lesson 1-4	1-4 Intervention	Activity 1-4	Diagnose and Prescribe Online
Lesson 1-5	1-5 Intervention	Activity 1-5	
Lesson 1-6	1-6 Intervention	Activity 1-6	
Lesson 1-7	1-7 Intervention	Activity 1-7	

YES ENRICH

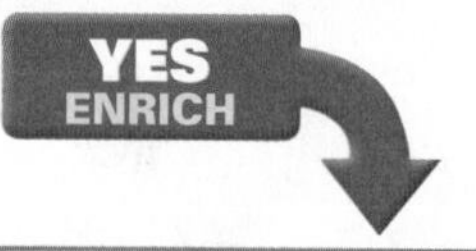

Ready to Go On? Enrichment, Section 1B
Worksheets
CD-ROM
Online

MULTI-STEP TEST PREP

Go for the Gold The table shows the number of medals won by the United States at four Summer Olympic Games.

Olympic Medals Won by U.S. Athletes				
Year	Site	Gold	Silver	Bronze
1992	Barcelona	37	34	37
1996	Atlanta	44	32	25
2000	Sydney	40	24	33
2004	Athens	35	39	29

1. Find the total number of medals won by the United States at each Olympics. Then order the Olympic sites from the greatest number of medals won to the least.
2. Estimate the total number of gold medals won by the United States at these four Olympics. Explain how you found your estimate.
3. To compare the performances of U.S. athletes at different Olympics, Jocelyn assigns 3 points to each gold medal, 2 points to each silver medal, and 1 point to each bronze medal. To find the total number of U.S. points for the Barcelona Olympics, she writes the expression $3 \times 37 + 2 \times 34 + 1 \times 37$. Explain how to evaluate this expression, and then find the point total.
4. In 1996, Romania won 2^2 gold medals, 7^1 silver medals, and 3^2 bronze medals. How many of each medal did Romania win? Find the difference in the number of medals won by the United States and the number of medals won by Romania in 1996. **4 gold, 7 silver, 9 bronze; 81**
5. The total number of medals won by the United States at each Summer Olympics since 1896 is $3^7 + 2$. About how many more medals do U.S. athletes need to win in order to have a total of 2,200? **about 10**

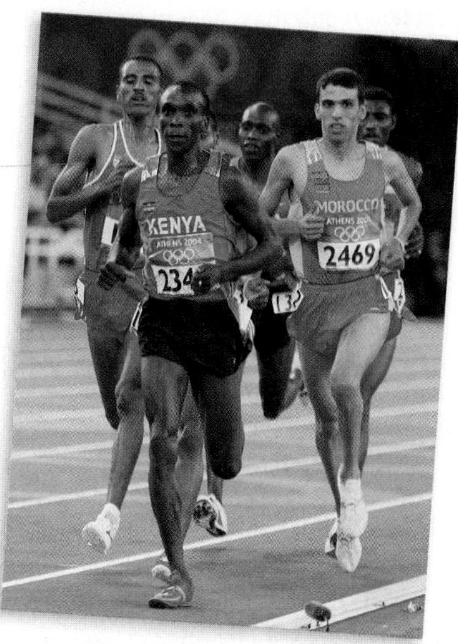

Multi-Step Test Prep

MULTI-STEP TEST PREP

Organizer

Objective: Assess students' ability to apply concepts and skills in Chapter 1 in a real-world format.

Online Edition

Resources

Middle School Assessments
www.mathtekstoolkit.org

Problem	Text reference
1	Lesson 1-1
2	Lesson 1-2
3	Lesson 1-4
4	Lesson 1-3
5	Lesson 1-4

Answers

1. Barcelona (108), Athens (103), Atlanta (101), Sydney (97)
2. Possible answer: 160; round the number of gold medals at each Olympics to 40, and then multiply by 4.
3. Multiply first, and then add; 216 points.

INTERVENTION

Scaffolding Questions

1. Should you use mental math, paper and pencil, or a calculator to add the numbers of medals for each Olympics? Answers will vary. How can you use mental math to find the total number of medals won in Barcelona? Possible answer: $3 \times 30 = 90$; then add $7 + 4 + 7 = 18$
2. What compatible numbers can you use to help with the estimate? Round the number of gold medals to 40 for each Olympics.
3. Which comes first in the order of operations: multiplication or addition? multiplication What expression do you get after performing the multiplications? $111 + 68 + 37$
4. What operation should you use to find the difference in the total number of medals won by the two countries? subtraction
5. How do you use the order of operations to evaluate $3^7 + 2$? First find the value of the number with the exponent. How do you find the value of 3^7? $3 \times 3 \times 3 \times 3 \times 3 \times 3 \times 3$ What is the value of $3^7 + 2$? 2,189

Extension

1. What is the average number of gold medals won at these Olympics? 39
2. Estimate the total number of medals that U.S. athletes are likely to win over the next five summer Olympics. Possible answer: about 500

Game Time

Organizer

Objective: Participate in games to practice and apply skills learned in Chapter 1.

 **Online Edition**

Resources

 ***Chapter 1 Resource Book***
Puzzles, Twisters & Teasers

Palindromes

Purpose: To apply the skill of addition to create palindrome numbers

Discuss Ask students to explain how the trick works. Ask them questions such as the following: How would you create a palindrome starting with the number 157? How many times must you repeat until the sum is a palindrome?
Possible answer: Begin with a number. Reverse its digits and add the resulting number to the original number. Repeat the process until the sum is a palindrome. It takes three steps:

157 + 751 = 908

908 + 809 = 1,717

1,717 + 7,171 = 8,888

Extend First have students use the trick to create a palindrome by starting with the number 6. Then have them start with 8. Have students note the number of steps until a palindrome is formed. Challenge students to explain why starting with a number from 5 through 9 always yields a palindrome in two steps.
Possible answer: 6 + 6 = 12; 12 + 21 = 33. 8 + 8 = 16; 16 + 61 = 77. Starting with a number from 5 through 9 yields a sum whose tens place is 1 and whose ones place is between 0 and 8. Interchanging the digits and adding means adding the same two numbers in different orders. There is no regrouping, so the sum will always be a palindrome.

Spin-a-Million

Purpose: To enhance the study of place value by creating numbers from numerals on a spinner.

Discuss Ask students what strategy they can use to help them win. Place smaller numerals in the smaller place values. Reserve the higher place values for larger numerals.

Game Time

Palindromes

A *palindrome* is a word, phrase, or number that reads the same forward and backward.

Examples:
race car Madam, I'm Adam. 3710173

You can turn almost any number into a palindrome with this trick.

Think of any number. 283
Now add that number in reverse. + 382
665

Use the sum to repeat the previous step and keep repeating until the final sum is a palindrome.

665
+ 566
1,231

1,231
+ 1,321
2,552

It took only three steps to create a palindrome by starting with the number 283. What happens if you start with the number 196? Do you think you will ever create a palindrome if you start with 196? One man who started with 196 did these steps until he had a number with 70,928 digits and he still had not created a palindrome!

Spin-a-Million

The object of this game is to create the number closest to 1,000,000.

Taking turns, spin the pointer and write the number on your place-value chart. The number cannot be moved once it has been placed.

After six turns, the player whose number is closest to one million wins the round and scores a point. The first player to get five points wins the game.

go.hrw.com
Game Time Extra
KEYWORD: MR7 Games

A complete copy of the rules and game pieces are available online.

Extend Given the numbers 2, 4, 3, 7, and 9, what is the largest number that could be formed in this game? the smallest number?
97,432; 23,479

PROJECT Picture This

Make a game in an empty DVD case to review concepts from this chapter.

Directions

1. Cut a piece of card stock that can be folded in half to fit inside the DVD case. Lay the card stock flat and draw a path for a board game. Be sure to have a start and a finish. **Figure A**

2. Close the game board and decorate the front. Glue a library pocket onto the front to hold the index cards. **Figure B**

3. On the index cards, write problems that can be solved using math from the chapter. Place the cards in the pocket.

4. Cut a piece of card stock to fit the other side of the DVD box. Glue directions for your game at the top. At the bottom, make a spinner the size of a DVD. Attach a brass fastener to the middle of the spinner, and then attach a paper clip to the fastener. **Figure C**

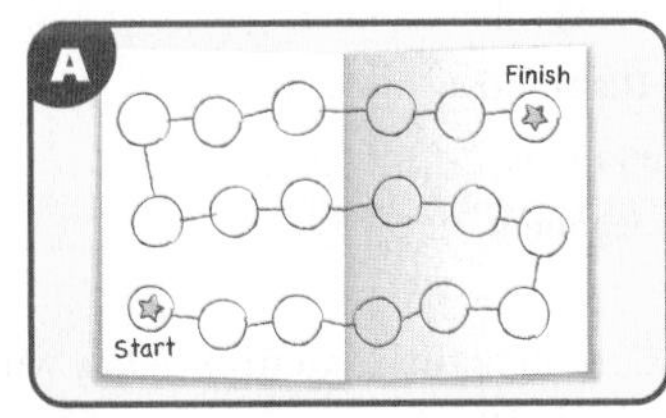

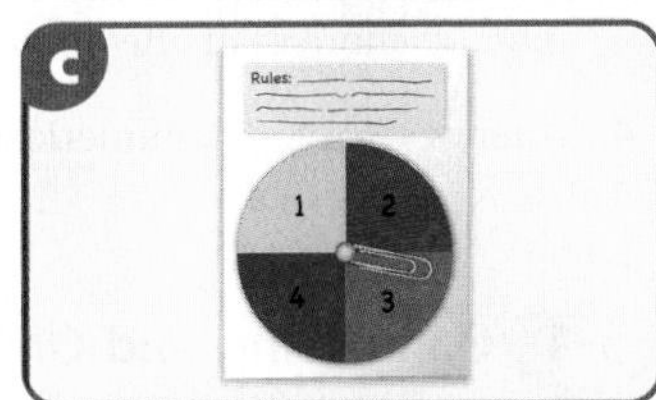

Putting the Math into Action

Play your game with a partner. Use buttons or coins as playing pieces. Players should take turns spinning the spinner and then be required to solve a problem correctly in order to move their piece.

Organizer

Objective: Make a board game to help review whole numbers and patterns.

Materials: Plastic DVD box, card-stock in various colors, markers, scissors, glue stick, library pocket, index cards, brass fastener, large paper clip

Online Edition

Using the Page

Preparing the Materials
Ask students to calculate how many index cards each student should receive if a stack of 200 index cards is distributed evenly among the class.

Making the Project
Encourage students to choose themes for their game boards (for example, favorite sports or movies) and have them decorate the game boards accordingly. Students might also include spaces on which players lose a turn or win a free turn.

Extending the Project
Have students make different spinners to see how this affects the play of the game.

Don't worry if library pockets aren't available. You can have students use business-size envelopes instead. In this case, have students seal the envelopes and then cut them in half crosswise. Each envelope makes two pockets that are just the right size for this project.

We save the free CD-ROMs that we receive in the mail from internet companies, because they always seem to come in handy. In this project, students can make their spinners by tracing around a CD-ROM or by drawing on it directly with a permanent marker.

CHAPTER 1 Study Guide: Review

Organizer

Objective: Help students organize and review key concepts and skills presented in Chapter 1.

Online Edition
Multilingual Glossary

Countdown to CRCT Week 2

Resources

PuzzlePro®
One-Stop Planner®

***Multilingual Glossary* Online**
go.hrw.com
KEYWORD: MR7 Glossary

Lesson Tutorial Videos
CD-ROM

Test & Practice Generator
One-Stop Planner®

Answers

1. sequence, term
2. base, exponent
3. order of operations
4. evaluate
5. 8,731; 8,735; 8,737; 8,740
6. 53,337; 53,341; 53,452; 53,456
7. 8,791; 81,790; 87,091; 87,901
8. 2,651; 22,561; 25,615; 26,551
9. 91,363; 93,613; 96,361; 96,631
10. 10,101; 10,110; 11,010; 11,110

CHAPTER 1 Study Guide: Review

Vocabulary

Complete the sentences below with vocabulary words from the list above.

1. An ordered set of numbers is called a(n) __?__. Each number in a sequence is called a(n) __?__.
2. In the expression 8^5, 8 is the __?__, and 5 is the __?__.
3. The __?__ is a set of rules used to evaluate an expression that contains more than one operation.
4. When you __?__ a numerical expression, you find its value.

Study Guide: Review

1-1 Comparing and Ordering Whole Numbers (pp. 6–9)

GPS M6P5.a

EXAMPLE

- **Order the numbers from least to greatest.**
4,913; 4,931; 4,391

4,913
4,931 *4,913 < 4,931*

4,931
4,391 *4,391 < 4,931*

4,913
4,391 *4,391 < 4,913*

4,391 < 4,913 < 4,931

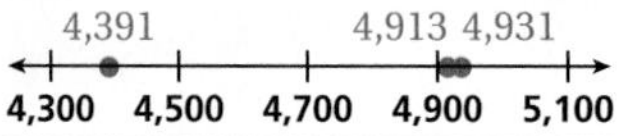

Number line: 4,300, 4,500, 4,700, 4,900, 5,100; points 4,391; 4,913; 4,931

EXERCISES

Order the numbers from least to greatest.

5. 8,731; 8,737; 8,735; 8,740
6. 53,341; 53,337; 53,456; 53,452
7. 87,091; 8,791; 87,901; 81,790
8. 26,551; 25,615; 2,651; 22,561
9. 96,361; 96,631; 93,613; 91,363
10. 10,101; 11,010; 10,110; 11,110

1-2 Estimating with Whole Numbers (pp. 10–13)

GPS M6P1.b

EXAMPLE

- **Estimate the sum 837 + 710 by rounding to the hundreds place.**
  800 + 700 = 1,500
  The sum is about 1,500.
- **Estimate the quotient of 148 and 31.**
  150 ÷ 30 = 5
  The quotient is about 5.

EXERCISES

Estimate each sum or difference by rounding to the place value indicated.

11. 4,671 − 3,954; thousands

12. 3,123 + 2,987; thousands

13. 53,465 − 27,465; ten thousands

14. Ralph has 38 photo album sheets with 22 baseball cards in each sheet. About how many baseball cards does he have?

1-3 Exponents (pp. 14–17)

GPS M6P1.c

EXAMPLE

- **Write 6 × 6 in exponential form.**
  6^2 *6 is a factor 2 times.*

Find each value.

- 5^2
  $5^2 = 5 \times 5$
  $= 25$
- 6^3
  $6^3 = 6 \times 6 \times 6$
  $= 216$

EXERCISES

Write each expression in exponential form.

15. 5 × 5 × 5	**16.** 3 × 3 × 3 × 3
17. 7 × 7 × 7 × 7 × 7	**18.** 8 × 8
19. 4 × 4 × 4 × 4	**20.** 1 × 1 × 1

Find each value.

21. 4^4	**22.** 2^4	**23.** 6^3
24. 3^3	**25.** 1^5	**26.** 7^4
27. 5^3	**28.** 10^2	**29.** 9^2

1-4 Order of Operations (pp. 22–25)

GPS M6P4.c

EXAMPLE

- **Evaluate $8 \div (7 - 5) \times 2^2 - 2 + 9$.**

$8 \div (7 - 5) \times 2^2 - 2 + 9$	
$8 \div 2 \times 2^2 - 2 + 9$	*Subtract in parentheses.*
$8 \div 2 \times 4 - 2 + 9$	*Simplify the exponent.*
$4 \times 4 - 2 + 9$	*Divide.*
$16 - 2 + 9$	*Multiply.*
$14 + 9$	*Subtract.*
23	*Add.*

EXERCISES

Evaluate each expression.

30. 9 × 8 − 13

31. 21 ÷ 3 + 4

32. 6 + 4 × 5

33. 19 − 12 ÷ 6

34. 30 ÷ 2 − 5 × 2

35. $(7 + 3) \div 2 \times 3^2$

36. $8 \times (7 + 5) \div 4^2 + 9 \div 3$

37. $3^2 \times 5 \div (10 \times 3 \div 2)$

Study Guide: Review

Answers

11. 1,000
12. 6,000
13. 20,000
14. 800
15. 5^3
16. 3^4
17. 7^5
18. 8^2
19. 4^4
20. 1^3
21. 256
22. 16
23. 216
24. 27
25. 1
26. 2,401
27. 125
28. 100
29. 81
30. 59
31. 11
32. 26
33. 17
34. 5
35. 45
36. 9
37. 3

Answers

38. 30
39. 520
40. 80
41. 1,080
42. 40
43. 320
44. 100
45. 130
46. 168
47. 135
48. 204
49. 152
50. 216
51. 165
52. 62°
53. Add 5; 24, 29.
54. Subtract 2; 13, 11.
55. Add 4 and subtract 2; 20, 22.
56. Multiply by 3; 81, 243, 729.
57. Add 5 and subtract 2; 71, 74.

1-5 Mental Math (pp. 26–29)

GPS M6P1.c

EXAMPLE

Evaluate.

■ $4 + 13 + 6 + 7$
$4 + 6 + 13 + 7$
$(4 + 6) + (13 + 7)$
$10 \quad + \quad 20$
30

■ $5 \times 9 \times 6$
$5 \times 6 \times 9$
$(5 \times 6) \times 9$
30×9
270

■ **Use the Distributive Property to find 3×16.**

$3 \times 16 = 3 \times (10 + 6)$
$= (3 \times 10) + (3 \times 6)$
$= 30 + 18$
$= 48$

EXERCISES

Evaluate.

38. $9 + 5 + 1 + 15$ **39.** $8 \times 13 \times 5$
40. $31 + 16 + 19 + 14$ **41.** $6 \times 12 \times 15$
42. $17 + 12 + 8 + 3$ **43.** $16 \times 5 \times 4$
44. $11 + 23 + 27 + 39$ **45.** $13 \times 5 \times 2$

Use the Distributive Property to find each product.

46. 7×24 **47.** 9×15
48. 6×34 **49.** 8×19
50. 8×27 **51.** 5×33

1-6 Choose the Method of Computation (pp. 30–32)

GPS M6P1.c

EXAMPLE

■ **Choose a solution method and solve. Explain your choice.**

The average annual rainfall in Washington, D.C., is 39 inches. How much rain does Washington, D.C., average in 8 years?

These numbers are not so big that you must use a calculator. Use pencil and paper to find the answer. $39 \times 8 = 312$ inches

EXERCISES

Choose a solution method and solve. Explain your choice.

52. The average high temperature for Washington, D.C., in January is 42°F. The record high temperature for Washington, D.C., is 104°F. How much higher is the record temperature than the average high temperature in January?

1-7 Patterns and Sequences (pp. 33–36)

GPS M6A2.a

EXAMPLE

Identify a pattern in the sequence. Name the missing terms.

■ 1, 3, 5, 7, ■, ■, . . .
+2 +2 +2 +2 +2

The pattern is to add 2 to each term. The missing terms are 9 and 11.

■ 6, 12, 11, 22, ■, 42, ■, . . .
×2 −1 ×2 −1 ×2 −1

The pattern is to multiply one term by 2 and subtract the next by 1. The missing terms are 21 and 41.

EXERCISES

Identify the pattern in the arithmetic sequence and then find the missing terms.

53. 4, 9, 14, 19, ■, ■, . . .
54. 21, 19, 17, 15, ■, ■, . . .

Identify a pattern in each sequence. Name the missing terms.

55. 16, 20, 18, 22, ■, 24, ■, . . .
56. 1, 3, 9, 27, ■, ■, . . .
57. 65, 70, 68, 73, ■, 76, ■, . . .

CHAPTER TEST

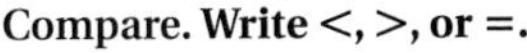

CHAPTER 1

Compare. Write <, >, or =.

1. 3,241 ▒ 324 >
2. 16,880,953 ▒ 16,221,773 >
3. 22,481,093 ▒ 23,662,840 <

Order the numbers from least to greatest.

4. 801; 798; 921 — 798; 801; 921
5. 4,835; 7,505; 4,310 — 4,310; 4,835; 7,505
6. 10,101; 101; 1,001 — 101; 1,001; 10,101

Estimate each sum or difference by rounding to the place value indicated.

7. 8,743 + 3,198; thousands 12,000
8. 62,524 − 17,831; ten thousands 40,000

Estimate.

9. Kaitlin's family is planning a trip from Washington, D.C., to New York City. New York City is 227 miles from Washington, D.C., and the family can drive an average of 55 mi/h. About how long will the trip take? about 4 hours

Write each expression in exponential form.

10. 4 × 4 × 4 × 4 × 4 4^5
11. 10 × 10 × 10 10^3
12. 6 × 6 × 6 × 6 6^4

Find each value.

13. 2^3 8
14. 5^2 25
15. 4^4 256
16. 11^2 121
17. 9^3 729

Evaluate each expression.

18. 12 + 8 ÷ 2 16
19. $3^2 \times 5 + 10 - 7$ 48
20. 12 + (28 − 15) + 4 × 2 33

Evaluate.

21. 15 + 23 + 47 + 5 90
22. 5 × 48 × 2 480
23. 2 × 5 × 11 110
24. 44 + 18 + 12 + 6 80

Use the Distributive Property to find each product.

25. 3 × 32 96
26. 52 × 6 312
27. 24 × 5 120
28. 81 × 6 486
29. 6 × 21 126

Choose a solution method and solve. Explain your choice.

30. At 5:00 A.M., the temperature was 41°F. By noon, the temperature was 69°F. By how many degrees did the temperature increase? paper and pencil; 28°F

Identify a pattern in each sequence. Name the missing terms.

31. 8, 22, 36, 50, ▒, ▒, ▒, . . . add 14; 64, 78, 92
32. 2, 10, 7, 15, ▒, 20, ▒, . . . add 8 and subtract 3; 12; 17

33. A tile pattern has 1 tile in the first row, 3 tiles in the second row, and 5 tiles in the third row. If this pattern continues, how many tiles are in the fifth row? 9 tiles

Chapter Test

CHAPTER TEST

CHAPTER 1

Organizer

Objective: Assess students' mastery of concepts and skills in Chapter 1.

Online Edition

Resources

Assessment Resources

Chapter 1 Tests
- Free Response (Levels A, B, C)
- Multiple Choice (Levels A, B, C)
- Performance Assessment

***IDEA Works!* CD-ROM**
Modified Chapter 1 Test

Organizer

Objective: Provide opportunities to learn and practice common test-taking strategies.

 **Online Edition**

Resources

 ***CRCT Prep* Workbook**

 ***CRCT Prep for MS and HS* CD-ROM**

 ***CRCT Practice* Online**

TEST PREP DOCTOR Students need to be aware that some of the choices given are distractors, intended to mislead them to believe that their wrong answer is indeed correct. Students should eliminate the most obvious wrong choices in order to concentrate on the other choices and verify that their answer is correct.

Standardized Test Strategies

Multiple Choice: Eliminate Answer Choices

You can solve some math problems without doing detailed calculations. You can use mental math, estimation, or logical reasoning to help you eliminate answer choices and save time.

Test Tackler

EXAMPLE 1

Which number is the closest estimate for 678 + 189?

Ⓐ 700 Ⓒ 1,000

Ⓑ 900 Ⓓ 5,000

You can use logical reasoning to eliminate choice A because it is too small. The estimated sum has to be greater than 700 because 678 + 189 is greater than 700.

Choice D may also be eliminated because the value is too large. The estimated sum will be less than 5,000.

Round 678 up to 700 and 189 up to 200. Then find the sum of 700 and 200: 700 + 200 = 900. You can eliminate choice C because it is greater than 900.

Choice B is the closest estimate.

EXAMPLE 2

Which of the following numbers is the standard form of four million, six hundred eight thousand, fifteen?

Ⓕ 468,015 Ⓗ 4,068,150

Ⓖ 4,608,015 Ⓙ 4,600,815,000

Logical reasoning can be used to eliminate choices. Numbers that have a place value in the millions must have at least seven but no more than nine digits. Choices F and J can be eliminated because they do not have the correct number of digits.

Both choices G and H have the correct range of digits, so narrow it down further. The number must end in 15. Choice H ends in 50, so it cannot be correct. Eliminate it.

The correct answer is G.

Some answer choices, called distracters, may seem correct because they are based on common errors made in calculations.

Read each item and answer the questions that follow.

Item A
Which number is the greatest?

Ⓐ 599,485
Ⓑ 5,571,987
Ⓒ 5,569,003
Ⓓ 5,399,879

1. Are there any answer choices you can eliminate immediately? If so, which ones and why?
2. Describe how you can find the correct answer.

City Middle School Populations	
Central Middle School	652
Eastside Middle School	718
Northside Middle School	663
Southside Middle School	731
Westside Middle School	842

Item B
The school district receives $30 a day in state funding for every student enrolled in a public school. Find the approximate number of students that attend all of the city middle schools.

Ⓕ 2,000
Ⓖ 3,300
Ⓗ 3,600
Ⓙ 4,000

3. Can F be eliminated? Why or why not?
4. Can H be eliminated? Why or why not?
5. Explain how to use mental math to solve this problem.

Item C
Which expression does NOT have the same value as $8 \times (52 + 12)$?

Ⓐ 8×64
Ⓑ $(8 \times 52) + (8 \times 12)$
Ⓒ $8(60) + 8(4)$
Ⓓ $8 \times 51 + 12$

6. Which answer choice can be eliminated immediately? Explain.
7. Explain how you can use the Distributive Property to solve this problem.

Item D
Stacey is beginning a new exercise program. She plans to cycle 2 kilometers on her first day. Each day after that, she will double the number of kilometers she cycled from the day before. Which expression shows how many kilometers she will cycle on the sixth day?

Ⓕ 2×6
Ⓖ $2 + 2 + 2 + 2 + 2 + 2$
Ⓗ 2^6
Ⓙ 6^2

8. Are there any answer choices you can eliminate immediately? If so, which choices and why?
9. Explain how you can use a table to help you solve this problem.

Item E
James is driving to his aunt's house. If he drives about 55 miles per hour for 5 hours, about how many miles will he have driven?

Ⓐ 12 miles
Ⓑ 300 miles
Ⓒ 60 miles
Ⓓ 600 miles

10. Which answer choice can be immediately eliminated and why?
11. Explain how to solve this problem.

Test Tackler

Answers

1. Yes, choice **A** can be eliminated because it has the fewest number of digits.
2. Use place value to compare the numbers. Move from left to right to compare each digit with the same place value.
3. Yes, choice **F** can be eliminated immediately because the value is too small.
4. No, you cannot immediately eliminate choice **H** because it is reasonable to think that there might be that many students.
5. Use compatible numbers to estimate the middle school population. The sum is about 3,600.
6. Choice **D** can be eliminated immediately because the parentheses can not be removed before the addition of 52 and 12.
7. If the Distributive Property is applied to $8 \times (52 + 12)$, choice **D** will be shown to be missing the product 8×12.
8. Choice **H** can be eliminated because the values should not be added.
9. Placing the data in a table will show that she cycled 64 km on the 6th day. Choice **G** has a value of 64.
10. Choice **A** and **C** are too small and can be eliminated immediately.
11. Round 55 to 60. Multiply 60×5 to get 300. James' aunt lives about 300 miles away.

Organizer

Objective: Provide review and practice for Chapter 1 and standardized tests.

Online Edition

Resources

Assessment Resources
Chapter 1 Cumulative Test

***CRCT Prep* Workbook**

***CRCT Prep* CD-ROM**

***CRCT Practice* Online**

go.hrw.com
KEYWORD: MR7 TestPrep

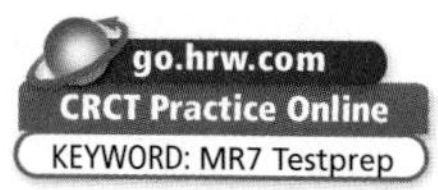

CRCT Prep

CUMULATIVE ASSESSMENT, CHAPTER 1

Multiple Choice

1. Jonah has 31 boxes of baseball cards. If each box contains 183 cards, about how many baseball cards does Jonah have in his collection?

Ⓐ 3,000 cards
Ⓑ 6,000 cards
Ⓒ 9,000 cards
Ⓓ 12,000 cards

2. Which of the following does NOT have a value of 27?

Ⓕ 3^3
Ⓖ $3^2 + 3 \times 7$
Ⓗ $3 \times 3 + 18$
Ⓙ $9^2 \div 3$

3. What are the next two terms in the following sequence?

6, 3, 12, 6, 24, ...

Ⓐ 3, 12
Ⓑ 6, 36
Ⓒ 12, 48
Ⓓ 18, 72

4. Which of the following correctly shows the use of the Distributive Property to find the product of 64 and 8?

Ⓕ $64 \times 8 = (8 \times 60) + (8 \times 4)$
Ⓖ $64 \times 8 = 8 \times 64$
Ⓗ $64 \times 8 = 8 + (60 + 4)$
Ⓙ $64 \times 8 = (8 \times 4) \times 60$

5. What is five billion, two hundred fifty-two million, six hundred thousand, three hundred eleven in standard form?

Ⓐ 5,252,603,011
Ⓑ 52,526,311
Ⓒ 5,252,600,311
Ⓓ 5,252,060,311

6. The attendance at a local library is shown in the table below. How many people visited the library last week

Last Week's Attendance	
Sunday	Closed
Monday	78
Tuesday	125
Wednesday	122
Thursday	96
Friday	104
Saturday	225

Ⓕ 450
Ⓖ 550
Ⓗ 650
Ⓙ 750

7. Which number is the greatest?

Ⓐ 5,432,873
Ⓑ 5,201,032
Ⓒ 5,221,754
Ⓓ 5,332,621

8. What is $6 \times 6 \times 6 \times 6$ written in exponential form?

Ⓕ 24^4
Ⓖ 1,296
Ⓗ 6^4
Ⓙ $1000 + 200 + 90 + 6$

9. The expression $6 \times 3 \times 4 = 3 \times 6 \times 4$ is an example of which property?

Ⓐ Associative
Ⓑ Commutative
Ⓒ Distributive
Ⓓ Exponential

TEST PREP DOCTOR

For **Item 3**, students may find more than one pattern in the sequence. It is important to be sure that the pattern works for all of the given terms before the two missing terms can be determined.

Answers

16a. $16

b. $30; $2 + 2^2 + 2^3 + 2^4 = 30$

17. Possible answer: $2(25 - 16) + 3^3$

$2(25 - 16) + 3^3$

$2(9) + 3^3$

$2(9) + 27$

$18 + 27$

45

18. See 4-Point Response work sample.

10. Which list of numbers is in order from least to greatest?

Ⓕ 1,231; 1,543; 1,267; 1,321

Ⓖ 3,210; 3,357; 3,366; 3,401

Ⓗ 4,321; 4,312; 4,211; 4,081

Ⓙ 5,019; 5,187; 5,143; 5,314

11. There are 2,347 seats in the town theater. A ticket to the Friday night concert costs $32. Which method of computation should be used to find how much money the theater will make if the Friday night concert sells out?

Ⓐ Paper and pencil

Ⓑ Calculator

Ⓒ Mental Math

Ⓓ Estimation

When you read a word problem, underline the information you need to help you answer the question.

12. What is the value of $3 + 8 \times 6 - (12 \div 4)$?

Ⓕ 13 Ⓗ 48

Ⓖ 27 Ⓙ 63

13. What is the value of 2^4?

Ⓐ 4 Ⓒ 8

Ⓑ 6 Ⓓ 16

14. At 2:00 P.M., the water temperature in the pool was 88°F. By 10:00 P.M. the water temperature in the pool was 75°F. By how many degrees did the water temperature drop?

Ⓕ 8° Ⓗ 52°

Ⓖ 13° Ⓙ 104°

15. Estimate the sum of 3,820 and 4,373 by rounding to the nearest thousand.

Ⓐ 8,000 Ⓒ 9,000

Ⓑ 8,100 Ⓓ 9,200

STANDARDIZED TEST PREP

Short Response

16. Megan deposited $2 into her savings account on the first Friday of the month. Each week she doubles her deposit from the week before.
    a. If this pattern continues, how much money will she deposit in week 4?
    b. What is the total amount in Megan's account after her fourth deposit? Explain how you found your answer.

17. Create a numerical expression that can be simplified in four steps. Include one set of parentheses and an exponent. The same mathematical operation may be used no more than two times. Show how to evaluate your expression.

Extended Response

18. The student population at Southside Middle School is listed in the table below.

Student Population at Southside Middle School		
	Boys	**Girls**
6th Grade	98	102
7th Grade	89	105
8th Grade	123	117

a. Use the information in the table to find the total number of students who attend Southside Middle School. Show your work.

b. About how many more girls are enrolled in the school than boys? Show your work. Explain how you found your answer.

c. The school board wants the school to have one teacher for every 20 students. If there are 8 sixth-grade teachers, does the school need to hire more sixth-grade teachers? If so, how many more? Explain your answer.

CRCT Prep

Short Response Rubric

Items 16–17

2 Points = The student's answer is an accurate and complete execution of the task or tasks.

1 Point = The student's answer contains attributes of an appropriate response but is flawed.

0 Points = The student's answer contains no attributes of an appropriate response.

Extended Response Rubric

Item 18

4 Points = The student demonstrates a thorough understanding of all concepts and shows all work correctly.

3 Points = The student demonstrates a basic understanding of all concepts, but the work shows some flaws reflecting inattentive execution of mathematical procedures or some misunderstanding of the underlying mathematics.

2 Points = The student demonstrates only a partial understanding of the concepts or procedures embodied in the tasks. The approach may be correct, but the work shows a misunderstanding of one or more important concepts.

1 Point = The student demonstrates a very limited understanding of the concepts or procedures embodied in the tasks. The response may show some understanding but exhibits many flaws or is incomplete.

0 Points = The student provides no response at all or a completely incorrect or uninterpretable response.

Student Work Samples for Item 18

4-Point Response

a. 98+102+89+105+123+117=634
A total of 634 student attend SMS.

b. Round the numbers to the nearest 10 and then add the number of girls and boys.

Boys	Girls
100	100
90	1 0
+1 20	120
310	330

There are about 20 more girls.

c. The 200 6th graders require 10 teachers.
200÷20=10
The school will need 2 more 6th grade teachers.

The student showed all work in finding the correct totals and explained the work when asked. The student correctly answered part **c** in a sentence.

3-Point Response

a) 634 students

b) about 20 more girls

c) yes

The student answered parts **a** and **b** correctly but failed to show the work or complete the explanation. The student did not show work in part **c** to support the answer.

2-Point Response

a. 310

b. 4 girls

c. 20×8=160
200−160=40 students need teachers

In part **a,** the student found only the total number of boys. In part **b,** an error was made and no explanation was given. The student did not complete part **c.**

CHAPTER 2

Introduction to Algebra

Section 2A

Understanding Variables and Expressions

- **2-1 Variables and Expressions**
- **2-2 Translate Between Words and Math**
- **2-3 Translating Between Tables and Expressions**
- **2-3 Hand-On Lab** Explore Area and Perimeter of Rectangles

Section 2B

Understanding Equations

- **2-4 Equations and Their Solutions**
- **2-5 Addition Equations**
- **2-6 Subtraction Equations**
- **2-7 Multiplication Equations**
- **2-8 Division Equations**
- **EXTENSION Inequalities**

Pacing Guide for 45-Minute Classes

Chapter 2

Countdown to Testing Weeks 3, 4

DAY 1	DAY 2	DAY 3	DAY 4	DAY 5
2-1 Lesson	2-2 Lesson	2-3 Lesson	2-3 Hands-On Lab Ready to Go On? Focus on Problem Solving	2-4 Lesson
DAY 6	**DAY 7**	**DAY 8**	**DAY 9**	**DAY 10**
2-5 Lesson	2-5 Lesson 2-6 Lesson	2-6 Lesson 2-7 Lesson	2-7 Lesson 2-8 Lesson	2-8 Lesson Ready to Go On? Multi-Step Test Prep
DAY 11	**DAY 12**	**DAY 13**		
EXTENSION	CHAPTER 2 REVIEW	CHAPTER 2 TEST		

Pacing Guide for 90-Minute Classes

Chapter 2

DAY 1	DAY 2	DAY 3	DAY 4	DAY 5
2-1 Lesson 2-2 Lesson	2-3 Lesson 2-3 Hands-On Lab Ready to Go On? Focus on Problem Solving	2-4 Lesson 2-5 Lesson	2-5 Lesson 2-6 Lesson 2-7 Lesson	2-7 Lesson 2-8 Lesson Ready to Go On? Multi-Step Test Prep
DAY 6	**DAY 7**			
EXTENSION CHAPTER 2 REVIEW	CHAPTER 2 TEST			

ONGOING ASSESSMENT and INTERVENTION

	DIAGNOSE	PRESCRIBE
Assess Prior Knowledge	**Before Chapter 2**	
	Diagnose readiness for the chapter.	Prescribe intervention.
	Are You Ready? SE p. 51	***Are You Ready? Intervention*** Skills 34, 36, 38
Formative Assessment	**Before Every Lesson**	
	Diagnose readiness for the lesson.	Prescribe intervention.
	Warm Up TE, every lesson	**Skills Bank** SE pp. 749–761
		Reteach CRB, Chapters 1–2
	During Every Lesson	
	Diagnose understanding of lesson concepts.	Prescribe intervention.
	Think and Discuss SE, every lesson	***Questioning Strategies*** pp. 15–30
	Write About It SE, lesson exercises	**Reading Strategies** CRB, every lesson
	Journal TE, lesson exercises	***Success for ELL*** pp. 15–30
	After Every Lesson	
	Diagnose mastery of lesson concepts.	Prescribe intervention.
	Lesson Quiz TE, every lesson	**Reteach** CRB, every lesson
	Test Prep SE, every lesson	**Problem Solving** CRB, every lesson
	Test and Practice Generator	**Test Prep Doctor** TE, lesson exercises
		***Homework Help* Online**
	Before Chapter 2 Testing	
	Diagnose mastery of concepts in the chapter.	Prescribe intervention.
	Ready to Go On? SE pp. 68, 88	***Ready to Go On? Intervention***
	Focus on Problem Solving SE p. 69	**Scaffolding Questions** TE p. 89
	Multi-Step Test Prep SE p. 89	
	Section Quizzes AR pp. 25–26	
	Test and Practice Generator 	
	Before High Stakes Testing	
	Diagnose mastery of benchmark concepts.	Prescribe intervention.
	CRCT Prep SE pp. 98–99	***CRCT Prep Workbook***
	***CRCT Prep* CD-ROM**	
Summative Assessment	**After Chapter 2**	
	Check mastery of chapter concepts.	Prescribe intervention.
	Multiple-Choice Tests (Forms A, B, C)	**Reteach** CRB, every lesson
	Free-Response Tests (Forms A, B, C)	***Lesson Tutorial Videos*** Chapter 2
	Performance Assessment AR pp. 27–40	
	Test and Practice Generator	
	Check mastery of benchmark concepts.	Prescribe intervention.
	CRCT	***CRCT Prep Workbook***

KEY: **SE** = *Student Edition* **TE** = *Teacher's Edition* **CRB** = *Chapter Resource Book* **AR** = *Assessment Resources* Available on CD-ROM Available online

Supporting the Teacher

Chapter 2 Resource Book

Practice A, B, C
pp. 3–5, 11–13, 19–21, 27–29, 35–37, 43–45, 51–53, 59–61

Reading Strategies ELL
pp. 9, 17, 25, 33, 41, 49, 57, 65

Puzzles, Twisters, and Teasers
pp. 10, 18, 26, 34, 42, 50, 58, 66

Reteach
pp. 6, 14, 22, 30, 38, 46, 54, 62

Problem Solving
pp. 8, 16, 24, 32, 40, 48, 56, 64

Challenge
pp. 7, 15, 23, 31, 39, 47, 55, 63

Parent Letter pp. 1–2

Transparencies

Lesson Transparencies, Volume 1 .... Chapter 2
- Teaching Tools
- Warm Ups
- Problem of the Day
- Teaching Transparencies
- Lesson Quizzes

Know-It Notebook .... Chapter 2
- Additional Examples
- Graphic Organizers
- Vocabulary
- Chapter Review
- Foldnotes
- Big Ideas

Alternate Openers: Explorations .... pp. 8–15

Countdown to CRCT .... pp. 5–8

Teacher Tools

Power Presentations®
Complete PowerPoint® presentations for Chapter 2 lessons

Lesson Tutorial Videos® SPANISH
Holt authors Ed Burger and Freddie Renfro present tutorials to support the Chapter 2 lessons.

One-Stop Planner® SPANISH
Easy access to all Chapter 2 resources and assessments, as well as software for lesson planning, test generation, and puzzle creation

IDEA Works!®
Key Chapter 2 resources and assessments modified to address special learning needs

Lesson Plans .... pp. 8–15

Questioning Strategies .... pp. 15–30

Solutions Key .... Chapter 2

Interdisciplinary Posters and Worksheets .... Chapter 2

TechKeys

Lab Resources

Project Teacher Support

Parent Resources 

Workbooks

Homework and Practice Workbook SPANISH
Teacher's Edition .... pp. 8–15

Know-It Notebook
Teacher's Guide .... Chapter 2

Problem Solving Workbook SPANISH
Teacher's Guide .... pp. 8–15

CRCT Prep Workbook
Teacher's Guide

Technology Highlights for the Teacher

 **Power Presentations**

Dynamic presentations to engage students. Complete PowerPoint® presentations for every lesson in Chapter 2.

2-1 Solving One-Step Equations

Isolate a variable by using inverse operations which "undo" operations on the variable.

An equation is like a balanced scale. To keep the balance, perform the same operation on both sides.

Inverse Operations	
Operation	**Inverse Operation**
Addition	Subtraction
Subtraction	Addition

 **One-Stop Planner** SPANISH

Easy access to Chapter 2 resources and assessments. Includes lesson-planning, test-generation, and puzzle-creation software.

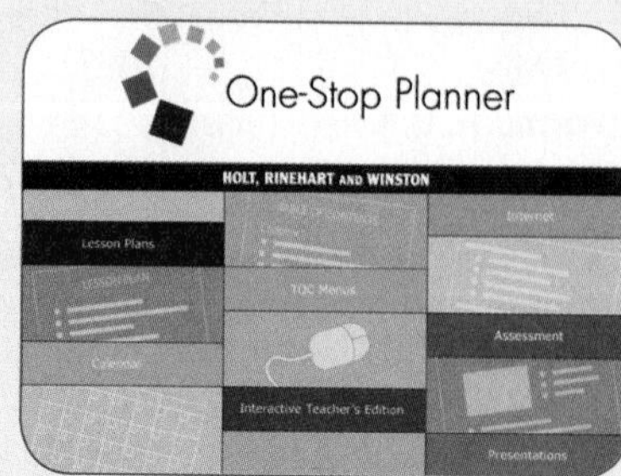

Premier Online Edition SPANISH

Chapter 2 includes Tutorial Videos, Lesson Activities, Lesson Quizzes, Homework Help, and Chapter Project.

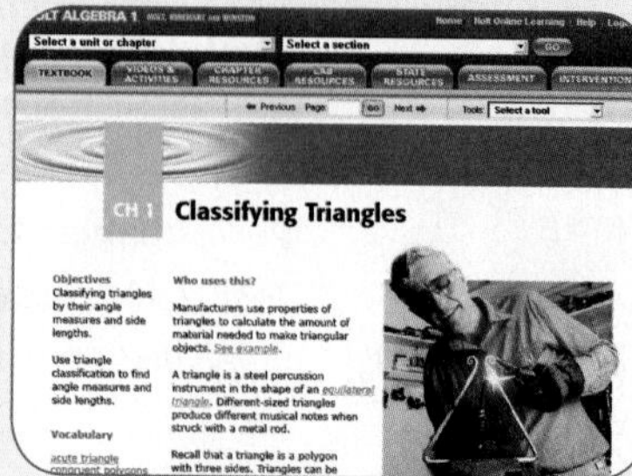

KEY: **SE** = *Student Edition* **TE** = *Teacher's Edition*  English Language Learners  Spanish version available  Available on CD-ROM

Reaching All Learners

Resources for All Learners

Hands-On Lab Activities ... Chapter 2
Technology Lab Activities ... Chapter 2
Homework and Practice Workbook SPANISH ... pp. 8–15
Know-It Notebook SPANISH ... Chapter 2
Problem Solving Workbook SPANISH ... pp. 8–15

DEVELOPING LEARNERS

Practice A ... CRB, every lesson
Reteach ... CRB, every lesson
Inclusion ... TE pp. 71, 79
Questioning Strategies ... pp. 15–30
Modified Chapter 2 Resources ... *IDEA Works!*
Homework Help Online

ON-LEVEL LEARNERS

Practice B ... CRB, every lesson
Puzzles, Twisters, and Teasers ... CRB, every lesson
Multiple Representations ... TE p. 90
Cognitive Strategies ... TE pp. 63, 82

ADVANCED LEARNERS

Practice C ... CRB, every lesson
Challenge ... CRB, every lesson
Extension ... TE pp. 53, 89, 92, 93
Critical Thinking ... TE p. 71

English Language Learners

ENGLISH LANGUAGE LEARNERS

Are You Ready? Vocabulary ... SE p. 51
Vocabulary Connections ... SE p. 52
Lesson Vocabulary ... SE, every lesson
Vocabulary Review ... SE p. 94
English Language Learners ... TE pp. 53, 58, 74, 101
Reading Strategies ... CRB, every lesson
Success for English Language Learners ... pp. 15–30
Multilingual Glossary

Reaching All Learners Through...

Inclusion ... TE pp. 71, 79
Visual Cues ... TE p. 82
Kinesthetic Experience ... TE p. 86
Concrete Manipulatives ... TE p. 75
Multiple Representations ... TE p. 90
Cognitive Strategies ... TE pp. 63, 82
Cooperative Learning ... TE p. 55
Modeling ... TE p. 75
Critical Thinking ... TE p. 71
Test Prep Doctor ... TE pp. 57, 61, 65, 73, 77, 84, 98
Common Error Alerts ... TE pp. 61, 63, 71, 73, 75, 79, 82, 86, 91
Scaffolding Questions ... TE p. 89

Technology Highlights for Reaching All Learners

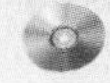

Lesson Tutorial Videos SPANISH

Starring Holt authors Ed Burger and Freddie Renfro! Live tutorials to support every lesson in Chapter 2.

Multilingual Glossary

Searchable glossary includes definitions in English, Spanish, Vietnamese, Chinese, Hmong, Korean, and 4 other languages.

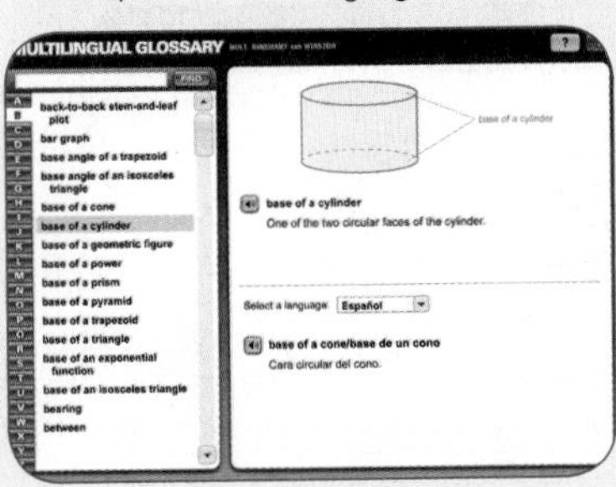

Online Interactivities

Interactive tutorials provide visually engaging alternative opportunities to learn concepts and master skills.

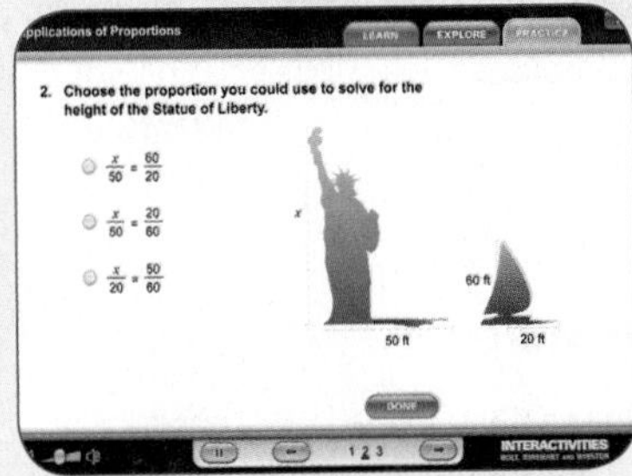

KEY: **SE** = *Student Edition* **TE** = *Teacher's Edition* **CRB** = *Chapter Resource Book*  Spanish version available  Available on CD-ROM 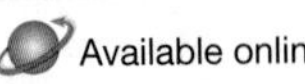 Available online

CHAPTER 2

Ongoing Assessment

Assessing Prior Knowledge

Determine whether students have the prerequisite concepts and skills for success in Chapter 2.

Are You Ready? SPANISH .... SE p. 51
Warm Up .... TE, every lesson

Test Preparation

Provide review and practice for Chapter 2 and standardized tests.

Multi-Step Test Prep .... SE p. 91
Study Guide: Review .... SE pp. 94–96
Standardized Test Prep .... SE pp. 98–99
Countdown to CRCT Transparencies .... pp. 5–8
CRCT Prep Workbook
***CRCT Prep* CD-ROM**
IDEA Works!

Alternative Assessment

Assess students' understanding of Chapter 2 concepts and combined problem-solving skills.

Chapter 2 Project .... SE p. 50
Performance Assessment SPANISH .... AR pp. 59–60
Portfolio Assessment SPANISH .... AR p. xxxiv

Daily Assessment

Provide formative assessment for each day of Chapter 2.

Questioning Strategies .... pp. 15–30
Think and Discuss .... SE, every lesson
Write About It .... SE, lesson exercises
Journal .... TE, lesson exercises
Lesson Quiz .... TE, every lesson
Modified Lesson Quizzes .... *IDEA Works!*

Weekly Assessment

Provide formative assessment for each week of Chapter 2.

Focus on Problem Solving .... SE p. 69
Multi-Step Test Prep .... SE p. 91
Ready to Go On? SPANISH .... SE pp. 68, 90
Cumulative Assessment .... SE pp. 98–99
Test and Practice Generator SPANISH .... *One-Stop Planner*

Formal Assessment

Provide summative assessment of Chapter 2 mastery.

Section Quizzes SPANISH .... AR pp. 25–26
Chapter 2 Test .... SE p. 97
Chapter Test (Levels A, B, C) SPANISH .... AR pp. 27–38
• Multiple Choice • Free Response
Cumulative Test SPANISH .... AR pp. 41–44
Test and Practice Generator SPANISH .... *One-Stop Planner*
Modified Chapter 2 Test .... *IDEA Works!*

Technology Highlights for Ongoing Assessment

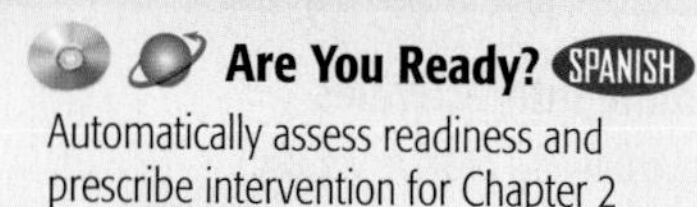

Automatically assess readiness and prescribe intervention for Chapter 2 prerequisite skills.

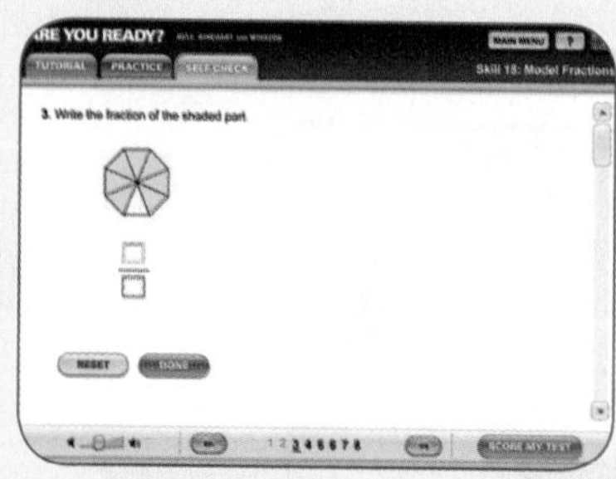

Automatically assess understanding of and prescribe intervention for Sections 2A and 2B.

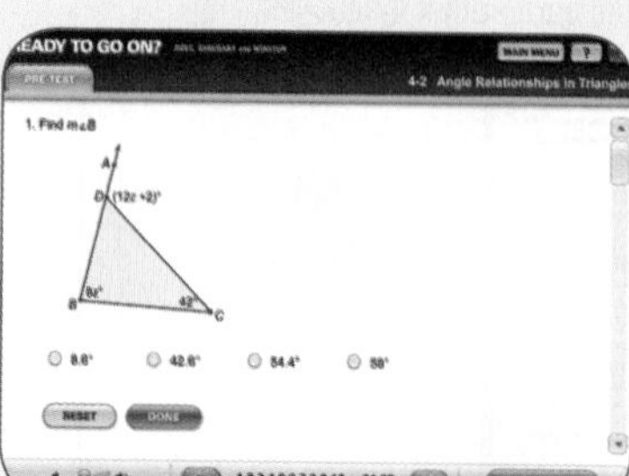

Test and Practice Generator SPANISH

Use Chapter 2 problem banks to create assessments and worksheets to print out or deliver online. Includes dynamic problems.

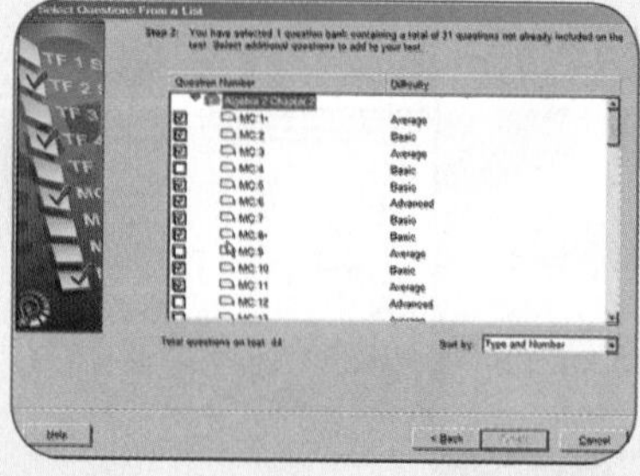

KEY: **SE** = *Student Edition* **TE** = *Teacher's Edition* **AR** = *Assessment Resources*  Spanish version available  Available on CD-ROM 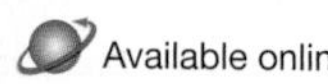 Available online

Formal Assessment

Three levels (A, B, C) of multiple-choice and free-response chapter tests are available in the *Assessment Resources.*

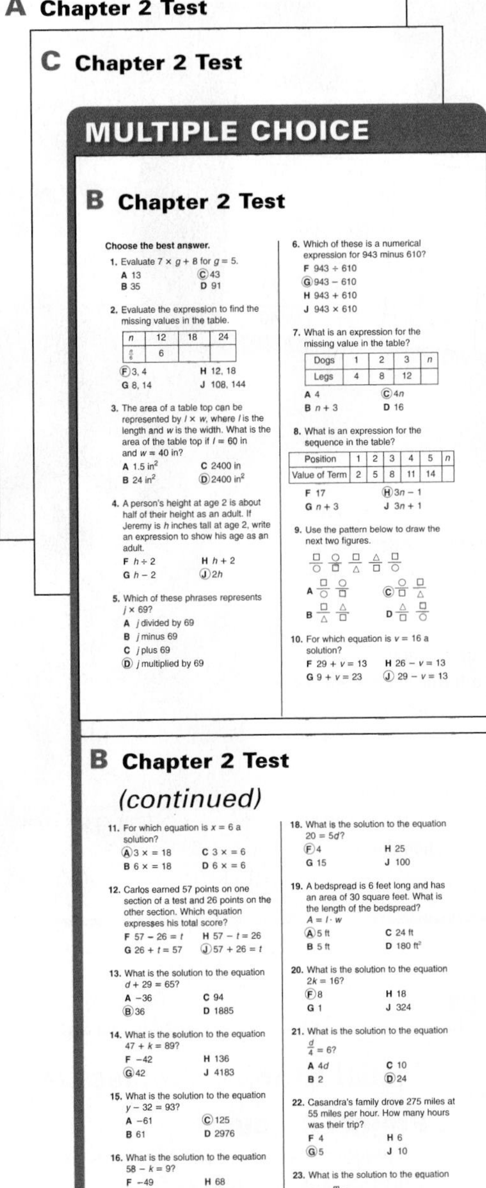

A Chapter 2 Test

C Chapter 2 Test

MULTIPLE CHOICE

B Chapter 2 Test

Choose the best answer.

1. Evaluate 7 × g + 8 for g = 5.
A 13 (C) 43
B 35 D 91

2. Evaluate the expression to find the missing values in the table.

n	12	18	24
$\frac{n}{2}$	6		

(F) 3, 4 H 12, 18
G 8, 14 J 108, 144

3. The area of a table top can be represented by l × w, where l is the length and w is the width. What is the area of the table top if l = 60 in and w = 40 in?
A 1.5 in² C 2400 in
B 24 in² (D) 2400 in²

4. A person's height at age 2 is about half of their height as an adult. If Jeremy is h inches tall at age 2, write an expression to show his age as an adult.
F h ÷ 2 H h + 2
G h − 2 (J) 2h

5. Which of these phrases represents j × 69?
A j divided by 69
B j minus 69
C j plus 69
(D) j multiplied by 69

6. Which of these is a numerical expression for 943 minus 610?
F 943 ÷ 610
(G) 943 − 610
H 943 + 610
J 943 × 610

7. What is an expression for the missing value in the table?

Dogs	1	2	3	n
Legs	4	8	12	

A 4 (C) 4n
B n + 3 D 16

8. What is an expression for the sequence in the table?

Position	1	2	3	4	5	n
Value of Term	2	5	8	11	14	

F 17 (H) 3n − 1
G n + 3 J 3n + 1

9. Use the pattern below to draw the next two figures.

10. For which equation is v = 16 a solution?
F 29 + v = 13 H 26 − v = 13
G 9 + v = 23 (J) 29 − v = 13

B Chapter 2 Test

(continued)

11. For which equation is x = 6 a solution?
(A) 3 × = 18 C 3 × = 6
B 6 × = 18 D 6 × = 6

12. Carlos earned 57 points on one section of a test and 26 points on the other section. Which equation expresses his total score?
F 57 − 26 = t H 57 − t = 26
G 26 + t = 57 (J) 57 + 26 = t

13. What is the solution to the equation d + 29 = 65?
A −36 C 94
(B) 36 D 1885

14. What is the solution to the equation 47 + k = 89?
F −42 H 136
(G) 42 J 4183

15. What is the solution to the equation y − 32 = 93?
A −61 (C) 125
B 61 D 2976

16. What is the solution to the equation 58 − k = 9?
F −49 H 68
(G) 49 J 522

17. Sara has a 13 ft. long canoe. Mike's canoe is 15 ft. long. Which equation shows how much longer Mike's canoe is?
(A) 15 − 13 = c C 13 − c = 15
B 15 + 13 = c D 15 + c = 13

18. What is the solution to the equation 20 = 5d?
(F) 4 H 25
G 15 J 100

19. A bedspread is 6 feet long and has an area of 30 square feet. What is the length of the bedspread? A = l · w
(A) 5 ft C 24 ft
B 5 ft D 180 ft²

20. What is the solution to the equation 2k = 16?
(F) 8 H 18
G 1 J 324

21. What is the solution to the equation $\frac{d}{4} = 6$?
A 4d C 10
B 2 (D) 24

22. Casandra's family drove 275 miles at 55 miles per hour. How many hours was their trip?
F 4 H 6
(G) 5 J 10

23. What is the solution to the equation $26 = \frac{m}{2}$?
A 2m C 28
B 24 (D) 52

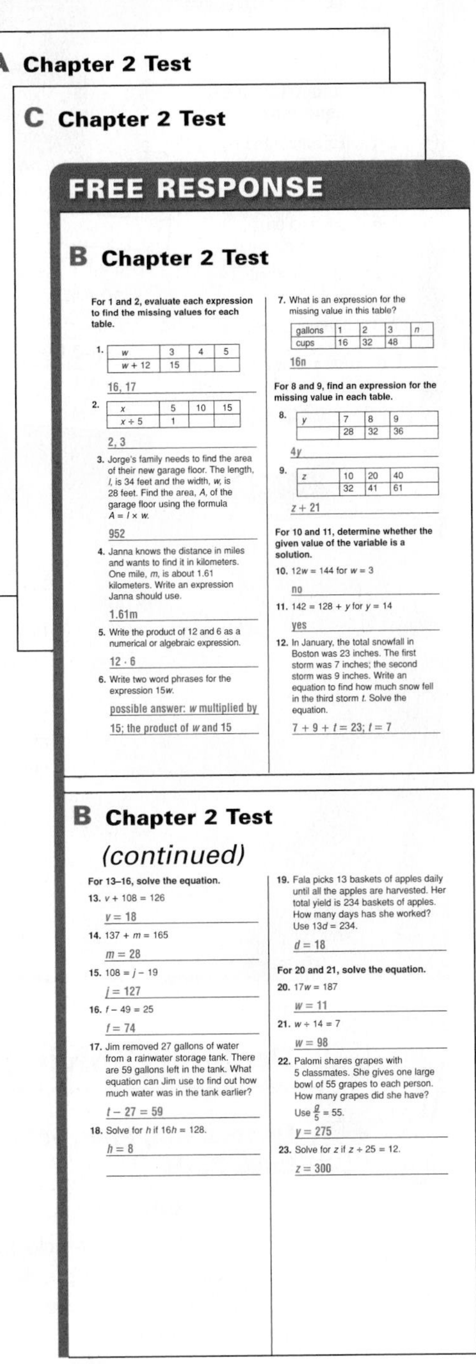

A Chapter 2 Test

C Chapter 2 Test

FREE RESPONSE

B Chapter 2 Test

For 1 and 2, evaluate each expression to find the missing values for each table.

1.

w	3	4	5
w + 12	15		

16, 17

2.

x	5	10	15
x ÷ 5	1		

2, 3

3. Jorge's family needs to find the area of their new garage floor. The length, l, is 34 feet and the width, w, is 28 feet. Find the area, A, of the garage floor using the formula A = l × w.
952

4. Janna knows the distance in miles and wants to find it in kilometers. One mile, m, is about 1.61 kilometers. Write an expression Janna should use.
1.61m

5. Write the product of 12 and 6 as a numerical or algebraic expression.
12 · 6

6. Write two word phrases for the expression 15w.
possible answer: w multiplied by 15; the product of w and 15

7. What is an expression for the missing value in this table?

gallons	1	2	3	n
cups	16	32	48	

16n

For 8 and 9, find an expression for the missing value in each table.

8.

y	7	8	9
	28	32	36

4y

9.

z	10	20	40
	32	41	61

z + 21

For 10 and 11, determine whether the given value of the variable is a solution.

10. 12w = 144 for w = 3
no

11. 142 = 128 + y for y = 14
yes

12. In January, the total snowfall in Boston was 23 inches. The first storm was 7 inches; the second storm was 9 inches. Write an equation to find how much snow fell in the third storm t. Solve the equation.
7 + 9 + t = 23; t = 7

B Chapter 2 Test

(continued)

For 13–16, solve the equation.

13. v + 108 = 126
v = 18

14. 137 + m = 165
m = 28

15. 108 = j − 19
j = 127

16. f − 49 = 25
f = 74

17. Jim removed 27 gallons of water from a rainwater storage tank. There are 59 gallons left in the tank. What equation can Jim use to find out how much water was in the tank earlier?
t − 27 = 59

18. Solve for h if 16h = 128.
h = 8

19. Fala picks 13 baskets of apples daily until all the apples are harvested. Her total yield is 234 baskets of apples. How many days has she worked? Use 13d = 234.
d = 18

For 20 and 21, solve the equation.

20. 17w = 187
w = 11

21. w ÷ 14 = 7
w = 98

22. Palomi shares grapes with 5 classmates. She gives one large bowl of 55 grapes to each person. How many grapes did she have? Use $\frac{g}{5} = 55$.
y = 275

23. Solve for z if z ÷ 25 = 12.
z = 300

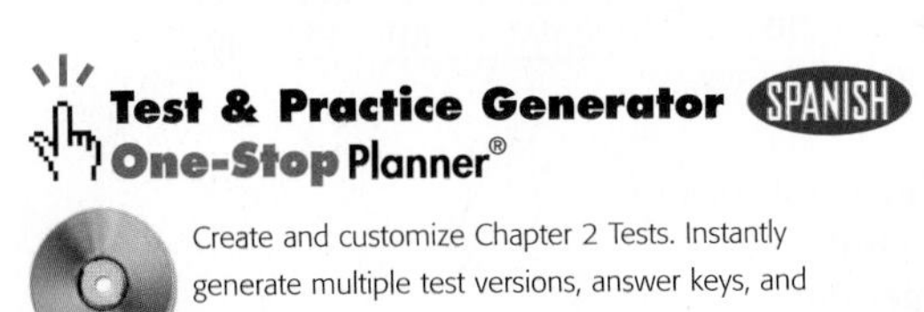

Create and customize Chapter 2 Tests. Instantly generate multiple test versions, answer keys, and Spanish versions of test items.

CHAPTER 2

Why Learn This?

Tell students that variables are used to take the place of quantities that change. For example, the number of cars heading north changes from one time period to the next. A traffic engineer might use a variable to represent the number of cars heading north and then use that variable in an equation to determine the timing of stoplights.

Using Data

To begin the study of this chapter, have students:

- Determine the number of cars heading east between noon and 2 P.M. 61
- Find the total number of cars passing through the intersection between 6 A.M. and 8 A.M. 255
- Offer suggestions as to why 114 cars head north during the morning rush hour, but only 11 head north during the evening rush hour. Possible answer: The intersection is located south of a city or other cluster of businesses.

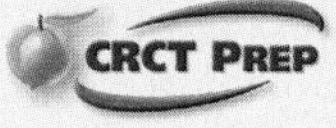

CRCT PREP On page 98, students will find cumulative CRCT practice.

CHAPTER 2

Introduction to Algebra

CRCT PREP

go.hrw.com
Chapter Project Online
KEYWORD: MR7 Ch2

Number of Cars Traveling in Each Direction

	North	South	East	West
6–8 A.M.	114	36	48	57
8–10 A.M.	97	52	57	52
10 A.M.–noon	35	24	65	56
noon–2 P.M.	23	109	61	56
2–4 P.M.	18	138	70	72
4–6 P.M.	11	54	47	40

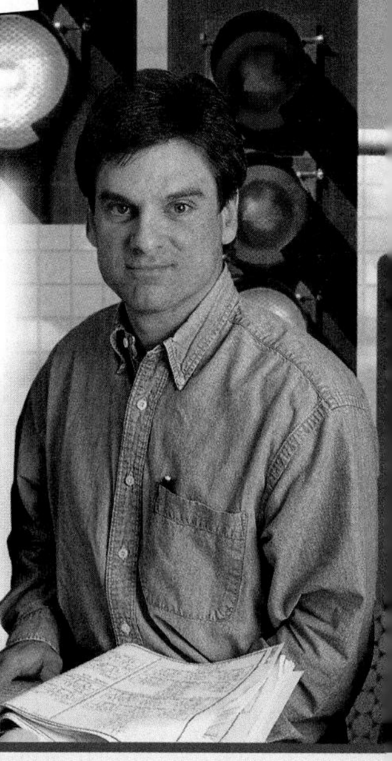

Career *Traffic Engineer*

Have you ever wondered why traffic moves quickly through one intersection but slowly through another? Traffic engineers program stoplights so that vehicles can move smoothly through intersections. There are many variables at a traffic intersection—the number of vehicles that pass, the time of day, and the direction in which each vehicle travels are examples. Traffic engineers use this information to control the timing of stoplights. The table lists traffic movement through a given intersection during a given weekday.

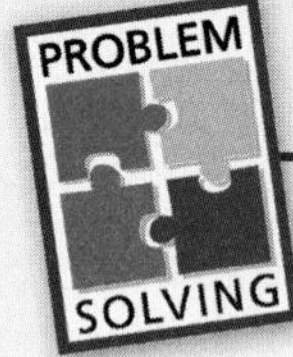

PROBLEM SOLVING

Problem Solving Project

Understand, Plan, Solve, and Look Back

Have students:

- Complete the Vehicle Travel worksheet to use simple equations to help them estimate amounts of traffic flow.
- Make a table listing the variables that would influence the pattern of stoplights at a corner. How do these variables help determine how long the red and green lights should be on?
- Research an intersection, what do they notice about the number of cars and trucks that enter the intersection at various times?

Social Studies Connection

Project Resources

All project resources for teachers and students are provided online.

Materials:

- Vehicle Travel worksheet

go.hrw.com
Project Teacher Support
KEYWORD: MR7 PSProject2

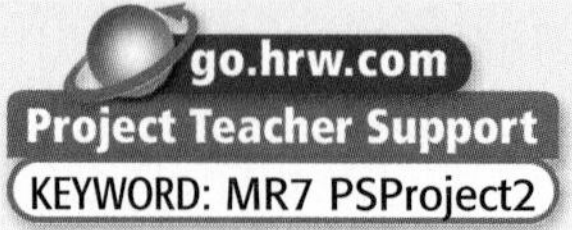

ARE YOU READY?

Vocabulary

Choose the best term from the list to complete each sentence.

1. Multiplication is the __?__ of division. inverse
2. The __?__ of 12 and 3 is 36. product
3. The __?__ of 12 and 3 is 15. sum
4. Addition, subtraction, multiplication, and division are called __?__. operations
5. The answer to a division problem is called the __?__. quotient

dividend
factor
inverse
operations
product
quotient
sum

Complete these exercises to review skills you will need for this chapter.

Multiplication Facts

Multiply.

6. 7 × 4 28 **7.** 8 × 9 72 **8.** 9 × 6 54 **9.** 7 × 7 49

10. 6 × 5 30 **11.** 3 × 8 24 **12.** 5 × 5 25 **13.** 2 × 9 18

Division Facts

Divide.

14. 64 ÷ 8 8 **15.** 63 ÷ 9 7 **16.** 56 ÷ 7 8 **17.** 54 ÷ 6 9

18. 49 ÷ 7 7 **19.** 30 ÷ 5 6 **20.** 32 ÷ 4 8 **21.** 18 ÷ 3 6

Whole Number Operations

Add, subtract, multiply, or divide.

22. 28 + 15 = 43 **23.** 71 + 38 = 109 **24.** 1,218 + 430 = 1,648 **25.** 2,218 + 1,135 = 3,353

26. 72 − 35 = 37 **27.** 98 − 45 = 53 **28.** 1,642 − 249 = 1,393 **29.** 3,408 − 1,649 = 1,759

30. 6 × 13 78 **31.** 8 × 15 120 **32.** 16 × 22 352 **33.** 20 × 35 700

34. 9)72 8 **35.** 7)84 12 **36.** 16)112 7 **37.** 23)1,472 64

ARE YOU READY? CHAPTER 2

Organizer

Objective: Assess students' understanding of prerequisite skills.

Prerequisite Skills

Multiplication Facts
Division Facts
Whole Number Operations

Assessing Prior Knowledge

INTERVENTION 

Diagnose and Prescribe

Use this page to determine whether intervention is necessary or whether enrichment is appropriate.

Resources

 ***Are You Ready? Intervention and Enrichment* Worksheets**

 ***Are You Ready?* CD-ROM**

 ***Are You Ready?* Online**

my.hrw.com

ARE YOU READY?
Diagnose and Prescribe

NO INTERVENE

Prerequisite Skill	*Are You Ready? Intervention*, Chapter 2 — Worksheets	CD-ROM	Online
Multiplication Facts	Skill 36	Activity 36	Diagnose and Prescribe Online
Division Facts	Skill 38	Activity 38	
Whole Number Operations	Skill 34	Activity 34	

YES ENRICH

***Are You Ready? Enrichment*, Chapter 2**
Worksheets
CD-ROM
Online

CHAPTER 2 Study Guide: Preview

Organizer

Objective: Help students organize the new concepts they will learn in Chapter 2.

Online Edition
Multilingual Glossary

Resources

PuzzlePro®
One-Stop Planner®

***Multilingual Glossary* Online**

go.hrw.com
KEYWORD: MR7 Glossary

Answers to *Vocabulary Connections*

Possible answers:

1. An algebraic expression contains variables.
2. If it is a constant, it does not change, even if it is in an expression.
3. A variable in an expression can be assigned any value.
4. an equal sign

CHAPTER 2

Study Guide: Preview

Where You've Been

Previously, you

- wrote numerical expressions involving whole numbers.
- solved problems using addition, subtraction, multiplication, and division of whole numbers.

In This Chapter

You will study

- writing algebraic expressions involving whole numbers.
- using addition, subtraction, multiplication, and division to solve one-step equations involving whole numbers.
- determining whether a number is a solution to an equation.

Where You're Going

You can use the skills learned in this chapter

- to solve one-step equations involving decimals and fractions.
- to solve one-step inequalities.

Key Vocabulary/Vocabulario

algebraic expression	expresión algebraica
constant	constante
equation	ecuación
solution of an equation	solución de una ecuación
variable	variable

Vocabulary Connections

To become familiar with some of the vocabulary terms in the chapter, consider the following. You may refer to the chapter, the glossary, or a dictionary if you like.

1. *Algebra* is a type of math that uses letters to represent numbers. The word *algebraic* means "relating to algebra." What do you think an **algebraic expression** contains?
2. When something is *constant,* it does not change. If there is a **constant** in an expression, do you think the number changes? Explain.
3. When something is *variable,* it is able to vary, or change. What do you think a **variable** in an expression is able to do?
4. An *equation* shows that two expressions are equal. What mathematical symbol would you expect to see in an **equation**?

Study Guide: Preview

Grade 6 CRCT GPS

M6A3. **Students will evaluate algebraic expressions, including those with exponents, and solve simple one-step equations using each of the four basic operations.**	

****Georgia Mathematics Performance Standards*** **statements are written out completely on pp. GA28–GA35.**

Writing Strategy: Use Your Own Words

Sometimes when you are reading about a new math concept for the first time from a textbook, the concept is difficult to understand.

As you go through each lesson, do the following:

- Look for the key ideas.
- Rewrite explanations given as paragraphs as steps or a list.
- Add an example when possible.

What Lupe Reads

To order numbers, you can compare them using place value and then write them in order from least to greatest.

What Lupe Writes

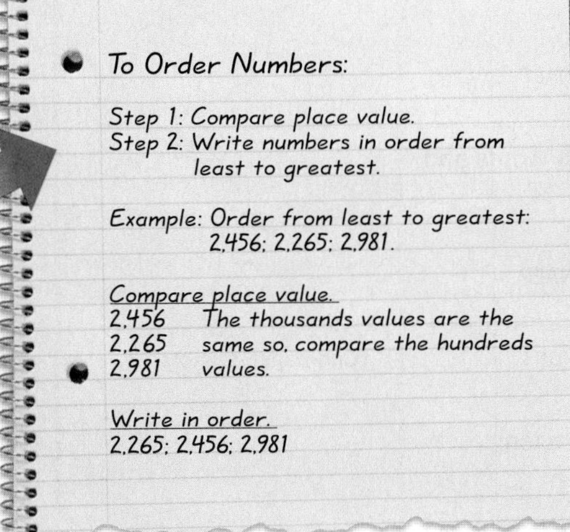

To Order Numbers:
Step 1: Compare place value.
Step 2: Write numbers in order from least to greatest.
Example: Order from least to greatest: 2,456; 2,265; 2,981.
Compare place value.
2,456 The thousands values are the
2,265 same so, compare the hundreds
2,981 values.
Write in order.
2,265; 2,456; 2,981

Reading and Writing Math

Try This

Rewrite the paragraph in your own words.

1. Sometimes in math you do not need an exact answer. Instead, you can use an estimate. Estimates are close to the exact answer but are usually easier and faster to find. When estimating, you can round the numbers in the problem to compatible numbers. Compatible numbers are close to the numbers in the problem, and they can help you do math mentally.

Grade 6 CRCT GPS

Standards	2-1	2-2	2-3	LAB 2-3	2-4	2-5	2-6	2-7	2-8	Ext.
M6A3	★	★	★	★	★	★	★	★	★	
M6P1		★				★	★	★	★	
M6P4					★					
M6P5	★	★	★	★	★	★	★			★

Reading and Writing Math

Organizer

Objective: Help students apply strategies to understand and retain key concepts.

Online Edition

Resources

Chapter 2 Resource Book
Reading Strategies

ENGLISH LANGUAGE LEARNERS

Writing Strategy: Use Your Own Words

Discuss Writing notes for yourself is like having a translation done to better understand another language. Students benefit from writing, in their own words, what they have just read.

Extend As students work through Chapter 2, have them use their own words to write new math concepts that are introduced. Before the end of class, have volunteers read what they have written.

Answers to *Try This*

Possible answer

1. Sometimes you need a close guess. To estimate, use numbers that are close to the ones you are working with but are easier to combine.

SECTION **2A**

Understanding Variables and Expressions

One-Minute Section Planner

Lesson	Materials	MiC and Lab Resources
Lesson 2-1 Variables and Expressions • Identify and evaluate expressions. ☑ CRCT ☑ SAT-10 ☑ ITBS ☑ CTBS ☑ NAEP		**MiC:** ***Comparing Quantities*** pp. 6–9 ***Technology Lab Activities*** 2-1
Lesson 2-2 Problem Solving Skill: Translate Between Words and Math • Translate between words and math. ☑ CRCT ☑ SAT-10 ☑ ITBS ☑ CTBS ☑ NAEP		**MiC:** ***Comparing Quantities*** pp. 28–31
Lesson 2-3 Translating Between Tables and Expressions • Write expressions for tables and sequences. **2-3 Hands-On Lab** Explore Area and Perimeter of Rectangles • Use grid paper to model the area and perimeter of different rectangles. ☑ CRCT ☑ SAT-10 ☑ ITBS ☑ CTBS ☑ NAEP	Grid paper, scissors	***Hands-On Lab Activities*** 2-3

MK = *Manipulatives Kit*

Mathematics in Context

The unit ***Comparing Quantities*** from the *Mathematics in Context* © 2006 series can be used with Section 2A. See Section Planner above for suggestions for integrating *MiC* with *Holt Mathematics*.

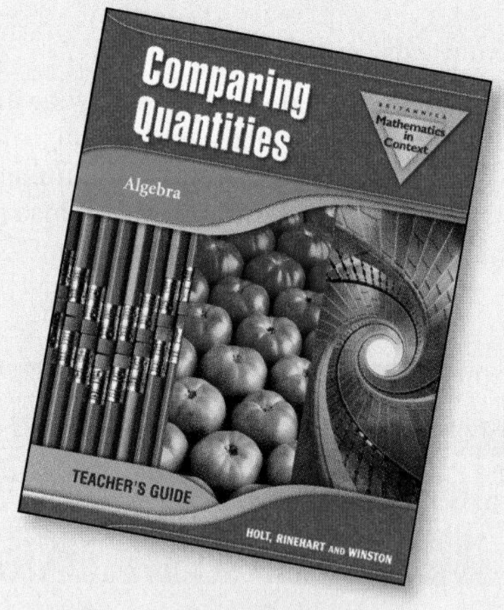

Section Overview

Professional Development

Evaluating Algebraic Expressions — Lesson 2-1

Why? Evaluating algebraic expressions allows you to give meaning to symbolic representations, such as formulas and equations.

An **algebraic expression** contains one or more variables and may contain operation symbols.

To **evaluate** an algebraic expression, substitute a number for the variable and then find the value.

Evaluate the **algebraic expression** $3x + 5$ for $x = 2$.

$3x + 5$
$3 \cdot 2 + 5$
$6 + 5$
11

The algebraic expression $3x + 5$ has the value 11 when $x = 2$.

Translating Between Words and Algebra — Lesson 2-2

Translating between words and algebra is used to solve real-world problems involving mathematics.

Operation	Action	Words	Expression	
+	Put together or combine.	• 5 added to 3 • 4 plus x • the sum of 7 and 2 • n more than 9	• $5 + 3$ • $4 + x$ • $7 + 2$ • $9 + n$	Numerical expression Algebraic expression Numerical expression Algebraic expression
−	Find how much more or how much less.	• 4 subtracted from b • 12 minus 5 • the difference of 7 and 3 • 2 less than y • take away 1 from 9	• $b - 4$ • $12 - 5$ • $7 - 3$ • $y - 2$ • $9 - 1$	Algebraic expression Numerical expression Numerical expression Algebraic expression Numerical expression
×	Put together groups of equal parts.	• t times 7 • 6 multiplied by s • the product of 4 and 3	• $t \times 7$, or $7t$ • $6 \times s$, or $6s$ • 4×3, or $(4)(3)$	Algebraic expression Algebraic expression Numerical expression
÷	Separate into equal groups.	• h divided by 2 • the quotient of 15 and 5	• $h \div 2$, or $\frac{h}{2}$ • $15 \div 5$, or $\frac{15}{5}$	Algebraic expression Numerical expression

Translating Between Tables and Expressions — Lesson 2-3

Why? Translating between tables and expressions allows students to generalize a pattern and make predictions.

Number of items	Total cost	
1	12	$1 \cdot 12 = 12$
2	24	$2 \cdot 12 = 24$
3	36	$3 \cdot 12 = 36$
4	48	$4 \cdot 12 = 48$
n	$12n$	

Position	Value of term	
1	5	$1 \cdot 3 + 2 = 5$
2	8	$2 \cdot 3 + 2 = 8$
3	11	$3 \cdot 3 + 2 = 11$
4	14	$4 \cdot 3 + 2 = 14$
n	$3n + 2$	

2-1 Organizer

Pacing: Traditional 1 day
Block $\frac{1}{2}$ day

Objective: Students identify and evaluate expressions.

GPS **M6A3**
Technology Lab
In *Technology Lab Activities*

Online Edition
Tutorial Videos, Interactivities

Countdown to CRCT Week 3

Power Presentations with PowerPoint®

Warm Up

Simplify.

1. 4 + 7 × 3 − 1 **24**

2. 87 − 15 ÷ 5 **84**

3. 6(9 + 2) + 7 **73**

4. 35 ÷ 7 × 5 **25**

Problem of the Day

How can the digits 1 through 5 be arranged in the boxes to make the greatest product?

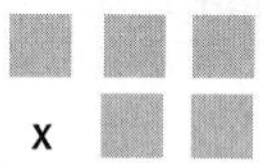

431
× 52

Also available on transparency

Math Humor

Overheard in math class:
Teacher: What is 7*Q* plus 3*Q*?
Student: 10*Q*
Teacher: You're welcome!

Georgia Performance Standards

M6A3 Students will evaluate algebraic expressions, including those with exponents, and solve simple one-step equations using each of the four basic operations.

M6P5.a Create and use representations to organize, record, and communicate mathematical ideas.

M6P5.c Use representations to model and interpret physical, social, and mathematical phenomena.

2-1 Variables and Expressions

Learn to identify and evaluate expressions.

Vocabulary
variable
constant
algebraic expression

Georgia Performance Standards

M6A3 Evaluate algebraic expressions. Also, M6P5.a, M6P5.c.

Inflation is the rise in prices that occurs over time. For example, you would have paid about \$7 in the year 2000 for something that cost only \$1 in 1950.

With this information, you can convert prices in 1950 to their equivalent prices in 2000.

1950	2000
\$1	\$7
\$2	\$14
\$3	\$21
\$*p*	\$*p* × 7

A **variable** is a letter or symbol that represents a quantity that can change. In the table above, *p* is a variable that stands for any price in 1950. A **constant** is a quantity that does not change. For example, the price of something in 2000 is always 7 times the price in 1950.

An **algebraic expression** contains one or more variables and may contain operation symbols. So *p* × 7 is an algebraic expression.

Algebraic Expressions	NOT Algebraic Expressions
150 + *y*	85 ÷ 5
35 × *w* + *z*	10 + 3 × 5

To evaluate an algebraic expression, substitute a number for the variable and then find the value.

EXAMPLE  **Evaluating Algebraic Expressions**

Evaluate each expression to find the missing values in the tables.

A

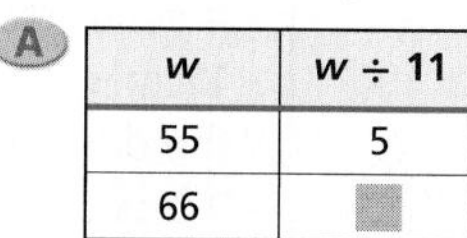

w	*w* ÷ 11
55	5
66	
77	

Substitute for w in w ÷ 11.

w = 55; 55 ÷ 11 = 5
w = 66; 66 ÷ 11 = 6
w = 77; 77 ÷ 11 = 7

The missing values are 6 and 7.

1 Introduce

Alternate Opener

EXPLORATION

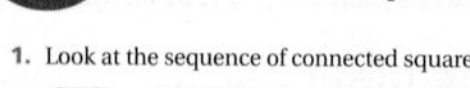

2-1 Variables and Expressions

1. Look at the sequence of connected squares.

1 + 3   1 + 3 + 3   1 + 3 + 3 + 3

a. Sketch the next two squares.
b. To complete the table for the connected squares, count the number of segments it takes to draw each square.

Number of Connected Squares	1	2	3	4	5	10	20	100
Number of Segments	4	7						

c. How can you find the number of segments if you know the number of squares?

Think and Discuss

2. **Explain** the reasoning you used to find the number of segments in one hundred connected squares.
3. **Explain** the reasoning you could use to find the number of segments in one thousand connected squares.

Motivate

List these expressions on the board: 4 + 6, 4 × 3, and 75 ÷ 5. Remind students that expressions do not contain an equal sign or an answer. Now list *x* + 6, *y* × 3, and *z* ÷ 5, and ask how these expressions are different. Explain that *x* + 6, *y* × 3, and *z* ÷ 5 are *algebraic expressions.*

Explorations and answers are provided in *Alternate Openers: Explorations Transparencies.*

Evaluate each expression to find the missing values in the tables.

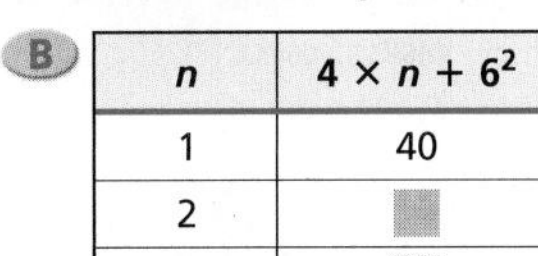

B

n	$4 \times n + 6^2$
1	40
2	
3	

Substitute for n in $4 \times n + 6^2$.
Use the order of operations.
$n = 1$; $4 \times 1 + 36 = 40$
$n = 2$; $4 \times 2 + 36 = 44$
$n = 3$; $4 \times 3 + 36 = 48$

The missing values are 44 and 48.

Writing Math

When you are multiplying a number times a variable, the number is written first. Write "3x" and not "x3." Read 3x as "three x."

You can write multiplication and division expressions without using the symbols × and ÷.

Instead of . . .	You can write . . .
$x \times 3$	$x \cdot 3$ $x(3)$ $3x$
$35 \div y$	$\frac{35}{y}$

EXAMPLE 2 Evaluating Expressions with Two Variables

A rectangle is 2 units wide. How many square units does the rectangle cover if it is 4, 5, 6, or 7 units long?

You can multiply length and width to find the number of square units. Let ℓ be length and w be width.

Make a table to help you find the number of square units for each length.

ℓ	w	$\ell \times w$
4	2	8
5	2	
6	2	
7	2	

$\ell = 4$; $4 \times 2 = 8$ square units
$\ell = 5$; $5 \times 2 = 10$ square units
$\ell = 6$; $6 \times 2 = 12$ square units
$\ell = 7$; $7 \times 2 = 14$ square units

The rectangle will cover 8, 10, 12, or 14 square units.

Check

Draw a rectangle 2 units wide. Then find the total number of units when the rectangle is 4, 5, 6, and 7 units long.

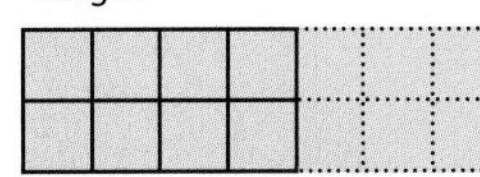

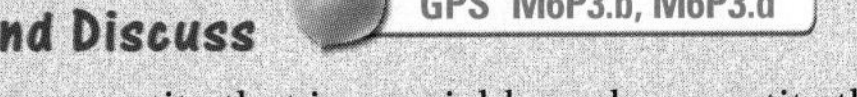

Think and Discuss GPS M6P3.b, M6P3.d

1. **Name** a quantity that is a variable and a quantity that is a constant.
2. **Explain** why $45 + x$ is an algebraic expression.

Answers to *Think and Discuss*:

1. Possible answer: Your age is a variable quantity. The number of days in a week is a constant quantity.
2. The expression contains one variable and the addition operation.

Power Presentations with PowerPoint®

Additional Examples

Example 1

Evaluate each expression to find the missing values in the tables.

A.

y	$5 \times y$
16	80
27	135
35	175

B.

z	$z \div 5 + 4^2$
20	20
45	25
60	28

Example 2

A rectangle is 4 units wide. How many square units does the rectangle cover if it is 3, 4, 5, or 6 units long?

ℓ	w	$\ell \times w$
3	4	12
4	4	16
5	4	20
6	4	24

Also available on transparency

Teaching Tip

Multiple Representations In example 2, point out that finding an expression is similar to finding a rule for a pattern. Each row individually will satisfy several possible expressions; you must find an expression that works for all rows in the table.

2 Teach

Guided Instruction

In this lesson, students learn to identify and evaluate expressions. Discuss the definitions of *variable*, *constant*, and *algebraic expression*. First, have students provide examples of algebraic and non-algebraic expressions. Then teach students to evaluate algebraic expressions by substituting given values for the variable. Next teach students to find missing expressions that will generate the sequence for a table.

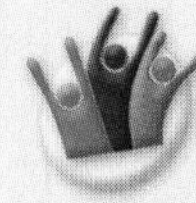

Reaching All Learners

Through Cooperative Learning

Have students work in groups to practice evaluating algebraic expressions. Have each group member write an algebraic expression. After the other group members take turns choosing numbers to substitute in the expression, have all the members evaluate for the chosen value. This process should continue until all members' expressions have been evaluated for several different values.

3 Close

Summarize

Discuss brief definitions of the new vocabulary in the lesson: *variable*, *constant*, and *algebraic expression*. Remind students that multiplication and division can be represented in different ways within an algebraic expression and that the order of operations must be followed.

2-1 Exercises

Assignment Guide

If you finished Example 1 assign:
Average 1–2, 4–5, 11–22, 24, 28–33
Advanced 1–2, 4–5, 11–22, 27–33

If you finished Example 2 assign:
Average 1–22, 28–33
Advanced 1–6, 11–33

Homework Quick Check

Quickly check key concepts.
Exercises: 4, 6, 8, 10

Math Background

François Viète (1540–1603) was a lawyer in France who devoted his spare time to mathematics. In his book *In Artem,* he introduced the idea of representing unknown quantities using vowels and constants using consonants. He also used our present symbols + and – but had no symbol for equality. To write "equals" he would use the Latin word *aequatur*.

Viète is sometimes called the Father of Algebra.

Answers

7a. 2 hr: 100–120 miles
3 hr: 150–180 miles
4 hr: 200–240 miles
5 hr: 250–300 miles

Georgia Performance Standards

M6P3.a Organize and consolidate their mathematical thinking through communication.

M6P3.c Analyze and evaluate the mathematical thinking and strategies of others.

2-1 Exercises

M6P3.a, M6P3.c

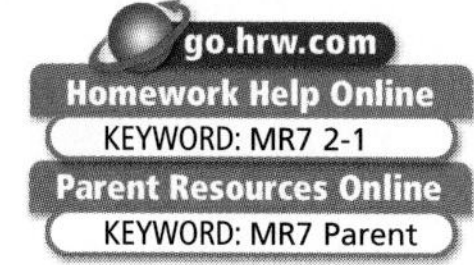

GUIDED PRACTICE

See Example 1

Evaluate each expression to find the missing values in the tables.

1.

n	$n + 7$
38	45
49	56
58	65

2.

x	$12x + 2^3$
8	104
9	116
10	128

See Example 2

3. A rectangle is 4 units wide. How many square units does the rectangle cover if it is 6, 7, 8, or 9 units long? 24; 28; 32; 36

INDEPENDENT PRACTICE

See Example 1

Evaluate each expression to find the missing values in the tables.

4.

x	$4x$
50	200
100	400
150	600

5.

n	$2n - 3^2$
10	11
16	23
17	25

See Example 2

6. A builder is designing a rectangular patio that has a length of 12 units. Find the total number of square units the patio will cover if the width is 4, 5, 6, or 7 units. 48; 60; 72; 84

PRACTICE AND PROBLEM SOLVING

Extra Practice pp. 746–7

7. Estimation Bobby drives his truck at a rate of 50 to 60 miles per hour.

a. Approximately how far can Bobby drive in 2, 3, 4, and 5 hours?

b. Bobby plans to take an 8-hour trip, which will include a 1-hour stop for lunch. What is a reasonable distance for Bobby to drive? between 350 and 420 miles

8. Multi-Step Each table in the cafeteria seats 8 people. Find the total number of people that can be seated at 7, 8, 9, and 10 tables. If the average bill per person is \$12, how much money can the cafeteria expect from 7, 8, 9, and 10 tables that have no empty seats? 56, 64; 72; 80; \$672; \$768; \$864; \$960

9. Measurement When traveling in Europe, Jessika converts the temperature given in degrees Celsius to a Fahrenheit temperature by using the expression $9x \div 5 + 32$, where x is the Celsius temperature. Find the temperature in degrees Fahrenheit when it is 0°C, 10°C, and 25°C. 32°F; 50°F; 77°F

10. Geometry To find the area of a triangle, you can use the expression $b \times h \div 2$, where b is the base of the triangle and h is its height. Find the area of a triangle with a base of 5 and a height of 6. 15

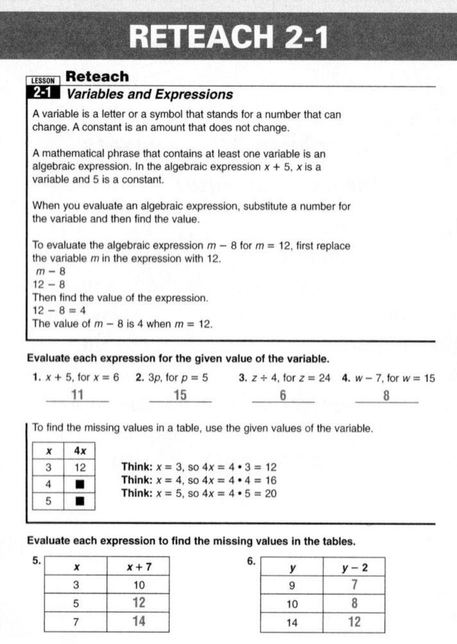

RETEACH 2-1

LESSON 2-1 **Reteach**
Variables and Expressions

A variable is a letter or a symbol that stands for a number that can change. A constant is an amount that does not change.

A mathematical phrase that contains at least one variable is an algebraic expression. In the algebraic expression $x + 5$, x is a variable and 5 is a constant.

When you evaluate an algebraic expression, substitute a number for the variable and then find the value.

To evaluate the algebraic expression $m - 8$ for $m = 12$, first replace the variable m in the expression with 12.
$m - 8$
$12 - 8$
Then find the value of the expression.
$12 - 8 = 4$
The value of $m - 8$ is 4 when $m = 12$.

Evaluate each expression for the given value of the variable.

1. $x + 5$, for $x = 6$ 11
2. $3p$, for $p = 5$ 15
3. $z \div 4$, for $z = 24$ 6
4. $w - 7$, for $w = 15$ 8

To find the missing values in a table, use the given values of the variable.

x	$4x$
3	12
4	■
5	■

Think: $x = 3$, so $4x = 4 \cdot 3 = 12$
Think: $x = 4$, so $4x = 4 \cdot 4 = 16$
Think: $x = 5$, so $4x = 4 \cdot 5 = 20$

Evaluate each expression to find the missing values in the tables.

5.

x	$x + 7$
3	10
5	12
7	14

6.

y	$y - 2$
9	7
10	8
14	12

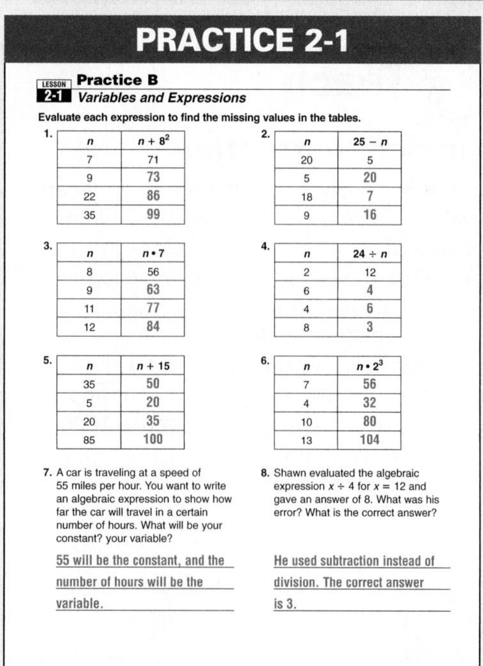

PRACTICE 2-1

LESSON 2-1 **Practice B**
Variables and Expressions

Evaluate each expression to find the missing values in the tables.

1.

n	$n + 8^2$
7	71
9	73
22	86
35	99

2.

n	$25 - n$
20	5
5	20
18	7
9	16

3.

n	$n \cdot 7$
8	56
9	63
11	77
12	84

4.

n	$24 \div n$
2	12
6	4
4	6
8	3

5.

n	$n + 15$
35	50
5	20
20	35
85	100

6.

n	$n \cdot 2^3$
7	56
4	32
10	80
13	104

7. A car is traveling at a speed of 55 miles per hour. You want to write an algebraic expression to show how far the car will travel in a certain number of hours. What will be your constant? your variable?

55 will be the constant, and the number of hours will be the variable.

8. Shawn evaluated the algebraic expression $x \div 4$ for $x = 12$ and gave an answer of 8. What was his error? What is the correct answer?

He used subtraction instead of division. The correct answer is 3.

Money

The Georgia quarter was the fourth quarter released under the 50 State Quarters® Program of the U.S. Mint.

go.hrw.com
Web Extra!
KEYWORD: MR7 Money

Evaluate each expression for the given value of the variable.

11. $3h + 2$ for $h = 10$ **32**
12. $2x^2$ for $x = 3$ **18**
13. $t - 7$ for $t = 20$ **13**
14. $4p - 3$ for $p = 20$ **77**
15. $\frac{c}{7}$ for $c = 56$ **8**
16. $10 + 2r$ for $r = 5$ **20**
17. $3x + 17$ for $x = 13$ **56**
18. $5p$ for $p = 12$ **60**
19. $s^2 - 15$ for $s = 5$ **10**
20. $14 - 2c$ for $c = 2$ **10**
21. $10x$ for $x = 11$ **110**
22. $4j + 12$ for $j = 9$ **48**

23. **Money** The zloty is the currency in Poland. In 2005, 1 U.S. dollar was worth 3 zlotys. How many zlotys were equivalent to 8 U.S. dollars? **24 zlotys**

24. Use the graph to complete the table.

Cups of Water	Number of Lemons
8	24
12	36
16	48
w	$3w$

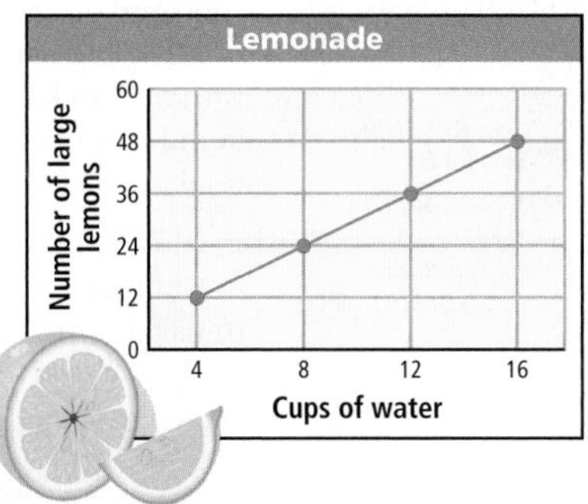

25. **What's the Error?** A student evaluated the expression $x \div 2$ for $x = 14$ and gave an answer of 28. What did the student do wrong? **The student multiplied 14 by 2 instead of dividing 14 by 2.**

26. **Write About It** How would you evaluate the expression $2x + 5$ for $x = 1, 2, 3,$ and 4? **Possible answer: Substitute each value of x into the expression and follow the order of operations.**

27. **Challenge** Using the algebraic expression $3n - 5$, what is the smallest whole-number value for n that will give you a result greater than 100? **36**

CRCT Prep • GPS Support • Spiral Review

28. **Multiple Choice** Evaluate $8m - 5$ for $m = 9$.

Ⓐ 67 Ⓑ 83 Ⓒ 84 Ⓓ 94

29. **Gridded Response** Evaluate the expression $4p + 18$ for $p = 5$. **38**

Write each expression in exponential form. (Lesson 1-3)

30. $3 \times 3 \times 3$ 3^3
31. $5 \times 5 \times 5 \times 5 \times 5 \times 5$ 5^6
32. $10 \times 10 \times 10 \times 10$ 10^4

Choose a solution method and solve. Explain your choice. (Lesson 1-6)

33. Al earns $16 per hour for his work at a factory. He works 32 hours per week and gets paid every 2 weeks. If the factory takes $105 out of each check for taxes, how much money will Al be paid? **$919**

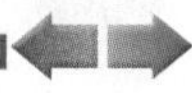

Ongoing Assessment and Intervention

Diagnose ***Before*** **the Lesson**
2-1 Warm Up, TE p. 54

Monitor ***During*** **the Lesson**
2-1 Know-It Notebook
2-1 Questioning Strategies

Assess ***After*** **the Lesson**
2-1 Lesson Quiz, TE p. 57

Test Prep Doctor In Exercise 28, remind students to follow the order of operations. The value of m should be multiplied by 8 before subtracting 5.

Journal

Have students write about situations, people, or things that are evaluated.

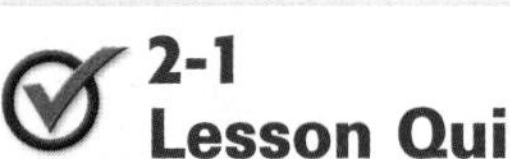

Power Presentations with PowerPoint®

2-1 Lesson Quiz

1. Evaluate the expression to find the missing values in the table.

x	$x^2 - 5$
10	95
7	44
5	20

2. A rectangle is 6 units wide. How many square units does the rectangle cover if it is 2, 3, 4, or 5 units long?

ℓ	w	$\ell \times w$
2	6	12
3	6	18
4	6	24
5	6	30

Also available on transparency

CHALLENGE 2-1

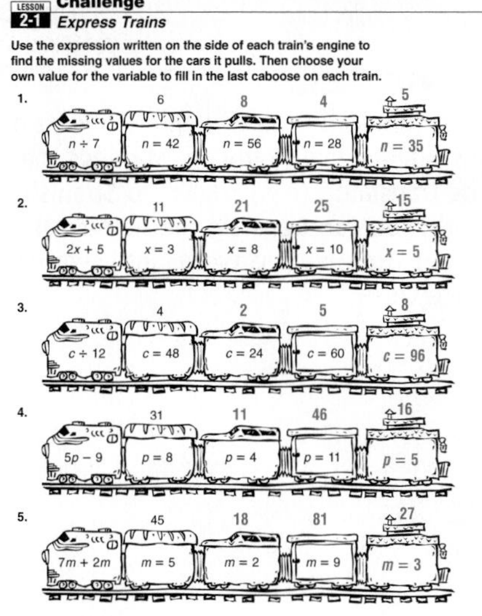

LESSON 2-1 **Challenge**
Express Trains

Use the expression written on the side of each train's engine to find the missing values for the cars it pulls. Then choose your own value for the variable to fill in the last caboose on each train.

1. $n \div 7$: $n = 42$ → 6; $n = 56$ → 8; $n = 28$ → 4; $n = 35$ → 5
2. $2x + 5$: $x = 3$ → 11; $x = 8$ → 21; $x = 10$ → 25; $x = 5$ → 15
3. $c \div 12$: $c = 48$ → 4; $c = 24$ → 2; $c = 60$ → 5; $c = 96$ → 8
4. $5p - 9$: $p = 8$ → 31; $p = 4$ → 11; $p = 11$ → 46; $p = 5$ → 16
5. $7m + 2m$: $m = 5$ → 45; $m = 2$ → 18; $m = 9$ → 81; $m = 3$ → 27

Possible answers are given on each caboose. Accept all answers that correctly match the chosen variable and the train's expression.

PROBLEM SOLVING 2-1

LESSON 2-1 **Problem Solving**
Variables and Expressions

Write the correct answer.

1. To cook 4 cups of rice, you use 8 cups of water. To cook 10 cups of rice, you use 20 cups of water. Write an expression to show how many cups of water you should use if you want to cook c cups of rice. How many cups of water should you use to cook 5 cups of rice?
2c; 10 cups of water

2. Sue earns the same amount of money for each hour that she tutors students in math. In 3 hours, she earns $27. In 8 hours, she earns $72. Write an expression to show how much money Sue earns working h hours. At this rate, how much money will Sue earn if she works 12 hours?
9h; $108

3. Bees are one of the fastest insects on Earth. They can fly 22 miles in 2 hours, and 55 miles in 5 hours. Write an expression to show how many miles a bee can fly in h hours. If a bee flies 4 hours at this speed, how many miles will it travel?
11h; 44 miles

4. A friend asks you to think of a number, triple it, and then subtract 2. Write an algebraic expression using the variable x to describe your friend's directions. Then find the value of the expression if the number you think of is 5.
3x − 2; 13

Circle the letter of the correct answer.

5. The ruble is the currency in Russia. In 2005, 1 United States dollar was worth 28 rubles. How many rubles were equivalent to 10 United States dollars?
A 28
B 38
Ⓒ 280
D 2,800

6. The peso is the currency in Mexico. In 2005, 1 United States dollar was worth 10 pesos. How many pesos were equivalent to 5 United States dollars?
F 1
G 10
H 15
Ⓙ 50

2-2 Organizer

Pacing: Traditional 1 day
Block $\frac{1}{2}$ day

Objective: Students translate between words and math.

Online Edition
Tutorial Videos, Interactivities

Countdown to CRCT Week 3

Warm Up

Evaluate each expression for $x = 9$.

1. $7 + x$ 16 **2.** $4x$ 36

3. $2x + 1$ 19 **4.** $\frac{36}{x}$ 4

Problem of the Day

Draw a square around the numbers of four adjacent days on the calendar for this month. Add all the numbers in the square and subtract four times the first number. What number do you get? 16

Also available on transparency

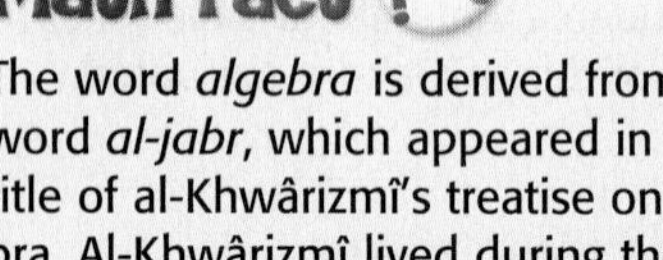

The word *algebra* is derived from the word *al-jabr*, which appeared in the title of al-Khwârizmî's treatise on algebra. Al-Khwârizmî lived during the late eighth and early ninth centuries.

2-2 Translate Between Words and Math

Problem Solving Skill

Learn to translate between words and math.

Georgia Performance Standards

M6P5.b Select, apply, and translate among mathematical representations to solve problems. Also, M6A3, M6P1.b, M6P1.c.

The earth's core is divided into two parts. The inner core is solid and dense, with a radius of 1,228 km. Let c stand for the thickness in kilometers of the liquid outer core. What is the total radius of the earth's core?

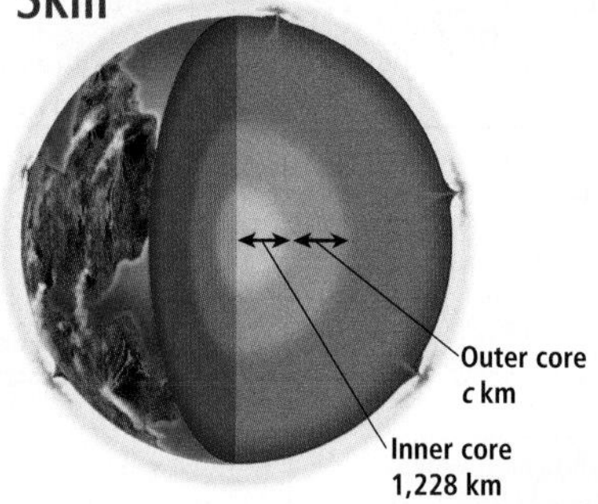

In word problems, you may need to identify the action to translate words to math.

Action	Put together or combine	Find how much more or less	Put together groups of equal parts	Separate into equal groups
Operation	Add	Subtract	Multiply	Divide

To solve this problem, you need to *put together* the measurements of the inner core and the outer core. To put things together, add.

$$1{,}228 + c$$

The total radius of the earth's core is $1{,}228 + c$ km.

EXAMPLE 1 *Social Studies Applications*

A **The Rio Grande is one of the longest rivers in the United States. It forms the border between Texas and Mexico. The Red River forms a border between Texas and Oklahoma and is 1,290 miles long. Write an expression to show how much longer the Rio Grande is than the Red River.**

To *find how much longer,* subtract the length of the Red River from the length of the Rio Grande.

$$n \quad - \quad 1{,}290$$

The Rio Grande is $n - 1{,}290$ miles longer than the Red River.

B **Let s represent the number of senators that each of the 50 states has in the U.S. Senate. Write an expression for the total number of senators.**

To *put together 50 equal groups of s,* multiply 50 times s.

$$50s$$

There are $50s$ senators in the U.S. Senate.

Georgia Performance Standards

M6A3 Students will evaluate algebraic expressions, including those with exponents, and solve simple one-step equations using each of the four basic operations.

M6P1.b Solve problems that arise in mathematics and in other contexts.

M6P1.c Apply and adapt a variety of appropriate strategies to solve problems.

M6P5.b Select, apply, and translate among mathematical representations to solve problems.

1 Introduce

Alternate Opener

EXPLORATION

2-2 Translate Between Words and Math

Drawing pictures and using formulas can help you translate between words and math.

A basketball court is 50 ft wide by 94 ft long. What is its area?

Formula for area

A = length × width

$A = 94 \times 50$

$A = 4{,}700$

Area = ? (50 ft, 94 ft)

The area is 4,700 ft^2.

In some word problems, word order may be confusing. For example, the following problems can be translated in at least two different ways.

Rewrite each problem to make it clearer.

	Word Problem	Possible Translations	Better Word Problem
1.	Write the expression "4 times x plus 6."	$4x + 6$ or $4(x + 6)$	
2.	Translate "the square root of n minus 3."	$\sqrt{n} - 3$ or $\sqrt{n - 3}$	

Think and Discuss

3. Explain what you did to rewrite numbers 1 and 2 to make them easier to translate into math.

Motivate

ENGLISH LANGUAGE LEARNERS

Discuss the word *translate* with students and have students give examples of things that can be translated (e.g., English to Spanish). Similarly, you can translate mathematical situations expressed as words into symbols, and vice versa.

Explorations and answers are provided in *Alternate Openers: Explorations Transparencies.*

There are several different ways to write math expressions with words.

Operation	+	−	×	÷
Numerical Expression	37 + 28	90 − 12	8 × 48 or 8 · 48 or (8)(48) or 8(48) or (8)48	327 ÷ 3 or $\frac{327}{3}$
Words	• 28 added to 37 • 37 plus 28 • the sum of 37 and 28 • 28 more than 37	• 12 subtracted from 90 • 90 minus 12 • the difference of 90 and 12 • 12 less than 90 • take away 12 from 90	• 8 times 48 • 48 multiplied by 8 • the product of 8 and 48 • 8 groups of 48	• 327 divided by 3 • the quotient of 327 and 3
Algebraic Expression	$x + 28$	$k - 12$	$8 \cdot w$ or $(8)(w)$ or $8w$	$n \div 3$ or $\frac{n}{3}$
Words	• 28 added to *x* • *x* plus 28 • the sum of *x* and 28 • 28 more than *x*	• 12 subtracted from *k* • *k* minus 12 • the difference of *k* and 12 • 12 less than *k* • take away 12 from *k*	• 8 times *w* • *w* multiplied by 8 • the product of 8 and *w* • 8 groups of *w*	• *n* divided by 3 • the quotient of *n* and 3

EXAMPLE 2 Translating Words into Math

Write each phrase as a numerical or algebraic expression.

A 287 plus 932

287 + 932

B b divided by 14

$b \div 14$ or $\frac{b}{14}$

EXAMPLE 3 Translating Math into Words

Write two phrases for each expression.

A $a - 45$
- a minus 45
- take away 45 from a

B (34)(7)
- the product of 34 and 7
- 34 multiplied by 7

Think and Discuss

GPS M6P3.b, M6P5.b

1. **Tell** how to write each of the following phrases as a numerical or algebraic expression: 75 less than 1,023; the product of 125 and z.
2. **Give** two examples of "$a \div 17$" expressed with words.

Power Presentations with PowerPoint®

Additional Examples

Example 1

A. Lake Superior is the largest lake in North America. Let a stand for the area in square miles of Lake Superior. Lake Erie has an area of 9,910 square miles. Write an expression to show how much larger Lake Superior is than Lake Erie.

$a - 9{,}910$

B. Let p represent the number of colored pencils in a box. If there are 26 boxes on the shelf, write an algebraic expression to represent the total number of pencils on the shelf.

$26 \cdot p$, or $26p$

Example 2

Write each phrase as a numerical or algebraic expression.

A. 987 minus 12

987 − 12

B. x times 45

$45 \cdot x$, or $45x$

Example 3

Write two phrases for each expression.

A. $\frac{16}{b}$ 16 divided by b; the quotient of 16 and b

B. (75)(32) 75 times 32; the product of 75 and 32

Also available on transparency

Answers to Think and Discuss

1. 1,023 − 75; $125z$; $125 \cdot z$; $(125)(z)$
2. a divided by 17; the quotient of a and 17

2 Teach

Guided Instruction

In this lesson, students learn to translate between words and mathematical expressions. First, describe the actions that signal each operation. (Teaching Transparency.) Then teach students to translate words into algebraic expressions. Next, teach students to write numerical and algebraic expressions with words.

Communicating Math Teach students to write all variables in a lowercase, cursive style. This eliminates confusion between x and ×, as well as between t and +.

Reaching All Learners

Through Home Connection

Have students record real-world math situations they experience at home, using both words and mathematical symbols. Possible answer: Mom works out for the same length of time each day. How long does she work out in a week? $7t$, where t represents the length of time she works out each day.

3 Close

Summarize

Direct the students' attention to the chart of operations, expressions, and words. Review each numerical and algebraic expression while connecting to the words that describe each expression. Have the students duplicate the chart for their own reference.

2-2 Exercises

M6P3.a, M6P4.c

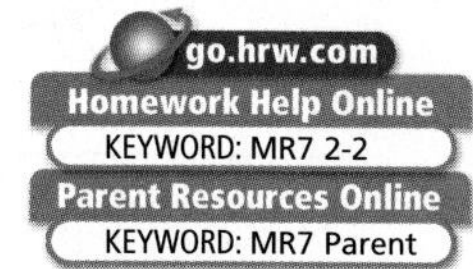

GUIDED PRACTICE

See Example 1

1. **Social Studies** The Big Island of Hawaii is the largest Hawaiian island, with an area of 4,028 mi^2. The next biggest island is Maui. Let m represent the area of Maui. Write an expression for the difference between the two areas. $4{,}028 - m$

See Example 2

Write each phrase as a numerical or algebraic expression.

2. 279 minus 125 $279 - 125$
3. the product of 15 and x $15x$
4. 17 plus 4 $17 + 4$
5. p divided by 5 $\frac{p}{5}$
6. the sum of 9 and q $9 + q$
7. 149 times 2 $(149)(2)$

See Example 3

Write two phrases for each expression.

8. $r + 87$
9. 345×196
10. $476 \div 28$
11. $d - 5$

INDEPENDENT PRACTICE

See Example 1

12. **Social Studies** In 2005, California had 21 more seats in the U.S. Congress than Texas had. If t represents the number of seats Texas had, write an expression for the number of seats California had. $t + 21$
13. Let x represent the number of television show episodes that are taped in a season. Write an expression for the number of episodes taped in 5 seasons. $5x$

See Example 2

Write each phrase as a numerical or algebraic expression.

14. 25 less than k $k - 25$
15. the quotient of 325 and 25 $325 \div 25$
16. 34 times w $34w$
17. 675 added to 137 $137 + 675$
18. the sum of 135 and p $135 + p$
19. take away 14 from j $j - 14$

See Example 3

Write two phrases for each expression.

20. $h + 65$
21. $243 - 19$
22. $125 \div n$
23. $342(75)$
24. $\frac{d}{27}$
25. $45 \cdot 23$
26. $629 + c$
27. $228 - b$

PRACTICE AND PROBLEM SOLVING

CRCT GPS

Extra Practice pp. 746–7

Translate each phrase into a numerical or algebraic expression.

28. 13 less than z $z - 13$
29. 15 divided by d $15 \div d$
30. 874 times 23 $874(23)$
31. m multiplied by 67 $67m$
32. the sum of 35, 74, and 21 $35 + 74 + 21$
33. 319 less than 678 $678 - 319$
34. **Critical Thinking** Paula and Manda were asked to write an expression to find the total number of shoes in a closet. Let s represent the number of pairs of shoes. Paula wrote s and Manda wrote $2s$. Who is correct? Explain.

35. **Write About It** Write a situation that could be modeled by the expression $x + 5$.

Assignment Guide

If you finished Example 1 assign:
Average 1, 12–13, 34, 36–37, 41–49
Advanced 1, 12–13, 35, 38–39, 41–49

If you finished Example 2 assign:
Average 1–7, 12–19, 28–37, 41–49
Advanced 1–7, 12–19, 28–34, 37–39, 41–49

If you finished Example 3 assign:
Average 1–37, 41–49
Advanced 1–34, 38–49

Homework Quick Check

Quickly check key concepts.
Exercises: 12, 14, 20, 28, 34

Math Background

We translate words into algebraic expressions using a consistent, universally understood system. This system has evolved over thousands of years. Archaeological records indicate that Babylonian mathematics had developed prose-based algebra by 2000 B.C.E.

The adoption of symbols to represent operations was also part of this evolution. The symbols + and − can be traced to Johann Widman (1498); the symbol · can be traced to Gottfried Leibniz (1698); and the symbol ÷ can be traced to Johann Heinrich Rahn (1659).

Answers

8–11, 20–27, 34–35. See p. A1.

Georgia Performance Standards

M6P3.a Organize and consolidate their mathematical thinking through communication.

M6P4.c Recognize and apply mathematics in contexts outside of mathematics.

RETEACH 2-2

LESSON 2-2 **Reteach**
Translate Between Words and Math

There are key words that tell you which operations to use for mathematical expressions.

Addition (combine)	Subtraction (less)	Multiplication (put together groups of equal parts)	Division (separate into equal groups)
add plus sum total increased by more than	minus difference subtract less than decreased by take away	product times multiply	quotient divide

You can use key words to help you translate between word phrases and mathematical phrases.

A. 3 plus 5 $3 + 5$ **B.** 3 times x $3x$ **C.** 5 less than p $p - 5$ **D.** h divided by 6 $h \div 6$

Write each phrase as a numerical or algebraic expression.

1. 4 less than 8 $8 - 4$
2. q divided by 3 $q \div 3$
3. f minus 6 $f - 6$
4. d multiplied by 9 $d \bullet 9$

You can use key words to write word phrases for mathematical phrases.

A. $7k$
- the product of 7 and k
- 7 times k

B. $5 - 2$
- 5 minus 2
- 2 less than 5

Write a phrase for each expression. Possible answers are given.

5. $z \div 4$ *z* divided by 4
6. $5 \bullet 6$ 5 times 6
7. $m - 6$ 6 less than *m*
8. $s + 3$ *s* plus 3

PRACTICE 2-2

LESSON 2-2 **Practice B**
Translate Between Words and Math

Write an expression.

1. Terry's essay has 9 more pages than Stacey's essay. If s represents the number of pages in Stacey's essay, write an expression for the number of pages in Terry's essay. $s + 9$
2. Let z represent the number of students in a class. Write an expression for the number of students in 3 equal groups. $\frac{z}{3}$

Write each phrase as a numerical or algebraic expression.

3. 24 multiplied by 3 $24 \bullet 3$
4. n multiplied by 14 $n \bullet 14$
5. w added to 64 $64 + w$
6. the difference of 58 and 6 $58 - 6$
7. m subtracted from 100 $100 - m$
8. the sum of 180 and 25 $180 + 25$
9. the product of 35 and x $35x$
10. the quotient of 63 and 9 $63 \div 9$
11. 28 divided by p $28 \div p$

Write two phrases for each expression. Possible answers are given.

12. $n + 91$ *n* plus 91; 91 more than *n*
13. $35 \div r$ 35 divided by *r*; the quotient of 35 and *r*
14. $20 - s$ 20 minus *s*; *s* less than 20
15. Charles is 3 years older than Paul. If y represents Paul's age, what expression represents Charles's age? $y + 3$
16. Maya bought some pizzas for $12 each. If p represents the number of pizzas she bought, what expression shows the total amount she spent? $12p$

Science 

The graph shows the number of U.S. space exploration missions from 1961 to 2005.

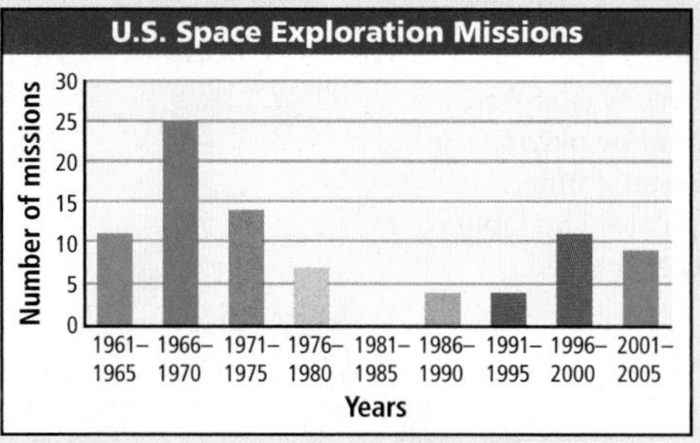

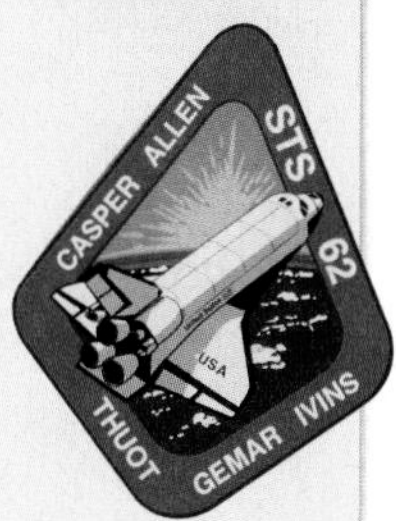

36. Between 1966 and 1970, the Soviet Union had m fewer space missions than the United States. Write an algebraic expression for this situation. $25 - m$

37. Let d represent the number of dollars that the United States spent on space missions from 1986 to 1990. Write an expression for the cost per mission. $d \div 4$

38. **Write a Problem** Use the data in the graph to write a word problem that can be answered with a numerical or algebraic expression.

39. **Critical Thinking** Let p stand for the number of missions between 1996 and 2000 that had people aboard. What operation would you use to write an expression for the number of missions without people? Explain.

40. **Challenge** Write an expression for the following: two more than the number of missions from 1971 to 1975, minus the number of missions from 1986 to 1990. Then evaluate the expression. $(14 + 2) - 4$; 12

CRCT Prep • GPS Support • Spiral Review

41. **Multiple Choice** Which expression represents the product of 79 and x?

Ⓐ $79 + x$ Ⓑ $x - 79$ Ⓒ $79x$ Ⓓ $\frac{x}{79}$

42. **Extended Response** Tim is driving from Ames, Iowa to Canton, Ohio. He is 280 miles from Ames when he stops for gas. Write an expression to represent the number of miles Tim has left to drive. Explain. Translate your expression into two different word phrases.

Use mental math to find each sum or product. (Lesson 1-5)

43. $8 \times 5 \times 9$ 360 **44.** $49 + 26 + 11 + 14$ 100 **45.** $4 \times 15 \times 6$ 360

Evaluate each expression for the given value of the variable. (Lesson 2-1)

46. $2y + 6$ for $y = 4$ 14 **47.** $\frac{z}{5}$ for $z = 40$ 8 **48.** $7r - 3$ for $r = 18$ 123 **49.** $\frac{p}{7} + 12$ for $p = 28$ 16

CHALLENGE 2-2

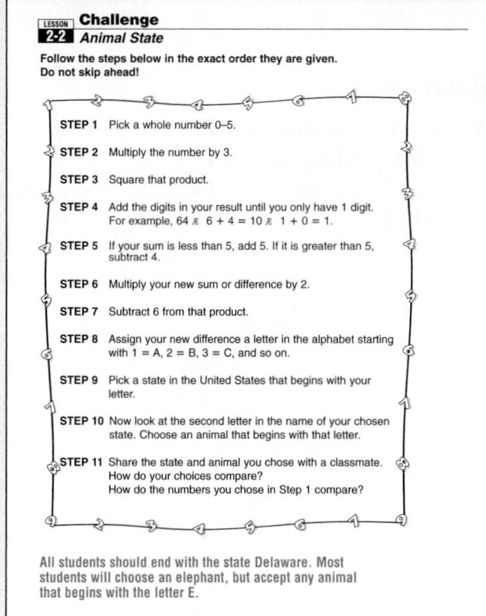

LESSON 2-2 **Challenge**
Animal State

Follow the steps below in the exact order they are given. Do not skip ahead!

STEP 1 Pick a whole number 0–5.
STEP 2 Multiply the number by 3.
STEP 3 Square that product.
STEP 4 Add the digits in your result until you only have 1 digit. For example, 64 → 6 + 4 = 10 → 1 + 0 = 1.
STEP 5 If your sum is less than 5, add 5. If it is greater than 5, subtract 4.
STEP 6 Multiply your new sum or difference by 2.
STEP 7 Subtract 6 from that product.
STEP 8 Assign your new difference a letter in the alphabet starting with 1 = A, 2 = B, 3 = C, and so on.
STEP 9 Pick a state in the United States that begins with your letter.
STEP 10 Now look at the second letter in the name of your chosen state. Choose an animal that begins with that letter.
STEP 11 Share the state and animal you chose with a classmate. How do your choices compare? How do the numbers you chose in Step 1 compare?

All students should end with the state Delaware. Most students will choose an elephant, but accept any animal that begins with the letter E.

PROBLEM SOLVING 2-2

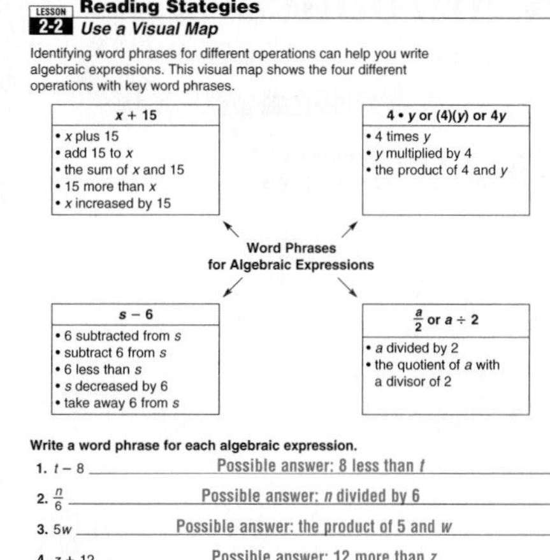

LESSON 2-2 **Reading Stategies**
Use a Visual Map

Identifying word phrases for different operations can help you write algebraic expressions. This visual map shows the four different operations with key word phrases.

Word Phrases for Algebraic Expressions

$x + 15$
• x plus 15 • add 15 to x • the sum of x and 15 • 15 more than x • x increased by 15

$4 \cdot y$ or $(4)(y)$ or $4y$
• 4 times y • y multiplied by 4 • the product of 4 and y

$s - 6$
• 6 subtracted from s • subtract 6 from s • 6 less than s • s decreased by 6 • take away 6 from s

$\frac{a}{2}$ or $a \div 2$
• a divided by 2 • the quotient of a with a divisor of 2

Write a word phrase for each algebraic expression.

1. $t - 8$ Possible answer: 8 less than t
2. $\frac{n}{6}$ Possible answer: n divided by 6
3. $5w$ Possible answer: the product of 5 and w
4. $z + 12$ Possible answer: 12 more than z

Write an algebraic expression for each word phrase.

5. the product of x and 12 $12x$ or $12 \cdot x$ or $(12)(x)$
6. m decreased by 5 $m - 5$
7. the quotient of p with a divisor of 3 $\frac{p}{3}$ or $p \div 3$
8. 25 more than r $r + 25$

Ongoing Assessment and Intervention

Diagnose ***Before*** **the Lesson**
2-2 Warm Up, TE p. 58

Monitor ***During*** **the Lesson**
2-2 Know-It Notebook
2-2 Questioning Strategies

Assess ***After*** **the Lesson**
2-2 Lesson Quiz, TE p. 61

COMMON ERROR ALERT

When translating between phrases and algebraic subtraction expressions, students may reverse the numbers. For example, they may answer $13 - z$ instead of $z - 13$ for Exercise 28. Caution students to read the phrases carefully, especially those involving subtraction and division, where order is important.

Answers

38–39, 42. See p. A1.

TEST PREP DOCTOR In Exercise 42, remind students to answer as completely as possible. There are four responses asked for in the exercise, including an explanation.

Journal

In language arts, the word *expression* means a phrase or a sentence. Have students write about how an algebraic expression is like a phrase.

Power Presentations with PowerPoint®

2-2 Lesson Quiz

1. Let x represent the number of minutes Kristen works out in one week. Write an expression for the number of minutes she works out in 4 weeks. $4x$

Write each phrase as a numerical or algebraic expression.

2. 7 less than x $x - 7$

3. The product of 12 and w $12w$

Write a phrase for each expression.

4. $17 + x$ x more than 17 or x added to 17

5. $n \div 12$ n divided by 12 or the quotient of n and 12

Also available on transparency

2-3 Organizer

Pacing: Traditional 1 day
Block $\frac{1}{2}$ day

Objective: Students write expressions for tables and sequences.

Online Edition
Tutorial Videos

Countdown to CRCT Week 3

Power Presentations with PowerPoint®

Warm Up

Name the next three terms in each sequence.

1. 7, 10, 13, 16, ▇, ▇, ▇ **19, 22, 25**
2. 105, 88, 71, 54, ▇, ▇, ▇ **37, 20, 3**
3. 64, 128, 256, 512, ▇, ▇, ▇ **1,024, 2,048, 4,096**

Problem of the Day

Sam's house is 3 blocks east and 5 blocks south of Tyra. If Tyra walks straight south and then straight east to Sam's house, does she walk more blocks east or more blocks south? How many more? **south; 2 blocks**

Also available on transparency

2-3 Translating Between Tables and Expressions

Learn to write expressions for tables and sequences.

Georgia Performance Standards

M6P5.b Select, apply, and translate among mathematical representations to solve problems. Also, M6A3, M6P5.a.

In 2004, International Chess Master Andrew Martin broke a world record by playing 321 games of chess at the same time. Each game required 32 chess pieces. The table shows the number of pieces needed for different numbers of games.

Games	Pieces
1	32
2	64
3	96
n	$32n$

The number of pieces is always 32 times the number of games. For n games, the expression $32n$ gives the number of pieces that are needed.

EXAMPLE 1 Writing an Expression

Write an expression for the missing value in each table.

A

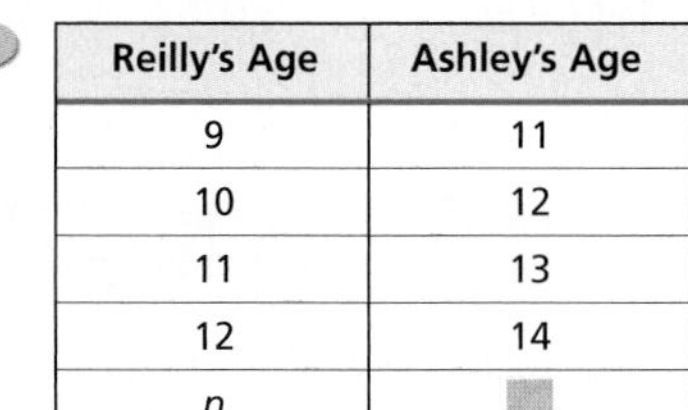

Reilly's Age	Ashley's Age
9	11
10	12
11	13
12	14
n	▇

Ashley's age is Reilly's age plus 2.

$9 + 2 = 11$
$10 + 2 = 12$
$11 + 2 = 13$
$12 + 2 = 14$
$n + 2$

When Reilly's age is n, Ashley's age is $n + 2$.

B

Eggs	Dozens
12	1
24	2
36	3
48	4
e	▇

The number of dozens is the number of eggs divided by 12.

$12 \div 12 = 1$
$24 \div 12 = 2$
$36 \div 12 = 3$
$48 \div 12 = 4$
$e \div 12$

When there are e eggs, the number of dozens is $e \div 12$, or $\frac{e}{12}$.

1 Introduce

Alternate Opener

EXPLORATION

2-3 Translating Between Tables and Expressions

You can explore geometric patterns to help you write algebraic expressions. Consider this sequence of figures.

Figure 1 Figure 2 Figure 3

The first figure has 5 segments, the second figure has 9 segments, and the third figure has 13 segments.

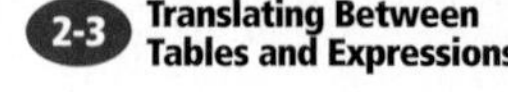

Figure Number	1	2	3
Number of Segments	5	9	13

1. Draw the next two figures in the pattern.
2. Complete the table.

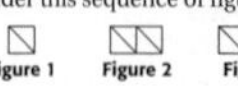

Figure Number	1	2	3	4	5
Number of Segments	5	9	13		

3. Describe any patterns you notice in the table.

Think and Discuss

4. **Explain** how you can find the number of segments in the 6th figure without drawing it.
5. **Explain** Explain how you can find the number of segments in any figure in the pattern if you know the number of the figure.

Motivate

Writing an expression from a table is very much like cracking the code used to send a message. Once you have the code, you have complete knowledge of the message. Once you write an expression for the values in the table, you can determine any desired outcome.

Explorations and answers are provided in *Alternate Openers: Explorations Transparencies.*

Georgia Performance Standards

M6A3 Students will evaluate algebraic expressions, including those with exponents, and solve simple one-step equations using each of the four basic operations.

M6P5.a Create and use representations to organize, record, and communicate mathematical ideas.

M6P5.b Select, apply, and translate among mathematical representations to solve problems.

You can look for a pattern in a table to help you write an expression.

EXAMPLE 2 Writing an Expression for a Sequence

Write an expression for the sequence in the table.

Position	1	2	3	4	5	n
Value of Term	3	5	7	9	11	■

Look for a relationship between the positions and the values of the terms in the sequence. Use guess and check.

Guess $2n$.
Check by substituting 3.
$2 \times 3 \neq 7$ ✗

Guess $2n + 1$.
Check by substituting 3.
$2 \times 3 + 1 = 7$ ✓

The expression $2n + 1$ works for the entire sequence.
$2 \times 1 + 1 = 3$, $2 \times 2 + 1 = 5$, $2 \times 3 + 1 = 7$,
$2 \times 4 + 1 = 9$, $2 \times 5 + 1 = 11$

The expression for the sequence is $2n + 1$.

Caution!

When you write an expression for data in a table, check that the expression works for *all* of the data in the table.

EXAMPLE 3 Writing an Expression for the Area of a Figure

A triangle has a base of 8 inches. The table shows the area of the triangle for different heights. Write an expression that can be used to find the area of the triangle when its height is h inches.

Base (in.)	Height (in.)	Area (in^2)	
8	1	4	$8 \times 1 = 8$, $8 \div 2 = 4$
8	2	8	$8 \times 2 = 16$, $16 \div 2 = 8$
8	3	12	$8 \times 3 = 24$, $24 \div 2 = 12$
8	4	16	$8 \times 4 = 32$, $32 \div 2 = 16$
8	h	■	$8 \times h = 8h$, $8h \div 2$

In each row of the table, the area is half the product of the base and the height. The expression is $\frac{8h}{2}$, or $4h$.

Think and Discuss

GPS M6P1.d, M6P3.d

1. **Describe** how to write an expression for a sequence given in a table.
2. **Explain** why it is important to check your expression for all of the data in a table.

Possible answers to *Think and Discuss:*

1. Look for a relationship between the positions and values. Check that the relationship works for all terms. Translate the relationship into an algebraic expression.
2. An expression might work for only the first one or two terms. It must work for all the data in the table.

COMMON ERROR ALERT

Students sometimes try to use the difference between the terms to define the operation to be used in the expression. Ask them to consider an operation involving the term's position and the value of the term.

Power Presentations with PowerPoint®

Additional Examples

Example 1

Write an expression for the missing value in the table.

Spike's Age	Rusty's Age
2	6
3	7
4	8
a	 $4a$

Example 2

Write an expression for the sequence in the table.

Position	1	2	3	4	n
Value	7	10	13	16	

$3n + 4$

Example 3

A triangle has a base of 6 inches. The table shows the area of the triangle for different heights. Write an expression that can be used to find the area of the triangle when its height is h inches.

Base (in.)	Height (in.)	Area (in^2)
6	1	3
6	2	6
6	4	12
6	h	 $3h$

Also available on transparency

2 Teach

Guided Instruction

In this lesson, students learn to write algebraic expressions for tables and sequences. First teach students how to discover a relationship between position 1 and the value of the term in position 1. Then check to see if the relationship holds for all other positions and values in the table. Then teach how to translate the relationship into an algebraic expression. Next apply the concept to real-world problems involving area.

Reaching All Learners

Through Cognitive Strategies

Have students develop a routine of examining individual operations in their attempts to discover a relationship between the positions and the terms in each row. If no relationship exists involving an individual operation, have students investigate multiplication in combination with addition or subtraction.

3 Close

Summarize

Review techniques for finding possible relationships in a table. Students need to remember to test the relationship for all terms in the table. Then remind them to translate the relationship into an algebraic expression.

2-3 Exercises

Assignment Guide

If you finished Example 1 assign:
Average 1, 4–5, 9–14, 17–26
Advanced 1, 4–5, 9–11, 13–15, 17–26

If you finished Example 2 assign:
Average 1–2, 4–7, 9–14, 17–26
Advanced 1–2, 4–7, 10–15, 17–26

If you finished Example 3 assign:
Average 1–14, 17–26
Advanced 1–8, 12–26

Homework Quick Check

Quickly check key concepts.
Exercises: 4, 6, 8, 14

2-3 Exercises

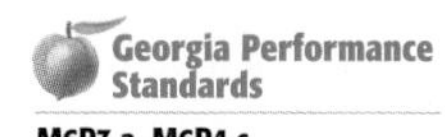
Georgia Performance Standards
M6P3.a, M6P4.c

go.hrw.com
Homework Help Online
KEYWORD: MR7 2-3
Parent Resources Online
KEYWORD: MR7 Parent

GUIDED PRACTICE

See Example 1 Write an expression for the missing value in each table.

1.

Go-Carts	1	2	3	4	n
Wheels	4	8	12	16	$4n$

See Example 2 Write an expression for the sequence in the table.

2.

Position	1	2	3	4	5	n
Value of Term	9	10	11	12	13	$n + 8$

See Example 3

3. A rectangle has a length of 5 inches. The table shows the area of the rectangle for different widths. Write an expression that can be used to find the area of the rectangle when its width is w inches.

Length (in.)	Width (in.)	Area (in^2)
5	2	10
5	4	20
5	6	30
5	8	40
5	w	$5w$

INDEPENDENT PRACTICE

See Example 1 Write an expression for the missing value in each table.

4.

Players	Soccer Teams
22	2
44	4
66	6
88	8
n	$\frac{n}{11}$

5.

Weeks	Days
4	28
8	56
12	84
16	112
n	$7n$

See Example 2 Write an expression for the sequence in the table.

6.

Position	1	2	3	4	5	n
Value of Term	7	12	17	22	27	

$5n + 2$

See Example 3

7. The table shows the area of a square with different side lengths. Write an expression that can be used to find the area of a square when its side length is s feet.

Length (ft)	2	4	6	8	s
Area (ft^2)	4	16	36	64	

Georgia Performance Standards

M6P3.a Organize and consolidate their mathematical thinking through communication.

M6P4.c Recognize and apply mathematics in contexts outside of mathematics.

RETEACH 2-3

LESSON 2-3 **Reteach**
Translating Between Tables and Expressions

You can write an expression for data in a table.
The expression must work for all of the data.

Cats	Legs
1	4
2	8
3	12
c	?

Think: When there is 1 cat, there are 4 legs. $4 \times 1 = 4$
When there are 2 cats, there are 8 legs. $4 \times 2 = 8$
When there are 3 cats, there are 12 legs. $4 \times 3 = 12$

So, when there are c cats, there are $4c$ legs.

You can write an expression for the sequence in a table.
Find a rule for the data in the table that works for the whole sequence.

Position	1	2	3	4	5	n
Value of Term	4	5	6	7	8	?

Step 1 Look at the value of the term in position 1.
4 is **3 more** than 1.
Step 2 Try the rule for position 2.
5 is **3 more** than 2.
Step 3 Try the rule for the rest of the positions.
6 is **3 more** than 3, 7 is **3 more** than 4, and 8 is **3 more** than 5.

So, the expression for the sequence is $n + 3$.

Write an expression for the missing value in each table.

1.

People	Legs
1	2
2	4
3	6
p	$2p$

2.

Yoko's Age	Mel's Age
9	19
10	20
11	21
y	$y + 10$

Write an expression for the sequence in the table.

3.

Position	1	2	3	4	5	n
Value of Term	3	6	9	12	15	$3n$

PRACTICE 2-3

LESSON 2-3 **Practice B**
Translating Between Tables and Expressions

Write an expression for the missing value in each table.

1.

Bicycles	Wheels
1	2
2	4
3	6
b	$2b$

2.

Ryan's Age	Mia's Age
14	7
16	9
18	11
r	$r - 7$

3.

Minutes	Hours
60	1
120	2
180	3
m	$m \div 60$

4.

Bags	Potatoes
3	21
4	28
5	35
b	$7b$

Write an expression for the sequence in each table.

5.

Position	1	2	3	4	5	n
Value of Term	3	4	5	6	7	$n + 2$

6.

Position	1	2	3	4	5	n
Value of Term	5	9	13	17	21	$4n + 1$

7. A rectangle has a width of 6 inches. The table shows the area of the rectangle for different widths. Write an expression that can be used to find the area of the rectangle when its length is l inches.

Width (in.)	Length (in.)	Area (in.^{2})
6	8	48
6	10	60
6	12	72
6	l	$6l$

PRACTICE AND PROBLEM SOLVING

Extra Practice pp. 746–7

Make a table for each sequence. Then write an expression for the sequence.

8. 2, 4, 6, 8, . . .
9. 6, 7, 8, 9, . . .
10. 10, 20, 30, 40, . . .

11. **Earth Science** The planet Mercury takes 88 days to make a complete orbit of the Sun. The table shows the number of orbits and the number of days it takes to make the orbits. Write an expression for the number of days it takes Mercury to make n orbits.

Orbits	Days
1	88
2	176
3	264
n	■ $88n$

12. **Multi-Step** The entry fee for a county fair is \$10. Each ride at the fair costs \$2. The table shows the total cost to go on various numbers of rides. Write an expression for the cost of r rides. Then use the expression to find the cost of 12 rides. $2r + 10$; \$34

Number of Rides	1	3	5	8	10	r
Total Cost (\$)	12	16	20	26	30	■

13. **Critical Thinking** Write two different expressions that describe the relationship in the table. Possible answer: $n + 7$; $3n + 1$

Position (n)	Value of Term
3	10

14. **Write About It** Explain how you can make a table of values for the expression $4n + 3$.

15. **Challenge** Can there be more than one expression that describes a set of data in a table? Explain.

CRCT Prep • GPS Support • Spiral Review

16. **Multiple Choice** Which expression describes the sequence in the table?

Position	1	2	3	4	5	n
Value of Term	6	11	16	21	26	■

Ⓐ $n + 5$ Ⓑ $5n + 1$ Ⓒ $6n$ Ⓓ $6n - 1$

17. **Multiple Choice** Find the missing value in the sequence 1, 3, 5, ■, 9, ...

Ⓕ 6 Ⓖ 7 Ⓗ 8 Ⓙ 9

Evaluate each expression. (Lesson 1-4)

18. $14 + 8 \times 2$ 30
19. $6^2 - (4 + 3)$ 29
20. $5 \times 8 \div (3 + 1)$ 10
21. $45 \div 3^2 + 16$ 21

Use the Distributive Property to find each product. (Lesson 1-5)

22. 3×21 63
23. 7×35 245
24. 6×19 114
25. 2×63 126

CHALLENGE 2-3

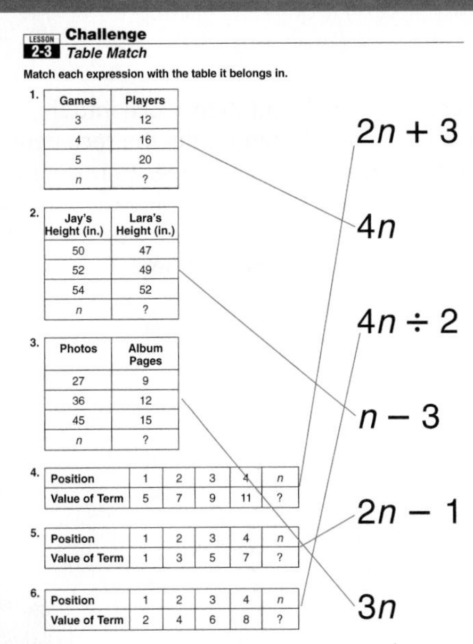

LESSON 2-3 **Challenge**
Table Match

Match each expression with the table it belongs in.

1.

Games	Players
3	12
4	16
5	20
n	?

2.

Jay's Height (in.)	Lara's Height (in.)
50	47
52	49
54	52
n	?

3.

Photos	Album Pages
27	9
36	12
45	15
n	?

4.

Position	1	2	3	4	n
Value of Term	5	7	9	11	?

5.

Position	1	2	3	4	n
Value of Term	1	3	5	7	?

6.

Position	1	2	3	4	n
Value of Term	2	4	6	8	?

$2n + 3$

$4n$

$4n \div 2$

$n - 3$

$2n - 1$

$3n$

PROBLEM SOLVING 2-3

LESSON 2-3 **Problem Solving**
Translating Between Tables and Expressions

Use the table to write an expression for the missing value. Then use your expression to answer the questions.

1. How many cars are produced on average each year?
1,250

2. How many cars will be produced in 6 years?
7,500

3. After how many years will there be an average production of 3,750 cars?
3

Cars Produced By Company X

Number of Years	Average Number of Cars Produced
2	2,500
5	6,250
7	8,750
10	12,500
12	15,000
14	17,500
n	$1,250n$

Circle the letter of the correct answer.
Company Y produces twice as many cars as Company X.

4. How many cars does Company Y produce on average in 8 years?
A 1,250
B 10,000
C 11,250
Ⓓ 20,000

5. How many more cars on average does Company Y produce in 4 years than Company X?
F 2,500
Ⓖ 5,000
H 6,125
J 7,500

6. Which company produces an average of 11,250 cars in 9 years?
Ⓐ Company X
B Company Y
C both companies
D neither company

7. How many cars are produced on average by both companies in 20 years?
F 3,750
G 12,500
H 25,000
Ⓙ 37,500

Ongoing Assessment and Intervention

Diagnose ***Before*** **the Lesson**
2-3 Warm Up, TE p. 62

Monitor ***During*** **the Lesson**
2-3 Know-It Notebook
2-3 Questioning Strategies

Assess ***After*** **the Lesson**
2-3 Lesson Quiz, TE p. 65

Answers

8–10, 14–15. See p. A1.

In Exercise 16, choices **A, B,** and **C** will work for the first term in the table. Remind students to test all terms in the table before reaching a conclusion.

Journal

Have students write about how they determine whether an expression is one that will work for a table of data.

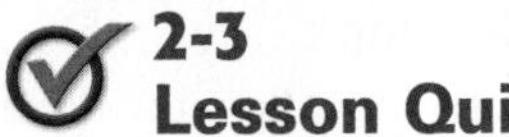

2-3 Lesson Quiz

1. Write an expression for the missing value in the table.

Scott's Age	Ray's Age
11	15
12	16
13	17
x	■

$x + 4$

2. Write an expression for the sequence in the table.

Position	1	2	3	n
Value of term	8	16	24	$8n$

3. A rectangle has a width of 7 in. The table shows the area of the rectangle for different lengths. Write an expression that can be used to find the area of the rectangle when its length is ℓ.

Width (in.)	Length (in.)	Area (in.^{2})
7	4	28
7	5	35
7	6	42
7	ℓ	■ 7ℓ

Also available on transparency

Organizer

Use with Lesson 2-3

Pacing:
Traditional $\frac{1}{2}$ day
Block $\frac{1}{4}$ day

Objective: Use grid paper to model the perimeter and area of rectangles.

Materials: Grid paper

Online Edition

Countdown to CRCT Week 3

Resources

Hands-On Lab Activities
Lab 2-3 Recording Sheet

Teach

Discuss

Have students discuss how to represent lengths on grid paper. Some students may start counting "one" at a corner of a rectangle and move one space and count "two." Have them count the length of each square as they move along each side of the rectangle.

Close

Key Concept

A table can show how the dimensions of a rectangle are used to calculate perimeter and area.

Assessment

Use grid paper and tables to find the perimeter and area of each rectangle.

1. length = 6, width = 8 **28, 48**
2. length = 9, width = 7 **32, 63**

Georgia Performance Standards

M6A3 Students will evaluate algebraic expressions, including those with exponents, and solve simple one-step equations using each of the four basic operations.

M6P5.a Create and use representations to organize, record, and communicate mathematical ideas.

M6P5.b Select, apply, and translate among mathematical representations to solve problems.

Explore Area and Perimeter of Rectangles

Use with Lesson 2-3

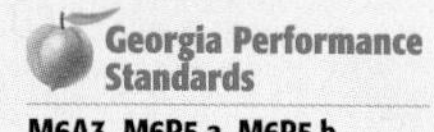

M6A3, M6P5.a, M6P5.b

REMEMBER
- Perimeter is the distance around a figure.
- Area is the amount of space a figure covers. It is measured in square units.

You can use graph paper to model the area of different rectangles.

Activity 1

Sarita is digging rectangular vegetable gardens. To prevent weeds from growing she will cover each garden with a mesh sheet the exact size of the garden before planting the vegetables. Complete the table to find the size of sheet needed for each garden.

Each sheet will be the same size as the garden it covers. Complete the table at right to show the area of each garden.

Garden A

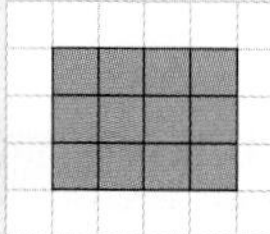

Garden B

Garden C

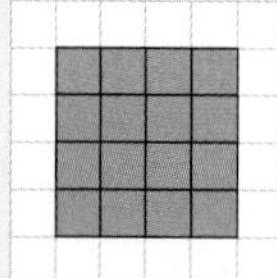

Garden D

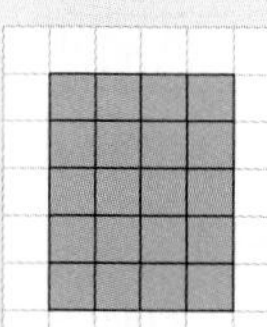

Areas of Gardens

Garden	Length (ℓ)	Width (w)	Area (A)
A	4	2	8
B	4	3	■ **12**
C	■ **4**	■ **4**	■ **16**
D	■ **4**	■ **5**	■ **20**

Think and Discuss

1. If you had a garden with a length of 4 and an area of 24, what would the width be? How did you get your answer?
2. The area of each garden is equal to its length times its width. Using the variables ℓ and w, what expression can you use to find the area of a rectangle? $A =$ ______. **$\ell \times w$**

Teacher to Teacher

It is important to approach concepts at the concrete level, and then move into the abstract level by making connections. For this lab, students can model the rectangular shapes with square tiles first, and then draw their models on grid paper to make the connecting representations. Move students to the abstract level by having them record the lengths, widths, and areas of their rectangles in a table. Finally, discuss the patterns seen in each row to develop the formulas for area and perimeter.

Jo Ann Hawkins
Abilene, Texas

Try This

Complete a table like the one in Activity 1 to find the area of each rectangle.

1. length = 10, width = 5 **2.** length = 10, width = 6 **3.** length = 10, width = 7

You can use graph paper to model the perimeters of different rectangles.

Activity 2

Jorge's family recently returned from vacation. They took many pictures that they want to frame, and they decide to make their own frames. Complete the table to find the amount of wood needed for each frame.

The amount of wood needed for each frame is the perimeter of the frame. Complete the table at right to show the perimeter of each frame.

Frame A **Frame B**

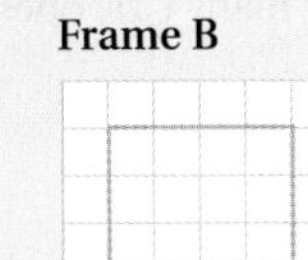

Perimeters of Picture Frames			
Frame	Length (ℓ)	Width (w)	Perimeter (P)
A	4	2	12
B	4	3	14
C	4	4	16
D	4	5	18

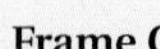

Frame C **Frame D**

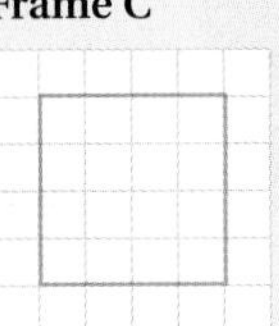

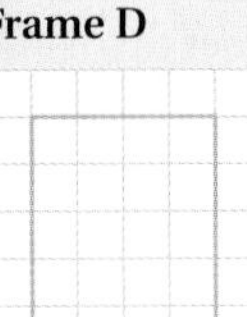

Think and Discuss

1. How did you find the perimeter of each frame?

2. A rectangle has one pair of sides with the same measure, called the length, and another pair with the same measure, called the width. We can say two lengths and two widths equal the perimeter. Using the variables ℓ and w, what expression can you use to find the perimeter of a rectangle?
$P =$ ______. $2\ell + 2w$

Try This

Complete a table like the one in Activity 2 to find the perimeter of each rectangle.

1. length = 8, width = 3 **2.** length = 20, width = 4 **3.** length = 7, width = 7

Activity 1

Answers to *Think and Discuss*

1. 6;

$A = \ell \times w$

$24 = 4 \times w$

$6 = w$

Answers to *Try This*

1–3.

Rectangle	ℓ	w	A
1	10	5	50
2	10	6	60
3	10	7	70

Activity 2

Answers to *Think and Discuss*

1. Possible answer: The perimeter of a rectangle is twice the sum of the length and the width.

Answers to *Try This*

1–3.

Rectangle	ℓ	w	P
1	8	3	22
2	20	4	48
3	7	7	28

Organizer

Objective: Assess students' mastery of concepts and skills in Lessons 2-1 through 2-3.

Resources

Assessment Resources
Section 2A Quiz

INTERVENTION 

Resources

***Ready to Go On? Intervention and Enrichment* Worksheets**

***Ready to Go On?* CD-ROM**

***Ready to Go On?* Online**

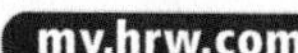

SECTION 2A

Ready to Go On?

Quiz for Lessons 2-1 Through 2-3

2-1 Variables and Expressions

Evaluate each expression to find the missing values in the tables.

1.

y	$23 + y$
17	40
27	50
37	60

2.

w	$w \times 3 + 10$
4	22
5	25
6	28

3. Stephanie's CD holder holds 6 CDs per page. How many CDs does Stephanie have if she fills 2, 3, 4, or 5 pages? 12; 18; 24; 30

2-2 Translate Between Words and Math

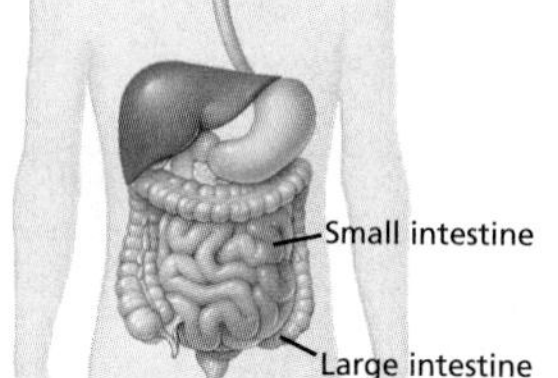

4. The small and large intestines are part of the digestive system. The small intestine is longer than the large intestine. Let n represent the length in feet of the small intestine. The large intestine is 5 feet long. Write an expression to show how much longer the small intestine is than the large intestine. $n - 5$

5. Let h represent the number of times your heart beats in 1 minute. Write an expression for the total number of times it beats in 1 hour. (*Hint:* 1 hour = 60 minutes) $60h$

Write each phrase as a numerical or algebraic expression.

6. 719 plus 210 $719 + 210$
7. t multiplied by 7 $7t$
8. the sum of n and 51 $n + 51$

Write two phrases for each expression. Possible answers:

9. $n + 19$ — n plus 19; 19 added to n
10. $12 \cdot 13$ — 12 times 13; 13 multiplied by 12
11. $72 - x$ — 17 minus x; x subtracted from 72
12. $\frac{t}{12}$ — t divided by 12; the quotient of t and 12
13. $15s$ — 13. 15 times s; s multiplied by 15

2-3 Translating Between Tables and Expressions

Write an expression for the sequence in the table.

14.

Position	1	2	3	4	5	n
Value of Term	8	16	24	32	40	

$8n$

Make a table for each sequence. Then write an expression for the sequence.

15. 3, 4, 5, 6, . . . $n + 2$
16. 4, 7, 10, 13, . . . $3n + 1$

READY TO GO ON?
Diagnose and Prescribe

NO INTERVENE

Ready to Go On? Intervention	Worksheets	CD-ROM	Online
	READY TO GO ON? Intervention, Section 2A		
Lesson 2-1	2-1 Intervention	Activity 2-1	Diagnose and Prescribe Online
Lesson 2-2	2-2 Intervention	Activity 2-2	
Lesson 2-3	2-3 Intervention	Activity 2-3	

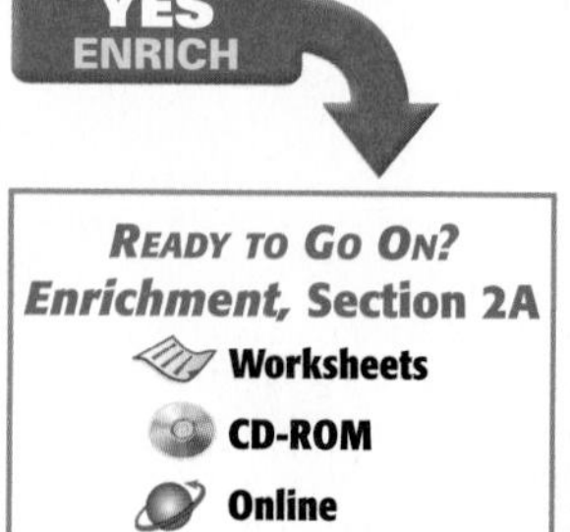

***READY TO GO ON? Enrichment,* Section 2A**
- Worksheets
- CD-ROM
- Online

Focus on Problem Solving

Understand the Problem

- **Identify too much or too little information**

Problems often give too much or too little information. You must decide whether you have enough information to work the problem.

Read the problem and identify the facts that are given. Can you use any of these facts to arrive at an answer? Are there facts in the problem that are not necessary to find the answer? These questions can help you determine whether you have too much or too little information.

If you cannot solve the problem with the information given, decide what information you need. Then read the problem again to be sure you haven't missed the information in the problem.

Copy each problem. Circle the important facts. Underline any facts that you do not need to answer the question. If there is not enough information, list the additional information you need.

1. The reticulated python is one of the longest snakes in the world. One was found in Indonesia in 1912 that was 33 feet long. At birth, a reticulated python is 2 feet long. Suppose an adult python is 29 feet long. Let f represent the number of feet the python grew since birth. What is the value of f?

2. The largest flying flag in the world is 7,410 square feet and weighs 180 pounds. There are a total of 13 horizontal stripes on it. Let h represent the height of each stripe. What is the value of h?

3. The elevation of Mt. McKinley is 20,320 ft. People who climb Mt. McKinley are flown to a base camp located at 7,200 ft. From there, they begin a climb that may last 20 days or longer. Let d represent the distance from the base camp to the summit of Mt. McKinley. What is the value of d?

4. Let c represent the cost of a particular computer in 1981. Six years later, in 1987, the price of the computer had increased to $3,600. What is the value of c?

Answers

1. $f = 27$ ft
2. not enough information given
3. 13,120 ft
4. not enough information given

3. You need to subtract the base-camp height from the peak height, and both are given. The length of the climb is extra information.
4. You need the cost of the computer in 1981, which is not given. All of the information is extra.

Focus on Problem Solving

Organizer

Objective: Focus on understanding the problem.

Online Edition

Resources

Chapter 2 Resource Book
Reading Strategies

Problem Solving Process

This page focuses on the first step of the problem-solving process: **Understand the Problem**

Discuss

Have students identify the information needed to solve each problem. Ask them whether all the information needed is given in the problem, and to identify any missing or extra information.

Possible answers:

1. You need to find the difference in length, so you need the length at birth and the adult length, and both are given. Everything else is extra information.
2. You need the height of the flag, which is missing. You would divide the height of the flag by the number of stripes, 13, to find the height of each stripe. If the width of the flag were given, you could find the height using the area. But, as the problem is written, the area and the weight of the flag are extra information.

SECTION
2B Understanding Equations

One-Minute Section Planner

Lesson	Materials	MiC and Lab Resources
Lesson 2-4 Equations and Their Solutions • Determine whether a number is a solution of an equation. ☑ CRCT ☑ SAT-10 ☑ ITBS ☑ CTBS ☐ NAEP	Balance scale	**MiC: *Comparing Quantities*** pp. 1–3
Lesson 2-5 Addition Equations • Solve whole-number addition equations. ☑ CRCT ☑ SAT-10 ☑ ITBS ☑ CTBS ☑ NAEP	Algebra tiles or counters (MK)	**MiC: *Comparing Quantities*** pp. 16–19 ***Hands-On Lab Activities*** 2-5
Lesson 2-6 Subtraction Equations • Solve whole-number subtraction equations. ☑ CRCT ☑ SAT-10 ☑ ITBS ☑ CTBS ☑ NAEP	Balance scale	**MiC: *Comparing Quantities*** pp. 16–19
Lesson 2-7 Multiplication Equations • Solve whole-number multiplication equations. ☑ CRCT ☑ SAT-10 ☑ ITBS ☑ CTBS ☑ NAEP		***Hands-On Lab Activities*** 2-7
Lesson 2-8 Division Equations • Solve whole-number division equations. ☑ CRCT ☑ SAT-10 ☑ ITBS ☑ CTBS ☑ NAEP	Index cards	
Extension Inequalities • Solve and graph whole-number inequalities. ☐ CRCT ☐ SAT-10 ☐ ITBS ☑ CTBS ☑ NAEP		***Technology Lab Activities*** Extension

MK = *Manipulatives Kit*

Mathematics in Context

The unit ***Comparing Quantities*** from the *Mathematics in Context* © 2006 series can be used with Section 2B. See Section Planner above for suggestions for integrating *MiC* with *Holt Mathematics*.

Section Overview

Determining Solutions of Equations

Lesson 2-4

Because equations are used to represent mathematical relationships in real situations, students can strengthen their problem-solving skills by learning to recognize and identify solutions to equations.

Situation: The Ferris wheel ride costs 3 tokens. After riding the Ferris wheel, Bailey had 5 tokens remaining. How many tokens did Bailey have before riding the Ferris wheel?

$$t - 3 = 5$$

$t = 9$ ***is not*** a solution because $9 - 3 = 5$ ***is not*** true.

$t = 8$ ***is*** a solution because $8 - 3 = 5$ ***is*** true.

Solving One-Step Equations

Lesson 2-5 through 2-8

Why? Many students can figure out the answers to problems without solving one-step equations. However, they will need to use the concepts learned at this level to solve equations involving fractions and decimals and multi-step equations later in this course.

Equation	Operation	Inverse Operation	Isolating the Variable
$a + 9 = 17$	Addition	Subtraction	$a + 9 = 17$ $\underline{-9} \quad \underline{-9}$ $a \quad = \quad 8$
$y - 11 = 25$	Subtraction	Addition	$y - 11 = 25$ $\underline{+11} \quad \underline{+11}$ $y \quad = 36$
$7b = 21$	Multiplication	Division	$7b = 21$ $\frac{7b}{7} = \frac{21}{7}$ $b = 3$
$\frac{x}{3} = 12$	Division	Multiplication	$\frac{x}{3} = 12$ $\frac{x}{3}(3) = 12(3)$ $x = 36$

2-4 Organizer

Pacing: Traditional 1 day
Block $\frac{1}{2}$ day

Objective: Students determine whether a number is a solution of an equation.

Online Edition
Tutorial Videos, Interactivities

Countdown to CRCT Week 3

Power Presentations with PowerPoint®

Warm Up

Evaluate each expression for $x = 8$.

1. $3x + 5$	29	**2.** $x + 8$	16
3. $2x - 7$	9	**4.** $8x \div 4$	16
5. $7x - 1$	55	**6.** $x - 3$	5

Problem of the Day

Complete the magic square so that every row, column, and diagonal add up to the same total.

9	2	10
8	7	6
4	12	5

Also available on transparency

What do "$x = 4$" and salt water have in common? Both can be called solutions.

2-4 Equations and Their Solutions

Learn to determine whether a number is a solution of an equation.

Vocabulary
equation
solution

Georgia Performance Standards
M6A3 Evaluate algebraic expressions. Also, M6P4.c, M6P5.b, M6P5.c.

An **equation** is a mathematical statement that two quantities are equal. You can think of a correct equation as a balanced scale.

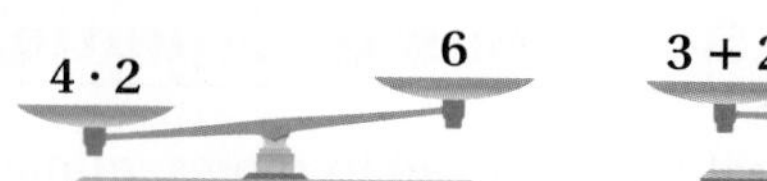

Equations may contain variables. If a value for a variable makes an equation true, that value is a **solution** of the equation.

You can test a value to see if it is a solution of an equation by substituting the value for the variable.

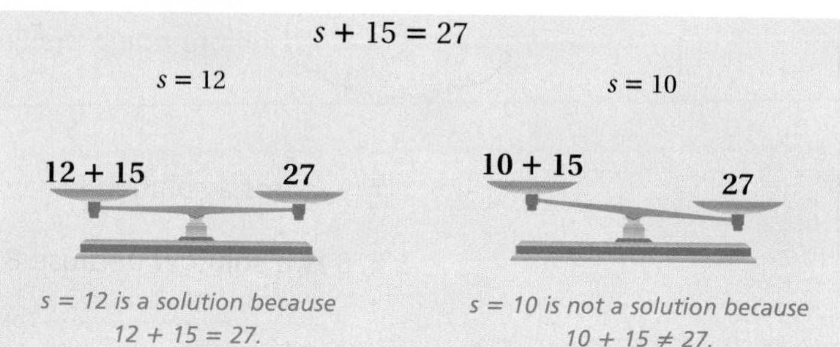

$s = 12$ is a solution because $12 + 15 = 27$.

$s = 10$ is not a solution because $10 + 15 \neq 27$.

Reading Math
The symbol $\neq$ means "is not equal to."

EXAMPLE 1 Determining Solutions of Equations

Determine whether the given value of the variable is a solution.

A $a + 23 = 82$ for $a = 61$

$a + 23 = 82$
$61 + 23 \stackrel{?}{=} 82$ *Substitute 61 for a.*
$84 \stackrel{?}{=} 82$ *Add.*

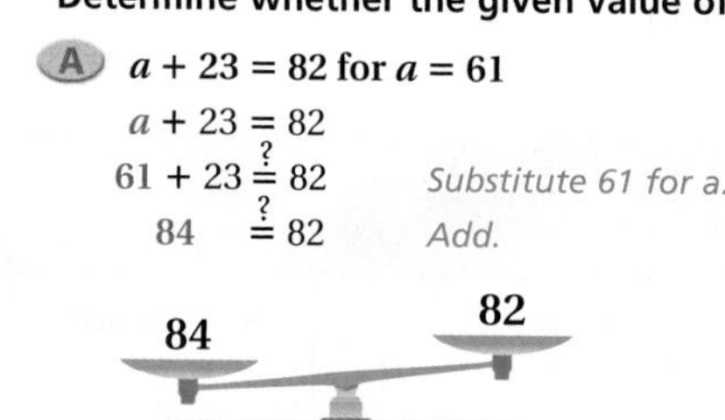

Since $84 \neq 82$, 61 is not a solution to $a + 23 = 82$.

Georgia Performance Standards

M6A3 Students will evaluate algebraic expressions, including those with exponents, and solve simple one-step equations using each of the four basic operations.

M6P4.c Recognize and apply mathematics in contexts outside of mathematics.

M6P5.b Select, apply, and translate among mathematical representations to solve problems.

M6P5.c Use representations to model and interpret physical, social, and mathematical phenomena.

1 Introduce

Alternate Opener

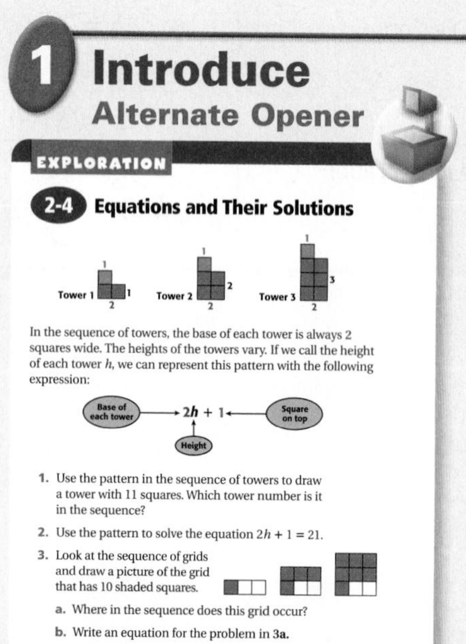

EXPLORATION

2-4 Equations and Their Solutions

In the sequence of towers, the base of each tower is always 2 squares wide. The heights of the towers vary. If we call the height of each tower h, we can represent this pattern with the following expression:

1. Use the pattern in the sequence of towers to draw a tower with 11 squares. Which tower number is it in the sequence?
2. Use the pattern to solve the equation $2h + 1 = 21$.
3. Look at the sequence of grids and draw a picture of the grid that has 10 shaded squares.
   a. Where in the sequence does this grid occur?
   b. Write an equation for the problem in **3a**.

Think and Discuss

4. **Discuss** what is meant by "a solution of an equation."

Motivate

Have students experiment with a balance scale, placing different combinations of items on each side of the scale until it is balanced. Lead students to understand that when the scale is balanced, the sum of the weights of the items on the left equals the sum of the weights of the items on the right.

Explorations and answers are provided in *Alternate Openers: Explorations Transparencies.*

Determine whether the given value of the variable is a solution.

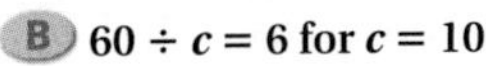

B $60 \div c = 6$ for $c = 10$

$60 \div c = 6$

$60 \div 10 \stackrel{?}{=} 6$ *Substitute 10 for c.*

$6 \stackrel{?}{=} 6$ *Divide.*

Because $6 = 6$, 10 is a solution to $60 \div c = 6$.

You can use equations to check whether measurements given in different units are equal.

For example, there are 12 inches in one foot. If you have a measurement in feet, multiply by 12 to find the measurement in inches: $12 \cdot$ feet = inches, or $12f = i$.

If you have one measurement in feet and another in inches, check whether the two numbers make the equation $12f = i$ true.

EXAMPLE 2 *Life Science Application*

One science book states that a manatee can grow to be 13 feet long. According to another book, a manatee may grow to 156 inches. Determine if these two measurements are equal.

$12f = i$

$12 \cdot 13 \stackrel{?}{=} 156$ *Substitute.*

$156 \stackrel{?}{=} 156$ *Multiply.*

Because $156 = 156$, 13 feet is equal to 156 inches.

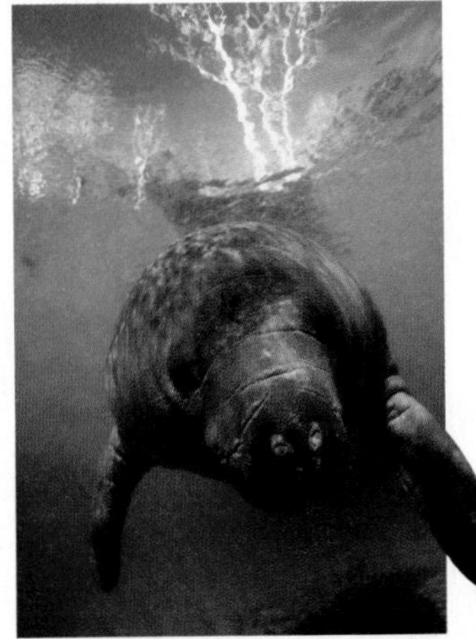

Think and Discuss

GPS M6P3.b

1. Tell which of the following is the solution to $y \div 2 = 9$: $y = 14$, $y = 16$, or $y = 18$. How do you know?

2. Give an example of an equation with a solution of 15.

COMMON ERROR ALERT

The equations in this lesson are relatively straightforward. Because of this, students may be careless, substituting the incorrect value for the variable. Caution students to double-check their work for accuracy.

Power Presentations with PowerPoint®

Additional Examples

Example 1

Determine whether the given value of each variable is a solution.

A. $b - 447 = 1{,}203$ for $b = 1{,}650$

1,650 is a solution to $b - 447 = 1{,}203$.

B. $27x = 1{,}485$ for $x = 54$

54 is not a solution to $27x = 1{,}485$.

Example 2

Paulo says that the park is 19 yards long. Jamie says that the park is 664 inches long. Determine if these two measurements are equal.

19 yards is not equal to 664 inches.

Also available on transparency

Answers to *Think and Discuss:*

1. $y = 18$ because $18 \div 2 = 9$.
2. Possible answer: $x \div 3 = 5$

2 Teach

Guided Instruction

In this lesson, students learn to determine whether a number is a solution of an equation. First teach students to determine whether given values for variables are solutions of equations. Then apply the concept to real-world problems.

Teaching Tip

Inclusion Always refer to an equation as a balanced mathematical statement and emphasize that only the correct solution will maintain the balance.

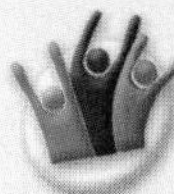

Reaching All Learners

Through Critical Thinking

Display a set of scales (Teaching Transparency). For each of the following equations, write the left side over the left scale and the right side over the right scale, and ask what the value of the variable must be for the scales to remain balanced.

1. $x + 3 = 7$ $x = 4$
2. $t - 5 = 3$ $t = 8$
3. $4y = 28$ $y = 7$
4. $\frac{w}{2} = 6$ $w = 12$

3 Close

Summarize

Give brief definitions of the new vocabulary in the lesson: *equation* and *solution*. Have a student explain to the class how equations are like balanced scales. Ask the students how they know when they have found the right answer.

2-4 Exercises

Assignment Guide

If you finished Example 1 assign:
Average 1–6, 8–19, 22–41, 46–52
Advanced 1–6, 8–19, 26–44, 46–52

If you finished Example 2 assign:
Average 1–34, 36–41, 46–52
Advanced 1–35, 42–52

Homework Quick Check

Quickly check key concepts.
Exercises: 8, 20, 22, 34, 40

Math Background

Much of the work students will do in their study of algebra will focus on equations. Because this chapter is an introduction to algebra, it is appropriate to highlight for students how equations relate to their earlier work in arithmetic.

Students realize that $2 + 2 = 4$ is a true statement and that $2 + 2 = 5$ is a false statement. Because of this, students may think that all algebraic equations have exactly one solution. Let them know that this is not the case, as they will discover through further work in algebra.

Answers

34. Possible answer: If 6 pizzas are cut into 8 slices, there will be 48 slices. If the 24 people eat 2 slices each, there will be enough. If any one wants more than 2 slices, there will not be enou

Georgi Standa

M6P1.b Solve mathematics a

M6P3.a Orga their mathematical thinking through communication.

2-4 Exercises

Georgia Performance Standards
M6P1.b, M6P3.a

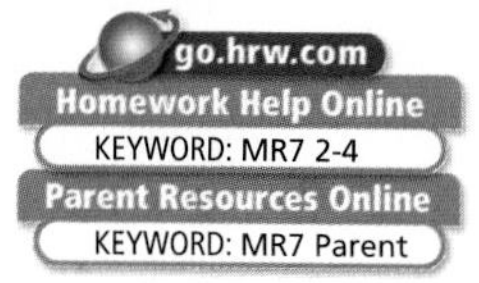

GUIDED PRACTICE

See Example 1 **Determine whether the given value of the variable is a solution.**

1. $c + 23 = 48$ for $c = 35$ no
2. $z + 31 = 73$ for $z = 42$ yes
3. $96 = 130 - d$ for $d = 34$ yes
4. $85 = 194 - a$ for $a = 105$ no
5. $75 \div y = 5$ for $y = 15$ yes
6. $78 \div n = 13$ for $n = 5$ no

See Example 2

7. **Social Studies** An almanac states that the Minnehaha Waterfall in Minnesota is 53 feet tall. A tour guide said the Minnehaha Waterfall is 636 inches tall. Determine if these two measurements are equal. 53 feet is equal to 636 inches.

INDEPENDENT PRACTICE

See Example 1 **Determine whether the given value of the variable is a solution.**

8. $w + 19 = 49$ for $w = 30$ yes
9. $d + 27 = 81$ for $d = 44$ no
10. $g + 34 = 91$ for $g = 67$ no
11. $k + 16 = 55$ for $k = 39$ yes
12. $101 = 150 - h$ for $h = 49$ yes
13. $89 = 111 - m$ for $m = 32$ no
14. $116 = 144 - q$ for $q = 38$ no
15. $92 = 120 - t$ for $t = 28$ yes
16. $80 \div b = 20$ for $b = 4$ yes
17. $91 \div x = 7$ for $x = 12$ no
18. $55 \div j = 5$ for $j = 10$ no
19. $49 \div r = 7$ for $r = 7$ yes

See Example 2

20. **Money** Kent earns \$6 per hour at his after-school job. One week, he worked 12 hours and received a paycheck for \$66. Determine if Kent was paid the correct amount of money. (*Hint:* \$6 · hours = total pay) No, he was not paid correctly.
21. **Measurement** The Eiffel Tower in Paris, France, is 300 meters tall. A fact page states that it is 30,000 centimeters tall. Determine if these two measurements are equal. (*Hint:* 1 m = 100 cm) 300 m is equal to 30,000 cm.

PRACTICE AND PROBLEM SOLVING

CRCT GPS
Extra Practice pp. 746–7

Determine whether the given value of the variable is a solution.

22. $93 = 48 + u$ for $u = 35$ no
23. $112 = 14 \times f$ for $f = 8$ yes
24. $13 = m \div 8$ for $m = 104$ yes
25. $79 = z - 23$ for $z = 112$ no
26. $64 = l - 34$ for $l = 98$ yes
27. $105 = p \times 7$ for $p = 14$ no
28. $94 \div s = 26$ for $s = 3$ no
29. $v + 79 = 167$ for $v = 88$ yes
30. $m + 36 = 54$ for $m = 18$ yes
31. $x - 35 = 96$ for $x = 112$ no
32. $12y = 84$ for $y = 7$ yes
33. $7x = 56$ for $x = 8$ yes
34. **Estimation** A large pizza has 8 slices. Determine if 6 large pizzas will be enough to feed 24 people, if each person eats 2 to 3 slices of pizza.

RETEACH 2-4

eteach
uations and Their Solutions

on is a mathematical sentence that says that two are equal.

ations contain variables. A solution for an equation is a a variable that makes the statement true.

write related facts using addition and subtraction.
13 $13 - 6 = 7$

write related facts using multiplication and division.
2 $12 \div 4 = 3$

use related facts to find solutions for equations. If the related fact matches the value for the variable, then that value is a solution.

A. $x + 5 = 9$, when $x = 3$
Think: $9 - 5 = x$
$x = 4$
$3 \neq 4$
So $x = 3$ is not a solution of $x + 5 = 9$.

B. $x - 7 = 5$, when $x = 12$
Think: $5 + 7 = x$
$x = 12$
$12 = 12$
So $x = 12$ is a solution of $x - 7 = 5$.

C. $2x = 14$, when $x = 9$
Think: $14 \div 2 = x$
$x = 7$
$9 \neq 7$
So $x = 9$ is not a solution for $2x = 14$.

D. $x \div 5 = 3$, when $x = 15$
Think: $3 \cdot 5 = x$
$x = 15$
$15 = 15$
So $x = 15$ is a solution for $x \div 5 = 3$.

Use related facts to determine whether the given value is a solution for each equation.

1. $x + 6 = 14$, when $x = 8$ yes
2. $s \div 4 = 5$, when $s = 24$ no
3. $g - 3 = 7$, when $g = 11$ no
4. $3a = 18$, when $a = 6$ yes
5. $26 = y - 9$, when $y = 35$ yes
6. $b \cdot 5 = 20$, when $b = 3$ no
7. $15 = v \div 3$, when $v = 45$ yes
8. $11 = p + 6$, when $p = 5$ yes
9. $6k = 78$, when $k = 12$ no

PRACTICE 2-4

LESSON 2-4 **Practice B**
Equations and Their Solutions

Determine whether the given value of the variable is a solution.

1. $9 + x = 21$ for $x = 11$ No
2. $n - 12 = 5$ for $n = 17$ Yes
3. $25 \cdot r = 75$ for $r = 3$ Yes
4. $72 \div q = 8$ for $q = 9$ Yes
5. $28 + c = 43$ for $c = 15$ Yes
6. $u \div 11 = 10$ for $u = 111$ No
7. $\frac{k}{8} = 4$ for $k = 24$ No
8. $16x = 48$ for $x = 3$ Yes
9. $73 - f = 29$ for $f = 54$ No
10. $67 - j = 25$ for $j = 42$ Yes
11. $39 \div v = 13$ for $v = 3$ Yes
12. $88 + d = 100$ for $d = 2$ No
13. $14p = 20$ for $p = 5$ No
14. $6w = 30$ for $w = 5$ Yes
15. $7 + x = 70$ for $x = 10$ No
16. $6 \cdot n = 174$ for $n = 29$ Yes

Replace each ? with a number that makes the equation correct.

17. $5 + 1 = 2 + ?$ 4
18. $10 - ? = 12 - 7$ 5
19. $? \cdot 3 = 2 \cdot 9$ 6
20. $28 \div 4 = 14 \div ?$ 2
21. $? + 8 = 6 + 3$ 1
22. $12 \cdot 0 = ? \cdot 15$ 0
23. Carla had \$15. After she bought lunch, she had \$8 left. Write an equation using the variable x to model this situation. What does your variable represent?
$15 - x = 8$; x = the amount she spent on lunch
24. Seventy-two people signed up for the soccer league. After the players were evenly divided into teams, there were 6 teams in the league. Write an equation to model this situation using the variable x.
$72 \div x = 6$

35. **Multi-Step** Rebecca has 17 one-dollar bills. Courtney has 350 nickels. Do the two girls have the same amount of money? (*Hint*: First find how many nickels are in a dollar.)
$17 \neq 350 \div 20$; No, they do not have the same amount of money.

Replace each ▒ with a number that makes the equation correct.

36. $4 + 1 =$ ▒ $+ 2$ 3
37. $2 +$ ▒ $= 6 + 2$ 6
38. ▒ $- 5 = 9 - 2$ 12
39. $5(4) = 10($▒$)$ 2
40. $3 + 6 =$ ▒ $- 4$ 13
41. $12 \div 4 = 9 \div$ ▒ 3

42. **Critical Thinking** Linda is building a rectangular playhouse. The width is x feet. The length is $x + 3$ feet. The distance around the base of the playhouse is 36 feet. Is 8 the value of x? Explain.

43. **Choose a Strategy** What should replace the question mark to keep the scale balanced? C

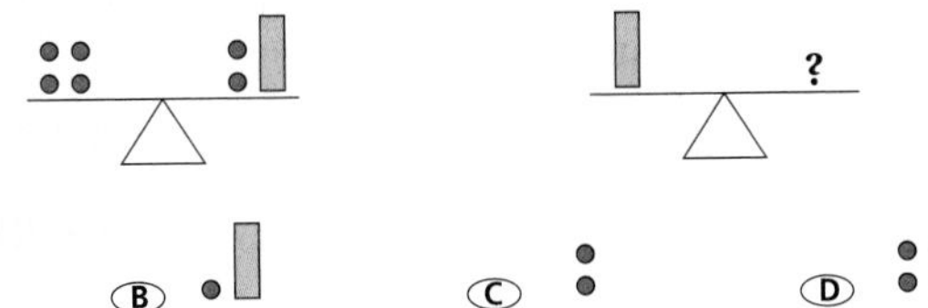

Ⓐ Ⓑ Ⓒ Ⓓ

44. **Write About It** Explain how to determine if a value is a solution to an equation.

45. **Challenge** Is $n = 4$ a solution for $n^2 + 79 = 88$? Explain.
no; The equation is not balanced when $n = 4$.

CRCT Prep • GPS Support • Spiral Review

46. **Multiple Choice** For which equation is $b = 8$ a solution?
Ⓐ $13 - b = 8$ Ⓑ $8 + b = 21$ Ⓒ $b - 13 = 21$ Ⓓ $b + 13 = 21$

47. **Multiple Choice** When Paul gets 53 more postcards, he will have 82 cards in his collection. Solve the equation $n + 53 = 82$ to find how many postcards Paul has in his collection now.
Ⓕ 135 Ⓖ 125 Ⓗ 29 Ⓙ 27

Write each expression in exponential form. (Lesson 1-3)

48. $3 \times 3 \times 3 \times 3 \times 3$ 3^5
49. $9 \times 9 \times 9 \times 9$ 9^4
50. $13 \times 13 \times 13$ 13^3
51. 8×8 8^2

Write an expression for the sequence in the table. (Lesson 2-3) $3n + 1$

52.

Position	1	2	3	4	5	n
Value of Term	4	7	10	13	16	▒

CHALLENGE 2-4

LESSON 2-4 **Challenge**
Keep It Balanced

Study the scales below. Then circle the solution below each scale that will keep it balanced.

1. $a + 17 = 25$
$a = 8$ (circled) $a = 9$

2. $6 = 24 \div x$
$x = 3$ $x = 4$ (circled)

3. $39 = 3n$
$n = 12$ $n = 13$ (circled)

4. $46 - c = 27$
$c = 19$ (circled) $c = 29$

5. $p \div 7 = 9$
$p = 49$ $p = 63$ (circled)

6. $52 + m = 100$
$m = 48$ (circled) $m = 58$

PROBLEM SOLVING 2-4

LESSON 2-4 **Problem Solving**
Equations and Their Solutions

Use the table to write and solve an equation to answer each question. Then use your answers to complete the table.

How Many Minutes Can Mammals Stay Underwater?	
Hippopotamus	15
Human	1
Muskrat	12
Platypus	10
Polar bear	2
Sea cow	16
Sea otter	5
Seal	22
Sperm whale	112

1. A hippopotamus can stay underwater 3 times as long as a sea otter can. How long can a sea otter stay underwater?
$3x = 15; x = 5;$
5 minutes

2. A seal can stay underwater 10 minutes longer than a muskrat can. How long can a muskrat stay underwater?
$x + 10 = 22; x = 12;$
12 minutes

3. A sperm whale can stay underwater 7 times longer than a sea cow can. How long can a sperm whale stay underwater?
$x \div 7 = 16; x = 112;$
112 minutes

Circle the letter of the correct answer.

4. The difference between the time a platypus and a polar bear can stay underwater is 8 minutes. How long can a polar bear stay underwater?
A 1 minute
Ⓑ 2 minutes
C 3 minutes
D 5 minutes

5. When you divide the amount of time any of the animals in the table can stay underwater by itself, the answer is always the amount of time the average human can stay underwater. How long can the average human stay underwater?
F 6 minutes
G 4 minutes
H 2 minutes
Ⓙ 1 minute

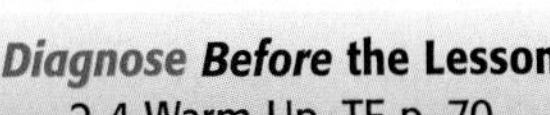

Ongoing Assessment and Intervention

***Diagnose Before* the Lesson**
2-4 Warm Up, TE p. 70

***Monitor During* the Lesson**
2-4 Know-It Notebook
2-4 Questioning Strategies

***Assess After* the Lesson**
2-4 Lesson Quiz, TE p. 73

Common Error Alert

Some students may be confused about how to approach Exercises 36–41 because there are operations shown on each side of the equal sign. Advise students to perform the operation on the side of the equation that only has numbers, and think of the gray box on the other side of the equation as a variable.

Answers

42. See p. A1.
44. Substitute the value for the variable and see if both sides are equal.

Test Prep Doctor In Exercise 46, students will need to substitute 8 for b in each equation in order to find the answer. Students who chose **A**, **B**, or **C** should recheck their work.

Journal

Have students write about other ways scales are used in everyday life.

Power Presentations with PowerPoint®

2-4 Lesson Quiz

Determine whether the given value of each variable is a solution.

1. $85 = 13x$ for $x = 5$ no
2. $w + 38 = 210$ for $w = 172$ yes
3. $8y = 88$ for $y = 11$ yes
4. $16 = w \div 6$ for $w = 98$ no
5. The local pizza shop charged Kylee $172 for 21 medium pizzas. The price of a medium pizza is $8. Determine whether Kylee paid the correct amount of money. (*Hint:* $8 • pizzas = total cost) no

Also available on transparency

2-5 Organizer

Pacing: Traditional $1\frac{1}{2}$ day
Block $\frac{3}{4}$ day

Objective: Students solve whole number addition equations.

GPS M6A3
Hands-On Lab
In *Hands-On Lab Activities*

Online Edition
Tutorial Videos, Interactivities

Countdown to CRCT Week 4

Power Presentations with PowerPoint®

Warm Up

Determine whether each value is a solution.

1. $86 + x = 102$ for $x = 16$ yes
2. $18 + x = 26$ for $x = 4$ no
3. $x + 46 = 214$ for $x = 168$ yes
4. $9 + x = 35$ for $x = 26$ yes

Problem of the Day

After Renee used 40 m of string for her kite and gave 5 m to her sister for her wagon, she had 8 m of string left. How much string did she have to start with? 53 m

Also available on transparency

Math Fact

The symbol for equality, =, was first used in Robert Recorde's book *The Whetstone of Witte,* published in 1557.

Georgia Performance Standards

M6A3 Students will evaluate algebraic expressions, including those with exponents, and solve simple one-step equations using each of the four basic operations.

M6P1.d Monitor and reflect on the process of mathematical problem solving.

M6P5.b Select, apply, and translate among mathematical representations to solve problems.

M6P5.c Use representations to model and interpret physical, social, and mathematical phenomena.

2-5 Addition Equations

Learn to solve whole-number addition equations.

Georgia Performance Standards

M6A3 Evaluate algebraic expressions and solve simple one-step equations using each of the four basic operations. Also, M6P1.d, M6P5.b, M6P5.c.

Some surfers recommend that the length of a beginner's surfboard be 14 inches greater than the surfer's height. If a surfboard is 82 inches, how tall should the surfer be to ride it?

The height of the surfer *combined* with 14 inches equals 82 inches. To combine amounts, you need to add.

Let h stand for the surfer's height. You can use the equation $h + 14 = 82$.

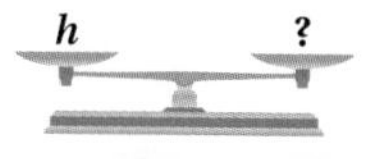

The equation $h + 14 = 82$ can be represented as a balanced scale.

To find the value of h, you need h by itself on one side of a balanced scale.

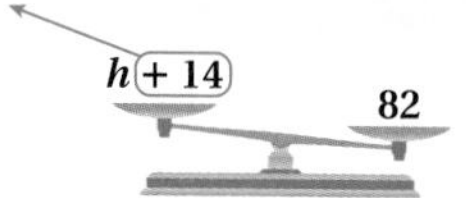

To get h by itself, first take away 14 from the left side of the scale. Now the scale is unbalanced.

To rebalance the scale, take away 14 from the other side.

Taking away 14 from both sides of the scale is the same as subtracting 14 from both sides of the equation.

$$\begin{aligned} h + 14 &= 82 \\ -14 & \quad -14 \\ h &= 68 \end{aligned}$$

A surfer using an 82-inch surfboard should be 68 inches tall.

Subtraction is the inverse, or opposite, of addition. If an equation contains addition, solve it by subtracting from both sides to "undo" the addition.

1 Introduce

Alternate Opener

EXPLORATION

2-5 Addition Equations

How much change from a dollar do you get when you buy something that costs 51 cents?

This problem can also be expressed as **what number plus 51 is 100?**

$n + 51 = 100$
$49 + 51 = 100$
$n = 49$ The change is 49¢.

Find the value of n in each equation.

1. $4 + n = 100$ $n =$ ______
2. $n + 45 = 100$ $n =$ ______
3. $19 + n = 100$ $n =$ ______
4. $n + 65 = 100$ $n =$ ______
5. $100 = 41 + n$ $n =$ ______

Think and Discuss

6. **Discuss** your strategies for solving the equations.
7. **Explain** how you can mentally find the solution to $n + 125 = 500$.

Motivate

ENGLISH LANGUAGE LEARNERS

Review the terms *constant, variable,* and *equation.* Have students give examples of addition equations that include a constant being added to a variable.

Explorations and answers are provided in *Alternate Openers: Explorations Transparencies.*

EXAMPLE 1 Solving Addition Equations

Solve each equation. Check your answers.

A $x + 62 = 93$

$$\begin{aligned} x + 62 &= 93 \\ -62 \quad & -62 \\ x &= 31 \end{aligned}$$

62 is added to x.
Subtract 62 from both sides to undo the addition.

Check $x + 62 = 93$

$31 + 62 \stackrel{?}{=} 93$ *Substitute 31 for x in the equation.*

$93 \stackrel{?}{=} 93$ ✔ *31 is the solution.*

B $81 = 17 + y$

$$\begin{aligned} 81 &= 17 + y \\ -17 \quad & -17 \\ 64 &= y \end{aligned}$$

17 is added to y.
Subtract 17 from both sides to undo the addition.

Check $81 = 17 + y$

$81 \stackrel{?}{=} 17 + 64$ *Substitute 64 for y in the equation.*

$81 \stackrel{?}{=} 81$ ✔ *64 is the solution.*

EXAMPLE 2 *Social Studies Application*

Texhoma, Stratford, and Dalhart are located along Highway 54 in Texas, as shown on the map. Find the distance *d* between Stratford and Texhoma.

distance between Texhoma and Dalhart	=	distance between Stratford and Dalhart	+	distance between Stratford and Texhoma
51	=	31	+	*d*

$$\begin{aligned} 51 &= 31 + d \\ -31 \quad & -31 \\ 20 &= d \end{aligned}$$

31 is added to d.
Subtract 31 from both sides to undo the addition.

The distance between Stratford and Texhoma is 20 miles.

Think and Discuss

1. Tell whether the solution of $c + 4 = 21$ will be less than 21 or greater than 21. Explain.

2. Describe how you could check your answer in Example 2.

COMMON ERROR ALERT

Some students may add the amount subtracted from one side of the equation to the other side. For example: $h + 14 = 82$; $h + 14 - 14 = 82 + 14$; $h = 96$. Stress that to keep the equation "balanced" the same amount must be taken away from each side.

Power Presentations with PowerPoint®

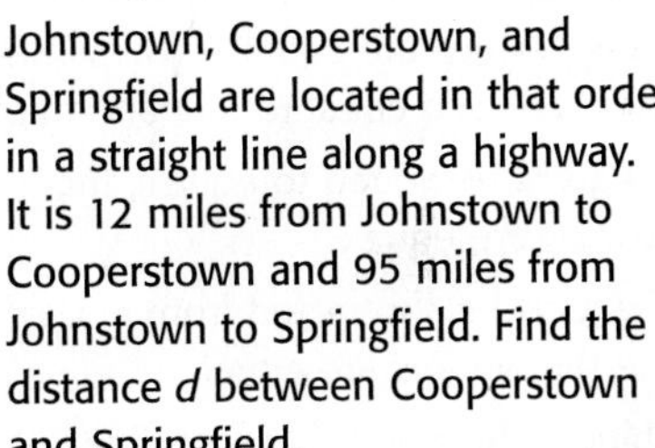

Additional Examples

Example 1

Solve each equation. Check your answers.

A. $x + 87 = 152$
$x = 65$

B. $72 = 18 + y$
$54 = y$

Example 2

Johnstown, Cooperstown, and Springfield are located in that order in a straight line along a highway. It is 12 miles from Johnstown to Cooperstown and 95 miles from Johnstown to Springfield. Find the distance *d* between Cooperstown and Springfield.

It is 83 miles from Cooperstown to Springfield.

Also available on transparency

Answers to *Think and Discuss*

1. Less than 21; you subtract 4 from both sides of the equation, which will make the answer 4 less than 21.
2. Substitute 19 for *d* in the equation $25 = 6 + d$. $6 + 19 = 25$ is true.

2 Teach

Guided Instruction

In this lesson, students learn to solve whole-number addition problems. First teach students to use a pictorial model of a balanced scale to solve an addition equation (Teaching Transparency). Then teach students to solve addition equations by using subtraction, the inverse of addition. Next, have students check their answers.

Modeling Have students draw balanced scale models when working through the exercises to give them a visual model to reinforce the concept.

Reaching All Learners

Through Concrete Manipulatives

Students may have difficulty grasping the concept of using subtraction to solve addition equations. Have students use manipulatives such as algebra tiles or counters provided in the Manipulatives Kit to solve addition equations such as the following:

1. $x + 7 = 12$ 5
2. $9 + z = 20$ 11
3. $8 = 5 + y$ 3
4. $11 = 4 + y$ 7

3 Close

Summarize

Walk students through the process of how to solve addition equations involving variables and how to check solutions. Emphasize that equations are balanced mathematical statements and that the balance must be maintained while finding the solution. Have a volunteer demonstrate how to properly write the steps for finding the solution and checking the answer.

2-5 Exercises

Assignment Guide

If you finished Example 1 assign:
Average 1–6, 8–16, 18–29, 37–43
Advanced 1–6, 8–16, 21–29, 30–32, 37–43

If you finished Example 2 assign:
Average 1–31, 37–43
Advanced 1–26, 32–43

Homework Quick Check

Quickly check key concepts.
Exercises: 8, 17–18, 30

Math Background

In his *Elements, Book I*, Euclid listed five axioms that he called "common notions."

1. Things which are equal to the same thing are also equal to one another.
2. If equals be added to equals, the wholes are equal.
3. If equals be subtracted from equals, the remainders are equal.
4. Things which coincide with one another are equal to one another.
5. The whole is greater than the part.

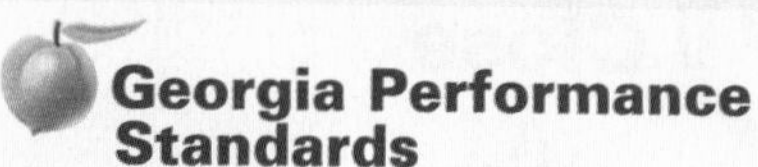

M6P3.a Organize and consolidate their mathematical thinking through communication.

M6P4.c Recognize and apply mathematics in contexts outside of mathematics.

2-5 Exercises

Georgia Performance Standards
M6P3.a, M6P4.c

Homework Help Online
KEYWORD: MR7 2-5
Parent Resources Online
KEYWORD: MR7 Parent

GUIDED PRACTICE

See Example 1

Solve each equation. Check your answers.

1. $x + 54 = 90$
2. $49 = 12 + y$
3. $n + 27 = 46$
4. $22 + t = 91$
5. $31 = p + 13$
6. $c + 38 = 54$

See Example 2

7. Lou, Michael, and Georgette live on Mulberry Street, as shown on the map. Lou lives 10 blocks from Georgette. Georgette lives 4 blocks from Michael. How many blocks does Michael live from Lou?

INDEPENDENT PRACTICE

See Example 1

Solve each equation. Check your answers.

8. $x + 19 = 24$
9. $10 = r + 3$
10. $s + 11 = 50$
11. $b + 17 = 42$
12. $12 + m = 28$
13. $z + 68 = 77$
14. $72 = n + 51$
15. $g + 28 = 44$
16. $27 = 15 + y$

See Example 2

17. What is the length of a killer whale?

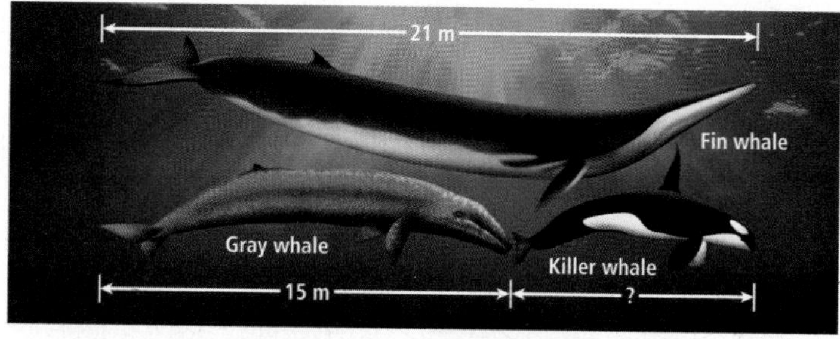

PRACTICE AND PROBLEM SOLVING

CRCT GPS
Extra Practice pp. 746–7

Solve each equation.

18. $x + 12 = 16$
19. $n + 32 = 39$
20. $23 + q = 34$
21. $52 + y = 71$
22. $73 = c + 35$
23. $93 = h + 15$
24. $125 = n + 85$
25. $87 = b + 18$
26. $12 + y = 50$
27. $t + 17 = 43$
28. $k + 9 = 56$
29. $25 + m = 47$

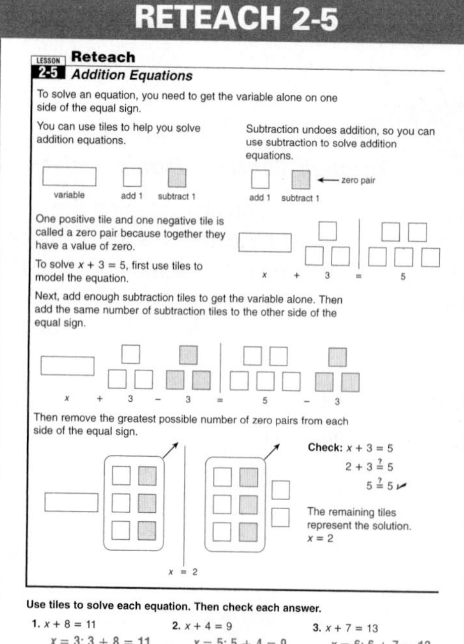

RETEACH 2-5

LESSON 2-5 **Reteach**
Addition Equations

To solve an equation, you need to get the variable alone on one side of the equal sign.

You can use tiles to help you solve addition equations.

variable add 1 subtract 1

Subtraction undoes addition, so you can use subtraction to solve addition equations.

add 1 subtract 1 ← zero pair

One positive tile and one negative tile is called a zero pair because together they have a value of zero.

To solve $x + 3 = 5$, first use tiles to model the equation.

$x + 3 = 5$

Next, add enough subtraction tiles to get the variable alone. Then add the same number of subtraction tiles to the other side of the equal sign.

$x + 3 - 3 = 5 - 3$

Then remove the greatest possible number of zero pairs from each side of the equal sign.

$x = 2$

Check: $x + 3 = 5$
$2 + 3 \stackrel{?}{=} 5$
$5 \stackrel{?}{=} 5$ ✓

The remaining tiles represent the solution.
$x = 2$

Use tiles to solve each equation. Then check each answer.

1. $x + 8 = 11$ — $x = 3; 3 + 8 = 11$
2. $x + 4 = 9$ — $x = 5; 5 + 4 = 9$
3. $x + 7 = 13$ — $x = 6; 6 + 7 = 13$

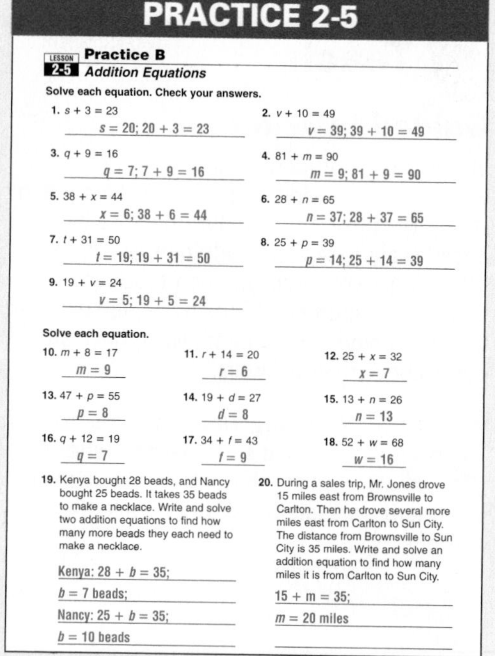

PRACTICE 2-5

LESSON 2-5 **Practice B**
Addition Equations

Solve each equation. Check your answers.

1. $s + 3 = 23$ — $s = 20; 20 + 3 = 23$
2. $v + 10 = 49$ — $v = 39; 39 + 10 = 49$
3. $q + 9 = 16$ — $q = 7; 7 + 9 = 16$
4. $81 + m = 90$ — $m = 9; 81 + 9 = 90$
5. $38 + x = 44$ — $x = 6; 38 + 6 = 44$
6. $28 + n = 65$ — $n = 37; 28 + 37 = 65$
7. $t + 31 = 50$ — $t = 19; 19 + 31 = 50$
8. $25 + p = 39$ — $p = 14; 25 + 14 = 39$
9. $19 + v = 24$ — $v = 5; 19 + 5 = 24$

Solve each equation.

10. $m + 8 = 17$ — $m = 9$
11. $r + 14 = 20$ — $r = 6$
12. $25 + x = 32$ — $x = 7$
13. $47 + p = 55$ — $p = 8$
14. $19 + d = 27$ — $d = 8$
15. $13 + n = 26$ — $n = 13$
16. $q + 12 = 19$ — $q = 7$
17. $34 + f = 43$ — $f = 9$
18. $52 + w = 68$ — $w = 16$

19. Kenya bought 28 beads, and Nancy bought 25 beads. It takes 35 beads to make a necklace. Write and solve two addition equations to find how many more beads they each need to make a necklace.

Kenya: $28 + b = 35$;
$b = 7$ beads;
Nancy: $25 + b = 35$;
$b = 10$ beads

20. During a sales trip, Mr. Jones drove 15 miles east from Brownsville to Carlton. Then he drove several more miles east from Carlton to Sun City. The distance from Brownsville to Sun City is 35 miles. Write and solve an addition equation to find how many miles it is from Carlton to Sun City.

$15 + m = 35$;
$m = 20$ miles

Physical Science

Popular items like the ball and the mood rings above are made of heat-sensitive materials. Changes in temperature, cause these materials to change color.

Write an equation for each statement.

30. The number of eggs e increased by 3 equals 14.

31. The number of new photos taken p added to 20 equals 36.

32. Physical Science Temperature can be measured in degrees Fahrenheit, degrees Celsius, or kelvins. To convert from degrees Celsius to kelvins, add 273 to the Celsius temperature. Complete the table.

	Kelvins (K)	°C + 273 = K	Celsius (°C)
Water Freezes	273	°C + 273 = 273	▒
Body Temperature	310	▒	▒
Water Boils	373	▒	▒

33. History In 1520, the explorer Ferdinand Magellan tried to measure the depth of the ocean. He weighted a 370 m rope and lowered it into the ocean. This rope was not long enough to reach the ocean floor. Suppose the depth at this location was 1,250 m. How much longer would Magellan's rope have to have been to reach the ocean floor?

34. Write a Problem Use data from your science book to write a problem that can be solved using an addition equation. Solve your problem.

35. Write About It Why are addition and subtraction called inverse operations?

36. Challenge In the magic square at right, each row, column, and diagonal has the same sum. Find the values of x, y, and z.

7	61	x
y	37	1
31	z	67

CRCT Prep • GPS Support • Spiral Review

37. Multiple Choice Pauline hit 6 more home runs than Danielle. Pauline hit 18 home runs. How many home runs did Danielle hit?

Ⓐ 3 Ⓑ 12 Ⓒ 18 Ⓓ 24

38. Multiple Choice Which is the solution to the equation $79 + r = 118$?

Ⓕ $r = 39$ Ⓖ $r = 52$ Ⓗ $r = 79$ Ⓙ $r = 197$

Order the numbers from least to greatest. (Lesson 1-1)

39. 798; 648; 923 **40.** 1,298; 876; 972 **41.** 1,498; 2,163; 1,036

Evaluate each expression to find the missing values in the tables. (Lesson 2-1)

42.

x	5	6	7	8
$9x$	45	▒	▒	▒

43.

y	121	99	77	55
$y \div 11$	11	▒	▒	▒

CHALLENGE 2-5

LESSON 2-5 Challenge
The Temperature's Rising

Each pair of thermometers shows a beginning temperature on the left and an ending temperature on the right. Write and solve an addition equation to find the change in temperature shown on each pair of thermometers.

1. $55 + x = 60$; $x = 5$°F
2. $20 + x = 30$; $x = 10$°F
3. $23 + x = 27$; $x = 4$°F
4. $8 + x = 15$; $x = 7$°F
5. $87 + x = 98$; $x = 11$°F
6. $14 + x = 27$; $x = 13$°F

PROBLEM SOLVING 2-5

LESSON 2-5 Problem Solving
Addition Equations

Use the bar graph and addition equations to answer the questions.

Most-Populated States

State: California, Florida, Illinois, Michigan, New York, Ohio, Pennsylvania, Texas

Population (in millions): 0, 5, 10, 15, 20, 25, 30, 35

1. How many more people live in California than in New York?
$19 + x = 34$; $x = 15$;
15 million people

2. How many more people live in Ohio than in Michigan?
$10 + x = 11$; $x = 1$;
1 million people

3. How many more people live in Florida than in Illinois?
$12 + x = 16$; $x = 4$;
4 million people

4. How many more people live in Texas than in Pennsylvania?
$12 + x = 21$; $x = 9$;
9 million people

Circle the letter of the correct answer.

5. Which two states' populations are used in the equation $12 + x = 12$?
A Pennsylvania and Texas
B Ohio and Florida
C Michigan and Illinois
Ⓓ Illinois and Pennsylvania

6. What is the value of x in the equation in Exercise 5?
Ⓕ 0
G 1
H 12
J 24

7. In 2003, the total population of the United States was 292 million. How many of those people did not live in one of the states shown on the graph?
A 416 million
B 73 million
Ⓒ 154 million
D 292 million

8. The combined population of Ohio and one other state is the same as the population of Texas. What is that state?
F California
G Florida
Ⓗ Michigan
J Pennsylvania

Ongoing Assessment and Intervention

***Diagnose Before* the Lesson**
2-5 Warm Up, TE p. 74

***Monitor During* the Lesson**
2-5 Know-It Notebook
2-5 Questioning Strategies

***Assess After* the Lesson**
2-5 Lesson Quiz, TE p. 77

Answer

34. Possible answer: 37 mL of glycerin was added to a solution to bring the total volume to 93 mL. What was the original volume of the solution? $37 + x = 93$, $x = 56$ The original volume was 56 mL.

Test Prep Doctor In Exercise 37, students need to identify which player hit more home runs and decide whether the answer should be greater or less than 18. Students who chose **D** should read the problem again carefully.

Journal

Have students write about why taking your shoes off before you stand on a scale is similar to solving an equation like $x + 2 = 95$.

Power Presentations with PowerPoint®

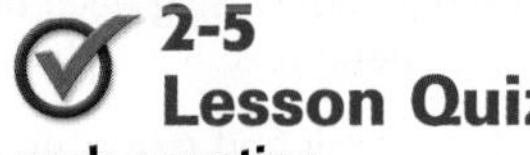

2-5 Lesson Quiz

Solve each equation.

1. $x + 15 = 72$ $x = 57$

2. $81 = x + 24$ $x = 57$

3. $x + 22 = 67$ $x = 45$

4. $93 = x + 14$ $x = 79$

5. Kaitlin is 2 inches taller than Reba. Reba is 54 inches tall. How tall is Kaitlin? 56 inches

Also available on transparency

2-6 Organizer

Pacing: Traditional 1 day
Block $\frac{1}{2}$ day

Objective: Students solve whole-number subtraction equations.

Online Edition
Tutorial Videos, Interactivities

Countdown to CRCT Week 4

Warm Up

Solve each equation.

1. $x + 7 = 22$ $x = 15$
2. $18 + x = 105$ $x = 87$
3. $16 = x + 9$ $x = 7$
4. $23 = x + 4$ $x = 19$

Problem of the Day

Bruce has 25 CDs remaining after giving 14 to John, 17 to Mary, and 25 to Sue. How many CDs did he begin with? 81

Also available on transparency

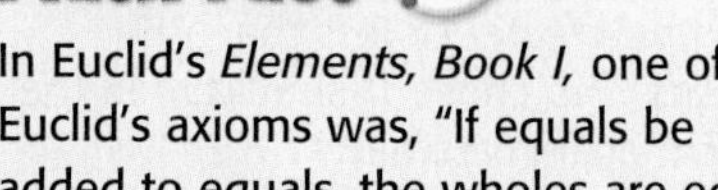

In Euclid's *Elements, Book I,* one of Euclid's axioms was, "If equals be added to equals, the wholes are equal."

Georgia Performance Standards

M6A3 Students will evaluate algebraic expressions, including those with exponents, and solve simple one-step equations using each of the four basic operations.

M6P1.d Monitor and reflect on the process of mathematical problem solving.

M6P5.b Select, apply, and translate among mathematical representations to solve problems.

2-6 Subtraction Equations

Learn to solve whole-number subtraction equations.

Georgia Performance Standards

M6A3 Evaluate algebraic expressions and solve simple one-step equations using each of the four basic operations. Also, M6P1.d, M6P5.b.

When John F. Kennedy became president of the United States, he was 43 years old. He was 8 years younger than Abraham Lincoln was when Lincoln became president. How old was Lincoln when he became president?

Kennedy was President from 1961 to 1963.

Lincoln was President from 1861 to 1865.

Let a represent Abraham Lincoln's age.

Abraham Lincoln's age	−	8	=	John F. Kennedy's age
a	−	8	=	43

Remember that addition and subtraction are inverse operations. When an equation contains subtraction, use addition to "undo" the subtraction. Remember to add the same amount to both sides of the equation.

$$\begin{aligned} a - 8 &= 43 \\ +8 \quad &\quad +8 \\ a \quad &= 51 \end{aligned}$$

Abraham Lincoln was 51 years old when he became president.

EXAMPLE 1 Solving Subtraction Equations

A **Solve $p - 2 = 5$. Check your answer.**

$$\begin{aligned} p - 2 &= 5 \\ +2 \quad &\quad +2 \\ p \quad &= 7 \end{aligned}$$

2 is subtracted from p. Add 2 to both sides to undo the subtraction.

Check $p - 2 = 5$

$7 - 2 \stackrel{?}{=} 5$ *Substitute 7 for p in the equation.*

$5 \stackrel{?}{=} 5$ ✔ *7 is the solution.*

1 Introduce

Alternate Opener

EXPLORATION

2-6 Subtraction Equations

After spending \$11, Jane has \$3 left in her purse. How much did she have to begin with?

Beginning amount $11 spent Amount left

$n - 11 = 3$
$14 - 11 = 3$
$n = 14$ She had \$14 to begin with.

Find the value of n in each equation.

1. $n - 25 = 75$ $n =$ ______
2. $n - 4 = 19$ $n =$ ______
3. $n - 7 = 35$ $n =$ ______
4. $n - 14 = 21$ $n =$ ______
5. $n - 20 = 83$ $n =$ ______

Think and Discuss

6. **Describe** your strategies for solving the subtraction equations.
7. **Explain** how you can find the solution to $n - 125 = 375$.

2 Teach

Guided Instruction

In this lesson, students learn to solve whole number subtraction equations. First, review the fact that addition and subtraction are inverse operations. Then teach students to use addition to solve subtraction equations, and check their solutions.

Explorations and answers are provided in *Alternate Openers: Explorations Transparencies.*

B Solve $40 = x - 11$. Check your answer.

$$\begin{aligned} 40 &= x - 11 \\ +11 &\quad\;\; +11 \\ 51 &= x \end{aligned}$$

11 is subtracted from x.
Add 11 to both sides to undo the subtraction.

Check $40 = x - 11$

$40 \stackrel{?}{=} 51 - 11$ *Substitute 51 for x in the equation.*

$40 \stackrel{?}{=} 40$ ✔ *51 is the solution.*

C Solve $x - 56 = 19$. Check your answer.

$$\begin{aligned} x - 56 &= 19 \\ +56 &\quad +56 \\ x &= 75 \end{aligned}$$

56 is subtracted from x.
Add 56 to both sides to undo the subtraction.

Check $x - 56 = 19$

$75 - 56 \stackrel{?}{=} 19$ *Substitute 75 for x in the equation.*

$19 \stackrel{?}{=} 19$ ✔ *75 is the solution.*

Think and Discuss

GPS M6P1.d, M6P2.c

1. **Tell** whether the solution of $b - 14 = 9$ will be less than 9 or greater than 9. Explain.
2. **Explain** how you know what number to add to both sides of an equation containing subtraction.

Answers to *Think and Discuss:*

1. Greater than 9; you add 14 to both sides of the equation to undo the subtraction, which means the solution will be 14 more than 9.
2. Add the number being subtracted from the variable to both sides of the equation to keep the equation balanced.

2-6 Exercises

Georgia Performance Standards
M6P3.c, M6P4.c

Homework Help Online
KEYWORD: MR7 2-6
Parent Resources Online
KEYWORD: MR7 Parent

GUIDED PRACTICE

See Example 1 Solve each equation. Check your answers.

1. $p - 8 = 9$ $p = 17$
2. $3 = x - 16$ $x = 19$
3. $a - 13 = 18$ $a = 31$
4. $15 = y - 7$ $y = 22$
5. $n - 24 = 9$ $n = 33$
6. $39 = d - 2$ $d = 41$

INDEPENDENT PRACTICE

See Example 1 Solve each equation. Check your answers.

7. $y - 18 = 7$ $y = 25$
8. $8 = n - 5$ $n = 13$
9. $a - 34 = 4$ $a = 38$
10. $c - 21 = 45$ $c = 66$
11. $a - 40 = 57$ $a = 97$
12. $31 = x - 14$ $x = 45$
13. $28 = p - 5$ $p = 33$
14. $z - 42 = 7$ $z = 49$
15. $s - 19 = 12$ $s = 31$

COMMON ERROR ALERT

Students just learned how to solve addition equations in the previous lesson. Because of this, they may try to subtract from each side of the subtraction equation to solve. Remind them to use the inverse operation, addition.

Power Presentations with PowerPoint®

Additional Examples

Example 

Solve each equation. Check your answer.

A. $y - 23 = 39$ $y = 62$
B. $78 = s - 15$ $93 = s$
C. $z - 3 = 12$ $z = 15$

Also available on transparency

2-6 Exercises

Assignment Guide

If you finished Example 1 assign:
Average 1–29, 33–41
Advanced 7–41

Homework Quick Check

Quickly check key concepts.
Exercises: 8, 16, 28

Reaching All Learners

Through Inclusion

Have students work with subtraction equations written on a balanced set of scales. Reinforce the concept of using the inverse operation to isolate the variable while maintaining the balance of the scales.

1. $x - 3 = 15$ $x = 18$
2. $y - 9 = 2$ $y = 11$
3. $7 = n - 6$ $n = 13$
4. $10 = z - 10$ $z = 20$

3 Close

Summarize

Briefly describe how to solve subtraction equations involving variables and how to check solutions. Have a student volunteer to provide the next step in the solution of a subtraction equation. Have another student give an explanation for the step provided by the previous student.

Georgia Performance Standards

M6P3.c Analyze and evaluate the mathematical thinking and strategies of others.

M6P4.c Recognize and apply mathematics in contexts outside of mathematics.

ONGOING ASSESSMENT and INTERVENTION

Diagnose Before the Lesson
2-6 Warm Up, TE p. 78

Monitor During the Lesson
2-6 Know-It Notebook
2-6 Questioning Strategies

Assess After the Lesson
2-6 Lesson Quiz, TE p. 80

Power Presentations with PowerPoint®

2-6 Lesson Quiz

Solve each equation.

1. $x - 9 = 21$ $x = 30$
2. $14 = x - 3$ $x = 17$
3. $x - 7 = 11$ $x = 18$
4. $16 = x - 14$ $x = 30$
5. $x - 9 = 11$ $x = 20$
6. Susan is taller than James. The difference in their height is 4 inches. James is 62 inches tall. How tall is Susan? 66 inches

Also available on transparency

Answers

28. $r = 14{,}162 + 248$; $r = 14{,}410$ ft

30–31. See p. A1.

PRACTICE AND PROBLEM SOLVING

CRCT GPS
Extra Practice pp. 746–7

Solve each equation.

16. $r - 57 = 7$ $r = 64$ **17.** $11 = x - 25$ $x = 36$ **18.** $8 = y - 96$ $y = 104$

19. $a - 6 = 15$ $a = 21$ **20.** $q - 14 = 22$ $q = 36$ **21.** $f - 12 = 2$ $f = 14$

22. $18 = j - 19$ $j = 37$ **23.** $109 = r - 45$ $r = 154$ **24.** $d - 8 = 29$ $d = 37$

25. $g - 71 = 72$ $g = 143$ **26.** $p - 13 = 111$ $p = 124$ **27.** $13 = m - 5$ $m = 18$

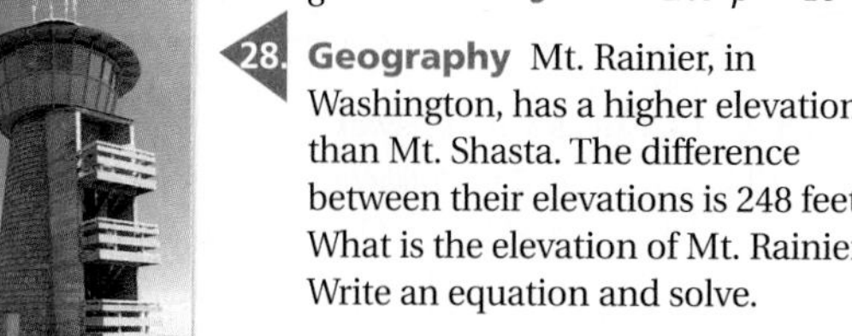

Georgia LINK Geography

Brasstown Bald is the highest mountain in Georgia. The observation tower at the top gives visitors a view from 4,784 feet above sea level.

28. Geography Mt. Rainier, in Washington, has a higher elevation than Mt. Shasta. The difference between their elevations is 248 feet. What is the elevation of Mt. Rainier? Write an equation and solve.

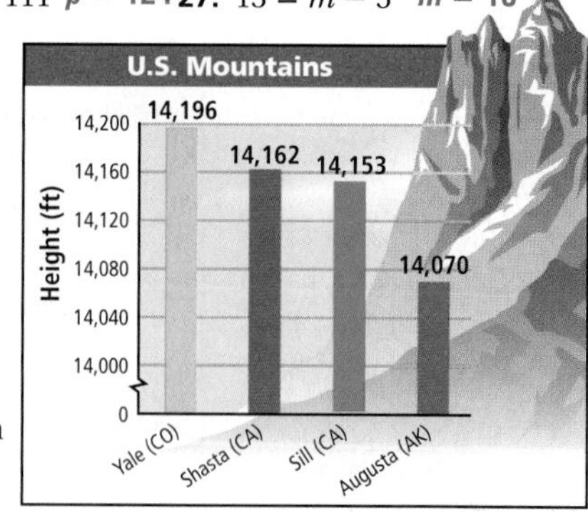

29. Social Studies In 2004, the population of New York City was 5 million less than the population of Shanghai, China. The population of New York City was 8 million. Solve the equation $8 = s - 5$ to find the population of Shanghai. 13 million

30. Write About It Suppose $n - 15$ is a whole number. What do you know about the value of n? Explain.

31. What's the Error? Look at the student paper at right. What did the student do wrong? What is the correct answer?

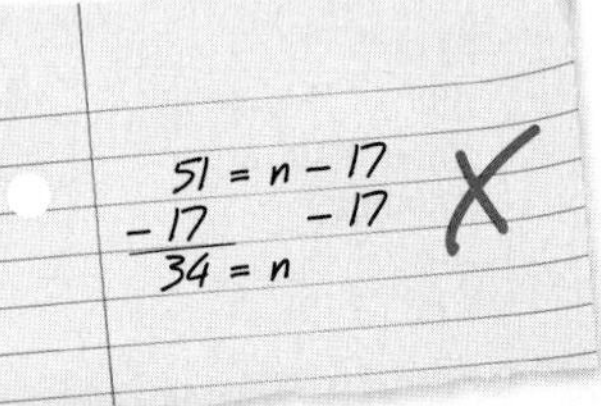

32. Challenge Write "the difference between n and 16 is 5" as an algebraic equation. Then find the solution. $n - 16 = 5$; $n = 21$

CRCT PREP • GPS SUPPORT • SPIRAL REVIEW

33. Multiple Choice Which is a solution to the equation $j - 39 = 93$?

Ⓐ $j = 54$ Ⓑ $j = 66$ Ⓒ $j = 93$ Ⓓ $j = 132$ (circled)

34. Short Response When 17 is subtracted from a number, the result is 64. Write an equation that can be used to find the original number. Then find the original number. $x - 17 = 64$; 81

Evaluate each expression. (Lesson 1-4)

35. $81 - 4 \times 3 + 18 \div (6 + 3)$ 71 **36.** $17 \times (5 - 3) + 16 \div 8$ 36 **37.** $3^2 - (15 - 8) + 4 \times 5$ 22

Solve each equation. (Lesson 2-5)

38. $a + 3 = 18$ $a = 15$ **39.** $y + 7 = 45$ $y = 38$ **40.** $x + 16 = 71$ $x = 55$ **41.** $87 = b + 31$ $b = 56$

CHALLENGE 2-6
PROBLEM SOLVING 2-6

LESSON 2-6 **Problem Solving**
Subtraction Equations

Write and solve subtraction equations to answer the questions.

1. Dr. Felix Hoffman invented aspirin in 1899. That was 29 years before Alexander Fleming invented penicillin. When was penicillin invented?
   $x - 29 = 1899$;
   $x = 1928$; in 1928
2. Kimberly was born on February 2. That is 10 days earlier than Kent's birthday. When is Kent's birthday?
   $x - 10 = 2$;
   $x = 12$; February 12
3. Kansas and North Dakota are the top wheat-producing states. In 2000, North Dakota produced 314 million bushels of wheat, which was 34 million bushels less than Kansas produced. How much wheat did Kansas farmers grow in 2000?
   $x - 34 = 314$;
   $x = 348$; 348 million bushels
4. Scientists assign every element an atomic number, which is the number of protons in the nucleus of that element. The atomic number of silver is 47, which is 32 less than the atomic number of gold. How many protons are in the nucleus of gold?
   $x - 32 = 47$;
   $x = 79$; 79 protons

Circle the letter of the correct answer.

5. The spine-tailed swift and the frigate bird are the two fastest birds on earth. A frigate bird can fly 95 miles per hour, which is 11 miles per hour slower than a spine-tailed swift. How fast can a spine-tailed swift fly?
   A 84 miles per hour
   B 101 miles per hour
   Ⓒ 106 miles per hour
   D 116 miles per hour
6. The Green Bay Packers and the Kansas City Chiefs played in the first Super Bowl in 1967. The Chiefs lost by 25 points, with a final score of 10. How many points did the Packers score in the first Super Bowl?
   Ⓕ 35
   G 25
   H 15
   J 0
7. The Rocky Mountains extend 3,750 miles across North America. That is 750 miles shorter than the Andes Mountains in South America. How long are the Andes Mountains?
   A 3,000 miles C 180 miles
   B 5 miles Ⓓ 4,500 miles
8. When the United States took its first census in 1790, only 4 million people lived here. That was 288 million fewer people than the population in 2003. What was the population of the United States in 2003?
   Ⓕ 292 million H 69 million
   G 284 million J 1,108 million

RETEACH 2-6

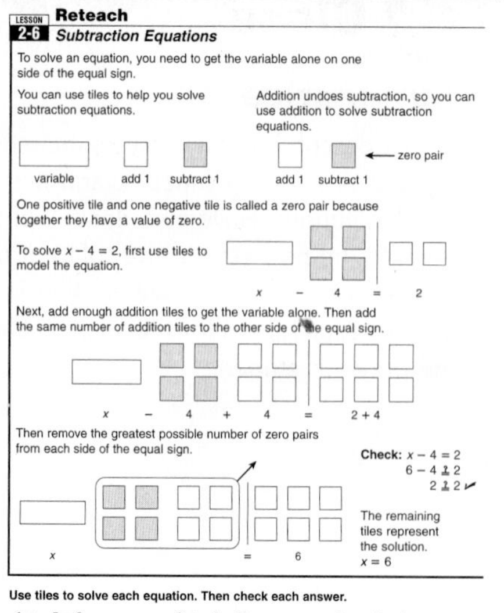

LESSON 2-6 **Reteach**
Subtraction Equations

To solve an equation, you need to get the variable alone on one side of the equal sign.

You can use tiles to help you solve subtraction equations.

Addition undoes subtraction, so you can use addition to solve subtraction equations.

variable add 1 subtract 1 add 1 subtract 1 ← zero pair

One positive tile and one negative tile is called a zero pair because together they have a value of zero.

To solve $x - 4 = 2$, first use tiles to model the equation.

$x - 4 = 2$

Next, add enough addition tiles to get the variable alone. Then add the same number of addition tiles to the other side of the equal sign.

$x - 4 + 4 = 2 + 4$

Then remove the greatest possible number of zero pairs from each side of the equal sign.

$x = 6$

Check: $x - 4 = 2$
$6 - 4 \stackrel{?}{=} 2$
$2 \stackrel{?}{=} 2$ ✓

The remaining tiles represent the solution.
$x = 6$

Use tiles to solve each equation. Then check each answer.

1. $x - 5 = 3$ $x = 8$; $8 - 5 = 3$
2. $x - 2 = 5$ $x = 7$; $7 - 2 = 5$
3. $x - 6 = 4$ $x = 10$; $10 - 6 = 4$
4. $x - 8 = 1$ $x = 9$; $9 - 8 = 1$
5. $x - 3 = 9$ $x = 12$; $12 - 3 = 9$
6. $x - 7 = 3$ $x = 10$; $10 - 7 = 3$

PRACTICE 2-6

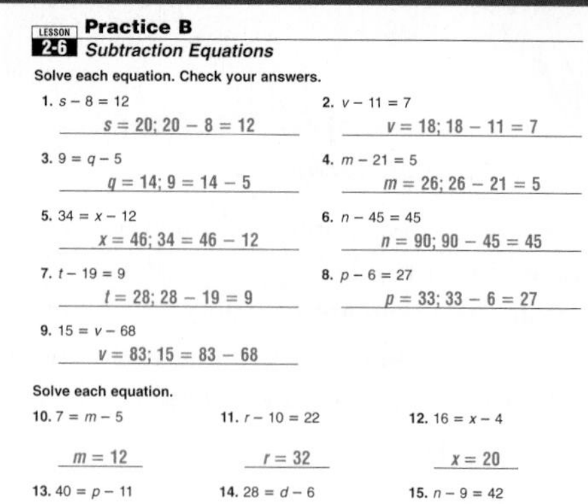

LESSON 2-6 **Practice B**
Subtraction Equations

Solve each equation. Check your answers.

1. $s - 8 = 12$ $s = 20$; $20 - 8 = 12$
2. $v - 11 = 7$ $v = 18$; $18 - 11 = 7$
3. $9 = q - 5$ $q = 14$; $9 = 14 - 5$
4. $m - 21 = 5$ $m = 26$; $26 - 21 = 5$
5. $34 = x - 12$ $x = 46$; $34 = 46 - 12$
6. $n - 45 = 45$ $n = 90$; $90 - 45 = 45$
7. $t - 19 = 9$ $t = 28$; $28 - 19 = 9$
8. $p - 6 = 27$ $p = 33$; $33 - 6 = 27$
9. $15 = v - 68$ $v = 83$; $15 = 83 - 68$

Solve each equation.

10. $7 = m - 5$ $m = 12$
11. $r - 10 = 22$ $r = 32$
12. $16 = x - 4$ $x = 20$
13. $40 = p - 11$ $p = 51$
14. $28 = d - 6$ $d = 34$
15. $n - 9 = 42$ $n = 51$
16. $q - 85 = 8$ $q = 93$
17. $f - 13 = 18$ $f = 31$
18. $47 = w - 38$ $w = 85$
19. Ted took 17 pictures at the aquarium. He now has 7 pictures left on the roll. Write and solve a subtraction equation to find out how many photos Ted had when he went to the aquarium.
   $x - 17 = 7$; $x = 24$ photos
20. Ted bought a dolphin poster for $12. He now has $5. Write and solve a subtraction equation to find out how much money Ted took to the aquarium.
   $x - 12 = 5$; $x = \$17$

2-7 Multiplication Equations

Learn to solve whole-number multiplication equations.

Georgia Performance Standards

M6A3 Evaluate algebraic expressions and solve simple one-step equations using each of the four basic operations. Also, M6P1.c, M6P1.d.

Nine-banded armadillos, the Texas state small mammal, are always born in groups of 4. If you count 32 babies, what is the number of mother armadillos?

To put together equal groups of 4, multiply. Let m represent the number of mother armadillos. There will be m equal groups of 4.

You can use the equation $4m = 32$.

Division is the inverse of multiplication. To solve an equation that contains multiplication, use division to "undo" the multiplication.

 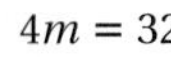

Caution!

$4m$ means "$4 \times m$."

$$4m = 32$$
$$\frac{4m}{4} = \frac{32}{4} \qquad \text{There are 8 mother armadillos.}$$
$$m = 8$$

EXAMPLE 1 Solving Multiplication Equations

Solve each equation. Check your answers.

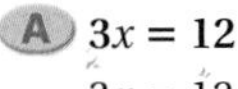

A $3x = 12$

$3x = 12$	*x is multiplied by 3.*
$\frac{3x}{3} = \frac{12}{3}$	*Divide both sides by 3 to undo the multiplication.*
$x = 4$	
Check $3x = 12$	
$3(4) \stackrel{?}{=} 12$	*Substitute 4 for x in the equation.*
$12 \stackrel{?}{=} 12$ ✔	*4 is the solution.*

B $8 = 4w$

$8 = 4w$	*w is multiplied by 4.*
$\frac{8}{4} = \frac{4w}{4}$	*Divide both sides by 4 to undo the multiplication.*
$2 = w$	
Check $8 = 4w$	
$8 \stackrel{?}{=} 4(2)$	*Substitute 2 for w in the equation.*
$8 \stackrel{?}{=} 8$ ✔	*2 is the solution.*

1 Introduce

Alternate Opener

EXPLORATION

2-7 Multiplication Equations

Bill bought 7 tickets to a basketball game for \$21. How much did each ticket cost?

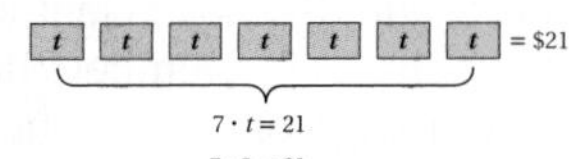

$7 \cdot t = 21$

$7 \cdot 3 = 21$

$t = 3$ Each ticket cost \$3.

Find the value of n in each equation.

1. $4 \cdot n = 36$ $n =$ ______
2. $100 \cdot n = 500$ $n =$ ______
3. $50 = 5 \cdot n$ $n =$ ______
4. $24 \cdot n = 48$ $n =$ ______
5. $10 \cdot n = 240$ $n =$ ______

Think and Discuss

6. **Discuss** your strategies for solving the equations.
7. **Explain** how you can find the solution to $4 \cdot n = 200$.

Motivate

Review with students how to solve addition and subtraction equations. Have students give examples of equations that have a constant multiplied by a variable. Ask them to predict how to solve a multiplication equation.

Explorations and answers are provided in *Alternate Openers: Explorations Transparencies.*

Organizer 2-7

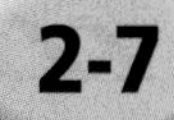

Pacing: Traditional 1 day
Block $\frac{1}{2}$ day

Objective: Students solve whole-number multiplication equations.

GPS M6A3
Hands-On Lab
In *Hands-On Lab Activities*

Online Edition
Tutorial Videos, Interactivities

Countdown to CRCT Week 4

Power Presentations with PowerPoint®

Warm Up

Divide.

1. $\frac{72}{12}$ 6
2. $\frac{65}{5}$ 13
3. $\frac{60}{6}$ 10
4. $\frac{40}{10}$ 4
5. $\frac{130}{5}$ 26
6. $\frac{91}{7}$ 13

Problem of the Day

Katie's little brother is building a tower with blocks. He adds 6 blocks and then removes 4 blocks. If he adds 8 more blocks, the tower will have twice as many blocks as when he started. How many blocks did he start with? **10 blocks**

Also available on transparency

Math Fact

The symbol × for multiplication was developed around 1600. It is not used in algebra because of its resemblance to the letter x.

Georgia Performance Standards

M6A3 Students will evaluate algebraic expressions, including those with exponents, and solve simple one-step equations using each of the four basic operations.

M6P1.c Apply and adapt a variety of appropriate strategies to solve problems.

M6P1.d Monitor and reflect on the process of mathematical problem solving.

COMMON ERROR ALERT

Caution students to be sure they are dividing in the correct order when solving multiplication equations. For example, to solve $4m = 32$, they should divide 32 by 4 as shown in the lesson opener, not 4 by 32.

Power Presentations with PowerPoint®

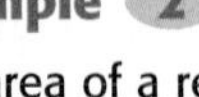

Additional Examples

Example 1

Solve each equation. Check your answers.

A. $5p = 75$ $\quad p = 15$

B. $16 = 8r$ $\quad 2 = r$

Example 2

The area of a rectangle is 56 square inches. Its length is 8 inches. What is its width? 7 inches

Also available on transparency

Answers to *Think and Discuss*

1. 15; because x is multiplied by 15
2. Possible answer: Less than 90; you divide both sides of the equation by 10, so the solution will be 9.

EXAMPLE 2 **PROBLEM SOLVING APPLICATION**

The area of a rectangle is 36 square inches. Its length is 9 inches. What is its width?

1 Understand the Problem

The **answer** will be the width of the rectangle in inches.

List the **important information:**

- The area of the rectangle is 36 square inches.
- The length of the rectangle is 9 inches.

Draw a diagram to represent this information.

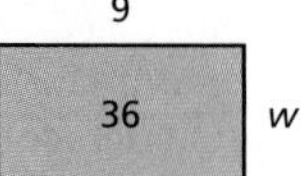

2 Make a Plan

You can write and solve an equation using the formula for area. To find the area of a rectangle, multiply its length by its width.

$A = \ell w$

$36 = 9w$

3 Solve

$36 = 9w$ *w is multiplied by 9.*

$\frac{36}{9} = \frac{9w}{9}$ *Divide both sides by 9 to undo the multiplication.*

$4 = w$

So the width of the rectangle is 4 inches.

4 Look Back

Arrange 36 identical squares in a rectangle. The length is 9, so line up the squares in rows of 9. You can make 4 rows of 9, so the width of the rectangle is 4.

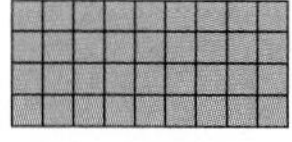

Think and Discuss

GPS M6P1.d, M6P2.c

1. **Tell** what number you would use to divide both sides of the equation $15x = 60$.
2. **Tell** whether the solution of $10c = 90$ will be less than 90 or greater than 90. Explain.

2 Teach

Guided Instruction

In this lesson, students learn to solve whole-number multiplication equations. First teach students to use division to solve multiplication equations. Then have students check their solutions.

Cognitive Strategies To demonstrate that division is the inverse of multiplication, have a student list the number sentences in the fact family for 3, 2, and 6. $3 \times 2 = 6$; $2 \times 3 = 6$; $6 \div 2 = 3$; $6 \div 3 = 2$

Reaching All Learners

Through Number Sense

Have students use the fraction bar to indicate division of both sides of the equation. This provides an easy visual check to compare the coefficient of the variable and the number chosen to divide both sides of the equation by.

3 Close

Summarize

Discuss with students how to solve multiplication equations involving variables and how to check solutions. Emphasize that the coefficient of the variable is the same number chosen to divide both sides of the equation by. Have a volunteer demonstrate the steps in solving and checking a multiplication equation.

2-7 Exercises

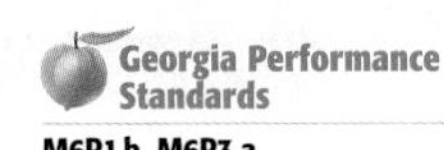

Georgia Performance Standards

M6P1.b, M6P3.a

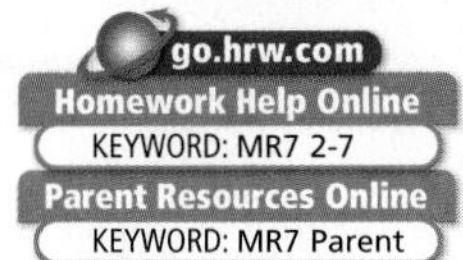

GUIDED PRACTICE

See Example 1

Solve each equation. Check your answers.

1. $7x = 21$ $x = 3$
2. $27 = 3w$ $w = 9$
3. $90 = 10a$ $a = 9$
4. $56 = 7b$ $b = 8$
5. $3c = 33$ $c = 11$
6. $12 = 2n$ $n = 6$

See Example 2

7. The area of a rectangular deck is 675 square feet. The deck's width is 15 feet. What is its length? 45 feet

INDEPENDENT PRACTICE

See Example 1

Solve each equation. Check your answers.

8. $12p = 36$ $p = 3$
9. $52 = 13a$ $a = 4$
10. $64 = 8n$ $n = 8$
11. $20 = 5x$ $x = 4$
12. $6r = 30$ $r = 5$
13. $77 = 11t$ $t = 7$
14. $14s = 98$ $s = 7$
15. $12m = 132$ $m = 11$
16. $9z = 135$ $z = 15$

See Example 2

17. Marcy spreads out a rectangular picnic blanket with an area of 24 square feet. Its width is 4 feet. What is its length? 6 feet

PRACTICE AND PROBLEM SOLVING

Extra Practice pp. 746–7

Solve each equation.

18. $5y = 35$ $y = 7$
19. $18 = 2y$ $y = 9$
20. $54 = 9y$ $y = 6$
21. $15y = 120$ $y = 8$
22. $4y = 0$ $y = 0$
23. $22y = 440$ $y = 20$
24. $3y = 63$ $y = 21$
25. $z - 6 = 34$ $z = 40$
26. $6y = 114$ $y = 19$
27. $161 = 7y$ $y = 23$
28. $135 = 3y$ $y = 45$
29. $y - 15 = 3$ $y = 18$
30. $81 = 9y$ $y = 9$
31. $4 + y = 12$ $y = 8$
32. $7y = 21$ $y = 3$
33. $a + 12 = 26$ $a = 14$
34. $10x = 120$ $x = 12$
35. $36 = 12x$ $x = 3$
36. $s - 2 = 7$ $s = 9$
37. $15 + t = 21$ $t = 6$
38. **Estimation** Colorado is almost a perfect rectangle on a map. Its border from east to west is about 387 mi, and its area is about 104,247 mi². Estimate the length of Colorado's border from north to south. (Area = length × width) $387w = 104{,}247$; about 250–350 miles

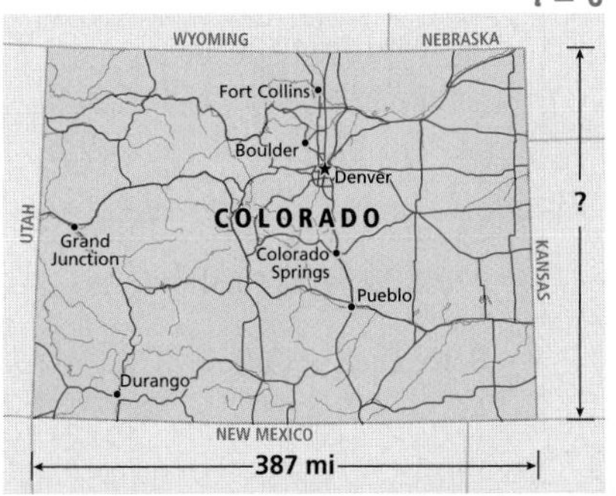

2-7 Exercises

Assignment Guide

If you finished Example 1 assign:
Average 1–6, 8–16, 37, 43–50
Advanced 1–6, 8–16, 41, 43–50

If you finished Example 2 assign:
Average 1–40, 43–50
Advanced 3–50

Homework Quick Check

Quickly check key concepts.
Exercises: 8, 18, 28, 38

Math Background

The equations in this lesson are of the form $ax = b$ $(a \neq 0)$ where $\frac{b}{a}$ is a whole number. Multiplication equations in general do not require that $\frac{b}{a}$ be a whole number. To solve all equations of the form $ax = b$ $(a \neq 0)$, rational numbers are needed.

RETEACH 2-7

LESSON 2-7 **Reteach**
Multiplication Equations

You can use tiles to help you solve multiplication equations.

variable add 1

Division undoes multiplication, so you can use division to solve multiplication equations.

To solve $3x = 12$, first use tiles to model the equation.

$3x = 12$

Next, divide each side of the equal sign into 3 equal groups

The number of tiles in one group represents the solution.

$x = 4$

Check: $3x = 12$
$3 \cdot 4 \stackrel{?}{=} 12$
$12 \stackrel{?}{=} 12$ ✓

$x = 4$

Use tiles to solve each equation. Then check each answer.

1. $5x = 15$ $x = 3$
2. $2x = 6$ $x = 3$
3. $4x = 16$ $x = 4$
4. $8x = 24$ $x = 3$
5. $3x = 18$ $x = 6$
6. $6x = 12$ $x = 2$
7. $7x = 21$ $x = 3$
8. $9x = 9$ $x = 1$
9. $4x = 24$ $x = 6$
10. $3x = 9$ $x = 3$
11. $8x = 16$ $x = 2$
12. $5x = 25$ $x = 5$

PRACTICE 2-7

LESSON 2-7 **Practice B**
Multiplication Equations

Solve each equation. Check your answers.

1. $8s = 72$ $s = 9;\ 8 \cdot 9 = 72$
2. $4v = 28$ $v = 7;\ 4 \cdot 7 = 28$
3. $27 = 9q$ $q = 3;\ 27 = 9 \cdot 3$
4. $12m = 60$ $m = 5;\ 12 \cdot 5 = 60$
5. $48 = 6x$ $x = 8;\ 48 = 6 \cdot 8$
6. $7n = 63$ $n = 9;\ 7 \cdot 9 = 63$
7. $10t = 130$ $t = 13;\ 10 \cdot 13 = 130$
8. $15p = 450$ $p = 30;\ 15 \cdot 30 = 450$
9. $84 = 6v$ $v = 14;\ 84 = 6 \cdot 14$

Solve each equation.

10. $49 = 7m$ $m = 7$
11. $20r = 80$ $r = 4$
12. $64 = 8x$ $x = 8$
13. $36 = 4p$ $p = 9$
14. $147 = 7d$ $d = 21$
15. $11n = 110$ $n = 10$
16. $12q = 144$ $q = 12$
17. $25f = 125$ $f = 5$
18. $128 = 16w$ $w = 8$
19. A hot-air balloon flew at 10 miles per hour. Using the variable h, write and solve a multiplication equation to find how many hours the balloon traveled if it covered a distance of 70 miles. $10h = 70$; $h = 7$ hours
20. A passenger helicopter can travel 300 miles in the same time it takes a hot-air balloon to travel 20 miles. Using the variable s, write and solve a multiplication equation to find how many times faster the helicopter can travel than the hot air balloon. $20s = 300$; $s = 15$ times faster

Georgia Performance Standards

M6P1.b Solve problems that arise in mathematics and in other contexts.

M6P3.a Organize and consolidate their mathematical thinking through communication.

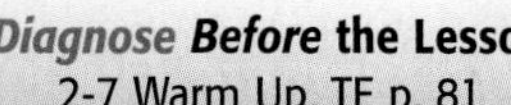

ONGOING ASSESSMENT and INTERVENTION

Diagnose ***Before*** **the Lesson**
2-7 Warm Up, TE p. 81

Monitor ***During*** **the Lesson**
2-7 Know-It Notebook
2-7 Questioning Strategies

Assess ***After*** **the Lesson**
2-7 Lesson Quiz, TE p. 84

Interdisciplinary LINK

Life Science

Exercises 39–44 involve information about arthropods. Arthropods are studied in middle school life science programs, such as *Holt Science & Technology.*

TEST PREP DOCTOR In Exercise 46, remind the students of the formula for the area of a rectangle. Then have them substitute the values for the area and the width into the formula, then solve for the length.

Journal

Have students write about the following situation. Four friends want to share the cost of a sandwich. Why is dividing the cost of the sandwich by four the same as solving the equation $4n = 12$?

Power Presentations with PowerPoint®

2-7 Lesson Quiz

Solve each equation.

1. $10y = 300$ $y = 30$
2. $2y = 82$ $y = 41$
3. $63 = 9y$ $y = 7$
4. $78 = 13x$ $x = 6$
5. The area of a board game is 468 square inches. Its width is 18 inches. What is the length? 26 inches

Also available on transparency

Life Science LINK

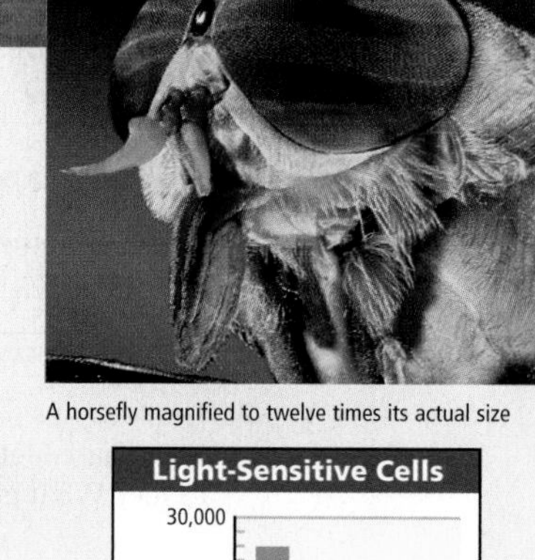

A horsefly magnified to twelve times its actual size

Arthropods make up the largest group of animals on Earth. They include insects, spiders, crabs, and centipedes. Arthropods have segmented bodies. In centipedes and millipedes, all of the segments are identical.

39. Centipedes have 2 legs per segment. They can have from 30 to 354 legs. Find a range for the number of segments a centipede can have.
15 to 177 segments

40. Millipedes have 4 legs per segment. The record number of legs on a millipede is 752. How many segments did this millipede have? 188

Many arthropods have compound eyes. Compound eyes are made up of tiny bundles of identical light-sensitive cells.

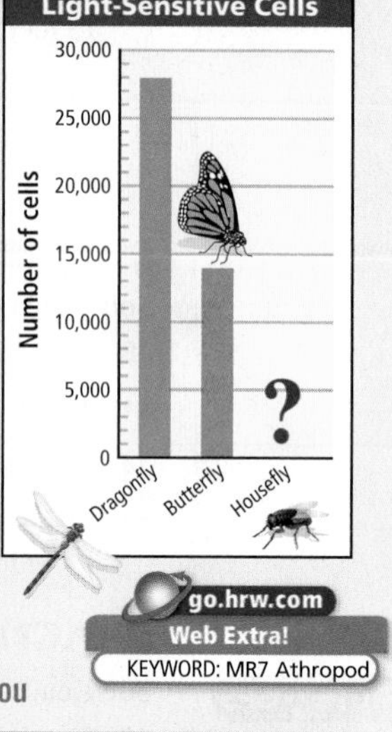

41. A dragonfly has 7 times as many light-sensitive cells as a housefly. How many of these cells does a housefly have?
4,000 light-sensitive cells

42. Find how many times more light-sensitive cells a dragonfly has than a butterfly. 2 times more

43. **Write About It** A trapdoor spider can pull with a force that is 140 times its own weight. What other information would you need to find the spider's weight? Explain.

44. **Challenge** There are about 6 billion humans in the world. Scientists estimate that there are a billion billion arthropods in the world. About how many times larger is the arthropod population than the human population?

go.hrw.com
Web Extra!
KEYWORD: MR7 Athropod

43. Possible answer: The force with which a trapdoor spider pulls; then you could solve $f = 140w$.

44. The arthropod population is about 167 million times larger than the human population.

CRCT PREP • GPS SUPPORT • SPIRAL REVIEW

45. Multiple Choice Solve the equation $25x = 175$.

Ⓐ $x = 5$ Ⓑ $x = 6$ Ⓒ $x = 7$ (circled) Ⓓ $x = 8$

46. Multiple Choice The area of a rectangle is 42 square inches. Its width is 6 inches. What is its length?

Ⓕ 5 inches Ⓖ 7 inches (circled) Ⓗ 9 inches Ⓙ 11 inches

Estimate each sum or difference by rounding to the place value indicated. (Lesson 1-2)

47. 4,798 + 2,118; thousands 7,000 **48.** 49,169 − 13,919; ten thousands 40,000

Solve each equation. (Lessons 2-5 and 2-6)

49. $b + 53 = 95$ $b = 42$ **50.** $a - 100 = 340$ $a = 440$ **51.** $n - 24 = 188$ $n = 212$ **52.** $w + 20 = 95$ $w = 75$

CHALLENGE 2-7

LESSON 2-7 **Challenge**
Regulation Sizes

Write a multiplication equation for the area of each regulation field or court. Then solve the equations to find the missing measurements. Remember: Area = length • width, or $A = l \cdot w$.

1. 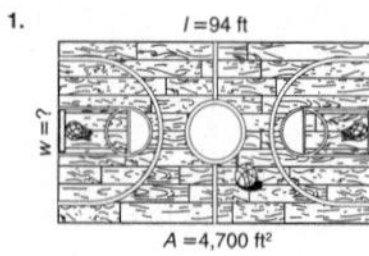

$4{,}700 = 94w$; $w = 50$

What is the width of a regulation basketball court?

50 feet

2. $l = ?$, $w = 75$ m, $A = 8{,}250$ m²

$8{,}250 = 75l$; $l = 110$

What is the length of a regulation soccer field?

110 meters

3. $l = ?$, $w = 26$ m, $A = 1{,}586$ m²

$1{,}586 = 26l$; $l = 61$

What is the length of a regulation ice hockey rink?

61 meters

4. $l = 90$ ft, $w = ?$, $A = 8{,}100$ ft²

$8{,}100 = 90w$; $w = 90$

What is the width of a regulation baseball diamond?

90 feet

PROBLEM SOLVING 2-7

LESSON 2-7 **Problem Solving**
Multiplication Equations

Write and solve a multiplication equation to answer each question.

1. In 1975, a person earning minimum wage made $80 for a 40-hour work week. What was the minimum wage per hour in 1975?

$40x = 80$; $x = 2$;
$2 per hour

2. If an ostrich could maintain its maximum speed for 5 hours, it could run 225 miles. How fast can an ostrich run?

$5x = 225$; $x = 45$;
45 miles per hour

3. About 2,000,000 people live in Paris, the capital of France. That is 80 times larger than the population of Paris, Texas. How many people live in Paris, Texas?

$80x = 2{,}000{,}000$; $x = 25{,}000$;
25,000 people

4. The average person in China goes to the movies 12 times per year. That is 3 times more than the average American goes to the movies. How many times per year does the average American go to the movies?

$3x = 12$; $x = 4$;
4 times per year

Circle the letter of the correct answer.

5. Recycling just 1 ton of paper saves 17 trees! If a city recycled enough paper to save 136 trees, how many tons of paper did it recycle?
A 7 tons
Ⓑ 8 tons (circled)
C 9 tons
D 119 tons

6. Seaweed found along the coast of California, called giant kelp, grows up to 18 inches per day. If a giant kelp plant has grown 162 inches at this rate, for how many days has it been growing?
F 180 days
G 144 days
Ⓗ 9 days (circled)
J 8 days

7. The distance between Atlanta, Georgia, and Denver, Colorado, is 1,398 miles. That is twice the distance between Atlanta and Detroit, Michigan. How many miles would you have to drive to get from Atlanta to Detroit?
A 2,796 miles
B 349.5 miles
Ⓒ 699 miles (circled)
D 1,400 miles

8. Jupiter has 2 times more moons than Neptune has, and 8 times more moons than Mars has. Jupiter has 16 moons. How many moons do Neptune and Mars each have?
Ⓕ 8 moons, 2 moons (circled)
G 2 moons, 8 moons
H 128 moons, 32 moons
J 32 moons, 128 moons

2-8 Division Equations

Learn to solve whole-number division equations.

Georgia Performance Standards

M6A3 Evaluate algebraic expressions and solve simple one-step equations using each of the four basic operations. Also, M6P1.b, M6P1.d.

Japanese pearl divers go as deep as 165 feet underwater in search of pearls. At this depth, the pressure on a diver is much greater than at the water's surface. Water pressure can be described using equations containing division.

Multiplication is the inverse of division. When an equation contains division, use multiplication to "undo" the division.

EXAMPLE 1 Solving Division Equations

Solve each equation. Check your answers.

A $\frac{y}{5} = 4$

$\frac{y}{5} = 4$ — *y is divided by 5.*

$5 \cdot \frac{y}{5} = 5 \cdot 4$ — *Multiply both sides by 5 to undo the division.*

$y = 20$

Check

$\frac{y}{5} = 4$

$\frac{20}{5} \stackrel{?}{=} 4$ — *Substitute 20 for y in the equation.*

$4 \stackrel{?}{=} 4$ ✔ — *20 is the solution.*

B $12 = \frac{z}{4}$

$12 = \frac{z}{4}$ — *z is divided by 4.*

$4 \cdot 12 = 4 \cdot \frac{z}{4}$ — *Multiply both sides by 4 to undo the division.*

$48 = z$

Check

$12 = \frac{z}{4}$

$12 \stackrel{?}{=} \frac{48}{4}$ — *Substitute 48 for z in the equation.*

$12 \stackrel{?}{=} 12$ ✔ — *48 is the solution.*

Organizer 2-8

Pacing: Traditional 1 day
Block $\frac{1}{2}$ day

Objective: Students solve whole-number division equations.

Online Edition
Tutorial Videos, Interactivities

Countdown to CRCT Week 4

Power Presentations with PowerPoint®

Warm Up

Solve.

1. $5x = 20$ — $x = 4$
2. $7n = 84$ — $n = 12$
3. $18 = y - 4$ — $y = 22$
4. $21 = n + 3$ — $n = 18$

Problem of the Day

If 11 is 4 less than 3 times a number, what is the number? 5

Also available on transparency

Math Humor

When he saw the expression "x over eight" in the equation, the student thought the solution was for x to take some stomach medicine.

1 Introduce

Alternate Opener

EXPLORATION

2-8 Division Equations

Four friends decided to share the cost of a gift for their dance teacher. After dividing the cost by 4, each friend's share is $25. What was the cost of the gift?

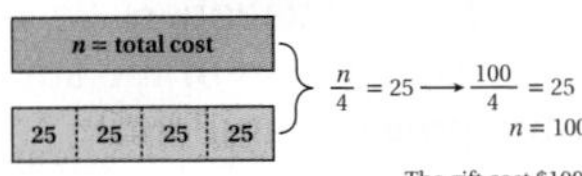

$\frac{n}{4} = 25 \rightarrow \frac{100}{4} = 25$

$n = 100$

The gift cost $100.

Find the value of n in each equation.

1. $\frac{n}{2} = 50$ $n =$ ______
2. $\frac{n}{10} = 2$ $n =$ ______
3. $20 = \frac{n}{3}$ $n =$ ______
4. $\frac{n}{7} = 5$ $n =$ ______

Think and Discuss

5. **Discuss** your strategies for solving the equations.
6. **Explain** how you can find the solution to $\frac{n}{2} = 26$.

2 Teach

Guided Instruction

In this lesson, students learn to solve whole number division equations. First explain that multiplication is the inverse of division, so multiplication is used to solve division equations. Then teach students to solve division equations. Next work through the science application with them.

Explorations and answers are provided in *Alternate Openers: Explorations Transparencies.*

Georgia Performance Standards

M6A3 Students will evaluate algebraic expressions, including those with exponents, and solve simple one-step equations using each of the four basic operations.

M6P1.b Solve problems that arise in mathematics and in other contexts.

M6P1.d Monitor and reflect on the process of mathematical problem solving.

Students may try to divide each side of the division equation to solve. Remind them to use the inverse operation, multiplication, to solve.

Power Presentations with PowerPoint®

Additional Examples

Example 

Solve each equation. Check your answers.

A. $\frac{x}{7} = 5$ $x = 35$ **B.** $13 = \frac{p}{6}$ $78 = p$

Example 

At Elk Meadows Park an aspen tree is one-third the height of a pine tree.

height of aspen $= \frac{\text{height of pine}}{3}$

The aspen tree is 14 feet tall. How tall is the pine tree? 42 feet

Also available on transparency

2-8 Exercises

Assignment Guide

If you finished Example 1 assign:
Average 1–8, 10–17, 19–26, 32–40
Advanced 1–8, 10–17, 19–25, 28, 32–40

If you finished Example 2 assign:
Average 1–28, 32–40
Advanced 5–25, 27–40

Homework Quick Check

Quickly check key concepts.
Exercises: 10, 18, 20, 28

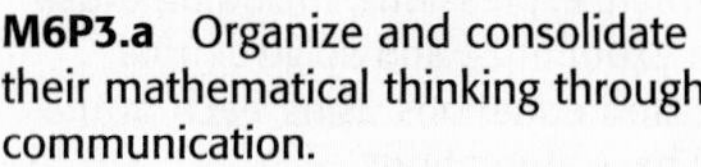

M6P3.a Organize and consolidate their mathematical thinking through communication.

M6P4.c Recognize and apply mathematics in contexts outside of mathematics.

EXAMPLE 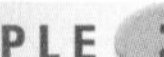 ***Physical Science Application***

Pressure is the amount of force exerted on an area. Pressure can be measured in pounds per square inch, or psi.

The pressure at the surface of the water is half the pressure at 30 ft underwater.

pressure at surface $= \frac{\text{pressure at 30 ft underwater}}{2}$

The pressure at the surface is 15 psi. What is the water pressure at 30 ft underwater?

Let p represent the pressure at 30 ft underwater.

$15 = \frac{p}{2}$ *Substitute 15 for pressure at the surface. p is divided by 2.*

$2 \cdot 15 = 2 \cdot \frac{p}{2}$ *Multiply both sides by 2 to undo the division.*

$30 = p$

The water pressure at 30 ft underwater is 30 psi.

Answers to *Think and Discuss*

1. Greater than 70; multiply both sides of the equation by 10 to undo the division; the solution will be the product of 70 and 10.
2. Substitute 30 for p in the equation. $15 = 30 \div 2$, so 30 is correct.
3. Possible answer: You are multiplying by 13 and dividing by 13, so the operations undo each other.

Think and Discuss GPS M6P1.d, M6P2.c

1. **Tell** whether the solution of $\frac{c}{10} = 70$ will be less than 70 or greater than 70. Explain.
2. **Describe** how you would check your answer to Example 2.
3. **Explain** why $13 \cdot \frac{x}{13} = x$.

2-8 Exercises

M6P3.a, M6P4.c

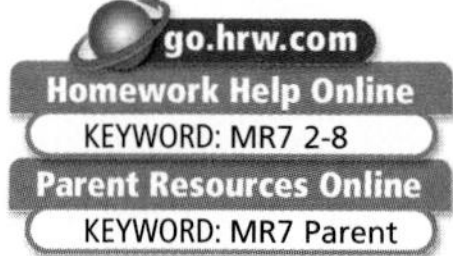

GUIDED PRACTICE

See Example 1 Solve each equation. Check your answers.

1. $\frac{y}{4} = 3$ $y = 12$
2. $14 = \frac{z}{2}$ $z = 28$
3. $\frac{r}{9} = 7$ $r = 63$
4. $\frac{s}{10} = \frac{4}{40}$ $s = 1$
5. $12 = \frac{j}{3}$ $j = 36$
6. $9 = \frac{x}{5}$ $x = 45$
7. $\frac{f}{12} = 5$ $f = 60$
8. $\frac{g}{2} = 1$ $g = 2$

See Example 2

9. Irene mowed the lawn and planted flowers. The amount of time she spent mowing the lawn was one-third the amount of time it took her to plant flowers. It took her 30 minutes to mow the lawn. Find the amount of time Irene spent planting flowers. 90 min

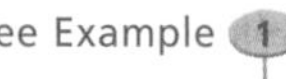

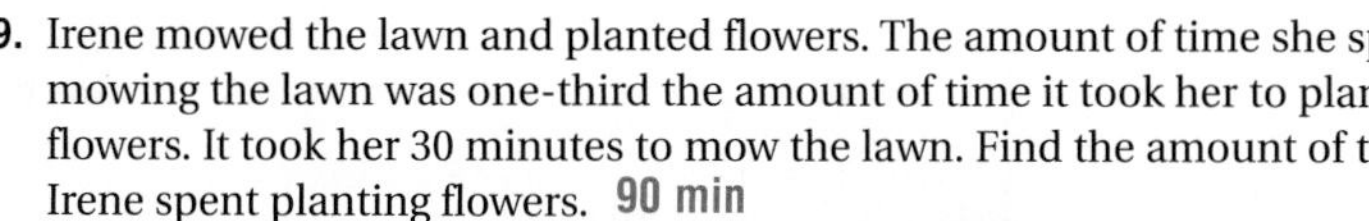

Reaching All Learners

Through Kinesthetic Experience

Give each group of students a set of nine cards numbered 1–9. On signal, each group picks a card at random and passes it to another group. The number on this card becomes the divisor in a division equation. On another signal, each group passes another card to the same group as before, and this card becomes the quotient. Groups solve the equations of the form (x ÷ first card) = (second card) and try to see which group finishes first.

3 Close

Summarize

Give brief descriptions of how to solve division equations involving variables and how to check solutions. Have a student volunteer to provide the next step in the solution of a division equation. Have another student give an explanation of the step provided by the previous student.

INDEPENDENT PRACTICE

See Example 1

Solve each equation. Check your answers.

10. $\frac{d}{3} = 12$ $d = 36$ 11. $\frac{c}{2} = 13$ $c = 26$ 12. $7 = \frac{m}{7}$ $m = 49$ 13. $\frac{g}{7} = 14$ $g = 98$

14. $6 = \frac{f}{4}$ $f = 24$ 15. $\frac{x}{12} = 12$ $x = 144$ 16. $\frac{j}{20} = 10$ $j = 200$ 17. $9 = \frac{r}{9}$ $r = 81$

See Example 2

18. The area of Danielle's garden is one-twelfth the area of her entire yard. The area of the garden is 10 square feet. Find the area of the yard. 120 square feet

PRACTICE AND PROBLEM SOLVING

Extra Practice pp. 746–7

Find the value of c in each equation.

19. $\frac{c}{12} = 8$ $c = 96$ 20. $4 = \frac{c}{9}$ $c = 36$ 21. $\frac{c}{15} = 11$ $c = 165$ 22. $c + 21 = 40$ $c = 19$

23. $14 = \frac{c}{5}$ $c = 70$ 24. $\frac{c}{4} = 12$ $c = 48$ 25. $\frac{c}{4} = 15$ $c = 60$ 26. $5c = 120$ $c = 24$

27. $\frac{w}{381} = 76$; $w = 28{,}956$ m

27. **Multi-Step** The Empire State Building is 381 m tall. At the Grand Canyon's widest point, 76 Empire State Buildings would fit end to end. Write and solve an equation to find the width of the Grand Canyon at this point.

29. Possible answer: Each of 15 people gave \$5 to a fund. What was the total given? $\frac{w}{15} = 5$

28. **Earth Science** You can estimate the distance of a thunderstorm in kilometers by counting the number of seconds between the lightning flash and the thunder and then dividing this number by 3. If a storm is 5 km away, how many seconds will you count between the lightning flash and the thunder? 15 seconds

29. **Write a Problem** Write a problem about money that can be solved with a division equation.

30. **Write About It** Use a numerical example to explain how multiplication and division undo each other. Possible answer: $9 \cdot 8 = 72$; $72 \div 8 = 9$

31. **Challenge** A number halved and then halved again is equal to 2. What was the original number? 8

CRCT PREP • GPS SUPPORT • SPIRAL REVIEW

32. **Multiple Choice** Carl has n action figures in his collection. He wants to place them in 6 bins with 12 figures in each bin. Solve the equation $\frac{n}{6} = 12$ to determine the number of action figures Carl has.

Ⓐ $n = 2$ Ⓑ $n = 6$ Ⓒ $n = 18$ Ⓓ $n = 72$

33. **Multiple Choice** Which equation does NOT have $k = 28$ as a solution?

Ⓕ $\frac{k}{14} = 2$ Ⓖ $\frac{k}{7} = 4$ Ⓗ $\frac{k}{28} = 1$ Ⓙ $\frac{k}{6} = 12$

Identify a pattern in each sequence. Name the next three terms. (Lesson 1-7)

34. 3, 10, 17, 24, . . . Add 7; 31, 38, 45
35. 5, 10, 15, 20, . . . Add 5; 25, 30, 35
36. 1, 4, 2, 5, 3, . . . Add 3, and then subtract 2; 6, 4, 7

Solve each equation. (Lesson 2-7)

37. $4r = 52$ $r = 13$ 38. $8k = 128$ $k = 16$ 39. $81 = 9p$ $p = 9$ 40. $119 = 17q$ $q = 7$

ONGOING ASSESSMENT and INTERVENTION

Diagnose ***Before*** **the Lesson**
2-8 Warm Up, TE p. 85

Monitor ***During*** **the Lesson**
2-8 Know-It Notebook
2-8 Questioning Strategies

Assess ***After*** **the Lesson**
2-8 Lesson Quiz, TE p. 87

Power Presentations with PowerPoint®

2-8 Lesson Quiz

Solve each equation. Check your answers.

1. $\frac{x}{10} = 7$ $x = 70$
2. $8 = \frac{x}{4}$ $x = 32$
3. $\frac{x}{9} = 11$ $x = 99$
4. $\frac{x}{15} = 7$ $x = 105$
5. The area of Sherry's flower garden is one-fourth the area of her vegetable garden. The area of the flower garden is 17 square feet. Let x represent the area of her vegetable garden. Find the area of her vegetable garden. 68 square feet

Also available on transparency

RETEACH 2-8

LESSON 2-8 **Reteach**
Division Equations

You can use multiplication and division to write related number facts.

$3 \cdot 4 = 12$ $12 \div 4 = 3$

Division and multiplication are inverse operations. They undo each other. So you can use multiplication to solve division equations.

To solve $\frac{x}{2} = 3$, think of a related number fact.

If $\frac{x}{2} = 3$, then $3 \cdot 2 = x$.

$3 \cdot 2 = x$
$x = 6$

Check: $\frac{x}{2} = 3$

$\frac{6}{2} \stackrel{?}{=} 3$ *substitute*

$3 \stackrel{?}{=} 3$ ✓

$x = 6$ is the solution for $\frac{x}{2} = 3$.

Use a related number fact to solve each equation. Then check each answer.

1. $\frac{x}{2} = 4$ $x = 8; \frac{8}{2} = 4$
2. $\frac{x}{8} = 2$ $x = 16; \frac{16}{8} = 2$
3. $\frac{x}{3} = 5$ $x = 15; \frac{15}{3} = 5$
4. $\frac{x}{5} = 1$ $x = 5; \frac{5}{5} = 1$
5. $\frac{x}{9} = 3$ $x = 27; \frac{27}{9} = 3$
6. $\frac{x}{6} = 3$ $x = 18; \frac{18}{6} = 3$
7. $\frac{x}{8} = 4$ $x = 32; \frac{32}{8} = 4$
8. $\frac{x}{2} = 9$ $x = 18; \frac{18}{2} = 9$
9. $\frac{x}{4} = 4$ $x = 16; \frac{16}{4} = 4$
10. $\frac{x}{5} = 4$ $x = 20; \frac{20}{5} = 4$
11. $\frac{x}{6} = 2$ $x = 12; \frac{12}{6} = 2$
12. $\frac{x}{9} = 4$ $x = 36; \frac{36}{9} = 4$

PRACTICE 2-8

LESSON 2-8 **Practice B**
Division Equations

Solve each equation. Check your answers.

1. $\frac{s}{6} = 7$ $s = 42; \frac{42}{6} = 7$
2. $\frac{v}{5} = 9$ $v = 45; \frac{45}{5} = 9$
3. $12 = \frac{q}{7}$ $q = 84; 12 = \frac{84}{7}$
4. $\frac{m}{2} = 16$ $m = 32; \frac{32}{2} = 16$
5. $26 = \frac{x}{3}$ $x = 78; 26 = \frac{78}{3}$
6. $\frac{n}{8} = 4$ $n = 32; \frac{32}{8} = 4$
7. $\frac{t}{11} = 11$ $t = 121; \frac{121}{11} = 11$
8. $\frac{p}{7} = 10$ $p = 70; \frac{70}{7} = 10$
9. $7 = \frac{v}{8}$ $v = 56; 7 = \frac{56}{8}$

Solve each equation.

10. $10 = \frac{m}{9}$ $m = 90$
11. $\frac{r}{5} = 8$ $r = 40$
12. $11 = \frac{x}{7}$ $x = 77$
13. $9 = \frac{p}{12}$ $p = 108$
14. $15 = \frac{d}{5}$ $d = 75$
15. $\frac{n}{4} = 28$ $n = 112$
16. $\frac{q}{2} = 134$ $q = 268$
17. $\frac{u}{16} = 1$ $u = 16$
18. $2 = \frac{w}{25}$ $w = 50$
19. All the seats in the theater are divided into 6 groups. There are 35 seats in each group. Using the variable s, write and solve a division equation to find how many seats there are in the theater. $\frac{s}{6} = 35$; $s = 210$ seats
20. There are 16 ounces in one pound. A box of nails weighs 4 pounds. Using the variable w, write and solve a division equation to find how many ounces the box weighs. $\frac{w}{16} = 4$; $w = 64$ ounces

CHALLENGE 2-8

PROBLEM SOLVING 2-8

LESSON 2-8 **Problem Solving**
Division Equations

Use the table to write and solve a division equation to answer each question.

Bakersville Sports League

Sport	Number of Teams	Players on Each Team
Baseball	7	20
Soccer	11	15
Football	8	24
Volleyball	12	9
Lacrosse	6	17
Basketball	10	10
Tennis	18	6

1. How many total people signed up to play soccer in Bakersville this year? $\frac{x}{11} = 15$; $x = 165$; 165 people
2. How many people signed up to play lacrosse this year? $\frac{x}{6} = 17$; $x = 102$; 102 people
3. What was the total number of people who signed up to play baseball this year? $\frac{x}{7} = 20$; $x = 140$; 140 people
4. Which two sports in the league have the same number of people signed up to play this year? How many people are signed up to play each of those sports? volleyball and tennis; 108 people

Circle the letter of the correct answer.

5. Which sport has a higher total number of players, football or tennis? How many more players?
   A football; 10 players
   B tennis; 144 players
   Ⓒ football; 84 players
   D tennis; 18 players
6. Only one sport this year has the same number of players on each team as its number of teams. Which sport is that?
   Ⓕ basketball
   G football
   H soccer
   J tennis

SECTION 2B

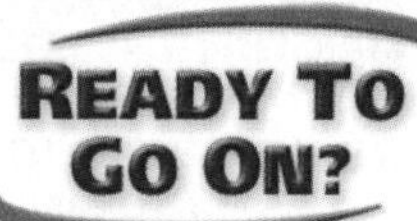

Organizer

Objective: Assess students' mastery of concepts and skills in Lessons 2-4 through 2-8.

Resources

Assessment Resources
Section 2B Quiz

Test & Practice Generator
One-Stop Planner®

INTERVENTION

Resources

***Ready to Go On? Intervention and Enrichment* Worksheets**

***Ready to Go On?* CD-ROM**

***Ready to Go On?* Online**

my.hrw.com

CHAPTER 2
SECTION 2B

READY TO GO ON?

Quiz for Lessons 2-4 Through 2-8

2-4 Equations and Their Solutions

Determine whether the given value of the variable is a solution.

1. $c - 13 = 54$ for $c = 67$ yes **2.** $5r = 65$ for $r = 15$ no **3.** $48 \div x = 6$ for $x = 8$ yes

4. Brady buys 2 notebooks and should get \$3 back in change. The cashier gives him 12 quarters. Determine if Brady was given the correct amount of change. 12 quarters is equal to \$3.

2-5 Addition Equations

Solve each equation. Check your answers.

5. $p + 51 = 76$ $p = 25$ **6.** $107 = 19 + j$ $j = 88$ **7.** $45 = s + 27$ $s = 18$

8. A large section of the original Great Wall of China is now in ruins. As measured today, the length of the wall is about 6,350 kilometers. When the length of the section now in ruins is included, the length of the wall is about 6,850 kilometers. Write and solve an equation to find the approximate length of the section of the Great Wall that is now in ruins. $6{,}350 + w = 6{,}850$; $w = 500$ km

2-6 Subtraction Equations

Solve each equation. Check your answers.

9. $k - 5 = 17$ $k = 22$ **10.** $150 = p - 30$ $p = 180$ **11.** $n - 24 = 72$ $n = 96$

12. The Kingda Ka roller coaster at Six Flags® Great Adventure in New Jersey is taller than the Top Thrill Dragster located at Cedar Point™ in Ohio. The difference between their heights is 36 feet. The Top Thrill Dragster is 420 feet high. Write and solve an equation to find the height of Kingda Ka. $k - 420 = 36$; $k = 456$ feet

2-7 Multiplication Equations

Solve each equation. Check your answers.

13. $6f = 18$ $f = 3$ **14.** $105 = 5d$ $d = 21$ **15.** $11x = 99$ $x = 9$

16. Taryn buys 8 identical glasses. Her total is \$48 before tax. Write and solve an equation to find out how much Taryn pays per glass. $8g = 48$; $g = \$6$

2-8 Division Equations

Solve each equation. Check your answers.

17. $10 = \frac{j}{9}$ $j = 90$ **18.** $5 = \frac{t}{6}$ $t = 30$ **19.** $\frac{r}{15} = 3$ $r = 45$

20. Paula is baking peach pies for a bake sale. Each pie requires 2 pounds of peaches. She bakes 6 pies. Write and solve an equation to find how many pounds of peaches Paula had to buy. $\frac{p}{2} = 6$; $p = 12$ lb

Ready to Go On?

READY TO GO ON?

Diagnose and Prescribe

NO
INTERVENE

Ready to Go On? Intervention	*Ready to Go On?* Intervention, Section 2B		
	Worksheets	CD-ROM	Online
Lesson 2-4	2-4 Intervention	Activity 2-4	Diagnose and Prescribe Online
Lesson 2-5	2-5 Intervention	Activity 2-5	
Lesson 2-6	2-6 Intervention	Activity 2-6	
Lesson 2-7	2-7 Intervention	Activity 2-7	
Lesson 2-8	2-8 Intervention	Activity 2-8	

YES
ENRICH

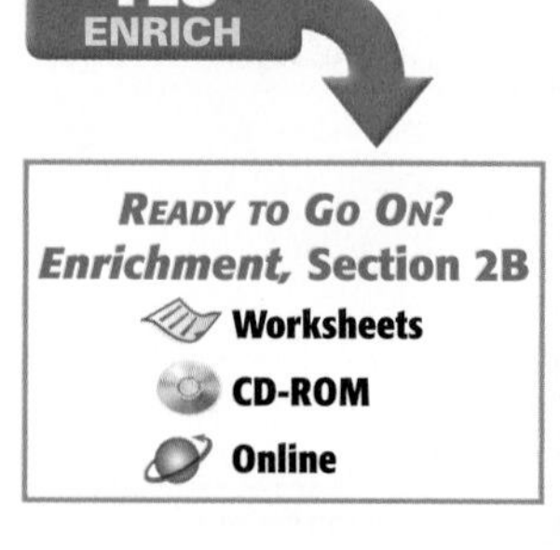

MULTI-STEP TEST PREP

Super Squid! For centuries, sailors have told tales of ships being captured by giant squid. Although the stories may be myths, scientists have concluded that giant squid can reach a total length of up to 60 feet.

The figure shows different ways a squid can be measured.

1. A giant squid washed ashore in New Zealand in 1887. It had a total length of 55 feet. In some sources, the squid's length is reported as 660 inches. Determine if these two measurements are equal. Explain.
2. The giant squid's total length of 55 feet was 49 feet more than its mantle length. What equation could you use to find the length of the mantle? Solve your equation. $55 = m + 49$; $m = 6$
3. The difference between the standard length and mantle length for this squid was 10 feet. Explain which operation you would use to write an equation to find the standard length of the squid, and then find the standard length.
4. Suppose the giant squid had 240 suction cups on each arm. Let n represent the number of arms. What expression could be used to find the total number of suction cups found on a giant squid? Explain. $240n$
5. The squid had a total of 1,920 suction cups. How many arms did the squid have? 8

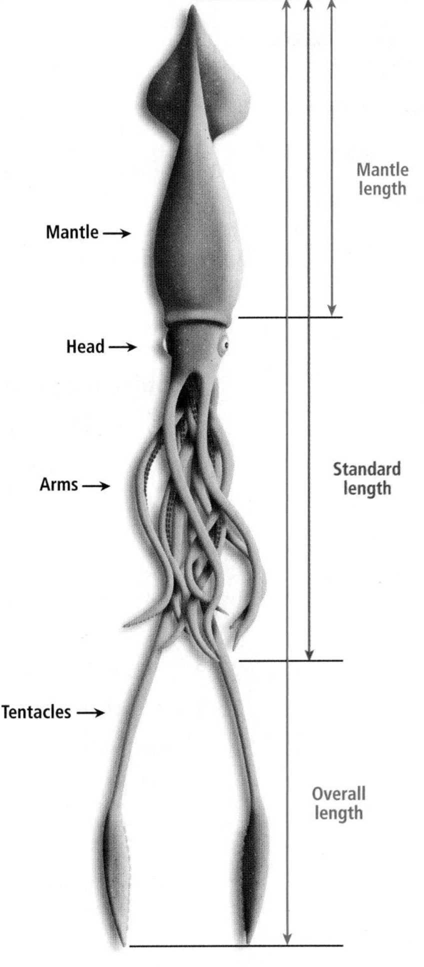

Organizer

Objective: Assess students' ability to apply concepts and skills in Chapter 2 in a real-world format.

Online Edition

Resources

Middle School Assessments
www.mathtekstoolkit.org

Problem	Text reference
1	Lesson 2-7
2	Lesson 2-5
3	Lesson 2-6
4	Lesson 2-7
5	Lesson 2-7

Answers

1. Yes; the values $f = 55$ and $i = 660$ are solutions to the equation $12f = i$.
3. Subtraction; the word *difference* means that you must use subtraction; $s - 6 = 10$; 16 ft.
4. $240n$; there are 240 suction cups on each arm. If you let n be the number of arms, you multiply 240 by n to find the total number of suction cups.

INTERVENTION

Scaffolding Questions

1. What equation relates measurements in feet to measurements in inches? $12f = i$ How can you use the equation to decide if the measurements are equal? Check to see whether $f = 55$ and $i = 660$ make the equation true.
2. What do you need to find in this problem? mantle length What variable can you use to represent the mantle length? Possible answer: m What operation will appear in your equation? addition
3. What information will you need from a previous problem? mantle length
4. What operation will you use to write the expression? Why? multiplication; because you know the number of suction cups per arm will be multiplied by the number of arms
5. What equation should you solve? $240n = 1{,}920$ How do you solve it? Divide both sides by 240.

Extension

1. A giant squid has a total length of 50 feet. The mantle length is one-tenth of the total length. The difference between the standard length and mantle length is 8 feet. Find the standard length? 13 feet
2. Estimate the total number of suction cups on a squid with 8 arms and 294 suction cups on each arm. Is it an overestimate or underestimate? 2400; overestimate

CHAPTER 2 Extension

Pacing: Traditional 1 day
Block $\frac{1}{2}$ day
Objective: Students solve and graph whole-number inequalities.

Technology Lab
In *Technology Lab Activities*

Online Edition

Countdown to CRCT Week 4

Using the Extension

In Lessons 2-4 through 2-8, students solved equations using addition, subtraction, multiplication, and division. In this extension, students will graph the solutions of inequalities on number lines. Students will also solve inequalities using addition, subtraction, multiplication, and division of whole numbers.

EXTENSION Inequalities

Learn to solve and graph whole-number inequalities.

Vocabulary
inequality

An **inequality** is a statement that two quantities are not equal.

$15 > 3$ $\quad 12 \le 29$ $\quad 41 \ge 18$ $\quad 17 < 90$

An inequality may contain a variable, as in the inequality $x > 3$. Values of the variable that make the inequality true are solutions of the inequality.

Helpful Hint

< means "is less than."
> means "is greater than."
≤ means "is less than or equal to."
≥ means "is greater than or equal to."

x	$x > 3$	Solution?
0	$0 \overset{?}{>} 3$	No; 0 is **not** greater than 3, so 0 is not a solution.
3	$3 \overset{?}{>} 3$	No; 3 is **not** greater than 3, so 3 is not a solution.
4	$4 \overset{?}{>} 3$	Yes; 4 is greater than 3, so 4 is a solution.
12	$12 \overset{?}{>} 3$	Yes; 12 is greater than 3, so 12 is a solution.

This table shows that an inequality may have more than one solution. You can use a number line to show all of the solutions.

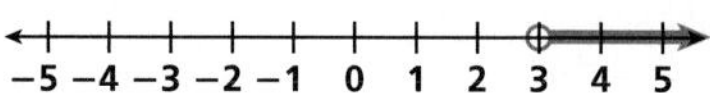

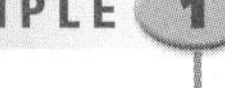

EXAMPLE 1 Graphing Inequalities

Graph the solutions to $w \le 4$ on a number line.

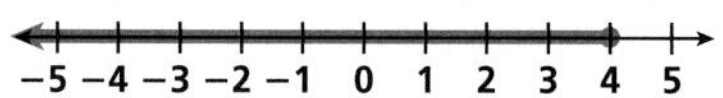

The closed circle on the point 4 shows that 4 is a solution.

Georgia Performance Standards
M6P5.a Create and use representations to organize, record, and communicate mathematical ideas. Also, M6P5.b.

You can solve inequalities in the same way that you solved equations.

EXAMPLE 2 Solving and Graphing Inequalities

Solve each inequality. Graph the solutions on a number line.

A $y + 7 < 9$

$y + 7 < 9$ — *7 is added to y.*
$\underline{-7} \quad \underline{-7}$ — *Subtract 7 from both sides to undo the addition.*
$y < 2$

−5 −4 −3 −2 −1 0 1 2 3 4 5

The open circle on the point 2 shows that 2 is not a solution.

Georgia Performance Standards

M6P5.a Create and use representations to organize, record, and communicate mathematical ideas.

M6P5.b Select, apply, and translate among mathematical representations to solve problems.

1 Introduce

Motivate

When comparing two numbers *a* and *b*, exactly one of the following statements is true: $a < b$, $a = b$, or $a > b$.

2 Teach

Guided Instruction

In this extension, students learn to solve and graph whole-number inequalities. Teach the students to graph inequalities. Then teach students to solve inequalities in a manner similar to how they solved equations. Have students graph their solutions on a number line.

Teaching Tip **Multiple Representations** For inequalities such as $7 < t$, have students rewrite the inequality placing the *t* to the left and reversing the inequality symbol. The inequality now reads $t > 7$. Having the variable come first makes the inequality easier to understand and to graph.

Solve each inequality. Graph the solutions on a number line.

B $2m \geq 12$

$2m \geq 12$ *m is multiplied by 2.*

$\frac{2m}{2} \geq \frac{12}{2}$ *Divide both sides by 2 to undo the multiplication.*

$m \geq 6$

−10 −8 −6 −4 −2 0 2 4 6 8 10

The closed circle on the point 6 shows that 6 is a solution.

In Exercise 5, some students may graph numbers that are less than 7 because the inequality reads "seven is less than *t*." Remind them that the inequality sign always "points to" the lesser of two numbers, which means that the values of *t* are greater than 7.

EXTENSION Exercises

Graph the solutions to each inequality on a number line.

1. $w \leq 0$
2. $x > 5$
3. $z \geq 9$
4. $g < 4$
5. $7 < t$
6. $m > 2$
7. $4 \geq q$
8. $h \leq 10$
9. $a \leq 8$
10. $6 > x$
11. $y < 3$
12. $1 \geq j$

Solve each inequality.

13. $3t \leq 27$ $t \leq 9$
14. $y - 5 \geq 0$ $y \geq 5$
15. $4x < 16$ $x < 4$
16. $x + 4 < 10$ $x < 6$
17. $2c > 2$ $c > 1$
18. $s + 2 \leq 10$ $s \leq 8$
19. $\frac{d}{6} \geq 1$ $d \geq 6$
20. $r + 9 \leq 23$ $r \leq 14$
21. $p - 4 > 2$ $p > 6$
22. $15n < 75$ $n < 5$
23. $4 + r \leq 7$ $r \leq 3$
24. $\frac{j}{2} \leq 4$ $j \leq 8$
25. $f - 11 > 16$ $f > 27$
26. $2k < 8$ $k < 4$
27. $3q \geq 9$ $q \geq 3$

Write an inequality for each sentence. Then graph your inequality.

28. *c* is less than or equal to two. $c \leq 2$
29. *p* is greater than 11. $p > 11$
30. 2 times *r* is less than 14. $2r < 14$
31. *s* plus 2 is greater than or equal to 5. $s + 2 \geq 5$
32. At some lakes, people who fish must throw back any trout that is less than 10 inches long. Write an inequality that represents the lengths of trout that may be kept. $t \geq 10$
33. **Geography** Mt. McKinley is the highest point in the United States, with an altitude of 20,320 ft. Let *a* be the altitude of any other U.S. location. Write an inequality relating *a* to Mt. McKinley's altitude. $a < 20{,}320$

34. **What's the Error?** A student graphed $x > 1$ as shown. What did the student do wrong? Draw the correct graph. The student drew a closed circle on 1 when it should have been open.

−5 −4 −3 −2 −1 0 1 2 3 4 5

Additional Examples

Example 

Graph the solutions to $x \geq 1$ on a number line.

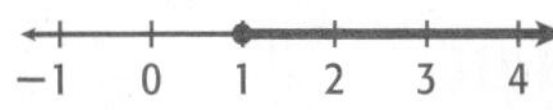

−1 0 1 2 3 4

Example 2

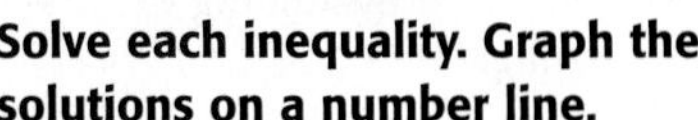

Solve each inequality. Graph the solutions on a number line.

A. $z - 2 > 1$

$z > 3$

−2 0 2 4 6 8 10

B. $\frac{x}{2} \leq 1$

$x \leq 2$

−2 0 2 4 6 8 10

Also available on transparency

3 Close

Summarize

Review by graphing the following: $x > 3$, $x = 3$, and $x \leq 3$. Then have students volunteer ways that solving inequalities is the same as solving equations and ways that solving inequalities is different from solving equations.

Answers

1. 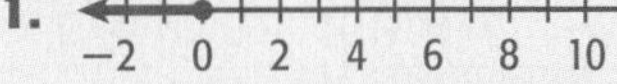
−2 0 2 4 6 8 10

2. −2 0 2 4 6 8 10

3. −2 0 2 4 6 8 10

4. −2 0 2 4 6 8 10

5. −2 0 2 4 6 8 10

6. −2 0 2 4 6 8 10

7. −2 0 2 4 6 8 10

8. −2 0 2 4 6 8 10

9. −2 0 2 4 6 8 10

10. −2 0 2 4 6 8 10

11. −2 0 2 4 6 8 10

12. −2 0 2 4 6 8 10

28. −2 0 2 4 6 8 10

29. −2 0 2 4 6 8 10 12

30. −2 0 2 4 6 8 10

31. −2 0 2 4 6 8 10

Game Time

Organizer

Objective: Participate in games to practice and apply skills learned in Chapter 2.

Online Edition

Resources

Chapter 2 Resource Book
Puzzles, Twisters, & Teasers

Math Magic

Purpose: To apply the problem-solving skill of writing and evaluating expressions to a magic trick

Discuss Ask students to explain how the charts were made. Possible answer: You can express any number using the expression $a + 3b + 9c$, with a, b, and c being 0, 1, or 2. For example, to express 7, let $a = 1$, $b = 2$, and $c = 0$. So 7 appears in the first chart once, in the second chart twice, and not in the third chart. How does algebra make this trick easier to understand? Writing the expression $a + 3b + 9c$ makes it easy to see why the trick works.

Extend Challenge students to explore why the charts contain only the numbers from 1 to 26.
Using the expression $a + 3b + 9c$ and the values 0, 1, and 2 for the variables, the least value for the expression is $0 + 3(0) + 9(0) = 0$, and the greatest is $2 + 3(2) + 9(2) = 26$. Zero is not in the charts because it appears zero times in each of the three charts.

Game Time

Math Magic

Guess what your friends are thinking with this math magic trick.

Copy the following number charts.

1	10	19
2, 2	11, 11	20, 20
4	13	22
5, 5	14, 14	23, 23
7	16	25
8, 8	17, 17	26, 26

3	12	21
4	13	22
5	14	23
6, 6	15, 15	24, 24
7, 7	16, 16	25, 25
8, 8	17, 17	26, 26

9	15	21, 21
10	16	22, 22
11	17	23, 23
12	18, 18	24, 24
13	19, 19	25, 25
14	20, 20	26, 26

Step 1: Ask a friend to think of a number from 1 to 26.
Example: Your friend thinks of 26.

Step 2: Show your friend the first chart and ask how many times the chosen number appears. Remember the answer.
Your friend says the chosen number appears twice on the first chart. — 2

Step 3: Show the second chart and ask the same question. Multiply the answer by 3. Add your result to the answer from step 2. Remember this answer.
Your friend says the chosen number appears twice. — $3 \cdot 2 = 6$
The answer from step 2 is 2. — $6 + 2 = 8$

Step 4: Show the third chart and ask the same question. Multiply the answer by 9. Add your result to the answer from step 3. The answer is your friend's number.
Your friend says the chosen number appears twice. — $9 \cdot 2 = 18$
The answer from step 3 is 8. — $18 + 8 = 26$ ← Your friend's number

How does it work?

Your friend's number will be the following:

(answer from step 2) + (3 · answer from step 3) + (9 · answer from step 4)

This is an expression with three variables: $a + 3b + 9c$. A number will be on a particular chart 0, 1, or 2 times, so a, b, and c will always be 0, 1, or 2. With these values, you can write expressions for each number from 1 to 26.

a	b	c	a + 3b + 9c
1	0	0	1 + 3(0) + 9(0) = 1
2	0	0	2 + 3(0) + 9(0) = 2
0	1	0	0 + 3(1) + 9(0) = 3

Can you complete the table for 4–26?

a	b	c	a + 3b + 9c
1	0	0	1 + 3(0) + 9(0) = 1
2	0	0	2 + 3(0) + 9(0) = 2
0	1	0	0 + 3(1) + 9(0) = 3
1	1	0	1 + 3(1) + 9(0) = 4
2	1	0	2 + 3(1) + 9(0) = 5
0	2	0	0 + 3(2) + 9(0) = 6
1	2	0	1 + 3(2) + 9(0) = 7
2	2	0	2 + 3(2) + 9(0) = 8
0	0	1	0 + 3(0) + 9(1) = 9
1	0	1	1 + 3(0) + 9(1) = 10
2	0	1	2 + 3(0) + 9(1) = 11
0	1	1	0 + 3(1) + 9(1) = 12
1	1	1	1 + 3(1) + 9(1) = 13

a	b	c	a + 3b + 9c
2	1	1	2 + 3(1) + 9(1) = 14
0	2	1	0 + 3(2) + 9(1) = 15
1	2	1	1 + 3(2) + 9(1) = 16
2	2	1	2 + 3(2) + 9(1) = 17
0	0	2	0 + 3(0) + 9(2) = 18
1	0	2	1 + 3(0) + 9(2) = 19
2	0	2	2 + 3(0) + 9(2) = 20
0	1	2	0 + 3(1) + 9(2) = 21
1	1	2	1 + 3(1) + 9(2) = 22
2	1	2	2 + 3(1) + 9(2) = 23
0	2	2	0 + 3(2) + 9(2) = 24
1	2	2	1 + 3(2) + 9(2) = 25
2	2	2	2 + 3(2) + 9(2) = 26

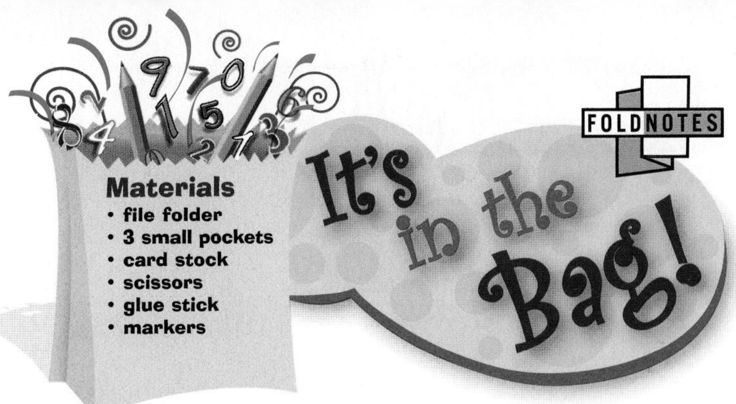

PROJECT Tri-Sided Equations

Use a colorful file folder to prepare a three-sided review of algebra!

Directions

1. Close the file folder. Fold one side down to the folded edge. Turn the folder over and fold the other side down to the folded edge. **Figure A**

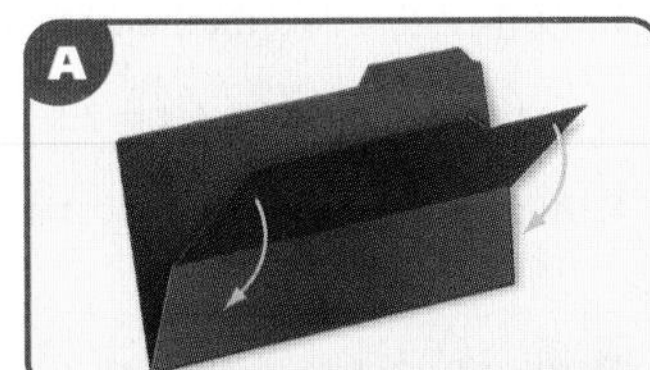

2. Open the folder. It will be divided into four sections. On the top section, cut off $\frac{1}{4}$ inch from each edge. On the bottom section, make a 1 inch diagonal slit in the top left corner and in the top right corner. **Figure B**

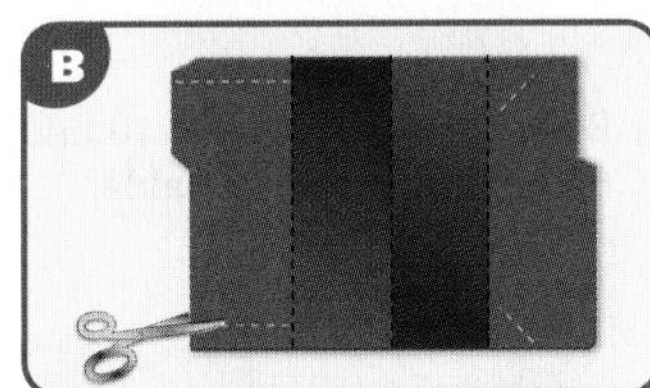

3. Fold the folder so that the corners of the smaller top section fit into the slits. This will create your three-sided holder for notes. **Figure C**

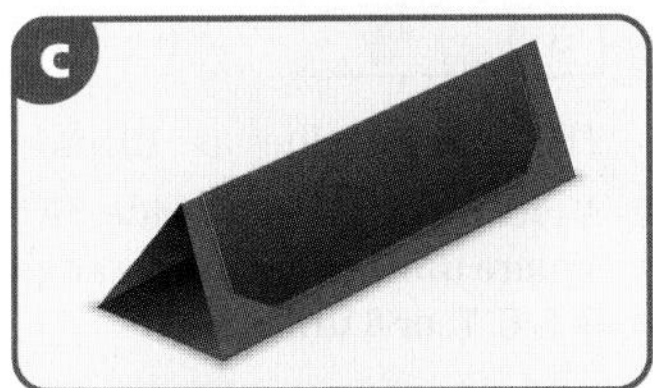

4. Write the definition of an equation on one side of your note holder. Write the order of operations on another side. Write examples of expressions on the third side.

Taking Note of the Math

Glue a small pocket made from construction paper or card stock onto each side of your note holder. On rectangular slips of card stock, write problems that demonstrate your knowledge of equations, order of operations, and expressions. Store the note cards in the appropriate pockets.

Over the last few years, we've found that a variety of snack foods are packaged in triangular prisms. These packages are perfect for this project! Students can also use flattened cereal boxes or poster board instead of file folders.

As a variation on the project, you might have students make the three-sided note holder so that it stands vertically. In this case, students will need to orient the pockets differently when they attach them to the note holder.

Organizer

Objective: Make a three-sided holder that stores notes on the algebra concepts.

Materials: Colored file folder, 3 small pockets made from construction paper or card stock (approx. 3 in. by 3 in.), small rectangular slips of colored card stock (approx. 4 in. by 2 in.), scissors, glue stick, markers

Using the Page

Preparing the Materials
If possible, use a large paper cutter to prepare the slips of cardstock ahead of time. Students will use these slips as note cards on which to write problems from the chapter.

Making the Project
Remind students to be especially careful when they use their scissors to cut the diagonal slits in the folder.

Extending the Project
Ask students how they would have to change their folds to make a four-sided or five-sided note holder.

CHAPTER 2 Study Guide: Review

Organizer

Objective: Help students organize and review key concepts and skills presented in Chapter 2.

Online Edition
Multilingual Glossary

Resources

PuzzlePro®
One-Stop Planner®

***Multilingual Glossary* Online**

go.hrw.com
KEYWORD: MR7 Glossary

Lesson Tutorial Videos
CD-ROM

Test & Practice Generator
One-Stop Planner®

Answers

1. algebraic expression
2. equation
3. variable
4. constant
5. 7, 6
6. 6, 10
7. 9, 18, 27, 36
8. 30, 33, 36, 39
9. 75, 80, 85, 90

CHAPTER 2

Study Guide: Review

Vocabulary

Complete the sentences below with vocabulary words from the list above.

1. A(n) __?__ contains one or more variables.
2. A(n) __?__ is a mathematical statement that says two quantities are equal.
3. In the equation $12 + t = 22$, t is a __?__.
4. A(n) __?__ is a quantity that does not change.

2-1 Variables and Expressions (pp. 54–57)

GPS M6A3

EXAMPLE

- **Evaluate the expression to find the missing values in the table.**

n	$3n + 4$	
1	7	$n = 1;\ 3 \times 1 + 4 = 7$
2	■	$n = 2;\ 3 \times 2 + 4 = 10$
3	■	$n = 3;\ 3 \times 3 + 4 = 13$

The missing values are 10 and 13.

- **A rectangle is 3 units wide. How many square units does the rectangle cover if it is 5, 6, 7, or 8 units long?**

ℓ	w	$\ell \times w$	
5	3	15	$5 \times 3 = 15$ square units
6	3	■	$6 \times 3 = 18$ square units
7	3	■	$7 \times 3 = 21$ square units
8	3	■	$8 \times 3 = 24$ square units

The rectangle will cover a total of 15, 18, 21, or 24 square units.

EXERCISES

Evaluate each expression to find the missing values in the tables.

5.

y	$y \div 7$
56	8
49	■
42	■

6.

k	$k \times 4 - 6$
2	2
3	■
4	■

7. A rectangle is 9 units long. How many square units does the rectangle cover if it is 1, 2, 3, or 4 units wide?
8. Karen buys 3 bouquets of flowers. How many flowers does she buy if each bouquet contains 10, 11, 12, or 13 flowers?
9. Ron buys 5 bags of marbles. How many marbles does he buy if each bag contains 15, 16, 17, or 18 marbles?

Study Guide: Review

2-2 Translate Between Words and Math (pp. 58–61)

GPS M6P5.b

EXAMPLE

Write each phrase as a numerical or algebraic expression.

- 617 minus 191
  $617 - 191$
- d multiplied by 5
  $5d$ or $5 \cdot d$ or $(5)(d)$

Write two phrases for each expression.

- $a \div 5$
  - a divided by 5
  - the quotient of a and 5
- $67 + 19$
  - the sum of 67 and 19
  - 19 more than 67

EXERCISES

Write each phrase as a numerical or algebraic expression.

10. 15 plus b

11. the product of 6 and 5

12. 9 times t

13. the quotient of g and 9

Write two phrases for each expression.

14. $4z$
15. $15 + x$

16. $54 \div 6$
17. $\frac{m}{20}$

18. $3 - y$
19. $5{,}100 + 64$

20. $y - 3$
21. $g - 20$

2-3 Translating Between Tables and Expressions (pp. 62–65)

GPS M6P5.b

EXAMPLE

- **Write an expression for the sequence in the table.**

Position	1	2	3	4	n
Value of Term	9	18	27	36	■

To go from the position to the value of the term, multiply the position by 9. The expression is $9n$.

EXERCISES

Write an expression for the sequence in each table.

22.

Position	1	2	3	4	n
Value of Term	4	7	10	13	■

23.

Position	1	2	3	4	n
Value of Term	0	1	2	3	■

2-4 Equations and Their Solutions (pp. 70–73)

GPS M6A3

EXAMPLE

- **Determine whether the given value of the variable is a solution.**

$f + 14 = 50$ for $f = 34$

$34 + 14 \stackrel{?}{=} 50$ *Substitute 34 for f.*

$48 \neq 50$ *Add.*

34 is not a solution.

EXERCISES

Determine whether the given value of each variable is a solution.

24. $28 + n = 39$ for $n = 11$

25. $12t = 74$ for $t = 6$

26. $y - 53 = 27$ for $y = 80$

27. $96 \div w = 32$ for $w = 3$

Study Guide: Review

Answers

10. $15 + b$
11. 6×5
12. $9t$
13. $g \div 9$
14. the product of 4 and z; 4 times z
15. 54 divided by 6; the quotient of 54 and 6
16. 3 minus y; the difference of 3 and y
17. y minus 3; the difference of y and 3
18. 15 plus x; the sum of 15 and x
19. m divided by 20; the quotient of m and 20
20. the sum of 5,100 and 64; 64 added to 5,100
21. g minus 20; the difference of g and 20
22. $3n + 1$
23. $n - 1$
24. yes
25. no
26. yes
27. yes

Answers

28. $x = 6$
29. $n = 14$
30. $c = 29$
31. $y = 6$
32. $p = 27$
33. $w = 9$
34. $b = 11$
35. $n = 44$
36. $p = 16$
37. $d = 57$
38. $k = 45$
39. $d = 9$
40. $p = 63$
41. $n = 67$
42. $r = 14$
43. $w = 144$
44. $h = 60$
45. $p = 167$
46. $v = 8$
47. $y = 9$
48. $c = 7$
49. $n = 2$
50. $s = 8$
51. $t = 10$
52. $a = 8$
53. $y = 8$
54. $r = 42$
55. $t = 15$
56. $y = 18$
57. $n = 72$
58. $z = 52$
59. $b = 100$
60. $n = 77$
61. $p = 90$

2-5 Addition Equations (pp. 74–77)

GPS M6A3

EXAMPLE

■ **Solve the equation $x + 18 = 31$.**

$$\begin{aligned} x + 18 &= 31 \\ -18 &\quad -18 \\ x &= 13 \end{aligned}$$

18 is added to x.
Subtract 18 from both sides to undo the addition.

EXERCISES

Solve each equation.

28. $4 + x = 10$
29. $n + 10 = 24$
30. $c + 71 = 100$
31. $y + 16 = 22$
32. $44 = p + 17$
33. $94 + w = 103$
34. $23 + b = 34$
35. $56 = n + 12$
36. $39 = 23 + p$
37. $d + 28 = 85$

2-6 Subtraction Equations (pp. 78–80)

GPS M6A3

EXAMPLE

■ **Solve the equation $c - 7 = 16$.**

$$\begin{aligned} c - 7 &= 16 \\ +7 &\quad +7 \\ c &= 23 \end{aligned}$$

7 is subtracted from c.
Add 7 to each side to undo the subtraction.

EXERCISES

Solve each equation.

38. $28 = k - 17$
39. $d - 8 = 1$
40. $p - 55 = 8$
41. $n - 31 = 36$
42. $3 = r - 11$
43. $97 = w - 47$
44. $12 = h - 48$
45. $9 = p - 158$

2-7 Multiplication Equations (pp. 81–84)

GPS M6A3

EXAMPLE

■ **Solve the equation $6x = 36$.**

$$\begin{aligned} 6x &= 36 \\ \frac{6x}{6} &= \frac{36}{6} \\ x &= 6 \end{aligned}$$

x is multiplied by 6.
Divide both sides by 6 to undo the multiplication.

EXERCISES

Solve each equation.

46. $5v = 40$
47. $27 = 3y$
48. $12c = 84$
49. $18n = 36$
50. $72 = 9s$
51. $11t = 110$
52. $7a = 56$
53. $8y = 64$

2-8 Division Equations (pp. 85–87)

GPS M6A3

EXAMPLE

■ **Solve the equation $\frac{k}{4} = 8$.**

$$\begin{aligned} \frac{k}{4} &= 8 \\ 4 \cdot \frac{k}{4} &= 4 \cdot 8 \\ k &= 32 \end{aligned}$$

k is divided by 4.
Multiply both sides by 4 to undo the division.

EXERCISES

Solve each equation.

54. $\frac{r}{7} = 6$
55. $\frac{t}{5} = 3$
56. $6 = \frac{y}{3}$
57. $12 = \frac{n}{6}$
58. $\frac{z}{13} = 4$
59. $20 = \frac{b}{5}$
60. $\frac{n}{11} = 7$
61. $10 = \frac{p}{9}$

CHAPTER TEST

CHAPTER 2

Evaluate each expression to find the missing values in the tables.

1.

a	$a + 18$
10	28
12	▒ **30**
14	▒ **32**

2.

y	$y \div 6$
18	3
30	▒ **5**
42	▒ **7**

3.

n	$n \div 5 + 7$
10	9
20	▒ **11**
30	▒ **13**

4. A van can seat 6 people. How many people can ride in 3, 4, 5, and 6 vans? **18; 24; 30; 36**

5. A rectangle is 5 units wide. How many square units does the rectangle cover if it is 10, 11, 12, or 13 units long? **50; 55; 60; 65**

Write an expression for the missing value in each table.

6.

Packages	Rolls
1	8
2	16
3	24
4	32
p	▒ **$8p$**

7.

Students	Groups
5	1
10	2
15	3
20	4
s	▒ **$\frac{s}{5}$**

Write an expression for the sequence in the table.

8.

Position	1	2	3	4	5	n
Value of Term	4	7	10	13	16	▒

$3n + 1$

3 3 3 3

9. There are more reptile species than amphibian species. There are 3,100 living species of amphibians. Write an expression to show how many more reptile species there are than amphibian species. **$n - 3{,}100$**

Write each phrase as a numerical or algebraic expression.

10. 26 more than n **$n + 26$** 11. g multiplied by 4 **$4g$** 12. the quotient of 180 and 15 **$180 \div 15$**

Write two phrases for each expression.

13. $(14)(16)$ 14. $n \div 8$ 15. $p + 11$ 16. $s - 6$

Determine whether the given value of the variable is a solution.

17. $5d = 70$ for $d = 12$ **no**

18. $29 = 76 - n$ for $n = 46$ **no**

19. $108 \div a = 12$ for $a = 9$ **yes**

20. $15 + m = 27$ for $m = 12$ **yes**

Solve each equation.

21. $a + 7 = 25$ **$a = 18$** 22. $121 = 11d$ **$d = 11$** 23. $3 = t - 8$ **$t = 11$** 24. $6 = \frac{k}{9}$ **$k = 54$**

25. Air typically has about 4,000 bacteria per cubic meter. If your room is 30 cubic meters, about how many bacteria would there be in the air in your room? **about 120,000 bacteria**

$\frac{4000 \text{ bac}}{m^3} \times 30 \, m^3 = 120{,}000 \text{ bac}$

Chapter Test

CHAPTER 2

Organizer

Objective: Assess students' mastery of concepts and skills in Chapter 2.

Online Edition

Resources

Assessment Resources

Chapter 2 Tests
- Free Response (Levels A, B, C)
- Multiple Choice (Levels A, B, C)
- Performance Assessment

***IDEA Works!* CD-ROM**
Modified Chapter 2 Test

Answers

13. 14 times 16; the product of 14 and 16
14. the quotient of n and 8; n divided by 8
15. p plus 11; the sum of p and 11
16. 6 less than s; s minus 6

Organizer

Objective: Provide review and practice for Chapters 1-2 and standardized tests.

Online Edition

Resources

Assessment Resources
Chapter 2 Cumulative Test

***CRCT Prep* Workbook**

***CRCT Prep* CD-ROM**

***CRCT Practice* Online**

go.hrw.com
KEYWORD: MR7 Test Prep

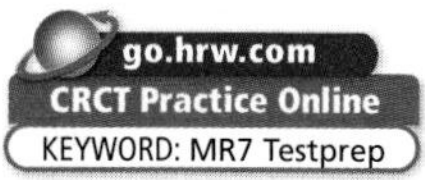

CRCT Prep

CUMULATIVE ASSESSMENT, CHAPTERS 1–2

Multiple Choice

1. Which is an algebraic expression for the product of 15 and x?

Ⓐ $15 - x$ Ⓒ $x + 15$
Ⓑ $15x$ Ⓓ $15 \div x$

2. Max earned $560 working as a landscaper. If he worked a total of 80 hours, which expression can be used to find how much he earned each hour?

Ⓕ $560 - 80$ Ⓗ $560 + 80$
Ⓖ $560 \div 80$ Ⓙ $560 \cdot 80$

3. Find the expression for the table.

w	
3	9
8	19
11	25
15	33

Ⓐ $3x$ Ⓒ $2x + 3$
Ⓑ $x + 18$ Ⓓ $3x - 5$

4. A rectangular classroom has an area of 252 square feet. The width of the classroom is 14 feet. What is its length?

Ⓕ 14 feet Ⓗ 18 feet
Ⓖ 16 feet Ⓙ 20 feet

5. What is the difference between 82,714 and 54,221 rounded to the nearest hundred?

Ⓐ 28,500 Ⓒ 26,900
Ⓑ 27,700 Ⓓ 26,000

6. What is the value of 8^3?

Ⓕ 11 Ⓗ 192
Ⓖ 24 Ⓙ 512

7. Zane biked 23 miles this week. This is 8 miles more than he biked the week before. Solve the equation $x + 8 = 23$ to find how many miles Zane biked last week?

Ⓐ 15 miles Ⓒ 31 miles
Ⓑ 23 miles Ⓓ 33 miles

8. Which team sold the most fund-raising products?

Fund-raising Results by Team	
Team	**Products Sold**
Golf	6,536
Soccer	6,421
Swim	6,879
Track	6,019

Ⓕ Soccer team Ⓗ Swim team
Ⓖ Golf team Ⓙ Track team

9. Which equation is an example of the Associative Property?

Ⓐ $3 + (4 + 6) = (3 + 4) + 6$
Ⓑ $(42 + 6) + 18 = (42 + 18) + 6$
Ⓒ $(3 \times 20) + (3 \times 4) = 3 \times 24$
Ⓓ $8(2 \times 6) = (8 \times 2) + (8 \times 6)$

TEST PREP DOCTOR

For item 2, students may have to be reminded the phrase "earn each hour" means that the pay has to be distributed evenly over 80 hours. The students should divide $560 by 80.

Answers

16a. $j + 7$; j represents the miles Jamie runs each week.

18. See 4-Point Response work sample.

10. Nicole is 15 years old. She is 3 years younger than her sister Jan. Solve the equation $j - 3 = 15$ to find Jan's age.

(F) 18 years (H) 12 years
(G) 17 years (J) 5 years

11. Ling created an arithmetic sequence that starts with 5 and then adds 8. Find the 6th term in this sequence.

(A) 30 (C) 40
(B) 38 (D) 45

When you read a word problem, underline the information you need to help you answer the question.

12. What is the value of $5^2 - (18 \div 6) \times 7$?

(F) 4 (H) 31
(G) 46 (J) 154

13. Scott spends 16 minutes in the pool treading water during swim practice. This is $\frac{1}{3}$ of his training time. How many total minutes is Scott's swim practice?

(A) 8 (C) 16
(B) 32 (D) 48

14. A case of pencils costs $15. The academic team spends $135 on pencils for the school tournament. How many cases of pencils did the academic team buy?

(F) 7 (H) 9
(G) 8 (J) 10

15. What value of x will make the expressions $2x + 4$ and $5x - 8$ equal 12?

(A) 2 (C) 4
(B) 6 (D) 8

STANDARDIZED TEST PREP

Short Response

16. Every week Brandi runs 7 more miles than her sister Jamie.

a. Write an expression for the number of miles that Brandi runs each week. Identify the variable.

b. Evaluate your expression to find the number of miles Brandi runs when Jamie runs 5 miles. **12 mi**

17. A vacation tour costs $450. Additional outings cost $25 each. The table shows the total cost to go on additional outings.

Outings	1	2	3	n
Total Cost ($)	475	500	525	■

Write an expression for the cost of n outings. Use the expression to find how much it costs to go on 5 outings.
$450 + 25n$; $575

Extended Response

18. Chrissy and Kathie are sisters. Chrissy was born on Kathie's birthday and is exactly 8 years younger. Chrissy celebrated her 16th birthday on December 8, 2005.

a. Complete the table to show the ages of the sisters in the years 2005, 2008, and 2011.

Year	Kathie's Age	Chrissy's Age
2005	■ 24	■ 16
2008	■ 27	■ 19
2011	■ 30	■ 22

b. Write an equation that could be used to find Chrissy's age in 2011. Identify the variable in the equation.

c. Solve the equation. Show your work. Compare your answer to the value in the table. Are the two solutions the same? Explain your answer.

CRCT Prep

Short Response Rubric

Items 16–17

2 Points = The student's answer is an accurate and complete execution of the task or tasks.

1 Point = The student's answer contains attributes of an appropriate response but is flawed.

0 Points = The student's answer contains no attributes of an appropriate response.

Extended Response Rubric

Item 18

4 Points = The student demonstrates a thorough understanding of all concepts and shows all work correctly.

3 Points = The student demonstrates a basic understanding of all concepts, but the work shows some flaws reflecting inattentive execution of mathematical procedures or some misunderstanding of the underlying mathematics.

2 Points = The student demonstrates only a partial understanding of the concepts or procedures embodied in the tasks. The approach may be correct, but the work shows a misunderstanding of one or more important concepts.

1 Point = The student demonstrates a very limited understanding of the concepts or procedures embodied in the tasks. The response may show some understanding but exhibits many flaws or is incomplete.

0 Points = The student provides no response at all or a completely incorrect or uninterpretable response.

Student Work Samples for Item 18

4-Point Response

a.

YEAR	KATHIE'S AGE	CHRISSY'S AGE
2005	24	16
2008	27	19
2011	30	22

b. Let k = Katnie's age.
k − 8 = 22

c. k − 8 = 22
k − 8 = 22
+8 +8
k = 30

The two solutions are both the same and reasonable. When 30 replaces k, each side of the equation equals 22.

The student showed all work in finding the correct totals and explained the work when asked. The student correctly answered part **c** in a sentence.

3-Point Response

a.

Year	Kathie's Age	Chrissy's Age
2005	24	16
2008	27	19
2011	30	22

b. Let k = Kathie's age
k + 8 = 22

c. k + 8 = 22
−8 −8
k = 14

The solution is correct. When 14 replaces k, each side of the equation equals 22.

The student answered part **a** correctly but wrote the wrong equation in part **b.** The student solved the equation but did not compare the solution to the value in the table.

2-Point Response

a. 24, 27, 30; 16, 19, 22

b. K + 2011 = 22

c. K + 2011 = 22
+2011 +2011
K = 2033

The two solutions are not the same.

In part **a,** the student found the correct data for the table. Parts **b** and **c**—the equation, solution, and conclusion—are incorrect.

Problem Solving on Location

Organizer

Objective: To solve real-world problems involving whole numbers, patterns, and basic algebraic ideas

Online Edition

The *Museum of Aviation*

Reading Strategies

ELL students may not be familiar with the word *aviation*. Have them read the page and use context clues to guess the meaning of the word. If students need guidance, ask them what type of museum would contain airplanes and helicopters. Then ask them what they think *aviation* means.

Using Data Check for understanding by asking students questions about the data in the bar graph. For example, Which helicopter can fly the fastest? The Jolly Green Giant At their top speeds, how much faster is the Workhorse than the Sioux? 32 mi/h

Georgia Performance Standards

M6P1.c Apply and adapt a variety of appropriate strategies to solve problems.

M6P4.c Recognize and apply mathematics in contexts outside of mathematics.

M6P5.a Create and use representations to organize, record, and communicate mathematical ideas.

Problem Solving on Location

GEORGIA

Georgia Performance Standards

M6P1.c, M6P4.c, M6P5.a

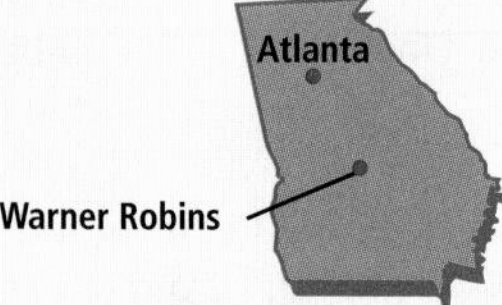

The Museum of Aviation

The Museum of Aviation, in Warner Robins, Georgia, is one of the largest aviation museums in the country. Its collection of more than 90 aircraft varies from helicopters to jets, like the SR-71 "Blackbird" shown at right.

Choose one or more strategies to solve each problem.

1. The museum consists of four buildings: the Eagle Building, the Century of Flight Hangar, Hangar One, and the Heritage Building. How many different ways can a visitor choose two of the buildings to explore? **6**

2. One of the planes at the museum is a Lockheed JetStar. The length of the JetStar is three times its height. The sum of the length and height is 80 feet. What are the length and height of the plane? **Length: 60 ft; height: 20 ft**

For 3, use the graph.

3. The graph shows the top speeds of several helicopters at the museum. The Iroquois's maximum speed is 17 mi/hr greater than that of the Choctaw. The Choctaw's maximum speed is 9 mi/hr less than that of the Workhorse. What is the maximum speed of the Iroquois? **140 mi/hr**

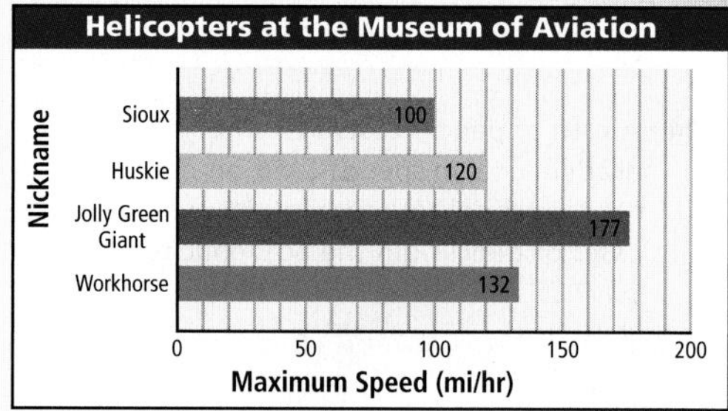

Problem Solving Focus

For problem 1, focus on the third step of the Problem Solving Process: Solve. In particular, ask students which strategy or strategies they used in solving the problem. If students used the strategy Make an Organized List, have them share their lists with the class. Then discuss whether there is more than one correct way to organize the information in the list.

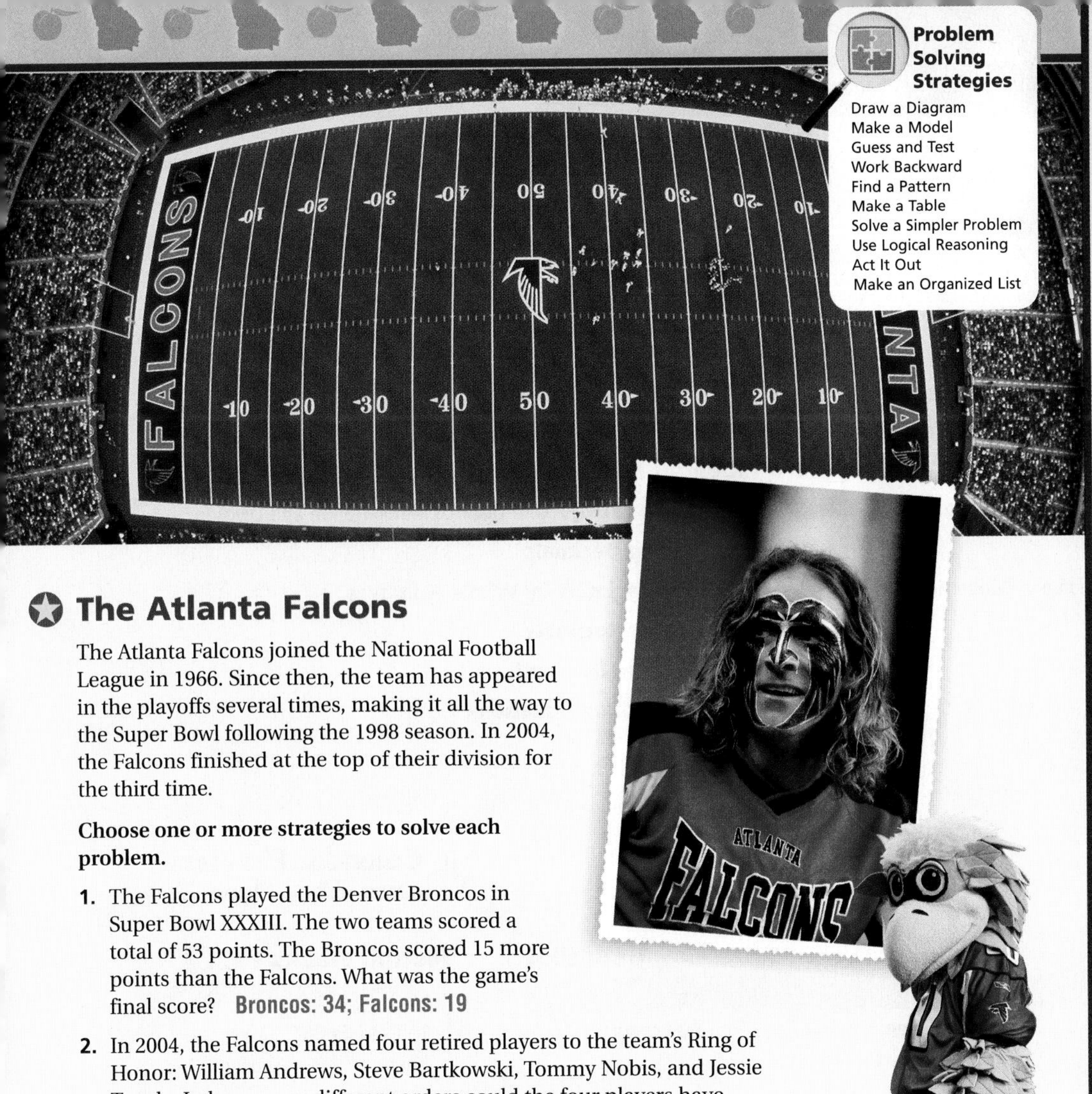

 The Atlanta Falcons

The Atlanta Falcons joined the National Football League in 1966. Since then, the team has appeared in the playoffs several times, making it all the way to the Super Bowl following the 1998 season. In 2004, the Falcons finished at the top of their division for the third time.

Choose one or more strategies to solve each problem.

1. The Falcons played the Denver Broncos in Super Bowl XXXIII. The two teams scored a total of 53 points. The Broncos scored 15 more points than the Falcons. What was the game's final score? **Broncos: 34; Falcons: 19**
2. In 2004, the Falcons named four retired players to the team's Ring of Honor: William Andrews, Steve Bartkowski, Tommy Nobis, and Jessie Tuggle. In how many different orders could the four players have lined up during the ceremony? **24**
3. The Falcons play 16 games each season, not including playoff games. In 2000, the Falcons won 4 games. In 2001, they lost 9 games. In 2002, they won two more games than they lost. In 2003, they won one more game than they won in 2000. What is the total number of games won by the Falcons from 2000 through 2003? (No games ended in a tie.) **25**
4. In 2004, the Falcons won 7 more games then they won in 2000. Use this and the information from Exercise 3 to make a graph displaying the number of wins recorded by the Falcons each season from 2000 through 2004.

4.

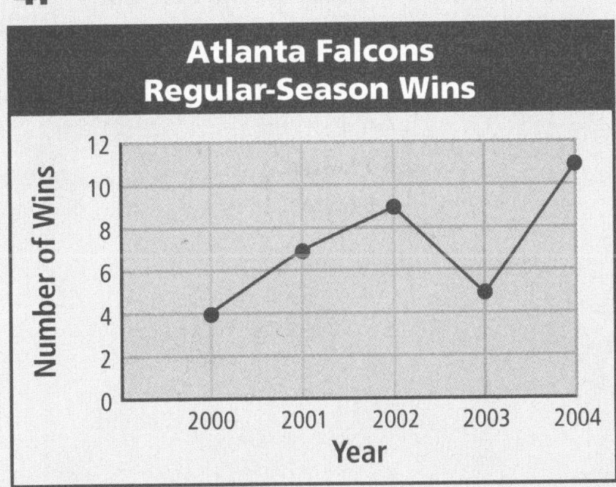

The *Atlanta Falcons*

Reading Strategies

English Language Learners

After students have read problem 1, ask them to give examples of information that is essential in solving the problem. Possible answer: The sum of the teams' scores is 53. Then have students give an example of information that is not essential in solving the problem. Possible answer: The teams played in Super Bowl XXXIII.

Problem Solving Focus

For problem 2, focus on the first step in the Problem Solving Process: Understand the Problem. Once students have read the problem, ask them what the answer will consist of. For example, for some problems, the answer is a number; for others, it is a list. In some cases, the answer is the name of a person or place. Help students understand that the phrase "In how many different orders..." means that the answer to this problem will be a number.

Discuss different strategies that could be used to solve problem 2. If no one suggests it, have students try using the strategy Act It Out. In this case, four students can assume the roles of the players while another student keeps track of the different orders in which they can line up.

Extension For problem 2, ask students how many different orders there would have been if five players had been honored at the ceremony. 120

CHAPTER 3

Decimals

Section 3A

Understanding Decimals

- **3-1 Hands-On Lab** Model Decimals
- **3-1 Representing, Comparing, and Ordering Decimals**
- **3-2 Estimating Decimals**
- **3-3 Hands-On Lab** Explore Decimal Addition and Subtraction
- **3-3 Adding and Subtracting Decimals**

Section 3B

Multiplying and Dividing Decimals

- **3-4 Scientific Notation**
- **3-5 Hands-On Lab** Explore Decimal Multiplication and Division
- **3-5 Multiplying Decimals**
- **3-6 Dividing Decimals by Whole Numbers**
- **3-7 Dividing by Decimals**
- **3-8 Interpret the Quotient**
- **3-9 Solving Decimal Equations**

Pacing Guide for 45-Minute Classes

Chapter 3

Countdown to Testing Weeks 5, 6

DAY 1	DAY 2	DAY 3	DAY 4	DAY 5
3-1 Hands-On Lab 3-1 Lesson	3-1 Lesson 3-2 Lesson	3-2 Lesson 3-3 Hands-On Lab	3-3 Lesson	Ready to Go On? Focus on Problem Solving 3-4 Lesson
DAY 6	**DAY 7**	**DAY 8**	**DAY 9**	**DAY 10**
3-4 Lesson 3-5 Hands-On Lab	3-5 Lesson	3-6 Lesson	3-7 Lesson	3-7 Lesson 3-8 Lesson
DAY 11	**DAY 12**	**DAY 13**	**DAY 14**	
3-8 Lesson 3-9 Lesson	3-9 Lesson Ready to Go On? Multi-Step Test Prep	Chapter 3 Review	Chapter 3 Test	

Pacing Guide for 90-Minute Classes

Chapter 3

DAY 1	DAY 2	DAY 3	DAY 4	DAY 5
3-1 Hands-On Lab 3-1 Lesson 3-2 Lesson	3-2 Lesson 3-3 Hands-On Lab 3-3 Lesson	Ready to Go On? Focus on Problem Solving 3-4 Lesson 3-5 Hands-On Lab	3-5 Lesson 3-6 Lesson	3-7 Lesson 3-8 Lesson
DAY 6	**DAY 7**			
3-8 Lesson 3-9 Lesson Ready to Go On? Multi-Step Test Prep	Chapter 3 Review Chapter 3 Test			

ONGOING ASSESSMENT and INTERVENTION

	DIAGNOSE	PRESCRIBE
Assess Prior Knowledge	**Before Chapter 3**	
	Diagnose readiness for the chapter.	Prescribe intervention.
	Are You Ready? SE p. 103	***Are You Ready? Intervention*** Skills 1, 12, 34, 58
Formative Assessment	**Before Every Lesson**	
	Diagnose readiness for the lesson.	Prescribe intervention.
	Warm Up TE, every lesson	**Skills Bank** SE pp. 749–761
		Reteach CRB, Chapters 1–3
	During Every Lesson	
	Diagnose understanding of lesson concepts.	Prescribe intervention.
	Think and Discuss SE, every lesson	***Questioning Strategies*** pp. 31–48
	Write About It SE, lesson exercises	**Reading Strategies** CRB, every lesson
	Journal TE, lesson exercises	***Success for ELL*** pp. 31–48
	After Every Lesson	
	Diagnose mastery of lesson concepts.	Prescribe intervention.
	Lesson Quiz TE, every lesson	**Reteach** CRB, every lesson
	Test Prep SE, every lesson	**Problem Solving** CRB, every lesson
	Test and Practice Generator	**Test Prep Doctor** TE, lesson exercises
		***Homework Help* Online**
	Before Chapter 3 Testing	
	Diagnose mastery of concepts in the chapter.	Prescribe intervention.
	Ready to Go On? SE pp. 122, 148	***Ready to Go On? Intervention***
	Focus on Problem Solving SE p. 123	**Scaffolding Questions** TE p. 149
	Multi-Step Test Prep SE p. 149	
	Section Quizzes AR pp. 45–46	
	Test and Practice Generator	
	Before High Stakes Testing	
	Diagnose mastery of benchmark concepts.	Prescribe intervention.
	Test Tackler SE pp. 156–157	***CRCT Prep Workbook***
	CRCT Prep SE pp. 158–159	
	***CRCT Prep* CD-ROM**	
Summative Assessment	**After Chapter 3**	
	Check mastery of chapter concepts.	Prescribe intervention.
	Multiple-Choice Tests (Forms A, B, C)	**Reteach** CRB, every lesson
	Free-Response Tests (Forms A, B, C)	***Lesson Tutorial Videos*** Chapter 3
	Performance Assessment AR pp. 47–60	
	Test and Practice Generator	
	Check mastery of benchmark concepts.	Prescribe intervention.
	CRCT	***CRCT Prep Workbook***

KEY: **SE** = *Student Edition* **TE** = *Teacher's Edition* **CRB** = *Chapter Resource Book* **AR** = *Assessment Resources* Available on CD-ROM Available online

CHAPTER 3

Supporting the Teacher

Chapter 3 Resource Book

Practice A, B, C
pp. 3–5, 12–14, 20–22, 28–30, 36–38, 44–46, 52–54, 60–62, 68–70

Reading Strategies ELL
pp. 10, 18, 26, 34, 42, 50, 58, 66, 74

Puzzles, Twisters, and Teasers
pp. 11, 19, 27, 35, 43, 51, 59, 67, 75

Reteach
pp. 6–7, 15, 23, 31, 39, 47, 55, 63, 71

Problem Solving
pp. 9, 17, 25, 33, 41, 49, 57, 65, 73

Challenge
pp. 8, 16, 24, 32, 40, 48, 56, 64, 72

Parent Letter pp. 1–2

Transparencies

Lesson Transparencies, Volume 1 .... Chapter 3
- Teaching Tools
- Warm Ups
- Problem of the Day
- Teaching Transparencies
- Lesson Quizzes

Know-It Notebook .... Chapter 3
- Additional Examples
- Graphic Organizers
- Vocabulary
- Chapter Review
- Foldnotes
- Big Ideas

Alternate Openers: Explorations .... pp. 16–24

Countdown to CRCT .... pp. 9–12

Teacher Tools

Power Presentations®
Complete PowerPoint® presentations for Chapter 3 lessons

Lesson Tutorial Videos® SPANISH
Holt authors Ed Burger and Freddie Renfro present tutorials to support the Chapter 3 lessons.

One-Stop Planner® SPANISH
Easy access to all Chapter 3 resources and assessments, as well as software for lesson planning, test generation, and puzzle creation

IDEA Works!®
Key Chapter 3 resources and assessments modified to address special learning needs

Lesson Plans .... pp. 16–24

Questioning Strategies .... pp. 31–48

Solutions Key .... Chapter 3

Interdisciplinary Posters and Worksheets .... Chapter 3

TechKeys

Lab Resources 

Project Teacher Support

Parent Resources

Workbooks

Homework and Practice Workbook SPANISH
Teacher's Edition .... pp. 16–24

Know-It Notebook
Teacher's Guide .... Chapter 3

Problem Solving Workbook SPANISH
Teacher's Guide .... pp. 16–24

CRCT Prep Workbook
Teacher's Guide

Technology Highlights for the Teacher

 **Power Presentations**

Dynamic presentations to engage students. Complete PowerPoint® presentations for every lesson in Chapter 3.

2-1 Solving One-Step Equations

Isolate a variable by using inverse operations which "undo" operations on the variable.

An equation is like a balanced scale. To keep the balance, perform the same operation on both sides.

Inverse Operations	
Operation	**Inverse Operation**
Addition	Subtraction
Subtraction	Addition

 **One-Stop Planner** SPANISH

Easy access to Chapter 3 resources and assessments. Includes lesson-planning, test-generation, and puzzle-creation software.

 **Premier Online Edition** SPANISH

Chapter 3 includes Tutorial Videos, Lesson Activities, Lesson Quizzes, Homework Help, and Chapter Project.

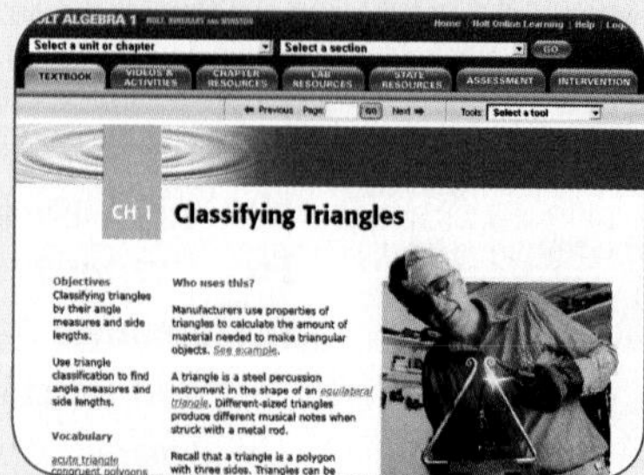

KEY: **SE** = *Student Edition* **TE** = *Teacher's Edition*  English Language Learners  Spanish version available  Available on CD-ROM 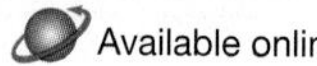

Reaching All Learners

Resources for All Learners

Hands-On Lab Activities .... Chapter 3
Technology Lab Activities .... Chapter 3
Homework and Practice Workbook SPANISH .... pp. 16–24
Know-It Notebook SPANISH .... Chapter 3
Problem Solving Workbook SPANISH .... pp. 16–24

DEVELOPING LEARNERS

Practice A .... CRB, every lesson
Reteach .... CRB, every lesson
Inclusion .... TE pp. 125, 138, 145
Questioning Strategies .... pp. 31–48
Modified Chapter 3 Resources .... *IDEA Works!*
Homework Help Online

ON-LEVEL LEARNERS

Practice B .... CRB, every lesson
Puzzles, Twisters, and Teasers .... CRB, every lesson
Cooperative Learning .... TE p. 131

ADVANCED LEARNERS

Practice C .... CRB, every lesson
Challenge .... CRB, every lesson
Extension .... TE pp. 105, 149, 150, 151
Critical Thinking .... TE p. 142

English Language Learners

ENGLISH LANGUAGE LEARNERS

Are You Ready? Vocabulary .... SE p. 103
Vocabulary Connections .... SE p. 104
Lesson Vocabulary .... SE, every lesson
Vocabulary Review .... SE p. 152
English Language Learners .... TE pp. 105, 108
Reading Strategies .... CRB, every lesson
Success for English Language Learners .... pp. 31–48
Multilingual Glossary

Reaching All Learners Through...

Inclusion .... TE pp. 125, 138, 145
Visual Cues .... TE pp. 109, 135
Kinesthetic Experience .... TE p. 138
Concrete Manipulatives .... TE p. 109
Cooperative Learning .... TE p. 131
Critical Thinking .... TE p. 142
Test Prep Doctor .... TE pp. 111, 115, 121, 127, 133, 140, 147, 156, 157, 158
Common Error Alert .... TE pp. 109, 113, 119, 125, 138, 145
Scaffolding Questions .... TE p. 149

Technology Highlights for Reaching All Learners

Lesson Tutorial Videos SPANISH

Starring Holt authors Ed Burger and Freddie Renfro! Live tutorials to support every lesson in Chapter 3.

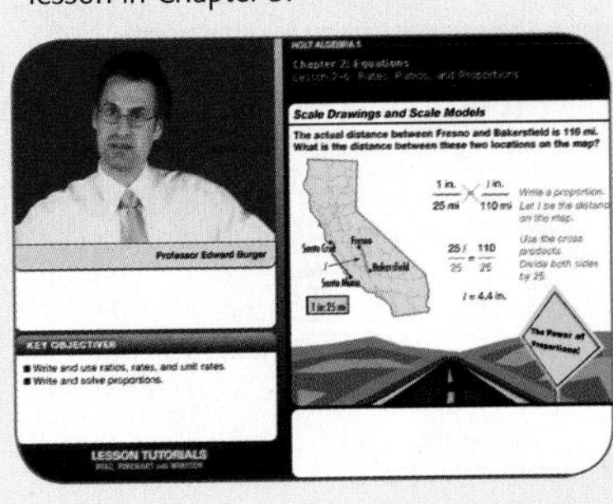

Multilingual Glossary

Searchable glossary includes definitions in English, Spanish, Vietnamese, Chinese, Hmong, Korean, and 4 other languages.

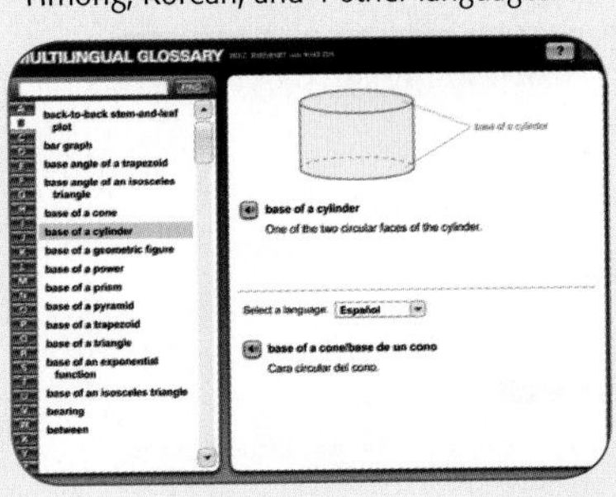

Online Interactivities

Interactive tutorials provide visually engaging alternative opportunities to learn concepts and master skills.

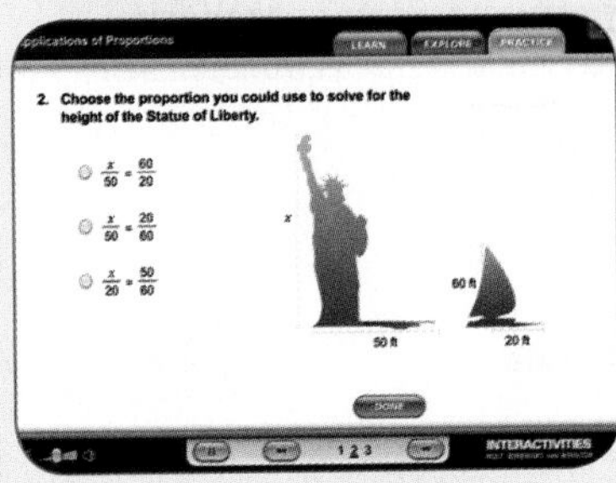

KEY: **SE** = *Student Edition* **TE** = *Teacher's Edition* **CRB** = *Chapter Resource Book*  Spanish version available 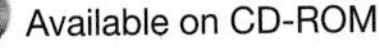 Available on CD-ROM 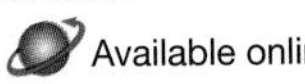 Available online

Ongoing Assessment

Assessing Prior Knowledge

Determine whether students have the prerequisite concepts and skills for success in Chapter 3.

Are You Ready? SPANISH .... SE p. 103
Warm Up .... TE, every lesson

Test Preparation

Provide review and practice for Chapter 3 and standardized tests.

Multi-Step Test Prep .... SE p. 149
Study Guide: Review .... SE pp. 152–154
Test Tackler .... SE pp. 156–159
Standardized Test Prep .... SE pp. 158–159
Countdown to CRCT Transparencies .... pp. 9–12
CRCT Prep Workbook
***CRCT Prep* CD-ROM**
IDEA Works!

Alternative Assessment

Assess students' understanding of Chapter 3 concepts and combined problem-solving skills.

Chapter 3 Project .... SE p. 102
Performance Assessment SPANISH .... AR pp. 59–60
Portfolio Assessment SPANISH .... AR p. xxxiv

Daily Assessment

Provide formative assessment for each day of Chapter 3.

Questioning Strategies .... pp. 31–48
Think and Discuss .... SE, every lesson
Write About It .... SE, lesson exercises
Journal .... TE, lesson exercises
Lesson Quiz .... TE, every lesson
Modified Lesson Quizzes .... *IDEA Works!*

Weekly Assessment

Provide formative assessment for each week of Chapter 3.

Focus on Problem Solving .... SE p. 123
Multi-Step Test Prep .... SE p. 149
Ready to Go On? SPANISH .... SE pp. 122, 148
Cumulative Assessment .... SE pp. 156–157
Test and Practice Generator SPANISH ... *One-Stop Planner*

Formal Assessment

Provide summative assessment of Chapter 3 mastery.

Section Quizzes SPANISH .... AR pp. 45–46
Chapter 3 Test .... SE p. 155
Chapter Test (Levels A, B, C) SPANISH .... AR pp. 47–58
• Multiple Choice • Free Response
Cumulative Test SPANISH .... AR pp. 61–64
Test and Practice Generator SPANISH ... *One-Stop Planner*
Modified Chapter 3 Test .... *IDEA Works!*

Technology Highlights for Ongoing Assessment

Are You Ready? SPANISH

Automatically assess readiness and prescribe intervention for Chapter 3 prerequisite skills.

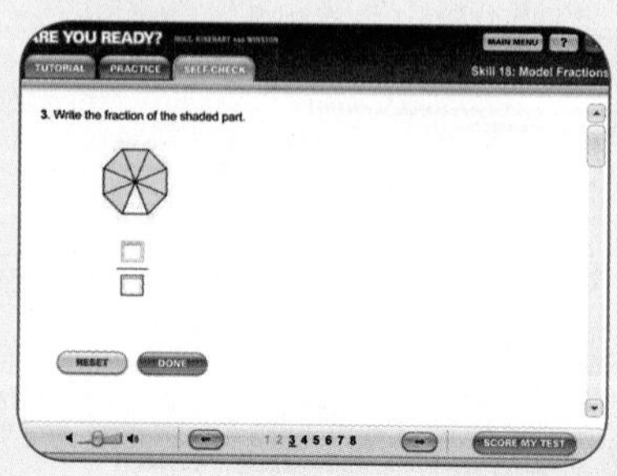

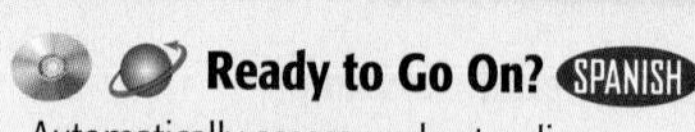

Ready to Go On? SPANISH

Automatically assess understanding of and prescribe intervention for Sections 3A and 3B.

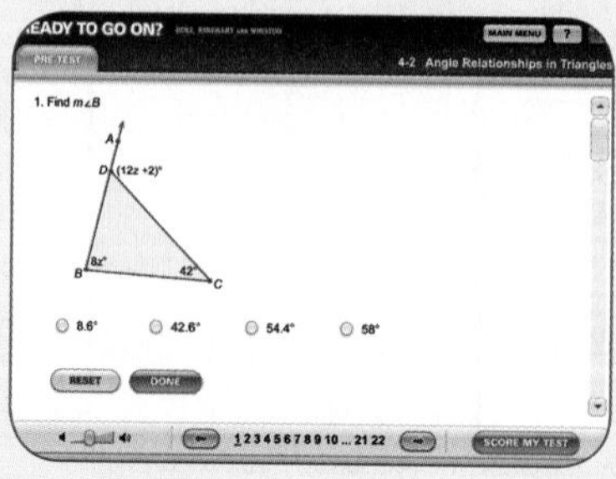

Test and Practice Generator SPANISH

Use Chapter 3 problem banks to create assessments and worksheets to print out or deliver online. Includes dynamic problems.

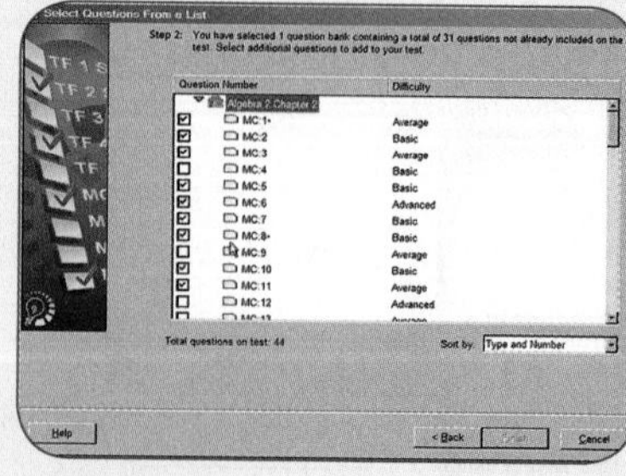

KEY: **SE** = *Student Edition* **TE** = *Teacher's Edition* **AR** = *Assessment Resources*  Spanish version available  Available on CD-ROM  Available online

Formal Assessment

Three levels (A, B, C) of multiple-choice and free-response chapter tests are available in the *Assessment Resources.*

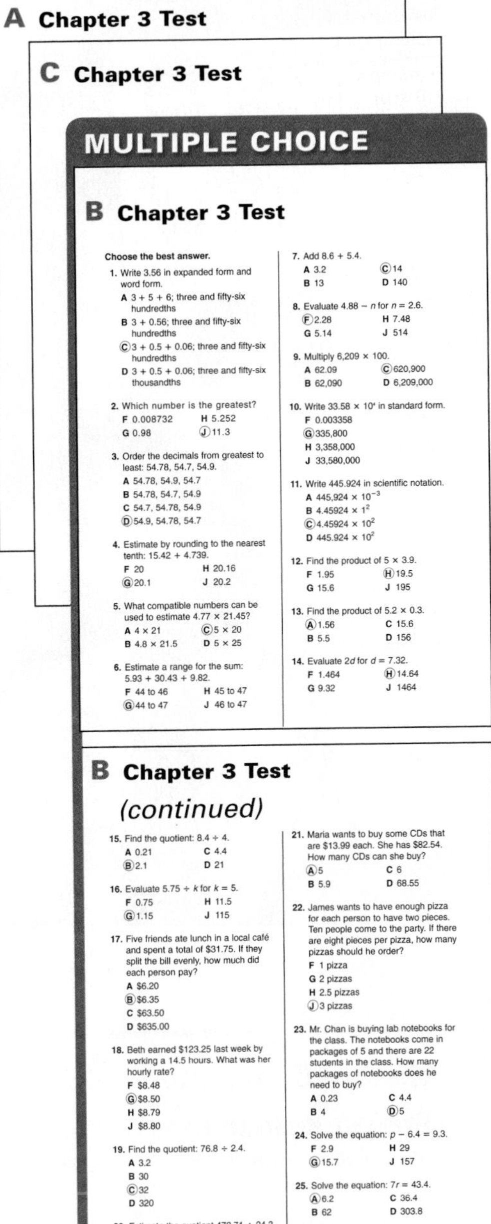

A Chapter 3 Test

C Chapter 3 Test

MULTIPLE CHOICE

B Chapter 3 Test

Choose the best answer.

1. Write 3.56 in expanded form and word form.
   A 3 + 5 + 6; three and fifty-six hundredths
   B 3 + 0.56; three and fifty-six hundredths
   (C) 3 + 0.5 + 0.06; three and fifty-six hundredths
   D 3 + 0.5 + 0.06; three and fifty-six thousandths

2. Which number is the greatest?
   F 0.008732   H 5.252
   G 0.98   (J) 11.3

3. Order the decimals from greatest to least: 54.78, 54.7, 54.9.
   A 54.78, 54.9, 54.7
   B 54.78, 54.7, 54.9
   C 54.7, 54.78, 54.9
   (D) 54.9, 54.78, 54.7

4. Estimate by rounding to the nearest tenth: 15.42 + 4.739.
   F 20   H 20.16
   (G) 20.1   J 20.2

5. What compatible numbers can be used to estimate 4.77 × 21.45?
   A 4 × 21   (C) 5 × 20
   B 4.8 × 21.5   D 5 × 25

6. Estimate a range for the sum: 5.93 + 30.43 + 9.82.
   F 44 to 46   H 45 to 47
   (G) 44 to 47   J 46 to 47

7. Add 8.6 + 5.4.
   A 3.2   (C) 14
   B 13   D 140

8. Evaluate 4.88 − *n* for *n* = 2.6.
   (F) 2.28   H 7.48
   G 5.14   J 514

9. Multiply 6,209 × 100.
   A 62.09   (C) 620,900
   B 62,090   D 6,209,000

10. Write 33.58 × 10^4 in standard form.
    F 0.003358
    (G) 335,800
    H 3,358,000
    J 33,580,000

11. Write 445.924 in scientific notation.
    A 445,924 × 10^{-3}
    B 4.45924 × 1^2
    (C) 4.45924 × 10^2
    D 445.924 × 10^2

12. Find the product of 5 × 3.9.
    F 1.95   (H) 19.5
    G 15.6   J 195

13. Find the product of 5.2 × 0.3.
    (A) 1.56   C 15.6
    B 5.5   D 156

14. Evaluate 2*d* for *d* = 7.32.
    F 1.464   (H) 14.64
    G 9.32   J 1464

B Chapter 3 Test *(continued)*

15. Find the quotient: 8.4 ÷ 4.
    A 0.21   C 4.4
    (B) 2.1   D 21

16. Evaluate 5.75 ÷ *k* for *k* = 5.
    F 0.75   H 11.5
    (G) 1.15   J 115

17. Five friends ate lunch in a local café and spent a total of $31.75. If they split the bill evenly, how much did each person pay?
    A $6.20
    (B) $6.35
    C $63.50
    D $635.00

18. Beth earned $123.25 last week by working a 14.5 hours. What was her hourly rate?
    F $8.48
    (G) $8.50
    H $8.79
    J $8.80

19. Find the quotient: 76.8 ÷ 2.4.
    A 3.2
    B 30
    (C) 32
    D 320

20. Estimate the quotient 478.71 ÷ 24.3.
    F 1.97   H 19.7
    G 2   (J) 20

21. Maria wants to buy some CDs that are $13.99 each. She has $82.54. How many CDs can she buy?
    (A) 5   C 6
    B 5.9   D 68.55

22. James wants to have enough pizza for each person to have two pieces. Ten people come to the party. If there are eight pieces per pizza, how many pizzas should he order?
    F 1 pizza
    G 2 pizzas
    H 2.5 pizzas
    (J) 3 pizzas

23. Mr. Chan is buying lab notebooks for the class. The notebooks come in packages of 5 and there are 22 students in the class. How many packages of notebooks does he need to buy?
    A 0.23   C 4.4
    B 4   (D) 5

24. Solve the equation: *p* − 6.4 = 9.3.
    F 2.9   H 29
    (G) 15.7   J 157

25. Solve the equation: 7*r* = 43.4.
    (A) 6.2   C 36.4
    B 62   D 303.8

26. Solve the equation: *t* + 3.9 = 11.2.
    F 2.87   H 15.1
    (G) 7.3   J 73

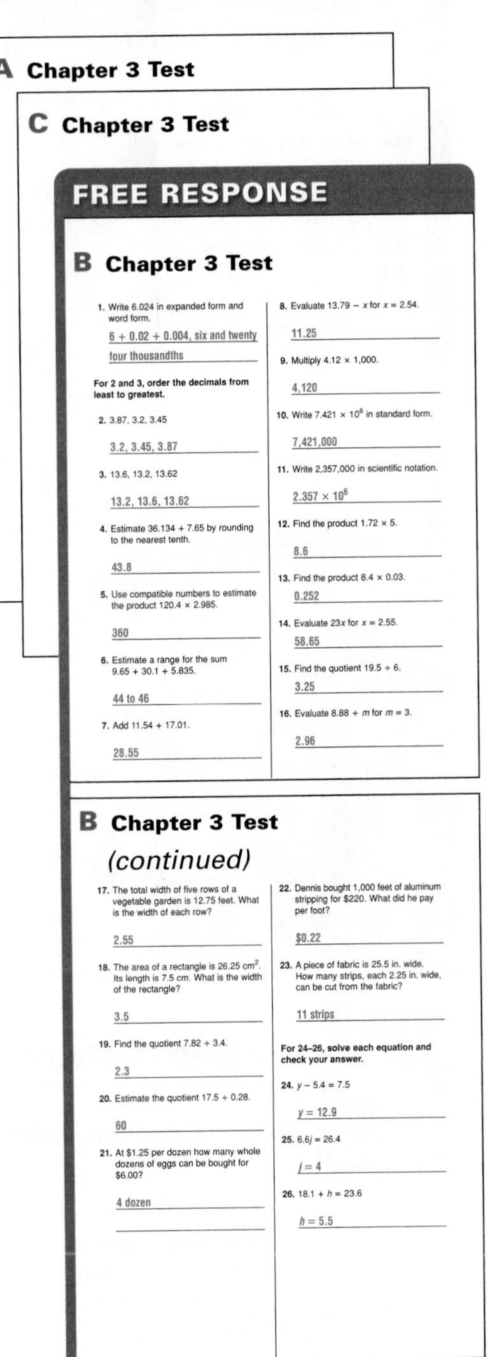

A Chapter 3 Test

C Chapter 3 Test

FREE RESPONSE

B Chapter 3 Test

1. Write 6.024 in expanded form and word form.
   6 + 0.02 + 0.004, six and twenty four thousandths

For 2 and 3, order the decimals from least to greatest.

2. 3.87, 3.2, 3.45
   3.2, 3.45, 3.87

3. 13.6, 13.2, 13.62
   13.2, 13.6, 13.62

4. Estimate 36.134 + 7.65 by rounding to the nearest tenth.
   43.8

5. Use compatible numbers to estimate the product 120.4 × 2.985.
   360

6. Estimate a range for the sum 9.65 + 30.1 + 5.835.
   44 to 46

7. Add 11.54 + 17.01.
   28.55

8. Evaluate 13.79 − *x* for *x* = 2.54.
   11.25

9. Multiply 4.12 × 1,000.
   4,120

10. Write 7.421 × 10^6 in standard form.
    7,421,000

11. Write 2,357,000 in scientific notation.
    2.357 × 10^6

12. Find the product 1.72 × 5.
    8.6

13. Find the product 8.4 × 0.03.
    0.252

14. Evaluate 23*x* for *x* = 2.55.
    58.65

15. Find the quotient 19.5 ÷ 6.
    3.25

16. Evaluate 8.88 ÷ *m* for *m* = 3.
    2.96

B Chapter 3 Test *(continued)*

17. The total width of five rows of a vegetable garden is 12.75 feet. What is the width of each row?
    2.55

18. The area of a rectangle is 26.25 cm^2. Its length is 7.5 cm. What is the width of the rectangle?
    3.5

19. Find the quotient 7.82 ÷ 3.4.
    2.3

20. Estimate the quotient 17.5 ÷ 0.28.
    60

21. At $1.25 per dozen how many whole dozens of eggs can be bought for $6.00?
    4 dozen

22. Dennis bought 1,000 feet of aluminum stripping for $220. What did he pay per foot?
    $0.22

23. A piece of fabric is 25.5 in. wide. How many strips, each 2.25 in. wide, can be cut from the fabric?
    11 strips

For 24–26, solve each equation and check your answer.

24. $y - 5.4 = 7.5$
    $y = 12.9$

25. $6.6j = 26.4$
    $j = 4$

26. $18.1 + h = 23.6$
    $h = 5.5$

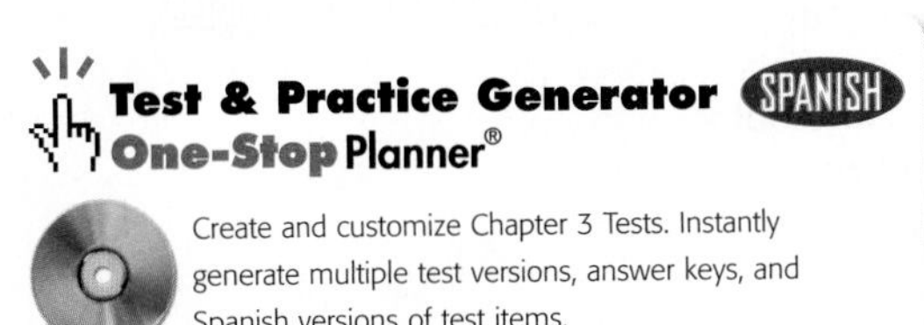

Test & Practice Generator SPANISH
One-Stop Planner®

Create and customize Chapter 3 Tests. Instantly generate multiple test versions, answer keys, and Spanish versions of test items.

CHAPTER 3

Why Learn This?

Tell students that decimals are essential to describe quantities accurately. For example, without decimals, the winning men's 100-meter times from 1928 and 1952 would appear to be equal. The more decimal places used, the more accurate the measurement.

Using Data

To begin the study of this chapter, have students:

- Identify the years from the table in which the women's 100 meters was held. 1928, 1952, 1988, 2000
- Identify the winning distance of the men's discus in 1988. 68.81 m
- Order the times in the women's 100 meters from fastest to slowest. 10.54 s, 10.75 s, 11.5 s, 12.2 s

On page 158, students will find cumulative CRCT practice.

CHAPTER 3

Decimals

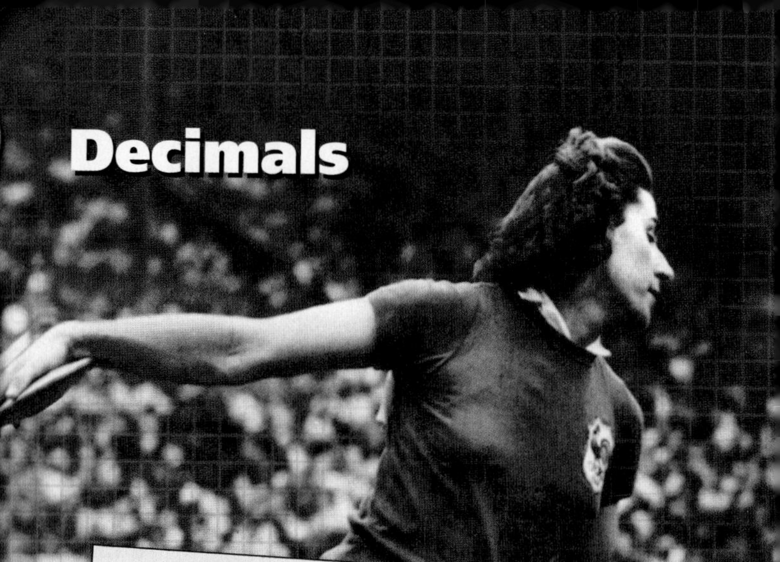

go.hrw.com
Chapter Project Online
KEYWORD: MR7 Ch3

Winning Olympic Performances

Year	Women's 100 Meters (s)	Women's Discus (m)	Men's 100 Meters (s)	Men's Discus (m)
1900	–	36.04	12.0	–
1928	12.2	39.62	10.8	47.32
1952	11.5	51.4	10.4	55.02
1988	10.54	72.3	9.92	68.81
2000	10.75	68.4	9.87	69.29

Career *Sports Historian*

Are people breaking records by running faster and jumping farther and higher? Records are kept for both professional and amateur sports. Many schools keep records of their individual athletes' and teams' performances. Keeping track of sports records is the job of sports historians. One of the most complete records is that of the Olympic games. The table shows the changes in the last century of the winning performances in some men's and women's Olympic sports.

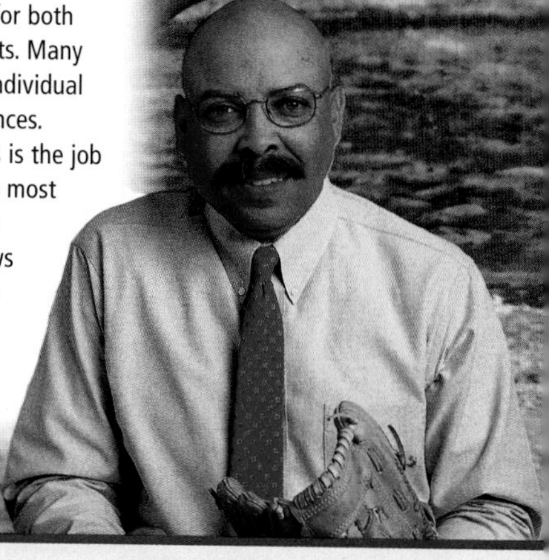

Problem Solving Project

Understand, Plan, Solve, and Look Back

Have students:

- Complete the Olympic History worksheet to learn about some changes in Olympic results in the last century.
- Make a chart comparing the women's and men's times in the 100 meters. Graph the results.
- Discover why there aren't any women's results in these events for 1900. Have students find out if there are any Olympic events today that men compete in but women do not.

History Connection

Project Resources

All project resources for teachers and students are provided online.

Materials:

- Olympic History worksheet

ARE YOU READY?

Vocabulary

Choose the best term from the list to complete each sentence.

1. The first place value to the left of the decimal point is the ___?___ place, and the place value two places to the left of the decimal point is the ___?___ place. ones; tens
2. In the expression $72 \div 9$, 72 is the ___?___, and 9 is the ___?___. dividend; divisor
3. The answer to a subtraction expression is the ___?___. difference
4. A(n) ___?___ is a mathematical statement that says two quantities are equivalent. equation

difference
dividend
divisor
equation
ones
quotient
tens

Complete these exercises to review skills you will need for this chapter.

Place Value of Whole Numbers

Identify the place value of each underlined digit.

5. 1<u>5</u>2 ten
6. <u>7</u>,903 thousand
7. <u>1</u>45,072 hundred thousand
8. 4,8<u>9</u>3,025 ten thousand
9. 1<u>3</u>,796,020 million
10. 1<u>4</u>5,683,032 ten million

Add and Subtract Whole Numbers

Find each sum or difference.

11. \$425 − \$75 \$350
12. 532 + 145 677
13. 160 − 82 78

Multiply and Divide Whole Numbers

Find each product or quotient.

14. \$320 × 5 \$1,600
15. $125 \div 5$ 25
16. 54 × 3 162

Exponents

Find each value.

17. 10^3 1,000
18. 3^6 729
19. 10^5 100,000
20. 4^5 1,024
21. 8^3 512
22. 2^7 128

Solve Whole Number Equations

Solve each equation.

23. $y + 382 = 743$ $y = 361$
24. $n - 150 = 322$ $n = 472$
25. $9x = 108$ $x = 12$

ARE YOU READY? CHAPTER 3

Organizer

Objective: Assess students' understanding of prerequisite skills.

Prerequisite Skills

Place Value of Whole Numbers
Add and Subtract Whole Numbers
Multiply and Divide Whole Numbers
Exponents
Solve Whole Number Equations

Assessing Prior Knowledge

INTERVENTION 

Diagnose and Prescribe

Use this page to determine whether intervention is necessary or whether enrichment is appropriate.

Resources

 ***Are You Ready? Intervention and Enrichment* Worksheets**

 ***Are You Ready?* CD-ROM**

 ***Are You Ready?* Online**

my.hrw.com

ARE YOU READY?

Diagnose and Prescribe

NO INTERVENE

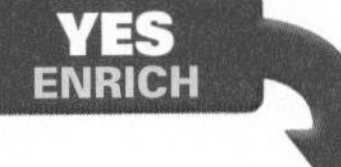

Prerequisite Skill	*ARE YOU READY? Intervention*, Chapter 3: Worksheets	CD-ROM	Online
Place Value of Whole Numbers	Skill 1	Activty 1	Diagnose and Prescribe Online
Add and Subtract Whole Numbers	Skill 34	Activty 34	
Multiply and Divide Whole Numbers	Skill 34	Activty 34	
Exponents	Skill 12	Activty 12	
Solve Whole Number Equation	Skill 58	Activty 58	

***ARE YOU READY? Enrichment*, Chapter 3**

 **Worksheets**

 **CD-ROM**

 **Online**

CHAPTER 3 Study Guide: Preview

Organizer

Objective: Help students organize the new concepts they will learn in Chapter 3.

 **Online Edition**
Multilingual Glossary

Resources

PuzzlePro®
One-Stop Planner®

 ***Multilingual Glossary* Online**

go.hrw.com
KEYWORD: MR7 Glossary

Answers to Vocabulary Connections

Possible answers:

1. You are using the whole-number part of the decimal when you perform front-end estimation.
2. We will use scientific notation in science class.
3. Clustering is a good method for estimating when the values of the numbers are close to each other.

CHAPTER 3 Study Guide: Preview

Where You've Been

Previously, you

- compared and ordered whole numbers.
- wrote large whole numbers in standard form.
- rounded numbers to a given place value.
- used addition, subtraction, multiplication, and division of whole numbers to solve problems.

In This Chapter

You will study

- reading, writing, comparing, and ordering decimals.
- writing large whole numbers in scientific notation.
- using rounding to estimate answers to problems that involve decimals.
- solving decimal equations.

Where You're Going

You can use the skills learned in this chapter

- to solve two-step decimal equations in higher-level math classes, such as Algebra 1.
- to solve problems using scientific notation in science classes, such as Astronomy.

Key Vocabulary/Vocabulario

clustering	aproximación
front-end estimation	estimación por partes
scientific notation	notación científica

Vocabulary Connections

To become familiar with some of the vocabulary terms in the chapter, consider the following. You may refer to the chapter, the glossary, or a dictionary if you like.

1. When you estimate, you approximate the value of something. What part of a decimal do you think you are using to approximate a value when you use **front-end estimation**?
2. *Notation* is a way of expressing something. In what other classes do you think you will use **scientific notation**?
3. A *cluster* is a close grouping of similar items. When do you think **clustering** might be a good method of estimation?

Grade 6 CRCT GPS

M6A3. **Students will evaluate algebraic expressions, including those with exponents, and solve simple one-step equations using each of the four basic operations.** M6N1. **Students will understand the meaning of the four arithmetic operations as related to positive rational numbers and will use these concepts to solve problems.** g. Solve problems involving fractions, decimals, and percents.	M6P1. **Students will solve problems (using appropriate technology).** M6P3. **Students will communicate mathematically.** M6P4. **Students will make connections among mathematical ideas and to other disciplines.** M6P5. **Students will represent mathematics in multiple ways.**

Georgia Mathematics Performance Standards statements are written out completely on pp. GA28–GA35.

Writing Strategy: Keep a Math Journal

You can help improve your writing and reasoning skills by keeping a math journal. When you express your thoughts on paper, you can make sense of confusing math concepts.

You can also record your thoughts about each lesson and reflect on what you learned in class. Your journal will become a personal math reference book from which to study.

Journal Entry: Read the entry Jaime wrote in his math journal about translating between math and words.

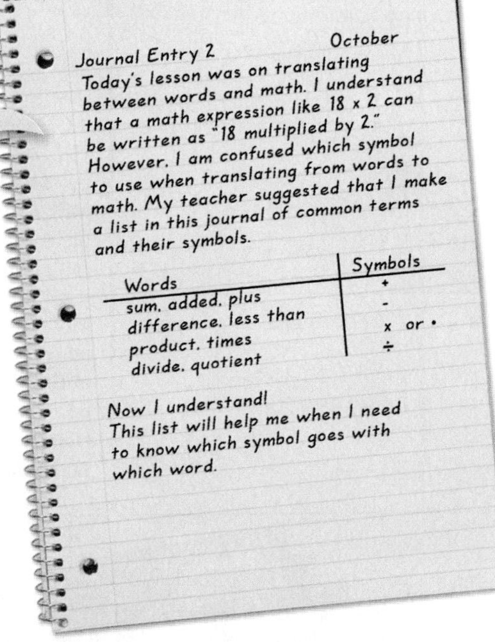

Journal Entry 2
October
Today's lesson was on translating between words and math. I understand that a math expression like 18 x 2 can be written as "18 multiplied by 2."
However, I am confused which symbol to use when translating from words to math. My teacher suggested that I make a list in this journal of common terms and their symbols.
Words
Symbols
sum, added, plus
+
difference, less than
-
product, times
x or •
divide, quotient
÷
Now I understand!
This list will help me when I need to know which symbol goes with which word.

Try This

Begin a math journal. Make an entry every day for one week. Use the following ideas to start your journal entries. Be sure to date each entry.

- What I already know about this lesson is . . .
- The skills I used to complete this lesson were . . .
- What problems did I have? How did I deal with these problems?
- What I liked/did not like about this lesson . . .

Reading and Writing Math

Reading and Writing Math

Organizer

Objective: Help students apply strategies to understand and retain key concepts.

Online Edition

Resources

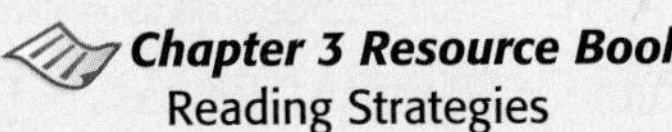

Reading Strategies

ENGLISH LANGUAGE LEARNERS

Writing Strategy: Keep a Math Journal

Discuss Students benefit from writing notes in their own words about new concepts. As they write in their journals, encourage them to include examples, diagrams, and drawings.

Extend Use fun devices, such as Foldnotes, to promote the creation and use of journals.

Answers to *Try This*

Check students' work.

Grade 6 CRCT GPS

Standards	LAB 3-1	3-1	3-2	LAB 3-3	3-3	3-4	LAB 3-5	3-5	3-6	3-7	3-8	3-9
M6A3								★	★			★
M6N1.g		★	★	★	★	★	★	★	★	★	★	★
M6P1		★	★		★	★		★	★	★	★	
M6P3		★	★		★	★		★	★	★	★	★
M6P4		★	★		★	★		★			★	★
M6P5	★	★		★	★		★	★			★	★

SECTION

3A

Understanding Decimals

One-Minute Section Planner

Lesson	Materials	MiC and Lab Resources
3-1 Hands-On Lab Model Decimals • Use decimal grids to represent decimals. **Lesson 3-1** Representing, Comparing, and Ordering Decimals • Write, compare, and order decimals using place value and number lines. ☑ CRCT ☑ SAT-10 ☑ ITBS ☐ CTBS ☑ NAEP	Decimal grids or grid paper, base-10 blocks (MK)	**MiC:** ***Models You Can Count On*** p. 29 ***Hands-On Lab Activities*** 3-1
Lesson 3-2 Estimating Decimals • Estimate decimal sums, differences, products, and quotients. ☑ CRCT ☑ SAT-10 ☑ ITBS ☑ CTBS ☑ NAEP		**MiC:** ***Models You Can Count On*** pp. 34–36, 44–46, 50–53 **MiC:** ***Expressions and Formulas*** pp. 6–8 **MiC:** ***More or Less*** pp. 1–4
3-3 Hands-On Lab Explore Decimal Addition and Subtraction Use decimal grids to model addition and subtraction of decimals. **Lesson 3-3** Adding and Subtracting Decimals • Add and subtract decimals. ☑ CRCT ☑ SAT-10 ☑ ITBS ☐ CTBS ☐ NAEP	Decimal grids or grid paper	**MiC:** ***Models You Can Count On*** pp. 7–8, 31–33, 53–55 **MiC:** ***Expressions and Formulas*** pp. 3, 6–8, 12–21, 40–41 ***Hands-On Lab Activities*** 3-3 ***Technology Lab Activities*** 3-3

MK = *Manipulatives Kit*

Mathematics in Context

The units ***Models You Can Count On, Expressions and Formulas,*** and ***More or Less*** from the *Mathematics in Context* © 2006 series can be used with Section 3A. See Section Planner above for suggestions for integrating *MiC* with *Holt Mathematics*.

Section Overview

Comparing and Ordering Decimals — Lesson 3-1

 Ordered lists of decimals are frequently found in sports statistics, such as batting averages in baseball.

121.0345 < 121.0543

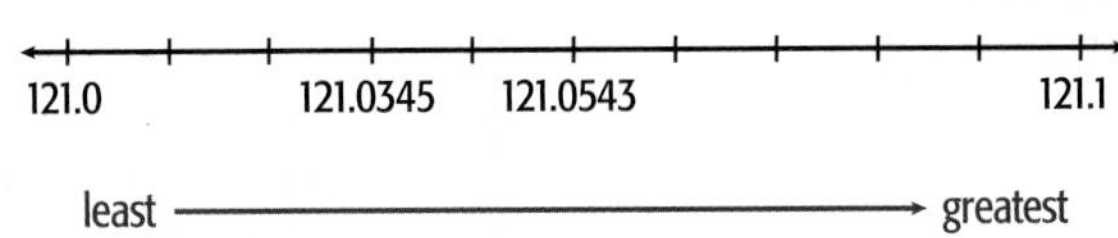

To order numbers, you can compare them using **place value.**

Numbers are **ordered** from least to greatest on the number line from left to right.

Estimating Decimals — Lesson 3-2

 You can use estimation to determine whether results of decimal operations are reasonable.

Estimate 3.**5**6 + 8.**3**1 to the nearest whole number.

4 + 8 = 12 The sum is about 12.

Estimate 9.7 ÷ 3.5.

9 ÷ **3** = 3 The quotient is about 3.

When rounding, look at the digit to the **right of the place to which you are rounding**.
- If that digit is 5 or greater, round up.
- If that digit is less than 5, round down.

Compatible numbers are close to the numbers in the problem, and they can help you do math mentally.

Adding and Subtracting Decimals — Lesson 3-3

 Using a checkbook requires adding and subtracting decimals.

Add 5 + 10.25 + 3.5.

$$\begin{array}{r} 5.\mathbf{00} \\ 10.25 \\ +\ 3.5\mathbf{0} \\ \hline 28.75 \end{array}$$

Use zeros to write an equivalent number to the same number of decimal places as the other numbers.

Subtract 3.57 from 9.

$$\begin{array}{r} 9.\mathbf{00} \\ -3.57 \\ \hline 5.43 \end{array}$$

Align the decimal points.

Organizer

Use with Lesson 3-1

Pacing:
Traditional $\frac{1}{2}$ day
Block $\frac{1}{4}$ day

Objective: Use decimal grids to represent decimals.

Materials: Decimal grids

Online Edition
Fraction/Decimal grids

Countdown to CRCT Week 5

Resources

Hands-On Lab Activities
Lab 3-1 Recording Sheet

Teach

Discuss

Discuss with students what each small square, row, and column represents. Discuss what number is represented by the entire grid.

Close

Key Concept

The decimal grid demonstrates the base-10 connection between whole numbers and decimals.

Assessment

Represent each decimal on a decimal grid.

1. 0.02

2. 3.4

Georgia Performance Standards

M6P5.a Create and use representations to organize, record, and communicate mathematical ideas.

M6P5.c Use representations to model and interpret physical, social, and mathematical phenomena.

Hands-On LAB 3-1 Model Decimals

Use with Lesson 3-1

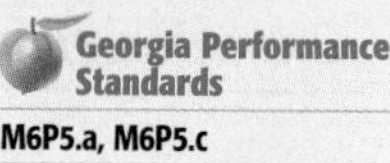

M6P5.a, M6P5.c

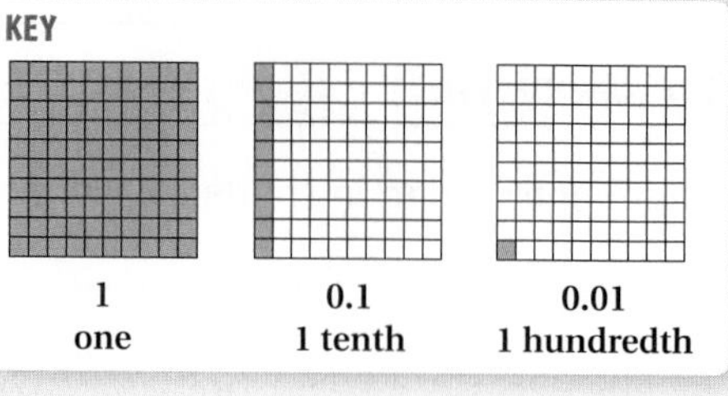

You can use decimal grids to model decimals. The grid is divided into 100 small squares. One square represents 1 hundredth, or 0.01. Ten squares form a column, which represents 1 tenth, or 0.1. Ten columns make up the grid, which represents one whole, or 1. By shading hundredths, tenths, or whole grids, you can model decimal numbers.

Activity 1

Write the decimal that is represented by each model.

a. *24 hundredths squares are shaded.*

So the model represents 0.24.

b. 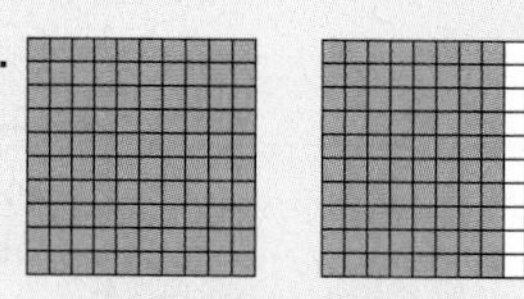

1 whole grid and 8 columns are shaded.

So the model represents 1.8.

c. 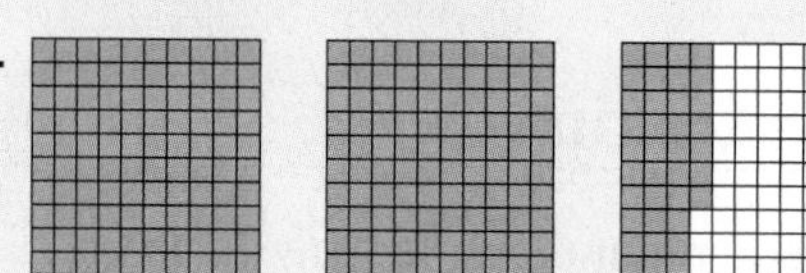

2 whole grids and 37 hundredths are shaded.

So the model represents 2.37.

Answers to *Assessment*

1.

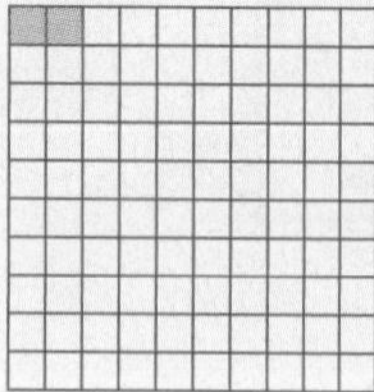

2.

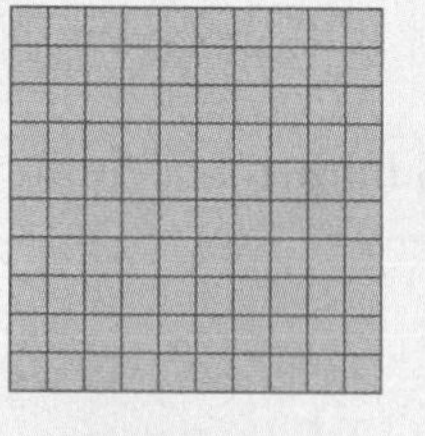
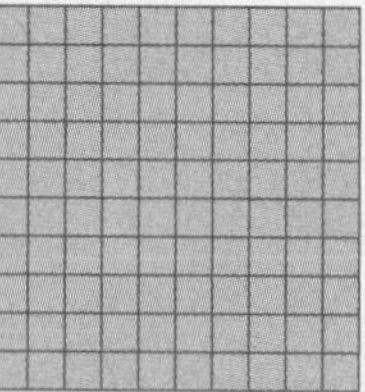
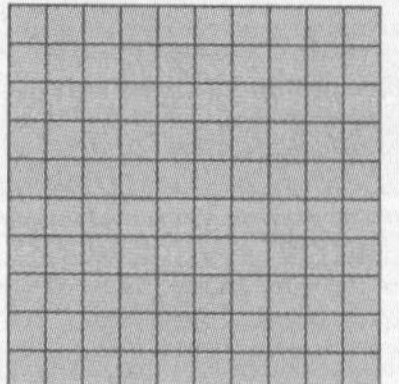
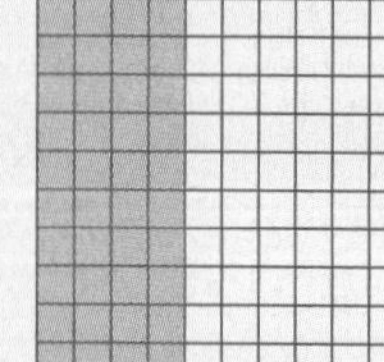

Think and Discuss

1. Explain how a decimal grid can show that 0.30 = 0.3.
   Possible answer: Shading 30 small squares is the same as shading 3 columns of 10.

Try This

Write the decimal that is represented by each model.

1. **0.56**
2. **0.99**
3. 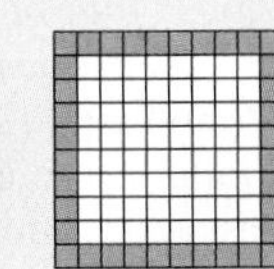 **1.36**

Activity 2

Use a decimal grid to model each decimal.

a. 0.42

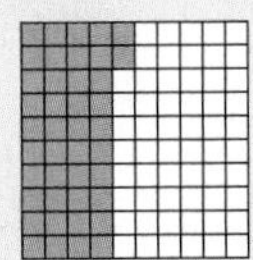

Shade 42 hundredths squares.

b. 1.88

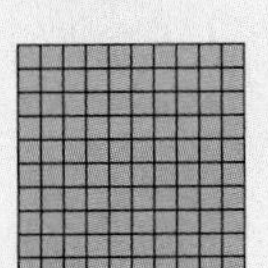
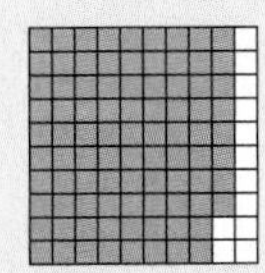

Shade 1 whole grid, 8 columns, and 8 small squares.

c. 2.75

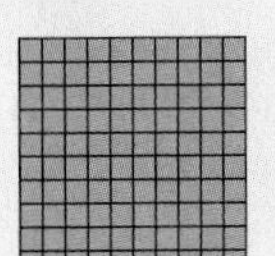
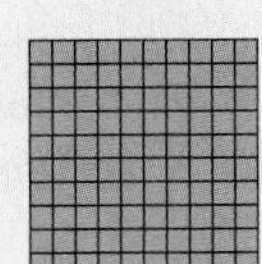
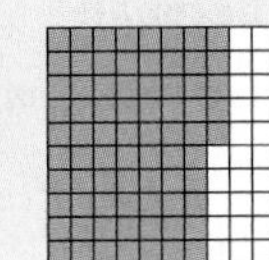

Shade 2 whole grids, 7 columns, and 5 small squares.

Think and Discuss

1. Explain how to model 0.46 by shading only 10 sections on the grid. (Hint: A section is a grid, column, or small square.)
   Possible answer: Shade 4 columns, plus 6 small squares.

Try This

Use a decimal grid to model each decimal.

1. 1.02 **2.** 0.04 **3.** 0.4 **4.** 2.14 **5.** 0.53

Activity 2

Answers to *Try This*

1.

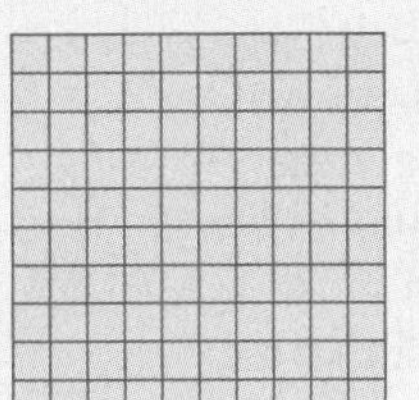
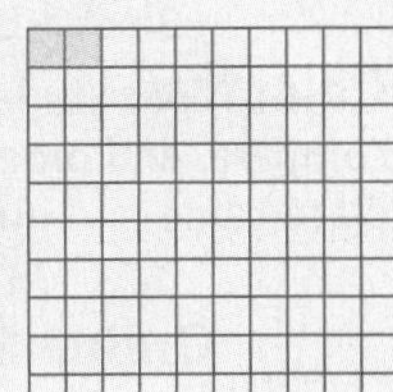

2.

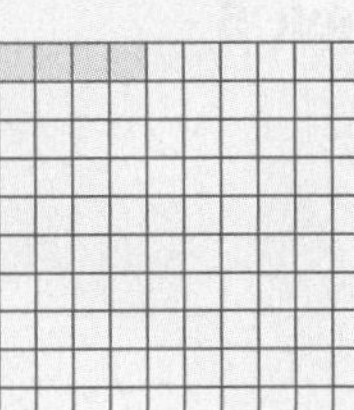

3.

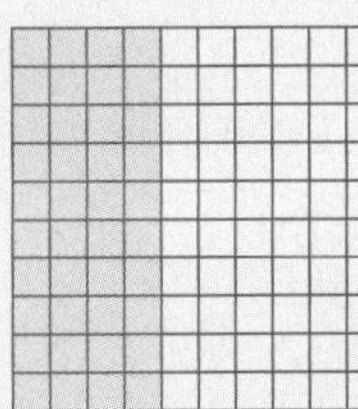

4.

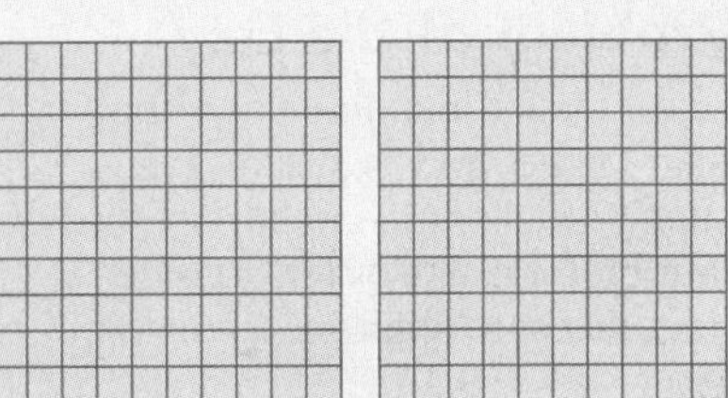

5.

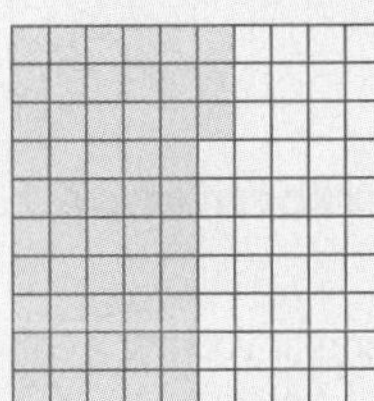

3-1 Organizer

Pacing: Traditional 1 day
Block $\frac{1}{2}$ day

Objective: Students write, compare, and order decimals using place value and number lines.

Online Edition
Tutorial Videos, Interactivities

Countdown to CRCT Week 5

Warm Up

Order the numbers from least to greatest.

1. 242, 156, 224, 165
   156, 165, 224, 242
2. 941, 148, 914, 814, 721
   148, 721, 814, 914, 941
3. 345, 376, 354, 397
   345, 354, 376, 397

Problem of the Day

Lupe is taller than Reba and shorter than Miguel. Tory is shorter than Lupe but taller than Reba. List the four brothers and sisters in order from tallest to shortest. Miguel, Lupe, Tory, Reba

Also available on transparency

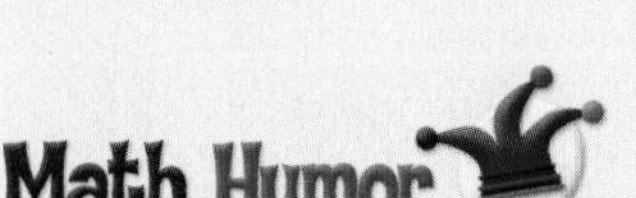

Did you hear about the decimal that found studying very difficult? It never seemed to get the point.

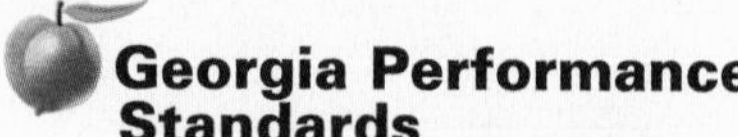

M6N1.g Solve problems involving fractions, decimals, and percents.

M6P1.b Solve problems that arise in mathematics and in other contexts.

M6P5.a Create and use representations to organize, record, and communicate mathematical ideas.

M6P5.b Select, apply, and translate among mathematical representations to solve problems.

3-1 Representing, Comparing, and Ordering Decimals

Learn to write, compare, and order decimals using place value and number lines.

M6N1.g Solve problems involving decimals. Also, M6P1.b, M6P5.a, M6P5.b.

The smaller the apparent magnitude of a star, the brighter the star appears when viewed from Earth. The magnitudes of some stars are listed in the table as decimal numbers.

Apparent Magnitudes of Stars

Star	Magnitude
Procyon	0.38
Proxima Centauri	11.0
Wolf 359	13.5
Vega	0.03

Decimal numbers represent combinations of whole numbers and numbers between whole numbers.

Place value can help you understand and write and compare decimal numbers.

Place Value

Hundreds	Tens	Ones	Tenths	Hundredths	Thousandths	Ten-Thousandths	Hundred-Thousandths
	2	3 •	0	0	5	0	3

EXAMPLE 1 **Reading and Writing Decimals**

Write each decimal in standard form, expanded form, and words.

A 1.05
Expanded form: 1 + 0.05
Word form: one *and* five hundredths

B 0.05 + 0.001 + 0.0007
Standard form: 0.0517
Word form: five hundred seventeen ten-thousandths

C sixteen and nine hundredths
Standard form: 16.09
Expanded form: 10 + 6 + 0.09

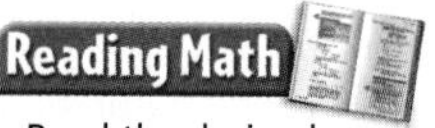

Read the decimal point as "and."

You can use place value to compare decimal numbers.

1 Introduce

Alternate Opener

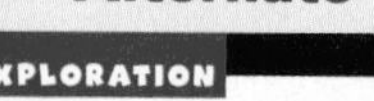

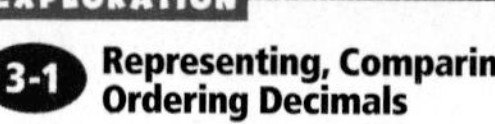

To model a decimal,
- color a 10-by-10-square grid for each whole in the decimal,
- color one 10-by-1-square strip for each tenth in the decimal, and color a small square for each hundredth in the decimal.

For example, the graph paper models the decimal 1.62.

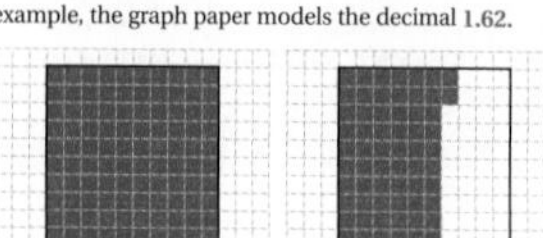

1. Draw a model for each decimal.
   a. 1.25 b. 2.13 c. 1.70 d. 1.7
2. Compare the models for 1c and 1d. What do you notice about these two decimals?
3. Order the decimals in numbers 1a–1d from least to greatest. Explain your reasoning.

Think and Discuss

4. **Explain** why 0.4 = 0.40.
5. **Explain** why 0.5 is greater than 0.10 even though 10 is greater than 5.

Motivate

ENGLISH LANGUAGE LEARNERS

Review the terms *standard form, expanded form,* and *word form.* Have students give examples of whole numbers expressed in standard, expanded, and word form (e.g., 3,025; 3,000 + 20 + 5; three thousand, twenty-five). Explain that decimals can also be expressed in standard, expanded, and word form.

Explorations and answers are provided in *Alternate Openers: Explorations Transparencies.*

EXAMPLE 2 Earth Science Application

Rigel and Betelgeuse are two stars in the constellation Orion. The apparent magnitude of Rigel is 0.12. The apparent magnitude of Betelgeuse is 0.50. Which star has the smaller magnitude? Which star appears brighter?

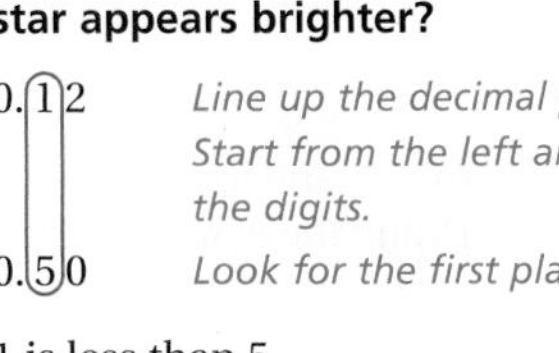

0.12 — *Line up the decimal points. Start from the left and compare the digits.*

0.50 — *Look for the first place where the digits are different.*

1 is less than 5.
$0.12 < 0.50$

Rigel has a smaller apparent magnitude than Betelgeuse. The star with the smaller magnitude appears brighter. When seen from Earth, Rigel appears brighter than Betelgeuse.

EXAMPLE 3 Comparing and Ordering Decimals

Helpful Hint

Writing zeros at the end of a decimal does not change the value of the decimal.

$0.3 = 0.30 = 0.300$

Order the decimals from least to greatest.
14.35, 14.3, 14.05

14.35 14.30	$14.30 < 14.35$	*Compare two of the numbers at a time. Write 14.3 as "14.30."*
14.35 14.05	$14.05 < 14.35$	*Start at the left and compare the digits.*
14.30 14.05	$14.05 < 14.30$	*Look for the first place where the digits are different.*

Graph the numbers on a number line.

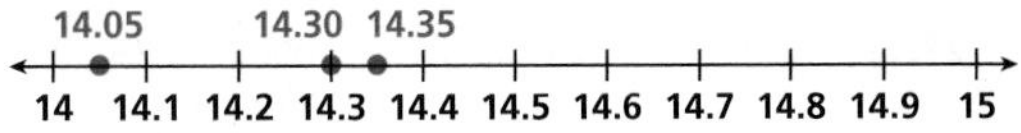

The numbers are ordered when you read the number line from left to right. The numbers in order from least to greatest are 14.05, 14.3, and 14.35.

Answers to *Think and Discuss:*

1. Possible answer: because five tenths is the same as 50 hundredths and 50 is greater than 29
2. 0.029
3. Possible answers: 1.51, 1.53, 1.57

Think and Discuss

GPS M6P2.c, M6P3.a

1. **Explain** why 0.5 is greater than 0.29 even though 29 is greater than 5.
2. **Name** the decimal with the least value: 0.29, 2.09, 2.009, 0.029
3. **Name** three numbers between 1.5 and 1.6.

COMMON ERROR ALERT

Some students try to align the digits farthest to the right, as with whole numbers, resulting in incorrect comparisons if the decimals have different numbers of decimal places. Many students will benefit from using graph paper to align their decimal numbers.

Power Presentations with PowerPoint®

Additional Examples

Example 1 

Write each decimal in standard form, expanded form, and words.

A. 1.07
1 + 0.07; one and seven hundredths

B. 0.03 + 0.006 + 0.0009
0.0369; three hundred sixty-nine ten-thousandths

C. fourteen and eight hundredths
14.08; 10 + 4 + 0.08

Example 2 

The star Wolf 359 has an apparent magnitude of 13.5. Suppose another star has an apparent magnitude of 13.05. Which star has the smaller magnitude?
The star with 13.05 has the smaller apparent magnitude.

Example 3 

Order the decimals from least to greatest.

16.67, 16.6, 16.07
The numbers in order are 16.07, 16.6, 16.67.

Also available on transparency

2 Teach

Guided Instruction

In this lesson, students learn to write, compare, and order decimals using place value and number lines. First point out the place-value chart (Teaching Transparency). Emphasize the names of the places to the right of the decimal point. Then teach how to properly name and write decimals in standard, word, and expanded form. Teach students to compare two decimals by lining up the decimal points. Next, demonstrate how to order three decimals by using a number line.

Teaching Tip — **Visual** Some students may benefit from using graph paper to align and compare decimal numbers.

Reaching All Learners

Through Concrete Manipulatives

Have students work with base-10 blocks, provided in the Manipulatives Kit, to reinforce their understanding of place value in decimal numbers. Base-10 blocks provide visual, tactile, auditory, and kinesthetic learning modalities to support all learners.

3 Close

Summarize

Have students name the place-value positions to the right of the decimal point and give examples of decimals in standard, expanded, and word form. Relate the tenths and the hundredths places to dimes and pennies to help in recalling place-value names.

3-1 Exercises

Assignment Guide

If you finished Example 1 assign:
Average 1–4, 9–12, 17–20, 45–51
Advanced 1–4, 9–12, 30–33, 45–51

If you finished Example 2 assign:
Average 1–5, 9–13, 17–33, 39–40, 45–51
Advanced 1–5, 9–13, 17–33, 41–42, 45–51

If you finished Example 3 assign:
Average 1–40, 45–51
Advanced 1–37, 42–51

Homework Quick Check

Quickly check key concepts.
Exercises: 10, 12, 14, 16, 26

Answers

9. 7 + 0.08 + 0.009 + 0.0003; seven and eight hundred ninety-three ten-thousandths
21. one hundred forty-two and six thousand, five hundred forty-one ten-thousandths
23. ninety-two thousand, seven hundred fifty-five hundred-thousandths

Math Background

The place-value system allows for the naming of whole numbers that are greater than any previously assigned value and for the naming of decimal numbers that are smaller than any previously assigned value.

Georgia Performance Standards

M6P3.a Organize and consolidate their mathematical thinking through communication.

M6P4.c Recognize and apply mathematics in contexts outside of mathematics.

3-1 Exercises

Georgia Performance Standards
M6P3.a, M6P4.c

go.hrw.com
Homework Help Online
KEYWORD: MR7 3-1
Parent Resources Online
KEYWORD: MR7 Parent

GUIDED PRACTICE

See Example 1 Write each decimal in standard form, expanded form, and words.

1. 1.98 — 1 + 0.9 + 0.08; one and ninety-eight hundredths
2. ten and forty-one thousandths — 10.041; 10 + 0.04 + 0.001
3. 0.07 + 0.006 + 0.0005 — 0.0765; seven hundred sixty-five ten-thousandths
4. 0.0472 — 0.04 + 0.007 + 0.0002; four hundred seventy-two ten-thousandths

See Example 2

5. **Physical Science** Osmium and iridium are precious metals. The density of osmium is 22.58 g/cm^3, and the density of iridium is 22.56 g/cm^3. Which metal is denser? Osmium

See Example 3 Order the decimals from least to greatest.

6. 9.5, 9.35, 9.65 — 9.35, 9.5, 9.65
7. 4.18, 4.1, 4.09 — 4.09; 4.1; 4.18
8. 12.39, 12.09, 12.92 — 12.09, 12.39, 12.92

INDEPENDENT PRACTICE

See Example 1 Write each decimal in standard form, expanded form, and words.

9. 7.0893
10. 12 + 0.2 + 0.005 — 12.205; twelve and two hundred five thousandths
11. seven and fifteen hundredths — 7.15; 7 + 0.1 + 0.05
12. 3 + 0.1 + 0.006 — 3.106; three and one hundred six thousandths

See Example 2

13. **Astronomy** Two meteorites landed in Mexico. The one found in Bacuberito weighed 24.3 tons, and the one found in Chupaderos weighed 26.7 tons. Which meteorite weighed more? the Chupaderos meteorite

See Example 3 Order the decimals from least to greatest.

14. 15.25, 15.2, 15.5 — 15.2, 15.25, 15.5
15. 1.56, 1.62, 1.5 — 1.5, 1.56, 1.62
16. 6.7, 6.07, 6.23 — 6.07, 6.23, 6.7

PRACTICE AND PROBLEM SOLVING

Extra Practice p. 718

Write each number in words.

17. 9.007 — nine and seven thousandths
18. 5 + 0.08 + 0.004 — five and eighty-four thousandths
19. 10.022 — ten and twenty-two thousandths
20. 4.28 — four and twenty-eight thousandths
21. 142.6541
22. 0.001 + 0.0007 — seventeen ten-thousandths
23. 0.92755
24. 1.02 — one and two hundredths

Compare. Write <, >, or =.

25. 8.04 ▭ 8.403 <
26. 0.907 ▭ 0.6801 >
27. 1.246 ▭ 1.29 <
28. one and fifty-two ten-thousandths ▭ 1.0052 =
29. ten and one hundredth ▭ 10.100 <

Write the value of the red digit in each number.

30. 3.026 — six thousandths
31. 17.53703 — three hundredths
32. 0.000598 — five ten-thousandths
33. 425.1055 — one tenth

Order the numbers from greatest to least.

34. 32.525, 32.5254, 31.6257 — 32.5254, 32.525, 31.6257
35. 0.34, 1.43, 4.034, 1.043, 1.424 — 4.034, 1.43, 1.424, 1.043, 0.34
36. 1.01, 1.1001, 1.101, 1.0001 — 1.101, 1.1001, 1.01, 1.0001
37. 652.12, 65.213, 65.135, 61.53 — 652.12, 65.213, 65.135, 61.53

RETEACH 3-1

LESSON 3-1 **Reteach**
Representing, Comparing, and Ordering Decimals

You can use place value to write decimals in standard form, expanded form, and word form.

To write 2.14 in expanded form, write the decimal as an addition expression using the place value of each digit.

Ones	Tenths	Hundredths	Thousandths	Ten Thousandths
2.	1	4		

2.14 can be written as 2 + 0.1 + 0.04.

When you write a decimal in word form, the number before the decimal point tells you how many wholes there are. The decimal point stands for the word "and."

Notice that the place value names to the right of the decimal begin with tenths, hundredths, and then thousandths. The "ths" ending indicates a decimal.

2.14 can also be written as *two and fourteen hundredths.*

1. How would you read a number with 4 decimal places?
The decimal should end with ten thousandths

Write each decimal in standard form, expanded form, and word form.

2.

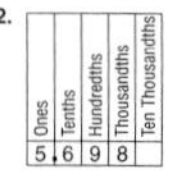

Ones	Tenths	Hundredths	Thousandths	Ten Thousandths
5.	6	9	8	

5 + 0.6 + 0.09 + 0.008; five and six hundred ninety-eight thousandths

3.

Ones	Tenths	Hundredths	Thousandths	Ten Thousandths
0.	0	9	4	

0 + 0.09 + 0.004; ninety-four thousandths

4. 7 + 0.8
7.8; seven and eight tenths

5. twelve-hundredths
0 + 0.1 + 0.02; 0.12

PRACTICE 3-1

LESSON 3-1 **Practice B**
Representing, Comparing, and Ordering Decimals

Write each decimal in standard form, expanded form, and words.

1. 2.07 — 2 + 0.07; two and seven hundredths
2. 5 + 0.007 — 5.007; five and seven thousandths
3. four and six tenths — 4.6; 4 + 0.6
4. sixteen and five tenths — 16.5; 10 + 6 + 0.5
5. 9 + 0.6 + 0.08 — 9.68; nine and sixty-eight hundredths
6. 1.037 — 1 + 0.03 + 0.007; one and thirty-seven thousandths
7. 2 + 0.1 + 0.003 — 2.103; two and one hundred three thousandths
8. eighteen hundredths — 0.18; 0.1 + 0.08
9. 6.11 — 6 + 0.1 + 0.01; six and eleven hundredths

Order the decimals from least to greatest.

10. 3.578, 3.758, 3.875 — 3.578; 3.758; 3.875
11. 0.0943, 0.9403, 0.9043 — 0.0943; 0.9043; 0.9403
12. 12.97, 12.957, 12.75 — 12.75; 12.957; 12.97
13. 1.09, 1.901, 1.9, 1.19 — 1.09; 1.19, 1.9; 1.901
14. Your seventh and eighth ribs are two of the longest bones in your body. The average seventh rib is nine and forty-five hundredths inches long, and the average eighth rib is 9.06 inches long. Which bone is longer? the seventh rib
15. The average female human heart weighs nine and three tenths ounces, while the average male heart weighs eleven and one tenth ounces. Which human heart weighs less, the male or the female? the female heart
16. The state has $42.3 million for a new theater. The theater that an architect designed would cost $42.25 million. Can the theater be built for the amount the state can pay? yes
17. Lyn traveled 79.47 miles on Saturday, 54.28 miles on Sunday, 65.5 miles on Monday, and 98.43 miles on Tuesday. Which day did she travel the greatest number of miles? Tuesday

Astronomy 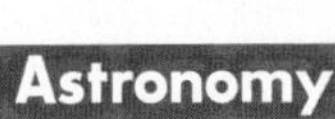

Proxima Centauri, the closest star to Earth other than the Sun, was discovered in 1913. It would take about 115,000 years for a spaceship traveling from Earth at 25,000 mi/h to reach Proxima Centauri.

Use the table for Exercises 38–44.

Star	Distance (light-years)
Alpha Centauri	4.35
Barnard's Star	5.98
Lalande 21185	8.22
Luyten 726-8	8.43
Proxima Centauri	4.22
Ross 154	9.45
Sirius	8.65

Distance of Stars from Earth

38. Order the stars Sirius, Luyten 726-8, and Lalande 21185 from closest to farthest from Earth. **Lalande 21185, Luyten 726-8, Sirius**

39. Which star in the table is farthest from Earth? **Ross 154**

40. How far in light-years is Ross 154 from Earth? Write the answer in words and expanded form. **Nine and forty-five hundredths, 9 + 0.4 + 0.05**

41. List the stars that are less than 5 light-years from Earth. **Alpha Centauri, Proxima Centauri**

42. **What's the Error?** A student wrote the distance of Proxima Centauri from Earth as "four hundred and twenty-two hundredths." Explain the error. Write the correct answer.

43. **Write About It** Which star is closer to Earth, Alpha Centauri or Proxima Centauri? Explain how you can compare the distances of these stars. Then answer the question. **43. Possible answer: Align the decimals and compare tenths; Proxima Centauri.**

44. **Challenge** Wolf 359 is located 7.75 light-years from Earth. If the stars in the table were listed in order from closest to farthest from Earth, between which two stars would Wolf 359 be located? **Barnard's Star and Lalande 21185**

42. See p. A1.

CRCT Prep • GPS Support • Spiral Review

45. **Multiple Choice** What is the standard form of "five and three hundred twenty-one hundred-thousandths"?

Ⓐ 5.321   Ⓑ 5.0321   **Ⓒ 5.00321** (circled)   Ⓓ 5.000321

46. **Gridded Response** Write 30 + 2 + 0.8 + 0.009 in standard form. **32.809**

Estimate each sum or difference by rounding to the place value indicated. (Lesson 1-2)

47. 6,832 + 2,078; thousands **9,000**   **48.** 52,854 − 25,318; ten thousands **20,000**

Solve each equation. (Lesson 2-6)

49. $n - 52 = 71$ $\mathbf{n = 123}$ **50.** $30 = k - 15$ $\mathbf{k = 45}$ **51.** $c - 22 = 30$ $\mathbf{c = 52}$

CHALLENGE 3-1

LESSON 3-1 Challenge
Place Your Values

Complete the tables below to show different numbers that can be written with the same digits. Do not use the same digit more than once for each place value. Possible answers are given.

1. Use the digits 1, 3, 5, 7, and 9 to write four 5-digit numbers of increasing value.

Hundreds	Tens	Ones	Tenths	Hundredths	Thousandths	Ten-Thousandths
		1	3	5	7	9
		3	1	9	5	7
		5	7	3	9	1
		7	9	1	3	5

2. Use the digits 0, 2, 4, 6, 7, and 8 to write four 6-digit numbers of decreasing value.

Hundreds	Tens	Ones	Tenths	Hundredths	Thousandths	Ten-Thousandths
	8	7	6	4	0	2
	6	8	0	2	7	4
	4	0	8	7	2	6
	2	6	4	0	8	7

3. Use the digits 0, 1, 2, 3, 4, 5, and 6 to write four 7-digit numbers of increasing value.

Hundreds	Tens	Ones	Tenths	Hundredths	Thousandths	Ten-Thousandths
1	0	2	3	4	5	6
2	1	0	4	3	6	5
3	5	6	2	0	1	4
4	3	5	6	2	0	1

PROBLEM SOLVING 3-1

LESSON 3-1 Problem Solving
Representing, Comparing, and Ordering Decimals

Use the table to answer the questions.

Largest Marine Mammals

Mammal	Length (ft)	Weight (T)
Blue whale	110.0	127.95
Fin whale	82.0	44.29
Gray whale	46.0	32.18
Humpback whale	49.2	26.08
Right whale	57.4	39.37
Sperm whale	59.0	35.43

1. What is the heaviest marine mammal on Earth?
   the blue whale
2. Which mammal in the table has the shortest length?
   a gray whale
3. Which mammal in the table is longer than a humpback whale, but shorter than a sperm whale?
   a right whale

Circle the letter of the correct answer.

4. Which mammal measures forty-nine and two tenths feet long?
   A blue whale
   B gray whale
   C sperm whale
   (D) humpback whale
5. Which mammal weighs thirty-five and forty-three hundredths tons?
   F right whale
   (G) sperm whale
   H gray whale
   J fin whale
6. Which of the following lists shows mammals in order from the least weight to the greatest weight?
   A sperm whale, right whale, fin whale, gray whale
   B fin whale, sperm whale, gray whale, blue whale
   C fin whale, right whale, sperm whale, gray whale
   (D) gray whale, sperm whale, right whale, fin whale
7. Which of the following lists shows mammals in order from the greatest length to the least length?
   (F) sperm whale, right whale, humpback whale, gray whale
   G gray whale, humpback whale, right whale, sperm whale
   H right whale, sperm whale, gray whale, humpback whale
   J humpback whale, gray whale, sperm whale, right whale

Ongoing Assessment and Intervention 

***Diagnose Before* the Lesson**
3-1 Warm Up, TE p. 108

***Monitor During* the Lesson**
3-1 Know-It Notebook
3-1 Questioning Strategies

***Assess After* the Lesson**
3-1 Lesson Quiz, TE p. 111

Interdisciplinary 

Astronomy

Exercises 38–44 involve using data about the distances of well-known stars from Earth. Astronomy is studied in middle school earth science programs such as *Holt Science & Technology*.

In Exercise 45, remind students that decimals are named by the place value of the last digit. The 1 in the decimal is in the fifth place to the right of the decimal point, or the hundred-thousandths position.

Journal

Have students write about a situation that does not involve money in which decimal numbers are used.

Power Presentations with PowerPoint®

3-1 Lesson Quiz

Write each in standard form, expanded form, and words.

1. 8.0342   8 + 0.03 + 0.004 + 0.0002; eight and three hundred forty-two ten-thousandths

2. 18 + 0.3 + 0.006   18.306; eighteen and three hundred six thousandths

3. eight and twelve hundredths **8.12; 8 + 0.1 + 0.02**

4. It takes Pluto 246.7 years to orbit the Sun, and it takes Neptune 164.8 years. Which planet takes longer to orbit the Sun?   Pluto

5. Order the decimals from least to greatest: 16.35, 16.3, 16.5. **16.3, 16.35, 16.5**

Also available on transparency

3-2 Organizer

Pacing: Traditional 1 day
Block $\frac{1}{2}$ day

Objective: Students estimate decimal sums, differences, products, and quotients.

Online Edition
Tutorial Videos

Countdown to CRCT Week 5

Power Presentations with PowerPoint®

Warm Up

Order the decimals from least to greatest.

1. 18.74, 18.7, 18.47
   18.47, 18.7, 18.74
2. 9.06, 9.66, 9.6, 9.076
   9.06, 9.076, 9.6, 9.66

Write each in words.

3. 3.072 three and seventy-two thousandths
4. 6.1258 six and one thousand two hundred fifty-eight ten-thousandths

Problem of the Day

Calculate your age in months.
Possible answer: 11 yr 8 mo = 140 mo

Also available on transparency

3-2 Estimating Decimals

Learn to estimate decimal sums, differences, products, and quotients.

Vocabulary
clustering
front-end estimation

Georgia Performance Standards
M6N1.g Solve problems involving decimals. Also, M6P1.b, M6P1.c.

Beth's health class is learning about fitness and nutrition. The table shows the approximate number of calories burned by someone who weighs 90 pounds.

Activity (45 min)	Calories Burned (App.)
Cycling	198.45
Playing ice hockey	210.6
Rowing	324
Water skiing	194.4

When numbers are about the same value, you can use *clustering* to estimate. **Clustering** means rounding the numbers to the same value.

EXAMPLE 1 Health Application

Beth wants to cycle, play ice hockey, and water ski. If Beth weighs 90 pounds and spends 45 minutes doing each activity, *about* how many calories will she burn in all?

198.45	→	200	*The addends cluster around 200.*
210.6	→	200	*To estimate the total number of calories,*
+ 194.4	→	+ 200	*round each addend to 200.*
		600	*Add.*

Beth burns about 600 calories.

EXAMPLE 2 Rounding Decimals to Estimate Sums and Differences

Estimate by rounding to the indicated place value.

A 3.92 + 6.48; ones

3.92 + 6.48 — *Round to the nearest whole number.*
4 + 6 = 10 — *The sum is about 10.*

B 8.6355 − 5.039; hundredths

8.6355	8.64	*Round to the hundredths.*
− 5.039	− 5.04	*Align the decimals.*
	3.60	*Subtract.*

Caution!
Look at the digit to the right of the place to which you are rounding.
- If it is *5 or greater,* round *up.*
- If it is *less than 5,* round *down.*

Georgia Performance Standards

M6N1.g Solve problems involving fractions, decimals, and percents.

M6P1.b Solve problems that arise in mathematics and in other contexts.

M6P1.c Apply and adapt a variety of appropriate strategies to solve problems.

1 Introduce

Alternate Opener

EXPLORATION

3-2 Estimating Decimals

For each problem, estimate a solution. Then compute with a calculator to see how close your estimated solutions are to the actual solutions.

	Problem	Estimate	Actual
1.	Seven people want to share the cost of a $33.75 boat rental. How much will each person pay?		
2.	You purchase items that cost the following amounts: $4.95, $1.29, $6.67, $4.19, and $10.39. What is the total cost?		
3.	How much change is there from $200.00 for an item that costs $157.98?		
4.	Ron's gas tank holds 21 gallons and is empty. If gas costs $2.499 per gallon, how much will it cost to fill Ron's tank?		

Think and Discuss

5. **Discuss** the estimation strategies you used.
6. **Describe** a situation in which all you need is an estimated solution and a situation in which you must calculate an exact solution.

Motivate

Have students brainstorm about real-world situations in which they may need to estimate decimal numbers (e.g., shopping, tipping, measurements). Then have students volunteer some estimation strategies to use in these situations.

Explorations and answers are provided in *Alternate Openers: Explorations Transparencies.*

EXAMPLE 3 **Using Compatible Numbers to Estimate Products and Quotients**

Remember!

Compatible numbers are close to the numbers that are in the problem and are helpful when you are solving the problem mentally.

Estimate each product or quotient.

A 26.76×2.93

$25 \times 3 = 75$ *25 and 3 are compatible.*

So 26.76×2.93 is about 75.

B $42.64 \div 16.51$

$45 \div 15 = 3$ *45 and 15 are compatible.*

So $42.64 \div 16.51$ is about 3.

You can also use *front-end estimation* to estimate with decimals. **Front-end estimation** means to use only the whole-number part of the decimal.

EXAMPLE 4 **Using Front-End Estimation**

Estimate a range for the sum.

$9.99 + 22.89 + 8.3$

Use front-end estimation.

9.99	→	9	*Add the whole numbers only.*
22.89	→	22	*The whole-number values of the decimals*
+ 8.30	→	+ 8	*are less than the actual numbers, so the*
		at least 39	*answer is an underestimate.*

The exact answer of $9.99 + 22.89 + 8.3$ is 39 or greater.

You can estimate a range for the sum by adjusting the decimal part of the numbers. Round the decimals to 0, 0.5, or 1.

0.99	→	1.00	*Add the decimal part of the numbers.*
0.89	→	1.00	*Add the whole-number estimate and the*
+ 0.30	→	+ 0.50	*adjusted estimate.*
		2.50	*The adjusted decimals are greater than the*
39.00 + 2.50 = 41.50			*actual decimals, so 41.50 is an overestimate.*

The estimated range for the sum is from 39.00 to 41.50.

Think and Discuss

GPS M6P3.a

1. Tell what number the following decimals cluster around: 34.5, 36.78, and 35.234.

2. Determine whether a front-end estimation without adjustment is always an overestimation or an underestimation.

Answers to *Think and Discuss:*

1. Possible answer: 35
2. It is always an underestimation.

Check that students are using front-end estimation correctly. Some students may round the numbers to the nearest whole number; they should simply truncate the numbers, dropping the decimal portion.

Power Presentations with PowerPoint®

Additional Examples

Example 

Nancy wants to cycle, ice skate, and water ski for 30 minutes each. About how many calories will she burn in all? (Cycling = 165.5 cal, ice skating = 177.5 cal, and water skiing = 171.5 cal)

Nancy burns about 510 calories.

Example 

Estimate by rounding to the indicated place value.

A. $7.13 + 4.68$; ones 12

B. $9.705 - 0.2683$; tenths 9.4

Example 

Estimate each product or quotient.

A. 33.83×1.98 70

B. $72.77 \div 26.14$ 3

Example 

Estimate a range for the sum.

$7.86 + 36.97 + 5.40$

The estimated range for the sum is from 48.00 to 50.50.

Also available on transparency

2 Teach

Guided Instruction

In this lesson, students learn to estimate decimal sums, differences, products, and quotients. First teach students to use clustering to estimate sums of numbers around the same value, and have them round decimals to estimate sums and differences. Then review compatible numbers and have students estimate products and quotients. Finally, teach front-end estimation and have students use the method to estimate sums.

Reaching All Learners

Through Curriculum Integration

Health Have students research the approximate number of calories burned for other activities. Students can use this information to write and solve application problems similar to the one in Example 1.

3 Close

Summarize

Review brief explanations for each type of estimation: *clustering, rounding, compatible numbers,* and *front-end estimation.* Have students work in pairs to solve estimation problems using the four techniques from the lesson. Then they can exchange papers and check each other's work.

3-2 Exercises

Assignment Guide

If you finished Example 1 assign:
Average 1, 11–12, 22, 27, 36–43
Advanced 1, 11–12, 25, 28, 36–43

If you finished Example 2 assign:
Average 1–5, 11–16, 22–24, 36–43
Advanced 1–5, 11–16, 25–27, 36–43

If you finished Example 3 assign:
Average 1–8, 11–19, 22–26, 36–43
Advanced 1–8, 11–19, 27–32, 36–43

If you finished Example 4 assign:
Average 1–21, 26–30, 36–43
Advanced 1–21, 31–43

Homework Quick Check

Quickly check key concepts.
Exercises: 12, 14, 18, 20

Math Background

Because of truncation, an estimate gained by front-end estimation will always be an underestimate. A quick way to obtain a guaranteed overestimate is to add the number of addends in the sum to the underestimate. This process works because you are adding 1 for each addend. Once you have the underestimate and the overestimate, you also have a range in which the true sum must lie.

Georgia Performance Standards

M6P3.a Organize and consolidate their mathematical thinking through communication.

M6P4.c Recognize and apply mathematics in contexts outside of mathematics.

3-2 Exercises

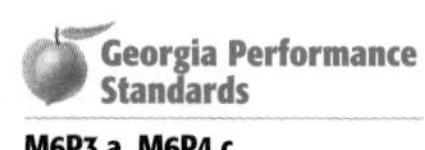

M6P3.a, M6P4.c

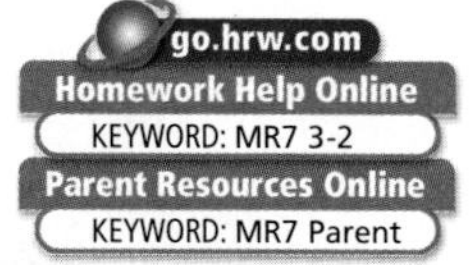

GUIDED PRACTICE

See Example 1

1. Elba runs every Monday, Wednesday, and Friday. Last week she ran 3.62 miles on Monday, 3.8 miles on Wednesday, and 4.3 miles on Friday. About how many miles did she run last week? **about 12 miles**

See Example 2

Estimate by rounding to the indicated place value.

2. 2.746 − 0.866; tenths **1.8**
3. 6.735 + 4.9528; ones **12**
4. 10.8071 + 5.392; hundredths **16.20**
5. 5.9821 − 0.48329; ten-thousandths **5.4988**

See Example 3

Estimate each product or quotient.

6. 38.92 ÷ 4.06 **10**
7. 14.51 × 7.89 **120**
8. 22.47 ÷ 3.22 **7**

See Example 4

Estimate a range for each sum.

9. 7.8 + 31.39 + 6.95 **from 44 to 46.5**
10. 14.27 + 5.4 + 21.86 **from 40 to 42**

INDEPENDENT PRACTICE

See Example 1

11. **Multi-Step** Before Mike's trip, the odometer in his car read 146.8 miles. He drove 167.5 miles to a friend's house and 153.9 miles to the beach. About how many miles did the odometer read when he arrived at the beach? **about 450 miles**
12. The rainfall in July, August, and September was 16.76 cm, 13.97 cm, and 15.24 cm, respectively. About how many total centimeters of rain fell during those three months? **about 45 cm**

See Example 2

Estimate by rounding to the indicated place value.

13. 2.0993 + 1.256; tenths **3.4**
14. 7.504 − 2.3792; hundredths **5.12**
15. 0.6271 + 4.53027; thousandths **5.157**
16. 13.274 − 8.5590; tenths **4.7**

See Example 3

Estimate each product or quotient.

17. 9.64 × 1.769 **20**
18. 11.509 ÷ 4.258 **3**
19. 19.03 ÷ 2.705 **6**

See Example 4

Estimate a range for each sum.

20. 17.563 + 4.5 + 2.31 **from 23 to 25**
21. 1.620 + 10.8 + 3.71 **from 14 to 17**

PRACTICE AND PROBLEM SOLVING

Extra Practice p. 718

Estimate by rounding to the nearest whole number.

22. 8.456 + 7.903 **16**
23. 12.43 × 3.72 **48**
24. 1,576.2 − 150.50 **1,425**
25. Estimate the quotient of 67.25 and 3.83. **17**
26. Estimate $79.45 divided by 17. **5**

RETEACH 3-2

LESSON 3-2 **Reteach**
Estimating Decimals

You can use rounding to estimate. Round to the indicated place value. Then add or subtract.

A. 3.478 + 7.136; tenths
3.478 — 7 ≥ 5, so round up — 3.5
7.136 — 3 < 5, so round down — +7.1
10.6
3.478 + 7.136 is about 10.6.

B. 12.848 − 6.124; hundredths
12.848 — 8 ≥ 5, so round up — 12.85
6.124 — 4 < 5, so round down — −6.12
6.73
12.848 − 6.124 is about 6.73.

Estimate by rounding to the indicated place value.

1. 1.04 + 9.37; tenths
1.04 rounds to **1.0**
9.37 rounds to **9.4**
estimate **10.4**

2. 2.17 + 3.56; tenths
2.17 rounds to **2.2**
3.56 rounds to **3.6**
estimate **5.8**

3. 6.753 − 4.245; hundredths
6.753 rounds to **6.75**
4.255 rounds to **4.26**
estimate **2.49**

You can use compatible numbers to estimate. Pick numbers that are close to the actual numbers that are easy to multiply or divide. Then multiply or divide.

A. 4.6 • 3.2
5 and 3 are compatible numbers.
5 • 3 = 15, so 4.6 • 3.2 is about 15.

B. 48.3 ÷ 13.2
48 and 12 are compatible numbers.
48 ÷ 12 = 4, so 48.3 ÷ 13.2 is about 4.

Use compatible numbers to estimate each product or quotient.

4. 9.4 • 5.6 **54**
5. 7.25 • 10.84 **77**
6. 84.8 ÷ 3.9 **21**
7. 21.9 ÷ 3.1 **7**
8. 8.3 • 7.6 **64**
9. 55.7 ÷ 6.9 **8**
10. 5.57 ÷ 2.7 **2**
11. 6.729 • 9.8 **70**

Possible answers are given.

PRACTICE 3-2

LESSON 3-2 **Practice B**
Estimating Decimals

Estimate by rounding to the indicated place value.

1. 7.462 + 1.809; tenths **9.3**
2. 15.3614 − 2.0573; hundredths **13.30**
3. 56.4059 − 4.837; ones **51**
4. 0.60871 + 1.2103; hundredths **1.82**

Estimate each product or quotient. Possible answers are given.

5. 42.1 ÷ 5.97 **7**
6. 11.8 • 6.125 **72**
7. 63.78 ÷ 8.204 **8**
8. 7.539 • 3.0642 **24**
9. 80.794 ÷ 8.61 **9**
10. 19.801 • 2.78 **60**

Estimate a range for each sum. Possible answers are given.

11. 6.8 + 4.3 + 5.6 **from 15 to 17.5**
12. 12.63 + 9.86 + 20.30 **from 41 to 43.5**
13. Two sixth-grade classes are collecting money to buy a present for one of their teachers. One class collected $24.68 and the other class collected $30.25. About how much money did they collect in all? The gift they want to buy costs $69.75. About how much more money do they need?
about $55.00; about $15.00
14. On the highway, Anita drove an average speed of 60.2 miles per hour. At that speed, about how far can she travel in three and a half hours? At that same speed, about how many hours will it take Anita to drive 400 miles?
about 240 miles; about 7 hours

Use the table for Exercises 27–31.

Long-Distance Costs for Callers in the United States	
Country	Cost per Minute (¢)
Venezuela	22
Russia	9.9
Japan	7.9
United States	3.7

27. **Money** Round each cost in the table to the nearest cent. Write your answer using a dollar sign and decimal point. **\$0.22, \$0.10, \$0.08, \$0.04**
28. About how much does it cost to phone someone in Russia and talk for 8 minutes? **about 80 cents**
29. About how much more does it cost to make a 12-minute call to Japan than to make an 18-minute call within the United States? **$(12 \times 8) - (18 \times 4) = 24$, or about 24 cents**
30. Will the cost of a 30-minute call to someone within the United States be greater or less than \$1.20? Explain.
31. **Multi-Step** Kim is in New York. She calls her grandmother in Venezuela and speaks for 20 minutes, then calls a friend in Japan and talks for 15 minutes, and finally calls her mother in San Francisco and talks for 30 minutes. Estimate the total cost of all her calls. **Possible answer: $(20 \times \$0.20) + (15 \times \$0.08) + (30 \times \$0.04) = \$4 + \$1.20 + \$1.20$, or about \$6.40**
32. **Health** The recommended daily allowance (RDA) for iron is 15 mg/day for teenage girls. Julie eats a hamburger that contains 3.88 mg of iron. About how many more milligrams of iron does she need to meet the RDA? **about 11 mg**
33. **Write a Problem** Write a problem with three decimal numbers that have a total sum between 30 and 32.5. **Possible answer: 8.56 + 12.36 + 10.74**

34. **Write About It** How do you adjust a front-end estimation? Why is this done?
35. **Challenge** Place a decimal point in each number so that the sum of the numbers is between 124 and 127: 1059 + 725 + 815 + 1263. **105.9 + 7.25 + 0.815 + 12.63**

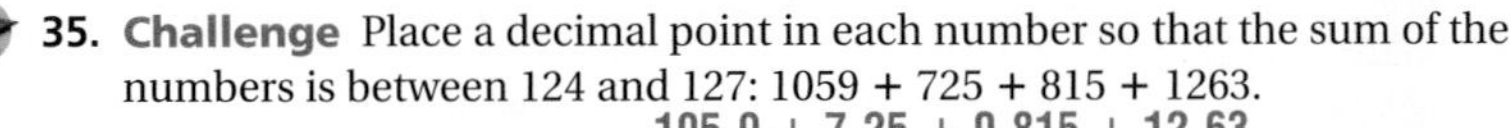

CRCT Prep • GPS Support • Spiral Review

36. **Multiple Choice** Which is the estimated difference of 34.45 − 24.71 by rounding to the nearest whole number?

Ⓐ 11 Ⓑ 10  Ⓒ 9 Ⓓ 8

37. **Short Response** The average rainfall in Oklahoma City is 2.8 inches in April, 5.3 inches in May, and 4.3 inches in June. A weather forecaster predicts that the rainfall one year will double the average in April and May and half the average in June. Estimate the predicted rainfall each month to the nearest inch. **6 inches in April, 10 inches in May, 2 inches in June**

Solve each equation. (Lesson 2-5)

38. $83 + n = 157$ **$n = 74$**
39. $x + 23 = 92$ **$x = 69$**
40. $25 + c = 145$ **$c = 120$**

Order the decimals from least to greatest. (Lesson 3-1)

41. 8.304, 8.009, 8.05 **8.009, 8.05, 8.304**
42. 5.62, 15.34, 1.589 **1.589, 5.62, 15.34**
43. 30.211, 30.709, 30.75 **30.211, 30.709, 30.75**

Ongoing Assessment and Intervention

***Diagnose Before* the Lesson**
3-2 Warm Up, TE p. 112

***Monitor During* the Lesson**
3-2 Know-It Notebook
3-2 Questioning Strategies

***Assess After* the Lesson**
3-2 Lesson Quiz, TE p. 115

Answers

30. Round 3.7 cents to 4 cents. $4 \times 30 = \$1.20$. \$1.20 is an overestimate, so it will cost less than \$1.20.
34. You round the decimal part of the addends to either 1.00, 0.5, or 0 and then add the estimated adjustment to the whole-number estimate. It gives a range for the sum.

Test Prep Doctor In Exercise 37, point out to students that three answers are required in this exercise. Students might list parts of the problem that need a response.

Journal

Have students write about how they can use estimation while shopping.

CHALLENGE 3-2

LESSON 3-2 Challenge
Out to Lunch

Use the restaurant bills below to estimate the total cost of each meal. Then estimate the amount each person should pay to split each check evenly. Possible answers are given.

Number of People: 2

Quantity	Item	Price
2	Large Soda	\$0.75 each
1	Cheeseburger	\$4.55
1	BLT	\$3.25
Estimated Total:		about \$10.00
Estimated Cost Per Person:		about \$5.00

Number of People: 4

Quantity	Item	Price
2	Slice of Pie	\$1.45 each
1	Brownie	\$1.25
3	Hot Tea	\$0.60 each
Estimated Total:		about \$6.00
Estimated Cost Per Person:		about \$1.50

Number of People: 4

Quantity	Item	Price
2	Bowl of Soup	\$2.89 each
1	Chicken Sandwich	\$4.95
1	Chef Salad	\$3.25
4	Coffee	\$0.50 each
Estimated Total:		about \$16.00
Estimated Cost Per Person:		about \$4.00

Number of People: 5

Quantity	Item	Price
1	Pizza	\$14.95
5	House Salad	\$2.85 each
4	Large Soda	\$0.75 each
1	Small Soda	\$0.55
Estimated Total:		about \$35.00
Estimated Cost Per Person:		about \$7.00

PROBLEM SOLVING 3-2

LESSON 3-2 Problem Solving
Estimating Decimals

Write the correct answer. Possible answers are given.

1. Men in Iceland have the highest average life expectancy in the world—76.8 years. The average life expectancy for a man in the United States is 73.1 years. About how much higher is a man's average life expectancy in Iceland? Round your answer to the nearest whole year.
   about 4 years
2. The average life expectancy for a woman in the United States is 79.1 years. Women in Japan have the highest average life expectancy—3.4 years higher than the United States. Estimate the average life expectancy of women in Japan. Round your answer to the nearest whole year.
   about 82 years
3. There are about 1.6093 kilometers in one mile. There are 26.2 miles in a marathon race. About how many kilometers are there in a marathon race? Round your answer to the nearest tenths.
   about 41.9 kilometers
4. At top speed, a hornet can fly 13.39 miles per hour. About how many hours would it take a hornet to fly 65 miles? Round your answer to the nearest whole number.
   about 5 hours

Circle the letter of the correct answer.

5. The average male human brain weighs 49.7 ounces. The average female human brain weighs 44.6 ounces. What is the difference in their weights?
   A about 95 ounces
   B about 7 ounces
   Ⓒ about 5 ounces
   D about 3 ounces
6. An official hockey puck is 2.54 centimeters thick. About how thick are two hockey pucks when one is placed on top of the other?
   F about 4 centimeters
   G about 4.2 centimeters
   Ⓗ about 5 centimeters
   J about 5.2 centimeters
7. Lydia earned \$9.75 per hour as a lifeguard last summer. She worked 25 hours a week. About how much did she earn in 8 weeks?
   A about \$250.00
   Ⓑ about \$2,000.00
   C about \$2,500.00
   D about \$200.00
8. Brent mixed 4.5 gallons of blue paint with 1.7 gallons of white paint and 2.4 gallons of red paint to make a light purple paint. About how many gallons of purple paint did he make?
   Ⓕ about 9 gallons
   G about 8 gallons
   H about 10 gallons
   J about 7 gallons

Power Presentations with PowerPoint®

3-2 Lesson Quiz

Estimate by rounding to the indicated place value.

1. $3.07442 + 1.352$; tenths **4.5**
2. $7.305 - 4.12689$; nearest whole number **3**

Estimate each product or quotient.

3. 6.75×1.82 **14**
4. $10.5 \div 3.42$ **3**
5. The snowfall in December, January, and February was 18.26 cm, 29.36 cm, and 32.87 cm, respectively. About how many total centimeters of snow fell during the three months? **80**

Also available on transparency

Organizer

Use with Lesson 3-3

Pacing:
Traditional $\frac{1}{2}$ day
Block $\frac{1}{4}$ day

Objective: Use decimal grids to model addition and subtraction of decimals.

Materials: Decimal grids

Resources

Hands-On Lab Activities
Lab 3-3 Recording Sheet

Teach

Discuss

While using the decimal grids, have students discuss the similarities between adding or subtracting decimals and adding or subtracting whole numbers.

Close

Key Concept

The decimal grid demonstrates the base-10 connection between whole numbers and decimals.

Assessment

Model each problem on a decimal grid. Then solve.

1. 0.2 + 0.33

2. 2.45 − 1.08

Georgia Performance Standards

M6N1.g Solve problems involving fractions, decimals, and percents.

M6P5.a Create and use representations to organize, record, and communicate mathematical ideas.

M6P5.b Select, apply, and translate among mathematical representations to solve problems.

Explore Decimal Addition and Subtraction

Use with Lesson 3-3

go.hrw.com
Lab Resources Online
KEYWORD: MR7 Lab3

Georgia Performance Standards
M6N1.g, M6P5.a, M6P5.b

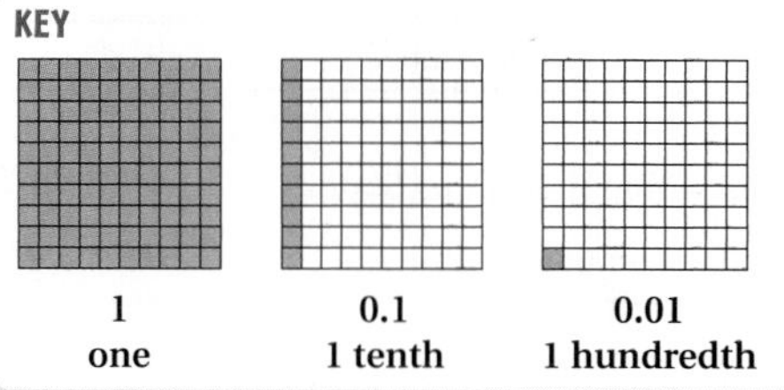

You can model addition and subtraction of decimals with decimal grids.

Activity 1

Use decimal grids to find each sum.

a. 0.24 + 0.32

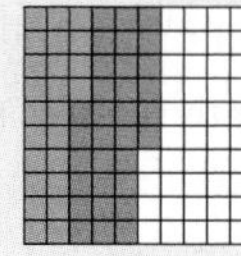

To represent 0.24, shade 24 squares.

To represent 0.32, shade 32 squares in another color.

There are 56 shaded squares representing 0.56.

0.24 + 0.32 = 0.56

b. 1.56 + 0.4

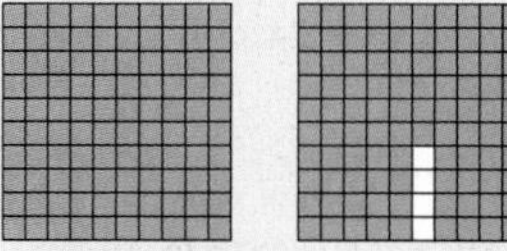

To represent 1.56, shade a whole grid and 56 squares of another.

To represent 0.4, shade 4 columns in another color.

One whole grid and 96 squares are shaded.

1.56 + 0.4 = 1.96

c. 0.75 + 0.68

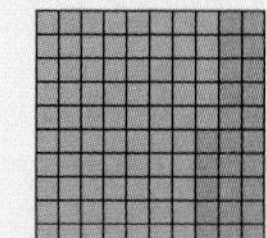
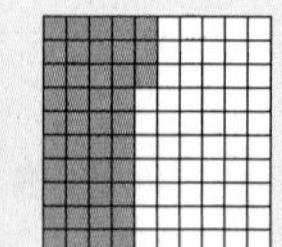

To represent 0.75, shade 75 squares.

To represent 0.68, shade 68 squares in another color. You will need to use another grid.

One whole grid and 43 squares are shaded.

0.75 + 0.68 = 1.43

Answers to *Assessment*

1. 0.53

2. 1.37

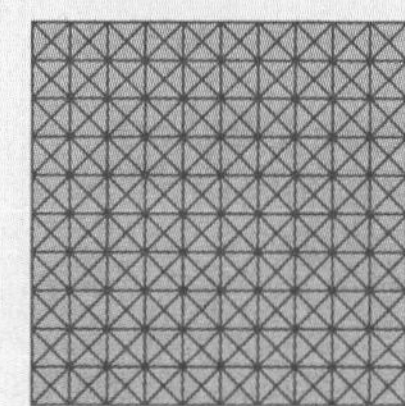
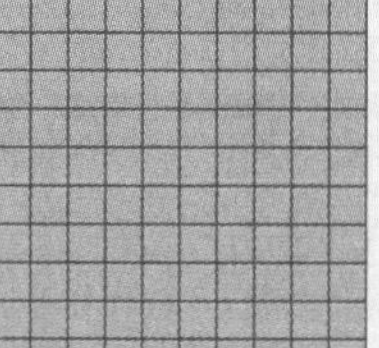
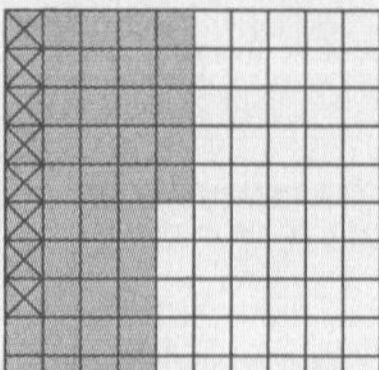

Think and Discuss

1. How would you shade a decimal grid to represent 0.2 + 0.18?
   Possible answer: To represent 0.2, shade 2 columns, and then shade 1 column plus 8 small squares in another color to represent 0.18.

Try This

Use decimal grids to find each sum.

1. 0.2 + 0.6 **0.8**	**2.** 1.07 + 0.03 **1.10**	**3.** 1.62 + 0.08 **1.70**
4. 0.45 + 0.29 **0.74**	**5.** 0.88 + 0.12 **1.00**	**6.** 1.29 + 0.67 **1.96**
7. 0.07 + 0.41 **0.48**	**8.** 0.51 + 0.51 **1.02**	**9.** 1.01 + 0.23 **1.24**

Activity 2

Use a decimal grid to find each difference.

a. 0.6 − 0.38

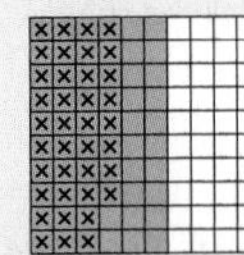

To represent 0.6, shade 6 columns.

Subtract 0.38 by removing 38 squares.

There are 22 remaining squares.

0.6 − 0.38 = 0.22

b. 1.22 − 0.41

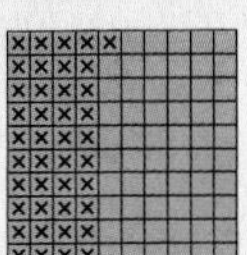

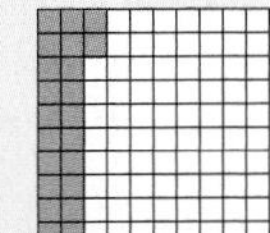

To represent 1.22, shade an entire decimal grid and 22 squares of another.

Subtract 0.41 by removing 41 squares.

There are 81 remaining squares.

1.22 − 0.41 = 0.81

Think and Discuss

1. How would you shade a decimal grid to represent 1.3 − 0.6?
   Possible answer: Shade 1 complete grid plus 3 columns of another to represent 1.3. Then remove 6 columns: 3 from the second grid and 3 from the first. This leaves 7 columns representing 0.7.

Try This

Use decimal grids to find each difference.

1. 0.9 − 0.3 **0.6**	**2.** 1.2 − 0.98 **0.22**	**3.** 0.6 − 0.41 **0.19**
4. 1.6 − 0.07 **1.53**	**5.** 0.35 − 0.03 **0.32**	**6.** 2.12 − 0.23 **1.89**
7. 2.0− 0.86 **1.14**	**8.** 0.78 − 0.76 **0.02**	**9.** 1.06 − 0.55 **0.51**

Activity 2

Answers to *Try This*

1–9. Complete answers on p. A1.

8.

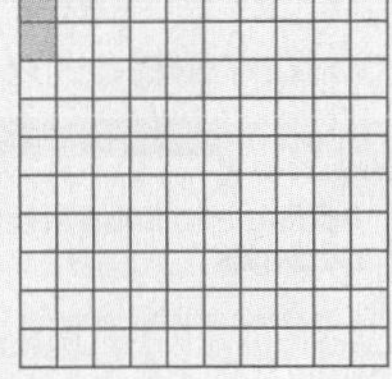

9.

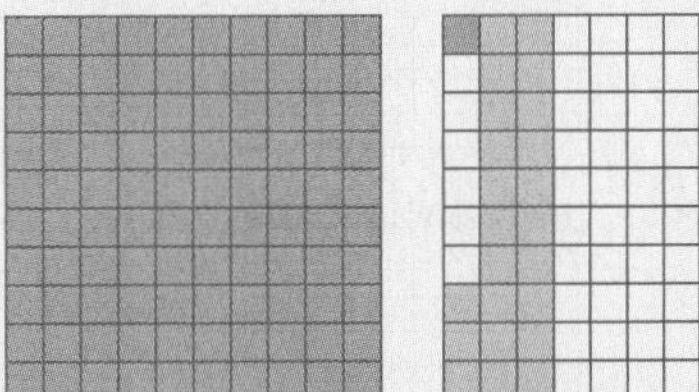

Activity 1

Answers to *Try This*

1.

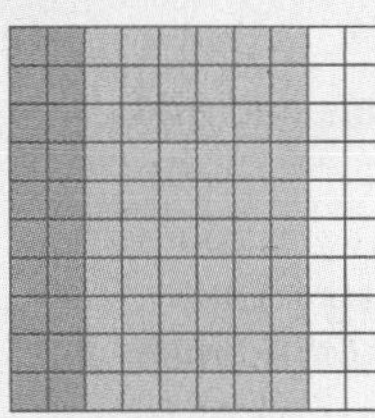

2.

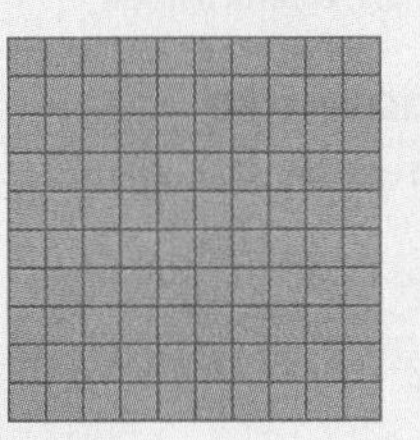

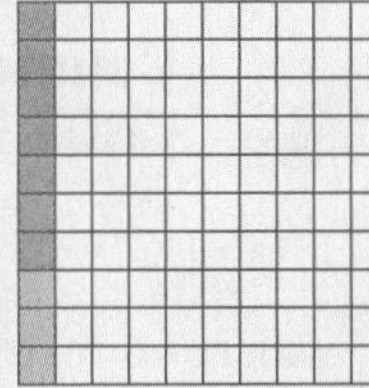

3.

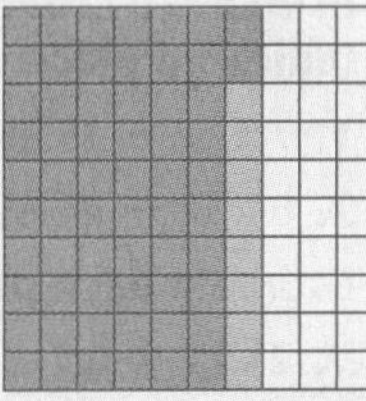

4.

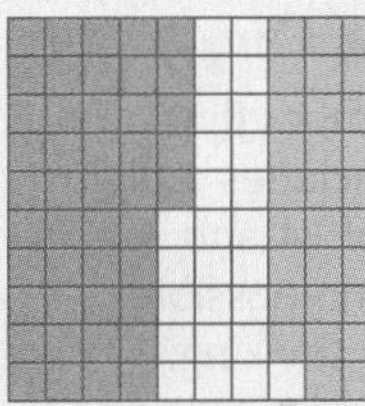

5.

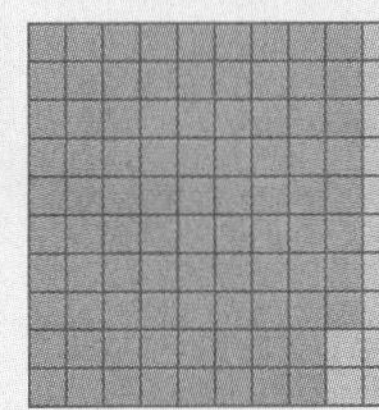

6.

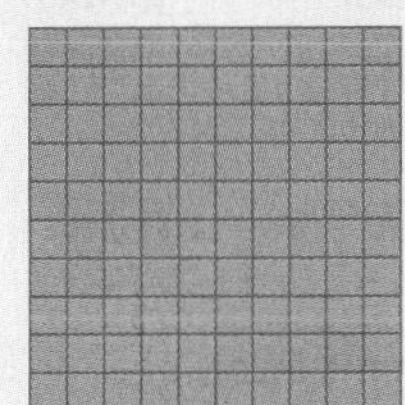

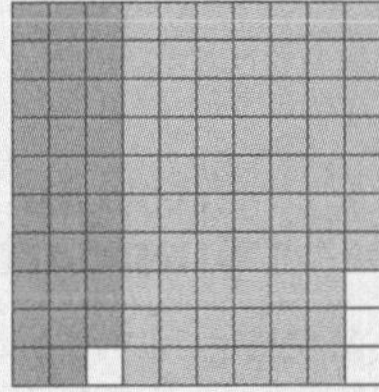

7.

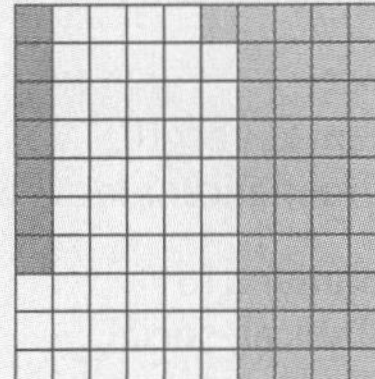

3-3 Organizer

Pacing: Traditional 1 day
Block $\frac{1}{2}$ day

Objective: Students add and subtract decimals.

Technology Lab
In *Technology Lab Activities*

Online Edition
Tutorial Videos, Interactivities

Countdown to CRCT Week 5

Warm Up

Estimate by rounding to the indicated place value.

1. 70.27 + 15.36; ones 85
2. 84.37 − 21.82; tenths 62.6

Estimate each product or quotient.

3. 27.25 × 8.7 270
4. 44.52 ÷ 3.27 15

Problem of the Day

Find a three-digit number that rounds to 440 and includes a digit that is the quotient of 24 and 3. Is there more than one possible answer? Explain your thinking.
438; no; the numbers that round to 440 are 435–444, 24 divided by 3 is 8, and 438 is the only number with 8 as a digit.

Also available on transparency

Math Fact

In some countries a comma is used in place of a decimal point to separate whole and fractional parts of a number.

M6N1.g Solve problems involving fractions, decimals, and percents.

M6P1.b Solve problems that arise in mathematics and in other contexts.

M6P5.a Create and use representations to organize, record, and communicate mathematical ideas.

M6P5.c Use representations to model and interpret physical, social, and mathematical phenomena.

3-3 Adding and Subtracting Decimals

Learn to add and subtract decimals.

M6N1.g Solve problems involving decimals. Also, M6P1.b, M6P5.a, M6P5.c.

At the 2004 U.S. Gymnastics Championships, Carly Patterson and Courtney Kupets tied for the All-Around title.

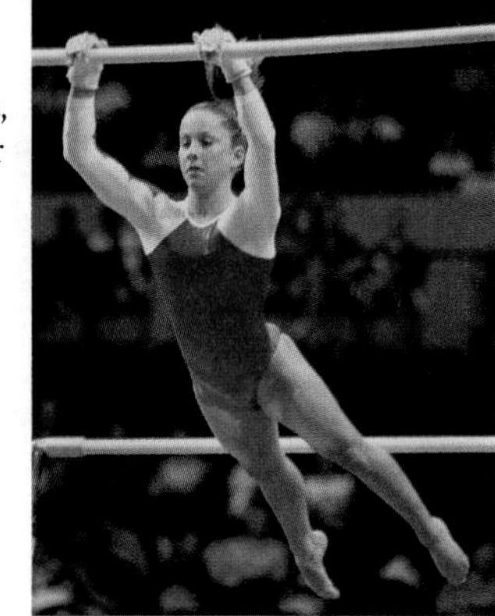

Carly Patterson also won a gold medal in the Women's Individual All-Around in the 2004 Olympic Games.

Carly Patterson's Preliminary Scores

Event	Points
Floor exercise	9.7
Balance beam	9.7
Vault	9.3
Uneven bars	9.45

To find the total number of points, you can add all of the scores.

EXAMPLE 1 *Sports Application*

Helpful Hint
Estimating before you add or subtract will help you check whether your answer is reasonable.

A What was Carly Patterson's preliminary total score in the 2004 U.S. Championships?

First estimate the sum of 9.7, 9.7, 9.3, and 9.45.

$$9.7 + 9.7 + 9.3 + 9.45$$
$$10 + 10 + 9 + 9 = 38$$

Estimate by rounding to the nearest whole number. The total is about 38 points.

Then add.

```
  9.70    Align the decimal points.
  9.70
  9.30    Use zeros as placeholders.
+ 9.45
 38.15    Add. Then place the decimal point.
```

Since 38.15 is close to the estimate of 38, the answer is reasonable. Patterson's total preliminary score was 38.15 points.

B How many more points did Patterson need on the uneven bars to have a perfect score of 10?

Find the difference between 10 and 9.45.

```
  10.00   Align the decimal points.
 − 9.45   Use zeros as placeholders.
   0.55   Subtract. Then place the decimal point.
```

Patterson needed another 0.55 points to have a perfect score.

1 Introduce

Alternate Opener

3-3 Adding and Subtracting Decimals

You have 19¢. How much more do you need to have $1.00? From 19¢ to 20¢, add 1¢. From 20¢ to $1.00, add 80¢. The answer is 1¢ + 80¢, or 81¢.

1. Draw arrows to connect each pair of amounts that would give you a sum of $1.00.

Amount 1	Amount 2
$0.19	$0.63
$0.25	$0.55
$0.76	$0.93
$0.07	$0.75
$0.65	$0.24
$0.37	$0.35
$0.45	$0.81

2. Compute the change from $10.00 on a purchase of each amount. Example: From $1.25 to $2.00, add $0.75. From $2.00 to $10.00, add $8.00. So the change on a purchase of $1.25 is $0.75 + $8.00 = $8.75.

Amount	Change from $10.00
$1.25	$8.75
$2.76	
$3.07	
$4.65	
$5.37	
$6.45	
$7.59	

Think and Discuss

3. **Name** five different pairs of numbers that each have a sum of $1.00.
4. **Describe** how you can use the strategy of "adding up" to find 200 − 176.25.

Motivate

Review procedures for adding and subtracting whole numbers: align digits according to place value (ones, tens, hundreds, etc.), perform the operation, and regroup when needed. Explain that the same steps are followed when adding and subtracting decimals.

Explorations and answers are provided in *Alternate Openers: Explorations Transparencies.*

EXAMPLE 2 Using Mental Math to Add and Subtract Decimals

Find each sum or difference.

A $1.6 + 0.4$

$1.6 + 0.4$ *Think: 0.6 + 0.4 = 1*

$1.6 + 0.4 = 2$

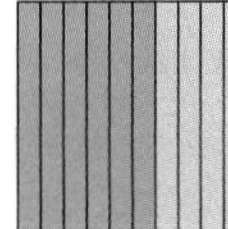

B $3 - 0.8$

$3 - 0.8$ *Think: What number added to 0.8 is 1? 0.8 + 0.2 = 1*

$3 - 0.8 = 2.2$ *So 1 − 0.8 = 0.2.*

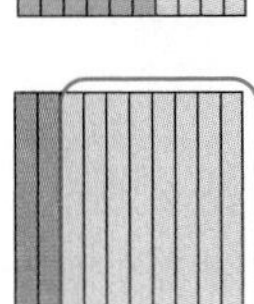

EXAMPLE 3 Evaluating Decimal Expressions

Evaluate 7.52 − *s* for each value of *s*.

A $s = 2.9$

$7.52 - s$

$7.52 - 2.9$ *Substitute 2.9 for s.*

$\begin{array}{r} 7.52 \\ -\ 2.90 \\ \hline 4.62 \end{array}$ *Align the decimal points. Use a zero as a placeholder. Subtract. Place the decimal point.*

Remember!

You can place any number of zeros at the end of a decimal number without changing its value.

B $s = 4.5367$

$7.52 - s$

$7.52 - 4.5367$ *Substitute 4.5367 for s.*

$\begin{array}{r} 7.5200 \\ -\ 4.5367 \\ \hline 2.9833 \end{array}$ *Align the decimal points. Use zeros as placeholders. Subtract. Place the decimal point.*

Possible answers to *Think and Discuss:*

1. Write the problem vertically while aligning the decimal points and place values. Use two zeros to the right of 124.5 as placeholders.
2. Estimating before you add or subtract allows you to check if your answer is reasonable.

Think and Discuss

GPS M6P1.d, M6P3.b

1. **Show** how you would write 2.678 + 124.5 to find the sum.
2. **Tell** why it is a good idea to estimate the answer before you add and subtract.
3. **Explain** how you can use mental math to find how many more points Carly Patterson would have needed to have scored a perfect 10 on the floor exercise.

COMMON ERROR ALERT

Students may try to align decimal numbers to the right instead of on the decimal point when adding or subtracting in vertical format. Explain that the place-value positions in each number must line up.

Power Presentations with PowerPoint®

Additional Examples

Example 1 

A. What was Carly Patterson's total for the events other than the floor exercise? 28.975

B. How many more points did Carly need on the vault to have a perfect score? 0.7

Example 2 

Find each sum or difference.

A. 1.8 + 0.2 2.0 **B.** 4 − 0.7 3.3

Example 3 

Evaluate 6.73 − *x* for each value of *x*.

A. *x* = 3.8 2.93 **B.** *x* = 2.9765 3.7535

Also available on transparency

Answers to *Think and Discuss*

3. 0.7 + 0.3 = 1, so 9.7 + 0.3 = 10. She would have needed 0.3 more of a point.

2 Teach

Guided Instruction

In this lesson, students learn to add and subtract decimals. First teach them to add four decimal addends, aligning decimal points and annexing zeros as placeholders. Then teach students to subtract a decimal from a whole number, aligning decimal points and using zeros as placeholders (that is, using zeros to write an equivalent number with the required number of decimal places). Next practice mental math strategies for adding and subtracting decimals. Finally, have students evaluate expressions for given variable values.

Reaching All Learners

Through Home Connection

Have students look through newspaper ads, at home or in the library, for items that, when combined, total less than $50. Have them subtract their totals from $50 to find out how much change they would receive. Possible answer: I found shoes for $12.95, a CD for $13.98, and a skateboard for $19.49. The total cost is $46.42. The amount of change I would get from $50.00 is $3.58.

3 Close

Summarize

Have students solve first a decimal addition problem and then a decimal subtraction problem (e.g., 8.34 + 3.7 + 5.029 and 12 − 7.62). Have them explain the steps they would follow to solve each. Emphasize the importance of aligning the decimals before solving the problem and using an estimate to check for reasonableness.

3-3 Exercises

Assignment Guide

If you finished Example 1 assign:
Average 1–3, 12–13, 35, 42, 49–56
Advanced 1–3, 12–13, 43–44, 49–56

If you finished Example 2 assign:
Average 1–7, 12–21, 30–35, 49–56
Advanced 1–7, 12–21, 33–35, 43–45, 49–56

If you finished Example 3 assign:
Average 1–35, 42–44, 49–56
Advanced 1–35, 45–56

Homework Quick Check

Quickly check key concepts.
Exercises: 12, 32, 34, 38, 42

Math Background

Place values to the right of a decimal point continue the same pattern as the pattern to the left of the decimal point. Specifically, the value of each place to the right of the decimal point in any number is 10 times as great as the value of the next place to its right. And the value of the ones place is 10 times as great as the value of the tenths place. Because of this, algorithms for addition and subtraction of whole numbers can be extended to decimal numbers.

3-3 Exercises

M6P3.a, M6P4.c

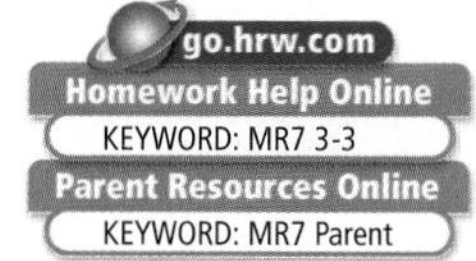

GUIDED PRACTICE

See Example 1 Use the table for Exercises 1–3.

1. How many miles in all is Rea's triathlon training? **20.2 miles**
2. How many miles did Rea run and swim in all? **5.95 miles**
3. How much farther did Rea cycle than swim? **12.65 miles**

Rea's Triathlon Training

Sport	Distance (mi)
Cycling	14.25
Running	4.35
Swimming	1.6

See Example 2 Find each sum or difference.

4. 2.7 + 0.3 **3**
5. 6 − 0.4 **5.6**
6. 5.2 + 2.8 **8**
7. 8.9 − 4 **4.9**

See Example 3 Evaluate 5.35 − m for each value of m.

8. $m = 2.37$ **2.98**
9. $m = 1.8$ **3.55**
10. $m = 4.7612$ **0.5888**
11. $m = 0.402$ **4.948**

INDEPENDENT PRACTICE

See Example 1

12. **Sports** During a diving competition, Phil performed two reverse dives and two dives from a handstand position. He received the following scores: 8.765, 9.45, 9.875, and 8.025. What was Phil's total score? **36.115**
13. Brad works after school at a local grocery store. How much did he earn in all for the month of October? **$567.38**

Brad's Earnings for October

Week	1	2	3	4
Earnings	$123.48	$165.18	$137.80	$140.92

See Example 2 Find each sum or difference.

14. 7.2 + 1.8 **9**
15. 8.5 − 7 **1.5**
16. 3.3 + 0.7 **4**
17. 15.9 + 2.1 **18**
18. 7 − 0.6 **6.4**
19. 7.55 − 3.25 **4.3**
20. 21.4 + 3.6 **25**
21. 5 − 2.7 **2.3**

See Example 3 Evaluate 9.67 − x for each value of x.

22. $x = 1.52$ **8.15**
23. $x = 3.8$ **5.87**
24. $x = 7.21$ **2.46**
25. $x = 0.635$ **9.035**
26. $x = 6.9$ **2.77**
27. $x = 1.001$ **8.669**
28. $x = 8$ **1.67**
29. $x = 9.527$ **0.143**

PRACTICE AND PROBLEM SOLVING

CRCT GPS
Extra Practice p. 718

Add or subtract.

30. 5.62 + 4.19 **9.81**
31. 10.508 − 6.73 **3.778**
32. 13.009 + 12.83 **25.839**
33. Find the sum of 0.0679 and 3.75. **3.8179**
34. Subtract 3.0042 from 7.435. **4.4308**
35. **Sports** Terin Humphrey was ranked third at the 2004 U.S. Gymnastics Championships with a score of 75.45. What was the difference between her score and Courtney Kupet's and Carly Patterson's score of 76.45? **1**

RETEACH 3-3

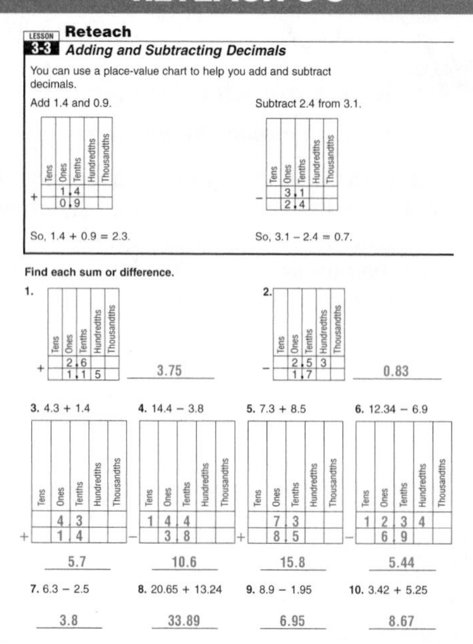
LESSON 3-3 **Reteach**
Adding and Subtracting Decimals

You can use a place-value chart to help you add and subtract decimals.

Add 1.4 and 0.9.

	Tens	Ones	Tenths	Hundredths	Thousandths
		1.	4		
+		0.	9		

So, 1.4 + 0.9 = 2.3.

Subtract 2.4 from 3.1.

	Tens	Ones	Tenths	Hundredths	Thousandths
		3.	1		
−		2.	4		

So, 3.1 − 2.4 = 0.7.

Find each sum or difference.

1.

	Tens	Ones	Tenths	Hundredths	Thousandths
		2.	6		
+		1.	1	5	

3.75

2.

	Tens	Ones	Tenths	Hundredths	Thousandths
		2.	5	3	
−		1.	7		

0.83

3. 4.3 + 1.4

	Tens	Ones	Tenths	Hundredths	Thousandths
		4.	3		
+		1.	4		

5.7

4. 14.4 − 3.8

	Tens	Ones	Tenths	Hundredths	Thousandths
	1	4.	4		
−		3.	8		

10.6

5. 7.3 + 8.5

	Tens	Ones	Tenths	Hundredths	Thousandths
		7.	3		
+		8.	5		

15.8

6. 12.34 − 6.9

	Tens	Ones	Tenths	Hundredths	Thousandths
	1	2.	3	4	
−		6.	9		

5.44

7. 6.3 − 2.5 3.8
8. 20.65 + 13.24 33.89
9. 8.9 − 1.95 6.95
10. 3.42 + 5.25 8.67

PRACTICE 3-3

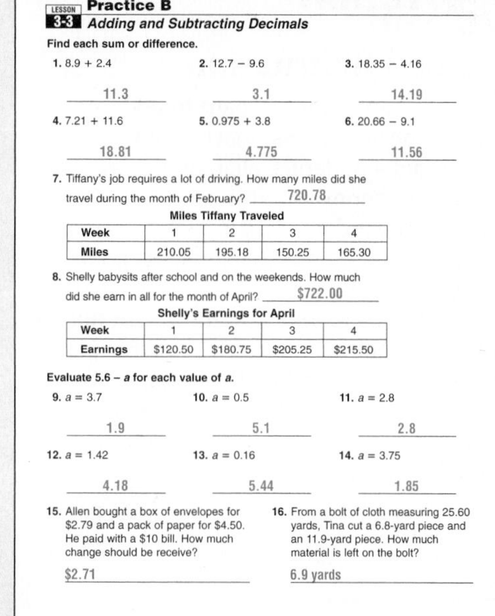
LESSON 3-3 **Practice B**
Adding and Subtracting Decimals

Find each sum or difference.

1. 8.9 + 2.4 11.3
2. 12.7 − 9.6 3.1
3. 18.35 − 4.16 14.19
4. 7.21 + 11.6 18.81
5. 0.975 + 3.8 4.775
6. 20.66 − 9.1 11.56
7. Tiffany's job requires a lot of driving. How many miles did she travel during the month of February? 720.78

Miles Tiffany Traveled

Week	1	2	3	4
Miles	210.05	195.18	150.25	165.30

8. Shelly babysits after school and on the weekends. How much did she earn in all for the month of April? $722.00

Shelly's Earnings for April

Week	1	2	3	4
Earnings	$120.50	$180.75	$205.25	$215.50

Evaluate 5.6 − *a* for each value of *a*.

9. $a = 3.7$ 1.9
10. $a = 0.5$ 5.1
11. $a = 2.8$ 2.8
12. $a = 1.42$ 4.18
13. $a = 0.16$ 5.44
14. $a = 3.75$ 1.85
15. Allen bought a box of envelopes for $2.79 and a pack of paper for $4.50. He paid with a $10 bill. How much change should be receive? $2.71
16. From a bolt of cloth measuring 25.60 yards, Tina cut a 6.8-yard piece and an 11.9-yard piece. How much material is left on the bolt? 6.9 yards

Georgia Performance Standards

M6P3.a Organize and consolidate their mathematical thinking through communication.

M6P4.c Recognize and apply mathematics in contexts outside of mathematics.

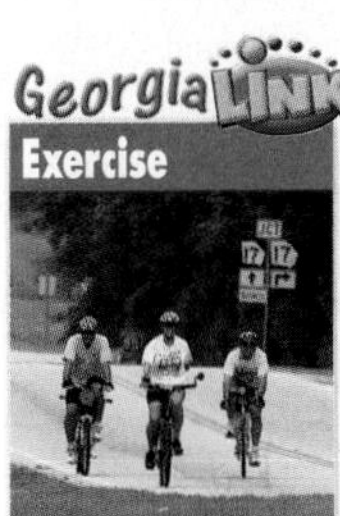

Georgia LINK Exercise

In 2005, almost 1800 cyclists participated in BRAG (The Bicycle Ride Across Georgia). The cyclists rode approximately 435 miles from Columbus to Jekyll's Island.

Evaluate each expression.

36. $8.09 - a$ for $a = 4.5$ **3.59**
37. $7.03 + 33.8 + n$ for $n = 12.006$ **52.836**
38. $b + (5.68 - 3.007)$ for $b = 6.134$ **8.807**
39. $(2 \times 14) - a + 1.438$ for $a = 0.062$ **29.376**
40. $5^2 - w$ for $w = 3.5$ **21.5**
41. $100 - p$ for $p = 15.034$ **84.966**
42. **Career** A fire helmet must be sturdy enough to protect the firefighter's head from dangerous objects and extremely hot temperatures while still being as lightweight as possible. One fire helmet weighs 1.616 kg, and another fire helmet weighs 1.403 kg. What is the difference in weights? **0.213 kg**
43. **Multi-Step** Logan wants to buy a new bike that costs $135.00. He started with $14.83 in his savings account. Last week, he deposited $15.35 into his account. Today, he deposited $32.40. How much more money does he need to buy the bike? **$72.42**
44. **Sports** With a time of 60.35 seconds, Martina Moracova broke Jennifer Thompson's world record time in the women's 100-meter medley. How much faster was Thompson than Moracova when, in the next heat, she reclaimed the record with a time of 59.30 seconds? **1.05 seconds**
45. **Sports** The highest career batting average ever achieved by a professional baseball player is 0.366. Bill Bergen finished with a career 0.170 average. How much lower is Bergen's career average than the highest career average? **0.196**
46. **What's the Question?** A cup of rice contains 0.8 mg of iron, and a cup of lima beans contains 4.4 mg of iron. If the answer is 6 mg, what is the question? **How many milligrams of iron are in 2 cups of rice and 1 cup of lima beans?**
47. **Write About It** Why is it important to align the decimal points before adding or subtracting decimal numbers? **Aligning the decimal points ensures that you add or subtract the digits in the same place value.**
48. **Challenge** Evaluate $(5.7 + a) \times (9.75 - b)$ for $a = 2.3$ and $b = 7.25$. **$(5.7 + 2.3) \times (9.75 - 7.25)$; 8×2.5; 20**

CRCT PREP • GPS SUPPORT • SPIRAL REVIEW

49. **Multiple Choice** What is the sum of 24.91 and 35.8?
    (A) 28.49 (B) 59.99 **(C) 60.71** (D) 60.99
50. **Multiple Choice** Lead has an atomic weight of 207.19. Mercury has an atomic weight of 200.6. How much greater is the atomic weight of lead than mercury?
    (F) 6.59 (G) 7.41 (H) 7.59 (J) 187.13

Solve each equation. (Lesson 2-6)

51. $s - 47 = 23$ **$s = 70$**
52. $73 = a - 78$ **$a = 151$**
53. $823 = t - 641$ **$t = 1{,}464$**

Estimate each product or quotient. (Lesson 3-2)

54. 15.72×4.08 **64**
55. 14.87×3.78 **60**
56. $53.67 \div 9.18$ **6**

Ongoing Assessment and Intervention

***Diagnose Before* the Lesson**
3-3 Warm Up, TE p. 118

***Monitor During* the Lesson**
3-3 Know-It Notebook
3-3 Questioning Strategies

***Assess After* the Lesson**
3-3 Lesson Quiz, TE p. 121

Test Prep Doctor In Exercise 49, students can eliminate wrong answers without finding the sum. The answer will have a 1 in the hundredths place because 35.8 does not have a digit in the hundredths place.

Journal

Have students write about a situation in which knowing an estimate is useful for making a decision.

CHALLENGE 3-3

Lesson 3-3 Challenge
A Penny Saved Is a Penny Earned

Next to each bank, describe three different coin combinations that equal the amount of money it holds. For each combination, use at least one quarter, one dime, one nickel, and one penny. **Possible combinations are given.**

1. 

2 quarters, 3 dimes, 1 nickel, 4 pennies
2 quarters, 2 dimes, 2 nickels, 9 pennies
1 quarter, 5 dimes, 2 nickels, 4 pennies

2. 

4 quarters, 2 dimes, 1 nickel, 3 pennies
2 quarters, 4 dimes, 5 nickels, 13 pennies
3 quarters, 4 dimes, 2 nickels, 3 pennies

3. 

1 quarter, 3 dimes, 1 nickel, 5 pennies
1 quarter, 1 dime, 4 nickels, 10 pennies
1 quarter, 2 dimes, 3 nickels, 5 pennies

4. 

8 quarters, 2 dimes, 1 nickel, 5 pennies
4 quarters, 10 dimes, 4 nickels, 10 pennies
6 quarters, 3 dimes, 4 nickels, 30 pennies

PROBLEM SOLVING 3-3

Lesson 3-3 Problem Solving
Adding and Subtracting Decimals

Use the table to answer the questions.

Busiest Ports in the United States

Port	Imports Per Year (millions of tons)	Exports Per Year (millions of tons)
South Louisiana, LA	30.6	57.42
Houston, TX	75.12	33.43
New York, NY & NJ	53.52	8.03
New Orleans, LA	26.38	21.73
Corpus Christi, TX	52.6	7.64

1. How many more tons of imports than exports does the Port of New Orleans handle each year? **4.65 million tons**
2. How many tons of imports and exports are shipped through the port of Houston, Texas, each year in all? **108.55 million tons**

Circle the letter of the correct answer.

3. Which port ships 0.39 more tons of exports each year than the port at Corpus Christi, Texas?
   A Houston
   (B) NY & NJ
   C New Orleans
   D South Louisiana
4. What is the difference between the imports and exports shipped in and out of Corpus Christi's port each year?
   F 45.04 million tons
   G 44.94 million tons
   (H) 44.96 million tons
   J 44.06 million tons
5. What is the total amount of imports shipped into the nation's 5 busiest ports each year?
   (A) 238.22 million tons
   B 366.47 million tons
   C 128.25 million tons
   D 109.97 million tons
6. What is the total amount of exports shipped out of the nation's 5 busiest ports each year?
   F 366.47 million tons
   (G) 128.25 million tons
   H 109.97 million tons
   J 238.22 million tons

Power Presentations with PowerPoint®

3-3 Lesson Quiz

Find each sum or difference.

1. $8.3 + 2.7$ **11**
2. $9.7 - 4$ **5.7**
3. $22.6 + 8.4$ **31**
4. Evaluate $12.76 - x$ for $x = 8.41$. **4.35**
5. During an ice-skating competition, Dawn received the following scores: 4.8, 5.2, 5.4. What was Dawn's total score? **15.4**

Also available on transparency

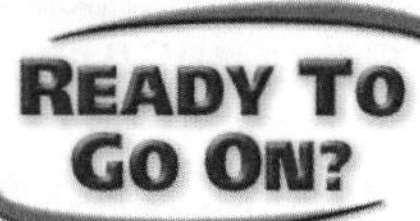

SECTION 3A

Organizer

Objective: Assess students' mastery of concepts and skills in Lessons 3-1 through 3-3.

Resources

 *Assessment Resources*
Section 3A Quiz

Test & Practice Generator
One-Stop Planner®

INTERVENTION

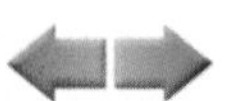

Resources

 *Ready to Go On? Intervention and Enrichment* **Worksheets**

 *Ready to Go On?* **CD-ROM**

 *Ready to Go On?* **Online**

my.hrw.com

CHAPTER 3

SECTION 3A

Quiz for Lessons 3-1 Through 3-3

3-1 Representing, Comparing, and Ordering Decimals

Write each decimal in standard form, expanded form, and words.

1. 4.012 **4 + 0.01 + 0.002; four and twelve thousandths**
2. ten and fifty-four thousandths **10 + 0.05 + 0.004; 10.054**
3. On Monday Jamie ran 3.54 miles. On Wednesday he ran 3.6 miles. On which day did he run farther? **Wednesday**

Order the decimals from least to greatest.

4. 3.406, 30.08, 3.6 **3.406, 3.6, 30.08**
5. 10.10, 10.01, 101.1 **10.01, 10.10, 101.1**
6. 16.782, 16.59, 16.79 **16.59, 16.782, 16.79**
7. 62.0581, 62.148, 62.0741 **62.0581, 62.0741, 62.148**
8. 123.05745, 132.05628, 123.05749 **123.05745, 123.05749, 132.05628**

3-2 Estimating Decimals

9. Matt drove 106.8 miles on Monday, 98.3 miles on Tuesday, and 103.5 miles on Wednesday. About how many miles did he drive in all? **about 300 miles**

Estimate.

10. 8.345 − 0.6051; round to the hundredths **7.74**
11. 16.492 − 2.613; round to the tenths **13.9**
12. 18.79 × 4.68 **100**
13. 71.378 ÷ 8.13 **9**
14. 52.055 × 7.18 **350**

Estimate a range for each sum.

15. 7.42 + 13.87 + 101.2 **from 121 to 123**
16. 1.79 + 3.45 + 7.92 **from 11 to 13.5**

3-3 Adding and Subtracting Decimals

17. Greg's scores at four gymnastic meets were 9.65, 8.758, 9.884, and 9.500. What was his total score for all four meets? **37.792**
18. Mrs. Henry buys groceries each week and uses a spreadsheet to keep track of how much she spends. How much did she spend in all for the month of December? **$263**

Grocery Spending for December				
Week	1	2	3	4
Amount Spent ($)	52.35	77.97	90.10	42.58

19. Sally walked 1.2 miles on Monday, 1.6 miles on Wednesday, and 2.1 miles on Friday. How many miles did she walk in all? **4.9 mi**

Find each sum or difference.

20. 0.47 + 0.03 **0.50**
21. 8 − 0.6 **7.4**
22. 2.2 + 1.8 **4**

Evaluate 8.67 − *s* for each value of *s*.

23. *s* = 3.4 **5.27**
24. *s* = 2.0871 **6.5829**
25. *s* = 7.205 **1.465**

Ready to Go On?

READY TO GO ON? Diagnose and Prescribe

NO INTERVENE

YES ENRICH

Ready to Go On? Intervention	READY TO GO ON? Intervention, Section 3A Worksheets	CD-ROM	Online
Lesson 3-1	3-1 Intervention	Activity 3-1	Diagnose and Prescribe Online
Lesson 3-2	3-2 Intervention	Activity 3-2	
Lesson 3-3	3-3 Intervention	Activity 3-3	

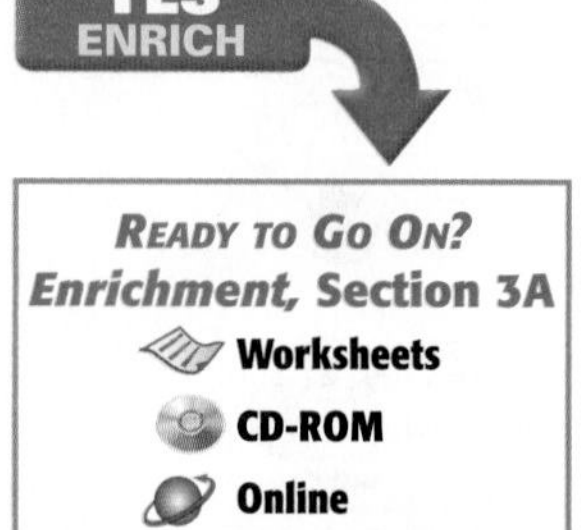

Focus on Problem Solving

Solve

• Write an equation

Read the whole problem before you try to solve it. Sometimes you need to solve the problem in more than one step.

Read the problem. Determine the steps needed to solve the problem.

Brian buys erasers and pens for himself and 4 students in his class. The erasers cost $0.79 each, and the pens cost $2.95 each. What is the total amount that Brian spends on the erasers and pens?

Here is one way to solve the problem.

5 erasers cost	5 pens cost
5 • $0.79	5 • $2.95

(5 • $0.79) + (5 • $2.95)

Read each problem. Decide whether you need more than one step to solve the problem. List the possible steps. Then choose an equation with which to solve the problem.

1. Joan is making some costumes. She cuts 3 pieces of fabric, each 3.5 m long. She has 5 m of fabric left. Which equation can you use to find f, the amount of fabric she had to start with?

   (A) $(3 \cdot 3.5) + 5 = f$
   (B) $3 + 3.5 + 5 = f$
   (C) $(5 \times 3.5) \div 3 = f$
   (D) $5 - (3 \cdot 3.5) = f$

2. Mario buys 4 chairs and a table. He spends $245.99 in all. If each chair costs $38.95, which equation can you use to find T, the cost of the table?

   (F) $4 + \$245.99 + \$38.95 = T$
   (G) $(4 \cdot \$38.95) + \$245.99 = T$
   (H) $\$245.99 - (4 \cdot \$38.95) = T$
   (J) $\$245.99 \div (4 \cdot \$38.95) = T$

3. Mya skis down Ego Bowl three times and down Fantastic twice. Ego Bowl is 5.85 km long, and Fantastic is 8.35 km long. Which equation can you use to estimate d, the distance Mya skis in all?

   (A) $(6 \cdot 3) + (8 \cdot 2) = d$
   (B) $(6 + 8) + (3 + 2) = d$
   (C) $3(6 + 8) = d$
   (D) $(6 \div 3) + (8 \div 2) = d$

Answers

1. A; 15.5 m
2. H; $90.19
3. A; 34 km

Focus on Problem Solving

Organizer

Objective: Focus on writing an equation.

Online Edition

Resources

Chapter 3 Resource Book
Reading Strategies

Problem Solving Process

This page focuses on the third step of the problem-solving process: **Solve**

Discuss

Have students discuss the steps required to solve each problem.

Possible answers:

1. Find the total amount of fabric used. Then add the amount left over to find the amount she had to start.
2. Find the total cost of the four chairs. Then subtract the cost from the total amount spent to find the amount spent on the table.
3. Estimate the total distance skied on each trail. Then add the distances together to estimate the total distance Mya skied.

SECTION 3B

Multiplying and Dividing Decimals

One-Minute Section Planner

Lesson	Materials	MiC and Lab Resources
Lesson 3-4 Scientific Notation • Write large numbers in scientific notation. ☑ CRCT ☑ SAT-10 ☑ ITBS ☐ CTBS ☑ NAEP		***Technology Lab Activities*** 3-4
3-5 Hands-On Lab Explore Decimal Multiplication and Division • Use decimal grids to model multiplication and division of decimals. ☑ CRCT ☑ SAT-10 ☑ ITBS ☐ CTBS ☑ NAEP **Lesson 3-5** Multiplying Decimals • Multiply decimals by whole numbers and by decimals.	Decimal grids or grid paper, colored pencils, transparency grids	**MiC:** ***Expressions and Formulas*** pp. 12–21 **MiC:** ***Fraction Times*** pp. 27–28 **MiC:** ***Reallotment*** pp. 15–17 **MiC:** ***More or Less*** pp. 5–7, 20–23 ***Hands-On Lab Activities*** 3-5
Lesson 3-6 Dividing Decimals by Whole Numbers • Divide decimals by whole numbers. ☑ CRCT ☑ SAT-10 ☑ ITBS ☐ CTBS ☑ NAEP	Graph paper	**MiC:** ***More or Less*** pp. 20–23
Lesson 3-7 Dividing by Decimals • Divide whole numbers and decimals by decimals. ☑ CRCT ☑ SAT-10 ☑ ITBS ☐ CTBS ☑ NAEP	Calculators, index cards	**MiC:** ***Expressions and Formulas*** p. 29 ***Technology Lab Activities*** 3-7
Lesson 3-8 Problem Solving Skill: Interpret the Quotient • Solve problems by interpreting the quotient. ☑ CRCT ☐ SAT-10 ☐ ITBS ☐ CTBS ☑ NAEP		
Lesson 3-9 Solving Decimal Equations • Solve equations involving decimals. ☑ CRCT ☑ SAT-10 ☑ ITBS ☐ CTBS ☑ NAEP		***Hands-On Lab Activities*** 3-9

MK = *Manipulatives Kit*

Mathematics in Context

The units ***Expressions and Formulas, Fraction Times, Reallotment,*** and ***More or Less*** from the *Mathematics in Context* © 2006 series can be used with Section 3B. See Section Planner above for suggestions for integrating *MiC* with *Holt Mathematics*.

Section Overview

Writing Numbers in Scientific Notation — *Lesson 3-4*

Why? Scientific notation is used to express very large or very small numbers.

A number written in scientific notation has two parts that are multiplied.

$$1.2345 \times 10^4$$

The **first part** is a number that is greater than 1 and less than 10.

The **second part** is a power of ten.

Multiplying and Dividing with Decimals — *Lessons 3-5, 3-6, and 3-7*

Why? Multiplying and dividing decimals is used to convert currency.

Multiply the digits. Then place the decimal point by adding the number of decimal places in the factors.

7.13	2 decimal places
× 0.2	+1 decimal place
1.426	3 decimal places

$0.36\overline{)11.2}$ →

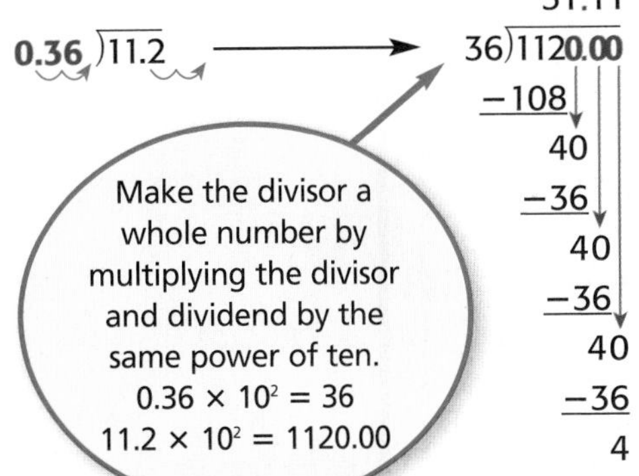

Make the divisor a whole number by multiplying the divisor and dividend by the same power of ten.
0.36 × 10² = 36
11.2 × 10² = 1120.00

$$\begin{array}{r} 31.11 \\ 36\overline{)1120.00} \\ -108 \\ 40 \\ -36 \\ 40 \\ -36 \\ 40 \\ -36 \\ 4 \end{array}$$

Align the decimal point in the quotient.

Interpreting the Quotient — *Lesson 3-8*

When you solve a division problem that has a remainder, you need to decide what the remainder represents.

When the question asks	→	You should
How many whole groups can be made when you divide?	→	Drop the decimal part of the quotient.
How many whole groups are needed to put all items from the dividend into a group?	→	Round the quotient up to the next highest whole number.
What is the exact number when you divide?	→	Use the entire quotient as the answer.

Solving Equations Containing Decimals — *Lesson 3-9*

To solve one-step equations with decimals, apply the rules for computing with decimals when you are isolating the variable.

Equation	Operation	Inverse Operation	Isolate the Variable
$x + 9.7 = 15$	Addition	**Subtraction**	$x = 5.3$
$y - 0.5 = -3.9$	Subtraction	**Addition**	$y = -3.4$
$-6 \cdot n = 2.4$	Multiplication	**Division**	$n = -0.4$
$\frac{a}{1.7} = 3$	Division	**Multiplication**	$a = 5.1$

3-4 Organizer

Pacing: Traditional 1 day
Block $\frac{1}{2}$ day

Objective: Students write large numbers in scientific notation.

GPS **M6N1.g**
Technology Lab
In Technology Lab Activities

Online Edition
Tutorial Videos, Interactivities

Countdown to CRCT Week 5

Power Presentations with PowerPoint®

Warm Up

Multiply.

1. 724×10^2 — 72,400
2. 837×10 — 8,370
3. 632.9×100 — 63,290

Problem of the Day

A rope ladder is hanging from the back of a yacht. At 10:00 A.M., the water reaches the third step on the ladder. If the water rises the height of 2 steps every 2 hours, at what step would the water level be at 5:00 P.M.? Explain. the third, because the boat will rise with the water

Also available on transparency

Math Fact !

For very large and very small numbers, *mega-* indicates 10^6, *giga-* indicates 10^9, *micro-* indicates 10^{-6}, *nano-* indicates 10^{-9}, and *pico-* indicates 10^{-12}.

Georgia Performance Standards

M6N1.g Solve problems involving fractions, decimals, and percents.

M6P4.a Recognize and use connections among mathematical ideas.

M6P4.b Understand how mathematical ideas interconnect and build on one another to produce a coherent whole.

M6P4.c Recognize and apply mathematics in contexts outside of mathematics.

3-4 Scientific Notation

Learn to write large numbers in scientific notation.

Vocabulary
scientific notation

Georgia Performance Standards

M6N1.g Solve problems involving decimals. Also, M6P4.a, M6P4.b, M6P4.c.

Artist Georges Seurat used the technique *pointillism* in his 1884 painting *A Sunday on La Grand Jatte.*

In pointillism, an artist places many small dots close together to create a picture. Seurat's painting is made up of about 3,456,000 dots.

The dots in the painting are as small as $\frac{1}{16}$ inch. It took Seurat about two years to complete the painting.

You can write large numbers such as 3,456,000 as the product of a number and a power of 10. Look for a pattern in the table below.

Number	×	Power of 10	Product	Number of Places the Decimal Point Moves
3.456	×	10	34.56	1
3.456	×	100	345.6	2
3.456	×	1,000	3,456	3
3.456	×	10,000	34,560	4

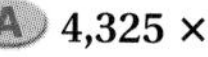

EXAMPLE 1 Multiplying by Powers of Ten

Find each product.

A $4{,}325 \times 1{,}000$

4,325.000 — *There are 3 zeros in 1,000.* *To multiply, move the decimal point 3 places right.*

= 4,325,000 — *Write 3 placeholder zeros.*

B $2.54 \times 10{,}000$

2.5400 — *There are 4 zeros in 10,000.* *To multiply, move the decimal point 4 places right.*

= 25,400 — *Write 2 placeholder zeros.*

Scientific notation is a shorthand method for writing large numbers.

A number written in scientific notation has two numbers that are multiplied.

$$4.123 \times 10^5$$

The first part is a number that is greater than 1 and less than 10. *The second part is a power of 10.*

1 Introduce

Alternate Opener

EXPLORATION

3-4 Scientific Notation

You can use exponents to represent powers of 10.

$10^1 = 10$
$10^2 = 10 \times 10 = 100$
$10^3 = 10 \times 10 \times 10 = 1{,}000$
$10^4 = 10 \times 10 \times 10 \times 10 = 10{,}000$

Find each product.
1. 6.25×10^1 2. 6.25×10^2 3. 6.25×10^3 4. 6.25×10^4

In scientific notation, numbers are written as the product of a power of 10 and a number that is greater than 1 and less than 10.

Number	Scientific Notation
6,250	6.25×10^3
62.50	6.25×10^1
625	6.25×10^2

Write each number in scientific notation by filling in the exponent for the power of 10.

5. $42.5 = 4.25 \times 10^{\square}$
6. $425 = 4.25 \times 10^{\square}$
7. $4250 = 4.25 \times 10^{\square}$
8. $42500 = 4.25 \times 10^{\square}$

Think and Discuss

9. **Explain** why 5.3×10^3 is greater than 1,000.
10. **Explain** how you know that $6.25 \times 10^6 = 6{,}250{,}000$.

Motivate

Write this number on the board: 5,880,000,000,000. Ask if anyone can read the number (5 trillion, 880 billion). Let the students know that this is approximately the number of miles light travels in one year (1 light-year). Tell students that they can write large numbers like these in a form called *scientific notation.*

Explorations and answers are provided in *Alternate Openers: Explorations Transparencies.*

EXAMPLE  **Writing Numbers in Scientific Notation**

Write 8,296,000 in scientific notation.

8,296,000

8,296,000 — *Move the decimal point 6 places left. The power of 10 is 6.*

$8{,}296{,}000 = 8.296 \times 10^6$

You can write a large number written in scientific notation in standard form. Look at the power of 10 and move the decimal point that number of places to the right.

EXAMPLE  **Writing Numbers in Standard Form**

Write 3.2×10^7 in standard form.

3.2×10^7 — *The power of 10 is 7.*

3.2000000 — *Move the decimal point 7 places right. Use zeros as placeholders.*

$3.2 \times 10^7 = 32{,}000{,}000$

EXAMPLE  ***Art Application***

Write the number of dots in Seurat's painting *A Sunday on La Grande Jatte*, 3,456,000, in scientific notation.

3,456,000 — *Move the decimal point left to form a number that is greater than 1 and less than 10.*

3,456,000 — *Multiply that number by a power of ten.*

3.456×10^6 — *The power of 10 is 6, because the decimal point is moved 6 places left.*

The number of dots in Seurat's painting is 3.456×10^6.

Possible answers to *Think and Discuss:*

1. Possible answer: Convert the number written in scientific notation back into standard form.
2. The part before the decimal point is not between 1 and 10. The correct way to write this number is 7.825×10^{10}.

Think and Discuss

1. **Explain** how you can check whether a number is written correctly in scientific notation.
2. **Tell** why 782.5×10^8 is not correctly written in scientific notation.
3. **Tell** the advantages of writing a number in scientific notation over writing it in standard form. Explain any disadvantages.

COMMON ERROR ALERT

Some students may multiply the power of ten by a number between 10 and 100 when trying to write a number in scientific notation. Have them make sure that they use a number between 1 and 10.

Power Presentations with PowerPoint®

Additional Examples

Example 

Find each product.

A. $5{,}892 \times 1{,}000$ 5,892,000

B. $47.75 \times 10{,}000$ 477,500

Example 

Write 6,000,000 in scientific notation. 6×10^6

Example 

Write 6.2174×10^3 in standard form. 6,217.4

Example 

Write the distance to the sun, 93,000,000 miles, in scientific notation. 9.3×10^7

Also available on transparency

Answers to *Think and Discuss*

3. Possible answer: Space and time can be saved by writing very large numbers in scientific notation. Space and time is wasted when scientific notation is used to write a smaller number such as in the tens or hundreds.

2 Teach

Guided Instruction

In this lesson, students learn to write large numbers in scientific notation. First, teach students to express a number that is written in standard form in scientific notation. Then teach students to express a number that is written in scientific notation in standard form.

Communicating Math Be sure students understand that the exponent indicates the number of times the decimal point must be moved and not the number of zeros to be added.

Reaching All Learners

Through Inclusion

Help students understand that writing a number in scientific notation is a two-part process. The first and most critical part is to create a number greater than 1 and less than 10 (i.e., a number that has only one digit to the left of the decimal point). Practice part one several times before proceeding to the next part. The second part is to count the number of places you have to move the decimal point to create the number in part one. The number of moves becomes the exponent of 10 in scientific notation.

3 Close

Summarize

Remind students what scientific notation is and give an example of a large number written in both standard form and scientific notation. Emphasize that a number in scientific notation is composed of a number between 1 and 10 multiplied by powers of ten.

3-4 Exercises

Assignment Guide

If you finished Example 1 assign:
Average 1–3, 11–16, 53–62
Advanced 1–3, 11–16, 53–62

If you finished Example 2 assign:
Average 1–6, 11–22, 36–44, 53–62
Advanced 1–6, 11–22, 40–48, 53–62

If you finished Example 3 assign:
Average 1–9, 11–28, 30–43, 53–62
Advanced 1–9, 11–28, 33–46, 53–62

If you finished Example 4 assign:
Average 1–47, 53–62
Advanced 1–43, 48–62

Homework Quick Check

Quickly check key concepts.
Exercises: 12, 16, 22, 24, 28

Math Background

Various methods have been used over the past 30 years to display numbers written in scientific notation on a calculator. For example, to express a number such as 4.35×10^{16}, most calculators use a notation such as 4.35 E16. The letter *E* signals exponent, with the base of 10 being assumed. Naturally, calculator users not familiar with scientific notation could become confused by such a display.

Georgia Performance Standards

M6P1.b Solve problems that arise in mathematics and in other contexts.

M6P3.c Analyze and evaluate the mathematical thinking and strategies of others.

3-4 Exercises

Georgia Performance Standards
M6P1.b, M6P3.c

go.hrw.com
Homework Help Online
KEYWORD: MR4 3-4
Parent Resources Online
KEYWORD: MR7 Parent

GUIDED PRACTICE

See Example 1 — **Find each product.**

1. $5{,}937 \times 100$ 593,700 **2.** $719.25 \times 1{,}000$ 719,250 **3.** $6.0912 \times 100{,}000$ 609,120

See Example 2 — **Write each number in scientific notation.**

4. 62,000 6.2×10^4 **5.** 500,000 5.0×10^5 **6.** 6,913,000 6.913×10^6

See Example 3 — **Write each number in standard form.**

7. 6.793×10^6 6,793,000 **8.** 1.4×10^4 14,000 **9.** 3.82×10^5 382,000

See Example 4 — **10. Geography** The Atlantic Ocean has a surface area of 31,660,000 square miles. Write the surface area of the Atlantic Ocean in scientific notation. 3.166×10^7 square miles

INDEPENDENT PRACTICE

See Example 1 — **Find each product.**

11. $278 \times 1{,}000$ 278,000 **12.** 74.1×100 741 **13.** $381.8 \times 10{,}000$ 3,818,000

14. $1.97 \times 10{,}000$ 19,700 **15.** $4{,}129 \times 100$ 412,900 **16.** $62.4 \times 1{,}000$ 62,400

See Example 2 — **Write each number in scientific notation.**

17. 90,000 9.0×10^4 **18.** 186,000 1.86×10^5 **19.** 1,607,000 1.607×10^6

20. 240,000 2.4×10^5 **21.** 6,000,000 6.0×10^6 **22.** 16,900,000 1.69×10^7

See Example 3 — **Write each number in standard form.**

23. 3.211×10^5 321,100 **24.** 1.63×10^6 1,630,000 **25.** 7.7×10^3 7,700

26. 2.14×10^4 21,400 **27.** 4.03×10^6 4,030,000 **28.** 8.1164×10^8 811,640,000

See Example 4 — **29. Entertainment** *Star Wars: Episode III—Revenge of the Sith* made $6,200,000 from its opening-night midnight screenings. Write this amount in scientific notation. $\$6.2 \times 10^6$

PRACTICE AND PROBLEM SOLVING

Extra Practice p. 718

Write each number in standard form.

30. 7.21×10^3 7,210 **31.** 1.234×10^5 123,400 **32.** 7.200×10^2 720

33. 2.08×10^5 208,000 **34.** 6.954×10^3 6,954 **35.** 5.43×10^1 54.3

Write each number in scientific notation.

36. 112,050 1.1205×10^5 **37.** 150,000 1.5×10^5 **38.** 4,562 4.562×10^3 **39.** 652 6.52×10^2

40. 1,000 1×10^3 **41.** 65,342 6.5342×10^4 **42.** 95 9.5×10^1 **43.** 28,001 2.8001×10^4

44. Technology In the year 2005, there were about 1 billion computers in the world. Write this number in standard form and scientific notation.

44. 1,000,000,000; 1.0×10^9

RETEACH 3-4

LESSON 3-4 **Reteach**
Scientific Notation

Scientific notation expresses a large number as the product of a number between one and ten and a power of ten.

To write 3,400 in scientific notation, move the decimal point to the left until the number falls between 1 and 10.

3,400 $1 < 3 < 10$, so move the decimal point 3 places to the left.

$3{,}400 = 3.4 \cdot 10^3$ The number of times you move the decimal point left is the power of ten.

Express each number in scientific notation.

1. 175,000 $1.75 \cdot 10^5$	2. 298 $2.98 \cdot 10^2$	3. 5,764 $5.764 \cdot 10^3$	4. 83 $8.3 \cdot 10^1$
5. 40,300 $4.03 \cdot 10^4$	6. 2,000,000 $2 \cdot 10^6$	7. 51,010 $5.101 \cdot 10^4$	8. 190,025 $1.90025 \cdot 10^5$

You can express numbers written in scientific notation in standard form.

The power of ten tells you how many places to move the decimal point to the right.

$3.2 \cdot 10^4 = 32{,}000$ To write $3.2 \cdot 10^4$ in standard form, move the decimal point 4 places to the right.

Write each number in standard form.

9. $5.62 \cdot 10^3$ 5,620	10. $7.238 \cdot 10^2$ 723.8	11. $9.9 \cdot 10^5$ 990,000	12. $6.53 \cdot 10^1$ 65.3
13. $5.36 \cdot 10^4$ 53,600	14. $2.4 \cdot 10^2$ 240	15. $4.35 \cdot 10^3$ 4,350	16. $8 \cdot 10^5$ 800,000
17. $1 \cdot 10^4$ 10,000	18. $2.03 \cdot 10^3$ 2030	19. $1.12 \cdot 10^2$ 112	20. $3.002 \cdot 10^6$ 3,002,000

PRACTICE 3-4

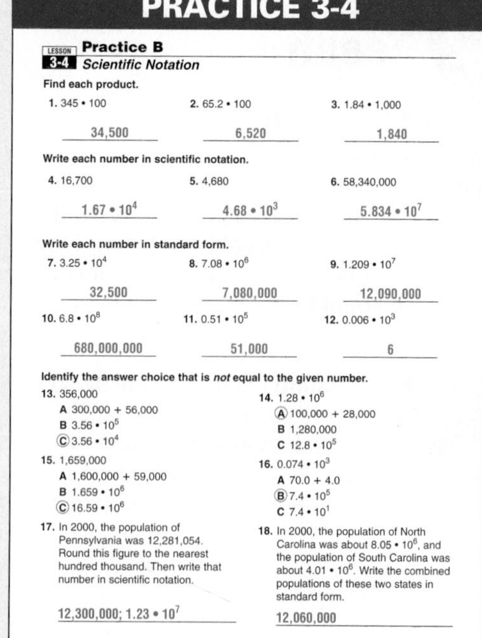

LESSON 3-4 **Practice B**
Scientific Notation

Find each product.

1. $345 \cdot 100$ 34,500	2. $65.2 \cdot 100$ 6,520	3. $1.84 \cdot 1{,}000$ 1,840

Write each number in scientific notation.

4. 16,700 $1.67 \cdot 10^4$	5. 4,680 $4.68 \cdot 10^3$	6. 58,340,000 $5.834 \cdot 10^7$

Write each number in standard form.

7. $3.25 \cdot 10^4$ 32,500	8. $7.08 \cdot 10^6$ 7,080,000	9. $1.209 \cdot 10^7$ 12,090,000
10. $6.8 \cdot 10^8$ 680,000,000	11. $0.51 \cdot 10^5$ 51,000	12. $0.006 \cdot 10^3$ 6

Identify the answer choice that is *not* equal to the given number.

13. 356,000
A $300{,}000 + 56{,}000$
B $3.56 \cdot 10^5$
(C) $3.56 \cdot 10^4$

14. $1.28 \cdot 10^6$
(A) $100{,}000 + 28{,}000$
B 1,280,000
C $12.8 \cdot 10^5$

15. 1,659,000
A $1{,}600{,}000 + 59{,}000$
B $1.659 \cdot 10^6$
(C) $16.59 \cdot 10^6$

16. $0.074 \cdot 10^3$
A $70.0 + 4.0$
(B) $7.4 \cdot 10^5$
C $7.4 \cdot 10^1$

17. In 2000, the population of Pennsylvania was 12,281,054. Round this figure to the nearest hundred thousand. Then write that number in scientific notation.
12,300,000; $1.23 \cdot 10^7$

18. In 2000, the population of North Carolina was about $8.05 \cdot 10^6$, and the population of South Carolina was about $4.01 \cdot 10^6$. Write the combined populations of these two states in standard form.
12,060,000

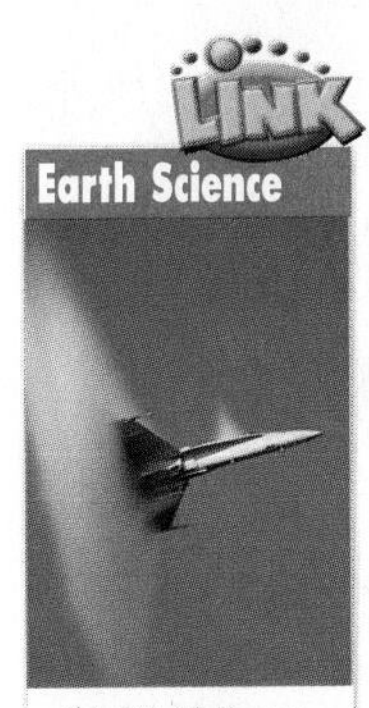

This F/A-18 Hornet makes a vapor cloud by flying at Mach 0.98, just under the speed of sound.

go.hrw.com
Web Extra!
KEYWORD: MR7 Sound

45. **Life Science** Genes carry the codes used for making proteins that are necessary for life. No one knows yet how many human genes there are. Estimates range from 3.8×10^4 to 1.2×10^5. Write a number in standard form that is within this range. **Range 38,000 to 120,000. Possible answer: 100,000**

46. **Earth Science** The speed of light is about 300,000 km/s. The speed of sound in air that has a temperature of 20°C is 1,125 ft/s. Write both of these values in scientific notation. **3.0×10^5 km/s; 1.125×10^3 ft/s**

Use the pictograph for Exercises 47 and 48.

47. Write the capacity of Rungnado Stadium in scientific notation. **$150,000 = 1.5 \times 10^5$**

48. **Estimation** Estimate the capacity of the largest stadium. Write the estimate in scientific notation. **Possible answer: 2.4×10^5**

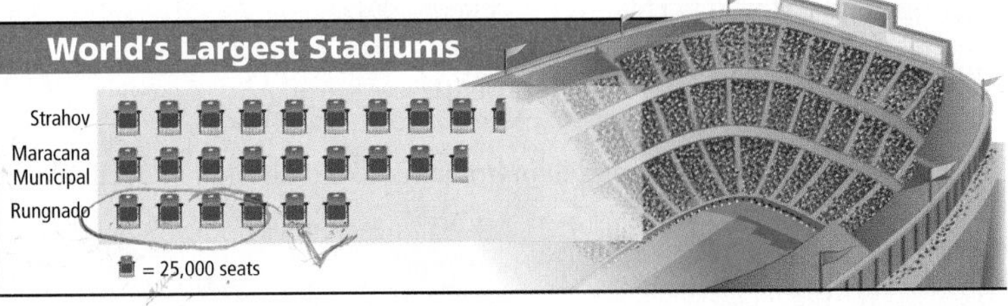

49. **Social Studies** The Library of Congress, in Washington, D.C., is the largest library in the world. It has 24,616,867 books. Round the number of books to the nearest hundred thousand, and write that number in scientific notation. **24,600,000; 2.46×10^7**

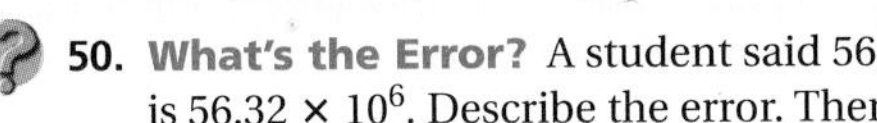

50. **What's the Error?** A student said 56,320,000 written in scientific notation is 56.32×10^6. Describe the error. Then write the correct answer.

51. **Write About It** How does writing numbers in scientific notation make it easier to compare and order the numbers?

52. **Challenge** What is 5.32 written in scientific notation? **5.32×10^0**

CRCT Prep • GPS Support • Spiral Review

53. **Multiple Choice** What is 23,600,000 in scientific notation?

(A) 236×10^5 (B) 23.6×10^6 (C) 2.36×10^6 **(D)** 2.36×10^7

54. **Gridded Response** North Dakota has an area of 7.07×10^4 square miles. What is this number in standard form? **70,700**

Identify the property illustrated by each equation. (Lesson 1-5)

55. $4 + 5 = 5 + 4$ **Commutative Property**
56. $3(4 - 1) = 3(4) - 3(1)$ **Distributive Property**
57. $(9 \times 80) \times 72 = 9 \times (80 \times 72)$ **Associative Property**

Evaluate each expression for $a = 4$, $b = 2.8$, and $c = 0.9$. (Lesson 3-3)

58. $a + b$ **6.8**
59. $b - c$ **1.9**
60. $a + c$ **4.9**
61. $a - b$ **1.2**
62. $a - c$ **3.1**

Ongoing Assessment and Intervention

Diagnose Before the Lesson
3-4 Warm Up, TE p. 124

Monitor During the Lesson
3-4 Know-It Notebook
3-4 Questioning Strategies

Assess After the Lesson
3-4 Lesson Quiz, TE p. 127

Answers

50. Scientific notation uses a decimal number that is at least 1 but less than 10. In scientific notation, the number would be written as 5.632×10^7

51. The powers of 10 can be compared. The number with the lowest power of 10 is the lesser number. If they have the same power of 10, the decimal numbers can be compared.

Test Prep Doctor In Exercise 53, students will need to understand that in scientific notation, there is only one digit to the left of the decimal point. Answers **A** and **B** can be eliminated because they are not in scientific notation.

Journal

Have students write about an imaginary visit to an amusement park. Have them use scientific notation to list their observations in the park (e.g., the number of people who visit the park in one year, the time in seconds a roller-coaster ride lasts, etc.).

CHALLENGE 3-4

LESSON 3-4 Challenge
The Solar System

Write each planet's average distance from the Sun in standard form. Then use the distances to label the planets in our solar system.

	Planet	Average Distance From the Sun (mi)	
		Scientific Notation	Standard Form
1.	Earth	$9.29 \cdot 10^7$	92,900,000
2.	Jupiter	$4.836 \cdot 10^8$	483,600,000
3.	Mars	$1.416 \cdot 10^8$	141,600,000
4.	Mercury	$3.6 \cdot 10^7$	36,000,000
5.	Neptune	$2.794 \cdot 10^9$	2,794,000,000
6.	Pluto	$3.675 \cdot 10^9$	3,675,000,000
7.	Saturn	$8.87 \cdot 10^8$	887,000,000
8.	Uranus	$1.784 \cdot 10^9$	1,784,000,000
9.	Venus	$6.72 \cdot 10^7$	67,200,000

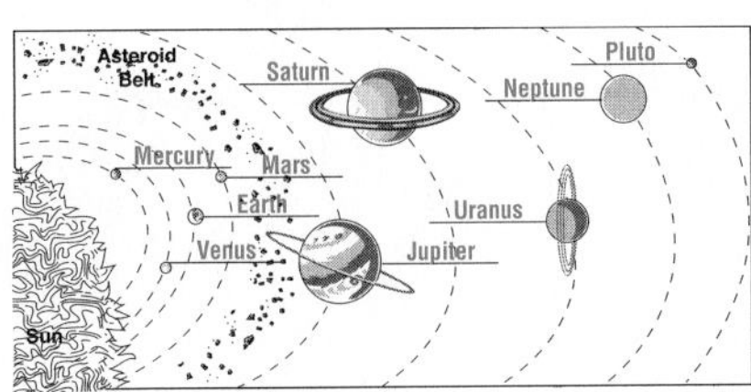

PROBLEM SOLVING 3-4

LESSON 3-4 Problem Solving
Scientific Notation

Write the correct answer.

1. The closest comet to approach Earth was called Lexell. On July 1, 1770, Lexell was observed about 874,200 miles from Earth's surface. Write this distance in scientific notation.
$8.742 \cdot 10^5$

2. Scientists estimate that it would take $1.4 \cdot 10^{10}$ years for light from the edge of our universe to reach Earth. How many years is that written in standard form?
14,000,000,000 years

3. In the United States, about 229,000,000 people speak English. About 18,000,000 people speak English in Canada. Write in scientific notation the total number of English speaking people in the United States and Canada.
$2.47 \cdot 10^8$ people

4. South Africa is the top gold-producing country in the world. Each year it produces $4.688 \cdot 10^8$ tons of gold! Written in standard form, how many tons of gold does South African produce each year?
468,800,000 tons

Circle the letter of the correct answer.

5. About $3.012 \cdot 10^6$ people visit Yellowstone National Park each year. What is that figure written in standard form?
A 30,120,000 people
(B) 3,012,000 people
C 301,200 people
D 30,120 people

6. In 2000, farmers in Iowa grew 1,740,000 bushels of corn. What is this amount written in scientific notation?
F $1.7 \cdot 10^5$
G $1.74 \cdot 10^5$
(H) $1.74 \cdot 10^6$
J $1.74 \cdot 10^7$

7. The temperature at the core of the Sun reaches 27,720,000°F. What is this temperature written in scientific notation?
A $2.7 \cdot 10^7$
B $2.72 \cdot 10^7$
C $2.772 \cdot 10^6$
(D) $2.772 \cdot 10^7$

8. Your body is constantly producing red blood cells—about $1.73 \cdot 10^{11}$ cells a day. How many blood cells is that written in standard form?
F 173,000,000 cells
G 17,300,000,000 cells
(H) 173,000,000,000 cells
J 1,730,000,000,000 cells

Power Presentations with PowerPoint®

3-4 Lesson Quiz

Write each number in scientific notation.

1. 6,300 **6.3×10^3**
2. 70,400,000 **7.04×10^7**

Write each number in standard form.

3. 7.241×10^4 **72,410**
4. 8.2137×10^7 **82,137,000**
5. A Wall Street report indicated that a fast-moving stock had sold 3,295,000 shares. Write this number in scientific notation. **3.295×10^6**

Also available on transparency

Organizer

Use with Lessons 3-5 and 3-6

Pacing:
Traditional $\frac{1}{2}$ day
Block $\frac{1}{4}$ day

Objective: Use decimal grids to model multiplication and division of decimals.

Materials: Decimal grids

Resources

Hands-On Lab Activities
Lab 3-5 Recording Sheet

Teach

Discuss

While using the decimal grids, have students discuss the similarities between multiplying or dividing decimals and multiplying or dividing whole numbers.

Close

Key Concept

The rules for multiplying and dividing decimals are based on the rules for multiplying and dividing whole numbers.

Assessment

Use decimal grids to find each product or quotient.

1. 2 · 0.35

2. 1.2 ÷ 2

Explore Decimal Multiplication and Division

Use with Lessons 3-5 and 3-6

Georgia Performance Standards
M6N1.g, M6P5.a, M6P5.b

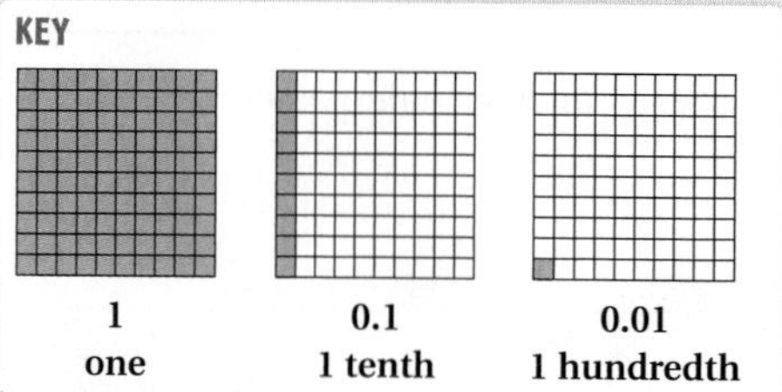

You can use decimal grids to model multiplication and division of decimals.

Activity 1

Use decimal grids to find each product.

a. 3 · 0.32

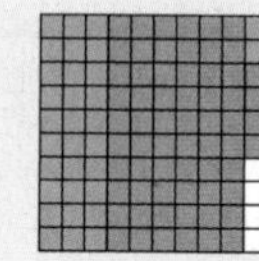

$3 \cdot 0.32 = 0.96$

To represent 3 · 0.32, shade 32 small squares three times.

Use a different color to shade a different group of 32 small squares each time.

There are 96 shaded squares.

b. 0.3 · 0.5

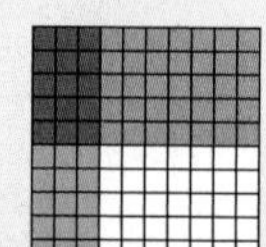

$0.3 \cdot 0.5 = 0.15$

To represent 0.3, shade 3 columns.

To represent 0.5, shade 5 rows in another color.

There are 15 squares in the area where the shading overlaps.

Think and Discuss

1. How is multiplying a decimal by a decimal different from multiplying a decimal by a whole number?
2. Why can you shade 5 rows to represent 0.5?

Try This

Use decimal grids to find each product.

1. 3 · 0.14 **0.42** **2.** 5 · 0.18 **0.90** **3.** 0.7 · 0.5 **0.35** **4.** 0.6 · 0.4 **0.24**

5. 4 · 0.25 **1** **6.** 0.2 · 0.9 **0.18** **7.** 9 · 0.07 **0.63** **8.** 8 · 0.15 **1.2**

Answers to *Assessment.*

1. 0.70

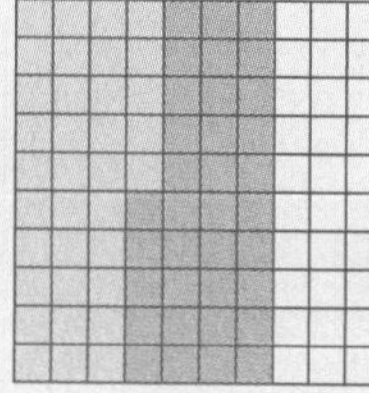

2. 0.60

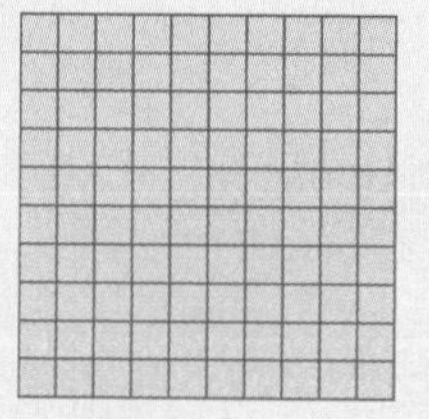

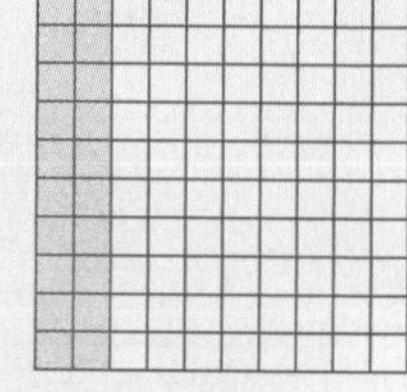

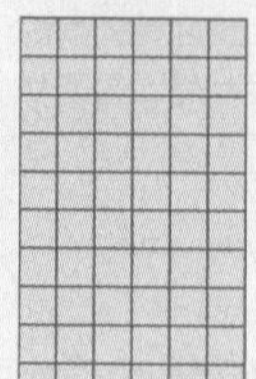

Georgia Performance Standards

M6N1.g Solve problems involving fractions, decimals, and percents.

M6P5.a Create and use representations to organize, record, and communicate mathematical ideas.

M6P5.b Select, apply, and translate among mathematical representations to solve problems.

Activity 2

Use decimal grids to find each quotient.

a. 3.66 ÷ 3

Shade 3 grids and 66 small squares of a fourth grid to represent 3.66.

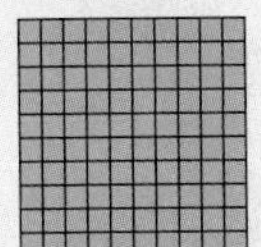
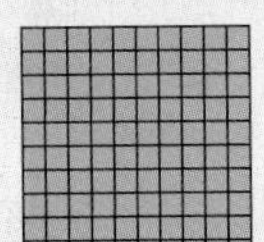
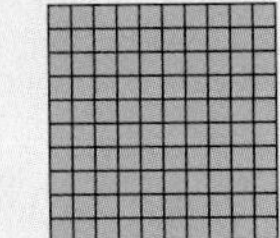
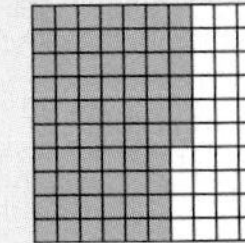

Divide the shaded wholes into 3 equal groups. Use scissors to divide the 66 hundredths into 3 equal groups.

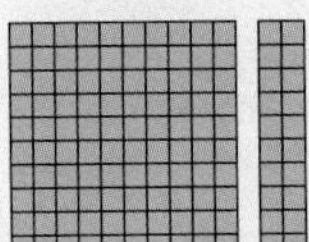
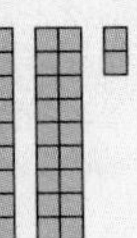
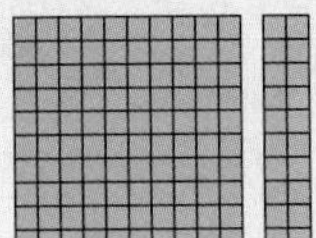
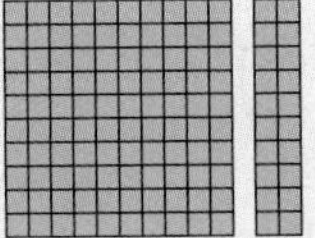

3.66 ÷ 3 = 1.22 *One whole grid and 22 small squares are in each group.*

b. 3.6 ÷ 1.2

Shade 3 grids and 6 columns of a fourth grid to represent 3.6. Cut apart the 6 tenths.

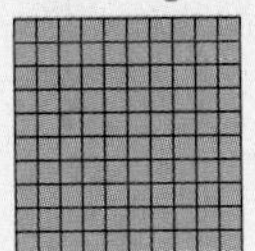
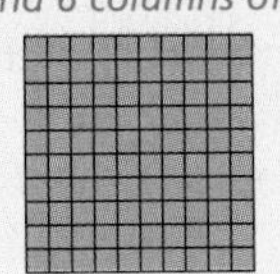
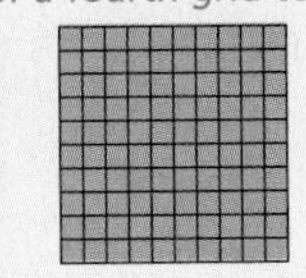
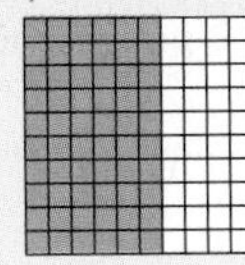

Divide the grids and tenths into equal groups of 1.2.

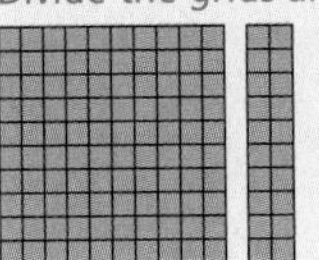
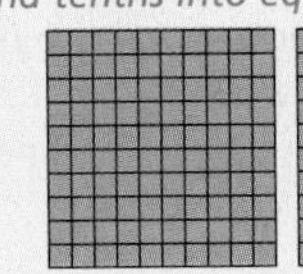
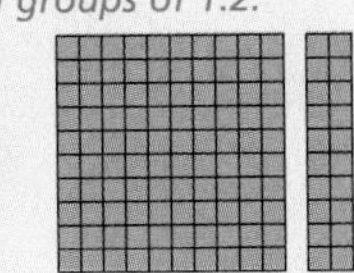

3.6 ÷ 1.2 = 3 *There are 3 equal groups of 1.2.*

Think and Discuss

1. Find 36 ÷ 12. How does this problem and its quotient compare to 3.6 ÷ 1.2?

Try This

Use decimal grids to find each quotient.

1. 4.04 ÷ 4 **1.01**
2. 3.25 ÷ 5 **0.65**
3. 7.8 ÷ 1.3 **6**
4. 5.6 ÷ 0.8 **7**
5. 6.24 ÷ 2 **3.12**
6. 5.1 ÷ 1.7 **3**
7. 5.7 ÷ 3 **1.9**
8. 5.4 ÷ 0.9 **6**

Teacher to Teacher

Teresa Roy
Round Rock, Texas

Have students use grid paper and color in their models of decimals. This makes a great connection when they get ready to do percents. For decimal multiplication, students can use different colors to model the decimals and see the overlapping area as the product. For decimal division, physically cutting the divisions really helps students make the connection.

You can also have students use virtual manipulatives on the computer for modeling decimal multiplication and division.

Activity 1

Answers to *Think and Discuss*

Possible answers:

1. When multiplying a decimal by a whole number n, model the decimal n times on the grid(s). The total number of squares is the product. When multiplying a decimal by a decimal, model one decimal with rows and the other with columns. The number of overlapping squares is the product.
2. Shading 5 rows and shading 5 columns both represent 0.5 because both 5 rows and 5 columns contain 50 squares. 50 squares is 0.50, the same as 0.5.

Answers to *Try This*

1.

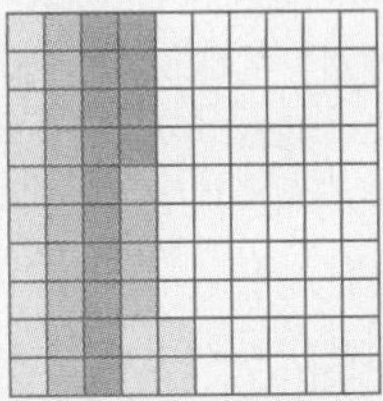

2.

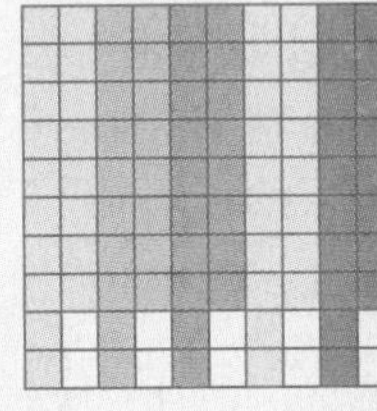

3.

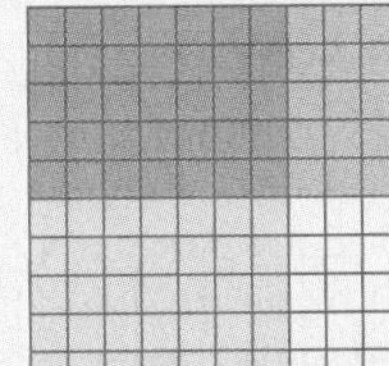

4.

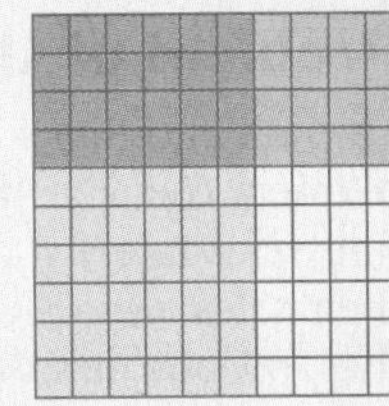

5–8. See p. A2.

Activity 2

Answers to *Think and Discuss*

1. 3; 36 ÷ 12 and 3.6 ÷ 1.2 have the same quotient; for 3.6 ÷ 1.2, you break up 3 whole grids and 6 columns into 3 groups of 1 grid and 2 columns each; for 36 ÷ 12, you break up 36 grids into 3 groups of 12 grids each.

Answers to *Try This*

1–8. Complete answers on pp. A2-A3.

3-5 Organizer

Pacing: Traditional 1 day
Block $\frac{1}{2}$ day

Objective: Students multiply decimals by whole numbers and by decimals.

Online Edition
Tutorial Videos

Countdown to CRCT Week 6

Power Presentations with PowerPoint®

Warm Up

Multiply.

1. 87 × 320 — 27,840
2. 943 × 800 — 754,400
3. 3,806 × 10 — 38,060
4. 1,207 × 100 — 120,700
5. 72 × 196 — 14,112
6. 120 × 523 — 62,760

Problem of the Day

Carmen and Rita sold homemade oatmeal cookies. After 8 days, they had sales totaling $70. Each day, their sales were $0.50 higher than the previous day. What were their sales on the first day? **$7.00**

Also available on transparency

Math Humor

Why is the computer-chip industry like multiplying two decimals between zero and one? It's always making a smaller product.

Georgia Performance Standards

M6A3 Students will evaluate algebraic expressions, including those with exponents, and solve simple one-step equations using each of the four basic operations.

M6N1.g Solve problems involving fractions, decimals, and percents.

M6P1.b Solve problems that arise in mathematics and in other contexts.

M6P5.a Create and use representations to organize, record, and communicate mathematical ideas.

3-5 Multiplying Decimals

Learn to multiply decimals by whole numbers and by decimals.

Georgia Performance Standards

M6A3 Evaluate algebraic expressions. Also, M6N1.g, M6P1.b, M6P5.a.

Because the Moon has less mass than Earth, it has a smaller gravitational effect. An object that weighs 1 pound on Earth weighs only 0.17 pound on the Moon.

You can multiply the weight of an object on Earth by 0.17 to find its weight on the Moon.

Gravity on Earth is about six times the gravity on the surface of the Moon.

You can multiply decimals by first multiplying as you would whole numbers. Then place the decimal point by finding the total of the number of decimal places in the factors. The product will have the same number of decimal places.

EXAMPLE 1  ***Science Application***

A flag weighs 3 pounds on Earth. What is the weight of the flag on the Moon?

3 × 0.17 Multiply 3 by 0.17, since 1 pound on Earth is 0.17 pound on the Moon.

$$\begin{array}{r} 17 \\ \times\ 3 \\ \hline 51 \end{array}$$

Multiply as you would with whole numbers.

Place the decimal point by adding the number of decimal places in the numbers multiplied.

Check

0.17	*2 decimal places*
× 3	*+ 0 decimal places*
0.51	*2 decimal places*

A 3 lb flag on Earth weighs 0.51 lb on the Moon.

EXAMPLE 2 **Multiplying a Decimal by a Decimal**

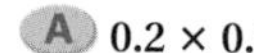

Helpful Hint

You can use a decimal grid to model multiplication of decimals.

Find each product.

A 0.2 × 0.6

Multiply. Then place the decimal point.

0.2	*1 decimal place*
× 0.6	*+ 1 decimal place*
0.12	*2 decimal places*

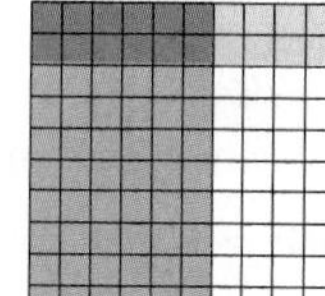

1 Introduce

Alternate Opener

EXPLORATION

 **3-5 Multiplying Decimals**

When you multiply decimals, you can use estimation to help you determine the position of the decimal point in the product.

Estimate each product. Then use a calculator to see how reasonable your estimate is.

		Estimate	Actual
1.	4.235 × 16.9		
2.	0.78 × 568		
3.	56.1 × 23		
4.	15.6 × 2.15		

Estimate each product. Use this estimate to decide where to place a decimal point in the answer. Check with your calculator.

5. 70.5 × 4.4 = 3 1 0 2
6. 0.75 × 692 = 5 1 9 0
7. 56 × 3.125 = 1 7 5 0
8. 45.6 × 2.15 = 9 8 0 4
9. 4.17 × 1.2 = 5 0 0 4
10. 125.2 × 7.4 = 9 2 6 4 8

Think and Discuss

11. **Discuss** your strategies for estimating in numbers 1–4.
12. **Explain** how you know where to place the decimal point in a product.

Motivate

Have students give examples of how to use the multiplication algorithm to multiply 3-digit numbers by 2-digit numbers and 4-digit numbers by 1-digit numbers. Explain that the algorithm for multiplying decimals is the same; however, students must make sure that the decimal point is placed in the product correctly.

Explorations and answers are provided in *Alternate Openers: Explorations Transparencies.*

John Young, a graduate of Georgia Tech, was the commander of the first space shuttle mission in 1981.

Find each product.

B 3.25 × 4.8

$3 \times 5 = 15$ — *Estimate the product. Round each factor to the nearest whole number.*

Multiply. Then place the decimal point.

$$\begin{array}{r} 3.25 \\ \times\ 4.8 \\ \hline 2600 \\ 13000 \\ \hline 15.600 \end{array}$$

2 decimal places
+ 1 decimal place
3 decimal places

15.600 is close to the estimate of 15. The answer is reasonable.

C 0.05 × 0.9

$0.05 \times 1 = 0.05$ — *Estimate the product. 0.9 is close to 1.*

Multiply. Then place the decimal point.

$$\begin{array}{r} 0.05 \\ \times\ 0.9 \\ \hline 0.045 \end{array}$$

2 decimal places
+ 1 decimal place
3 decimal places; use a placeholder zero.

0.045 is close to the estimate of 0.05. The answer is reasonable.

EXAMPLE 3 Evaluating Decimal Expressions

Remember!
These notations all mean multiply 3 times *x*.
$3 \cdot x$ $3x$ $3(x)$

Evaluate 3*x* for each value of *x*.

A $x = 4.047$

$3x = 3(4.047)$ — *Substitute 4.047 for x.*

$$\begin{array}{r} 4.047 \\ \times\ \ \ 3 \\ \hline 12.141 \end{array}$$

3 decimal places
+ 0 decimal places
3 decimal places

B $x = 2.95$

$3x = 3(2.95)$ — *Substitute 2.95 for x.*

$$\begin{array}{r} 2.95 \\ \times\ \ 3 \\ \hline 8.85 \end{array}$$

2 decimal places
+ 0 decimal places
2 decimal places

Think and Discuss

GPS M6P3.b

1. **Tell** how many decimal places are in the product of 235.2 and 0.24.
2. **Tell** which is greater, 4 × 0.6 or 4 × 0.006.
3. **Describe** how the products of 0.3 × 0.5 and 3 × 5 are similar. How are they different?

Power Presentations with PowerPoint®

Additional Examples

Example 1

Something that weighs 1 lb on Earth weighs 0.17 lb on the Moon. How much would a 4 lb dumbbell weigh on the Moon? **0.68 lb**

Example 2

Find each product.

A. 0.3 × 0.4 **0.12**
B. 0.07 × 0.8 **0.056**
C. 1.34 × 2.5 **3.350**

Example 3

Evaluate 5*x* for each value of *x*.

A. $x = 3.062$ **15.310**
B. $x = 4.79$ **23.95**

Also available on transparency

Answers to *Think and Discuss*

1. 3 decimal places (to the thousandths place)
2. 4 × 0.6 is greater than 4 × 0.006.
3. Possible answer: Both have the number 15 in their product; the product of 3 × 5 is 15, and the product of 0.3 × 0.5 is 0.15.

2 Teach

Guided Instruction

In this lesson, students learn to multiply decimals by whole numbers and by decimals. First show students how repeated addition of a decimal is related to the multiplication of that decimal by a whole number. Then teach students to multiply a decimal by a decimal. Next have them evaluate multiplication expressions for given values of *x*.

Number Sense In working with positive numbers, make sure students understand that multiplication by a number less than one gives a product less than the other factor (e.g., 0.8 × 15 = 12 and 12 < 15).

Reaching All Learners

Through Cooperative Learning

Have students work in groups to identify the expressions in the list that have a product of 0.48.

0.2 × 2.4 ✓	0.3 × 1.6 ✓
0.2 × 0.24	3 × 0.16 ✓
2 × 2.4	3 × 1.6
2 × 0.24 ✓	0.3 × 0.16
0.4 × 1.2 ✓	0.6 × 0.8 ✓
0.4 × 0.12	6 × 0.8
4 × 1.2	8 × 0.06 ✓
4 × 0.12 ✓	8 × 0.6

3 Close

Summarize

Outline the steps to follow when multiplying decimals. Emphasize the fact that the algorithm for multiplying decimals is the same as that for multiplying whole numbers except that the placement of the decimal in the product is determined by the total number of digits behind the decimal points in both factors.

3-5 Exercises

Assignment Guide

If you finished Example 1 assign:
Average 1–2, 11–12, 49, 55–65
Advanced 1–2, 11–12, 51, 55–65

If you finished Example 2 assign:
Average 1–6, 11–20, 29–42, 49–50, 55–65
Advanced 1–6, 11–20, 29–42, 51–52, 55–65

If you finished Example 3 assign:
Average 1–51, 55–65
Advanced 1–48, 52–65

Homework Quick Check

Quickly check key concepts.
Exercises: 12, 14, 18, 24, 36, 44

Math Background

The shifting of the decimal point when multiplying decimals can be justified by considering the following example:

$$5.42 \times 1.6$$

$$\frac{542}{100} \times \frac{16}{10} = \frac{8{,}672}{1{,}000}$$

$$= 8.672$$

Georgia Performance Standards

M6P3.c Analyze and evaluate the mathematical thinking and strategies of others.

M6P4.c Recognize and apply mathematics in contexts outside of mathematics.

3-5 Exercises

M6P3.c, M6P4.c

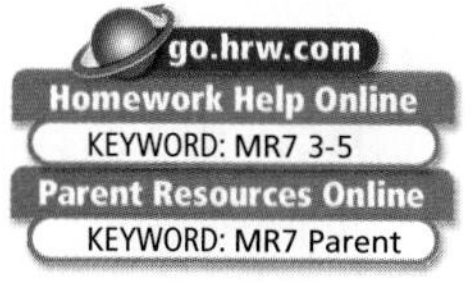

GUIDED PRACTICE

See Example 1

1. Each can of cat food costs \$0.28. How much will 6 cans of cat food cost? **\$1.68**
2. Jorge buys 8 baseballs for \$9.29 each. How much does he spend in all? **\$74.32**

See Example 2

Find each product.

3. 0.6×0.4 **0.24**
4. 0.008×0.5 **0.0040**
5. 3.0×0.07 **0.21**
6. 0.12×0.6 **0.072**

See Example 3

Evaluate $5x$ for each value of x.

7. $x = 3.304$ **16.52**
8. $x = 4.58$ **22.90**
9. $x = 7.126$ **35.63**
10. $x = 1.9$ **9.5**

INDEPENDENT PRACTICE

See Example 1

11. Gwenyth walks her dog each morning. If she walks 0.37 kilometers each morning, how many kilometers will she have walked in 7 days? **2.59 km**
12. **Consumer Math** Apples are on sale for \$0.49 per pound. What is the price for 4 pounds of apples? **\$1.96**

See Example 2

Find each product.

13. 0.9×0.03 **0.027**
14. 4.5×0.5 **2.25**
15. 0.31×0.7 **0.217**
16. 1.6×0.08 **0.128**
17. 0.007×0.06 **0.00042**
18. 0.04×3.0 **0.12**
19. 2.0×0.006 **0.012**
20. 0.005×0.003 **0.000015**

See Example 3

Evaluate $7x$ for each value of x.

21. $x = 1.903$ **13.321**
22. $x = 2.461$ **17.227**
23. $x = 3.72$ **26.04**
24. $x = 4.05$ **28.35**
25. $x = 0.164$ **1.148**
26. $x = 5.89$ **41.23**
27. $x = 0.3702$ **2.5914**
28. $x = 1.82$ **12.74**

PRACTICE AND PROBLEM SOLVING

Extra Practice p. 719

Multiply.

29. 0.3×0.03 **0.009**
30. 1.4×0.21 **0.294**
31. 0.06×1.02 **0.0612**
32. 8.2×4.1 **33.62**
33. 12.6×2.1 **26.46**
34. 3.04×0.6 **1.824**
35. 0.66×2.52 **1.6632**
36. 3.08×0.7 **2.156**
37. $0.2 \times 0.94 \times 1.3$ **0.2444**
38. $1.54 \times 3.05 \times 2.6$ **12.2122**
39. $1.98 \times 0.4 \times 5.2$ **4.1184**
40. $1.7 \times 2.41 \times 0.5$ **2.0485**
41. $2.5 \times 1.52 \times 3.7$ **14.06**
42. $6.5 \times 0.15 \times 3.8$ **3.705**

Evaluate.

43. $6n$ for $n = 6.23$ **37.38**
44. $5t + 0.462$ for $t = 3.04$ **15.662**
45. $8^2 - 2b$ for $b = 0.95$ **62.1**
46. $4^3 + 5c$ for $c = 1.9$ **73.5**
47. $3h - 15 + h$ for $h = 5.2$ **5.8**
48. $5^2 + 6j + j$ for $j = 0.27$ **26.89**

RETEACH 3-5

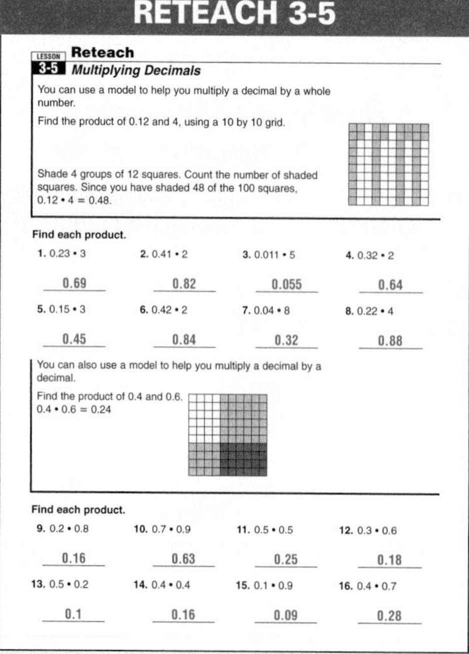

LESSON 3-5 **Reteach**
Multiplying Decimals

You can use a model to help you multiply a decimal by a whole number.

Find the product of 0.12 and 4, using a 10 by 10 grid.

Shade 4 groups of 12 squares. Count the number of shaded squares. Since you have shaded 48 of the 100 squares, 0.12 • 4 = 0.48.

Find each product.

1. 0.23 • 3 **0.69**	2. 0.41 • 2 **0.82**	3. 0.011 • 5 **0.055**	4. 0.32 • 2 **0.64**
5. 0.15 • 3 **0.45**	6. 0.42 • 2 **0.84**	7. 0.04 • 8 **0.32**	8. 0.22 • 4 **0.88**

You can also use a model to help you multiply a decimal by a decimal.

Find the product of 0.4 and 0.6.
0.4 • 0.6 = 0.24

Find each product.

9. 0.2 • 0.8 **0.16**	10. 0.7 • 0.9 **0.63**	11. 0.5 • 0.5 **0.25**	12. 0.3 • 0.6 **0.18**
13. 0.5 • 0.2 **0.1**	14. 0.4 • 0.4 **0.16**	15. 0.1 • 0.9 **0.09**	16. 0.4 • 0.7 **0.28**

PRACTICE 3-5

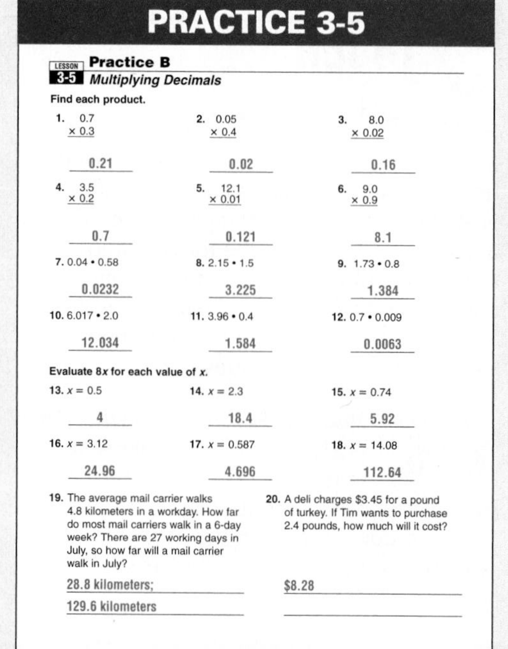

LESSON 3-5 **Practice B**
Multiplying Decimals

Find each product.

1. 0.7 × 0.3 **0.21**	2. 0.05 × 0.4 **0.02**	3. 8.0 × 0.02 **0.16**
4. 3.5 × 0.2 **0.7**	5. 12.1 × 0.01 **0.121**	6. 9.0 × 0.9 **8.1**
7. 0.04 • 0.58 **0.0232**	8. 2.15 • 1.5 **3.225**	9. 1.73 • 0.8 **1.384**
10. 6.017 • 2.0 **12.034**	11. 3.96 • 0.4 **1.584**	12. 0.7 • 0.009 **0.0063**

Evaluate 8*x* for each value of *x*.

13. *x* = 0.5 **4**	14. *x* = 2.3 **18.4**	15. *x* = 0.74 **5.92**
16. *x* = 3.12 **24.96**	17. *x* = 0.587 **4.696**	18. *x* = 14.08 **112.64**

19. The average mail carrier walks 4.8 kilometers in a workday. How far do most mail carriers walk in a 6-day week? There are 27 working days in July, so how far will a mail carrier walk in July? **28.8 kilometers; 129.6 kilometers**

20. A deli charges \$3.45 for a pound of turkey. If Tim wants to purchase 2.4 pounds, how much will it cost? **\$8.28**

Physical Science LINK

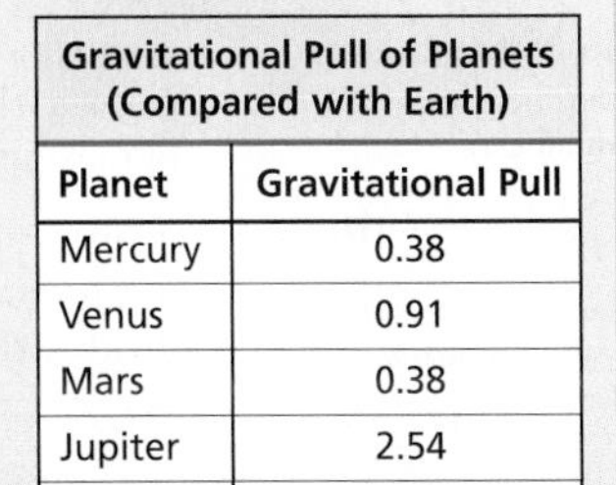

Saturn is the second-largest planet in the solar system. Saturn is covered by thick clouds. Saturn's density is very low. Suppose you weigh 180 pounds on Earth. If you were able to stand on Saturn, you would weigh only 165 pounds. To find the weight of an object on another planet, multiply its weight on Earth by the gravitational pull listed in the table.

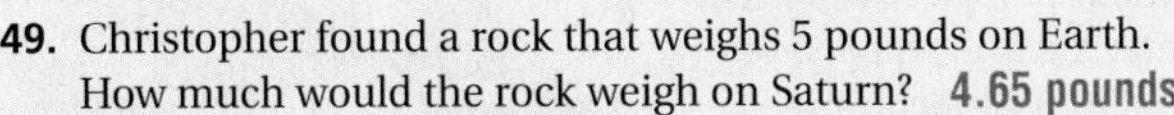

Gravitational Pull of Planets (Compared with Earth)	
Planet	**Gravitational Pull**
Mercury	0.38
Venus	0.91
Mars	0.38
Jupiter	2.54
Saturn	0.93
Neptune	1.2

49. Christopher found a rock that weighs 5 pounds on Earth. How much would the rock weigh on Saturn? **4.65 pounds**

50. On which two planets would the weight of an object be the same? **Mercury and Mars**

51. **Multi-Step** An object weighs 9 pounds on Earth. How much more would this object weigh on Neptune than on Mars? **7.38 lb**

52. **Write a Problem** Use the data in the table to write a word problem that can be answered by evaluating an expression with multiplication. Solve your problem.

53. **What's the Error?** A student said that his new baby brother, who weighs 10 pounds, would weigh 120 pounds on Neptune. What is the error? Write the correct answer.

54. **Challenge** An object weighs between 2.79 lb and 5.58 lb on Saturn. Give a range for the object's weight on Earth.

Galileo Galilei was the first person to look at Saturn through a telescope. He thought there were groups of stars on each side of the planet, but it was later determined that he had seen Saturn's rings.

go.hrw.com
Web Extra!
KEYWORD: MR7 Saturn

Possible answer: $2.79 \div 0.93 = 3$, and $5.58 \div 0.93 = 6$; the object must weigh between 3 lb and 6 lb.

53. Possible answer: The student forgot to place the decimal point in the answer. It should be 12 lb.

CRCT Prep • GPS Support • Spiral Review

55. **Multiple Choice** Max uses 1.6 liters of gasoline each hour mowing lawns. How much gas does he use in 5.8 hours?

Ⓐ 7.4 liters (B) 9.28 liters (circled) Ⓒ 92.8 liters Ⓓ 928 liters

56. **Multiple Choice** What is the value of $5x$ when $x = 3.2$?

(F) 16 (circled) Ⓖ 1.6 Ⓗ 0.16 Ⓙ 8.2

Solve each equation. (Lesson 2-8)

57. $\frac{x}{8} = 4$ **$x = 32$**
58. $\frac{y}{12} = 5$ **$y = 60$**
59. $3 = \frac{t}{17}$ **$t = 51$**
60. $2 = \frac{s}{21}$ **$s = 42$**

Write each decimal in expanded form. (Lesson 3-1)

61. 1.23 **1 + 0.2 + 0.03**
62. 0.45 **0.4 + 0.05**
63. 26.07 **20 + 6 + 0.07**
64. 116.2 **100 + 10 + 6 + 0.2**
65. 80.002 **80 + 0.002**

CHALLENGE 3-5

LESSON 3-5 Challenge
Decimal Growth

Use the growth rate for each plant below to find how much it will grow in 1 week.

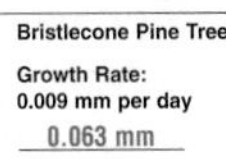

Eucalyptus Tree	Bristlecone Pine Tree	Trumpet Tree
Growth Rate: 2.5 cm per day	Growth Rate: 0.009 mm per day	Growth Rate: 0.28 in. per day
17.5 cm	**0.063 mm**	**1.96 in**

Use the growth rate for each plant below to find how much it will grow in 0.25 day.

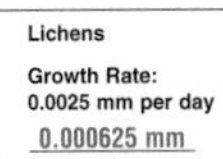
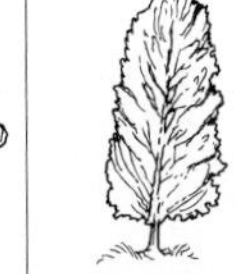

Oak Tree	Lichens	Poplar Tree
Growth Rate: 1.4 mm per day	Growth Rate: 0.0025 mm per day	Growth Rate: 0.118 in. per day
0.35 mm	**0.000625 mm**	**0.0295 in.**

PROBLEM SOLVING 3-5

LESSON 3-5 Problem Solving
Multiplying Decimals

Use the table to answer the questions.

United States Minimum Wage

Year	Hourly Rate
1940	$0.30
1950	$0.75
1960	$1.00
1970	$1.60
1980	$3.10
1990	$3.80
2000	$5.15

1. At the minimum wage, how much did a person earn for a 40-hour workweek in 1950? **$30.00**
2. At the minimum wage, how much did a person earn for working 25 hours in 1970? **$40.00**
3. If you had a minimum-wage job in 1990, and worked 15 hours a week, how much would you have earned each week? **$57.00**
4. About how many times higher was the minimum wage in 1960 than in 1940? **about 3 times**

Circle the letter for the correct answer.

5. Ted's grandfather had a minimum-wage job in 1940. He worked 40 hours a week for the entire year. How much did Ted's grandfather earn in 1940?
   A $12.00
   (B) $624.00 (circled)
   C $642.00
   D $6,240.00
6. Marci's mother had a minimum-wage job in 1980. She worked 12 hours a week. How much did Marci's mother earn each week?
   F $3.72
   G $37.00
   H $37.10
   (J) $37.20 (circled)
7. Having one dollar in 1960 is equivalent to having $5.82 today. If you worked 40 hours a week in 1960 at minimum wage, how much would your weekly earnings be worth today?
   A $40.00
   B $5.82
   (C) $232.80 (circled)
   D $2,328.00
8. In 2000, Cindy had a part-time job at a florist, where she earned minimum wage. She worked 18 hours each week for the whole year. How much did she earn from this job in 2000?
   F $927.00
   (G) $4,820.40 (circled)
   H $10,712.00
   J $2,142.40

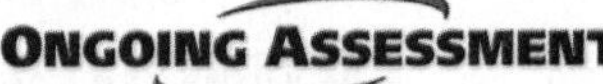

Ongoing Assessment and Intervention

Diagnose ***Before*** **the Lesson**
3-5 Warm Up, TE p. 130

Monitor ***During*** **the Lesson**
3-5 Know-It Notebook
3-5 Questioning Strategies

Assess ***After*** **the Lesson**
3-5 Lesson Quiz, TE p. 133

Interdisciplinary LINK

Physical Science

Exercises 49–54 involve using information about the gravitational pull on various planets. The force of gravity is studied in middle school physical science programs such as *Holt Science & Technology*.

Answers

52. Possible answer: If an object weighs 100 pounds on Earth, how much will that object weigh on Jupiter? 2.54 × 100 = 254 pounds

Test Prep Doctor In Exercise 56, remind students that an estimate can help to eliminate wrong answers. A good estimate is 5 • 3, or 15. This estimate eliminates choices **G, H,** and **J.**

Journal

Have students write about situations in a grocery store in which decimal numbers are multiplied by whole numbers or decimal numbers.

Power Presentations with PowerPoint®

3-5 Lesson Quiz

Find each product.

1. 0.8 × 0.07 **0.056**
2. 0.006 × 0.07 **0.00042**

Evaluate $8x$ for each value of x.

3. $x = 2.705$ **21.64**
4. $x = 0.804$ **6.432**
5. "Pick your own" peaches sell for $0.95 per pound. You picked 92 pounds of peaches. How much were you charged? **$87.40**

Also available on transparency

3-6 Organizer

Pacing: Traditional 1 day
Block $\frac{1}{2}$ day

Objective: Students divide decimals by whole numbers.

Online Edition
Tutorial Videos

Countdown to CRCT Week 6

Power Presentations with PowerPoint®

Warm Up

Divide.

1. 56,000 ÷ 8 7,000
2. 5,219 ÷ 17 307
3. 9,180 ÷ 12 765

Problem of the Day

In his pocket, Bill has $0.77 made up of 10 coins. What are the coins?
1 quarter, 3 dimes, 4 nickels, and 2 pennies

Also available on transparency

Math Humor

Why is the student holding his math book to his ears and dancing? The teacher told him the book contained some good algorithms.

3-6 Dividing Decimals by Whole Numbers

Learn to divide decimals by whole numbers.

Georgia Performance Standards

M6A3 Evaluate algebraic expressions. Also, M6N1.g, M6P1.b.

Ethan and two of his friends are going to share equally the cost of making a sculpture for the art fair.

To find how much each person should pay for the materials, you will need to divide a decimal by a whole number.

EXAMPLE 1 Dividing a Decimal by a Whole Number

Remember!

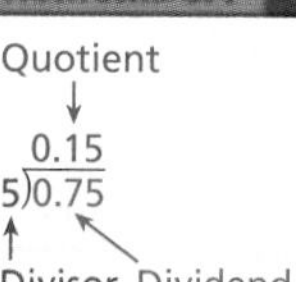

Find each quotient.

A 0.75 ÷ 5

```
   0.15
5)0.75
 − 5
   25
 − 25
    0
```

Place a decimal point in the quotient directly above the decimal point in the dividend.

Divide as you would with whole numbers.

B 2.52 ÷ 3

```
   0.84
3)2.52
 − 2 4
    12
  − 12
     0
```

Place a decimal point in the quotient directly above the decimal point in the dividend.

Divide as you would with whole numbers.

EXAMPLE 2 Evaluating Decimal Expressions

Evaluate 0.435 ÷ x for each given value of x.

A $x = 3$

0.435 ÷ x

0.435 ÷ 3 *Substitute 3 for x.*

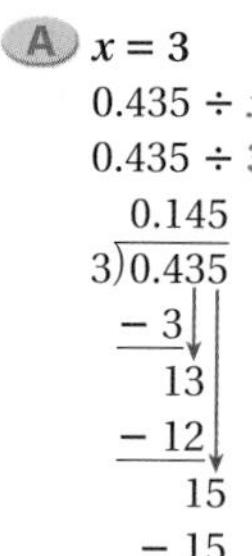

```
   0.145
3)0.435
 − 3
   13
 − 12
    15
  − 15
     0
```

Divide as you would with whole numbers.

B $x = 15$

0.435 ÷ x

0.435 ÷ 15 *Substitute 15 for x.*

```
    0.029
15)0.435
  − 0
    43
  − 30
    135
  −135
      0
```

Sometimes you need to use a zero as a placeholder.

15 > 4, so place a zero in the quotient and divide 15 into 43.

Georgia Performance Standards

M6A3 Students will evaluate algebraic expressions, including those with exponents, and solve simple one-step equations using each of the four basic operations.

M6N1.g Solve problems involving fractions, decimals, and percents.

M6P1.b Solve problems that arise in mathematics and in other contexts.

1 Introduce

Alternate Opener

EXPLORATION

3-6 Dividing Decimals by Whole Numbers

1. Four friends go on a vacation together. They decide to share all expenses evenly. Estimate the cost of each item per person, and then compute the actual cost with a calculator.

Item	Total Cost	Estimated Cost per Person	Actual Cost per Person
Cab fare	$50.00		
Pizza	$13.92		
Movie rental	$10.00		
Dinner	$76.20		
Boat ride	$35.96		

Estimate each quotient. Use this estimate to decide where to place a decimal point in the answer. Check with your calculator.

2. 125.2 ÷ 25 = 5 0 0 8
3. 40 ÷ 16 = 2 5
4. 7.5 ÷ 5 = 1 5
5. 75 ÷ 12 = 6 2 5

Think and Discuss

6. **Discuss** your strategies for estimating in number 1.
7. **Explain** how you know where to place the decimal point in a quotient.

2 Teach

Guided Instruction

In this lesson, students learn to divide decimals by whole numbers. First teach them to divide a decimal by a whole number using the division algorithm, and have them check the answer. Then teach them to evaluate division expressions for given whole-number values of x. Finally, explain how to apply division in a consumer application.

Explorations and answers are provided in *Alternate Openers: Explorations Transparencies.*

EXAMPLE 3 Consumer Math Application

Possible answers to *Think and Discuss:*

1. Place the decimal point in the quotient directly above the decimal point in the dividend.

Remember!

Multiplication can "undo" division. To check your answer to a division problem, multiply the divisor by the quotient.

Ethan and two of his friends are making a papier-mâché sculpture using balloons, strips of paper, and paint. The materials cost $11.61. If they share the cost equally, how much should each person pay?

$11.61 should be divided into three equal groups.
Divide $11.61 by 3.

```
   3.87      Place a decimal point in the quotient directly
 3)11.61     above the decimal point in the dividend.
  -9
   26        Divide as you would with whole numbers.
  -24
    21
   -21
     0
```

Check

3.87 × 3 = 11.61

Each person should pay $3.87.

2. Possible answer: Multiplication can "undo" division. The product of the divisor and the quotient should be the dividend.

Think and Discuss

1. **Tell** how you know where to place the decimal point in the quotient.
2. **Explain** why you can use multiplication to check your answer to a division problem.

Power Presentations with PowerPoint®

Additional Examples

Example 1 

Find each quotient.

A. 0.84 ÷ 3 0.28 **B.** 3.56 ÷ 4 0.89

Example 2 

Evaluate 0.936 ÷ *x* for each given value of *x*.

A. $x = 9$ 0.104 **B.** $x = 18$ 0.052

Example 3 

Jodi and three of her friends are making a tile design. The materials cost $10.12. If they share the cost equally, how much should each person pay? $2.53

Also available on transparency

3-6 Exercises

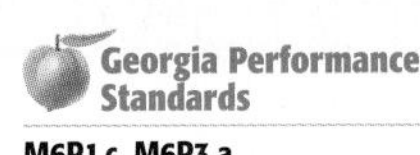

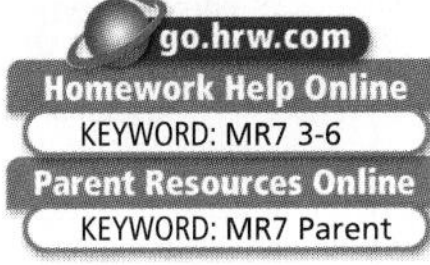

GUIDED PRACTICE

See Example 1 Find each quotient.

1. 1.38 ÷ 6 0.23
2. 0.96 ÷ 8 0.12
3. 1.75 ÷ 5 0.35
4. 0.72 ÷ 4 0.18

See Example 2 Evaluate 0.312 ÷ *x* for each given value of *x*.

5. $x = 4$ 0.078
6. $x = 6$ 0.052
7. $x = 3$ 0.104
8. $x = 12$ 0.026

See Example 3

9. **Consumer Math** Mr. Richards purchased 8 T-shirts for the volleyball team. The total cost of the T-shirts was $70.56. How much did each shirt cost? $8.82

3-6 Exercises

Assignment Guide

If you finished Example 1 assign:
Average 1–4, 10–13, 31–39
Advanced 1–4, 10–13, 31–39

If you finished Example 2 assign:
Average 1–8, 10–17, 22–23, 31–39
Advanced 1–8, 10–17, 24–25, 31–39

If you finished Example 3 assign:
Average 1–27, 31–39
Advanced 1–25, 28–39

Homework Quick Check

Quickly check key concepts.
Exercises: 12, 16, 18, 20, 22

Reaching All Learners

Through Visual Cues

If students are having difficulty keeping a division problem organized, encourage them to use graph paper (Teacher Tools in Lesson Transparencies) for setting up and working their division problems. Have them write each digit in a separate square to maintain the alignment of columns and rows.

3 Close

Summarize

Explain that the steps to follow when dividing a decimal by a whole number are the same steps involved in division of whole numbers except for the placement of the decimal in the quotient. Remind and encourage the students to check their solutions.

Georgia Performance Standards

M6P1.c Apply and adapt a variety of appropriate strategies to solve problems.

M6P3.a Organize and consolidate their mathematical thinking through communication.

Ongoing Assessment and Intervention

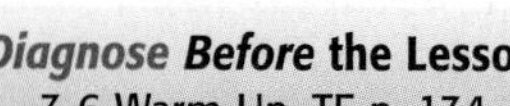

***Diagnose Before* the Lesson**
3-6 Warm Up, TE p. 134

***Monitor During* the Lesson**
3-6 Know-It Notebook
3-6 Questioning Strategies

***Assess After* the Lesson**
3-6 Lesson Quiz, TE p. 136

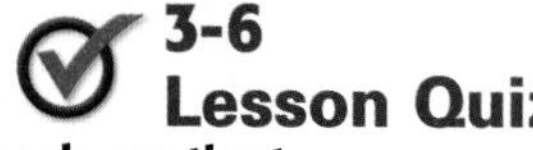

Answers

27. Possible answer: Round 5.58 to 6; 6 ÷ 6 = 1, so the answer 0.93 is reasonable.

Power Presentations with PowerPoint®

3-6 Lesson Quiz

Find each quotient.

1. 3.12 ÷ 8 0.39

2. 5.68 ÷ 8 0.71

Evaluate the expression 1.25 ÷ *x* for the given value of *x*.

3. $x = 5$ 0.25

4. $x = 25$ 0.05

5. The tennis team is having 3 tennis rackets restrung. The total cost is $54.75. What is the average cost per racket? $18.25

Also available on transparency

Independent Practice

See Example 1 **Find each quotient.**

10. 0.91 ÷ 7 **0.13** **11.** 1.32 ÷ 6 **0.22** **12.** 4.68 ÷ 9 **0.52** **13.** 0.81 ÷ 3 **0.27**

See Example 2 **Evaluate 0.684 ÷ *x* for each given value of *x*.**

14. $x = 3$ **0.228** **15.** $x = 4$ **0.171** **16.** $x = 18$ **0.038** **17.** $x = 9$ **0.076**

See Example 3 **18. Consumer Math** Charles, Kate, and Kim eat lunch in a restaurant. The bill is $27.12. If they share the bill equally, how much will each person pay? **$9.04**

Practice and Problem Solving

CRCT GPS
Extra Practice p. 719

Find the value of each expression.

19. (0.49 + 0.045) ÷ 5 **0.107** **20.** (4.9 − 3.125) ÷ 5 **0.355** **21.** (13.28 − 7.9) ÷ 4 **1.345**

Evaluate the expression *x* ÷ 4 for each value of *x*.

22. $x = 0.504$ **0.126** **23.** $x = 0.944$ **0.236** **24.** $x = 57.484$ **14.371** **25.** $x = 1.648$ **0.412**

26. Multi-Step At the grocery store, a 6 lb bag of oranges costs $2.04. Is this more or less expensive than the price shown at the farmers' market?

Oranges $0.30/lb

26. More expensive. 6 lb at farmers' market cost $1.80.

27. Critical Thinking How could you use rounding to check your answer to the problem 5.58 ÷ 6?

28. Choose a Strategy Sarah had $1.19 in coins. Jeff asked her for change for a dollar, but she did not have the correct change. What coins did she have? **Possible answer: 3 quarters, 4 dimes, and 4 pennies**

29. Write About It When do you use a placeholder zero in the quotient?

30. Challenge Evaluate the expression *x* ÷ 2 for the following values of $x = 520$, 52, and 5.2. Try to predict the value of the same expression for $x = 0.52$. **260, 26, 2.6; 0.26**

29. when the divisor is greater than the portion of the dividend being divided into

CRCT Prep • GPS Support • Spiral Review

31. Multiple Choice What is the value of 0.98 ÷ *x* when $x = 2$?

Ⓐ 49 Ⓑ 4.9 **Ⓒ 0.49** Ⓓ 0.049

32. Gridded Response Danika spent $89.24 on two pairs of shoes. Each pair of shoes cost the same amount. How much, in dollars, did each pair cost? **44.62**

Identify a pattern in each sequence. Name the missing term. (Lesson 1-7)

33. 85, 80, 75, 70, 65, ■, . . . **Subtract 5; 60**

34. 2, 6, 5, 9, 8, ■, . . . **Alteranate adding 4 and subtracting 1; 12**

35. 10, 17, 12, 19, 14, ■, . . . **Alternate adding 7 and subtracting 5; 21**

Write each number in standard form. (Lesson 3-4)

36. 6.479×10^3 **6,479** **37.** 0.208×10^2 **20.8** **38.** 13.507×10^4 **135,070** **39.** 7.1×10^5 **710,000**

Challenge 3-6
Problem Solving 3-6

LESSON 3-6 **Problem Solving**
Dividing Decimals by Whole Numbers

Write the correct answer.

1. Four friends had lunch together. The total bill for lunch came to $33.40, including tip. If they shared the bill equally, how much did they each pay?
$8.35

2. There are 7.2 milligrams of iron in a dozen eggs. Because there are 12 eggs in a dozen, how many milligrams of iron are in 1 egg?
0.6 milligrams

3. Kyle bought a sheet of lumber 8.7 feet long to build fence rails. He cut the strip into 3 equal pieces. How long is each piece?
2.9 feet

4. An albatross has a wingspan greater than the length of a car—3.7 meters! Wingspan is the length from the tip of one wing to the tip of the other wing. What is the length of each albatross wing (assuming wing goes from center of body)?
1.85 meters

Circle the letter of the correct answer.

5. The City Zoo feeds its three giant pandas 181.5 pounds of bamboo shoots every day. Each panda is fed the same amount of bamboo. How many pounds of bamboo does each panda eat every day?
A 6.05 pounds
Ⓑ 60.5 pounds
C 61.5 pounds
D 605 pounds

6. Emma bought 22.5 yards of cloth to make curtains for two windows in her apartment. She used the same amount of cloth on each window. How much cloth did she use to make each set of curtains?
F 1.125 yards
G 10.25 yards
Ⓗ 11.25 yards
J 11.52 yards

7. Aerobics classes cost $153.86 for 14 sessions. What is the fee for one session?
Ⓐ $10.99
B $1.99
C about $25.00
D about $20.00

8. An entire apple pie has 36.8 grams of saturated fat. If the pie is cut into 8 slices, how many grams of saturated fat are in each slice?
F 4.1 grams
G 0.46 grams
Ⓗ 4.6 grams
J 4.11 grams

Reteach 3-6

LESSON 3-6 **Reteach**
Dividing Decimals by Whole Numbers

You can use decimal grids to help you divide decimals by whole numbers.

To divide 0.35 by 7, first shade in a decimal grid to show thirty-five hundredths.

0.35 ÷ 7 means "divide 0.35 into 7 equal groups." Show this on the decimal grid.

The number of units in each group is the quotient.

So, 0.35 ÷ 7 = 0.05.

Use decimal grids to find each quotient.

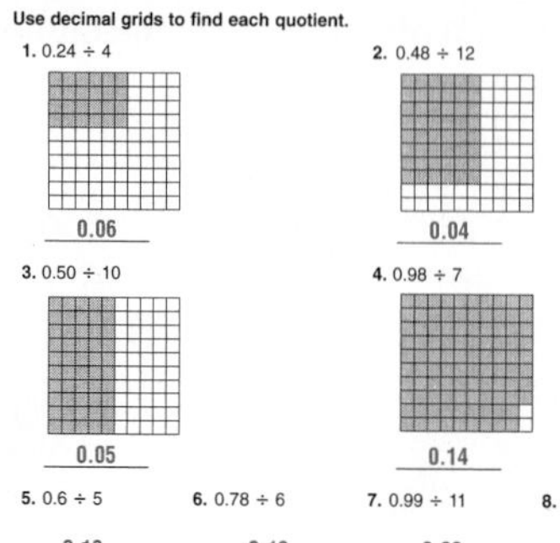

1. 0.24 ÷ 4 0.06

2. 0.48 ÷ 12 0.04

3. 0.50 ÷ 10 0.05

4. 0.98 ÷ 7 0.14

5. 0.6 ÷ 5 0.12 **6.** 0.78 ÷ 6 0.13 **7.** 0.99 ÷ 11 0.09 **8.** 0.32 ÷ 4 0.08

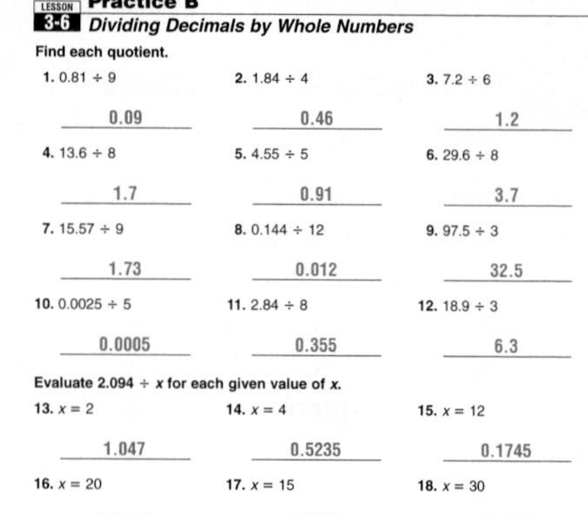

Practice 3-6

LESSON 3-6 **Practice B**
Dividing Decimals by Whole Numbers

Find each quotient.

1. 0.81 ÷ 9 0.09 **2.** 1.84 ÷ 4 0.46 **3.** 7.2 ÷ 6 1.2

4. 13.6 ÷ 8 1.7 **5.** 4.55 ÷ 5 0.91 **6.** 29.6 ÷ 8 3.7

7. 15.57 ÷ 9 1.73 **8.** 0.144 ÷ 12 0.012 **9.** 97.5 ÷ 3 32.5

10. 0.0025 ÷ 5 0.0005 **11.** 2.84 ÷ 8 0.355 **12.** 18.9 ÷ 3 6.3

Evaluate 2.094 ÷ *x* for each given value of *x*.

13. $x = 2$ 1.047 **14.** $x = 4$ 0.5235 **15.** $x = 12$ 0.1745

16. $x = 20$ 0.1047 **17.** $x = 15$ 0.1396 **18.** $x = 30$ 0.0698

19. There are three grizzly bears in the city zoo. Yogi weighs 400.5 pounds, Winnie weighs 560.35 pounds, and Nyla weighs 618.29 pounds. What is the average weight of the three bears?
526.38 pounds

20. The bill for dinner came to $75.48. The four friends decided to leave a $15.00 tip. If they shared the bill equally, how much will they each pay?
$22.62

3-7 Dividing by Decimals

Learn to divide whole numbers and decimals by decimals.

Georgia Performance Standards

M6N1.g Solve problems involving decimals. Also, M6P1.c, M6P1.d.

Julie and her family traveled to the Grand Canyon. They stopped to refill their gas tank with 13.4 gallons of gasoline after they had driven 368.5 miles.

To find the miles that they drove per gallon, you will need to divide a decimal by a decimal.

EXAMPLE 1 Dividing a Decimal by a Decimal

Helpful Hint

Multiplying the divisor and the dividend by the same number does not change the quotient.

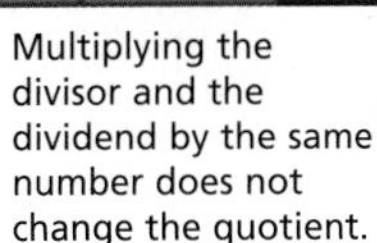

42 ÷ 6 = 7
× 10 ↓ × 10 ↓
420 ÷ 60 = 7

42 ÷ 6 = 7
× 100 ↓ × 100 ↓
4,200 ÷ 600 = 7

Find each quotient.

A **3.6 ÷ 1.2**

```
1.2)3.6
```

Multiply the divisor and dividend by the same power of ten.

```
    3
12)36
  -36
    0
```

There is one decimal place in the divisor. Multiply by 10^1, or 10.

Think: 1.2 × 10 = 12 3.6 × 10 = 36

Divide.

3.6 ÷ 1.2 = 3

B **42.3 ÷ 0.12**

```
0.12)42.3
```

Make the divisor a whole number by multiplying the divisor and dividend by 10^2, or 100.

Think: 0.12 × 100 = 12 42.3 × 100 = 4,230

```
     352.5
12)4230.0
  -36
    63
   -60
     30
    -24
      60
     -60
       0
```

Place the decimal point in the quotient. Divide.

When there is a remainder, place a zero after the decimal point in the dividend and continue to divide.

42.3 ÷ 0.12 = 352.5

Organizer 3-7

Pacing: Traditional $1\frac{1}{2}$ day
Block $\frac{3}{4}$ day

Objective: Students divide whole numbers and decimals by decimals.

Technology Lab
In *Technology Lab Activities*

Online Edition
Tutorial Videos

Countdown to CRCT Week 6

Power Presentations with PowerPoint®

Warm Up

Divide.

1. 4.8 ÷ 2 2.4
2. 16.1 ÷ 7 2.3
3. 0.36 ÷ 3 0.12
4. 25.28 ÷ 4 6.32

Problem of the Day

In the following magic square, 3.375 is the product of the numbers in every row, column, and diagonal. Fill in the missing numbers.

4.5	0.25	3
1	1.5	2.25
0.75	9	0.5

Also available on transparency

Math Humor

What kinds of decimals do the most talking? Repeating decimals

1 Introduce

Alternate Opener

EXPLORATION

3-7 Dividing by Decimals

A CD store carries the packages of recordable CDs listed in the table. The third column shows the cost of one CD for different packages. This is called the ***unit cost.*** The fourth column shows how many CDs one dollar can buy. For example, if you buy the 5-pack at $4.95, one dollar buys 1.01 CD (a little more than one CD). This is called the ***purchasing power*** of $1.00.

Use a calculator to find the cost of 1 CD and the purchasing power of $1.00 for each package.

	Item	Cost	Cost of 1 CD	Purchasing Power of $1.00
1.	Single CD	$1.19		
2.	5-pack	$4.95	4.95 ÷ 5 = 0.99	5 ÷ 4.95 = 1.01
3.	10-pack	$8.95		
4.	20-pack	$16.95		
5.	50-pack	$35.95		

6. Which package gives you the highest unit cost?
7. Which package gives you the lowest unit cost?
8. Which package gives you the greatest purchasing power per dollar? the least purchasing power per dollar?

Think and Discuss

9. **Describe** the relationship between unit cost and purchasing power by looking at the numbers in the third and fourth columns above.

Motivate

Solve the following problem for the class: 760 ÷ 8 (95). Ask a student to use a calculator to solve 7,600 ÷ 80 (95). Explain that multiplying the dividend and divisor by the same number, 10, did not change the solution. This fact is a key component of this lesson.

Explorations and answers are provided in *Alternate Openers: Explorations Transparencies.*

Georgia Performance Standards

M6N1.g Solve problems involving fractions, decimals, and percents.

M6P1.c Apply and adapt a variety of appropriate strategies to solve problems.

M6P1.d Monitor and reflect on the process of mathematical problem solving.

COMMON ERROR ALERT

Some students may position the decimal for the quotient before multiplying the divisor and dividend by a power of ten. Remind them that the decimal is positioned only after multiplication by a power of ten has occurred

Power Presentations with PowerPoint®

Additional Examples

Example 

Find each quotient.

A. 5.2 ÷ 1.3 4

B. 61.3 ÷ 0.36 $170.2\overline{7}$

Example 2

After driving 216.3 mi, the Yorks filled up with 10.5 gal of gas. On average, how many miles did they drive per gallon of gas?
They averaged 20.6 miles per gallon.

Also available on transparency

EXAMPLE  **PROBLEM SOLVING APPLICATION**

After driving 368.5 miles, Julie and her family refilled the tank of their car with 13.4 gallons of gasoline. On average, how many miles did they drive per gallon of gas?

1 Understand the Problem

The **answer** will be the average number of miles per gallon.

List the **important information:**

- They drove 368.5 miles.
- They used 13.4 gallons of gas.

 **Make a Plan**

Solve a simpler problem by replacing the decimals in the problem with whole numbers.

If they drove 10 miles using 2 gallons of gas, they averaged 5 miles per gallon. You need to divide miles by gallons to solve the problem.

 **Solve**

First estimate the answer. You can use compatible numbers.
368.5 ÷ 13.4 ⟶ 360 ÷ 12 = 30

13.4)368.5 — *Multiply the divisor and the dividend by 10. Think: 13.4 × 10 = 134   368.5 × 10 = 3,685*

```
      27.5
134)3685.0
   − 268
     1005
    − 938
      67 0
    − 67 0
         0
```

Place the decimal point in the quotient. Divide.

Julie and her family averaged 27.5 miles per gallon.

 **Look Back**

The answer is reasonable, since 27.5 is close to the estimate of 30.

Think and Discuss  GPS M6P3.b

1. **Tell** how the quotient of 48 ÷ 12 is similar to the quotient of 4.8 ÷ 1.2. How is it different?

Answers to *Think and Discuss*

1. 48 ÷ 12 and 4.8 ÷ 1.2 both have a quotient of 4. The difference is that the first expression contains whole numbers and the second contains decimals.

2 Teach

Guided Instruction

In this lesson, students learn to divide whole numbers and decimals by decimals. First teach students to make the divisor a whole number when dividing a decimal by a decimal. Then teach them the notation used to signify repeating decimals. Finally, teach students to solve an application problem involving average gas mileage.

Inclusion Remind students that both the divisor *and* the dividend must be multiplied by the same power of ten to get the correct quotient.

Reaching All Learners

Through Kinesthetic Experience

Have students work in groups of three or four. Give each group a set of index cards labeled 0–9. Have the groups mix and place the cards face down in a pile. Students should then draw three cards to make a dividend and two cards to make a divisor. Have students take turns determining where to place decimal points in each number and then do the division individually. Group members should compare answers and work a problem together if they do not all get the same quotient.

 Close

Summarize

Explain how to change the divisor and the dividend to solve 2.4 ÷ 0.9.
(Multiply the divisor, 0.9, by 10 to make it a whole number. Multiply the dividend, 2.4, by 10. Divide: 24 ÷ 9 = 2.6... .)
Remind them that the placement of the decimal point must follow the multiplication by a power of ten.

3-7 Exercises

M6P3.a, M6P3.c

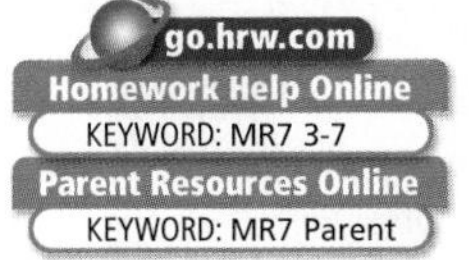

GUIDED PRACTICE

See Example 1

Find each quotient.

1. 6.5 ÷ 1.3
2. 20.7 ÷ 0.6
3. 25.5 ÷ 1.5
4. 5.4 ÷ 0.9
5. 13.2 ÷ 2.2
6. 63.39 ÷ 0.24

See Example 2

7. Marcus drove 354.9 miles in 6.5 hours. On average, how many miles per hour did he drive?
8. **Consumer Math** Anthony spends \$87.75 on shrimp. The shrimp cost \$9.75 per pound. How many pounds of shrimp does Anthony buy?

INDEPENDENT PRACTICE

See Example 1

Find each quotient.

9. 3.6 ÷ 0.6
10. 8.2 ÷ 0.5
11. 18.4 ÷ 2.3
12. 4.8 ÷ 1.2
13. 52.2 ÷ 0.24
14. 32.5 ÷ 2.6
15. 49.5 ÷ 4.5
16. 96.6 ÷ 0.42
17. 6.5 ÷ 1.3

See Example 2

18. Jen spends \$5.98 on ribbon. Ribbon costs \$0.92 per meter. How many meters of ribbon does Jen buy?
19. Kyle's family drove 329.44 miles. Kyle calculated that the car averaged 28.4 miles per gallon of gas. How many gallons of gas did the car use?
20. **Consumer Math** Peter is saving \$4.95 each week to buy a DVD that costs \$24.75, including tax. For how many weeks will he have to save?

PRACTICE AND PROBLEM SOLVING

Extra Practice p. 719

Divide.

21. 2.52 ÷ 0.4
22. 12.586 ÷ 0.35
23. 0.5733 ÷ 0.003
24. 10.875 ÷ 1.2
25. 92.37 ÷ 0.5
26. 8.43 ÷ 0.12

Evaluate.

27. $0.732 \div n$ for $n = 0.06$
28. $73.814 \div c$ for $c = 1.3$
29. $b \div 0.52$ for $b = 6.344$
30. $r \div 4.17$ for $r = 10.5918$

Find the value of each expression.

31. $6.35 \times 10^2 \div 0.5$
32. $8.1 \times 10^2 \div 0.9$
33. $4.5 \times 10^3 \div 4$
34. $20.1 \times 10^3 \div 0.1$
35. $2.76 \times 10^2 \div 0.3$
36. $6.2 \times 10^3 \div 8$
37. **Multi-Step** Find the value of $6.45 \times 10^6 \div 0.3$. Write your answer in scientific notation.

RETEACH 3-7

LESSON 3-7 **Reteach**
Dividing by Decimals

You can use powers of ten to help you divide a decimal by a decimal.

To divide 0.048 by 0.12, first multiply each number by the least power of ten that makes the divisor a whole number.

0.048 ÷ 0.12

$0.12 \cdot 10^2 = 12$ Move the decimal point 2 places to the right.

$0.048 \cdot 10^2 = 4.8$ Move the decimal point 2 places to the right.

Then divide.

4.8 ÷ 12 **Step 1:** Divide as you would divide a whole number by a whole number.

$$\begin{array}{r} 0.4 \\ 12\overline{)4.8} \\ \underline{4\,8} \\ 0 \end{array}$$

Step 2: Think 48 ÷ 12 = 4.

Step 3: Bring the decimal into the quotient and add a zero placeholder if necessary.

So, 0.048 ÷ 0.12 = 0.4.

Find each quotient.

1. $0.7\overline{)0.42}$ 0.6
2. $0.08\overline{)0.4}$ 5
3. $0.5\overline{)0.125}$ 0.25
4. $0.02\overline{)0.3}$ 15
5. $0.4\overline{)0.08}$ 0.2
6. $0.9\overline{)0.63}$ 0.7
7. $0.008\overline{)0.4}$ 50
8. $0.04\overline{)0.032}$ 0.8
9. $0.3\overline{)0.06}$ 0.2
10. $0.04\overline{)0.2}$ 5
11. $0.007\overline{)4.9}$ 700
12. $0.6\overline{)0.012}$ 0.02

PRACTICE 3-7

LESSON 3-7 **Practice B**
Dividing by Decimals

Find each quotient.

1. 9.0 ÷ 0.9   10
2. 29.6 ÷ 3.7   8
3. 10.81 ÷ 2.3   4.7
4. 10.5 ÷ 1.5   7
5. 15.36 ÷ 4.8   3.2
6. 9.75 ÷ 1.3   7.5
7. 20.4 ÷ 5.1   4
8. 37.5 ÷ 2.5   15
9. 9.24 ÷ 1.1   8.4
10. 16.56 ÷ 6.9   2.4
11. 28.9 ÷ 8.5   3.4
12. 14.35 ÷ 0.7   20.5

Evaluate $x \div 1.2$ for each value of x.

13. $x = 40.8$ 34
14. $x = 1.8$ 1.5
15. $x = 10.8$ 9
16. $x = 14.4$ 12
17. $x = 4.32$ 3.6
18. $x = 0.06$ 0.05

19. Anna is saving \$6.35 a week to buy a computer game that costs \$57.15. How many weeks will she have to save to buy the game?
9 weeks

20. Ben ran a 19.5-mile race last Saturday. His average speed during the race was 7.8 miles per hour. How long did it take Ben to finish the race?
2.5 hours

3-7 Exercises

Assignment Guide

If you finished Example 1 assign:
Average 1–6, 9–17, 21–26, 45–54
Advanced 1–6, 9–17, 31–36, 45–54

If you finished Example 2 assign:
Average 1–40, 45–54
Advanced 1–36, 41–54

Homework Quick Check
Quickly check key concepts.
Exercises: 14, 16, 20, 28, 30

Math Background

To determine whether a quotient will be a terminating or repeating decimal, it is necessary only to examine the ratio of dividend to divisor in lowest whole terms. If the divisor can be expressed as a product of twos and fives, then the quotient will be a terminating decimal; otherwise, it will be a repeating decimal.

For example, the expression 0.04 ÷ 1.6 is translated by the division algorithm to 0.4 ÷ 16. In lowest terms, this is equivalent to the ratio 1:40 (0.4:16 = 4:160 = 1:40). Then, because 40 = 2 × 2 × 2 × 5, the quotient is a terminating decimal.

Georgia Performance Standards

M6P3.a Organize and consolidate their mathematical thinking through communication.

M6P3.c Analyze and evaluate the mathematical thinking and strategies of others.

ONGOING ASSESSMENT and INTERVENTION

***Diagnose Before* the Lesson**
3-7 Warm Up, TE p. 137

***Monitor During* the Lesson**
3-7 Know-It Notebook
3-7 Questioning Strategies

***Assess After* the Lesson**
3-7 Lesson Quiz, TE p. 140

History LINK

The U.S. Mint was established by the Coinage Act in 1792. The first coins were copper and were made in Philadelphia.

38. **Earth Science** A planet's year is the time it takes that planet to revolve around the Sun. A Mars year is 1.88 Earth years. If you are 13 years old in Earth years, about how old would you be in Mars years?

39. **History** The U.S. Treasury first printed paper money in 1862. The paper money we use today is 0.0043 inch thick. Estimate the number of bills you would need to stack to make a pile that is 1 inch thick. If you stacked $20 bills, what would be the total value of the money in the pile?

Use the map for Exercises 40 and 41.

40. **Multi-Step** Bill drove from Washington, D.C., to Charlotte in 6.5 hours. What was his average speed in miles per hour?

41. **Estimation** Betty drove a truck from Richmond to Washington, D.C. It took her about 2.5 hours. Estimate the average speed she was driving.

42. **What's the Error?** A student incorrectly answered the division problem below. Explain the error and write the correct quotient.

$$0.004\overline{)53.824} = 13.456$$

43. **Write About It** Explain how you know where to place the decimal point in the quotient when you divide by a decimal number.

44. **Challenge** Find the value of a in the division problem.

$$0.4a3\overline{)0.41713} = 1.01$$

CRCT PREP • GPS SUPPORT • SPIRAL REVIEW

45. **Multiple Choice** Nick bought 2.5 pounds of popcorn for $8.35. How much did he pay for each pound of popcorn?

Ⓐ $20.88 Ⓑ $3.43 Ⓒ $3.34 Ⓓ $33.40

46. **Extended Response** In the 2004–2005 NBA season, Tracy McGrady earned a salary of $14,487,000. He played in 78 games and averaged 40.8 minutes per game. How much money did Tracy McGrady earn each minute he played? Round your answer to the nearest dollar. Explain how you solved the problem.

Compare. Write <, >, or =. (Lesson 1-1)

47. 56,902 ▪ 56,817 48. 14,562 ▪ 14,581 49. 1,240,518 ▪ 1,208,959

Evaluate 4*y* for each value of *y*. (Lesson 3-5)

50. $y = 2.13$ 51. $y = 4.015$ 52. $y = 3.6$ 53. $y = 0.78$ 54. $y = 1.4$

TEST PREP DOCTOR In Exercise 46, point out to students that there is more than one way to solve this problem. Students can divide the salary by 78 to find his earnings per game and then divide by 40.8. Or they can multiply 78 times 40.8 to find the total number of minutes played that year and then divide the salary by the total minutes.

Journal

Have students explain the similarities and differences between dividing whole numbers by whole numbers and decimals by decimals.

Power Presentations with PowerPoint®

3-7 Lesson Quiz

Find each quotient.

1. 49 ÷ 0.7 **70**
2. 21.63 ÷ 2.1 **10.3**
3. 38.43 ÷ 6.1 **6.3**
4. 16.9 ÷ 5.2 **3.25**
5. John spent $13.44 renting 4 videos for the weekend. What was the cost per video? **$3.36**

Also available on transparency

CHALLENGE 3-7

LESSON 3-7 Challenge
Cutting Decimals

The strips of cloth below need to be cut into equal pieces of given lengths. Draw lines on each strip of cloth to show how many pieces will be cut.

1. Total Length: 9.8 yards Piece Length: 1.4 yards
Students should draw 6 lines across the cloth to cut it into 7 equal pieces.

2. Total Length: 2.5 yards Piece Length: 0.5 yards
Students should draw 4 lines across the cloth to cut it into 5 equal pieces.

3. Total Length: 10.2 yards Piece Length: 1.7 yards
Students should draw 5 lines across the cloth to cut it into 6 equal pieces.

4. Total Length: 6.4 yards Piece Length: 0.8 yards
Students should draw 7 lines across the cloth to cut it into 8 equal pieces.

5. Total Length: 13.6 yards Piece Length: 3.4 yards
Students should draw 3 lines across the cloth to cut it into 4 equal pieces.

PROBLEM SOLVING 3-7

LESSON 3-7 Problem Solving
Dividing by Decimals

Write the correct answer.

1. Jamal spent $6.75 on wire to build a rabbit hutch. Wire costs $0.45 per foot. How many feet of wire did Jamal buy?
15 feet

2. Peter drove 195.3 miles in 3.5 hours. On average, how many miles per hour did he drive?
55.8 miles per hour

3. Lisa's family drove 830.76 miles to visit her grandparents. Lisa calculated that they used 30.1 gallons of gas. How many miles per gallon did the car average?
27.6 miles per gallon

4. A chef bought 84.5 pounds of ground beef. He uses 0.5 pound of ground beef for each hamburger. How many hamburgers can he make?
169 hamburgers

Circle the letter of the correct answer.

5. Mark earned $276.36 for working 23.5 hours last week. He earned the same amount of money for each hour that he worked. What is Mark's hourly rate of pay?
A $1.17
B $10.76
Ⓒ $11.76
D $117.60

6. Alicia wants to cover a section of her wall that is 2 feet wide and 12 feet long with mirrors. Each mirror tile is 2 feet wide and 1.5 feet long. How many mirror tiles does she need to cover that section?
F 4 tiles
G 6 tiles
Ⓗ 8 tiles
J 12 tiles

7. John ran the city marathon in 196.5 minutes. The marathon is 26.2 miles long. On average, how many miles per hour did John run the race?
A 7 miles per hour
B 6.2 miles per hour
Ⓒ 7.5 miles per hour
D 5.5 miles per hour

8. Shaneeka is saving $5.75 of her allowance each week to buy a new camera that costs $51.75. How many weeks will she have to save to have enough money to buy it?
Ⓕ 9 weeks
G 9.5 weeks
H 8.1 weeks
J 8 weeks

3-8 Interpret the Quotient

 Problem Solving Skill

Learn to solve problems by interpreting the quotient.

In science lab, Kim learned to make slime from corn starch, water, and food coloring. She has 0.87 kg of corn starch, and the recipe for one bag of slime calls for 0.15 kg. To find the number of bags of slime Kim can make, you need to divide.

EXAMPLE 1 ***Measurement Application***

> **Remember!**
> To divide decimals, first write the divisor as a whole number. Multiply the divisor and dividend by the same power of ten.

Kim will use 0.87 kg of corn starch to make gift bags of slime for her friends. If each bag requires 0.15 kg of corn starch, how many bags of slime can she make?

The question asks how many whole bags of slime can be made when the corn starch is divided into groups of 0.15 kg.

$0.87 \div 0.15 = ?$

$87 \div 15 = 5.8$

Think: The quotient shows that there is not enough to make 6 bags of slime that are 0.15 kg each. There is only enough for 5 bags. The decimal part of the quotient will not be used in the answer.

Kim can make 5 gift bags of slime.

EXAMPLE 2 ***Photography Application***

> **Georgia Performance Standards**
> **M6N1.g** Solve problems involving decimals. Also, M6P1.d, M6P4.c, M6P5.c.

There are 246 students in the sixth grade. If Ms. Lee buys rolls of film with 24 exposures each, how many rolls will she need to take every student's picture?

The question asks how many whole rolls are needed to take a picture of every one of the students.

$246 \div 24 = ?$

$246 \div 24 = 10.25$

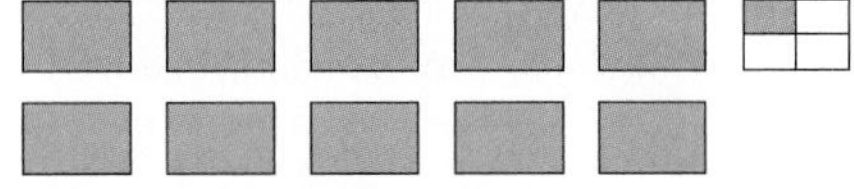

Think: Ten rolls of film will not be enough to take every student's picture. Ms. Lee will need to buy another roll of film. The quotient must be rounded up to the next highest whole number.

Ms. Lee will need 11 rolls of film.

Organizer 3-8

Pacing: Traditional 1 day
Block $\frac{1}{2}$ day

Objective: Students solve problems by interpreting the quotient.

Online Edition
Tutorial Videos

Countdown to CRCT Week 6

Power Presentations with PowerPoint®

Warm Up

Divide.

1. 15.264 ÷ 3 **5.088**
2. 3.78 ÷ 3 **1.26**
3. 342 ÷ 7.6 **45**
4. 28.32 ÷ 4.8 **5.9**

Problem of the Day

Divide your age in months by 12. What does the quotient tell you? my age in years

Also available on transparency

Math Humor

Teacher: Why does your division assignment feel so cold?

Student: A lot of the answers had remainders, and my mom always told me to put leftovers in the refrigerator.

1 Introduce

Alternate Opener

EXPLORATION

3-8 Interpret the Quotient

For each problem, estimate a solution. Then compute with a calculator.

		Estimate	Actual
1.	At Juan's school, each lunch special costs $3.65. How many lunches can Juan buy with $20.00?		
2.	Gasoline costs $2.499 per gallon. How many gallons can Sue buy with $25.00?		
3.	On Jorge's map, 0.15 cm represents 1 mi. He measures a road which is 7.8 cm. How many mi long is the actual road?		
4.	Ofelia makes $6.79 per hour at her summer job. If she wants to make $200 per week, how many hours should she work?		

Think and Discuss

5. **Explain** the estimation strategies you used.
6. **Describe** a problem that can be solved by division.

2 Teach

Guided Instruction

In this lesson, students learn to solve problems by interpreting the quotient. First present the measurement application, in which the decimal part of the quotient is not used to answer the question. Then present Example 2, in which the quotient is rounded up to answer the question. Finally, present the situation in which an exact quotient is needed to answer the question. Explain the reasons for each different interpretation of the quotient.

Explorations and answers are provided in *Alternate Openers: Explorations Transparencies.*

Georgia Performance Standards

M6N1.g Solve problems involving fractions, decimals, and percents.

M6P1.d Monitor and reflect on the process of mathematical problem solving.

M6P4.c Recognize and apply mathematics in contexts outside of mathematics.

M6P5.c Use representations to model and interpret physical, social, and mathematical phenomena.

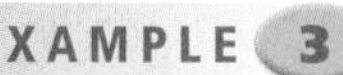

Power Presentations with PowerPoint®

Additional Examples

Example 1

Suppose Mark wants to make bags of slime. If each bag of slime requires 0.15 kg of corn starch and he has 1.23 kg, how many bags of slime can he make? 8

Example 2

There are 237 students in the seventh grade. If Mr. Jones buys rolls of film with 36 exposures each, how many rolls will he need to take every student's picture? 7

Example 3

Gary has 42.25 meters of rope. If he cuts it into 13 equal pieces, how long is each piece? 3.25 meters

Also available on transparency

3-8 Exercises

Assignment Guide

If you finished Example 1 assign:
Average 1, 4, 7, 13–22
Advanced 1, 4, 8, 13–22

If you finished Example 2 assign:
Average 1–2, 4–5, 7–8, 13–22
Advanced 1–2, 4–5, 8–9, 13–22

If you finished Example 3 assign:
Average 1–9, 13–22
Advanced 1–6, 10–22

Homework Quick Check

Quickly check key concepts.
Exercises: 4, 6, 8

Georgia Performance Standards

M6P1.b Solve problems that arise in mathematics and in other contexts.

M6P3.a Organize and consolidate their mathematical thinking through communication.

EXAMPLE 3 ***Social Studies Application***

Marissa is drawing a time line of the Stone Age. She plans for 6 equal sections, two each for the Paleolithic, Mesolithic, and Neolithic periods. If she has 7.8 meters of paper, how long is each section?

The question asks exactly how long each section will be when the paper is divided into 6 sections.

$7.8 \div 6 = 1.3$ *Think: The question asks for an exact answer, so do not estimate. Use the entire quotient.*

Each section will be **1.3** meters long.

When the question asks	→ You should
How many whole groups can be made when you divide?	→ Drop the decimal part of the quotient.
How many whole groups are needed to put all items from the dividend into a group?	→ Round the quotient up to the next highest whole number.
What is the exact number when you divide?	→ Use the entire quotient as the answer.

Possible answers to *Think and Discuss:*
1. Round up the quotient to the next highest whole number. They will need 3 vans.

Think and Discuss GPS M6P3.b

1. Tell how you would interpret the quotient: A group of 27 students will ride in vans that carry 12 students each. How many vans are needed?

3-8 Exercises

Georgia Performance Standards
M6P1.b, M6P3.a

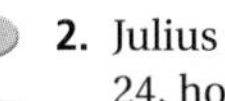

go.hrw.com
Homework Help Online KEYWORD: MR7 3-8
Parent Resources Online KEYWORD: MR7 Parent

GUIDED PRACTICE

See Example 1
1. Kay is making beaded belts for her friends from 6.5 meters of cord. One belt uses 0.625 meter of cord. How many belts can she make? 10 belts

See Example 2
2. Julius is supplying cups for a party of 136 people. If cups are sold in packs of 24, how many packs of cups will he need? 6 packs

See Example 3
3. Miranda is decorating for a party. She has 13 balloons and 29.25 meters of ribbon. She wants to tie the same length of ribbon on each balloon. How long will each ribbon be? 2.25 meters

Reaching All Learners
Through Critical Thinking

Have students make up and write a numerical division problem that would have a remainder. Then using the examples as a guide, challenge them to write three different word problems to go along with the division problem, each one requiring a different interpretation of the quotient.

3 Close

Summarize

Direct students' attention to the table following Example 3. Review the different ways to interpret quotients and the questions that signal each action to take.

INDEPENDENT PRACTICE

See Example 1 — 4. There are 0.454 kg of corn starch in a container. How many 0.028 kg portions are in one container? **16 portions**

See Example 2 — 5. Tina needs 36 flowers for her next project. The flowers are sold in bunches of 5. How many bunches will she need? **8 bunches**

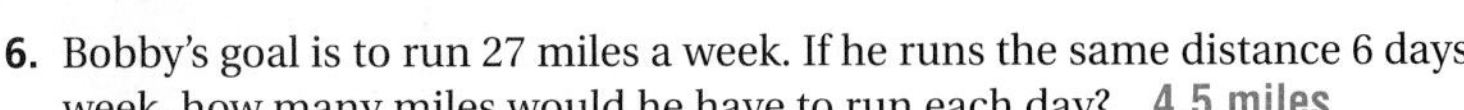

See Example 3 — 6. Bobby's goal is to run 27 miles a week. If he runs the same distance 6 days a week, how many miles would he have to run each day? **4.5 miles**

PRACTICE AND PROBLEM SOLVING

CRCT GPS
Extra Practice p. 719

7. Nick wants to write thank-you notes to 15 of his friends. The cards are sold in packs of 6. How many packs does Nick need to buy? **3 packs**

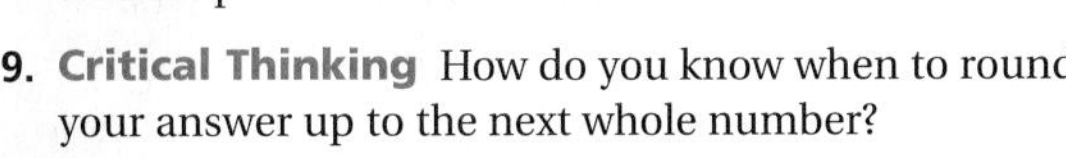

8. **Multi-Step** The science teacher has 7 packs of seeds and 36 students. If the students should each plant the same number of seeds, how many can each student plant? **4 seeds**

9. **Critical Thinking** How do you know when to round your answer up to the next whole number?

10. **Write a Problem** Create a problem that is solved by interpreting the quotient.

11. **Write About It** Explain how a calculator shows the remainder when you divide 145 by 8.

12. **Challenge** Leonard wants to place a fence on both sides of a 10-meter walkway. If he puts a post at both ends and at every 2.5 meters in between, how many posts does he use? **10 posts**

10. Possible answer: A cookie recipe calls for 1.75 cups of chocolate pieces. How many batches of cookies can you make with 6 cups of chocolate pieces?

11. Possible answer: A calculator shows the remainder as the decimal part of the quotient 18.125.

CRCT PREP • GPS SUPPORT • SPIRAL REVIEW

13. **Multiple Choice** There are 375 students going on a field trip. Each bus holds 65 students. How many buses are needed for the field trip?

Ⓐ 4　　Ⓑ 5　　 Ⓒ 6　　Ⓓ 7

14. **Multiple Choice** Mrs. Neal has 127 stickers. She wants to give each of the 22 students in her class the same number of stickers. Which expression can be used to find how many stickers each student will get?

Ⓕ 127 − 22　　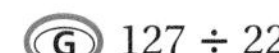 Ⓖ 127 ÷ 22　　Ⓗ 127 + 22　　Ⓙ 127 × 22

Solve for y. (Lessons 2-4, 2-5, 2-6)

15. $y - 23 = 40$ **$y = 63$**　16. $14y = 168$ **$y = 12$**　17. $36 + y = 53$ **$y = 17$**　18. $\frac{y}{5} = 7$ **$y = 35$**

Find each quotient. (Lesson 3-7)

19. $45.5 \div 5$ **9.1**　20. $103.7 \div 2$ **51.85**　21. $35 \div 2.5$ **14**　22. $4.25 \div 0.25$ **17**

ONGOING ASSESSMENT and INTERVENTION

Diagnose **Before** the Lesson
3-8 Warm Up, TE p. 141

Monitor **During** the Lesson
3-8 Know-It Notebook
3-8 Questioning Strategies

Assess **After** the Lesson
3-8 Lesson Quiz, TE p. 143

Answers

9. Possible answer: Round up to the next whole number when your answer, if it was rounded down, is not enough for what is needed.

Power Presentations with PowerPoint®

3-8 Lesson Quiz

Solve.

1. The cross-country team's goal is to run 26.25 mi next week. If they run only 5 days next week, how many miles would they have to run each day? **5.25 mi**
2. Shannon is having a surprise party for her parents. She wants to invite 22 friends. Invitations come in packages of 8. How many packages does Shannon need to buy? **3**

Also available on transparency

PRACTICE 3-8

LESSON 3-8 **Practice B**
Interpret the Quotient

Circle the letter of the correct answer.

1. You spent a total of $6.75 for 15 yards of ribbon. How much did the ribbon cost per yard?
   A $0.50
   (B) $0.45
   C $1.35
   D $1.45
2. Buttons come in packs of 12. How many packs should you buy if you need 100 buttons?
   F 10
   G 8
   (H) 9
   J 12
3. Your sewing cabinet has compartments that hold 8 spools of thread each. You have 50 spools of thread. How many compartments can you fill?
   (A) 6
   B 7
   C 5
   D 8
4. You spent a total of $35.75 for velvet cloth. Each yard of the velvet costs $3.25. How many yards did you buy?
   F 10
   G 10.5
   (H) 11
   J 11.5

Write the correct answer.

5. You used a total of 67.5 yards of cotton material to make costumes for the play. Each costume used 11.25 yards of cloth. How many costumes did you make?
   6 costumes
6. You are saving $17.00 each week to buy a new sewing machine that costs $175.50. How many weeks will you have to save to have enough money to buy the sewing machine?
   11 weeks
7. Sequins come in packs of 75. You use 12 sequins on each costume. If you have one pack of sequins, how many costumes can you make?
   6 costumes
8. You pay $26.28 for a subscription to *Sewing Magazine*. You get an issue every month for a year. How much does each issue cost?
   $2.19

RETEACH 3-8

LESSON 3-8 **Reteach**
Interpret the Quotient

There are three ways the decimal part of a quotient can be interpreted when you solve a problem.

If the question asks for an exact number, use the entire quotient.
If the question asks how many whole groups are needed to put the dividend into a group, round the quotient up to the next whole number.
If the question asks how many whole groups can be made when you divide, drop the decimal part of the quotient.

To interpret the quotient, decide what the question is asking.

In the school library, there are tables that seat 4 students each. If there are 30 students in a class, how many tables are needed to seat all of the students?

To solve, divide 30 by 4.

$30 \div 4 = 7.5$

The question is asking how many tables (whole groups) are needed to put all of the students in the class (dividend) into a group.

So, round 7.5 up to the next whole number.

8 tables are needed to seat all of the students.

Interpret the quotient to solve each problem.

1. A recipe that serves 6 requires 9 cups of milk. How much milk is needed for each serving?
   1.5 cups are needed for each serving.
2. A storage case holds 24 model cars. Marla has 84 model cars. How many storage cases does she need to store all of her cars?
   Marla needs 4 cases.
3. Kenny has $4.25 to spend at the school carnival. If game tickets are $0.50 each, how many games can Kenny play?
   Kenny can play 8 games.

CHALLENGE 3-8
PROBLEM SOLVING 3-8

LESSON 3-8 **Problem Solving**
Interpret the Quotient

Write the correct answer.

1. Five friends split a pizza that costs $16.75. If they shared the bill equally, how much did they each pay?
   $3.35
2. There are 45 choir members going to the recital. Each van can carry 8 people. How many vans are needed?
   6 vans
3. Tara bought 150 beads. She needs 27 beads to make each necklace. How many necklaces can she make?
   5 necklaces
4. Cat food costs $2.85 for five cans. Ben only wants to buy one can. How much will it cost?
   $0.57

Circle the letter of the correct answer.

5. Tennis balls come in cans of 3. The coach needs 50 tennis balls for practice. How many cans should he order?
   A 16 cans
   (B) 17 cans
   C 18 cans
   D 20 cans
6. The rainfall for three months was 4.6 inches, 3.5 inches, and 4.2 inches. What was the average monthly rainfall during that time?
   F 41 inches
   G 12.3 inches
   H 4.3 inches
   (J) 4.1 inches
7. Tom has $15.86 to buy marbles that cost $1.25 each. He wants to know how many marbles he can buy. What should he do after he divides?
   (A) Drop the decimal part of the quotient when he divides.
   B Drop the decimal part of the dividend when he divides.
   C Round the quotient up to the next highest whole number to divide.
   D Use the entire quotient of his division as the answer.
8. Mei needs 135 hot dog rolls for the class picnic. The rolls come in packs of 10. She wants to know how many packs to buy. What should she do after she divides?
   F Drop the decimal part of the quotient when she divides.
   G Drop the decimal part of the dividend when she divides.
   (H) Round the quotient up to the next highest whole number.
   J Use the entire quotient of her division as the answer.

3-9 Organizer

Pacing: Traditional 1 day
Block $\frac{1}{2}$ day

Objective: Students solve equations involving decimals.

GPS M6A3
Hands-On Lab
In *Hands-On Lab Activities*

Online Edition
Tutorial Videos, Interactivities

Countdown to CRCT Week 6

Solve.

1. $x - 3 = 11$ $\quad x = 14$
2. $18 = x + 4$ $\quad x = 14$
3. $\frac{x}{7} = 42$ $\quad x = 294$
4. $2x = 52$ $\quad x = 26$
5. $x - 82 = 172$ $\quad x = 254$

Problem of the Day

Find the missing entries in the magic square. 11.25 is the sum of every row, column, and diagonal.

3	6.75	1.5
2.25	3.75	5.25
6	0.75	4.5

Also available on transparency

Georgia Performance Standards

M6A3 Students will evaluate algebraic expressions, including those with exponents, and solve simple one-step equations using each of the four basic operations.

M6N1.g Solve problems involving fractions, decimals, and percents.

M6P4.c Recognize and apply mathematics in contexts outside of mathematics.

M6P5.b Select, apply, and translate among mathematical representations to solve problems.

3-9 Solving Decimal Equations

Learn to solve equations involving decimals.

Georgia Performance Standards

M6A3 Evaluate algebraic expressions and solve simple one-step equations. Also, M6N1.g, M6P4.c, M6P5.b.

Felipe has earned \$45.20 by mowing lawns for his neighbors. He wants to buy inline skates that cost \$69.95. Write and solve an equation to find how much more money Felipe must earn to buy the skates.

Let m be the amount of money Felipe needs. $\$45.20 + m = \$69.95$

You can solve equations with decimals using inverse operations just as you solved equations with whole numbers.

$$\begin{aligned} \$45.20 + m &= \$69.95 \\ -\$45.20 \quad\;\; &\quad -\$45.20 \\ m &= \$24.75 \end{aligned}$$

Felipe needs \$24.75 more to buy the inline skates.

EXAMPLE 1 Solving One-Step Equations with Decimals

Remember!
Use inverse operations to get the variable alone on one side of the equation.

Solve each equation. Check your answer.

A $g - 3.1 = 4.5$

$g - 3.1 = 4.5$ — *3.1 is subtracted from g.*
$\underline{+3.1 \quad +3.1}$ — *Add 3.1 to both sides to undo the subtraction.*
$g = 7.6$

Check
$g - 3.1 = 4.5$
$7.6 - 3.1 \stackrel{?}{=} 4.5$ — *Substitute 7.6 for g in the equation.*
$4.5 \stackrel{?}{=} 4.5$ ✔ — *7.6 is the solution.*

B $3k = 8.1$

$3k = 8.1$ — *k is multiplied by 3.*
$\frac{3k}{3} = \frac{8.1}{3}$ — *Divide both sides by 3 to undo the multiplication.*
$k = 2.7$

Check
$3k = 8.1$
$3(2.7) \stackrel{?}{=} 8.1$ — *Substitute 2.7 for k in the equation.*
$8.1 \stackrel{?}{=} 8.1$ ✔ — *2.7 is the solution.*

1 Introduce

Alternate Opener

EXPLORATION

3-9 Solving Decimal Equations

For each equation, estimate the solution. Then use a calculator to solve the equation. Compare the calculated solution with your estimated solution.

		Estimate	Actual
1.	$1.25 + x = 10$		
2.	$20 - x = 1.95$		
3.	$6x = 15$		
4.	$\frac{x}{4.5} = 10$		
5.	$\frac{x}{100} = 1.609$		

6. Write a real-world situation for the equation in Exercise 3.

Think and Discuss

7. **Explain** which equations it was easiest to estimate a solution for.
8. **Describe** a real-world situation that you could model with a decimal equation.

Motivate

Present a simple equation to students, such as $x + 15 = 43$. Have students explain how to solve the equation. Subtract 15 from both sides. $x + 15 - 15 = 43 - 15$, so $x = 28$. Tell students that decimal equations are also solved by using inverse operations.

Explorations and answers are provided in *Alternate Openers: Explorations Transparencies.*

Solve each equation. Check your answer.

C $\frac{m}{5} = 1.5$

$\frac{m}{5} = 1.5$ — *m is divided by 5.*

$\frac{m}{5} \cdot 5 = 1.5 \cdot 5$ — *Multiply both sides by 5 to undo the division.*

$m = 7.5$

Check

$\frac{m}{5} = 1.5$

$\frac{7.5}{5} \stackrel{?}{=} 1.5$ — *Substitute 7.5 for m in the equation.*

$1.5 \stackrel{?}{=} 1.5$ ✔ — *7.5 is the solution.*

EXAMPLE 2 *Measurement Application*

Remember!

The area of a rectangle is its length times its width.

$A = \ell w$

A **The area of the floor in Jonah's bedroom is 28 square meters. If its length is 3.5 meters, what is the width of the bedroom?**

area = length · width

$28 = 3.5 \cdot w$ — *Write the equation for the problem.*

$28 = 3.5w$ — *Let w be the width of the room.*

$\frac{28}{3.5} = \frac{3.5w}{3.5}$ — *w is multiplied by 3.5. Divide both sides by 3.5 to undo the multiplication.*

$8 = w$

The width of Jonah's bedroom is 8 meters.

B **Jonah is carpeting his bedroom. The carpet costs $22.50 per square meter. What is the total cost to carpet the bedroom?**

total cost = area · cost of carpet per square meter

$C = 28 \cdot 22.50$ — *Let C be the total cost. Write the equation for the problem.*

$C = 630$ — *Multiply.*

The cost of carpeting the bedroom is $630.

Possible answers to *Think and Discuss:*

1. Possible answers: The value of m will be less than 1 because 4.5 ÷ 5 is less than 1; the value of m will be less than 1 because 4.5 is the product of 5 and *m*.

Think and Discuss

GPS M6P1.d, M6P2.c

1. Explain whether the value of m will be less than or greater than 1 when you solve $5m = 4.5$.

2. Tell how you can check the answer in Example 2A.

COMMON ERROR ALERT

Caution students to be sure they are using the inverse operation to get the variable alone on one side of the equation. Remind them that addition and subtraction are inverse operations; so are multiplication and division.

Power Presentations with PowerPoint®

Additional Examples

Example 1

Solve each equation. Check your answer.

A. $k - 6.2 = 9.5$ $k = 15.7$

B. $6k = 7.2$ $k = 1.2$

C. $\frac{m}{7} = 0.6$ $m = 4.2$

Example 2

A. The area of Emily's floor is 33.75 m^2. If its length is 4.5 meters, what is its width?
The width of the floor is 7.5 meters.

B. If carpet costs $23 per m^2, what is the total cost to carpet the floor?
The total cost of carpeting the floor is $776.25.

Also available on transparency

Answers to *Think and Discuss*

2. Substitute 8 for *w* in the equation $28 = 3.5w$. If both sides of the equation are equal, then 8 is the correct solution.
$28 \stackrel{?}{=} 3.5w$
$28 \stackrel{?}{=} 3.5 \cdot 8$
$28 \stackrel{?}{=} 28$ ✔

2 Teach

Guided Instruction

In this lesson, students learn to solve equations involving decimals. First teach them to solve subtraction, multiplication, and division equations involving decimals by using the inverse operations of addition, division, and multiplication, respectively. Then teach students to apply the concept to real-world applications.

Inclusion If students are intimidated by the use of decimals in equations, have them solve a simpler problem, substituting whole numbers for the decimals. This should give students the reinforcement they need to solve decimal equations.

Reaching All Learners

Through Communication

Ask students to work in pairs, with one demonstrating the solution of a decimal equation to the other. Each step should be shown and explained. Have students reverse roles to solve another decimal equation. Let them know that they can assist their partner if necessary.

3 Close

Summarize

Have students volunteer to solve decimal equations for the class. As they work, emphasize the inverse operations being used and the placement of the decimal points.

3-9 Exercises

Assignment Guide

If you finished Example 1 assign:
Average 1–6, 9–17, 20–25, 41–49
Advanced 1–6, 9–17, 26–31, 41–49

If you finished Example 2 assign:
Average 1–35, 41–49
Advanced 1–31, 36–49

Homework Quick Check

Quickly check key concepts.
Exercises: 10, 12, 16, 18

Math Background

As long ago as 2000 B.C.E., the mathematics of Babylonia included algebra. The methods relied on prose for exposition. The problems included equations of 2nd, 3rd, and 4th degree.

Georgia Performance Standards

M6P3.a Organize and consolidate their mathematical thinking through communication.

M6P3.c Analyze and evaluate the mathematical thinking and strategies of others.

3-9 Exercises

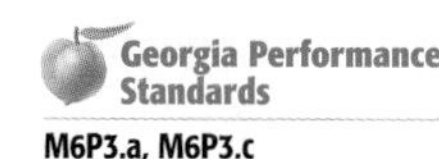

M6P3.a, M6P3.c

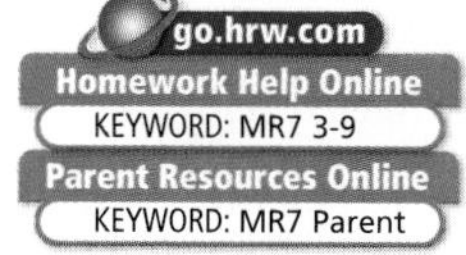

GUIDED PRACTICE

See Example 1 Solve each equation. Check your answer.

1. $a - 2.3 = 4.8$ $a = 7.1$
2. $6n = 8.4$ $n = 1.4$
3. $\frac{c}{4} = 3.2$ $c = 12.8$
4. $8.5 = 2.49 + x$ $x = 6.01$
5. $\frac{d}{3.2} = 1.09$ $d = 3.488$
6. $1.6 = m \cdot 4$ $m = 0.4$

See Example 2

7. The length of a window is 10.5 meters, and the width is 5.75 meters. Solve the equation $a \div 10.5 = 5.75$ to find the area of the window. $60.375\ m^2$
8. Gretchen wants to add a wallpaper border along the top of the walls of her square room. The distance around her room is 20.4 meters.
   a. What is the length of each wall of Gretchen's room? 5.1 m
   b. The price of wallpaper border is $1.25 per meter. What is the total cost to add the border to her room? $25.50

INDEPENDENT PRACTICE

See Example 1 Solve each equation. Check your answer.

9. $b - 5.6 = 3.7$ $b = 9.3$
10. $1.6 = \frac{p}{7}$ $p = 11.2$
11. $3r = 62.4$ $r = 20.8$
12. $9.5 = 5x$ $x = 1.9$
13. $a - 4.8 = 5.9$ $a = 10.7$
14. $\frac{n}{8} = 0.8$ $n = 6.4$
15. $8 + f = 14.56$ $f = 6.56$
16. $5.2s = 10.4$ $s = 2$
17. $1.95 = z - 2.05$ $z = 4$

See Example 2

18. **Geometry** The area of a rectangle is 65.8 square units. The length is 7 units. Solve the equation $7 \cdot w = 65.8$ to find the width of the rectangle. 9.4 units
19. Ken wants to fence his square garden. He will need 6.4 meters of fence to enclose all four sides of the garden.
   a. How long is each side of his garden? 1.6 meters
   b. The price of fencing is $2.25 per meter. What is the total cost to fence Ken's garden? $14.40

PRACTICE AND PROBLEM SOLVING

CRCT GPS
Extra Practice p. 719

Solve each equation and check your answer.

20. $9.8 = t - 42.1$ $t = 51.9$
21. $q \div 2.6 = 9.5$ $q = 24.7$
22. $45.36 = 5.6 \cdot m$ $m = 8.1$
23. $1.3b = 5.46$ $b = 4.2$
24. $4.93 = 0.563 + m$ $m = 4.367$
25. $\frac{a}{5} = 2.78$ $a = 13.9$
26. $w - 64.99 = 13.044$ $w = 78.034$
27. $6.205z = 80.665$ $z = 13$
28. $74.2 = 38.06 + c$ $c = 36.14$
29. **Geometry** The shortest side of the triangle is 10 units long.
   a. What are the lengths of the other two sides of the triangle? 19.5 units, 21 units
   b. What is the perimeter of the triangle? 50.5 units

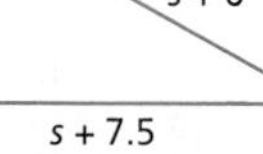

RETEACH 3-9

LESSON 3-9 **Reteach**
Solving Decimal Equations

You can write related equations for addition and subtraction equations.
$7.4 + 6.2 = 13.6$ $13.6 - 6.2 = 7.4$

Use related equations to solve each of the following.

A. $x + 4.5 = 7.9$
Think: $7.9 - 4.5 = x$
$x = 3.4$
Check $x + 4.5 = 7.9$
$3.4 + 4.5 \stackrel{?}{=} 7.9$ substitute
$7.9 = 7.9$

B. $x - 0.08 = 6.2$
Think: $6.2 + 0.08 = x$
$x = 6.28$
Check $x - 0.08 = 6.2$
$6.28 - 0.08 \stackrel{?}{=} 6.2$ substitute
$6.2 = 6.2$

Use related facts to solve each equation. Then check each answer.

1. $x + 8.7 = 12.9$ $x = 4.2$
2. $x + 8.4 = 16.6$ $x = 8.2$
3. $x - 2.65 = 7.8$ $x = 10.45$
4. $x - 0.8 = 2.3$ $x = 3.1$

You can write related equations for multiplication and division equations.
$3.2 \cdot 2.4 = 7.68$ $7.68 \div 2.4 = 3.2$

Use related equations to solve each of the following.

C. $3x = 1.5$
Think: $1.5 \div 3 = x$
$x = 0.5$
Check: $3x = 1.5$
$3 \cdot 0.5 \stackrel{?}{=} 1.5$ substitute
$1.5 = 1.5$

D. $x \div 6 = 1.2$
Think: $1.2 \cdot 6 = x$
$x = 7.2$
Check: $x \div 6 = 1.2$
$7.2 \div 6 \stackrel{?}{=} 1.2$ substitute
$1.2 = 1.2$

Use related facts to solve each equation. Then check each answer.

5. $x \div 3 = 6.3$ $x = 18.9$
6. $x \div 0.2 = 3.4$ $x = 0.68$
7. $7x = 4.2$ $x = 0.6$
8. $5x = 4.5$ $x = 0.9$

PRACTICE 3-9

LESSON 3-9 **Practice B**
Solving Decimal Equations

Solve each equation. Check your answer.

1. $a - 2.7 = 4.8$ $a = 7.5$; $7.5 - 2.7 = 4.8$
2. $b \div 7 = 1.9$ $b = 13.3$; $13.3 \div 7 = 1.9$
3. $w - 6.5 = 3.8$ $w = 10.3$; $10.3 - 6.5 = 3.8$
4. $p \div 0.4 = 1.7$ $p = 0.68$; $0.68 \div 0.4 = 1.7$
5. $4.5 + x = 8$ $x = 3.5$; $4.5 + 3.5 = 8$
6. $b \div 3 = 2.5$ $b = 7.5$; $7.5 \div 3 = 2.5$
7. $7.8 + s = 15.2$ $s = 7.4$; $7.8 + 7.4 = 15.2$
8. $1.63q = 9.78$ $q = 6$; $1.63 \cdot 6 = 9.78$
9. $0.05 + x = 2.06$ $x = 2.01$; $0.05 + 2.01 = 2.06$
10. $1.7n = 2.38$ $n = 1.4$; $1.7 \cdot 1.4 = 2.38$
11. $t - 6.08 = 12.59$ $t = 18.67$; $18.67 - 6.08 = 12.59$
12. $9q = 16.2$ $q = 1.8$; $9 \cdot 1.8 = 16.2$
13. $w - 8.9 = 10.3$ $w = 19.2$; $19.2 - 8.9 = 10.3$
14. $1.4n = 3.22$ $n = 2.3$; $1.4 \cdot 2.3 = 1.3$
15. $t - 12.7 = 0.8$ $t = 13.5$; $13.5 - 12.7 = 0.8$
16. $3.8 + a = 6.5$ $a = 2.7$; $3.8 + 2.7 = 6.5$
17. The distance around a square photograph is 12.8 centimeters. What is the length of each side of the photograph? 3.2 centimeters
18. You buy two rolls of film for $3.75 each. You pay with a $10 bill. How much change should you get back? $2.50

The London Eye is the world's largest Ferris wheel. Use the table for Exercises 30–32.

30. Write the height of the wheel in kilometers. **0.135 km**

31. Multi-Step There are 1,000 kilograms in a metric ton. What is the weight of the wheel in kilograms written in scientific notation? **1.9×10^6**

32. a. How many seconds does it take for the wheel to make one revolution? **1,800 sec**

b. The wheel moves at a rate of 0.26 meters per second. Use the equation $d \div 0.26 = 1{,}800$ to find the distance of one revolution. **468 m**

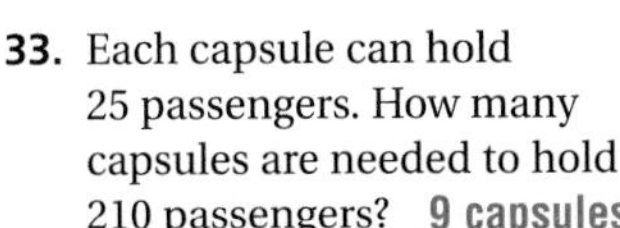

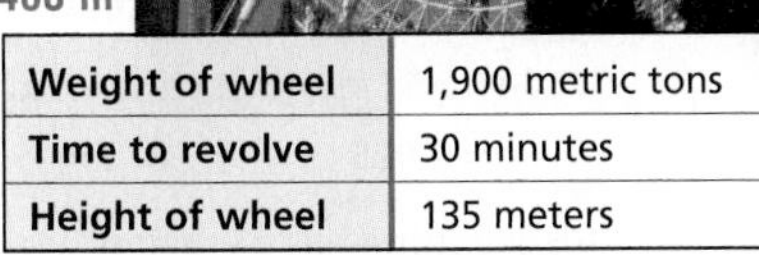

33. Each capsule can hold 25 passengers. How many capsules are needed to hold 210 passengers? **9 capsules**

Weight of wheel	1,900 metric tons
Time to revolve	30 minutes
Height of wheel	135 meters

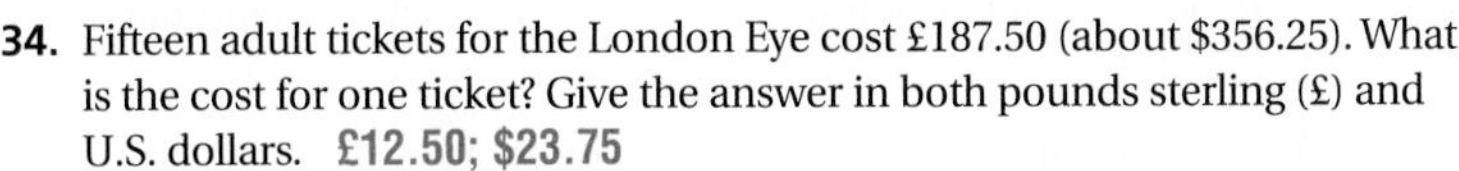

34. Fifteen adult tickets for the London Eye cost £187.50 (about $356.25). What is the cost for one ticket? Give the answer in both pounds sterling (£) and U.S. dollars. **£12.50; $23.75**

35. What's the Error? When solving the equation $b - 12.98 = 5.03$, a student said that $b = 7.95$. Describe the error. What is the correct value for b?
Possible answer: The student subtracted 5.03 from 12.98 rather than adding; $b = 18.01$

36. Write About It Explain how you solve for the variable in a multiplication equation such as $2.3a = 4.6$.
Possible answer: Divide both sides of the equation by 2.3, so $a = 2$.

37. Challenge Solve $1.45n \times 3.2 = 23.942 + 4.13$. **6.05**

CRCT Prep • GPS Support • Spiral Review

38. Multiple Choice Solve the equation $d \div 4 = 6.7$ for d.

(A) $d = 26.8$ (circled) (B) $d = 10.7$ (C) $d = 2.7$ (D) $d = 1.675$

39. Multiple Choice Kelly bought 2.8 pounds of beef for $5.04. How much did she pay for each pound of beef?

(F) $18.00 (G) $7.84 (H) $1.80 (circled) (J) $0.18

Write each phrase as a numerical or algebraic expression. (Lesson 2-2)

40. 103 less than 739 **739 − 103**

41. the product of 7 and z **$7z$**

42. the difference of 12 and n **$12 - n$**

Find each quotient. (Lesson 3-6)

43. $25.5 \div 5$ **5.1**

44. $44.7 \div 3$ **14.9**

45. $96.48 \div 6$ **16.08**

46. $0.0378 \div 9$ **0.0042**

Ongoing Assessment and Intervention

***Diagnose Before* the Lesson**
3-9 Warm Up, TE p. 144

***Monitor During* the Lesson**
3-9 Know-It Notebook
3-9 Questioning Strategies

***Assess After* the Lesson**
3-9 Lesson Quiz, TE p. 147

Test Prep Doctor In Exercises 38 and 39, point out that both problems involve division. An estimate, using compatible numbers, can be helpful in eliminating wrong answers.

Journal

Have students write and solve a decimal equation. Then have them place the equation in a real-world context.

CHALLENGE 3-9

LESSON 3-9 Challenge
Playing Weight

In professional sports, each ball has a maximum, or greatest, weight allowed in play. The lightest official weight for a table tennis ball is only 0.009 ounces. Use the equations below to find the maximum weights, in ounces, of some other sports' balls.

+ 1.601 =

− = 0.45

− 1.87 = • 2

= + 3.87

Golf Ball	Tennis Ball	Billiard Ball	Volleyball	Bowling Ball
Weight: 1.61 ounces	Weight: 2.06 ounces	Weight: 5.99 ounces	Weight: 9.86 ounces	Weight: 255.55 ounces

PROBLEM SOLVING 3-9

LESSON 3-9 Problem Solving
Solving Decimal Equations

Write the correct answer.

1. Bee hummingbirds weigh only 0.0056 ounces. They have to eat half their body weight every day to survive. How much food does a bee hummingbird have to eat each day?
0.0028 ounces

2. The desert locust, a type of grasshopper, can jump 10 times the length of its body. The locust is 1.956 inches long. How far can it jump in one leap?
19.56 inches

3. In 1900, there were about 1.49 million people living in California. In 2000, the population was 33.872 million. How much did the population grow between 1900 and 2000?
by 32.382 million

4. Juanita has $567.89 in her checking account. After she deposited her paycheck and paid her rent of $450.00, she had $513.82 left in the account. How much was her paycheck?
$395.93

Circle the letter of the correct answer.

5. The average body temperature for people is 98.6°F. The average body temperature for most dogs is 3.4°F higher than for people. The average body temperature for cats is 0.5°F lower than for dogs. What is the normal body temperature for dogs and cats?
A dogs: 101.5°F; cats 102°F
(B) dogs: 102°F; cats 101.5°F
C dogs: 102.5°F; cats 103°F
D dogs: 102.5°F; cats 102.5°F

6. Seattle, Washington, is famous for its rainy climate. Winter is the rainiest season there. From November through December the city gets an average of 5.85 inches of rain each month. Seattle usually gets 6 inches of rain in December. What is the city's average rainfall in November?
F 6 inches
G 5.925 inches
H 5.8 inches
(J) 5.7 inches

7. The equation to convert from Celsius to Kelvin degrees is K = 273.16 + C. If it is 303.66°K outside, what is the temperature in Celsius degrees?
A 576.82°C
(B) 30.5°C
C 305°C
D 257.68°C

8. The distance around a square mirror is 6.8 feet. Which of the following equations finds the length of each side of the mirror?
F $6.8 - x = 4$
G $x \div 4 = 6.8$
(H) $4x = 6.8$
J $6.8 + 4 = x$

Power Presentations with PowerPoint®

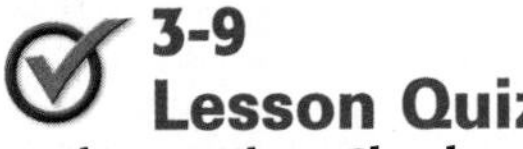

3-9 Lesson Quiz

Solve each equation. Check your answer.

1. $x - 3.9 = 14.2$ $x = 18.1$
2. $\frac{x}{4} = 8.3$ $x = 33.2$
3. $x - 4.9 = 16.2$ $x = 21.1$
4. $7x = 47.6$ $x = 6.8$
5. The area of the floor in Devon's room is 35.7 m^2. If the width is 4.2 m, what is the length of the bedroom? **8.5 m**

Also available on transparency

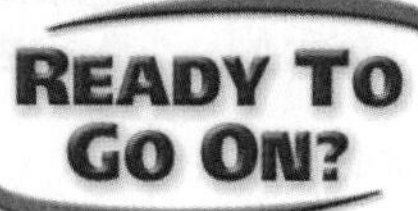

Organizer

Objective: Assess students' mastery of concepts and skills in Lessons 3-4 through 3-9.

Resources

 ***Assessment Resources***
Section 3B Quiz

INTERVENTION 

Resources

 *Ready to Go On? Intervention and Enrichment* Worksheets

 *Ready to Go On?* CD-ROM

 *Ready to Go On?* Online

my.hrw.com

CHAPTER 3 SECTION 3B

Ready to Go On?

Quiz for Lessons 3-4 Through 3-9

3-4 Scientific Notation

Find each product.

1. $516 \times 10{,}000$ 5,160,000
2. 16.82×100 1,682
3. $5{,}217 \times 1{,}000$ 5,217,000

Write each number in scientific notation.

4. 102,000 1.02×10^5
5. 5,480,000 5.48×10^6
6. 100,000,000 1×10^8

3-5 Multiplying Decimals

Evaluate $5x$ for each value of x.

7. $x = 1.025$ 5.125
8. $x = 6.2$ 31
9. $x = 2.64$ 13.2
10. Neptune has a gravitational pull 1.2 times that of Earth. If an object weighs 15 pounds on Earth, how much would it weigh on Neptune? 18 pounds

3-6 Dividing Decimals by Whole Numbers

Find each quotient.

11. $17.5 \div 5$ 3.5
12. $11.6 \div 8$ 1.45
13. $23.4 \div 6$ 3.9
14. $35.5 \div 5$ 7.1
15. Five apples cost \$4.90. How much does each apple cost? \$0.98

3-7 Dividing Decimals

Find each quotient.

16. $2.226 \div 0.42$ 5.3
17. $13.49 \div 7.1$ 1.9
18. $35.34 \div 6.2$ 5.7
19. $178.64 \div 81.2$ 2.2
20. Peri spent \$21.89 on material to make a skirt. The material cost \$3.98 per yard. How many yards did Peri buy? 5.5 yards

3-8 Interpret the Quotient

21. There are 352 students graduating from high school. The photographer takes one picture of each student as the student receives his or her diploma. If the photographer has 36 exposures on each roll of film, how many rolls will she have to buy to take each student's picture? 10 rolls

3-9 Solving Decimal Equations

Solve each equation.

22. $t - 6.3 = 8.9$ $t = 15.2$
23. $4h = 20.4$ $h = 5.1$
24. $\frac{p}{7} = 4.6$ $p = 32.2$
25. $d + 2.8 = 9.5$ $d = 6.7$

READY TO GO ON? Diagnose and Prescribe

NO INTERVENE

Ready to Go On? Intervention	*Ready to Go On? Intervention*, Section 3B Worksheets	CD-ROM	Online
Lesson 3-4	3-4 Intervention	Activity 3-4	Diagnose and Prescribe Online
Lesson 3-5	3-5 Intervention	Activity 3-5	
Lesson 3-6	3-6 Intervention	Activity 3-6	
Lesson 3-7	3-7 Intervention	Activity 3-7	
Lesson 3-8	3-8 Intervention	Activity 3-8	
Lesson 3-9	3-9 Intervention	Activity 3-9	

YES ENRICH

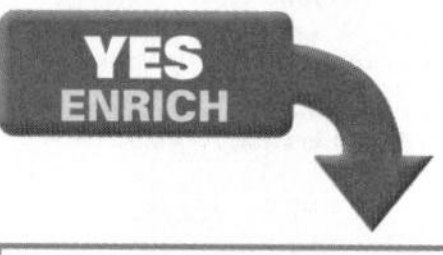

MULTI-STEP TEST PREP

Read All About It! Most Americans read a newspaper at least once a week. In fact, about 55 million newspapers are sold in the United States each day. The table shows the approximate daily circulation of some of the most popular U.S. newspapers.

1. Order the newspapers from the least daily circulation to the greatest.
2. Estimate the total circulation of the eight newspapers. Explain how you made your estimate.
3. The *Wall Street Journal*, the *New York Post*, and the *New York Times* are all published in New York. What is the total circulation for these newspapers? **3,862,000**
4. Write the circulation of the *Wall Street Journal* in scientific notation. (*Hint:* 2.09 million is the same as 2,090,000.) **2.09×10^6**
5. The circulation of *USA Today* is about 4.2 times the circulation of the *San Francisco Chronicle*. Find the circulation of *USA Today*. **2,154,600**
6. The daily circulation of the *Los Angeles Times* is about 3 times the daily circulation of the *Orange County Register*. Write and solve an equation to find the daily circulation of the *Orange County Register*.
$0.915 = 3x$; $x = 0.305$; the circulation of the *Orange County Register* is about 305,000.

U.S. Newspaper Circulation	
Newspaper	**Daily Circulation (Millions)**
Chicago Tribune	0.681
Dallas Morning News	0.51
Houston Chronicle	0.553
Los Angeles Times	0.915
New York Post	0.652
New York Times	1.12
San Francisco Chronicle	0.513
Wall Street Journal	2.09

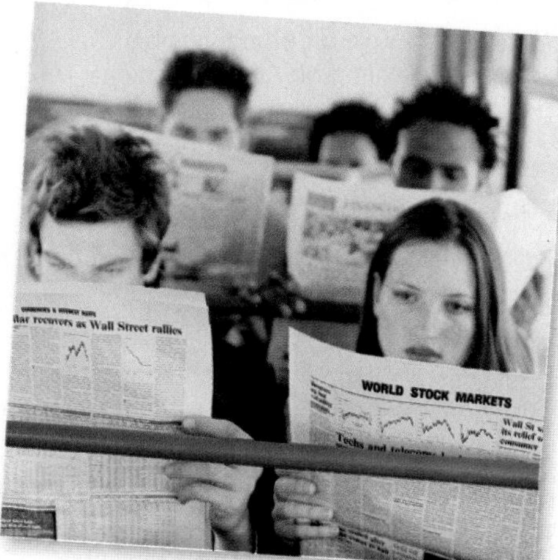

Organizer

Objective: Assess students' ability to apply concepts and skills in Chapter 3 in a real-world format.

 **Online Edition**

Resources

 ***Middle School Assessments***
www.mathtekstoolkit.org

Problem	Text Reference
1	Lesson 3-1
2	Lesson 3-2
3	Lesson 3-3
4	Lesson 3-4
5	Lesson 3-5
6	Lesson 3-9

Answers

1. *Dallas Morning News, San Francisco Chronicle, Houston Chronicle, New York Post, Chicago Tribune, Los Angeles Times, New York Times, Wall Street Journal*
2. 7.5 million; three paper circulations were rounded to 0.5, four paper circulations were rounded to 1, and one paper circulation was rounded to 2

INTERVENTION 

Scaffolding Questions

1. Which newspaper has the smallest circulation? Dallas Morning News Which newspaper has the largest circulation? Wall Street Journal
2. How can you use rounding to help make the estimate? Round each decimal to 0.5, 1, or 2.
3. What operation should you use to solve this problem? addition What decimals should you add? 2.09, 1.12, and 0.652
4. What is the first step in writing 2,090,000 in scientific notation? Move the decimal point left to form a number greater than 1 and less than 10.
5. What operation should you use to solve the problem? multiplication What product do you need to find? 4.2×0.513 How many decimal places will the product have? 4
6. What should the variable in the equation represent? the circulation of the *Orange County Register* How can you translate the problem into an equation? $3x = 0.915$ How can you solve the equation? divide both sides by 3.

Extension

1. How many more copies of the *New York Times* are sold each day than the *Chicago Tribune*? 0.439 million or 439,000
2. Are more than 10 million copies of the *Wall Street Journal* sold each Monday to Friday? Why or why not? Yes; 5×2.09 is greater than 5×2, which is 10.

Game Time

Organizer

Objective: Participate in games to practice and apply skills learned in Chapter 3.

 **Online Edition**

Resources

 ***Chapter 3 Resource Book***
Puzzles, Twisters & Teasers

Jumbles

Purpose: *To apply the skill of using operations with decimals to solving a riddle*

Discuss Discuss with students the best way to order a large group of numbers. Possible answer: Make several different lists (e.g., numbers less than 1, numbers between 1 and 2, 2 and 3, etc.). Order the numbers within each list, and then combine the lists so that the entire set is ordered from least to greatest.

Extend Challenge students to create a puzzle using decimal operations and their favorite riddle. Have them trade riddles and solve.

Make a Buck

Purpose: *To practice adding decimals by playing a money game*

Discuss Suppose the sum of the values on the cards in your hand is \$0.67. You draw the wild card. What value should you assign the wild card in order to win a point? \$0.33

Extend Have students play the game again, altering the rules so that each player is allowed 8 cards in his or her hand and the target sum is \$2.00.

Game Time

Jumbles

Do you know what eleven plus two equals?

Use your calculator to evaluate each expression. Keep the letters under the expressions with the answers you get. Then order the answers from least to greatest, and write down the letters in that order. You will spell the answer to the riddle. TWELVE PLUS ONE

4 − 1.893	0.21 ÷ 0.3	0.443 − 0.0042	4.509 − 3.526	3.14 · 2.44	1.56 · 3.678
E (2.107)	L (0.7)	E (.4388)	V (.983)	E (7.6616)	N (5.73768)

6.34 ÷ 2.56	1.19 + 1.293	8.25 ÷ 2.5	7.4 − 2.356
P (2.4765625)	L (2.483)	U (3.3)	S (5.044)

0.0003 + 0.003	0.3 · 0.04	2.17 + 3.42
T (0.0033)	W (.012)	O (5.59)

Make A Buck

The object of the game is to win the most points by adding decimal numbers to make a sum close to but not over \$1.00.

Most cards have a decimal number on them representing an amount of money. Others are wild cards: The person who receives a wild card decides its value.

The dealer gives each player four cards. Taking turns, players add the numbers in their hand. If the sum is less than \$1.00, a player can either draw a card from the top of the deck or pass.

When each player has taken a turn or passed, the player whose sum is closest to but not over \$1.00 scores a point. If players tie for the closest sum, each of those players scores a point. All cards are then discarded and four new cards are dealt to each player.

When all of the cards have been dealt, the player with the most points wins.

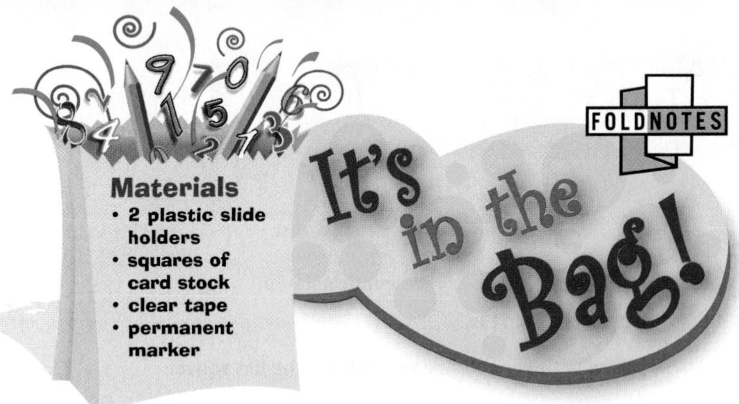

PROJECT Project E Z 2 C Decimals

Practice reading decimals by making this see-through decimal holder.

Directions

1. Cut out about 40 small squares of colored card stock. Remove ten of the squares. On these squares, write "Ones," "Tens," "Hundreds," "Thousands," "Ten-Thousands," "Tenths," "Hundredths," "Thousandths," "Ten-Thousandths," and "Hundred-Thousandths." **Figure A**
2. On each of the remaining squares, write a number from 0 to 9.
3. Tape the two slide holders together. Using a permanent marker, draw decimal points down the middle where the holders are taped together. **Figure B**
4. Put the squares with the names of the place values in the correct slots along the top row.

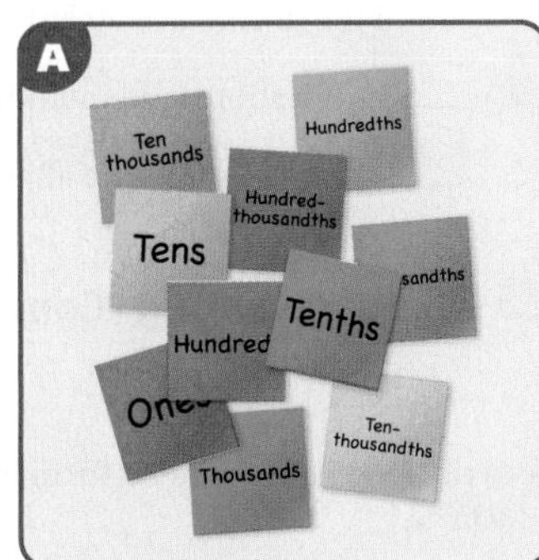

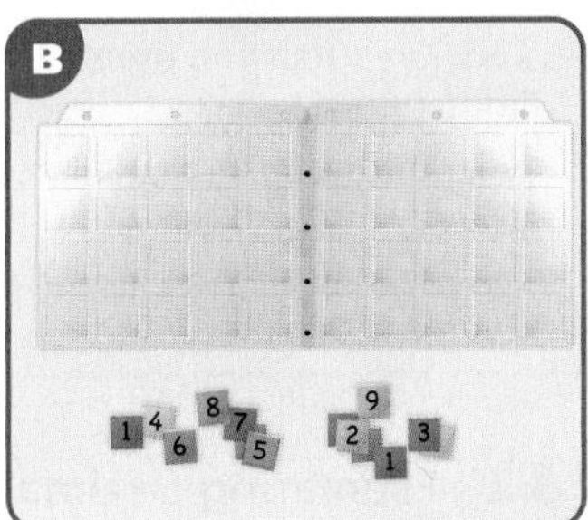

Putting the Math into Action

Put numbered squares in the remaining slots. Work with a partner to practice reading the resulting decimals. Mix up the numbered squares and repeat the process several more times, sometimes using all of the slots in a row and sometimes making shorter decimals.

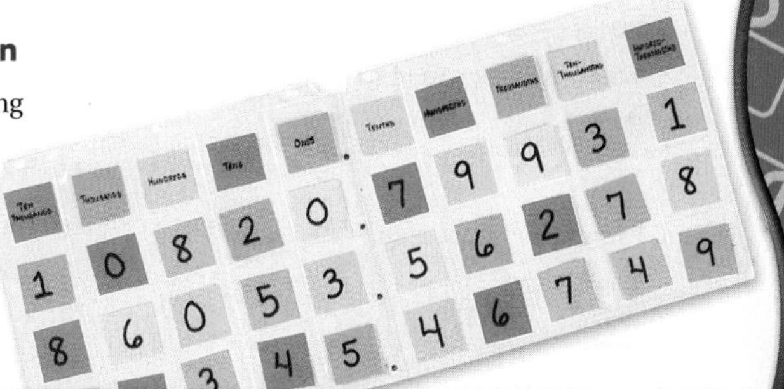

Organizer

Objective: Make a decimal holder that gives students practice in reading decimals.

Materials: 2 plastic slide holders, about 40 squares of colored cardstock (approx. 1 in. by 1 in.), clear tape, black permanent marker

Online Edition

Using the Page

Preparing the Materials
Before beginning the project, ask students to name the place-value positions to the left and right of the decimal point. These names will be written on the squares that go across the top row of the decimal holder.

Making the Project
As students make the numbered squares, have them underscore the 6 and the 9 so that they can tell them apart later on.

Extending the Project
Challenge students to create the largest number possible using the available numbered squares.

Tips from the Bag Ladies!

You can find slide holders at office-supply stores and photo-developing centers. If you want to extend the project, get extra slide holders and have students tape three or more of them together. This will make it possible for students to create very large or very small numbers.

Once the decimal holders have been made, there are lots of ways to use them! For example, you might have students put the numbered squares into a hat and choose them at random before placing them into the slots.

CHAPTER 3 Study Guide: Review

Organizer

Objective: Help students organize and review key concepts and skills presented in Chapter 3.

Online Edition
Multilingual Glossary

Resources

PuzzlePro®
One-Stop Planner®

***Multilingual Glossary* Online**

go.hrw.com
KEYWORD: MR7 Glossary

Lesson Tutorial Videos
CD-ROM

Test & Practice Generator
One-Stop Planner®

Answers

1. front-end estimation
2. scientific notation
3. clustering
4. 5 + 0.6 + 0.08; five and sixty-eight hundredths
5. 1 + 0.007 + 0.0006; one and seventy-six ten-thousandths
6. 1 + 0.2 + 0.003; one and two hundred three thousandths
7. 20 + 3 + 0.005; twenty-three and five thousandths
8. 70 + 1 + 0.03 + 0.008; seventy-one and thirty-eight thousandths
9. 90 + 9 + 0.9 + 0.09 + 0.009 + 0.0009; ninety-nine and nine thousand, nine hundred ninety-nine ten thousandths
10. 1.12, 1.2, 1.3
11. 11.07, 11.17, 11.7
12. 0.033, 0.3, 0.303
13. 5.009, 5.5, 5.950
14. 101.025, 101.25, 101.52
15. 11.32
16. 2.3
17. 14
18. 80
19. 9
20. 5

CHAPTER 3 Study Guide: Review

Vocabulary

clustering 112
front-end estimation 113
scientific notation 124

Complete the sentences below with vocabulary words from the list above.

1. When you estimate a sum by using only the whole-number part of the decimals, you are using __?__.
2. __?__ is a shorthand method for writing large numbers.
3. __?__ means rounding all the numbers to the same value.

3-1 Representing, Comparing, and Ordering Decimals (pp. 108–111)

GPS M6N1.g

EXAMPLE

- **Write 4.025 in expanded form and words.**

  Expanded form: 4 + 0.02 + 0.005

  Word form: four and twenty-five thousandths

- **Order the decimals from least to greatest. 7.8, 7.83, 7.08**

  7.08 < 7.80 < 7.83 *Compare the numbers.*
  7.08, 7.8, 7.83 *Then order the numbers.*

EXERCISES

Write each in expanded form and words.

4. 5.68
5. 1.0076
6. 1.203
7. 23.005
8. 71.038
9. 99.9999

Order the decimals from least to greatest.

10. 1.2, 1.3, 1.12
11. 11.17, 11.7, 11.07
12. 0.3, 0.303, 0.033
13. 5.009, 5.950, 5.5
14. 101.52, 101.25, 101.025

3-2 Estimating Decimals (pp. 112–115)

GPS M6N1.g

EXAMPLE

- **Estimate.**

  5.35 − 0.7904; round to tenths

  5.4 *Align the decimals.*
  − 0.8 *Subtract.*
  4.6

- **Estimate 49.67 × 2.88.**

  49.67 × 2.88
  50 × 3 = 150

EXERCISES

Estimate.

15. 8.0954 + 3.218; round to the hundredths
16. 6.8356 − 4.507; round to the tenths
17. 9.258 + 4.97; round to the ones

Estimate each product or quotient.

18. 21.19 × 4.23
19. 53.98 ÷ 5.97
20. 102.89 × 19.95

3-3 Adding and Subtracting Decimals (pp. 118–121)

GPS M6N1.g

EXAMPLE

■ **Find the sum.**

7.62 + 0.563

7.620 *Align the decimal points.*
+ 0.563 *Use zeros as placeholders.*
8.183 *Add. Place the decimal point.*

EXERCISES

Find each sum or difference.

21. 7.08 + 4.5 + 13.27 **22.** 6 − 0.7
23. 6.21 + 5.8 + 21.01 **24.** 7.001 − 2.0785
25. 5.1 + 7.98 + 19.25 **26.** 15.704 − 1.08

Evaluate 6.48 − s for each value of s.

27. $s = 3.9$ **28.** $s = 3.6082$
29. $s = 5.01$ **30.** $s = 0.057$
31. $s = 4.48$ **32.** $s = 1.65$

3-4 Scientific Notation (pp. 124–127)

GPS M6N1.g

EXAMPLE

■ **Find the product.**

326 × 10,000 *Move the decimal point 4 places right.*
= 326.0000
= 3,260,000 *Write 4 placeholder zeros.*

■ **Write the number in scientific notation.**

60,000 *Move the decimal point 4 places to the left.*
$= 6.0 \times 10^4$

■ **Write each number in standard form.**

7.18×10^5
= 718,000 *Move the decimal point 5 places right.*

EXERCISES

Find each product.

33. 12.6 × 10,000 **34.** 546 × 100
35. 67 × 100,000 **36.** 180.6 × 1,000
37. 4.2 × 1,000 **38.** 78.9 × 100

Write each number in scientific notation.

39. 550,000 **40.** 7,230
41. 1,300,000 **42.** 14.8
43. 902.4 **44.** 891,402,000

Write each number in standard form.

45. 3.02×10^4 **46.** 4.293×10^5
47. 1.7×10^6 **48.** 5.39×10^3
49. 6.85×10^2 **50.** 1.45×10^7

3-5 Multiplying Decimals (pp. 130–133)

GPS M6A3, M6N1.g

EXAMPLE

■ **Find the product.**

0.3 *1 decimal place*
× 0.08 *+ 2 decimal places*
0.024 *3 decimal places*

EXERCISES

Find each product.

51. 4 × 2.36 **52.** 0.5 × 1.73
53. 0.6 × 0.012 **54.** 8 × 3.052
55. 1.2 × 0.45 **56.** 9.7 × 1.084
57. 9 × 1.08 **58.** 7.2 × 5.49

Study Guide: Review

Answers

21. 24.85
22. 5.3
23. 33.02
24. 4.9225
25. 32.33
26. 14.624
27. 2.58
28. 2.8718
29. 1.47
30. 6.423
31. 2
32. 4.83
33. 126,000
34. 54,600
35. 6,700,000
36. 180,600
37. 4,200
38. 7,890
39. 5.5×10^5
40. 7.23×10^3
41. 1.3×10^6
42. 1.48×10^1
43. 9.024×10^2
44. 8.91402×10^8
45. 30,200
46. 429,300
47. 1,700,000
48. 5,390
49. 685
50. 14,500,000
51. 9.44
52. 0.865
53. 0.0072
54. 24.416
55. 0.54
56. 10.5148
57. 9.72
58. 39.528

Answers

59. 1.03
60. 0.72
61. 3.85
62. 2.59
63. $3.64
64. 8.1
65. $6.1\overline{6}$
66. $3.87\overline{6}$
67. 52.275
68. 0.75 meter
69. 14 containers
70. 9 cars
71. $a = 13.38$
72. $y = 2.62$
73. $n = 2.29$
74. $p = 60.2$
75. $5.00

3-6 Dividing Decimals by Whole Numbers (pp. 134–136)

EXAMPLE

■ **Find the quotient.**

0.95 ÷ 5

Place a decimal point directly above the decimal point in the dividend. Then divide.

$$5\overline{)0.95} = 0.19$$

EXERCISES

Find each quotient.

59. 6.18 ÷ 6 **60.** 2.16 ÷ 3

61. 34.65 ÷ 9 **62.** 20.72 ÷ 8

63. If four people equally share a bill for $14.56, how much should each person pay?

3-7 Dividing by Decimals (pp. 137–140)

EXAMPLE

■ **Find the quotient.**

9.65 ÷ 0.5

Make the divisor a whole number.
Place the decimal point in the quotient.

$$5\overline{)96.5} = 19.3$$

EXERCISES

Find each quotient.

64. 4.86 ÷ 0.6 **65.** 1.85 ÷ 0.3

66. 34.89 ÷ 9 **67.** 62.73 ÷ 1.2

68. Ana cuts some wood that is 3.75 meters long into 5 pieces of equal length. How long is each piece?

3-8 Interpret the Quotient (pp. 141–143)

EXAMPLE

■ **Ms. Ald needs 26 stickers for her preschool class. Stickers are sold in packs of 8. How many packs should she buy?**

26 ÷ 8 = 3.25

3.25 is between 3 and 4.
3 packs will not be enough.

Ms. Ald should buy 4 packs of stickers.

EXERCISES

69. Billy has 3.6 liters of juice. How many 0.25 L containers can he fill?

70. There are 34 people going on a field trip. If each car holds 4 people, how many cars will they need for the field trip?

3-9 Solving Decimal Equations (pp. 144–147)

GPS M6A3., M6N1.g

EXAMPLE

■ **Solve $4x = 20.8$.**

$4x = 20.8$ *x is multiplied by 4.*

$\frac{4x}{4} = \frac{20.8}{4}$ *Divide both sides by 4.*

$x = 5.2$

EXERCISES

Solve each equation.

71. $a - 6.2 = 7.18$ **72.** $3y = 7.86$

73. $n + 4.09 = 6.38$ **74.** $\frac{p}{7} = 8.6$

75. Jasmine buys 2.25 kg of apples for $11.25. How much does 1 kg of apples cost?

Study Guide: Review

CHAPTER TEST

CHAPTER 3

1. The New York Philharmonic Orchestra performs at Avery Fisher Hall in New York City. It seats 2,738 people. The Boston Symphony Orchestra performs at Symphony Hall in Boston, Massachusetts. It seats 2,625 people. Which hall seats more people? **Avery Fisher Hall**

Order the decimals from least to greatest.

2. 12.6, 12.07, 12.67 **12.07, 12.6, 12.67**
3. 3.5, 3.25, 3.08 **3.08, 3.25, 3.5**
4. 0.10301, 0.10318, 0.10325 **0.10301, 0.10318, 0.10325**

Estimate by rounding to the indicated place value.

5. 6.178 − 0.2805; hundredths **5.90**
6. 7.528 + 6.075; ones **14**

Estimate.

7. 21.35 × 3.18 **60**
8. 98.547 ÷ 4.93 **20**
9. 11.855 × 8.45 **96**

Estimate a range for each sum.

10. 3.89 + 42.71 + 12.32 **at least 57, but not more than 59.5**
11. 20.751 + 2.55 + 17.4 **at least 39, but not more than 41**
12. 4.987 + 28.27 + 0.098 **at least 32, but not more than 33.5**

13. Britney wants to exercise in a step aerobics class. The class uses the 4-inch step for 15 minutes and the 6-inch step for 15 minutes. About how many calories will she burn in all? **about 150 calories**

Step Height (in.)	Calories Burned in 15 minutes
4	67.61
6	82.2
8	96

Evaluate.

14. 0.76 + 2.24 **3**
15. 7 − 0.4 **6.6**
16. 0.12 × 0.006 **0.00072**
17. 5.85 ÷ 3.9 **1.5**

Find each product.

18. 516 × 10,000 **5,160,000**
19. 16.82 × 100 **1,682**
20. 521.7 × 100,000 **52,170,000**
21. 423.6 × 1,000 **423,600**

Write each number in scientific notation.

22. 16,900 1.69×10^4
23. 180,500 1.805×10^5
24. 3,190,000 3.19×10^6

Write each number in standard form.

25. 3.08×10^5 **308,000**
26. 1.472×10^6 **1,472,000**
27. 2.973×10^4 **29,730**

Solve each equation.

28. $b - 4.7 = 2.1$ $b = 6.8$
29. $5a = 4.75$ $a = 0.95$
30. $\frac{y}{6} = 7.2$ $y = 43.2$
31. $c + 1.9 = 26.04$ $c = 24.14$

32. The school band is going to a competition. There are 165 students in the band. If each bus holds 25 students, how many buses will be needed? **7 buses**

33. Six girls went shopping. All sweaters were on sale for the same price. Each girl chose a sweater. The total bill was $126.24. How much did each sweater cost? **$21.04**

Chapter Test

CHAPTER TEST

CHAPTER 3

Organizer

Objective: Assess students' mastery of concepts and skills in Chapter 3.

Online Edition

Resources

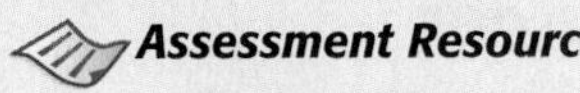

Assessment Resources

Chapter 3 Tests
- Free Response (Levels A, B, C)
- Multiple Choice (Levels A, B, C)
- Performance Assessment

***IDEA Works!* CD-ROM**
Modified Chapter 3 Test

Organizer

Objective: Provide opportunities to learn and practice common test-taking strategies.

Online Edition

Resources

 ***CRCT Prep* Workbook**

 ***CRCT Prep for MS and HS* CD-ROM**

 ***CRCT Practice* Online**

KEYWORD: MR7 TestPrep

TEST PREP DOCTOR This test tackler focuses on how to write a complete short-answer response using the two-point rubric. It is common for a student to quickly solve the problem without giving a full explanation or examples as directed by the question. Students should read the problem once to understand what is being asked and then again to underline the main point or question needed to answer the question completely. Terms such as "explain" or "show all work" should be stressed so that the student fulfils the requirements of the problem. Also, the student needs to know to never leave a short-answer response blank. At least some credit will be given for some work even if the answer is not correct.

Standardized Test Strategies

Test Tackler

Short Response: Write Short Responses

Short-response test items require a solution to the problem and the reasoning or work used to get that solution. Short-response test items are scored according to a 2-point scoring rubric. A sample scoring rubric is provided below.

EXAMPLE

Short Response Coach Mott needs to order jackets for the boys' basketball team. Each jacket costs $28.75. The team has $125 from their fund-raiser to go toward the total cost of the jackets. If there are 10 players on the team, how much money will each player need to give to Coach Mott for a jacket so he can place the order? Explain.

Scoring Rubric

2 points: The student correctly answers the question, shows all work, and provides a complete and correct explanation.

1 point: The student correctly answers the question but does not show all work or does not provide a complete explanation; or the student makes minor errors resulting in an incorrect solution but shows all work and provides a complete explanation.

0 points: The student gives an incorrect answer and shows no work or explanation, or the student gives no response.

2-point response:

Cost of one jacket: $28.75
Total cost for team jackets (10 players):
$28.75 × 10 = $287.50

Subtract the money the team already has from the total cost.
$287.50 − $125 = $162.50

Divide the remaining cost by the number of players on the team.
$162.50 ÷ 10 = $16.25

Each player needs to give Coach Mott $16.25 so he can place the order for the jackets.

1-point response:

($287.50 − $125) ÷ $10 = $16.25

He will need $16.25 from each player.

The student correctly solved the problem but did not show all of his or her work or did not provide an explanation.

0-point response:

$16.25

The student gave a correct answer but did not show any work or give an explanation.

Never leave a short-response test item blank. Showing your work and providing a reasonable explanation will result in at least some credit.

Read each test item and answer the questions that follow by using the scoring rubric below.

Item A
Short Response Write two equations that each have a solution of 12. You cannot use the same mathematical operation for both equations. Explain how to solve both equations.

Student's Answer

One equation that has a solution of 12 is $\frac{x}{6} = 2$. To solve this equation, I must undo the division by multiplying by 6 on both sides.

$$\frac{x}{6} = 2$$
$$6 \cdot \left(\frac{x}{6}\right) = 6 \cdot 2$$
$$x = 12$$

Another equation with a solution of 12 is $x - 8 = 20$.
To solve this equation, I must add the opposite of 8 to both sides.

$$x - 8 = 20$$
$$-8 = -8$$
$$x = 12$$

1. The student's answer will not receive full credit. Find the error in the student's answer.
2. Rewrite the student's answer so that it receives full credit.

Item B
Short Response June is 8 years older than her cousin Liv. Write an expression to find June's age. Identify the variable and list three possible solutions showing the ages of June and Liv.

Student's Answer

Let x = Liv's age. Since June is 8 years older, the expression $x + 8$ can be used to find June's age.
Three possible solutions for Liv and June follow:
$x = 3$, $3 + 8 = 11$; Liv: 3, June: 11
$x = 8$, $8 + 8 = 16$; Liv: 8, June: 16
$x = 11$, $11 + 8 = 19$; Liv: 11, June: 19

3. What score should the student's answer receive? Explain your reasoning.
4. What additional information, if any, should the student's answer include in order to receive full credit?

Item C
Short Response Write an equation to represent the following situation. Define the variable. Solve the problem. *Sam has two kittens. The larger kitten weighs 3.2 kg. The other kitten needs to gain 1.9 kg to weigh as much as the larger kitten. How much does the smaller kitten weigh?*

Student's Answer

Let x = the weight of the smaller kitten.
$x + 1.9 = 3.2$
$3.2 + 1.9 = 5.1$

5. How would you score the student's response? Explain.
6. Rewrite the response so that it receives full credit.

Test Tackler

As you practice short-answer responses, show students the difference between a 2-point, 1-point, and 0-point response. Challenge students to rewrite answers for any questions that do not have a 2-point response.

Answers

1. This student gets a score of 1 because the second equation does not have a solution of 12.
2. Another equation with a solution of 12 is $x - 8 = 4$. To solve this equation, I must add 8 to both sides.
$$x - 8 = 4$$
$$+8 + 8$$
$$x = 12$$
3. This answer gets a score of 2 points because the answer is correct and the results are clearly labeled.
4. No additional information is required.
5. This student gets a score of 1 point because the answer is incorrect. The student identified the variable and wrote an acceptable equation, but the solution is incorrect.
6. Let x = the weight of the smaller kitten.
$$x + 1.9 = 3.2$$
$$x + 1.9 = 3.2$$
$$-1.9 - 1.9$$
$$x = 1.3$$
I need to add the opposite of 1.9 to both sides to undo the addition.
The kitten needs to gain 1.3 kg to weigh as much as the larger kitten.

Organizer

Objective: Provide review and practice for Chapters 1–3 and standardized tests.

Online Edition

Resources

Assessment Resources
Chapter 3 Cumulative Test

***CRCT Prep* Workbook**

***CRCT Prep* CD-ROM**

***CRCT Practice* Online**

go.hrw.com
KEYWORD: MR7 TestPrep

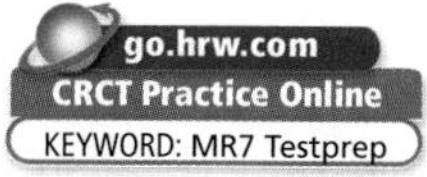

CUMULATIVE ASSESSMENT, CHAPTERS 1–3

Multiple Choice

1. Which of the following is the standard form for six and eighty-six thousandths?
   Ⓐ 6.860 Ⓒ 6.0086
   Ⓑ 6.086 Ⓓ 6.00086

2. The weights of three backpacks are 15.8 pounds, 18.1 pounds, and 16.7 pounds. About how many pounds do the backpacks weigh all together?
   Ⓕ 30 pounds Ⓗ 50 pounds
   Ⓖ 40 pounds Ⓙ 60 pounds

3. For which equation is $c = 8$ NOT a solution?
   Ⓐ $\frac{c}{4} = 2$ Ⓒ $4c = 28$
   Ⓑ $c + 4 = 12$ Ⓓ $c - 5 = 3$

4. Jerah scored 15 more points in a basketball game than his brother Jim did. Jim scored 7 points. Which expression can be used to find the number of points Jim scored?
   Ⓕ $15 - 7$ Ⓗ $15 \div 7$
   Ⓖ 15×7 Ⓙ $15 + 7$

5. Find the sum of 1.4 and 0.9.
   Ⓐ 0.1 Ⓒ 1.3
   Ⓑ 0.5 Ⓓ 2.3

6. Which number is the greatest?
   Ⓕ 18.095 Ⓗ 18.907
   Ⓖ 18.9 Ⓙ 18.75

7. The heights of four different plants are listed below. Which statement is supported by the data?

Plant Height (in.)				
Plant	T	S	U	W
Week 1	15.9	23.6	17.1	12.5
Week 2	21.4	27.4	22.9	16.4

   Ⓐ Plant T was the shortest during week 1.
   Ⓑ Plant S grew more than 4 inches between week 1 and week 2.
   Ⓒ Plant U grew the most between week 1 and week 2.
   Ⓓ Plant W is the tallest.

8. What is the value of 3^4?
   Ⓕ 7 Ⓗ 81
   Ⓖ 12 Ⓙ 96

9. There are 58,000 seats in a football stadium. Which of the following is the correct way to write 58,000 in scientific notation?
   Ⓐ 580×10^2 Ⓒ 5.8×10^4
   Ⓑ 58×10^3 Ⓓ 0.58×10^5

10. Tomas needs 42 cups for a party. The cups are sold in packages of 5. How many packages should he buy?
   Ⓕ 10 packages Ⓗ 8 packages
   Ⓖ 9 packages Ⓙ 7 packages

11. What is $7.89 \div 3$?
   Ⓐ 263 Ⓒ 0.263
   Ⓑ 26.3 Ⓓ 2.63

CRCT Prep

For item 10, remind the students to interpret the quotient. Some might make the mistake of rounding their answer after dividing 42 by 5. Remind them that the remainder in this problem means that another package of cups is needed.

Answers

18. $5b = 43.75$; $b = 8.75$

19a. 17 packs; Possible answer: She has 64 pencils, and she needs 136 more pencils to have a total of 200.
$136 \div 8 = 17$

b. $13.43

20. See 4-Point Response work sample.

12. Which set of numbers is in order from least to greatest?

Ⓕ 23.7, 23.07, 23.13, 23.89

Ⓖ 21.4, 21.45, 21.79, 21.8

Ⓗ 22, 22.09, 21.9, 22.1

Ⓙ 25.4, 25.09, 25.6, 25.7

13. Megan is beginning an exercise routine. She plans to walk 1 mile on day 1 and increase her distance each day by 0.25 mile. How many miles will she be walking on day 10?

Ⓐ 2.5 miles Ⓒ 4.75 miles

Ⓑ 3.25 miles Ⓓ 6.0 miles

Estimate your answer before solving the question. Use your estimate to check the reasonableness of your answer.

14. What is the value of c in the equation $\frac{c}{6} = 3.4$?

Ⓕ 0.57 Ⓗ 9.4

Ⓖ 4 Ⓙ 20.4

15. What is the missing term in the following sequence?

5, 12, 26, 47, ■, 110, . . .

Ⓐ 68 Ⓒ 78.5

Ⓑ 75 Ⓓ 99

16. Cindy bought 3 bunches of daisies and 4 bunches of carnations. There are 6 daisies and 10 carnations in a bunch. How many flowers does she have in all?

Ⓕ 58 Ⓗ 112

Ⓖ 72 Ⓙ 720

17. Bart and his 2 friends buy lunch. The total is \$13.74. If they share the cost equally, how much, in dollars, should each person pay?

Ⓐ \$4.58 Ⓒ \$6.37

Ⓑ \$5.87 Ⓓ \$6.87

STANDARDIZED TEST PREP

Short Response

18. Kevin buys 5 steaks for \$43.75. Let b equal the cost of one steak. Write and solve the equation to find the cost of one steak.

19. Ms. Maier has 8 packs of pencils to give out to students taking a state test. Each pack has 8 pencils. There are 200 students taking the test who need pencils.

a. How many more packs of pencils does Ms. Maier need to buy? Explain your answer and show your work.

b. If each pack of pencils costs \$0.79, how much money will Ms. Maier need to spend to buy the extra pencils? Show your work.

Extended Response

20. Admission to the Children's Museum is listed below. Use the chart to answer the following questions.

Admission Costs (\$)	
Adult	7.50
Child	5.75

a. Write an expression to find the cost of admission for 2 adults and c children.

b. Use your expression to find the total cost for Mr. and Mrs. Chu and their 8-year-old triplets. Show your work.

c. If Mr. Chu pays for admission using a \$50 bill, how much change does he get back? Show your work.

d. On the Chu's next visit, Mrs. Chu plans to use a coupon and will only pay \$28.50 for the family. How much will she save using the coupon?

CRCT Prep

Short Response Rubric

Items 18–19

2 Points = The student's answer is an accurate and complete execution of the task or tasks.

1 Point = The student's answer contains attributes of an appropriate response but is flawed.

0 Points = The student's answer contains no attributes of an appropriate response.

Extended Response Rubric

Item 20

4 Points = The student demonstrates a thorough understanding of all concepts and all work is shown correctly.

3 Points = The student demonstrates a basic understanding of all concepts, but the work shows some flaws reflecting inattentive execution of mathematical procedures or some misunderstanding of the underlying mathematics.

2 Points = The student demonstrates only a partial understanding of the concepts and/or procedures embodied in the tasks. The approach may be correct but the work shows a misunderstanding of one or more important concepts.

1 Point = The student demonstrates a very limited understanding of the concepts and/or procedures embodied in the tasks. The response may show some understanding but exhibits many flaws and/or is incomplete.

0 Points = The student has provided no response at all, or a completely incorrect or uninterpretable response.

Student Work Samples for Item 20

4-Point Response

a. 15 + 5.75c

b. 15 + 5.75(3)
15 + 17.25
\$32.25

c. Mr. Lopez will receive \$17.75 in change because 50 − 32.25 = 17.75.

d. They would save \$3.75.

The student's answers are correct. All work asked for is shown and questions were answered in complete sentences.

3-Point Response

a. 15 + 5.75c

b. 15 + 5.75 (3)
\$32.25

c. 50 − 32.25 = 27.75

d. \$3.75

The student's answers are correct except for part **c.** Work is not shown when asked for and questions were not answered in complete sentences.

2-Point Response

a. 15 + 5.75c

b. 15 + 5.75(5)
\$43.75

c. \$6.25

d. \$5.25

A mistake was made in substitution in part **b,** making other answers incorrect. No work is shown and questions are not answered in complete sentences.

CHAPTER 4

Number Theory and Fractions

Section 4A
Number Theory

- 4-1 Divisibility
- 4-2 Hands-On Lab Explore Factors
- 4-2 Factors and Prime Factorization
- 4-3 Greatest Common Factor
- 4-3 Technology Lab Greatest Common Factor

Section 4B
Understanding Fractions

- 4-4 Hands-On Lab Explore Decimals and Fractions
- 4-4 Decimals and Fractions
- 4-5 Hands-On Lab Model Equivalent Fractions
- 4-5 Equivalent Fractions
- 4-5B Hands-On Lab Explore Fraction Measurement
- 4-6 Mixed Numbers and Improper Fractions

Section 4C
Introduction to Fraction Operations

- 4-7 Comparing and Ordering Fractions
- 4-8 Adding and Subtracting with Like Denominators
- 4-9 Estimating Fraction Sums and Differences
- EXTENSION Sets of Numbers

Pacing Guide for 45-Minute Classes

Chapter 4

Countdown to Testing Weeks 7, 8, 9

DAY 1	DAY 2	DAY 3	DAY 4	DAY 5
4-1 Lesson	4-2 Hands-On Lab 4-2 Lesson	4-2 Lesson 4-3 Lesson	4-3 Lesson	4-3 Technology Lab Ready to Go On? Focus on Problem Solving
DAY 6	**DAY 7**	**DAY 8**	**DAY 9**	**DAY 10**
4-4 Hands-On Lab 4-4 Lesson	4-4 Lesson 4-5 Hands-On Lab	4-5 Lesson	4-5 Hands-On Lab 4-6 Lesson	4-6 Lesson Ready to Go On? Focus on Problem Solving
DAY 11	**DAY 12**	**DAY 13**	**DAY 14**	**DAY 15**
4-7 Lesson	4-8 Lesson	4-9 Lesson	4-9 Lesson Ready to Go On? Multi-Step Test Prep	EXTENSION
DAY 16	**DAY 17**			
Chapter 4 Review	Chapter 4 Test			

Pacing Guide for 90-Minute Classes

Chapter 4

DAY 1	DAY 2	DAY 3	DAY 4	DAY 5
4-1 Lesson 4-2 Hands-On Lab 4-2 Lesson	4-2 Lesson 4-3 Lesson	4-3 Technology Lab Ready to Go On? Focus on Problem Solving 4-4 Hands-On Lab 4-4 Lesson	4-4 Lesson 4-5 Hands-On Lab 4-5 Lesson	4-5 Hands-On Lab 4-6 Lesson Ready to Go On? Focus on Problem Solving
DAY 6	**DAY 7**	**DAY 8**	**DAY 9**	
4-7 Lesson 4-8 Lesson	4-9 Lesson Ready to Go On? Multi-Step Test Prep	EXTENSION Chapter 4 Review	Chapter 4 Test	

ONGOING ASSESSMENT and INTERVENTION

	DIAGNOSE	PRESCRIBE
Assess Prior Knowledge	**Before Chapter 4**	
	Diagnose readiness for the chapter.	Prescribe intervention.
	Are You Ready? SE p. 161	***Are You Ready? Intervention*** Skills 7, 8, 15, 64
Formative Assessment	**Before Every Lesson**	
	Diagnose readiness for the lesson.	Prescribe intervention.
	Warm Up TE, every lesson	**Skills Bank** SE pp. 749–761
		Reteach CRB, Chapters 1–4
	During Every Lesson	
	Diagnose understanding of lesson concepts.	Prescribe intervention.
	Think and Discuss SE, every lesson	***Questioning Strategies*** pp. 49–66
	Write About It SE, lesson exercises	**Reading Strategies** CRB, every lesson
	Journal TE, lesson exercises	***Success for ELL*** pp. 49–66
	After Every Lesson	
	Diagnose mastery of lesson concepts.	Prescribe intervention.
	Lesson Quiz TE, every lesson	**Reteach** CRB, every lesson
	Test Prep SE, every lesson	**Problem Solving** CRB, every lesson
	Test and Practice Generator	**Test Prep Doctor** TE, lesson exercises
		***Homework Help* Online**
	Before Chapter 4 Testing	
	Diagnose mastery of concepts in the chapter.	Prescribe intervention.
	Ready to Go On? SE pp. 178, 210	***Ready to Go On? Intervention***
	Focus on Problem Solving SE p. 179	**Scaffolding Questions** TE p. 211
	Multi-Step Test Prep SE p. 211	
	Section Quizzes AR pp. 65–67	
	Test and Practice Generator	
	Before High Stakes Testing	
	Diagnose mastery of benchmark concepts.	Prescribe intervention.
	CRCT Prep SE pp. 220–221	***CRCT Prep Workbook***
	***CRCT Prep* CD-ROM**	
Summative Assessment	**After Chapter 4**	
	Check mastery of chapter concepts.	Prescribe intervention.
	Multiple-Choice Tests (Forms A, B, C)	**Reteach** CRB, every lesson
	Free-Response Tests (Forms A, B, C)	***Lesson Tutorial Videos*** Chapter 4
	Performance Assessment AR pp. 68–81	
	Test and Practice Generator	
	Check mastery of benchmark concepts.	Prescribe intervention.
	CRCT	***CRCT Prep Workbook***

KEY: **SE** = *Student Edition* **TE** = *Teacher's Edition* **CRB** = *Chapter Resource Book* **AR** = *Assessment Resources* Available on CD-ROM  Available online

CHAPTER 4

Supporting the Teacher

Chapter 4 Resource Book

Practice A, B, C
pp. 3–5, 12–14, 20–22, 28–30,37–39, 45–47, 53–55, 62–64, 70–72

Reading Strategies ELL
pp. 10, 18, 26, 35, 43, 51, 60, 68, 76

Puzzles, Twisters, and Teasers
pp. 11, 19, 27, 36, 44, 52, 61, 69, 77

Reteach
pp. 6–7, 15, 23, 31–32, 40, 48, 56–57, 65, 73

Problem Solving
pp. 9, 17, 25, 34, 42, 50, 59, 67, 75

Challenge
pp. 8, 16, 24, 33, 41, 49, 58, 66, 74

Parent Letter pp. 1–2

Transparencies

Lesson Transparencies, Volume 1 .... Chapter 4
- Teaching Tools
- Warm Ups
- Problem of the Day
- Teaching Transparencies
- Lesson Quizzes

Know-It Notebook .... Chapter 4
- Additional Examples
- Graphic Organizers
- Vocabulary
- Chapter Review
- Foldnotes
- Big Ideas

Alternate Openers: Explorations .... pp. 25–33

Countdown to CRCT .... pp. 13–18

Teacher Tools

Power Presentations®
Complete PowerPoint® presentations for Chapter 4 lessons

Lesson Tutorial Videos® SPANISH
Holt authors Ed Burger and Freddie Renfro present tutorials to support the Chapter 4 lessons.

One-Stop Planner® SPANISH
Easy access to all Chapter 4 resources and assessments, as well as software for lesson planning, test generation, and puzzle creation

IDEA Works!®
Key Chapter 4 resources and assessments modified to address special learning needs

Lesson Plans .... pp. 25–33

Questioning Strategies .... pp. 49–66

Solutions Key .... Chapter 4

Interdisciplinary Posters and Worksheets .... Chapter 4

TechKeys

Lab Resources

Project Teacher Support

Parent Resources 

Workbooks

Homework and Practice Workbook SPANISH
Teacher's Edition .... pp. 25–33

Know-It Notebook
Teacher's Guide .... Chapter 4

Problem Solving Workbook SPANISH
Teacher's Guide .... pp. 25–33

CRCT Prep Workbook
Teacher's Guide

Technology Highlights for the Teacher

 **Power Presentations**

Dynamic presentations to engage students. Complete PowerPoint® presentations for every lesson in Chapter 4.

2-1 Solving One-Step Equations

Isolate a variable by using inverse operations which "undo" operations on the variable.

An equation is like a balanced scale. To keep the balance, perform the same operation on both sides.

Inverse Operations	
Operation	**Inverse Operation**
Addition	Subtraction
Subtraction	Addition

 **One-Stop Planner** SPANISH

Easy access to Chapter 4 resources and assessments. Includes lesson-planning, test-generation, and puzzle-creation software.

 **Premier Online Edition** SPANISH

Chapter 4 includes Tutorial Videos, Lesson Activities, Lesson Quizzes, Homework Help, and Chapter Project.

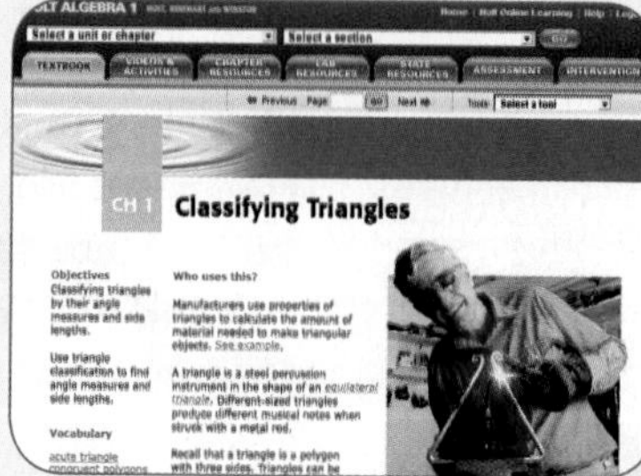

KEY: **SE** = *Student Edition* **TE** = *Teacher's Edition*  English Language Learners  Spanish version available  Available on CD-ROM 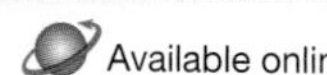 Available online

Reaching All Learners

Resources for All Learners

Hands-On Lab Activities ..... Chapter 4
Technology Lab Activities ..... Chapter 4
Homework and Practice Workbook SPANISH ..... pp. 25–33
Know-It Notebook SPANISH ..... Chapter 4
Problem Solving Workbook SPANISH ..... pp. 25–33

DEVELOPING LEARNERS

Practice A ..... CRB, every lesson
Reteach ..... CRB, every lesson
Inclusion ..... TE p. 174
Questioning Strategies ..... pp. 49–66
Modified Chapter 4 Resources ..... *IDEA Works!*
Homework Help Online

ON-LEVEL LEARNERS

Practice B ..... CRB, every lesson
Puzzles, Twisters, and Teasers ..... CRB, every lesson
Multiple Representations ..... TE pp. 170, 182
Cognitive Strategies ..... TE p. 182

ADVANCED LEARNERS

Practice C ..... CRB, every lesson
Challenge ..... CRB, every lesson
Extension ..... TE pp. 163, 211, 214, 215
Critical Thinking ..... TE pp. 170, 203

English Language Learners

ENGLISH LANGUAGE LEARNERS

Are You Ready? Vocabulary ..... SE p. 161
Vocabulary Connections ..... SE p. 162
Lesson Vocabulary ..... SE, every lesson
Vocabulary Review ..... SE p. 216
English Language Learners ..... TE pp. 163, 165, 173, 179, 182, 187, 199, 206, 207, 213, 222, 223
Reading Strategies ..... CRB, every lesson
Success for English Language Learners ..... pp. 49–66
Multilingual Glossary

Reaching All Learners Through...

Inclusion ..... TE p. 174
Kinesthetic Experience ..... TE pp. 165, 193
Multiple Representations ..... TE pp. 170, 182
Congnitive Strategies ..... TE p. 182
Cooperative Learning ..... TE pp. 174, 187
Modeling ..... TE p. 199
Graphic Organizers ..... TE p. 212
Critical Thinking ..... TE pp. 170, 203
Test Prep Doctor ..... TE pp. 167, 172, 176, 184, 189, 195, 201, 205, 209, 220
Common Error Alert ..... TE pp. 165, 170, 174, 176, 193
Scaffolding Questions ..... TE p. 211

Technology Highlights for Reaching All Learners

Lesson Tutorial Videos SPANISH

Starring Holt authors Ed Burger and Freddie Renfro! Live tutorials to support every lesson in Chapter 4.

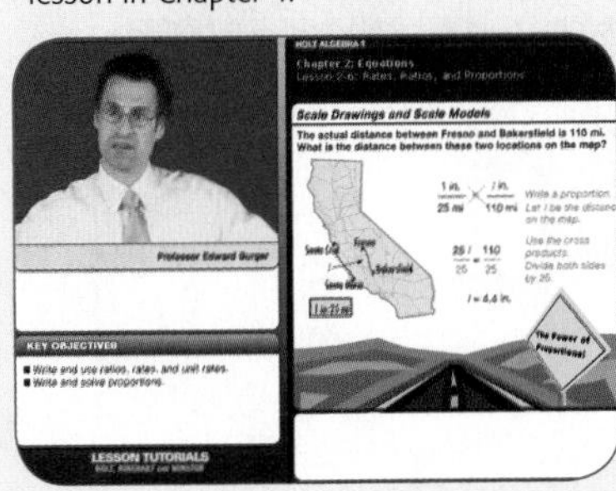

Multilingual Glossary

Searchable glossary includes definitions in English, Spanish, Vietnamese, Chinese, Hmong, Korean, and 4 other languages.

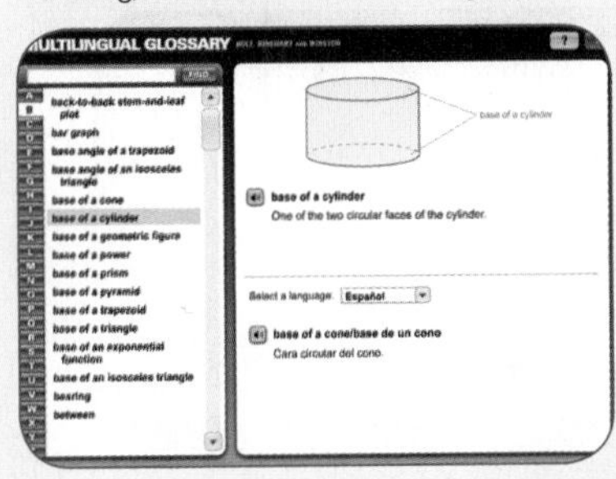

Online Interactivities

Interactive tutorials provide visually engaging alternative opportunities to learn concepts and master skills.

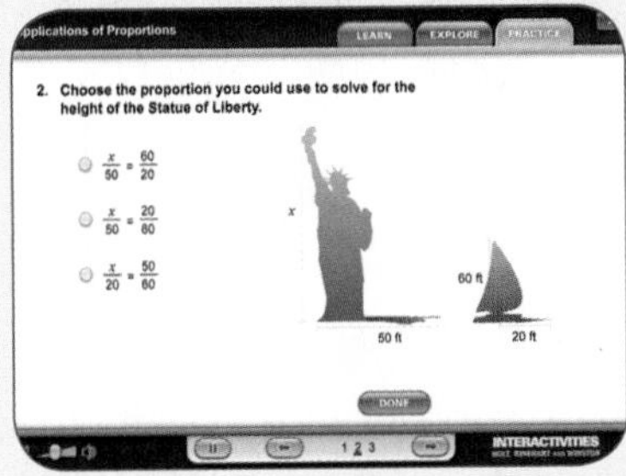

KEY: **SE** = *Student Edition* **TE** = *Teacher's Edition* **CRB** = *Chapter Resource Book* 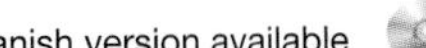 Spanish version available  Available on CD-ROM 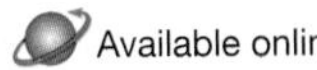 Available online

Ongoing Assessment

Assessing Prior Knowledge

Determine whether students have the prerequisite concepts and skills for success in Chapter 4.

Are You Ready? SPANISH .... SE p. 161
Warm Up .... TE, every lesson

Test Preparation

Provide review and practice for Chapter 4 and standardized tests.

Multi-Step Test Prep .... SE p. 211
Study Guide: Review .... SE pp. 216–218
Standardized Test Prep .... SE pp. 220–221
Countdown to CRCT Transparencies .... pp. 13–18
CRCT Prep Workbook
***CRCT Prep* CD-ROM**
IDEA Works!

Alternative Assessment

Assess students' understanding of Chapter 4 concepts and combined problem-solving skills.

Chapter 4 Project .... SE p. 160
Performance Assessment SPANISH .... AR pp. 80–81
Portfolio Assessment SPANISH .... AR p. xxxiv

Daily Assessment

Provide formative assessment for each day of Chapter 4.

Questioning Strategies .... pp. 49–66
Think and Discuss .... SE, every lesson
Write About It .... SE, lesson exercises
Journal .... TE, lesson exercises
Lesson Quiz .... TE, every lesson
Modified Lesson Quizzes .... *IDEA Works!*

Weekly Assessment

Provide formative assessment for each week of Chapter 4.

Focus on Problem Solving .... SE p. 179
Multi-Step Test Prep .... SE p. 211
Ready to Go On? SPANISH .... SE pp. 178, 210
Cumulative Assessment .... SE pp. 220–221
Test and Practice Generator SPANISH .... *One-Stop Planner*

Formal Assessment

Provide summative assessment of Chapter 4 mastery.

Section Quizzes SPANISH .... AR pp. 65–67
Chapter 4 Test .... SE p. 219
Chapter Test (Levels A, B, C) SPANISH .... AR pp. 68–79
• Multiple Choice • Free Response
Cumulative Test SPANISH .... AR pp. 82–85
Test and Practice Generator SPANISH .... *One-Stop Planner*
Modified Chapter 4 Test .... *IDEA Works!*

Technology Highlights for Ongoing Assessment

Automatically assess readiness and prescribe intervention for Chapter 4 prerequisite skills.

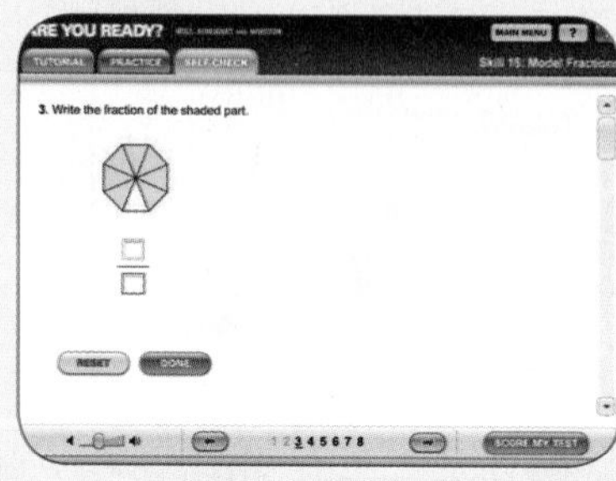

Automatically assess understanding of and prescribe intervention for Sections 4A, 4B, and 4C.

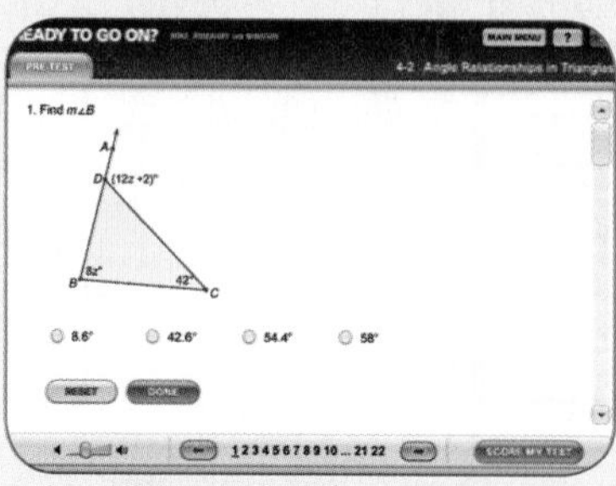

Test and Practice Generator SPANISH

Use Chapter 4 problem banks to create assessments and worksheets to print out or deliver online. Includes dynamic problems.

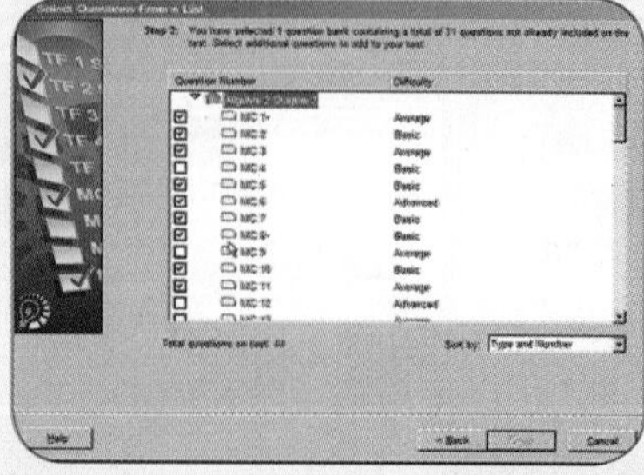

KEY: **SE** = *Student Edition* **TE** = *Teacher's Edition* **AR** = *Assessment Resources*  Spanish version available  Available on CD-ROM 

Formal Assessment

Three levels (A, B, C) of multiple-choice and free-response chapter tests are available in the *Assessment Resources.*

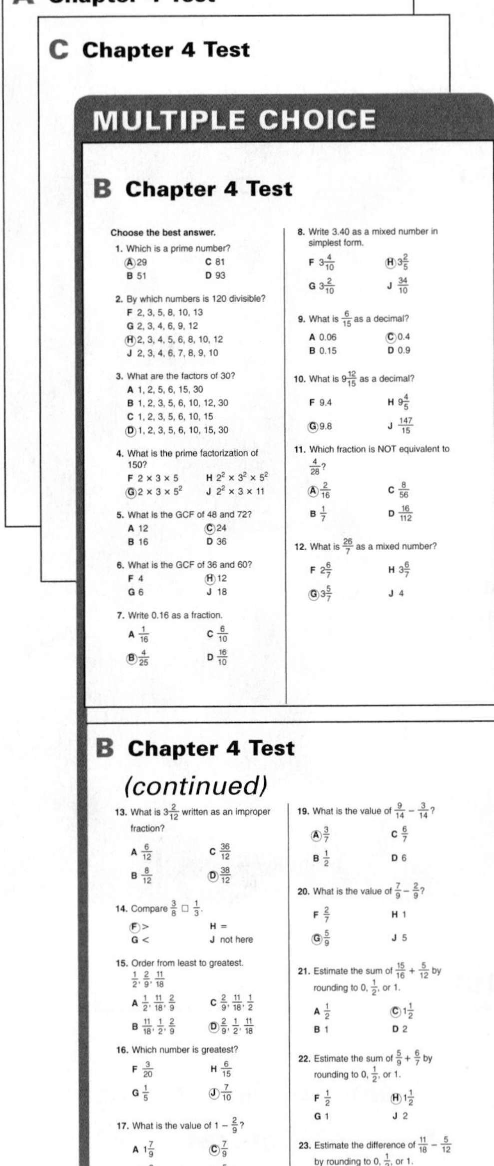

A Chapter 4 Test

C Chapter 4 Test

MULTIPLE CHOICE

B Chapter 4 Test

Choose the best answer.

1. Which is a prime number?
   (A) 29 C 81
   B 51 D 93
2. By which numbers is 120 divisible?
   F 2, 3, 5, 8, 10, 13
   G 2, 3, 4, 6, 9, 12
   (H) 2, 3, 4, 5, 6, 8, 10, 12
   J 2, 3, 4, 6, 7, 8, 9, 10
3. What are the factors of 30?
   A 1, 2, 5, 6, 15, 30
   B 1, 2, 3, 5, 6, 10, 12, 30
   C 1, 2, 3, 5, 6, 10, 15
   (D) 1, 2, 3, 5, 6, 10, 15, 30
4. What is the prime factorization of 150?
   F $2 \times 3 \times 5$ H $2^2 \times 3^2 \times 5^2$
   (G) $2 \times 3 \times 5^2$ J $2^2 \times 3 \times 11$
5. What is the GCF of 48 and 72?
   A 12 (C) 24
   B 16 D 36
6. What is the GCF of 36 and 60?
   F 4 (H) 12
   G 6 J 18
7. Write 0.16 as a fraction.
   A $\frac{1}{16}$ C $\frac{6}{10}$
   (B) $\frac{4}{25}$ D $\frac{16}{10}$
8. Write 3.40 as a mixed number in simplest form.
   F $3\frac{4}{10}$ (H) $3\frac{2}{5}$
   G $3\frac{2}{10}$ J $\frac{34}{10}$
9. What is $\frac{6}{15}$ as a decimal?
   A 0.06 (C) 0.4
   B 0.15 D 0.9
10. What is $9\frac{12}{15}$ as a decimal?
    F 9.4 H $9\frac{4}{5}$
    (G) 9.8 J $\frac{147}{15}$
11. Which fraction is NOT equivalent to $\frac{4}{28}$?
    (A) $\frac{2}{16}$ C $\frac{8}{56}$
    B $\frac{1}{7}$ D $\frac{16}{112}$
12. What is $\frac{26}{7}$ as a mixed number?
    F $2\frac{6}{7}$ H $3\frac{6}{7}$
    (G) $3\frac{5}{7}$ J 4

B Chapter 4 Test (continued)

13. What is $3\frac{2}{12}$ written as an improper fraction?
    A $\frac{6}{12}$ C $\frac{36}{12}$
    B $\frac{8}{12}$ (D) $\frac{38}{12}$
14. Compare $\frac{3}{8}$ □ $\frac{1}{3}$.
    (F) > H =
    G < J not here
15. Order from least to greatest. $\frac{1}{2}, \frac{2}{9}, \frac{11}{18}$
    A $\frac{1}{2}, \frac{11}{18}, \frac{2}{9}$ C $\frac{2}{9}, \frac{11}{18}, \frac{1}{2}$
    B $\frac{11}{18}, \frac{1}{2}, \frac{2}{9}$ (D) $\frac{2}{9}, \frac{1}{2}, \frac{11}{18}$
16. Which number is greatest?
    F $\frac{3}{20}$ H $\frac{6}{15}$
    G $\frac{1}{5}$ (J) $\frac{7}{10}$
17. What is the value of $1 - \frac{2}{9}$?
    A $1\frac{7}{9}$ (C) $\frac{7}{9}$
    B $1\frac{2}{9}$ D $\frac{5}{9}$
18. Add $\frac{5}{12} + \frac{4}{12}$.
    F $\frac{1}{12}$ H $\frac{2}{3}$
    G $\frac{9}{24}$ (J) $\frac{3}{4}$
19. What is the value of $\frac{9}{14} - \frac{3}{14}$?
    (A) $\frac{3}{7}$ C $\frac{6}{7}$
    B $\frac{1}{2}$ D 6
20. What is the value of $\frac{7}{9} - \frac{2}{9}$?
    F $\frac{2}{7}$ H 1
    (G) $\frac{5}{9}$ J 5
21. Estimate the sum of $\frac{15}{16} + \frac{5}{12}$ by rounding to 0, $\frac{1}{2}$, or 1.
    A $\frac{1}{2}$ (C) $1\frac{1}{2}$
    B 1 D 2
22. Estimate the sum of $\frac{5}{9} + \frac{6}{7}$ by rounding to 0, $\frac{1}{2}$, or 1.
    F $\frac{1}{2}$ (H) $1\frac{1}{2}$
    G 1 J 2
23. Estimate the difference of $\frac{11}{18} - \frac{5}{12}$ by rounding to 0, $\frac{1}{2}$, or 1.
    (A) 0 C 1
    B $\frac{1}{2}$ D $1\frac{1}{2}$

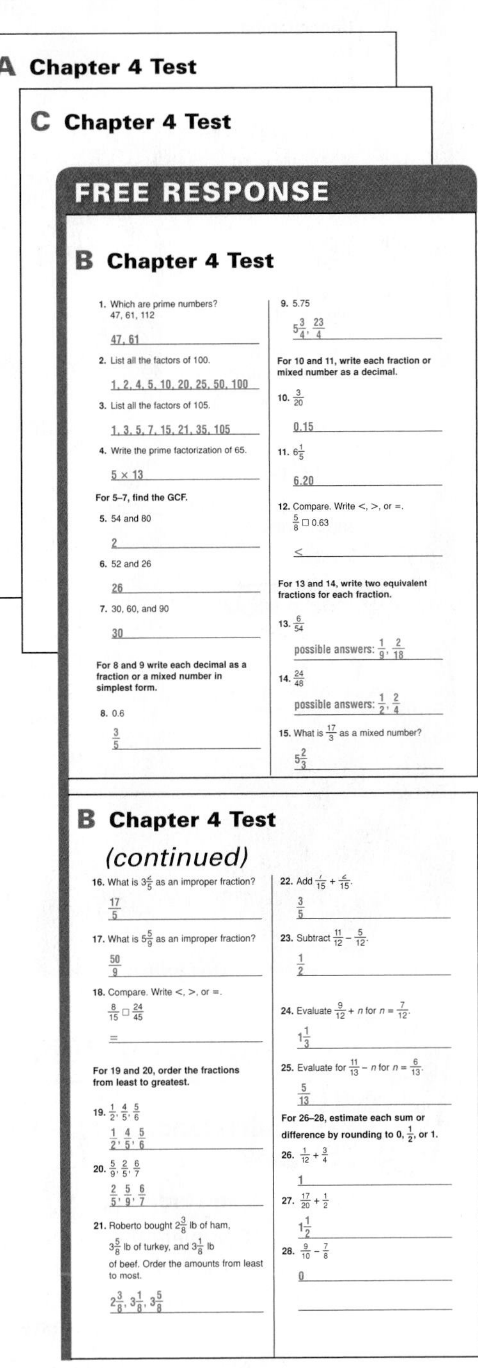

A Chapter 4 Test

C Chapter 4 Test

FREE RESPONSE

B Chapter 4 Test

1. Which are prime numbers? 47, 61, 112
   47, 61
2. List all the factors of 100.
   1, 2, 4, 5, 10, 20, 25, 50, 100
3. List all the factors of 105.
   1, 3, 5, 7, 15, 21, 35, 105
4. Write the prime factorization of 65.
   5×13

For 5–7, find the GCF.

5. 54 and 80
   2
6. 52 and 26
   26
7. 30, 60, and 90
   30

For 8 and 9 write each decimal as a fraction or a mixed number in simplest form.

8. 0.6
   $\frac{3}{5}$
9. 5.75
   $5\frac{3}{4}, \frac{23}{4}$

For 10 and 11, write each fraction or mixed number as a decimal.

10. $\frac{3}{20}$
    0.15
11. $6\frac{1}{5}$
    6.20
12. Compare. Write <, >, or =.
    $\frac{5}{8}$ □ 0.63
    <

For 13 and 14, write two equivalent fractions for each fraction.

13. $\frac{6}{54}$
    possible answers: $\frac{1}{9}, \frac{2}{18}$
14. $\frac{24}{48}$
    possible answers: $\frac{1}{2}, \frac{2}{4}$
15. What is $\frac{17}{3}$ as a mixed number?
    $5\frac{2}{3}$

B Chapter 4 Test (continued)

16. What is $3\frac{2}{5}$ as an improper fraction?
    $\frac{17}{5}$
17. What is $5\frac{5}{9}$ as an improper fraction?
    $\frac{50}{9}$
18. Compare. Write <, >, or =.
    $\frac{8}{15}$ □ $\frac{24}{45}$
    =

For 19 and 20, order the fractions from least to greatest.

19. $\frac{1}{2}, \frac{4}{5}, \frac{5}{6}$
    $\frac{1}{2}, \frac{4}{5}, \frac{5}{6}$
20. $\frac{5}{9}, \frac{2}{5}, \frac{6}{7}$
    $\frac{2}{5}, \frac{5}{9}, \frac{6}{7}$
21. Roberto bought $2\frac{3}{8}$ lb of ham, $3\frac{5}{8}$ lb of turkey, and $3\frac{1}{8}$ lb of beef. Order the amounts from least to most.
    $2\frac{3}{8}, 3\frac{1}{8}, 3\frac{5}{8}$
22. Add $\frac{4}{15} + \frac{5}{15}$.
    $\frac{3}{5}$
23. Subtract $\frac{11}{12} - \frac{5}{12}$.
    $\frac{1}{2}$
24. Evaluate $\frac{9}{12} + n$ for $n = \frac{7}{12}$.
    $1\frac{1}{3}$
25. Evaluate for $\frac{11}{13} - n$ for $n = \frac{6}{13}$.
    $\frac{5}{13}$

For 26–28, estimate each sum or difference by rounding to 0, $\frac{1}{2}$, or 1.

26. $\frac{1}{12} + \frac{3}{4}$
    1
27. $\frac{17}{20} + \frac{1}{2}$
    $1\frac{1}{2}$
28. $\frac{9}{10} - \frac{7}{8}$
    0

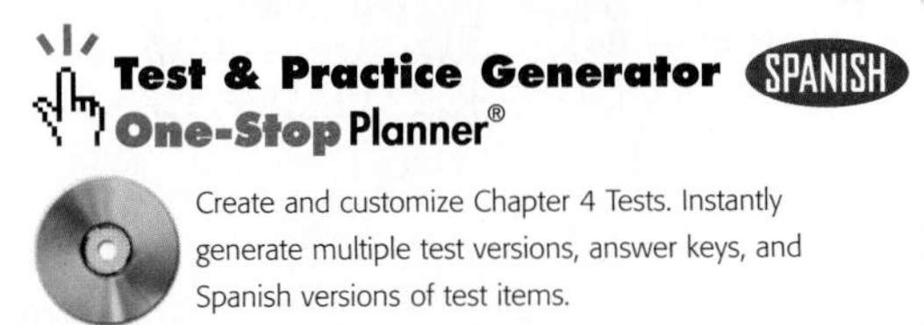

Test & Practice Generator SPANISH
One-Stop Planner®

Create and customize Chapter 4 Tests. Instantly generate multiple test versions, answer keys, and Spanish versions of test items.

Why Learn This?

Tell students that many formulas used in the real world involve division. Tell them that when they are performing division, it is helpful to understand fractions and the relationship between fractions and decimals. For example, in the plumber's formula, it may be helpful to realize that $\frac{\text{cost of pipe}}{3}$ can be interpreted as (cost of pipe) ÷ 3 or as $\frac{1}{3}$ × (cost of pipe).

Using Data

To begin the study of this chapter, have students:

- Estimate the cost of installing a 4 in. × 10 ft pipe with one $\frac{1}{8}$-bend connection. about $18
- Calculate the exact cost of installing a 4 in. × 20 ft pipe with one straight coupling. $24.76
- Round the cost of each connection to the nearest half-dollar and then write each cost as a mixed number. $\frac{1}{4}$ bend: $6\frac{1}{2}$; $\frac{1}{8}$ bend: 6; $\frac{1}{6}$ bend: $7\frac{1}{2}$

On page 220, students will find cumulative CRCT practice.

CHAPTER 4

Number Theory and Fractions

CRCT PREP

go.hrw.com
Chapter Project Online
KEYWORD: MR7 Ch4

ABS Plastic Drain Pipe	
Component	**Cost ($)**
Pipe 4 in. × 10 ft	11.99
Pipe 4 in. × 20 ft	22.57
Straight coupling	2.19
$\frac{1}{4}$-bend connection	6.49
$\frac{1}{8}$-bend connection	5.99
$\frac{1}{6}$-bend connection	7.49

Career *Plumber*

Do you like working with your hands to solve problems? If so, you might want to become a skilled trade worker, such as a master plumber.

To calculate the cost of parts and labor, plumbers use basic mathematical formulas. For example, some plumbers might calculate the cost of a new sewer line with a formula like the following:

cost of installed line = $\frac{\text{cost of pipe}}{3} \times 49 + \frac{\text{cost of pipe fittings}}{2}$

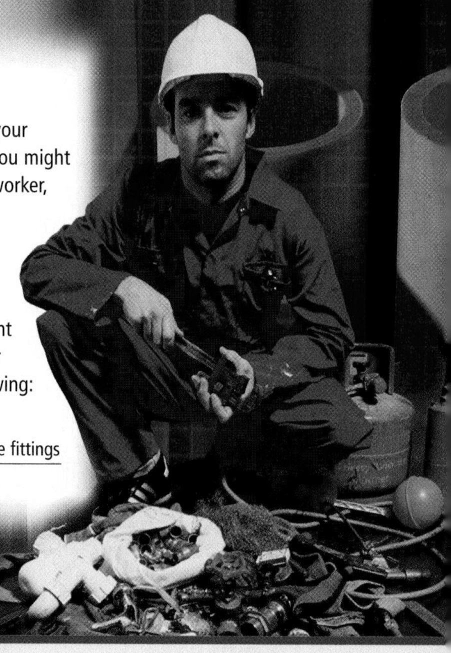

Problem Solving Project

Understand, Plan, Solve, and Look Back

Have students:

- Complete the Plumber's Cost/Profit Analysis worksheet to learn how to use fractions and decimals to determine prices.
- Research to find out what the word *plumber* means.
- Research to find out what an ABS plastic pipe is, why it is used for drainpipe, and what other kinds of plastic pipe are used in building construction.

Physical Science and Social Studies Connection

Project Resources

All project resources for teachers and students are provided online.

Materials:

- Plumber's Cost/Profit Analysis worksheet

Are You Ready?

Vocabulary

Choose the best term from the list to complete each sentence.

1. To find the sum of two numbers, you should ___?___. add
2. Fractions are written as a ___?___ over a ___?___. numerator; denominator
3. In the equation $4 \cdot 3 = 12$, 12 is the ___?___. product
4. The ___?___ of 18 and 10 is 8. difference
5. The numbers 18, 27, and 72 are ___?___ of 9. multiples

add
denominator
difference
multiples
numerator
product
quotient

Complete these exercises to review skills you will need for this chapter.

Write and Read Decimals

Write each decimal in word form.

6. 0.5 five tenths
7. 2.78 two and seventy-eight hundredths
8. 0.125 one hundred twenty-five thousandths
9. 12.8 twelve and eight tenths
10. 125.49 one hundred twenty-five and forty-nine hundredths
11. 8.024 eight and twenty-four thousandths

Multiples

List the first four multiples of each number.

12. 6 6, 12, 18, 24
13. 8 8, 16, 24, 32
14. 5 5, 10, 15, 20
15. 12 12, 24, 36, 48
16. 7 7, 14, 21, 28
17. 20 20, 40, 60, 80
18. 14 14, 28, 42, 56
19. 9 9, 18, 27, 36

Evaluate Expressions

Evaluate each expression for the given value of the variable.

20. $y + 4.3$ for $y = 3.2$ 7.5
21. $\frac{x}{5}$ for $x = 6.4$ 1.28
22. $3c$ for $c = 0.75$ 2.25
23. $a + 4 \div 8$ for $a = 3.75$ 4.25
24. $27.8 - d$ for $d = 9.25$ 18.55
25. $2.5b$ for $b = 8.4$ 21

Factors

Find all the whole-number factors of each number.

26. 8 1, 2, 4, 8
27. 12 1, 2, 3, 4, 6, 12
28. 24 1, 2, 3, 4, 6, 8, 12, 24
29. 30 1, 2, 3, 5, 6, 10, 15, 30
30. 45 1, 3, 5, 9, 15, 45
31. 52 1, 2, 4, 13, 26, 52
32. 75 1, 3, 5, 15, 25, 75
33. 150 1, 2, 3, 5, 6, 10, 15, 25, 30, 50, 75, 150

CHAPTER 4

Organizer

Objective: Assess students' understanding of prerequisite skills.

Prerequisite Skills

Write and Read Decimals
Multiples
Evaluate Expressions
Factors

Assessing Prior Knowledge

INTERVENTION 

Diagnose and Prescribe

Use this page to determine whether intervention is necessary or enrichment is appropriate.

Resources

 ***Are You Ready? Intervention and Enrichment* Worksheets**

 ***Are You Ready?* CD-ROM**

 ***Are You Ready?* Online**

my.hrw.com

Are You Ready?

Diagnose and Prescribe

NO INTERVENE

Prerequisite Skill	*Are You Ready? Intervention*, Chapter 4 Worksheets	CD-ROM	Online
Write and Read Decimals	Skill 15	Activity 15	Diagnose and Prescribe Online
Multiples	Skill 7	Activity 7	
Evaluate Expressions	Skill 64	Activity 64	
Factors	Skill 8	Activity 8	

YES ENRICH

CHAPTER 4 Study Guide: Preview

Organizer

Objective: Help students organize the new concepts they will learn in Chapter 4.

Online Edition
Multilingual Glossary

Resources

PuzzlePro®
One-Stop Planner®

***Multilingual Glossary* Online**

go.hrw.com
KEYWORD: MR7 Glossary

Answers to *Vocabulary Connections*

Possible answers:

1. Equivalent fractions are fractions that are equal in value.
2. When you are dividing and the quotient is a decimal with no remainder, the quotient is a terminating decimal.
3. Common denominators share the same value; they are equal.
4. An improper fraction will have a numerator that is larger than the denominator.

Study Guide: Preview

Where You've Been

Previously, you

- identified a number as prime or composite.
- identified common factors of a set of whole numbers.
- generated equivalent fractions.
- compared two fractions with common denominators.

In This Chapter

You will study

- writing the prime factorization of a number.
- finding the greatest common factor (GCF) of a set of whole numbers.
- generating equivalent forms of numbers, including whole numbers, fractions, and decimals.
- comparing and ordering fractions, decimals, and whole numbers.

Where You're Going

You can use the skills learned in this chapter

- to double or halve recipes when cooking.
- to add together fractions when determining volume in a science class.

Key Vocabulary/Vocabulario

common denominator	denominador común
composite number	número compuesto
equivalent fractions	fracciones equivalentes
factor	factor
greatest common factor (GCF)	máximo común divisor (MCD)
improper fraction	fracción impropia
prime factorization	factorización prima
prime number	número primo
terminating decimal	decimal cerrado

Vocabulary Connections

To become familiar with some of the vocabulary terms in the chapter, consider the following. You may refer to the chapter, the glossary, or a dictionary if you like.

1. The word *equivalent* means "equal in value." What do you think **equivalent fractions** are?
2. To *terminate* something means to bring it to an end. If a decimal is a **terminating decimal**, what do you think happens to it? Explain.
3. When people have something in *common*, they have something that they share. What do you think **common denominators** share?
4. If something is *improper*, it is not right. In fractions, it is *improper* to have the numerator be greater than the denominator. How would you expect an **improper fraction** to look?

Grade 6 CRCT GPS

M6N1.
Students will understand the meaning of the four arithmetic operations as related to positive rational numbers and will use these concepts to solve problems.

a. Apply factors and multiples.
b. Decompose numbers into their prime factorization (Fundamental Theorem of Arithmetic).
c. Determine the greatest common factor (GCF) and the least common multiple (LCM) for a set of numbers.
f. Use fractions, decimals, and percents interchangeably.
g. Solve problems involving fractions, decimals, and percents.

M6M2.
Students will use appropriate units of measure for finding length, perimeter, area and volume and will express each quantity using the appropriate unit.

a. Measure length to the nearest half, fourth, eighth and sixteenth of an inch.

M6A2.
Students will consider relationships between varying quantities.

a. Analyze and describe patterns arising from mathematical rules, tables, and graphs.

M6A3.
Students will evaluate algebraic expressions, including those with exponents, and solve simple one-step equations using each of the four basic operations.

***Georgia Mathematics Performance Standards* statements are written out completely on pp. GA28–GA35.**

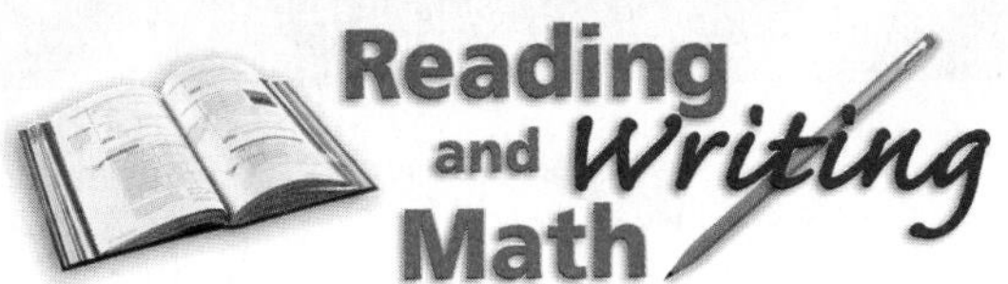

Reading Strategy: Read a Lesson for Understanding

Reading ahead will prepare you for new ideas and concepts presented in class. As you read a lesson, make notes. Write down the main points of the lesson, math terms that you do not understand, examples that need more explanation, and questions you can ask during class.

Learn to solve equations involving decimals.

The objective tells you the main idea of the lesson.

Work through the examples and write down any questions you have.

Solving One-Step Equations with Decimals

Solve each equation. Check your answer.

A $g - 3.1 = 4.5$

$g - 3.1 = 4.5$ — *3.1 is subtracted from g.*

$\underline{+3.1} \quad \underline{+3.1}$ — *Add 3.1 to both sides to undo the subtraction.*

$g = 7.6$

Check

$g - 3.1 = 4.5$

$7.6 - 3.1 \stackrel{?}{=} 4.5$ — *Substitute 7.6 for g in the equation.*

$4.5 \stackrel{?}{=} 4.5$ ✔ — *7.6 is the solution.*

Questions:
- *How do I know what operation to use?*
- *What should I do if I check my answer and the two sides are not equal?*

Write down questions you have as you read the lesson.

Try This

Read Lesson 4-1 before your next class and answer the following questions.

1. What is the objective of the lesson?
2. Are there new vocabulary terms, formulas, or symbols? If so, what are they?

Reading and Writing Math

Organizer

Objective: Help students apply strategies to understand and retain key concepts.

Online Edition

Resources

Chapter 4 Resource Book
Reading Strategies

ENGLISH LANGUAGE LEARNERS

Reading Strategy: Read a Lesson for Understanding

Discuss Have students compare reviewing their notes for a test with reading ahead in their textbooks.

Extend Encourage students to read ahead in lessons, quizzes, labs, tests, and projects for all of their classes.

Answers to *Try This*

1. Use divisibility rules.
2. divisible, composite numbers, prime numbers

Grade 6 CRCT GPS

Standards	4-1	LAB 4-2	4-2	4-3	LAB 4-3	LAB 4-4	4-4	LAB 4-5A	4-5	LAB 4-5B	4-6	4-7	4-8	4-9	Ext.
M6N1.a		★	★												
M6N1.b			★	★											
M6N1.c				★	★										
M6N1.f						★	★								
M6N1.g									★		★	★	★	★	
M6M2.a										★					
M6A2.a										★					
M6A3													★		
M6P1	★			★	★						★		★	★	
M6P4				★		★	★								
M6P5		★	★			★	★	★	★		★	★	★	★	★

SECTION 4A

Number Theory

One-Minute Section Planner

Lesson	Materials	MiC and Lab Resources
Lesson 4-1 Divisibility • Use divisibility rules. ☐ CRCT ☐ SAT-10 ☑ ITBS ☑ CTBS ☑ NAEP	Number cubes (MK)	
4-2 Hands-On Lab Explore Factors • Use graph paper or unit cubes to model prime and composite numbers. Graph paper or unit cubes (MK) **Lesson 4-2** Factors and Prime Factorization • Write prime factorizations of composite numbers. ☑ CRCT ☑ SAT-10 ☑ ITBS ☑ CTBS ☑ NAEP	Graph paper or unit cubes (MK)	***Hands-On Lab Activities*** 4-2
Lesson 4-3 Greatest Common Factor • Find the greatest common factor (GCF) of a set of numbers. ☑ CRCT ☑ SAT-10 ☐ ITBS ☐ CTBS ☐ NAEP **4-3 Technology Lab** Greatest Common Factor • Use a graphing calculator to find the greatest common factor (GCF) of two or more numbers.	Grid paper, graphing calculators	***Technology Lab Activities*** 4-3

MK = *Manipulatives Kit*

Mathematics in Context

No units from the *Mathematics in Context* © 2006 series can be used with Section 4A.

Section Overview

Divisibility

Lesson 4-1

Why? You need to find factors of numbers when operating with fractions.

A number is divisible by . . .	Example	Explanation
2 if the last digit is even (0, 2, 4, 6, or 8).	176	**6** is even.
3 if the sum of the digits is divisible by 3.	**525**	**5** + **2** + **5** = 12; 12 is divisible by 3.
4 if the last two digits form a number divisible by 4.	3,**516**	**16** is divisible by 4.
5 if the last digit is 0 or 5.	11,27**5**	The last digit is **5**.
6 if the number is divisible by both 2 and 3.	**24**	**24** is divisible by both 2 and 3.
9 if the sum of the digits is divisible by 9.	**4,860**	**4** + **8** + **6** + **0** = 18; 18 is divisible by 9.
10 if the last digit is 0.	35,39**0**	The last digit is **0**.

Factors and Prime Factorization

Lesson 4-2

Why? Prime factorization is used to operate with and simplify fractions.

A **prime number** is greater than 1 and has factors of only 1 and itself: 2, 3, 5, 7, 11, . . .

A **composite number** is greater than 1 and is not prime: 4, 6, 8, 9, 10, . . .

Write the prime factorization of 84.

Use a **factor tree.**

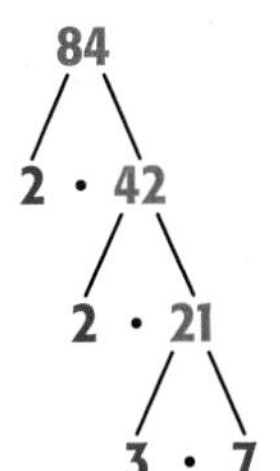

Use a **ladder diagram.**

2 | 84
2 | 42
3 | 21
7 | 7
1

The number 84 is **composite.**

84 = **2** · **2** · **3** · **7** The factors 2, 3, and 7 are **prime.**

Greatest Common Factor

Lesson 4-3

Finding the GCF of a set of numbers is used in operations with fractions.

Find the GCF of 24 and 60.		
Method 1	factors of 24: 1, 2, 3, 4, 6, 8, (12), 24 factors of 60: 1, 2, 3, 4, 5, 6, 10, (12), 15, 20, 30, 60	*List all the factors of each number.* *Circle the greatest common factor.*
Method 2	24 = (2) · (2) · 2 · (3) 60 = (2) · (2) · (3) · 5 2 · 2 · 3 = 12	*Write the prime factorization of each number.* *Circle the common prime factors.* *Find the product of the common prime factors.*

The greatest common factor of 24 and 60 is 12.

4-1 Organizer

Pacing: Traditional 1 day
Block $\frac{1}{2}$ day

Objective: Students use divisibility rules.

Online Edition
Tutorial Videos, Interactivities

Countdown to CRCT Week 7

Power Presentations with PowerPoint®

Warm Up

Write each number as a product of two whole numbers in as many ways as possible.

1. 20 $1 \times 20, 2 \times 10, 4 \times 5$
2. 48 $1 \times 48, 2 \times 24, 3 \times 16, 4 \times 12, 6 \times 8$
3. 16 $1 \times 16, 2 \times 8, 4 \times 4$

Problem of the Day

In this magic square, every row, column, and diagonal has the same sum, 34. Complete the square using the whole numbers from 1 to 16.

4	15	14	1
9	6	7	12
5	10	11	8
16	3	2	13

Also available on transparency

Georgia Performance Standards

M6P1.b Solve problems that arise in mathematics and in other contexts.

4-1 Divisibility

Learn to use divisibility rules.

Vocabulary
divisible
composite number
prime number

Georgia Performance Standards
M6P1.b Solve problems that arise in mathematics.

This year, 42 girls signed up to play basketball for the Junior Girls League, which has 6 teams. To find whether each team can have the same number of girls, decide if 42 is divisible by 6.

A number is **divisible** by another number if the quotient is a whole number with no remainder.

$42 \div 6 = 7 \leftarrow$ Quotient

Since there is no remainder, 42 is divisible by 6. The Junior Girls League can have 6 teams with 7 girls each.

Divisibility Rules

A number is divisible by...	Divisible	Not Divisible
2 if the last digit is even (0, 2, 4, 6, or 8).	3,978	4,975
3 if the sum of the digits is divisible by 3.	315	139
4 if the last two digits form a number divisible by 4.	8,512	7,518
5 if the last digit is 0 or 5.	14,975	10,978
6 if the number is divisible by both 2 and 3.	48	20
9 if the sum of the digits is divisible by 9.	711	93
10 if the last digit is 0.	15,990	10,536

EXAMPLE 1 Checking Divisibility

A **Tell whether 610 is divisible by 2, 3, 4, and 5.**

2	*The last digit, 0, is even.*	Divisible
3	*The sum of the digits is 6 + 1 + 0 = 7. 7 is not divisible by 3.*	Not divisible
4	*The last two digits form the number 10. 10 is not divisible by 4.*	Not divisible
5	*The last digit is 0.*	Divisible

So 610 is divisible by 2 and 5.

1 Introduce

Alternate Opener

EXPLORATION

4-1 Divisibility

Some calculators have an INT ÷ key, which returns a quotient and a remainder.

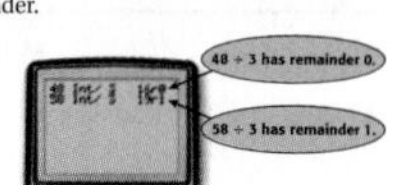
48 ÷ 3 has remainder 0.
58 ÷ 3 has remainder 1.

1. Use mental math or a calculator to determine each quotient and remainder. Then add the digits of the dividend.

	Dividend	Divisor	Quotient	Remainder	Sum of Digits
a.	48	3	16	0	4 + 8 = 12
b.	58	3	19	1	5 + 8 = 13
c.	256	3			
d.	1,011	3			
e.	72	3			
f.	74	3			
g.	129	3			
h.	130	3			

Think and Discuss

2. **Explain** whether 3,129 is divisible by 3.
3. **Describe** the pattern between the remainder and the sum of the digits in the table.

Motivate

Review division facts through $81 \div 9$ with students by using number families or by having students in pairs quiz each other. Point out that the quotients in division facts are all whole numbers without remainders. Ask students which numbers in the division facts you just reviewed are only divided by 1 and themselves (2, 3, 5, 7).

Explorations and answers are provided in *Alternate Openers: Explorations Transparencies.*

B Tell whether 387 is divisible by 6, 9, and 10.

6	*The last digit, 7, is odd, so 387 is not divisible by 2.*	Not divisible
9	*The sum of the digits is 3 + 8 + 7 = 18. 18 is divisible by 9.*	Divisible
10	*The last digit is 7, not 0.*	Not divisible

So 387 is divisible by 9.

Any number greater than 1 is divisible by at least two numbers—1 and the number itself. Numbers that are divisible by more than two numbers are called **composite numbers**.

A **prime number** is divisible by only the numbers 1 and itself. For example, 11 is a prime number because it is divisible by only 1 and 11. The numbers 0 and 1 are neither prime nor composite.

EXAMPLE 2 Identifying Prime and Composite Numbers

Tell whether each number is prime or composite.

A **45**
divisible by 1, 3, 5, 9, 15, 45
composite

B **13**
divisible by 1, 13
prime

C **19**
divisible by 1, 19
prime

D **49**
divisible by 1, 7, 49
composite

The prime numbers from 1 through 50 are highlighted below.

1	2	3	4	5	6	7	8	9	10
11	12	13	14	15	16	17	18	19	20
21	22	23	24	25	26	27	28	29	30
31	32	33	34	35	36	37	38	39	40
41	42	43	44	45	46	47	48	49	50

Think and Discuss

GPS M6P3.b

1. **Tell** which whole numbers are divisible by 1.
2. **Explain** how you know that 87 is a composite number.
3. **Tell** how the divisibility rules help you identify composite numbers.

COMMON ERROR ALERT

Some students may incorrectly think that they can use the sum of the digits to check for divisibility by numbers other than 3 and 9.

Power Presentations with PowerPoint®

Additional Examples

Example 1

A. Tell whether 462 is divisible by 2, 3, 4, and 5.
462 is divisible by 2 and 3.

B. Tell whether 540 is divisible by 6, 9, and 10.
540 is divisible by 6, 9, and 10.

Example 2

Tell whether each number is prime or composite.

A. 23 prime **B.** 48 composite
C. 31 prime **D.** 18 composite

Also available on transparency

Answers to *Think and Discuss*

1. all whole numbers
2. You know 87 is divisible by 3 because 8 + 7 = 15. Therefore, 87 has factors other than 1 and itself, making it composite.
3. The rules help you quickly check to see whether a number is divisible by more than two numbers.

2 Teach

Guided Instruction

In this lesson, students learn to use divisibility rules. First teach the divisibility rules for the numbers 2–6 and 9–10 (Teaching Transparency). Then teach students to use these rules to check for divisibility by these numbers. Finally, explain the terms *prime* and *composite* and how to identify prime and composite numbers.

Teaching Tip

Communicating Math Students should know that divisibility rules are most handy when working with very large numbers. Divisibility rules provide information about a number without requiring the use of more complicated division.

Reaching All Learners

Through Kinesthetic Experience

Provide number cubes with the numbers 2, 3, 4, 5, 6, and 9 (available in the Manipulatives Kit). Have students work in groups. Generate a list of at least twenty 3-digit numbers. To play the game, students choose a 3-digit number, toss the number cube, state the divisibility rule for the number tossed, and check for divisibility by that number. Then they toss the number cube again and check for divisibility by a different number. Have students take turns and repeat the process until all the numbers in the list have been chosen.

3 Close

Summarize

ENGLISH LANGUAGE LEARNERS

Review the terms *divisible*, *composite number*, and *prime number* with students. Discuss how the terms relate to each other.

Possible answer: A number is divisible by another number if the quotient is a whole number with no remainder. Composite numbers are divisible by more than two numbers; prime numbers are numbers greater than 1 that are divisible only by 1 and themselves.

4-1 Exercises

Assignment Guide

If you finished Example 1 assign:
Average 1–4, 33–36, 48, 55–62
Advanced 13–20, 49, 55–62

If you finished Example 2 assign:
Average 1–50, 55–62
Advanced 1–46, 51–62

Homework Quick Check

Quickly check key concepts.
Exercises: 14, 20, 26, 32, 38, 42

Answers

33.		no	no		no	no	
34.		no	no	yes	no	no	yes
35.	yes	no	yes	no	no	no	no
36.	yes	yes	yes	yes	yes	no	yes

Math Background

The divisibility rule for 9 works because numbers are written in the base-10 system, and every positive power of 10 is 1 greater than a multiple of 9.

Consider the number 243.

$243 = 2 \times 100 + 4 \times 10 + 3$
$243 = 2 \times (99 + 1) + 4 \times (9 + 1) + 3$
$243 = (2 \times 99) + (2 \times 1) + (4 \times 9) + (4 \times 1) + 3$
$243 = (2 \times 99) + (4 \times 9) + (2 \times 1) + (4 \times 1) + 3$
$243 = (2 \times 99) + (4 \times 9) + 2 + 4 + 3$
$(2 \times 99) + (4 \times 9)$ is divisible by 9.

So 243 is divisible by 9 if $2 + 4 + 3$ is divisible by 9.

Georgia Performance Standards

M6P3.a Organize and consolidate their mathematical thinking through communication.

M6P3.c Analyze and evaluate the mathematical thinking and strategies of others.

4-1 Exercises

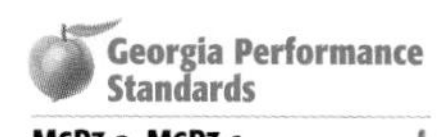

M6P3.a, M6P3.c

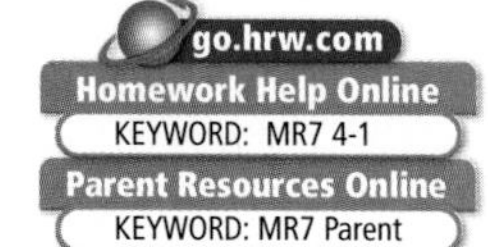

GUIDED PRACTICE

See Example 1 Tell whether each number is divisible by 2, 3, 4, 5, 6, 9, and 10.

1. 508 2, 4 **2.** 432 2, 3, 4, 6, 9 **3.** 247 none **4.** 189 3, 9

See Example 2 Tell whether each number is prime or composite.

5. 75 composite **6.** 17 prime **7.** 27 composite **8.** 63 composite
9. 72 composite **10.** 83 prime **11.** 99 composite **12.** 199 prime

INDEPENDENT PRACTICE

See Example 1 Tell whether each number is divisible by 2, 3, 4, 5, 6, 9, and 10.

13. 741 3 **14.** 810 2, 3, 5, 6, 9, 10 **15.** 675 3, 5, 9 **16.** 480 2, 3, 4, 5, 6, 10
17. 908 2, 4 **18.** 146 2 **19.** 514 2 **20.** 405 3, 5, 9

See Example 2 Tell whether each number is prime or composite.

21. 34 composite **22.** 29 prime **23.** 61 prime **24.** 81 composite
25. 51 composite **26.** 23 prime **27.** 97 prime **28.** 93 composite
29. 77 composite **30.** 41 prime **31.** 67 prime **32.** 39 composite

PRACTICE AND PROBLEM SOLVING

Extra Practice p. 720

Copy and complete the table. Write *yes* if the number is divisible by the given number. Write *no* if it is not.

		2	3	4	5	6	9	10
33.	677	*no*	■	■	*no*	■	■	*no*
34.	290	*yes*	■	■	■	■	■	■
35.	1,744	■	■	■	■	■	■	■
36.	12,180	■	■	■	■	■	■	■

Possible answers:

Tell whether each statement is true or false. Explain your answers.

37. All even numbers are divisible by 2. True

38. All odd numbers are divisible by 3. False

39. Some even numbers are divisible by 5. True

40. All odd numbers are prime. False

Replace each box with a digit that will make the number divisible by 3.

41. 74■ 1, 4, or 7 **42.** 8,10■ 0, 3, 6, or 9 **43.** 3,■41 1, 4, or 7
44. ■,335 1, 4, or 7 **45.** 67,■11 0, 3, 6, or 9 **46.** 10,0■1 1, 4, or 7

RETEACH 4-1

LESSON 4-1 **Reteach**
Divisibility

A number is divisible by another number if the quotient is a whole number with no remainder.

15 is divisible by 3 because $15 \div 3 = 5$. There are rules to help you figure out if a number is divisible by another number.

Divisibility Rules

A number is divisible by:

2 if the last digit is even.
3 if the sum of the digits is divisible by 3.
4 if the last two digits form a number that is divisible by 4.
5 if the last digit is 0 or 5.
6 if the number is divisible by both 2 and 3.
9 if the sum of the digits is divisible by 9.
10 if the last digit is 0.

To tell whether 315 is divisible by 2, 3, 4, 5, 6, 9, and 10, you can use the divisibility rules listed above.

5 is not an even number, so 315 **is not divisible** by 2.
$3 + 1 + 5 = 9$. 9 is divisible by 3, so 315 **is divisible** by 3.
15 is not divisible by 4, so 315 **is not divisible** by 4.
The last digit is 0 or 5, so 315 **is divisible** by 5.
315 is divisible by 3, but not 2. So, 315 **is not divisible** by 6.
The sum of the digits is 9 and 9 is divisible by 9. So 315 **is divisible** by 9.
The last digit is not 0, so 315 **is not divisible** by 10.

315 is divisible by 3, 5, and 9.

Use divisibility rules to tell whether each number is divisible by 2, 3, 4, 5, 6, 9, and 10.

1. 120 2; 3; 4; 5; 6; 10
2. 435 3; 5
3. 228 2; 3; 4; 6
4. 540 2; 3; 4; 5; 6; 9; 10
5. 144 2; 3; 4; 6; 9
6. 634 2
7. 402 2; 3; 6
8. 320 2; 4; 5; 10

PRACTICE 4-1

LESSON 4-1 **Practice B**
Divisibility

Tell whether each number is divisible by 2, 3, 4, 5, 6, 9, and 10.

1. 90 2; 3; 5; 6; 9; 10
2. 416 2; 4
3. 308 2; 4
4. 540 2; 3; 4; 5; 6; 9; 10
5. 804 2; 3; 4; 6
6. 225 3; 5; 9
7. 663 3
8. 972 2; 3; 4; 6; 9
9. 836 2; 4

Tell whether each number is prime or composite.

10. 33 composite
11. 69 composite
12. 41 prime
13. 45 composite
14. 58 composite
15. 87 composite
16. 61 prime
17. 53 prime
18. 99 composite

19. Dan counted all the coins in his bank, and he had 72 quarters. Can he exchange the quarters for an even amount of dollar bills? How do you know?

Yes; because there are 4 quarters in 1 dollar, and 72 is divisible by 4.

20. A small town purchased 196 American flags for its Memorial Day parade. Eight locations were selected to display the flags. Can each location have the same number of flags? If no, explain why not. If yes, how many flags will be displayed at each location?

No; because 196 is not divisible by 8.

47. Make a table that shows the prime numbers from 50 to 100. **prime numbers from 50 to 100 are 53, 59, 61, 67, 71, 73, 79, 83, 89, and 97.**

48. **Astronomy** Earth has a diameter of 7,926 miles. Tell whether this number is divisible by 2, 3, 4, 5, 6, 9, and 10. **2, 3, and 6**

49. On which of the bridges in the table could a light fixture be placed every 6 meters so that the first light is at the beginning of the bridge and the last light is at the end of the bridge? Explain. **Mackinac Straits**

Golden Gate Bridge

Longest Bridges in the U.S.

Name and State	Length (m)
Verrazano Narrows, NY	1,298
Golden Gate, CA	1,280
Mackinac Straits, MI	1,158
George Washington, NY	1,067

50. **Critical Thinking** A number is between 80 and 100 and is divisible by both 5 and 6. What is the number? **90**

51. **Choose a Strategy** Find the greatest four-digit number that is divisible by 1, 2, 3, and 4. **9,996**

52. **What's the Error?** To find whether 3,463 is divisible by 4, a student added the digits. The sum, 16, is divisible by 4, so the student stated that 3,463 is divisible by 4. Explain the error.

53. **Write About It** If a number is divisible by both 4 and 9, by what other numbers is it divisible? Explain.

54. **Challenge** Find a number that is divisible by 2, 3, 4, 5, 6, and 10, but not 9. **Possible answer: 240**

CRCT Prep • GPS Support • Spiral Review

55. **Multiple Choice** ___?___ numbers are divisible by more than two numbers.

(A) Whole (B) Prime (C) Equivalent (D) Composite

56. **Short Response** What is the least three-digit number that is divisible by both 5 and 9? Show your work. 5×9=45 45 90 135

Use the pattern to write the first five terms of each sequence. (Lesson 1-7)

57. Start with 7; add 4. **7, 11, 15, 19, 23**

58. Start with 78; subtract 9. **78, 69, 60, 51, 42**

59. Start with 6; multiply by 5. **6, 30, 150, 750, 3,750**

Evaluate each expression for the given value of the variable. (Lesson 2-1)

60. $2x + 28$ for $x = 4$ **36**

61. $x + 18$ for $x = 12$ **30**

62. $\frac{x}{5}$ for $x = 25$ **5**

CHALLENGE 4-1

LESSON 4-1 Challenge
The Chinese Calendar

The Chinese calendar runs in cycles of 12 years. Each year in a cycle is named after an animal. The Chinese believe the animal ruling the year in which you were born has a great effect on your personality. They say, "This is the animal that hides in your heart."

2000 was a year of the dragon.

The Chinese calendar cycle below is for the years 1983–1994. Use the clues to write the last two digits in the year that goes with each animal. Then read the character traits associated with the animals. Which animal hides in your heart?

Tiger: 19 86 Divisible by: 2 and 43 Traits: bold, adventurous	Sheep: 19 91 Divisible by: 7 Traits: charming, artistic	Pig: 19 83 Divisible by: 1 and 83 Traits: loyal, tolerant
Dog: 19 94 Divisible by: 2 and 47 Traits: honest, faithful	Dragon: 19 88 Divisible by: 2, 4, and 8 Traits: fun, energetic	Rat: 19 84 Divisible by: 4 and 6 Traits: generous, creative
Horse: 19 90 Divisible by: 5 and 9 Traits: friendly, hardworking	Rooster: 19 93 Divisible by: 3 and 31 Traits: decisive, proud	Ox: 19 85 Divisible by: 5 Traits: confident, leaderlike
Snake: 19 89 Divisible by: 1 and 89 Traits: charming, wise	Monkey: 19 92 Divisible by: 2 and 4 Traits: smart, likable	Rabbit: 19 87 Divisible by: 3 and 29 Traits: friendly, cooperative

PROBLEM SOLVING 4-1

LESSON 4-1 Problem Solving
Divisibility

Use the table to answer the questions.

Subways Around the World

City, Country	Length (mi)
New York, U.S.	247
Mexico City, Mexico	111
Paris, France	125
Moscow, Russia	152
Seoul, South Korea	83
Tokyo, Japan	105

1. Which city's subway has a length that is a prime number of miles? **Seoul, South Korea**
2. Which subway could be evenly broken into sections of 2 miles each? **Moscow, Russia**
3. Which subways could be evenly broken into sections of 5 miles each? **Paris, France, and Tokyo, Japan**

Circle the letter of the correct answer.

4. Which subway's length is divisible by 4 miles?
A New York, United States
B Paris, France
C Tokyo, Japan
(D) Moscow, Russia

5. Which subway's length is not a prime number, but is also not divisible by 2, 3, 4, 5, 6, or 9?
F Mexico City, Mexico
(G) New York, United States
H Seoul, South Korea
J Paris, France

6. The subway in Hong Kong, China, has a length that is a prime number of miles. Which of the following is its length?
A 260 miles
B 268 miles
(C) 269 miles
D 265 miles

7. The subway in St. Petersburg, Russia, has a length that is divisible by 3 miles. Which of the following is its length?
(F) 57 miles
G 56 miles
H 55 miles
J 58 miles

Ongoing Assessment and Intervention

Diagnose ***Before*** **the Lesson**
4-1 Warm Up, TE p. 164

Monitor ***During*** **the Lesson**
4-1 Know-It Notebook
4-1 Questioning Strategies

Assess ***After*** **the Lesson**
4-1 Lesson Quiz, TE p. 167

Answers

49. Mackinac Straits; Possible answer: 1,158 is divisible by 6, so there will be 6 meters between each light.

52. A number is divisible by 4 only if the number formed by the last two digits is divisible by 4, not if the sum of the digits is divisible by 4.

53. 2, 3, and 6; 2 is a factor of 4, 3 is a factor of 9, and if a number is divisible by 2 and 3 it is also divisible by 6.

56. 135; the LCM is 5 × 9 = 45. The LCM with three digits is 5 × 9 × 3 = 135.

Test Prep Doctor In Exercise 56, students will need to apply their knowledge of the divisibility rules. The number will have 5 and 9 as factors. 45 is the smallest such number. Therefore, the answer will be a multiple of 45.

Journal

Have students explain the difference between prime and composite numbers using the term *divisible*. Have students give examples of both types of numbers.

Power Presentations with PowerPoint®

4-1 Lesson Quiz

Tell whether each number is divisible by 2, 3, 4, 5, 6, 9, and 10.

1. 256 **2, 4**
2. 720 **2, 3, 4, 5, 6, 9, 10**
3. 615 **3, 5**

Tell whether each number is prime or composite.

4. 47 prime
5. 38 composite

Also available on transparency

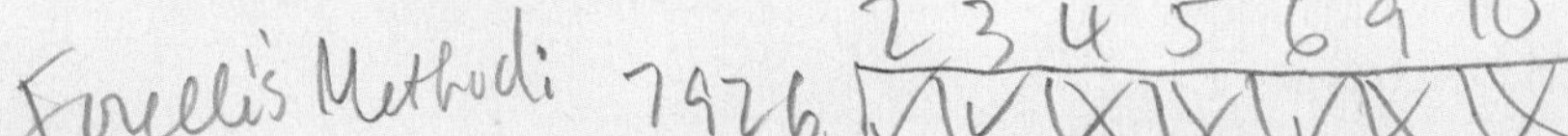

Organizer

Use with Lesson 4-2

Pacing:
Traditional $\frac{1}{2}$ day
Block $\frac{1}{4}$ day

Objective: Use grid paper or unit cubes to model prime and composite numbers.

Materials: Grid paper or unit cubes

Online Edition

Countdown to CRCT Week 7

Resources

Hands-On Lab Activities
Lab 4-2 Recording Sheet

Teach

Discuss

Encourage students to suggest different ways a number can be represented by forming a rectangle using grid paper or unit cubes.

Call their attention to those numbers that have only one form, a rectangle one square wide.

Close

Key Concept

Grid paper or unit cubes can provide concrete examples of why numbers are considered to be either prime or composite.

Assessment

Use grid paper to represent each number by forming two different rectangles.

1. 9

2. 12

Georgia Performance Standards

M6N1.a Apply factors and multiples.

M6P5.c Use representations to model and interpret physical, social, and mathematical phenomena.

Explore Factors

Use with Lesson 4-2

Georgia Performance Standards
M6N1.a, M6P5.c

You can use graph paper or unit cubes to model *factors* of a number and determine whether the number is a prime number or a composite number.

Activity

Use graph paper to show the different ways the number 16 can be modeled.

1 The number 16 can be modeled by drawing a rectangle 2 units wide and 8 units long. The dimensions, 2 and 8, are factors of 16. This means that 2 × 8 = 16.

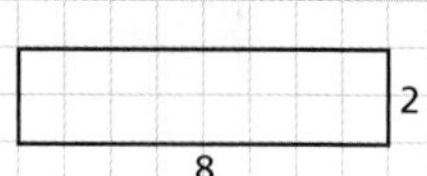

What other ways can 16 be modeled?
A rectangle 1 unit wide and 16 units long and a 4-unit-by-4 unit square can also model 16.

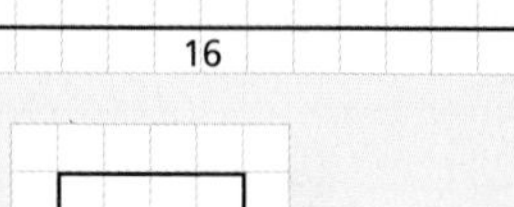

The factors of 16 are 1, 2, 4, 8, and 16. Because you can model 16 in more than one way, 16 is a composite number.

Use graph paper to show the different ways the number 3 can be modeled.

2 The number 3 can be modeled by drawing a rectangle 1 unit wide and 3 units long. The dimensions, 1 and 3, are factors of 3. This means that 1 × 3 = 3. Because 3 cannot be modeled any other way, 3 is a prime number.

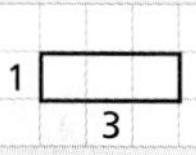

Think and Discuss

1. How can you use the rules of divisibility to determine whether there is more than one way to model a number?
2. Find the factors of 2. Is 2 prime or composite? Explain.

Try This

1. Use graph paper to model two prime numbers and two composite numbers. Find their factors.

Possible Answers to *Assessment*

1.

2.

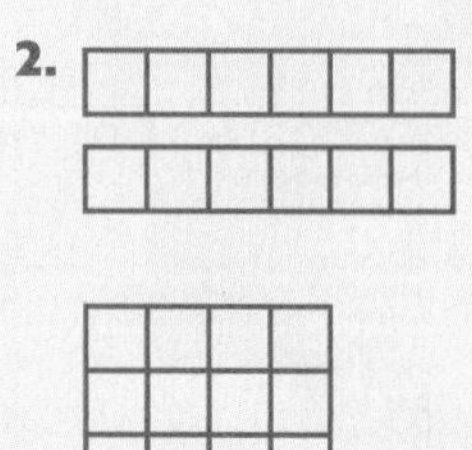

Possible Answers to *Think and Discuss*

1. If a divisibility rule applies to a number, then that number can be modeled in more than one way.
2. 1, 2; 2 is prime; the factors of 2 are 1 and 2, and no others.

Possible Answers to *Try This*

1. Two prime numbers are 3 and 5. 3 has factors of 1 and 3. 5 has factors of 1 and 5. Two composite numbers are 6 and 9. 6 has factors of 1, 2, 3, and 6. 9 has factors of 1, 3, and 9.

4-2 Factors and Prime Factorization

Learn to write prime factorizations of composite numbers.

Vocabulary
factor
prime factorization

Whole numbers that are multiplied to find a product are called **factors** of that product. A number is divisible by its factors.

$2 \cdot 3 = 6$ (2 and 3: Factors; 6: Product)

$6 \div 3 = 2$
$6 \div 2 = 3$
6 is divisible by 3 and 2.

EXAMPLE 1 Finding Factors

Georgia Performance Standards
M6N1.b Decompose numbers into their prime factorization. Also, M6N1.a, M6P5.a, M6P5.b.

Helpful Hint
When the pairs of factors begin to repeat, then you have found all of the factors of the number you are factoring.

List all of the factors of each number.

A 18

Begin listing factors in pairs.

$18 = 1 \cdot 18$	*1 is a factor.*
$18 = 2 \cdot 9$	*2 is a factor.*
$18 = 3 \cdot 6$	*3 is a factor.*
	4 is not a factor.
	5 is not a factor.
$18 = 6 \cdot 3$	*6 and 3 have already been listed, so stop here.*
1 2 3 6 9 18	*You can draw a diagram to illustrate the factor pairs.*

The factors of 18 are 1, 2, 3, 6, 9, and 18.

B 13

$13 = 1 \cdot 13$ — *Begin listing factors in pairs. 13 is not divisible by any other whole numbers.*

The factors of 13 are 1 and 13.

You can use factors to write a number in different ways.

Factorization of 12			
$1 \cdot 12$	$2 \cdot 6$	$3 \cdot 4$	$3 \cdot 2 \cdot 2$

Notice that these factors are all prime.

The **prime factorization** of a number is the number written as the product of its prime factors.

Organizer 4-2

Pacing: Traditional 1 day
Block $\frac{1}{2}$ day

Objective: Students write prime factorizations of composite numbers.

Online Edition
Tutorial Videos, Interactivities

Countdown to CRCT Week 7

Power Presentations with PowerPoint®

Warm Up

Identify each number as prime or composite.

1. 19 prime
2. 82 composite
3. 57 composite
4. 85 composite
5. 101 prime
6. 121 composite

Problem of the Day

At the first train stop, 7 people disembarked. At the second stop, 8 people disembarked. At the fourth stop, the last 6 people disembarked. If there were 28 people on the train before the first stop, how many people left at the third stop? 7

Also available on transparency

Math Humor

Teacher: All prime numbers are odd, with one exception; two is even.
Student: That's odd.

1 Introduce

Alternate Opener

EXPLORATION

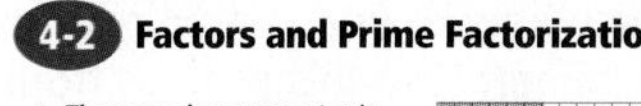

4-2 Factors and Prime Factorization

1. The rectangle measures 4 units by 6 units and has an area of 24 square units. Use graph paper to draw rectangles that have different whole-number dimensions but still have an area of 24 square units. (*Hint:* 4 × 6 = 24. What factors other than 1 × 24 give you 24?)
2. The rectangle measures 3 units by 5 units and has an area of 15 square units. Is it possible to draw rectangles that have whole-number dimensions other than 3 × 5 (and 1 × 15) and still have an area of 15 square units?

Think and Discuss

3. **Explain** how you can use rectangles to determine factors of numbers.
4. **Explain** why it is possible to draw more than two different rectangles with an area of 24 square units, but it is not possible to draw more than two different rectangles with an area of 15 square units.

Motivate

Ask students to name numbers that can be multiplied to get certain numbers. For example, you might ask them to name numbers that can be multiplied to get 28 (1 and 28; 2 and 14; 4 and 7).

Explorations and answers are provided in *Alternate Openers: Explorations Transparencies.*

Georgia Performance Standards

M6N1.a Apply factors and multiples.

M6N1.b Decompose numbers into their prime factorization (Fundamental Theorem of Arithmetic).

M6P5.a Create and use representations to organize, record, and communicate mathematical ideas.

M6P5.b Select, apply, and translate among mathematical representations to solve problems.

COMMON ERROR ALERT

When asked to write the prime factorization of a number, students may list all factors of a number instead of just the prime factors. For example, when factoring 12 they may write 1 · 2 · 3 · 4 · 6 · 12 instead of 3 · 2 · 2.

Power Presentations with PowerPoint®

Additional Examples

Example 

List all of the factors of each number.

A. 16 1, 2, 4, 8, 16

B. 19 1,19

Example 

Write the prime factorization of each number.

A. 24 $2^3 \cdot 3$

B. 45 $3^2 \cdot 5$

Also available on transparency

Answers to *Think and Discuss*

1. Possible answer: when the factor pairs start to repeat
2. Possible answer: when all the factors are prime and their product is the original number
3. *Prime factors* of a number are all prime; *factors* of a number don't have to be prime.

EXAMPLE  **Writing Prime Factorizations**

Write the prime factorization of each number.

A 36

Method 1: Use a factor tree.

Choose any two factors of 36 to begin. Keep finding factors until each branch ends at a prime factor.

Helpful Hint

You can use exponents to write prime factorizations. Remember that an exponent tells you how many times the base is a factor.

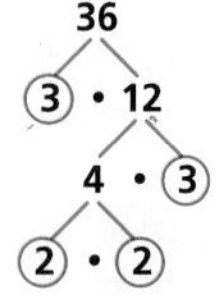

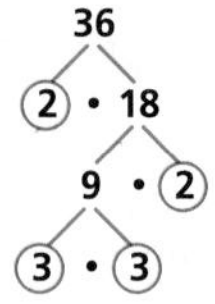

$36 = 3 \cdot 2 \cdot 2 \cdot 3$ $36 = 2 \cdot 3 \cdot 3 \cdot 2$

The prime factorization of 36 is $2 \cdot 2 \cdot 3 \cdot 3$, or $2^2 \cdot 3^2$.

B 54

Method 2: Use a ladder diagram.

Choose a prime factor of 54 to begin. Keep dividing by prime factors until the quotient is 1.

Divisor	Quotient
2	54
3	27
3	9
3	3
	1

Divisor	Quotient
3	54
3	18
2	6
3	3
	1

$54 = 2 \cdot 3 \cdot 3 \cdot 3$ $54 = 3 \cdot 3 \cdot 2 \cdot 3$

The prime factorization of 54 is $2 \cdot 3 \cdot 3 \cdot 3$, or $2 \cdot 3^3$.

In Example 2, notice that the prime factors may be written in a different order, but they are still the same factors. Except for changes in the order, there is only one way to write the prime factorization of a number.

Think and Discuss GPS M6P3.b, M6P3.d

1. **Tell** how you know when you have found all of the factors of a number.
2. **Tell** how you know when you have found the prime factorization of a number.
3. **Explain** the difference between factors of a number and prime factors of a number.

2 Teach

Guided Instruction

In this lesson, students learn to write prime factorizations of composite numbers. First explain the term *factors* and teach students to list all factors of a number. Then teach them to find the prime factors of a number, using a factor tree and a ladder diagram. Have students practice finding factors and prime factors of other numbers before introducing *Think and Discuss.*

Teaching Tip **Multiple Representations** Some students may prefer using a factor tree, while others may prefer the ladder diagram. Encourage students to use the method that works best for them.

Reaching All Learners

Through Critical Thinking

Have students name five numbers that have the prime factors 2, 3, and 5. Each factor may be used more than once.

Possible answers:

$30 = 2 \times 3 \times 5$

$60 = 2 \times 2 \times 3 \times 5$, or $2^2 \times 3 \times 5$

$120 = 2 \times 2 \times 2 \times 3 \times 5$, or $2^3 \times 3 \times 5$

$180 = 2 \times 2 \times 3 \times 3 \times 5$, or $2^2 \times 3^2 \times 5$

$900 = 2 \times 2 \times 3 \times 3 \times 5 \times 5$, or $2^2 \times 3^2 \times 5^2$

3 Close

Summarize

Review how to find factors of a number, and differentiate this process from finding the prime factorization of a number. Have students give examples of each.

Possible answer: factors of 40: 1, 2, 4, 5, 8, 10, 20, 40; prime factorization of 40:
$2 \times 2 \times 2 \times 5$, or $2^3 \times 5$

4-2 Exercises

M6P3.a, M6P3.c

GUIDED PRACTICE

See Example 1

List all of the factors of each number.

1. 12 1, 2, 3, 4, 6, 12
2. 21 1, 3, 7, 21
3. 52 1, 2, 4, 13, 26, 52
4. 75 1, 3, 5, 15, 25, 75

See Example 2

Write the prime factorization of each number.

5. 48 $2^4 \cdot 3$
6. 20 $2^2 \cdot 5$
7. 66 $2 \cdot 3 \cdot 11$
8. 34 $2 \cdot 17$

INDEPENDENT PRACTICE

See Example 1

List all of the factors of each number.

9. 24 1, 2, 3, 4, 6, 8, 12, 24
10. 37 1, 37
11. 42 1, 2, 3, 6, 7, 14, 21, 42
12. 56 1, 2, 4, 7, 8, 14, 28, 56
13. 67 1, 67
14. 72 1, 2, 3, 4, 6, 8, 9, 12, 18, 24, 36, 72
15. 85 1, 5, 17, 85
16. 92 1, 2, 4, 23, 46, 92

See Example 2

Write the prime factorization of each number.

17. 49 7^2
18. 38 $2 \cdot 19$
19. 76 $2^2 \cdot 19$
20. 60 $2^2 \cdot 3 \cdot 5$
21. 81 3^4
22. 132 $2^2 \cdot 3 \cdot 11$
23. 140 $2^2 \cdot 5 \cdot 7$
24. 87 $3 \cdot 29$

PRACTICE AND PROBLEM SOLVING

Extra Practice p. 720

Write each number as a product in two different ways. Possible answers:

25. 34 $2 \cdot 17$; $1 \cdot 34$
26. 82 $2 \cdot 41$; $1 \cdot 82$
27. 88 $8 \cdot 11$; $4 \cdot 22$
28. 50 $2 \cdot 25$; $10 \cdot 5$
29. 15 $3 \cdot 5$; $15 \cdot 1$
30. 78 $26 \cdot 3$; $2 \cdot 39$
31. 94 $47 \cdot 2$; $94 \cdot 1$
32. 35 $7 \cdot 5$; $1 \cdot 35$

33. **Sports** Little League Baseball began in 1939 in Pennsylvania. When it first started, there were 45 boys on 3 teams. 15 boys per team
    a. If the teams were equally sized, how many boys were on each team?
    b. Name another way the boys could have been divided into equally sized teams. (Remember that a baseball team must have at least 9 players.) 5 teams of 9 players

34. **Critical Thinking** Use the divisibility rules to list the factors of 171. Explain how you determined the factors. 1, 3, 9, 19, 57, 171; possible answer: list factors as pairs

Find the prime factorization of each number.

35. 99 $3^2 \cdot 11$
36. 249 $3 \cdot 83$
37. 284 $2^2 \cdot 71$
38. 620 $2^2 \cdot 5 \cdot 31$
39. 840 $2^3 \cdot 3 \cdot 5 \cdot 7$
40. 150 $2 \cdot 3 \cdot 5^2$
41. 740 $2^2 \cdot 5 \cdot 37$
42. 402 $2 \cdot 3 \cdot 67$

43. The prime factorization of 50 is $2 \cdot 5^2$. Without dividing or using a diagram, find the prime factorization of 100. $2^2 \cdot 5^2$

44. **Geometry** The area of a rectangle is the product of its length and width. Suppose the area of a rectangle is 24 in^2. What are the possible whole number measurements of its length and width? Possible answers: $1 \cdot 24$; $24 \cdot 1$; $2 \cdot 12$; $12 \cdot 2$; $3 \cdot 8$; $8 \cdot 3$; $4 \cdot 6$; $6 \cdot 4$

45. **Physical Science** The speed of sound at sea level at 20°C is 343 meters per second. Write the prime factorization of 343. 7^3

RETEACH 4-2

LESSON 4-2 **Reteach**

Factors and Prime Factorization

Factors of a product are the numbers that are multiplied to find that product. A factor is also a whole number that divides the product with no remainder.

To find all of the factors of 24, make a list of multiplication facts.

$1 \cdot 24 = 24$
$2 \cdot 12 = 24$
$3 \cdot 8 = 24$
$4 \cdot 6 = 24$

The factors of 24 are 1, 2, 3, 4, 6, 8, 12, and 24.

Write multiplication facts to find the factors of each number.

1. 20 $1 \cdot 20 = 20$; $2 \cdot 10 = 20$; $4 \cdot 5 = 20$
2. 16 $1 \cdot 16 = 16$; $2 \cdot 8 = 16$; $4 \cdot 4 = 16$
3. 35 $1 \cdot 35 = 35$; $5 \cdot 7 = 35$
4. 31 $1 \cdot 31 = 31$

A number written as the product of prime factors is called the prime factorization of the number.

To write the prime factorization of 24, first write it as product of 2 numbers. Then rewrite each factor as the product of 2 numbers until all of the factors are prime numbers.

$24 = \mathbf{4} \cdot 6$ (Write 24 as the product of 2 numbers.)
$= 2 \cdot 2 \cdot \mathbf{6}$ (Rewrite 4 as the product of 2 prime numbers.)
$= 2 \cdot 2 \cdot 2 \cdot 3$ (Rewrite 6 as the product of 2 prime numbers.)

So, the prime factorization of 24 is $2 \cdot 2 \cdot 2 \cdot 3$ or $2^3 \cdot 3$.

Find the prime factorization of each number.

5. 28 $2^2 \cdot 7$
6. 45 $3^2 \cdot 5$
7. 50 $2 \cdot 5^2$
8. 72 $2^3 \cdot 3^2$

PRACTICE 4-2

LESSON 4-2 **Practice B**

Factors and Prime Factorization

List all of the factors of each number.

1. 15 1; 3; 5; 15
2. 24 1; 2; 3; 4; 6; 8; 12; 24
3. 33 1; 3; 11; 33
4. 72 1; 2; 3; 4; 6; 8; 9; 12; 18; 24; 36; 72
5. 48 1; 2; 3; 4; 6; 8; 12; 16; 24; 48
6. 95 1; 5; 19; 95
7. 66 1; 2; 3; 6; 11; 22; 33; 66
8. 87 1; 3; 29; 87
9. 36 1; 2; 3; 4; 6; 9; 12; 18; 36

Write the prime factorization of each number.

10. 44 $2^2 \cdot 11$
11. 56 $2^3 \cdot 7$
12. 42 $2 \cdot 3 \cdot 7$
13. 39 $3 \cdot 13$
14. 36 $2^2 \cdot 3^2$
15. 125 5^3
16. 85 $5 \cdot 17$
17. 100 $2^2 \cdot 5^2$
18. 32 2^5

19. James has an assigned seat for his flight to Denver. The seats on the plane are numbered 1–49. James's seat number is an odd number greater than 10 that is factor of 100. What is his seat number for the flight? 25

20. Linda writes the prime factorization of 40 as $2 \cdot 2 \cdot 2 \cdot 5$ on the board. Phil writes the prime factorization of 40 as $2^3 \cdot 5$. Who is correct? They both are.

4-2 Exercises

Assignment Guide

If you finished Example 1 assign:
Average 1–4, 25–32, 34, 52–62
Advanced 9–16, 25–28, 50, 52–62

If you finished Example 2 assign:
Average 1–45, 52–62
Advanced 1–32, 35–42, 46–62

Homework Quick Check

Quickly check key concepts.
Exercises: 12, 14, 18, 24, 26, 36

Math Background

Eratosthenes (275–194 B.C.E., Greece) developed the following method for finding prime numbers: Make a table from 1 to 100. One is not a prime, so cross it out. Circle 2 because it is a prime. Starting at 2, cross out multiples of 2. Circle 3 because it is a prime. Starting at 3, cross out every third number (even though some may have been crossed out before) in the list. Continue this process until all the numbers in the list have either been circled or crossed out.

Remind students that they are crossing out multiples of each prime. For example, with the prime number 5, every fifth number afterwards (10, 15, 20, 25, ...) is a multiple of 5.

Georgia Performance Standards

M6P3.a Organize and consolidate their mathematical thinking through communication.

M6P3.c Analyze and evaluate the mathematical thinking and strategies of others.

ONGOING ASSESSMENT

and INTERVENTION 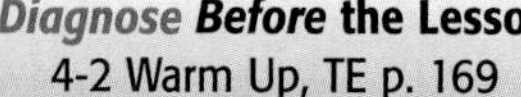

Diagnose **Before** the Lesson
4-2 Warm Up, TE p. 169

Monitor **During** the Lesson
4-2 Know-It Notebook
4-2 Questioning Strategies

Assess **After** the Lesson
4-2 Lesson Quiz, TE p. 172

Interdisciplinary 

Life Science

Exercises 46–51 involve using data about endangered species. Protection of endangered species is studied in middle school life science programs such as *Holt Science & Technology*.

TEST PREP DOCTOR Remembering the Commutative Property will help students in Exercise 53. Commuting the second and third numbers creates compatible pairs, making it easy to compute the product of 60.

Journal

Have students explain which is easier to use for finding the prime factorization of a number, a factor tree or a ladder diagram, and why.

Power Presentations with PowerPoint®

4-2 Lesson Quiz

List all the factors of each number.

1. 22 — 1, 2, 11, 22

2. 40 — 1, 2, 4, 5, 8, 10, 20, 40

3. 51 — 1, 3, 17, 51

Write the prime factorization of each number.

4. 32 — 2^5

5. 120 — $2^3 \times 3 \times 5$

Also available on transparency

Life Science 

Climate changes, habitat destruction, and overhunting can cause animals and plants to die in large numbers. When the entire population of a species begins to die out, the species is considered endangered.

The graph shows the number of endangered species in each category of animal.

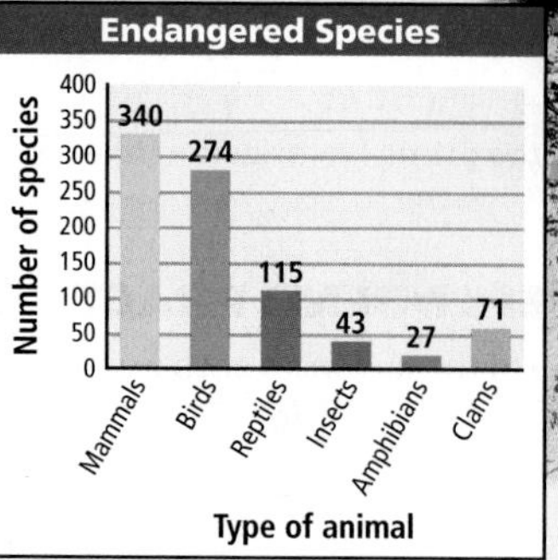

Laysan albatross chicks often die from eating plastic that pollutes the oceans and beaches. Clean-up efforts may prevent the albatross from becoming endangered.

46. How many species of mammals are endangered? Write this number as the product of prime factors. **340; $2^2 \cdot 5 \cdot 17$**

47. Which categories of animals have a prime number of endangered species? **Insects; Clams**

48. How many species of reptiles and amphibians combined are endangered? Write the answer as the product of prime factors. **142; $2 \cdot 71$**

49. **What's the Error?** When asked to write the prime factorization of the number of endangered amphibian species, a student wrote 3 × 9. Explain the error and write the correct answer. **9 is not a prime number; 3^3**

50. **Write About It** A team of five scientists is going to study endangered insect species. The scientists want to divide the species evenly among them. Will they be able to do this? Why or why not?

50. No, because there are 43 endangered insect species and five scientists and 43 is not divisible by 5.

51. **Challenge** Add the number of endangered mammal species to the number of endangered bird species. Find the prime factorization of this number. **$2 \cdot 307$**

go.hrw.com
Web Extra!
KEYWORD: MR7 Endangered

CRCT PREP • GPS SUPPORT • SPIRAL REVIEW

52. **Multiple Choice** Which expression shows the prime factorization of 50?

Ⓐ 2×5^2　　Ⓑ 2×5^{10}　　Ⓒ 10^5　　Ⓓ 5×10

53. **Gridded Response** What number has a prime factorization of $2 \times 2 \times 3 \times 5$? **60**

54. Damien's favorite song is 4.2 minutes long. Jan's favorite song is 2.89 minutes long. Estimate the difference in the lengths of the songs by rounding to the nearest whole number. (Lesson 3-2) **1 minute**

Tell whether each number is divisible by 2, 3, 4, 5, 6, 9, and 10. (Lesson 4-1)

55. 105 **3, 5**　**56.** 198 **2, 3, 6, 9**　**57.** 360 **2, 3, 4, 5, 6, 9, 10**　**58.** 235 **5**

59. 100 **2, 4, 5, 10**　**60.** 92 **2, 4**　**61.** 540 **2, 3, 4, 5, 6, 9, 10**　**62.** 441 **3, 9**

CHALLENGE 4-2

LESSON 4-2 Challenge
Prime Shades

For each given number, shade one box in each row of the table to show a prime factor. Then use your shaded boxes to write each number's prime factorization.

1. 12

7	2
3	5
2	11

Prime factorization: $2^2 \cdot 3$

2. 70

5	3
2	11
3	7

Prime factorization: $2 \cdot 5 \cdot 7$

3. 63

3	5
2	3
11	7

Prime factorization: $3^2 \cdot 7$

4. 150

13	5
3	7
2	11
17	5

Prime factorization: $2 \cdot 3 \cdot 5^2$

5. 84

11	7
5	2
13	2
3	17

Prime factorization: $2^2 \cdot 3 \cdot 7$

6. 260

5	11
3	2
17	13
2	7

Prime factorization: $2^2 \cdot 5 \cdot 13$

7. 80

5	7
17	2
2	13
11	2
2	3

Prime factorization: $2^4 \cdot 5$

8. 1,750

17	5
13	7
31	5
5	3
2	11

Prime factorization: $2 \cdot 5^3 \cdot 7$

9. 3,234

5	3
17	7
31	11
2	13
7	23

Prime factorization: $2 \cdot 3 \cdot 7^2 \cdot 11$

PROBLEM SOLVING 4-2

LESSON 4-2 Problem Solving
Factors and Prime Factorization

Write the correct answer.

1. The area of a rectangle is the product of its length and width. If a rectangular board has an area of 30 square feet, what are the possible measurements of its length and width?
   1, 2, 3, 5, 6, 10, 15, or 30 feet
2. The first-floor apartments in Jenna's building are numbered 100 to 110. How many apartments on that floor are a prime number? What are those apartment numbers?
   4 apartments; 101, 103, 107, and 109
3. A Russian mathematician named Christian Goldbach came up with a theory that every even number greater than 4 can be written as the sum of two odd primes. Test Goldbach's theory with the numbers 6 and 50. Possible answers:
   6 = 3 + 3; 50 = 19 + 31
4. Mr. Samuels has 24 students in his math class. He wants to divide the students into equal groups, and he wants the number of students in each group to be prime. What are his choices for group sizes? How many groups can he make?
   12 groups of 2 students each or 8 groups of 3 students each

Circle the letter of the correct answer.

5. Why is 2 the only even prime number?
   A It is the smallest prime number.
   Ⓑ All other even numbers are divisible by 2.
   C It only has 1 and 2 as factors.
   D All odd numbers are prime.
6. What prime numbers are factors of both 60 and 105?
   F 2 and 3
   G 2 and 5
   Ⓗ 3 and 5
   J 5 and 7
7. If a composite number has the first five prime numbers as factors, what is the smallest number it could be? Write that number's prime factorization.
   A 30
   B 210
   Ⓒ 2,310
   D 30,030
8. Tim's younger brother, Bryant, just had a birthday. Bryant's age only has one factor, and is not a prime number. How old is Bryant?
   F 10 years old
   G 7 years old
   H 3 years old
   Ⓙ 1 year old

4-3 Greatest Common Factor

Learn to find the greatest common factor (GCF) of a set of numbers.

Vocabulary

greatest common factor (GCF)

Factors shared by two or more whole numbers are called common factors. The largest of the common factors is called the **greatest common factor**, or **GCF**.

Factors of 24: 1, 2, 3, 4, 6, 8, 12, 24

Factors of 36: 1, 2, 3, 4, 6, 9, 12, 18, 36

Common factors: 1, 2, 3, 4, 6, (12)

The greatest common factor (GCF) of 24 and 36 is 12.

Example 1 shows three different methods for finding the GCF.

EXAMPLE 1 Finding the GCF

Find the GCF of each set of numbers.

Georgia Performance Standards

M6N1.c Determine the greatest common factor (GCF) for a set of numbers. Also, M6N1.b, M6P1.c, M6P4.a, M6P4.b.

A 16 and 24

Method 1: List the factors.

factors of 16: 1, 2, 4, (8), 16 — *List all the factors.*

factors of 24: 1, 2, 3, 4, 6, (8), 12, 24 — *Circle the GCF.*

The GCF of 16 and 24 is 8.

B 12, 24, and 32

Method 2: Use prime factorization.

$12 = 2 \cdot 2 \cdot 3$ — *Write the prime factorization of each number.*

$24 = 2 \cdot 2 \cdot 2 \cdot 3$

$32 = 2 \cdot 2 \cdot 2 \cdot 2 \cdot 2$ — *Find the common prime factors.*

$2 \cdot 2 = 4$ — *Find the product of the common prime factors.*

The GCF of 12, 24, and 32 is 4.

C 12, 18, and 60

Method 3: Use a ladder diagram.

```
2 | 12 | 18 | 60
3 |  6 |  9 | 30
     2    3   10
```

Begin with a factor that divides into each number. Keep dividing until the three numbers have no common factors.

$2 \cdot 3 = 6$ — *Find the product of the numbers you divided by.*

The GCF is 6.

1 Introduce

Alternate Opener

EXPLORATION

4-3 Greatest Common Factor

The sixth-grade band, which has 60 members, and the seventh-grade band, which has 48 members, are getting ready for a parade. How can they march together in blocks with the same number of columns? The model and table below show one possible formation.

1. Use graph paper to draw a model of two other formations that would work.
2. Complete the table to show the number of rows and columns in the other two formations.

	Formation 1		Formation 2		Formation 3	
	Rows	Columns	Rows	Columns	Rows	Columns
6th Grade	10	6				
7th Grade	8	6				

Think and Discuss

3. **Discuss** which formation the band director should select if she wants the bands to pass through the parade as quickly as possible.
4. **Explain** why both 48 and 60 must be divisible by the number of columns.

Motivate

ENGLISH LANGUAGE LEARNERS

Ask students what it means to have something in *common* with someone (e.g., to have a similar interest, have the same eye color, be the same height, etc.). Give students several numbers and have them list the factors of each number. Have them identify any factors that appear in more than one list.

Explorations and answers are provided in *Alternate Openers: Explorations Transparencies.*

Organizer 4-3

Pacing: Traditional $1\frac{1}{2}$ day
Block $\frac{3}{4}$ day

Objective: Students find the greatest common factor (GCF) of a set of numbers.

Online Edition
Tutorial Videos, Interactivities

Countdown to CRCT Week 7

Power Presentations with PowerPoint®

Warm Up

Write the prime factorization of each number.

1. 14 2×7

2. 18 2×3^2

3. 63 $3^2 \times 7$

4. 54 2×3^3

Problem of the Day

In a parade, there are 15 riders on bicycles and tricycles. In all, there are 34 cycle wheels. How many bicycles and how many tricycles are in the parade? 11 bicycles and 4 tricycles

Also available on transparency

Math Fact

When the greatest common factor of two whole numbers is 1, those numbers are said to be *relatively prime*. The idea is not that they are necessarily prime, but that they are prime *relative to* each other.

Georgia Performance Standards

M6N1.b Decompose numbers into their prime factorization (Fundamental Theorem of Arithmetic).

M6N1.c Determine the greatest common factor (GCF) and the least common multiple (LCM) for a set of numbers.

M6P1.c Apply and adapt a variety of appropriate strategies to solve problems.

M6P4.a Recognize and use connections among mathematical ideas.

M6P4.b Understand how mathematical ideas interconnect and build on one another to produce a coherent whole.

COMMON ERROR ALERT

Some students may find *any* common factor, instead of the *greatest* common factor. Remind them to find the *greatest* of the common factors.

Power Presentations with PowerPoint®

Additional Examples

Example 1

Find the GCF of each set of numbers.

A. 28 and 42   14

B. 18, 30, and 24   6

C. 45, 18, and 27   9

Example 2

Jenna has 16 red flowers and 24 yellow flowers. She wants to make bouquets with the same number of each color flower in each bouquet. What is the greatest number of bouquets she can make?   8

Also available on transparency

Answers to *Think and Discuss*

1. The GCF of two prime numbers is 1 because a prime number has only two factors, 1 and the number itself. Two prime numbers will have only the factor 1 in common.
2. The least common factor of a group of numbers is 1.

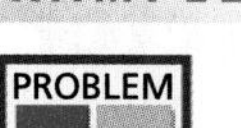

EXAMPLE 2 **PROBLEM SOLVING APPLICATION**

PROBLEM SOLVING

There are 12 boys and 18 girls in Mr. Ruiz's science class. The students must form lab groups. Each group must have the same number of boys and the same number of girls. What is the greatest number of groups Mr. Ruiz can make if every student must be in a group?

1 Understand the Problem

The **answer** will be the *greatest* number of groups 12 boys and 18 girls can form so that each group has the same number of boys, and each group has the same number of girls.

2 Make a Plan

You can make an organized list of the possible groups.

3 Solve

Helpful Hint

If more students are put in each group, there will be fewer groups. You need the most groups possible, so put the smallest possible number of students in each team. Start with 1 boy in each group.

There are more girls than boys in the class, so there will be more girls than boys in each group.

Boys	Girls	Groups
1	2	(B GG) (B GG) (B GG) (B GG) (B GG) (B GG) (B GG) (B GG) (B GG) 9 boys, 18 girls: There are 3 boys not in groups. ✗
2	3	(BB GGG) (BB GGG) (BB GGG) (BB GGG) (BB GGG) (BB GGG) 12 boys, 18 girls: Every student is in a group. ✓

The greatest number of groups is 6.

4 Look Back

The number of groups will be a common factor of the number of boys and the number of girls. To form the largest number of groups, find the GCF of 12 and 18.

factors of 12: 1, 2, 3, 4, ⑥, 12   factors of 18: 1, 2, 3, ⑥, 9, 18

The GCF of 12 and 18 is 6.

Think and Discuss

GPS M6P3.b

1. **Explain** what the GCF of two prime numbers is.
2. **Tell** what the least common factor of a group of numbers would be.

2 Teach

Guided Instruction

In this lesson, students learn to find the greatest common factor (GCF) of a set of numbers. Teach the students three methods for finding the GCF: listing factors, using prime factorization, and using a ladder diagram. GCF is used in later lessons involving fractions and algebraic expressions.

Teaching Tip

Inclusion Be sure that students using the prime factorization method realize that the common prime factors will not always line up neatly like they do in Example 1B. Let them know that they can always reorganize the factors.

Reaching All Learners

Through Cooperative Learning

Have students work in groups of three to find the GCF. Each member of the group will use a different method for finding the GCF on the same problem. Each member should explain their method as they compare their answers. For the next problem, the group members will switch methods within the group and proceed as before to find the GCF. Allow group members to assist other group members when necessary.

3 Close

Summarize

Review the terms *factor* and *greatest common factor*. Have students work in pairs using the prime factorization and ladder diagram methods of finding the GCF of two or more numbers. Then have volunteers illustrate for the class the methods used.

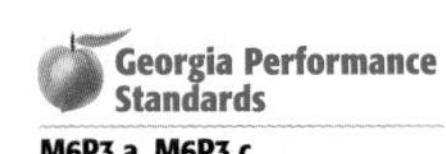

M6P3.a, M6P3.c

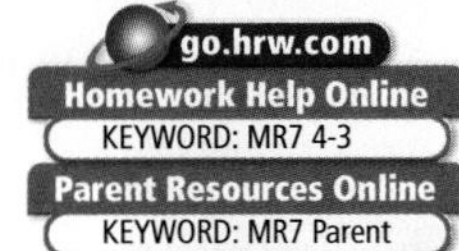

GUIDED PRACTICE

See Example 1

Find the GCF of each set of numbers.

1. 18 and 27 **9**
2. 32 and 72 **8**
3. 21, 42, and 56 **7**
4. 15, 30, and 60 **15**
5. 18, 24, and 36 **6**
6. 9, 36, and 81 **9**

See Example 2

7. Kim is making flower arrangements. She has 16 red roses and 20 pink roses. Each arrangement must have the same number of red roses and the same number of pink roses. What is the greatest number of arrangements Kim can make if every flower is used? **4 arrangements**

INDEPENDENT PRACTICE

See Example 1

Find the GCF of each set of numbers.

8. 10 and 35 **5**
9. 28 and 70 **14**
10. 36 and 72 **36**
11. 26, 48, and 62 **2**
12. 16, 40, and 88 **8**
13. 12, 60, and 68 **4**
14. 30, 45, and 75 **15**
15. 24, 48, and 84 **12**
16. 16, 48, and 72 **8**

See Example 2

17. The local recreation center held a scavenger hunt. There were 15 boys and 9 girls at the event. The group was divided into the greatest number of teams possible with the same number of boys on each team and the same number of girls on each team. How many teams were made if each person was on a team? **3 teams**
18. Ms. Kline makes balloon arrangements. She has 32 blue balloons, 24 yellow balloons, and 16 white balloons. Each arrangement must have the same number of each color. What is the greatest number of arrangements that Ms. Kline can make if every balloon is used? **8 arrangements**

PRACTICE AND PROBLEM SOLVING

Extra Practice p. 720

Write the GCF of each set of numbers.

19. 60 and 84 **12**
20. 14 and 17 **1**
21. 10, 35, and 110 **5**
22. 21 and 306 **3**
23. 630 and 712 **2**
24. 16, 24, and 40 **8**
25. 75, 225, and 150 **75**
26. 42, 112, and 105 **7**
27. 12, 16, 20, and 24 **4**
28. Jared has 12 jars of grape jam, 16 jars of strawberry jam, and 24 jars of raspberry jam. He wants to place the jam into the greatest possible number of boxes so that each box has the same number of jars of each kind of jam. How many boxes does he need? **4 boxes**
29. Pam is making fruit baskets. She has 30 apples, 24 bananas, and 12 oranges. What is the greatest number of baskets she can make if each type of fruit is distributed equally among the baskets? **6 baskets**
30. **Critical Thinking** Write a set of three different numbers that have a GCF of 9. Explain your method. **Possible answer: 9, 18, 27; I started with 9 and wrote the next 2 multiples of 9.**

4-3 Exercises

Assignment Guide

If you finished Example 1 assign:
Average 1–6, 19–27, 31–36, 43–53
Advanced 8–16, 19–24, 31–36, 43–53

If you finished Example 2 assign:
Average 1–39, 43–53
Advanced 1–36, 40–53

Homework Quick Check

Quickly check key concepts.
Exercises: 12, 16, 18, 24, 28

Math Background

Euclid's work *The Elements* contains a method for determining the greatest common factor of two whole numbers that is known as the Euclidean algorithm.

Here is a simple variation of the Euclidean algorithm: If $a > b$, the GCF of a and b equals the GCF of b and $a - b$. For example, the GCF of 48 and 30 equals the GCF of 30 and 18. This process can be continued until one of the terms divides the other: the GCF of 30 and 18 equals the GCF of 18 and 12; the GCF of 18 and 12 equals the GCF of 12 and 6. Because 6 divides 12, the GCF of 48 and 30 is 6.

RETEACH 4-3

LESSON 4-3 **Reteach**
Greatest Common Factor

The greatest common factor, or GCF, is the largest number that is the factor of any set of at least two numbers.

You can use prime factorization to find the GCF of two or more numbers.

To find the GCF of 18 and 24, first write the prime factorization of each number. Then identify the common prime factors.

18 = **2** • **3** • 3
24 = **2** • 2 • 2 • **3**

Next, find the product of the common prime factors.
2 • 3 = 6

The GCF of 18 and 24 is 6.

Find the GCF of each set of numbers.

1. 32 and 48
   32 = 2^5
   48 = $2^4 \cdot 3$
   16
2. 45 and 81
   45 = $3^2 \cdot 5$
   81 = 3^4
   9
3. 18 and 36
   18 = $2 \cdot 3^2$
   36 = $2^2 \cdot 3^2$
   18
4. 14 and 35
   14 = $2 \cdot 7$
   35 = $5 \cdot 7$
   7
5. 42 and 72
   42 = $2 \cdot 3 \cdot 7$
   72 = $2^3 \cdot 3^2$
   6
6. 56 and 64
   56 = $2^3 \cdot 7$
   64 = 2^6
   8
7. 28, 56, and 84
   28 = $2^2 \cdot 7$
   56 = $2^3 \cdot 7$
   84 = $2^2 \cdot 3 \cdot 7$
   28
8. 30, 45, and 75
   30 = $2 \cdot 3 \cdot 5$
   45 = $3^2 \cdot 5$
   75 = $3 \cdot 5^2$
   15
9. 36, 45, and 54
   36 = $2^2 \cdot 3^2$
   45 = $3^2 \cdot 5$
   54 = $2 \cdot 3^3$
   9

PRACTICE 4-3

LESSON 4-3 **Practice B**
Greatest Common Factor

Find the GCF of each set of numbers.

1. 12 and 15 — 3
2. 18 and 24 — 6
3. 15 and 25 — 5
4. 16 and 24 — 8
5. 36 and 45 — 9
6. 24 and 54 — 6
7. 48 and 64 — 16
8. 27 and 72 — 9
9. 55 and 77 — 11
10. 16, 28, and 48 — 4
11. 15, 35, and 95 — 5
12. 20, 30, and 80 — 10
13. 18, 36, and 54 — 18
14. 27, 36, and 45 — 9
15. 21, 49, and 63 — 7
16. 25, 35, and 45 — 5
17. 28, 42, and 63 — 7
18. 25, 75, and 115 — 5
19. Mr. Thompson's sixth-grade class is competing in the school field day. There are 16 boys and 12 girls in his class. He divided the class into the greatest number of teams possible with the same number of boys on each team and the same number of girls on each team. How many teams were made if each person was on a team? How many girls were on each team? How many boys?
    4 teams with 3 girls and 4 boys on each team
20. Barbara is making candy bags for her birthday party. She has 24 lollipops, 12 candy bars, and 42 pieces of gum. She wants each bag to have the same number of each kind of candy. What is the greatest number of bags she can make if all the candy is used? How many pieces of each kind of candy will be in each bag?
    6 bags with 4 lollipops, 2 candy bars, and 7 pieces of gum in each bag

Georgia Performance Standards

M6P3.a Organize and consolidate their mathematical thinking through communication.

M6P3.c Analyze and evaluate the mathematical thinking and strategies of others.

ONGOING ASSESSMENT and INTERVENTION

Diagnose **Before** the Lesson
4-3 Warm Up, TE p. 173

Monitor **During** the Lesson
4-3 Know-It Notebook
4-3 Questioning Strategies

Assess **After** the Lesson
4-3 Lesson Quiz, TE p. 176

COMMON ERROR ALERT

When finding the GCF of a set of three numbers, some students may neglect one of the numbers and find the GCF of only two of the numbers. But what the students can do is find the GCF of the first two numbers and then find the GCF of that GCF and the third number. This will be the GCF of all three numbers.

Answers

40. See p. A3.

TEST PREP DOCTOR In Exercise 43, remind students that 16 will be a factor in all the numbers in the correct set. With this information, choices **B, C,** and **D** can be eliminated.

Journal

Have students write a real-world problem involving GCF similar to the one in Example 2. Have them solve the problem and explain their solution.

Power Presentations with PowerPoint®

4-3 Lesson Quiz

Find the greatest common factor of each set of numbers.

1. 18 and 30 — 6
2. 20 and 35 — 5
3. 8, 28, 52 — 4
4. 44, 66, 88 — 22
5. Mrs. Lovejoy makes flower arrangements. She has 36 red carnations, 60 white carnations, and 72 pink carnations. Each arrangement must have the same number of each color. What is the greatest number of arrangements she can make if she uses every carnation? — 12 arrangements

Also available on transparency

LINK Life Science

The biggest flower in the world is the Rafflesia. It grows in the Indonesian rain forest. Blossoms can measure four feet across, weigh about 15 pounds, and contain about 1.5 gallons of water.

Write the GCF of each set of numbers.

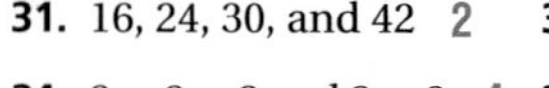

31. 16, 24, 30, and 42   2   **32.** 25, 90, 45, and 100   5   **33.** 27, 90, 135, and 72   9

34. $2 \times 2 \times 3$ and 2×2 4   **35.** $2 \times 3^2 \times 7$ and $2^2 \times 3$ 6   **36.** $3^2 \times 7$ and $2 \times 3 \times 5^2$ 3

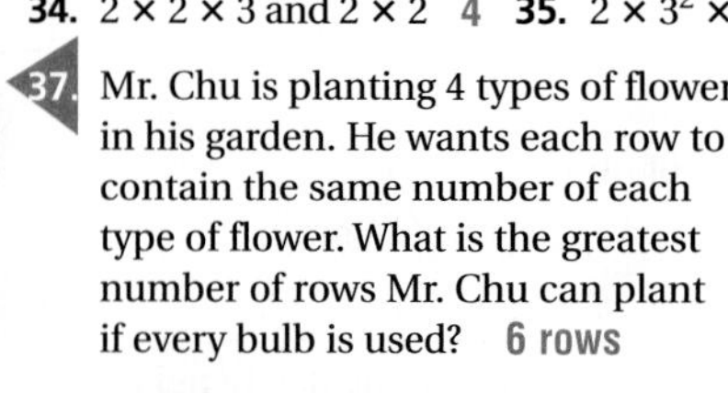

37. Mr. Chu is planting 4 types of flowers in his garden. He wants each row to contain the same number of each type of flower. What is the greatest number of rows Mr. Chu can plant if every bulb is used?   6 rows

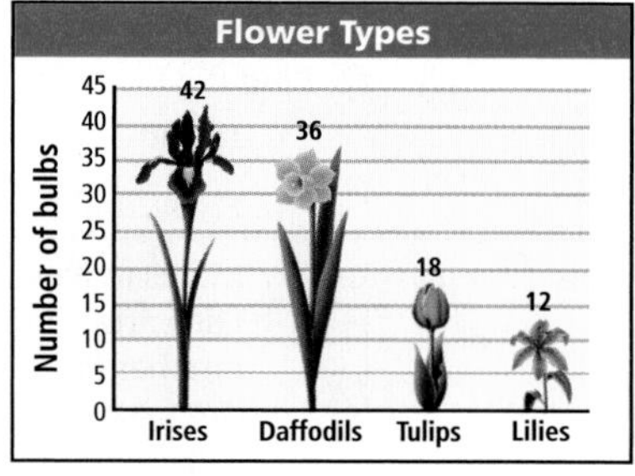

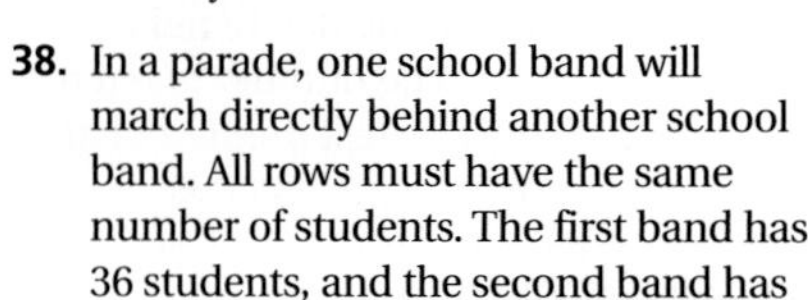

38. In a parade, one school band will march directly behind another school band. All rows must have the same number of students. The first band has 36 students, and the second band has 60 students. What is the greatest number of students who can be in each row?   12

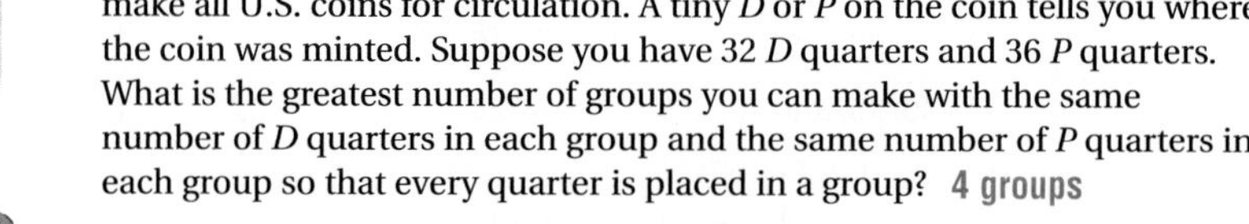

39. Social Studies Branches of the U.S. Mint in Denver and Philadelphia make all U.S. coins for circulation. A tiny *D* or *P* on the coin tells you where the coin was minted. Suppose you have 32 *D* quarters and 36 *P* quarters. What is the greatest number of groups you can make with the same number of *D* quarters in each group and the same number of *P* quarters in each group so that every quarter is placed in a group?   4 groups

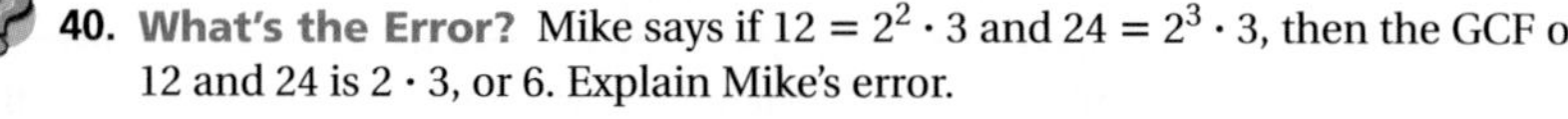

40. What's the Error? Mike says if $12 = 2^2 \cdot 3$ and $24 = 2^3 \cdot 3$, then the GCF of 12 and 24 is $2 \cdot 3$, or 6. Explain Mike's error.

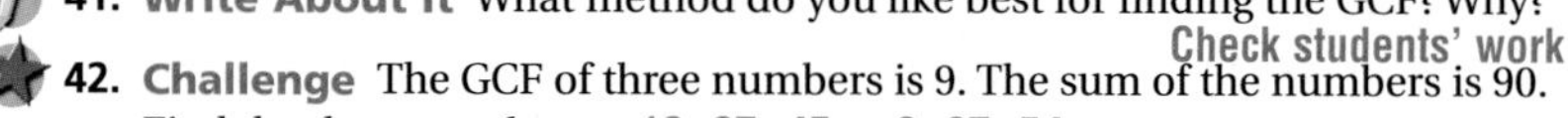

41. Write About It What method do you like best for finding the GCF? Why?   Check students' work.

42. Challenge The GCF of three numbers is 9. The sum of the numbers is 90. Find the three numbers.   18, 27, 45 or 9, 27, 54

CRCT PREP • GPS SUPPORT • SPIRAL REVIEW

43. Multiple Choice For which set of numbers is 16 the GCF?

Ⓐ 16, 32, 48   Ⓑ 12, 24, 32   Ⓒ 24, 48, 60   Ⓓ 8, 80, 100

44. Multiple Choice Mrs. Lyndon is making baskets of muffins. She has 48 lemon muffins, 120 blueberry muffins, and 112 banana nut muffins. How many baskets can Mrs. Lyndon make with each type of muffin distributed evenly?

Ⓕ 4   Ⓖ 6   Ⓗ 8   Ⓙ 12

Solve each equation. (Lessons 2-4, 2-5, 2-6, 2-7)

45. $y + 37 = 64$ $y = 27$ **46.** $43 - c = 19$ $c = 24$ **47.** $72 \div z = 9$ $z = 8$ **48.** $3v = 81$ $v = 27$

Write the prime factorization of each number. (Lesson 4-2)

49. 42 $2 \times 3 \times 7$ **50.** 19 1×19 **51.** 51 3×17 **52.** 132 $2^2 \times 3 \times 11$ **53.** 200 $5^2 \times 2^3$

CHALLENGE 4-3

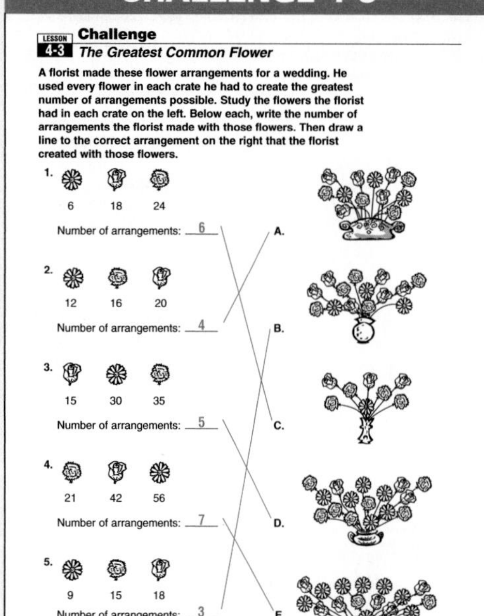

LESSON 4-3 **Challenge**
The Greatest Common Flower

A florist made these flower arrangements for a wedding. He used every flower in each crate he had to create the greatest number of arrangements possible. Study the flowers the florist had in each crate on the left. Below each, write the number of arrangements the florist made with those flowers. Then draw a line to the correct arrangement on the right that the florist created with those flowers.

1. 6   18   24 — Number of arrangements: 6   A.
2. 12   16   20 — Number of arrangements: 4   B.
3. 15   30   35 — Number of arrangements: 5   C.
4. 21   42   56 — Number of arrangements: 7   D.
5. 9   15   18 — Number of arrangements: 3   E.

PROBLEM SOLVING 4-3

LESSON 4-3 **Problem Solving**
Greatest Common Factor

Write the correct answer.

1. Carolyn has 24 bottles of shampoo, 36 tubes of hand lotion, and 60 bars of lavender soap to make gift baskets. She wants to have the same number of each item in every basket. What is the greatest number of baskets she can make without having any of the items left over?
   12 baskets
2. There are 40 girls and 32 boys who want to participate in the relay race. If each team must have the same number of girls and boys, what is the greatest number of teams that can race? How many boys and girls will be on each team?
   8 teams with 5 girls and 4 boys each
3. Ming has 15 quarters, 30 dimes, and 48 nickels. He wants to group his money so that each group has the same number of each coin. What is the greatest number of groups he can make? How many of each coin will be in each group? How much money will each group be worth?
   3 groups with 5 quarters, 10 dimes, and 16 nickels each; $3.05
4. A gardener has 27 tulip bulbs, 45 tomato plants, 108 rose bushes, and 126 herb seedlings to plant in the city garden. He wants each row of the garden to have the same number of each kind of plant. What is the greatest number of rows that the gardener can make if he uses all the plants?
   9 rows

Circle the letter of the correct answer.

5. Kim packed 6 boxes with identical supplies. It was the greatest number she could pack and use all the supplies. Which of these is her supply list?
   A 24 pencils, 36 pens, 10 rulers
   B 12 rulers, 30 pencils, 45 pens
   Ⓒ 42 pencils, 18 rulers, 72 pens
   D 60 pens, 54 pencils, 32 rulers
6. The sum of three numbers is 60. Their greatest common factor is 4. Which of the following lists shows those three numbers?
   F 4, 16, 36
   Ⓖ 8, 20, 32
   H 14, 16, 30
   J 10, 18, 32

Greatest Common Factor

Use with Lesson 4-3

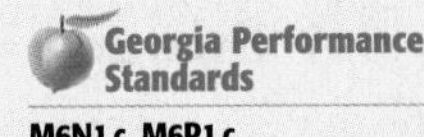

Georgia Performance Standards
M6N1.c, M6P1.c

go.hrw.com
Lab Resources Online
KEYWORD: MR7 Lab4

You can use a graphing calculator to quickly find the greatest common factor (GCF) of two or more numbers. A calculator is particularly useful when you need to find the GCF of large numbers.

Activity

Find the GCF of 504 and 3,150.

The GCF is also known as the *greatest common divisor,* or GCD. The GCD function is found on the **MATH** menu.

To find the GCD on a graphing calculator, press MATH. Press ▶ to highlight NUM, and then use ▼ to scroll down and highlight 9:.

Press ENTER 504 , 3150) ENTER.

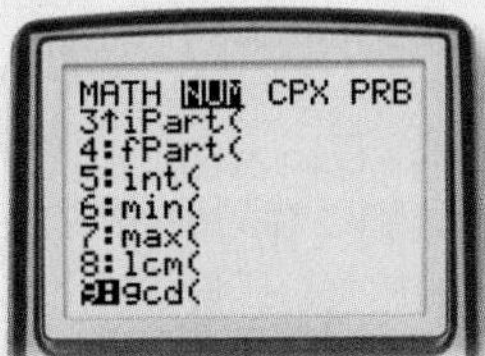

The greatest common factor of 504 and 3,150 is 126.

Think and Discuss

1. Suppose your calculator will not allow you to enter three numbers into the GCD function. How could you still use your calculator to find the GCF of the three following numbers: 4,896; 2,364; and 656? Explain your strategy and why it works. **Possible answer: Find the GCF of 4,896 and 2,364. Then find the GCF of 2,364 and 656, and then the GCF of 656 and 4,896. The greatest common factor of these three numbers (12, 4, and 16) would be the greatest common factor of 4,896, 2,364, and 656; in this case, it is 4.**
2. Would you use your calculator to find the GCF of 6 and 18? Why or why not? **Possible answer: No, because it can be done quickly mentally.**

Try This

Find the GCF of each set of numbers.

1. 14, 48 **2**
2. 18, 54 **18**
3. 99, 121 **11**
4. 144, 196 **4**
5. 200, 136 **8**
6. 246, 137 **1**
7. 72, 860 **4**
8. 55, 141, 91 **1**

Organizer

Use with Lesson 4-3

Pacing:
Traditional $\frac{1}{2}$ day
Block $\frac{1}{4}$ day

Objective: Using a graphing calculator to find the GCF of two or more numbers.

Materials: Graphing calculator

Online Edition
Scientific Calculator

Countdown to CRCT Week 7

Resources

Technology Lab Activities
Lab 4-3 Recording Sheet

Teach

Discuss

Have students share their ideas about whether using a calculator makes a difference in finding the GCF or GCD.

Close

Key Concept

Calculators can be most helpful in finding the GCF of large numbers, as well as finding the GCF of sets of three or more numbers.

Assessment

1. What should you enter into the calculator when the display shows **gcd(**? the numbers whose greatest common divisor you are trying to find, separated by a comma
2. Find the greatest common factor of 48 and 88. 8
3. What is the greatest common divisor of 288, 200, and 212? 4

Georgia Performance Standards

M6N1.c Determine the greatest common factor (GCF) and the least common multiple (LCM) for a set of numbers.

M6P1.c Analyze and adapt a variety of appropriate strategies to solve problems.

Organizer

Objective: Assess students' mastery of concepts and skills in Lessons 4-1 through 4-3.

Resources

Assessment Resources
Section 4A Quiz

Test & Practice Generator
One-Stop Planner®

INTERVENTION

Resources

***Ready to Go On? Intervention and Enrichment* Worksheets**

***Ready to Go On?* CD-ROM**

***Ready to Go On?* Online**

my.hrw.com

Answers

5. Yes; Possible answer: 45 is divisible by 5.

SECTION 4A

Ready to Go On?

Quiz for Lessons 4-1 Through 4-3

4-1 Divisibility

Tell whether each number is divisible by 2, 3, 4, 5, 6, 9, and 10.

1. 708 2, 3, 4, 6
2. 514 2
3. 470 2, 5, 10
4. 338 2
5. A highway loop around a city is 45 miles long. If exits are placed every 5 miles, will the exits be evenly spaced around the loop? Explain.
6. Hoover Dam is 1,244 feet across at the top. Tell whether this number is divisible by 2, 3, 4, 5, 6, 9, and 10. 2, 4

Tell whether each number is prime or composite.

7. 76 composite
8. 59 prime
9. 69 composite
10. 33 composite

4-2 Factors and Prime Factorization

List all of the factors of each number.

11. 26 1, 2, 13, 26
12. 32 1, 2, 4, 8, 16, 32
13. 39 1, 3, 13, 39
14. 84 1, 2, 3, 4, 6, 7, 12, 14, 21, 28, 42, 84
15. Mr. Collins's bowling league has 48 members. If the league splits into 12 teams, how many equally sized teams will there be? 4

Write the prime factorization of each number.

16. 96 $2^5 \times 3$
17. 50 2×5^2
18. 104 $2^3 \times 13$
19. 63 $3^2 \times 7$
20. Scientists classify many sunflowers in the genus *Helianthus*. There are approximately 67 species of *Helianthus*. Write the prime factorization of 67. 1×67

4-3 Greatest Common Factor

Find the GCF of each set of numbers.

21. 16 and 36 4
22. 22 and 88 22
23. 65 and 91 13
24. 20, 55, and 85 5
25. There are 36 sixth-graders and 40 seventh-graders. What is the greatest number of teams that the students can form if each team has the same number of sixth-graders and the same number of seventh-graders and every student must be on a team? 4 teams
26. There are 14 girls and 21 boys in Mrs. Sutter's gym class. To play a certain game, the students must form teams. Each team must have the same number of girls and the same number of boys. What is the greatest number of teams Mrs. Sutter can make if every student is on a team? 7 teams
27. Mrs. Young, an art teacher, is organizing the art supplies. She has 76 red markers, 52 blue markers, and 80 black markers. She wants to divide the markers into boxes with the same number of red, the same number of blue, and the same number of black markers in each box. What is the greatest number of boxes she can have if every marker is placed in a box? 4 boxes

READY TO GO ON?
Diagnose and Prescribe

NO — INTERVENE

Ready to Go On? Intervention	*Ready to Go On? Intervention,* Section 4A: Worksheets	CD-ROM	Online
Lesson 4-1	4-1 Intervention	Activity 4-1	Diagnose and Prescribe Online
Lesson 4-2	4-2 Intervention	Activity 4-2	
Lesson 4-3	4-3 Intervention	Activity 4-3	

YES — ENRICH

***Ready to Go On? Enrichment,* Section 4A**
Worksheets
CD-ROM

Online

Focus on Problem Solving

Understand the Problem

• **Interpret unfamiliar words**

You must understand the words in a problem in order to solve it. If there is a word you do not know, try to use context clues to figure out its meaning. Suppose there is a problem about red, green, blue, and chartreuse fabric. You may not know the word *chartreuse*, but you can guess that it is probably a color. To make the problem easier to understand, you could replace *chartreuse* with the name of a familiar color, like *white*.

In some problems, the name of a person, place, or thing might be difficult to pronounce, such as *Mr. Joubert*. When you see a proper noun that you do not know how to pronounce, you can use another proper noun or a pronoun in its place. You could replace *Mr. Joubert* with *he*. You could replace *Koenisburg Street* with *K Street*.

Copy each problem. Underline any words that you do not understand. Then replace each word with a more familiar word.

1. Grace is making flower bouquets. She has 18 chrysanthemums and 42 roses. She wants to arrange them in groups that each have the same number of chrysanthemums and the same number of roses. What is the fewest number of flowers that Grace can have in each group? How many chrysanthemums and how many roses will be in each group?

2. Most marbles are made from glass. The glass is liquefied in a furnace and poured. It is then cut into cylinders that are rounded off and cooled. Suppose 1,200 cooled marbles are put into packages of 8. How many packages could be made? Would there be any marbles left over?

3. In ancient times, many civilizations used calendars that divided the year into months of 30 days. A year has 365 days. How many whole months were in these ancient calendars? Were there any days left over? If so, how many?

4. Mrs. LeFeubre is tiling her garden walkway. It is a rectangle that is 4 feet wide and 20 feet long. Mrs. LeFeubre wants to use square tiles, and she does not want to have to cut any tiles. What is the size of the largest square tile that Mrs. LeFeubre can use?

Answers

1. 10 flowers in each group; 7 roses and 3 chrysanthemums
2. 150 packages; no
3. 12 months; yes; 5
4. Mrs. LeFeubre can use square tiles with side lengths of 4 ft.

Focus on Problem Solving

Organizer

Objective: Focus on understanding the problem by interpreting unfamiliar words.

Online Edition

Resources

Chapter 4 Resource Book
Reading Strategies

Problem Solving Process

This page focuses on the first step of the problem-solving process: **Understand the Problem.**

ENGLISH LANGUAGE LEARNERS

Discuss

Have students read each problem and list the words they did not understand. Then ask them to give a simpler, or more familiar, replacement word for each of the words they mentioned.

Possible answers:

1. *Bouquets* and *chrysanthemums;* replace *bouquets* with *arrangements* and replace *chrysanthemums* with *carnations*.
2. *Liquefied* and *furnace;* replace *liquefied* with *melted* and replace *furnace* with *fire*.
3. *Ancient* and *civilizations;* replace *ancient* with *old* and replace *civilizations* with *people*.
4. *LeFeubre;* replace *Mrs. LeFeubre* with *Mrs. L.*

Understanding Fractions

One-Minute Section Planner

Lesson	Materials	MiC and Lab Resources
4-4 Hands-On Lab Explore Decimals and Fractions • Use decimal grids to show the relationship between decimals and fractions. **Lesson 4-4** Decimals and Fractions • Convert between decimals and fractions. ☑ CRCT ☐ SAT-10 ☑ ITBS ☐ CTBS ☑ NAEP	Decimal grids or grid paper, fraction bars (MK)	**MiC:** ***Fraction Times*** p. 29 **MiC:** ***More or Less*** pp. 20–21 ***Hands-On Lab Activities*** 4-4
4-5 Hands-On Lab Model Equivalent Fractions • Use pattern blocks to model equivalent fractions. **Lesson 4-5** Equivalent Fractions • Write equivalent fractions. ☑ CRCT ☐ SAT-10 ☐ ITBS ☑ CTBS ☐ NAEP **4-5B Hands-On Lab** Explore Fraction Measurement • Use handmade rulers to study equivalent fractions.	Pattern blocks (MK), fraction bars (MK), number cubes (MK), customary rulers (MK), paper strips, transparency ruler (MK)	**MiC:** ***Models You Can Count On*** pp. 3–8 ***Hands-On Lab Activities*** 4-5
Lesson 4-6 Mixed Numbers and Improper Fractions • Convert between mixed numbers and improper fractions. ☑ CRCT ☐ SAT-10 ☐ ITBS ☐ CTBS ☐ NAEP	Fraction bars (MK), customary rulers (MK)	***Hands-On Lab Activities*** 4-6

MK = *Manipulatives Kit*

Mathematics in Context

The units ***Models You Can Count On, Fraction Times,*** and ***More or Less*** from the *Mathematics in Context* © 2006 series can be used with Section 4B. See Section Planner above for suggestions for integrating *MiC* with *Holt Mathematics*.

Section Overview

Professional Development

Decimals and Fractions

Lesson 4-4

To compare numbers, you sometimes need to convert between fraction form and decimal form.

Write 0.27 as a fraction.

The place value of the digit farthest to the right is hundredths, so 0.27 is 27 hundredths.

$$0.27 = \frac{27}{100}$$

Write $\frac{3}{8}$ as a decimal.

Divide 3 by 8 to convert $\frac{3}{8}$ to a decimal.

$$8\overline{)3.000} = 0.375$$

$$\frac{3}{8} = 0.375$$

Equivalent Fractions

Lessons 4-5

In order to work with fractions with unlike denominators, you need to know how to write them as equivalent fractions with like denominators.

Equivalent fractions

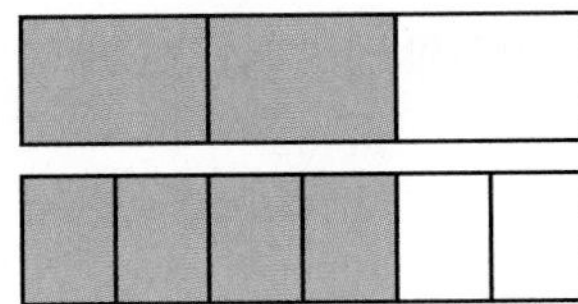

$$\frac{2}{3} = \frac{4}{6}$$

Find the missing number that makes the fractions equivalent.

$$\frac{3}{4} = \frac{\blacksquare}{20}$$

$$\frac{4}{5} = \frac{16}{\blacksquare}$$

$$\frac{3 \cdot 5}{4 \cdot 5} = \frac{15}{20}$$

$$\frac{4 \cdot 4}{5 \cdot 4} = \frac{16}{20}$$

Mixed Numbers and Improper Fractions

Lesson 4-6

To operate with fractions, you sometimes need to convert between mixed numbers and improper fractions.

Convert the improper fraction $\frac{11}{4}$ to a mixed number:

$$4\overline{)11} = 2\tfrac{3}{4}$$
$$-8$$
$$3$$

Divide the numerator by the denominator.

The remainder becomes the numerator, and the divisor remains the denominator.

$$\frac{11}{4} = 2\frac{3}{4}$$

From a mixed number to an improper fraction:

$$2\frac{3}{4} = \frac{4 \times 2 + 3}{4}$$

$$= \frac{11}{4}$$

Organizer

Use with Lesson 4-4

Pacing:
Traditional $\frac{1}{2}$ day
Block $\frac{1}{4}$ day

Objective: To use decimal grids to show the relationship between decimals and fractions.

Materials: Decimal grids

Online Edition
Fraction/Decimal Grids

Countdown to CRCT Week 8

Resources

Hands-On Lab Activities
Lab 4-4 Recording Sheet

Teach

Discuss

Discuss with students what each small square on the decimal grid represents. Also discuss the decimal represented by each column or row.

Close

Key Concept

The decimal grid allows a concrete connection between decimals and their equivant fractions.

Assessment

Represent each decimal on a decimal grid.

1. 0.4

2. 0.64

M6N1.f Use fractions, decimals, and percents interchangeably.

M6P4.a Recognize and use connections among mathematical ideas.

M6P5.a Create and use representations to organize, record, and communicate mathematical ideas.

Explore Decimals and Fractions

Use with Lesson 4-4

M6N1.f, M6P4.a, M6P5.a

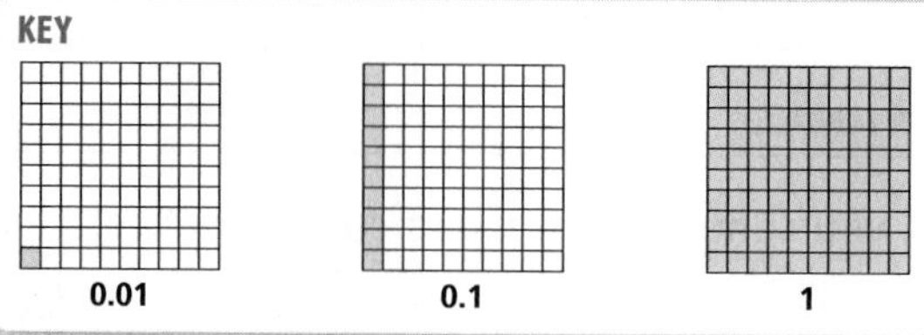

You can use decimal grids to show the relationship between fractions and decimals.

Activity

Write the number represented on each grid as a fraction and as a decimal.

1

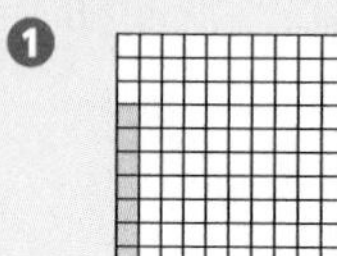

Seven hundredths squares are shaded → 0.07
How many squares are shaded? 7 ← numerator
How many squares are in the whole? 100 ← denominator

$0.07 = \frac{7}{100}$

2

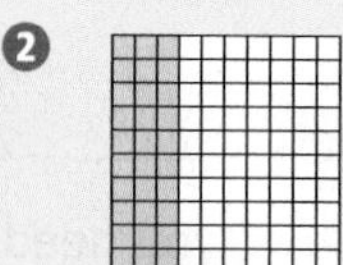

Three tenths columns are shaded → 0.3
How many complete columns are shaded? 3
How many columns are in the whole? 10

$0.3 = \frac{3}{10}$

Think and Discuss

1. Is 0.09 the same as $\frac{9}{10}$? Use decimal grids to support your answer.

Possible answer: No, 0.09 is not the same as $\frac{9}{10}$. $\frac{9}{10}$ is the same as 0.9 (nine tenths), not 0.09 (nine hundredths).

Try This

Use decimal grids to represent each number.

1. 0.8 **2.** $\frac{37}{100}$ **3.** 0.53 **4.** $\frac{1}{10}$ **5.** $\frac{67}{100}$

6. For 1–5, write each decimal as a fraction and each fraction as a decimal. $\frac{4}{5}$; 0.37; $\frac{53}{100}$; 0.1; 0.67

Answers to *Assessment*

1.

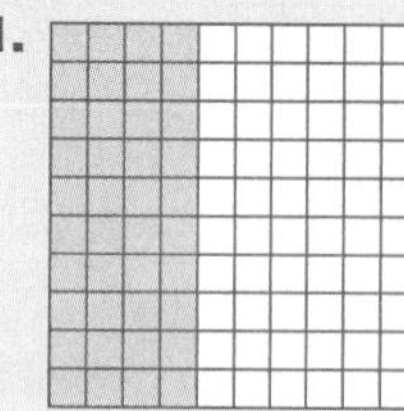

2.

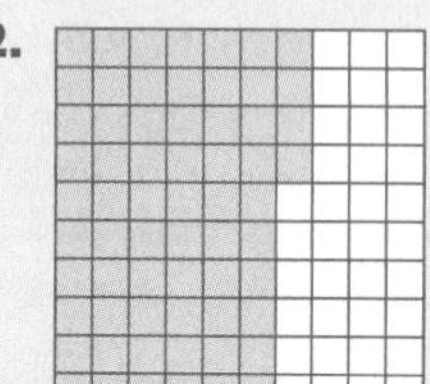

Answers to *Try This*

1.

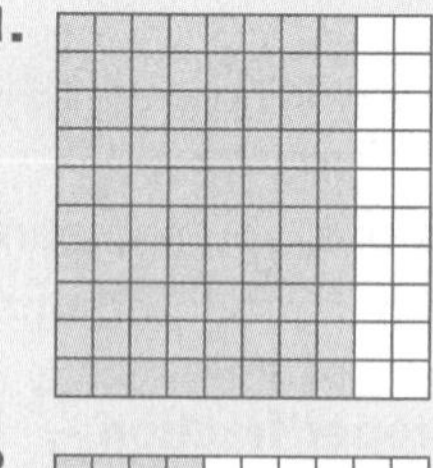

2.

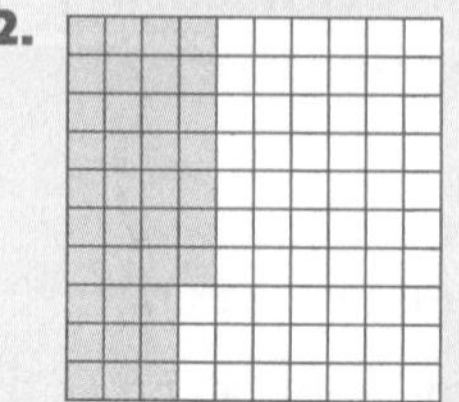

3.

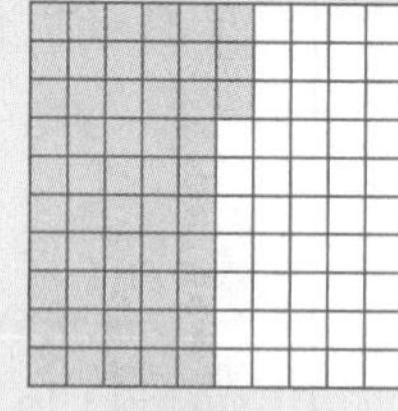

4.

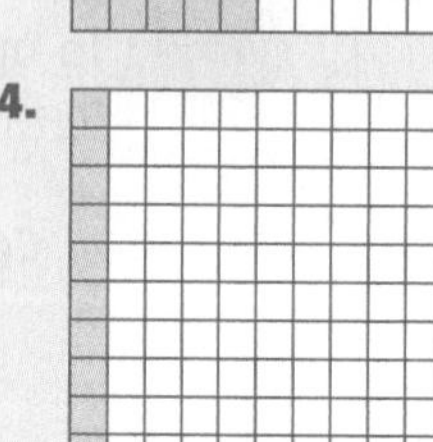

5.

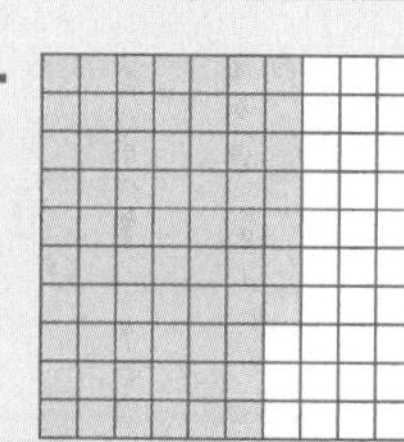

4-4 Decimals and Fractions

The University of Texas baseball team has participated in the College World Series more times than any other school.

Learn to convert between decimals and fractions.

Vocabulary
mixed number
terminating decimal
repeating decimal

Georgia Performance Standards

M6N1.f Use fractions and decimals interchangeably. Also, M6P4.a, M6P4.b, M6P5.c.

Decimals and fractions can often be used to represent the same number.

For example, a baseball player's or baseball team's batting average can be represented as a fraction:

$$\frac{\text{number of hits}}{\text{number of times at bat}}$$

In 2005, the University of Texas baseball team won its sixth College World Series title. During that season, the team had 734 hits and 2,432 at bats. The team's batting average was $\frac{734}{2{,}432}$.

$$734 \div 2{,}432 = 0.3018092105\ldots$$

The 2005 batting average for the University of Texas baseball team is reported as .302.

Decimals can be written as fractions or mixed numbers. A number that contains both a whole number greater than 0 and a fraction, such as $1\frac{3}{4}$, is called a **mixed number**.

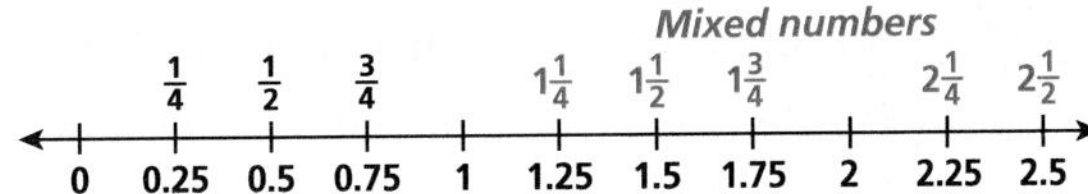

EXAMPLE 1 Writing Decimals as Fractions or Mixed Numbers

Remember!

Place Value			
Ones	Tenths	Hundredths	Thousandths

Write each decimal as a fraction or mixed number.

A 0.23

0.23 *Identify the place value of the digit farthest to the right.*

$\frac{23}{100}$ *The 3 is in the **hundred**ths place, so use **100** as the denominator.*

B 1.7

1.7 *Identify the place value of the digit farthest to the right.*

$1\frac{7}{10}$ *Write the whole number, 1. The 7 is in the **ten**ths place, so use **10** as the denominator.*

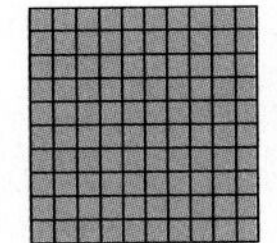
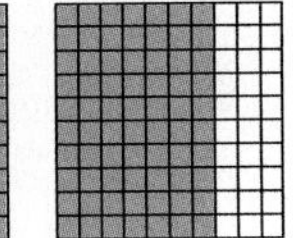

Organizer 4-4

Pacing: Traditional 1 day
Block $\frac{1}{2}$ day

Objective: Students convert between decimals and fractions.

Online Edition
Tutorial Videos, Interactivities

Countdown to CRCT Week 8

Power Presentations with PowerPoint®

Warm Up

Find the GCF of each set of numbers.

1. 15, 24 3 **2.** 30, 60 30
3. 54, 102 6 **4.** 12, 16, 24 4

Problem of the Day

Write the day of the month as the product of two factors. Possible answer: 12th of the month, 6 × 2

Also available on transparency

Math Humor

The class was changing decimals to fractions, so the teacher asked, "What's one point four?" The student on the basketball team said, "You get one *point* for making a foul shot."

1 Introduce

Alternate Opener

EXPLORATION

4-4 Decimals and Fractions

Use the model to complete the table of equivalent fractions and decimals.

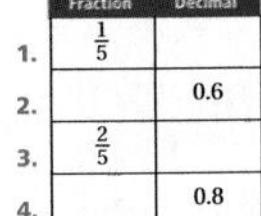

	Fraction	Decimal
1.	$\frac{1}{5}$	
2.		0.6
3.	$\frac{2}{5}$	
4.		0.8

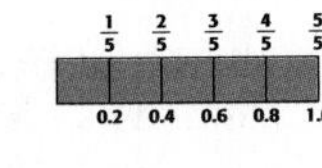

Use the model to complete the table of equivalent fractions and decimals.

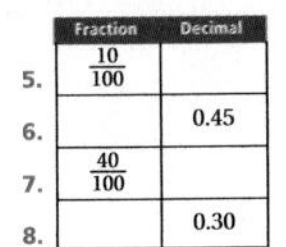

	Fraction	Decimal
5.	$\frac{10}{100}$	
6.		0.45
7.	$\frac{40}{100}$	
8.		0.30

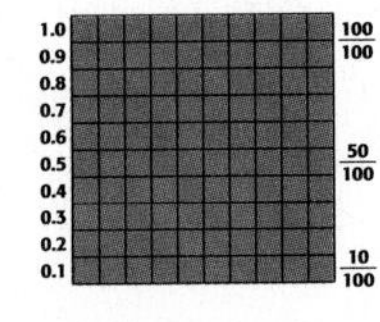

Think and Discuss

9. Describe a situation in which decimals are used.
10. Describe a situation in which fractions are used.

Motivate

Ask students to name different ways to order a set of decimals.

Possible answers: Use a number line; line up decimal points and compare numbers two at a time by comparing digits in the same place-value position, beginning with the greatest position.

Tell students that in this lesson they will order a group of numbers containing both decimals and fractions.

Explorations and answers are provided in *Alternate Openers: Explorations Transparencies.*

Georgia Performance Standards

M6N1.f Use fractions, decimals, and precents interchangeably.

M6P4.a Recognize and use connections among mathematical ideas.

M6P4.b Understand how mathematical ideas interconnect and build on one another to produce a coherent whole.

M6P5.c Use representations to model and interpret physical, social, and mathematical phenomena.

Power Presentations with PowerPoint®

Additional Examples

Example 1

Write each decimal as a fraction or mixed number.

A. 0.67 $\frac{67}{100}$ **B.** 5.9 $5\frac{9}{10}$

Example 2

Write each fraction or mixed number as a decimal.

A. $\frac{3}{20}$ 0.15 **B.** $6\frac{1}{3}$ $6.\overline{3}$

Example 3

Order the fractions and decimal from least to greatest.

$\frac{3}{4}$, 0.8, $\frac{7}{10}$ $\frac{7}{10}$, $\frac{3}{4}$, 0.8

Also available on transparency

Teaching Tip **Multiple Representations** For Example 3, discuss with students the reason for converting the fractions to decimals instead of converting the decimal to a fraction: Decimals are generally easier to compare than fractions.

Answers to *Think and Discuss*

1. Possible answer: By saying it this way you know that you must write 6 first, and then to write the rest as a fraction, you just write 9 over 10.
2. No; Although the digits follow a pattern, the same combination of digits does not repeat.

EXAMPLE 2 **Writing Fractions as Decimals**

Write each fraction or mixed number as a decimal.

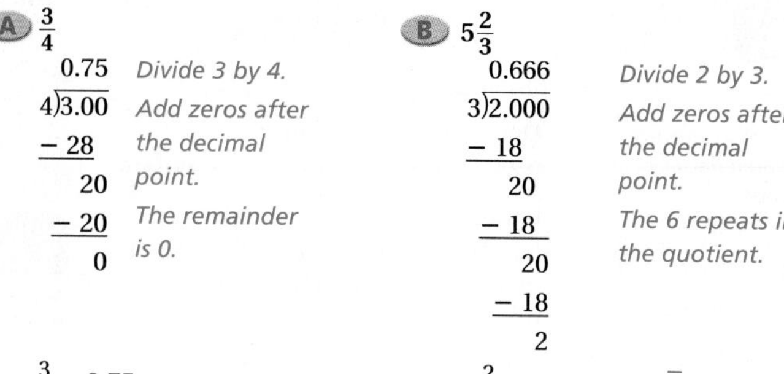

A $\frac{3}{4}$

$$\begin{array}{r} 0.75 \\ 4\overline{)3.00} \\ -28 \\ \hline 20 \\ -20 \\ \hline 0 \end{array}$$

Divide 3 by 4.
Add zeros after the decimal point.
The remainder is 0.

$\frac{3}{4} = 0.75$

B $5\frac{2}{3}$

$$\begin{array}{r} 0.666 \\ 3\overline{)2.000} \\ -18 \\ \hline 20 \\ -18 \\ \hline 20 \\ -18 \\ \hline 2 \end{array}$$

Divide 2 by 3.
Add zeros after the decimal point.
The 6 repeats in the quotient.

$5\frac{2}{3} = 5.666... = 5.\overline{6}$

Writing Math

To write a repeating decimal, you can show three dots or draw a bar over the repeating part: $0.666... = 0.\overline{6}$

A **terminating decimal**, such as 0.75, has a finite number of decimal places. A **repeating decimal**, such as 0.666..., has a block of one or more digits that repeat continuously.

Common Fractions and Equivalent Decimals

$\frac{1}{5}$	$\frac{1}{4}$	$\frac{1}{3}$	$\frac{2}{5}$	$\frac{1}{2}$	$\frac{3}{5}$	$\frac{2}{3}$	$\frac{3}{4}$	$\frac{4}{5}$
0.2	0.25	$0.\overline{3}$	0.4	0.5	0.6	$0.\overline{6}$	0.75	0.8

EXAMPLE 3 **Comparing and Ordering Fractions and Decimals**

Order the fractions and decimals from least to greatest.

0.5, $\frac{1}{5}$, 0.37

First rewrite the fraction as a decimal. $\frac{1}{5} = 0.2$

Order the three decimals.

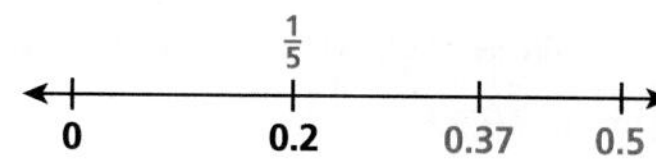

The numbers in order from least to greatest are $\frac{1}{5}$, 0.37, and 0.5.

Think and Discuss GPS M6P2.c, M6P3.b

1. **Tell** how reading the decimal 6.9 as "six and nine tenths" helps you to write 6.9 as a mixed number.
2. **Look** at the decimal 0.121122111222.... If the pattern continues, is this a repeating decimal? Why or why not?

2 Teach

Guided Instruction

In this lesson, students learn to convert between decimals and fractions. Begin by showing students a number line with mixed numbers and their decimal equivalents (Teaching Transparency). Next teach students to change decimals to fractions and then to change fractions to decimals. Teach them to distinguish between a terminating decimal and a repeating decimal and how to write a repeating decimal. Show students common fractions and their decimal equivalents. Finally, teach how to order a set of numbers containing both fractions and decimals.

Reaching All Learners

Through Cognitive Strategies

Have students match common fractions with their decimal equivalents. Knowing these fractions and their decimal equivalents will help students gain confidence in working with fractions.

1. $0.\overline{3}$ f	**a.** $\frac{3}{4}$
2. 0.5 b	**b.** $\frac{1}{2}$
3. $0.\overline{6}$ d	**c.** $\frac{1}{4}$
4. 0.25 c	**d.** $\frac{2}{3}$
5. 0.75 a	**e.** $\frac{1}{5}$
6. 0.2 e	**f.** $\frac{1}{3}$

3 Close

English Language Learners

Summarize

Review the terms *mixed number, terminating decimal,* and *repeating decimal* by having students give brief definitions of each.

Possible answer: A mixed number is a number that contains a whole number and a fraction. A terminating decimal is a decimal that has a finite number of decimal places. A repeating decimal repeats the same digit or group of digits without end.

4-4 Exercises

Georgia Performance Standards
M6P3.a, M6P3.c

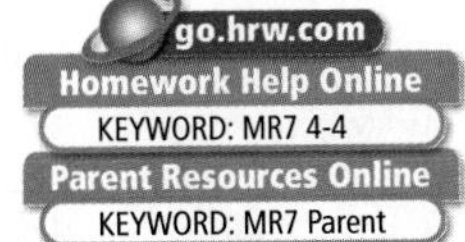
go.hrw.com
Homework Help Online
KEYWORD: MR7 4-4
Parent Resources Online
KEYWORD: MR7 Parent

GUIDED PRACTICE

Accept equivalent fractions.

See Example 1 Write each decimal as a fraction or mixed number.

1. 0.15 $\frac{3}{20}$
2. 1.25 $1\frac{1}{4}$
3. 0.43 $\frac{43}{100}$
4. 2.6 $2\frac{3}{5}$

See Example 2 Write each fraction or mixed number as a decimal.

5. $\frac{2}{5}$ 0.4
6. $2\frac{7}{8}$ 2.875
7. $\frac{1}{8}$ 0.125
8. $4\frac{1}{10}$ 4.1

See Example 3 Order the fractions and decimals from least to greatest.

9. $\frac{2}{3}$, 0.78, 0.21 0.21, $\frac{2}{3}$, 0.78
10. $\frac{5}{16}$, 0.67, $\frac{1}{6}$ $\frac{1}{6}$, $\frac{5}{16}$, 0.67
11. 0.52, $\frac{1}{9}$, 0.3 $\frac{1}{9}$, 0.3, 0.52

INDEPENDENT PRACTICE

Accept equivalent fractions.

See Example 1 Write each decimal as a fraction or mixed number.

12. 0.31 $\frac{31}{100}$
13. 5.71 $5\frac{71}{100}$
14. 0.13 $\frac{13}{100}$
15. 3.23 $3\frac{23}{100}$
16. 0.5 $\frac{1}{2}$
17. 2.7 $2\frac{7}{10}$
18. 0.19 $\frac{19}{100}$
19. 6.3 $6\frac{3}{10}$

See Example 2 Write each fraction or mixed number as a decimal.

20. $\frac{1}{9}$ $0.\overline{1}$
21. $1\frac{3}{5}$ 1.6
22. $\frac{8}{9}$ $0.\overline{8}$
23. $3\frac{11}{40}$ 3.275
24. $2\frac{5}{6}$ $2.8\overline{3}$
25. $\frac{3}{8}$ 0.375
26. $4\frac{4}{5}$ 4.8
27. $\frac{5}{8}$ 0.625

See Example 3 Order the fractions and decimals from least to greatest.

28. 0.49, 0.82, $\frac{1}{2}$ 0.49, $\frac{1}{2}$, 0.82
29. $\frac{3}{8}$, 0.29, $\frac{1}{9}$ $\frac{1}{9}$, 0.29, $\frac{3}{8}$
30. 0.94, $\frac{4}{5}$, 0.6 0.6, $\frac{4}{5}$, 0.94
31. 0.11, $\frac{1}{10}$, 0.13 $\frac{1}{10}$, 0.11, 0.13
32. $\frac{2}{3}$, 0.42, $\frac{2}{5}$ $\frac{2}{5}$, 0.42, $\frac{2}{3}$
33. $\frac{3}{7}$, 0.76, 0.31 0.31, $\frac{3}{7}$, 0.76

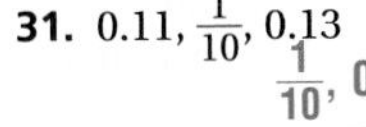

PRACTICE AND PROBLEM SOLVING

CRCT GPS
Extra Practice p. 720

Write each decimal in expanded form and use a whole number or fraction for each place value.

34. 0.81
35. 92.3
36. 13.29
37. 107.17

Write each fraction as a decimal. Tell whether the decimal terminates or repeats.

38. $\frac{7}{9}$ $0.\overline{7}$; repeats
39. $\frac{1}{6}$ $0.1\overline{6}$; repeats
40. $\frac{17}{20}$ 0.85; terminates
41. $\frac{5}{12}$ $0.41\overline{6}$; repeats
42. $\frac{7}{8}$ 0.875; terminates
43. $\frac{4}{5}$ 0.8; terminates
44. $\frac{9}{5}$ 1.8; terminates
45. $\frac{15}{18}$ $0.8\overline{3}$; repeats
46. $\frac{7}{3}$ $2.\overline{3}$; repeats
47. $\frac{11}{12}$ $0.91\overline{6}$; repeats

Compare. Write <, >, or =.

48. 0.75 ■ $\frac{3}{4}$ =
49. $\frac{5}{8}$ ■ 0.5 >
50. 0.78 ■ $\frac{7}{9}$ >
51. $\frac{1}{3}$ ■ 0.35 <
52. $\frac{2}{5}$ ■ 0.4 =
53. 0.75 ■ $\frac{4}{5}$ <
54. $\frac{3}{8}$ ■ 0.25 >
55. 0.8 ■ $\frac{5}{6}$ <

56. **Multi-Step** Peter walked $1\frac{3}{5}$ miles on a treadmill. Sally walked 1.5 miles on the treadmill. Who walked farther? Explain.

RETEACH 4-4

LESSON 4-4 **Reteach**
Decimals and Fractions

You can write decimals as fractions or mixed numbers. A place value chart will help you read the decimal. Remember the decimal point is read as the word "and."

To write 0.47 as a fraction, first think about the decimal in words.

Ones	Tenths	Hundredths	Thousandths	Ten Thousandths
0.	4	7		

0.47 is read "forty-seven hundredths." The place value of the decimal tells you the denominator is 100.

$0.47 = \frac{47}{100}$

To write 8.3 as a mixed number, first think about the decimal in words.

Ones	Tenths	Hundredths	Thousandths	Ten Thousandths
8.	3			

8.3 is read "eight and three tenths." The place value of the decimal tells you the denominator is 10. The decimal point is read as the word "and."

$8.3 = 8\frac{3}{10}$

Write each decimal as a fraction or mixed number.

1. 0.61 $\frac{61}{100}$
2. 3.43 $3\frac{43}{100}$
3. 0.009 $\frac{9}{1,000}$
4. 4.7 $4\frac{7}{10}$
5. 1.5 $1\frac{5}{10}$ or $1\frac{1}{2}$
6. 0.13 $\frac{13}{100}$
7. 5.002 $5\frac{2}{1,000}$ or $5\frac{1}{500}$
8. 0.021 $\frac{21}{1,000}$

PRACTICE 4-4

LESSON 4-4 **Practice B**
Decimals and Fractions

Write each decimal as a fraction or mixed number.

1. 0.23 $\frac{23}{100}$
2. 0.1 $\frac{1}{10}$
3. 3.25 $3\frac{25}{100}$ or $3\frac{1}{4}$
4. $1.\overline{3}$ $1\frac{1}{3}$
5. 5.5 $5\frac{5}{10}$ or $5\frac{1}{2}$
6. 3.7 $3\frac{7}{10}$

Write each fraction or mixed number as a decimal.

7. $\frac{4}{5}$ 0.8
8. $\frac{1}{9}$ $0.\overline{1}$
9. $1\frac{2}{3}$ $1.\overline{6}$
10. $3\frac{3}{5}$ 3.6
11. $2\frac{1}{3}$ $2.\overline{3}$
12. $\frac{8}{9}$ $0.\overline{8}$

Order the fractions and decimals from least to greatest.

13. $\frac{1}{4}$, 0.7, $\frac{3}{5}$ $\frac{1}{4}$, $\frac{3}{5}$, 0.7
14. 0.25, $\frac{1}{8}$, 0.3 $\frac{1}{8}$, 0.25, 0.3
15. $\frac{9}{10}$, 0.49, $\frac{1}{2}$ 0.49, $\frac{1}{2}$, $\frac{9}{10}$

Order the fractions and decimals from greatest to least.

16. 0.13, $\frac{1}{10}$, 0.9 0.9, 0.13, $\frac{1}{10}$
17. $\frac{2}{5}$, 0.7, $\frac{2}{3}$ 0.7, $\frac{2}{3}$, $\frac{2}{5}$
18. 0.65, $\frac{4}{5}$, $\frac{3}{4}$ $\frac{4}{5}$, $\frac{3}{4}$, 0.65

19. Derrick has a dollar bill and three dimes, Jane has a dollar bill and one quarter, and Kelly has a dollar bill and ten nickels. Who has the most money? the least?
Kelly has the most, and Jane has the least.

20. It rained three and one half inches in April. In May it rained $3\frac{3}{4}$ inches, and in June it rained 3.6 inches. Write the months in order from the greatest to the least amount of rain.
May, June, April

4-4 Exercises

Assignment Guide

If you finished Example 1 assign:
Average 1–4, 63, 67–75
Advanced 12–19, 67–75

If you finished Example 2 assign:
Average 1–8, 38–47, 63, 67–75
Advanced 12–27, 64, 67–75

If you finished Example 3 assign:
Average 1–42, 52–75
Advanced 12–75

Homework Quick Check
Quickly check key concepts.
Exercises: 14, 16, 22, 26, 32, 40

Answers

34. $0 + \frac{8}{10} + \frac{1}{100}$
35. $90 + 2 + \frac{3}{10}$
36. $10 + 3 + \frac{2}{10} + \frac{9}{100}$
37. $100 + 7 + \frac{1}{10} + \frac{7}{100}$
56. See p. A3.

Math Background

As long ago as 1100 B.C.E., people in China were using the concepts of fractions and mixed numbers. They did not use numerical symbols, but rather words to express these ideas.

Our method of writing fractions probably traces to Hindu mathematicians, although they did not employ the fraction bar. For example, to write the fraction $\frac{1}{2}$, Hindu mathematicians of the first millennium would write $\begin{matrix}1\\2\end{matrix}$. The fraction bar was introduced by Arab mathematicians.

Georgia Performance Standards

M6P3.a Organize and consolidate their mathematical thinking through communication.

M6P3.c Analyze and evaluate the mathematical thinking and strategies of others.

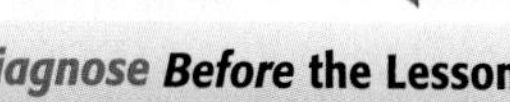

ONGOING ASSESSMENT and INTERVENTION

Diagnose Before the Lesson
4-4 Warm Up, TE p. 181

Monitor During the Lesson
4-4 Know-It Notebook
4-4 Questioning Strategies

Assess After the Lesson
4-4 Lesson Quiz, TE p. 184

Answers

64. Only the 8 repeats, so it should be the only digit with a line over it. $0.3\overline{8}$

65. 0.24 is the decimal for $\frac{6}{25}$. To find this you could multiply 0.04 by 6.

TEST PREP DOCTOR In Exercise 67, students will need to read the problem carefully. Choices **B** and **C** can be eliminated easily if students realize that the decimal numbers are in the wrong order. Remind students that converting a fraction to a decimal involves dividing the numerator by the denominator.

Journal

Tell students to write about one example of a fraction and one example of a decimal number and how they are used in the real world.

Power Presentations with PowerPoint®

4-4 Lesson Quiz

Write each decimal as a fraction or mixed number.

1. 0.24 $\frac{6}{25}$

2. 6.75 $6\frac{3}{4}$

Write each fraction or mixed number as a decimal.

3. $2\frac{3}{5}$ 2.6

4. $\frac{7}{8}$ 0.875

5. Order the fractions and decimals from least to greatest.
0.38, $\frac{3}{4}$, $\frac{1}{5}$ $\frac{1}{5}$, 0.38, $\frac{3}{4}$

6. Jamal ran the following distances on three different days: 0.87 mile, $\frac{2}{3}$ mile, and 0.13 mile. Order the distances from least to greatest.
0.13, $\frac{2}{3}$, 0.87

Also available on transparency

Georgia LINK Sports

Andruw Jones of the Atlanta Braves hit 51 homeruns in the 2005 season, which broke the previous franchise record.

Order the mixed numbers and decimals from greatest to least.

57. 4.48, 3.92, $4\frac{1}{2}$ $4\frac{1}{2}$, 4.48, 3.92

58. $10\frac{5}{9}$, 10.5, $10\frac{1}{5}$ $10\frac{5}{9}$, 10.5, $10\frac{1}{5}$

59. 125.205, 125.25, $125\frac{1}{5}$ 125.25, 125.205, $125\frac{1}{5}$

Sports The table shows batting averages for two baseball seasons. Use the table for Exercises 60–62.

Player	Season 1	Season 2
Pedro	0.360	$\frac{3}{10}$
Jill	0.380	$\frac{3}{8}$
Lamar	0.290	$\frac{1}{3}$
Britney	0.190	$\frac{3}{20}$

60. Which players had higher batting averages in season 1 than they had in season 2? Pedro, Jill, and Britney

61. Who had the highest batting average in either season? Jill

62. **Multi-Step** Whose batting average changed the most between season 1 and season 2? Pedro

63. **Life Science** Most people with color deficiency (often called color blindness) have trouble distinguishing shades of red and green. About 0.05 of men in the world have color deficiency. What fraction of men have color deficiency? $\frac{1}{20}$

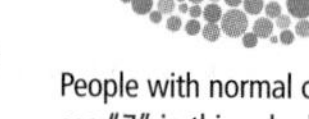

People with normal color vision will see "7" in this color-blindness test.

64. **What's the Error?** A student found the decimal equivalent of $\frac{7}{18}$ to be $0.\overline{38}$. Explain the error. What is the correct answer?

65. **Write About It** The decimal for $\frac{1}{25}$ is 0.04, and the decimal for $\frac{2}{25}$ is 0.08. Without dividing, find the decimal for $\frac{6}{25}$. Explain how you found your answer.

66. **Challenge** Write $\frac{1}{999}$ as a decimal. $0.\overline{001}$

CRCT PREP • GPS SUPPORT • SPIRAL REVIEW

67. **Multiple Choice** Which numbers are listed from least to greatest?

Ⓐ 0.65, 0.81, $\frac{4}{5}$ Ⓑ 0.81, 0.65, $\frac{4}{5}$ Ⓒ $\frac{4}{5}$, 0.81, 0.65 Ⓓ 0.65, $\frac{4}{5}$, 0.81

68. **Gridded Response** Write $5\frac{1}{8}$ as a decimal. 5.125

Find each sum or difference. (Lesson 3-3)

69. 12.56 + 8.91 21.47 **70.** 19.05 − 2.27 16.78 **71.** 5 + 8.25 + 10.2 23.45

Find the GCF of each set of numbers. (Lesson 4-3)

72. 235 and 35 5 **73.** 28 and 154 14 **74.** 90 and 56 2 **75.** 16 and 112 16

CHALLENGE 4-4

LESSON 4-4 Challenge
Fractions of Pizza

Write the fractions as decimals. Then slice and shade pieces of each pizza to represent each fraction. Finally, compare the pizzas in each row by writing $<$, $>$, or $=$.

1. $\frac{3}{4}$ 0.75 $<$ $\frac{4}{5}$ 0.8
2. $\frac{3}{6}$ 0.5 $=$ $\frac{1}{2}$ 0.5
3. $\frac{2}{3}$ $0.\overline{6}$ $>$ $\frac{3}{5}$ 0.6
4. $\frac{1}{5}$ 0.2 $<$ $\frac{1}{3}$ $0.\overline{3}$

PROBLEM SOLVING 4-4

LESSON 4-4 Problem Solving
Decimals and Fractions

Electricity is measured in amperes, or the rate electrical currents flow. A high ampere measurement means that a lot of electricity is being used. The table below shows the average amount of electricity some household appliances use per hour. Use the table to answer the questions.

Electricity Use in the Home

Appliance	Amps per Hour
Blender	$2\frac{1}{2}$
Coffeemaker	$6\frac{2}{3}$
Computer and printer	$1\frac{5}{6}$
Microwave oven	$12\frac{1}{2}$
Popcorn popper	$2\frac{1}{12}$
25-inch television	$1\frac{1}{4}$
VCR	$\frac{1}{3}$

1. How much electricity does an average 25-inch television use each hour? Write your answer as a decimal.
1.25 amperes

2. Which appliance uses an average of 2.5 amps per hour?
blender

3. Which appliance uses the most electricity per hour? Write its ampere measurement as a decimal.
microwave oven;
12.5 amperes

Circle the letter of the correct answer.

4. How much electricity do most computers and printers use in an hour?
A 1.38 amperes
B 1.8 amperes
Ⓒ 1.83 amperes
D 1.88 amperes

5. Which of the appliances has an hourly ampere measurement that is a repeating decimal?
F blender
Ⓖ coffee maker
H microwave oven
J 25-inch television

6. In most years, 39.7 percent of the world's energy comes from burning oil. What is this percent written as a fraction?
A $\frac{39}{7}$ percent
B $39\frac{1}{7}$ percent
C $3\frac{9}{7}$ percent
Ⓓ $39\frac{7}{10}$ percent

7. The United States produces about 13.2 percent of the world's hydroelectric power. What fraction of hydroelectric power does the United States produce?
Ⓕ $13\frac{1}{5}$ percent
G $\frac{13}{2}$ percent
H $1\frac{3}{2}$ percent
J $13\frac{1}{2}$ percent

Model Equivalent Fractions

Use with Lesson 4-5

Georgia Performance Standards
M6P5.a, M6P5.b

go.hrw.com
Lab Resources Online
KEYWORD: MR7 Lab4

KEY

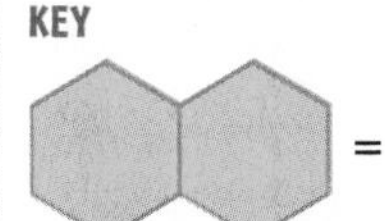 = 1 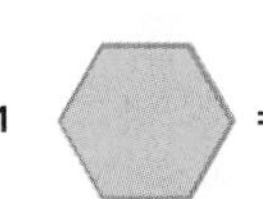 = $\frac{1}{2}$ 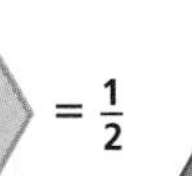 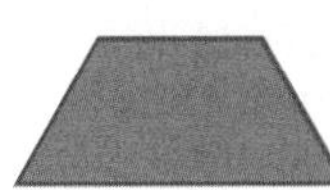 = $\frac{1}{4}$  = $\frac{1}{6}$ 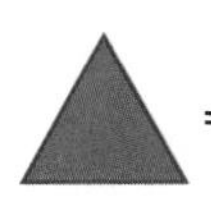 = $\frac{1}{12}$

Pattern blocks can be used to model equivalent fractions. To find a fraction that is equivalent to $\frac{1}{2}$, first choose the pattern block that represents $\frac{1}{2}$. Then find all the pieces of one color that will fit evenly on the $\frac{1}{2}$ block. Count these pieces to find the equivalent fraction. You may be able to find more than one equivalent fraction.

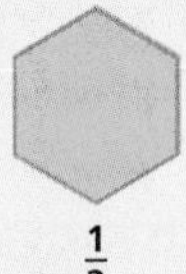 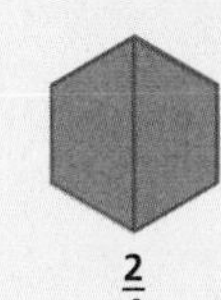 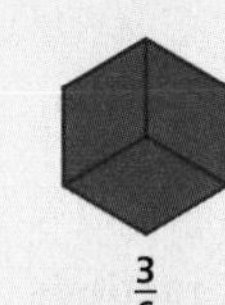 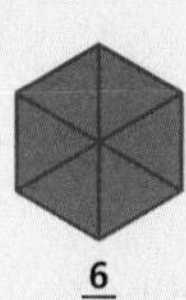

$\frac{1}{2} = \frac{2}{4} = \frac{3}{6} = \frac{6}{12}$

Activity

Use pattern blocks to find an equivalent fraction for $\frac{8}{12}$.

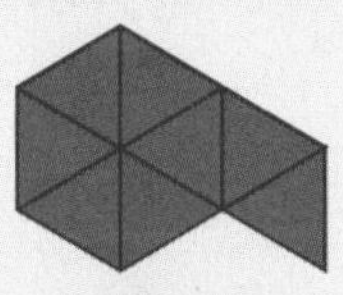

First show $\frac{8}{12}$.

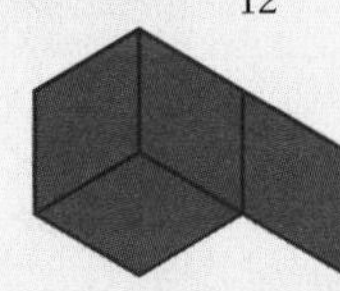

You can cover $\frac{8}{12}$ with four of the $\frac{1}{6}$ pieces.

$\frac{8}{12} = \frac{4}{6}$

Think and Discuss

1. Can you find a combination of pattern blocks for $\frac{1}{3}$? Find an equivalent fraction for $\frac{1}{3}$.
2. Are $\frac{9}{12}$ and $\frac{3}{6}$ equivalent? Use pattern blocks to support your answer.

Try This

Write the fraction that is modeled. Then find an equivalent fraction.

1. 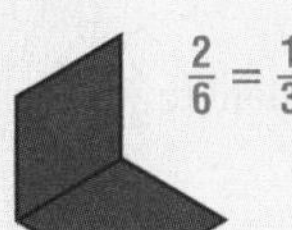 $\frac{2}{6} = \frac{1}{3}$

2. 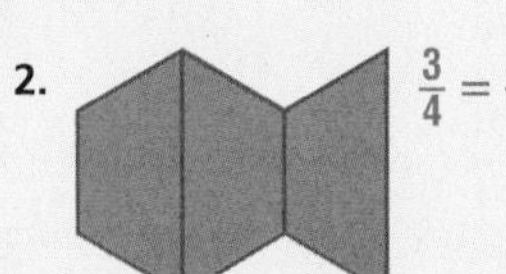 $\frac{3}{4} = \frac{9}{12}$

Answers to *Think and Discuss*

1. Possible answer: Two blue rhombus-shaped pattern blocks are equivalent to $\frac{1}{3}$. $\frac{2}{6}$ is an equivalent fraction for $\frac{1}{3}$.
2. Possible answer: No, $\frac{9}{12}$ and $\frac{3}{6}$ are not equivalent. $\frac{9}{12}$ can be represented by 9 green triangle-shaped pattern blocks, and $\frac{3}{6}$ can be represented by 3 blue rhombus-shaped pattern blocks or 6, not 9, green triangle-shaped pattern blocks.

Answers to *Assessment*

1. 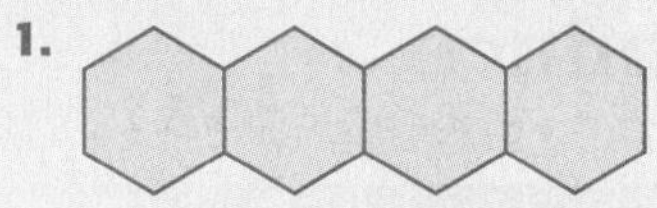
2. 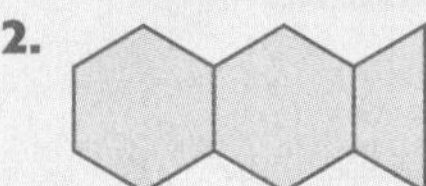
3. 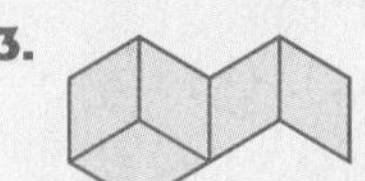

Organizer

Use with Lesson 4-5

Pacing:
Traditional $\frac{1}{2}$ day
Block $\frac{1}{4}$ day

Objective: To use pattern blocks to model equivalent fractions

Materials: Pattern blocks

Online Edition

Countdown to CRCT Week 8

Resources

Hands-On Lab Activities
Lab 4-5A Recording Sheet

Teach

Discuss

Discuss with students what fractional part of a whole each pattern block represents.

Close

Key Concept

The pattern blocks allow a concrete and visual connection between equivalent fractions.

Assessment

Model each fraction or mixed number with pattern blocks.

1. 2
2. $1\frac{1}{4}$
3. $\frac{5}{6}$

Georgia Performance Standards

M6P5.a Create and use representations to organize, record, and communicate mathematical ideas.

M6P5.b Select, apply, and translate among mathematical representations to solve problems.

4-5 Organizer

Pacing: Traditional 1 day
Block $\frac{1}{2}$ day

Objective: Students write equivalent fractions and mixed numbers.

Online Edition
Tutorial Videos, Interactivities

Countdown to CRCT Week 8

Power Presentations with PowerPoint®

Warm Up

List the factors of each number.

1. 8 — 1, 2, 4, 8
2. 10 — 1, 2, 5, 10
3. 16 — 1, 2, 4, 8, 16
4. 20 — 1, 2, 4, 5, 10, 20
5. 30 — 1, 2, 3, 5, 6, 10, 15, 30

Problem of the Day

John has 3 coins, 2 of which are the same. Ellen has 1 fewer coin than John, and Anna has 2 more coins than John. Each girl has only 1 kind of coin. Who has coins that could equal the value of a half dollar?
Ellen and Anna

Also available on transparency

Math Humor

The fraction one-fifth went to the doctor because it wasn't feeling very well. The doctor said, "You need to calm down. You're too tense (two-tenths)."

Georgia Performance Standards

M6N1.g Solve problems involving fractions, decimals, and percents.

M6P5.a Create and use representations to organize, record, and communicate mathematical ideas.

M6P5.b Select, apply, and translate among mathematical representations to solve problems.

M6P5.c Use representations to model and interpret physical, social, and mathematical phenomena.

4-5 Equivalent Fractions

Learn to write equivalent fractions.

Vocabulary
equivalent fractions
simplest form

Georgia Performance Standards
M6N1.g Solve problems involving fractions. Also, M6P5.a, M6P5.b, M6P5.c.

Rulers often have marks for inches, $\frac{1}{2}$, $\frac{1}{4}$, and $\frac{1}{8}$ inches.

Notice that $\frac{1}{2}$ in., $\frac{2}{4}$ in., and $\frac{4}{8}$ in. all name the same length. Fractions that represent the same value are **equivalent fractions**. So $\frac{1}{2}$, $\frac{2}{4}$, and $\frac{4}{8}$ are equivalent fractions.

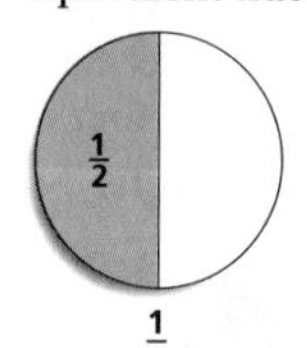

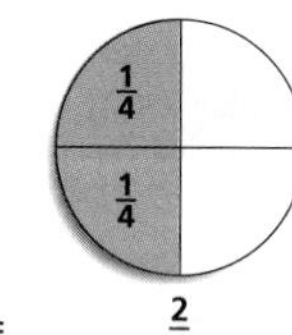

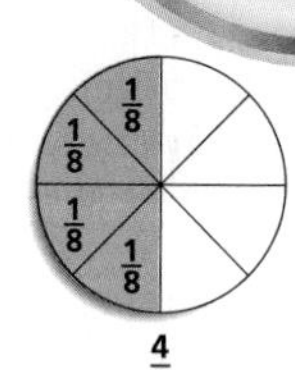

$$\frac{1}{2} = \frac{2}{4} = \frac{4}{8}$$

EXAMPLE 1 Finding Equivalent Fractions

Find two equivalent fractions for $\frac{6}{8}$.

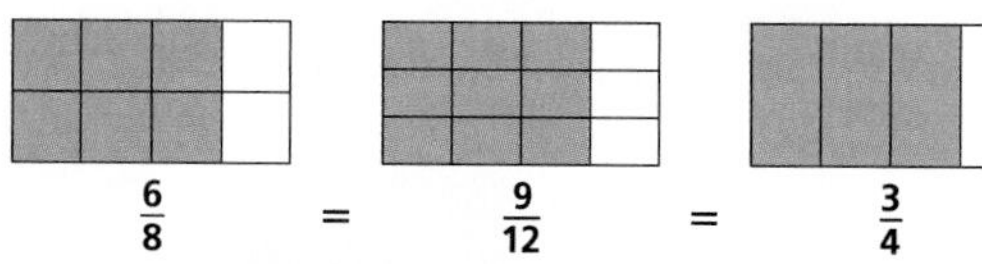

$$\frac{6}{8} = \frac{9}{12} = \frac{3}{4}$$

The same area is shaded when the rectangle is divided into 8 parts, 12 parts, and 4 parts.

So $\frac{6}{8}$, $\frac{9}{12}$, and $\frac{3}{4}$ are all equivalent fractions.

EXAMPLE 2 Multiplying and Dividing to Find Equivalent Fractions

Find the missing number that makes the fractions equivalent.

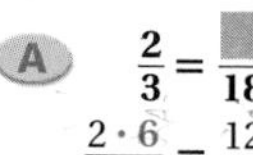

A $\frac{2}{3} = \frac{\square}{18}$

$\frac{2 \cdot 6}{3 \cdot 6} = \frac{12}{18}$ *In the denominator, 3 is multiplied by 6 to get 18. Multiply the numerator, 2, by the same number, 6.*

So $\frac{2}{3}$ is equivalent to $\frac{12}{18}$.

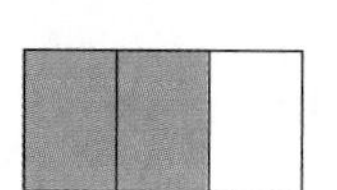

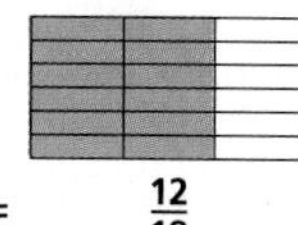

$$\frac{2}{3} = \frac{12}{18}$$

1 Introduce

Alternate Opener

EXPLORATION

4-5 Equivalent Fractions

Equivalent fractions are fractions that have the same value.

Use the models below to find equivalent fractions.

1. $\frac{1}{2} = \square = \square = \square$
2. $\frac{2}{3} = \square = \square$

Think and Discuss

3. **Describe** how you could write $\frac{1}{2}$ as an equivalent fraction with a denominator of 24.
4. **Discuss** whether $\frac{6}{12}$ and $\frac{9}{18}$ are equivalent fractions.

Motivate

Set up fraction bars (Manipulatives Kit) in groups of three, with each group representing the same fractional amount (e.g., $\frac{1}{2}$, $\frac{3}{6}$, $\frac{4}{8}$). Ask students to state how the fractions in each group are alike and how they are different.

Possible answer: The same amount is represented in each group. Different numbers of bars were used to represent the same fractional amount.

Explorations and answers are provided in *Alternate Openers: Explorations Transparencies.*

Find the missing number that makes the fractions equivalent.

B $\frac{70}{100} = \frac{7}{\blacksquare}$

$\frac{70 \div 10}{100 \div 10} = \frac{7}{10}$ *In the numerator, 70 is divided by 10 to get 7. Divide the denominator by the same number, 10.*

So $\frac{70}{100}$ is equivalent to $\frac{7}{10}$.

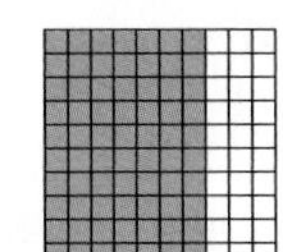
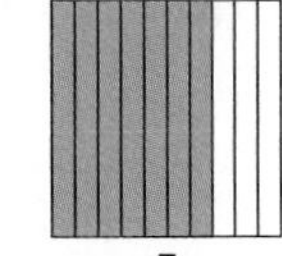

$\frac{70}{100} = \frac{7}{10}$

Every fraction has one equivalent fraction that is called the simplest form of the fraction. A fraction is in **simplest form** when the GCF of the numerator and the denominator is 1.

Example 3 shows two methods for writing a fraction in simplest form.

EXAMPLE 3 Writing Fractions in Simplest Form

Write each fraction in simplest form.

A $\frac{18}{24}$

The GCF of 18 and 24 is 6, so $\frac{18}{24}$ is not in simplest form.

Method 1: Use the GCF.

$\frac{18 \div 6}{24 \div 6} = \frac{3}{4}$ *Divide 18 and 24 by their GCF, 6.*

Method 2: Use prime factorization.

$\frac{18}{24} = \frac{\cancel{2} \cdot \cancel{3} \cdot 3}{\cancel{2} \cdot 2 \cdot 2 \cdot \cancel{3}} = \frac{3}{4}$ *Write the prime factors of 18 and 24. Simplify.*

So $\frac{18}{24}$ written in simplest form is $\frac{3}{4}$.

Helpful Hint

Method 2 is useful when you know that the numerator and denominator have common factors, but you are not sure what the GCF is.

B $\frac{8}{9}$

The GCF of 8 and 9 is 1, so $\frac{8}{9}$ is already in simplest form.

Think and Discuss GPS M6P2.c, M6P3.b

1. **Explain** whether a fraction is equivalent to itself.
2. **Tell** which of the following fractions are in simplest form: $\frac{9}{21}$, $\frac{20}{25}$, and $\frac{5}{13}$. Explain.
3. **Explain** how you know that $\frac{7}{16}$ is in simplest form.

COMMON ERROR ALERT

Watch for students who add to or subtract from the numerator and denominator instead of multiplying or dividing when making equivalent fractions.

Power Presentations with PowerPoint®

Additional Examples

Example 1

Find two equivalent fractions for $\frac{10}{12}$.

Possible answer: $\frac{10}{12}$, $\frac{15}{18}$, $\frac{5}{6}$

Example 2

Find the missing number that makes the fractions equivalent.

A. $\frac{3}{5} = \frac{\blacksquare}{20}$ 12

B. $\frac{4}{5} = \frac{80}{\blacksquare}$ 100

Example 3

Write each fraction in simplest form.

A. $\frac{20}{48}$ $\frac{5}{12}$

B. $\frac{7}{10}$ $\frac{7}{10}$ is already in simplest form.

Also available on transparency

Answers to Think and Discuss

1. Yes, because a fraction would have the same value as itself.
2. $\frac{5}{13}$ is the only fraction whose numerator and denominator have a GCF of 1, so it is the only fraction that is in simplest form.
3. Possible answer: The GCF of 7 and 16 is 1.

2 Teach

Guided Instruction

In this lesson, students learn to write equivalent fractions and mixed numbers. Teach students to use models to find equivalent fractions. Then teach them to multiply and divide to find equivalent fractions and to write a fraction in simplest form using the GCF or a ladder diagram. Students using the GCF method may need to check their final fractions to be sure they are indeed in simplest form.

Teaching Tip

Technology Show students how to use a fraction-capable calculator to check whether fractions are in simplest form.

Reaching All Learners

Through Cooperative Learning

Have students work in groups to find equivalent fractions. Groups toss two number cubes (provided in the Manipulatives Kit). The lesser number becomes the numerator of a fraction, and the greater number becomes the denominator. If the numbers are the same, the number is both the numerator and the denominator. Each group member names one equivalent fraction. Then the group decides which one of the two fractions, if either, is in simplest form. If students are having difficulty, encourage them to draw the fraction generated by the number cube and its equivalent.

3 Close

Summarize

ENGLISH LANGUAGE LEARNERS

Review the terms *equivalent fractions* and *simplest form*. Have the students explain how to find equivalent fractions and how to write fractions in simplest form.

Possible answer: You can find equivalent fractions by multiplying or dividing the numerator and denominator by the same number. You can write a fraction in simplest form by dividing the numerator and denominator by their GCF.

4-5 Exercises

Assignment Guide

If you finished Example 1 assign:
Average 1–4, 37–40, 45, 51–60
Advanced 13–20, 45, 51–60

If you finished Example 2 assign:
Average 1–8, 37–40, 45, 51–60
Advanced 13–28, 51–60

If you finished Example 3 assign:
Average 1–47, 51–60
Advanced 1–44, 48–60

Homework Quick Check

Quickly check key concepts.
Exercises: 22, 26, 28, 38

Math Background

In the sixteenth century, before the common acceptance of using places to the right of a decimal point to represent numbers less than 1, fractions were used exclusively. Writing fractions in simplest form made any further computation simpler. Today, with the use of calculators, writing fractions in simplest form is not as necessary.

Writing a fraction in simplest form was once called *abbreviating* the fraction. To abbreviate fractions, people learned the divisibility rules discussed in Lesson 4-1, as well as the Euclidean algorithm discussed in the Math Background of Lesson 4-3.

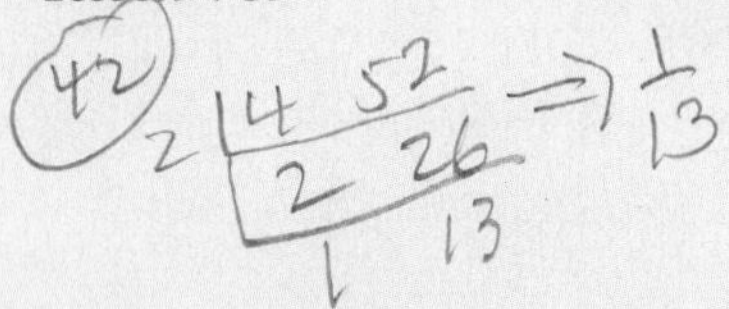

Georgia Performance Standards

M6P1.b Solve problems that arise in mathematics and in other contexts.

M6P3.a Organize and consolidate their mathematical thinking through communication.

4-5 Exercises

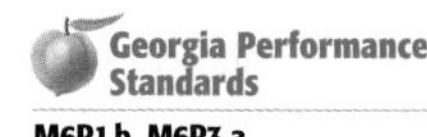

Georgia Performance Standards
M6P1.b, M6P3.a

go.hrw.com
Homework Help Online
KEYWORD: MR4 4-5
Parent Resources Online
KEYWORD: MR7 Parent

GUIDED PRACTICE

See Example 1 — Find two equivalent fractions for each fraction. Possible answers:

1. $\frac{4}{6}$ $\frac{2}{3}, \frac{8}{12}$
2. $\frac{3}{12}$ $\frac{1}{4}, \frac{2}{8}$
3. $\frac{3}{6}$ $\frac{1}{2}, \frac{5}{10}$
4. $\frac{6}{16}$ $\frac{3}{8}, \frac{9}{24}$

See Example 2 — Find the missing numbers that make the fractions equivalent.

5. $\frac{2}{5} = \frac{10}{\blacksquare}$ 25
6. $\frac{7}{21} = \frac{1}{\blacksquare}$ 3
7. $\frac{3}{4} = \frac{\blacksquare}{28}$ 21
8. $\frac{8}{12} = \frac{\blacksquare}{3}$ 2

See Example 3 — Write each fraction in simplest form.

9. $\frac{2}{10}$ $\frac{1}{5}$
10. $\frac{6}{18}$ $\frac{1}{3}$
11. $\frac{4}{16}$ $\frac{1}{4}$
12. $\frac{9}{15}$ $\frac{3}{5}$

INDEPENDENT PRACTICE

See Example 1 — Find two equivalent fractions for each fraction. Possible answers:

13. $\frac{3}{9}$ $\frac{1}{3}, \frac{2}{6}$
14. $\frac{2}{10}$ $\frac{1}{5}, \frac{5}{25}$
15. $\frac{3}{21}$ $\frac{1}{7}, \frac{2}{14}$
16. $\frac{3}{18}$ $\frac{1}{6}, \frac{2}{12}$
17. $\frac{12}{15}$ $\frac{4}{5}, \frac{20}{25}$
18. $\frac{4}{10}$ $\frac{2}{5}, \frac{8}{20}$
19. $\frac{10}{12}$ $\frac{5}{6}, \frac{20}{24}$
20. $\frac{6}{10}$ $\frac{3}{5}, \frac{9}{15}$

See Example 2 — Find the missing numbers that make the fractions equivalent.

21. $\frac{3}{7} = \frac{\blacksquare}{35}$ 15
22. $\frac{6}{48} = \frac{1}{\blacksquare}$ 8
23. $\frac{2}{5} = \frac{28}{\blacksquare}$ 70
24. $\frac{12}{18} = \frac{\blacksquare}{3}$ 2
25. $\frac{2}{7} = \frac{\blacksquare}{21}$ 6
26. $\frac{8}{32} = \frac{\blacksquare}{4}$ 1
27. $\frac{2}{7} = \frac{40}{\blacksquare}$ 140
28. $\frac{3}{5} = \frac{21}{\blacksquare}$ 35

See Example 3 — Write each fraction in simplest form.

29. $\frac{2}{8}$ $\frac{1}{4}$
30. $\frac{10}{15}$ $\frac{2}{3}$
31. $\frac{6}{30}$ $\frac{1}{5}$
32. $\frac{6}{14}$ $\frac{3}{7}$
33. $\frac{12}{16}$ $\frac{3}{4}$
34. $\frac{4}{28}$ $\frac{1}{7}$
35. $\frac{4}{8}$ $\frac{1}{2}$
36. $\frac{10}{35}$ $\frac{2}{7}$

PRACTICE AND PROBLEM SOLVING

CRCT GPS
Extra Practice p. 721

37. $\frac{3}{6} = \frac{1}{2}$
38. $\frac{1}{4} = \frac{2}{8}$
39. $\frac{2}{3} = \frac{8}{12}$
40. $\frac{2}{4} = \frac{1}{2}$

Write the equivalent fractions represented by each picture.

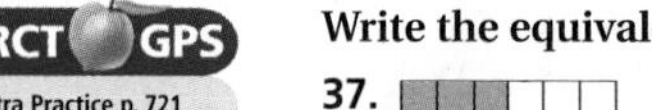

37. ▭ = ▭
38. ◯ = ◯
39. ⬡ = ⬡
40. ⇔ = ⇔

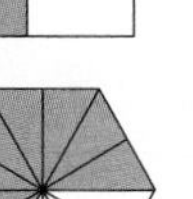

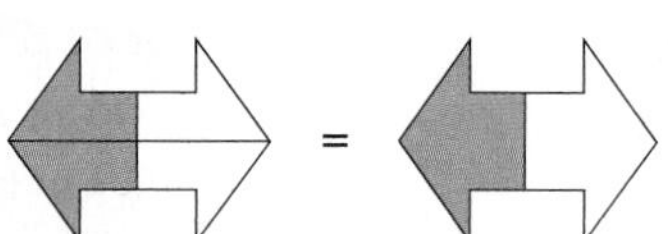

Write each fraction in simplest form. Show two ways to simplify.

41. $\frac{5}{20}$ $\frac{1}{4}$
42. $\frac{4}{52}$ $\frac{1}{13}$
43. $\frac{14}{35}$ $\frac{2}{5}$
44. $\frac{112}{220}$ $\frac{28}{55}$

RETEACH 4-5

LESSON 4-5 **Reteach** *Equivalent Fractions*

Fractions that have the same value are equivalent fractions.

$\frac{3}{4} = \frac{6}{8}$

$\frac{3}{4}$ and $\frac{6}{8}$ are equivalent fractions.

You can use fraction strips to help you find equivalent fractions.

To solve $\frac{2}{3} = \frac{?}{12}$, first use fraction strips to model the first fraction.

Then use $\frac{1}{12}$ fraction pieces to make a length as long as the $\frac{2}{3}$ strip.

You need eight $\frac{1}{12}$ pieces, so $\frac{2}{3} = \frac{8}{12}$.

Find the missing number that makes the fractions equivalent.

1. $\frac{3}{4} = \frac{?}{12}$ 9
2. $\frac{8}{10} = \frac{?}{5}$ 4
3. $\frac{6}{9} = \frac{?}{3}$ 2
4. $\frac{5}{6} = \frac{?}{12}$ 10

A fraction is in simplest form when the GCF of the numerator and the denominator is 1.

To write $\frac{4}{6}$ in simplest form, divide the numerator and the denominator by their GCF, 2.

$4 \div 2 = 2$
$6 \div 2 = 3$

So, $\frac{4}{6}$ in simplest form is $\frac{2}{3}$.

Write each fraction in simplest form.

5. $\frac{3}{9}$ $\frac{1}{3}$
6. $\frac{12}{16}$ $\frac{3}{4}$
7. $\frac{14}{18}$ $\frac{7}{9}$
8. $\frac{8}{20}$ $\frac{2}{5}$

PRACTICE 4-5

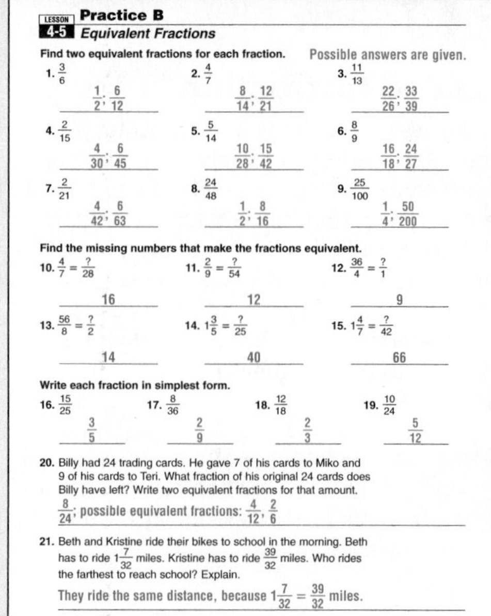

LESSON 4-5 **Practice B** *Equivalent Fractions*

Find two equivalent fractions for each fraction. Possible answers are given.

1. $\frac{3}{6}$ $\frac{1}{2}, \frac{6}{12}$
2. $\frac{4}{7}$ $\frac{8}{14}, \frac{12}{21}$
3. $\frac{11}{13}$ $\frac{22}{26}, \frac{33}{39}$
4. $\frac{2}{15}$ $\frac{4}{30}, \frac{6}{45}$
5. $\frac{5}{14}$ $\frac{10}{28}, \frac{15}{42}$
6. $\frac{8}{9}$ $\frac{16}{18}, \frac{24}{27}$
7. $\frac{2}{21}$ $\frac{4}{42}, \frac{6}{63}$
8. $\frac{24}{48}$ $\frac{1}{2}, \frac{8}{16}$
9. $\frac{25}{100}$ $\frac{1}{4}, \frac{50}{200}$

Find the missing numbers that make the fractions equivalent.

10. $\frac{4}{7} = \frac{?}{28}$ 16
11. $\frac{2}{9} = \frac{?}{54}$ 12
12. $\frac{36}{4} = \frac{?}{1}$ 9
13. $\frac{56}{8} = \frac{?}{2}$ 14
14. $1\frac{3}{5} = \frac{?}{25}$ 40
15. $1\frac{4}{7} = \frac{?}{42}$ 66

Write each fraction in simplest form.

16. $\frac{15}{25}$ $\frac{3}{5}$
17. $\frac{8}{36}$ $\frac{2}{9}$
18. $\frac{12}{18}$ $\frac{2}{3}$
19. $\frac{10}{24}$ $\frac{5}{12}$

20. Billy had 24 trading cards. He gave 7 of his cards to Miko and 9 of his cards to Teri. What fraction of his original 24 cards does Billy have left? Write two equivalent fractions for that amount.
$\frac{8}{24}$; possible equivalent fractions: $\frac{4}{12}, \frac{2}{6}$

21. Beth and Kristine ride their bikes to school in the morning. Beth has to ride $1\frac{7}{32}$ miles. Kristine has to ride $\frac{39}{32}$ miles. Who rides the farthest to reach school? Explain.
They ride the same distance, because $1\frac{7}{32} = \frac{39}{32}$ miles.

Social Studies LINK

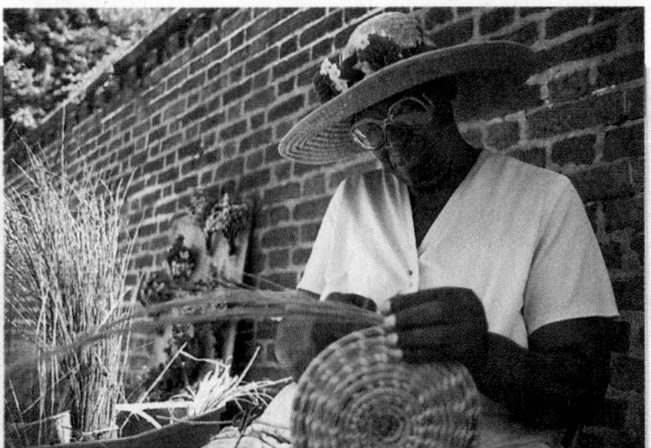

The Old City Market is a public market in Charleston, South Carolina. Local artists, craftspeople, and vendors display and sell their goods in open-sided booths.

45. You can buy food, such as southern sesame seed cookies, at $\frac{1}{10}$ of the booths. Write two equivalent fractions for $\frac{1}{10}$. **Possible answers: $\frac{2}{20}$; $\frac{4}{40}$**

46. Handwoven sweetgrass baskets are a regional specialty. About 8 out of every 10 baskets sold are woven at the market. Write a fraction for "8 out of 10." Then write this fraction in simplest form. **$\frac{8}{10} = \frac{4}{5}$**

47. Suppose the circle graph shows the number of each kind of craft booth at the Old City Market. For each type of booth, tell what fraction it represents of the total number of craft booths. Write these fractions in simplest form.

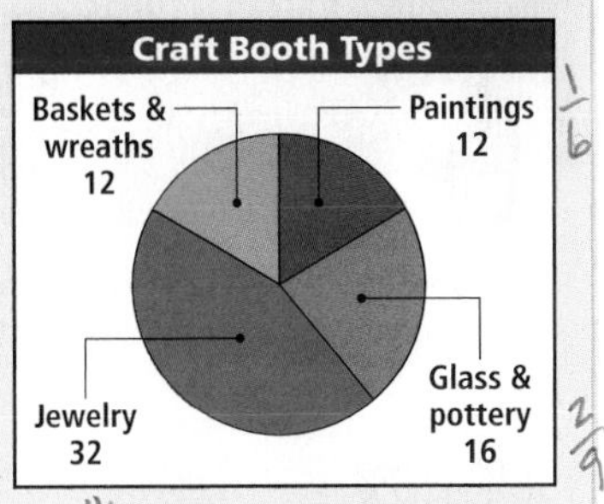

48. Customers can buy packages of dried rice and black-eyed peas, which can be made into black-eyed pea soup. One recipe for black-eyed pea soup calls for $\frac{1}{2}$ tsp of basil. How could you measure the basil if you had only a $\frac{1}{4}$ tsp measuring spoon? What if you had only a $\frac{1}{8}$ tsp measuring spoon?

49. **Write About It** The recipe for soup also calls for $\frac{1}{4}$ tsp of pepper. How many fractions are equivalent to $\frac{1}{4}$? Explain.

50. **Challenge** Silver jewelry is a popular item at the market. Suppose there are 28 bracelets at one jeweler's booth and that $\frac{3}{7}$ of these bracelets have red stones. How many bracelets have red stones? **12**

CRCT Prep • GPS Support • Spiral Review

51. Multiple Choice Which fraction is NOT equivalent to $\frac{1}{6}$?

Ⓐ $\frac{2}{12}$ **Ⓑ $\frac{6}{1}$** Ⓒ $\frac{3}{18}$ Ⓓ $\frac{6}{36}$

52. Multiple Choice Which denominator makes the fractions $\frac{7}{28}$ and $\frac{21}{\square}$ equivalent?

Ⓕ 3 Ⓖ 4 **Ⓗ 84** Ⓙ 112

Solve each equation. Check your answer. (Lesson 2-7)

53. $\frac{x}{3} = 15$ **$x = 45$** **54.** $8 = \frac{h}{8}$ **$h = 64$** **55.** $\frac{w}{2} = 9$ **$w = 18$** **56.** $\frac{p}{5} = 10$ **$p = 50$**

Write each fraction or mixed number as a decimal. (Lesson 4-4)

57. $\frac{2}{3}$ **$0.\overline{6}$** **58.** $\frac{7}{8}$ **0.875** **59.** $3\frac{1}{5}$ **3.2** **60.** $2\frac{9}{16}$ **2.5625**

Ongoing Assessment and Intervention

Diagnose **Before** the Lesson
4-5 Warm Up, TE p. 186

Monitor **During** the Lesson
4-5 Know-It Notebook
4-5 Questioning Strategies

Assess **After** the Lesson
4-5 Lesson Quiz, TE p. 189

Interdisciplinary LINK

Social Studies

Exercises 45–50 involve using information about a public market in South Carolina. The economy of different regions in the United States is studied in middle school social studies programs such as Holt, Rinehart & Winston's *People, Places, and Change.*

Answers

47–49. See p. A3.

Test Prep Doctor In Exercise 52, ask students to compare the numerators. 7 must be multiplied by 3 to get 21. The denominator, 28, must also be multiplied by 3.

Journal

Have students explain which method of writing a fraction in simplest form (GCF or ladder diagram) is the most efficient and why.

CHALLENGE 4-5

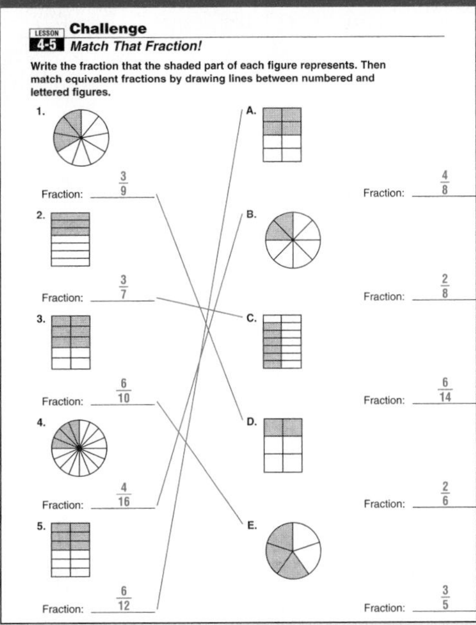

LESSON 4-5 **Challenge**
Match That Fraction!

Write the fraction that the shaded part of each figure represents. Then match equivalent fractions by drawing lines between numbered and lettered figures.

1. Fraction: $\frac{3}{9}$
2. Fraction: $\frac{3}{7}$
3. Fraction: $\frac{6}{10}$
4. Fraction: $\frac{4}{16}$
5. Fraction: $\frac{6}{12}$

A. Fraction: $\frac{4}{8}$
B. Fraction: $\frac{2}{8}$
C. Fraction: $\frac{6}{14}$
D. Fraction: $\frac{2}{6}$
E. Fraction: $\frac{3}{5}$

PROBLEM SOLVING 4-5

LESSON 4-5 **Problem Solving**
Equivalent Fractions

About 60 million Americans exercise 100 times or more each year. Their top activities and the fraction of those 60 million people who did them are shown on the circle graph. Use the graph to answer the questions.

Exercise in the U.S.: Fitness walking $\frac{17}{60}$; Free weights $\frac{1}{5}$; Stationary bike $\frac{3}{20}$; Running/Jogging $\frac{3}{20}$; Treadmill $\frac{7}{60}$; Resistance machines $\frac{1}{10}$

1. Which two activities did the same number of people use to keep in shape? **stationary bike and running/jogging**
2. Which activity had the most participants? Write an equivalent fraction for that activity's participants. **fitness walking; possible answer: $\frac{34}{120}$**
3. Which activity had the fewest participants? Write two equivalent fractions for that activity's participants. **resistance machines; possible answers: $\frac{2}{20}$; $\frac{3}{30}$**

Circle the letter of the correct answer.

4. Which activity did $\frac{3}{15}$ of the people use to exercise?
   Ⓐ free weights
   B treadmill
   C fitness walking
   D stationary bike
5. Which activity did $\frac{35}{300}$ of the people use to stay healthy?
   F running/jogging
   G resistance machines
   H free weights
   Ⓙ treadmill
6. An average-sized person can burn about $6\frac{1}{2}$ calories a minute while riding a bike. Which of the following is equivalent to that amount?
   A $1\frac{2}{2}$ **Ⓒ $6\frac{2}{4}$**
   B $5\frac{6}{2}$ D $6\frac{2}{6}$
7. An average-sized person can burn about 11.25 calories a minute while jogging. Which of the following is not equivalent to that amount?
   F $11\frac{1}{4}$ H $11\frac{2}{8}$
   Ⓖ $11\frac{1}{2}$ J $11\frac{3}{12}$

Power Presentations with PowerPoint®

4-5 Lesson Quiz

Find two equivalent fractions for each given fraction. Possible answers:

1. $\frac{4}{10}$ $\frac{2}{5}$, $\frac{8}{20}$

2. $\frac{7}{14}$ $\frac{1}{2}$, $\frac{14}{28}$

Find the missing number that makes the fractions equivalent.

3. $\frac{2}{7} = \frac{\square}{21}$ 6

4. $\frac{4}{15} = \frac{20}{\square}$ 75

Write each fraction in simplest form.

5. $\frac{4}{8}$ $\frac{1}{2}$

6. $\frac{7}{49}$ $\frac{1}{7}$

Also available on transparency

Organizer

Use with Lesson 4-5

Pacing:
Traditional $\frac{1}{2}$ day
Block $\frac{1}{4}$ day

Objective: Use handmade rulers to study equivalent fractions.

Materials: Strips of paper

Online Edition

Countdown to CRCT Week 8

Resources

Hands-On Lab Activities
Lab 4-5B Recording Sheet

Teach

Discuss

Discuss how rulers should be aligned to the line that is being measured.

Ask students to explain how a standard ruler takes the place of four rulers they made.

Close

Key Concept

Standard rulers provide a convenient way of measuring, and they may be used to convert equivalent fractions to their simplest form.

Assessment

1. When measuring a line, how should you align the ruler to the line?
2. If a line measures 7 quarter inches, how long is it?
3. How does a standard ruler take the place of the four rulers you made?

Georgia Performance Standards

M6M2.a Measure length to the nearest half, fourth, eighth, and sixteenth of an inch.

M6A2.a Analyze and describe patterns arising from mathematical rules, tables, and graphs.

Explore Fraction Measurement

Use with Lesson 4-5

Georgia Performance Standards
M6M2.a, M6A2.a

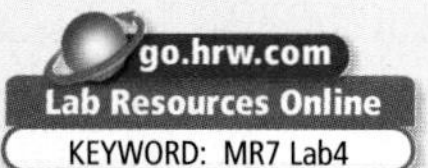

Look at a standard ruler. It probably has marks for inches, half inches, quarter inches, eighth inches, and sixteenth inches.

In this activity, you will make some of your own rulers and use them to help you find and understand equivalent fractions.

Activity

1. You will need four strips of paper. On one strip, use your ruler to make a mark for every half inch. Number each mark, beginning with 0. Label this strip "half-inch ruler."

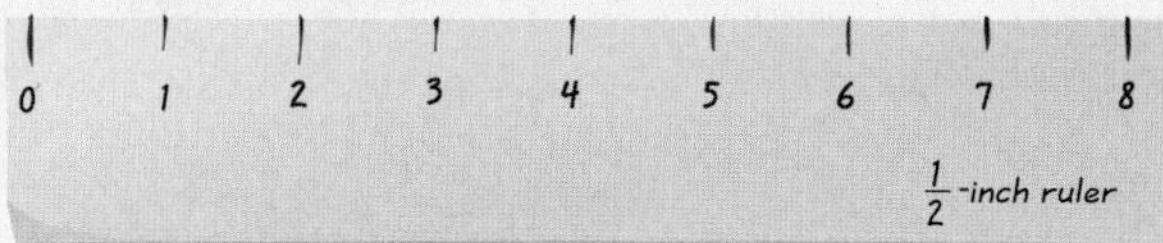

On a second strip, make a mark for every quarter inch. Again, number each mark, beginning with 0. Label this strip "quarter-inch ruler."

Do the same thing for eighth inches and sixteenth inches.

0 5 10 15 20 25 30 35 40 45 50 55 60 65
$\frac{1}{16}$-inch ruler

Answers to *Assessment*

1. Make sure the end of the line matches up with 0 on the ruler.
2. $1\frac{3}{4}$ inches
3. A standard ruler has markings to show half-, quarter-, eighth-, and sixteenth-inch measurements.

2. Now use the half-inch ruler you made to measure the green line segment at right. How many half inches long is the segment?

Use your quarter-inch ruler to measure the line segment again. How many quarter inches long is the segment?

How many eighth inches long is the segment?

How many sixteenth inches?

Fill in the blanks: $\frac{1}{2} = \frac{\blacksquare}{4} = \frac{\blacksquare}{8} = \frac{\blacksquare}{16}$. **2; 4; 8**

3. Use your quarter-inch ruler to measure the green line segment below.

How long is the segment?

Now use your eighth-inch ruler to measure the line segment again. How many eighth inches long is the segment?

How many sixteenth inches?

Fill in the blanks: $\frac{3}{4} = \frac{\blacksquare}{8} = \frac{\blacksquare}{16}$. **6; 12**

Think and Discuss

1. Possible answer: A ruler shows that equivalent fractions have the same value, because the measurements are equivalent. For example, $\frac{1}{2}$ inch is equivalent to $\frac{4}{8}$ inch.

1. How does a ruler show that equivalent fractions have the same value?
2. Look at your lists of equivalent fractions from 2 and 3. Do you notice any patterns? Describe them. **Possible answer: Both the numerators and the denominators are doubling (being multiplied by 2) from fraction to fraction.**
3. Use your rulers to measure an object longer than 1 inch. Use your measurements to write equivalent fractions. What do you notice about these fractions? **Possible answer: The numerators are greater than the denominators.**

Try This

1. Use your rulers to measure the length of the items below. Use your measurements to write equivalent fractions. **Check students' measurements.**

2. Use your rulers to measure several items in your classroom. Use your measurements to write equivalent fractions. **Check students' work.**

Sandy R. Puckett
Taipei American School
Taipei, Taiwan

Teacher to Teacher

Graphing fractions can be a very powerful way to display equivalent fractions and later to compare fractions.

Draw the positive *x*- and *y*-axes, number equal intervals from 0 to 20, and label the respective axes "numerator" and "denominator." Graph $\frac{1}{2}$ by graphing (1, 2) on the coordinate plane, and label it as $\frac{1}{2}$. Continue graphing and labeling $\frac{2}{4}$, $\frac{3}{6}$, $\frac{4}{8}$, etc. The points for these fractions lie on a straight line that goes through the origin. Every fraction along this line is equivalent to $\frac{1}{2}$. My students graph many common equivalent fractions, using a different color for each line. They then cut out the graphs and tape them in the back of their math books for quick reference.

4-6 Organizer

Pacing: Traditional 1 day
Block $\frac{1}{2}$ day

Objective: Students convert between mixed numbers and improper fractions.

Hands-On Lab
In *Hands-On Lab Activities*

Online Edition
Tutorial Videos, Interactivities

Countdown to CRCT Week 9

Warm Up

Order the fractions from least to greatest.

1. $\frac{2}{9}, \frac{1}{6}, \frac{2}{3}$ $\frac{1}{6}, \frac{2}{9}, \frac{2}{3}$
2. $\frac{2}{3}, \frac{7}{12}, \frac{5}{6}$ $\frac{7}{12}, \frac{2}{3}, \frac{5}{6}$
3. $\frac{5}{8}, \frac{1}{2}, \frac{4}{11}$ $\frac{4}{11}, \frac{1}{2}, \frac{5}{8}$

Problem of the Day

Two numbers have a product of 48. When the larger number is divided by the smaller, the quotient is 3. What are the numbers? 4 and 12

Also available on transparency

Math Fact

Many people learn that π equals the mixed number $3\frac{1}{7}$ or the equivalent improper fraction $\frac{22}{7}$. However, these are approximations of the true value of π, because π cannot be expressed as a ratio of whole numbers.

Georgia Performance Standards

M6N1.g Solve problems involving fractions, decimals, and percents.

M6P1.b Solve problems that arise in mathematics and in other contexts.

M6P5.b Select, apply, and translate among mathematical representations to solve problems.

M6P5.c Use representations to model and interpret physical, social, and mathematical phenomena.

4-6 Mixed Numbers and Improper Fractions

Learn to convert between mixed numbers and improper fractions.

Vocabulary
improper fraction
proper fraction

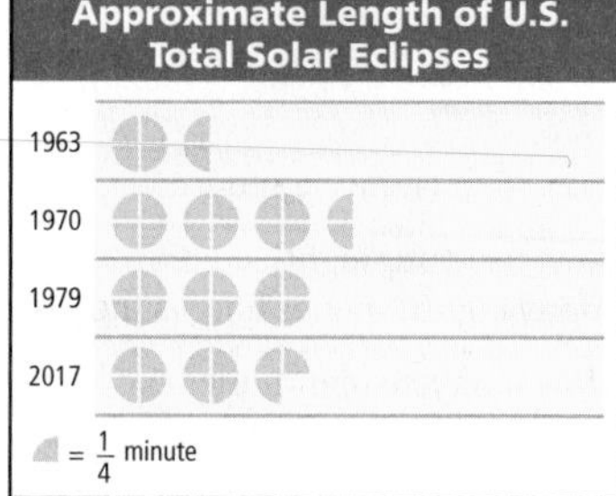

Approximate Length of U.S. Total Solar Eclipses

1963
1970
1979
2017
= $\frac{1}{4}$ minute

Have you ever witnessed a total eclipse of the sun? It occurs when the sun's light is completely blocked out. A total eclipse is rare—only three have been visible in the continental United States since 1963.

The graph shows that the eclipse in 2017 will last $2\frac{3}{4}$ minutes. There are eleven $\frac{1}{4}$-minute sections, so $2\frac{3}{4} = \frac{11}{4}$.

Reading Math
$\frac{11}{4}$ is read as "eleven-fourths."

An **improper fraction** is a fraction in which the numerator is greater than or equal to the denominator, such as $\frac{11}{4}$.

Whole numbers can be written as improper fractions. The whole number is the numerator, and the denominator is 1. For example, $7 = \frac{7}{1}$.

When the numerator is less than the denominator, the fraction is called a **proper fraction**.

Improper and Proper Fractions		
Improper Fractions		
• Numerator equals denominator → fraction is equal to 1	$\frac{3}{3} = 1$	$\frac{102}{102} = 1$
• Numerator greater than denominator → fraction is greater than 1	$\frac{9}{5} > 1$	$\frac{13}{1} > 1$
Proper Fractions		
• Numerator less than denominator → fraction is less than 1	$\frac{2}{5} < 1$	$\frac{102}{351} < 1$

You can write an improper fraction as a mixed number.

EXAMPLE 1 *Astronomy Application*

Georgia Performance Standards
M6N1.g Solve problems involving fractions. Also, M6P1.b, M6P5.b, M6P5.c.

The longest total solar eclipse in the next 200 years will take place in 2186. It will last about $\frac{15}{2}$ minutes. Write $\frac{15}{2}$ as a mixed number.

Method 1: Use a model.

Draw squares divided into half sections. Shade 15 of the half sections.

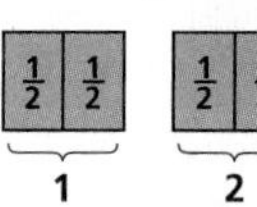
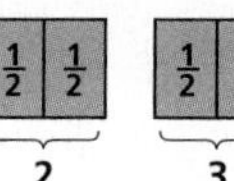
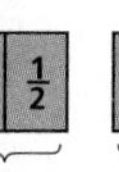
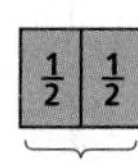
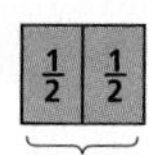
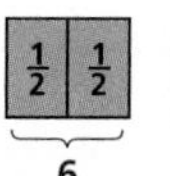
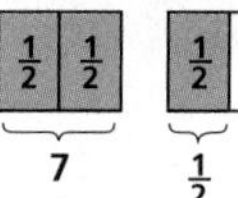

1 2 3 4 5 6 7 $\frac{1}{2}$

There are 7 whole squares and 1 half square, or $7\frac{1}{2}$ squares, shaded.

1 Introduce

Alternate Opener

EXPLORATION

4-6 Mixed Numbers and Improper Fractions

An *improper fraction* is a fraction in which the numerator is greater than or equal to the denominator. The model shows that $\frac{7}{4} = \frac{4}{4} + \frac{3}{4} = 1 + \frac{3}{4}$.

The mixed number $1\frac{3}{4} = 1 + \frac{3}{4}$.

For each improper fraction, complete the model and write the improper fraction as a mixed number.

1. $\frac{5}{3}$ ____
2. $\frac{7}{6}$ ____
3. $\frac{6}{4}$ ____

Think and Discuss
4. **Explain** why $\frac{6}{4} = 1\frac{1}{2}$.
5. **Discuss** a situation in which mixed numbers are used.

Motivate

Ask a volunteer to represent, in a drawing, the amount of pizza that 27 students would eat if each student got one slice of pizza and each pizza had been cut into 8 pieces.

Possible answer: 4 circles are divided into eighths, and 3 circles are completely shaded. Only 3 slices in the fourth circle are shaded.

Then ask students how much pizza this represents. $3\frac{3}{8}$ pizzas

Explorations and answers are provided in *Alternate Openers: Explorations Transparencies.*

Method 2: Use division.

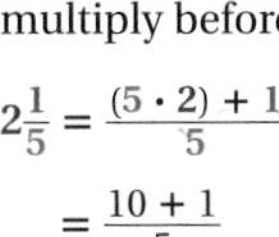

$$\begin{array}{r} 7\frac{1}{2} \\ 2\overline{)15} \\ -14 \\ \hline 1 \end{array}$$

Divide the numerator by the denominator.

To form the fraction part of the quotient, use the remainder as the numerator and the divisor as the denominator.

The 2186 eclipse will last about $7\frac{1}{2}$ minutes.

Mixed numbers can be written as improper fractions.

EXAMPLE 2 **Writing Mixed Numbers as Improper Fractions**

Write $2\frac{1}{5}$ as an improper fraction.

Method 1: Use a model.

You can draw a diagram to illustrate the whole and fractional parts.

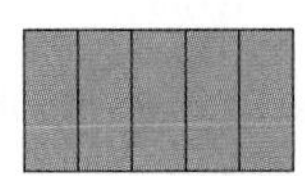
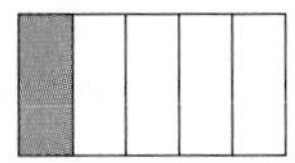

There are 11 fifths, or $\frac{11}{5}$. *Count the fifths in the diagram.*

Method 2: Use multiplication and addition.

When you are changing a mixed number to an improper fraction, spiral clockwise as shown in the picture. The order of operations will help you remember to multiply before you add.

$$2\frac{1}{5} = \frac{(5 \cdot 2) + 1}{5}$$
$$= \frac{10 + 1}{5}$$
$$= \frac{11}{5}$$

Multiply the whole number by the denominator and add the numerator. Keep the same denominator.

Think and Discuss

GPS M6P2.c, M6P3.b

1. **Read** each improper fraction: $\frac{10}{7}, \frac{25}{9}, \frac{31}{16}$.
2. **Tell** whether each fraction is less than 1, equal to 1, or greater than 1: $\frac{21}{21}, \frac{54}{103}, \frac{9}{11}, \frac{7}{3}$.
3. **Explain** why any mixed number written as a fraction will be improper.

Some students may multiply the numerator by the whole number and add the denominator when changing from a mixed number to an improper fraction. Have students change the resulting improper fraction back to a mixed number and compare with the original mixed number.

Power Presentations with PowerPoint®

Additional Examples

Example 1

Ella hiked for $\frac{9}{4}$ hours yesterday. Write $\frac{9}{4}$ as a mixed number. $2\frac{1}{4}$

Example 2

Write $3\frac{2}{3}$ as an improper fraction. $\frac{11}{3}$

Also available on transparency

Answers to *Think and Discuss*

1. ten sevenths; twenty-five ninths; thirty-one sixteenths
2. equal to 1; less than 1; less than 1; greater than 1
3. A mixed number consists of a whole number and a fraction, so it will always be greater than one. Numbers greater than one are improper when written as fractions.

2 Teach

Guided Instruction

In this lesson, students learn to convert between mixed numbers and improper fractions. Define *improper fraction* and *proper fraction.* Teach two ways to convert each type of fraction: using a model and using division (for improper to mixed) and multiplication and addition (for mixed to improper). Students should understand that being able to change the form of a fraction can make working with it easier without changing its value.

Reaching All Learners

Through Kinesthetic Experience

Have students use inch rulers (provided in the Manipulatives Kit) to measure various items in the classroom. For each item, have students record the measurement as both a mixed number and an improper fraction.

Possible answer:
pencil: $7\frac{1}{2}$ inches or $\frac{15}{2}$ inches

3 Close

Summarize

Have students explain how to change from an improper fraction to a mixed number and vice versa and give an example.

Possible answer: To change from an improper fraction to a mixed number, divide the numerator by the denominator. For example, $\frac{8}{5} = 8 \div 5 = 1\frac{3}{5}$. To change from a mixed number to an improper fraction, multiply the denominator by the whole number, add the numerator, and keep the same denominator. For example, $2\frac{1}{3} = \frac{(3 \cdot 2) + 1}{3} = \frac{7}{3}$.

4-6 Exercises

Assignment Guide

If you finished Example 1 assign:
Average 1, 16–23, 35, 41, 47–57
Advanced 6–7, 16–23, 35, 47–57

If you finished Example 2 assign:
Average 1–43, 47–57
Advanced 1–39, 44–57

Homework Quick Check

Quickly check key concepts.
Exercises: 6, 10, 18, 26, 30

Math Background

Improper fractions are really not improper at all. Indeed, they help us to multiply mixed numbers. To multiply $1\frac{1}{4} \times 2\frac{4}{5}$, change the mixed numbers to improper fractions: $\frac{5}{4} \times \frac{14}{5}$.

Georgia Performance Standards

M6P3.a Organize and consolidate their mathematical thinking through communication.

M6P4.c Recognize and apply mathematics in contexts outside of mathematics.

4-6 Exercises

M6P3.a, M6P4.c

go.hrw.com
Homework Help Online
KEYWORD: MR7 4-6
Parent Resources Online
KEYWORD: MR7 Parent

GUIDED PRACTICE

See Example 1

1. The fifth largest meteorite found in the United States is named the Navajo. The Navajo weighs $\frac{12}{5}$ tons. Write $\frac{12}{5}$ as a mixed number. $2\frac{2}{5}$

See Example 2

Write each mixed number as an improper fraction.

2. $1\frac{1}{4}$ $\frac{5}{4}$ 3. $2\frac{2}{3}$ $\frac{8}{3}$ 4. $1\frac{2}{7}$ $\frac{9}{7}$ 5. $2\frac{2}{5}$ $\frac{12}{5}$

INDEPENDENT PRACTICE

See Example 1

6. **Astronomy** Saturn is the sixth planet from the Sun. It takes Saturn $\frac{59}{2}$ years to revolve around the Sun. Write $\frac{59}{2}$ as a mixed number. $29\frac{1}{2}$
7. **Astronomy** Pluto has the lowest surface gravity of all the planets in the solar system. A person who weighs 143 pounds on Earth weighs $\frac{43}{5}$ pounds on Pluto. Write $\frac{43}{5}$ as a mixed number. $8\frac{3}{5}$

See Example 2

Write each mixed number as an improper fraction.

8. $1\frac{3}{5}$ $\frac{8}{5}$ 9. $2\frac{2}{9}$ $\frac{20}{9}$ 10. $3\frac{1}{7}$ $\frac{22}{7}$ 11. $4\frac{1}{3}$ $\frac{13}{3}$
12. $2\frac{3}{8}$ $\frac{19}{8}$ 13. $4\frac{1}{6}$ $\frac{25}{6}$ 14. $1\frac{4}{9}$ $\frac{13}{9}$ 15. $3\frac{4}{5}$ $\frac{19}{5}$

PRACTICE AND PROBLEM SOLVING

CRCT GPS
Extra Practice p. 721

18. $6\frac{2}{3}$; mixed number
22. $8\frac{10}{11}$; mixed number

Write each improper fraction as a mixed number or whole number. Tell whether your answer is a mixed number or whole number.

16. $\frac{21}{4}$ $5\frac{1}{4}$; mixed number 17. $\frac{32}{8}$ 4; whole number 18. $\frac{20}{3}$ 19. $\frac{43}{5}$ $8\frac{3}{5}$; mixed number
20. $\frac{108}{9}$ 12; whole number 21. $\frac{87}{10}$ $8\frac{7}{10}$; mixed number 22. $\frac{98}{11}$ 23. $\frac{105}{7}$ 15; whole number

Write each mixed number as an improper fraction.

24. $9\frac{1}{4}$ $\frac{37}{4}$ 25. $4\frac{9}{11}$ $\frac{53}{11}$ 26. $11\frac{4}{9}$ $\frac{103}{9}$ 27. $18\frac{3}{5}$ $\frac{93}{5}$

28. **Measurement** The actual dimensions of a piece of lumber called a 2-by-4 are $1\frac{1}{2}$ inches and $3\frac{1}{2}$ inches. Write these numbers as improper fractions. $\frac{3}{2}, \frac{7}{2}$

Replace each shape with a number that will make the equation correct.

29. $■\frac{2}{5} = \frac{17}{●}$ 3; 5 30. $■\frac{6}{11} = \frac{83}{●}$ 7; 11 31. $■\frac{1}{9} = \frac{118}{●}$ 13;9
32. $■\frac{6}{7} = \frac{55}{●}$ 7; 7 33. $■\frac{9}{10} = \frac{29}{●}$ 2; 10 34. $■\frac{1}{3} = \frac{55}{●}$ 18; 3

35. Daniel is a costume designer for movies and music videos. He recently purchased $\frac{256}{9}$ yards of metallic fabric for space-suit costumes. Write a mixed number to represent the number of yards of fabric Daniel purchased. $28\frac{4}{9}$ yards

Write the improper fraction as a decimal. Then use $<$, $>$, or $=$ to compare.

36. $\frac{7}{5}$ ■ 1.8 $<$ 37. 6.875 ■ $\frac{55}{8}$ $=$ 38. $\frac{27}{2}$ ■ 13 $>$ 39. $\frac{20}{5}$ ■ 4.25 $<$

RETEACH 4-6

LESSON 4-6 **Reteach**
Mixed Numbers and Improper Fractions

A proper fraction is a fraction whose numerator is less than its denominator.
$\frac{2}{3}$, $\frac{1}{4}$, and $\frac{2}{7}$ are examples of proper fractions.

An improper fraction is a fraction whose numerator is greater than or equal to its denominator.
$\frac{3}{2}$, $\frac{8}{3}$, and $\frac{5}{5}$ are examples of improper fractions.

Some improper fractions can be written as mixed numbers.
To write $\frac{7}{4}$ as a mixed number, draw circles divided into $\frac{1}{4}$ sections.
Then shade in 7 of the $\frac{1}{4}$ sections.

There is one circle and $\frac{3}{4}$ of a circle shaded.
So, $\frac{7}{4} = 1\frac{3}{4}$.

Write each improper fraction as a mixed number.

1. $\frac{14}{3}$ $4\frac{2}{3}$ 2. $\frac{11}{2}$ $5\frac{1}{2}$ 3. $\frac{15}{4}$ $3\frac{3}{4}$ 4. $\frac{19}{6}$ $3\frac{1}{6}$

Mixed numbers can be written as improper fractions.
To write $2\frac{1}{3}$ as an improper fraction, draw 3 circles. Divide each circle into $\frac{1}{3}$ sections. Next, shade in 2 whole circles and one $\frac{1}{3}$ section of the last circle.

Then find the total number of $\frac{1}{3}$ sections that are shaded.
Seven $\frac{1}{3}$ sections are shaded, so $2\frac{1}{3} = \frac{7}{3}$.

Write each mixed number as an improper fraction.

5. $3\frac{1}{4}$ $\frac{13}{4}$ 6. $5\frac{2}{3}$ $\frac{17}{3}$ 7. $4\frac{1}{2}$ $\frac{9}{2}$ 8. $1\frac{5}{6}$ $\frac{11}{6}$

PRACTICE 4-6

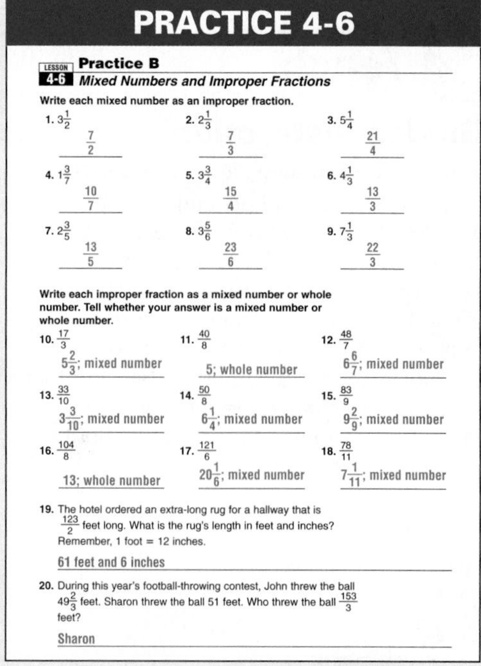

LESSON 4-6 **Practice B**
Mixed Numbers and Improper Fractions

Write each mixed number as an improper fraction.

1. $3\frac{1}{2}$ $\frac{7}{2}$ 2. $2\frac{1}{3}$ $\frac{7}{3}$ 3. $5\frac{1}{4}$ $\frac{21}{4}$
4. $1\frac{3}{7}$ $\frac{10}{7}$ 5. $3\frac{3}{4}$ $\frac{15}{4}$ 6. $4\frac{1}{3}$ $\frac{13}{3}$
7. $2\frac{3}{5}$ $\frac{13}{5}$ 8. $3\frac{5}{6}$ $\frac{23}{6}$ 9. $7\frac{1}{3}$ $\frac{22}{3}$

Write each improper fraction as a mixed number or whole number. Tell whether your answer is a mixed number or whole number.

10. $\frac{17}{3}$ $5\frac{2}{3}$; mixed number 11. $\frac{40}{8}$ 5; whole number 12. $\frac{48}{7}$ $6\frac{6}{7}$; mixed number
13. $\frac{33}{10}$ $3\frac{3}{10}$; mixed number 14. $\frac{50}{8}$ $6\frac{1}{4}$; mixed number 15. $\frac{83}{9}$ $9\frac{2}{9}$; mixed number
16. $\frac{104}{8}$ 13; whole number 17. $\frac{121}{6}$ $20\frac{1}{6}$; mixed number 18. $\frac{78}{11}$ $7\frac{1}{11}$; mixed number

19. The hotel ordered an extra-long rug for a hallway that is $\frac{123}{2}$ feet long. What is the rug's length in feet and inches? Remember, 1 foot = 12 inches.
61 feet and 6 inches

20. During this year's football-throwing contest, John threw the ball $49\frac{2}{3}$ feet. Sharon threw the ball 51 feet. Who threw the ball $\frac{153}{3}$ feet?
Sharon

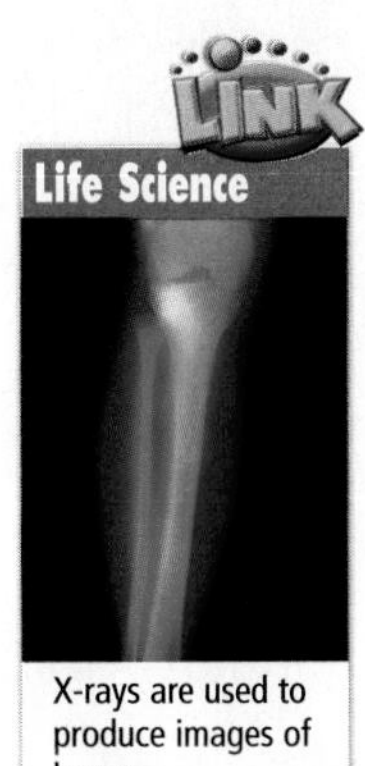

LINK — Life Science

X-rays are used to produce images of bones.

go.hrw.com Web Extra! KEYWORD: MR7 X-ray

Life Science **The table lists the lengths of the longest bones in the human body. Use the table for Exercises 40–42.**

40. Write the length of the ulna as an improper fraction. Then do the same for the length of the humerus. $\frac{141}{5}$, $\frac{73}{2}$

41. Write the length of the fibula as a mixed number. Then do the same for the length of the femur. $40\frac{1}{2}$; $50\frac{1}{2}$

42. Use the mixed-number form of each length. Compare the whole-number part of each length to write the bones in order from longest to shortest.

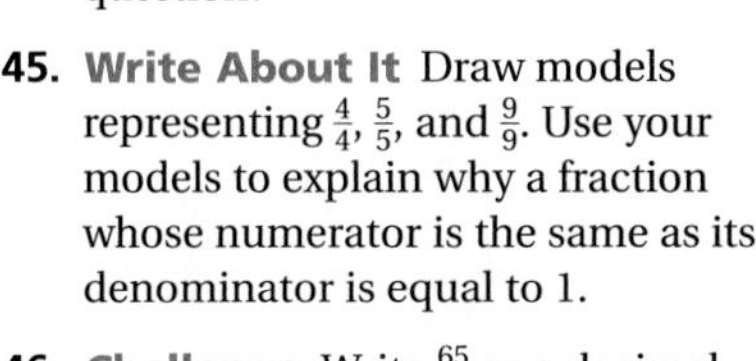

43. **Social Studies** The European country of Monaco, with an area of only $1\frac{4}{5}$ km^2, is one of the smallest countries in the world. Write $1\frac{4}{5}$ as an improper fraction. $\frac{9}{5}$

44. **What's the Question?** The lengths of Victor's three favorite movies are $\frac{11}{4}$ hours, $\frac{9}{4}$ hours, and $\frac{7}{4}$ hours. The answer is $2\frac{1}{4}$ hours. What is the question?

45. **Write About It** Draw models representing $\frac{4}{4}$, $\frac{5}{5}$, and $\frac{9}{9}$. Use your models to explain why a fraction whose numerator is the same as its denominator is equal to 1.

46. **Challenge** Write $\frac{65}{12}$ as a decimal. $5.41\overline{6}$

Longest Human Bones	
Fibula (outer lower leg)	$\frac{81}{2}$ cm
Ulna (inner lower arm)	$28\frac{1}{5}$ cm
Femur (upper leg)	$\frac{101}{2}$ cm
Humerus (upper arm)	$36\frac{1}{2}$ cm
Tibia (inner lower leg)	43 cm

CRCT Prep • GPS Support • Spiral Review

47. Multiple Choice What is $3\frac{2}{11}$ written as an improper fraction?

(A) $\frac{35}{11}$ (B) $\frac{35}{3}$ (C) $\frac{33}{22}$ (D) $\frac{70}{11}$

48. Multiple Choice It takes $\frac{24}{5}$ new pencils placed end to end to be the same length as one yardstick. What is this improper fraction written as a mixed number?

(F) $3\frac{4}{5}$ (G) $4\frac{1}{4}$ (H) $4\frac{1}{5}$ (J) $4\frac{4}{5}$

Order the numbers from least to greatest. (Lesson 1-1)

49. 1,497; 2,560; 1,038 — 1,038; 1,497; 2,560

50. 10,462; 9,198; 11,320 — 9,198; 10,462; 11,320

51. 4,706; 11,765; 1,765 — 1,765; 4,706; 11,765

Estimate a range for each sum. (Lesson 3-2)

52. 19.85 + 6.7 + 12.4 — 37 to 39.5

53. 2.456 + 8.3 + 11.05 — 21 to 22

54. 15.36 + 10.75 + 6.1 — 31 to 32.5

List all the factors of each number. (Lesson 4-2)

55. 57 — 1, 3, 19, 57

56. 36 — 1, 2, 3, 4, 6, 9, 12, 18, 36

57. 54 — 1, 2, 3, 6, 9, 18, 27, 54

CHALLENGE 4-6

LESSON 4-6 Challenge
Mixed Up Mixed Numbers

Find the whole number and fraction in the box to make a mixed number to match each improper fraction listed below. Cross out each whole number and fraction as you use it. When you have finished, the unused items in the box will form the mixed number that answers the question at the bottom of the page.

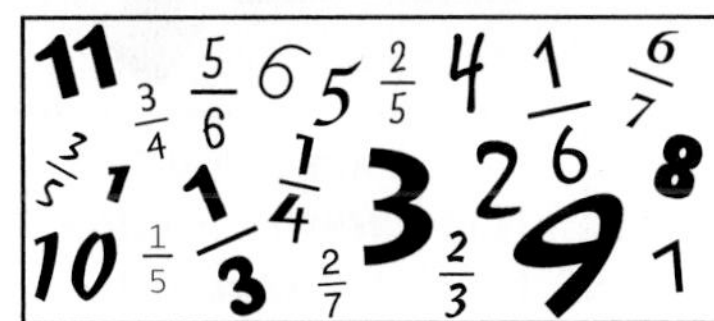

1. $\frac{7}{3}$ = $2\frac{1}{3}$
2. $\frac{20}{3}$ = $6\frac{2}{3}$
3. $\frac{21}{4}$ = $5\frac{1}{4}$
4. $\frac{31}{4}$ = $7\frac{3}{4}$
5. $\frac{41}{5}$ = $8\frac{1}{5}$
6. $\frac{57}{5}$ = $11\frac{2}{5}$
7. $\frac{59}{6}$ = $9\frac{5}{6}$
8. $\frac{19}{6}$ = $3\frac{1}{6}$
9. $\frac{13}{7}$ = $1\frac{6}{7}$
10. $\frac{72}{7}$ = $10\frac{2}{7}$

How old is the moon? $4\frac{3}{5}$ billion years old!

PROBLEM SOLVING 4-6

LESSON 4-6 Problem Solving
Mixed Numbers and Improper Fractions

Write the correct answer.

1. If stretched end-to-end, the total length of the blood vessels inside your body could wrap around Earth's equator $\frac{5}{2}$ times! Write this fact as a mixed number. $2\frac{1}{2}$ times

2. In 2000, the average 12-year-old child in the United States earned an allowance of 9 dollars and $\frac{7}{25}$ cents a week. Write this amount as an improper fraction and a decimal. $\frac{232}{25}$; \$9.28

3. The normal body temperature for a rattlesnake is between $53\frac{3}{5}$°F and $64\frac{2}{5}$°F. Write this range as improper fractions. $\frac{268}{5}$°F to $\frac{322}{5}$°F

4. A professional baseball can weigh no less than $\frac{45}{9}$ ounces and no more than $\frac{21}{4}$ ounces. Write this range as mixed numbers. 5 ounces to $5\frac{1}{4}$ ounces

Circle the letter of the correct answer.

5. Betty needs a piece of lumber that is $\frac{14}{3}$ feet long. Which size should she look for at the hardware store?
A $3\frac{3}{3}$ feet
B $3\frac{1}{4}$ feet
(C) $4\frac{2}{3}$ feet
D $4\frac{1}{4}$ feet

6. What operations are used to change a mixed number to an improper fraction?
(F) multiplication and addition
G division and subtraction
H division and addition
J multiplication and subtraction

7. Adult bees only eat nectar, the substance in flowers used to make honey. A bee could fly 4 million miles on the energy it would get from eating $\frac{9}{2}$ liters of nectar. What is this amount of nectar written as a mixed number.
A $9\frac{1}{2}$ liters
B) $4\frac{1}{2}$ liters
C $4\frac{1}{9}$ liters
D $2\frac{1}{2}$ liters

8. An astronaut who weighs 250 pounds on Earth would weigh $41\frac{1}{2}$ pounds on the moon. What is the astronaut's moon weight written as an improper fraction?
F $\frac{41}{2}$ pounds
G $\frac{42}{2}$ pounds
H $\frac{82}{2}$ pounds
(J) $\frac{83}{2}$ pounds

ONGOING ASSESSMENT and INTERVENTION

***Diagnose Before* the Lesson**
4-6 Warm Up, TE p. 192

***Monitor During* the Lesson**
4-6 Know-It Notebook
4-6 Questioning Strategies

***Assess After* the Lesson**
4-6 Lesson Quiz, TE p. 195

Answers

42. femur, tibia, fibula, humerus, ulna

44. Possible answer: What mixed number represents the length of the movie that is $\frac{9}{4}$ hours long?

45. because you shade all 4 out of 4, 5 out of 5, and 9 out of 9 pieces in your drawings representing one whole

TEST PREP DOCTOR In Exercise 47, remind students to multiply the denominator by the whole number and then add the product to the numerator to get the new numerator. Choices **B** and **C** can be eliminated because the denominator should not change if the fraction is in simplest form.

TEST PREP DOCTOR For Exercise 48, remind students to divide the numerator by the denominator, and any remainder will be the numerator in the fractional part of the mixed number.

Journal

Have students write how mixed numbers and improper fractions are used in real-world situations.

Power Presentations with PowerPoint®

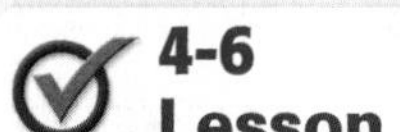

4-6 Lesson Quiz

Write each mixed number as an improper fraction.

1. Janet watches $\frac{7}{4}$ hours of television per day. Write $\frac{7}{4}$ as a mixed number. $1\frac{3}{4}$
2. $3\frac{3}{5}$ — $\frac{18}{5}$
3. $6\frac{1}{9}$ — $\frac{55}{9}$
4. $10\frac{1}{2}$ — $\frac{21}{2}$
5. $4\frac{1}{8}$ — $\frac{33}{8}$

Also available on transparency

SECTION 4B

Organizer

Objective: Assess students' mastery of concepts and skills in Lessons 4-4 through 4-6.

Resources

Assessment Resources
Section 4B Quiz

Test & Practice Generator
One-Stop Planner®

INTERVENTION

Resources

Ready to Go On? Intervention and Enrichment Worksheets

Ready to Go On? CD-ROM

Ready to Go On? Online

my.hrw.com

CHAPTER 4

SECTION 4B

Ready to Go On?

Quiz for Lessons 4-4 Through 4-6

4-4 Decimals and Fractions

Write each decimal as a fraction.

1. 0.67 $\frac{67}{100}$
2. 0.9 $\frac{9}{10}$
3. 0.43 $\frac{43}{100}$

Write each fraction as a decimal.

4. $\frac{2}{5}$ 0.4
5. $\frac{1}{6}$ $0.1\overline{6}$
6. $\frac{3}{4}$ 0.75

Compare. Write $<$, $>$, or $=$.

7. $\frac{7}{10}$ ■ 0.9 $<$
8. 0.4 ■ $\frac{2}{5}$ $=$
9. $\frac{3}{5}$ ■ 0.5 $>$
10. Jamal got $\frac{4}{5}$ of the questions correct on his quiz. Dominic got 0.75 of the questions correct. Who got more questions correct? Jamal

4-5 Equivalent Fractions

Write two equivalent fractions for each fraction.

11. $\frac{9}{12}$ $\frac{3}{4}$, $\frac{6}{8}$
12. $\frac{18}{42}$ $\frac{9}{21}$, $\frac{3}{7}$
13. $\frac{25}{30}$ $\frac{5}{6}$, $\frac{30}{36}$

Write each fraction in simplest form.

14. $\frac{20}{24}$ $\frac{5}{6}$
15. $\frac{14}{49}$ $\frac{2}{7}$
16. $\frac{12}{28}$ $\frac{3}{7}$
17. Mandy ate $\frac{1}{6}$ of a pizza. Write two equivalent fractions for $\frac{1}{6}$.

17. Possible answers: $\frac{2}{12}$, $\frac{3}{18}$

18. Liane is making fruit salad. The recipe calls for $\frac{1}{2}$ cup shredded coconut. Liane has only a $\frac{1}{4}$-cup measure. How can she measure the correct $\frac{1}{2}$-cup amount? Use 2 of the $\frac{1}{4}$-cup measures.

4-6 Mixed Numbers and Improper Fractions

Replace each shape with a number that will make the equation correct.

19. ■$\frac{2}{7} = \frac{9}{●}$ [1; 7]
20. $6\frac{■}{8} = \frac{49}{●}$ [1; 8]
21. ■$\frac{4}{9} = \frac{157}{●}$ [17; 9]

Use the table for Exercises 22–24.

22. Write the lengths of *1900* and *Empire* as mixed numbers in simplest form. $5\frac{3}{10}$; 8
23. Write the lengths of *Fanny and Alexander* and *War and Peace* as improper fractions. $\frac{26}{5}$, $\frac{511}{60}$
24. Write the movies in order from longest to shortest.
25. The proboscis bat, with a length of $\frac{19}{5}$ cm, is one of the smallest bats. Write $\frac{19}{5}$ as a mixed number. $3\frac{4}{5}$

World's Longest Movies	
Title	**Length (h)**
1900	$\frac{318}{60}$
Empire	$\frac{480}{60}$
Fanny and Alexander	$5\frac{1}{5}$
War and Peace	$8\frac{31}{60}$

24. *War and Peace, Empire, 1900, Fanny and Alexander*

READY TO GO ON?
Diagnose and Prescribe

NO INTERVENE

YES ENRICH

Ready to Go On? Intervention	*Ready to Go On? Intervention,* Section 4B Worksheets	CD-ROM	Online
Lesson 4-4	4-4 Intervention	Activity 4-4	Diagnose and Prescribe Online
Lesson 4-5	4-5 Intervention	Activity 4-5	
Lesson 4-6	4-6 Intervention	Activity 4-6	

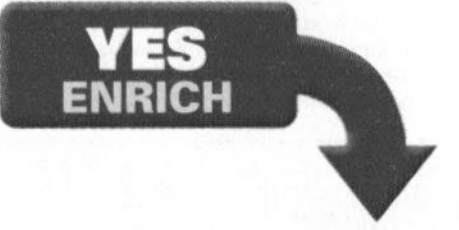

Ready to Go On? Enrichment, Section 4B

Worksheets

CD-ROM

Online

Focus on Problem Solving

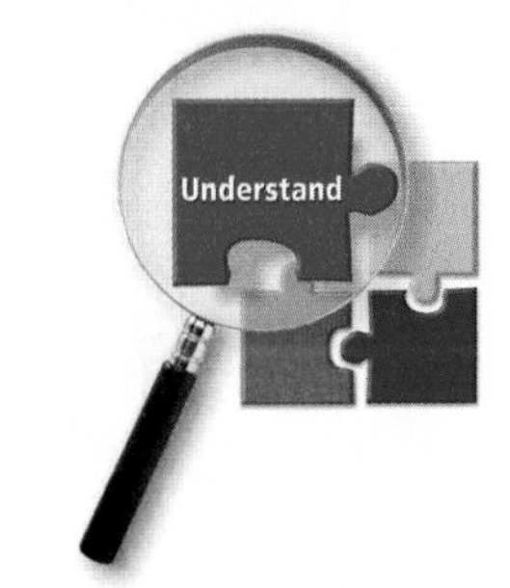

Understand the Problem

• **Write the problem in your own words**

One way to understand a problem better is to write it in your own words. Before you do this, you may need to read it over several times, perhaps aloud so that you can hear yourself say the words.

When you write a problem in your own words, try to make the problem simpler. Use smaller words and shorter sentences. Leave out any extra information, but make sure to include all the information you need to answer the question.

Write each problem in your own words. Check that you have included all the information you need to answer the question.

1. Martin is making muffins for his class bake sale. The recipe calls for $2\frac{1}{3}$ cups of flour, but Martin's only measuring cup holds $\frac{1}{3}$ cup. How many of his measuring cups should he use?

2. Mariko sold an old book to a used bookstore. She had hoped to sell it for \$0.80, but the store gave her $\frac{3}{4}$ of a dollar. What is the difference between the two amounts?

3. Koalas of eastern Australia feed mostly on eucalyptus leaves. They select certain trees over others to find the $1\frac{1}{4}$ pounds of food they need each day. Suppose a koala has eaten $1\frac{1}{8}$ pounds of food. Has the koala eaten enough food for the day?

4. The first day of the Tour de France is called the prologue. Each of the days after that is called a stage, and each stage covers a different distance. The total distance covered in the race is about 3,600 km. If a cyclist has completed $\frac{1}{3}$ of the race, how many kilometers has he ridden?

Focus on Problem Solving

Organizer

Objective: Focus on understanding the problem by restating the problem in your own words.

Online Edition

Resources

Chapter 4 Resource Book
Reading Strategies

Problem Solving Process

This page focuses on the first step of the problem-solving process:
Understand the Problem

Discuss

Have students identify the unnecessary information in each problem. Then have them rewrite each problem in their own words and include only the important information.

Possible answers:

1. The muffins are for a bake sale. How many times must Martin fill his $\frac{1}{3}$-cup measuring cup in order to get $2\frac{1}{3}$ cups of flour?
2. Mariko sold an old book to a used bookstore. What is the difference between \$0.80 and $\frac{3}{4}$ of a dollar?
3. Koalas feed mostly on eucalyptus, and they select certain trees over others.
   If a koala needs $1\frac{1}{4}$ pounds of food and has eaten $1\frac{1}{8}$ pounds of food, has it eaten enough food?
4. The first day of the Tour de France is called the Prologue; each of the days after that is called a stage, and each stage covers a different distance. What is $\frac{1}{3}$ of 3,600 km?

Answers

1. 7
2. \$0.05 (a nickel)
3. No, the koala needs another $\frac{1}{8}$ lb of food.
4. 1,200 km

SECTION 4C

Introduction to Fraction Operations

Lesson	Materials	MiC and Lab Resources
Lesson 4-7 Comparing and Ordering Fractions • Use pictures and number lines to compare and order fractions. ☑ CRCT ☐ SAT-10 ☐ ITBS ☑ CTBS ☑ NAEP	Fraction bars (MK)	**MiC:** ***Models You Can Count On*** pp. 26–28 **MiC:** ***Fraction Times*** pp. 4–9, 18–21 ***Hands-On Lab Activities*** 4-7 ***Technology Lab Activities*** 4-7
Lesson 4-8 Adding and Subtracting with Like Denominators • Add and subtract fractions with like denominators. ☑ CRCT ☑ SAT-10 ☑ ITBS ☐ CTBS ☑ NAEP	Fraction bars (MK)	**MiC:** ***Models You Can Count On*** pp. 13–14
Lesson 4-9 Estimating Fraction Sums and Differences • Estimate sums and differences of fractions and mixed numbers. ☑ CRCT ☑ SAT-10 ☑ ITBS ☑ CTBS ☑ NAEP		**MiC:** ***Fraction Times*** pp. 4–9, 18–21
Extension Set of Numbers • Make Venn diagrams to describe number sets. ☐ CRCT ☐ SAT-10 ☐ ITBS ☐ CTBS ☐ NAEP		

MK = *Manipulatives Kit*

Mathematics in Context

The units ***Models You Can Count On*** and ***Fraction Times*** from the *Mathematics in Context* © 2006 series can be used with Section 4C. See Section Planner above for suggestions for integrating *MiC* with *Holt Mathematics*.

Section Overview

Professional Development

Comparing and Ordering Fractions — Lesson 4-7

Why? You often need to compare and order fractions that have unlike denominators.

Order from least to greatest: $\frac{3}{8}, \frac{1}{3}$, 0.35

Write all the numbers in decimal form.

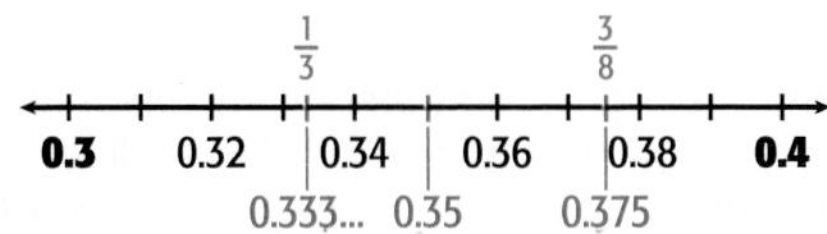

The numbers in order from least to greatest are:

$\frac{1}{3}$, 0.35, and $\frac{3}{8}$.

Order from least to greatest: $\frac{1}{2}, \frac{5}{12}, \frac{2}{5}$.

Rename with like denominators.

$\frac{1 \cdot 30}{2 \cdot 30} = \frac{30}{60}$ $\frac{5 \cdot 5}{12 \cdot 5} = \frac{25}{60}$ $\frac{2 \cdot 12}{5 \cdot 12} = \frac{24}{60}$

$\frac{24}{60}$ $\frac{25}{60}$ $\frac{30}{60}$

$\frac{2}{5}$ $\frac{5}{12}$ $\frac{1}{2}$

The numbers in order from least to greatest are:

$\frac{2}{5}, \frac{5}{12}$, and $\frac{1}{2}$.

Adding and Subtracting with Like Denominators — Lesson 4-8

Why? Solving real-world problems often involves adding and subtracting fractions and mixed numbers.

When adding or subtracting fractions with like denominators, add or subtract the numerators and keep the same denominator.

$$\frac{1}{10} + \frac{3}{10} = \frac{4}{10} = \frac{2}{5}$$

$$1 - \frac{1}{4} = \frac{4}{4} - \frac{1}{4} = \frac{3}{4}$$

Estimating Fraction Sums and Differences — Lesson 4-9

Why? Estimation skills are often used in daily life.

Kristi is looking for a two-bedroom apartment. In one apartment, the master bedroom is $14\frac{3}{4}$ feet wide and the other bedroom is $12\frac{1}{3}$ feet wide. About how much wider is the master bedroom than the other bedroom?

$14\frac{3}{4}$
The numerator is about the same as the denominator, so the fraction is closest to 1. You can round this number to 15.

$12\frac{1}{3}$
The numerator is much less than half the denominator, so the fraction is closest to 0. You can round this number to 12.

$$14\frac{3}{4} - 12\frac{1}{3} \approx 15 - 12 \approx 3$$

The master bedroom is about 3 feet wider than the other bedroom.

4-7 Organizer

Pacing: Traditional 1 day
Block $\frac{1}{2}$ day

Objective: Students use pictures and number lines to compare and order fractions.

GPS M6N1.g
Technology Lab
In *Technology Lab Activities*

Online Edition
Tutorial Videos

Countdown to CRCT Week 9

Warm Up

Find the missing number that makes the fractions equivalent.

1. $\frac{3}{5} = \frac{\blacksquare}{15}$ 9
2. $\frac{2}{3} = \frac{\blacksquare}{12}$ 8
3. $\frac{3}{4} = \frac{\blacksquare}{20}$ 15
4. $\frac{5}{8} = \frac{\blacksquare}{24}$ 15

Problem of the Day

From 4:00 to 5:30, Carlos, Lisa, and Toni took turns playing the same computer game. Carlos played for $\frac{1}{2}$ hour, and Lisa played for $\frac{3}{4}$ hour. For how many minutes did Toni play the game? 15 minutes

Also available on transparency

Math Fact

The word *fraction* comes from the Latin word *frangere*, which means "to break". Thus, a fraction is a broken number, or a piece of a number.

Georgia Performance Standards

M6N1.g Solve problems involving fractions, decimals, and percents.

M6P5.a Create and use representations to organize, record, and communicate mathematical ideas.

M6P5.b Select, apply, and translate among mathematical representations to solve problems.

M6P5.c Use representations to model and interpret physical, social, and mathematical phenomena.

4-7 Comparing and Ordering Fractions

Learn to use pictures and number lines to compare and order fractions.

Vocabulary
like fractions
unlike fractions
common denominator

Georgia Performance Standards
M6N1.g Solve problems involving fractions. Also, M6P5.a, M6P5.b, M6P5.c.

Rachel and Hannah are making a kind of cookie called *hamantaschen.* They have $\frac{1}{2}$ cup of strawberry jam, but the recipe requires $\frac{1}{3}$ cup.

Hamantaschen
1/2 cup butter
2 egg yolks
1 1/2 cups flour
2 tablespoons sugar
3 tablespoons ice water
1/3 cup strawberry jam

To determine if they have enough for the recipe, they need to compare the fractions $\frac{1}{2}$ and $\frac{1}{3}$.

When you are comparing fractions, first check their denominators. When fractions have the same denominator, they are called **like fractions**. For example, $\frac{1}{8}$ and $\frac{5}{8}$ are like fractions. When two fractions have different denominators, they are called **unlike fractions**. For example, $\frac{7}{10}$ and $\frac{1}{2}$ are unlike fractions.

EXAMPLE 1 Comparing Fractions

Helpful Hint
When two fractions have the same denominator, the one with the larger numerator is greater.
$\frac{2}{5} < \frac{3}{5}$ $\frac{3}{8} > \frac{1}{8}$

Compare. Write <, >, or =.

A $\frac{1}{8} \blacksquare \frac{5}{8}$

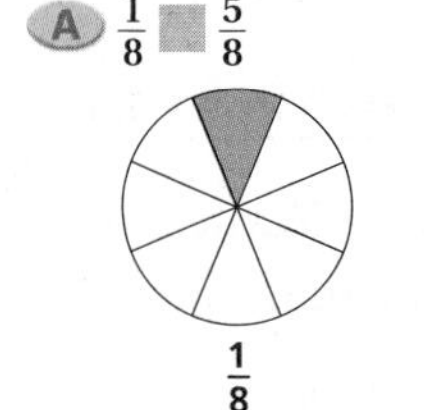

Model $\frac{1}{8}$ and $\frac{5}{8}$.

From the model, $\frac{1}{8} < \frac{5}{8}$.

B $\frac{7}{10} \blacksquare \frac{1}{2}$

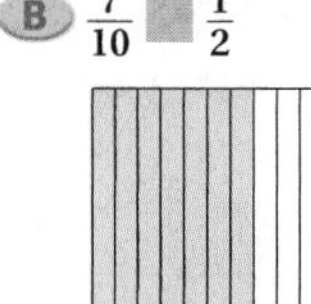

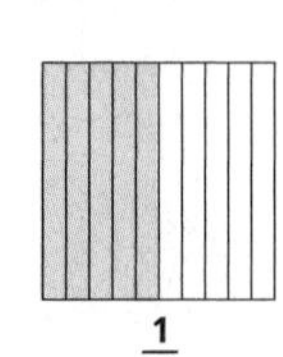

Model $\frac{7}{10}$ and $\frac{1}{2}$. $\frac{1}{2}$ and $\frac{5}{10}$ are equivalent fractions.

From the model, $\frac{7}{10} > \frac{1}{2}$.

1 Introduce

Alternate Opener

EXPLORATION

Use the model to decide whether the fraction on the left is greater than (>), less than (<), or equal to (=) the fraction on the right.

1. $\frac{1}{2} \square \frac{1}{3}$
2. $\frac{1}{2} \square \frac{1}{4}$
3. $\frac{1}{2} \square \frac{2}{3}$
4. $\frac{1}{3} \square \frac{1}{4}$
5. $\frac{3}{4} \square \frac{2}{3}$
6. $\frac{3}{4} \square \frac{5}{6}$
7. $\frac{1}{6} \square \frac{1}{4}$

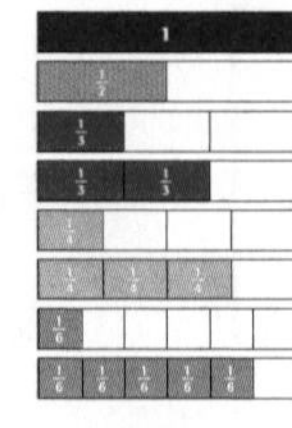

8. Look at the calculator screen to compare $\frac{1}{2}$ and $\frac{2}{3}$. Which fraction is greater? How do you know?

Think and Discuss

9. **Explain** how you could compare a fraction and a decimal.
10. **Explain** why $\frac{1}{17}$ is greater than $\frac{1}{18}$.

Motivate

Ask students to give examples of fractions in different contexts (e.g., $\frac{1}{2}$ gal of ice cream, $\frac{3}{4}$ cup of flour, $\frac{1}{8}$ inch, etc.). Then use the same units of measure, but provide a different fraction (e.g., $\frac{1}{3}$ gal of ice cream, $\frac{2}{3}$ cup of flour, $\frac{1}{16}$ inch, etc.). Explain that, as in the lesson opener, amounts represented as fractions sometimes must be compared in order to make decisions, such as determining whether $\frac{2}{3}$ cup or $\frac{3}{4}$ cup is more.

Explorations and answers are provided in *Alternate Openers: Explorations Transparencies.*

To compare unlike fractions without models, first rename the fractions so they have the same denominator. This is called finding a **common denominator**. This method can be used to compare mixed numbers as well.

EXAMPLE 2 *Cooking Application*

Rachel and Hannah have $1\frac{2}{3}$ cups of flour. They need $1\frac{1}{2}$ cups to make hamantaschen. Do they have enough flour for the recipe?

Compare $1\frac{2}{3}$ and $1\frac{1}{2}$.

Compare the whole-number parts of the numbers.

$1 = 1$ The whole-number parts are equal.

Compare the fractional parts. Find a common denominator by multiplying the denominators. $2 \cdot 3 = 6$

Find equivalent fractions with 6 as the denominator.

$$\frac{2}{3} = \frac{\blacksquare}{6} \qquad \frac{1}{2} = \frac{\blacksquare}{6}$$

$$\frac{2 \cdot 2}{3 \cdot 2} = \frac{4}{6} \qquad \frac{1 \cdot 3}{2 \cdot 3} = \frac{3}{6}$$

$$\frac{2}{3} = \frac{4}{6} \qquad \frac{1}{2} = \frac{3}{6}$$

Compare the like fractions. $\frac{4}{6} > \frac{3}{6}$, so $\frac{2}{3} > \frac{1}{2}$.

Therefore, $1\frac{2}{3}$ is greater than $1\frac{1}{2}$.

Since $1\frac{2}{3}$ cups is more than $1\frac{1}{2}$ cups, they have enough flour.

EXAMPLE 3 **Ordering Fractions**

Order $\frac{3}{7}$, $\frac{3}{4}$, and $\frac{1}{4}$ from least to greatest.

$\frac{3 \cdot 4}{7 \cdot 4} = \frac{12}{28}$ $\frac{3 \cdot 7}{4 \cdot 7} = \frac{21}{28}$ $\frac{1 \cdot 7}{4 \cdot 7} = \frac{7}{28}$ *Rename with like denominators.*

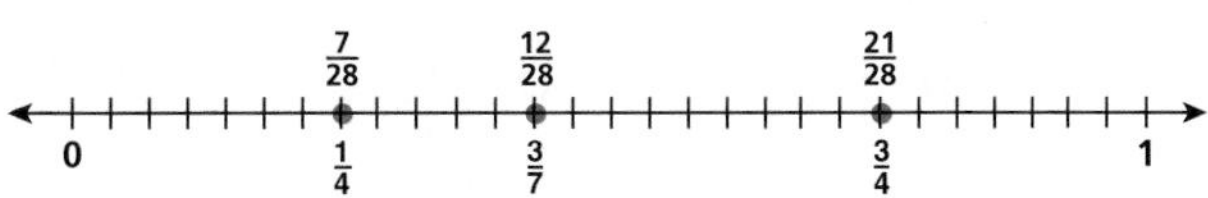

Remember!

Numbers increase in value as you move from left to right on a number line.

The fractions in order from least to greatest are $\frac{1}{4}, \frac{3}{7}, \frac{3}{4}$.

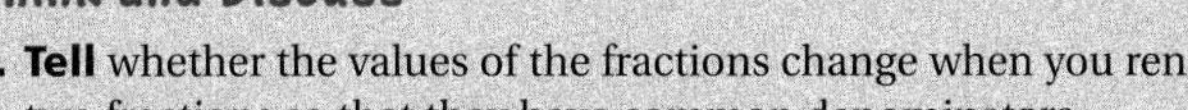

Think and Discuss GPS M6P3.b

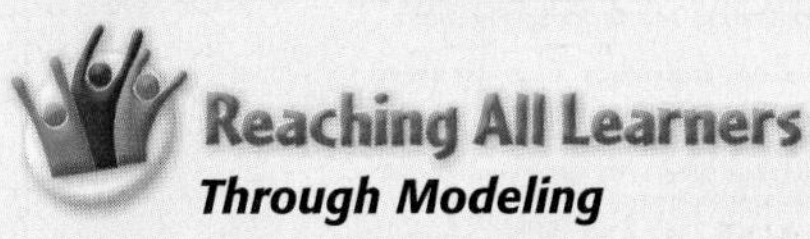

1. Tell whether the values of the fractions change when you rename two fractions so that they have common denominators.

2. Explain how to compare $\frac{2}{5}$ and $\frac{4}{5}$.

COMMON ERROR ALERT

When renaming fractions so that they have the same denominator, some students multiply just the denominator and not the numerator. Remind students that they have to multiply both the numerator and the denominator by the same value to create equivalent fractions.

Power Presentations with PowerPoint®

Additional Examples

Example 1

Compare. Write <, >, or =.

A. $\frac{6}{7}$ ■ $\frac{4}{7}$ $>$

B. $\frac{1}{9}$ ■ $\frac{5}{9}$ $<$

Example 2

Ray has $\frac{2}{3}$ cup of nuts. He needs $\frac{3}{4}$ cup to make cookies. Does he have enough nuts for the recipe?

No

Example 3

Order the fractions from least to greatest. $\frac{4}{5}, \frac{2}{3}, \frac{1}{3}$ $\frac{1}{3}, \frac{2}{3}, \frac{4}{5}$

Also available on transparency

Answers to Think and Discuss

1. No; when you multiply both the numerator and the denominator of a fraction by the same number, the resulting fraction is equivalent.
2. Since the denominators are the same, compare the numerators. $2 < 4$, so $\frac{2}{5} < \frac{4}{5}$.

2 Teach

Guided Instruction

In this lesson, students learn to use models and number lines to compare and order fractions. Teach them to use models to compare like fractions, then explain how to compare unlike fractions by first changing them to like fractions. Finally, teach students to order three unlike fractions by using a number line.

Teaching Tip **Communicating Math** If the denominator of one fraction is a multiple of the denominator of the other fraction, only one of the fractions needs to be changed to compare them.

Reaching All Learners

Through Modeling

Have each student or group of students model the fractions being compared in the lesson examples and exercises. Have them use fraction bars (provided in the Manipulatives Kit) to verify their results.

3 Close

Summarize

ENGLISH LANGUAGE LEARNERS

Have students define *unlike fractions* and explain how to compare them.

Possible answer: Unlike fractions are fractions with different denominators. To compare unlike fractions, change them to equivalent fractions with like denominators and then compare the numerators.

4-7 Exercises

Assignment Guide

If you finished Example 1 assign:
Average 1–4, 27–34, 43, 53–63
Advanced 10–17, 27–30, 44, 53–63

If you finished Example 2 assign:
Average 1–5, 27–34, 43, 53–63
Advanced 10–18, 27–30, 44, 53–63

If you finished Example 3 assign:
Average 1–49, 53–63
Advanced 1–47, 50–63

Homework Quick Check

Quickly check key concepts.
Exercises: 12, 24, 32, 36, 40

Math Background

The relationship between fractions and decimals provides an alternative method for comparing and ordering unlike fractions. By writing each fraction as a decimal, the fractions can be compared without resorting to the introduction of a common denominator.

Georgia Performance Standards

M6P3.a Organize and consolidate their mathematical thinking through communication.

M6P4.c Recognize and apply mathematics in contexts outside of mathematics.

4-7 Exercises

Georgia Performance Standards
M6P3.a, M6P4.c

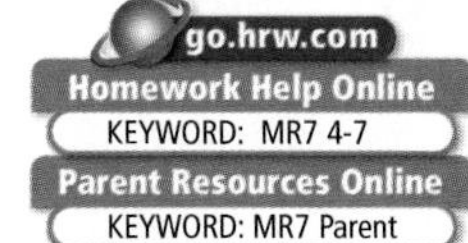

GUIDED PRACTICE

See Example 1 Compare. Write <, >, or =.

1. $\frac{3}{5}$ ▢ $\frac{2}{5}$ $>$
2. $\frac{1}{9}$ ▢ $\frac{2}{9}$ $<$
3. $\frac{6}{8}$ ▢ $\frac{3}{4}$ $=$
4. $\frac{3}{7}$ ▢ $\frac{6}{7}$ $<$

See Example 2

5. Arsenio has $\frac{2}{3}$ cup of brown sugar. The recipe he is using requires $\frac{1}{4}$ cup of brown sugar. Does he have enough brown sugar for the recipe? Explain. yes; possible answer: $\frac{2}{3}$ cup is greater than $\frac{1}{4}$ cup.

See Example 3 Order the fractions from least to greatest.

6. $\frac{3}{8}, \frac{1}{5}, \frac{2}{3}$ $\frac{1}{5}, \frac{3}{8}, \frac{2}{3}$
7. $\frac{1}{4}, \frac{2}{5}, \frac{1}{3}$ $\frac{1}{4}, \frac{1}{3}, \frac{2}{5}$
8. $\frac{5}{9}, \frac{1}{8}, \frac{2}{7}$ $\frac{1}{8}, \frac{2}{7}, \frac{5}{9}$
9. $\frac{1}{2}, \frac{1}{6}, \frac{2}{3}$ $\frac{1}{6}, \frac{1}{2}, \frac{2}{3}$

INDEPENDENT PRACTICE

See Example 1 Compare. Write <, >, or =.

10. $\frac{2}{5}$ ▢ $\frac{4}{5}$ $<$
11. $\frac{1}{10}$ ▢ $\frac{3}{10}$ $<$
12. $\frac{3}{4}$ ▢ $\frac{3}{8}$ $>$
13. $\frac{5}{6}$ ▢ $\frac{4}{6}$ $>$
14. $\frac{4}{5}$ ▢ $\frac{5}{5}$ $<$
15. $\frac{2}{4}$ ▢ $\frac{1}{2}$ $=$
16. $\frac{4}{8}$ ▢ $\frac{16}{24}$ $<$
17. $\frac{11}{16}$ ▢ $\frac{9}{16}$ $>$

See Example 2

18. Kelly needs $\frac{2}{3}$ gallon of paint to finish painting her deck. She has $\frac{5}{8}$ gallon of paint. Does she have enough paint to finish her deck? Explain. no; possible answer: $\frac{5}{8}$ gallon is less than $\frac{2}{3}$ gallon.

See Example 3 Order the fractions from least to greatest.

19. $\frac{1}{2}, \frac{3}{5}, \frac{3}{7}$ $\frac{3}{7}, \frac{1}{2}, \frac{3}{5}$
20. $\frac{1}{6}, \frac{2}{5}, \frac{1}{4}$ $\frac{1}{6}, \frac{1}{4}, \frac{2}{5}$
21. $\frac{4}{9}, \frac{3}{8}, \frac{1}{3}$ $\frac{1}{3}, \frac{3}{8}, \frac{4}{9}$
22. $\frac{1}{4}, \frac{5}{6}, \frac{5}{9}$ $\frac{1}{4}, \frac{5}{9}, \frac{5}{6}$
23. $\frac{3}{4}, \frac{7}{10}, \frac{2}{3}$ $\frac{2}{3}, \frac{7}{10}, \frac{3}{4}$
24. $\frac{13}{18}, \frac{5}{9}, \frac{5}{6}$ $\frac{5}{9}, \frac{13}{18}, \frac{5}{6}$
25. $\frac{3}{8}, \frac{1}{4}, \frac{2}{3}$ $\frac{1}{4}, \frac{3}{8}, \frac{2}{3}$
26. $\frac{3}{10}, \frac{2}{3}, \frac{5}{11}$ $\frac{3}{10}, \frac{5}{11}, \frac{2}{3}$

PRACTICE AND PROBLEM SOLVING

Extra Practice p. 721

Compare. Write <, >, or =.

27. $\frac{4}{15}$ ▢ $\frac{3}{10}$ $<$
28. $\frac{7}{12}$ ▢ $\frac{13}{30}$ $>$
29. $\frac{5}{9}$ ▢ $\frac{4}{11}$ $>$
30. $\frac{8}{14}$ ▢ $\frac{8}{9}$ $<$
31. $\frac{3}{5}$ ▢ $\frac{26}{65}$ $>$
32. $\frac{3}{5}$ ▢ $\frac{2}{21}$ $>$
33. $\frac{24}{41}$ ▢ $\frac{2}{7}$ $>$
34. $\frac{10}{38}$ ▢ $\frac{1}{4}$ $>$

Order the fractions from least to greatest.

35. $\frac{2}{5}, \frac{1}{2}, \frac{3}{10}$ $\frac{3}{10}, \frac{2}{5}, \frac{1}{2}$
36. $\frac{3}{4}, \frac{3}{5}, \frac{7}{10}$ $\frac{3}{5}, \frac{7}{10}, \frac{3}{4}$
37. $\frac{7}{15}, \frac{2}{3}, \frac{1}{5}$ $\frac{1}{5}, \frac{7}{15}, \frac{2}{3}$
38. $\frac{3}{4}, \frac{1}{3}, \frac{8}{15}$ $\frac{1}{3}, \frac{8}{15}, \frac{3}{4}$
39. $\frac{2}{5}, \frac{4}{9}, \frac{11}{15}$ $\frac{2}{5}, \frac{4}{9}, \frac{11}{15}$
40. $\frac{7}{12}, \frac{5}{8}, \frac{1}{2}$ $\frac{1}{2}, \frac{7}{12}, \frac{5}{8}$
41. $\frac{5}{8}, \frac{3}{4}, \frac{5}{12}$ $\frac{5}{12}, \frac{5}{8}, \frac{3}{4}$
42. $\frac{2}{3}, \frac{7}{8}, \frac{7}{15}$ $\frac{7}{15}, \frac{2}{3}, \frac{7}{8}$

43. Laura and Kim receive the same amount of allowance each week. Laura spends $\frac{3}{5}$ of it on going to the movies. Kim spends $\frac{4}{7}$ of it on a CD. Which girl spent more of her allowance? Explain. Laura; $\frac{3}{5} > \frac{4}{7}$

44. Kyle operates a hot dog cart in a large city. He spends $\frac{2}{5}$ of his budget on supplies, $\frac{1}{12}$ on advertising, and $\frac{2}{25}$ on taxes and fees. Does Kyle spend more on advertising or more on taxes and fees? advertising

RETEACH 4-7

LESSON 4-7 **Reteach**
Comparing and Ordering Fractions

$\frac{3}{4}$ and $\frac{2}{3}$ are unlike fractions because they have different denominators. To compare these fractions, graph the fractions on the same number line.

The fraction that is farther to the right on the number line is greater in value.

$\frac{9}{12} > \frac{8}{12}$, so $\frac{3}{4} > \frac{2}{3}$.

(number line: 0, $\frac{8}{12}$ ($\frac{2}{3}$), $\frac{9}{12}$ ($\frac{3}{4}$), 1)

Use the number line to compare the fractions. Write < or >.

1. $\frac{1}{3}$ $<$ $\frac{5}{6}$
2. $\frac{5}{10}$ $>$ $\frac{1}{4}$
3. $\frac{11}{12}$ $>$ $\frac{4}{6}$
4. $\frac{6}{9}$ $>$ $\frac{1}{6}$

You can use number lines to order fractions from least to greatest.

To order $\frac{1}{2}, \frac{5}{6}$, and $\frac{3}{4}$, graph the values on a number line.

Then list the fractions as they appear from left to right. From least to greatest the fractions are $\frac{1}{2}, \frac{3}{4}$, and $\frac{5}{6}$.

(number line: 0, $\frac{6}{12}$ ($\frac{1}{2}$), $\frac{9}{12}$ ($\frac{3}{4}$), $\frac{10}{12}$ ($\frac{5}{6}$), 1)

Use the number line to order the fractions from least to greatest.

5. $\frac{7}{12}, \frac{1}{4}, \frac{4}{8}$ $\frac{1}{4}, \frac{4}{8}, \frac{7}{12}$
6. $\frac{2}{3}, \frac{7}{12}, \frac{2}{8}$ $\frac{2}{8}, \frac{7}{12}, \frac{2}{3}$
7. $\frac{1}{2}, \frac{3}{4}, \frac{3}{9}$ $\frac{3}{9}, \frac{1}{2}, \frac{3}{4}$
8. $\frac{5}{12}, \frac{1}{3}, \frac{5}{6}$ $\frac{1}{3}, \frac{5}{12}, \frac{5}{6}$

PRACTICE 4-7

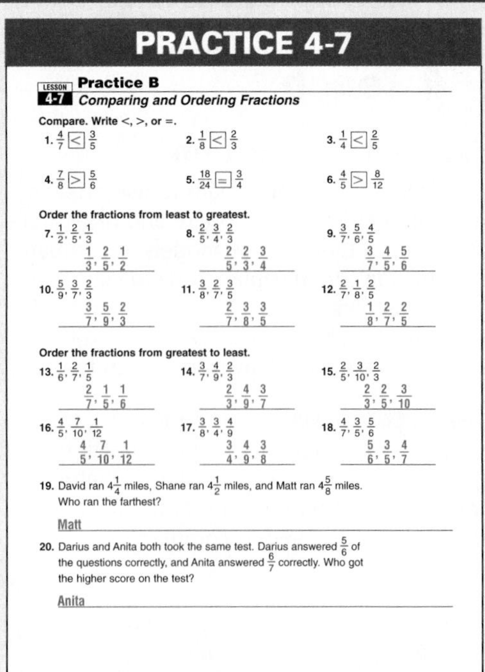
LESSON 4-7 **Practice B**
Comparing and Ordering Fractions

Compare. Write <, >, or =.

1. $\frac{4}{7}$ $<$ $\frac{3}{5}$
2. $\frac{1}{8}$ $<$ $\frac{2}{3}$
3. $\frac{1}{4}$ $<$ $\frac{2}{5}$
4. $\frac{7}{8}$ $>$ $\frac{5}{6}$
5. $\frac{18}{24}$ $=$ $\frac{3}{4}$
6. $\frac{4}{5}$ $>$ $\frac{8}{12}$

Order the fractions from least to greatest.

7. $\frac{1}{2}, \frac{2}{5}, \frac{1}{3}$ $\frac{1}{3}, \frac{2}{5}, \frac{1}{2}$
8. $\frac{2}{5}, \frac{3}{4}, \frac{2}{3}$ $\frac{2}{5}, \frac{2}{3}, \frac{3}{4}$
9. $\frac{3}{7}, \frac{5}{6}, \frac{4}{5}$ $\frac{3}{7}, \frac{4}{5}, \frac{5}{6}$
10. $\frac{5}{9}, \frac{3}{7}, \frac{2}{3}$ $\frac{3}{7}, \frac{5}{9}, \frac{2}{3}$
11. $\frac{3}{8}, \frac{2}{7}, \frac{3}{5}$ $\frac{2}{7}, \frac{3}{8}, \frac{3}{5}$
12. $\frac{2}{7}, \frac{1}{8}, \frac{2}{5}$ $\frac{1}{8}, \frac{2}{7}, \frac{2}{5}$

Order the fractions from greatest to least.

13. $\frac{1}{6}, \frac{2}{7}, \frac{1}{5}$ $\frac{2}{7}, \frac{1}{5}, \frac{1}{6}$
14. $\frac{3}{7}, \frac{4}{9}, \frac{2}{3}$ $\frac{2}{3}, \frac{4}{9}, \frac{3}{7}$
15. $\frac{2}{5}, \frac{3}{10}, \frac{2}{3}$ $\frac{2}{3}, \frac{2}{5}, \frac{3}{10}$
16. $\frac{4}{5}, \frac{7}{10}, \frac{1}{12}$ $\frac{4}{5}, \frac{7}{10}, \frac{1}{12}$
17. $\frac{3}{8}, \frac{3}{4}, \frac{4}{9}$ $\frac{3}{4}, \frac{4}{9}, \frac{3}{8}$
18. $\frac{4}{7}, \frac{3}{5}, \frac{5}{6}$ $\frac{5}{6}, \frac{3}{5}, \frac{4}{7}$

19. David ran $4\frac{1}{4}$ miles, Shane ran $4\frac{1}{2}$ miles, and Matt ran $4\frac{5}{8}$ miles. Who ran the farthest?

Matt

20. Darius and Anita both took the same test. Darius answered $\frac{5}{6}$ of the questions correctly, and Anita answered $\frac{6}{7}$ correctly. Who got the higher score on the test?

Anita

LINK Agriculture

There are over 3,500 different uses for corn products, from ethanol fuel and industrial products to the household items you see above.

Order the numbers from least to greatest.

45. $1\frac{2}{5}, 1\frac{1}{8}, 3\frac{4}{5}, 3, 3\frac{2}{5}$ **46.** $7\frac{1}{2}, 9\frac{4}{7}, 9\frac{1}{2}, 8, 8\frac{3}{4}$ **47.** $\frac{1}{2}, 3\frac{1}{5}, 3\frac{1}{10}, \frac{3}{4}, 3\frac{1}{15}$

48. Agriculture The table shows the fraction of the world's total corn each country produces. List the countries in order from the country that produces the most corn to the country that produces the least corn.
United States, China, Brazil

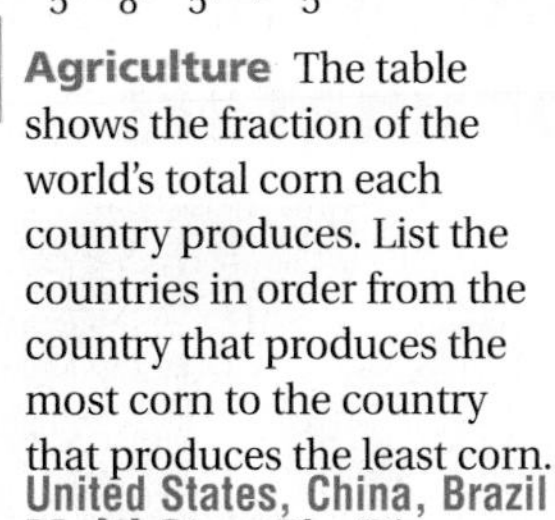

World's Corn Production	
United States	$\frac{41}{100}$
China	$\frac{1}{5}$
Brazil	$\frac{1}{20}$

49. Multi-Step The Dixon Dragons must win at least $\frac{3}{7}$ of their remaining games to qualify for their district playoffs. If they have 15 games left and they win 7 of them, will the Dragons compete in the playoffs? Explain.
yes; possible answer: $\frac{7}{15}$ is greater than $\frac{3}{7}$

50. Write a Problem Write a problem that involves comparing two fractions with different denominators.

51. Write About It Compare the following fractions.

$\frac{1}{2}$ ■ $\frac{1}{4}$ $\frac{2}{3}$ ■ $\frac{2}{5}$ $\frac{3}{4}$ ■ $\frac{3}{7}$ $\frac{4}{5}$ ■ $\frac{4}{9}$

What do you notice about two fractions that have the same numerator but different denominators? Which one is greater?

52. Challenge Name a fraction that would make the inequality true.

$\frac{1}{4} >$ ■ $> \frac{1}{5}$ Possible answer: $\frac{9}{40}$

45. $1\frac{1}{8}, 1\frac{2}{5}, 3, 3\frac{2}{5}, 3\frac{4}{5}$

46. $7\frac{1}{2}, 8, 8\frac{3}{4}, 9\frac{1}{2}, 9\frac{4}{7}$

47. $\frac{1}{2}, \frac{3}{4}, 3\frac{1}{15}, 3\frac{1}{10}, 3\frac{1}{5}$

CRCT Prep • GPS Support • Spiral Review

53. Multiple Choice Which fraction has the least value?

Ⓐ $\frac{1}{5}$ Ⓑ $\frac{3}{11}$ Ⓒ $\frac{2}{15}$ Ⓓ $\frac{4}{18}$

54. Extended Response Kevin is making potato soup. The recipe shows that he needs $\frac{1}{2}$ gallon of milk and 3.5 pounds of potatoes. He has $\frac{2}{5}$ gallon of milk and $\frac{21}{5}$ pounds of potatoes. Does Kevin have enough milk and potatoes to make the soup? Show your work and explain your answer.

Write each number in scientific notation. (Lesson 3-4)

55. 45 4.5×10^1 **56.** 405,000 4.05×10^5 **57.** 1,600,000 1.6×10^6 **58.** 23,000,000 2.3×10^7

Write each fraction in simplest form. (Lesson 4-5)

59. $\frac{3}{36}$ $\frac{1}{12}$ **60.** $\frac{4}{42}$ $\frac{2}{21}$ **61.** $\frac{6}{20}$ $\frac{3}{10}$ **62.** $\frac{12}{30}$ $\frac{2}{5}$ **63.** $\frac{5}{55}$ $\frac{1}{11}$

CHALLENGE 4-7

LESSON 4-7 **Challenge**
Light as a Feather

The pygmy shrew is the lightest mammal on Earth. It weighs only 0.05 ounces. That's lighter than most feathers! Use the clues below to complete the table with each tiny animal's weight.

Lightest Mammals

Mammal	Weight (oz)
Pygmy shrew	$\frac{1}{20}$
Pipistrelle bat	$\frac{11}{100}$
Kitti's hog-nosed bat	$\frac{7}{100}$
Harvest mouse	$\frac{9}{50}$
Masked shrew	$\frac{2}{25}$

The smallest pygmy shrews are only $1\frac{1}{2}$ inches long!

1. Thousands of masked shrews live all over North America, but they are rarely seen. Although tiny, they have enormous appetites—often eating more than their body weight each day in bugs, slugs, and other crawly things. A masked shrew weighs more than a kitti's hog-nosed bat, but less than a pipistrelle bat.
2. Several different speices of harvest mice live in the United States. They are excellent climbers and spend much of the night scampering around in search of seeds and bugs to eat. During the day, they stay at home to avoid their worst enemies: hawks, owls, and snakes. A harvest mouse weighs more than any other animal listed in the table.
3. Kitti's hog-nosed bats live only in Asia. They spend most of the day hanging in deep, dark caves. At night, they leave the cave and fly around catching bugs to eat. About the size of a bumblebee, a kitti's hog-nosed bat weighs more than a pygmy shrew, but less than a masked shrew.
4. Pipistrelle bats are the smallest bats in the United States. They are unusual for bats, because they often fly in daylight to catch beetles and other bugs to eat. In winter, they hibernate in caves or other dark places. During that time, the bats are often covered with droplets of water, which sparkle and give them a pearly glow. A pipistrelle bat weighs less than a harvest mouse, but more than a masked shrew.

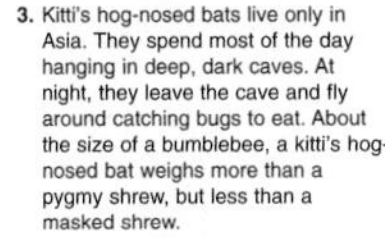

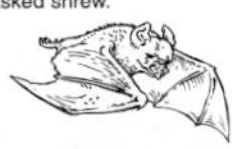

PROBLEM SOLVING 4-7

LESSON 4-7 **Problem Solving**
Comparing and Ordering Fractions

The table shows what fraction of Earth's total land area each of the continents makes up. Use the table to answer the questions.

Earth's Land

Continent	Fraction of Earth's Land
Africa	$\frac{1}{5}$
Antarctica	$\frac{1}{10}$
Asia	$\frac{3}{10}$
Australia	$\frac{1}{20}$
Europe	$\frac{7}{100}$
North America	$\frac{4}{25}$
South America	$\frac{6}{50}$

1. Which continent makes up most of Earth's land?
   Asia
2. Which continent makes up the least part of Earth's land?
   Australia
3. Explain how you would compare the part of Earth's total land area that Australia and Europe make up.
   Change $\frac{1}{20}$ to $\frac{5}{100}$ and then compare it to $\frac{7}{100}$.

Circle the letter of the correct answer.

4. Which of these continents covers the greatest part of Earth's total land area?
   (A) North America
   B South America
   C Europe
   D Australia
5. Which of these continents covers the least part of Earth's total land area?
   F Africa
   G Antarctica
   H Asia
   (J) Australia
6. Which of the following lists shows the continents written in order from the greatest part of Earth's total land they cover to the least part?
   (A) Asia, Africa, North America
   B Africa, Asia, North America
   C Asia, South America, North America
   D North America, Asia, South America
7. Which of the following lists shows the continents written in order from the least part of Earth's total land they cover to the greatest part?
   F Antarctica, Europe, South America
   G South America, Antarctica, Europe
   (H) Australia, Europe, Antarctica
   J Antarctica, Europe, Australia

Ongoing Assessment and Intervention

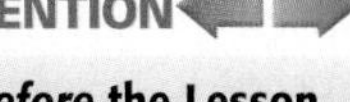

Diagnose Before the Lesson
4-7 Warm Up, TE p. 198

Monitor During the Lesson
4-7 Know-It Notebook
4-7 Questioning Strategies

Assess After the Lesson
4-7 Lesson Quiz, TE p. 201

Answers

50. Possible answer: $\frac{2}{7}$ of Hanna's birthday gifts were in bags and $\frac{3}{5}$ were in boxes. Did Hanna receive more gifts in bags or more in boxes?

51. >; >; >; >; Possible answer: When two fractions have the same numerator, the one with the least denominator is greatest.

54. See p. A3.

Test Prep Doctor To help students compare fractions in Exercise 53, suggest that converting the fraction to a decimal will be easier than writing fractions with the same denominator. To convert the fraction to a decimal, divide the numerator by the denominator.

Journal

Have students write a real-world problem in which unlike fractions are compared. Then have students solve the problem and explain the solution

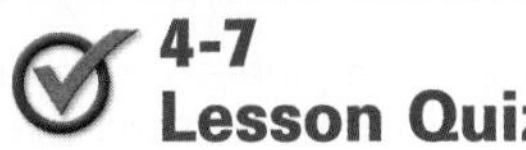

Power Presentations with PowerPoint®

4-7 Lesson Quiz

Compare. Write <, >, or =.

1. $\frac{3}{6}$ ■ $\frac{4}{8}$ = **2.** $\frac{5}{8}$ ■ $\frac{9}{16}$ >

3. You drilled three holes in a piece of wood. The diameters of the holes are $\frac{1}{8}$, $\frac{3}{8}$, and $\frac{3}{16}$ inches. Which hole is the largest? $\frac{3}{8}$

Order the fractions from least to greatest.

4. $\frac{7}{8}, \frac{5}{8}, \frac{2}{3}$ $\frac{5}{8}, \frac{2}{3}, \frac{7}{8}$

5. $\frac{3}{4}, \frac{5}{8}, \frac{5}{6}$ $\frac{5}{8}, \frac{3}{4}, \frac{5}{6}$

Also available on transparency

4-8 Organizer

Pacing: Traditional 1 day
Block $\frac{1}{2}$ day

Objective: Students add and subtract fractions with like denominators.

Online Edition
Tutorial Videos

Countdown to CRCT Week 9

Power Presentations with PowerPoint®

Warm Up

Write each mixed number as an improper fraction.

1. $6\frac{1}{3}$ $\frac{19}{3}$
2. $2\frac{1}{5}$ $\frac{11}{5}$
3. $3\frac{2}{7}$ $\frac{23}{7}$
4. $8\frac{1}{2}$ $\frac{17}{2}$
5. $9\frac{4}{5}$ $\frac{49}{5}$
6. $4\frac{8}{11}$ $\frac{52}{11}$

Problem of the Day

Marge has six coins that total \$1.15. She cannot make change for \$1.00, a half dollar, a quarter, a dime, or a nickel. What coins does she have?
half dollar, quarter, 4 dimes

Also available on transparency

Math Humor

Why do they call that stuff you pour in coffee "half and half"? Why not just call it "one whole"?

Georgia Performance Standards

M6N1.g Solve problems involving fractions, decimals, and percents.

M6A.3 Students will evaluate algebraic expressions, including those with exponents, and solve simple one-step equations using each of the four basic operations.

M6P1.b Solve problems that arise in mathematics and in other contexts.

M6P5.b Select, apply, and translate among mathematical representations to solve problems.

4-8 Adding and Subtracting with Like Denominators

Learn to add and subtract fractions with like denominators.

Georgia Performance Standards

M6N1.g Solve problems involving fractions. Also, M6A3, M6P1.b, M6P5.b.

You can estimate the age of an oak tree by measuring around the trunk at four feet above the ground.

The distance around a young oak tree's trunk increases at a rate of approximately $\frac{1}{8}$ inch per month.

EXAMPLE 1 *Life Science Application*

Sophie plants a young oak tree in her backyard. The distance around the trunk grows at a rate of $\frac{1}{8}$ inch per month. Use pictures to model how much this distance will increase in two months, then write your answer in simplest form.

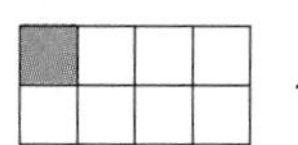 + 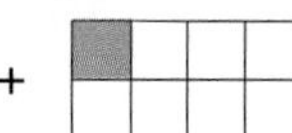 =

$\frac{1}{8} + \frac{1}{8}$

$\frac{1}{8} + \frac{1}{8} = \frac{2}{8}$ *Add the numerators. Keep the same denominator.*

$= \frac{1}{4}$ *Write your answer in simplest form.*

The distance around the trunk will increase by $\frac{1}{4}$ inch.

EXAMPLE 2 **Subtracting Like Fractions and Mixed Numbers**

Subtract. Write each answer in simplest form.

A $1 - \frac{2}{3}$

$\frac{3}{3} - \frac{2}{3} = \frac{1}{3}$

To get a common denominator, rewrite 1 as a fraction with a denominator of 3.

Subtract the numerators. Keep the same denominator.

Check

 − 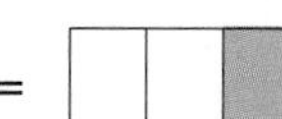 =

Remember!
When the numerator equals the denominator, the fraction is equal to 1.
$\frac{3}{3} = 1$ $\frac{173}{173} = 1$

1 Introduce

Alternate Opener

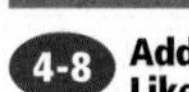

EXPLORATION

4-8 Adding and Subtracting with Like Denominators

Suzanne runs on a $\frac{3}{4}$-mile track. She ran one lap and then decided to run one more lap.

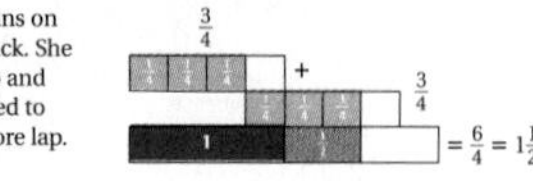

Susan ran $1\frac{1}{2}$ miles.

Draw a model to solve each addition problem.

1. $\frac{3}{5} + \frac{4}{5}$
2. $\frac{3}{10} + \frac{7}{10}$

Paul is recording a CD and has $\frac{1}{6}$ of the work completed. How much recording is left?

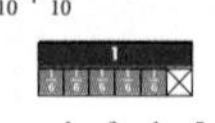

Paul needs to record $\frac{5}{6}$ of the CD. $1 - \frac{1}{6} = \frac{6}{6} - \frac{1}{6} = \frac{5}{6}$

Draw a model to solve each subtraction problem.

3. $\frac{4}{5} - \frac{3}{5}$
4. $1 - \frac{3}{10}$

Think and Discuss

5. **Explain** how to add and subtract fractions with like denominators.
6. **Explain** how to subtract a fraction from 1.

Motivate

Discuss fractions as they relate to time (e.g., quarter hour and half hour). Ask students how many quarter hours are equal to one half hour. (2 quarter hours) Have students explain how they know this.

Possible answers: Because $\frac{1}{4} + \frac{1}{4} = \frac{1}{2}$, students may refer to a clock face to illustrate their answer.

Explorations and answers are provided in *Alternate Openers: Explorations Transparencies.*

Subtract. Write each answer in simplest form.

B $3\frac{7}{12} - 1\frac{1}{12}$

$3\frac{7}{12} - 1\frac{1}{12}$ — *Subtract the fractions. Then subtract the whole numbers.*

$2\frac{6}{12}$

$2\frac{1}{2}$ — *Write your answer in simplest form.*

Check

EXAMPLE 3 Evaluating Expressions with Fractions

Evaluate each expression for $x = \frac{3}{8}$. Write each answer in simplest form.

A $\frac{5}{8} - x$

$\frac{5}{8} - x$ — *Write the expression.*

$\frac{5}{8} - \frac{3}{8} = \frac{2}{8}$ — *Substitute $\frac{3}{8}$ for x and subtract the numerators. Keep the same denominator.*

$= \frac{1}{4}$ — *Write your answer in simplest form.*

B $x + 1\frac{1}{8}$

$x + 1\frac{1}{8}$ — *Write the expression.*

$\frac{3}{8} + 1\frac{1}{8} = 1\frac{4}{8}$ — *Substitute $\frac{3}{8}$ for x. Add the fractions. Then add the whole numbers.*

$= 1\frac{1}{2}$ — *Write your answer in simplest form.*

C $x + \frac{7}{8}$

$x + \frac{7}{8}$ — *Write the expression.*

$\frac{3}{8} + \frac{7}{8} = \frac{10}{8}$ — *Substitute $\frac{3}{8}$ for x and add the numerators. Keep the same denominator.*

$= \frac{5}{4}$ or $1\frac{1}{4}$ — *Write your answer in simplest form.*

Helpful Hint

When adding a fraction to a mixed number, you can think of the fraction as having a whole number of 0.

$\frac{3}{8} = 0\frac{3}{8}$

Answers to *Think and Discuss*

1. Possible answer: First add or subtract the numerators. Then write the answer over the same denominator.
2. When adding like fractions, the denominator stays the same. So the correct sum is $\frac{4}{5}$.

Think and Discuss

GPS M6P2.c, M6P3.b

1. **Explain** how to add or subtract like fractions.
2. **Tell** why the sum of $\frac{1}{5}$ and $\frac{3}{5}$ is not $\frac{4}{10}$. Give the correct sum.
3. **Describe** how you would add $2\frac{3}{8}$ and $1\frac{1}{8}$. How would you subtract $1\frac{1}{8}$ from $2\frac{3}{8}$?

Watch for students who add or subtract the numerators *and* the denominators, instead of keeping the same denominator.

Power Presentations with PowerPoint®

Additional Examples

Example 1

Snow was falling at a rate of $\frac{1}{4}$ inch per hour. How much snow fell after two hours? Write your answer in simplest form. $\frac{1}{2}$ inch

Example 2

Subtract. Write each answer in simplest form.

A. $1 - \frac{3}{5}$ $\frac{2}{5}$

B. $5\frac{5}{12} - 2\frac{1}{12}$ $3\frac{1}{3}$

Example 3

Evaluate each expression for $x = \frac{2}{9}$. Write each answer in simplest form.

A. $\frac{5}{9} - x$ $\frac{1}{3}$

B. $x + 2\frac{4}{9}$ $2\frac{2}{3}$, or $\frac{8}{3}$

C. $x + \frac{8}{9}$ $\frac{10}{9}$, or $1\frac{1}{9}$

Also available on transparency

Answers to *Think and Discuss*

1. Possible answer: First add or subtract the numerators. Then write the answer over the same denominator.
2. When adding like fractions, the denominator stays the same. So the correct sum is $\frac{4}{5}$.

2 Teach

Guided Instruction

In this lesson, students learn to add and subtract fractions with like denominators. Teach them to add like fractions by adding the numerators and keeping the same denominator. (Use a pie to model how adding fifths does not change the denominator, only the numerator.) Then teach students to subtract by subtracting the numerators and keeping the same denominator. Finally, have students evaluate expressions involving adding and subtracting fractions with like denominators.

Reaching All Learners

Through Critical Thinking

Have students complete the magic square, expressing all missing fractions in simplest form. The sum of every row, column, and major diagonal is one.

$\frac{2}{15}$	$\frac{7}{15}$	$\frac{2}{5}$
$\frac{3}{5}$	$\frac{1}{3}$	$\frac{1}{15}$
$\frac{4}{15}$	$\frac{1}{5}$	$\frac{8}{15}$

3 Close

Summarize

Have the students explain how to solve $\frac{5}{8} + \frac{7}{8}$ and $\frac{7}{8} - \frac{5}{8}$.

Possible answer: Add 5 and 7 and keep the same denominator. Write the answer as a mixed number in simplest form. $\frac{5}{8} + \frac{7}{8} = \frac{12}{8} = \frac{3}{2} = 1\frac{1}{2}$

Subtract 5 from 7 and keep the same denominator. Write the difference in simplest form. $\frac{7}{8} - \frac{5}{8} = \frac{2}{8} = \frac{1}{4}$

4-8 Exercises

Assignment Guide

If you finished Example 1 assign:
Average 1, 28, 38, 44–53
Advanced 10, 28, 38, 44–53

If you finished Example 2 assign:
Average 1–5, 19–28, 36–38, 44–53
Advanced 10–14, 19–28, 40–42, 44–53

If you finished Example 3 assign:
Average 1–35, 39–40, 44–53
Advanced 1–35, 41–53

Homework Quick Check
Quickly check key concepts.
Exercises: 10, 14, 18, 22, 26

Math Background

In teaching students to work with fractions, some educators move from addition to subtraction to multiplication and finally to division, the same route used for whole numbers; others begin with multiplication of fractions because it is easier to master than addition and subtraction.

Georgia Performance Standards

M6P3.a Organize and consolidate their mathematical thinking through communication.

M6P3.c Analyze and evaluate the mathematical thinking and strategies of others.

4-8 Exercises

Georgia Performance Standards
M6P3.a, M6P3.c

go.hrw.com
Homework Help Online
KEYWORD: MR7 4-8
Parent Resources Online
KEYWORD: MR7 Parent

GUIDED PRACTICE

See Example 1
1. Marta is filling a bucket with water. The height of the water is increasing $\frac{1}{6}$ foot each minute. Use pictures to model how much the height of the water will change in three minutes, and then write your answer in simplest form. $\frac{1}{2}$ foot

See Example 2
Subtract. Write each answer in simplest form.

2. $2 - \frac{3}{5}$ $1\frac{2}{5}$
3. $8 - \frac{6}{7}$ $7\frac{1}{7}$
4. $4\frac{2}{3} - 1\frac{1}{3}$ $3\frac{1}{3}$
5. $8\frac{7}{12} - 3\frac{5}{12}$ $5\frac{1}{6}$

See Example 3
Evaluate each expression for $x = \frac{3}{10}$. Write each answer in simplest form.

6. $\frac{9}{10} - x$ $\frac{3}{5}$
7. $x + \frac{1}{10}$ $\frac{2}{5}$
8. $x + \frac{9}{10}$ $\frac{6}{5}$ or $1\frac{1}{5}$
9. $x - \frac{1}{10}$ $\frac{1}{5}$

INDEPENDENT PRACTICE

See Example 1
10. Wesley drinks $\frac{2}{13}$ gallon of juice each day. Use pictures to model the number of gallons of juice Wesley drinks in 5 days, and then write your answer in simplest form. $\frac{10}{13}$ gallon

See Example 2
Subtract. Write each answer in simplest form.

11. $1 - \frac{5}{7}$ $\frac{2}{7}$
12. $1 - \frac{3}{8}$ $\frac{5}{8}$
13. $2\frac{4}{5} - 1\frac{1}{5}$ $1\frac{3}{5}$
14. $9\frac{9}{14} - 5\frac{3}{14}$ $4\frac{3}{7}$

See Example 3
Evaluate each expression for $x = \frac{11}{20}$. Write each answer in simplest form.

15. $x + \frac{13}{20}$ $\frac{6}{5}$ or $1\frac{1}{5}$
16. $x - \frac{3}{20}$ $\frac{2}{5}$
17. $x - \frac{9}{20}$ $\frac{1}{10}$
18. $x + \frac{17}{20}$ $\frac{7}{5}$ or $1\frac{2}{5}$

PRACTICE AND PROBLEM SOLVING

Extra Practice p. 721

Write each sum or difference in simplest form.

19. $\frac{1}{16} + \frac{9}{16}$ $\frac{5}{8}$
20. $\frac{15}{26} - \frac{11}{26}$ $\frac{2}{13}$
21. $\frac{10}{33} + \frac{4}{33}$ $\frac{14}{33}$
22. $1 - \frac{9}{10}$ $\frac{1}{10}$
23. $\frac{26}{75} + \frac{24}{75}$ $\frac{2}{3}$
24. $\frac{100}{999} + \frac{899}{999}$ 1
25. $37\frac{13}{18} - 24\frac{7}{18}$ $13\frac{1}{3}$
26. $\frac{1}{20} + \frac{7}{20} + \frac{3}{20}$ $\frac{11}{20}$
27. $\frac{11}{24} + \frac{1}{24} + \frac{5}{24}$ $\frac{17}{24}$
28. Lily took $\frac{5}{6}$ lb of peanuts to a baseball game. She ate $\frac{2}{6}$ lb. How many pounds of peanuts does she have left? Write the answer in simplest form. $\frac{1}{2}$ lb

Evaluate. Write each answer in simplest form.

29. $a + \frac{7}{18}$ for $a = \frac{1}{18}$ $\frac{4}{9}$
30. $\frac{6}{13} - j$ for $j = \frac{4}{13}$ $\frac{2}{13}$
31. $c + c$ for $c = \frac{5}{14}$ $\frac{5}{7}$
32. $m - \frac{6}{17}$ for $m = 1$ $\frac{11}{17}$
33. $8\frac{14}{15} - z$ for $z = \frac{4}{15}$ $8\frac{2}{3}$
34. $13\frac{1}{24} + y$ for $y = 2\frac{5}{24}$ $15\frac{1}{4}$
35. Sheila spent x hour studying on Tuesday and $\frac{1}{4}$ hour studying on Thursday. What was the total amount of time in hours Sheila spent studying if $x = \frac{2}{4}$? $\frac{3}{4}$ hour

RETEACH 4-8

LESSON 4-8 **Reteach**
Adding and Subtracting with Like Denominators

You can use fraction strips to add like fractions.

To find $\frac{1}{8} + \frac{3}{8}$, first model the expression using $\frac{1}{8}$ fraction pieces.

$\boxed{\frac{1}{8}} + \boxed{\frac{1}{8}}\boxed{\frac{1}{8}}\boxed{\frac{1}{8}}$

The total number of fraction pieces is 4.
So, $\frac{1}{8} + \frac{3}{8} = \frac{4}{8}$.
Then write the sum in simplest form. $\frac{4}{8} = \frac{1}{2}$.

Write each sum in simplest form.

1. $\frac{1}{4} + \frac{1}{4}$ $\frac{1}{2}$
2. $\frac{1}{5} + \frac{3}{5}$ $\frac{4}{5}$
3. $\frac{1}{6} + \frac{5}{6}$ 1
4. $\frac{5}{12} + \frac{1}{12}$ $\frac{1}{2}$

You can use fraction strips to subtract like fractions.

To find $\frac{5}{6} - \frac{1}{6}$, use fraction strips to model the first fraction.

$\boxed{\frac{1}{6}}\boxed{\frac{1}{6}}\boxed{\frac{1}{6}}\boxed{\frac{1}{6}}\boxed{\frac{1}{6}}$

Next, take away fraction strips that represent the second fraction.

$\boxed{\frac{1}{6}}\boxed{\frac{1}{6}}\boxed{\frac{1}{6}}\boxed{\frac{1}{6}}\boxed{\frac{1}{6}}$

The remaining fraction strips represent the difference.
$\frac{5}{6} - \frac{1}{6} = \frac{4}{6}$

$\frac{4}{6} = \frac{2}{3}$ in simplest form.

Write each difference in simplest form.

5. $\frac{5}{8} - \frac{3}{8}$ $\frac{1}{4}$
6. $\frac{7}{12} - \frac{5}{12}$ $\frac{1}{6}$
7. $\frac{3}{4} - \frac{1}{4}$ $\frac{1}{2}$
8. $\frac{9}{10} - \frac{3}{10}$ $\frac{3}{5}$

PRACTICE 4-8

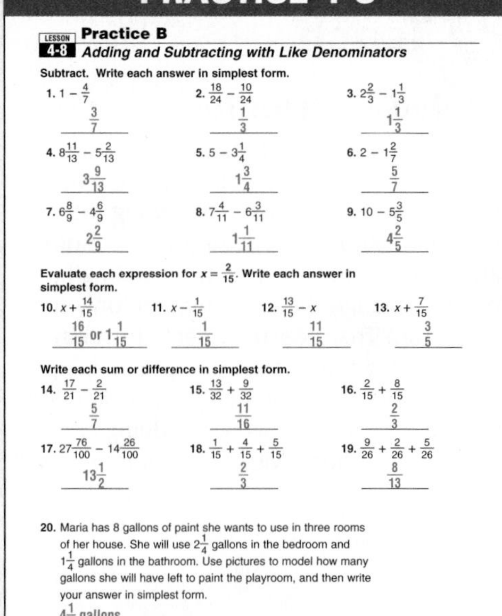
LESSON 4-8 **Practice B**
Adding and Subtracting with Like Denominators

Subtract. Write each answer in simplest form.

1. $1 - \frac{4}{7}$ $\frac{3}{7}$
2. $\frac{18}{24} - \frac{10}{24}$ $\frac{1}{3}$
3. $2\frac{2}{3} - 1\frac{1}{3}$ $1\frac{1}{3}$
4. $8\frac{11}{13} - 5\frac{2}{13}$ $3\frac{9}{13}$
5. $5 - 3\frac{1}{4}$ $1\frac{3}{4}$
6. $2 - 1\frac{2}{7}$ $\frac{5}{7}$
7. $6\frac{8}{9} - 4\frac{6}{9}$ $2\frac{2}{9}$
8. $7\frac{4}{11} - 6\frac{3}{11}$ $1\frac{1}{11}$
9. $10 - 5\frac{3}{5}$ $4\frac{2}{5}$

Evaluate each expression for $x = \frac{2}{15}$. Write each answer in simplest form.

10. $x + \frac{14}{15}$ $\frac{16}{15}$ or $1\frac{1}{15}$
11. $x - \frac{1}{15}$ $\frac{1}{15}$
12. $\frac{13}{15} - x$ $\frac{11}{15}$
13. $x + \frac{7}{15}$ $\frac{3}{5}$

Write each sum or difference in simplest form.

14. $\frac{17}{21} - \frac{2}{21}$ $\frac{5}{7}$
15. $\frac{13}{32} + \frac{9}{32}$ $\frac{11}{16}$
16. $\frac{2}{15} + \frac{8}{15}$ $\frac{2}{3}$
17. $27\frac{76}{100} - 14\frac{26}{100}$ $13\frac{1}{2}$
18. $\frac{1}{15} + \frac{4}{15} + \frac{5}{15}$ $\frac{2}{3}$
19. $\frac{9}{26} + \frac{2}{26} + \frac{5}{26}$ $\frac{8}{13}$
20. Maria has 8 gallons of paint she wants to use in three rooms of her house. She will use $2\frac{1}{4}$ gallons in the bedroom and $1\frac{1}{4}$ gallons in the bathroom. Use pictures to model how many gallons she will have left to paint the playroom, and then write your answer in simplest form. $4\frac{1}{2}$ gallons

Life Science

Each fall, Callaway Gardens, near Pine Mountain, Georgia, holds a Chrysanthemum Festival.

36. Carlos had 7 cups of chocolate chips. He used $1\frac{2}{3}$ cups to make a chocolate sauce and $3\frac{1}{3}$ cups to make cookies. How many cups of chocolate chips does Carlos have now? **2 cups**

37. A concert was $2\frac{1}{4}$ hr long. The first musical piece lasted $\frac{1}{4}$ hr. The intermission also lasted $\frac{1}{4}$ hr. How long was the rest of the concert? **$1\frac{3}{4}$ hr**

38. A flight from Washington, D.C., stops in San Francisco and then continues to Seattle. The trip to San Francisco takes $4\frac{5}{8}$ hr. The trip to Seattle takes $1\frac{1}{8}$ hr. What is the total flight time? **$5\frac{6}{8}$ or $5\frac{3}{4}$ hr**

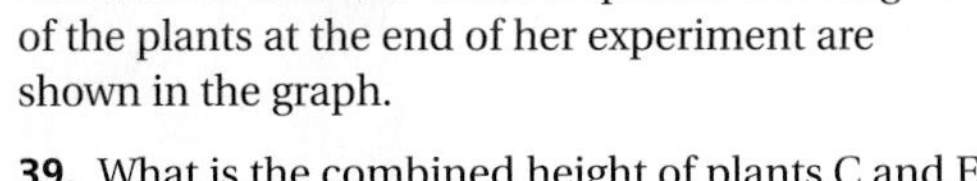

Life Science Use the graph for Exercises 39–41. Sheila performed an experiment to find the most effective plant fertilizer. She used a different fertilizer on each of 5 different plants. The heights of the plants at the end of her experiment are shown in the graph.

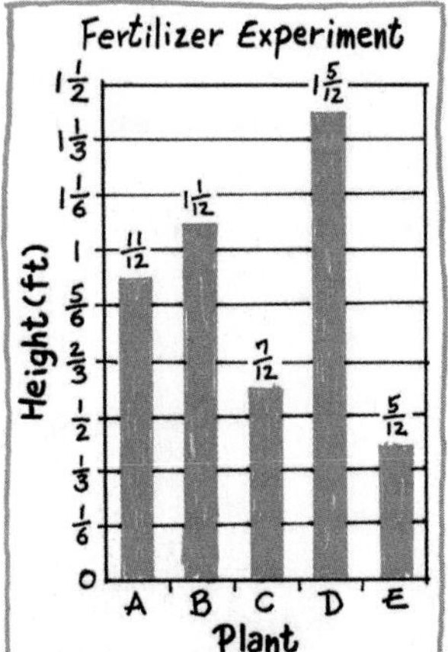

39. What is the combined height of plants C and E? **1 foot**

40. What is the difference in height between the tallest plant and the shortest plant? **1 foot**

41. What's the Error? Sheila found the combined heights of plants B and E to be $1\frac{6}{24}$ feet. Explain the error and give the correct answer in simplest form.

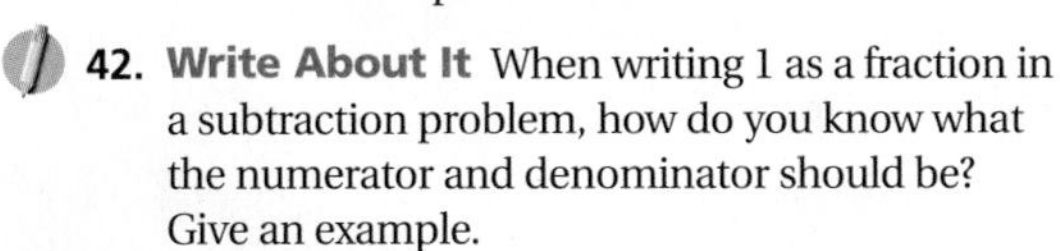

42. Write About It When writing 1 as a fraction in a subtraction problem, how do you know what the numerator and denominator should be? Give an example.

43. Challenge Explain how you might estimate the difference between $\frac{3}{4}$ and $\frac{6}{23}$. **Possible answer: $\frac{6}{23}$ is almost equal to $\frac{1}{4}$. Subtract $\frac{1}{4}$ from $\frac{3}{4}$ to find an estimate of $\frac{2}{4}$, or $\frac{1}{2}$.**

CRCT Prep • GPS Support • Spiral Review

44. Multiple Choice Solve. $x - \frac{6}{11} = \frac{5}{11}$

Ⓐ $\frac{1}{22}$ Ⓑ $\frac{1}{11}$ **Ⓒ 1** Ⓓ 11

45. Short Response Your friend was absent from school and asked you for help with the math assignment. Give your friend detailed instructions on how to subtract $4\frac{7}{12}$ from $13\frac{11}{12}$.

Find two equivalent fractions for each fraction. (Lesson 4-5) **Possible answers:**

46. $\frac{4}{7}$ **$\frac{8}{14}, \frac{12}{21}$** **47.** $\frac{3}{4}$ **$\frac{6}{8}, \frac{9}{12}$** **48.** $\frac{2}{9}$ **$\frac{4}{18}, \frac{6}{27}$** **49.** $\frac{3}{5}$ **$\frac{6}{10}, \frac{9}{15}$** **50.** $\frac{1}{10}$ **$\frac{2}{20}, \frac{3}{30}$**

Order the fractions from least to greatest. (Lesson 4-7)

51. $\frac{3}{7}, \frac{5}{4}, \frac{2}{6}$ **$\frac{2}{6}, \frac{3}{7}, \frac{5}{4}$** **52.** $\frac{2}{3}, \frac{4}{11}, \frac{5}{8}$ **$\frac{4}{11}, \frac{5}{8}, \frac{2}{3}$** **53.** $\frac{3}{10}, \frac{3}{8}, \frac{1}{3}$ **$\frac{3}{10}, \frac{1}{3}, \frac{3}{8}$**

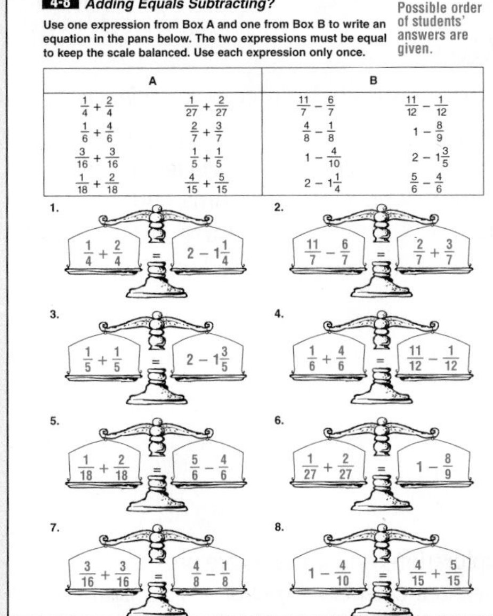

CHALLENGE 4-8

LESSON 4-8 **Challenge**
Adding Equals Subtracting?

Use one expression from Box A and one from Box B to write an equation in the pans below. The two expressions must be equal to keep the scale balanced. Use each expression only once.

Possible order of students' answers are given.

A		B	
$\frac{1}{4}+\frac{2}{4}$	$\frac{1}{27}+\frac{2}{27}$	$\frac{11}{7}-\frac{6}{7}$	$\frac{11}{12}-\frac{1}{12}$
$\frac{1}{6}+\frac{4}{6}$	$\frac{2}{7}+\frac{3}{7}$	$\frac{4}{8}-\frac{1}{8}$	$1-\frac{8}{9}$
$\frac{3}{16}+\frac{3}{16}$	$\frac{1}{5}+\frac{1}{5}$	$1-\frac{4}{10}$	$2-1\frac{3}{5}$
$\frac{1}{18}+\frac{2}{18}$	$\frac{4}{15}+\frac{5}{15}$	$2-1\frac{1}{4}$	$\frac{5}{6}-\frac{4}{6}$

1. $\frac{1}{4}+\frac{2}{4} = 2-1\frac{1}{4}$
2. $\frac{11}{7}-\frac{6}{7} = \frac{2}{7}+\frac{3}{7}$
3. $\frac{1}{5}+\frac{1}{5} = 2-1\frac{3}{5}$
4. $\frac{1}{6}+\frac{4}{6} = \frac{11}{12}-\frac{1}{12}$
5. $\frac{1}{18}+\frac{2}{18} = \frac{5}{6}-\frac{4}{6}$
6. $\frac{1}{27}+\frac{2}{27} = 1-\frac{8}{9}$
7. $\frac{3}{16}+\frac{3}{16} = \frac{4}{8}-\frac{1}{8}$
8. $1-\frac{4}{10} = \frac{4}{15}+\frac{5}{15}$

PROBLEM SOLVING 4-8

LESSON 4-8 **Problem Solving**
Adding and Subtracting with Like Denominators

Write the answers in simplest form.

1. About $\frac{3}{10}$ of Earth's surface is covered by land, and the rest is water. What fraction of Earth's surface is covered by water?
$\frac{7}{10}$ of Earth's surface

2. A recipe for cookies calls for $\frac{3}{8}$ cup of chocolate chips. Tameeka wants to double the recipe. How much chocolate chips will she use?
$\frac{3}{4}$ cup

3. In Mr. Chesterfield's science class, $\frac{2}{9}$ of the boys like his class. Three times as many girls like his science class. How many girls like Mr. Chesterfield's science class?
$\frac{2}{3}$ of the girls

4. In the United States, $\frac{6}{50}$ of the population is left-handed men and $\frac{5}{50}$ of the population is left-handed women. What part of the population is left-handed?
$\frac{11}{50}$

Circle the letter of the correct answer.

5. In the United States, about $\frac{1}{10}$ of the population is born with black hair, and $\frac{7}{10}$ of the population is born with brown hair. What fraction of the total population in the U.S. is born with brown or black hair?
A $\frac{1}{10}$ C $\frac{3}{5}$
B $\frac{1}{5}$ **Ⓓ $\frac{4}{5}$**

6. In the United States, about $\frac{3}{20}$ of the population is born with blond hair, and $\frac{1}{20}$ of the population is born with red hair. What fraction of the total population in the U.S. is born with blond or red hair?
F $\frac{1}{10}$ H $\frac{3}{5}$
Ⓖ $\frac{1}{5}$ J $\frac{4}{5}$

7. The average height for men in the United States is $5\frac{2}{3}$ feet tall. Bill is $\frac{1}{3}$ foot shorter than average. How tall is Bill?
Ⓐ $5\frac{1}{3}$ feet C 6 feet
B $5\frac{3}{6}$ feet D $5\frac{1}{6}$ feet

8. The average height for women in the United States is $5\frac{1}{3}$ feet tall. Katie is $\frac{2}{3}$ foot taller than average. How tall is Katie?
F $5\frac{1}{3}$ feet **Ⓗ 6 feet**
G $5\frac{3}{6}$ feet J $5\frac{1}{6}$ feet

Ongoing Assessment and Intervention

Diagnose ***Before*** **the Lesson**
4-8 Warm Up, TE p. 202

Monitor ***During*** **the Lesson**
4-8 Know-It Notebook
4-8 Questioning Strategies

Assess ***After*** **the Lesson**
4-8 Lesson Quiz, TE p. 205

Answers

41. Sheila added the numerators and the denominators. She should have added just the numerators, and the answer would have been $1\frac{1}{2}$ feet.

42. The numerator and denominator should be the same as the denominator of the fraction you are subtracting. For example, in $1 - \frac{1}{3}$, you should write 1 as $\frac{3}{3}$ and then subtract the numerators.

45. Possible answer: First, find the difference between the fractions. The denominators are alike, so subtract 7 from 11, and write the difference over 12. Then find the difference between the whole numbers.

Test Prep Doctor In Exercise 44, students need to remember to use the inverse operation when solving an equation. The solution is found by adding $\frac{6}{11}$ to both sides of the equation.

Journal

Have students think of and write real-world situations in which like fractions are added and subtracted. Have them describe how to solve each problem.

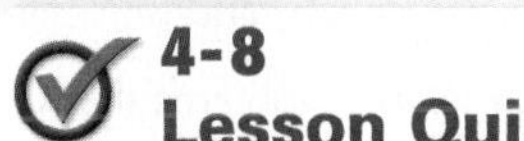

Power Presentations with PowerPoint®

4-8 Lesson Quiz

1. Weston walks $\frac{3}{4}$ mile every day. How far will he have walked in 4 days? 3 miles

Subtract. Write each answer in simplest form.

2. $1 - \frac{9}{11}$ $\frac{2}{11}$

3. $1 - \frac{8}{9}$ $\frac{1}{9}$

4. Evaluate $\frac{16}{21} - x$ for $x = \frac{6}{21}$. $\frac{10}{21}$

Also available on transparency

4-9 Organizer

Pacing: Traditional $1\frac{1}{2}$ day
Block $\frac{3}{4}$

Objective: Students estimate sums and differences of fractions and mixed numbers.

Online Edition
Tutorial Videos

Countdown to CRCT Week 9

Power Presentations with PowerPoint®

Warm Up

Write each sum or difference in simplest form.

1. $\frac{3}{8} + \frac{5}{8}$ 1
2. $\frac{9}{10} - \frac{3}{10}$ $\frac{3}{5}$
3. $2\frac{1}{4} + 1\frac{1}{4}$ $3\frac{1}{2}$
4. $5\frac{8}{9} - 1\frac{2}{9}$ $4\frac{2}{3}$

Problem of the Day

Students at a school dance formed equal teams to play a game. When they formed teams of 3, 4, 5, or 6, there was always one person left. What is the smallest number of people that there could have been at the dance? 61, the LCM of all the numbers, plus 1

Also available on transparency

Math Humor

What was the movie about?
About $2\frac{1}{2}$ hours

Georgia Performance Standards

M6N1.g Solve problems involving fractions, decimals, and percents.

M6P1.b Solve problems that arise in mathematics and in other contexts.

M6P5.a Create and use representations to organize, record, and communicate mathematical ideas.

M6P5.b Select, apply, and translate among mathematical representations to solve problems.

4-9 Estimating Fraction Sums and Differences

Learn to estimate sums and differences of fractions and mixed numbers.

Georgia Performance Standards

M6N1.g Solve problems involving fractions. Also, M6P1.b, M6P5.a, M6P5.b.

Members of the Nature Club went mountain biking in Canyonlands National Park, Utah. They biked $10\frac{3}{10}$ miles on Monday.

You can estimate fractions by rounding to 0, $\frac{1}{2}$, or 1.

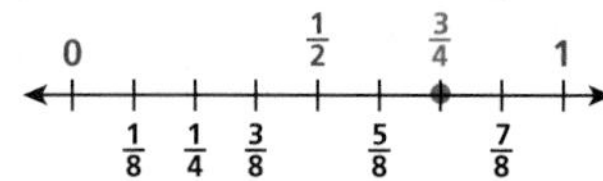
0
$\frac{1}{2}$
$\frac{3}{4}$
1
$\frac{1}{8}$ $\frac{1}{4}$ $\frac{3}{8}$ $\frac{5}{8}$ $\frac{7}{8}$

Canyonlands National Park, Utah, is a 337,570-acre park that has many canyons, mesas, arches, and spires.

The fraction $\frac{3}{4}$ is halfway between $\frac{1}{2}$ and 1, but we usually round up. So the fraction $\frac{3}{4}$ rounds to 1.

You can round fractions by comparing the numerator and denominator.

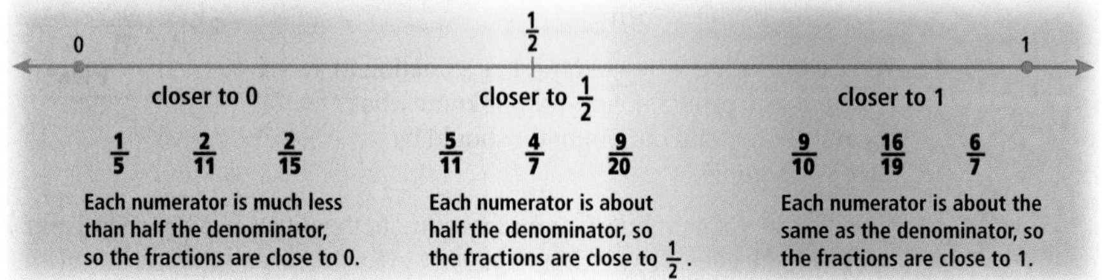
0
$\frac{1}{2}$
1
closer to 0
$\frac{1}{5}$ $\frac{2}{11}$ $\frac{2}{15}$
Each numerator is much less than half the denominator, so the fractions are close to 0.
closer to $\frac{1}{2}$
$\frac{5}{11}$ $\frac{4}{7}$ $\frac{9}{20}$
Each numerator is about half the denominator, so the fractions are close to $\frac{1}{2}$.
closer to 1
$\frac{9}{10}$ $\frac{16}{19}$ $\frac{6}{7}$
Each numerator is about the same as the denominator, so the fractions are close to 1.

EXAMPLE 1 Estimating Fractions

Estimate each sum or difference by rounding to 0, $\frac{1}{2}$, or 1.

A $\frac{8}{9} + \frac{2}{11}$

$\frac{8}{9} + \frac{2}{11}$ *Think: $\frac{8}{9}$ rounds to 1 and $\frac{2}{11}$ rounds to 0.*

$1 + 0 = 1$

$\frac{8}{9} + \frac{2}{11}$ is about 1.

B $\frac{7}{12} - \frac{8}{15}$

$\frac{7}{12} - \frac{8}{15}$ *Think: $\frac{7}{12}$ rounds to $\frac{1}{2}$ and $\frac{8}{15}$ rounds to $\frac{1}{2}$.*

$\frac{1}{2} - \frac{1}{2} = 0$

$\frac{7}{12} - \frac{8}{15}$ is about 0.

1 Introduce

Alternate Opener

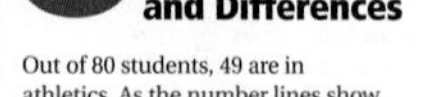

EXPLORATION

4-9 Estimating Fraction Sums and Differences

Out of 80 students, 49 are in athletics. As the number lines show, approximately half the students are in athletics. In other words, $\frac{49}{80}$ is close to $\frac{1}{2}$.

0 49 80
0 $\frac{1}{2}$ 1

Use a number line to determine whether each fraction is closest to 0, $\frac{1}{2}$, or 1.

1. $\frac{79}{99}$
2. $\frac{22}{213}$
3. $\frac{15}{27}$
4. $\frac{22}{45}$
5. $\frac{300}{475}$
6. $\frac{400}{475}$

Use the estimates you found in numbers 1–6 to estimate each sum or difference.

7. $\frac{79}{99} + \frac{15}{27}$
8. $\frac{22}{213} + \frac{22}{45}$
9. $\frac{300}{475} - \frac{22}{45}$
10. $\frac{15}{27} - \frac{22}{45}$

Think and Discuss

11. **Discuss** your strategies for determining whether the fractions were closest to 0, $\frac{1}{2}$, or 1.
12. **Explain** how you know $\frac{237}{475}$ is less than $\frac{1}{2}$.

Motivate

ENGLISH LANGUAGE LEARNERS

Ask students what it means to *estimate*. Possible answer: to find an answer that is close to the exact answer. Have students estimate whole-number sums and differences and explain how they estimated each.

Explorations and answers are provided in *Alternate Openers: Explorations Transparencies.*

You can also estimate by rounding mixed numbers. Compare the mixed number to the two nearest whole numbers and the nearest $\frac{1}{2}$.

Does $10\frac{3}{10}$ round to 10, $10\frac{1}{2}$, or 11?

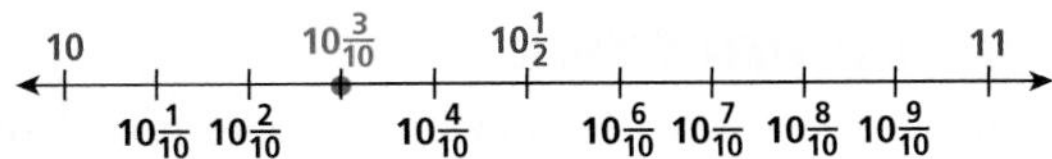

The mixed number $10\frac{3}{10}$ rounds to $10\frac{1}{2}$.

EXAMPLE 2 *Sports Application*

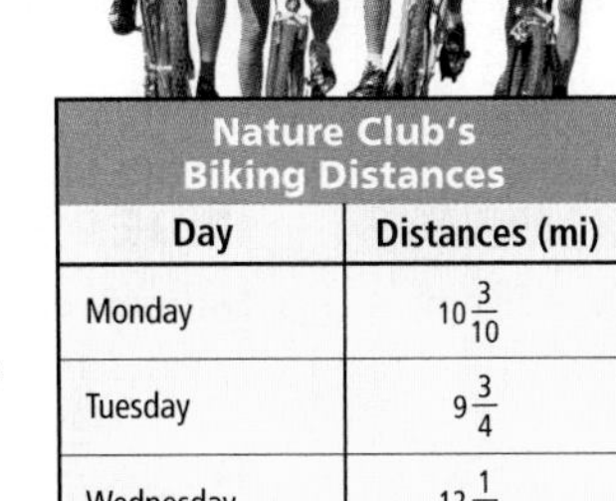

A **About how far did the Nature Club ride on Monday and Tuesday?**

$10\frac{3}{10} + 9\frac{3}{4}$

$10\frac{1}{2} + 10 = 20\frac{1}{2}$

They rode about $20\frac{1}{2}$ miles.

Nature Club's Biking Distances	
Day	Distances (mi)
Monday	$10\frac{3}{10}$
Tuesday	$9\frac{3}{4}$
Wednesday	$12\frac{1}{4}$
Thursday	$4\frac{7}{10}$

B **About how much farther did the Nature Club ride on Wednesday than on Thursday?**

$12\frac{1}{4} - 4\frac{7}{10}$

$12\frac{1}{2} - 4\frac{1}{2} = 8$

They rode about 8 miles farther on Wednesday than on Thursday.

Helpful Hint

$\frac{1}{4}$ is halfway between 0 and $\frac{1}{2}$. Round $\frac{1}{4}$ up to $\frac{1}{2}$.

C **Estimate the total distance that the Nature Club rode on Monday, Tuesday, and Wednesday.**

$10\frac{3}{10} + 9\frac{3}{4} + 12\frac{1}{4}$

$10\frac{1}{2} + 10 + 12\frac{1}{2} = 33$

They rode about 33 miles.

Answers to *Think and Discuss:*

1. 1; 0; $\frac{1}{2}$
2. If the fraction part of the mixed number is less than $\frac{1}{2}$, drop the fraction to round to the whole number. If the fraction part of the mixed number is $\frac{1}{2}$ or greater, round up to the next whole number.
3. Yes, they rode a total of about 10 + 10 + 12 + 5 = 37 miles.

Think and Discuss

GPS M6P3.b

1. **Tell** whether each fraction rounds to 0, $\frac{1}{2}$, or 1: $\frac{5}{6}, \frac{2}{15}, \frac{7}{13}$.
2. **Explain** how to round mixed numbers to the nearest whole number.
3. **Determine** whether the Nature Club met their goal to ride at least 35 total miles.

Students may be confused by the concept of rounding to a fraction, because they have more practice with rounding to whole numbers. Spend as much time as needed explaining rounding to a fraction.

Power Presentations with PowerPoint®

Additional Examples

Example 1

Estimate each sum or difference by rounding to 0, $\frac{1}{2}$, or 1.

A. $\frac{6}{7} + \frac{3}{8}$ about $1\frac{1}{2}$

B. $\frac{9}{10} - \frac{7}{8}$ about 0

Example 2

Tosha's Walking Distances	
Day	Distance (miles)
Tuesday	$5\frac{1}{10}$
Thursday	$4\frac{7}{8}$
Saturday	$6\frac{3}{7}$
Sunday	$8\frac{9}{10}$

A. About how far did Tosha walk on Tuesday and Thursday? about 10 miles

B. About how much farther did Tosha walk on Sunday than on Thursday? about 4 miles farther

C. Estimate the total distance Tosha walked on Thursday, Saturday, and Sunday. about $20\frac{1}{2}$ miles

Also available on transparency

2 Teach

Guided Instruction

In this lesson, students learn to estimate sums and differences of fractions and mixed numbers. First teach students the rule for rounding fractional parts. If the numerator is much less than half the denominator, the fraction is close to 0. If the numerator is about half the denominator, the fraction is close to $\frac{1}{2}$. If the numerator is about the same as the denominator, the fraction is close to 1. You may use the Teaching Transparency. Then teach them to estimate fraction sums and differences and then mixed-number sums and differences.

Reaching All Learners

Through Curriculum Integration

Language Arts Discuss with students that many words in the English language have Latin origins. The word *fraction* comes from the Latin word *frangere*, which means "to break." The word *estimate* comes from the Latin word *aestimatus*, which means "to value." Encourage students to research the origins of other math terms and to report to the class what they discover.

3 Close

Summarize

Close the lesson by reviewing with students how to estimate fraction sums and differences: Round each fraction to 0, $\frac{1}{2}$, or 1, and then add or subtract the rounded fractions. Have students estimate a sum and a difference to make sure they understand the process.

4-9 Exercises

Assignment Guide

If you finished Example 1 assign:
Average 1–4, 37–43
Advanced 7–10, 37–43

If you finished Example 2 assign:
Average 1–21, 27–33, 37–43
Advanced 7–30, 34–43

Homework Quick Check

Quickly check key concepts.
Exercises: 10, 12, 16, 18, 22

Math Background

To estimate the sum of many mixed numbers or decimal numbers, the following strategy is both efficient and effective: If there are n addends in all, add the whole parts only and then add $\frac{n}{2}$ to the sum of the whole parts.

The rationale behind the method is as follows: If there are many addends, the fractional or decimal parts should be distributed in a fairly uniform manner between 0 and 1. Therefore the average value of a fractional or decimal part of a number should be near $\frac{1}{2}$. Because there are n addends in all, the sum of these parts should be near $n \cdot \frac{1}{2} = \frac{n}{2}$.

Answers

24. Possible answer: a task requiring a number of people

Georgia Performance Standards

M6P3.a Organize and consolidate their mathematical thinking through communication.

M6P4.c Recognize and apply mathematics in contexts outside of mathematics.

4-9 Exercises

Georgia Performance Standards
M6P3.a, M6P4.c

Homework Help Online
KEYWORD: MR7 4-9
Parent Resources Online
KEYWORD: MR7 Parent

GUIDED PRACTICE

See Example 1 Estimate each sum or difference by rounding to 0, $\frac{1}{2}$, or 1.

1. $\frac{8}{9} + \frac{1}{6}$ about 1
2. $\frac{11}{12} - \frac{4}{9}$ about $\frac{1}{2}$
3. $\frac{3}{7} + \frac{1}{12}$ about $\frac{1}{2}$
4. $\frac{6}{13} - \frac{2}{5}$ about 0

See Example 2 Use the table for Exercises 5 and 6.

5. About how far did Mark run during week 1 and week 2? 16 miles
6. About how much farther did Mark run during week 2 than during week 3? 1 mile

Mark's Running Distances

Week	Distance (mi)
1	$8\frac{3}{4}$
2	$7\frac{1}{5}$
3	$5\frac{5}{6}$

INDEPENDENT PRACTICE

See Example 1 Estimate each sum or difference by rounding to 0, $\frac{1}{2}$, or 1.

7. $\frac{7}{8} - \frac{3}{8}$ about $\frac{1}{2}$
8. $\frac{3}{10} + \frac{3}{4}$ about $1\frac{1}{2}$
9. $\frac{5}{6} - \frac{7}{8}$ about 0
10. $\frac{7}{10} + \frac{1}{6}$ about 1
11. $\frac{3}{4} + \frac{7}{10}$ about $1\frac{1}{2}$
12. $\frac{9}{20} - \frac{1}{6}$ about $\frac{1}{2}$
13. $\frac{8}{9} + \frac{4}{5}$ about 2
14. $\frac{19}{20} + \frac{9}{10}$ about 2

See Example 2 Use the table for Exercises 15–17.

15. About how much do the meteorites in Brenham and Goose Lake weigh together? 4 tons
16. About how much more does the meteorite in Willamette weigh than the meteorite in Norton County? $15\frac{1}{2}$ tons
17. About how much do the two meteorites in Kansas weigh together? $3\frac{1}{2}$ tons

Meteorites in the United States

Location	Weight (tons)
Willamette, AZ	$16\frac{1}{2}$
Brenham, KS	$2\frac{3}{5}$
Goose Lake, CA	$1\frac{3}{10}$
Norton County, KS	$1\frac{1}{10}$

PRACTICE AND PROBLEM SOLVING

CRCT GPS
Extra Practice p. 721

Estimate each sum or difference to compare. Write < or >.

18. $\frac{5}{6} + \frac{7}{9}$ ■ 3 <
19. $2\frac{8}{15} - 1\frac{1}{11}$ ■ 1 >
20. $1\frac{2}{21} + \frac{3}{7}$ ■ 2 <
21. $1\frac{7}{13} - \frac{8}{9}$ ■ 1 <
22. $3\frac{2}{10} + 2\frac{2}{5}$ ■ 6 <
23. $4\frac{6}{9} - 2\frac{3}{19}$ ■ 2 >

24. **Critical Thinking** Describe a situation in which it is better to round a mixed number up to the next whole number even if the fraction in the mixed number is closer to $\frac{1}{2}$ than 1.

Estimate.

25. $\frac{7}{8} + \frac{4}{7} + \frac{7}{13}$ about 2
26. $\frac{6}{11} + \frac{9}{17} + \frac{3}{5}$ about $1\frac{1}{2}$
27. $\frac{8}{9} + \frac{3}{4} + \frac{9}{10}$ about 3
28. $1\frac{5}{8} + 2\frac{1}{15} + 2\frac{12}{13}$ about $6\frac{1}{2}$
29. $4\frac{11}{12} + 3\frac{1}{19} + 5\frac{4}{7}$ about $13\frac{1}{2}$
30. $10\frac{1}{9} + 8\frac{5}{9} + 11\frac{13}{14}$ about $30\frac{1}{2}$

RETEACH 4-9

LESSON 4-9 **Reteach**
Estimating Fraction Sums and Differences

You can use number lines to help you estimate fraction sums and differences.

To estimate the sum of $\frac{5}{6}$ and $\frac{1}{3}$, locate each fraction on a number line. Then round each fraction to 0, $\frac{1}{2}$, or 1.

$\frac{5}{6} + \frac{1}{3} \approx$

$1 + \frac{1}{2} = 1\frac{1}{2}$

So, $\frac{5}{6} + \frac{1}{3}$ is about $1\frac{1}{2}$.

To estimate the difference between $\frac{7}{8}$ and $\frac{2}{4}$, locate each fraction on a number line. Then round each fraction to 0, $\frac{1}{2}$, or 1.

$\frac{7}{8} - \frac{2}{4} \approx$

$1 - \frac{1}{2} = \frac{1}{2}$

So, $\frac{7}{8} - \frac{2}{4}$ is about $\frac{1}{2}$.

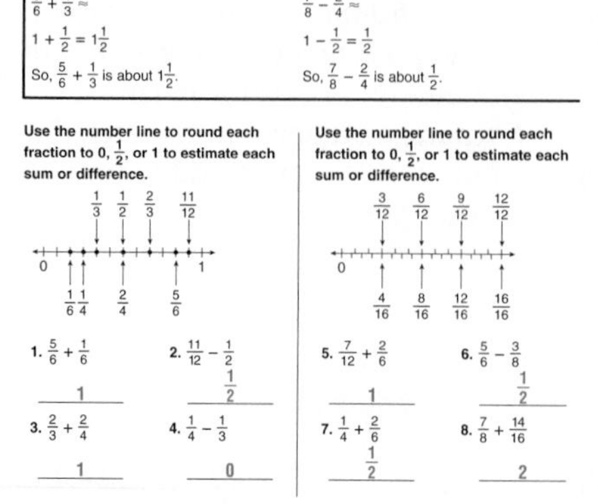

Use the number line to round each fraction to 0, $\frac{1}{2}$, or 1 to estimate each sum or difference.

1. $\frac{5}{6} + \frac{1}{6}$ 1
2. $\frac{11}{12} - \frac{1}{2}$ $\frac{1}{2}$
3. $\frac{2}{3} + \frac{2}{4}$ 1
4. $\frac{1}{4} - \frac{1}{3}$ 0

Use the number line to round each fraction to 0, $\frac{1}{2}$, or 1 to estimate each sum or difference.

5. $\frac{7}{12} + \frac{2}{6}$ 1
6. $\frac{5}{6} - \frac{3}{8}$ $\frac{1}{2}$
7. $\frac{1}{4} + \frac{2}{6}$ $\frac{1}{2}$
8. $\frac{7}{8} + \frac{14}{16}$ 2

PRACTICE 4-9

LESSON 4-9 **Practice B**
Estimating Fraction Sums and Differences

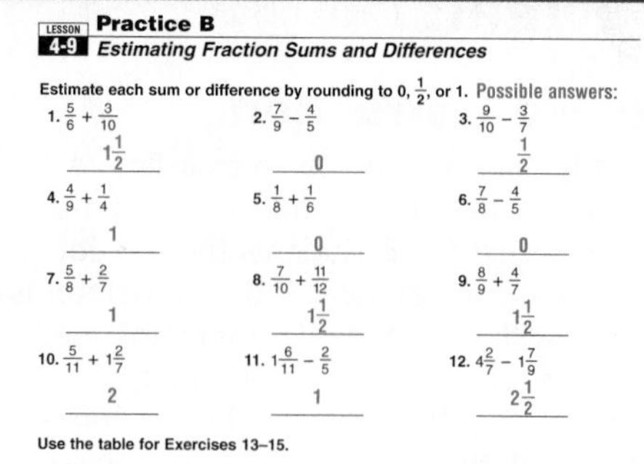

Estimate each sum or difference by rounding to 0, $\frac{1}{2}$, or 1. Possible answers:

1. $\frac{5}{6} + \frac{3}{10}$ $1\frac{1}{2}$
2. $\frac{7}{9} - \frac{4}{5}$ 0
3. $\frac{9}{10} - \frac{3}{7}$ $\frac{1}{2}$
4. $\frac{4}{9} + \frac{1}{4}$ 1
5. $\frac{1}{8} + \frac{1}{6}$ 0
6. $\frac{7}{8} - \frac{4}{5}$ 0
7. $\frac{5}{8} + \frac{2}{7}$ 1
8. $\frac{7}{10} + \frac{11}{12}$ $1\frac{1}{2}$
9. $\frac{8}{9} + \frac{4}{7}$ $1\frac{1}{2}$
10. $\frac{5}{11} + 1\frac{2}{7}$ 2
11. $1\frac{6}{11} - \frac{2}{5}$ 1
12. $4\frac{2}{7} - 1\frac{7}{9}$ $2\frac{1}{2}$

Use the table for Exercises 13–15.

Fruit Punch

Ingredient	Amount (cups)
Orange juice	$4\frac{3}{5}$
Cranberry juice	$2\frac{1}{4}$
Ginger ale	$\frac{7}{8}$

13. About how much more orange juice than ginger ale is used in the punch? about $3\frac{1}{2}$ cups
14. About how much juice is used in the punch? about 7 cups
15. About how many cups of fruit punch does this recipe make? about 8 cups
16. Damonte rolled the medicine ball $9\frac{3}{4}$ feet. Zachary rolled it $9\frac{7}{12}$ feet. Who rolled the medicine ball the farthest? About how much farther? Damonte; about $\frac{1}{2}$ foot farther
17. Sara ran $5\frac{6}{7}$ miles on Monday and $4\frac{1}{4}$ miles on Tuesday. About how many miles did she run in all during those two days? about $10\frac{1}{2}$ miles

Life Science Use an inch ruler for Exercises 31–32. Measure to the nearest $\frac{1}{4}$ inch.

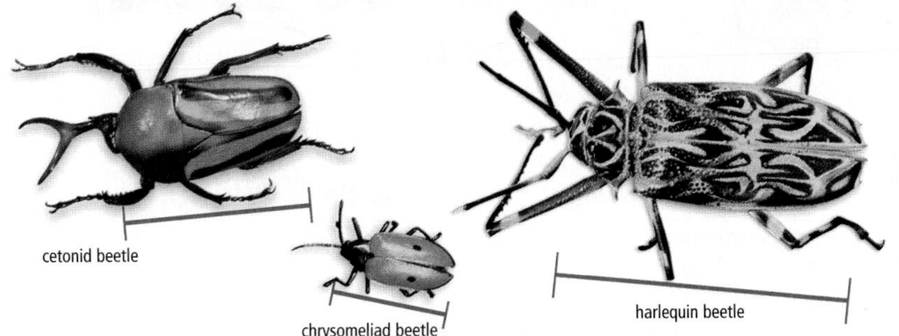

31. About how much longer is the harlequin beetle than the cetonid beetle? $\frac{1}{2}$ in.
32. About how much longer is the harlequin beetle than the chrysomeliad beetle? 1 in.
33. Use the table to estimate the total weekly snowfall. about $9\frac{1}{2}$ in.

Day	Mon	Tue	Wed	Thu	Fri	Sat	Sun
Snowfall (in.)	$3\frac{4}{7}$	$\frac{7}{8}$	0	$2\frac{1}{6}$	$\frac{2}{11}$	$1\frac{9}{20}$	$1\frac{4}{7}$

34. **Write a Problem** Write a problem about a trip that can be solved by estimating fractions. Exchange with a classmate and solve.
35. **Write About It** Explain how to estimate the sum of two mixed numbers. Give an example to explain your answer.
36. **Challenge** Estimate. $\left[5\frac{7}{8} - 2\frac{3}{20}\right] + 1\frac{4}{7}$ about $5\frac{1}{2}$

CRCT Prep • GPS Support • Spiral Review

37. **Multiple Choice** Larry ran $3\frac{1}{3}$ miles on Monday and $5\frac{3}{4}$ miles on Tuesday. About how many miles did Larry run on Monday and Tuesday?

Ⓐ 8 (B) 9 Ⓒ 10 Ⓓ 11

38. **Multiple Choice** Marie used $2\frac{3}{5}$ cups of flour for a recipe. Linda used $1\frac{1}{4}$ cups of flour for a recipe. About how many more cups of flour did Marie use than Linda?

Ⓕ 1 (G) 2 Ⓗ 3 Ⓙ 4

Evaluate each expression. (Lesson 1-4)

39. $6 \times (21 - 15) \div 12$ 3
40. $72 \div 8 + 2^3 \times 5 - 19$ 30
41. $5 + (6 - 1) \times 2 \div 2$ 10

Write an expression for the missing value in each table. (Lesson 2-3)

42.

Games Played	2	4	6	8	n
Points Scored	14	28	42	56	▢

$7n$

43.

Month	1	3	5	7	n
Hours Worked	6	8	10	12	▢

$n + 5$

CHALLENGE 4-9

LESSON 4-9 **Challenge**
What's on the Menu?

The menu below shows the average amounts of food most Americans eat each day. Use the menu to complete the diet estimation chart that follows.

Average American Daily Menu

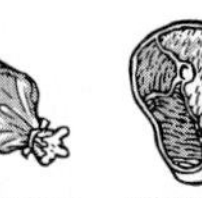
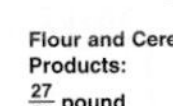
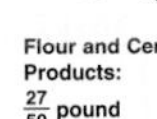
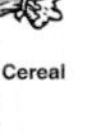

Dairy Products: $1\frac{2}{5}$ pounds

Processed Fruits and Vegetables: $1\frac{1}{20}$ pounds

Flour and Cereal Products: $\frac{27}{50}$ pound

Red Meat: $\frac{9}{25}$ pound

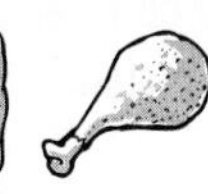
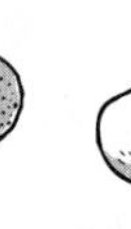

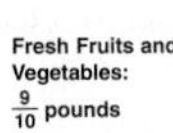
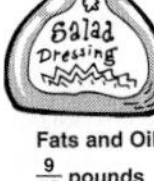

Sweetener Products: $\frac{21}{50}$ pound

Poultry: $\frac{9}{50}$ pounds

Fresh Fruits and Vegetables: $\frac{9}{10}$ pounds

Fats and Oils: $\frac{9}{50}$ pounds

Estimated American Diet

Foods	Estimated Daily Consumption
Red meat and poultry	about $\frac{1}{2}$ pound
Fruits and vegetables	about 2 pounds
Sweetener products and fats and oils	about $\frac{1}{2}$ pound
Dairy and flour and cereal products	about 2 pounds
Total Daily Food Consumption:	about 5 pounds

PROBLEM SOLVING 4-9

LESSON 4-9 **Problem Solving**
Estimating Fraction Sums and Differences

Use the table to answer the questions. Possible answers:

Portland, Oregon, Average Monthly Rainfall

Month	Jan	Feb	Mar	Apr	May	Jun	Jul	Aug	Sep	Oct	Nov	Dec
Rain (in.)	$5\frac{2}{5}$	$3\frac{9}{10}$	$3\frac{3}{5}$	$2\frac{2}{5}$	$2\frac{1}{10}$	$1\frac{1}{2}$	$\frac{3}{5}$	$1\frac{1}{10}$	$1\frac{4}{5}$	$2\frac{7}{10}$	$5\frac{3}{10}$	$6\frac{1}{10}$

1. About how much does it rain in Portland in January and February combined?
   about $9\frac{1}{2}$ inches
2. About how much more does it rain in Portland in October than in September?
   about 1 inch more
3. In most years, about how much rain does Portland receive from May through July?
   about 4 inches
4. What is the difference between Portland's average rainfall in March and May?
   about $1\frac{1}{2}$ inches

Circle the letter of the correct answer.

5. What is the difference in rainfall between Portland's rainiest and driest months?
   A about $2\frac{1}{2}$ inches
   (B) about 5 inches
   C about $6\frac{1}{2}$ inches
   D about $7\frac{1}{2}$ inches
6. About how much rain does Portland receive in most years all together?
   F about $25\frac{1}{2}$ inches
   G about $30\frac{1}{2}$ inches
   H about $32\frac{1}{2}$ inches
   (J) about $36\frac{1}{2}$ inches
7. About how much rain does Portland receive during its three rainiest months all together?
   (A) about 17 inches
   B about 16 inches
   C about 18 inches
   D about 15 inches
8. In which month in Portland can you expect about $\frac{1}{2}$ inch less rainfall than in June?
   F May
   G July
   H September
   (J) August

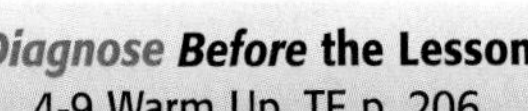

ONGOING ASSESSMENT and INTERVENTION

Diagnose ***Before*** **the Lesson**
4-9 Warm Up, TE p. 206

Monitor ***During*** **the Lesson**
4-9 Know-It Notebook
4-9 Questioning Strategies

Assess ***After*** **the Lesson**
4-9 Lesson Quiz, TE p. 209

Answers

34. Possible answer: Bob will drive 426 miles to visit his grandmother. He drives $\frac{3}{8}$ of the trip and stops to buy gasoline. Then Bob drives $\frac{1}{5}$ of the trip before he makes a rest stop. About how much of the trip has Bob driven?
35. See p. A3.

TEST PREP DOCTOR In Exercises 37 and 38, students will need to read each exercise carefully. They should round to the nearest whole number and get an estimate instead of trying to solve the problem exactly.

Journal

Have students describe situations when fraction sums and differences may be estimated as well as situations when an exact sum or difference would be needed.

Power Presentations with PowerPoint®

4-9 Lesson Quiz

Estimate each sum or difference by rounding to 0, $\frac{1}{2}$, or 1.

1. $\frac{9}{10} - \frac{2}{5}$ $\frac{1}{2}$
2. $\frac{3}{8} + \frac{8}{9}$ $1\frac{1}{2}$
3. $\frac{10}{11} - \frac{8}{9}$ 0
4. $\frac{1}{4} + \frac{8}{15}$ 1
5. The conservation club picked up trash along the road for three weeks. The table shows the number of pounds of trash that was collected. About how many pounds did they collect in weeks 2 and 3?

Week	Pounds Picked Up
1	$18\frac{1}{2}$
2	$16\frac{1}{3}$
3	$20\frac{9}{10}$

37 pounds

Also available on transparency

Organizer

Objective: Assess students' mastery of concepts and skills in Lessons 4-7 through 4-9.

Resources

Assessment Resources
Section 4C Quiz

Test & Practice Generator
One-Stop Planner®

INTERVENTION

Resources

***Ready to Go On? Intervention and Enrichment* Worksheets**

***Ready to Go On?* CD-ROM**

***Ready to Go On?* Online**

my.hrw.com

CHAPTER 4

SECTION 4C

READY TO GO ON?

Quiz for Lessons 4-7 Through 4-9

4-7 Comparing and Ordering Fractions

Compare. Write <, >, or =.

1. $\frac{3}{4}$ ■ $\frac{2}{3}$ >
2. $\frac{7}{9}$ ■ $\frac{5}{6}$ <
3. $\frac{4}{9}$ ■ $\frac{4}{7}$ <
4. $\frac{5}{11}$ ■ $\frac{3}{5}$ <

Order the fractions from least to greatest.

5. $\frac{5}{8}, \frac{1}{2}, \frac{3}{4}$ $\frac{1}{2}, \frac{5}{8}, \frac{3}{4}$
6. $\frac{3}{4}, \frac{3}{5}, \frac{7}{10}$ $\frac{3}{5}, \frac{7}{10}, \frac{3}{4}$
7. $\frac{1}{3}, \frac{3}{8}, \frac{1}{4}$ $\frac{1}{4}, \frac{1}{3}, \frac{3}{8}$
8. $\frac{2}{5}, \frac{4}{9}, \frac{11}{15}$ $\frac{2}{5}, \frac{4}{9}, \frac{11}{15}$
9. Mrs. Wilson split a bag of marbles between her three sons. Ralph got $\frac{1}{10}$, Pete got $\frac{1}{2}$, and Jon got $\frac{8}{20}$. Who got the most marbles? Pete

4-8 Adding and Subtracting with Like Denominators

10. The average growth rate for human hair is $\frac{1}{2}$ inch per month. On average, how much hair will a person grow in 3 months? Write your answer in simplest form. $\frac{3}{2}$ or $1\frac{1}{2}$
11. A recipe for fruit salad calls for $\frac{1}{5}$ cup coconut. Ryan wants to double the recipe. How much coconut should he use? Write your answer in simplest form. $\frac{2}{5}$

Subtract. Write each answer in simplest form.

12. $1 - \frac{3}{4}$ $\frac{1}{4}$
13. $6\frac{5}{9} - 5\frac{1}{9}$ $1\frac{4}{9}$
14. $10\frac{7}{16} - 4\frac{3}{16}$ $6\frac{1}{4}$
15. $5\frac{8}{9} - 1\frac{7}{9}$ $4\frac{1}{9}$
16. $8\frac{4}{17} - 6\frac{2}{17}$ $2\frac{2}{17}$
17. $1 - \frac{7}{8}$ $\frac{1}{8}$

Evaluate each expression for $x = \frac{5}{7}$. Write your answer in simplest form.

18. $x + 2\frac{1}{7}$ $2\frac{6}{7}$
19. $x - \frac{3}{7}$ $\frac{2}{7}$
20. $10 + x$ $10\frac{5}{7}$
21. $3\frac{2}{7} + x$ 4
22. $6\frac{6}{7} - x$ $6\frac{1}{7}$
23. $x + \frac{2}{7}$ 1

4-9 Estimating Fraction Sums and Differences

Estimate each sum or difference.

24. $\frac{3}{4} - \frac{1}{10}$ about 1
25. $\frac{7}{9} + \frac{7}{9}$ about 2
26. $\frac{15}{16} - \frac{4}{5}$ about 0
27. $3\frac{7}{8} - 1\frac{1}{10}$ about 3

Use the table for problems 28–30.

28. About how far did Mrs. Ping walk during week 1 and week 2? about 6 mi
29. About how much farther did Mrs. Ping walk in week 2 than in week 3? about $\frac{1}{2}$ mi
30. About how far did Mrs. Ping walk during the three weeks? about $8\frac{1}{2}$ mi

Mrs. Ping's Walking Distances

Week	Distance (mi)
1	$2\frac{3}{4}$
2	$3\frac{1}{8}$
3	$2\frac{4}{7}$

Ready to Go On?

READY TO GO ON?

Diagnose and Prescribe

NO INTERVENE

Ready to Go On? Intervention	*Ready to Go On? Intervention*, Section 4C		
	Worksheets	CD-ROM	Online
Lesson 4-7	4-7 Intervention	Activity 4-7	Diagnose and Prescribe Online
Lesson 4-8	4-8 Intervention	Activity 4-8	
Lesson 4-9	4-9 Intervention	Activity 4-9	

***Ready to Go On? Enrichment*, Section 4C**

Worksheets

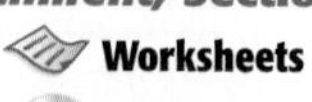

CD-ROM

Online

MULTI-STEP TEST PREP

CHAPTER 4

A Party with Palm Trees

Jamal and Sarah are planning an end-of-year party for the Spanish Club. They want it to have a tropical theme.

1. There will be 16 girls and 12 boys at the party. Jamal wants to set up the tables so that every table has the same number of girls and the same number of boys. How many tables will there be? How many girls and boys will be at each table?
   4 tables; 4 girls and 3 boys
2. Sarah finds three recipes for fruit punch. She wants to choose the recipe that calls for the greatest amount of pineapple juice per serving. Which recipe should she choose? Explain.

3. Jamal thinks they should choose the recipe that makes the largest serving of punch. Which recipe should they choose in this case? Explain.
4. Each punch glass holds 2 cups of liquid. If they use the recipe that makes the largest serving, will there be room in each glass for ice? Explain.
   Yes; $2 - 1\frac{2}{3} = \frac{1}{3}$; there will be $\frac{1}{3}$ of the glass not filled.

Multi-Step Test Prep

MULTI-STEP TEST PREP

CHAPTER 4

Organizer

Objective: Assess students' ability to apply concepts and skills in Chapter 4 in a real-world format.

Online Edition

Resources

Middle School Assessments
www.mathtekstoolkit.org

Problem	Text Reference
1	Lesson 4-3
2	Lesson 4-7
3	Lesson 4-8
4	Lesson 4-8

Answers

2. Sea Breeze; possible answer: the amount of pineapple juice in Sea Breeze is $\frac{3}{4}$ cup, and $\frac{3}{4}$ cup is greater than $\frac{2}{3}$ cup and 0.5 cup.
3. Thirst Quencher; possible answer: when you add the amount of cups per recipe, Thirst Quencher has $1\frac{2}{3}$ cups, which is more than Sea Breeze at $1\frac{1}{4}$ cups and Tropical Mist at $1\frac{1}{2}$ cups.

INTERVENTION

Scaffolding Questions

1. How can you find the number of tables Jamal should set up? Find the GCF of 16 and 12. How do you find the GCF? Write the factors of 16 and 12 and choose the greatest number that appears in both lists.
2. How can you compare the amount of pineapple juice in each recipe? Convert the fractions to decimals, or compare the fractions $\frac{2}{3}$, $\frac{3}{4}$, and $\frac{1}{2}$.
3. What should you do in order to compare the serving sizes? Add the amounts of the ingredients in each recipe, then compare the sums. How do you add the fractions in the Thirst Quencher recipe? Add the numerators and keep the same denominator.
4. What subtraction problem do you need to solve to answer this question? $2 - 1\frac{2}{3}$. How can you solve it? Write it as $\frac{6}{3} - \frac{5}{3}$.

Extensions

1. How much pineapple juice is needed to make 5 servings of Thirst Quencher? $3\frac{1}{3}$ cups
2. Jamal has a quart (4 cups) of orange juice. Is this enough to make 6 servings of Thirst Quencher? yes

Extension

Pacing: Traditional 1 day
Block $\frac{1}{2}$ day

Objective: Students make Venn diagrams to describe number sets.

Online Edition

Using the Extension

In Lesson 4-2, students wrote prime factorizations of composite numbers. In this extension, students make Venn diagrams to describe number sets. Students will identify elements in sets and use Venn diagrams to analyze relationships between those sets.

EXTENSION

Sets of Numbers

Learn to make Venn diagrams to describe number sets.

Vocabulary
set
empty set
element
subset
intersection
union
Venn diagram

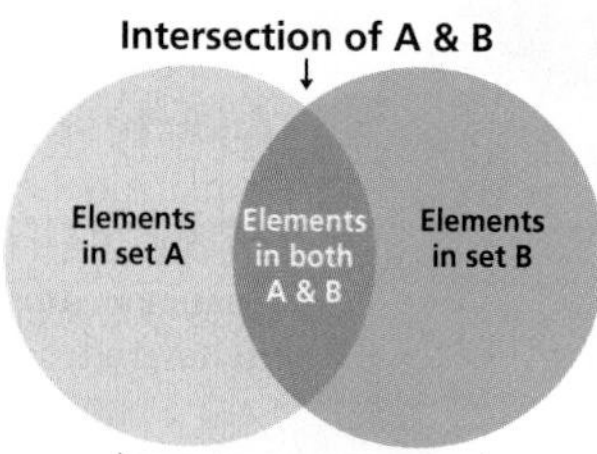

A group of items is called a **set**. The items in a set are called **elements**. In this chapter, you saw several sets of numbers, such as prime numbers, composite numbers, and factors.

In a **Venn diagram**, circles are used to show relationships between sets. The overlapped region represents elements that are in both set A *and* set B. This set is called the **intersection** of A and B. Elements that are in set A *or* set B make up the **union** of A and B.

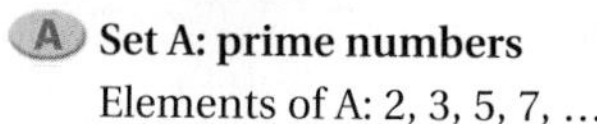

Identifying Elements and Drawing Venn Diagrams

Georgia Performance Standards

M6P5.a Create and use representations to organize, record, and communicate mathematical ideas. Also, M6P5.b, M6P5.c.

Identify the elements in each set. Then draw a Venn diagram. What is the intersection? What is the union?

A **Set A: prime numbers** **Set B: composite numbers**
Elements of A: 2, 3, 5, 7, ... Elements of B: 4, 6, 8, 9, ...

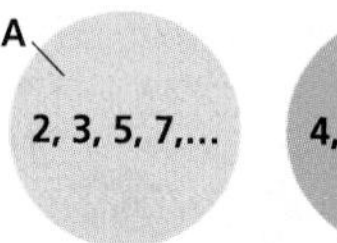

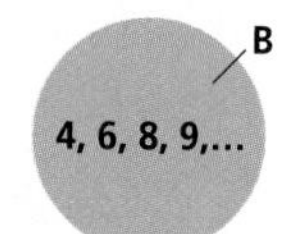

The circles do not overlap because no number is both prime and composite.

Intersection: none. When a set has no elements, it is called an **empty set**. The intersection of A and B is empty.

Union: all numbers that are prime *or* composite—all whole numbers except 0 and 1.

Set A: factors of 36 **Set B: factors of 24**
Elements of A: 1, 2, 3, 4, 6, 9, 12, 18, 36
Elements of B: 1, 2, 3, 4, 6, 8, 12, 24

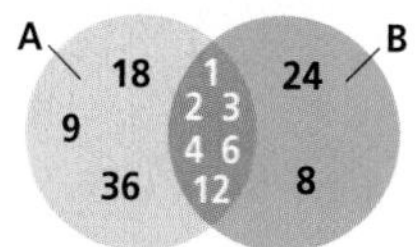

The circles overlap because some factors of 36 are also factors of 24.

Intersection: 1, 2, 3, 4, 6, 12 — *factors of 36* ***and*** *24*
Union: 1, 2, 3, 4, 6, 8, 9, 12, 18, 24, 36 — *factors of 36* ***or*** *24*

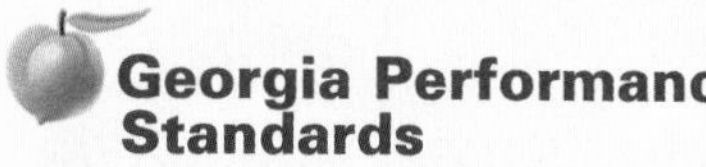

Georgia Performance Standards

M6P5.a Create and use representations to organize, record, and communicate mathematical ideas.

M6P5.b Select, apply, and translate among mathematical representations to solve problems.

M6P5.c Use representations to model and interpret physical, social, and mathematical phenomena.

1 Introduce

Motivate

Discuss with students how they use graphic organizers in Language Arts, Science, and Social Studies.

Relate how circles, lines, and boxes are used to show the relationships among ideas in the composition of an effective essay.

In science, dot diagrams and three-dimensional drawings are used to represent the way molecules are formed. Lines and arrows are used to illustrate the water cycle and food chain.

In Social studies, graphic organizers such as time lines are used to represent the sequence of events, and organizational flowcharts are used to illustrate the structure of governments and the process a bill goes through to become law.

Identify the elements in each set. Then draw a Venn diagram. What is the intersection? What is the union?

C Set A: factors of 36   Set B: factors of 12

Elements of A: 1, 2, 3, 4, 6, 9, 12, 18, 36

Elements of B: 1, 2, 3, 4, 6, 12

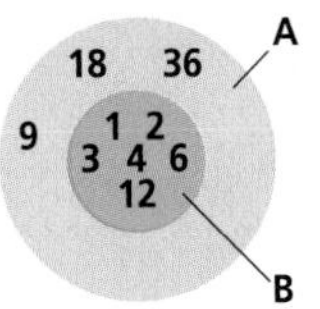

The circle for set B is entirely inside the circle for set A because all factors of 12 are also factors of 36.

Intersection: 1, 2, 3, 4, 6, 12   *factors of 36 **and** 12*

Union: 1, 2, 3, 4, 6, 9, 12, 18, 36   *factors of 36 **or** 12*

Helpful Hint

To decide whether set B is a subset of set A, ask yourself, "Is every element of B also in A?" If the answer is yes, then B is a subset of A.

Look at Example 1C. When one set is entirely contained in another set, we say the first set is a **subset** of the second set.

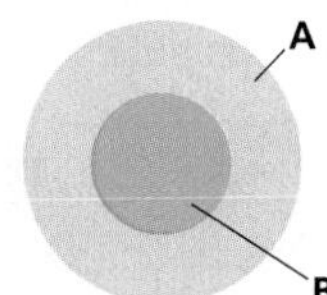

B is a subset of A.

EXTENSION Exercises

Identify the elements in each set. Then draw a Venn diagram. What is the intersection? What is the union?

1. Set A: even numbers
   Set B: odd numbers
2. Set A: factors of 18
   Set B: factors of 40
3. Set A: factors of 72
   Set B: factors of 36
4. Set A: even numbers
   Set B: composite numbers

Tell whether set A is a subset of set B.

5. Set A: whole numbers less than 10
   Set B: whole numbers less than 12
   yes
6. Set A: whole numbers less than 8
   Set B: whole numbers greater than 9
   no
7. Set A: prime numbers
   Set B: odd numbers
   no
8. Set A: numbers divisible by 6
   Set B: numbers divisible by 3
   yes

9. **Write About It** How could you use a Venn diagram to help find the greatest common factor of two numbers? Give an example.

10. **Challenge** How could you use a Venn diagram to help find the greatest common factor of three numbers? Give an example.

Additional Examples

Example 

Identify the elements in each set. Then draw a Venn diagram. What is the intersection? What is the union?

A. Set A: whole numbers
Set B: even numbers

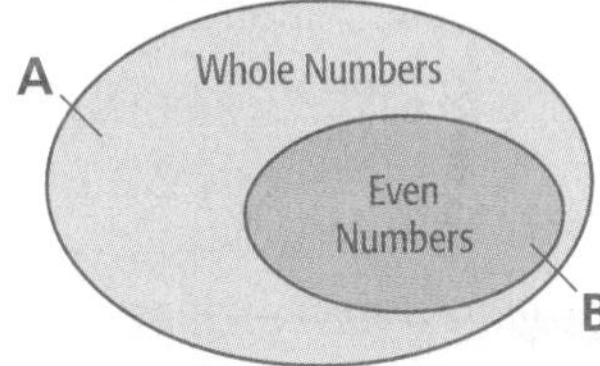

intersection: even number
union: whole numbers

B. Set A: factors of 12
Set B: factors of 18

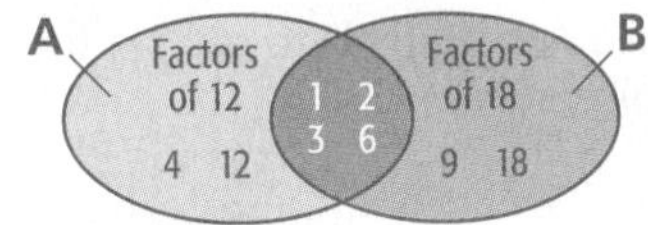

intersection: 1, 2, 3, 6
union: 1, 2, 3, 4, 6, 9, 12, 18

C. Set A: factors of 10
Set B: factors of 7

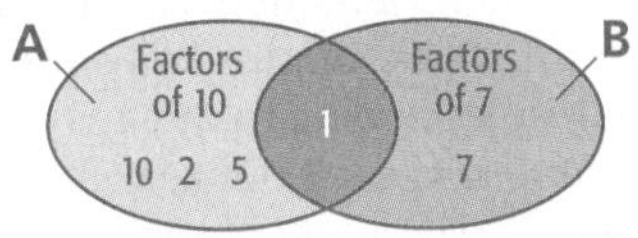

intersection: 1
union: 1, 2, 5, 7, 10

Also available on transparency

Answers

1–4, 9–10. See p. A3–A4.

2 Teach

Guided Instruction

In this extension, students learn to make Venn diagrams to describe number sets. First teach students to identify elements in two sets. Then teach students to draw a Venn diagram of the sets and find the union and intersection of those sets. Then explain that the empty set has no elements, the word *and* indicates intersection, and the word *or* indicates union. Finally, teach students to determine whether one set is a subset of another set.

ENGLISH LANGUAGE LEARNERS

Teaching Tip

Reading Math Remind students that in Venn diagrams, *or* means one or the other or both.

3 Close

Summarize

Have the students explain how to find the union and intersection of the set of factors of 6 and the set of factors of 12. Then have students explain whether one of those sets is a subset of the other.

Possible answer: The set of factors of 6 is 1, 2, 3, 6. The set of factors of 12 is 1, 2, 3, 4, 6, 12. The union is all the factors of both 6 and 12. The intersection is only the factors that appear in the diagrams for both 6 and 12. The union is 1, 2, 3, 4, 6, 12. The intersection is 1, 2, 3, 6. Because all the factors of 6 are factors of 12, the factors of six are a subset of the factors of 12.

Game Time

Organizer

Objective: Participate in games to practice and apply skills learned in Chapter 4.

 **Online Edition**

Resources

 ***Chapter 4 Resource Book***
Puzzles, Twisters, & Teasers

Riddle Me This

Purpose: To apply divisibility rules to solving a riddle

Discuss Ask students to explain the divisibility rule for 3. Find the sum of the digits in the number. If the sum is divisible by 3, then the number is divisible by 3.

Extend Challenge students to create a grid similar to the one in this activity. Have them design the grid so that each square contains a number that a classmate must check for divisibility and must shade according to the answer. Have the results spell out a word or message. Check students' work.

On a Roll

Purpose: To use knowledge of fractions to play a game

Materials: Number cubes (Manipulatives Kit)

Discuss When a student has completed the game board, have the student explain how he or she knows that the squares have been filled in correctly.

Extend Have students create a new game board using different expressions in each square. For example, they could use the following:

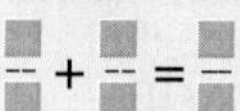

Then have them play the game using their new game boards.

Game Time

Riddle Me This

"When you go from there to here,
you'll find I disappear.
Go from here to there, and then
you'll see me again.
What am I?" **the letter *T***

To solve this riddle, copy the square below. If a number is divisible by 3, color that box red. Remember the divisibility rule for 3. If a number is not divisible by 3, color that box blue.

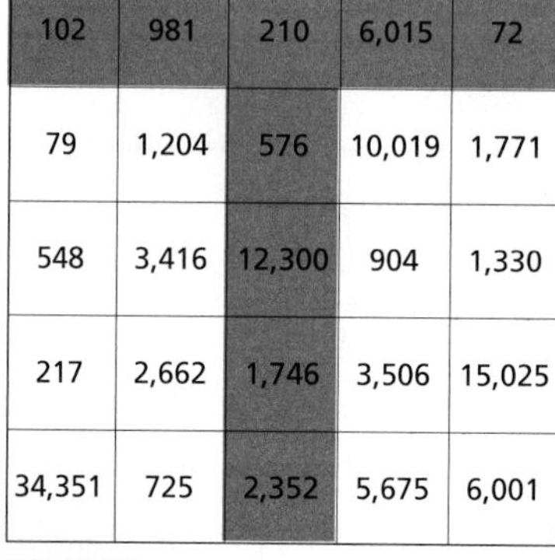

102	981	210	6,015	72
79	1,204	576	10,019	1,771
548	3,416	12,300	904	1,330
217	2,662	1,746	3,506	15,025
34,351	725	2,352	5,675	6,001

On a Roll

The object is to be the first person to fill in all the squares on your game board.

On your turn, roll a number cube and record the number rolled in any blank square on your game board. Once you have placed a number in a square, you cannot move that number. If you cannot place the number in a square, then your turn is over. The winner is the first player to complete their game board correctly.

go.hrw.com
Game Time Extra
KEYWORD: MR7 Games

A complete copy of the rules and game pieces are available online.

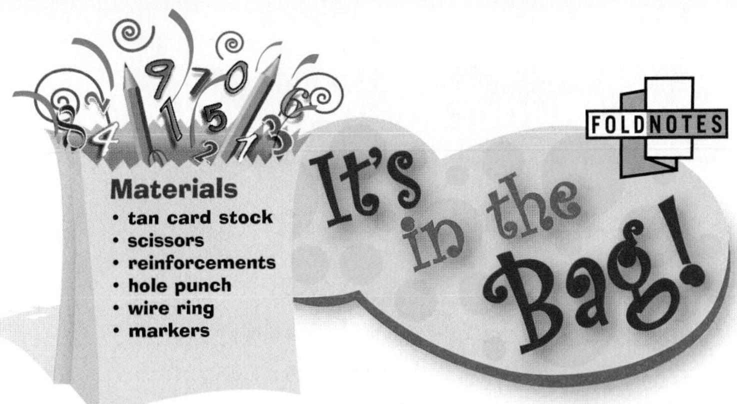

PROJECT Spec-Tag-Ular Number Theory

Tags will help you keep notes about number theory and fractions on an easy-to-use reference ring.

Directions

1. Make tags by cutting ten rectangles from card stock, each approximately $2\frac{3}{4}$ inches by $1\frac{1}{2}$ inches.
2. Use scissors to clip off two corners at the end of each tag. **Figure A**
3. Punch a hole between the clipped corners of each tag. Put a reinforcement around the hole on both sides of the tag. **Figure B**
4. Hook all of the tags together on a wire ring. On one of the tags, write the number and name of the chapter. **Figure C**

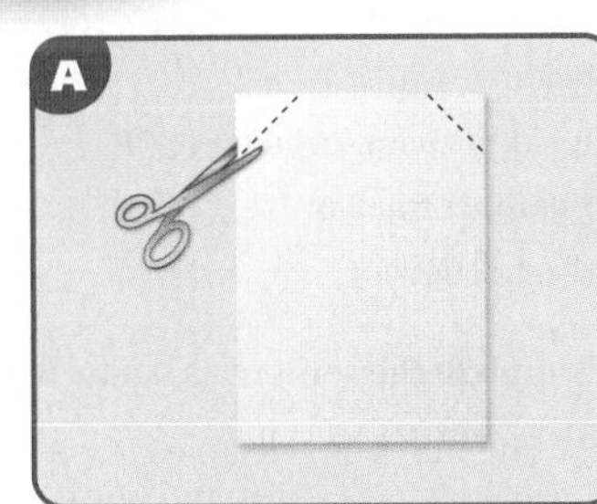

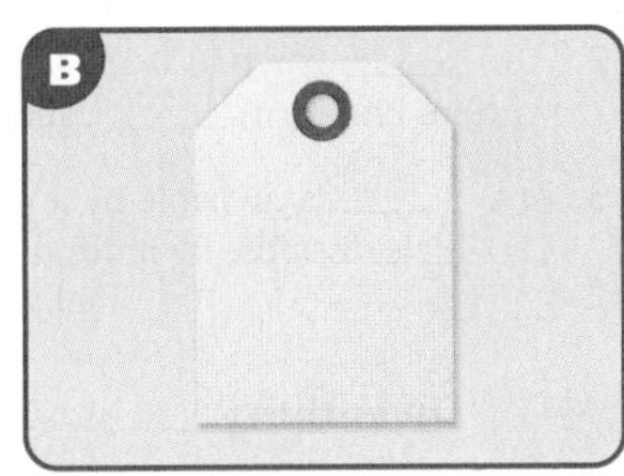

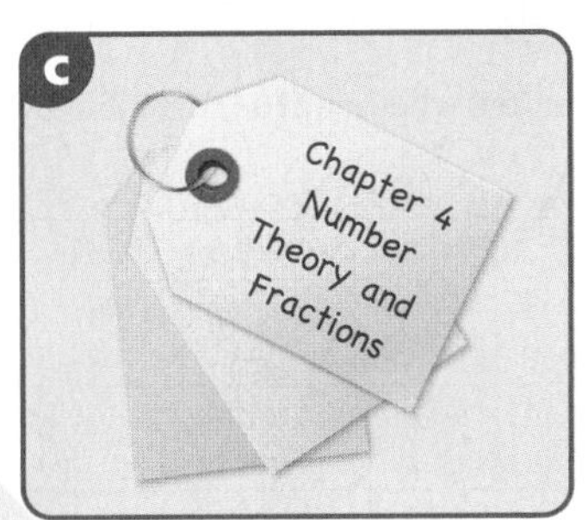

Taking Note of the Math

On each tag, write a divisibility rule from the chapter. You can also use the tags to record important facts about fractions.

Organizer

Objective: Make tags on which to record notes about number theory and fractions.

Materials: tan cardstock, scissors, reinforcements, hole punch, wire ring, markers

Online Edition

Using the Page

Preparing the Materials
Tell students they will be cutting out ten rectangular tags, each approximately $2\frac{3}{4}$ in. by $1\frac{1}{2}$ in. Ask them to calculate the size of the sheet of cardstock that they should start with.

Making the Project
To speed things along, remind students that they can stack several tags and punch a hole through all of them at the same time.

Extending the Project
Have students make extra tags. Throughout the remainder of the course, students can add tags with additional notes on fractions, decimals, and percents. Students can use extra rings to sort their notes by chapter.

Tips from the Bag Ladies!

To save a little time, you can buy ready-made tags at an office-supply store. The tags are even available in different sizes and colors. As for the wire rings, you can use key rings, chicken rings, or chenille sticks that have been bent into loops.

Students enjoy using the tags as a study aid. They can turn the tags into flashcards or use the tags to quiz each other before an exam. Students might also clip the rings onto a spiral notebook so that the tags are always available as a handy reference.

CHAPTER 4 Study Guide: Review

Organizer

Objective: Help students organize and review key concepts and skills presented in Chapter 4.

Online Edition
Multilingual Glossary

Countdown to CRCT Week 9

Resources

PuzzlePro®
One-Stop Planner®

***Multilingual Glossary* Online**

go.hrw.com
KEYWORD: MR7 Glossary

***Lesson Tutorial Videos* CD-ROM**

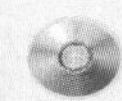

Test & Practice Generator
One-Stop Planner®

Answers

1. improper fraction; mixed number
2. repeating decimal; terminating decimal
3. prime number; composite number
4. 2
5. 2, 3, 5, 6, 9, 10
6. 2, 3, 6, 9
7. 2, 4
8. 2, 5, 10
9. 3
10. composite
11. composite
12. prime
13. composite
14. prime
15. composite
16. composite
17. prime
18. composite
19. prime

CHAPTER 4

Study Guide: Review

Vocabulary

common denominator	199	mixed number	181
composite number	165	prime factorization	169
divisible	164	prime number	165
equivalent fractions	186	proper fraction	192
factor	169	repeating decimal	182
greatest common factor (GCF)	173	simplest form	187
improper fraction	192	terminating decimal	182
like fractions	198	unlike fractions	198

Complete the sentences below with vocabulary words from the list above.

1. The number $\frac{11}{9}$ is an example of a(n) __?__, and $3\frac{1}{6}$ is an example of a(n) __?__.
2. A(n) __?__, such as 0.3333..., has a block of one or more digits that repeat without end. A(n) __?__, such as 0.25, has a finite number of decimal places.
3. A(n) __?__ is divisible by only two numbers, 1 and itself. A(n) __?__ is divisible by more than two numbers.

Study Guide: Review

4-1 Divisibility (pp. 164–167)

GPS M6P1.b

EXAMPLE

■ **Tell whether 210 is divisible by 2, 3, 4, and 6.**

2	*The last digit, 0, is even.*	Divisible
3	*The sum of the digits is divisible by 3.*	Divisible
4	*The number formed by the last two digits is not divisible by 4.*	Not divisible
6	*210 is divisible by 2 and 3.*	Divisible

■ **Tell whether each number is prime or composite.**

17 *only divisible by 1 and 17* prime
25 *divisible by 1, 5, and 25* composite

EXERCISES

Tell whether each number is divisible by 2, 3, 4, 5, 6, 9, and 10.

4. 118
5. 90
6. 342
7. 284
8. 170
9. 393

Tell whether each number is prime or composite.

10. 121
11. 77
12. 13
13. 118
14. 67
15. 93
16. 39
17. 97
18. 85
19. 61

4-2 Factors and Prime Factorization (pp. 169–172)

GPS M6N1.b

EXAMPLE

- **List all the factors of 10.**

  $10 = 1 \cdot 10$ $\quad$ $10 = 2 \cdot 5$

  The factors of 10 are 1, 2, 5, and 10.

- **Write the prime factorization of 30.**

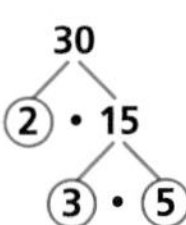

$30 = 2 \cdot 3 \cdot 5$

EXERCISES

List all the factors of each number.

20. 60	**21.** 72
22. 29	**23.** 56
24. 85	**25.** 71

Write the prime factorization of each number.

26. 65	**27.** 94	**28.** 110
29. 81	**30.** 99	**31.** 76
32. 97	**33.** 55	**34.** 46

4-3 Greatest Common Factor (pp. 173–176)

GPS M6N1.c

EXAMPLE

- **Find the GCF of 35 and 50.**

  factors of 35: 1, (5), 7, 35
  factors of 50: 1, 2, (5), 10, 25, 50

  The GCF of 35 and 50 is 5.

EXERCISES

Find the GCF of each set of numbers.

35. 36 and 60

36. 50, 75, and 125

37. 45, 81, and 99

4-4 Decimals and Fractions (pp. 181–184)

GPS M6N1.f

EXAMPLE

- **Write 1.29 as a mixed number.**

  $1.29 = 1\frac{29}{100}$

- **Write $\frac{3}{5}$ as a decimal.**

  $5\overline{)3.0}$ = 0.6 $\qquad \frac{3}{5} = 0.6$

EXERCISES

Write as a fraction or mixed number.

38. 0.37	**39.** 1.8	**40.** 0.4

Write as a decimal.

41. $\frac{7}{8}$	**42.** $\frac{2}{5}$	**43.** $\frac{7}{9}$

4-5 Equivalent Fractions (pp. 186–189)

GPS M6N1.g

EXAMPLE

- **Find an equivalent fraction for $\frac{4}{5}$.**

  $\frac{4}{5} = \frac{\blacksquare}{15}$ $\qquad \frac{4 \cdot 3}{5 \cdot 3} = \frac{12}{15}$

- **Write $\frac{8}{12}$ in simplest form.**

  $\frac{8 \div 4}{12 \div 4} = \frac{2}{3}$

EXERCISES

Find two equivalent fractions.

44. $\frac{4}{6}$	**45.** $\frac{4}{5}$	**46.** $\frac{3}{12}$

Write each fraction in simplest form.

47. $\frac{14}{16}$	**48.** $\frac{9}{30}$	**49.** $\frac{7}{10}$

Study Guide: Review

Answers

20. 1, 2, 3, 4, 5, 6, 10, 12, 15, 20, 30, 60
21. 1, 2, 3, 4, 6, 8, 9, 12, 18, 24, 36, 72
22. 1, 29
23. 1, 2, 4, 7, 8, 14, 28, 56
24. 1, 5, 17, 85
25. 1, 71
26. $5 \cdot 13$
27. $2 \cdot 47$
28. $2 \cdot 5 \cdot 11$
29. 3^4
30. $3^2 \cdot 11$
31. $2^2 \cdot 19$
32. 97
33. $5 \cdot 11$
34. $2 \cdot 23$
35. 12
36. 25
37. 9
38. $\frac{37}{100}$
39. $1\frac{4}{5}$
40. $\frac{2}{5}$
41. 0.875
42. 0.4
43. $0.\overline{7}$
44. Possible answer: $\frac{2}{3}, \frac{8}{12}$
45. Possible answer: $\frac{8}{10}, \frac{16}{20}$
46. Possible answer: $\frac{1}{4}, \frac{2}{8}$
47. $\frac{7}{8}$
48. $\frac{3}{10}$
49. $\frac{7}{10}$

Answers

50. $\frac{34}{9}$
51. $\frac{29}{12}$
52. $\frac{37}{7}$
53. $3\frac{5}{6}$
54. $3\frac{2}{5}$
55. $5\frac{1}{8}$
56. >
57. >
58. $\frac{3}{8}, \frac{2}{3}, \frac{7}{8}$
59. $\frac{3}{12}, \frac{1}{3}, \frac{4}{6}$
60. 1
61. $\frac{3}{4}$
62. $\frac{3}{5}$
63. $6\frac{5}{7}$
64. 1
65. $\frac{1}{2}$
66. 11
67. $2\frac{1}{2}$

Study Guide: Review

4-6 Mixed Numbers and Improper Fractions (pp. 192–195)  GPS M6N1.g

EXAMPLE

- Write $3\frac{5}{6}$ as an improper fraction.

$3\frac{5}{6} = \frac{(3 \cdot 6) + 5}{6} = \frac{18 + 5}{6} = \frac{23}{6}$

- Write $\frac{19}{4}$ as a mixed number.

$4\overline{)19}$ = 4R3 $\quad \frac{19}{4} = 4\frac{3}{4}$

EXERCISES

Write as an improper fraction.

50. $3\frac{7}{9}$ **51.** $2\frac{5}{12}$ **52.** $5\frac{2}{7}$

Write as a mixed number.

53. $\frac{23}{6}$ **54.** $\frac{17}{5}$ **55.** $\frac{41}{8}$

4-7 Comparing and Ordering Fractions (pp. 198–201)  GPS M6N1.g

EXAMPLE

- Order from least to greatest.

$\frac{3}{5}, \frac{2}{3}, \frac{1}{3}$ *Rename with like denominators.*

$\frac{3 \cdot 3}{5 \cdot 3} = \frac{9}{15} \quad \frac{2 \cdot 5}{3 \cdot 5} = \frac{10}{15} \quad \frac{1 \cdot 5}{3 \cdot 5} = \frac{5}{15}$

$\frac{1}{3}, \frac{3}{5}, \frac{2}{3}$

EXERCISES

Compare. Write <, >, or =.

56. $\frac{6}{8}$ ■ $\frac{3}{8}$ **57.** $\frac{7}{9}$ ■ $\frac{2}{3}$

Order from least to greatest.

58. $\frac{3}{8}, \frac{2}{3}, \frac{7}{8}$ **59.** $\frac{4}{6}, \frac{3}{12}, \frac{1}{3}$

4-8 Adding and Subtracting with Like Denominators (pp. 202–205)  GPS M6N1.g

EXAMPLE

- Subtract $4\frac{5}{6} - 2\frac{1}{6}$. Write your answer in simplest form.

$4\frac{5}{6} - 2\frac{1}{6} = 2\frac{4}{6} = 2\frac{2}{3}$

EXERCISES

Add or subtract. Write each answer in simplest form.

60. $\frac{1}{5} + \frac{4}{5}$ **61.** $1 - \frac{3}{12}$

62. $\frac{9}{10} - \frac{3}{10}$ **63.** $4\frac{2}{7} + 2\frac{3}{7}$

4-9 Estimating Fraction Sums and Differences (pp. 206–209) GPS M6N1.g

EXAMPLE

- Estimate the sum or difference by rounding fractions to 0, $\frac{1}{2}$, or 1.

$\frac{7}{8} + \frac{1}{7}$ *Think: 1 + 0.*

$\frac{7}{8} + \frac{1}{7}$ is about 1.

EXERCISES

Estimate each sum or difference by rounding fractions to 0, $\frac{1}{2}$, or 1.

64. $\frac{3}{5} + \frac{3}{7}$ **65.** $\frac{6}{7} - \frac{5}{9}$

66. $4\frac{9}{10} + 6\frac{1}{5}$ **67.** $7\frac{5}{11} - 4\frac{3}{4}$

CHAPTER TEST

CHAPTER 4

List all the factors of each number. Then tell whether each number is prime or composite.

1. 98 1, 2, 7, 14, 49, 98; composite
2. 40 1, 2, 4, 5, 8, 10, 20, 40; composite
3. 45 1, 3, 5, 9, 15, 45; composite

Write the prime factorization of each number.

4. 64 $2 \times 2 \times 2 \times 2 \times 2 \times 2$
5.  130 $2 \times 5 \times 13$
6. 49 7×7

Find the GCF of each set of numbers.

7. 24 and 108 12
8.  45, 18, and 39 3
9. 49, 77, and 84 7

10. Ms. Arrington is making supply boxes for her students. She has 63 pencils, 42 pens, and 21 packs of markers. Each type of supply must be evenly distributed. What is the greatest number of supply boxes she can make if every supply is used? 7 supply boxes

Write each decimal as a fraction or mixed number.

11. 0.37 $\frac{37}{100}$
12. 1.9 $1\frac{9}{10}$
13. 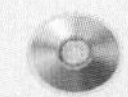 0.92 $\frac{23}{25}$

Write each fraction or mixed number as a decimal.

14. $\frac{3}{8}$ 0.375
15. $9\frac{3}{5}$ 9.6
16. $\frac{2}{3}$ $0.\overline{6}$

Write each fraction in simplest form.

17. $\frac{4}{12}$ $\frac{1}{3}$
18. $\frac{6}{9}$ $\frac{2}{3}$
19. $\frac{3}{15}$ $\frac{1}{5}$

Write each mixed number as an improper fraction.

20. $4\frac{7}{8}$ $\frac{39}{8}$
21. $7\frac{5}{12}$ $\frac{89}{12}$
22. $3\frac{5}{7}$ $\frac{26}{7}$

Compare. Write <, >, or =.

23. $\frac{5}{6}$ ■ $\frac{3}{6}$ >
24. $\frac{3}{4}$ ■ $\frac{7}{8}$ <
25. $\frac{4}{5}$ ■ $\frac{7}{10}$ >

Order the fractions and decimals from least to greatest.

26. 2.17, 2.3, $2\frac{1}{9}$ $2\frac{1}{9}$, 2.17, 2.3
27. 0.1, $\frac{3}{8}$, 0.3 0.1, 0.3, $\frac{3}{8}$
28. 0.9, $\frac{2}{8}$, 0.35 $\frac{2}{8}$, 0.35, 0.9

29. On Monday, it snowed $2\frac{1}{4}$ inches. On Tuesday, an additional $3\frac{3}{4}$ inches of snow fell. How much snow fell altogether on Monday and Tuesday? 6 inches

Estimate each sum or difference by rounding to 0, $\frac{1}{2}$, or 1.

30. $\frac{1}{8} + \frac{4}{7}$ $\frac{1}{2}$
31. $\frac{11}{12} - \frac{4}{9}$ $\frac{1}{2}$
32. $\frac{4}{5} + \frac{1}{9}$ 1
33. $2\frac{9}{10} - 2\frac{1}{7}$ 1

Chapter Test

CHAPTER TEST

CHAPTER 4

Organizer

Objective: Assess students' mastery of concepts and skills in Chapter 4.

Online Edition

Resources

Assessment Resources

Chapter 4 Tests
- Free Response (Levels A, B, C)
- Multiple Choice (Levels A, B, C)
- Performance Assessment

***IDEA Works!* CD-ROM**
Modified Chapter 4 Test

Test & Practice Generator
One-Stop Planner®

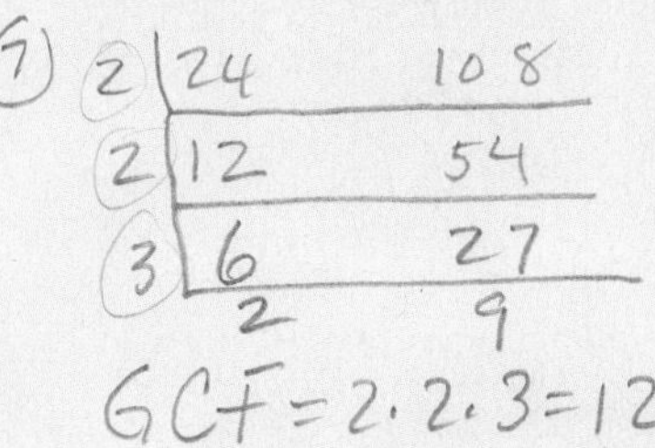

Organizer

Objective: Provide review and practice for Chapters 1–4 and standardized tests.

Online Edition

Resources

Assessment Resources
Chapter 4 Cumulative Test

***CRCT Prep* Workbook**

***CRCT Prep* CD-ROM**

***CRCT Practice* Online**

go.hrw.com
KEYWORD: MR7 TestPrep

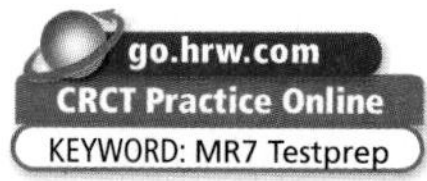

CRCT Prep

CUMULATIVE ASSESSMENT, CHAPTERS 1–4

Multiple Choice

1. Which of the following numbers is divisible by 3, 4, and 8?

(A) 12 (C) 20
(B) 16 (D) 24

2. When June sits down today to read, she notices she is on page 20 of a 200-page book. She decides to read 4 pages of this book every day until she is finished. If this pattern continues, what page of the book will June be on in 10 more days?

(F) 24 (H) 60
(G) 44 (J) 120

3. Alice is using three different colors of beads to make necklaces. She has 48 blue beads, 56 pink beads, and 32 white beads. She wants to use the same number of pink, same number of blue, and same number of white beads on each necklace. What is the greatest number of necklaces she can make if she uses all of the beads?

(A) 16 (C) 8
(B) 12 (D) 4

4. A writer spends $144.75 on 5 ink cartridges. Which equation can be used to find the cost c of one ink cartridge?

(F) $5c = 144.75$
(G) $\frac{c}{144.75} = 5$
(H) $5 + c = 144.75$
(J) $144.75 - c = 5$

5. Which fraction is equal to 0.25?

(A) $\frac{1}{3}$ (C) $\frac{2}{5}$
(B) $\frac{1}{4}$ (D) $\frac{1}{25}$

6. Which fraction is NOT equivalent to $\frac{4}{6}$?

(F) $\frac{2}{3}$ (H) $\frac{8}{12}$
(G) $\frac{10}{15}$ (J) $\frac{16}{18}$

7. Which fraction is equivalent to the shaded area of the model?

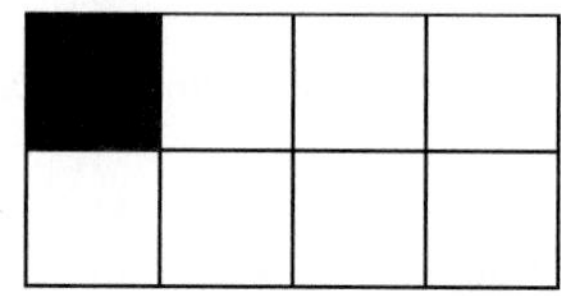

(A) $\frac{2}{4}$ (C) $\frac{6}{32}$
(B) $\frac{3}{24}$ (D) $\frac{4}{40}$

8. Steve bought a movie ticket for $6.25, a box of popcorn for $2.25, and a large drink for $4.75. How much money did he spend at the movie?

(F) $12.00 (H) $13.25
(G) $12.75 (J) $13.50

9. Four boys each order their own small pizza. William eats $\frac{2}{3}$ of his pizza. Mike eats $\frac{2}{5}$ of his pizza. Julio eats $\frac{1}{2}$ of his pizza. Lee eats $\frac{3}{8}$ of his pizza. Who ate the least amount of pizza?

(A) Lee
(B) Mike
(C) Julio
(D) William

TEST PREP DOCTOR

For item 10, remind students that the quotient resulting from dividing 78 by 4 needs to be interpreted. There are 19 groups of 4, with 2 as a remainder, meaning that the 2 remaining students also need an adult leader. Therefore, 20 adult leaders are needed.

Answers

16. $9\frac{1}{4}$ yd; Possible answer: $9\frac{2}{8}$, $\frac{74}{8}$, 9.25

17. No, 348 is not divisible by 8. 348 is also divisible by 3 because the sum of the digits is divisible by 3.

18. $315 = 3 \times 3 \times 5 \times 7$;
$225 = 3 \times 3 \times 5 \times 5$;
Factors of 315 are 1, 3, 5, 7, 9, 15, 21, 35, 45, 63, 105, and 315.
Factors of 225 are 1, 3, 5, 9, 15, 25, 45, 75, and 225. GCF = 45. The numbers are composite because they contain factors other than 1 and themselves.

20. See 4-Point Response work sample.

10. There are 78 students going on a field trip to the state capitol. The students are in groups of 4. Each group must have an adult leader. How many adult leaders are needed for each student group to have an adult leader?

(F) 15 (H) 20
(G) 19 (J) 22

11. Which of the following is equivalent to 2.52?

(A) $2\frac{52}{100}$ (C) $\frac{52}{200}$
(B) $2\frac{52}{10}$ (D) $\frac{2}{52}$

You can answer some problems without doing many calculations. Use mental math, estimation, or logical reasoning to eliminate answer choices and save time.

12. Which of the following numbers is prime?

(F) 91 (H) 97
(G) 93 (J) 98

13. What is the least common multiple of 4 and 6.

(A) 2 (C) 12
(B) 6 (D) 24

14. Suppose you are making fruit baskets that contain 4 oranges and 5 apples each. If you have 100 oranges and 100 apples, how many baskets can you make?

(F) 20 (H) 100
(G) 25 (J) 500

15. What is the prime factorization of 120?

(A) $2^2 \times 3 \times 5$
(B) $2^3 \times 3 \times 5$
(C) $2^3 \times 3^2 \times 5$
(D) $2 \times 4 \times 3 \times 5$

STANDARDIZED TEST PREP

Short Response

16. Stacie has $16\frac{3}{8}$ yards of material. She uses $7\frac{1}{8}$ yards for a skirt. How much material does she have left? Write your answer as a mixed number in simplest form. Then give three other equivalent answers, including one decimal.

17. Maggie says that 348 is divisible by 2, 4, and 8. Is she correct? Give any other numbers by which 348 is divisible. Explain.

18. Write the numbers 315 and 225 as products of prime factors. Then list all the factors of each number and find the GCF. Are 315 and 225 prime or composite? Explain.

19. Suzanne has 317 flyers to mail. Each flyer requires 1 stamp. If she buys books of stamps that contain 20 stamps each, how many books will she need to mail the flyers? **16 books; $20 \times 16 = 320$; that is enough stamps to mail the 317 flyers.**

Extended Response

20. Mr. Peters needs to build a rectangular pig pen $14\frac{4}{5}$ meters long and $5\frac{1}{5}$ meters wide.

a. How much fencing does Mr. Peters need to buy? Show how you found your answer. Write your answer in simplest form.

b. Mr. Peters's pig pen will need 6 meters more fencing than the rectangular pig pen his neighbor is building. Write and solve an equation to find how much fencing his neighbor needs to buy. Show your work.

c. If the neighbor's pig pen is going to be 4 meters wide, how long will it be? Show your work.

CRCT Prep

Short Response Rubric

Items 16–19

2 Points = The student's answer is an accurate and complete execution of the task or tasks.

1 Point = The student's answer contains attributes of an appropriate response but is flawed.

0 Points = The student's answer contains no attributes of an appropriate response.

Extended Response Rubric

Item 20

4 Points = The student demonstrates a thorough understanding of all concepts and all work is shown correctly.

3 Points = The student demonstrates a basic understanding of all concepts, but the work shows some flaws reflecting inattentive execution of mathematical procedures or some misunderstanding of the underlying mathematics.

2 Points = The student demonstrates only a partial understanding of the concepts and/or procedures embodied in the tasks. The approach may be correct but the work shows a misunderstanding of one or more important concepts.

1 Point = The student demonstrates a very limited understanding of the concepts and/or procedures embodied in the tasks. The response may show some understanding but exhibits many flaws and/or is incomplete.

0 Points = The student provides no response at all, or a completely incorrect or uninterpretable response.

Student Work Samples for Item 20

4-Point Response

a. 40 m; find the sum of the length of the sides of the pig pen.
$14\frac{4}{5} + 14\frac{4}{5} + 5\frac{1}{5} + 5\frac{1}{5} = 40$
b. $n + 6 = 40$
$n = 34$
The neighbor needs to buy 34 m of fencing.
c. 13 m; since he bought 34 m and the width of 1 side was 4 m, find the overall length by doubling the width and subtracting that from the amount of fencing he bought. $34 - 8 = 26$. Since 26 represents 2 sides of the pen, divide 26 in half. The neighbor's pen will be 13 m long.

The student's answers are correct. All work is shown when asked for, and questions are answered in complete sentences.

3-Point Response

a. 40 ft
b. The neighbor needs to buy 34 ft of fencing.
c. The neighbor's pen will be 13 ft long.

The student's answers are correct. A mistake was made in identifying the units of measure, and all work is not shown.

2-Point Response

a. 40m
b. $n - 6 = 40$
$n = 46$
The neighbor needs 46m of fencing.
c. $46 - 4 = 42$; the neighbor's pen is 42m long.

The answer to part **a** is correct. The equation in part **b** was solved correctly, but the equation was not correctly set up. Student did not understand part **c**.

Problem Solving on Location

Organizer

Objective: To solve real-world problems involving decimals, number theory, and fractions

Online Edition

The Appalachian Trail

ENGLISH LANGUAGE LEARNERS

Reading Strategies

Remind students that certain words correspond to specific mathematical operations. For example, the word *difference* usually means that subtraction will be involved in the solution of the problem. Have students read problem 1 and identify any words that are clues to the operations that may be used in solving the problem. "25 times longer": multiplication; "combined length": addition

Using Data Be sure students understand what is meant by the mile markings in the map. Explain that the trail starts at Mile 0 and that the subsequent markings give distances along the trail from the starting point.

Problem Solving on Location

GEORGIA

Georgia Performance Standards

M6P1.c, M6P4.c, M6P5.a

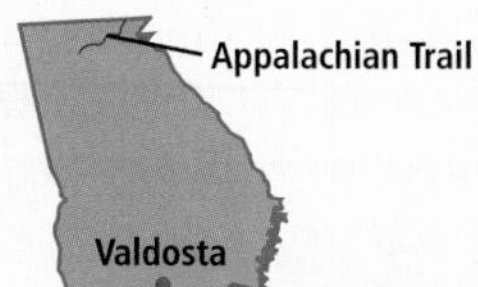

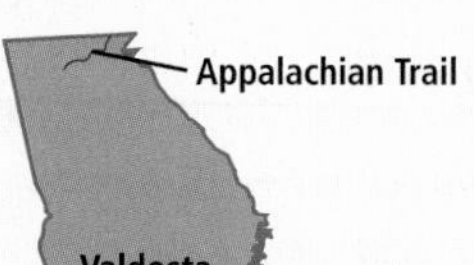

The Appalachian Trail

The Appalachian Trail is the nation's longest marked footpath. The 2,200-mile trail crosses 14 states, from Maine to the northwest corner of Georgia. The section of the trail in Georgia is known for its steep climbs and spectacular views.

Choose one or more strategies to solve each problem.

1. There are several access trails in Georgia that link to the Appalachian Trail. Among these, Benton MacKaye Trail is 25 times longer than Andrews Cove Trail. The two trails have a combined length of 52 miles. How long is each trail? Andrews Cove Trail: 2 mi; Benton MacKaye Trail: 50 mi

For 2 and 3, use the map.

2. The Appalachian Trail is indicated by white marks on trees along the trail. The marks occur every 0.2 miles. Assume there is a marked tree at Blood Mountain and at Neels Gap. How many marked trees occur between these two points? 11
3. Hiking north from Tray Mountain, hikers pass a shelter after 0.3 miles. They pass a second shelter after hiking another 7.1 miles. How far is the second shelter from Bly Gap? 12.3 mi

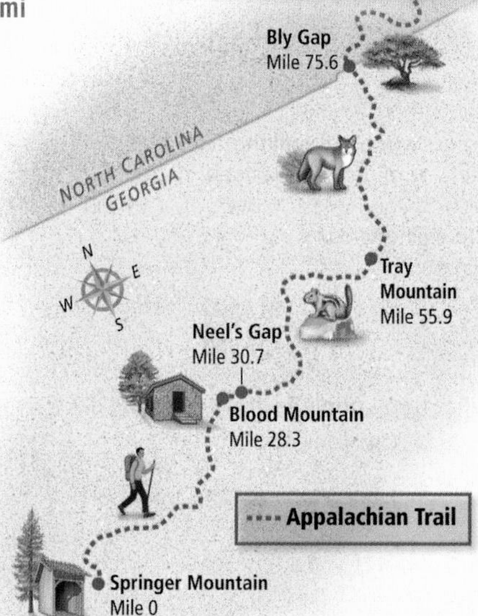

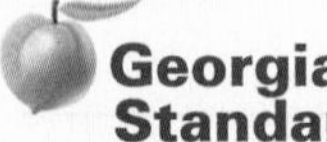

Georgia Performance Standards

M6P1.c Apply and adapt a variety of appropriate strategies to solve problems.

M6P4.c Recognize and apply mathematics in contexts outside of mathematics.

M6P5.b Select, apply, and translate among mathematical representations to solve problems.

Problem Solving Focus

For problem 3, focus on the strategy Draw a Diagram. Have students share any diagrams that they drew in order to solve the problem. Point out that diagrams can often be much simpler than the objects they represent. For example, the path from Tray Mountain to Bly Gap can be represented with a line segment.

Wild Adventures

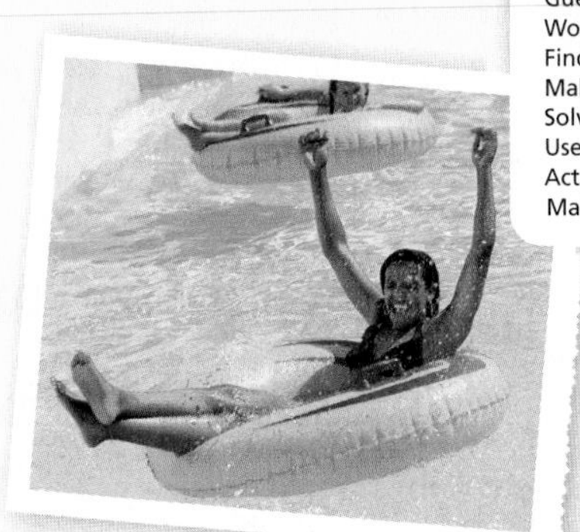

Problem Solving Strategies
- Draw a Diagram
- Make a Model
- Guess and Test
- Work Backward
- Find a Pattern
- Make a Table
- Solve a Simpler Problem
- Use Logical Reasoning
- Act It Out
- Make an Organized List

Wild Adventures Theme Park in Valdosta, Georgia, is an amusement park with a beastly twist. Scattered among the roller coasters and water rides are more than 500 wild animals in a variety of natural habitats.

Choose one or more strategies to solve each problem.

1. The Wild Adventures water park includes a wave pool. Throughout the day, the waves are on for 15 minutes, then off for 15 minutes, then on for 15 minutes, and so on. How many times are the waves on during a 10-hour period? 20
2. Pharaoh's Fury is a thrill ride based on a giant swinging boat. The boat has 10 rows of seats. Each row can hold either 4 adults or 6 children. Adults and children are not mixed in the same row. When all the seats are filled and there are 52 people on the ride, how many rows of adults are there? 4

For 3, use the table.

3. The table shows the heights of some of the unusual mammals at Wild Adventures. One of these mammals is also known as a horned oryx. The horned oryx is shorter than the zebu. It is also more than a foot taller than the blackbuck. Which mammal is the horned oryx? Scimitar

Mammals at Wild Adventures

Mammal	Height (ft)
Addax	$3\frac{1}{4}$
Blackbuck	$2\frac{2}{3}$
Impala	$3\frac{1}{12}$
Sable antelope	$4\frac{2}{3}$
Scimitar	$4\frac{1}{5}$
Zebu	$4\frac{1}{2}$

The sable antelope is native to eastern and southern Africa

Wild Adventures

Reading Strategies

ENGLISH LANGUAGE LEARNERS

If students have difficulty getting started in solving a problem, suggest that they restate the problem in their own words. Have students use problem 1 to practice this skill. After reading the problem as a class, have volunteers restate the problem in their own words. Ask the class whether all of the important information was included in each restatement.

Using Data Have students identify the key data that is given in problem 2. To help students organize this data, suggest that they write the information in a list. For example:
Number of rows: 10
Number of people in each row: 4 adults or 6 children
Number of people on ride: 52

Problem Solving Focus

For problem 3, focus on the strategy Use Logical Reasoning. Ask students what logical conclusions they can make based on each sentence of the problem. For instance, based on the sentence "The horned oryx is shorter than the zebu," students can conclude that neither the zebu nor the sable antelope are the horned oryx.

Discuss strategies that can be used to keep track of the logical conclusions that students make in problem 3. As an example, students might begin by writing a list of all of the animals. Then they can cross them off as they are logically eliminated.

CHAPTER 5

Fraction Operations

Section 5A

Adding and Subtracting Fractions

- **5-1 Least Common Multiple**
- **5-2 Hands-On Lab** Model Fraction Addition and Subtraction
- **5-2 Adding and Subtracting with Unlike Denominators**
- **5-3 Adding and Subtracting Mixed Numbers**
- **5-4 Hands-On Lab** Model Subtraction with Regrouping
- **5-4 Regrouping to Subtract Mixed Numbers**
- **5-5 Solving Fraction Equations: Addition and Subtraction**

Section 5B

Multiplying and Dividing Fractions

- **5-6 Multiplying Fractions by Whole Numbers**
- **5-7 Hands-On Lab** Model Fraction Multiplication
- **5-7 Multiplying Fractions**
- **5-8 Multiplying Mixed Numbers**
- **5-9 Hands-On Lab** Model Fraction Division
- **5-9 Dividing Fractions and Mixed Numbers**
- **5-10 Solving Fraction Equations: Multiplication and Division**

Pacing Guide for 45-Minute Classes

Chapter 5

Countdown to Testing Weeks 10, 11

DAY 1	DAY 2	DAY 3	DAY 4	DAY 5
5-1 Lesson	5-1 Lesson	5-2 Hands-On Lab 5-2 Lesson	5-2 Lesson	5-2 Lesson 5-3 Lesson
DAY 6	**DAY 7**	**DAY 8**	**DAY 9**	**DAY 10**
5-3 Lesson 5-4 Hands-On Lab	5-4 Lesson	5-4 Lesson	5-5 Lesson	Ready to Go On? Focus on Problem Solving 5-6 Lesson
DAY 11	**DAY 12**	**DAY 13**	**DAY 14**	**DAY 15**
5-6 Lesson 5-7 Hands-On Lab	5-7 Lesson	5-8 Lesson	5-9 Hands-On Lab 5-9 Lesson	5-9 Lesson 5-10 Lesson
DAY 16	**DAY 17**	**DAY 18**		
5-10 Lesson Ready to Go On? Multi-Step Test Prep	Chapter 5 Review	Chapter 5 Test		

Pacing Guide for 90-Minute Classes

Chapter 5

DAY 1	DAY 2	DAY 3	DAY 4	DAY 5
5-1 Lesson	5-2 Hands-On Lab 5-2 Lesson	5-2 Lesson 5-3 Lesson 5-4 Hands-On Lab	5-4 Lesson	5-5 Lesson Ready to Go On? Focus on Problem Solving 5-6 Lesson
DAY 6	**DAY 7**	**DAY 8**	**DAY 9**	
5-6 Lesson 5-7 Hands-On Lab 5-7 Lesson	5-8 Lesson 5-9 Hands-On Lab 5-9 Lesson	5-9 Lesson 5-10 Lesson Ready to Go On? Multi-Step Test Prep	Chapter 5 Review Chapter 5 Test	

ONGOING ASSESSMENT and INTERVENTION

	DIAGNOSE	PRESCRIBE
Assess Prior Knowledge	**Before Chapter 5**	
	Diagnose readiness for the chapter.	Prescribe intervention.
	Are You Ready? SE p. 225	***Are You Ready? Intervention*** Skills 19, 22, 36, 43
Formative Assessment	**Before Every Lesson**	
	Diagnose readiness for the lesson.	Prescribe intervention.
	Warm Up TE, every lesson	**Skills Bank** SE pp. 749–761 **Reteach** CRB, Chapters 1–5
	During Every Lesson	
	Diagnose understanding of lesson concepts.	Prescribe intervention.
	Think and Discuss SE, every lesson **Write About It** SE, lesson exercises **Journal** TE, lesson exercises	***Questioning Strategies*** Chapter 5 **Reading Strategies** CRB, every lesson ***Success for ELL*** pp. 67–86
	After Every Lesson	
	Diagnose mastery of lesson concepts.	Prescribe intervention.
	Lesson Quiz TE, every lesson **Test Prep** SE, every lesson ***Test and Practice Generator***	**Reteach** CRB, every lesson **Problem Solving** CRB, every lesson **Test Prep Doctor** TE, lesson exercises ***Homework Help* Online**
	Before Chapter 5 Testing	
	Diagnose mastery of concepts in the chapter.	Prescribe intervention.
	Ready to Go On? SE pp. 252, 278 **Focus on Problem Solving** SE p. 253 **Multi-Step Test Prep** SE p. 279 **Section Quizzes** AR pp. 86–87 ***Test and Practice Generator***	***Ready to Go On? Intervention*** **Scaffolding Questions** TE p. 279
	Before High Stakes Testing	
	Diagnose mastery of benchmark concepts.	Prescribe intervention.
	Test Tackler SE pp. 286–287 **CRCT Prep** SE pp. 288–289 ***CRCT Prep* CD-ROM**	***CRCT Prep Workbook***
Summative Assessment	**After Chapter 5**	
	Check mastery of chapter concepts.	Prescribe intervention.
	Multiple-Choice Tests (Forms A, B, C) **Free-Response Tests (Forms A, B, C)** **Performance Assessment** AR pp. 88–101 ***Test and Practice Generator***	**Reteach** CRB, every lesson ***Lesson Tutorial Videos*** Chapter 5
	Check mastery of benchmark concepts.	Prescribe intervention.
	CRCT	***CRCT Prep Workbook***

KEY: **SE** = *Student Edition* **TE** = *Teacher's Edition* **CRB** = *Chapter Resource Book* **AR** = *Assessment Resources* Available online Available on CD-ROM

CHAPTER 5

Supporting the Teacher

Chapter 5 Resource Book

Practice A, B, C
pp. 3–5, 11–13, 19–21, 27–29, 35–37, 43–45, 51–53, 59–61, 67–69, 75–77

Reading Strategies ELL
pp. 9, 17, 25, 33, 41, 49, 57, 65, 73, 81

Puzzles, Twisters, and Teasers
pp. 10, 18, 26, 34, 42, 50, 58, 66, 74, 82

Reteach
pp. 6, 14, 22, 30, 38, 46, 54, 62, 70, 78

Problem Solving
pp. 8, 16, 24, 32, 40, 48, 56, 64, 72, 80

Challenge
pp. 7, 15, 23, 31, 39, 47, 55, 63, 71, 79

Parent Letter pp. 1–2

Transparencies

Lesson Transparencies, Volume 1 .... Chapter 5
- Teaching Tools
- Warm Ups
- Problem of the Day
- Teaching Transparencies
- Lesson Quizzes

Know-It Notebook .... Chapter 5
- Additional Examples
- Vocabulary
- Chapter Review
- Big Ideas

Alternate Openers: Explorations .... pp. 34–43

Countdown to CRCT .... pp. 19–22

Teacher Tools

Power Presentations®
Complete PowerPoint® presentations for Chapter 5 lessons

Lesson Tutorial Videos® SPANISH
Holt authors Ed Burger and Freddie Renfro present tutorials to support the Chapter 5 lessons.

One-Stop Planner® SPANISH
Easy access to all Chapter 5 resources and assessments, as well as software for lesson planning, test generation, and puzzle creation

IDEA Works!®
Key Chapter 5 resources and assessments modified to address special learning needs

Lesson Plans .... pp. 34–43

Questioning Strategies .... Chapter 5

Solutions Key .... Chapter 5

Interdisciplinary Posters and Worksheets .... Chapter 5

TechKeys

Lab Resources

Project Teacher Support

Parent Resources

Workbooks

Homework and Practice Workbook SPANISH
Teacher's Guide .... pp. 17–22

Know-It Notebook
Teacher's Guide .... Chapter 5

Problem Solving Workbook SPANISH
Teacher's Guide .... pp. 17–22

CRCT Prep
Teacher's Guide

Technology Highlights for the Teacher

Power Presentations

Dynamic presentations to engage students. Complete PowerPoint® presentations for every lesson in Chapter 5.

2-1 Solving One-Step Equations

Isolate a variable by using inverse operations which "undo" operations on the variable.

An equation is like a balanced scale. To keep the balance, perform the same operation on both sides.

Inverse Operations	
Operation	**Inverse Operation**
Addition	Subtraction
Subtraction	Addition

One-Stop Planner SPANISH

Easy access to Chapter 5 resources and assessments. Includes lesson-planning, test-generation, and puzzle-creation software.

Premier Online Edition SPANISH

Chapter 5 includes Tutorial Videos, Lesson Activities, Lesson Quizzes, Homework Help, and Chapter Project.

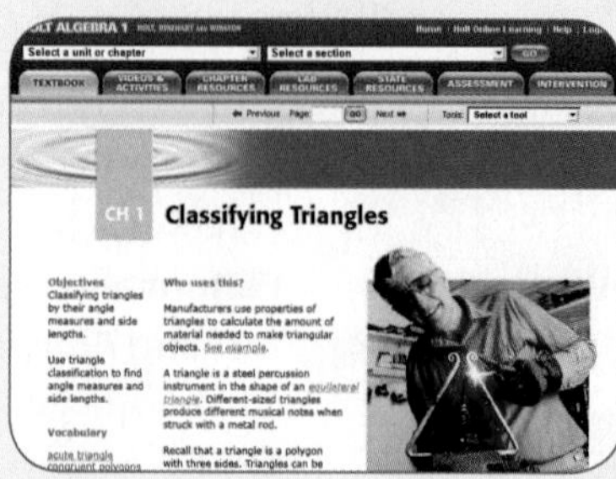

KEY: **SE** = *Student Edition* **TE** = *Teacher's Edition*  English Language Learners  Spanish version available 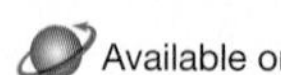 Available online  Available on CD-ROM

Reaching All Learners

Resources for All Learners

Hands-On Lab Activities	Chapter 5
Technology Lab Activities	Chapter 5
Homework and Practice Workbook SPANISH	pp. 34–43
Know-It Notebook SPANISH	Chapter 5
Problem Solving Workbook SPANISH	pp. 34–43

DEVELOPING LEARNERS

Practice A	CRB, every lesson
Reteach	CRB, every lesson
Inclusion	TE p. 255
Questioning Strategies	Chapter 5
Modified Chapter 5 Resources	*IDEA Works!*
Homework Help Online	

ON-LEVEL LEARNERS

Practice B	CRB, every lesson
Puzzles, Twisters, and Teasers	CRB, every lesson
Multiple Representations	TE pp. 229, 261
Cognitive Strategies	TE p. 235

ADVANCED LEARNERS

Practice C	CRB, every lesson
Challenge	CRB, every lesson
Extension	TE pp. 227, 279, 280, 281
Critical Thinking	TE pp. 245, 265, 271

English Language Learners

ENGLISH LANGUAGE LEARNERS

Are You Ready? Vocabulary	SE p. 225
Vocabulary Connections	SE p. 226
Lesson Vocabulary	SE, every lesson
Vocabulary Review	SE p. 282
English Language Learners	TE pp. 229, 235, 271
Reading Strategies	CRB, every lesson
Success for English Language Learners	pp. 67–86
Multilingual Glossary	

Reaching All Learners Through...

Inclusion	TE p. 255
Diversity	TE p. 249
Kinesthetic Experience	TE pp. 239, 261
Concrete Manipulatives	TE p. 229
Multiple Representations	TE pp. 229, 261
Cognitive Strategies	TE p. 235
Cooperative Learning	TE pp. 255, 275
Modeling	TE pp. 235, 265
Critical Thinking	TE pp. 245, 265, 271
Test Prep Doctor	TE pp. 231, 237, 241, 247, 251, 257, 263, 267, 273, 277, 286, 288
Common Error Alert	TE pp. 229, 235, 239, 245, 249, 255, 261, 263, 265, 271, 275
Scaffolding Questions	TE p. 279

Technology Highlights for Reaching All Learners

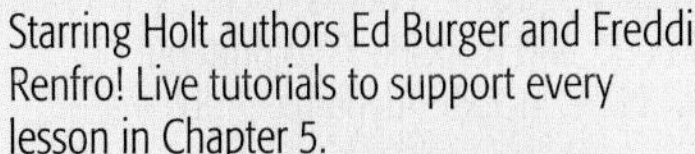

Lesson Tutorial Videos SPANISH

Starring Holt authors Ed Burger and Freddie Renfro! Live tutorials to support every lesson in Chapter 5.

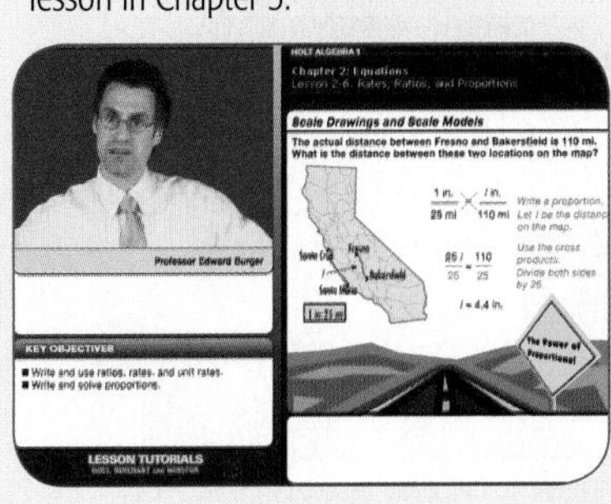

Multilingual Glossary

Searchable glossary includes definitions in English, Spanish, Vietnamese, Chinese, Hmong, Korean, and 4 other languages.

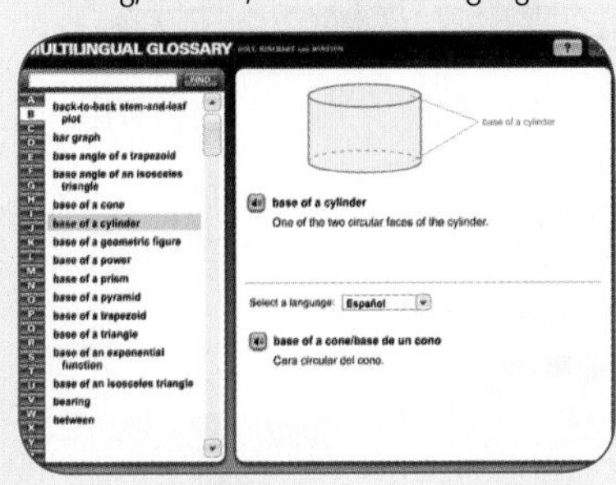

Online Interactivities

Interactive tutorials provide visually engaging alternative opportunities to learn concepts and master skills.

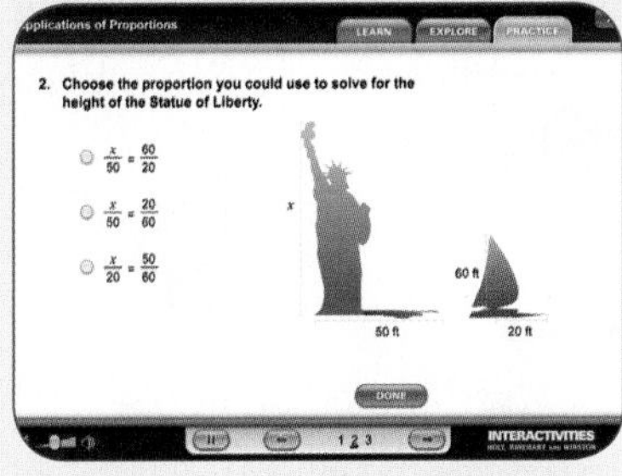

KEY: **SE** = *Student Edition* **TE** = *Teacher's Edition* **CRB** = *Chapter Resource Book* SPANISH Spanish version available 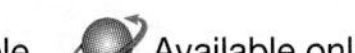 Available online  Available on CD-ROM

Ongoing Assessment

Assessing Prior Knowledge

Determine whether students have the prerequisite concepts and skills for success in Chapter 5.

Are You Ready? SPANISH .... SE p. 225

Warm Up .... TE, every lesson

Test Preparation

Provide review and practice for Chapter 5 and standardized tests.

Multi-Step Test Prep .... SE p. 279

Study Guide: Review .... SE pp. 282–284

Standardized Test Prep .... SE pp. 286–287

Test Tackler .... SE pp. 288–289

Countdown to CRCT Transparencies .... pp. 19–22

CRCT Prep Workbook

***CRCT Prep* CD-ROM**

IDEA Works!

Alternative Assessment

Assess students' understanding of Chapter 5 concepts and combined problem-solving skills.

Chapter 5 Project .... SE p. 224

Performance Assessment .... AR pp. 100–101

Portfolio Assessment .... AR p. xxxiv

Daily Assessment

Provide formative assessment for each day of Chapter 5.

Questioning Strategies .... Chapter 5

Think and Discuss .... SE, every lesson

Write About It .... SE, lesson exercises

Journal .... TE, lesson exercises

Lesson Quiz .... TE, every lesson

Modified Lesson Quizzes .... *IDEA Works!*

Weekly Assessment

Provide formative assessment for each week of Chapter 5.

Focus on Problem Solving .... SE p. 253

Multi-Step Test Prep .... SE p. 279

Ready to Go On? SPANISH .... SE pp. 252, 278

Cumulative Assessment .... SE pp. 286–287

Test and Practice Generator SPANISH .... *One-Stop Planner*

Formal Assessment

Provide summative assessment of Chapter 5 mastery.

Section Quizzes SPANISH .... AR pp. 86–87

Chapter 5 Test .... SE p. 285

Chapter Test (Levels A, B, C) SPANISH .... AR pp. 88–99
- Multiple Choice
- Free Response

Cumulative Test SPANISH .... AR pp. 102–105

Test and Practice Generator SPANISH .... *One-Stop Planner*

Modified Chapter 5 Test .... *IDEA Works!*

Technology Highlights for Ongoing Assessment

Are You Ready? SPANISH

Automatically assess readiness and prescribe intervention for Chapter 5 prerequisite skills.

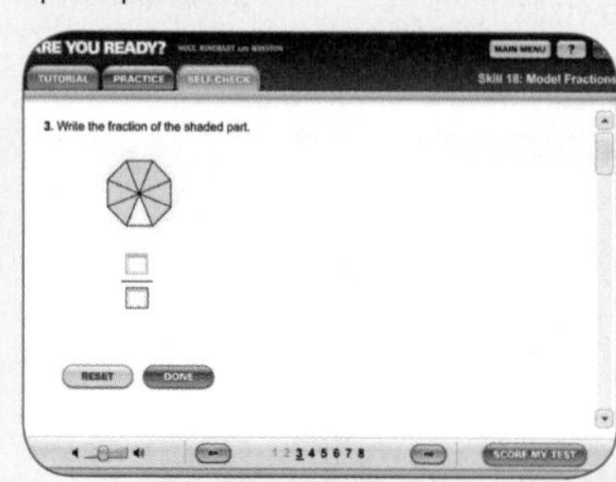

Ready to Go On? SPANISH

Automatically assess understanding of and prescribe intervention for Sections 5A and 5B.

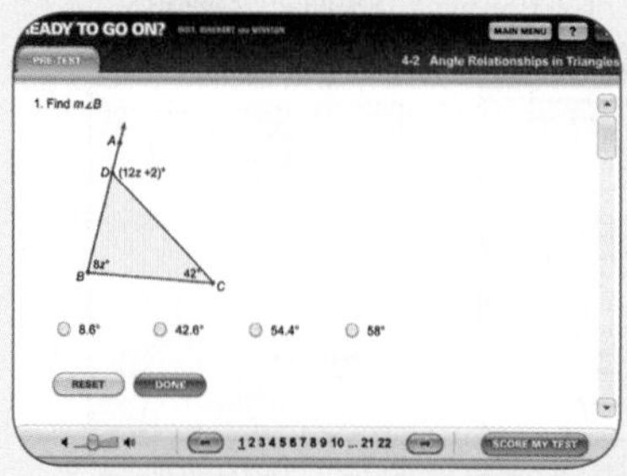

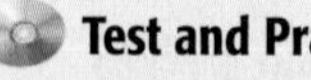

Test and Practice Generator SPANISH

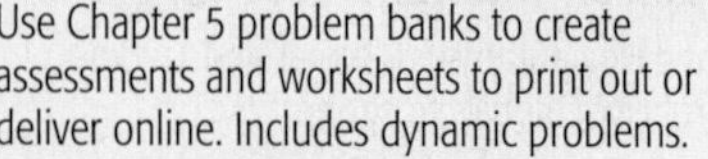

Use Chapter 5 problem banks to create assessments and worksheets to print out or deliver online. Includes dynamic problems.

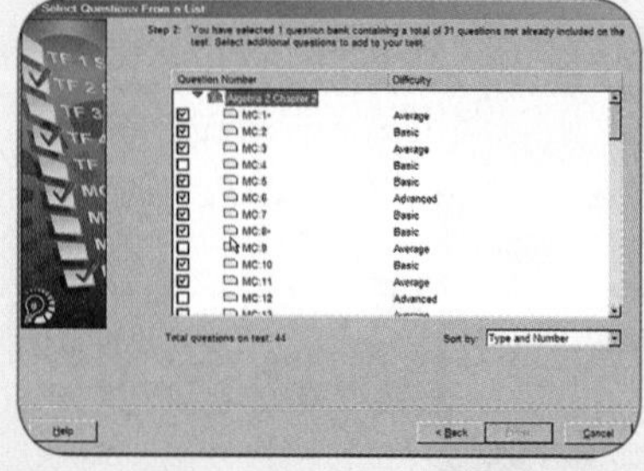

KEY: **SE** = *Student Edition* **TE** = *Teacher's Edition* **AR** = *Assessment Resources* 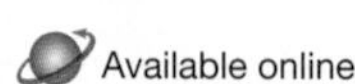 SPANISH Spanish version available; Available online; Available on CD-ROM

Formal Assessment

Three levels (A, B, C) of multiple-choice and free-response chapter tests are available in the *Assessment Resources.*

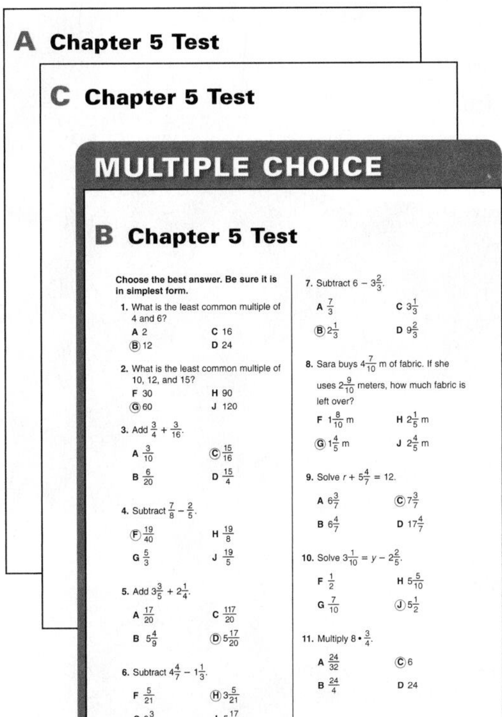

A Chapter 5 Test

C Chapter 5 Test

MULTIPLE CHOICE

B Chapter 5 Test

Choose the best answer. Be sure it is in simplest form.

1. What is the least common multiple of 4 and 6?
   A 2 C 16
   Ⓑ 12 D 24
2. What is the least common multiple of 10, 12, and 15?
   F 30 H 90
   Ⓖ 60 J 120
3. Add $\frac{3}{4} + \frac{3}{16}$.
   A $\frac{3}{10}$ Ⓒ $\frac{15}{16}$
   B $\frac{6}{20}$ D $\frac{15}{4}$
4. Subtract $\frac{7}{8} - \frac{2}{5}$.
   Ⓕ $\frac{19}{40}$ H $\frac{19}{8}$
   G $\frac{5}{3}$ J $\frac{19}{5}$
5. Add $3\frac{3}{5} + 2\frac{1}{4}$.
   A $\frac{17}{20}$ C $\frac{117}{20}$
   B $5\frac{4}{9}$ Ⓓ $5\frac{17}{20}$
6. Subtract $4\frac{4}{7} - 1\frac{1}{3}$.
   F $\frac{5}{21}$ Ⓗ $3\frac{5}{21}$
   G $3\frac{3}{4}$ J $5\frac{17}{21}$
7. Subtract $6 - 3\frac{2}{3}$.
   A $\frac{7}{3}$ C $3\frac{1}{3}$
   Ⓑ $2\frac{1}{3}$ D $9\frac{2}{3}$
8. Sara buys $4\frac{7}{10}$ m of fabric. If she uses $2\frac{9}{10}$ meters, how much fabric is left over?
   F $1\frac{8}{10}$ m H $2\frac{1}{5}$ m
   Ⓖ $1\frac{4}{5}$ m J $2\frac{4}{5}$ m
9. Solve $r + 5\frac{4}{7} = 12$.
   A $6\frac{3}{7}$ Ⓒ $7\frac{3}{7}$
   B $6\frac{4}{7}$ D $17\frac{4}{7}$
10. Solve $3\frac{1}{10} = y - 2\frac{2}{5}$.
    F $\frac{1}{2}$ H $5\frac{5}{10}$
    G $\frac{7}{10}$ Ⓙ $5\frac{1}{2}$
11. Multiply $8 \cdot \frac{3}{4}$.
    A $\frac{24}{32}$ Ⓒ 6
    B $\frac{24}{4}$ D 24

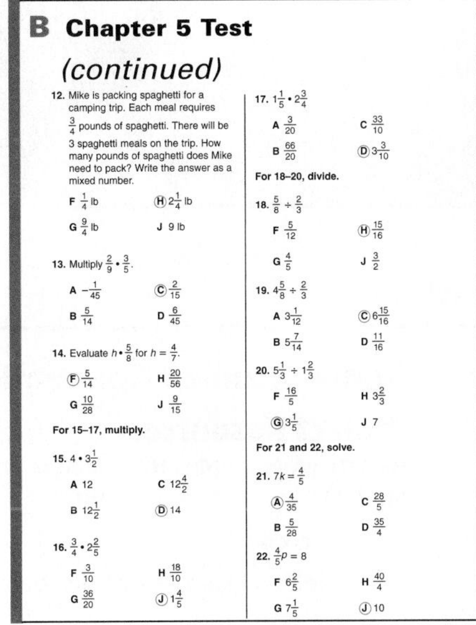

B Chapter 5 Test

(continued)

12. Mike is packing spaghetti for a camping trip. Each meal requires $\frac{3}{4}$ pounds of spaghetti. There will be 3 spaghetti meals on the trip. How many pounds of spaghetti does Mike need to pack? Write the answer as a mixed number.
    F $\frac{1}{4}$ lb Ⓗ $2\frac{1}{4}$ lb
    G $\frac{9}{4}$ lb J 9 lb
13. Multiply $\frac{2}{9} \cdot \frac{3}{5}$.
    A $-\frac{1}{45}$ Ⓒ $\frac{2}{15}$
    B $\frac{5}{14}$ D $\frac{6}{45}$
14. Evaluate $h \cdot \frac{5}{8}$ for $h = \frac{4}{7}$.
    Ⓕ $\frac{5}{14}$ H $\frac{20}{56}$
    G $\frac{10}{28}$ J $\frac{9}{15}$

For 15–17, multiply.

15. $4 \cdot 3\frac{1}{2}$
    A 12 C $12\frac{4}{2}$
    B $12\frac{1}{2}$ Ⓓ 14
16. $\frac{3}{4} \cdot 2\frac{2}{5}$
    F $\frac{3}{10}$ H $\frac{18}{10}$
    G $\frac{36}{20}$ Ⓙ $1\frac{4}{5}$
17. $1\frac{1}{5} \cdot 2\frac{3}{4}$
    A $\frac{3}{20}$ C $\frac{33}{10}$
    B $\frac{66}{20}$ Ⓓ $3\frac{3}{10}$

For 18–20, divide.

18. $\frac{5}{6} \div \frac{2}{3}$
    F $\frac{5}{12}$ Ⓗ $\frac{15}{16}$
    G $\frac{4}{5}$ J $\frac{3}{2}$
19. $4\frac{5}{8} \div \frac{2}{3}$
    A $3\frac{1}{12}$ Ⓒ $6\frac{15}{16}$
    B $5\frac{7}{14}$ D $\frac{11}{16}$
20. $5\frac{1}{3} \div 1\frac{2}{3}$
    F $\frac{16}{5}$ H $3\frac{2}{3}$
    Ⓖ $3\frac{1}{5}$ J 7

For 21 and 22, solve.

21. $7k = \frac{4}{5}$
    Ⓐ $\frac{4}{35}$ C $\frac{28}{5}$
    B $\frac{5}{28}$ D $\frac{35}{4}$
22. $\frac{4}{5}p = 8$
    F $6\frac{2}{5}$ H $\frac{40}{4}$
    G $7\frac{1}{5}$ Ⓙ 10

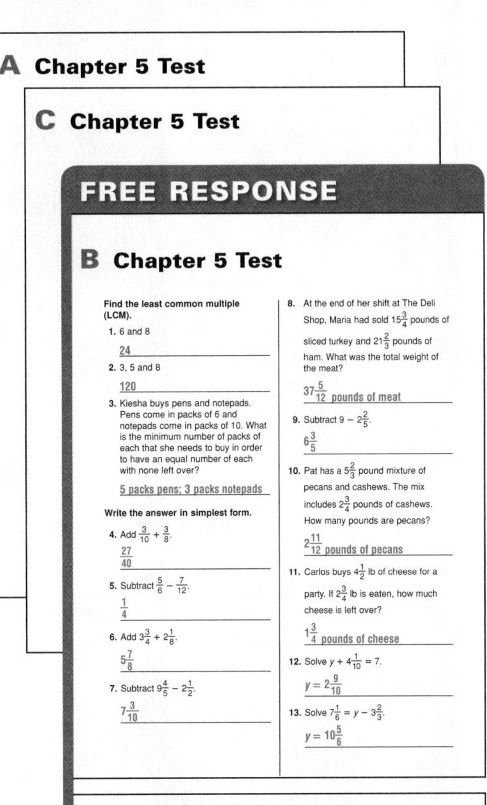

A Chapter 5 Test

C Chapter 5 Test

FREE RESPONSE

B Chapter 5 Test

Find the least common multiple (LCM).

1. 6 and 8
   24
2. 3, 5 and 8
   120
3. Kiesha buys pens and notepads. Pens come in packs of 6 and notepads come in packs of 10. What is the minimum number of packs of each that she needs to buy in order to have an equal number of each with none left over?
   5 packs pens; 3 packs notepads

Write the answer in simplest form.

4. Add $\frac{3}{10} + \frac{3}{8}$.
   $\frac{27}{40}$
5. Subtract $\frac{5}{6} - \frac{7}{12}$.
   $\frac{1}{4}$
6. Add $3\frac{3}{4} + 2\frac{1}{8}$.
   $5\frac{7}{8}$
7. Subtract $9\frac{4}{5} - 2\frac{1}{2}$.
   $7\frac{3}{10}$
8. At the end of her shift at The Deli Shop, Maria had sold $15\frac{3}{4}$ pounds of sliced turkey and $21\frac{2}{3}$ pounds of ham. What was the total weight of the meat?
   $37\frac{5}{12}$ pounds of meat
9. Subtract $9 - 2\frac{2}{5}$.
   $6\frac{3}{5}$
10. Pat has a $5\frac{2}{3}$ pound mixture of pecans and cashews. The mix includes $2\frac{3}{4}$ pounds of cashews. How many pounds are pecans?
    $2\frac{11}{12}$ pounds of pecans
11. Carlos buys $4\frac{1}{2}$ lb of cheese for a party. If $2\frac{3}{4}$ lb is eaten, how much cheese is left over?
    $1\frac{3}{4}$ pounds of cheese
12. Solve $y + 4\frac{1}{10} = 7$.
    $y = 2\frac{9}{10}$
13. Solve $7\frac{1}{6} = y - 3\frac{2}{3}$.
    $y = 10\frac{5}{6}$

B Chapter 5 Test

(continued)

14. Multiply $6 \cdot \frac{2}{3}$.
    4
15. Evaluate $4t$ for $t = \frac{3}{7}$.
    $1\frac{5}{7}$
16. Pete is packing dog food for a 4-day camping trip. Pete's dog will eat $\frac{2}{3}$ pounds of food a day. How many pounds of dog food does Pete need to pack? Write the answer as a mixed number.
    $2\frac{2}{3}$ lb
17. Multiply $\frac{5}{7} \cdot \frac{3}{4}$.
    $\frac{15}{28}$
18. Evaluate $y \cdot \frac{1}{8}$ for $y = \frac{16}{17}$.
    $\frac{2}{17}$
19. Marcus spent $\frac{1}{2}$ of his time for evening chores shoveling snow. For $\frac{2}{3}$ of that time, he shoveled the driveway. Express in simplest form how much of his total chore time he spent shoveling the driveway.
    $\frac{1}{3}$

Multiply. Write the answer in simplest form.

20. $3 \cdot 4\frac{2}{5}$
    $13\frac{1}{5}$
21. $\frac{2}{3} \cdot 4\frac{1}{2}$
    3
22. $1\frac{1}{2} \cdot 3\frac{1}{6}$
    $4\frac{3}{4}$

Divide. Write the answer in simplest form.

23. $\frac{2}{3} \div \frac{4}{5}$
    $\frac{5}{6}$
24. $3\frac{3}{5} \div \frac{3}{4}$
    $4\frac{4}{5}$
25. $2\frac{9}{10} \div 3\frac{1}{3}$
    $\frac{87}{100}$

Solve each equation. Write the solution in simplest form.

26. Solve $4a = \frac{2}{3}$.
    $a = \frac{1}{6}$
27. Solve $\frac{8}{11}y = 6$.
    $y = 8\frac{1}{4}$

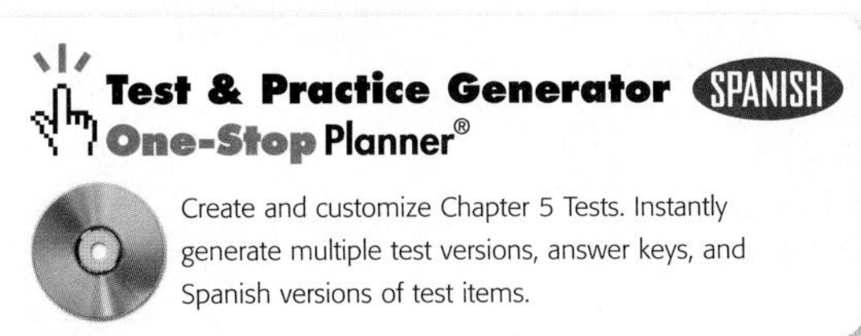

Test & Practice Generator SPANISH
One-Stop Planner®

Create and customize Chapter 5 Tests. Instantly generate multiple test versions, answer keys, and Spanish versions of test items.

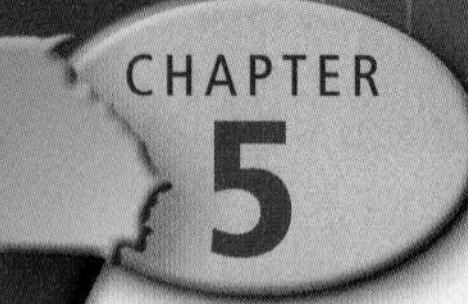

Why Learn This?

Tell students that fractions are essential for describing quantities in the real world. Many quantities cannot accurately be described using only whole numbers. Have students look at the chart to see how a painter describes times using fractions. For example, it may be more useful for a painter to describe 30 minutes as $\frac{1}{2}$ hour.

Using Data

To begin the study of this chapter, have students:

- Find the total amount of time it takes to paint a window with oil-based paint and to paint 100 ft of chair rail with latex paint. $1\frac{1}{2}$ hours = 1hr 30 min
- Determine the number of minutes it takes to paint a door with oil-based paint. 30 min
- Compare the number of minutes it takes to paint 100 ft of chair rail with latex paint and with stain. It takes 45 minutes with latex paint and 36 minutes with stain.

On page 288, students will find cumulative CRCT practice.

CHAPTER 5

Fraction Operations

go.hrw.com
Chapter Project Online
KEYWORD: MR7 Ch5

Painting Times

Object	Paint	Time (hr)
Wall (100 ft^2)	Oil-based	$\frac{3}{10}$
Wall (100 ft^2)	Latex	$\frac{2}{5}$
Chair rail (100 ft)	Latex	$\frac{3}{4}$
Chair rail (100 ft)	Stain	$\frac{3}{5}$
Door	Oil-based	$\frac{1}{2}$
Window	Oil-based	$\frac{3}{4}$

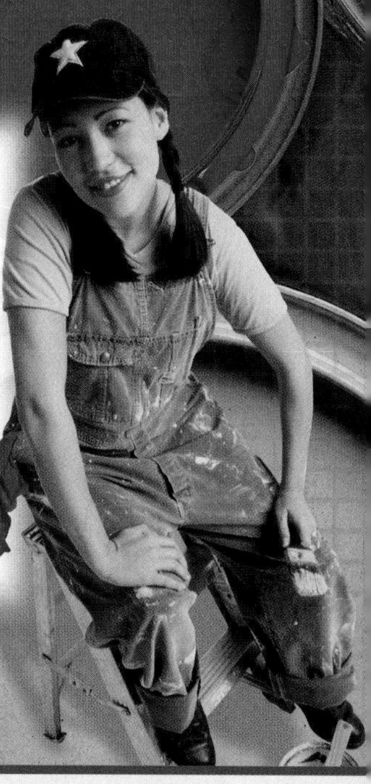

Career *Painter*

Have you ever wondered how painters estimate how much to charge for a job? Professional painters might paint houses, schools, office buildings, sports stadiums, or even music halls. To estimate how much to charge, many painters use a table that lists the average time it should take to prepare and paint certain objects. The table shows some painting jobs and the amount of time they take to complete.

PROBLEM SOLVING

Problem Solving Project

Understand, Plan, Solve, and Look Back

Have students:

- Complete the Painter's Estimates worksheet to learn to use fractions to calculate the time needed to complete an interior painting project.
- Research to find the difference between oil-based paint and latex paint. Why do we need more than one kind of paint? Why would you choose latex or oil-based paint for a particular job? Why does it take longer to paint with oil-based paint than to paint with latex paint?

Social Studies Connection

Project Resources

All project resources for teachers and students are provided online.

Materials:

- Painter's Estimates worksheet

go.hrw.com
Project Teacher Support
KEYWORD: MR7 PSProject5

ARE YOU READY?

Vocabulary

Choose the best term from the list to complete each sentence.

1. The first five ___?___ of 6 are 6, 12, 18, 24, and 30. The ___?___ of 6 are 1, 2, 3, and 6. multiples; factors
2. Fractions with the same denominator are called ___?___. like fractions
3. A fraction is in ___?___ when the GCF of the numerator and the denominator is 1. simplest form
4. The fraction $\frac{13}{9}$ is a(n) ___?___ because the ___?___ is greater than the ___?___. improper fraction; numerator; denominator

denominator
factors
improper fraction
like fractions
multiples
numerator
proper fraction
simplest form
unlike fractions

Complete these exercises to review skills you will need for this chapter.

Simplify Fractions

Write each fraction in simplest form.

5. $\frac{6}{10}$ $\frac{3}{5}$
6. $\frac{5}{15}$ $\frac{1}{3}$
7. $\frac{14}{8}$ $1\frac{3}{4}$
8. $\frac{8}{12}$ $\frac{2}{3}$
9. $\frac{10}{100}$ $\frac{1}{10}$
10. $\frac{12}{144}$ $\frac{1}{12}$
11. $\frac{33}{121}$ $\frac{3}{11}$
12. $\frac{15}{17}$ $\frac{15}{17}$

Write Mixed Numbers as Fractions

Write each mixed number as an improper fraction.

13. $1\frac{1}{8}$ $\frac{9}{8}$
14. $2\frac{3}{4}$ $\frac{11}{4}$
15. $2\frac{4}{5}$ $\frac{14}{5}$
16. $1\frac{7}{9}$ $\frac{16}{9}$
17. $3\frac{1}{5}$ $\frac{16}{5}$
18. $5\frac{2}{3}$ $\frac{17}{3}$
19. $4\frac{4}{7}$ $\frac{32}{7}$
20. $3\frac{11}{12}$ $\frac{47}{12}$

Add and Subtract Like Fractions

Add or subtract. Write each answer in simplest form.

21. $\frac{5}{8}+\frac{1}{8}$ $\frac{3}{4}$
22. $\frac{3}{7}+\frac{5}{7}$ $1\frac{1}{7}$
23. $\frac{9}{10}-\frac{3}{10}$ $\frac{3}{5}$
24. $\frac{5}{9}-\frac{2}{9}$ $\frac{1}{3}$
25. $\frac{1}{2}+\frac{1}{2}$ 1
26. $\frac{7}{12}-\frac{5}{12}$ $\frac{1}{6}$
27. $\frac{3}{5}+\frac{4}{5}$ $1\frac{2}{5}$
28. $\frac{4}{15}-\frac{1}{15}$ $\frac{1}{5}$

Multiplication Facts

Multiply.

29. 8×11 88
30. 7×8 56
31. 4×12 48
32. 12×7 84
33. 10×13 130
34. 9×7 63
35. 6×8 48
36. 11×12 132

ARE YOU READY?

CHAPTER 5

Organizer

Objective: Assess students' understanding of prerequisite skills.

Prerequisite Skills

Simplify Fractions
Write Mixed Numbers as Fractions
Add and Subtract Like Fractions
Multiplication Facts

Assessing Prior Knowledge

INTERVENTION 

Diagnose and Prescribe

Use this page to determine whether intervention is necessary or enrichment is appropriate.

Resources

 ***Are You Ready? Intervention and Enrichment* Worksheets**

 ***Are You Ready?* CD-ROM**

 ***Are You Ready?* Online**

my.hrw.com

ARE YOU READY?

Diagnose and Prescribe

NO INTERVENE

YES ENRICH

Prerequisite Skill	*Are You Ready? Intervention,* Chapter 5 — Worksheets	CD-ROM	Online
Simplify Fractions	Skill 19	Activity 19	Diagnose and Prescribe Online
Write Mixed Numbers as Fractions	Skill 22	Activity 22	
Add and Subtract Like Fractions	Skill 43	Activity 43	
Multiplication Facts	Skill 36	Activity 36	

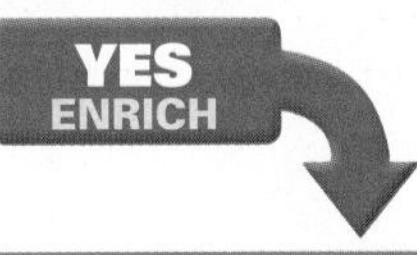

CHAPTER 5 Study Guide: Preview

Organizer

Objective: Help students organize the new concepts they will learn in Chapter 5.

Online Edition
Multilingual Glossary

Resources

***Multilingual Glossary* Online**

go.hrw.com
KEYWORD: MR7 Glossary

Answers to *Vocabulary Connections*

Possible answers:

1. The reciprocal of a fraction is the inverse or the inverted fraction.
2. Two numbers that have a common multiple are both factors of that number. Least common multiple is the smallest multiple common to both numbers.
3. The least common denominator is the smallest number that the original denominators are a factor of.

CHAPTER 5 Study Guide: Preview

Where You've Been

Previously, you

- modeled addition and subtraction of fractions with like denominators.
- estimated sums and differences of whole numbers.
- wrote equivalent fractions.

In This Chapter

You will study

- modeling addition and subtraction situations involving fractions.
- estimating sums and differences of fractions.
- adding, subtracting, multiplying, and dividing fractions and mixed numbers with unlike denominators.
- solving equations with fractions.

Where You're Going

You can use the skills learned in this chapter

- to solve measurement problems that involve fractions and mixed numbers.
- to estimate sums and differences between distances that involve fractions.

Key Vocabulary/Vocabulario

least common denominator (LCD)	mínimo común denominador (MCD)
least common multiple (LCM)	mínimo común múltiplo (MCM)
reciprocals	recíproco

Vocabulary Connections

To become familiar with some of the vocabulary terms in the chapter, consider the following. You may refer to the chapter, the glossary, or a dictionary if you like.

1. The word *reciprocal* means "inversely related or opposite." What do you think the **reciprocal** of a fraction will look like?
2. When people have something in *common*, they have something that they share. What do you think two numbers with a common multiple share? What do you think the **least common multiple** of two numbers is?
3. Fractions with the same denominator have a common denominator. What do you think the **least common denominator** of two fractions is?

Study Guide: Preview

Grade 6 CRCT GPS

M6N1.
Students will understand the meaning of the four arithmetic operations as related to positive rational numbers and will use these concepts to solve problems.
c. Determine the greatest common factor (GCF) and the least common multiple (LCM) for a set of numbers.
d. Add and subtract fractions and mixed numbers with unlike denominators.
e. Multiply and divide fractions and mixed numbers.
f. Use fractions, decimals, and percents interchangeably.
g. Solve problems involving fractions, decimals, and percents.

M6A3.
Students will evaluate algebraic expressions, including those with exponents, and solve simple one-step equations using each of the four basic operations.

M6P1.
Students will solve problems (using appropriate technology).

M6P4.
Students will make connections among mathematical ideas and to other disciplines.

M6P5.
Students will represent mathematics in multiple ways.

***Georgia Mathematics Performance Standards* statements are written out completely on pp. GA28–GA35.**

Reading and Writing Math

Study Strategy: Make Flash Cards

Create flash cards to help you learn a sequence of steps, vocabulary, math symbols, formulas, or mathematical rules. Study your flash cards often.

Use these suggestions to make flash cards.

- Label each card with the lesson number so you can look back at your textbook when studying.
- Write the name of the formula, term, or rule on one side of the card, and the meaning or an example on the other side of the card.
- Write definitions using your own words.

From Lesson 4-8

Life Science Application

Sophie plants a young oak tree in her backyard. The distance around the trunk grows at a rate of $\frac{1}{8}$ inch per month. Use pictures to model how much this distance will increase in two months, then write your answer in simplest form.

$\frac{1}{8} + \frac{1}{8}$

$\frac{1}{8} + \frac{1}{8} = \frac{2}{8}$ *Add the numerators. Keep the same denominator.*

$= \frac{1}{4}$ *Write your answer in simplest form.*

The distance around the trunk will increase by $\frac{1}{4}$ inch.

Sample Flash Card

Front

Lesson 4-8
Pages 202-205

Adding and Subtracting Fractions with Like Denominators

Back

	$\frac{1}{8} + \frac{1}{8}$
Keep the denominators.	$\frac{1}{8} + \frac{1}{8} = \frac{\ }{8}$
Add the numerators.	$\frac{1}{8} + \frac{1}{8} = \frac{2}{8}$
Write in simplest form.	$\frac{1}{4}$

Try This

1. Use Lesson 4-6 to make flash cards for the rules for writing mixed numbers as improper fractions.

Organizer

Objective: Help students apply strategies to understand and retain key concepts.

Online Edition

Resources

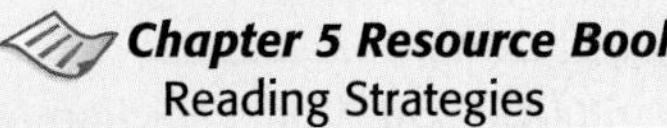

Chapter 5 Resource Book
Reading Strategies

Study Strategy: Make Flash Cards

Discuss Help students to understand the advantage of having a note-taking system that is flexible and can be customized. It is easier to study alone because definitions, examples, and solutions are on the back side of the card. Students can use flash cards to review as few or as many concepts as needed.

Extend A project for one or more grading periods can be designed around students maintaining a creative flash card system.

Answers to *Try This*

1. Check students' work.

Grade 6 CRCT GPS

Standards	5-1	LAB 5-2	5-2	5-3	LAB 5-4	5-4	5-5	5-6	LAB 5-7	5-7	5-8	LAB 5-9	5-9	5-10
M6N1.c	★													
M6N1.d		★	★	★	★	★	★							
M6N1.e								★	★	★	★	★	★	★
M6N1.g			★	★		★	★	★	★	★	★	★	★	★
M6A3							★	★		★				★
M6P1	★		★	★		★		★						★
M6P4			★				★							
M6P5	★	★			★	★			★	★		★	★	

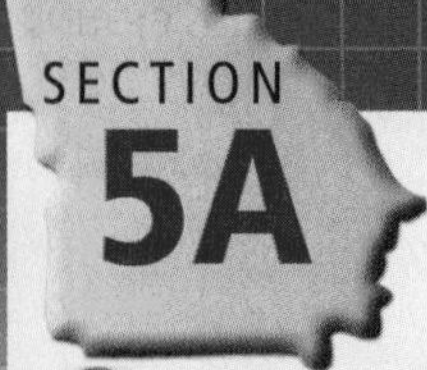

Adding and Subtracting Fractions

One-Minute Section Planner

Lesson	Materials	MiC and Lab Resources
Lesson 5-1 Least Common Multiple • Find the least common multiple (LCM) of a group of numbers. ☑ CRCT ☑ SAT-10 ☑ ITBS ☑ CTBS ☑ NAEP	Spinners (MK)	**MiC:** ***Fraction Times*** p. 7 ***Technology Lab Activities*** 5-1
8-5 Hands-On Lab Model Fraction Addition and Subtraction • Use fraction bars to model addition and subtraction of fractions. **Lesson 5-2** Adding and Subtracting with Unlike Denominators • Add and subtract fractions with unlike denominators. ☑ CRCT ☐ SAT-10 ☑ ITBS ☐ CTBS ☑ NAEP	Fraction bars (MK), grid paper, fraction bar transparency	**MiC:** ***Fraction Times*** pp. 20–21 **MiC:** ***Expressions and Formulas*** pp. 39–40 ***Hands-On Lab Activities*** 5-2 ***Technology Lab Activities*** 5-2
Lesson 5-3 Adding and Subtracting Mixed Numbers • Add and subtract mixed numbers with unlike denominators. ☑ CRCT ☑ SAT-10 ☑ ITBS ☐ CTBS ☑ NAEP	Rulers (MK)	**MiC:** ***Reallotment*** pp. 18–21, 30–31 ***Technology Lab Activities*** 5-3
5-4 Hands-On Lab Model Subtraction witk Regrouping • Use fraction bars to model subtraction of fractions by regrouping them. **Lesson 5-4** Regrouping to Subtract Mixed Numbers • Regroup mixed numbers to subtract. ☑ CRCT ☑ SAT-10 ☑ ITBS ☐ CTBS ☑ NAEP	Fraction bars (MK), grid paper, fraction bar transparency	**MiC:** ***Reallotment*** pp. 18–21 ***Hands-On Lab Activities*** 5-4
Lesson 5-5 Solving Fraction Equations: Addition and Subtraction • Solve equations by adding and subtracting fractions. ☑ CRCT ☑ SAT-10 ☑ ITBS ☐ CTBS ☑ NAEP		

MK = *Manipulatives Kit*

Mathematics in Context

The units ***Fraction Times, Expressions and Formulas,*** and ***Reallotment*** from the *Mathematics in Context* © 2006 series can be used with Section 5A. See Section Planner above for suggestions for integrating *MiC* with *Holt Mathematics.*

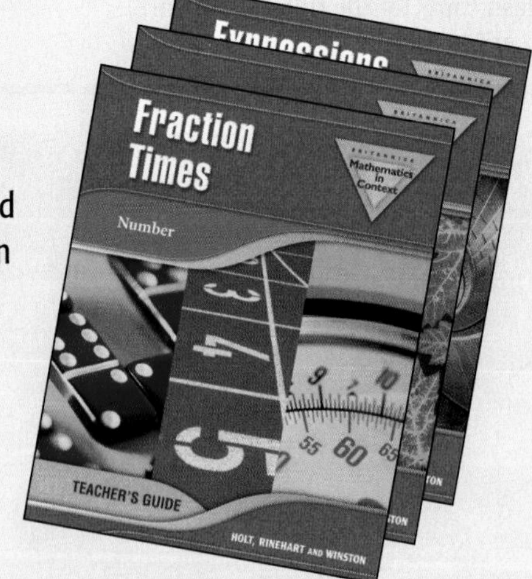

Section Overview

Professional Development

Adding and Subtracting Fractions

Lesson 5-1, 5-2, 5-3

Why? Adding and subtracting fractions is necessary in many problems-solving situations.

To add or subtract unlike fractions, first rewrite them as equivalent fractions with a **common denominator**.

$$\frac{1}{6} + \frac{7}{10}$$

$$\frac{1 \cdot 5}{6 \cdot 5} + \frac{7 \cdot 3}{10 \cdot 3}$$

$$\frac{5}{30} + \frac{21}{30}$$

$$\frac{26}{30}$$

$$\frac{13}{15}$$

To find a **common denominator**, find the LCM of 6 and 10.

List the multiples.

6: 6, 12, 18, 24, **30**, . . .

10: 10, 20, **30**, . . .

Use prime factorization.

$6 = 2 \cdot 3$

$10 = 2 \cdot 5$

LCM = $2 \cdot 3 \cdot 5 = 30$

Regrouping to Subtract Fractions

Lesson 5-4

Why? In order to solve fraction equations, you may need to regroup to subtract.

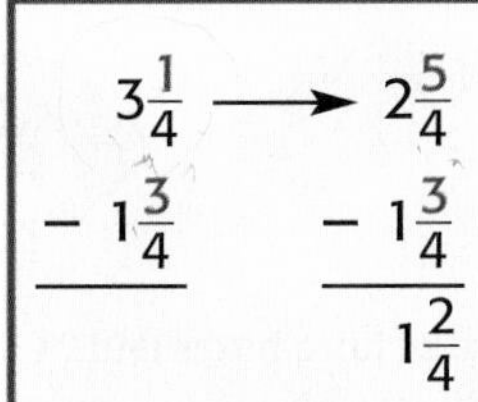

$$3\frac{1}{4} - 1\frac{3}{4} \longrightarrow 2\frac{5}{4} - 1\frac{3}{4} = 1\frac{2}{4}$$

Rename $3\frac{1}{4}$ as $2\frac{5}{4}$ in order to subtract the numerators.

Fraction Equations with Addition and Subtraction

Lesson 5-5

Why? Many equations that model real-world situations contain fractions.

Subtract $1\frac{3}{4}$ from both sides to undo the addition.

$$\begin{aligned} x + 1\tfrac{3}{4} &= 3\tfrac{1}{4} \\ -\,1\tfrac{3}{4} &\quad -\,1\tfrac{3}{4} \\ x &= 1\tfrac{2}{4} \\ x &= 1\tfrac{1}{2} \end{aligned}$$

5-1 Organizer

Pacing: Traditional 2 day
Block 1 day

Objective: Students find the least common multiple (LCM) of a group of numbers.

GPS M6N1.c
Technology Lab
In *Technology Lab Activities*

Online Edition
Tutorial Videos

Countdown to CRCT Week 10

Power Presentations with PowerPoint®

Warm Up

Write the first five multiples of each number.

1. 5 — 5, 10, 15, 20, 25
2. 6 — 6, 12, 18, 24, 30
3. 10 — 10, 20, 30, 40, 50
4. 12 — 12, 24, 36, 48, 60

Problem of the Day

Greg, Sam, and Mary all work at the same high school. One of them is a principal, one of them is a teacher, and one of them is a janitor. Sam is older than Mary. Mary does not live in the same town as the principal. The teacher, the oldest of the three, often plays golf with Greg. What is each person's job? Greg, principal; Sam, teacher; Mary, janitor

Also available on transparency

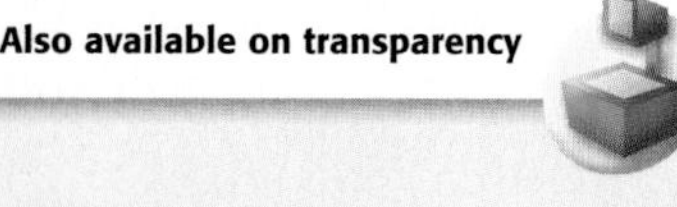

Georgia Performance Standards

M6N1.c Determine the greatest common factor (GCF) and the least common multiple (LCM) for a set of numbers.

M6P1.b Solve problems that arise in mathematics and in other contexts.

M6P5.c Use representations to model and interpret physical, social, and mathematical phenomena.

5-1 Least Common Multiple

Learn to find the least common multiple (LCM) of a group of numbers.

Vocabulary
least common multiple (LCM)

Georgia Performance Standards

M6N1.c Determine the least common multiple (LCM) for a set of numbers. Also, M6P1.b, M6P5.c.

After games in Lydia's soccer league, one player's family brings snacks for both teams to share. This week Lydia's family will provide juice boxes and granola bars for 24 players.

You can make a model to help you find the least number of juice and granola packs Lydia's family should buy. Use colored counters, drawings, or pictures to illustrate the problem.

EXAMPLE 1 *Consumer Application*

Remember!
A multiple of a number is the product of the number and any nonzero whole number.

Juice comes in packs of 6, and granola bars in packs of 8. If there are 24 players, what is the least number of packs needed so that each player has a drink and granola bar and there are none left over?

Draw juice boxes in groups of 6. Draw granola bars in groups of 8. Stop when you have drawn the same number of each.

There are 24 juice boxes and 24 granola bars.

Lydia's family should buy 4 packs of juice and 3 packs of granola bars.

The smallest number that is a multiple of two or more numbers is the **least common multiple (LCM)**. In Example 1, the LCM of 6 and 8 is 24.

1 Introduce

Alternate Opener

EXPLORATION

5-1 Least Common Multiple

1. Sarah and Jane enter a walkathon for charity. They start together, but Sarah completes one lap every 6 minutes while Jane completes one lap every 8 minutes.

Number of Laps Completed	Sarah's Time (min)	Jane's Time (min)
1	6 · 1 = 6	8 · 1 = 8
2	6 · 2 = 12	8 · 2 = 16
3	6 · 3 = 18	8 · 3 = 24
4	6 · 4 = 24	8 · 4 = 32
5	6 · 5 = 30	8 · 5 = 40
6	6 · 6 = 36	8 · 6 = 48
7	6 · 7 = 42	8 · 7 = 56
8	6 · 8 = 48	8 · 8 = 64

a. After how many minutes will Sarah and Jane meet at the start again?

b. When will they meet the next time?

Think and Discuss

2. **Discuss** the solution to number **1a** using the term *common multiple.*
3. **Compare** the solution to number **1a** with the solution to number **1b**, and describe these solutions using the terms *common multiple* and *least common multiple.*

Motivate

Have students work on the following problem. Two faucets are dripping. One faucet will drip every 4 seconds and the other faucet drips every 9 seconds. If a drop of water falls from both faucets at the same time, how many seconds will it be before you see the faucets drip at the same time again? 36 seconds

Explorations and answers are provided in *Alternate Openers: Explorations Transparencies.*

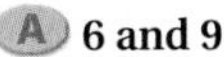

EXAMPLE 2 Using Multiples to Find the LCM

Find the least common multiple (LCM).

Method 1: Use a number line.

A **6 and 9**

Use a number line to skip count by 6 and 9.

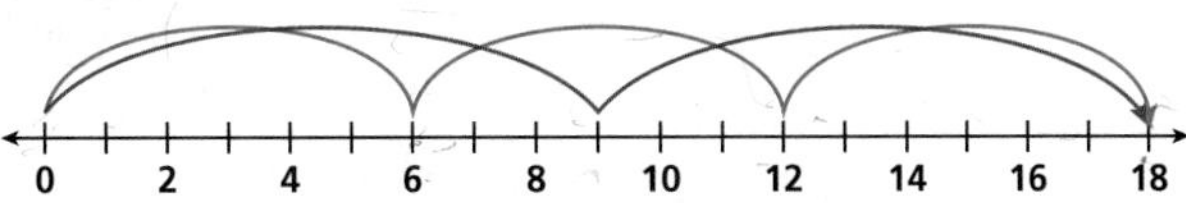

The least common multiple (LCM) of 6 and 9 is 18.

Method 2: Use a list.

B **3, 5, and 6**

3: 3, 6, 9, 12, 15, 18, 21, 24, 27, 30, 33, . . .
5: 5, 10, 15, 20, 25, 30, 35, . . .
6: 6, 12, 18, 24, 30, 36, . . .

List multiples of 3, 5, and 6. Find the smallest number that is in all the lists.

LCM: 30

Method 3: Use prime factorization.

C **8 and 12**

$8 = 2 \cdot 2 \cdot 2$
$12 = 2 \cdot 2 \cdot \quad 3$
$\downarrow \; \downarrow \; \downarrow \; \downarrow$
$2 \cdot 2 \cdot 2 \cdot 3$
$2 \cdot 2 \cdot 2 \cdot 3 = 24$

Write the prime factorization of each number. Line up the common factors. To find the LCM, multiply one number from each column.

LCM: 24

D **12, 10, and 15**

$12 = 2^2 \cdot 3$
$10 = 2 \cdot \quad 5$
$15 = \quad 3 \cdot 5$
$\downarrow \; \downarrow \; \downarrow$
$2^2 \cdot 3 \cdot 5$
$2^2 \cdot 3 \cdot 5 = 60$

Write the prime factorization of each number in exponential form.

To find the LCM, multiply each prime factor once with the greatest exponent used in any of the prime factorizations.

LCM: 60

Remember!

The prime factorization of a number is the number written as a product of its prime factors.

Think and Discuss

GPS M6P2.c, M6P3.b

1. **Explain** why you cannot find a greatest common multiple for a group of numbers.
2. **Tell** whether the LCM of a set of numbers can ever be smaller than any of the numbers in the set.

Answers to *Think and Discuss*

1. Possible answer: For any common multiple found, you can always create a greater common multiple by continuing to multiply the common multiple by any whole number.

2. No, the LCM of a set of numbers can be equal to one of the numbers in the set, but never smaller than any number in the set.

COMMON ERROR ALERT

Some students may confuse LCM with GCF. Tell them to concentrate on the words *multiple* and *factor* to keep their meanings straight. Finding the GCF and LCM for the same set of numbers helps students see the difference.

Power Presentations with PowerPoint®

Additional Examples

Example 1

English muffins come in packs of 8, and eggs come in cartons of 12. If there are 24 students, what is the least number of packs and cartons needed so that each student has a muffin sandwich with one egg?

Three packs of English muffins and 2 cartons of eggs are needed.

Example 2

Find the least common multiple (LCM).

A. 3 and 4 **12**
B. 4, 5, and 8 **40**
C. 6 and 20 **60**
D. 15, 6, and 4 **60**

Also available on transparency

2 Teach

Guided Instruction

In this lesson, students learn to find the least common multiple (LCM) for a group of numbers. First show them a real-world application of the LCM. Then teach them three methods for finding the LCM of a group of numbers: use a number line, use a list, and use prime factorization.

Teaching Tip **Multiple Representations** For Example 2, have students use each of the three methods for finding the LCM for each given set of numbers.

Reaching All Learners
Through Concrete Manipulatives

Give students spinners labeled with the digits 1–9 (provided in the Manipulatives Kit). Have students spin their spinners to generate sets of three or four 1- and 2-digit numbers. Have students use each of the three given methods to find the LCM for each set of numbers.

3 Close

Summarize

ENGLISH LANGUAGE LEARNERS

Review the term *least common multiple* (LCM) and have students explain how the LCM differs from the GCF.

Possible answer: The LCM is the *least* number that is a *multiple* of all numbers in a given set. The GCF is the *greatest* number that is a *factor* of all numbers in a given set (or by which all numbers in a set are divisible). The GCF is smaller than the LCM unless all of the numbers are equal.

5-1 Exercises

Assignment Guide

If you finished Example 1 assign:
Average 1, 41–52
Advanced 14, 41–52

If you finished Example 2 assign:
Average 1–38, 41–52
Advanced 1–36, 38–52

Homework Quick Check

Quickly check key concepts.
Exercises: 14, 16, 24, 32

Math Background

An alternative method for finding the least common multiple of two numbers is to divide their product by their greatest common factor. For example, because the greatest common factor of 10 and 12 is 2, the least common multiple of 10 and 12 is $(10 \cdot 12) \div 2 = 60$. This method has the advantage of not requiring the enumeration of multiples.

Georgia Performance Standards

M6P1.c Apply and adapt a variety of appropriate strategies to solve problems.

M6P3.a Organize and consolidate their mathematical thinking through communication.

M6P5.c Use representations to model and interpret physical, social, and mathematical phenomena.

5-1 Exercises

Georgia Performance Standards
M6P1.c, M6P3.a, M6P5.c

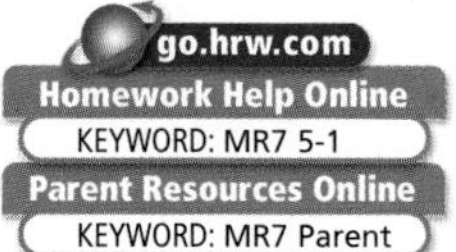

go.hrw.com
Homework Help Online
KEYWORD: MR7 5-1
Parent Resources Online
KEYWORD: MR7 Parent

GUIDED PRACTICE

See Example 1

1. Pencils are sold in packs of 12, and erasers in packs of 9. Mr. Joplin wants to give each of 36 students a pencil and an eraser. What is the least number of packs he should buy so there are none left over? **3 packs of pencils and 4 packs of erasers**

See Example 2

Find the least common multiple (LCM).

2. 3 and 5 **15**
3. 4 and 9 **36**
4. 2, 3, and 6 **6**
5. 2, 4, and 5 **20**
6. 4 and 12 **12**
7. 6 and 16 **48**
8. 4, 6, and 8 **24**
9. 2, 5, and 8 **40**
10. 6 and 10 **30**
11. 21 and 63 **63**
12. 3, 5, and 9 **45**
13. 5, 6, and 25 **150**

INDEPENDENT PRACTICE

See Example 1

14. String-cheese sticks are sold in packs of 10, and celery sticks in packs of 15. Ms. Sobrino wants to give each of 30 students one string-cheese stick and one celery stick. What is the least number of packs she should buy so there are none left over? **3 packs of string cheese sticks and 2 packs of celery sticks**

See Example 2

Find the least common multiple (LCM).

15. 2 and 8 **8**
16. 3 and 7 **21**
17. 4 and 10 **20**
18. 3 and 9 **9**
19. 3, 6, and 9 **18**
20. 4, 8, and 10 **40**
21. 4, 6, and 12 **12**
22. 4, 6, and 7 **84**
23. 3, 8, and 12 **24**
24. 3, 7, and 10 **210**
25. 2, 6, and 11 **66**
26. 2, 3, 6, and 9 **18**
27. 2, 4, 5, and 6 **60**
28. 10 and 11 **110**
29. 4, 5, and 7 **140**
30. 2, 3, 6, and 8 **24**

PRACTICE AND PROBLEM SOLVING

Extra Practice p. 722

31. What is the LCM of 6 and 12? **12**
32. What is the LCM of 5 and 11? **55**
33. **The diagram at right is a Venn diagram. The numbers in the red circle are multiples of 4. The numbers in the blue circle are multiples of 6. The numbers in the purple section are multiples of both 4 and 6.**

Find the missing numbers in the Venn diagram.

Multiples of 4 | Multiples of 6
a, 4 | c, 24, d | 6, b

a. a two-digit multiple of 4 that is not a multiple of 6 **Possible answers: 16, 20, 28**
b. a two-digit multiple of 6 that is not a multiple of 4 **Possible answers: 18, 30, 42**
c. the LCM of 4 and 6 **12**
d. a three-digit common multiple of 4 and 6 **120, 144, 168, and 192**

Find a pair of numbers that has the given characteristics.

34. The LCM of the two numbers is 26. One number is even and one is odd. **13 and 26**
35. The LCM of the two numbers is 48. The sum of the numbers is 28. **12 and 16**
36. The LCM of the two numbers is 60. The difference of the two numbers is 3. **12 and 15**

RETEACH 5-1

LESSON 5-1 **Reteach**
Least Common Multiple

The smallest number that is a multiple of two or more numbers is called the least common multiple (LCM).

To find the least common multiple of 3, 6, and 8, list the multiples for each number and put a circle around the LCM in the three list.

Multiples of 3: 3, 6, 9, 12, 15, 18, 21, 24
Multiples of 6: 6, 12, 18, 24, 30, 36, 42
Multiples of 8: 8, 16, 24, 32, 40, 48, 56
So 24 is the LCM of 3, 6, and 8.

List the multiples of each number to help you find the least common multiple of each group.

1. 3 and 4
Multiples of 3: ____
Multiples of 4: ____
LCM: 12

2. 5 and 7
Multiples of 5: ____
Multiples of 7: ____
LCM: 35

3. 8 and 12
Multiples of 8: ____
Multiples of 12: ____
LCM: 24

4. 2 and 9
Multiples of 2: ____
Multiples of 9: ____
LCM: 18

5. 4 and 6
Multiples of 4: ____
Multiples of 6: ____
LCM: 12

6. 4 and 10
Multiples of 4: ____
Multiples of 10: ____
LCM: 20

7. 2, 5, and 6
Multiples of 2: ____
Multiples of 5: ____
Multiples of 6: ____
LCM: 30

8. 3, 4, and 9
Multiples of 3: ____
Multiples of 4: ____
Multiples of 9: ____
LCM: 36

9. 8, 10, and 12
Multiples of 8: ____
Multiples of 10: ____
Multiples of 12: ____
LCM: 120

PRACTICE 5-1

LESSON 5-1 **Practice B**
Least Common Multiple

Find the least common multiple (LCM).

1. 2 and 5 — 10
2. 4 and 3 — 12
3. 6 and 4 — 12
4. 6 and 8 — 24
5. 5 and 9 — 45
6. 4 and 5 — 20
7. 10 and 15 — 30
8. 8 and 12 — 24
9. 6 and 10 — 30
10. 3, 6, and 9 — 18
11. 2, 5, and 10 — 10
12. 4, 7, and 14 — 28
13. 3, 5, and 9 — 45
14. 2, 5, and 8 — 40
15. 3, 9, and 12 — 36

16. Mr. Stevenson is ordering shirts and hats for his Boy Scout troop. There are 45 scouts in the troop. Hats come in packs of 3, and shirts come in packs of 5. What is the least number of packs of each he should order to so that each scout will have 1 hat and 1 shirt, and none will be left over?
15 packs of hats and 9 packs of shirts

17. Tony wants to make 36 party bags. Glitter pens come in packs of 6. Stickers come in sheets of 4, and balls come in packs of 3. What is the least number of each package he should buy to have 1 of each item in every party bag, and no supplies left over?
6 packs of pens, 9 sheets of stickers, and 12 packs of balls

18. Glenda is making 30 school supply baskets. Notepads come in packs of 5. Erasers come in packs of 15, and markers come in packs of 3. What is the least number of each package she should buy to have 1 of each item in every basket, and no supplies left over?
6 packs of notepads, 2 packs of erasers, and 10 packs of markers

Georgia LINK
Career

Paula Deen runs the award-winning Lady & Sons Restaurant in Savannah. She also has a cooking show on the Food Network and is the author of several cookbooks.

37. During its grand opening weekend, a restaurant gave every eighth customer a free appetizer, every twelfth customer a free beverage, and every fifteenth customer a free dish of frozen yogurt.
   a. Which customer was the first to receive all three free items? **120**
   b. Which customer was the first to receive a free appetizer and frozen yogurt? **120**
   c. If the restaurant served 500 customers that weekend, how many of those customers received all three free items? **4**

38. **Choose a Strategy** Sophia gave $\frac{1}{2}$ of her semi-precious-rock collection to her son. She gave $\frac{1}{2}$ of what she had left to her grandson. Then she gave $\frac{1}{2}$ of what she had left to her great-grandson. She kept 10 rocks for herself. How many rocks did she have in the beginning?

Ⓐ 40　　Ⓑ 80 (circled)　　Ⓒ 100　　Ⓓ 160

39. **Write About It** Explain the steps you can use to find the LCM of two numbers. Choose two numbers to show an example of your method.

40. **Challenge** Find the LCM of each pair of numbers.
   a. 4 and 6　　b. 8 and 9　　c. 5 and 7　　d. 8 and 10

   When is the LCM of two numbers equal to the product of the two numbers?
   a. 12　b. 72　c. 35　d. 40; when they have no common prime factors

CRCT Prep • GPS Support • Spiral Review

41. **Multiple Choice** Cheese cubes are sold in packs of 60. Crackers are sold in packs of 12. To make 60 snacks of 2 cheese cubes and 1 cracker, what is the least number of packs of each type needed?

Ⓐ 2 cheese, 1 cracker　　Ⓒ 2 cheese, 2 cracker
Ⓑ 2 cheese, 5 cracker (circled)　　Ⓓ 5 cheese, 2 cracker

42. **Multiple Choice** What is the least common multiple of 5 and 8?

Ⓕ 40 (circled)　　Ⓖ 20　　Ⓗ 80　　Ⓙ 60

Multiply. (Lesson 3-6)

43. 0.3×0.1 **0.03**　44. 0.16×0.5 **0.08**　45. 1.2×0.2 **0.24**　46. 0.7×9 **6.3**

Compare. Write <, >, or =. (Lesson 4-7)

47. $\frac{2}{9}$ ▪ $\frac{2}{13}$ **>**　48. $\frac{10}{11}$ ▪ $\frac{100}{110}$ **=**　49. $5\frac{2}{7}$ ▪ $3\frac{5}{7}$ **>**

Add or subtract. (Lesson 4-8)

50. $\frac{5}{6} + \frac{11}{6}$ **$2\frac{2}{3}$**　51. $\frac{3}{7} + 4\frac{2}{7}$ **$4\frac{5}{7}$**　52. $6\frac{2}{3} - 3\frac{1}{3}$ **$3\frac{1}{3}$**

CHALLENGE 5-1

LESSON 5-1 **Challenge**
Moons Over Neptune

We measure one month by our moon's orbital period, or the time it takes the Moon to travel once around Earth, which is about 30 days. But what if you lived on Neptune? It has 8 moons! How could you pick just one moon to measure your months? One possible solution is to calculate one month based on when two of Neptune's moons are in conjunction at some arbitrary starting point in the sky, or appear to be in the same place in the sky. The diagram below shows some of the moons you could use to measure your months on Neptune.

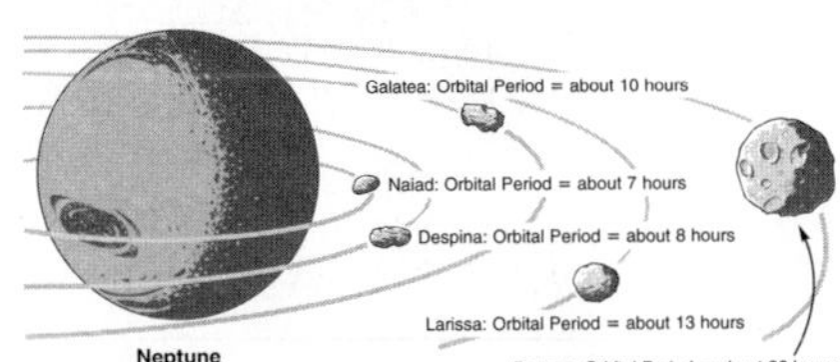

Use the diagram and least common multiples to complete the chart below. For each row, write how long your month on Neptune would be if you used those moons in conjunction as the length of one month.

Neptune Moons to Use	Length of One Neptune Month
Naiad and Despina	about 56 hours
Larissa and Proteus	about 26 hours
Galatea and Despina	about 40 hours
Despina and Proteus	about 104 hours

PROBLEM SOLVING 5-1

LESSON 5-1 **Problem Solving**
Least Common Multiple

Use the table to answer the questions.

Party Supplies

Item	Number per Pack
Invitations	12
Balloons	30
Paper plates	10
Paper napkins	24
Plastic cups	15
Noise makers	5

1. You want to have an equal number of plastic cups and paper plates. What is the least number of packs of each you can buy?
   3 packs of plates and
   2 packs of cups
2. You want to invite 48 people to a party. What is the least number of packs of invitations and napkins you should buy to have one for each person and none left over?
   4 packs of invitations and
   2 packs of napkins

Circle the letter of the correct answer.

3. You want to have an equal number of noisemakers and balloons at your party. What is the least number of packs of each you can buy?
   A 1 pack of balloons and 1 pack of noise makers
   B 1 pack of balloons and 2 packs of noise makers
   Ⓒ 1 pack of balloons and 6 packs of noise makers
   D 6 packs of balloons and 1 pack of noise makers
4. You bought an equal number of packs of plates and cups so that each of your 20 guests would have 3 cups and 2 plates. How many packs of each item did you buy?
   F 1 pack of cups and 1 pack of plates
   G 3 packs of cups and 4 packs of plates
   H 4 packs of cups and 3 packs of plates
   Ⓙ 4 packs of cups and 4 packs of plates
5. The LCM for three items listed in the table is 60 packs. Which of the following are those three items?
   A balloons, plates, noise makers
   Ⓑ noise makers, invitations, balloons
   C napkins, cups, plates
   D balloons, napkins, plates
6. To have one of each item for 120 party guests, you buy 10 packs of one item and 24 packs of the other. What are those two items?
   F plates and invitations
   G balloons and cups
   H napkins and plates
   Ⓙ invitations and noise makers

Ongoing Assessment and Intervention

***Diagnose Before* the Lesson**
5-1 Warm Up, TE p. 228

***Monitor During* the Lesson**
5-1 Know-It Notebook
5-1 Questioning Strategies

***Assess After* the Lesson**
5-1 Lesson Quiz, TE p. 231

Answers

39. Possible answer: Choose 3 and 4. List multiples of the first number: 3, 6, 9, 12, 15.... List multiples of the second number: 4, 8, 12, 16.... Find the smallest number they have in common. The LCM is 12.

Test Prep Doctor For Exercise 42, students may select any method for finding the LCM. However, they may choose to test each answer choice. Choices **G** and **J** can be eliminated because 8 is not a factor. 8 and 5 are factors of choices **F** and **H,** but choice **F** is the smaller number and therefore is correct.

Journal

Have students list three numbers and find their LCM. Have students explain two methods they could use for finding the LCM.

Power Presentations with PowerPoint®

5-1 Lesson Quiz

Find the least common multiple (LCM).

1. 6, 14　**42**
2. 9, 12　**36**
3. 5, 6, 10　**30**
4. 12, 16, 24, 36　**144**
5. Two students in Mrs. Albring's preschool class are stacking blocks, one on top of the other. Reece's blocks are 4 cm high, and Maddy's blocks are 9 cm high. How tall will their stacks be when they are the same height for the first time?
   36 cm

Also available on transparency

Organizer

Use with Lesson 5-2

Pacing:
Traditional $\frac{1}{2}$ day
Block $\frac{1}{4}$ day

Objective: Use fraction bars to model addition and subtraction of fractions.

Materials: Fraction bars

Online Edition
Fraction Bars

Resources

Hands-On Lab Activities
Lab 5-2 Recording Sheet

Teach

Discuss

Discuss with students what each fraction bar represents.

Close

Key Concept

Addition and subtraction of fractions can occur only when the fractions have common denominators.

Assessment

Represent each fraction using fraction bars.

1. $\frac{3}{8}$ — $\frac{1}{8}$ $\frac{1}{8}$ $\frac{1}{8}$
2. $\frac{5}{12}$ — $\frac{1}{12}$ $\frac{1}{12}$ $\frac{1}{12}$ $\frac{1}{12}$ $\frac{1}{12}$
3. How can you use $\frac{1}{6}$ bars to represent $\frac{1}{2}$? Use three $\frac{1}{6}$ bars.

Model Addition and Subtraction of Fractions

Use with Lesson 5-2 and 5-3

Georgia Performance Standards
M6N1.d, M6P5.a, M6P5.b

go.hrw.com
Lab Resources Online
KEYWORD: MR7 Lab5

When fractions have different denominators, you need to find a common denominator before you can add or subtract them. Write equivalent fractions with the same denominator and then perform the operation.

Activity 1

1 Find $\frac{1}{8} + \frac{1}{4}$.

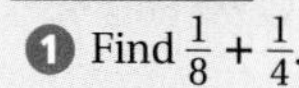

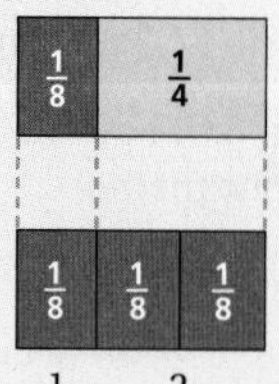

$\frac{1}{8} + \frac{2}{8} = \frac{3}{8}$

Use fraction bars to represent both fractions.

Find one size fraction bar to model both fractions.

$\frac{1}{8} = \frac{1}{8}$ and $\frac{1}{4}$ is equivalent to $\frac{2}{8}$.

Find the total number of $\frac{1}{8}$ fraction bars.

2 Find $\frac{2}{3} + \frac{1}{2}$.

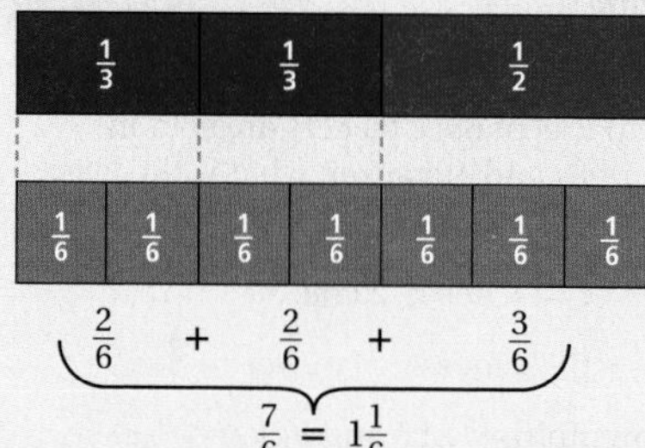

$\frac{2}{6} + \frac{2}{6} + \frac{3}{6}$

$\frac{7}{6} = 1\frac{1}{6}$

Use fraction bars to represent both fractions.

Find one size fraction bar to model both fractions.

$\frac{1}{3}$ is equivalent to $\frac{2}{6}$, and $\frac{1}{2}$ is equivalent to $\frac{3}{6}$.

Find the total number of $\frac{1}{6}$ fraction bars.

Think and Discuss

1. Explain what the denominators of $\frac{1}{6}, \frac{1}{4}, \frac{2}{3}$, and $\frac{1}{2}$ have in common? *(Hint: Think of common multiples.)* **The denominators 6, 4, 3, and 2 have a LCM of 12.**

Try This

Model each addition expression with fraction bars, draw the model, and find the sum.

1. $\frac{1}{4} + \frac{1}{2}$ $\frac{3}{4}$
2. $\frac{3}{8} + \frac{1}{4}$ $\frac{5}{8}$
3. $\frac{1}{2} + \frac{2}{5}$ $\frac{9}{10}$
4. $\frac{3}{4} + \frac{1}{6}$ $\frac{11}{12}$
5. $\frac{1}{3} + \frac{1}{6}$ $\frac{3}{4}$, or $\frac{1}{2}$
6. $\frac{7}{8} + \frac{3}{4}$ $\frac{13}{8}$, or $1\frac{5}{8}$
7. $\frac{2}{3} + \frac{1}{4}$ $\frac{11}{12}$
8. $\frac{5}{8} + \frac{1}{4}$ $\frac{7}{8}$

Georgia Performance Standards

M6N1.d Add and subtract fractions and mixed numbers with unlike denominators.

M6P5.a Create and use representations to organize, record, and communicate mathematical ideas.

M6P5.b Select, apply, and translate among mathematical representations to solve problems.

Activity 1

Answers to *Try This*

1. $\frac{1}{4}$ $\frac{1}{2}$ / $\frac{1}{4}$ $\frac{1}{4}$ $\frac{1}{4}$ $= \frac{3}{4}$
2. $\frac{1}{8}$ $\frac{1}{8}$ $\frac{1}{8}$ $\frac{1}{4}$ / $\frac{1}{8}$ $\frac{1}{8}$ $\frac{1}{8}$ $\frac{1}{8}$ $\frac{1}{8}$ $= \frac{5}{8}$
3. $\frac{1}{2}$ $\frac{1}{5}$ $\frac{1}{5}$ / $\frac{1}{10}$ × 9 $= \frac{9}{10}$
4. $\frac{1}{4}$ $\frac{1}{4}$ $\frac{1}{4}$ $\frac{1}{6}$ / $\frac{1}{12}$ × 11 $= \frac{11}{12}$
5. $\frac{1}{3}$ $\frac{1}{6}$ / $\frac{1}{6}$ $\frac{1}{6}$ $\frac{1}{6}$ or $\frac{1}{3}$ $\frac{1}{6}$ / $\frac{1}{2}$ $= \frac{1}{2}$
6. 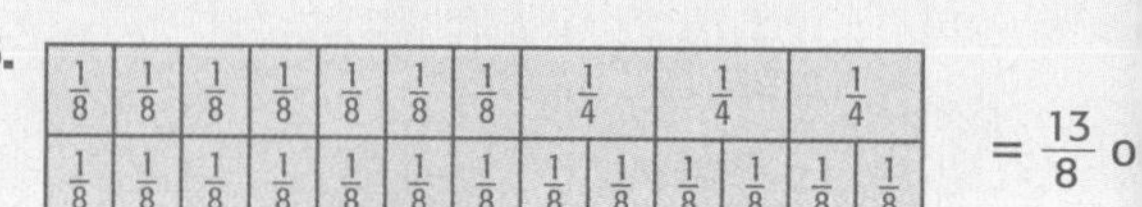 $= \frac{13}{8}$ o
7. 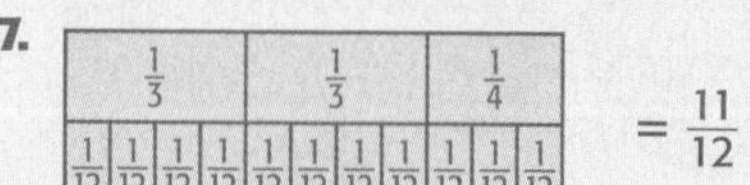 $= \frac{11}{12}$
8. $\frac{1}{8}$ $\frac{1}{8}$ $\frac{1}{8}$ $\frac{1}{8}$ $\frac{1}{8}$ $\frac{1}{4}$ / $\frac{1}{8}$ × 7 $= \frac{7}{8}$

Activity 2

1. Find $\frac{1}{3} - \frac{1}{6}$.

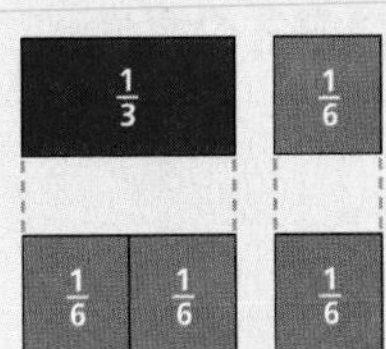

Use fraction bars to represent both fractions.

Find one size fraction bar to model both fractions.

$\frac{1}{3}$ is equivalent to $\frac{2}{6}$ and $\frac{1}{6} = \frac{1}{6}$.

Take away $\frac{1}{6}$ from $\frac{2}{6}$.

$\frac{2}{6} - \frac{1}{6} = \frac{1}{6}$

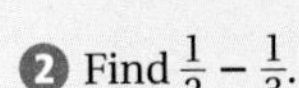

2. Find $\frac{1}{2} - \frac{1}{3}$.

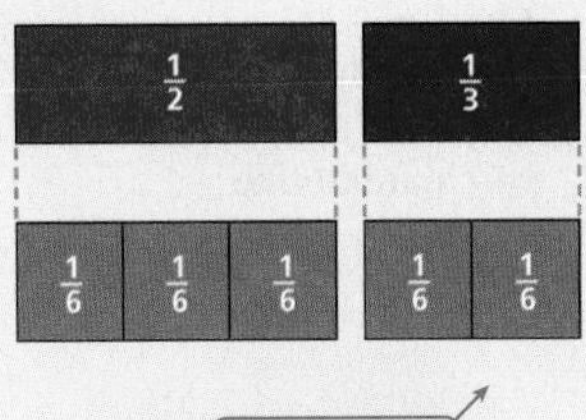

Use fraction bars to represent both fractions.

Find one size fraction bar to model both fractions.

$\frac{1}{2}$ is equivalent to $\frac{3}{6}$ and $\frac{1}{3}$ is equivalent to $\frac{2}{6}$.

Take away $\frac{2}{6}$ from $\frac{3}{6}$.

$\frac{3}{6} - \frac{2}{6} = \frac{1}{6}$

Think and Discuss

1. What size fraction bar would you use to model $\frac{1}{2} - \frac{1}{4}$? Is there another size fraction bar you could use? Explain. $\frac{1}{4}, \frac{1}{8}; \frac{1}{2} = \frac{4}{8}$ and $\frac{1}{4} = \frac{2}{8}$
2. What size fraction bar would you use to model $\frac{4}{5} - \frac{1}{2}$? Explain. $\frac{1}{10}$; the least common multiple of 5 and 2 is 10.

Try This

Model each subtraction expression with fraction bars, draw the model, and find the difference.

1. $\frac{3}{4} - \frac{1}{3}$ $\frac{5}{12}$
2. $\frac{1}{3} - \frac{1}{4}$ $\frac{1}{12}$
3. $\frac{1}{2} - \frac{2}{5}$ $\frac{1}{10}$
4. $\frac{5}{6} - \frac{1}{3}$ $\frac{3}{6}$, or $\frac{1}{2}$
5. $\frac{1}{2} - \frac{5}{12}$ $\frac{1}{12}$
6. $\frac{7}{8} - \frac{3}{4}$ $\frac{1}{8}$
7. $\frac{1}{4} - \frac{1}{8}$ $\frac{1}{8}$
8. $\frac{1}{4} - \frac{1}{6}$ $\frac{1}{12}$

Activity 2

Answers to *Try This*

1.

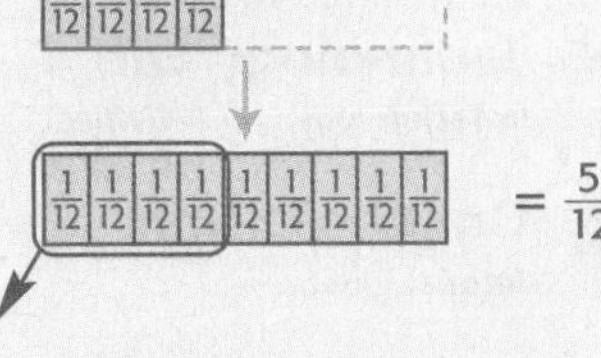

$= \frac{5}{12}$

2.

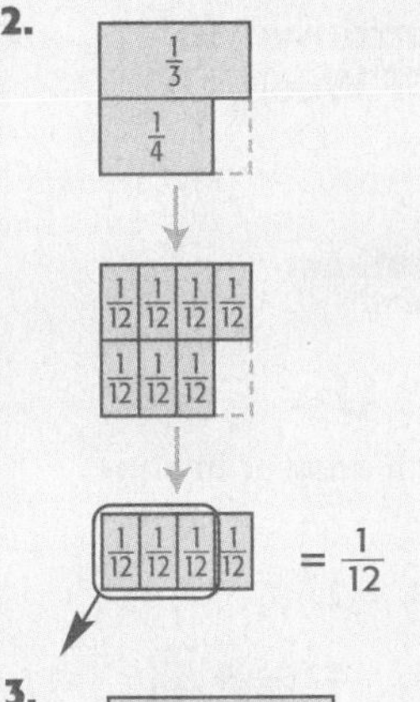

$= \frac{1}{12}$

3.

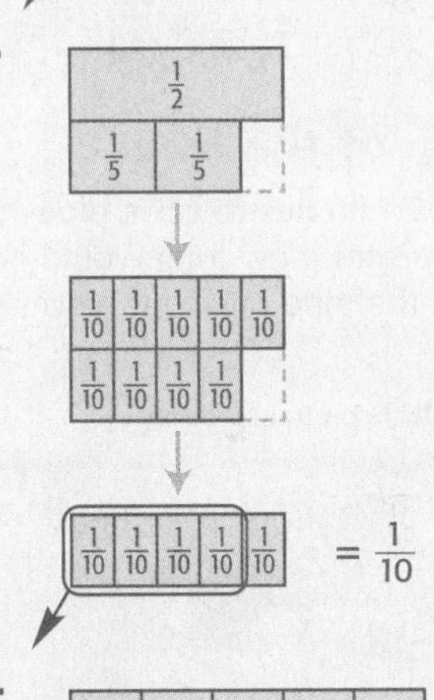

$= \frac{1}{10}$

4.

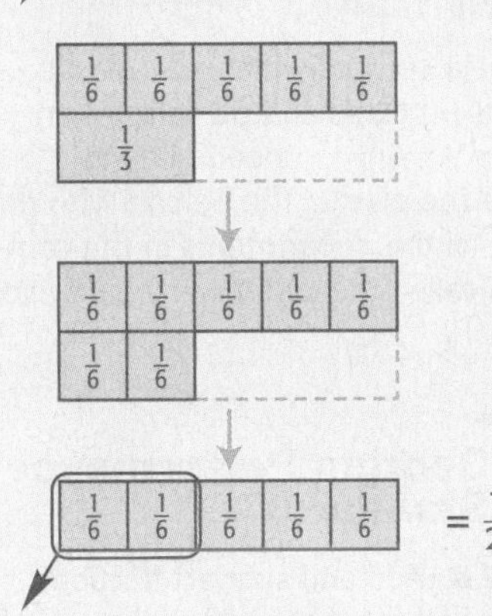

$= \frac{1}{2}$

5.

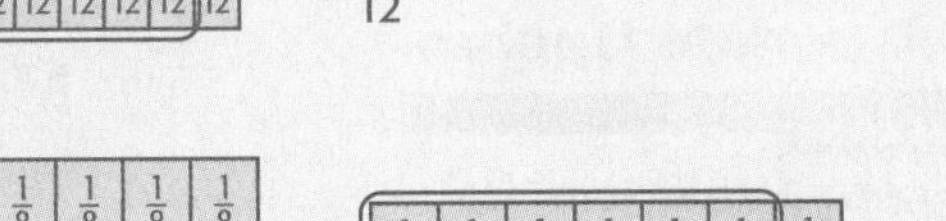

$= \frac{1}{12}$

6.

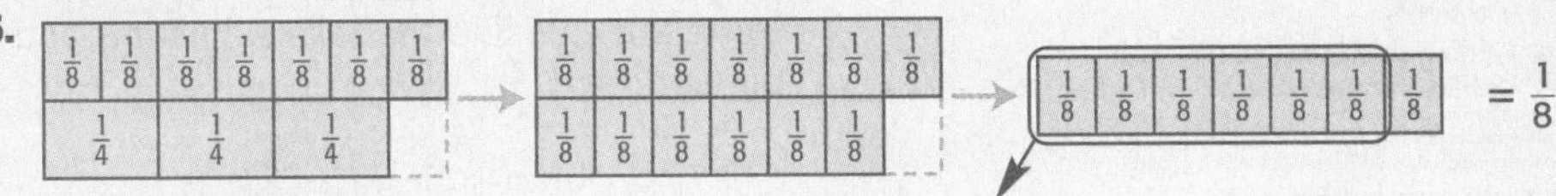

$= \frac{1}{8}$

7.

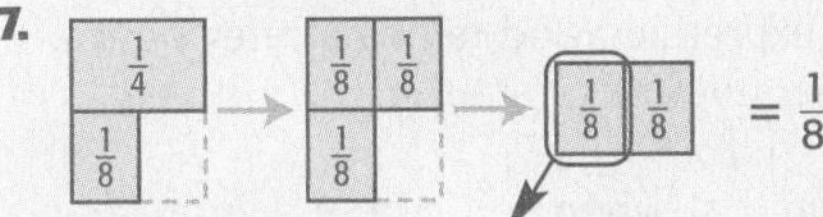

$= \frac{1}{8}$

8.

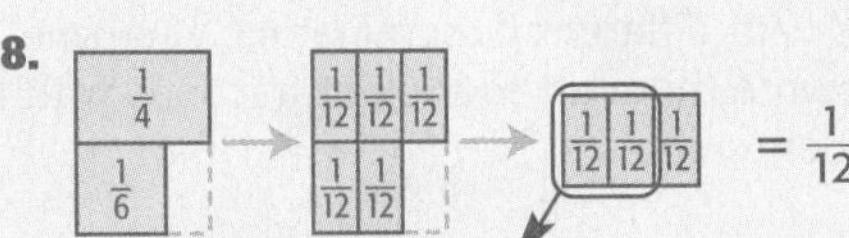

$= \frac{1}{12}$

5-2 Organizer

Pacing: Traditional 2 day
Block 1 day

Objective: Students add and subtract fractions with unlike denominators.

GPS M6N1.d, M6N1.g
Technology Lab
In *Technology Lab Activities*

Online Edition
Tutorial Videos

Countdown to CRCT Week 10

Warm Up

Add. Write each answer in simplest form.

1. $\frac{1}{7}+\frac{1}{7}$ $\frac{2}{7}$
2. $\frac{8}{15}+\frac{3}{15}$ $\frac{11}{15}$
3. $\frac{7}{9}+\frac{2}{9}$ 1
4. $\frac{11}{20}+\frac{4}{20}$ $\frac{3}{4}$

Problem of the Day

If it takes 12 minutes to cut a pipe into three pieces, how long would it take to cut the pipe into four pieces? 18 minutes

Also available on transparency

Math Humor

Imagine a company that puts plastic coatings on cards and posters. When things go wrong, someone has to remove the plastic. The person who does this for all the departments in the company is called the *common delaminator*.

Georgia Performance Standards

M6N1.d Add and subtract fractions and mixed numbers with unlike denominators.

M6N1.g Solve problems involving fractions, decimals, and percents.

M6P1.c Apply and adapt a variety of appropriate strategies to solve problems.

M6P4.c Recognize and apply mathematics in contexts outside of mathematics.

5-2 Adding and Subtracting with Unlike Denominators

Learn to add and subtract fractions with unlike denominators.

Vocabulary
least common denominator (LCD)

Georgia Performance Standards
M6N1.d Add and subtract fractions and mixed numbers with unlike denominators. Also, M6N1.g, M6P1.c, M6P4.c.

Remember!
Fractions that represent the same value are equivalent.

The Pacific Ocean covers $\frac{1}{3}$ of Earth's surface. The Atlantic Ocean covers $\frac{1}{5}$ of Earth's surface. To find the fraction of Earth's surface that is covered by both oceans, you can add $\frac{1}{3}$ and $\frac{1}{5}$, which are unlike fractions.

To add or subtract unlike fractions, first rewrite them as equivalent fractions with a common denominator.

EXAMPLE 1 *Social Studies Application*

What fraction of Earth's surface is covered by the Atlantic and Pacific Oceans? Add $\frac{1}{3}$ and $\frac{1}{5}$.

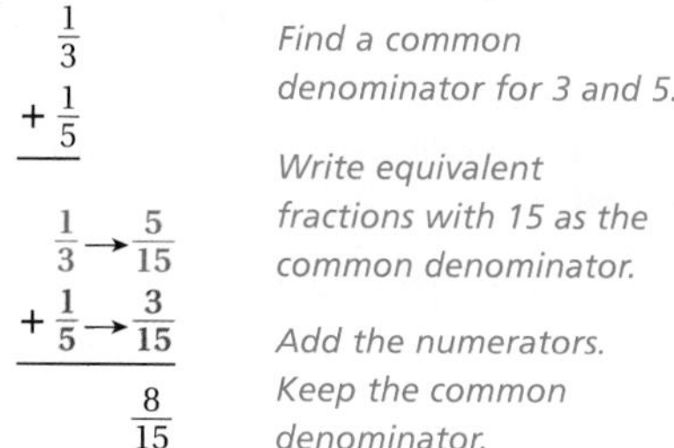

$\frac{1}{3} + \frac{1}{5}$ — *Find a common denominator for 3 and 5.*

$\frac{1}{3} \rightarrow \frac{5}{15}$, $+\frac{1}{5} \rightarrow \frac{3}{15}$ — *Write equivalent fractions with 15 as the common denominator.*

$\frac{8}{15}$ — *Add the numerators. Keep the common denominator.*

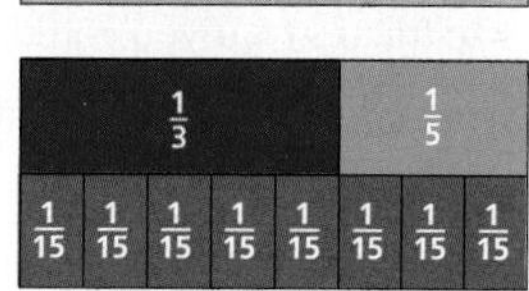

The Pacific and Atlantic Oceans cover $\frac{8}{15}$ of Earth's surface.

You can use *any* common denominator or the *least common denominator* to add and subtract unlike fractions. The **least common denominator (LCD)** is the least common multiple of the denominators.

1 Introduce

Alternate Opener

EXPLORATION

5-2 Adding and Subtracting with Unlike Denominators

Fractions are pieces of a whole. When you add or subtract fractions with unlike denominators, you are usually adding or subtracting pieces of different sizes. Look at the model used to solve the problem below.

Phil combines $\frac{1}{4}$ gallon of paint with $\frac{1}{2}$ gallon of paint. How much paint does he have now?

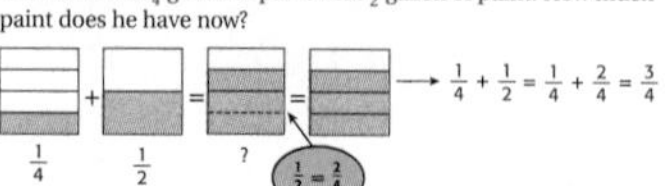

Phil has $\frac{3}{4}$ gallon of paint.

1. Draw a model to show that $1-\frac{1}{4}=\frac{3}{4}$.

Draw a model to solve each problem. Simplify your answers.

2. $\frac{1}{2}+\frac{1}{3}$
3. $\frac{4}{5}-\frac{1}{2}$

Think and Discuss

4. **Explain** how to add and subtract fractions with unlike denominators.
5. **Draw** a model to show $\frac{1}{2}+\frac{2}{3}=1\frac{1}{6}$.

Motivate

Have students find the following sums and differences: $\frac{2}{7}+\frac{3}{7}$; $\frac{1}{8}+\frac{3}{8}$; $\frac{10}{11}-\frac{4}{11}$; $\frac{11}{12}-\frac{7}{12}$. $\frac{5}{7}$, $\frac{4}{8}$, or $\frac{1}{2}$; $\frac{6}{11}$; $\frac{4}{12}$, or $\frac{1}{3}$

Have students compare the denominators in each expression and tell what they notice. The denominators are the same in each expression.

Explain that when you add or subtract fractions with different denominators, you have to rewrite them as equivalent fractions with like denominators.

Explorations and answers are provided in *Alternate Openers: Explorations Transparencies.*

EXAMPLE 2 Adding and Subtracting Unlike Fractions

Add or subtract. Write each answer in simplest form.

Method 1: Multiply the denominators.

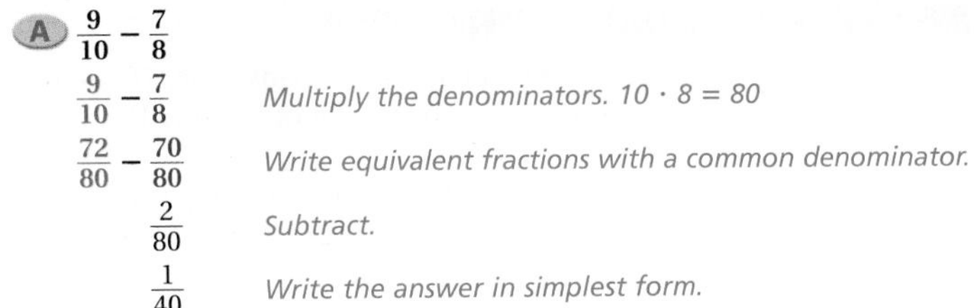

A $\frac{9}{10} - \frac{7}{8}$

$\frac{9}{10} - \frac{7}{8}$ *Multiply the denominators. $10 \cdot 8 = 80$*

$\frac{72}{80} - \frac{70}{80}$ *Write equivalent fractions with a common denominator.*

$\frac{2}{80}$ *Subtract.*

$\frac{1}{40}$ *Write the answer in simplest form.*

Method 2: Use the LCD.

B $\frac{9}{10} - \frac{7}{8}$ *Multiples of 10: 10, 20, 30, 40, . . .*

$\frac{9}{10} - \frac{7}{8}$ *Multiples of 8: 8, 16, 24, 32, 40, . . . The LCD is 40.*

$\frac{36}{40} - \frac{35}{40}$ *Write equivalent fractions with a common denominator.*

$\frac{1}{40}$ *Subtract.*

Method 3: Use mental math.

C $\frac{5}{12} + \frac{1}{6}$

$\frac{5}{12} + \frac{1}{6}$ *Think: 12 is a multiple of 6, so the LCD is 12.*

$\frac{5}{12} + \frac{2}{12}$ *Rewrite $\frac{1}{6}$ with a denominator of 12.*

$\frac{7}{12}$ *Add.*

D $\frac{1}{3} - \frac{2}{9}$

$\frac{1}{3} - \frac{2}{9}$ *Think: 9 is a multiple of 3, so the LCD is 9.*

$\frac{3}{9} - \frac{2}{9}$ *Rewrite $\frac{1}{3}$ with a denominator of 9.*

$\frac{1}{9}$ *Subtract.*

Answers to *Think and Discuss*

1. Possible answer: Using the LCD will give the smallest possible fractions to work with, which may reduce the number of steps needed to express the answer in simplest form.

Think and Discuss

1. Explain an advantage of using the least common denominator (LCD) when adding unlike fractions.

2. Tell when the least common denominator (LCD) of two fractions is the product of their denominators.

3. Explain how you can use mental math to subtract $\frac{1}{12}$ from $\frac{3}{4}$.

COMMON ERROR ALERT

Some students may forget to find a common denominator for the fractions and add or subtract both numerators and denominators. Watch for this especially when they are adding denominators.

Power Presentations with PowerPoint®

Additional Examples

Example 1

Mark made a pizza with pepperoni covering $\frac{1}{4}$ of the pizza and onions covering another $\frac{1}{3}$. What fraction of the pizza is covered by pepperoni and onions? $\frac{7}{12}$

Example 2

Add or subtract. Write each answer in simplest form.

A. $\frac{7}{10} - \frac{3}{8}$ $\frac{13}{40}$

B. $\frac{11}{12} - \frac{3}{8}$ $\frac{13}{24}$

C. $\frac{5}{16} + \frac{1}{8}$ $\frac{7}{16}$

D. $\frac{5}{16} - \frac{1}{8}$ $\frac{3}{16}$

Also available on transparency

Answers to *Think and Discuss*

2. When the denominators have no factors other than 1 in common, the LCD is the product of the two denominators.
3. Because 12 is a multiple of 4, the LCD is 12. $\frac{9}{12} - \frac{1}{12} = \frac{8}{12}$, or $\frac{2}{3}$

2 Teach

Guided Instruction

In this lesson, students learn to add and subtract fractions with unlike denominators. First define *unlike fractions*. Teach students to find a common denominator to add unlike fractions. Then teach students to use the least common denominator to add unlike fractions. Point out that when one denominator is a multiple of the other, the greater denominator is the LCD.

Cognitive Strategies You may want to compare the denominators of fractions with units of measure. For example, just as you cannot add 2 in. and 3 cm, you cannot add $\frac{2}{5}$ and $\frac{3}{10}$ without first writing them with a common denominator.

Reaching All Learners

Through Modeling

Have students work in groups using fraction bars to complete the addition square. Work across and down; the sum of the first and second will equal the third.

The addition square is shown below.

$\frac{1}{4}$	$\frac{1}{12}$	$\frac{1}{3}$
$\frac{1}{3}$	$\frac{1}{6}$	$\frac{1}{2}$
$\frac{7}{12}$	$\frac{1}{4}$	$\frac{5}{6}$

3 Close

ENGLISH LANGUAGE LEARNERS

Summarize

Review the terms *unlike fractions* and *least common denominator* (LCD). Discuss how the terms relate to each other.

Possible answers: *Unlike fractions* are fractions with different denominators. The *least common denominator* is the least common multiple of the denominators of unlike fractions. Use the LCD or any common multiple of the denominators when adding and subtracting unlike fractions.

5-2 Exercises

Assignment Guide

If you finished Example 1 assign:
Average 1, 48–57
Advanced 6–7, 48–57

If you finished Example 2 assign:
Average 1–43, 48–57
Advanced 1–39, 44–57

Homework Quick Check
Quickly check key concepts.
Exercises: 6, 8, 14, 18, 26

Math Background

Example 2 makes clear that both the method of using the LCD and the method of multiplying denominators are suitable for adding or subtracting fractions. The LCD method generally has the advantage of working with simpler numbers, but the method of multiplying denominators is actually the method found most often historically. This method can be found in use as early as the twelfth century.

The use of the LCD is found occasionally in the work of some fifteenth- and sixteenth-century arithmeticians. This method did not gain general acceptance until the seventeenth century.

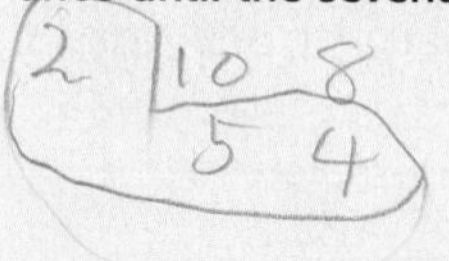

Georgia Performance Standards

M6P3.c Analyze and evaluate the mathematical thinking and strategies of others.

M6P4.c Recognize and apply mathematics in contexts outside of mathematics.

5-2 Exercises

M6P3.c, M6P4.c

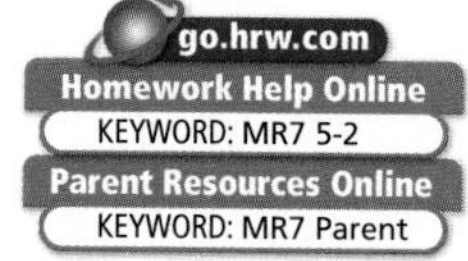

GUIDED PRACTICE

See Example 1

1. A trailer hauling wood weighs $\frac{2}{3}$ ton. The trailer weighs $\frac{1}{4}$ ton without the wood. What is the weight of the wood? $\frac{5}{12}$ ton

See Example 2

Add or subtract. Write each answer in simplest form.

2. $\frac{1}{3}+\frac{1}{9}$ $\frac{4}{9}$
3. $\frac{7}{10}-\frac{2}{5}$ $\frac{3}{10}$
4. $\frac{2}{3}-\frac{2}{5}$ $\frac{4}{15}$
5. $\frac{1}{2}+\frac{3}{7}$ $\frac{13}{14}$

INDEPENDENT PRACTICE

See Example 1

6. **Social Studies** Approximately $\frac{1}{5}$ of the world's population lives in China. The people of India make up about $\frac{1}{6}$ of the world's population. What fraction of the world's people live in either China or India? $\frac{11}{30}$
7. Cedric is making an Italian dish using a recipe that calls for $\frac{2}{3}$ cup of grated mozarella cheese. If Cedric has grated $\frac{1}{2}$ cup of mozarella cheese, how much more does he need to grate? $\frac{1}{6}$ cup

See Example 2

Add or subtract. Write each answer in simplest form.

8. $\frac{3}{4}-\frac{1}{2}$ $\frac{1}{4}$
9. $\frac{1}{6}+\frac{5}{12}$ $\frac{7}{12}$
10. $\frac{5}{6}-\frac{3}{4}$ $\frac{1}{12}$
11. $\frac{1}{5}+\frac{1}{4}$ $\frac{9}{20}$
12. $\frac{7}{10}+\frac{1}{8}$ $\frac{33}{40}$
13. $\frac{1}{3}+\frac{4}{5}$ $1\frac{2}{15}$
14. $\frac{8}{9}-\frac{2}{3}$ $\frac{2}{9}$
15. $\frac{5}{8}+\frac{1}{2}$ $1\frac{1}{8}$

PRACTICE AND PROBLEM SOLVING

CRCT GPS
Extra Practice p. 722

Find each sum or difference. Write your answer in simplest form.

16. $\frac{3}{10}+\frac{1}{2}$ $\frac{4}{5}$
17. $\frac{4}{5}-\frac{1}{3}$ $\frac{7}{15}$
18. $\frac{5}{8}-\frac{1}{6}$ $\frac{11}{24}$
19. $\frac{1}{6}+\frac{2}{9}$ $\frac{7}{18}$
20. $\frac{2}{7}+\frac{2}{5}$ $\frac{24}{35}$
21. $\frac{7}{12}-\frac{1}{4}$ $\frac{1}{3}$
22. $\frac{7}{8}-\frac{2}{3}$ $\frac{5}{24}$
23. $\frac{2}{11}+\frac{2}{3}$ $\frac{28}{33}$

Evaluate each expression for $b=\frac{1}{2}$. Write your answer in simplest form.

24. $b+\frac{1}{3}$ $\frac{5}{6}$
25. $\frac{8}{9}-b$ $\frac{7}{18}$
26. $b-\frac{2}{11}$ $\frac{7}{22}$
27. $\frac{7}{10}-b$ $\frac{1}{5}$
28. $\frac{2}{7}+b$ $\frac{11}{14}$
29. $b+b$ $\frac{2}{2}$ or 1
30. $b-b$ 0
31. $b+\frac{5}{8}$ $1\frac{1}{8}$

Evaluate. Write each answer in simplest form.

32. $\frac{1}{3}+\frac{1}{9}+\frac{1}{3}$ $\frac{7}{9}$
33. $\frac{9}{10}-\frac{2}{10}-\frac{1}{5}$ $\frac{1}{2}$
34. $\frac{1}{2}+\frac{1}{4}-\frac{1}{8}$ $\frac{5}{8}$
35. $\frac{3}{7}+\frac{1}{14}+\frac{2}{28}$ $\frac{4}{7}$
36. $\frac{5}{6}-\frac{2}{3}+\frac{7}{12}$ $\frac{3}{4}$
37. $\frac{2}{3}+\frac{1}{4}-\frac{1}{6}$ $\frac{3}{4}$
38. $\frac{2}{9}+\frac{1}{6}+\frac{1}{3}$ $\frac{13}{18}$
39. $\frac{1}{2}-\frac{1}{4}+\frac{5}{8}$ $\frac{7}{8}$
40. Bailey spent $\frac{2}{3}$ of his monthly allowance at the movies and $\frac{1}{5}$ of it on baseball cards. What fraction of Bailey's allowance is left? $\frac{2}{15}$
41. **Multi-Step** Betty is making punch for a party. She needs a total of $\frac{9}{10}$ gallon of water to add to fruit juice. In one container she has $\frac{1}{3}$ gallon water, and in another she has $\frac{2}{5}$ gallon. How much more water does she need? $\frac{1}{6}$ gallon

RETEACH 5-2

LESSON 5-2 **Reteach**
Adding and Subtracting with Unlike Denominators

Unlike fractions have different denominators. To add and subtract fractions, you must have a common denominator. The least common denominator (LCD) is the least common multiple of the denominators.

To add or subtract unlike fractions, first find the LCD of the fractions.

$\frac{2}{3}+\frac{1}{4}$
Multiples of 4: 4, 8, **12**,...
Multiples of 3: 3, 6, 9, **12**,...
The LCD is 12.

Next, use fraction strips to find equivalent fractions.

$\frac{1}{3}$	$\frac{1}{3}$	

$\frac{1}{4}$			

$\frac{1}{12}$	$\frac{1}{12}$	$\frac{1}{12}$	$\frac{1}{12}$	$\frac{1}{12}$	$\frac{1}{12}$	$\frac{1}{12}$	$\frac{1}{12}$				

$\frac{1}{12}$	$\frac{1}{12}$	$\frac{1}{12}$									

Then use fraction strips to find the sum or difference.

$\frac{1}{12}$	$\frac{1}{12}$	$\frac{1}{12}$	$\frac{1}{12}$	$\frac{1}{12}$	$\frac{1}{12}$	$\frac{1}{12}$	$\frac{1}{12}$				

+

$\frac{1}{12}$	$\frac{1}{12}$	$\frac{1}{12}$									

$\frac{8}{12}+\frac{3}{12}=\frac{11}{12}$

So, $\frac{2}{3}+\frac{1}{4}=\frac{11}{12}$.

Use fraction strips to find each sum or difference. Write your answer in simplest form.

1. $\frac{1}{4}+\frac{1}{8}$ $\frac{3}{8}$
2. $\frac{5}{6}-\frac{2}{3}$ $\frac{1}{6}$
3. $\frac{3}{4}-\frac{1}{3}$ $\frac{5}{12}$
4. $\frac{3}{5}+\frac{3}{10}$ $\frac{9}{10}$
5. $\frac{3}{4}+\frac{1}{6}$ $\frac{11}{12}$
6. $\frac{1}{2}+\frac{3}{8}$ $\frac{7}{8}$
7. $\frac{2}{3}-\frac{1}{6}$ $\frac{1}{2}$
8. $\frac{1}{3}-\frac{1}{4}$ $\frac{1}{12}$

PRACTICE 5-2

LESSON 5-2 **Practice B**
Adding and Subtracting with Unlike Denominators

Add or subtract. Write each answer in simplest form.

1. $\frac{6}{7}+\frac{1}{3}$ $1\frac{4}{21}$
2. $\frac{3}{7}-\frac{2}{5}$ $\frac{1}{35}$
3. $\frac{1}{4}+\frac{3}{8}$ $\frac{5}{8}$
4. $\frac{7}{8}-\frac{2}{3}$ $\frac{5}{24}$
5. $\frac{1}{6}+\frac{3}{5}$ $\frac{23}{30}$
6. $\frac{5}{6}-\frac{2}{3}$ $\frac{1}{6}$
7. $\frac{5}{9}-\frac{1}{3}$ $\frac{2}{9}$
8. $\frac{7}{8}+\frac{3}{4}$ $1\frac{5}{8}$
9. $\frac{5}{12}-\frac{1}{6}$ $\frac{1}{4}$
10. $\frac{4}{5}-\frac{7}{11}$ $\frac{9}{55}$
11. $\frac{4}{9}+\frac{5}{6}$ $1\frac{5}{18}$
12. $\frac{5}{8}+\frac{2}{3}$ $1\frac{7}{24}$

Evaluate each expression for $b=\frac{1}{3}$. Write your answer in simplest form.

13. $b+\frac{5}{8}$ $\frac{23}{24}$
14. $\frac{7}{9}-b$ $\frac{4}{9}$
15. $\frac{2}{7}+b$ $\frac{13}{21}$
16. $b+b$ $\frac{2}{3}$
17. $\frac{11}{12}-b$ $\frac{7}{12}$
18. $\frac{3}{4}-b$ $\frac{5}{12}$
19. There are three grades in Kyle's middle school—sixth, seventh, and eighth. One-third of the students are in sixth grade and $\frac{1}{4}$ are in seventh grade. What fraction of the schools' students are in eighth grade?
$\frac{5}{12}$ of the students
20. Sarah is making a dessert that calls for $\frac{4}{5}$ cup of crushed cookies. If she has already crushed $\frac{7}{10}$ cup, how much more does she need?
$\frac{1}{10}$ cup

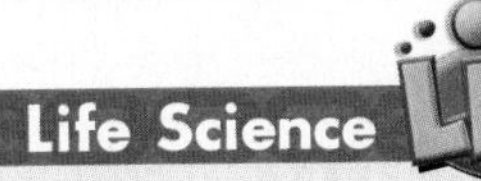

Life Science LINK

The red lorikeet, galah cockatoo, and green-cheeked Amazon are three very colorful birds. The African grey parrot is known for its ability to mimic sounds it hears. In fact, one African grey named Prudle had a vocabulary of almost 1,000 words.

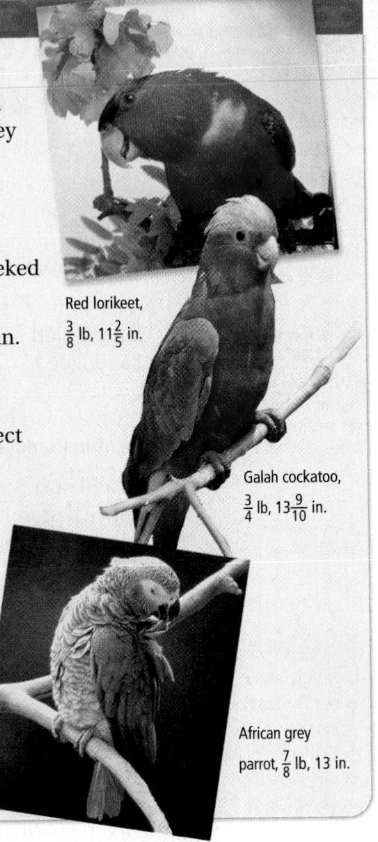

Red lorikeet, $\frac{3}{8}$ lb, $11\frac{2}{5}$ in.

Galah cockatoo, $\frac{3}{4}$ lb, $13\frac{9}{10}$ in.

African grey parrot, $\frac{7}{8}$ lb, 13 in.

42. Which bird weighs more, the green-cheeked Amazon or the red lorikeet? green-cheeked Amazon

43. What is the difference in weights between the green-cheeked Amazon and the red lorikeet? $\frac{9}{40}$ lb

44. Does the red lorikeet weigh more or less than $\frac{1}{2}$ lb? Explain.

45. **What's the Error?** A student found the difference in weight between the African grey parrot and the galah cockatoo to be 1 lb. Explain the error. Then find the correct difference between the weights of these birds.

46. **Write About It** Explain how you find the difference in weight between the galah cockatoo and green-cheeked Amazon.

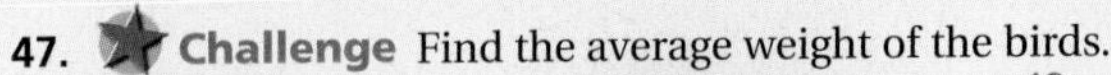

47. **Challenge** Find the average weight of the birds. $\frac{13}{20}$ lb

Green-cheeked Amazon, $\frac{3}{5}$ lb, $13\frac{1}{5}$ in.

CRCT Prep • GPS Support • Spiral Review

48. **Multiple Choice** One apple weighs $\frac{1}{4}$ lb and another apple weighs $\frac{3}{16}$ lb. Find the difference in their weights.

(A) $\frac{1}{16}$ lb (B) $\frac{1}{6}$ lb (C) $\frac{1}{4}$ lb (D) $\frac{7}{16}$ lb

49. **Short Response** Wanda walked $\frac{7}{24}$ mile more than Lori. Lori walked $\frac{5}{6}$ mile less than Jack. Wanda walked $\frac{3}{8}$ mile. How many miles did Jack walk? Give your answer in simplest form. Explain how you solved the problem. $\frac{11}{12}$ mi

Divide. (Lesson 3-7)

50. 1.40 ÷ 2 0.70 **51.** 3.3 ÷ 3 1.1 **52.** 0.85 ÷ 5 0.17 **53.** 0.375 ÷ 3 0.125

Estimate each sum or difference to compare. Write < or >. (Lesson 4-9)

54. $\frac{4}{5} + \frac{2}{3}$ ▪ 1 > **55.** $6\frac{1}{3} - 2\frac{1}{9}$ ▪ 4 > **56.** $8\frac{7}{10} - 1\frac{3}{7}$ ▪ 8 < **57.** $5\frac{1}{5} + \frac{8}{9}$ ▪ 6 >

CHALLENGE 5-2

LESSON 5-2 **Challenge**
Egyptian Fractions

Did you know that ancient Egyptians used fractions 5,000 years ago? Some of their fractions were like the ones we use today. However, the Egyptians only used **unit fractions,** or fractions with a numerator of 1. All other fractions had to be written as a sum of unit fractions. And no sum could repeat the same unit fraction! For example, the Egyptians would write $\frac{3}{4}$ as $\frac{1}{2} + \frac{1}{4}$. They would not write $\frac{1}{4} + \frac{1}{4} + \frac{1}{4}$.

Ancient Egyptians did not have paper. They recorded their math work on papyrus, or thin strips of dried plants. Study the Egyptian fractions recorded on the papyrus scrolls below. Then write each fraction the way we do today.

1. 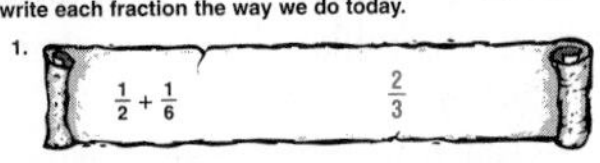
$\frac{1}{2} + \frac{1}{6}$ $\frac{2}{3}$

2. 
$\frac{1}{2} + \frac{1}{4} + \frac{1}{20}$ $\frac{4}{5}$

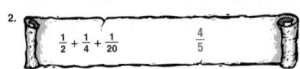

3. 
$\frac{1}{2} + \frac{1}{3}$ $\frac{5}{6}$

4. 
$\frac{1}{4} + \frac{1}{8}$ $\frac{3}{8}$

5. 
$\frac{1}{2} + \frac{1}{3} + \frac{1}{15}$ $\frac{9}{10}$

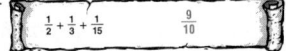

PROBLEM SOLVING 5-2

LESSON 5-2 **Problem Solving**
Adding and Subtracting with Unlike Denominators

Use the circle graph to answer the questions. Write each answer in simplest form.

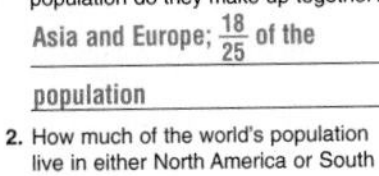

1. On which two continents do most people live? How much of the total population do they make up together?
Asia and Europe; $\frac{18}{25}$ of the population

2. How much of the world's population live in either North America or South America?
$\frac{7}{50}$ of the population

3. How much more of the world's total population lives in Asia than in Africa?
$\frac{1}{2}$ of the population

Circle the letter of the correct answer.

4. How much of Earth's total population do people in Asia and Africa make up all together?
A $\frac{3}{10}$ of the population
B $\frac{2}{5}$ of the population
(C) $\frac{7}{10}$ of the population
D $\frac{7}{5}$ of the population

5. What is the difference between North America's part of the total population and Africa's part?
(F) Africa has $\frac{1}{50}$ more.
G Africa has $\frac{1}{50}$ less.
H Africa has $\frac{9}{50}$ more.
J Africa has $\frac{9}{50}$ less.

6. How much more of the population lives in Europe than in North America?
(A) $\frac{1}{25}$ of the population
B $\frac{1}{5}$ of the population
C $\frac{1}{15}$ of the population
D $\frac{1}{10}$ of the population

7. How much of the world's population lives in North America and Europe?
F $\frac{1}{25}$ of the population
G $\frac{1}{15}$ of the population
(H) $\frac{1}{5}$ of the population
J $\frac{1}{20}$ of the population

Ongoing Assessment and Intervention

***Diagnose Before* the Lesson**
5-2 Warm Up, TE p. 234

***Monitor During* the Lesson**
5-2 Know-It Notebook
5-2 Questioning Strategies

***Assess After* the Lesson**
5-2 Lesson Quiz, TE p. 237

Interdisciplinary LINK

Life Science

Exercises 42–47 involve information about the weights of some birds. Students study mammals and birds in middle school life science programs such as *Holt Science & Technology*.

Answers

44. Possible answer: less than $\frac{1}{2}$ lb because $\frac{4}{8}$ lb $= \frac{1}{2}$ lb and $\frac{3}{8} < \frac{4}{8}$.

45–46. See p. A4.

Test Prep Doctor For Exercise 49, encourage students to read the problem more than once. Identify each bit of informaton and write an equation to represent what is given. It may be helpful to draw a diagram to understand who walked more or less than the others.

Journal

Have students explain how adding or subtracting unlike fractions and adding or subtracting like fractions are different and how they are alike.

Power Presentations with PowerPoint®

5-2 Lesson Quiz

Add or subtract. Write each answer in simplest form.

1. $\frac{3}{8} + \frac{1}{6}$ $\frac{13}{24}$ **2.** $\frac{1}{2} - \frac{1}{8}$ $\frac{3}{8}$

3. $\frac{5}{12} - \frac{1}{6}$ $\frac{1}{4}$ **4.** $\frac{1}{6} + \frac{1}{8}$ $\frac{7}{24}$

5. Bonnie is making oatmeal bars, and the recipe calls for $\frac{3}{4}$ cup of brown sugar. If she has $\frac{1}{3}$ cup of brown sugar, how much more does she need? $\frac{5}{12}$ cup

Also available on transparency

5-3 Organizer

Pacing: Traditional 1 day
Block $\frac{1}{2}$ day

Objective: Students add and subtract mixed numbers with unlike denominators.

GPS M6N1.d, M6N1.g
Technology Lab
In Technology Lab Activities

Online Edition
Tutorial Videos

Countdown to CRCT Week 10

Power Presentations with PowerPoint®

Warm Up

Add or subtract. Write each answer in simplest form.

1. $\frac{7}{12} - \frac{1}{2}$ $\frac{1}{12}$
2. $\frac{3}{11} + \frac{2}{3}$ $\frac{31}{33}$
3. $\frac{1}{6} + \frac{3}{4}$ $\frac{11}{12}$
4. $\frac{11}{12} - \frac{1}{3}$ $\frac{7}{12}$

Problem of the Day

The sum of every row, column, and diagonal is the same. Complete the magic square.

$\frac{3}{4}$	$1\frac{1}{3}$	$\frac{11}{12}$
$1\frac{1}{6}$	1	$\frac{5}{6}$
$1\frac{1}{12}$	$\frac{2}{3}$	$1\frac{1}{4}$

Also available on transparency

5-3 Adding and Subtracting Mixed Numbers

Learn to add and subtract mixed numbers with unlike denominators.

M6N1.d Add and subtract fractions and mixed numbers with unlike denominators. Also, M6N1.g, M6P1.b.

Chameleons can change color at any time to camouflage themselves. They live high in trees and are seldom seen on the ground.

A Parsons chameleon, which is the largest kind of chameleon, can extend its tongue $1\frac{1}{2}$ times the length of its body. This allows the chameleon to capture food it otherwise would not be able to reach.

The chameleon is the only animal capable of moving each eye independently of the other. A chameleon can turn its eyes about 360°.

To add or subtract mixed numbers with unlike denominators, you must first find a common denominator for the fractions.

EXAMPLE 1 Adding and Subtracting Mixed Numbers

Find each sum or difference. Write the answer in simplest form.

A $2\frac{3}{4} + 1\frac{1}{6}$

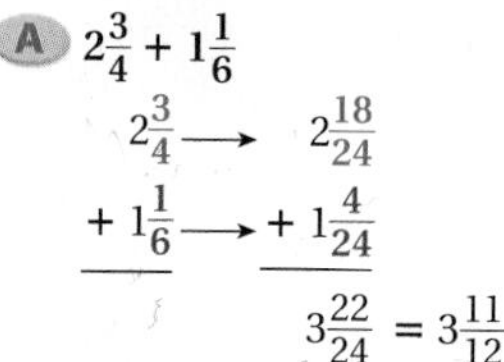

$2\frac{3}{4} \to 2\frac{18}{24}$

$+1\frac{1}{6} \to +1\frac{4}{24}$

$3\frac{22}{24} = 3\frac{11}{12}$

Multiply the denominators. 4 · 6 = 24
Write equivalent fractions with a common denominator of 24.
Add the fractions and then the whole numbers, and simplify.

B $4\frac{5}{6} - 2\frac{2}{9}$

$4\frac{5}{6} \to 4\frac{15}{18}$

$-2\frac{2}{9} \to -2\frac{4}{18}$

$2\frac{11}{18}$

The LCD of 6 and 9 is 18.
Write equivalent fractions with a common denominator of 18.
Subtract the fractions and then the whole numbers.

C $2\frac{2}{3} + 1\frac{3}{4}$

$2\frac{2}{3} \to 2\frac{8}{12}$

$+1\frac{3}{4} \to +1\frac{9}{12}$

$3\frac{17}{12} = 4\frac{5}{12}$

The LCD of 3 and 4 is 12.
Write equivalent fractions with a common denominator of 12.
Add the fractions and then the whole numbers, and simplify. $3\frac{17}{12} = 3 + 1\frac{5}{12}$

Georgia Performance Standards

M6N1.d Add and subtract fractions and mixed numbers with unlike denominators.

M6N1.g Solve problems involving fractions, decimals, and percents.

M6P1.b Solve problems that arise in mathematics and in other contexts.

1 Introduce

Alternate Opener

EXPLORATION

5-3 Adding and Subtracting Mixed Numbers

The graph shows typical rainfall levels for a city in the Southwest for the first 5 months of the year. What is the approximate total rainfall from January through May?

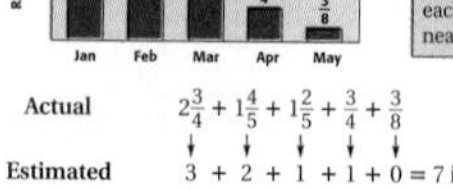

Actual $2\frac{3}{4} + 1\frac{4}{5} + 1\frac{2}{5} + \frac{3}{4} + \frac{3}{8}$

Estimated $3 + 2 + 1 + 1 + 0 = 7$ in.

The total rainfall is about 7 inches.

Estimate each sum or difference.

1. $13\frac{1}{2} - 9\frac{27}{32}$
2. $1\frac{1}{2} + 9\frac{3}{8} - 2\frac{1}{4}$
3. $17\frac{7}{8} + 19\frac{1}{10}$
4. $4\frac{1}{8} - 1\frac{3}{10} + 3\frac{1}{4}$

Think and Discuss

5. **Discuss** the estimation strategies you used.
6. **Describe** a real-world situation in which mixed numbers are added or subtracted.

Motivate

Have students give examples of situations when they would need to add or subtract mixed numbers. Ask students what they needed to do in the previous lesson to add or subtract fractions with unlike denominators. Write equivalent fractions with common denominators. Explain that the same rule applies to mixed number addition and subtraction.

Explorations and answers are provided in *Alternate Openers: Explorations Transparencies.*

Find each sum or difference. Write the answer in simplest form.

D $8\frac{2}{5} - 6\frac{3}{10}$

$$\begin{array}{rcr} 8\frac{2}{5} & \longrightarrow & 8\frac{4}{10} \\ -\,6\frac{3}{10} & \longrightarrow & -\,6\frac{3}{10} \\ \hline & & 2\frac{1}{10} \end{array}$$

Think: 10 is a multiple of 5, so 10 is the LCD.

Write equivalent fractions with a common denominator of 10.

Subtract the fractions and then the whole numbers.

EXAMPLE 2 *Life Science Application*

The length of a Parsons chameleon's body is $23\frac{1}{2}$ inches. The chameleon can extend its tongue $35\frac{1}{4}$ inches. What is the total length of its body and its tongue?

Add $23\frac{1}{2}$ and $35\frac{1}{4}$.

$$\begin{array}{rcr} 23\frac{1}{2} & \longrightarrow & 23\frac{2}{4} \\ +\,35\frac{1}{4} & \longrightarrow & +\,35\frac{1}{4} \\ \hline & & 58\frac{3}{4} \end{array}$$

Find a common denominator. Write equivalent fractions with the LCD, 4, as the denominator.

Add the fractions and then the whole numbers.

The total length of the chameleon's body and tongue is $58\frac{3}{4}$ inches.

Helpful Hint

You can use mental math to find an LCD. *Think:* 4 is a multiple of 2 and 4.

Think and Discuss

GPS M6P3.b, M6P3.c

1. **Tell** what mistake was made when subtracting $2\frac{1}{2}$ from $5\frac{3}{5}$ gave the following result: $5\frac{3}{5} - 2\frac{1}{2} = 3\frac{2}{3}$. Then find the correct answer.
2. **Explain** why you first find equivalent fractions when adding $1\frac{1}{5}$ and $1\frac{1}{2}$.
3. **Tell** how you know that $5\frac{1}{2} - 3\frac{1}{4}$ is more than 2.

Answers to *Think and Discuss*

1. Instead of using equivalent fractions with a common denominator, the numerators were subtracted and the denominators were subtracted.

COMMON ERROR ALERT

When renaming mixed numbers using a common denominator, some students, concentrating on the fractions, may overlook keeping the whole number as part of the newly renamed mixed number. Remind students that the whole number part of this mixed number should not be separated from the part that is a fraction.

Power Presentations with PowerPoint®

Additional Examples

Example 1

Find each sum or difference. Write the answer in simplest form.

A. $3\frac{1}{8} + 1\frac{5}{6}$ $4\frac{23}{24}$

B. $5\frac{2}{3} - 1\frac{1}{4}$ $4\frac{5}{12}$

C. $2\frac{1}{2} + 4\frac{4}{5}$ $7\frac{3}{10}$

D. $6\frac{2}{3} - 3\frac{2}{9}$ $3\frac{4}{9}$

Example 2

The length of Jen's kitten's body is $10\frac{1}{4}$ inches long. Its tail is $5\frac{1}{8}$ inches long. What is the total length of its body and tail? $15\frac{3}{8}$ inches

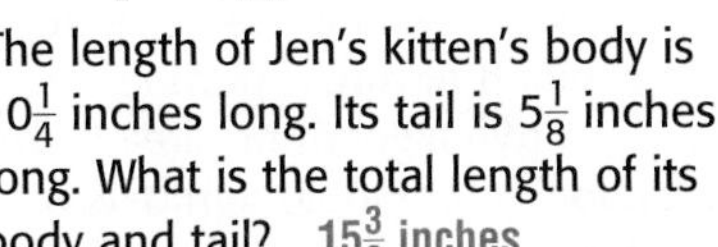

Also available on transparency

Answers to *Think and Discuss*

2. Possible answer: You need to have common denominators before you can add the numerators.
3. 5 minus 3 is 2, and $\frac{1}{2}$ is greater than $\frac{1}{4}$, so the answer would be greater than 2.

2 Teach

Guided Instruction

In this lesson, students learn to add and subtract mixed numbers with unlike denominators. Teach them to find sums and differences by writing equivalent fractions with common denominators. Then apply the concept to a measurement situation.

Reaching All Learners

Through Kinesthetic

Have students measure, in inches, several objects around the classroom and then record their findings. (Rulers are provided in the Manipulatives Kit.) Then move some of the objects next to one another. Have students use their findings to calculate the combined width of adjacent objects and to check the results by making an actual measurement. Ask the students to explain any discrepancies.

3 Close

Summarize

Review adding and subtracting mixed numbers with unlike denominators. Have students explain how they would add $12\frac{3}{4} + 3\frac{5}{6}$.

Possible answer: Write equivalent fractions with a denominator of 12. Add the fractions, and then add the whole numbers. $12\frac{9}{12} + 3\frac{10}{12} = 15\frac{19}{12} = 16\frac{7}{12}$

5-3 Exercises

Assignment Guide

If you finished Example 1 assign:
Average 1–4, 15–22, 50–59
Advanced 6–13, 24–27, 50–59

If you finished Example 2 assign:
Average 1–44, 50–59
Advanced 1–42, 45–59

Homework Quick Check

Quickly check key concepts.
Exercises: 6, 12, 14, 18, 36, 40

Math Background

The Associative and Commutative Properties of Addition allow one to conceive of the sum of two mixed numbers as two separate sums: the sum of their whole parts and the sum of their fractional parts. By treating the sums separately, addition of mixed numbers is reduced to two algorithms already mastered: addition of whole numbers and addition of fractions.

Georgia Performance Standards

M6P3.a Organize and consolidate their mathematical thinking through communication.

M6P4.c Recognize and apply mathematics in context outside of mathematics.

5-3 Exercises

Georgia Performance Standards
M6P3.a, M6P4.c

go.hrw.com
Homework Help Online
KEYWORD: MR7 5-3
Parent Resources Online
KEYWORD: MR7 Parent

GUIDED PRACTICE

See Example 1 — Find each sum or difference. Write the answer in simplest form.

1. $7\frac{1}{12} + 3\frac{1}{3}$ $10\frac{5}{12}$ **2.** $2\frac{1}{6} + 2\frac{3}{8}$ $4\frac{13}{24}$ **3.** $8\frac{5}{6} - 2\frac{3}{4}$ $6\frac{1}{12}$ **4.** $6\frac{6}{7} - 1\frac{1}{2}$ $5\frac{5}{14}$

See Example 2 — **5. Life Science** A sea turtle traveled $7\frac{3}{4}$ hours in two days. It traveled $3\frac{1}{2}$ hours on the first day. How many hours did it travel on the second day? $4\frac{1}{4}$

INDEPENDENT PRACTICE

See Example 1 — Find each sum or difference. Write the answer in simplest form.

6. $3\frac{9}{10} - 1\frac{2}{5}$ $2\frac{1}{2}$ **7.** $2\frac{1}{6} + 4\frac{5}{12}$ $6\frac{7}{12}$ **8.** $5\frac{9}{11} + 5\frac{1}{3}$ $11\frac{5}{33}$ **9.** $9\frac{3}{4} - 3\frac{1}{2}$ $6\frac{1}{4}$

10. $6\frac{3}{10} + 3\frac{2}{5}$ $9\frac{7}{10}$ **11.** $10\frac{2}{3} - 2\frac{1}{12}$ $8\frac{7}{12}$ **12.** $14\frac{3}{4} - 6\frac{5}{12}$ $8\frac{1}{3}$ **13.** $19\frac{1}{10} + 10\frac{1}{2}$ $29\frac{3}{5}$

See Example 2 — **14. School** The drama club rehearsed $1\frac{3}{4}$ hours Friday and $3\frac{1}{6}$ hours Saturday. How many total hours did the students rehearse? $4\frac{11}{12}$

PRACTICE AND PROBLEM SOLVING

CRCT GPS
Extra Practice p. 722

Add or subtract. Write each answer in simplest form.

15. $15\frac{5}{6} + 18\frac{2}{3}$ $34\frac{1}{2}$ **16.** $17\frac{1}{6} + 12\frac{1}{4}$ $29\frac{5}{12}$ **17.** $23\frac{9}{10} - 20\frac{3}{9}$ $3\frac{51}{90}$ **18.** $32\frac{5}{7} - 13\frac{2}{5}$ $19\frac{3}{5}$

19. $28\frac{11}{12} - 8\frac{5}{9}$ $20\frac{13}{36}$ **20.** $12\frac{2}{11} + 20\frac{2}{3}$ $32\frac{28}{33}$ **21.** $36\frac{5}{8} - 24\frac{5}{12}$ $12\frac{5}{24}$ **22.** $48\frac{9}{11} + 2\frac{1}{4}$ $51\frac{3}{44}$

23. Measurement Kyle's backpack weighs $14\frac{7}{20}$ lb. Kirsten's backpack weighs $12\frac{1}{4}$ lb.

a. How much do the backpacks weigh together? $26\frac{3}{5}$ pounds

b. How much more does Kyle's backpack weigh than Kirsten's backpack? $2\frac{1}{10}$ lb

c. Kyle takes his $3\frac{1}{4}$ lb math book out of his backpack. How much does his backpack weigh now? $11\frac{1}{10}$ lb

Add or subtract. Write each answer as a fraction in simplest form.

24. $0.3 + \frac{2}{5}$ $\frac{7}{10}$ **25.** $\frac{4}{5} + 0.9$ $1\frac{7}{10}$ **26.** $5\frac{4}{5} - 3.2$ $2\frac{3}{5}$ **27.** $14\frac{1}{4} + 9.5$ $23\frac{3}{4}$

28. $6.3 + \frac{4}{5}$ $7\frac{1}{10}$ **29.** $23\frac{3}{4} - 10.5$ $13\frac{1}{4}$ **30.** $18.9 - 6\frac{1}{2}$ $12\frac{2}{5}$ **31.** $21.8 - 3\frac{3}{5}$ $18\frac{1}{5}$

32. A wheelbarrow can hold $52\frac{1}{2}$ lb. Five rocks that weigh $10\frac{5}{8}$ lb, $12\frac{1}{6}$ lb, $9\frac{1}{4}$ lb, $11\frac{1}{8}$ lb, and $10\frac{1}{2}$ lb are to be loaded into the wheelbarrow. Can the wheelbarrow hold all five rocks? Explain.

32. no; the total weight of the rocks is $52\frac{2}{3}$ lb and the wheelbarrow only holds $52\frac{1}{2}$ lb; $52\frac{2}{3} > 52\frac{1}{2}$

33. The route Jo usually takes to work is $4\frac{2}{5}$ mi. After heavy rains, when that road is flooded, she must take a different route that is $4\frac{9}{10}$ mi. How much longer is Jo's alternate route? $\frac{1}{2}$ mi

34. Multi-Step Mr. Hansley used $1\frac{2}{3}$ c of flour to make muffins and $4\frac{1}{2}$ c to make bread. If he has $3\frac{5}{6}$ c left, how much flour did Mr. Hansley have before making the muffins and bread? 10 c

RETEACH 5-3

LESSON 5-3 **Reteach**
Adding and Subtracting Mixed Numbers

You can use what you know about improper fractions to add and subtract mixed numbers.

To find the sum or difference of mixed numbers, first write the mixed numbers as improper fractions.

A. $3\frac{1}{4} + 2\frac{1}{3}$ $= \frac{13}{4} + \frac{7}{3}$ B. $4\frac{1}{2} - 2\frac{2}{3}$ $= \frac{9}{2} - \frac{8}{3}$

Next, find equivalent fractions with a least common denominator.

$\frac{13}{4} + \frac{7}{3}$ $= \frac{39}{12} + \frac{28}{12}$ $\frac{9}{2} - \frac{8}{3}$ $= \frac{27}{6} - \frac{16}{6}$

Then add or subtract the like fractions.

$\frac{39}{12} + \frac{28}{12}$ $= \frac{67}{12}$ $\frac{27}{6} - \frac{16}{6}$ $= \frac{11}{6}$

Write the answer as a mixed number in simplest form.

$\frac{67}{12}$ $= 5\frac{7}{12}$ $\frac{11}{6}$ $= 1\frac{5}{6}$

So, $3\frac{1}{4} + 2\frac{1}{3} = 5\frac{7}{12}$. So, $4\frac{1}{2} - 2\frac{2}{3} = 1\frac{5}{6}$.

Find each sum or difference. Write your answer in simplest form.

1. $1\frac{1}{4} + 1\frac{1}{2}$ $= \frac{5}{4} + \frac{3}{2}$ $= \frac{5}{4} + \frac{6}{4}$ $2\frac{3}{4}$
2. $3\frac{1}{6} + 1\frac{2}{3}$ $= \frac{19}{6} + \frac{5}{3}$ $= \frac{19}{6} + \frac{10}{6}$ $4\frac{5}{6}$
3. $2\frac{1}{8} + 4\frac{1}{2}$ $= \frac{17}{8} + \frac{9}{2}$ $= \frac{17}{8} + \frac{36}{8}$ $6\frac{5}{8}$
4. $4\frac{1}{3} + 1\frac{1}{2}$ $= \frac{13}{3} + \frac{3}{2}$ $= \frac{26}{6} + \frac{9}{6}$ $5\frac{5}{6}$
5. $2\frac{3}{5} + 1\frac{1}{10}$ $3\frac{7}{10}$
6. $3\frac{1}{6} + 1\frac{1}{12}$ $4\frac{1}{4}$
7. $2\frac{5}{8} - 1\frac{1}{4}$ $1\frac{3}{8}$
8. $5\frac{2}{3} - 2\frac{1}{4}$ $3\frac{5}{12}$

PRACTICE 5-3

LESSON 5-3 **Practice B**
Adding and Subtracting Mixed Numbers

Find each sum or difference. Write the answer in simplest form.

1. $4\frac{3}{8} + 5\frac{1}{4}$ $9\frac{5}{8}$
2. $11\frac{2}{5} - 8\frac{1}{3}$ $3\frac{1}{15}$
3. $7\frac{1}{3} + 3\frac{2}{9}$ $10\frac{5}{9}$
4. $22\frac{5}{6} - 17\frac{1}{4}$ $5\frac{7}{12}$
5. $32\frac{4}{7} - 14\frac{1}{3}$ $18\frac{5}{21}$
6. $12\frac{1}{4} + 5\frac{1}{12}$ $17\frac{1}{3}$
7. $29\frac{1}{3} - 14\frac{1}{6}$ $15\frac{1}{6}$
8. $5\frac{3}{4} - 1\frac{7}{11}$ $4\frac{5}{44}$
9. $21\frac{1}{6} + 1\frac{3}{8}$ $22\frac{13}{24}$
10. $15\frac{7}{12} - 14\frac{3}{8}$ $1\frac{5}{24}$
11. $5\frac{6}{15} + 4\frac{3}{10}$ $9\frac{7}{10}$
12. $25\frac{1}{7} + 25\frac{2}{5}$ $50\frac{19}{35}$
13. $3\frac{2}{5} + 1\frac{1}{3}$ $4\frac{11}{15}$
14. $1\frac{2}{5} - 1\frac{2}{10}$ $\frac{1}{5}$
15. $3\frac{3}{5} - 2\frac{1}{2}$ $1\frac{1}{10}$
16. $6\frac{3}{4} - 3\frac{3}{10}$ $3\frac{9}{20}$
17. $4\frac{4}{5} + 2\frac{1}{10}$ $6\frac{9}{10}$
18. $32\frac{1}{2} + 5\frac{1}{3}$ $37\frac{5}{6}$

19. Donald is making a party mix. He bought $2\frac{1}{4}$ pounds of pecans and $3\frac{1}{5}$ pounds of walnuts. How many pounds of nuts did Donald buy in all? $5\frac{9}{20}$ pounds

20. Mrs. Watson's cookie recipe calls for $3\frac{4}{7}$ cups of sugar. Mr. Clark's cookie recipe calls for $4\frac{2}{3}$ cups of sugar. How much more sugar does Mr. Clark's recipe use? $1\frac{2}{21}$ cups more

21. Tasha's cat weighs $15\frac{5}{12}$ lb. Naomi's cat weighs $11\frac{1}{3}$ lb. Can they bring both of their cats to the vet in a carrier that can hold up to 27 pounds? Explain.

Yes; because the cats' combined weight is $26\frac{3}{4}$ pounds, which is less the 27 pounds

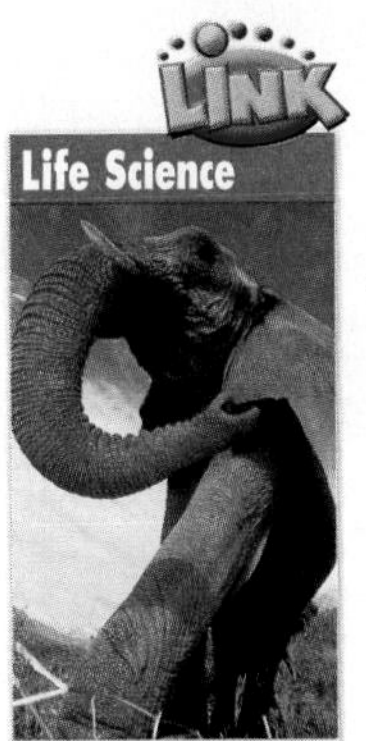

Research shows that elephants hear through their feet. The feet act as drums, sending vibrations through the bones to the elephant's ears.

Evaluate each expression for $n = 2\frac{1}{3}$. Write your answer in simplest form.

35. $2\frac{2}{3} + n$ **5** **36.** $5 - \left(1\frac{2}{3} + n\right)$ **1** **37.** $n - 1\frac{1}{4}$ $1\frac{1}{12}$ **38.** $5 - n$ $2\frac{2}{3}$

39. $n + 5\frac{7}{9}$ $8\frac{1}{9}$ **40.** $6 + \left(3\frac{4}{9} + n\right)$ $11\frac{7}{9}$ **41.** $2\frac{1}{3} - n$ **0** **42.** $3 + \left(2\frac{3}{4} - n\right)$ $3\frac{5}{12}$

43. Life Science Elephants can communicate through low-frequency infrasonic rumbles. Such sounds can travel from $\frac{1}{8}$ km to $9\frac{1}{2}$ km. Find the difference between these two distances. $9\frac{3}{8}$ **km**

Use the drawing for Exercises 44–47.

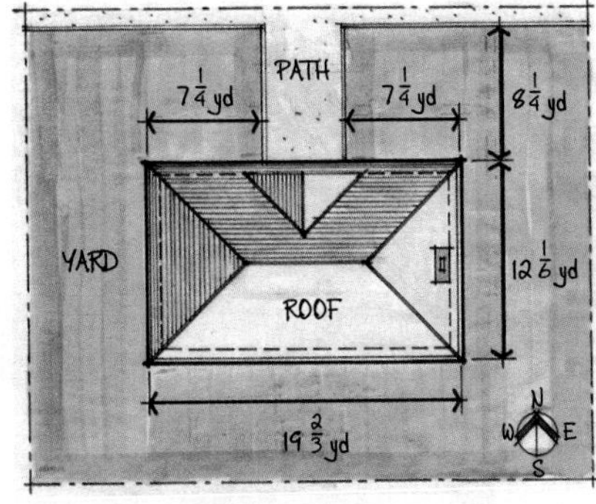

44. Sarah is a landscape architect designing a garden. Based on her drawing, how much longer is the south side of the building than the west side? $7\frac{1}{2}$ **yd**

45. Sarah needs to determine how many azalea bushes she can plant along both sides of the path. What is the sum of the lengths of the two sides of the path? $16\frac{1}{2}$ **yards**

46. How wide is the path? $5\frac{1}{6}$ **yards**

47. What's the Question? The answer is $63\frac{2}{3}$ yd. What is the question?

48. Write About It Explain how you would use the sum of $\frac{2}{5}$ and $\frac{1}{3}$ to find the sum of $10\frac{2}{5}$ and $6\frac{1}{3}$. **Possible answer: Find the sum of the whole numbers and add it to the sum of $\frac{2}{5}$ and $\frac{1}{3}$.**

49. Challenge Find each missing numerator.

a. $3\frac{x}{9} + 4\frac{2}{9} = 7\frac{7}{9}$ $x = 5$ **b.** $1\frac{3}{10} + 9\frac{x}{2} = 10\frac{4}{5}$ $x = 1$

CRCT Prep • GPS Support • Spiral Review

50. Multiple Choice Which expression does NOT have a sum of $6\frac{3}{10}$?

Ⓐ $1\frac{1}{20} + 5\frac{1}{4}$ Ⓑ $3\frac{1}{5} + 3\frac{1}{10}$ **Ⓒ** $3\frac{2}{5} + 3\frac{1}{5}$ Ⓓ $8\frac{9}{20} - 2\frac{3}{20}$

51. Multiple Choice A bumblebee bat is $1\frac{1}{5}$ inches in length. A thread snake is $4\frac{1}{4}$ inches in length. How much longer is a thread snake than a bumblebee bat?

Ⓕ $3\frac{1}{4}$ inches Ⓖ $3\frac{1}{5}$ inches Ⓗ $3\frac{1}{10}$ inches **Ⓙ** $3\frac{1}{20}$ inches

Write each decimal as a fraction or mixed number. (Lesson 4-4)

52. 0.35 $\frac{7}{20}$ **53.** 1.5 $1\frac{1}{2}$ **54.** 0.7 $\frac{7}{10}$ **55.** 1.4 $1\frac{2}{5}$

Evaluate each expression for $x = \frac{2}{5}$. Write your answer in simplest form. (Lesson 5-2)

56. $x - \frac{3}{10}$ $\frac{1}{10}$ **57.** $x + \frac{5}{12}$ $\frac{49}{60}$ **58.** $\frac{7}{8} - x$ $\frac{19}{40}$ **59.** $\frac{2}{3} + x$ $1\frac{1}{15}$

CHALLENGE 5-3

LESSON 5-3 Challenge
Maximum Snakes

The bar graph below shows the maximum lengths for the longest snakes in the world. Use the graph to find how much each of the snakes in the City Zoo is below its maximum length.

World's Longest Snakes

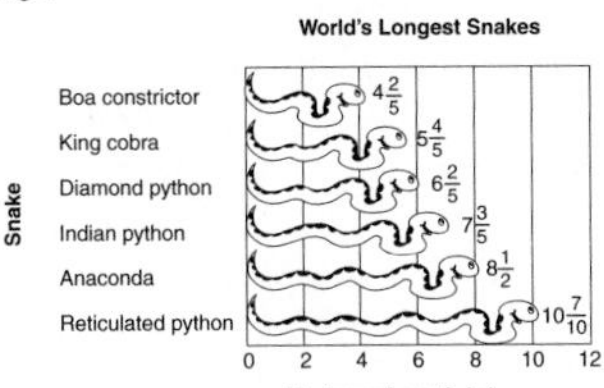

Snakes in the City Zoo

Snake	Length (in meters)	Difference from Maximum Length
Kevin (king cobra)	$3\frac{1}{2}$	$2\frac{3}{10}$ meters
Annie (anaconda)	$5\frac{1}{3}$	$3\frac{1}{6}$ meters
Bob (boa constrictor)	$3\frac{1}{4}$	$1\frac{3}{20}$ meters
Ivy (Indian python)	$4\frac{2}{7}$	$3\frac{11}{35}$ meters
Reggie (reticulated python)	$8\frac{3}{5}$	$2\frac{1}{10}$ meters
Diana (diamond python)	$4\frac{3}{8}$	$2\frac{1}{40}$ meters

PROBLEM SOLVING 5-3

LESSON 5-3 Problem Solving
Adding and Subtracting Mixed Numbers

Write the correct answer in simplest form.

1. Of the planets in our solar system, Jupiter and Neptune have the greatest surface gravity. Jupiter's gravitational pull is $2\frac{16}{25}$ stronger than Earth's, and Neptune's is $1\frac{1}{5}$ stronger. What is the difference between Jupiter's and Neptune's surface gravity levels?

Jupiter's is $1\frac{11}{25}$ higher.

2. Escape velocity is the speed a rocket must attain to overcome a planet's gravitational pull. Earth's escape velocity is $6\frac{9}{10}$ miles per second! The Moon's escape velocity is $5\frac{2}{5}$ miles per second slower. How fast does a rocket have to launch to escape the moon's gravity?

$1\frac{1}{2}$ miles per second

3. The two longest total solar eclipses occurred in 1991 and 1992. The first one lasted $6\frac{5}{6}$ minutes. The eclipse of 1992 lasted $5\frac{1}{3}$ minutes. How much longer was 1991's eclipse?

$1\frac{1}{2}$ minutes

4. The two largest meteorites found in the U.S. landed in Canyon Diablo, Arizona, and Willamette, Oregon. The Arizona meteorite weighs $33\frac{1}{10}$ tons! Oregon's weighs $16\frac{1}{2}$ tons. How much do the two meteorites weigh in all?

$49\frac{3}{5}$ tons

Circle the letter of the correct answer.

5. Not including the Sun, Proxima Centauri is the closest star to Earth. It is $4\frac{11}{50}$ light years away! The next closest star is Alpha Centauri. It is $\frac{13}{100}$ light years farther than Proxima. How far is Alpha Centauri from Earth?

Ⓐ $4\frac{7}{20}$ light years
B $4\frac{13}{100}$ light years
C $4\frac{6}{25}$ light years
D $4\frac{1}{50}$ light years

6. It takes about $5\frac{1}{3}$ minutes for light from the Sun to reach Earth. The Moon is closer to Earth, so its light reaches Earth faster—about $5\frac{19}{60}$ minutes faster than from the Sun. How long does light from the Moon take to reach Earth?

F $\frac{3}{10}$ of a minute
Ⓖ $\frac{1}{60}$ of a minute
H $\frac{1}{3}$ of a minute
J $\frac{4}{15}$ of a minute

Ongoing Assessment and Intervention

***Diagnose Before* the Lesson**
5-3 Warm Up, TE p. 238

***Monitor During* the Lesson**
5-3 Know-It Notebook
5-3 Questioning Strategies

***Assess After* the Lesson**
5-3 Lesson Quiz, TE p. 241

Answers

47. What is the distance around, or the perimeter of, the house?

Test Prep Doctor In Exercise 51, point out to students that this exercise requires an exact answer. None of the answers can be eliminated by estimation. *How much longer* means that the student should subtract, using an LCD of 20.

Journal

Have students outline the steps involved in adding and subtracting mixed numbers with unlike denominators. Have them give an example for each operation.

Power Presentations with PowerPoint®

5-3 Lesson Quiz

Find each sum or difference. Write the answer in simplest form.

1. $7\frac{11}{12} - 4\frac{2}{3}$ $3\frac{1}{4}$ **2.** $9\frac{1}{6} + 7\frac{3}{8}$ $16\frac{13}{24}$

3. $6\frac{7}{8} + 1\frac{3}{10}$ $8\frac{7}{40}$ **4.** $10\frac{2}{5} - 4\frac{1}{6}$ $6\frac{7}{30}$

5. Miles worked $5\frac{3}{4}$ hours on Friday and $8\frac{2}{3}$ hours on Saturday. How many total hours did he work?
$14\frac{5}{12}$ hours

Also available on transparency

Organizer

Use with Lesson 5-4

Pacing:
Traditional $\frac{1}{2}$ day
Block $\frac{1}{4}$ day

Objective: Use fraction bars to model subtracting fractions by regrouping them.

Materials: Fraction bars

Online Edition
Fraction Bars

Resources

Hands-On Lab Activities
Lab 5-4 Recording Sheet

Teach

Discuss

Discuss with students what each fraction bar represents, how to regroup a whole unit, and how to model subtraction using fraction bars.

Close

Key Concept

Mixed numbers can be regrouped when subtraction calls for it.

Assessment

Model each subtraction problem using fraction bars.

1. $\frac{1}{2} - \frac{1}{3}$
2. $\frac{5}{12} - \frac{1}{3}$
3. $\frac{7}{8} - \frac{1}{4}$

Georgia Performance Standards

M6N1.d Add and subtract fractions and mixed numbers with unlike denominators.

M6P5.a Create and use representations to organize, record, and communicate mathematical ideas.

M6P5.b Select, apply, and translate among mathematical representations to solve problems.

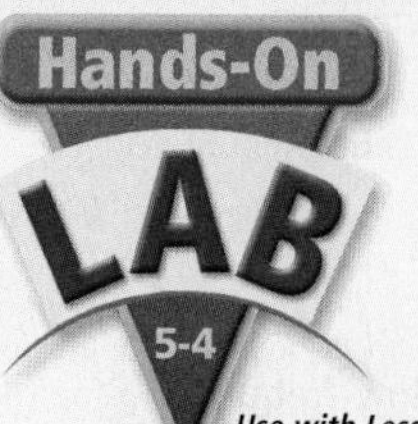

Regroup to Subtract Fractions

Use with Lesson 5-4

Georgia Performance Standards
M6N1.d, M6P5.a, M6P5.b

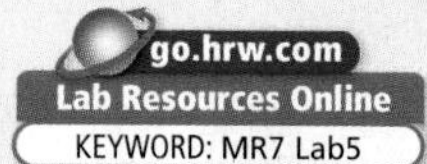

go.hrw.com
Lab Resources Online
KEYWORD: MR7 Lab5

Sometimes you need to regroup a mixed number before you can subtract. To regroup a mixed number, divide one or more of the whole numbers into fractional parts.

Activity

1. Find $1\frac{1}{3} - \frac{2}{3}$.

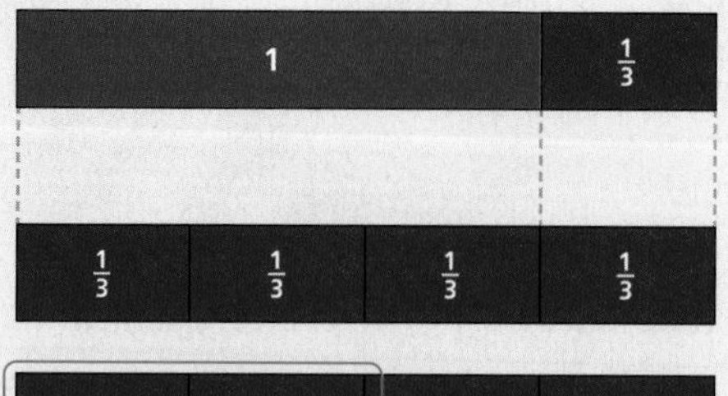

Use fraction bars to model the first mixed number, $1\frac{1}{3}$.

The model does not show $\frac{2}{3}$ that can be removed. You need to regroup $1\frac{1}{3}$.

1 is equivalent to $\frac{3}{3}$.

Now you can subtract $\frac{2}{3}$ from $\frac{4}{3}$.

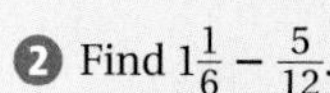

$1\frac{1}{3} - \frac{2}{3} \rightarrow \frac{4}{3} - \frac{2}{3} = \frac{2}{3}$

2. Find $1\frac{1}{6} - \frac{5}{12}$.

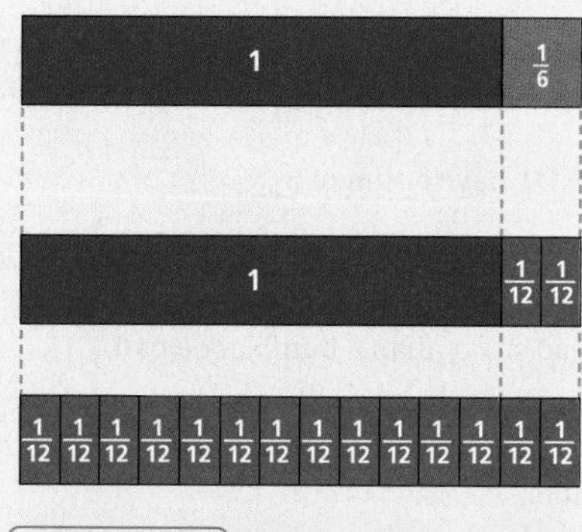

Use fraction bars to model the first mixed number, $1\frac{1}{6}$.

You need to remove $\frac{5}{12}$, so model $1\frac{1}{6}$ using $\frac{1}{12}$ fraction bars.

The model does not show $\frac{5}{12}$ that can be removed. You need to regroup $1\frac{1}{6}$.

1 is equivalent to $\frac{12}{12}$.

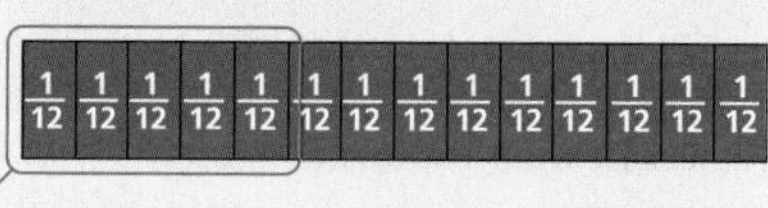

Now you can subtract $\frac{5}{12}$ from $\frac{14}{12}$.

$1\frac{1}{6} - \frac{5}{12} \rightarrow \frac{14}{12} - \frac{5}{12} - \frac{9}{12}$, or $\frac{3}{4}$

Answers to *Assessment*

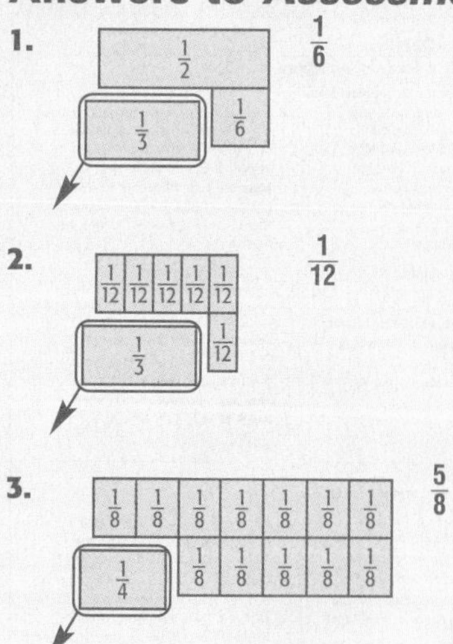

1. $\frac{1}{6}$
2. $\frac{1}{12}$
3. $\frac{5}{8}$

Answers to *Try This*

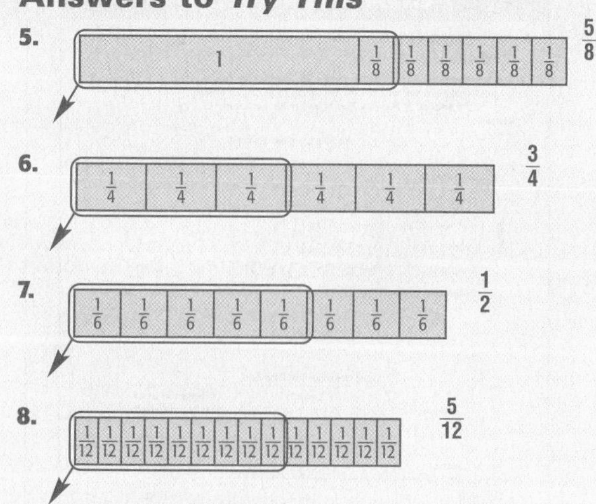

5. $\frac{5}{8}$
6. $\frac{3}{4}$
7. $\frac{1}{2}$
8. $\frac{5}{12}$

3 Find $1\frac{1}{3} - \frac{1}{2}$.

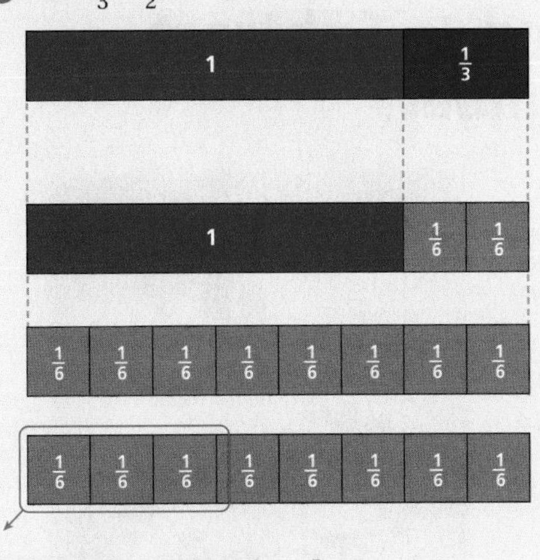

Use fraction bars to model the first mixed number, $1\frac{1}{3}$.

You need to remove $\frac{1}{2}$. Model $1\frac{1}{3}$ using one size fraction bar that can model $1\frac{1}{3}$ and $\frac{1}{2}$.

The model does not show $\frac{1}{2}$ that can be removed. You need to regroup $1\frac{1}{3}$.

1 is equivalent to $\frac{6}{6}$.

Now you can subtract $\frac{1}{2}$ from $\frac{8}{6}$.

$$1\frac{1}{3} - \frac{1}{2} \rightarrow \frac{8}{6} - \frac{1}{2} = \frac{5}{6}$$

Think and Discuss

1. Tell whether you need to regroup before you subtract $3\frac{3}{8} - 1\frac{1}{8}$. **no**
2. Tell whether you need to regroup before you subtract $4\frac{3}{5} - 1\frac{7}{10}$. **yes**

Try This

Give the subtraction expression that is modeled.

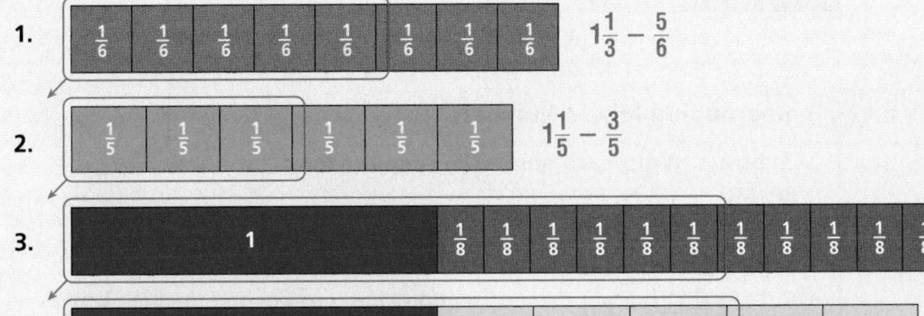

1. $1\frac{1}{3} - \frac{5}{6}$
2. $1\frac{1}{5} - \frac{3}{5}$
3. $2\frac{3}{8} - 1\frac{3}{4}$
4. $2\frac{1}{4} - 1\frac{3}{4}$

Model each subtraction expression with fraction bars, draw the model, and find the difference.

5. $1\frac{3}{4} - 1\frac{1}{8}$ $\frac{5}{8}$
6. $1\frac{1}{2} - \frac{3}{4}$ $\frac{3}{4}$
7. $1\frac{2}{6} - \frac{5}{6}$ $\frac{1}{2}$
8. $1\frac{1}{6} - \frac{3}{4}$ $\frac{5}{12}$
9. $2\frac{3}{8} - 1\frac{1}{2}$ $\frac{7}{8}$
10. $3\frac{1}{3} - 1\frac{2}{3}$ $1\frac{2}{3}$
11. $4\frac{1}{4} - 2\frac{5}{6}$ $1\frac{5}{12}$
12. $3\frac{1}{6} - 1\frac{1}{4}$ $1\frac{11}{12}$

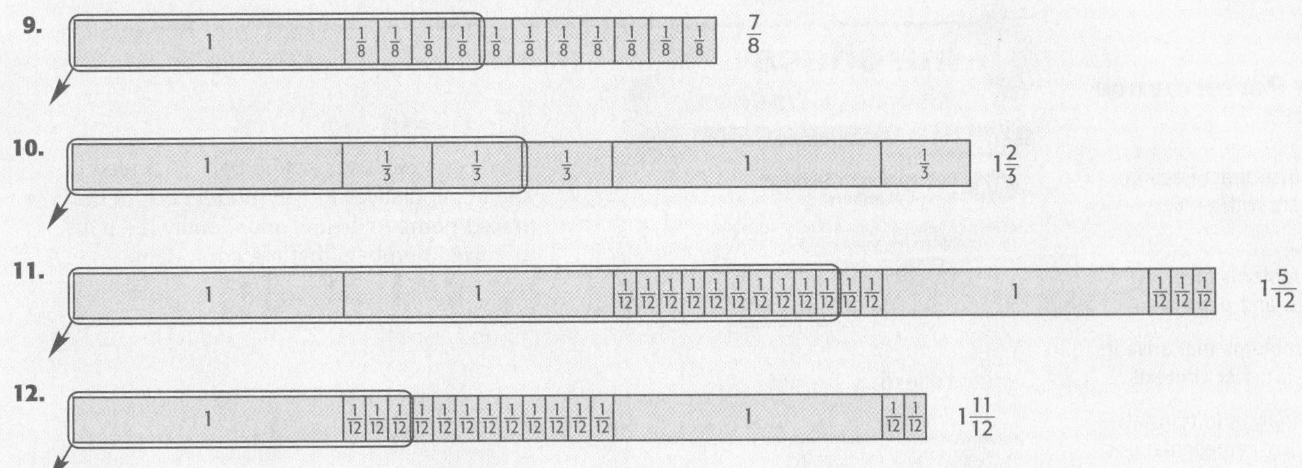

9. $\frac{7}{8}$

10. $1\frac{2}{3}$

11. $1\frac{5}{12}$

12. $1\frac{11}{12}$

5-4 Organizer

Pacing: Traditional 2 day
Block 1 day

Objective: Students rename mixed numbers to subtract.

Online Edition
Tutorial Videos

Countdown to CRCT Week 10

Warm Up

Add or subtract.

1. $3\frac{2}{5} + 1\frac{3}{5}$ 5 **2.** $7\frac{9}{11} + \frac{11}{11}$ $8\frac{9}{11}$

3. $8\frac{4}{5} - 2\frac{1}{4}$ $6\frac{11}{20}$ **4.** $6\frac{1}{3} - 1\frac{1}{9}$ $5\frac{2}{9}$

Problem of the Day

Complete the magic square so that every row, column, and diagonal has the same sum. Answer:

$1\frac{7}{8}$	$\frac{5}{8}$	$\frac{1}{2}$	$2\frac{1}{4}$
$1\frac{1}{4}$	$1\frac{1}{2}$	$1\frac{5}{8}$	$\frac{7}{8}$
$1\frac{3}{4}$	1	$1\frac{1}{8}$	$1\frac{3}{8}$
$\frac{3}{8}$	$2\frac{1}{8}$	2	$\frac{3}{4}$

Also available on transparency

5-4 Regrouping to Subtract Mixed Numbers

Learn to regroup mixed numbers to subtract.

Georgia Performance Standards

M6N1.d Subtract fractions and mixed numbers with unlike denominators. Also, M6N1.g, M6P1.b, M6P5.b.

Jimmy and his family planted a tree when it was $1\frac{3}{4}$ ft tall. Now the tree is $2\frac{1}{4}$ ft tall. How much has the tree grown since it was planted?

The difference in the heights can be represented by the expression $2\frac{1}{4} - 1\frac{3}{4}$.

You will need to regroup $2\frac{1}{4}$ because the fraction in $1\frac{3}{4}$ is greater than $\frac{1}{4}$.

Divide *one whole* of $2\frac{1}{4}$ into fourths.

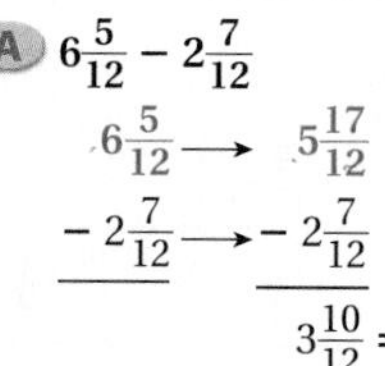

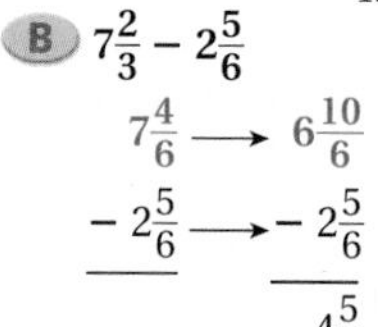

Regroup $2\frac{1}{4}$ as $1\frac{5}{4}$.

$$\begin{array}{r} 2\frac{1}{4} \rightarrow \quad 1\frac{5}{4} \\ -\,1\frac{3}{4} \rightarrow -\,1\frac{3}{4} \\ \hline \frac{2}{4} = \frac{1}{2} \end{array}$$

The tree has grown $\frac{1}{2}$ ft since it was planted.

EXAMPLE 1 Regrouping Mixed Numbers

Subtract. Write each answer in simplest form.

A $6\frac{5}{12} - 2\frac{7}{12}$

$$\begin{array}{r} 6\frac{5}{12} \longrightarrow \quad 5\frac{17}{12} \\ -\,2\frac{7}{12} \longrightarrow -\,2\frac{7}{12} \\ \hline 3\frac{10}{12} = 3\frac{5}{6} \end{array}$$

Regroup $6\frac{5}{12}$ as $5 + 1\frac{5}{12} = 5 + \frac{12}{12} + \frac{5}{12}$.

Subtract the fractions and then the whole numbers.

Write the answer in simplest form.

B $7\frac{2}{3} - 2\frac{5}{6}$

$$\begin{array}{r} 7\frac{4}{6} \longrightarrow \quad 6\frac{10}{6} \\ -\,2\frac{5}{6} \longrightarrow -\,2\frac{5}{6} \\ \hline 4\frac{5}{6} \end{array}$$

6 is a multiple of 3, so 6 is a common denominator.

Regroup $7\frac{4}{6}$ as $6 + 1\frac{4}{6} = 6 + \frac{6}{6} + \frac{4}{6}$.

Subtract the fractions and then the whole numbers.

Georgia Performance Standards

M6N1.d Add and subtract fractions and mixed numbers with unlike denominators.

M6N1.g Solve problems involving fractions, decimals, and percents.

M6P1.b Solve problems that arise in mathematics and in other contexts.

M6P5.b Select, apply, and translate among mathematical representations to solve problems.

1 Introduce

Alternate Opener

EXPLORATION

5-4 Regrouping to Subtract Mixed Numbers

A baker starts the day with $2\frac{1}{4}$ lemon cakes and sells $1\frac{1}{2}$ lemon cakes during the day. How much cake is left over?

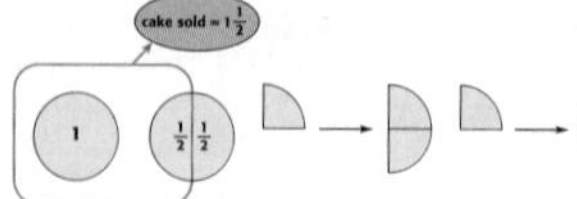

initial amount of cake = $2\frac{1}{4}$ cake left = $\frac{3}{4}$

There is $\frac{3}{4}$ of a cake left over.

Use a model to solve each subtraction problem.

1. $2 - 1\frac{1}{4}$
2. $4 - 1\frac{1}{2}$
3. $5\frac{1}{4} - 3\frac{1}{2}$
4. $1\frac{1}{8} - \frac{3}{4}$

Think and Discuss

5. **Discuss** your method for subtracting mixed numbers.
6. **Explain** why the method used to solve the problem about the lemon cakes is called regrouping.

Motivate

Have students use fraction bars (provided in the Manipulatives Kit) to model each of the mixed numbers below and identify the pairs of mixed numbers that are equivalent.

$1\frac{11}{8}$ $1\frac{13}{8}$ $2\frac{3}{8}$ $2\frac{1}{8}$ $2\frac{5}{8}$ $1\frac{9}{8}$

$1\frac{9}{8}$ and $2\frac{1}{8}$; $1\frac{11}{8}$ and $2\frac{3}{8}$; $1\frac{13}{8}$ and $2\frac{5}{8}$

Explorations and answers are provided in *Alternate Openers: Explorations Transparencies.*

Subtract. Write each answer in simplest form.

C $8\frac{1}{4} - 5\frac{2}{3}$

$$\begin{array}{rcr} 8\frac{3}{12} & \longrightarrow & 7\frac{15}{12} \\ -\,5\frac{8}{12} & \longrightarrow & -\,5\frac{8}{12} \\ \hline & & 2\frac{7}{12} \end{array}$$

The LCM of 4 and 3 is 12.
Regroup $8\frac{3}{12}$ as $7 + 1\frac{3}{12} = 7 + \frac{12}{12} + \frac{3}{12}$.
Subtract the fractions and then the whole numbers.

D $8 - 5\frac{3}{4}$

$$\begin{array}{rcr} 8 & \longrightarrow & 7\frac{4}{4} \\ -\,5\frac{3}{4} & \longrightarrow & -\,5\frac{3}{4} \\ \hline & & 2\frac{1}{4} \end{array}$$

Write 8 as a mixed number with a denominator of 4. Regroup 8 as $7 + \frac{4}{4}$.
Subtract the fractions and then the whole numbers.

EXAMPLE 2 *Measurement Application*

Dave is re-covering an old couch and cushions. He determines that he needs 17 yards of fabric for the job.

A **Dave has $1\frac{2}{3}$ yards of fabric. How many more yards does he need?**

$$\begin{array}{rcr} 17 & \longrightarrow & 16\frac{3}{3} \\ -\,1\frac{2}{3} & \longrightarrow & -\,1\frac{2}{3} \\ \hline & & 15\frac{1}{3} \end{array}$$

Write 17 as a mixed number with a denominator of 3. Regroup 17 as $16 + \frac{3}{3}$.
Subtract the fractions and then the whole numbers.

Dave needs another $15\frac{1}{3}$ yards of material.

B **If Dave uses $9\frac{5}{6}$ yards of fabric to cover the couch frame, how much of the 17 yards will he have left?**

$$\begin{array}{rcr} 17 & \longrightarrow & 16\frac{6}{6} \\ -\,9\frac{5}{6} & \longrightarrow & -\,9\frac{5}{6} \\ \hline & & 7\frac{1}{6} \end{array}$$

Write 17 as a mixed number with a denominator of 6. Regroup 17 as $16 + \frac{6}{6}$.
Subtract the fractions and then the whole numbers.

Dave will have $7\frac{1}{6}$ yards of material left.

Think and Discuss

GPS M6P1.d, M6P3.b

1. **Explain** why you regroup 2 as $1\frac{8}{8}$ instead of $1\frac{3}{3}$ when you find $2 - 1\frac{3}{8}$.
2. **Give** an example of a subtraction expression in which you would need to regroup the first mixed number to subtract.

Answers to *Think and Discuss*

1. Possible answer: You need to use a denominator of 8 so that you can subtract $\frac{3}{8}$ from it.
2. Answers should show a mixed number subtracted from a second mixed number, where the fraction in the number being subtracted is greater than the fraction in the number from which it is subtracted.

COMMON ERROR ALERT

Some students may have difficulty regrouping the mixed number(s) being subtracted. Have these students use fraction models to help them with this step.

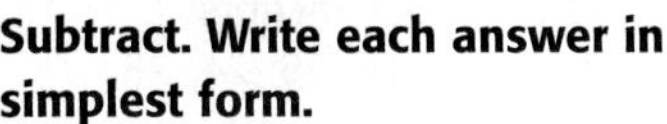

Power Presentations with PowerPoint®

Additional Examples

Example 1

Subtract. Write each answer in simplest form.

A. $7\frac{1}{6} - 2\frac{5}{6}$ $4\frac{1}{3}$

B. $8\frac{2}{5} - 6\frac{7}{10}$ $1\frac{7}{10}$

C. $6 - 3\frac{2}{3}$ $2\frac{1}{3}$

D. $5\frac{1}{3} - 2\frac{3}{4}$ $2\frac{7}{12}$

Example 2

Li is making a quilt. She needs 15 yards of fabric.

A. Li has $2\frac{3}{4}$ yards of fabric. How many more yards does she need? another $12\frac{1}{4}$ yards

B. If Li uses $11\frac{1}{6}$ yards of fabric, how much of the 15 yards will she have left? $3\frac{5}{6}$ yards

Also available on transparency

2 Teach

Guided Instruction

In this lesson, students learn to regroup mixed numbers to subtract. You may use the Teaching Transparency. Teach students to regroup to subtract mixed numbers with like and unlike denominators. Then teach students to subtract a mixed number from a whole number.

Reaching All Learners
Through Critical Thinking

Challenge students to identify a rule and complete the following subtraction pattern.

$10\frac{3}{5}, 8\frac{4}{5}, 7, 5\frac{1}{5}$, ▢, ▢, . . .

Subtract $1\frac{4}{5}$ from each term to get the next one; $3\frac{2}{5}$, $1\frac{3}{5}$.

Have students make up their own mixed number subtraction patterns for a partner to solve.

3 Close

Summarize

Review the steps for subtracting mixed numbers:

- Regroup the mixed numbers so that they have like denominators.
- Regroup the mixed number being subtracted from, if its fraction is less than the fraction in the mixed number being subtracted.
- Subtract the fractions and then the whole numbers.
- Write the answer in simplest form.

5-4 Exercises

Assignment Guide

If you finished Example 1 assign:
Average 1–4, 16–23, 47–55
Advanced 6–13, 26–29, 47–55

If you finished Example 2 assign:
Average 1–43, 47–55
Advanced 1–40, 44–55

Homework Quick Check

Quickly check key concepts.
Exercises: 6, 12, 14, 18, 24, 28

Math Background

The method taught here for subtracting mixed numbers is directly analogous to the method for subtracting whole numbers and decimal numbers. The only new element is that the manipulation involves increasing a digit not by 10 but by a fraction that equals 1.

Similar regrouping occurs when finding elapsed time. To find the elapsed time from 10:40 to 11:10, you would subtract 11:10 from 10:40. Because 1 hour = 60 minutes, when you regroup, you get 10:70 − 10:40 = 0:30. The elapsed time is 30 minutes.

Georgia Performance Standards

M6P3.a Organize and consolidate their mathematical thinking through communication.

M6P3.c Analyze and evaluate the mathematical thinking and strategies of others.

5-4 Exercises

Georgia Performance Standards
M6P3.a, M6P3.c

go.hrw.com
Homework Help Online
KEYWORD: MR7 5-4
Parent Resources Online
KEYWORD: MR7 Parent

GUIDED PRACTICE

See Example 1

Subtract. Write each answer in simplest form.

1. $2\frac{1}{2} - 1\frac{3}{4}$ $\frac{3}{4}$
2. $8\frac{2}{9} - 2\frac{7}{9}$ $5\frac{4}{9}$
3. $3\frac{2}{6} - 1\frac{2}{3}$ $1\frac{2}{3}$
4. $7\frac{1}{4} - 4\frac{11}{12}$ $2\frac{1}{3}$

See Example 2

5. Mr. Jones purchased a 4-pound bag of flour. He used $1\frac{2}{5}$ pounds of flour to make bread. How many pounds of flour are left? $2\frac{3}{5}$

INDEPENDENT PRACTICE

See Example 1

Subtract. Write each answer in simplest form.

6. $6\frac{3}{11} - 3\frac{10}{11}$ $2\frac{4}{11}$
7. $9\frac{2}{5} - 5\frac{3}{5}$ $3\frac{4}{5}$
8. $4\frac{3}{10} - 3\frac{3}{5}$ $\frac{7}{10}$
9. $10\frac{1}{2} - 2\frac{5}{8}$ $7\frac{7}{8}$
10. $11\frac{3}{4} - 9\frac{1}{8}$ $2\frac{5}{8}$
11. $7\frac{5}{9} - 2\frac{5}{6}$ $4\frac{13}{18}$
12. $6 - 2\frac{2}{3}$ $3\frac{1}{3}$
13. $5\frac{7}{10} - 3\frac{1}{2}$ $2\frac{1}{5}$

See Example 2

14. **Measurement** A standard piece of notebook paper has a length of 11 inches and a width of $8\frac{1}{2}$ inches. What is the difference between these two measures? $2\frac{1}{2}$ inches
15. Chad opened a 10-pound bag of birdseed to refill his feeders. He used $3\frac{1}{3}$ pounds to fill them. How many pounds of birdseed were left? $6\frac{2}{3}$

PRACTICE AND PROBLEM SOLVING

CRCT GPS
Extra Practice p. 722

Find each difference. Write the answer in simplest form.

16. $8 - 6\frac{4}{7}$ $1\frac{3}{7}$
17. $13\frac{1}{9} - 11\frac{2}{3}$ $1\frac{4}{9}$
18. $10\frac{3}{4} - 6\frac{1}{2}$ $4\frac{1}{4}$
19. $13 - 4\frac{2}{11}$ $8\frac{9}{11}$
20. $15\frac{2}{5} - 12\frac{3}{4}$ $2\frac{13}{20}$
21. $17\frac{5}{9} - 6\frac{1}{3}$ $11\frac{2}{9}$
22. $18\frac{1}{4} - 14\frac{3}{8}$ $3\frac{7}{8}$
23. $20\frac{1}{6} - 7\frac{4}{9}$ $12\frac{13}{18}$

24. **Economics** A single share of stock in a company cost $\$23\frac{2}{5}$ on Monday. By Tuesday, the cost of a share in the company had fallen to $\$19\frac{1}{5}$. By how much did the price of a share fall? $\$4\frac{1}{5}$
25. Jasmine is $62\frac{1}{2}$ inches tall. Her brother, Antoine, is $69\frac{3}{4}$ inches tall. What is the difference, in inches, in their heights? $7\frac{1}{4}$ in.

Simplify each expression. Write the answer in simplest form.

26. $4\frac{2}{3} + 5\frac{1}{3} - 7\frac{1}{8}$ $2\frac{7}{8}$
27. $12\frac{5}{9} - 6\frac{2}{3} + 1\frac{4}{9}$ $7\frac{1}{3}$
28. $7\frac{7}{8} - 4\frac{1}{8} + 1\frac{1}{4}$ 5
29. $7\frac{4}{11} - 2\frac{8}{11} - \frac{10}{11}$ $3\frac{8}{11}$
30. $8\frac{1}{3} - 5\frac{8}{9} + 8\frac{1}{2}$ $10\frac{17}{18}$
31. $5\frac{2}{7} - 2\frac{1}{14} + 8\frac{5}{14}$ $11\frac{4}{7}$

32. **Multi-Step** Octavio used a brand new 6-hour tape to record some television shows. He recorded a movie that is $1\frac{1}{2}$ hours long and a cooking show that is $1\frac{1}{4}$ hours long. How much time is left on the tape? $3\frac{1}{4}$

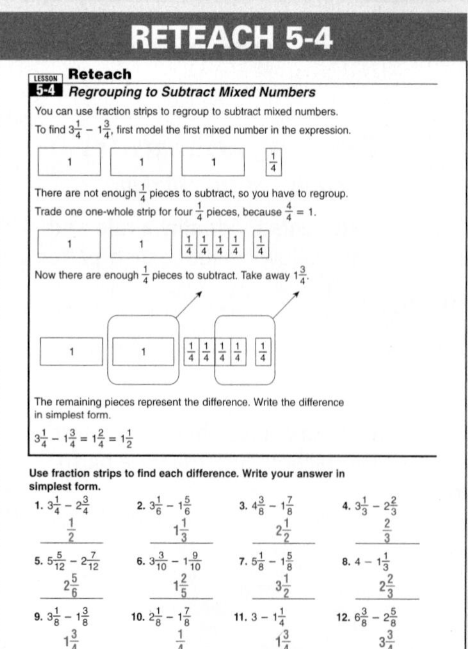

RETEACH 5-4

LESSON 5-4 **Reteach**
Regrouping to Subtract Mixed Numbers

You can use fraction strips to regroup to subtract mixed numbers.

To find $3\frac{1}{4} - 1\frac{3}{4}$, first model the first mixed number in the expression.

1 | 1 | 1 | $\frac{1}{4}$

There are not enough $\frac{1}{4}$ pieces to subtract, so you have to regroup.
Trade one one-whole strip for four $\frac{1}{4}$ pieces, because $\frac{4}{4} = 1$.

1 | 1 | $\frac{1}{4}$ $\frac{1}{4}$ $\frac{1}{4}$ $\frac{1}{4}$ | $\frac{1}{4}$

Now there are enough $\frac{1}{4}$ pieces to subtract. Take away $1\frac{3}{4}$.

1 | 1 | $\frac{1}{4}$ $\frac{1}{4}$ $\frac{1}{4}$ $\frac{1}{4}$ | $\frac{1}{4}$

The remaining pieces represent the difference. Write the difference in simplest form.

$3\frac{1}{4} - 1\frac{3}{4} = 1\frac{2}{4} = 1\frac{1}{2}$

Use fraction strips to find each difference. Write your answer in simplest form.

1. $3\frac{1}{4} - 2\frac{3}{4}$ $\frac{1}{2}$
2. $3\frac{1}{6} - 1\frac{5}{6}$ $1\frac{1}{3}$
3. $4\frac{3}{8} - 1\frac{7}{8}$ $2\frac{1}{2}$
4. $3\frac{1}{3} - 2\frac{2}{3}$ $\frac{2}{3}$
5. $5\frac{5}{12} - 2\frac{7}{12}$ $2\frac{5}{6}$
6. $3\frac{3}{10} - 1\frac{9}{10}$ $1\frac{2}{5}$
7. $5\frac{1}{8} - 1\frac{5}{8}$ $3\frac{1}{2}$
8. $4 - 1\frac{1}{3}$ $2\frac{2}{3}$
9. $3\frac{1}{8} - 1\frac{3}{8}$ $1\frac{3}{4}$
10. $2\frac{1}{8} - 1\frac{7}{8}$ $\frac{1}{4}$
11. $3 - 1\frac{1}{4}$ $1\frac{3}{4}$
12. $6\frac{3}{8} - 2\frac{5}{8}$ $3\frac{3}{4}$

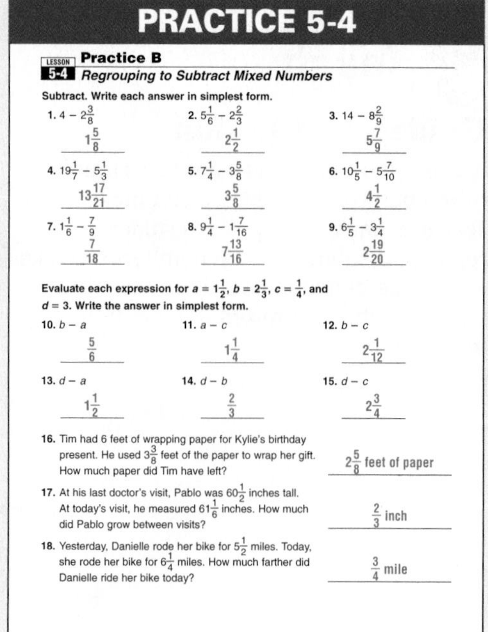

PRACTICE 5-4

LESSON 5-4 **Practice B**
Regrouping to Subtract Mixed Numbers

Subtract. Write each answer in simplest form.

1. $4 - 2\frac{3}{8}$ $1\frac{5}{8}$
2. $5\frac{1}{6} - 2\frac{2}{3}$ $2\frac{1}{2}$
3. $14 - 8\frac{2}{9}$ $5\frac{7}{9}$
4. $19\frac{1}{7} - 5\frac{1}{3}$ $13\frac{17}{21}$
5. $7\frac{1}{4} - 3\frac{5}{8}$ $3\frac{5}{8}$
6. $10\frac{1}{5} - 5\frac{7}{10}$ $4\frac{1}{2}$
7. $1\frac{1}{6} - \frac{7}{9}$ $\frac{7}{18}$
8. $9\frac{1}{4} - 1\frac{7}{16}$ $7\frac{13}{16}$
9. $6\frac{1}{5} - 3\frac{1}{4}$ $2\frac{19}{20}$

Evaluate each expression for $a = 1\frac{1}{2}$, $b = 2\frac{1}{3}$, $c = \frac{1}{4}$, and $d = 3$. Write the answer in simplest form.

10. $b - a$ $\frac{5}{6}$
11. $a - c$ $1\frac{1}{4}$
12. $b - c$ $2\frac{1}{12}$
13. $d - a$ $1\frac{1}{2}$
14. $d - b$ $\frac{2}{3}$
15. $d - c$ $2\frac{3}{4}$

16. Tim had 6 feet of wrapping paper for Kylie's birthday present. He used $3\frac{3}{8}$ feet of the paper to wrap her gift. How much paper did Tim have left? $2\frac{5}{8}$ feet of paper
17. At his last doctor's visit, Pablo was $60\frac{1}{2}$ inches tall. At today's visit, he measured $61\frac{1}{6}$ inches. How much did Pablo grow between visits? $\frac{2}{3}$ inch
18. Yesterday, Danielle rode her bike for $5\frac{1}{2}$ miles. Today, she rode her bike for $6\frac{1}{4}$ miles. How much farther did Danielle ride her bike today? $\frac{3}{4}$ mile

Evaluate each expression for $a = 6\frac{2}{3}$, $b = 8\frac{1}{2}$, and $c = 1\frac{3}{4}$. Write the answer in simplest form.

33. $a - c$ $4\frac{11}{12}$ **34.** $b - c$ $6\frac{3}{4}$ **35.** $b - a$ $1\frac{5}{6}$ **36.** $10 - b$ $1\frac{1}{2}$

37. $b - (a + c)$ $\frac{1}{12}$ **38.** $c + (b - a)$ $3\frac{7}{12}$ **39.** $(a + b) - c$ $13\frac{5}{12}$ **40.** $(10 - c) - a$ $1\frac{7}{12}$

Use the table for Exercises 41–44.

41. Gustavo is working at a gift wrap center. He has 2 yd² of wrapping paper to wrap a small box. How much wrapping paper will be left after he wraps the gift? $1\frac{1}{12}$ yards²

42. Gustavo must now wrap two extra-large boxes. If he has 6 yd² of wrapping paper, how much more wrapping paper will he need to wrap the two gifts? $\frac{2}{9}$ yards²

43. To wrap a large box, Gustavo used $\frac{3}{4}$ yd² less wrapping paper than the amount listed in the table. How many square yards did he use to wrap the gift? $1\frac{11}{12}$ yards²

Gustavo's Gift Wrap Table

Gift Size	Paper Needed (yd²)
Small	$\frac{11}{12}$
Medium	$1\frac{5}{9}$
Large	$2\frac{2}{3}$
X-large	$3\frac{1}{9}$

44. What's the Error? Gustavo calculated the difference between the amount needed to wrap an extra-large box and the amount needed to wrap a medium box to be $2\frac{4}{9}$ yd². Explain his error and find the correct answer.

45. Write About It Explain why you write equivalent fractions before you regroup them. Explain why you do not regroup them first.

46. Challenge Fill in the box with a mixed number that makes the inequality true.

$$12\frac{1}{2} - 8\frac{3}{4} > 10 - \blacksquare$$ Any number $> 6\frac{1}{4}$

CRCT Prep • GPS Support • Spiral Review

47. Multiple Choice Find the difference of $5 - \frac{4}{9}$.

Ⓐ $5\frac{5}{9}$ Ⓑ $5\frac{1}{9}$ Ⓒ $4\frac{5}{9}$ Ⓓ $4\frac{1}{9}$

48. Gridded Response Tami worked 4 hours on Saturday at the city pool. She spent $1\frac{3}{4}$ hours cleaning the pool and the remaining time working as a lifeguard. How many hours did Tami spend working as a lifeguard? $2\frac{1}{4}$

Find the missing numbers that make the fractions equivalent. (Lesson 4-5)

49. $\frac{1}{2} = \frac{8}{a}$ $a = 16$ **50.** $\frac{x}{5} = \frac{3}{15}$ $x = 1$ **51.** $\frac{3}{z} = \frac{7}{21}$ $z = 9$ **52.** $\frac{7}{8} = \frac{d}{56}$ $d = 49$

Estimate. (Lesson 4-9)

53. $6\frac{7}{8} + 3\frac{2}{15} + 7\frac{1}{20}$ 17 **54.** $2\frac{3}{4} + 8\frac{9}{10} + 3\frac{1}{9}$ 15 **55.** $12\frac{8}{15} + 2\frac{1}{6} + 7\frac{3}{5}$ 23

CHALLENGE 5-4

LESSON 5-4 **Challenge**
Popular First Names

What are the most popular first names in the United States?

Regroup fractions or mixed numbers to solve each problem below. Write your answers in simplest form. Then, in the box at the bottom of the page, write each problem's letter in the blanks above its solution. When you have solved all the problems, you will have found the answer to the question.

$8\frac{7}{12} - 7\frac{3}{4}$ $\frac{5}{6}$ A

$9\frac{1}{8} - 8\frac{3}{4}$ $\frac{3}{8}$ E

$10\frac{1}{3} - 9\frac{2}{3}$ $\frac{2}{3}$ J

$6\frac{1}{2} - 5\frac{4}{5}$ $\frac{7}{10}$ M

$5\frac{1}{5} - 4\frac{4}{5}$ $\frac{2}{5}$ R

$7\frac{2}{9} - 6\frac{2}{3}$ $\frac{5}{9}$ S

$12\frac{2}{5} - 11\frac{1}{2}$ $\frac{9}{10}$ Y

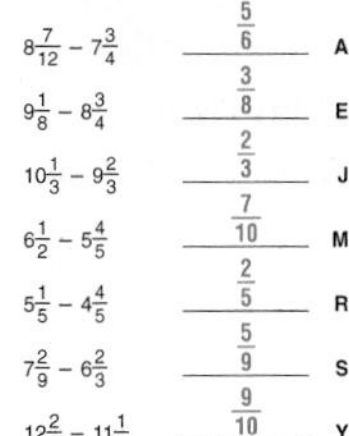

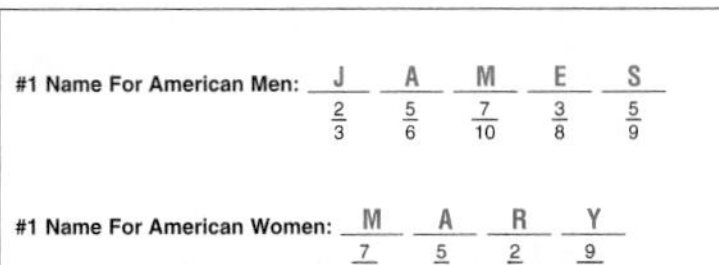

#1 Name For American Men: J ($\frac{2}{3}$) A ($\frac{5}{6}$) M ($\frac{7}{10}$) E ($\frac{3}{8}$) S ($\frac{5}{9}$)

#1 Name For American Women: M ($\frac{7}{10}$) A ($\frac{5}{6}$) R ($\frac{2}{5}$) Y ($\frac{9}{10}$)

PROBLEM SOLVING 5-4

LESSON 5-4 **Problem Solving**
Regrouping to Subtract Mixed Numbers

Write the correct answer in simplest form.

1. The average person in the United States eats $6\frac{13}{16}$ pounds of potato chips each year. The average person in Ireland eats $5\frac{15}{16}$ pounds. How much more potato chips do Americans eat a year than people in Ireland?
$\frac{7}{8}$ pound more

2. The average person in the United States eats $270\frac{1}{16}$ pounds of meat each year. The average person in Australia eats $238\frac{1}{2}$ pounds. How much more meat do Americans eat a year than people in Australia?
$31\frac{9}{16}$ pounds more

3. The average Americans eats $24\frac{1}{2}$ pounds of ice cream every year. The average person in Israel eats $15\frac{4}{5}$ pounds. How much more ice cream do Americans eat each year?
$8\frac{7}{10}$ pounds more

4. People in Switzerland eat the most chocolate—26 pounds a year per person. Most Americans eat $12\frac{9}{16}$ pounds each year. How much more chocolate do the Swiss eat?
$13\frac{7}{16}$ pounds more

5. The average person in the United States chews $1\frac{9}{16}$ pounds of gum each year. The average person in Japan chews $\frac{7}{8}$ pound. How much more gum do Americans chew?
$\frac{11}{16}$ pound more

6. Norwegians eat the most frozen foods—$78\frac{1}{2}$ pounds per person each year. Most Americans eat $35\frac{15}{16}$ pounds. How much more frozen foods do people in Norway eat?
$42\frac{9}{16}$ pounds more

Circle the letter of the correct answer.

7. Most people around the world eat $41\frac{7}{8}$ pounds of sugar each year. Most Americans eat $66\frac{3}{4}$ pounds. How much more sugar do Americans eat than the world's average?
A $25\frac{7}{8}$ pounds more
B $25\frac{1}{8}$ pounds more
Ⓒ $24\frac{7}{8}$ pounds more
D $24\frac{1}{8}$ pounds more

8. The average person eats 208 pounds of vegetables and $125\frac{5}{8}$ pounds of fruit each year. How much more vegetables do most people eat than fruit?
F $83\frac{5}{8}$ pounds more
Ⓖ $82\frac{3}{8}$ pounds more
H $123\frac{5}{8}$ pounds more
J $83\frac{3}{8}$ pounds more

Ongoing Assessment and Intervention

***Diagnose Before* the Lesson**
5-4 Warm Up, TE p. 244

***Monitor During* the Lesson**
5-4 Know-It Notebook
5-4 Questioning Strategies

***Assess After* the Lesson**
5-4 Lesson Quiz, TE p. 247

Answers

44. Gustavo did not regroup $3\frac{1}{9}$, and he subtracted 1 from 5 instead of 5 from 1. The correct difference is $1\frac{5}{9}$ yd².

45. Possible answer: It is easier to determine if you need to regroup after you find equivalent fractions; unnecessary steps may be involved if you regroup before finding equivalent fractions.

Test Prep Doctor In Exercise 47, students should realize that the answer should be less than 5, which eliminates choices **A** and **B.**

Journal

Have students explain the steps they follow when subtracting mixed numbers. Have them address situations when the fraction part of the first mixed number is less than the fraction part of the mixed number being subtracted.

Power Presentations with PowerPoint®

5-4 Lesson Quiz

Subtract. Write each answer in simplest form.

1. $7\frac{4}{7} - 3\frac{6}{7}$ $3\frac{5}{7}$

2. $8\frac{7}{10} - 3\frac{4}{5}$ $4\frac{9}{10}$

3. $7 - 5\frac{2}{9}$ $1\frac{7}{9}$

4. $10\frac{3}{8} - 4\frac{9}{16}$ $5\frac{13}{16}$

5. Irena put 10 cups of food in the bird feeder. The birds ate $3\frac{3}{8}$ cups. How many cups are left? $6\frac{5}{8}$ cups

Also available on transparency

5-5 Organizer

Pacing: Traditional 1 day
Block $\frac{1}{2}$ day

Objective: Students solve equations by adding and subtracting fractions.

Online Edition
Tutorial Videos, Interactivities

Countdown to CRCT Week 10

Power Presentations with PowerPoint®

Warm Up

Solve.

1. $x - 15 = 9$ $\quad x = 24$
2. $x + 21 = 34$ $\quad x = 13$
3. $17 = x - 11$ $\quad x = 28$
4. $22 = x - 34$ $\quad x = 56$

Problem of the Day

If a newborn baby weighs two pounds plus three-fourths its own weight, how much does it weigh?
8 pounds

Also available on transparency

Math Humor

Two crooked tailors made pleats in a skirt to sew in some stolen money. One made four pleats, and the other made only one. Both were arrested, but the second tailor went free because in court he *pleated the fifth*.

Georgia Performance Standards

M6N1.d Add and subtract fractions and mixed numbers with unlike denominators.

M6N1.g Solve problems involving fractions, decimals, and percents.

M6A3 Students will evaluate algebraic expressions, including those with exponents, and solve simple one-step equations using each of the four basic operations.

M6P4.c Recognize and apply mathematics in contexts outside of mathematics.

5-5 Solving Fraction Equations: Addition and Subtraction

Learn to solve equations by adding and subtracting fractions.

Georgia Performance Standards

M6N1.g Solve problems involving fractions. Also, M6N1.d, M6A3, M6P4.c.

Sugarcane is the main source of the sugar we use to sweeten our foods. It grows in tropical areas, such as Costa Rica and Haiti.

In one year, the average person in Costa Rica consumes $24\frac{1}{4}$ lb less sugar than the average person in the United States consumes.

This painting depicts the landscape of Haiti, a tropical area where sugarcane grows.

EXAMPLE 1 Solving Equations by Adding and Subtracting

Solve each equation. Write the solution in simplest form.

A $x + 6\frac{2}{3} = 11$

$x + 6\frac{2}{3} = 11$

$-6\frac{2}{3} \quad -6\frac{2}{3}$ — *Subtract $6\frac{2}{3}$ from both sides to undo the addition.*

$x = 10\frac{3}{3} - 6\frac{2}{3}$ — *Regroup 11 as $10\frac{3}{3}$.*

$x = 4\frac{1}{3}$ — *Subtract.*

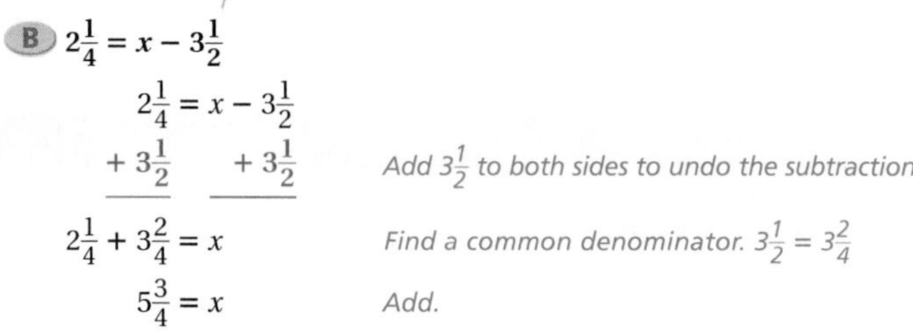

B $2\frac{1}{4} = x - 3\frac{1}{2}$

$2\frac{1}{4} = x - 3\frac{1}{2}$

$+3\frac{1}{2} \quad +3\frac{1}{2}$ — *Add $3\frac{1}{2}$ to both sides to undo the subtraction.*

$2\frac{1}{4} + 3\frac{2}{4} = x$ — *Find a common denominator. $3\frac{1}{2} = 3\frac{2}{4}$*

$5\frac{3}{4} = x$ — *Add.*

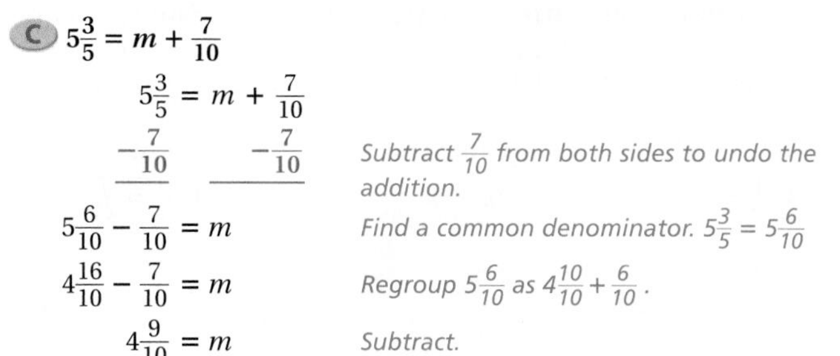

C $5\frac{3}{5} = m + \frac{7}{10}$

$5\frac{3}{5} = m + \frac{7}{10}$

$-\frac{7}{10} \quad -\frac{7}{10}$ — *Subtract $\frac{7}{10}$ from both sides to undo the addition.*

$5\frac{6}{10} - \frac{7}{10} = m$ — *Find a common denominator. $5\frac{3}{5} = 5\frac{6}{10}$*

$4\frac{16}{10} - \frac{7}{10} = m$ — *Regroup $5\frac{6}{10}$ as $4\frac{10}{10} + \frac{6}{10}$.*

$4\frac{9}{10} = m$ — *Subtract.*

1 Introduce

Alternate Opener

EXPLORATION

5-5 Solving Fraction Equations: Addition and Subtraction

You can use mental math to solve addition and subtraction equations that contain fractions. Look at the reasoning used to solve $\frac{7}{9} - x = \frac{2}{9}$.

Since the denominators of the fractions are the same, you can rewrite $\frac{7}{9} - x = \frac{2}{9}$ as a simpler equation: $7 - ■ = 2$.

$7 - ■ = 2$ — *Think:* 7 minus what number equals 2?
$7 - 5 = 2$ — Use mental math.
$\frac{7}{9} - \frac{5}{9} = \frac{2}{9}$ — Write the equation, using the denominator.
$x = \frac{5}{9}$ — Write the value of x.

Using the example above as a guide, complete the table below.

	Equation	Simpler Equation	Value of x
1.	$\frac{1}{2} + x = \frac{7}{2}$	$1 + ■ = 7$	
2.	$x - \frac{2}{5} = \frac{1}{5}$	$■ - 2 = 1$	
3.	$x + \frac{1}{3} = \frac{2}{3}$	$■ + 1 = 2$	
4.	$x - \frac{1}{3} = \frac{2}{3}$	$■ - 1 = 2$	

Think and Discuss

5. **Explain** how you could use mental math to solve the equation $\frac{1}{3} + x = \frac{5}{6}$.

Motivate

Review how to solve equations. Ask students what operation undoes addition. subtraction Ask what operation undoes subtraction. addition Have students explain how to solve an equation where a whole number is added to a variable. Subtract the whole number added to the variable from both sides of the equation.

Explorations and answers are provided in *Alternate Openers: Explorations Transparencies.*

Solve each equation. Write the solution in simplest form.

D $w - \frac{1}{2} = 2\frac{3}{4}$

$w - \frac{1}{2} = 2\frac{3}{4}$

$\underline{+\frac{1}{2} \quad +\frac{1}{2}}$ — *Add $\frac{1}{2}$ to both sides to undo the subtraction.*

$w = 2\frac{3}{4} + \frac{1}{2}$

$w = 2\frac{3}{4} + \frac{2}{4}$ — *Find a common denominator. $\frac{1}{2} = \frac{2}{4}$*

$w = 2\frac{5}{4}$ — *Add.*

$w = 3\frac{1}{4}$ — *$2\frac{5}{4} = 2 + 1\frac{1}{4}$*

EXAMPLE 2 ***Social Studies Application***

On average, a person in Costa Rica consumes $132\frac{1}{4}$ lb of sugar per year. If the average person in Costa Rica consumes $24\frac{1}{4}$ lb less than the average person in the U.S., what is the average sugar consumption per year by a person in the U.S.?

Costa Rica

$u - 24\frac{1}{4} = 132\frac{1}{4}$ — *Let u represent the average amount of sugar consumed in the U.S.*

$\underline{+24\frac{1}{4} \quad +24\frac{1}{4}}$ — *Add $24\frac{1}{4}$ to both sides to undo the subtraction.*

$u = 156\frac{2}{4} = 156\frac{1}{2}$ — *Simplify.*

Check

$u - 24\frac{1}{4} = 132\frac{1}{4}$

$156\frac{1}{2} - 24\frac{1}{4} \stackrel{?}{=} 132\frac{1}{4}$ — *Substitute $156\frac{1}{2}$ for u.*

$156\frac{2}{4} - 24\frac{1}{4} \stackrel{?}{=} 132\frac{1}{4}$ — *Find a common denominator.*

$132\frac{1}{4} \stackrel{?}{=} 132\frac{1}{4}$ ✔ — *$156\frac{1}{2}$ is the solution.*

On average, a person in the U.S. consumes $156\frac{1}{2}$ lb of sugar per year.

Think and Discuss  GPS M6P1.d

1. **Explain** how regrouping a mixed number when subtracting is similar to regrouping when subtracting whole numbers.
2. **Give** an example of an addition equation with a solution that is a fraction between 3 and 4.

COMMON ERROR ALERT

Students may use the wrong operation when solving equations, for example, using addition to solve an addition equation. Remind them that the *inverse* operation isolates the variable.

Power Presentations with PowerPoint®

Additional Examples

Example 1

Solve each equation. Write the solution in simplest form.

A. $x + 5\frac{3}{5} = 14$ — $x = 8\frac{2}{5}$

B. $3\frac{2}{9} = x - 4\frac{1}{3}$ — $7\frac{5}{9} = x$

C. $6\frac{1}{6} = m + \frac{7}{12}$ — $5\frac{7}{12} = m$

D. $w - \frac{4}{5} = 3\frac{3}{10}$ — $w = 4\frac{1}{10}$

Example 2

Linda's dog weighs $85\frac{1}{4}$ pounds. If Linda's dog weighs $17\frac{1}{2}$ pounds less than Ian's dog, how much does Ian's dog weigh? $102\frac{3}{4}$ pounds

Also available on transparency

Possible Answers to *Think and Discuss*

1. You must regroup one whole from the whole numbers place to add to the fractions place, just like borrowing 1 group of 10 from the tens place to add to the ones place.
2. $a + \frac{1}{2} = 4, a = 3\frac{1}{2}$

2 Teach

Guided Instruction

In this lesson, students learn how to solve equations by adding and subtracting fractions. After students solve addition and subtraction equations that require regrouping and finding common denominators, have them apply the concept to a real-world situation. Remind students that addition and subtraction are inverse operations.

Reaching All Learners

Through Diversity

Have students find recipes at home that involve mixed numbers that can be placed into addition and subtraction equations. Have students bring in their problems to share with the class.

Possible answer: Steve's chicken recipe calls for $1\frac{1}{2}$ teaspoons of garlic. The amount of garlic is $1\frac{1}{4}$ teaspoons more than the amount of salt called for. How much salt does the recipe call for?

$s + 1\frac{1}{4} = 1\frac{1}{2}; s = \frac{1}{4}$

The recipe requires $\frac{1}{4}$ teaspoon of salt.

3 Close

Summarize

Work through the following problem with the class to review the lesson.

$y + \frac{3}{5} = 7\frac{1}{2}$

$y + \frac{3}{5} - \frac{3}{5} = 7\frac{1}{2} - \frac{3}{5}$

$y = 7\frac{5}{10} - \frac{6}{10}$

$y = 6\frac{15}{10} - \frac{6}{10}$

$y = 6\frac{9}{10}$

5-5 Exercises

Assignment Guide

If you finished Example 1 assign:
Average 1–6, 16–21, 37–45
Advanced 8–13, 26–31, 37–45

If you finished Example 2 assign:
Average 1–33, 37–45
Advanced 1–31, 34–45

Homework Quick Check

Quickly check key concepts.
Exercises: 10, 12, 18, 20, 22

Math Background

Although the equations in this lesson are no different in structure from those encountered earlier involving whole numbers, the introduction of fractions and mixed numbers could be enough to confuse some students.

For example, some students may find Example 2 difficult as written, but they would have no problem with it if the numbers were whole. Therefore, a good strategy for students to use is *Solve a Simpler Problem*. Here, students could set up the equation, imagining whole numbers instead of mixed numbers. Then, once solved, the equation can be set up again and solved using the original mixed numbers.

Georgia Performance Standards

M6P1.b Solve problems that arise in mathematics and in other contexts.

M6P3.a Organize and consolidate their mathematical thinking through communication.

5-5 Exercises

Georgia Performance Standards
M6P1.b, M6P3.a

go.hrw.com
Homework Help Online
KEYWORD: MR7 5-5
Parent Resources Online
KEYWORD: MR7 Parent

GUIDED PRACTICE

See Example 1 Solve each equation. Write the solution in simplest form.

1. $x + 2\frac{1}{2} = 7$ $4\frac{1}{2}$
2. $3\frac{1}{3} = x - 5\frac{1}{9}$ $8\frac{4}{9}$
3. $9\frac{3}{4} = x + 4\frac{1}{8}$ $5\frac{5}{8}$
4. $x + 1\frac{1}{5} = 5\frac{3}{10}$ $4\frac{1}{10}$
5. $3\frac{2}{5} + x = 7\frac{1}{2}$ $4\frac{1}{10}$
6. $8\frac{7}{10} = x - 4\frac{1}{4}$ $12\frac{19}{20}$

See Example 2

7. A tailor increased the length of a robe by $2\frac{1}{4}$ inches. The new length of the robe is 60 inches. What was the original length? $57\frac{3}{4}$ in.

INDEPENDENT PRACTICE

See Example 1 Solve each equation. Write the solution in simplest form.

8. $x - 4\frac{3}{4} = 1\frac{1}{12}$ $5\frac{5}{6}$
9. $x + 5\frac{3}{8} = 9$ $3\frac{5}{8}$
10. $3\frac{1}{2} = 1\frac{3}{10} + x$ $2\frac{1}{5}$
11. $4\frac{2}{3} = x - \frac{1}{6}$ $4\frac{5}{6}$
12. $6\frac{3}{4} + x = 9\frac{1}{8}$ $2\frac{3}{8}$
13. $x - 3\frac{7}{9} = 5$ $8\frac{7}{9}$

See Example 2

14. Robert is taking a movie-making class in school. He edited his short video and cut $3\frac{2}{5}$ minutes. The new length of the video is $12\frac{1}{10}$ minutes. How long was his video before he cut it? $15\frac{1}{2}$ minutes
15. An extension for a table increased its length by $2\frac{1}{2}$ feet. The new length of the table is $8\frac{3}{4}$ feet. What was the original length? $6\frac{1}{4}$ feet

PRACTICE AND PROBLEM SOLVING

Extra Practice p. 722

Find the solution to each equation. Check your answers.

16. $y + 8\frac{2}{4} = 10$ $1\frac{1}{2}$
17. $p - 1\frac{2}{5} = 3\frac{7}{10}$ $5\frac{1}{10}$
18. $6\frac{2}{3} + n = 7\frac{5}{6}$ $1\frac{1}{6}$
19. $5\frac{3}{5} = s - 2\frac{3}{10}$ $7\frac{9}{10}$
20. $k - 8\frac{1}{4} = 1\frac{1}{3}$ $9\frac{7}{12}$
21. $\frac{23}{24} = c + \frac{5}{8}$ $\frac{1}{3}$
22. The difference between Cristina's and Erin's heights is $\frac{1}{2}$ foot. Erin's height is $4\frac{1}{4}$ feet, and she is shorter than Cristina. How tall is Cristina? $4\frac{3}{4}$ feet
23. **Measurement** Lori used $2\frac{5}{8}$ ounces of shampoo to wash her dog. When she was finished, the bottle contained $13\frac{3}{8}$ ounces of shampoo. How many ounces of shampoo were in the bottle before Lori washed her dog? 16 ounces
24. **Sports** Jack decreased his best time in the 400-meter race by $1\frac{3}{10}$ seconds. His new best time is $52\frac{3}{5}$ seconds. What was Jack's old time in the 400-meter race? $53\frac{9}{10}$ seconds
25. **Crafts** Juan makes bracelets to sell at his mother's gift shop. He alternates between green and blue beads.

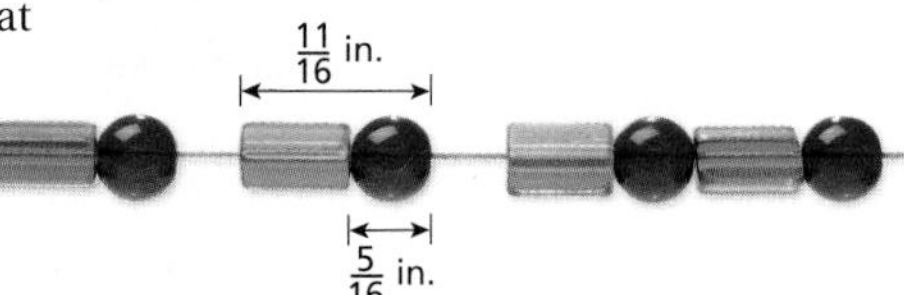

What is the length of the green bead? $\frac{3}{8}$ in.

RETEACH 5-5

LESSON 5-5 Reteach
Solving Fraction Equations: Addition and Subtraction

You can write related facts using addition and subtraction.

$3 + 4 = 7$ $7 - 4 = 3$

You can use related facts to solve equations.

A. $x + 2\frac{1}{2} = 4$

Think: $4 - 2\frac{1}{2} = x$

$x = 4 - 2\frac{1}{2}$

$x = 3\frac{2}{2} - 2\frac{1}{2}$ Regroup 4 as $3\frac{2}{2}$.

$x = 1\frac{1}{2}$

B. $x - 4\frac{1}{3} = 3\frac{1}{2}$

Think: $3\frac{1}{2} + 4\frac{1}{3} = x$

$x = 3\frac{1}{2} + 4\frac{1}{3}$

$x = \frac{7}{2} + \frac{13}{3}$ Write the mixed numbers as improper fractions.

$x = \frac{21}{6} + \frac{26}{6}$ Write the fractions using a common denominator.

$x = \frac{47}{6}$

$x = 7\frac{5}{6}$ Write the sum as a mixed number.

Use related facts to solve each equation.

1. $x + 3\frac{1}{3} = 7$; $x = 7 - 3\frac{1}{3}$; $x = 6\frac{3}{3} - 3\frac{1}{3}$; $x = 3\frac{2}{3}$
2. $x - 2\frac{1}{4} = 4\frac{1}{2}$; $x = 4\frac{1}{2} + 2\frac{1}{4}$; $x = \frac{9}{2} + \frac{9}{4}$; $x = \frac{18}{4} + \frac{9}{4}$; $x = 6\frac{3}{4}$
3. $x + \frac{3}{8} = 5\frac{1}{4}$; $x = 5\frac{1}{4} - \frac{3}{8}$; $x = \frac{21}{4} - \frac{3}{8}$; $x = \frac{42}{8} - \frac{3}{8}$; $x = 4\frac{7}{8}$
4. $x - \frac{5}{12} = 2\frac{1}{2}$; $x = 2\frac{1}{2} + \frac{5}{12}$; $x = \frac{5}{2} + \frac{5}{12}$; $x = \frac{30}{12} + \frac{5}{12}$; $x = 2\frac{11}{12}$
5. $x - 1\frac{3}{4} = 7\frac{1}{2}$ $x = 9\frac{1}{4}$
6. $x - 3\frac{2}{3} = 1\frac{1}{3}$ $x = 5$
7. $x + 3\frac{1}{2} = 6\frac{1}{4}$ $x = 2\frac{3}{4}$
8. $x - 2\frac{2}{5} = 1\frac{3}{10}$ $x = 3\frac{7}{10}$

PRACTICE 5-5

LESSON 5-5 Practice B
Solving Fraction Equations: Addition and Subtraction

Solve each equation. Write the solution in simplest form. Check your answers.

1. $k + 3\frac{3}{4} = 5\frac{2}{3} - 1\frac{1}{3}$ $k = \frac{7}{12}$
2. $a - 2\frac{2}{11} = 2\frac{5}{22} - 1\frac{2}{11}$ $a = 3\frac{5}{22}$
3. $2\frac{2}{7} = n - 4\frac{2}{3} - 1\frac{1}{3}$ $n = 8\frac{2}{7}$
4. $6\frac{1}{4} = z + 1\frac{5}{8}$ $z = 4\frac{5}{8}$
5. $5\frac{1}{4} = x + \frac{7}{16}$ $x = 4\frac{13}{16}$
6. $r + 6 = 9\frac{2}{5} - 2\frac{1}{2}$ $r = \frac{9}{10}$
7. $11\frac{2}{5} = q - 4\frac{2}{7} + 2\frac{1}{7}$ $q = 13\frac{19}{35}$
8. $4\frac{2}{5} - 2\frac{1}{2} = p + \frac{3}{10}$ $p = 1\frac{3}{5}$
9. $\frac{3}{8} + \frac{1}{6} = c - 4\frac{5}{6}$ $c = 5\frac{3}{8}$
10. $2\frac{1}{4} + c = 2\frac{1}{3} + 1\frac{1}{6}$ $c = 1\frac{1}{4}$
11. A seamstress raised the hem on Helen's skirt by $1\frac{1}{3}$ inches. The skirt's original length was 16 inches. What is the new length? $14\frac{2}{3}$ inches
12. The bike trail is $5\frac{1}{4}$ miles long. Jessie has already cycled $2\frac{5}{8}$ miles of the trail. How much farther does she need to go to finish the trail? $2\frac{5}{8}$ miles

Find the solution to each equation. Check your answers.

26. $m + 4 = 6\frac{3}{8} - 1\frac{1}{4}$ $1\frac{1}{8}$ **27.** $3\frac{2}{9} - 1\frac{1}{3} = p - 5\frac{1}{2}$ $7\frac{7}{18}$ **28.** $q - 4\frac{1}{4} = 1\frac{1}{6} + 1\frac{1}{2}$ $6\frac{11}{12}$

29. $a + 5\frac{1}{4} + 2\frac{1}{2} = 13\frac{1}{6}$ $5\frac{5}{12}$ **30.** $11\frac{2}{7} = w + 3\frac{1}{2} - 1\frac{1}{7}$ $8\frac{13}{14}$ **31.** $9 - 5\frac{7}{8} = x - 1\frac{1}{8}$ $4\frac{1}{4}$

32. Music A string quartet is performing Antonio Vivaldi's *The Four Seasons*. The concert is scheduled to last 45 minutes.

Antonio Vivaldi's *The Four Seasons*

"Spring"
"Summer"
"Autumn"
"Winter"
= 1 minute

a. After playing "Spring," "Summer," and "Autumn," how much time will be left in the concert? $15\frac{3}{4}$ min

b. Is the concert long enough to play the four movements and another piece that is $6\frac{1}{2}$ minutes long? Explain.

33. Write a Problem Use the pictograph to write a subtraction problem with two mixed numbers. Possible answer: What is the difference in time between Summer and Spring?

34. Choose a Strategy How can you draw a line that is 5 inches long using only one sheet of $8\frac{1}{2}$ in. × 11 in. notebook paper?

35. Write About It Explain how you know whether to add a number to or subtract a number from both sides of an equation in order to solve the equation. You would do the opposite of the operation that was in front of the number you wanted to move.

36. Challenge Use the numbers 1, 2, 3, 4, 5, and 6 to write a subtraction problem with two mixed numbers that have a difference of $4\frac{13}{20}$. $6\frac{2}{5} - 1\frac{3}{4}$

CRCT Prep • GPS Support • Spiral Review

37. Multiple Choice Solve $4\frac{1}{2} + x = 6\frac{1}{6}$ for x.

Ⓐ $x = 1\frac{1}{4}$ Ⓑ $x = 1\frac{2}{3}$ Ⓒ $x = 2\frac{1}{4}$ Ⓓ $x = 2\frac{2}{3}$

38. Multiple Choice Ambra's hair was $7\frac{2}{3}$ inches long. After she got her hair cut, the length of her hair was $5\frac{4}{5}$ inches. How many inches of hair were cut?

Ⓕ $1\frac{13}{15}$ Ⓖ $2\frac{2}{5}$ Ⓗ $2\frac{2}{3}$ Ⓙ $2\frac{13}{15}$

Find the least common multiple (LCM). (Lesson 5-1)

39. 4 and 12 12 **40.** 7, 14, and 21 42 **41.** 6, 9, and 24 72

Evaluate. Write each answer as a fraction in simplest form. (Lesson 5-3)

42. $2.5 + 5\frac{3}{8}$ $7\frac{7}{8}$ **43.** $3.1 - 2\frac{3}{4}$ $\frac{7}{20}$ **44.** $15\frac{1}{5} - 8.2$ 7 **45.** $6\frac{1}{6} + 1.4$ $7\frac{17}{30}$

Ongoing Assessment and Intervention

***Diagnose Before* the Lesson**
5-5 Warm Up, TE p. 248

***Monitor During* the Lesson**
5-5 Know-It Notebook
5-5 Questioning Strategies

***Assess After* the Lesson**
5-5 Lesson Quiz, TE p. 251

Answers

32. b. Yes. The total time for the four movements and another piece is $44\frac{1}{2}$ minutes.

34. Fold the top right corner to the left side of the page. The distance from the top right corner to the bottom left corner is 2.5 inches (11−8.5). Draw a line segment that is twice this length.

Test Prep Doctor In Exercise 37, students should understand that solving equations involving fractions requires the same steps as solving equations involving whole numbers. Use the inverse operation, subtraction, and rerouping to find the difference between $6\frac{1}{6}$ and $4\frac{1}{2}$.

Journal

Have students write algebraic equations involving adding and subtracting fractions. Have them solve the equations and outline the steps they followed to solve one of the addition equations and one of the subtraction equations.

CHALLENGE 5-5

LESSON 5-5 Challenge
You Read My Mind!

Here's a trick you can use to amaze your friends and family. Start by asking your friends to think of a number—any number. Pretend you are reading their minds while you write the number 6 on a piece of paper. (Don't show it to them.) Then use the steps below to tell them what to do. The fraction $\frac{2}{5}$ is used as an example choice, but the trick works for any chosen fraction, mixed number, decimal, or whole number.

Step	Example
1. Double your number.	$\frac{2}{5} + \frac{2}{5} = \frac{4}{5}$
2. Add 12 to your sum.	$\frac{4}{5} + 12 = 12\frac{4}{5}$
3. Divide your new sum by 2.	$12\frac{4}{5} \div 2 = 6\frac{2}{5}$
4. Subtract your chosen number from that quotient.	$6\frac{2}{5} - \frac{2}{5} = 6$

Now amaze your friends by showing that you wrote the same number they ended with. No matter what number is chosen, this trick always ends in 6. Equations explain why it works—but don't tell your friends this part.

Let x = the chosen number.

STEP 1	STEP 2	STEP 3	STEP 4
$2x$	$2x + 12$	$(2x + 12) \div 2 = x + 6$	$x + 6 - x = 6$

Before you try the trick, practice it on the fractions below. Use the equations for each step and show all your work.

1. Chosen Number: $\frac{7}{9}$
   STEP 1: $2 \bullet \frac{7}{9} = \frac{14}{9} = 1\frac{5}{9}$
   STEP 2: $1\frac{5}{9} + 12 = 13\frac{5}{9}$
   STEP 3: $13\frac{5}{9} \div 2 = \frac{122}{18} = 6\frac{14}{18} = 6\frac{7}{9}$
   STEP 4: $6\frac{7}{9} - \frac{7}{9} = 6$

2. Chosen Number: $3\frac{1}{4}$
   STEP 1: $2 \bullet 3\frac{1}{4} = \frac{26}{4} = 6\frac{2}{4} = 6\frac{1}{2}$
   STEP 2: $6\frac{1}{2} + 12 = 18\frac{1}{2}$
   STEP 3: $18\frac{1}{2} \div 2 = \frac{37}{4} = 9\frac{1}{4}$
   STEP 4: $9\frac{1}{4} - 3\frac{1}{4} = 6$

PROBLEM SOLVING 5-5

LESSON 5-5 Problem Solving
Solving Fraction Equations: Addition and Subtraction

Write the correct answer in simplest form.

1. It usually takes Brian $1\frac{1}{2}$ hours to get to work from the time he gets out of bed. His drive to the office takes $\frac{3}{4}$ hour. How much time does he spend getting ready for work?
   $\frac{3}{4}$ of an hour

2. Before she went to the hairdresser, Sheila's hair was $7\frac{1}{4}$ inches long. When she left the salon, it was $5\frac{1}{2}$ inches long. How much of her hair did Sheila get cut off?
   $1\frac{3}{4}$ inches

3. One lap around the gym is $\frac{1}{3}$ mile long. Kim has already run 5 times around. If she wants to run 2 miles total, how much farther does she have to go?
   $\frac{1}{3}$ mile more

4. Darius timed his speech at $5\frac{1}{6}$ minutes. His time limit for the speech is $4\frac{1}{2}$ minutes. How much does he need to cut from his speech?
   $\frac{2}{3}$ minute

Circle the letter of the correct answer.

5. Mei and Alex bought the same amount of food at the deli. Mei bought $1\frac{1}{4}$ pounds of turkey and $1\frac{1}{3}$ pounds of cheese. Alex bought $1\frac{1}{2}$ pounds of turkey. How much cheese did Alex buy?
   Ⓐ $1\frac{1}{12}$ pounds C $1\frac{1}{4}$ pounds
   B $1\frac{1}{6}$ pounds D $4\frac{1}{12}$ pounds

6. When Lynn got her dog, Max, he weighed $10\frac{1}{2}$ pounds. During the next 6 months, he gained $8\frac{4}{5}$ pounds. At his one-year check-up he had gained another $4\frac{1}{3}$ pounds. How much did Max weigh when he was 1 year old?
   F $22\frac{19}{30}$ pounds H $23\frac{29}{30}$ pounds
   Ⓖ $23\frac{19}{30}$ pounds J $23\frac{49}{50}$ pounds

7. Charlie picked up 2 planks of wood at the hardware store. One is $6\frac{1}{4}$ feet long and the other is $5\frac{5}{8}$ feet long. How much should he cut from the first plank to make them the same length?
   Ⓐ $\frac{5}{8}$ foot C $1\frac{3}{8}$ feet
   B $\frac{1}{2}$ foot D $1\frac{5}{8}$ feet

8. Carmen used $3\frac{3}{4}$ cups of flour to make a cake. She had $\frac{1}{2}$ cup of flour left over. Which equation can you use to find how much flour she had before baking the cake?
   F $x + \frac{1}{2} = 3\frac{3}{4}$ H $3\frac{3}{4} - \frac{1}{2} = x$
   Ⓖ $x - 3\frac{3}{4} = \frac{1}{2}$ J $3\frac{3}{4} - x = \frac{1}{2}$

Power Presentations with PowerPoint®

5-5 Lesson Quiz

Solve each equation. Write the solution in simplest form.

1. $x - 3\frac{3}{4} = 2\frac{5}{12}$ $x = 6\frac{1}{6}$

2. $x + 6\frac{5}{8} = 11$ $x = 4\frac{3}{8}$

3. $1\frac{7}{10} = x - 2\frac{4}{5}$ $x = 4\frac{1}{2}$

4. $5\frac{3}{4} = x - \frac{1}{2}$ $x = 6\frac{1}{4}$

5. Marco needs to work 40 hours per week. He has worked $31\frac{5}{8}$ hours so far this week. How many hours does he need to work on Friday to meet his 40-hour requirement? $8\frac{3}{8}$ hours

Also available on transparency

Organizer

Objective: Assess students' mastery of concepts and skills in Lessons 5-1 through 5-5.

Resources

Assessment Resources
Section 5A Quiz

Test & Practice Generator
One-Stop Planner®

INTERVENTION

Resources

***Ready to Go On? Intervention and Enrichment* Worksheets**

***Ready to Go On?* CD-ROM**

***Ready to Go On?* Online**

my.hrw.com

SECTION 5A

Ready to Go On?

Quiz for Lessons 5-1 Through 5-5

5-1 Least Common Multiple

1. Markers are sold in packs of 8, and crayons are sold in packs of 16. If there are 32 students in Mrs. Reading's art class, what is the least number of packs needed so that each student can have one marker and one crayon and none will be left over? **4 packs of markers and 2 packs of crayons**
2. Cans of soup are sold in packs of 24, and packets of crackers are sold in groups of 4. If there are 120 people to be fed and each will get one can of soup and one packet of crackers, what is the least number of packs needed to feed everyone such that no crackers or soup are left over? **5 packs of soup and 30 packets of crackers**

Find the least common multiple (LCM).

3. 4 and 6 **12**
4. 2 and 15 **30**
5. 3, 5, and 9 **45**
6. 4, 6, and 10 **60**

5-2 Adding and Subtracting with Unlike Denominators

Add or subtract. Write each answer in simplest form.

7. $\frac{5}{7} - \frac{3}{14}$ **$\frac{1}{2}$**
8. $\frac{7}{8} + \frac{1}{24}$ **$\frac{11}{12}$**
9. $\frac{8}{9} - \frac{1}{10}$ **$\frac{71}{90}$**
10. $\frac{1}{6} + \frac{1}{2}$ **$\frac{2}{3}$**
11. Alexia needs to add $\frac{2}{3}$ cup of sugar for the recipe she is making. She has added $\frac{1}{2}$ cup already. How much more sugar does she need to add? **$\frac{1}{6}$ c**

5-3 Adding and Subtracting Mixed Numbers

Find each sum or difference. Write each answer in simplest form.

12. $2\frac{9}{13} - 1\frac{1}{26}$ **$1\frac{17}{26}$**
13. $9\frac{5}{10} + 11\frac{4}{5}$ **$21\frac{3}{10}$**
14. $7\frac{8}{9} - 1\frac{1}{18}$ **$6\frac{5}{6}$**
15. $2\frac{4}{5} + 1\frac{1}{10}$ **$3\frac{9}{10}$**

5-4 Regrouping to Subtract Mixed Numbers

Subtract. Write each answer in simplest form.

16. $2\frac{1}{13} - 1\frac{1}{26}$ **$1\frac{1}{26}$**
17. $7\frac{1}{3} - 5\frac{7}{9}$ **$1\frac{5}{9}$**
18. $3\frac{3}{10} - 1\frac{4}{5}$ **$1\frac{1}{2}$**
19. $10\frac{1}{2} - 5\frac{2}{3}$ **$4\frac{5}{6}$**
20. Mary Ann buys $4\frac{2}{5}$ pounds of bananas. She uses $1\frac{1}{2}$ pounds making banana bread. How many pounds of bananas does she have left? **$2\frac{9}{10}$**

5-5 Solving Fraction Equations: Addition and Subtraction

Solve each equation. Write the solution in simplest form.

21. $t + 2\frac{5}{8} = 9$ **$t = 6\frac{3}{8}$**
22. $5\frac{1}{6} = x - \frac{7}{8}$ **$x = 6\frac{1}{24}$**
23. $g + \frac{1}{4} = 2\frac{9}{10}$ **$g = 2\frac{13}{20}$**
24. $a + \frac{3}{5} = 1\frac{7}{10}$ **$a = 1\frac{1}{10}$**
25. Bryn bought $5\frac{1}{8}$ yards of material. She used $3\frac{7}{9}$ yards to make a dress. How much material does she have left? **$1\frac{25}{72}$ yd**

READY TO GO ON?
Diagnose and Prescribe

NO INTERVENE

Ready to Go On? Intervention	*Ready to Go On? Intervention*, Section 5A		
	Worksheets	CD-ROM	Online
Lesson 5-1	5-1 Intervention	Activity 5-1	Diagnose and Prescribe Online
Lesson 5-2	5-2 Intervention	Activity 5-2	
Lesson 5-3	5-3 Intervention	Activity 5-3	
Lesson 5-4	5-4 Intervention	Activity 5-4	
Lesson 5-5	5-5 Intervention	Activity 5-5	

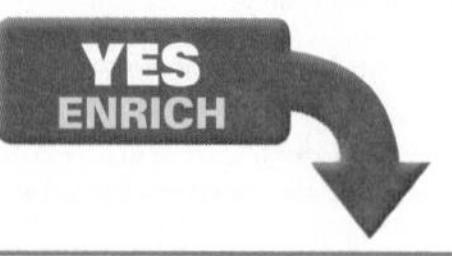

***Ready to Go On? Enrichment*, Section 5A**
- Worksheets
- CD-ROM
- Online

Focus on Problem Solving

Solve

Choose the operation: multiplication or division

Read the whole problem before you try to solve it. Determine what action is taking place in the problem. Then decide whether you need to multiply or divide in order to solve the problem.

If you are asked to combine equal groups, you need to multiply. If you are asked to share something equally or to separate something into equal groups, you need to divide.

Action	Operation	
Combining equal groups	Multiplication	
Sharing things equally or separating into equal groups	Division	

Read each problem, and determine the action taking place. Choose an operation to solve the problem. Then solve, and write the answer in simplest form.

1. Jason picked 30 cups of raspberries. He put them in giant freezer bags with 5 cups in each bag. How many bags does he have?
2. When the cranberry flowers start to open in June, cranberry growers usually bring in about $2\frac{1}{2}$ beehives per acre of cranberries to pollinate the flowers. A grower has 36 acres of cranberries. About how many beehives does she need?
3. A recipe that makes 3 cranberry banana loaves calls for 4 cups of cranberries. Linh wants to make only 1 loaf. How many cups of cranberries does she need?
4. Clay wants to double a recipe for blueberry muffins that calls for 1 cup of blueberries. How many blueberries will he need?

Focus on Problem Solving

Organizer

Objective: Focus on choosing an operation to solve the problem.

Online Edition

Resources

Chapter 5 Resource Book
Reading Strategies

Problem Solving Process

This page focuses on the third step of the problem-solving process:
Solve

Discuss

Have students identify the key words or phrases that indicate which operation to use. Determine the action taking place and name the operation.

Possible answers:

1. 5 cups *in each* bag; separating into equal groups; division
2. $2\frac{1}{2}$ beehives *per* acre; combining equal groups; multiplication
3. recipe that makes 3 loaves . . . *only* wants 1; separating into equal groups; division
4. *double* a recipe; combining equal groups; multiplication

Answers

1. 6 bags
2. about 90 beehives
3. $1\frac{1}{3}$ cups of cranberries
4. 2 cups blueberries

SECTION 5B Multiplying and Dividing Fractions

One-Minute Section Planner

Lesson	Materials	MiC and Lab Resources
Lesson 5-6 Multiplying Fractions by Whole Numbers • Multiply fractions by whole numbers. ☑ CRCT ☑ SAT-10 ☑ ITBS ☐ CTBS ☑ NAEP		
5-7 Hands-On Lab Model Fraction Multplication • Use grids to model fraction multiplication. **Lesson 5-7** Multiplying Fractions • Multiply fractions. ☑ CRCT ☑ SAT-10 ☑ ITBS ☐ CTBS ☑ NAEP	Grid paper, transparency grid	**MiC:** ***Reallotment*** pp. 20–21 ***Hands-On Lab Activities*** 5-7 ***Technology Lab Activities*** 5-7
Lesson 5-8 Multiplying Mixed Numbers • Multiply mixed numbers. ☑ CRCT ☑ SAT-10 ☑ ITBS ☐ CTBS ☑ NAEP		**MiC:** ***Fraction Times*** pp. 43–45
5-9 Hands-On Lab Model Fraction Division • Use grids to model division of fractions. **Lesson 5-9** Dividing Fractions and Mixed Numbers • Divide fractions and mixed numbers. ☑ CRCT ☑ SAT-10 ☑ ITBS ☐ CTBS ☑ NAEP	Grid paper, transparency grid	**MiC:** ***Reallotment*** pp. 30–31 **MiC:** ***More or Less*** pp. 20–21
Lesson 5-10 Solving Fraction Equations: Multiplication and Division • Solve equations by multiplying and dividing fractions. ☑ CRCT ☑ SAT-10 ☑ ITBS ☐ CTBS ☑ NAEP		

MK = *Manipulatives Kit*

Mathematics in Context

The units ***Fraction Times, Reallotment,*** and ***More or Less*** from the *Mathematics in Context* © 2006 series can be used with Section 5B. See Section Planner above for suggestions for integrating *MiC* with *Holt Mathematics*.

Section Overview

Multiplying Fractions by Whole Numbers — Lesson 5-6

Why? Some practical problems require multiplying fractions by whole numbers.

If Jo and Helena each ate $\frac{3}{8}$ of a pizza, how much of the pizza did they eat altogether?

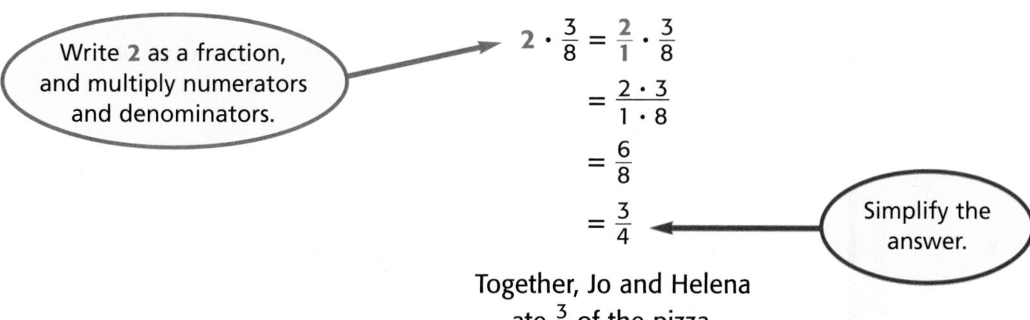

Write 2 as a fraction, and multiply numerators and denominators.
Simplify the answer.

$$2 \cdot \frac{3}{8} = \frac{2}{1} \cdot \frac{3}{8}$$
$$= \frac{2 \cdot 3}{1 \cdot 8}$$
$$= \frac{6}{8}$$
$$= \frac{3}{4}$$

Together, Jo and Helena ate $\frac{3}{4}$ of the pizza.

Multiplying and Dividing Fractions and Mixed Numbers — Lessons 5-7, 5-8, 5-9

Why? Solving real-world problems often involves multiplying or dividing fractions and mixed numbers.

Joe ran two-thirds as far as Adam. If Adam ran $1\frac{4}{5}$ miles, how far did Joe run?

$$\frac{2}{3} \cdot 1\frac{4}{5}$$

Write the mixed number as an improper fraction.

Multiply numerators.
Multiply denominators.

$$\frac{2}{3} \cdot \frac{9}{5} = \frac{18}{15}$$
$$= \frac{6}{5}, \text{ or } 1\frac{1}{5}$$

Joe ran $1\frac{1}{5}$ miles.

Mary has $2\frac{1}{2}$ yards if ribbon. How many $\frac{1}{4}$ yard lengths of ribbon can she make?

$$2\frac{1}{2} \div \frac{1}{4} = \frac{5}{\cancel{2}_1} \cdot \frac{\cancel{4}^2}{1}$$
$$= \frac{10}{1}, \text{ or } 10$$

Write the division as multiplication by the reciprocal.

Mary can make 10 lengths of ribbon.

Fraction Equations with Addition and Subtraction — Lesson 5-10

Why? Many application problems can be solved using fraction equations.

Cathy uses 3 cans of paint to paint $\frac{2}{3}$ of her room. How many cans of paint will she use to paint the whole room?

Multiply both sides of the equation by $\frac{3}{2}$, the reciprocal of $\frac{2}{3}$.

$$\frac{2}{3}r = 3$$
$$\frac{3}{2} \cdot \frac{2}{3}r = \frac{3}{2} \cdot \frac{3}{1}$$
$$r = \frac{9}{2}, \text{ or } 4\frac{1}{2}$$

Write the solution as a mixed number to represent cans of paint.

Cathy will use $4\frac{1}{2}$ cans of paint.

5-6 Organizer

Pacing: Traditional 1 day
Block $\frac{1}{2}$ day

Objective: Students multiply fractions by whole numbers.

Online Edition
Tutorial Videos, Interactivities

Countdown to CRCT Week 11

Warm Up

Multiply.

1. 15 × 2 30 **2.** 12 × 8 96
3. 9 × 16 144 **4.** 6 × 11 66
5. 8 × 15 120

Problem of the Day

The lengths of 3 dowels are 13 inches, 27 inches, and 19 inches. How can you use the three dowels to mark off a length of 5 inches?
13 + 19 − 27

Also available on transparency

Math Fact

European writers of mathematics during medieval times and Renaissance times did not understand how the product of a fraction and a whole number could be less than the whole number.

5-6 Multiplying Fractions by Whole Numbers

Learn to multiply fractions by whole numbers.

Georgia Performance Standards

M6N1.g Solve problems involving fractions. Also, M6N1.e, M6A3, M6P1.b.

Recall that multiplication by a whole number can be represented as repeated addition. For example, 4 • 5 = 5 + 5 + 5 + 5. You can multiply a whole number by a fraction using the same method.

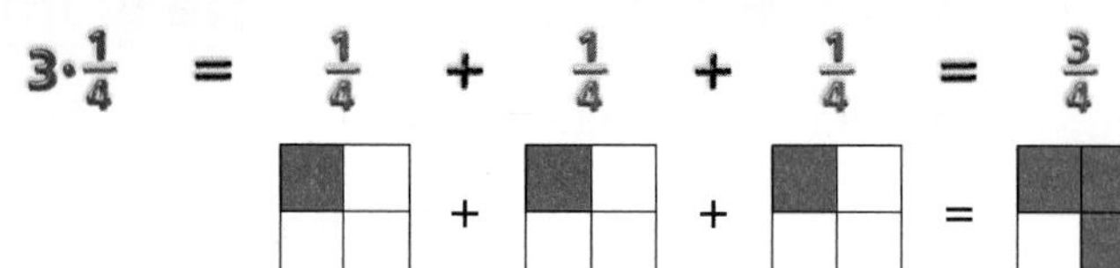

$$3 \cdot \frac{1}{4} = \frac{1}{4} + \frac{1}{4} + \frac{1}{4} = \frac{3}{4}$$

There is another way to multiply with fractions. Remember that a whole number can be written as an improper fraction with 1 in the denominator. So $3 = \frac{3}{1}$.

$$\frac{3}{1} \cdot \frac{1}{4} = \frac{3 \cdot 1}{1 \cdot 4} = \frac{3}{4}$$ ← Multiply numerators. ← Multiply denominators.

EXAMPLE 1 Multiplying Fractions and Whole Numbers

Multiply. Write each answer in simplest form.

Method 1: Use repeated addition.

A $5 \cdot \frac{1}{8}$

$5 \cdot \frac{1}{8} = \frac{1}{8} + \frac{1}{8} + \frac{1}{8} + \frac{1}{8} + \frac{1}{8}$ *Write $5 \cdot \frac{1}{8}$ as addition. Add the numerators.*

$= \frac{5}{8}$

B $3 \cdot \frac{1}{9}$

$3 \cdot \frac{1}{9} = \frac{1}{9} + \frac{1}{9} + \frac{1}{9}$ *Write $3 \cdot \frac{1}{9}$ as addition. Add the numerators.*

$= \frac{3}{9}$

$= \frac{1}{3}$ *Write your answer in simplest form.*

Method 2: Multiply.

C $4 \cdot \frac{7}{8}$

$\frac{4}{1} \cdot \frac{7}{8} = \frac{28}{8}$ *Multiply.*

$= \frac{7}{2}$ or $3\frac{1}{2}$ *Write your answer in simplest form.*

1 Introduce

Alternate Opener

EXPLORATION

5-6 Multiplying Fractions by Whole Numbers

Rosario requires $\frac{3}{4}$ of a 1-pound bag of clay to make one bowl. How many 1-pound bags of clay will she need to make a set of 6 bowls?

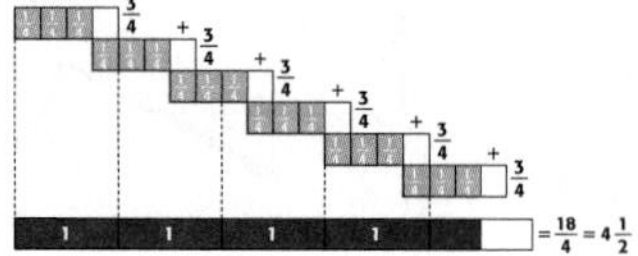

She will need $4\frac{1}{2}$ 1-pound bags of clay.

Draw a model to find each product.

1. $3 \cdot \frac{3}{4}$
2. $4 \cdot \frac{1}{2}$
3. $5 \cdot \frac{2}{3}$
4. $7 \cdot \frac{1}{4}$

Think and Discuss

5. Explain how you know that $3 \cdot \frac{3}{4}$ is less than 3.

Motivate

Write these two expressions: $\frac{2}{5} + \frac{2}{5} + \frac{2}{5}$ and $\frac{3}{4} + \frac{3}{4} + \frac{3}{4}$. Have a student evaluate each one. Tell the students that these expressions can be represented using multiplication, just as with expressions involving the addition of like whole numbers.

Explorations and answers are provided in *Alternate Openers: Explorations Transparencies.*

Georgia Performance Standards

M6N1.e Multiply and divide fractions and mixed numbers.

M6N1.g Solve problems involving fractions, decimals, and percents.

M6A3 Students will evaluate algebraic expressions, including those with exponents, and solve simple one-step equations using each of the four basic operations.

M6P1.b Solve problems that arise in mathematics and in other contexts.

EXAMPLE 2 Evaluating Fraction Expressions

Evaluate 6x for each value of x. Write each answer in simplest form.

A $x = \frac{1}{8}$

$6x$ — *Write the expression.*

$6 \cdot \frac{1}{8}$ — *Substitute $\frac{1}{8}$ for x.*

$\frac{6}{1} \cdot \frac{1}{8} = \frac{6}{8}$ — *Multiply.*

$= \frac{3}{4}$ — *Write your answer in simplest form.*

B $x = \frac{2}{3}$

$6x$ — *Write the expression.*

$6 \cdot \frac{2}{3}$ — *Substitute $\frac{2}{3}$ for x.*

$\frac{6}{1} \cdot \frac{2}{3} = \frac{12}{3}$ — *Multiply.*

$= \frac{4}{1}$

$= 4$

Remember!

$\frac{12}{3}$ means $12 \div 3$.

Sometimes the denominator of an improper fraction will divide into the numerator without a remainder, as in Example 2B. When this happens, the improper fraction is equivalent to a whole number, not a mixed number.

$$\frac{12}{3} = 4$$

EXAMPLE 3 *Social Studies Application*

Any proposed amendment to the U.S. Constitution must be ratified, or approved, by $\frac{3}{4}$ of the states. When the 13th Amendment abolishing slavery was proposed in 1865, there were 36 states. How many states needed to ratify this amendment in order for it to pass?

To find $\frac{3}{4}$ of 36, multiply.

$\frac{3}{4} \cdot 36 = \frac{3}{4} \cdot \frac{36}{1}$

$= \frac{108}{4}$

$= 27$ — *Divide 108 by 4 and write your answer in simplest form.*

For the 13th Amendment to pass, 27 states had to ratify it.

Answers to *Think and Discuss*

1. Possible answer: 4 circles, each divided into fifths, with one-fifth of each circle shaded.
2. The first expression is correct because the whole number was multiplied by the numerator and not by the denominator.
3. Possible answer: because multiplying by $\frac{5}{8}$, which is greater than $\frac{1}{2}$, yields a product greater than half of 16.

Think and Discuss

GPS M6P2.c, M6P5.c

1. **Describe** a model you could use to show the product of $4 \cdot \frac{1}{5}$.
2. **Choose** the expression that is correctly multiplied.
   $2 \cdot \frac{3}{7} = \frac{6}{7}$ $\qquad 2 \cdot \frac{3}{7} = \frac{6}{14}$
3. **Explain** how you know without actually multiplying that $\frac{5}{8} \cdot 16$ is greater than 8.

COMMON ERROR ALERT

Because students learned how to add and subtract like fractions, in this lesson some may multiply the numerator, leaving the denominator alone. When practical, have students use repeated addition to check their multiplication.

Power Presentations with PowerPoint®

Additional Examples

Example 

Multiply. Write each answer in simplest form.

A. $7 \cdot \frac{1}{9}$ $\quad \frac{7}{9}$

B. $6 \cdot \frac{1}{8}$ $\quad \frac{3}{4}$

C. $8 \cdot \frac{2}{3}$ $\quad \frac{16}{3}$, or $5\frac{1}{3}$

Example 

Evaluate 4x for each value of x. Write each answer in simplest form.

A. $x = \frac{1}{10}$ $\quad \frac{2}{5}$ $\qquad$ **B.** $x = \frac{3}{8}$ $\quad \frac{3}{2}$, or $1\frac{1}{2}$

Example 

There are 25 students in the music club. Of those students, $\frac{3}{5}$ are also in the band. How many music club students are in the band?

15 students

Also available on transparency

2 Teach

Guided Instruction

In this lesson, students learn to multiply fractions by whole numbers. Teach students to find the product of two fractions by multiplying the numerators to get the new numerator and multiplying the denominators to get the new denominator. Then teach them to evaluate expressions and solve real-world problems in which a fraction and a whole number are multiplied.

Teaching Tip

Inclusion Remind students that a whole number can be written as a fraction with a denominator of 1.

Reaching All Learners

Through Cooperative Learning

A trail mix recipe called for the following ingredients to make one batch: $\frac{3}{4}$ cup oat cereal, $\frac{2}{3}$ cup wheat cereal, $\frac{1}{3}$ cup raisins, and $\frac{1}{4}$ cup mini pretzels. Have students work in groups to decide how much of each ingredient would be needed for 12 batches of the recipe? 9 cups oat cereal, 8 cups wheat cereal, 4 cups raisins, 3 cups mini pretzels

3 Close

Summarize

Have students explain how multiplying fractions by whole numbers is different from adding and subtracting fractions with like denominators.

Possible answer: When multiplying fractions by whole numbers, you multiply the numerator by the whole number. When adding or subtracting fractions with like denominators, you only add or subtract the numerators, you do not multiply them.

5-6 Exercises

Assignment Guide

If you finished Example 1 assign:
Average 1–8, 55–63
Advanced 14–21, 55–63

If you finished Example 2 assign:
Average 1–12, 31–34, 55–63
Advanced 14–29, 55–63

If you finished Example 3 assign:
Average 1–51, 55–63
Advanced 1–48, 52–63

Homework Quick Check

Quickly check key concepts.
Exercises: 18, 20, 24, 28, 34, 40

Math Background

Before the seventeenth century, writers of mathematics generally did not try to explain the process of multiplication as it applies to fractions. One exception is Trenchant (1566), who used a square cut into smaller squares to illustrate multiplication.

Georgia Performance Standards

M6P3.a Organize and consolidate their mathematical thinking through communication.

M6P4.c Recognize and apply mathematics in contexts outside of mathematics.

5-6 Exercises

Georgia Performance Standards
M6P3.a, M6P4.c

go.hrw.com
Homework Help Online
KEYWORD: MR7 5-6
Parent Resources Online
KEYWORD: MR7 Parent

GUIDED PRACTICE

See Example 1 Multiply. Write each answer in simplest form.

1. $8 \cdot \frac{1}{9}$ $\frac{8}{9}$
2. $2 \cdot \frac{1}{5}$ $\frac{2}{5}$
3. $12 \cdot \frac{1}{4}$ 3
4. $7 \cdot \frac{4}{9}$ $3\frac{1}{9}$
5. $3 \cdot \frac{1}{7}$ $\frac{3}{7}$
6. $4 \cdot \frac{2}{11}$ $\frac{8}{11}$
7. $8 \cdot \frac{3}{4}$ 6
8. $18 \cdot \frac{1}{3}$ 6

See Example 2 Evaluate $12x$ for each value of x. Write each answer in simplest form.

9. $x = \frac{2}{3}$ 8
10. $x = \frac{1}{2}$ 6
11. $x = \frac{3}{4}$ 9
12. $x = \frac{5}{6}$ 10

See Example 3
13. The school Community Service Club has 45 members. Of these 45 members, $\frac{3}{5}$ are boys. How many boys are members of the Community Service Club? 27 boys

INDEPENDENT PRACTICE

See Example 1 Multiply. Write each answer in simplest form.

14. $4 \cdot \frac{1}{10}$ $\frac{2}{5}$
15. $6 \cdot \frac{1}{8}$ $\frac{3}{4}$
16. $3 \cdot \frac{1}{12}$ $\frac{1}{4}$
17. $2 \cdot \frac{2}{5}$ $\frac{4}{5}$
18. $6 \cdot \frac{10}{11}$ $5\frac{5}{11}$
19. $2 \cdot \frac{3}{11}$ $\frac{6}{11}$
20. $15 \cdot \frac{2}{15}$ 2
21. $20 \cdot \frac{1}{2}$ 10

See Example 2 Evaluate $8x$ for each value of x. Write each answer in simplest form.

22. $x = \frac{1}{2}$ 4
23. $x = \frac{3}{4}$ 6
24. $x = \frac{1}{8}$ 1
25. $x = \frac{1}{4}$ 2
26. $x = \frac{2}{5}$ $3\frac{1}{5}$
27. $x = \frac{5}{7}$ $5\frac{5}{7}$
28. $x = \frac{7}{8}$ 7
29. $x = \frac{4}{9}$ $3\frac{5}{9}$

See Example 3
30. **School** Kiesha spent 120 minutes completing her homework last night. Of those minutes, $\frac{1}{6}$ were spent on Spanish. How many minutes did Kiesha spend on her Spanish homework? 20 minutes

PRACTICE AND PROBLEM SOLVING

CRCT GPS
Extra Practice p. 722

Evaluate each expression. Write each answer in simplest form.

31. $12b$ for $b = \frac{7}{12}$ 7
32. $20m$ for $m = \frac{1}{20}$ 1
33. $33z$ for $z = \frac{5}{11}$ 15
34. $\frac{2}{3}y$ for $y = 18$ 12
35. $\frac{1}{4}x$ for $x = 20$ 5
36. $\frac{3}{5}a$ for $a = 30$ 18
37. $\frac{4}{5}c$ for $c = 12$ $\frac{48}{5}$ or $9\frac{3}{5}$
38. $14x$ for $x = \frac{3}{8}$ $\frac{21}{4}$ or $5\frac{1}{4}$
39. $\frac{9}{10}n$ for $n = 50$ 45

Compare. Write <, >, or =.

40. $9 \cdot \frac{1}{16}$ ■ $\frac{1}{2}$ >
41. $15 \cdot \frac{2}{5}$ ■ 5 >
42. $\frac{8}{13}$ ■ $4 \cdot \frac{2}{13}$ =
43. $3 \cdot \frac{2}{9}$ ■ $\frac{2}{3}$ =
44. $6 \cdot \frac{4}{15}$ ■ $\frac{11}{24}$ >
45. 5 ■ $12 \cdot \frac{3}{4}$ <
46. $3 \cdot \frac{1}{7}$ ■ $3 \cdot \frac{1}{5}$ <
47. $7 \cdot \frac{3}{4}$ ■ $6 \cdot \frac{3}{7}$ >
48. $2 \cdot \frac{5}{6}$ ■ $6 \cdot \frac{2}{5}$ <

49. Denise spent \$55 shopping. Of that \$55, she spent $\frac{3}{5}$ on a pair of shoes. How much money did Denise spend on the pair of shoes? \$33

RETEACH 5-6

LESSON 5-6 **Reteach**
Multiplying Fractions Using Repeated Addition

You can use fraction strips to multiply fractions by whole numbers.
To find $3 \cdot \frac{2}{3}$, first think about the expression in words.
$3 \cdot \frac{2}{3}$ means "3 groups of $\frac{2}{3}$."
Then model the expression.

The total number of $\frac{1}{3}$ fraction pieces is 6.
So, $3 \cdot \frac{2}{3} = \frac{2}{3} + \frac{2}{3} + \frac{2}{3} = \frac{6}{3} = 2$ in simplest form.

Use fraction strips to find each product.

1. $4 \cdot \frac{1}{8}$ $\frac{1}{2}$
2. $2 \cdot \frac{2}{5}$ $\frac{4}{5}$
3. $6 \cdot \frac{1}{8}$ $\frac{3}{4}$
4. $8 \cdot \frac{1}{4}$ 2

You can also use counters to multiply fractions by whole numbers.
To find $\frac{1}{2} \cdot 12$, first think about the expression in words.
$\frac{1}{2} \cdot 12 = \frac{12}{2}$, which means "12 divided into 2 equal groups."
Then model the expression.

The number of counters in each group is the product.
$\frac{1}{2} \cdot 12 = 6$.

Use counters to find each product.

5. $\frac{1}{3} \cdot 15$ 5
6. $\frac{1}{8} \cdot 24$ 3
7. $\frac{1}{4} \cdot 16$ 4
8. $\frac{1}{12} \cdot 24$ 2

PRACTICE 5-6

LESSON 5-6 **Practice B**
Multiplying Fractions Using Repeated Addition

Multiply. Write each answer in simplest form.

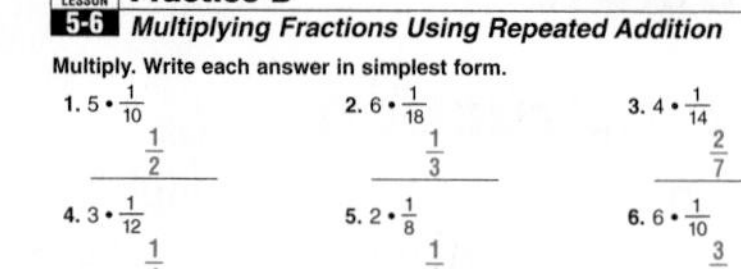

1. $5 \cdot \frac{1}{10}$ $\frac{1}{2}$
2. $6 \cdot \frac{1}{18}$ $\frac{1}{3}$
3. $4 \cdot \frac{1}{14}$ $\frac{2}{7}$
4. $3 \cdot \frac{1}{12}$ $\frac{1}{4}$
5. $2 \cdot \frac{1}{8}$ $\frac{1}{4}$
6. $6 \cdot \frac{1}{10}$ $\frac{3}{5}$
7. $3 \cdot \frac{1}{6}$ $\frac{1}{2}$
8. $3 \cdot \frac{5}{12}$ $1\frac{1}{4}$
9. $3 \cdot \frac{2}{7}$ $\frac{6}{7}$
10. $2 \cdot \frac{3}{8}$ $\frac{3}{4}$
11. $10 \cdot \frac{3}{15}$ 2
12. $8 \cdot \frac{2}{14}$ $1\frac{1}{7}$
13. $5 \cdot \frac{2}{10}$ 1
14. $4 \cdot \frac{4}{12}$ $1\frac{1}{3}$
15. $2 \cdot \frac{13}{20}$ $1\frac{3}{10}$

Evaluate $6x$ for each value of x. Write the answer in simplest form.

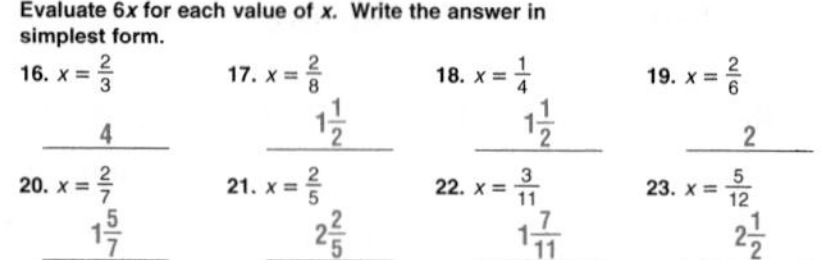

16. $x = \frac{2}{3}$ 4
17. $x = \frac{2}{8}$ $1\frac{1}{2}$
18. $x = \frac{1}{4}$ $1\frac{1}{2}$
19. $x = \frac{2}{6}$ 2
20. $x = \frac{2}{7}$ $1\frac{5}{7}$
21. $x = \frac{2}{5}$ $2\frac{2}{5}$
22. $x = \frac{3}{11}$ $1\frac{7}{11}$
23. $x = \frac{5}{12}$ $2\frac{1}{2}$

24. Thomas spends 60 minutes exercising. For $\frac{1}{4}$ of that time, he jumps rope. How many minutes does he spend jumping rope? 15 minutes

25. Kylie made a 4-ounce milk shake. Two-thirds of the milk shake was ice cream. How many ounces of ice cream did Kylie use in the shake? $2\frac{2}{3}$ ounces

Life Science LINK

The General Sherman, a giant sequoia tree in California's Sequoia National Park, is one of the largest trees in the world at 275 ft tall.

California also has some of the nation's tallest grand firs, ponderosa pines, and sugar pines. The table shows how the heights of these trees compare with the height of the General Sherman. For example, the grand fir is $\frac{23}{25}$ the height of the General Sherman.

50. Find the heights of the trees in the table. Write your answers in simplest form. 253; $225\frac{1}{2}$; 231

51. The world's tallest bluegum eucalyptus tree is $\frac{3}{5}$ the height of the General Sherman tree. How tall is this bluegum eucalyptus? 165 feet tall

52. **What's the Question?** Joshua trees can grow to be 40 ft tall. The answer is $\frac{8}{55}$. What is the question?

53. **Write About It** Find $\frac{1}{5}$ the height of the General Sherman. Then divide the height of the General Sherman by 5. What do you notice? Why does this make sense?

54. **Challenge** The world's tallest incense cedar tree is 152 ft tall. What is $\frac{1}{5}$ of $\frac{1}{2}$ of $\frac{1}{4}$ of 152? $3\frac{4}{5}$

52. Possible answer: The height of the Joshua tree is what fraction of the height of the General Sherman tree?

Tree Heights Compared with the General Sherman	
Tallest Grand Fir	$\frac{23}{25}$
Tallest Ponderosa Pine	$\frac{41}{50}$
Tallest Sugar Pine	$\frac{21}{25}$

Source: The Top 10 of Everything 2000

CRCT Prep • GPS Support • Spiral Review

55. Multiple Choice A recipe uses $\frac{1}{3}$ cup of sugar. Daniela doubled the recipe. How much sugar did she use?

Ⓐ $\frac{1}{4}$ cup Ⓑ $\frac{1}{3}$ cup 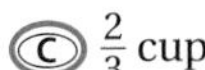 Ⓒ $\frac{2}{3}$ cup Ⓓ $\frac{3}{4}$ cup

56. Extended Response Mario bought $\frac{1}{5}$ pound of turkey. Rose bought four times as much turkey as Mario. And Celia bought 2 times as much as Rose. How many pounds of turkey did Rose buy? How many pounds did Celia buy? How much more did Celia buy than Mario? Show your work. $\frac{4}{5}$ lb; $1\frac{3}{5}$ lb; $1\frac{2}{5}$ lb

Write each phrase as a numerical or algebraic expression. (Lesson 2-2)

57. w less than 75 $75 - w$ **58.** the product of n and 16 $16n$ **59.** the quotient of p and 7 $p \div 7$

Subtract. Write each answer in simplest form. (Lesson 5-4)

60. $5\frac{2}{3} - 4\frac{5}{6}$ $\frac{5}{6}$ **61.** $12\frac{4}{7} - 3\frac{6}{7}$ $8\frac{5}{7}$ **62.** $9\frac{7}{12} - 2\frac{1}{3}$ $7\frac{1}{4}$ **63.** $11\frac{5}{8} - 5\frac{1}{4}$ $6\frac{3}{8}$

CHALLENGE 5-6

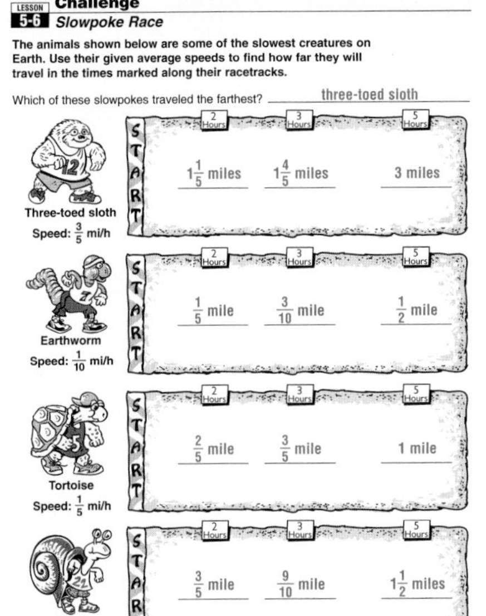

LESSON 5-6 **Challenge**
Slowpoke Race

The animals shown below are some of the slowest creatures on Earth. Use their given average speeds to find how far they will travel in the times marked along their racetracks.

Which of these slowpokes traveled the farthest? three-toed sloth

Animal	2 Hours	3 Hours	5 Hours
Three-toed sloth, Speed: $\frac{3}{5}$ mi/h	$1\frac{1}{5}$ miles	$1\frac{4}{5}$ miles	3 miles
Earthworm, Speed: $\frac{1}{10}$ mi/h	$\frac{1}{5}$ mile	$\frac{3}{10}$ mile	$\frac{1}{2}$ mile
Tortoise, Speed: $\frac{1}{5}$ mi/h	$\frac{2}{5}$ mile	$\frac{3}{5}$ mile	1 mile
Snail, Speed: $\frac{3}{10}$ mi/h	$\frac{3}{5}$ mile	$\frac{9}{10}$ mile	$1\frac{1}{2}$ miles

PROBLEM SOLVING 5-6

LESSON 5-6 **Problem Solving**
Multiplying Fractions Using Repeated Addition

Write the answers in simplest form.

1. Did you know that some people have more bones than the rest of the population? About $\frac{1}{20}$ of all people have an extra rib bone. In a crowd of 60 people, about how many people are likely have an extra rib bone?

   3 people

2. The Appalachian National Scenic Trail is the longest marked walking path in the United States. It extends through 14 states for about 2,000 miles. Last year, Carla hiked $\frac{1}{5}$ of the trail. How many miles of the trail did she hike?

   400 miles

3. Human fingernails can grow up to $\frac{1}{10}$ of a millimeter each day. How much can fingernails grow in one week?

   $\frac{7}{10}$ millimeter

4. Most people dream about $\frac{1}{4}$ of the time they sleep. How long will you probably dream tonight if you sleep for 8 hours?

   2 hours

Circle the letter of the correct answer.

5. Today, the United States flag has 50 stars—one for each state. The first official U.S. flag was approved in 1795. It had $\frac{3}{10}$ as many stars as today's flag. How many stars were on the first official U.S. flag?

   A 5 stars
   B 10 stars
   (C) 15 stars
   D 35 stars

6. The Statue of Liberty is about 305 feet tall from the ground to the tip of her torch. The statue's pedestal makes up about $\frac{1}{2}$ of its height. About how tall is the pedestal of the Statue of Liberty?

   F 610 feet
   (G) 152 1/2 feet
   H 150 1/2 feet
   J 102 1/2 feet

7. The Caldwells own a 60-acre farm. They planted $\frac{3}{5}$ of the land with corn. How many acres of corn did they plant?

   A 12 acres
   (B) 36 acres
   C 20 acres
   D 18 acres

8. Objects on Uranus weigh about $\frac{4}{5}$ of their weight on Earth. If a dog weighs 40 pounds on Earth, how much would it weigh on Uranus?

   (F) 32 pounds
   G 10 pounds
   H 8 pounds
   J 30 pounds

Ongoing Assessment and Intervention

Diagnose ***Before*** **the Lesson**
5-6 Warm Up, TE p. 254

Monitor ***During*** **the Lesson**
5-6 Know-It Notebook
5-6 Questioning Strategies

Assess ***After*** **the Lesson**
5-6 Lesson Quiz, TE p. 257

Interdisciplinary LINK

Life Science

Exercises 50–54 involve comparing the heights of extremely large trees with the height of the famous General Sherman sequoia tree in California. Plants are studied in middle school life science programs, such as *Holt Science & Technology*.

Answers

53. See p. A4.

Test Prep Doctor In Exercise 56, students need to identify the responses asked for in this exercise. Remind them to show their work.

Journal

Have students explain why the product of a fraction and a whole number can be a fraction, a whole number, or a mixed number.

Power Presentations with PowerPoint®

5-6 Lesson Quiz

Multiply. Write each answer in simplest form.

1. $10 \cdot \frac{2}{5}$ 4

2. $6 \cdot \frac{1}{10}$ $\frac{3}{5}$

Evaluate 6x for each value of x. Write your answer in simplest form.

3. $x = \frac{1}{4}$ $\frac{3}{2}$, or $1\frac{1}{2}$

4. $x = \frac{5}{6}$ 5

5. Alicia spent 15 minutes making a pizza. Of those minutes, $\frac{1}{3}$ were spent rolling out the crust. How many minutes did Alicia spend rolling out the crust? 5 minutes

Also available on transparency

Organizer

Use with Lessons 5-7 and 5-8

Pacing:
Traditional $\frac{1}{2}$ day
Block $\frac{1}{4}$ day

Objective: Use grids to model fraction multiplication.

Materials: Fraction bars

Online Edition
Fraction Bars

Resources

Hands-On Lab Activities
Lab 5-7 Recording Sheet

Teach

Discuss

Discuss with students what each square represents and how to represent fractions with a grid.

Close

Key Concept

Fraction multiplication can be modeled by dividing a square horizontally and vertically.

Assessment

Represent each product with a grid.

1. $\frac{2}{3} \times \frac{2}{3}$ $\frac{4}{9}$
2. $\frac{4}{5} \times \frac{1}{2}$ $\frac{4}{10}$
3. $\frac{1}{3} \times 1\frac{3}{4}$ $\frac{7}{12}$

Georgia Performance Standards

M6N1.e Multiply and divide fractions and mixed numbers.

M6N1.g Solve problems involving fractions, decimals, and percents.

M6P5.b Select, apply, and translate among mathematical representations to solve problems.

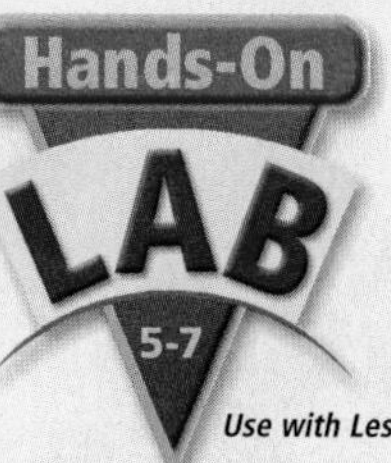

Model Fraction Multiplication

Use with Lessons 5-7 and 5-8

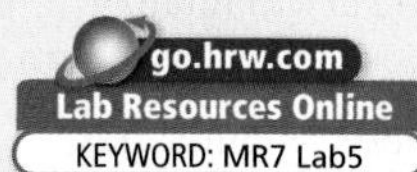

M6N1.e, M6N1.g, M6P5.b

You can use grids to help you understand fraction multiplication.

Activity 1

1. Think of $\frac{1}{2} \cdot \frac{1}{3}$ as $\frac{1}{2}$ of $\frac{1}{3}$.

Shade $\frac{1}{3}$ of a square.

Divide the square into halves.

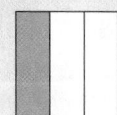

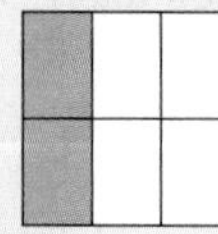

Look at $\frac{1}{2}$ of the part you shaded.

What fraction of the whole is this?

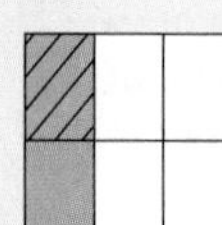

$\frac{1}{2}$ of $\frac{1}{3}$ is $\frac{1}{6}$.

2. Think of $\frac{2}{3} \cdot \frac{1}{2}$ as $\frac{2}{3}$ of $\frac{1}{2}$.

Shade $\frac{1}{2}$ of a square.

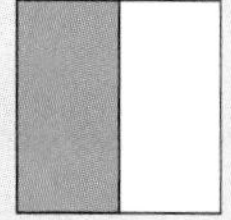

Divide the square into thirds.

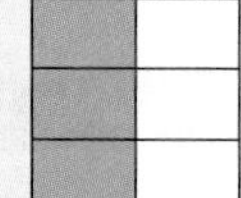

$\frac{2}{3}$ of $\frac{1}{2}$ is $\frac{2}{6}$, or $\frac{1}{3}$.

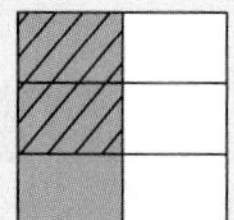

Think and Discuss

1. Tell whether the product is greater than or less than the fractions you started with. **The product will be smaller than both of the fractions.**

Try This

Write the multiplication expression modeled on each grid.

1. 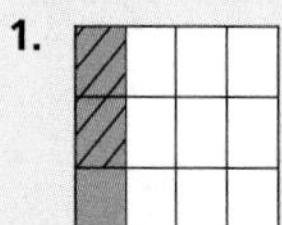 $\frac{2}{3} \cdot \frac{1}{4}$

2. 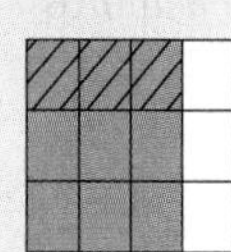 $\frac{1}{3} \cdot \frac{3}{4}$

3. 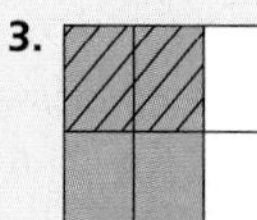 $\frac{1}{2} \cdot \frac{2}{3}$

Answers to *Assessment*

1. 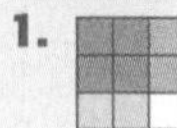

2. 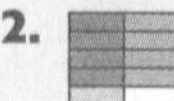

3. 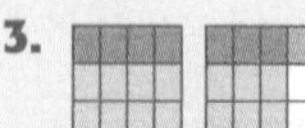

Use a grid to model each multiplication expression.

4. $\frac{1}{3} \cdot \frac{1}{2}$ $\frac{1}{6}$ 5. $\frac{2}{3} \cdot \frac{1}{3}$ $\frac{2}{9}$ 6. $\frac{1}{4} \cdot \frac{2}{3}$ $\frac{2}{12}$, or $\frac{1}{6}$ 7. $\frac{1}{3} \cdot \frac{3}{4}$ $\frac{3}{12}$, or $\frac{1}{4}$

You can also use grids to model multiplication of mixed numbers.

Activity 2

Think of $\frac{1}{2} \cdot 2\frac{1}{2}$ as $\frac{1}{2}$ of $2\frac{1}{2}$.

Shade $2\frac{1}{2}$ squares.

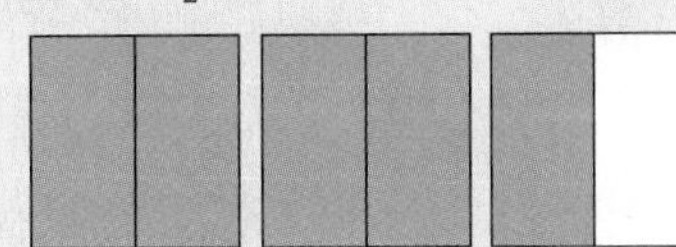

Divide the squares into halves.

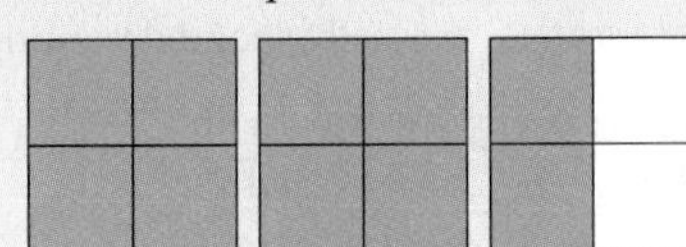

Look at $\frac{1}{2}$ of the part you shaded.

What fraction of the model is this?

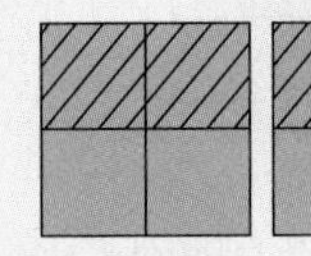
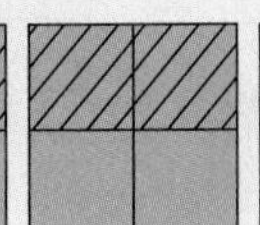
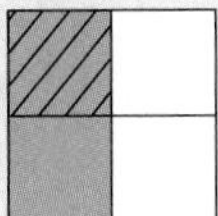

$\frac{1}{2}$ of $2\frac{1}{2}$ is $1\frac{1}{4}$.

Think and Discuss

1. Describe how modeling multiplication of mixed numbers is like modeling multiplication of fractions.

Try This

Write the multiplication expression modeled on each grid.

1. 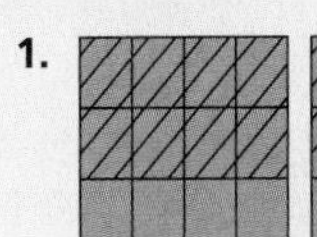 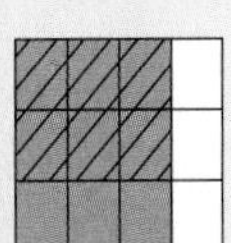 $\frac{2}{3} \cdot 1\frac{3}{4}$

2.  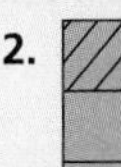 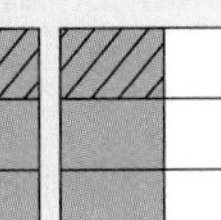 $\frac{1}{3} \cdot 1\frac{1}{2}$

3. 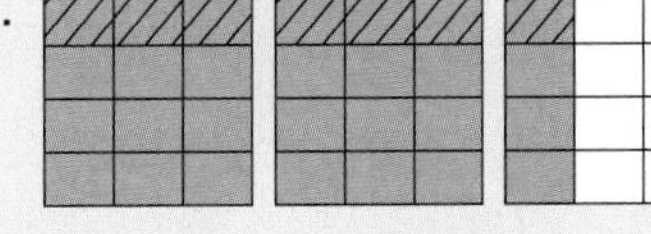 $\frac{1}{4} \cdot 2\frac{1}{3}$

Use a grid to model each multiplication expression.

4. $\frac{1}{3} \cdot 1\frac{1}{2}$ $\frac{3}{6}$, or $\frac{1}{2}$ 5. $\frac{2}{3} \cdot 2\frac{1}{3}$ $\frac{14}{9}$, or $1\frac{5}{9}$ 6. $\frac{1}{4} \cdot 2\frac{2}{3}$ $\frac{8}{12}$, or $\frac{2}{3}$ 7. $\frac{1}{3} \cdot 1\frac{3}{4}$ $\frac{7}{12}$

8. $\frac{3}{4} \cdot 1\frac{1}{3}$ $\frac{12}{12}$, or 1 9. $\frac{1}{2} \cdot 3\frac{1}{3}$ $\frac{10}{6}$, or $1\frac{2}{3}$ 10. $\frac{2}{3} \cdot 1\frac{3}{4}$ $\frac{7}{6}$, or $1\frac{1}{6}$ 11. $\frac{1}{4} \cdot 2\frac{1}{2}$ $\frac{5}{8}$

Activity 1

Answers to *Try This*

4. 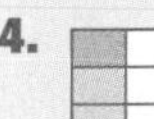

5. 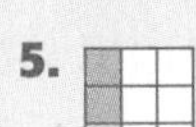

6. 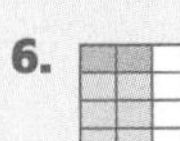

7. 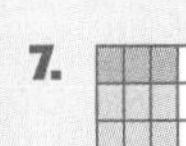

Activity 2

Answers to *Think and Discuss*

1. When you multiply mixed numbers, you should model the second factor first, as you would when you multiply fractions. Divide the model of the second factor into the number of equal groups indicated by the denominator of the first factor. Then shade the portion of the equal groups indicated by the first factor.

Answers to *Try This*

4. 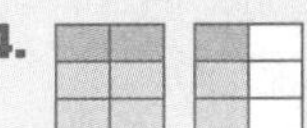

5. 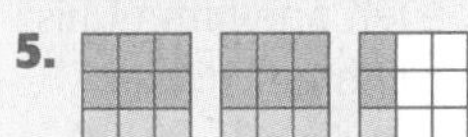

6. 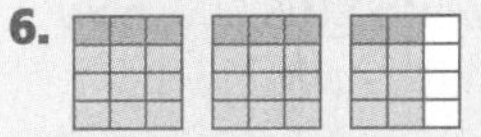

7. 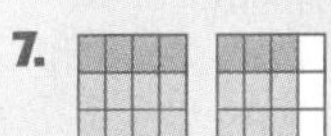

8. 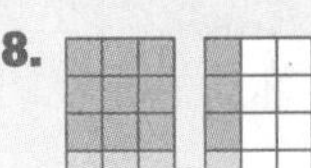

9. 

10. 

11. 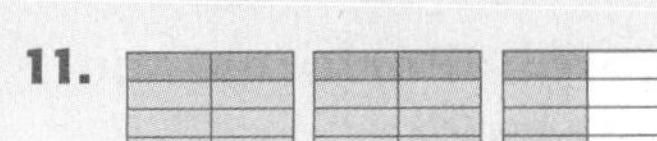

5-7 Organizer

Pacing: Traditional 1 day
Block $\frac{1}{2}$ day

Objective: Students multiply fractions.

GPS M6N1.e, M6N1.g
Technology Lab
In *Technology Lab Activities*

Online Edition
Tutorial Videos, Interactivities

Countdown to CRCT Week 11

Power Presentations with PowerPoint®

Warm Up

1. What is $\frac{1}{2}$ of 12? 6
2. What is $\frac{1}{2}$ of 100? 50
3. What is $\frac{1}{2}$ of 120? 60
4. What is $\frac{1}{4}$ of 100? 25
5. What is $\frac{1}{4}$ of 480? 120

Problem of the Day

Your favorite uncle left one-fifth of his estate to each of his three children and the rest to his favorite charity. If his estate was worth \$105,000, how much was given to charity? \$42,000

Also available on transparency

Math Humor

The golfer wondered if $\frac{p}{3} \cdot \frac{ar}{2} = 66$ is a true equation. After all, the product is $\frac{par}{6}$, or *6 under par*, which does equal 66 on most golf courses.

Georgia Performance Standards

M6N1.e Multiply and divide fractions and mixed numbers.

M6N1.g Solve problems involving fractions, decimals, and percents.

M6A3 Students will evaluate algebraic expressions, including those with exponents, and solve simple one-step equations using each of the four basic operations.

M6P5.c Use representations to model and interpret physical, social, and mathematical phenomena.

5-7 Multiplying Fractions

Learn to multiply fractions.

M6N1.e Multiply fractions. Also, M6N1.g, M6A3, M6P5.c.

On average, people spend $\frac{1}{3}$ of their lives asleep. About $\frac{1}{4}$ of the time they sleep, they dream. What fraction of a lifetime does a person typically spend dreaming?

One way to find $\frac{1}{4}$ of $\frac{1}{3}$ is to make a model.

Find $\frac{1}{4}$ of $\frac{1}{3}$.

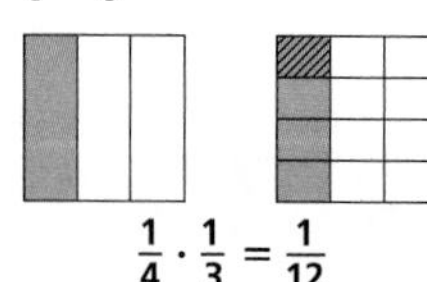

$$\frac{1}{4} \cdot \frac{1}{3} = \frac{1}{12}$$

Your brain keeps working even when you're asleep. It makes sure that you keep breathing and that your heart keeps beating.

You can also multiply fractions without making a model.

$\frac{1}{4} \cdot \frac{1}{3} = \frac{1 \cdot 1}{4 \cdot 3}$ ← *Multiply the numerators.* ← *Multiply the denominators.*

$= \frac{1}{12}$ *The answer is in simplest form.*

A person typically spends $\frac{1}{12}$ of his or her lifetime dreaming.

EXAMPLE 1 Multiplying Fractions

Multiply. Write each answer in simplest form.

A $\frac{1}{3} \cdot \frac{3}{5}$

$\frac{1}{3} \cdot \frac{3}{5} = \frac{1 \cdot 3}{3 \cdot 5}$ *Multiply numerators. Multiply denominators.*

$= \frac{3}{15}$ *The GCF of 3 and 15 is 3.*

$= \frac{1}{5}$ *The answer is in simplest form.*

B $\frac{6}{7} \cdot \frac{2}{3}$

$\frac{\overset{2}{\cancel{6}}}{7} \cdot \frac{2}{\underset{1}{\cancel{3}}} = \frac{2}{7} \cdot \frac{2}{1}$ *Use the GCF to simplify the fractions before multiplying. The GCF of 6 and 3 is 3.*

$= \frac{2 \cdot 2}{7 \cdot 1}$ *Multiply numerators. Multiply denominators.*

$= \frac{4}{7}$ *The answer is in simplest form.*

1 Introduce

Alternate Opener

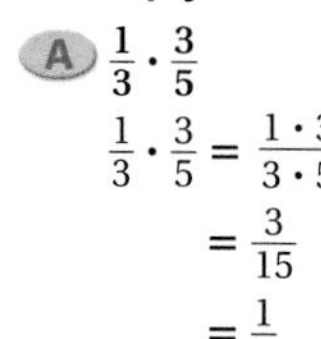

EXPLORATION

5-7 Multiplying Fractions

You can use paper folding to find the product of two fractions. To find $\frac{3}{4}$ of $\frac{1}{2}$, fold the paper in half vertically to model $\frac{1}{2}$. Then fold it horizontally into four sections to create fourths.

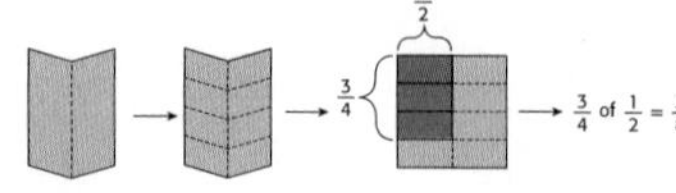

Use paper folding to find each product. Sketch a picture for each product.

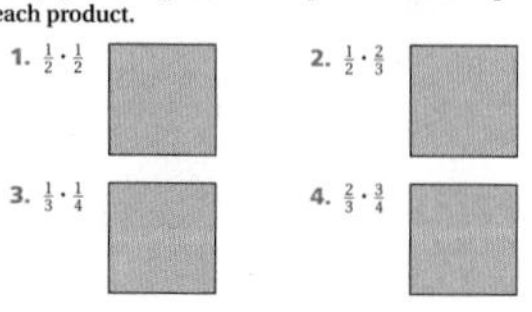

1. $\frac{1}{2} \cdot \frac{1}{2}$
2. $\frac{1}{2} \cdot \frac{2}{3}$
3. $\frac{1}{3} \cdot \frac{1}{4}$
4. $\frac{2}{3} \cdot \frac{3}{4}$

Think and Discuss

5. **Explain** how to multiply two fractions.

Motivate

Pose this situation to students:

In this class, $\frac{1}{2}$ of the students are girls. Of those girls, $\frac{1}{3}$ packed a lunch today. What fraction of the class packed a lunch today? $\frac{1}{6}$

Ask students to explain how they would find the answer. Point out that the situation in the lesson opener also involves multiplication of fractions.

Explorations and answers are provided in *Alternate Openers: Explorations Transparencies.*

Multiply. Write each answer in simplest form.

C $\frac{3}{8} \cdot \frac{2}{9}$

$\frac{3}{8} \cdot \frac{2}{9} = \frac{3 \cdot 2}{8 \cdot 9}$ *Multiply numerators. Multiply denominators.*

$= \frac{6}{72}$ *The GCF of 6 and 72 is 6.*

$= \frac{1}{12}$ *The answer is in simplest form.*

EXAMPLE 2 Evaluating Fraction Expressions

Evaluate the expression $a \cdot \frac{1}{3}$ for each value of a. Write the answer in simplest form.

A $a = \frac{5}{8}$

$a \cdot \frac{1}{3}$

$\frac{5}{8} \cdot \frac{1}{3}$ *Substitute $\frac{5}{8}$ for a.*

$\frac{5 \cdot 1}{8 \cdot 3}$ *Multiply.*

$\frac{5}{24}$ *The answer is in simplest form.*

B $a = \frac{9}{10}$

$a \cdot \frac{1}{3}$

$\frac{9}{10} \cdot \frac{1}{3}$ *Substitute $\frac{9}{10}$ for a.*

$\frac{\overset{3}{\cancel{9}}}{10} \cdot \frac{1}{\underset{1}{\cancel{3}}}$ *Use the GCF to simplify.*

$\frac{3 \cdot 1}{10 \cdot 1}$ *Multiply.*

$\frac{3}{10}$ *The answer is in simplest form.*

C $a = \frac{3}{4}$

$a \cdot \frac{1}{3}$

$\frac{3}{4} \cdot \frac{1}{3}$ *Substitute $\frac{3}{4}$ for a.*

$\frac{3 \cdot 1}{4 \cdot 3}$ *Multiply numerators. Multiply denominators.*

$\frac{3}{12}$ *The GCF of 3 and 12 is 3.*

$\frac{1}{4}$ *The answer is in simplest form.*

Helpful Hint

You can look for a common factor in a numerator and a denominator to determine whether you can simplify before multiplying.

Answers to *Think and Discuss*

1. Possible answer: The product of two proper fractions is less than each factor because you are finding a fraction of another fraction.
2. 7

Think and Discuss GPS M6P1.c, M6P2.c

1. **Determine** whether the product of two proper fractions is greater than or less than each factor.
2. **Name** the missing denominator in the equation $\frac{1}{\blacksquare} \cdot \frac{2}{3} = \frac{2}{21}$.
3. **Tell** how to find the product of $\frac{4}{21} \cdot \frac{6}{10}$ in two different ways.

When multiplying like fractions, some students may multiply the numerators but not the denominators. Explain that rules for multiplying fractions are different from those for adding and subtracting fractions.

Power Presentations with PowerPoint®

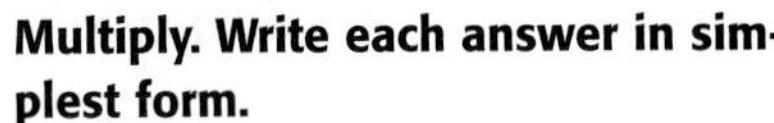

Example 1

Multiply. Write each answer in simplest form.

A. $\frac{1}{4} \cdot \frac{2}{5}$ $\frac{1}{10}$

B. $\frac{5}{7} \cdot \frac{4}{15}$ $\frac{4}{21}$

C. $\frac{4}{9} \cdot \frac{6}{10}$ $\frac{4}{15}$

Example 2

Evaluate the expression $b \cdot \frac{2}{5}$ for each value of b. Write the answer in simplest form.

A. $b = \frac{1}{3}$ $\frac{2}{15}$

B. $b = \frac{3}{8}$ $\frac{3}{20}$

C. $b = \frac{5}{7}$ $\frac{2}{7}$

Also available on transparency

Answers to *Think and Discuss*

3. First way: Multiply the numerators and the denominators, and then simplify the product. $\frac{4}{21} \cdot \frac{6}{10} = \frac{24}{210} = \frac{4}{35}$
Second way: Use the GCF to simplify the fractions before multiplying. $\frac{\overset{2}{\cancel{4}}}{\underset{7}{\cancel{21}}} \cdot \frac{\overset{2}{\cancel{6}}}{\underset{5}{\cancel{10}}} = \frac{2}{7} \cdot \frac{2}{5} = \frac{4}{35}$

2 Teach

Guided Instruction

In this lesson, students learn to multiply fractions. Show students how to use a model to find the product of two fractions, and then teach them to multiply fractions without using a model. (Teaching Transparency) Have students evaluate expressions involving multiplication of fractions.

Multiple Representations Have students use shaded models as they work through the examples.

Reaching All Learners

Through Kinesthetic Experience

Have students work in groups to practice multiplying fractions. Students toss number cubes to generate fractions to multiply, using the smaller number for the numerator and the larger number for the denominator.

For example, a toss of [die showing 3] [die showing 2] would be the fraction $\frac{2}{3}$. Group members work together to multiply the fractions and express the answers in simplest form, taking turns recording the steps they follow.

3 Close

Summarize

Remind students that the procedure for multiplying fractions differs from that for adding and subtracting fractions with like denominators. Have students explain how they are different.

Possible answers: When adding or subtracting like fractions, you add or subtract the numerators and keep the same denominator. When multiplying fractions, you multiply the numerators and you also multiply the denominators.

5-7 Exercises

Assignment Guide

If you finished Example 1 assign:
Average 1–4, 25–28, 49–58
Advanced 9–16, 49–58

If you finished Example 2 assign:
Average 1–44, 49–58
Advanced 1–40, 45–58

Homework Quick Check

Quickly check key concepts.
Exercises: 12, 16, 20, 24, 32, 34

Math Background

When multiplying fractions, early writers of arithmetic generally did not practice cancellation before multiplication, as we do in this lesson. Thus, they would express a product such as $\frac{6}{11} \cdot \frac{5}{12}$ first as $\frac{30}{132}$ and then reduced as $\frac{5}{22}$, rather than looking for common factors among the numerators and denominators. One can, of course, practice this method today as well, but it is generally easier to simplify before multiplying.

COMMON ERROR ALERT

When answering Exercises 35–40, students may assume that they can compare any two fractions. Explain that they must multiply first and then compare the products.

Georgia Performance Standards

M6P3.a Organize and consolidate their mathematical thinking through communication.

M6P4.c Recognize and apply mathematics in contexts outside of mathematics.

5-7 Exercises

M6P3.a, M6P4.c

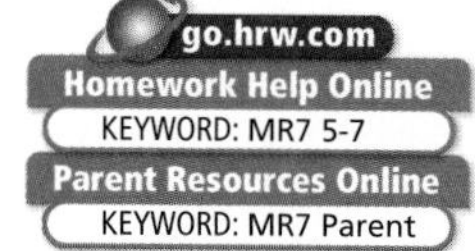

Homework Help Online
KEYWORD: MR7 5-7
Parent Resources Online
KEYWORD: MR7 Parent

GUIDED PRACTICE

See Example 1 Multiply. Write each answer in simplest form.

1. $\frac{1}{2} \cdot \frac{1}{3}$ $\frac{1}{6}$
2. $\frac{2}{5} \cdot \frac{1}{4}$ $\frac{1}{10}$
3. $\frac{4}{7} \cdot \frac{3}{4}$ $\frac{3}{7}$
4. $\frac{5}{6} \cdot \frac{3}{5}$ $\frac{1}{2}$

See Example 2 Evaluate the expression $b \cdot \frac{1}{5}$ for each value of b. Write the answer in simplest form.

5. $b = \frac{2}{3}$ $\frac{2}{15}$
6. $b = \frac{5}{8}$ $\frac{1}{8}$
7. $b = \frac{1}{4}$ $\frac{1}{20}$
8. $b = \frac{3}{5}$ $\frac{3}{25}$

INDEPENDENT PRACTICE

See Example 1 Multiply. Write each answer in simplest form.

9. $\frac{1}{3} \cdot \frac{2}{7}$ $\frac{2}{21}$
10. $\frac{1}{3} \cdot \frac{1}{5}$ $\frac{1}{15}$
11. $\frac{5}{6} \cdot \frac{2}{3}$ $\frac{5}{9}$
12. $\frac{1}{3} \cdot \frac{6}{7}$ $\frac{2}{7}$
13. $\frac{3}{10} \cdot \frac{5}{6}$ $\frac{1}{4}$
14. $\frac{7}{9} \cdot \frac{3}{5}$ $\frac{7}{15}$
15. $\frac{1}{2} \cdot \frac{10}{11}$ $\frac{5}{11}$
16. $\frac{3}{5} \cdot \frac{3}{4}$ $\frac{9}{20}$

See Example 2 Evaluate the expression $x \cdot \frac{1}{6}$ for each value of x. Write the answer in simplest form.

17. $x = \frac{4}{5}$ $\frac{2}{15}$
18. $x = \frac{6}{7}$ $\frac{1}{7}$
19. $x = \frac{3}{4}$ $\frac{1}{8}$
20. $x = \frac{5}{6}$ $\frac{5}{36}$
21. $x = \frac{8}{9}$ $\frac{4}{27}$
22. $x = \frac{9}{10}$ $\frac{3}{20}$
23. $x = \frac{5}{8}$ $\frac{5}{48}$
24. $x = \frac{3}{8}$ $\frac{1}{16}$

PRACTICE AND PROBLEM SOLVING

CRCT GPS
Extra Practice p. 723

Find each product. Simplify the answer.

25. $\frac{3}{5} \cdot \frac{4}{9}$ $\frac{4}{15}$
26. $\frac{5}{12} \cdot \frac{9}{10}$ $\frac{3}{8}$
27. $\frac{2}{5} \cdot \frac{2}{7} \cdot \frac{5}{8}$ $\frac{1}{14}$
28. $\frac{2}{7} \cdot \frac{1}{8}$ $\frac{1}{28}$
29. $\frac{6}{7} \cdot \frac{9}{10}$ $\frac{27}{35}$
30. $\frac{4}{9} \cdot \frac{2}{3}$ $\frac{8}{27}$
31. $\frac{1}{2} \cdot \frac{2}{5} \cdot \frac{9}{11}$ $\frac{9}{55}$
32. $\frac{1}{12} \cdot \frac{3}{7}$ $\frac{1}{28}$

33. A walnut muffin recipe calls for $\frac{3}{4}$ cup walnuts. Mrs. Hooper wants to make $\frac{1}{3}$ of the recipe. What fraction of a cup of walnuts will she need? $\frac{1}{4}$ cup

34. Jim spent $\frac{5}{6}$ of an hour doing chores. He spent $\frac{2}{5}$ of that time washing dishes. What fraction of an hour did he spend washing dishes? $\frac{1}{3}$ of an hour

Compare. Write <, >, or =.

35. $\frac{2}{3} \cdot \frac{1}{4}$ ■ $\frac{1}{3} \cdot \frac{3}{4}$ $<$
36. $\frac{3}{5} \cdot \frac{3}{4}$ ■ $\frac{1}{2} \cdot \frac{9}{10}$ $=$
37. $\frac{5}{6} \cdot \frac{2}{3}$ ■ $\frac{1}{3} \cdot \frac{2}{3}$ $>$
38. $\frac{5}{8} \cdot \frac{1}{4}$ ■ $\frac{2}{9} \cdot \frac{1}{7}$ $>$
39. $\frac{2}{5} \cdot \frac{1}{10}$ ■ $\frac{3}{5} \cdot \frac{2}{5}$ $<$
40. $\frac{1}{2} \cdot \frac{4}{5}$ ■ $\frac{10}{20} \cdot \frac{16}{20}$ $=$

41. A multiplying number machine uses a rule to change one fraction into another fraction. The machine changed $\frac{1}{2}$ into $\frac{1}{8}$, $\frac{1}{5}$ into $\frac{1}{20}$, and $\frac{5}{7}$ into $\frac{5}{28}$.
    a. What is the rule? Multiply by $\frac{1}{4}$
    b. Into what fraction will the machine change $\frac{1}{3}$? $\frac{1}{12}$

RETEACH 5-7

LESSON 5-7 **Reteach**
Multiplying Fractions

To multiply fractions, multiply the numerators and multiply the denominators.

When multiplying fractions, you can sometimes divide by the GCF to make the problem simpler.

You can divide by the GCF even if the numerator and denominator of the same fraction have a common factor.

$\frac{1}{2} \cdot \frac{2}{3}$

$\frac{1}{\not 2} \cdot \frac{\not 2}{3}$

The problem is now $\frac{1}{1} \cdot \frac{1}{3}$.

$\frac{1 \cdot 1}{1 \cdot 3} = \frac{1}{3}$

So, $\frac{1}{2} \cdot \frac{2}{3} = \frac{1}{3}$

Is it possible to simplify before you multiply? If so, what is the GCF?

1. $\frac{1}{4} \cdot \frac{1}{2}$ no
2. $\frac{1}{6} \cdot \frac{3}{4}$ yes; 3
3. $\frac{1}{8} \cdot \frac{2}{3}$ yes; 2
4. $\frac{1}{3} \cdot \frac{2}{5}$ no

Multiply.

5. $\frac{1}{6} \cdot \frac{3}{5}$ $\frac{1}{10}$
6. $\frac{1}{4} \cdot \frac{1}{3}$ $\frac{1}{12}$
7. $\frac{7}{8} \cdot \frac{4}{5}$ $\frac{7}{10}$
8. $\frac{1}{6} \cdot \frac{2}{3}$ $\frac{1}{9}$
9. $\frac{1}{5} \cdot \frac{1}{2}$ $\frac{1}{10}$
10. $\frac{3}{5} \cdot \frac{1}{4}$ $\frac{3}{20}$
11. $\frac{3}{7} \cdot \frac{1}{9}$ $\frac{1}{21}$
12. $\frac{3}{4} \cdot \frac{1}{2}$ $\frac{3}{8}$
13. $\frac{1}{3} \cdot \frac{6}{7}$ $\frac{2}{7}$
14. $\frac{1}{4} \cdot \frac{2}{3}$ $\frac{1}{6}$
15. $\frac{3}{4} \cdot \frac{1}{3}$ $\frac{1}{4}$
16. $\frac{1}{4} \cdot \frac{1}{8}$ $\frac{1}{32}$

PRACTICE 5-7

LESSON 5-7 **Practice B**
Multiplying Fractions

Multiply. Write each answer in simplest form.

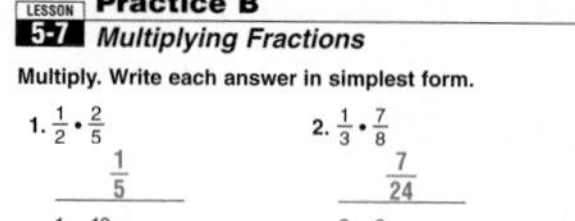

1. $\frac{1}{2} \cdot \frac{2}{5}$ $\frac{1}{5}$
2. $\frac{1}{3} \cdot \frac{7}{8}$ $\frac{7}{24}$
3. $\frac{2}{3} \cdot \frac{4}{6}$ $\frac{4}{9}$
4. $\frac{1}{4} \cdot \frac{10}{11}$ $\frac{5}{22}$
5. $\frac{3}{5} \cdot \frac{2}{3}$ $\frac{2}{5}$
6. $\frac{8}{9} \cdot \frac{3}{4}$ $\frac{2}{3}$
7. $\frac{3}{8} \cdot \frac{4}{5}$ $\frac{3}{10}$
8. $\frac{2}{7} \cdot \frac{3}{4}$ $\frac{3}{14}$
9. $\frac{1}{6} \cdot \frac{2}{3}$ $\frac{1}{9}$

Evaluate the expression $x \cdot \frac{1}{5}$ for each value of x. Write the answer in simplest form.

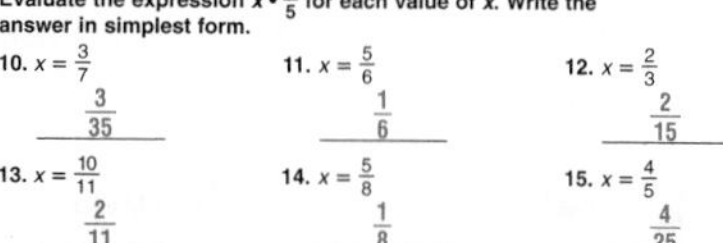

10. $x = \frac{3}{7}$ $\frac{3}{35}$
11. $x = \frac{5}{6}$ $\frac{1}{6}$
12. $x = \frac{2}{3}$ $\frac{2}{15}$
13. $x = \frac{10}{11}$ $\frac{2}{11}$
14. $x = \frac{5}{8}$ $\frac{1}{8}$
15. $x = \frac{4}{5}$ $\frac{4}{25}$

16. A cookie recipe calls for $\frac{2}{3}$ cup of brown sugar. Sarah is making $\frac{1}{4}$ of the recipe. How much brown sugar will she need?
    $\frac{1}{6}$ cup

17. Nancy spent $\frac{7}{8}$ hour working out at the gym. She spent $\frac{5}{7}$ of that time lifting weights. What fraction of an hour did she spend lifting weights?
    $\frac{5}{8}$ hour

There are about 1,000 species of bats in the world. Bats make up about $\frac{1}{4}$ of the world's mammals.

42. Alex exercised for $\frac{3}{4}$ hour. He lifted weights for $\frac{1}{5}$ of that time. What fraction of an hour did he spend lifting weights? $\frac{3}{20}$ **hr**

43. **Life Science** A bat can eat half its weight in insects in one night. If a bat weighing $\frac{3}{4}$ lb eats half its weight in insects, how much do the insects weigh? $\frac{3}{8}$ **lb**

44. **Multi-Step** The number of American bison has steadily declined throughout the years. Once, 20 million bison roamed the United States. Now, there are only $\frac{1}{80}$ of that number of bison. Of those, only $\frac{8}{125}$ roam in the wild. The number of American bison currently roaming in the wild is what fraction of 20 million? How many bison is that? $\frac{1}{1,250}$; **16,000 bison**

45. The seating plan shows Oak School's theater. The front section has $\frac{3}{4}$ of the seats, and the rear section has $\frac{1}{4}$ of the seats. The school has reserved $\frac{1}{2}$ of the seats in the front section for students. What fraction of the seating is reserved for students? $\frac{3}{8}$

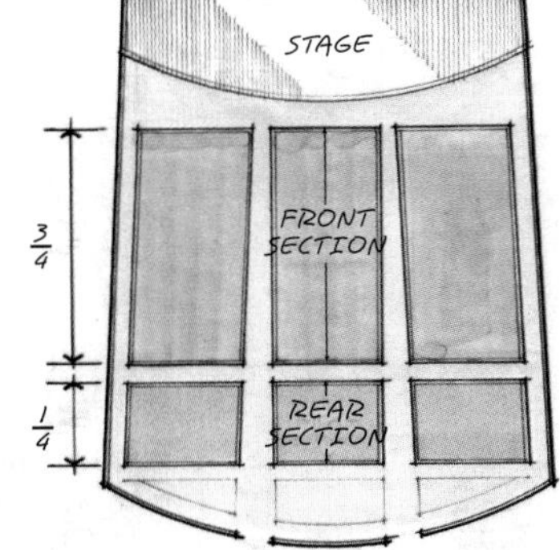

46. **Write a Problem** Use the seating plan to write a problem in which you need to multiply two fractions. Then solve the problem.

47. **Write About It** Explain how you can use the GCF before multiplying so that the product of two fractions is in simplest form.

48. **Challenge** Evaluate the expression. Then simplify your answer.

$$\frac{(2+6)}{5} \cdot \frac{1}{4} \cdot 6 \quad 2\frac{2}{5}$$

CRCT Prep • GPS Support • Spiral Review

49. **Multiple Choice** Which shows the product of $\frac{4}{5}$ and $\frac{3}{5}$ in simplest form?

Ⓐ $1\frac{2}{5}$ Ⓑ $1\frac{1}{3}$ Ⓒ $\frac{3}{5}$ **Ⓓ** $\frac{12}{25}$

50. **Multiple Choice** Julie spent $\frac{1}{3}$ of her birthday money on new clothes. She spent $\frac{3}{10}$ of that money on shoes. What fraction of her birthday money did Julie spend on shoes?

Ⓕ $\frac{1}{30}$ **Ⓖ** $\frac{1}{10}$ Ⓗ $\frac{2}{15}$ Ⓙ $\frac{3}{13}$

Solve each equation. (Lesson 2-7)

51. $15n = 45$ $n = 3$ **52.** $7t = 147$ $t = 21$ **53.** $6a = 78$ $a = 13$ **54.** $12b = 216$ $b = 18$

Find each sum or difference. (Lesson 5-2)

55. $\frac{1}{9} + \frac{1}{3}$ $\frac{4}{9}$ **56.** $\frac{11}{12} - \frac{5}{6}$ $\frac{1}{12}$ **57.** $\frac{2}{7} + \frac{6}{21}$ $\frac{12}{21}$ **58.** $\frac{1}{5} + \frac{3}{10} - \frac{1}{15}$ $\frac{13}{30}$

ONGOING ASSESSMENT and INTERVENTION

Diagnose **Before the Lesson**
5-7 Warm Up, TE p. 260

Monitor **During the Lesson**
5-7 Know-It Notebook
5-7 Questioning Strategies

Assess **After the Lesson**
5-7 Lesson Quiz, TE p. 263

Answers

46. Possible answer: If $\frac{1}{3}$ of the rear seating is reserved for teachers, what fraction of the seating is reserved for teachers? $\frac{1}{12}$

47. Possible answer: You find a common factor in the numerator and denominator. Divide each by the common factor. Repeat the process as many times as possible. Then multiply the fractions. The product will be in simplest form.

TEST PREP DOCTOR In Exercise 50, students need to understand how to interpret the phrase: $\frac{3}{10}$ *of that money.* To get the correct answer, $\frac{1}{3}$ is multiplied by $\frac{3}{10}$.

Journal

Have students write real-world problems where fractions are multiplied. Have students solve their problems.

CHALLENGE 5-7

LESSON 5-7 Challenge
Fractions of Flowers

For each flower below, shade the two petals whose fractions have a product equal to the fraction written in the center of that flower.

1. 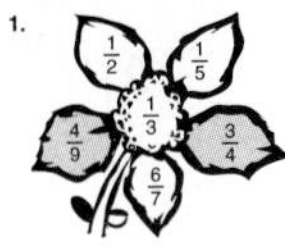

2. 

3. 

4. 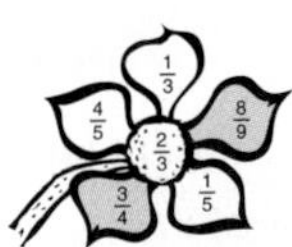

5. 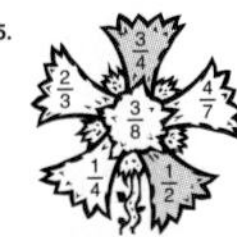

6. 

PROBLEM SOLVING 5-7

LESSON 5-7 Problem Solving
Multiplying Fractions

Use the circle graph to answer the questions. Write each answer in simplest form.

School Orchestra: Strings $\frac{1}{2}$, Brass $\frac{1}{8}$, Woodwind $\frac{1}{4}$, Percussion $\frac{1}{8}$

1. Of the students playing stringed instruments, $\frac{3}{4}$ play the violin. What fraction of the whole orchestra is violin players?
$\frac{3}{8}$ of the orchestra

2. Of the students playing woodwind instruments, $\frac{1}{2}$ play the clarinet. What fraction of the whole orchestra is clarinet players?
$\frac{1}{8}$ of the orchestra

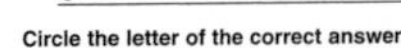

Circle the letter of the correct answer.

3. Two-thirds of the students who play a percussion instrument are boys. What fraction of the musicians in the orchestra is boys who play percussion? girls who play percussion?
A $\frac{1}{24}$ of the orchestra
B $\frac{1}{12}$ of the orchestra
C $\frac{1}{4}$ of the orchestra
D $\frac{2}{3}$ of the orchestra

4. The brass section is evenly divided into horns, trumpets, trombones, and tubas. What fraction of the whole orchestra do players of each of those brass instruments make up?
F $\frac{1}{32}$ of the orchestra
G $\frac{1}{8}$ of the orchestra
H $\frac{1}{4}$ of the orchestra
J $\frac{1}{2}$ of the orchestra

5. There are 40 students in the orchestra. How many students play either percussion or brass instruments?
A 5 students
B 10 students
C 8 students
D 16 students

6. If 2 more violinists join the orchestra, what fraction of all the musicians would play a stringed instrument?
F $\frac{11}{21}$
G $\frac{11}{20}$
H $\frac{1}{20}$
J $\frac{1}{26}$

Power Presentations with PowerPoint®

5-7 Lesson Quiz

Multiply. Write each answer in simplest form.

1. $\frac{1}{4} \cdot \frac{3}{5}$ $\frac{3}{20}$ **2.** $\frac{3}{10} \cdot \frac{5}{7}$ $\frac{3}{14}$

Evaluate the expression $x \cdot \frac{1}{8}$ for each value of x. Write the answer in simplest form.

3. $x = \frac{4}{5}$ $\frac{1}{10}$ **4.** $x = \frac{1}{8}$ $\frac{1}{64}$

5. At a particular college $\frac{2}{5}$ of the students take a math class. Of these students, $\frac{1}{4}$ take basic algebra. What fraction of all students take basic algebra? $\frac{1}{10}$

Also available on transparency

5-8 Organizer

Pacing: Traditional 1 day
Block $\frac{1}{2}$ day

Objective: Students multiply mixed numbers.

Online Edition
Tutorial Videos

Countdown to CRCT Week 11

Power Presentations with PowerPoint®

Warm Up

Multiply.

1. $\frac{1}{3} \cdot \frac{1}{2}$ $\quad \frac{1}{6}$ **2.** $\frac{4}{5} \cdot \frac{3}{8}$ $\quad \frac{3}{10}$

3. $\frac{3}{11} \cdot 2$ $\quad \frac{6}{11}$ **4.** $\frac{3}{8} \cdot \frac{5}{8}$ $\quad \frac{15}{64}$

Problem of the Day

Tracy and Zachary are sharing a large pizza. Tracy cuts the pizza in half. Zachary says he cannot eat that much. Zachary cuts his half into fourths and eats one piece. What fraction of the whole pizza does Zachary **not** eat? $\frac{7}{8}$

Also available on transparency

Math Humor

When you multiply $23\frac{17}{19} \times 14\frac{31}{87}$, what do you get? Tired

5-8 Multiplying Mixed Numbers

Learn to multiply mixed numbers.

Georgia Performance Standards

M6N1.e Multiply fractions and mixed numbers. Also, M6N1.g.

Janice and Carlos are making homemade pasta from a recipe that calls for $1\frac{1}{2}$ cups of flour. They want to make $\frac{1}{3}$ of the recipe.

You can find $\frac{1}{3}$ of $1\frac{1}{2}$, or multiply $\frac{1}{3}$ by $1\frac{1}{2}$, to find how much flour Janice and Carlos need.

EXAMPLE 1 Multiplying Fractions and Mixed Numbers

Remember!

To write a mixed number as an improper fraction, start with the whole number, multiply by the denominator, and add the numerator. Use the same denominator.

$1\frac{1}{5} = \frac{1 \cdot 5 + 1}{5} = \frac{6}{5}$

Multiply. Write each answer in simplest form.

A $\frac{1}{3} \cdot 1\frac{1}{2}$

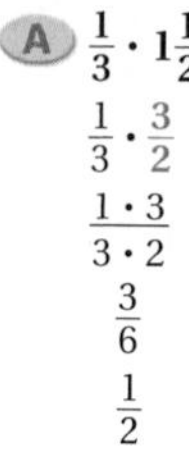

$\frac{1}{3} \cdot \frac{3}{2}$ *Write $1\frac{1}{2}$ as an improper fraction. $1\frac{1}{2} = \frac{3}{2}$*

$\frac{1 \cdot 3}{3 \cdot 2}$ *Multiply numerators. Multiply denominators.*

$\frac{3}{6}$

$\frac{1}{2}$ *Write the answer in simplest form.*

B $1\frac{1}{5} \cdot \frac{2}{3}$

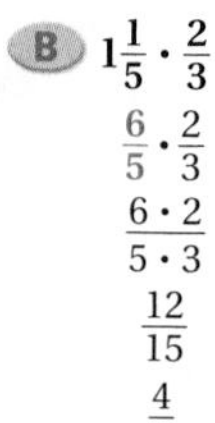

$\frac{6}{5} \cdot \frac{2}{3}$ *Write $1\frac{1}{5}$ as an improper fraction. $1\frac{1}{5} = \frac{6}{5}$*

$\frac{6 \cdot 2}{5 \cdot 3}$ *Multiply numerators. Multiply denominators.*

$\frac{12}{15}$

$\frac{4}{5}$ *Write the answer in simplest form.*

C $\frac{3}{4} \cdot 2\frac{1}{3}$

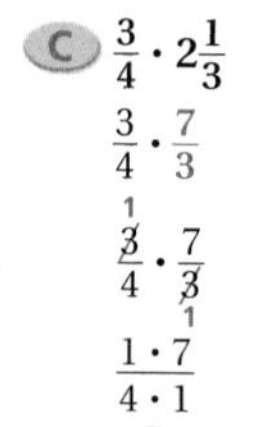

$\frac{3}{4} \cdot \frac{7}{3}$ *Write $2\frac{1}{3}$ as an improper fraction. $2\frac{1}{3} = \frac{7}{3}$*

$\frac{\overset{1}{\cancel{3}}}{4} \cdot \frac{7}{\underset{1}{\cancel{3}}}$ *Use the GCF to simplify before multiplying.*

$\frac{1 \cdot 7}{4 \cdot 1}$

$\frac{7}{4} = 1\frac{3}{4}$ *You can write the answer as a mixed number.*

Georgia Performance Standards

M6N1.e Multiply and divide fractions and mixed numbers.

M6N1.g Solve problems involving fractions, decimals, and percents.

1 Introduce

Alternate Opener

EXPLORATION

5-8 Multiplying Mixed Numbers

You can use paper folding to find products of mixed numbers. To find $\frac{1}{2} \cdot 1\frac{1}{2}$, first fold two sheets of paper in half vertically to represent $1\frac{1}{2}$. To represent $\frac{1}{2}$ of $1\frac{1}{2}$, fold both sheets in half again horizontally.

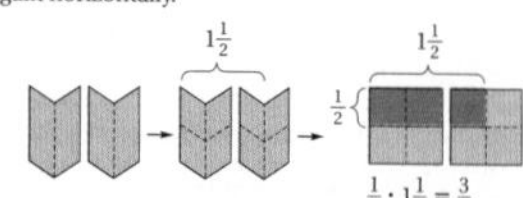

Use paper folding to find each product. Sketch a picture for each product.

1. $\frac{2}{3} \cdot 1\frac{1}{2}$

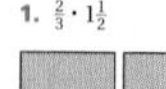

2. $\frac{1}{3} \cdot 1\frac{3}{4}$

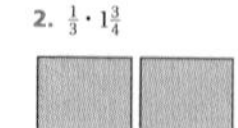

Think and Discuss

3. **Explain** how to multiply a fraction times a mixed number.
4. **Explain** why the product of a proper fraction and a mixed number is less than the mixed number.

Motivate

To introduce students to multiplying with mixed numbers, show them a model of $2\frac{1}{4}$ like the one below.

Ask students how they would show $\frac{1}{2}$ of $2\frac{1}{4}$.
Possible answer: Take one-half of the two wholes and one-half of $\frac{1}{4}$. $1 + \frac{1}{8} = 1\frac{1}{8}$

Explorations and answers are provided in *Alternate Openers: Explorations Transparencies.*

EXAMPLE 2 Multiplying Mixed Numbers

Find each product. Write the answer in simplest form.

A $2\frac{1}{2} \cdot 1\frac{1}{3}$

$\frac{5}{2} \cdot \frac{4}{3}$ — *Write the mixed numbers as improper fractions. $2\frac{1}{2} = \frac{5}{2}$ $\quad 1\frac{1}{3} = \frac{4}{3}$*

$\frac{5 \cdot 4}{2 \cdot 3}$ — *Multiply numerators. Multiply denominators.*

$\frac{20}{6}$

$3\frac{2}{6}$ — *Write the improper fraction as a mixed number.*

$3\frac{1}{3}$ — *Simplify.*

B $1\frac{1}{4} \cdot 1\frac{1}{3}$

$\frac{5}{4} \cdot \frac{4}{3}$ — *Write the mixed numbers as improper fractions. $1\frac{1}{4} = \frac{5}{4}$ $\quad 1\frac{1}{3} = \frac{4}{3}$*

$\frac{5}{\cancel{4}_1} \cdot \frac{\cancel{4}^1}{3}$ — *Use the GCF to simplify before multiplying.*

$\frac{5 \cdot 1}{1 \cdot 3}$ — *Multiply numerators. Multiply denominators.*

$\frac{5}{3}$

$1\frac{2}{3}$ — *Write the answer as a mixed number.*

C $5 \cdot 3\frac{2}{11}$

$5 \cdot 3\frac{2}{11}$

$5 \cdot \left(3 + \frac{2}{11}\right)$

$(5 \cdot 3) + \left(5 \cdot \frac{2}{11}\right)$ — *Use the Distributive Property.*

$(5 \cdot 3) + \left(\frac{5}{1} \cdot \frac{2}{11}\right)$

$15 + \frac{10}{11}$ — *Multiply.*

$15\frac{10}{11}$ — *Add.*

Think and Discuss

GPS M6P2.c, M6P3.b

1. **Tell** how you multiply a mixed number by a mixed number.
2. **Explain** two ways you would multiply a mixed number by a whole number.
3. **Tell** how multiplying mixed numbers is similar to multiplying fractions.

Answers to *Think and Discuss*

1. Change each mixed number to an improper fraction. Multiply the numerators, and multiply the denominators.

Express the product in simplest form, and change any improper fractions to mixed numbers.

2. Write the mixed number as an improper fraction and multiply by the whole number written as a fraction. Or multiply the whole number by the whole number part of the mixed number and by the fraction part of the mixed number. Then add the products.

3. Mixed numbers must be written as improper fractions before they can be multiplied. Once this occurs, there is no difference in how mixed numbers and fractions are multiplied.

COMMON ERROR ALERT

Some students may multiply the fraction part by the fraction part and the whole number part by the whole number part separately when multiplying two mixed numbers. Show students that this method results in an incorrect product and emphasize that mixed numbers must first be written as improper fractions before multiplying.

Power Presentations with PowerPoint®

Additional Examples

Example 1 

Multiply. Write each answer in simplest form.

A. $\frac{1}{4} \cdot 1\frac{1}{3}$ $\quad \frac{1}{3}$

B. $3\frac{1}{2} \cdot \frac{4}{5}$ $\quad 2\frac{4}{5}$

C. $\frac{12}{13} \cdot 2\frac{3}{8}$ $\quad 2\frac{5}{26}$

Example 2 

Find each product. Write the answer in simplest form.

A. $1\frac{2}{3} \cdot 2\frac{1}{7}$ $\quad 3\frac{4}{7}$

B. $1\frac{3}{8} \cdot 2\frac{2}{5}$ $\quad 3\frac{3}{10}$

C. $2 \cdot 4\frac{2}{5}$ $\quad 8\frac{4}{5}$

Also available on transparency

2 Teach

Guided Instruction

In this lesson, students learn to multiply mixed numbers. Begin by teaching students to multiply a fraction and a mixed number. Then teach students to multiply mixed numbers by mixed numbers and whole numbers by mixed numbers.

Teaching Tip **Modeling** Have students draw or make models to help conceptualize some of the simpler examples in the lesson.

Reaching All Learners

Through Critical Thinking

Challenge students to use each of the following numbers to form two multiplication number sentences: $\frac{1}{4}, \frac{3}{4}, \frac{7}{8}, 1\frac{7}{8}, 2\frac{1}{2}, 3\frac{1}{2}$.

Possible answer: $\frac{1}{4} \cdot 3\frac{1}{2} = \frac{7}{8}$ and $\frac{3}{4} \cdot 2\frac{1}{2} = 1\frac{7}{8}$

3 Close

Summarize

Have the students solve three problems: one in which a fraction and a mixed number are multiplied, one in which two mixed numbers are multiplied, and one in which a whole number and a mixed number are multiplied. After students have solved the problems on their own, work through them together, explaining the steps as you go.

5-8 Exercises

Assignment Guide

If you finished Example 1 assign:
Average 1–6, 29–33, 59–68
Advanced 13–20, 29–31, 59–68

If you finished Example 2 assign:
Average 1–55, 59–68
Advanced 1–52, 56–68

Homework Quick Check

Quickly check key concepts.
Exercises: 18, 22, 26, 34, 40, 46

Math Background

The expression *improper fractions* carries unfortunate connotations. As this lesson demonstrates, a fraction such as $\frac{25}{9}$ is called improper because its numerator is greater than its denominator. Therefore it is rewritten as $2\frac{7}{9}$. This mixed number has the advantage of making clear the whole numbers between which the fractional expression lies. However, $\frac{25}{9}$ is generally easier to use in arithmetic than $2\frac{7}{9}$. When it comes to deciding how a number should be expressed, students should consider how the number is going to be used.

Georgia Performance Standards

M6P1.b Solve problems that arise in mathematics and in other contexts.

M6P3.a Organize and consolidate their mathematical thinking through communication.

5-8 Exercises

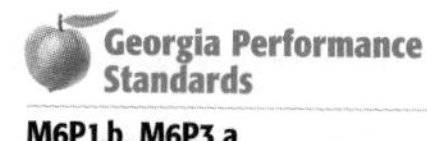
Georgia Performance Standards
M6P1.b, M6P3.a

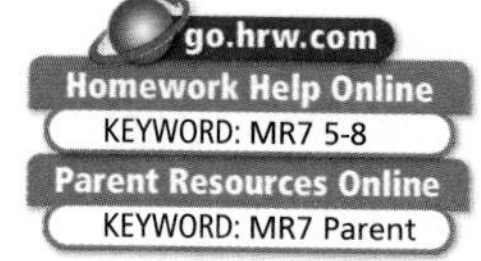

GUIDED PRACTICE

See Example 1 Multiply. Write each answer in simplest form.

1. $1\frac{1}{4} \cdot \frac{2}{3}$ $\frac{5}{6}$
2. $2\frac{2}{3} \cdot \frac{1}{4}$ $\frac{2}{3}$
3. $\frac{3}{7} \cdot 1\frac{5}{6}$ $\frac{11}{14}$
4. $1\frac{1}{3} \cdot \frac{6}{7}$ $1\frac{1}{7}$
5. $\frac{2}{3} \cdot 1\frac{3}{10}$ $\frac{13}{15}$
6. $2\frac{6}{11} \cdot \frac{2}{7}$ $\frac{8}{11}$

See Example 2 Find each product. Write the answer in simplest form.

7. $1\frac{5}{6} \cdot 1\frac{1}{8}$ $2\frac{1}{16}$
8. $2\frac{2}{5} \cdot 1\frac{1}{12}$ $2\frac{3}{5}$
9. $4 \cdot 5\frac{3}{7}$ $21\frac{5}{7}$
10. $2\frac{3}{4} \cdot 1\frac{5}{6}$ $5\frac{1}{24}$
11. $2\frac{3}{8} \cdot 5\frac{1}{5}$ $12\frac{7}{20}$
12. $10\frac{1}{2} \cdot 1\frac{1}{4}$ $13\frac{1}{8}$

INDEPENDENT PRACTICE

See Example 1 Multiply. Write each answer in simplest form.

13. $1\frac{1}{4} \cdot \frac{3}{4}$ $\frac{15}{16}$
14. $\frac{4}{7} \cdot 1\frac{1}{4}$ $\frac{5}{7}$
15. $1\frac{1}{6} \cdot \frac{2}{5}$ $\frac{7}{15}$
16. $2\frac{1}{6} \cdot \frac{3}{7}$ $\frac{13}{14}$
17. $\frac{5}{9} \cdot 1\frac{9}{10}$ $1\frac{1}{18}$
18. $2\frac{2}{9} \cdot \frac{3}{5}$ $1\frac{1}{3}$
19. $1\frac{3}{10} \cdot \frac{5}{7}$ $\frac{13}{14}$
20. $\frac{3}{4} \cdot 1\frac{2}{5}$ $1\frac{1}{20}$

See Example 2 Find each product. Write the answer in simplest form.

21. $1\frac{1}{3} \cdot 1\frac{5}{7}$ $2\frac{2}{7}$
22. $1\frac{2}{3} \cdot 2\frac{3}{10}$ $3\frac{5}{6}$
23. $4 \cdot 3\frac{7}{8}$ $15\frac{1}{2}$
24. $6 \cdot 2\frac{1}{3}$ 14
25. $5 \cdot 4\frac{7}{10}$ $23\frac{1}{2}$
26. $2\frac{2}{3} \cdot 3\frac{5}{8}$ $9\frac{2}{3}$
27. $1\frac{1}{2} \cdot 2\frac{2}{5}$ $3\frac{3}{5}$
28. $3\frac{5}{6} \cdot 2\frac{3}{4}$ $10\frac{13}{24}$

PRACTICE AND PROBLEM SOLVING

Extra Practice p. 723

Write each product in simplest form.

29. $1\frac{2}{3} \cdot \frac{2}{9}$ $\frac{10}{27}$
30. $3\frac{1}{3} \cdot \frac{7}{10}$ $2\frac{1}{3}$
31. $2 \cdot \frac{5}{8}$ $1\frac{1}{4}$
32. $2\frac{8}{11} \cdot \frac{3}{10}$ $\frac{9}{11}$
33. $\frac{3}{8} \cdot \frac{4}{9}$ $\frac{1}{6}$
34. $2\frac{1}{12} \cdot 1\frac{3}{5}$ $3\frac{1}{3}$
35. $3\frac{3}{10} \cdot 4\frac{1}{6}$ $13\frac{3}{4}$
36. $2\frac{1}{4} \cdot 1\frac{2}{9}$ $2\frac{3}{4}$
37. $2 \cdot \frac{4}{5} \cdot 1\frac{2}{3}$ $2\frac{2}{3}$
38. $3\frac{5}{6} \cdot \frac{9}{10} \cdot 4\frac{2}{3}$ $16\frac{1}{10}$
39. $1\frac{7}{8} \cdot 2\frac{1}{3} \cdot 4$ $17\frac{1}{2}$
40. $1\frac{2}{7} \cdot 3 \cdot 2\frac{5}{8}$ $10\frac{1}{8}$

41. Jared used $1\frac{2}{5}$ bags of soil for his garden. He is digging another garden that will need $\frac{1}{5}$ as much soil as the original. How much will he use? $\frac{7}{25}$ of a bag

42. Milo is making $1\frac{1}{2}$ batches of muffins. If one batch calls for $1\frac{3}{4}$ cups flour, how much flour will he need? $2\frac{5}{8}$ cups

43. **Critical Thinking** Is the product of two mixed numbers always greater than 1? Explain. Yes; mixed numbers are always greater than 1, and the product of two numbers greater than 1 is always greater than 1.

Evaluate each expression.

44. $\frac{1}{2} \cdot c$ for $c = 4\frac{2}{5}$ $2\frac{1}{5}$
45. $1\frac{5}{7} \cdot x$ for $x = \frac{5}{6}$ $1\frac{3}{7}$
46. $1\frac{3}{4} \cdot b$ for $b = 1\frac{1}{7}$ 2
47. $1\frac{5}{9} \cdot n$ for $n = 18$ 28
48. $2\frac{5}{9} \cdot t$ for $t = 4$ $10\frac{2}{9}$
49. $3\frac{3}{4} \cdot p$ for $p = \frac{1}{2}$ $1\frac{7}{8}$
50. $\frac{4}{5} \cdot m$ for $m = 2\frac{2}{3}$ $2\frac{2}{15}$
51. $6y$ for $y = 3\frac{5}{8}$ $21\frac{3}{4}$
52. $2\frac{3}{5} \cdot c$ for $c = 1\frac{1}{5}$ $3\frac{3}{25}$

RETEACH 5-8

LESSON 5-8 **Reteach**
Multiplying Mixed Numbers

To find $\frac{1}{3}$ of $2\frac{1}{2}$, first change $2\frac{1}{2}$ to an improper fraction.

$2\frac{1}{2} = \frac{5}{2}$

Then multiply as you would with two proper fractions.

Check to see if you can divide by the GCF to make the problem simpler. Then multiply the numerators and multiply the denominators.

The problem is now $\frac{1}{3} \cdot \frac{5}{2}$.

$\frac{1 \cdot 5}{3 \cdot 2} = \frac{5}{6}$

So, $\frac{1}{3} \cdot 2\frac{1}{2}$ is $\frac{5}{6}$.

Rewrite each mixed number as an improper fraction. Is it possible to simplify before you multiply? If so, what is the GCF?

1. $\frac{1}{4} \cdot 1\frac{1}{3} = \frac{1}{4} \cdot \frac{4}{3}$ $\frac{1}{3}$
2. $\frac{1}{6} \cdot 2\frac{1}{2} = \frac{1}{6} \cdot \frac{5}{2}$ $\frac{5}{12}$
3. $\frac{1}{8} \cdot 1\frac{1}{2} = \frac{1}{8} \cdot \frac{3}{2}$ $\frac{3}{16}$
4. $\frac{1}{3} \cdot 1\frac{2}{5} = \frac{1}{3} \cdot \frac{7}{5}$ $\frac{7}{15}$
5. $1\frac{1}{3} \cdot 1\frac{2}{3}$ $\frac{4}{3} \cdot \frac{5}{3}$ $2\frac{2}{9}$
6. $1\frac{1}{2} \cdot 1\frac{1}{3}$ $\frac{3}{2} \cdot \frac{4}{3}$ 2
7. $1\frac{3}{4} \cdot 2\frac{1}{2}$ $\frac{7}{4} \cdot \frac{5}{2}$ $4\frac{3}{8}$
8. $1\frac{1}{6} \cdot 2\frac{2}{3}$ $\frac{7}{6} \cdot \frac{8}{3}$ $3\frac{1}{9}$
9. $3\frac{1}{3} \cdot \frac{2}{5}$ $1\frac{1}{3}$
10. $2\frac{1}{2} \cdot \frac{1}{5}$ $\frac{1}{2}$
11. $1\frac{3}{4} \cdot 2\frac{1}{2}$ $4\frac{3}{8}$
12. $3\frac{1}{3} \cdot 1\frac{1}{5}$ 4

PRACTICE 5-8

LESSON 5-8 **Practice B**
Multiplying Mixed Numbers

Multiply. Write each answer in simplest form.

1. $1\frac{2}{3} \cdot \frac{4}{5}$ $1\frac{1}{3}$
2. $1\frac{7}{8} \cdot \frac{4}{5}$ $1\frac{1}{2}$
3. $2\frac{3}{4} \cdot \frac{1}{5}$ $\frac{11}{20}$
4. $2\frac{1}{6} \cdot \frac{2}{3}$ $1\frac{4}{9}$
5. $2\frac{2}{5} \cdot \frac{3}{8}$ $\frac{9}{10}$
6. $1\frac{3}{4} \cdot \frac{5}{6}$ $1\frac{11}{24}$
7. $1\frac{1}{6} \cdot \frac{3}{5}$ $\frac{7}{10}$
8. $\frac{2}{9} \cdot 2\frac{1}{7}$ $\frac{10}{21}$
9. $2\frac{3}{11} \cdot \frac{7}{10}$ $1\frac{13}{22}$

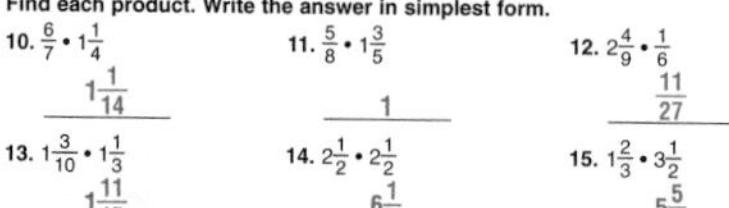

Find each product. Write the answer in simplest form.

10. $\frac{6}{7} \cdot 1\frac{1}{4}$ $1\frac{1}{14}$
11. $\frac{5}{8} \cdot 1\frac{3}{5}$ 1
12. $2\frac{4}{9} \cdot \frac{1}{6}$ $\frac{11}{27}$
13. $1\frac{3}{10} \cdot 1\frac{1}{3}$ $1\frac{11}{15}$
14. $2\frac{1}{2} \cdot 2\frac{1}{2}$ $6\frac{1}{4}$
15. $1\frac{2}{3} \cdot 3\frac{1}{2}$ $5\frac{5}{6}$

16. Dominick lives $1\frac{3}{4}$ miles from his school. If his mother drives him half the way, how far will Dominick have to walk to get to school? $\frac{7}{8}$ mile

17. Katoni bought $2\frac{1}{2}$ dozen donuts to bring to the office. Since there are 12 donuts in a dozen, how many donuts did Katoni buy? 30 donuts

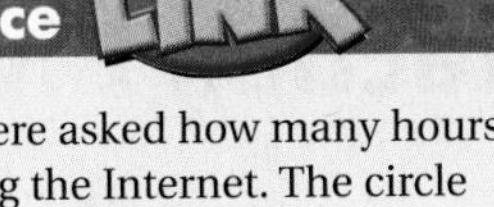

Computer Science LINK

In a survey, 240 people were asked how many hours per week they spend using the Internet. The circle graph shows which fractions of the people use the Internet for which amounts of time.

Using the Internet

More than 36 hr: $\frac{1}{4}$
12 hr to 24 hr: $\frac{1}{3}$
25 hr to 36 hr: $\frac{3}{8}$
Less than 12 hr: $\frac{1}{24}$

Use the graph for Exercises 53–58.

53. How many people in all were surveyed? **240 people**

54. Find the number of people who said they use the Internet for 12 hours to 24 hours a week. **$\frac{1}{3} \cdot 240 = 80$ people**

55. Toni's grandfather uses the Internet for $1\frac{1}{2}$ hours each day.

a. How many hours does he use the Internet in one week? (Write the answer as a mixed number.) **$1\frac{1}{2} \cdot 7 = 10\frac{1}{2}$ h**

b. If Toni's grandfather were included in the survey, in which time section of the circle graph would his data be? **Less than 12 h**

56. **Choose a Strategy** Which set of tallies could represent the number of people who use the Internet for fewer than 12 hours a week?

(A) 𝍸 𝍸 (B) 𝍸 𝍸 || (C) 𝍸 𝍸 𝍸 𝍸 (D) 𝍸 𝍸 𝍸 𝍸 ||||

57. **Write About It** Explain how you can find the number of people surveyed who use the Internet for more than 36 hours a week.

58. **Challenge** Five-sixths of the people who use the Internet for 25 hours to 36 hours said they use it for 30 hours each week. Find the number of people who use the Internet for 30 hours each week. **75 people**

CRCT PREP • GPS SUPPORT • SPIRAL REVIEW

59. **Multiple Choice** A chef uses $2\frac{1}{4}$ cups of water for a recipe. The chef doubled the recipe. How much water did the chef use?

(A) 4 cups (B) $4\frac{1}{4}$ cups **(C) $4\frac{1}{2}$ cups** (D) $4\frac{3}{4}$ cups

60. **Gridded Response** Keith ate $\frac{1}{3}$ pound of grapes last week. Jamal ate five times as many grapes as Keith last week. How many pounds of grapes did Jamal eat? **$1\frac{2}{3}$**

Write each number in scientific notation. (Lesson 3-4)

61. 540 **5.4×10^2** **62.** 1,400 **1.4×10^3** **63.** 54,000 **5.4×10^4** **64.** 508,000,000 **5.08×10^8**

Multiply. Write each answer in simplest form. (Lesson 5-6)

65. $5 \times \frac{1}{10}$ **$\frac{1}{2}$** **66.** $21 \times \frac{1}{3}$ **7** **67.** $\frac{2}{7} \times 14$ **4** **68.** $\frac{5}{12} \times 2$ **$\frac{5}{6}$**

CHALLENGE 5-8

LESSON 5-8 **Challenge**
And They're Off!

Like many sports, horse racing uses a special system of measurement. Horse races are measured in units called *furlongs*. One furlong equals $\frac{1}{8}$ mile. The races described below have different furlong lengths, but they all offer the same prize money to their winners—$1,000,000!

Write the length in miles of each of these horse races in simplest form.

1. Santa Anita Derby, California
Race Length: 9 furlongs **Length in Miles:** $1\frac{1}{8}$ miles

2. Kentucky Derby, Kentucky
Race Length: 10 furlongs **Length in Miles:** $1\frac{1}{4}$ miles

3. Preakness Stakes, Maryland
Race Length: $9\frac{1}{2}$ furlongs **Length in Miles:** $1\frac{3}{16}$ miles

4. Belmont Stakes, New York
Race Length: 12 furlongs **Length in Miles:** $1\frac{1}{2}$ miles

5. Breeders' Cup Juvenile, New York
Race Length: $8\frac{1}{2}$ furlongs **Length in Miles:** $1\frac{1}{16}$ miles

PROBLEM SOLVING 5-8

LESSON 5-8 **Problem Solving**
Multiplying Mixed Numbers

Use the recipe to answer the questions.

CHOCOLATE CHIP COOKIES Servings: 1 batch
$1\frac{2}{3}$ cups flour
$\frac{3}{4}$ teaspoon baking soda
$\frac{1}{2}$ cup white sugar
$2\frac{1}{3}$ cups semisweet chocolate chips
$\frac{1}{2}$ cup brown sugar
$\frac{3}{4}$ cup butter
1 egg
$1\frac{1}{4}$ teaspoons vanilla

1. If you want to make $2\frac{1}{2}$ batches, how much flour would you need? **$4\frac{1}{6}$ cups**
2. If you want to make only $1\frac{1}{2}$ batches, how much chocolate chips would you need? **$3\frac{1}{2}$ cups**
3. You want to bake $3\frac{1}{4}$ batches. How much vanilla do you need in all? **$4\frac{1}{16}$ teaspoons**

Choose the letter for the best answer.

4. If you make $1\frac{1}{4}$ batches, how much baking soda would you need?
A $\frac{3}{16}$ teaspoon C $\frac{3}{5}$ teaspoon
B $\frac{5}{16}$ teaspoon **(D) $\frac{15}{16}$ teaspoon**

5. How many cups of white sugar do you need to make $3\frac{1}{2}$ batches of cookies?
F $3\frac{1}{2}$ cups H $1\frac{1}{2}$ cups
(G) $1\frac{3}{4}$ cups J $1\frac{1}{4}$ cups

6. Dan used $2\frac{1}{4}$ cups of butter to make chocolate chip cookies using the above recipe. How many batches of cookies did he make?
(A) 3 batches C 5 batches
B 4 batches D 6 batches

7. One bag of chocolate chips holds 2 cups. If you buy five bags, how many cups of chips will you have left over after baking $2\frac{1}{2}$ batches of cookies?
(F) $4\frac{1}{6}$ cups H $2\frac{1}{3}$ cups
G $5\frac{5}{6}$ cups J $\frac{1}{3}$ cup

ONGOING ASSESSMENT and INTERVENTION

***Diagnose Before* the Lesson**
5-8 Warm Up, TE p. 264

***Monitor During* the Lesson**
5-8 Know-It Notebook
5-8 Questioning Strategies

***Assess After* the Lesson**
5-8 Lesson Quiz, TE p. 267

Interdisciplinary LINK

Computer Science

Exercises 53–58 involve using data about Internet usage to solve problems involving fraction multiplication.

Answers

57. Possible answer: Find $\frac{1}{4}$ of 240. Use the GCF of 4 and 240 to simplify. $1 \cdot 60 = 60$, so 60 people said they use the Internet for more than 36 hours.

In Exercise 60, students may use repeated addition of a fraction or multiplication by a whole number. Either way, the result will be $\frac{5}{3}$. Remember to simplify the fraction.

Journal

Have students explain in their own words how to multiply mixed numbers by fractions, by whole numbers, and by mixed numbers.

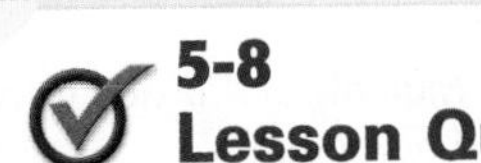

5-8 Lesson Quiz

Multiply. Write each answer in simplest form.

1. $3\frac{1}{5} \cdot \frac{5}{8}$ **2** **2.** $1\frac{7}{10} \cdot \frac{5}{7}$ **$1\frac{3}{14}$**

Find each product. Write the answer in simplest form.

3. $2\frac{1}{5} \cdot 1\frac{1}{4}$ **$2\frac{3}{4}$** **4.** $5 \cdot 3\frac{1}{5}$ **16**

5. A nurse gave a patient $3\frac{1}{2}$ tablets of a medication. If each tablet contained $\frac{1}{20}$ grain of the medication, how much medication did the patient receive? **$\frac{7}{40}$ grain**

Also available on transparency

Organizer

Use with Lesson 5-9

Pacing:
Traditional $\frac{1}{2}$ day
Block $\frac{1}{4}$ day

Objective: Use grids to model division of fractions.

Materials: Fraction bars

Online Edition
Fraction Bars

Resources

Hands-On Lab Activities
Lab 5-9 Recording Sheet

Teach

Discuss

Discuss with students what a grid represents and how to use grids to model fractions and mixed numbers.

Close

Key Concept

Using grids will yield the same result as applying the rules for dividing fractions and mixed numbers.

Assessment

Evaluate.

1. $1\frac{1}{3} \div 4$ $\frac{1}{3}$
2. $2\frac{1}{2} \div 5$ $\frac{1}{2}$
3. $2\frac{2}{5} \div 3$ $\frac{4}{5}$

Model Fraction Division

Use with Lesson 5-9

Georgia Performance Standards
M6N1.e, M6N1.g, M6P5.b

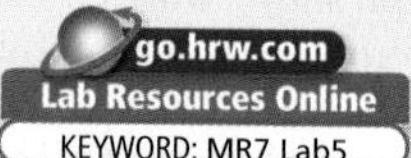

You can use grids to help you understand division of fractions.

Activity 1

Find $4\frac{1}{2} \div 3$.

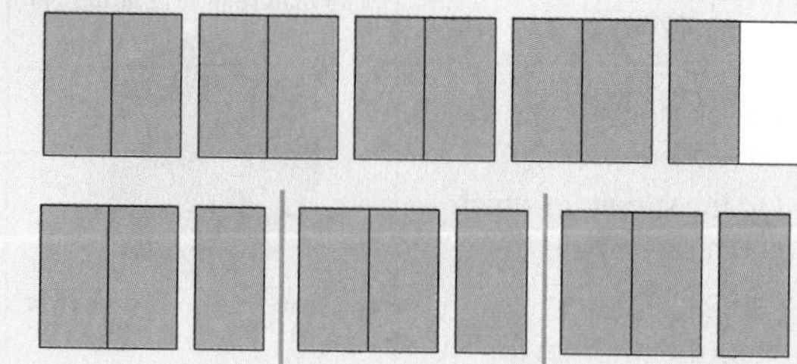

Think of $4\frac{1}{2} \div 3$ as dividing $4\frac{1}{2}$ into 3 equal groups.

Shade $4\frac{1}{2}$ squares.

Divide the squares into 3 equal groups.

Look at one of the shaded groups.

What fraction is this?

$4\frac{1}{2} \div 3 = 1\frac{1}{2}$

Think and Discuss

1. Explain how you know the number of groups into which you must divide the squares. **The number of groups is the number you are dividing by.**

Try This

Write the division expression modeled on each grid.

1. 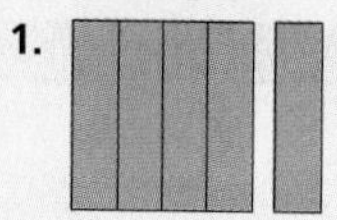 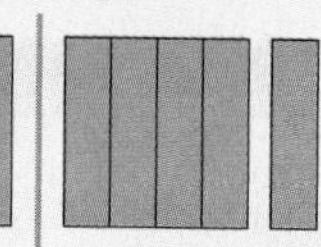 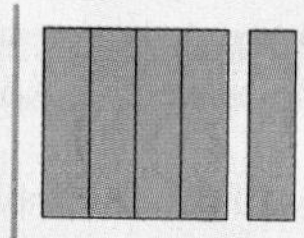 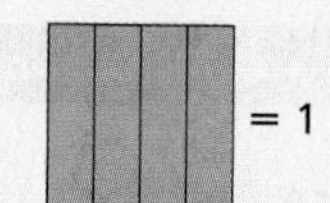 = 1 $3\frac{3}{4} \div 3$

Draw a model for each division expression. Then find the value of the expression.

2. $9\frac{1}{3} \div 4$ $2\frac{1}{3}$
3. $3\frac{3}{4} \div 5$ $\frac{3}{4}$
4. $4\frac{2}{3} \div 2$ $2\frac{1}{3}$
5. $4\frac{1}{5} \div 3$ $1\frac{2}{5}$

Activity 2

1. Find $2\frac{2}{3} \div \frac{2}{3}$.

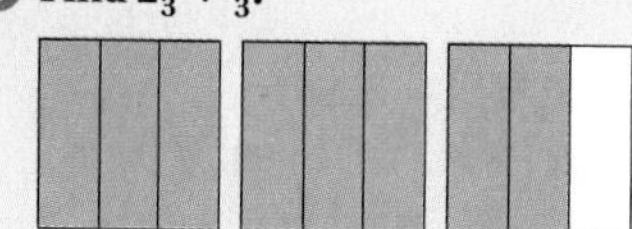

Shade $2\frac{2}{3}$ squares.

Georgia Performance Standards

M6N1.e Multiply and divide fractions and mixed numbers.

M6N1.g Solve problems involving fractions, decimals, and percents.

M6P5.b Select, apply, and translate among mathematical representations to solve problems.

Activity 1

Answers to *Try This*

2. 

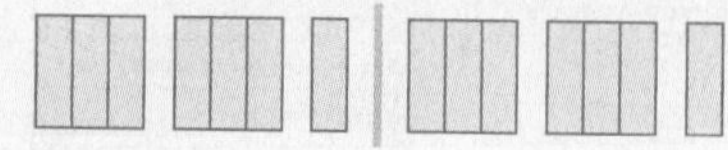

 = 1

3. 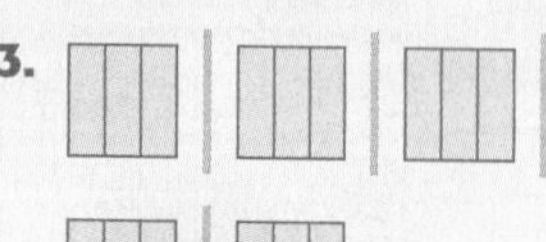

 = 1

4. 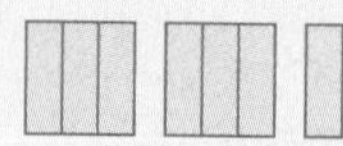

= 1

5. 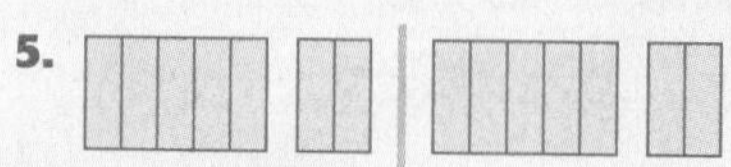

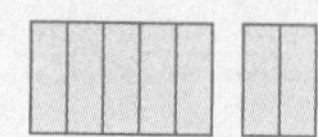

= 1

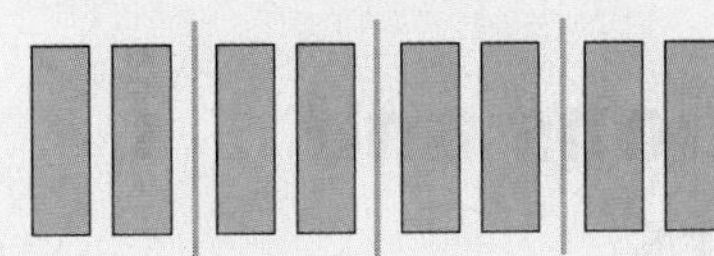

Divide the shaded squares and shaded thirds into equal groups of $\frac{2}{3}$.

There are 4 groups of $\frac{2}{3}$ in $2\frac{2}{3}$.

$2\frac{2}{3} \div \frac{2}{3} = 4$

2 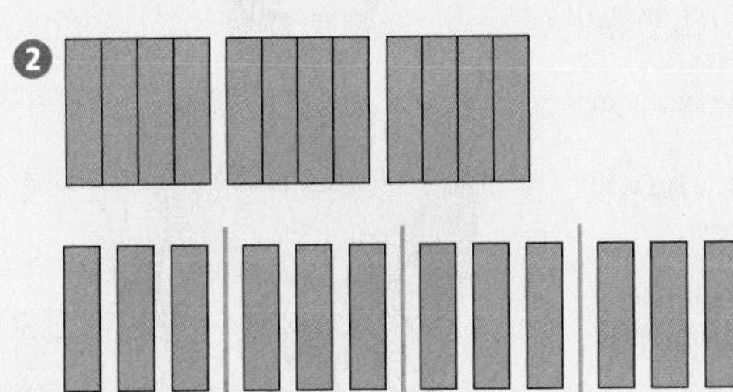

To find $3 \div \frac{3}{4}$, think, "How many groups of $\frac{3}{4}$ are in 3?"

Shade 3 squares. Then divide the squares into fourths because the denominator of $\frac{3}{4}$ is 4.

Divide the shaded squares into equal groups of $\frac{3}{4}$.

There are 4 groups of $\frac{3}{4}$ in 3.

$3 \div \frac{3}{4} = 4$

Think and Discuss

1. Explain what prediction you can make about the value of $6 \div \frac{3}{4}$ if you know that $3 \div \frac{3}{4}$ is 4. **You can predict that the value would be twice as much, 8, because there will be twice as many groups of $\frac{3}{4}$ in 6 as there were in 3. This is because 3 times 2 is 6.**

Try This

Write the division expression modeled by each grid.

1. 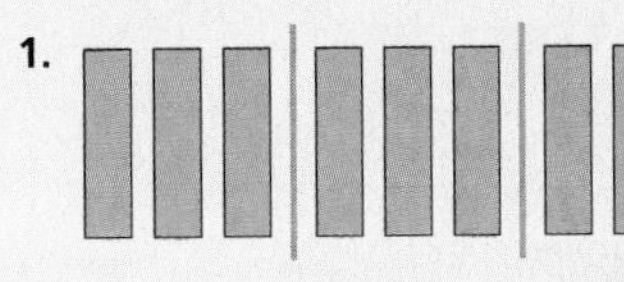 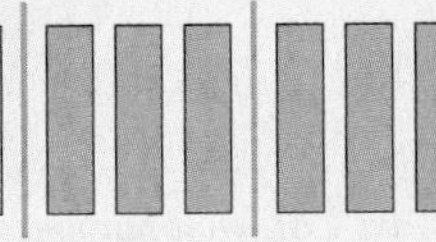 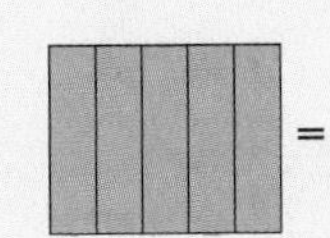 = 1 $2\frac{2}{5} \div \frac{3}{5}$

2. 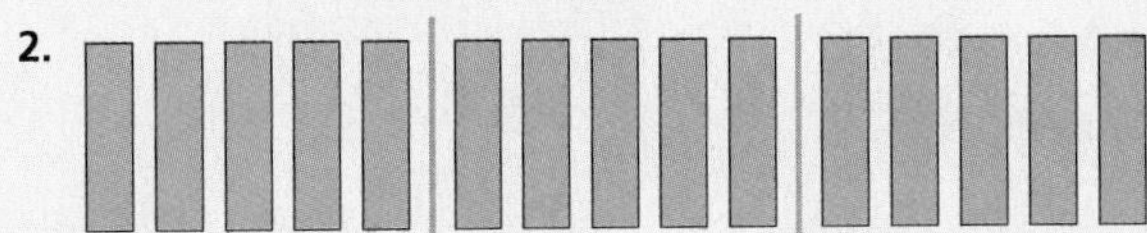 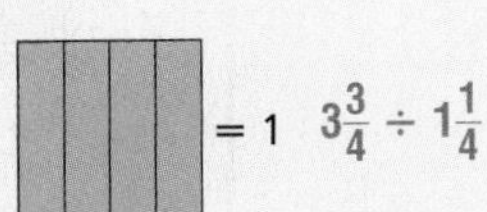 = 1 $3\frac{3}{4} \div 1\frac{1}{4}$

Draw a model for each division expression. Then find the value of the expression.

3. $4 \div 1\frac{1}{3}$ **3**
4. $3\frac{3}{4} \div \frac{3}{4}$ **5**
5. $5\frac{1}{3} \div \frac{2}{3}$ **8**
6. $6\frac{2}{3} \div 1\frac{2}{3}$ **4**

Activity 2

Answers to *Try This*

3. 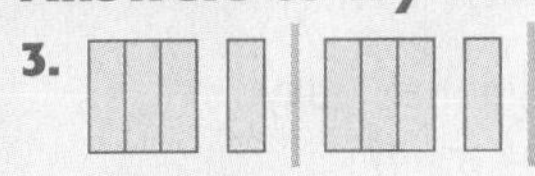

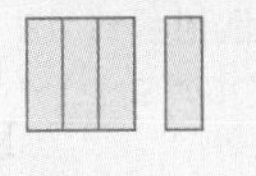

= 1

4. 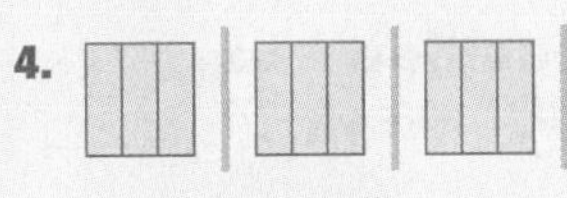

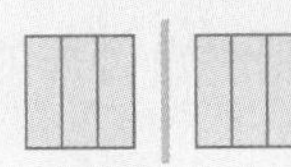

= 1

5. 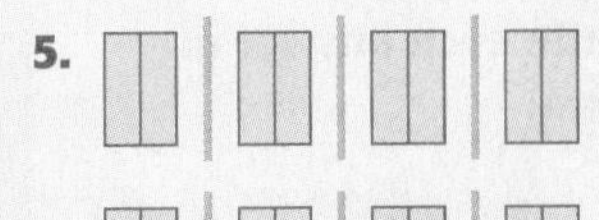

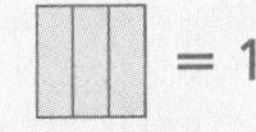 = 1

6. 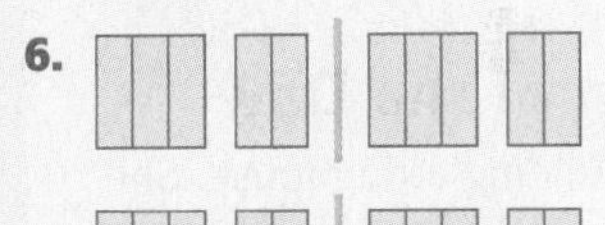

= 1

Dawn Schiller
Temple, Texas

Teacher to Teacher

Several of my students have a difficult time dividing fractions. I give each student a set of fraction bars, a Dry-Erase™ board, and a marker. Students model the dividend by drawing a train. Then they draw another train below the first train to represent the divisor. The students then count the number of sections in the second train, which gives them the answer. Fraction bars can be used to model dividing whole numbers by fractions, dividing fractions by fractions, and dividing mixed numbers.

5-9 Organizer

Pacing: Traditional 1 day
Block $\frac{1}{2}$ day

Objective: Students divide fractions and mixed numbers.

Online Edition
Tutorial Videos

Countdown to CRCT Week 11

Power Presentations with PowerPoint®

Warm Up

Multiply. Write each answer in simplest form.

1. $2\frac{1}{2} \cdot 2$ — 5
2. $1\frac{1}{2} \cdot 3\frac{1}{2}$ — $\frac{21}{4}$ or $5\frac{1}{4}$
3. $3\frac{1}{3} \cdot 3$ — 10
4. $2\frac{1}{5} \cdot 1\frac{1}{4}$ — $\frac{11}{4}$ or $2\frac{3}{4}$

Problem of the Day

Rachel is building a doghouse. She needs to cut a 12-foot-long board into lengths of 65 in. How many lengths can she cut, and will there be any wood left? If so, how much?
2 cuts; yes, 14 in.

Also available on transparency

Math Humor

What is the best time to divide a half dollar evenly between two people?
A quarter to two

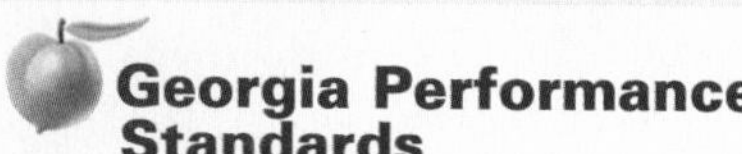

Georgia Performance Standards

M6N1.e Multiply and divide fractions and mixed numbers.

M6N1.g Solve problems involving fractions, decimals, and percents.

M6P5.c Use representations to model and interpret physical, social, and mathematical phenomena.

5-9 Dividing Fractions and Mixed Numbers

Learn to divide fractions and mixed numbers.

Vocabulary
reciprocal

Georgia Performance Standards

M6N1.e Divide fractions and mixed numbers. Also, M6N1.g, M6P5.c.

Curtis is making sushi rolls. First, he will place a sheet of seaweed, called *nori,* on the sushi rolling mat. Then, he will use the mat to roll up rice, cucumber, avocado, and crabmeat. Finally, he will slice the roll into smaller pieces.

Curtis has 2 cups of rice and will use $\frac{1}{3}$ cup for each sushi roll. How many sushi rolls can he make?

Think: How many $\frac{1}{3}$ pieces equal 2 wholes?

There are six $\frac{1}{3}$ pieces in 2 wholes.

Curtis can make 6 sushi rolls.

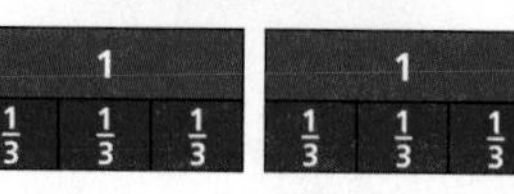

Reciprocals can help you divide by fractions. Two numbers are **reciprocals** if their product is 1.

EXAMPLE 1 Finding Reciprocals

Find the reciprocal.

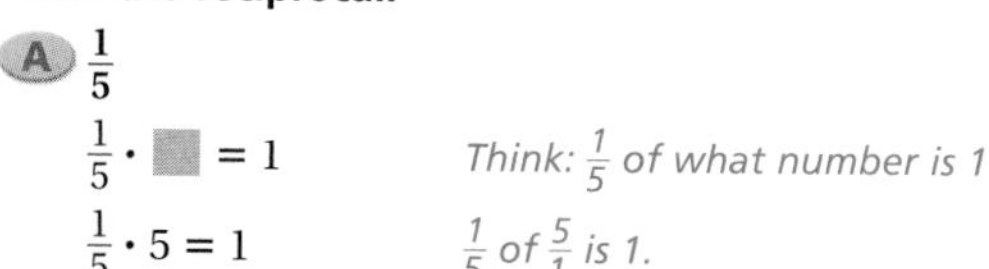

A $\frac{1}{5}$

$\frac{1}{5} \cdot \blacksquare = 1$ — *Think: $\frac{1}{5}$ of what number is 1?*

$\frac{1}{5} \cdot 5 = 1$ — *$\frac{1}{5}$ of $\frac{5}{1}$ is 1.*

The reciprocal of $\frac{1}{5}$ is 5.

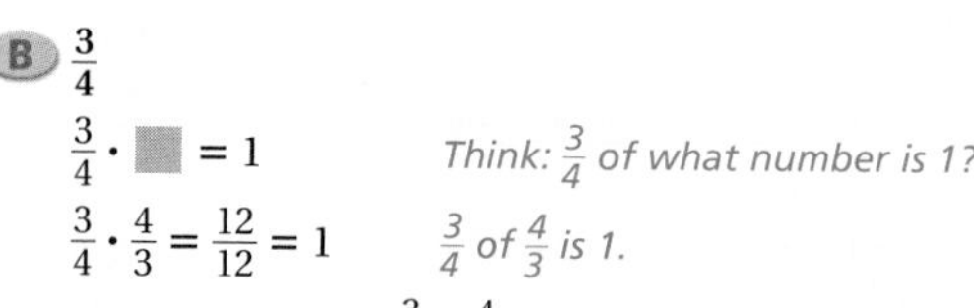

B $\frac{3}{4}$

$\frac{3}{4} \cdot \blacksquare = 1$ — *Think: $\frac{3}{4}$ of what number is 1?*

$\frac{3}{4} \cdot \frac{4}{3} = \frac{12}{12} = 1$ — *$\frac{3}{4}$ of $\frac{4}{3}$ is 1.*

The reciprocal of $\frac{3}{4}$ is $\frac{4}{3}$.

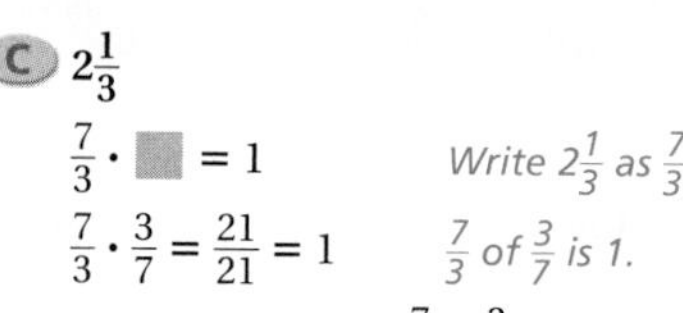

C $2\frac{1}{3}$

$\frac{7}{3} \cdot \blacksquare = 1$ — *Write $2\frac{1}{3}$ as $\frac{7}{3}$.*

$\frac{7}{3} \cdot \frac{3}{7} = \frac{21}{21} = 1$ — *$\frac{7}{3}$ of $\frac{3}{7}$ is 1.*

The reciprocal of $\frac{7}{3}$ is $\frac{3}{7}$.

1 Introduce

Alternate Opener

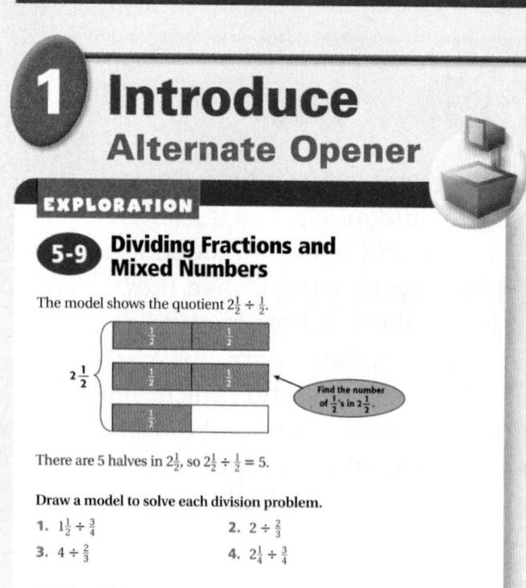

EXPLORATION

5-9 Dividing Fractions and Mixed Numbers

The model shows the quotient $2\frac{1}{2} \div \frac{1}{2}$.

There are 5 halves in $2\frac{1}{2}$, so $2\frac{1}{2} \div \frac{1}{2} = 5$.

Draw a model to solve each division problem.

1. $1\frac{1}{2} \div \frac{3}{4}$
2. $2 \div \frac{2}{3}$
3. $4 \div \frac{2}{3}$
4. $2\frac{1}{4} \div \frac{3}{4}$

Think and Discuss

5. **Describe** how to model fraction division by using fraction bars.
6. **Explain** why $3 \div \frac{3}{4} = 4$.

Motivate

List the following fractions:
$\frac{2}{3}, \frac{2}{5}, \frac{3}{2}, \frac{3}{4}, \frac{4}{3}, \frac{5}{2}, \frac{5}{6}, \frac{6}{5}$

Have students identify the pairs of fractions with a product of 1.
$\frac{2}{3}$ and $\frac{3}{2}$; $\frac{2}{5}$ and $\frac{5}{2}$; $\frac{3}{4}$ and $\frac{4}{3}$; $\frac{5}{6}$ and $\frac{6}{5}$

When a fraction is inverted, the result is the reciprocal of the original fraction. When reciprocals are multiplied, the product is 1.

Explorations and answers are provided in *Alternate Openers: Explorations Transparencies.*

Look at the relationship between the fractions $\frac{3}{4}$ and $\frac{4}{3}$. If you switch the numerator and denominator of a fraction, you will find its reciprocal. Dividing by a number is the same as multiplying by its reciprocal.

$$24 \div 4 = 6 \qquad 24 \cdot \frac{1}{4} = 6$$

EXAMPLE 2 Using Reciprocals to Divide Fractions and Mixed Numbers

Divide. Write each answer in simplest form.

A $\frac{4}{5} \div 5$

$\frac{4}{5} \div 5 = \frac{4}{5} \cdot \frac{1}{5}$ — *Rewrite as multiplication using the reciprocal of 5, $\frac{1}{5}$.*

$= \frac{4 \cdot 1}{5 \cdot 5}$ — *Multiply by the reciprocal.*

$= \frac{4}{25}$ — *The answer is in simplest form.*

B $\frac{3}{4} \div \frac{1}{2}$

$\frac{3}{4} \div \frac{1}{2} = \frac{3}{4} \cdot \frac{2}{1}$ — *Rewrite as multiplication using the reciprocal of $\frac{1}{2}$, $\frac{2}{1}$.*

$= \frac{3 \cdot \overset{1}{\cancel{2}}}{\underset{2}{\cancel{4}} \cdot 1}$ — *Simplify before multiplying.*

$= \frac{3}{2}$ — *Multiply.*

$= 1\frac{1}{2}$ — *You can write the answer as a mixed number.*

C $2\frac{2}{3} \div 1\frac{1}{6}$

$2\frac{2}{3} \div 1\frac{1}{6} = \frac{8}{3} \div \frac{7}{6}$ — *Write the mixed numbers as improper fractions. $2\frac{2}{3} = \frac{8}{3}$ and $1\frac{1}{6} = \frac{7}{6}$*

$= \frac{8}{3} \cdot \frac{6}{7}$ — *Rewrite as multiplication.*

$= \frac{8 \cdot \overset{2}{\cancel{6}}}{\underset{1}{\cancel{3}} \cdot 7}$ — *Simplify before multiplying.*

$= \frac{16}{7}$ — *Multiply.*

$= 2\frac{2}{7}$ — *You can write the answer as a mixed number.*

Think and Discuss

GPS M6P1.d, M6P3.b

1. **Explain** how you can use mental math to find the value of n in the equation $\frac{5}{8} \cdot n = 1$.
2. **Explain** how to find the reciprocal of $3\frac{6}{11}$.

COMMON ERROR ALERT

Some students may forget that a division problem involving fractions has two parts: changing from division to multiplication and finding the reciprocal of the divisor. Remind them that both steps are necessary to solve the problem correctly.

Power Presentations with PowerPoint®

Additional Examples

Example 1

Find the reciprocal.

A. $\frac{1}{9}$ The reciprocal of $\frac{1}{9}$ is 9.

B. $\frac{2}{3}$ The reciprocal of $\frac{2}{3}$ is $\frac{3}{2}$.

C. $3\frac{1}{5}$ The reciprocal of $\frac{16}{5}$ is $\frac{5}{16}$.

Example 2

Divide. Write each answer in simplest form.

A. $\frac{8}{7} \div 7$ $\frac{8}{49}$

B. $\frac{5}{6} \div \frac{2}{3}$ $1\frac{1}{4}$

C. $2\frac{3}{4} \div 1\frac{1}{12}$ $2\frac{7}{13}$

Also available on transparency

Answers to Think and Discuss

1. Possible answer: You know the product of a fraction and its reciprocal is 1. Therefore, n must be the reciprocal of $\frac{5}{8}$, or $\frac{8}{5}$.
2. First change $3\frac{6}{11}$ to an improper fraction, and then switch the numerator and denominator. $3\frac{6}{11} = \frac{39}{11}$, so the reciprocal of $3\frac{6}{11}$ is $\frac{11}{39}$.

2 Teach

Guided Instruction

ENGLISH LANGUAGE LEARNERS

In this lesson, students learn to divide fractions and mixed numbers. First explain what a *reciprocal* is, and have students find reciprocals for fractions and mixed numbers. Then teach students to use a reciprocal and multiplication to divide by a fraction or mixed number.

Reaching All Learners

Through Critical Thinking

Challenge students to find the missing numbers in the following division problems. Have them check their answers.

1. $\frac{3}{4} \div$ ▇ $= 3\frac{3}{4}$ $\frac{1}{5}$
2. ▇ $\div \frac{5}{6} = 1\frac{4}{5}$ $1\frac{1}{2}$
3. $2\frac{1}{2} \div$ ▇ $= 1\frac{3}{7}$ $1\frac{3}{4}$
4. ▇ $\div 2\frac{1}{10} = 1\frac{2}{3}$ $3\frac{1}{2}$

3 Close

Summarize

Review the term *reciprocal*, and have students explain how it is used in division of fractions.

Possible answers: Two numbers are reciprocals if their product is 1. To divide by a fraction or mixed number, multiply the dividend by the reciprocal of the divisor.

5-9 Exercises

Assignment Guide

If you finished Example 1 assign:
Average 1–5, 66–75
Advanced 14–23, 66–75

If you finished Example 2 assign:
Average 1–56, 60–61, 66–75
Advanced 1–53, 57–59, 62–75

Homework Quick Check

Quickly check key concepts.
Exercises: 16, 20, 26, 30, 38, 42

Math Background

The use of multiplication by the reciprocal to divide by a fraction can be traced to Hindu and Arab mathematicians in the early Middle Ages.

A second method, which was taught in arithmetic books in the past, is to first rewrite the dividend and divisor using a common denominator. Thus, $\frac{5}{6} \div \frac{7}{8}$ could be rewritten as $\frac{20}{24} \div \frac{21}{24}$. Then the quotient of the numerators is found: $\frac{20}{24} \div \frac{21}{24} = \frac{20}{21}$.

This method has the advantage of fitting in nicely with the algorithms learned for addition and subtraction. Its disadvantage lies in the need for a common denominator.

5-9 Exercises

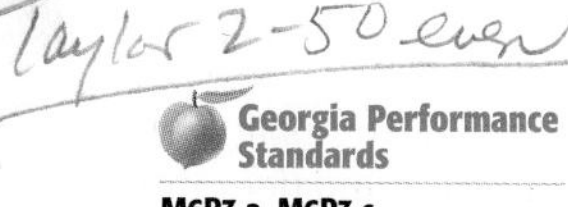

Georgia Performance Standards
M6P3.a, M6P3.c

go.hrw.com
Homework Help Online
KEYWORD: MR7 5-9
Parent Resources Online
KEYWORD: MR7 Parent

GUIDED PRACTICE

See Example 1 **Find the reciprocal.**

1. $\frac{2}{7}$ $\frac{7}{2}$
2. $\frac{5}{9}$ $\frac{9}{5}$
3. $\frac{1}{9}$ $\frac{9}{1}$, or 9
4. $\frac{3}{11}$ $\frac{11}{3}$
5. $2\frac{3}{5}$ $\frac{5}{13}$

See Example 2 **Divide. Write each answer in simplest form.**

6. $\frac{5}{6} \div 3$ $\frac{5}{18}$
7. $2\frac{1}{7} \div 1\frac{1}{4}$ $1\frac{5}{7}$
8. $\frac{5}{12} \div 5$ $\frac{1}{12}$
9. $1\frac{5}{8} \div \frac{3}{4}$ $2\frac{1}{6}$
10. $\frac{2}{3} \div \frac{1}{6}$ 4
11. $\frac{3}{10} \div 1\frac{2}{3}$ $\frac{9}{50}$
12. $\frac{4}{7} \div 1\frac{1}{7}$ $\frac{1}{2}$
13. $4 \div \frac{7}{8}$ $4\frac{4}{7}$

INDEPENDENT PRACTICE

See Example 1 **Find the reciprocal.**

14. $\frac{7}{8}$ $\frac{8}{7}$
15. $\frac{1}{10}$ $\frac{10}{1}$, or 10
16. $\frac{3}{8}$ $\frac{8}{3}$
17. $\frac{11}{12}$ $\frac{12}{11}$
18. $2\frac{5}{8}$ $\frac{8}{21}$
19. $\frac{8}{11}$ $\frac{11}{8}$
20. $\frac{5}{6}$ $\frac{6}{5}$
21. $\frac{6}{7}$ $\frac{7}{6}$
22. $\frac{2}{9}$ $\frac{9}{2}$
23. $5\frac{1}{4}$ $\frac{4}{21}$

See Example 2 **Divide. Write each answer in simplest form.**

24. $\frac{7}{8} \div 4$ $\frac{7}{32}$
25. $2\frac{3}{8} \div 1\frac{3}{4}$ $1\frac{5}{14}$
26. $\frac{8}{9} \div 12$ $\frac{2}{27}$
27. $9 \div \frac{3}{4}$ 12
28. $3\frac{5}{6} \div 1\frac{5}{9}$ $2\frac{13}{28}$
29. $\frac{9}{10} \div 3$ $\frac{3}{10}$
30. $2\frac{4}{5} \div 1\frac{5}{7}$ $1\frac{19}{30}$
31. $3\frac{1}{5} \div 1\frac{2}{7}$ $2\frac{22}{45}$
32. $\frac{5}{8} \div \frac{1}{2}$ $1\frac{1}{4}$
33. $1\frac{1}{2} \div 2\frac{1}{4}$ $\frac{2}{3}$
34. $\frac{7}{12} \div 2\frac{5}{8}$ $\frac{2}{9}$
35. $\frac{1}{8} \div 5$ $\frac{1}{40}$

PRACTICE AND PROBLEM SOLVING

CRCT GPS
Extra Practice p. 723

Multiply or divide. Write each answer in simplest form.

36. $2\frac{3}{4} \div 2\frac{1}{5}$ $1\frac{1}{4}$
37. $4\frac{4}{5} \div 2\frac{6}{7}$ $1\frac{17}{25}$
38. $\frac{3}{8} \cdot \frac{5}{12}$ $\frac{5}{32}$
39. $6 \cdot \frac{7}{9}$ $4\frac{2}{3}$
40. $3\frac{1}{7} \div 5$ $\frac{22}{35}$
41. $\frac{9}{14} \cdot \frac{1}{6}$ $\frac{3}{28}$

$12 \div \frac{3}{4} = 12 \cdot \frac{4}{3} = 16$

42. At Lina's restaurant, one serving of chili is $1\frac{1}{2}$ cups. The chef makes 48 cups of chili each night. How many servings of chili are in 48 cups? **32 servings**
43. Rhula bought 12 lb of raisins. She packed them into freezer bags so that each bag weighs $\frac{3}{4}$ lb. How many freezer bags did she pack? **16 bags**

Decide whether the fractions in each pair are reciprocals. If not, write the reciprocal of each fraction.

44. $\frac{1}{2}, 2$ yes
45. $\frac{3}{8}, \frac{16}{6}$ yes
46. $\frac{7}{9}, \frac{21}{27}$ $\frac{9}{7}, \frac{27}{21}$
47. $\frac{5}{6}, \frac{12}{10}$ yes
48. $1\frac{1}{2}, \frac{2}{3}$ yes
49. $\frac{2}{5}, \frac{4}{25}$ $\frac{5}{2}, \frac{25}{4}$
50. $\frac{3}{7}, 2\frac{1}{3}$ yes
51. $5, \frac{5}{1}$ $\frac{1}{5}, \frac{1}{5}$
52. Lisa had some wood that was $12\frac{1}{2}$ feet long. She cut it into 5 pieces that are equal in length. How long is each piece of wood? **$2\frac{1}{2}$ ft long or 30 in.**
53. **Critical Thinking** How can you recognize the reciprocal of a fraction?

53. The reciprocal of a fraction has the fraction's numerator as its denominator and has the fraction's denominator as its numerator. The product of a fraction and its reciprocal is 1.

Georgia Performance Standards

M6P3.a Organize and consolidate their mathematical thinking through communication.

M6P3.c Analyze and evaluate the mathematical thinking and strategies of others.

RETEACH 5-9

LESSON 5-9 **Reteach**
Dividing Fractions and Mixed Numbers

Two numbers are reciprocals if their product is 1. $\frac{2}{3}$ and $\frac{3}{2}$ are reciprocals because $\frac{2}{3} \cdot \frac{3}{2} = \frac{6}{6} = 1$.

Dividing by a fraction is the same as multiplying by its reciprocal.

$\frac{1}{4} \div 2 = \frac{1}{8}$ $\qquad$ $\frac{1}{4} \cdot \frac{1}{2} = \frac{1}{8}$

So, you can use reciprocals to divide by fractions.

To find $\frac{2}{3} \div 4$, first rewrite the expression as a multiplication expression using the reciprocal of the divisor, 4.

$\frac{2}{3} \cdot \frac{1}{4}$

Then use canceling to find the product in simplest form.

$\frac{2}{3} \div 4 = \frac{2}{3} \cdot \frac{1}{4} = \frac{1}{3} \cdot \frac{1}{2} = \frac{1}{6}$

To find $3\frac{1}{4} \div 1\frac{1}{2}$, first rewrite the expression using improper fractions.

$\frac{13}{4} \div \frac{3}{2}$

Next, write the expression as a multiplication expression.

$\frac{13}{4} \cdot \frac{2}{3}$

$3\frac{1}{4} \div 1\frac{1}{2} = \frac{13}{4} \div \frac{3}{2} = \frac{13}{4} \cdot \frac{2}{3} = \frac{13}{2} \cdot \frac{1}{3} = \frac{13}{6} = 2\frac{1}{6}$

Divide. Write each answer in simplest form.

1. $\frac{1}{4} \div 3$; $\frac{1}{4} \div \frac{3}{1}$; $\frac{1}{4} \cdot \frac{1}{3}$; $\frac{1}{12}$
2. $1\frac{1}{2} \div 1\frac{1}{4}$; $\frac{3}{2} \div \frac{5}{4}$; $\frac{3}{2} \cdot \frac{4}{5}$; $1\frac{1}{5}$
3. $\frac{3}{8} \div 2$; $\frac{3}{8} \div \frac{2}{1}$; $\frac{3}{8} \cdot \frac{1}{2}$; $\frac{3}{16}$
4. $2\frac{1}{3} \div 1\frac{3}{4}$; $\frac{7}{3} \div \frac{7}{4}$; $\frac{7}{3} \cdot \frac{4}{7}$; $1\frac{1}{3}$
5. $\frac{1}{5} \div 2$ $\frac{1}{10}$
6. $1\frac{1}{6} \div 2\frac{2}{3}$ $\frac{7}{16}$
7. $\frac{1}{8} \div 4$ $\frac{1}{32}$
8. $3\frac{1}{8} \div \frac{1}{2}$ $6\frac{1}{4}$

PRACTICE 5-9

LESSON 5-9 **Practice B**
Dividing Fractions and Mixed Numbers

Find the reciprocal.

1. $\frac{5}{7}$ $\frac{7}{5}$
2. $\frac{9}{8}$ $\frac{8}{9}$
3. $\frac{3}{5}$ $\frac{5}{3}$
4. $\frac{1}{10}$ 10
5. $\frac{4}{9}$ $\frac{9}{4}$
6. $\frac{13}{14}$ $\frac{14}{13}$
7. $1\frac{1}{3}$ $\frac{3}{4}$
8. $2\frac{4}{5}$ $\frac{5}{14}$
9. $3\frac{1}{6}$ $\frac{6}{19}$

Divide. Write each answer in simplest form.

10. $\frac{5}{6} \div 5$ $\frac{1}{6}$
11. $2\frac{3}{4} \div 1\frac{4}{7}$ $1\frac{3}{4}$
12. $\frac{7}{8} \div \frac{2}{3}$ $1\frac{5}{16}$
13. $3\frac{1}{4} \div 2\frac{3}{4}$ $1\frac{2}{11}$
14. $\frac{9}{10} \div 3$ $\frac{3}{10}$
15. $\frac{3}{4} \div 9$ $\frac{1}{12}$
16. $2\frac{6}{9} \div \frac{6}{7}$ $3\frac{1}{9}$
17. $\frac{5}{6} \div 2\frac{3}{10}$ $\frac{25}{69}$
18. $2\frac{1}{8} \div 3\frac{1}{4}$ $\frac{17}{26}$
19. The rope in the school gymnasium is $10\frac{1}{2}$ feet long. To make it easier to climb, the gym teacher tied a knot in the rope every $\frac{3}{4}$ foot. How many knots are in the rope? **14 knots**
20. Mr. Fulton bought $12\frac{1}{2}$ pounds of ground beef for the cookout. He plans on using $\frac{1}{4}$ pound of beef for each hamburger. How many hamburgers can he make? **50 hamburgers**
21. Mrs. Marks has $9\frac{1}{4}$ ounces of fertilizer for her plants. She plans on using $\frac{3}{4}$ ounce of fertilizer for each plant. How many plants can she fertilizer? **12 plants**

Multiply or divide. Write each answer in simplest form.

54. $\frac{11}{12} \cdot \frac{9}{10} \div 1\frac{1}{4}$ $\frac{33}{50}$ 55. $2\frac{3}{4} \cdot 1\frac{2}{3} \div 5$ $\frac{11}{12}$ 56. $1\frac{1}{2} \div \frac{3}{4} \cdot \frac{2}{5}$ $\frac{4}{5}$

57. $\frac{3}{4} \cdot \left(\frac{5}{7} \div \frac{1}{2}\right)$ $1\frac{1}{14}$ 58. $4\frac{2}{3} \div \left(6 \cdot \frac{3}{5}\right)$ $1\frac{8}{27}$ 59. $5\frac{1}{5} \cdot \left(3\frac{2}{5} \cdot 2\frac{1}{3}\right)$ $41\frac{19}{75}$

Life Science The bar graph shows the lengths of some species of snakes found in the United States. Use the bar graph for Exercises 60–62.

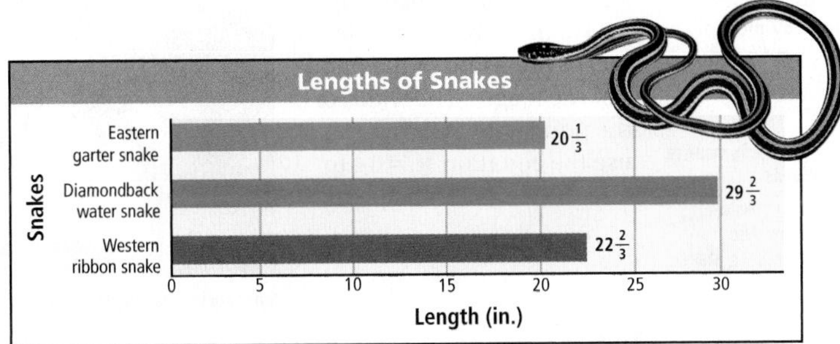

60. Is the length of the eastern garter snake greater than or less than $\frac{1}{2}$ yd? Explain. **Greater than, because $\frac{1}{2}$ yd = 18 in. and $20\frac{1}{3} > 18$.**

61. What is the average length of all the snakes? **$24\frac{2}{9}$ in.**

62. Jim measured the length of a rough green snake. It was $27\frac{1}{3}$ in. long. What would the average length of the snakes be if Jim's measure of a rough green snake were added? **25 in.**

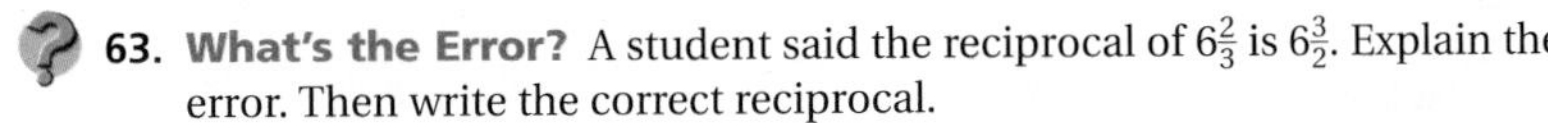

63. **What's the Error?** A student said the reciprocal of $6\frac{2}{3}$ is $6\frac{3}{2}$. Explain the error. Then write the correct reciprocal.

64. **Write About It** Explain how to divide fractions to find $\frac{3}{4} \div 2\frac{1}{3}$.

65. **Challenge** Evaluate the expression $\frac{(6-3)}{4} \div \frac{1}{8} \cdot 5$. **30**

CRCT Prep • GPS Support • Spiral Review

66. **Multiple Choice** A piece of wood was 12 feet long. Gene cut the wood pieces $\frac{2}{3}$ foot long. How many pieces did Gene have?

Ⓐ 4 Ⓑ 8 Ⓒ 16 **Ⓓ 18**

67. **Multiple Choice** Which product is NOT equal to 1?

Ⓕ $\frac{2}{3} \cdot \frac{3}{2}$ Ⓖ $8 \cdot \frac{1}{8}$ **Ⓗ $\frac{1}{9} \cdot \frac{9}{3}$** Ⓙ $\frac{2}{13} \cdot \frac{13}{2}$

Find the number of decimal places in each product. Then multiply. (Lesson 3-5)

68. 2.4 × 1.8 **2; 4.32** 69. 19 × 0.5 **1; 9.5** 70. 7.04 × 2.3 **3; 16.192** 71. 0.4 × 0.1 **2; 0.04**

Find each product. (Lesson 5-8)

72. $2\frac{2}{3} \cdot \frac{1}{8}$ $\frac{1}{3}$ 73. $\frac{1}{4} \cdot 3\frac{1}{2}$ $\frac{7}{8}$ 74. $1\frac{1}{4} \cdot 1\frac{2}{5}$ $1\frac{3}{4}$ 75. $2\frac{1}{5} \cdot 2\frac{2}{3}$ $5\frac{13}{15}$

CHALLENGE 5-9

LESSON 5-9 Challenge
Inching Across the U.S.A.

You can use a map and a ruler to find the distance between places. On the map below, for example, you measure that 2 inches separate Kansas City, Missouri, and Richmond, Virginia. The map scale shows that $\frac{1}{4}$ inch on the map equals 140 miles. So the distance between Kansas City and Richmond is 1,120 miles.

Calculations:
$2 \div \frac{1}{4} = 8$
8 × 140 = 1,120

Use the map and a ruler to find the distance in miles between each pair of cities.

1. Miami, Florida, and New Orleans, Louisiana **770 miles**
2. Denver, Colorado, and Los Angeles, California **1,015 miles**
3. Seattle, Washington, and Minneapolis, Minnesota **1,540 miles**
4. Washington, D.C., and Atlanta, Georgia **665 miles**
5. Oklahoma City, Oklahoma, and Pittsburgh, Pennsylvania **1,120 miles**
6. San Francisco, California, and Boston, Massachusetts **3,080 miles**

PROBLEM SOLVING 5-9

LESSON 5-9 Problem Solving
Dividing Fractions and Mixed Numbers

Write the correct answer in simplest form.

1. Horses are measured in units called *hands*. One inch equals $\frac{1}{4}$ hand. The average Clydesdale horse is $17\frac{1}{5}$ hands high. What is the horse's height in inches? in feet?
$68\frac{4}{5}$ inches; $5\frac{11}{15}$ feet

2. Cloth manufacturers use a unit of measurement called a *finger*. One finger is equal to $4\frac{1}{2}$ inches. If 25 inches are cut off a bolt of cloth, how many fingers of cloth were cut?
$5\frac{5}{9}$ fingers

3. People in England measure weights in units called *stones*. One pound equals $\frac{1}{14}$ of a stone. If a cat weighs $\frac{3}{4}$ stone, how many pounds does it weigh?
$10\frac{1}{2}$ pounds

4. The hiking trail is $\frac{9}{10}$ mile long. There are 6 markers evenly posted along the trail to direct hikers. How far apart are the markers placed?
$\frac{3}{20}$ mile

Choose the letter for the best answer.

5. A cake recipe calls for $1\frac{1}{2}$ cups of butter. One tablespoon equals $\frac{1}{16}$ cup. How many tablespoons of butter do you need to make the cake?
Ⓐ 24 tablespoons
B 8 tablespoons
C $\frac{3}{32}$ tablespoon
D 9 tablespoons

6. Printed letters are measured in units called *points*. One point equals $\frac{1}{72}$ inch. If you want the title of a paper you are typing on a computer to be $\frac{1}{2}$ inch tall, what type point size should you use?
F 144 point
Ⓖ 36 point
H $\frac{1}{36}$ point
J $\frac{1}{144}$ point

7. Phyllis bought 14 yards of material to make chair cushions. She cut the material into pieces $1\frac{3}{4}$ yards long to make each cushion. How many cushions did Phyllis make?
A 4 cushions
Ⓒ 8 cushions
B 6 cushions
D $24\frac{1}{2}$ cushions

8. Dry goods are sold in units called *pecks* and *bushels*. One peck equals $\frac{1}{4}$ bushel. If Peter picks $5\frac{1}{2}$ bushels of peppers, how many pecks of peppers did Peter pick?
F $1\frac{3}{8}$ pecks
H 20 pecks
G 11 pecks
Ⓙ 22 pecks

ONGOING ASSESSMENT and INTERVENTION

***Diagnose Before* the Lesson**
5-9 Warm Up, TE p. 270

***Monitor During* the Lesson**
5-9 Know-It Notebook
5-9 Questioning Strategies

***Assess After* the Lesson**
5-9 Lesson Quiz, TE p. 273

Answers

Possible answers:

63. The student did not write $6\frac{2}{3}$ as an improper fraction before switching the denominator and numerator in the fraction. The correct answer is $\frac{3}{20}$.

64. Find the reciprocal of $2\frac{1}{3}$, which is $\frac{3}{7}$. Then multiply $\frac{3}{4} \cdot \frac{3}{7} = \frac{9}{28}$.

TEST PREP DOCTOR + In Exercise 67, students will need to know that two fractions whose product is one are reciprocals. Students who recognize the reciprocals can eliminate choices **F** and **J.** Also, knowing that any whole number can be written as a fraction by placing it over 1 can help students eliminate choice **G.**

Journal

Have students compare and contrast division by fractions and mixed numbers with division by whole numbers and decimals. Have them support their comparisons with examples.

Power Presentations with PowerPoint®

5-9 Lesson Quiz

Find the reciprocal.

1. $\frac{1}{11}$ $\frac{11}{1}$ 2. $\frac{8}{13}$ $\frac{13}{8}$

Divide. Write each answer in simplest form.

3. $\frac{4}{7} \div 20$ $\frac{1}{35}$

4. $3\frac{1}{2} \div 2\frac{1}{2}$ $\frac{7}{5}$, or $1\frac{2}{5}$

5. Rhonda put $2\frac{3}{4}$ pounds of pecans into $\frac{1}{4}$-pound bags. How many bags did Rhonda fill? **11 bags**

Also available on transparency

5-10 Organizer

Pacing: Traditional 1 day
Block $\frac{1}{2}$ day

Objective: Students solve equations by multiplying and dividing fractions.

Online Edition
Tutorial Videos, Interactivities

Countdown to CRCT Week 11

Power Presentations with PowerPoint®

Warm Up

Solve.

1. $x - 5 = 17$ $x = 22$
2. $5x = 125$ $x = 25$
3. $x + 12 = 86$ $x = 74$
4. $9x = 108$ $x = 12$

Problem of the Day

Stephen forgot his locker number, but he remembered that the sum of the digits is 11 and that the digits are all odd numbers. The locker numbers are from 1 to 120. What is Stephen's locker number? 119

Also available on transparency

Math Humor

Needing 75 cents is like solving the equation $\frac{4}{3}x = 1$. In both cases, the solution is 3 quarters.

Georgia Performance Standards

M6N1.e Multiply and divide fractions and mixed numbers.

M6N1.g Solve problems involving fractions, decimals, and percents.

M6A3 Students will evaluate algebraic expressions, including those with exponents, and solve simple one-step equations using each of the four basic operations.

M6P1.c Apply and adapt a variety of appropriate strategies to solve problems.

M6P1.d Monitor and reflect on the process of mathematical problem solving.

5-10 Solving Fraction Equations: Multiplication and Division

Learn to solve equations by multiplying and dividing fractions.

M6N1.g Solve problems involving fractions. Also, M6N1.e, M6A3, M6P1.c, M6P1.d.

Josef is building a fish pond for koi in his backyard. He makes the width of the pond $\frac{2}{3}$ of the length. The width of the pond is 14 feet. You can use the equation $\frac{2}{3}\ell = 14$ to find the length of the pond.

Small koi in a backyard pond usually grow 2 to 4 inches per year.

Remember!
Dividing by a number is the same as multiplying by its reciprocal.

EXAMPLE 1 Solving Equations by Multiplying and Dividing

Solve each equation. Write the answer in simplest form.

A $\frac{2}{3}\ell = 14$

$\frac{2}{3}\ell = 14$

$\frac{2}{3}\ell \div \frac{2}{3} = 14 \div \frac{2}{3}$ *Divide both sides of the equation by $\frac{2}{3}$.*

$\frac{2}{3}\ell \cdot \frac{3}{2} = 14 \cdot \frac{3}{2}$ *Multiply by $\frac{3}{2}$, the reciprocal of $\frac{2}{3}$.*

$\ell = 14 \cdot \frac{3}{2}$

$\ell = \frac{14 \cdot 3}{1 \cdot 2}$

$\ell = \frac{42}{2}$, or 21

B $2x = \frac{1}{3}$

$2x = \frac{1}{3}$

$\frac{2x}{1} \cdot \frac{1}{2} = \frac{1}{3} \cdot \frac{1}{2}$ *Multiply both sides by the reciprocal of 2.*

$x = \frac{1 \cdot 1}{3 \cdot 2}$

$x = \frac{1}{6}$ *The answer is in simplest form.*

C $\frac{5x}{6} = 4$

$\frac{5x}{6} = 4$

$\frac{5x}{6} \div \frac{5}{6} = \frac{4}{1} \div \frac{5}{6}$ *Divide both sides by $\frac{5}{6}$.*

$\frac{5x}{6} \cdot \frac{6}{5} = \frac{4}{1} \cdot \frac{6}{5}$ *Multiply by the reciprocal of $\frac{5}{6}$.*

$x = \frac{24}{5}$, or $4\frac{4}{5}$

1 Introduce

Alternate Opener

EXPLORATION

Solving Fraction Equations: Multiplication and Division

You can use a number line to solve fraction equations. Look at the reasoning used to solve the equation $\frac{1}{2}n = 50$.

If $\frac{1}{2}$ of a number is 50, . . .
then the number must be 100.

0 50 100
0 $\frac{1}{2}$ 1

$\frac{1}{2}n = 50$
$n = 100$

Complete the number line to solve each equation.

1. $\frac{1}{2}n = 125$ (0, 125, n; 0, $\frac{1}{2}$, 1)
2. $\frac{1}{3}n = 12$ (0, 12, n; 0, $\frac{1}{3}$, $\frac{2}{3}$, 1)
3. $\frac{3}{4}n = 60$ (0, 60, n; 0, $\frac{1}{4}$, $\frac{1}{2}$, $\frac{3}{4}$, 1)
4. $\frac{2}{3}n = 20$ (0, 20, n; 0, $\frac{1}{3}$, $\frac{2}{3}$, 1)

Think and Discuss

5. **Describe** a real-world situation that could be represented by the equation in number 3.
6. **Discuss** another way of solving equations that contain fractions and involve multiplication.

Motivate

Have students explain how to solve the equation $7b = 35$. Divide both sides of the equation by 7. Then ask students, keeping that in mind, to tell how they would solve the equation $\frac{2}{3}d = 10$. Divide both sides of the equation by $\frac{2}{3}$, or multiply both sides by $\frac{3}{2}$, the reciprocal of $\frac{2}{3}$.

Explorations and answers are provided in *Alternate Openers: Explorations Transparencies.*

EXAMPLE 2 PROBLEM SOLVING APPLICATION

Dexter makes dog biscuits for the animal shelter. He makes $\frac{3}{4}$ of a recipe and uses 15 cups of powdered milk. How many cups of powdered milk are in the recipe?

1 Understand the Problem

The **answer** will be the number of cups of powdered milk in the recipe.

List the **important information:**

- He makes $\frac{3}{4}$ of the recipe.
- He uses 15 cups of powdered milk.

2 Make a Plan

You can write and solve an equation. Let x represent the number of cups in the recipe.

He uses 15 cups, which is three-fourths of the amount in the recipe.
$15 = \frac{3}{4}x$

3 Solve

$15 = \frac{3}{4}x$

$15 \cdot \frac{4}{3} = \frac{3}{4}x \cdot \frac{4}{3}$ *Multiply both sides by $\frac{4}{3}$, the reciprocal of $\frac{3}{4}$.*

$\frac{\overset{5}{\cancel{15}}}{1} \cdot \frac{4}{\underset{1}{\cancel{3}}} = x$ *Simplify. Then multiply.*

$20 = x$

There are 20 cups of powdered milk in the recipe.

4 Look Back

Check $15 = \frac{3}{4}x$

$15 \stackrel{?}{=} \frac{3}{4}(20)$ *Substitute 20 for x.*

$15 \stackrel{?}{=} \frac{\overset{15}{\cancel{60}}}{\underset{1}{\cancel{4}}}$ *Multiply and simplify.*

$15 \stackrel{?}{=} 15$ ✓ *20 is the solution.*

Georgia LINK Life Science

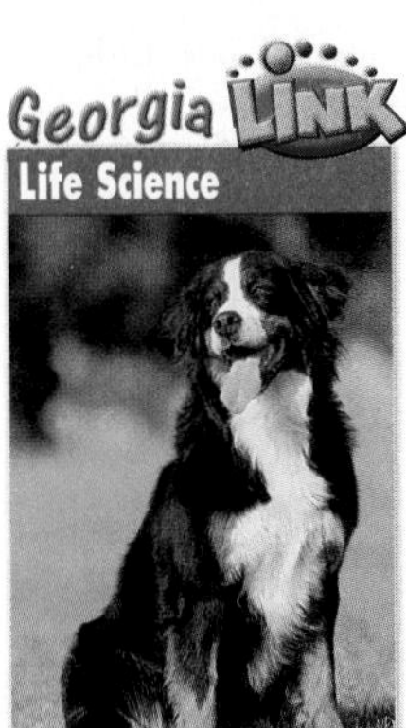

The University of Georgia College of Veterinary Medicine runs a program called Dog Doctors. Veterinary students bring Bernese Mountain dogs to schools across Georgia to educate students about pet care.

Think and Discuss

GPS M6P1.d, M6P2.c

1. **Explain** whether $\frac{2}{3}x = 4$ is the same as $\frac{2}{3} = 4x$.
2. **Tell** how you know which numbers to divide by in the following equations: $\frac{2}{3}x = 4$ and $\frac{4}{5} = 8x$.

COMMON ERROR ALERT

Some students may solve the problem $\frac{2}{5}x = 4$ and get $x = 4 \cdot \frac{2}{5}$. Remind students that they need to multiply by the reciprocal.

Power Presentations with PowerPoint®

Additional Examples

Example 1

Solve each equation. Write the answer in simplest form.

A. $\frac{3}{5}\ell = 25$ $\ell = \frac{125}{3}$, or $41\frac{2}{3}$

B. $7x = \frac{2}{5}$ $x = \frac{2}{35}$

C. $\frac{5y}{8} = 6$ $y = \frac{48}{5}$, or $9\frac{3}{5}$

Example 2

Dexter makes $\frac{2}{3}$ of a recipe, and he uses 12 cups of powdered milk. How many cups of powdered milk are in the recipe? 18 cups

Also available on transparency

Answers to *Think and Discuss*

1. Possible answer: No, if $\frac{2}{3}x = 4$, $x = 6$. If $\frac{2}{3} = 4x$, $x = \frac{1}{6}$.
2. With $\frac{2}{3}x = 4$, divide by $\frac{2}{3}$ because that's the number that the variable is multiplied by; with $\frac{4}{5} = 8x$, divide by 8 because that's the number that the variable is being multiplied by.

2 Teach

Guided Instruction

In this lesson, students learn to solve equations by multiplying and dividing fractions. First teach students to solve equations where they multiply by a reciprocal to solve. Then teach students to translate a word problem into an equation that can be solved by multiplying by a reciprocal. Have students check the answers in Example 1 by substituting the values for each variable.

Reaching All Learners

Through Cooperative Learning

Have students work in groups to solve equations involving variables multiplied by fractions and mixed numbers. Each student writes an equation on a strip of paper. Then, as a group, students solve and check the solutions to each equation, explaining each step as they work through the problems.

3 Close

Summarize

Review using reciprocals to solve equations. Explain that solving any equation containing multiplication involves dividing both sides of the equation by the number that is being multiplied by the variable. If that number happens to be a fraction, then the rule for dividing by a fraction applies. In other words, both sides of the equation are multiplied by the reciprocal of that fraction.

5-10 Exercises

Assignment Guide

If you finished Example 1 assign:
Average 1–4, 16–21, 41–51
Advanced 6–13, 22–23, 41–51

If you finished Example 2 assign:
Average 1–35, 41–51
Advanced 1–31, 36–51

Homework Quick Check

Quickly check key concepts.
Exercises: 8, 12, 18, 20, 22, 26

Math Background

Consider $\frac{2}{3} \div \frac{3}{5}$. To understand how this can be rewritten as $\frac{2}{3} \cdot \frac{5}{3}$, follow these steps:

Steps	Explanation
$\frac{2}{3} \div \frac{3}{5} = \frac{2}{3} \cdot \frac{5}{3} \cdot \frac{3}{5} \div \frac{3}{5}$	This is valid because $\frac{5}{3} \cdot \frac{3}{5} = \frac{15}{15} = 1$.
$\frac{2}{3} \div \frac{3}{5} = \frac{2}{3} \cdot \frac{5}{3}$	This is valid because $\frac{3}{5} \div \frac{3}{5} = 1$.

Georgia Performance Standards

M6P3.a Organize and consolidate their mathematical thinking through communication.

M6P4.c Recognize and apply mathematics in contexts outside of mathematics.

5-10 Exercises

Georgia Performance Standards
M6P3.a, M6P4.c

go.hrw.com
Homework Help Online
KEYWORD: MR7 5-10
Parent Resources Online
KEYWORD: MR7 Parent

GUIDED PRACTICE

See Example 1

Solve each equation. Write the answer in simplest form.

1. $\frac{3}{4}z = 12$ $z = 16$
2. $4n = \frac{3}{5}$ $n = \frac{3}{20}$
3. $\frac{2x}{3} = 5$ $x = 7\frac{1}{2}$
4. $2c = \frac{9}{10}$ $c = \frac{9}{20}$

See Example 2

5. **School** In PE class, $\frac{3}{8}$ of the students want to play volleyball. If 9 students want to play volleyball, how many students are in the class? 24

INDEPENDENT PRACTICE

See Example 1

Solve each equation. Write the answer in simplest form.

6. $3t = \frac{2}{7}$ $t = \frac{2}{21}$
7. $\frac{1}{3}x = 3$ $x = 9$
8. $\frac{3r}{5} = 9$ $r = 15$
9. $8t = \frac{4}{5}$ $t = \frac{1}{10}$
10. $\frac{4}{5}a = 1$ $a = 1\frac{1}{4}$
11. $\frac{y}{4} = 5$ $y = 20$
12. $2b = \frac{6}{7}$ $b = \frac{3}{7}$
13. $\frac{7}{9}j = 10$ $j = 12\frac{6}{7}$

See Example 2

14. Jason uses 2 cans of paint to paint $\frac{1}{2}$ of his room. How many cans of paint will he use to paint the whole room? 4 cans
15. Cassandra baby-sits for $\frac{4}{5}$ of an hour and earns \$8. What is her hourly rate? \$10

PRACTICE AND PROBLEM SOLVING

CRCT GPS
Extra Practice p. 723

Solve each equation. Write the answer in simplest form.

16. $m = \frac{3}{8} \cdot 4$ $m = 1\frac{1}{2}$
17. $\frac{3y}{5} = 6$ $y = 10$
18. $4z = \frac{7}{10}$ $z = \frac{7}{40}$
19. $t = \frac{4}{5} \cdot 20$ $t = \frac{80}{5}$ or 16
20. $\frac{3}{5}a = \frac{3}{5}$ $a = 1$
21. $\frac{1}{6}b = 2\frac{1}{3}$ $b = 14$
22. $5c = \frac{2}{3} \div \frac{2}{3}$ $c = \frac{1}{5}$
23. $\frac{3}{4}x = 7$ $x = 9\frac{1}{3}$
24. $\frac{1}{2} = \frac{w}{4}$ $w = 2$
25. $8 = \frac{2n}{3}$ $n = 12$
26. $\frac{1}{4} \cdot \frac{1}{2} = 4d$ $d = \frac{1}{32}$
27. $2y = \frac{4}{5} \div \frac{3}{5}$ $y = \frac{2}{3}$

Write each equation. Then solve, and check the solution.

28. A number n is divided by 4 and the quotient is $\frac{1}{2}$. $\frac{n}{4} = \frac{1}{2}$; $n = 2$
29. A number n is multiplied by $1\frac{1}{2}$ and the product is 9. $\frac{3}{2}n = 9$; $n = 6$
30. A recipe for a loaf of bread calls for $\frac{3}{4}$ cup of oatmeal.
    a. How much oatmeal do you need if you make half the recipe? $\frac{3}{8}$ cup
    b. How much oatmeal do you need if you double the recipe? $1\frac{1}{2}$ cups
31. **Entertainment** Connie rode the roller coaster at the amusement park. After 3 minutes, the ride was $\frac{3}{4}$ complete. How long did the entire ride take? 4 minutes
32. Zac moved $\frac{1}{5}$ of the things from his old bedroom to his new dorm room in $32\frac{1}{2}$ minutes. How long will it take in minutes for him to move all of his things to his new dorm room? $162\frac{1}{2}$ minutes
33. A dress pattern requires $3\frac{1}{8}$ yards of fabric. Jody wants to make matching dresses for the girls in her sewing club so she purchased $34\frac{3}{8}$ yards of fabric. How many dresses can Jody make using this pattern? 11 dresses

RETEACH 5-10

LESSON 5-10 **Reteach**
Solving Fraction Equations: Multiplication and Division

You can write related facts using multiplication and division.

$3 \cdot 4 = 12 \qquad 4 = 12 \div 3$

You can use related facts to solve equations.

A. $\frac{2}{3} \cdot x = 12$

Think: $12 \div \frac{2}{3} = x$
$x = 12 \cdot \frac{3}{2}$
$x = \frac{12}{1} \cdot \frac{3}{2}$
$x = \frac{36}{2}$
$x = 18$

Check: $\frac{2}{3} \cdot x = 12$
$\frac{2}{3} \cdot 18 \stackrel{?}{=} 12$ Substitute
$\frac{2}{3} \cdot \frac{18}{1} \stackrel{?}{=} 12$
$\frac{36}{3} \stackrel{?}{=} 12$
$12 = 12$ ✓

B. $\frac{2x}{5} = 3$
$\frac{2}{5} \cdot x = 3$

Think: $3 \div \frac{2}{5} = x$
$x = 3 \cdot \frac{5}{2}$
$x = \frac{3}{1} \cdot \frac{5}{2}$
$x = \frac{15}{2}$
$x = 7\frac{1}{2}$

Check: $\frac{2x}{5} = 3$
$\frac{2}{5} \cdot x \stackrel{?}{=} 3$
$\frac{2}{5} \cdot \frac{15}{2} \stackrel{?}{=} 3$ Substitute
$\frac{30}{10} \stackrel{?}{=} 3$
$3 = 3$ ✓

Use related facts to solve each equation. Then check each answer.

1. $\frac{1}{4} \cdot x = 3$ $x = 12$ ✓
2. $\frac{3x}{4} = 2$ $x = 2\frac{2}{3}$ ✓
3. $\frac{3}{5} \cdot x = \frac{2}{3}$ $x = 1\frac{1}{9}$ ✓
4. $\frac{1}{3} \cdot x = 6$ $x = 18$ ✓
5. $\frac{2x}{5} = 1$ $x = 2\frac{1}{2}$ ✓
6. $\frac{1}{8} \cdot x = 3$ $x = 24$ ✓

PRACTICE 5-10

LESSON 5-10 **Practice B**
Solving Fraction Equations: Multiplication and Division

Solve each equation. Write the answer in simplest form. Check your answers.

1. $\frac{1}{4}x = 6$ $x = 24$; $\frac{1}{4} \cdot 24 = 6$ ✓
2. $2t = \frac{4}{7}$ $t = \frac{2}{7}$; $2 \cdot \frac{2}{7} = \frac{4}{7}$ ✓
3. $\frac{3}{5}a = 3$ $a = 5$; $\frac{3}{5} \cdot 5 = 3$ ✓
4. $\frac{r}{6} = 8$ $r = 48$; $\frac{48}{6} = 8$ ✓
5. $\frac{2b}{9} = 4$ $b = 18$; $\frac{(2 \cdot 18)}{9} = 4$ ✓
6. $3y = \frac{4}{5}$ $y = \frac{4}{15}$; $3 \cdot \frac{4}{15} = \frac{4}{5}$ ✓
7. $\frac{2}{3}d = 5$ $d = 7\frac{1}{2}$; $\frac{2}{3} \cdot 7\frac{1}{2} = 5$ ✓
8. $2f = \frac{1}{6}$ $f = \frac{1}{12}$; $2 \cdot \frac{1}{12} = \frac{1}{6}$ ✓
9. $4q = \frac{2}{9}$ $q = \frac{1}{18}$; $4 \cdot \frac{1}{18} = \frac{2}{9}$ ✓
10. $\frac{1}{2}s = 2$ $s = 4$; $\frac{1}{2} \cdot 4 = 2$ ✓
11. $\frac{h}{7} = 5$ $h = 35$; $\frac{35}{7} = 5$ ✓
12. $\frac{1}{4}c = 9$ $c = 36$; $\frac{1}{4} \cdot 36 = 9$ ✓
13. $5g = \frac{5}{6}$ $g = \frac{1}{6}$; $5 \cdot \frac{1}{6} = \frac{5}{6}$ ✓
14. $3k = \frac{1}{9}$ $k = \frac{1}{27}$; $3 \cdot \frac{1}{27} = \frac{1}{9}$ ✓
15. $\frac{3x}{5} = 6$ $x = 10$; $\frac{(3 \cdot 10)}{5} = 6$ ✓
16. It takes 3 buckets of water to fill $\frac{1}{3}$ of a fish tank. How many buckets are needed to fill the whole tank? 9 buckets
17. Jenna got 12, or $\frac{3}{5}$, of her answers on the test right. How many questions were on the test? 20 questions
18. It takes Charles 2 minutes to run $\frac{1}{4}$ of a mile. How long will it take Charles to run a mile? 8 minutes

Life Science

The northwest corner of Madagascar is home to black lemurs. These primates live in groups of 7–10, and they have an average life span of 20–25 years. Much of their habitat is being destroyed by human agricultural activity.

34. **Multi-Step** Alder cut 3 pieces of fabric from a roll. Each piece of fabric she cut is $1\frac{1}{2}$ yd long. She has 2 yards of fabric left on the roll. How much fabric was on the roll before she cut it? $6\frac{1}{2}$ yards

35. **Life Science** Sasha's book report is about animals in Madagascar. She writes 10 pages, which represents $\frac{1}{3}$ of her report, about lemurs. How many more pages does Sasha have to write to complete her book report? 20 more pages

36. **Critical Thinking** How can you tell, without solving the equation $\frac{1}{2}x = 4\frac{7}{8}$, that x is greater that $4\frac{7}{8}$? One-half of a number is $4\frac{7}{8}$, so the whole number must be greater than $4\frac{7}{8}$.

Use the circle graph for Exercises 37 and 38.

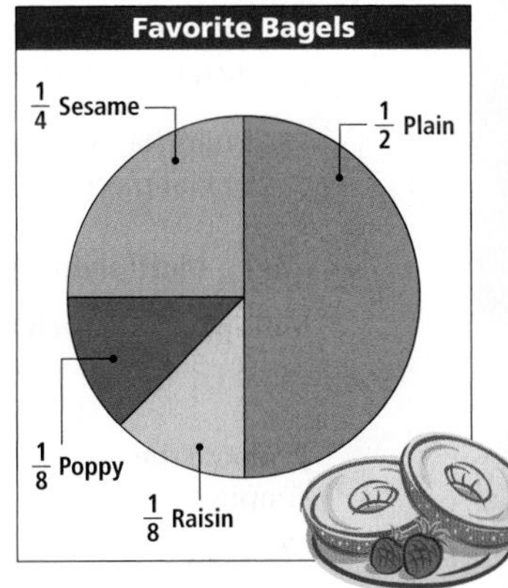

37. The circle graph shows the results of a survey of people who were asked to choose their favorite kind of bagel.
    a. One hundred people chose plain bagels as their favorite kind of bagel. How many people were surveyed in all? 200 people
    b. One-fifth of the people who chose sesame bagels also chose plain cream cheese as their favorite spread. How many people chose plain cream cheese? (*Hint*: Use the answer to part **a** to help you solve this problem.) 10 people

38. **What's the Question?** If the answer is 25 people, what is the question?

39. **Write About It** Explain how to solve $\frac{3}{5}x = 4$.

40. **Challenge** Solve $2\frac{3}{4}n = \frac{11}{12}$ $\frac{1}{3}$

CRCT Prep • GPS Support • Spiral Review

41. **Multiple Choice** Solve $\frac{3}{10}x = 9$.

    (A) $x = 15$ (B) $x = 30$ (C) $x = 60$ (D) $x = 90$

42. **Multiple Choice** Which of the following is a solution to $4x = \frac{3}{4}$?

    (F) $x = \frac{3}{16}$ (G) $x = \frac{3}{4}$ (H) $x = 3$ (J) $x = 5\frac{1}{3}$

43. **Gridded Response** What value of y is a solution to $\frac{4}{5}y = 28$? 35

Find the GCF of each set of numbers. (Lesson 4-3)

44. 6 and 15 3
45. 18 and 56 2
46. 12, 16, and 32 4
47. 24, 63, and 81 3

Divide. Write each answer in simplest form. (Lesson 5-9)

48. $\frac{2}{3} \div \frac{1}{3}$ 2
49. $\frac{9}{10} \div \frac{3}{4}$ $1\frac{1}{5}$
50. $2\frac{3}{8} \div \frac{1}{4}$ $9\frac{1}{2}$
51. $1\frac{1}{4} \div 2\frac{1}{3}$ $\frac{15}{28}$

CHALLENGE 5-10

LESSON 5-10 Challenge
Crawly Creature Equations

A millipede called the *Illacme plenipes* holds the record for the creature with the most legs—750! However, most millipedes have only 30 legs. Shown below are some other many-legged creatures.

Let [millipede] = the number of legs most millipedes have. Use this information to solve the equations and find how many legs each other crawly creature has.

$\frac{8}{15}$ • [millipede] = [caterpillar]

$\frac{3}{5}$ • [caterpillar] • $\frac{5}{6}$ = [spider]

$\frac{3}{4}$ • [spider] = [insect]

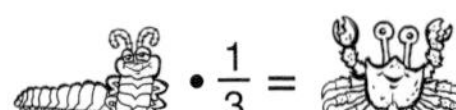

[caterpillar] • $\frac{1}{3}$ = [crab]

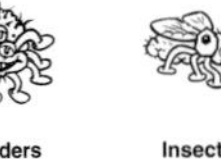
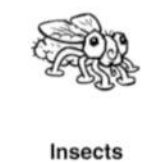

Caterpillars	Spiders	Insects	Crabs
16 legs	8 legs	6 legs	10 legs

PROBLEM SOLVING 5-10

LESSON 5-10 Problem Solving
Solving Fraction Equations: Multiplication and Division

Solve.

1. The number of T-shirts is multiplied by $\frac{1}{2}$ and the product is 18. Write and solve an equation for the number of T-shirts, where t represents the number of T-shirts.
   $t \bullet \frac{1}{2} = 18; t = 36$

2. The number of students is divided by 18 and the quotient is $\frac{1}{6}$. Write and solve an equation for the number of students, where s represents the number of students.
   $s \div 18 = \frac{1}{6}; s = 3$

3. The number of players is multiplied by $2\frac{1}{2}$ and the product is 25. Write and solve an equation for the number of players, where p represents the number of players.
   $p \bullet 2\frac{1}{2} = 25; p = 10$

4. The number of chairs is divided by $\frac{1}{4}$ and the quotient is 12. Write and solve an equation for the number of chairs, where c represents the number of chairs.
   $c \div \frac{1}{4} = 12; c = 3$

Circle the letter of the correct answer.

5. Paco bought 10 feet of rope. He cut it into several $\frac{5}{6}$-foot pieces. Which equation can you use to find how many pieces of rope Paco cut?
   A $\frac{5}{6} \div 10 = x$
   B $\frac{5}{6} \div x = 10$
   (C) $10 \div x = \frac{5}{6}$
   D $10x = \frac{5}{6}$

6. Each square on the graph paper has an area of $\frac{4}{9}$ square inch. What is the length and width of each square?
   F $\frac{1}{9}$ inch
   (G) $\frac{2}{3}$ inch
   H $\frac{2}{9}$ inch
   J $\frac{1}{3}$ inch

7. Which operation should you use to solve the equation $6x = \frac{3}{8}$?
   A addition
   B subtraction
   C multiplication
   (D) division

8. A fraction divided by $\frac{2}{3}$ is equal to $1\frac{1}{4}$. What is that fraction?
   F $\frac{1}{3}$
   (G) $\frac{5}{6}$
   H $\frac{1}{4}$
   J $\frac{1}{2}$

Ongoing Assessment and Intervention

Diagnose **Before** the Lesson
5-10 Warm Up, TE p. 274

Monitor **During** the Lesson
5-10 Know-It Notebook
5-10 Questioning Strategies

Assess **After** the Lesson
5-10 Lesson Quiz, TE p. 277

Answers

38. Possible answer: How many people chose raisin bagels as their favorite kind of bagel?

39. Possible answer: Divide both sides of the equation by $\frac{3}{5}$. To divide by $\frac{3}{5}$, you can multiply by $\frac{5}{3}$, the reciprocal of $\frac{3}{5}$. Write the answer, $\frac{20}{3}$, in simplest form, $6\frac{2}{3}$.

Test Prep Doctor In Exercises 41 and 42, remind students that each solution involves dividing both sides of the equation by the coefficient of the variable, which is the same as multiplying by its reciprocal.

Journal

Have students explain and give an example of how to solve an equation whose solution involves multiplication of both sides by a reciprocal.

Power Presentations with PowerPoint®

5-10 Lesson Quiz

Solve each equation. Write the answer in simplest form.

1. $3x = \frac{1}{8}$ $x = \frac{1}{24}$
2. $\frac{1}{4}x = 4$ $x = 16$
3. $\frac{3}{7}x = 14$ $x = \frac{98}{3}$ or $32\frac{2}{3}$
4. $\frac{y}{7} = 9$ $y = 63$
5. Rebecca used 3 pt of paint to paint $\frac{1}{4}$ of the trim in her bedroom. How many pints will Rebecca use for the trim in the entire bedroom? 12

Also available on transparency

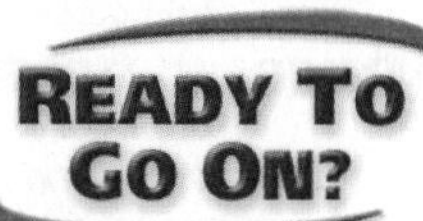

SECTION 5B READY TO GO ON?

Organizer

Objective: Assess students' mastery of concepts and skills in Lessons 5-6 through 5-10.

Resources

Assessment Resources
Section 5B Quiz

Test & Practice Generator
One-Stop Planner®

INTERVENTION

Resources

***Ready to Go On? Intervention and Enrichment* Worksheets**

***Ready to Go On?* CD-ROM**

***Ready to Go On?* Online**

my.hrw.com

CHAPTER 5
SECTION 5B

READY TO GO ON?

Quiz for Lessons 5-6 Through 5-10

5-6 Multiplying Fractions by Whole Numbers

1. Multiply $4 \cdot \frac{2}{3}$. Write your answer in simplest form. $2\frac{2}{3}$
2. Michelle ordered 5 lb of fruit for a family picnic. Of that fruit, $\frac{1}{3}$ was watermelon. How much of the fruit was watermelon? $1\frac{2}{3}$ lb.
3. Philip has 35 comic books. Of those comics, $\frac{2}{10}$ take place in space. How many of Philip's comic books take place in space? 7

5-7 Multiplying Fractions

Multiply. Write each answer in simplest form.

4. $\frac{2}{7} \cdot \frac{3}{4}$ $\frac{3}{14}$
5. $\frac{3}{5} \cdot \frac{2}{3}$ $\frac{2}{5}$
6. $\frac{7}{12} \cdot \frac{4}{5}$ $\frac{7}{15}$

Evaluate the expression $t \cdot \frac{1}{8}$ for each value of t. Write the answer in simplest form.

7. $t = \frac{4}{9}$ $\frac{1}{18}$
8. $t = \frac{4}{5}$ $\frac{1}{10}$
9. $t = \frac{2}{3}$ $\frac{1}{12}$

5-8 Multiplying Mixed Numbers

Multiply. Write each answer in simplest form.

10. $\frac{1}{4} \cdot 2\frac{1}{3}$ $\frac{7}{12}$
11. $1\frac{1}{6} \cdot \frac{2}{3}$ $\frac{7}{9}$
12. $\frac{7}{8} \cdot 2\frac{2}{3}$ $2\frac{1}{3}$

Find each product. Write the answer in simplest form.

13. $2\frac{1}{4} \cdot 1\frac{1}{6}$ $2\frac{5}{8}$
14. $1\frac{2}{3} \cdot 2\frac{1}{5}$ $3\frac{2}{3}$
15. $3 \cdot 4\frac{2}{7}$ $12\frac{6}{7}$

5-9 Dividing Fractions and Mixed Numbers

Find the reciprocal.

16. $\frac{2}{7}$ $\frac{7}{2}$
17. $\frac{5}{12}$ $\frac{12}{5}$
18. $\frac{3}{5}$ $\frac{5}{3}$

Divide. Write each answer in simplest form.

19. $\frac{3}{5} \div 4$ $\frac{3}{20}$
20. $1\frac{3}{10} \div 3\frac{1}{4}$ $\frac{2}{5}$
21. $1\frac{1}{5} \div 2\frac{1}{3}$ $\frac{18}{35}$

5-10 Solving Fraction Equations: Multiplication and Division

Solve each equation.

22. $\frac{2y}{3} = 10$ 15
23. $6p = \frac{3}{4}$ $\frac{1}{8}$
24. $\frac{2x}{3} = 9$ $13\frac{1}{2}$
25. Michael has a black cat and a gray kitten. The black cat weighs 12 pounds. The gray kitten weighs $\frac{3}{5}$ the weight of the black cat. How much does the gray kitten weigh? $7\frac{1}{5}$ pounds

Ready to Go On?

READY TO GO ON?

Diagnose and Prescribe

NO INTERVENE | **YES ENRICH**

Ready to Go On? Intervention	*Ready to Go On? Intervention,* Section 5B — Worksheets	CD-ROM	Online
Lesson 5-6	5-6 Intervention	Activity 5-6	Diagnose and Prescribe Online
Lesson 5-7	5-7 Intervention	Activity 5-7	
Lesson 5-8	5-8 Intervention	Activity 5-8	
Lesson 5-9	5-9 Intervention	Activity 5-9	
Lesson 5-10	5-10 Intervention	Activity 5-10	

***Ready to Go On? Enrichment,* Section 5B**

Worksheets

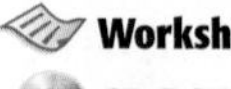

CD-ROM

Online

MULTI-STEP TEST PREP

CHAPTER 5

Something's Fishy! Maria and Victor are setting up a 20-gallon aquarium. They want to choose fish for the aquarium using the rule "1 inch of fish per gallon of water." This means that the total length of the fish in their tank should be no more than 20 inches.

1. Maria considers getting one of each fish shown in the table. Estimate the total length of the fish. Could she add more fish? Explain.
2. Victor would like to have a neon tetra and a guppy in the tank. What is the total length of the two fish?
3. What is the total length of the remaining fish that Victor could add to the tank? Explain.
4. Is there enough room left for Victor to add 4 clown barbs to the tank? Why or why not?
5. Maria and Victor decide to fill the tank with neon tetras only. Write and solve an equation to find out how many neon tetras they can put in the tank.

Common Aquarium Fish	
Name	**Length (in.)**
Zebra danio	$2\frac{1}{2}$
Neon tetra	$1\frac{1}{4}$
Clown barb	$4\frac{7}{16}$
Platy	$1\frac{3}{4}$
Guppy	$2\frac{3}{8}$

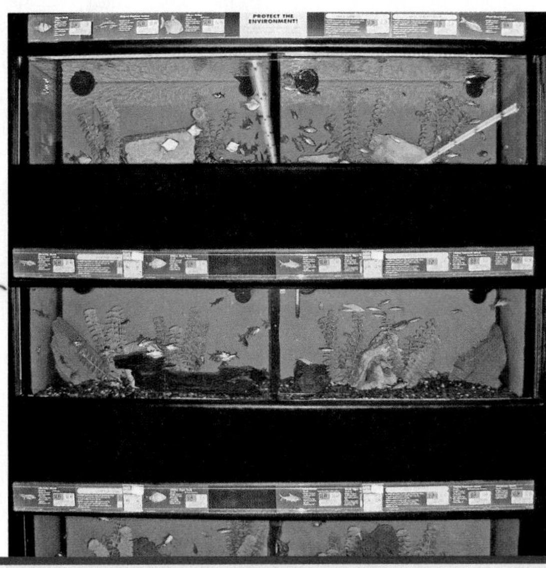

Multi-Step Test Prep

MULTI-STEP TEST PREP

CHAPTER 5

Organizer

Objective: Assess students' ability to apply concepts and skills in Chapter 5 in a real-world format.

 **Online Edition**

Resources

 ***Middle School Assessments***
www.mathtekstoolkit.org

Problem	Text reference
1	Lesson 5-2
2	Lesson 5-2
3	Lesson 5-4
4	Lesson 5-6
5	Lesson 5-10

Answers

1. $12\frac{1}{2}$ in.; the rule of 1 inch of fish per gallon of water will allow her to add $7\frac{1}{2}$ more inches of fish.
2. $3\frac{5}{8}$ in.
3. $16\frac{3}{8}$ in.; according to the rule, it would be $20 - 3\frac{5}{8}$, or $16\frac{3}{8}$.
4. No; 4 clown barbs would measure $17\frac{3}{4}$ in., which is more than the $16\frac{3}{8}$ in. allowed under the rule.
5. $1\frac{1}{4}n = 20$, $n = 16$

INTERVENTION

Scaffolding Questions

1. How can you estimate the sum of the lengths? Round each mixed number to the nearest $\frac{1}{2}$. Round each mixed number in the table. $2\frac{1}{2}$, 1, $4\frac{1}{2}$, 2, $2\frac{1}{2}$
2. What mixed numbers should you add? $1\frac{1}{4}$ and $2\frac{3}{8}$ What are the steps in adding these mixed numbers? Find a common denominator (8) and write $1\frac{1}{4}$ as $1\frac{2}{8}$. Add the fractions, and then add the whole numbers.
3. Will you add or subtract to solve this problem? subtract
What subtraction problem should you solve? $20 - 3\frac{5}{8}$ How can you rename 20? $19\frac{8}{8}$
4. How can you find the total length of four clown barbs? Multiply: $4 \times 4\frac{7}{16}$. How do you find this product? Write it as $4 \times (4 + \frac{7}{16})$ and use the Distributive Property
5. What should the variable represent in this problem? the number of neon tetras What equation should you solve? $1\frac{1}{4}x = 20$ or $\frac{5}{4}x = 20$ How do you solve the equation? Divide both sides by $\frac{5}{4}$.

Game Time

Organizer

Objective: Participate in games to practice and apply skills learned in Chapter 5.

 **Online Edition**

Resources

 ***Chapter 5 Resource Book***
Puzzles, Twisters & Teasers

Fraction Riddles

Purpose: To apply using operations with fractions to solving riddles

Discuss Ask students to explain how the riddle in problem 1 works. Is the problem as difficult as it sounds? Explain.

Possible answer:

When you multiply the first nine factors, $\frac{1}{2} \cdot \frac{2}{3} \cdot \frac{3}{4} \cdot \frac{4}{5} \cdot \frac{5}{6} \cdot \frac{7}{8} \cdot \frac{8}{9} \cdot \frac{9}{10}$, you find that the product simplifies to $\frac{1}{10}$ because each factor in the denominator, except for 10, is also in the numerator. $\frac{1}{10}$ of 1000 is 100.

Extend Challenge students to create their own fraction riddles. Have them use problems 1–5 as models. Check students' work.

Fraction Bingo

Purpose: To practice using fraction operations and equivalent fractions in a game format

Discuss When students get a "bingo," have them demonstrate for the class how each winning solution was obtained.

Extend Have students create new expression cards for each solution on their bingo cards. Use the new cards to play again.

Game Time

Fraction Riddles

1. What is the value of one-half of two-thirds of three-fourths of four-fifths of five-sixths of six-sevenths of seven-eighths of eight-ninths of nine-tenths of one thousand? **100**

2. What is the next fraction in the sequence below?
$\frac{1}{12}, \frac{1}{6}, \frac{1}{4}, \frac{1}{3}, \ldots$ **$\frac{5}{12}$; The sequence is $\frac{1}{12}, \frac{2}{12} = \frac{1}{6}, \frac{3}{12} = \frac{1}{4}, \frac{4}{12} = \frac{1}{3}, \ldots$**

3. I am a three-digit number. My hundreds digit is one-third of my tens digit. My tens digit is one-third of my ones digit. What number am I? **139**

4. A *splorg* costs three-fourths of a dollar plus three-fourths of a *splorg*. How much does a *splorg* cost? **$3**

5. How many cubic inches of dirt are in a hole that measures $\frac{1}{3}$ feet by $\frac{1}{4}$ feet by $\frac{1}{2}$ feet?
None; there is no dirt in a hole.

Fraction Bingo

The object is to be the first player to cover five squares in a row horizontally, vertically, or diagonally.

One person is the caller. On each of the caller's cards, there is an expression containing fractions. When the caller draws a card, he or she reads the expression aloud for the players.

The players must find the value of the expression. If a square on the player's card has that value or a fraction equivalent to that value, they cover the square.

The first player to cover five squares in a row is the winner. Take turns being the caller. A variation can be played in which the winner is the first person to cover all their squares.

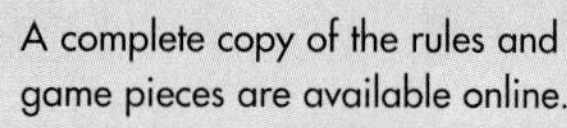

A complete copy of the rules and game pieces are available online.

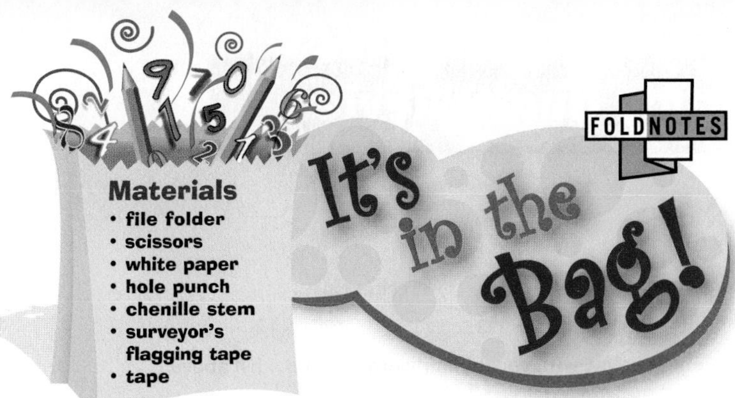

PROJECT

Flipping over Fractions

Make a flip-flop book to take notes and work sample problems related to fraction operations.

Directions

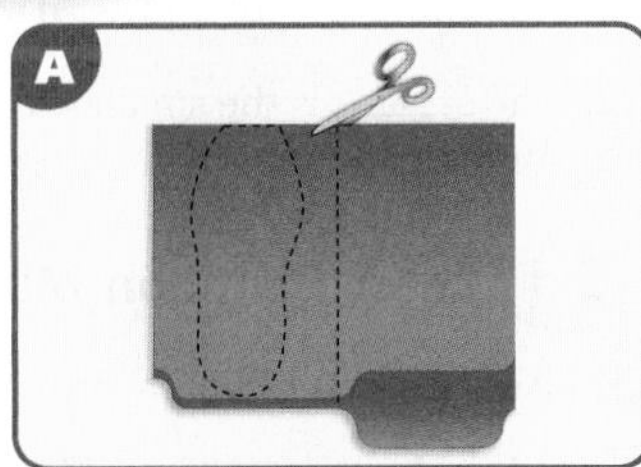

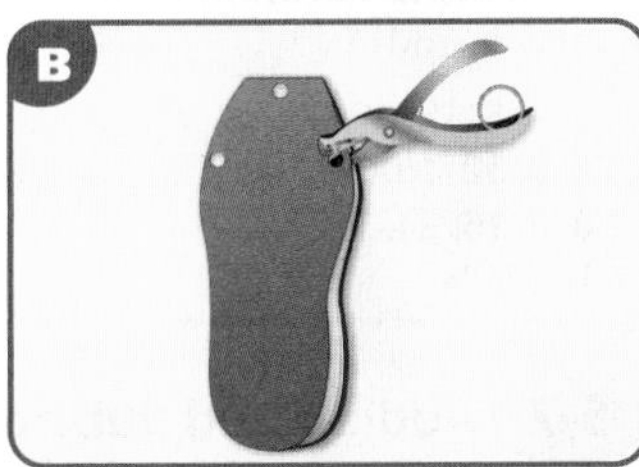

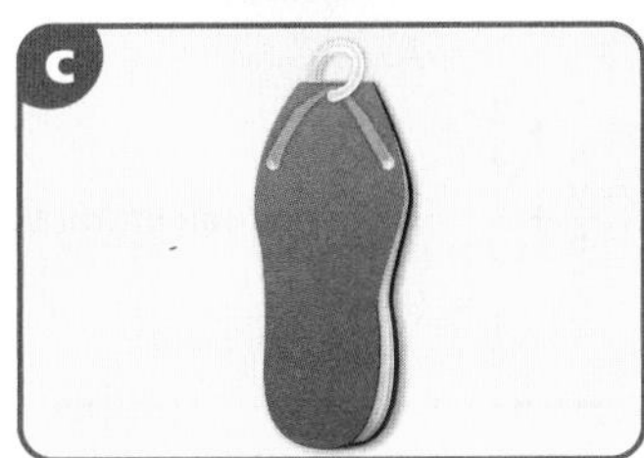

1. Cut the folder in half from the fold to the edge. Then cut out a flip-flop shape, with the "toe" of the flip-flop along the folded edge. **Figure A**

2. Cut about ten flip-flop shapes out of the white paper. They should be slightly smaller than the flip-flop you cut out of the file folder.

3. Put the white flip-flops inside the file-folder flip-flop. Punch a hole at the top through all the layers. Also punch holes at the sides of the flip-flip cover. These side holes should go through only the cover. **Figure B**

4. Insert the chenille stem into the hole at the top, make a loop, and trim. Insert the surveyor's flagging tape through the loop, and insert the ends into the holes at the sides of the flip-flop. Tape the surveyor's flagging tape to the back of the cover to hold it in place. **Figure C**

Write the chapter number and title on the flip-flop. Then use the inside pages to work problems from the chapter. Choose problems that will help you remember the most important concepts.

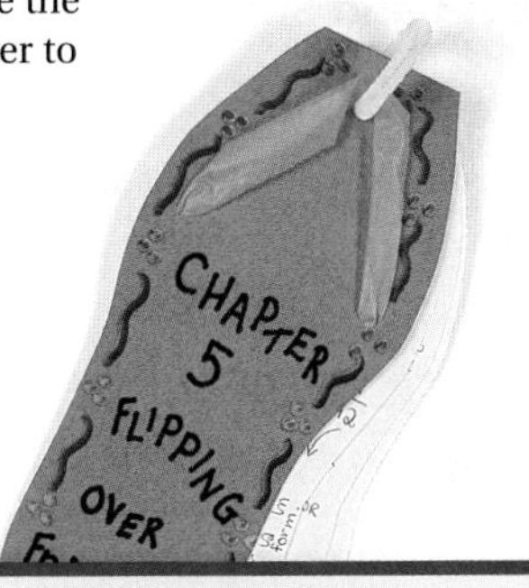

Organizer

Objective: Make a flip-flop book in which to record sample problems related to fraction operations.

Materials: file folder, scissors, white paper, hole punch, chenille stick, surveyor's flagging tape (about 10 in. long), tape, markers

Online Edition

Using the Page

Preparing the Materials
Have students work in pairs. Give each pair one file folder to share. Once the folder has been cut in two, each student can take one of the halves to make his or her own flip-flop book.

Making the Project
Remind students that the holes at the sides of the flip-flop should go through only the top layer (i.e., the cover).

Extending the Project
Have students turn over their flip-flop book and use the other side to record additional sample problems.

You can buy surveyor's flagging tape at home-improvement stores. It's perfect for this project because it's inexpensive and comes in bright colors. If you have trouble finding it, you can use ribbon or yarn instead. Speaking of colors, file folders are available in every color of the rainbow. We also like to provide students with gel markers so that the text really pops.

CHAPTER 5 Study Guide: Review

Organizer

Objective: Help students organize and review key concepts and skills presented in Chapter 5.

Online Edition
Multilingual Glossary

Resources

PuzzlePro®
One-Stop Planner®

***Multilingual Glossary* Online**

go.hrw.com
KEYWORD: MR7 Glossary

Lesson Tutorial Videos
CD-ROM

Test & Practice Generator
One-Stop Planner®

Answers

1. reciprocals
2. least common denominator
9. $\frac{33}{40}$
10. $\frac{3}{4}$
11. $\frac{1}{15}$
12. $\frac{5}{24}$
13. $4\frac{7}{10}$
14. $3\frac{1}{18}$
15. $\frac{7}{15}$

CHAPTER 5

Study Guide: Review

Study Guide: Review

Vocabulary

least common denominator (LCD) 234
least common multiple (LCM) 228
reciprocals 270

Complete the sentences below with vocabulary words from the list above.

1. Two numbers are ___?___ if their product is 1.
2. The ___?___ is the smallest number that is a common multiple of two or more denominators.

5-1 Least Common Multiple (pp. 228–231)

GPS M6N1.c

EXAMPLE

- **Find the least common multiple (LCM) of 4, 6, and 8.**

  4: 4, 8, 12, 16, 20, 24, 28, . . .
  6: 6, 12, 18, 24, 30, . . .
  8: 8, 16, 24, 32, . . .
  LCM: 24

EXERCISES

Find the least common multiple (LCM).

3. 3, 5, and 10
4. 6, 8, and 16
5. 3, 9, and 27
6. 4, 12, and 30
7. 25 and 45
8. 12, 22, and 30

5-2 Adding and Subtracting with Unlike Denominators (pp. 234–237)

GPS M6N1.d

EXAMPLE

- $\frac{7}{9} + \frac{2}{3}$

  $\frac{7}{9} + \frac{2}{3}$ *Write equivalent fractions. Add.*

  $\frac{7}{9} + \frac{6}{9} = \frac{13}{9} = 1\frac{4}{9}$

EXERCISES

Add or subtract. Write each answer in simplest form.

9. $\frac{1}{5} + \frac{5}{8}$
10. $\frac{1}{6} + \frac{7}{12}$
11. $\frac{13}{15} - \frac{4}{5}$
12. $\frac{7}{8} - \frac{2}{3}$

5-3 Adding and Subtracting Mixed Numbers (pp. 238–241)

GPS M6N1.d

EXAMPLE

- **Find the difference. Write the answer in simplest form.**

  $5\frac{5}{8} - 3\frac{1}{6}$

  $5\frac{15}{24} - 3\frac{4}{24}$ *Write equivalent fractions.*

  $2\frac{11}{24}$ *Subtract.*

EXERCISES

Find each sum or difference. Write the answer in simplest form.

13. $1\frac{3}{10} + 3\frac{2}{5}$
14. $4\frac{5}{9} - 1\frac{1}{2}$
15. Angela had $\frac{7}{10}$ gallon of paint. She used $\frac{1}{3}$ gallon for a project. How much paint did she have left?

5-4 Regrouping to Subtract Mixed Numbers (pp. 244–247)

GPS M6N1.d

EXAMPLE

■ **Subtract.**

$4\frac{7}{10} - 2\frac{9}{10}$

$3\frac{17}{10} - 2\frac{9}{10}$ *Regroup $4\frac{7}{10}$. Subtract.*

$1\frac{8}{10}$

$1\frac{4}{5}$

EXERCISES

Subtract. Write each answer in simplest form.

16. $7\frac{2}{9} - 3\frac{5}{9}$ **17.** $3\frac{1}{5} - 1\frac{7}{10}$

18. $8\frac{7}{12} - 2\frac{11}{12}$ **19.** $5\frac{3}{8} - 2\frac{3}{4}$

20. $11\frac{6}{7} - 4\frac{13}{14}$ **21.** $10 - 8\frac{7}{8}$

22. Georgette needs 8 feet of ribbon to decorate gifts. She has $3\frac{1}{4}$ feet of ribbon. How many more feet of ribbon does Georgette need?

5-5 Solving Fraction Equations: Addition and Subtraction (pp. 248–251)

GPS M6N1.g

EXAMPLE

■ **Solve $n + 2\frac{5}{7} = 8$.**

$n + 2\frac{5}{7} - 2\frac{5}{7} = 8 - 2\frac{5}{7}$

$n = 8 - 2\frac{5}{7}$

$n = 7\frac{7}{7} - 2\frac{5}{7}$

$n = 5\frac{2}{7}$

EXERCISES

Solve each equation. Write the solution in simplest form.

23. $x - 12\frac{3}{4} = 17\frac{2}{5}$ **24.** $t + 6\frac{11}{12} = 21\frac{5}{6}$

25. $3\frac{2}{3} = m - 1\frac{3}{4}$ **26.** $5\frac{2}{3} = p + 2\frac{2}{9}$

27. $y - 1\frac{2}{3} = 3\frac{4}{5}$ **28.** $4\frac{2}{5} + j = 7\frac{7}{10}$

29. Jon poured $1\frac{1}{2}$ oz of lemon juice onto a salad. He has $5\frac{1}{2}$ oz lemon juice left in the bottle. How many ounces of lemon juice were in the bottle before Jon poured some on the salad?

5-6 Multiplying Fractions by Whole Numbers (pp. 254–257)

GPS M6N1.g

EXAMPLE

■ **Multiply $3 \cdot \frac{3}{5}$. Write your answer in simplest form.**

$3 \cdot \frac{3}{5} = \frac{3}{5} + \frac{3}{5} + \frac{3}{5} = \frac{9}{5}$ or $1\frac{4}{5}$

EXERCISES

Multiply. Write each answer in simplest form.

30. $5 \cdot \frac{1}{7}$ **31.** $2 \cdot \frac{3}{8}$ **32.** $3 \cdot \frac{6}{7}$

33. $4 \cdot \frac{5}{8}$ **34.** $6 \cdot \frac{1}{2}$ **35.** $2 \cdot \frac{3}{5}$

36. There are 105 members of the high school band. Of these members, $\frac{1}{5}$ play percussion instruments. How many members play percussion?

Study Guide: Review

Answers

16. $3\frac{2}{3}$
17. $1\frac{1}{2}$
18. $5\frac{2}{3}$
19. $2\frac{5}{8}$
20. $6\frac{13}{14}$
21. $1\frac{1}{8}$
22. $4\frac{3}{4}$ feet
23. $30\frac{3}{20}$
24. $14\frac{11}{12}$
25. $5\frac{5}{12}$
26. $3\frac{4}{9}$
27. $5\frac{7}{15}$
28. $3\frac{3}{10}$
29. 7 oz
30. $\frac{5}{7}$
31. $\frac{3}{4}$
32. $2\frac{4}{7}$
33. $2\frac{1}{2}$
34. 3
35. $1\frac{1}{5}$
36. 21 members

Answers

37. $\frac{1}{3}$
38. $\frac{15}{28}$
39. $\frac{1}{10}$
40. $\frac{7}{25}$
41. $\frac{5}{81}$
42. $\frac{3}{14}$
43. $\frac{2}{5}$
44. $\frac{9}{10}$
45. $1\frac{1}{4}$
46. 2
47. $\frac{4}{21}$
48. $\frac{3}{20}$
49. $\frac{5}{9}$
50. 8 times
51. $a = \frac{1}{8}$
52. $b = 2$
53. $m = 17\frac{1}{2}$
54. $g = \frac{2}{15}$
55. $r = 10\frac{4}{5}$
56. $s = 50$
57. $p = \frac{1}{9}$
58. $j = 1\frac{53}{64}$

Study Guide: Review

5-7 Multiplying Fractions (pp. 260–263)

GPS M6N1.e

EXAMPLE

- **Multiply. Write the answer in simplest form.**

$\frac{3}{4} \cdot \frac{1}{3}$ *Multiply. Then simplify.*

$\frac{3 \cdot 1}{4 \cdot 3} = \frac{3}{12} = \frac{1}{4}$

EXERCISES

Multiply. Write each answer in simplest form.

37. $\frac{5}{6} \cdot \frac{2}{5}$
38. $\frac{5}{7} \cdot \frac{3}{4}$
39. $\frac{4}{5} \cdot \frac{1}{8}$
40. $\frac{7}{10} \cdot \frac{2}{5}$
41. $\frac{1}{9} \cdot \frac{5}{9}$
42. $\frac{1}{4} \cdot \frac{6}{7}$
43. Andrew's hockey team won $\frac{4}{5}$ of their games. Andrew scored in $\frac{2}{3}$ of the games his team won. In what fraction of his team's games did Andrew score?

5-8 Multiplying Mixed Numbers (pp. 264–267)

GPS M6N1.e

EXAMPLE

- **Multiply. Write the answer in simplest form.**

$\frac{2}{5} \cdot 1\frac{2}{3} = \frac{2}{5} \cdot \frac{5}{3} = \frac{10}{15} = \frac{2}{3}$

EXERCISES

Multiply. Write each answer in simplest form.

44. $\frac{2}{5} \cdot 2\frac{1}{4}$
45. $\frac{3}{4} \cdot 1\frac{2}{3}$
46. $3\frac{1}{3} \cdot \frac{3}{5}$

5-9 Dividing Fractions and Mixed Numbers (pp. 270–273)

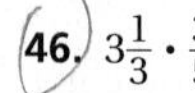

GPS M6N1.e

EXAMPLE

- **Divide. Write the answer in simplest form.**

$\frac{3}{4} \div 6 = \frac{3 \cdot 1}{4 \cdot 6} = \frac{3}{24} = \frac{1}{8}$

EXERCISES

Divide. Write each answer in simplest form.

47. $\frac{4}{7} \div 3$
48. $\frac{3}{10} \div 2$
49. $1\frac{1}{3} \div 2\frac{2}{5}$
50. Beverly needs to measure $2\frac{2}{3}$ cups of bread crumbs. She has a $\frac{1}{3}$ cup measuring scoop. How many times must she fill the $\frac{1}{3}$ cup measuring scoop to get $2\frac{2}{3}$ cups of bread crumbs?

5-10 Solving Fraction Equations: Multiplication and Division (pp. 274–277)

GPS M6N1.g

EXAMPLE

- **Solve the equation.**

$\frac{4}{5}n = 12$

$\frac{4}{5}n \div \frac{4}{5} = 12 \div \frac{4}{5}$ *Divide both sides by $\frac{4}{5}$.*

$\frac{4}{5}n \cdot \frac{5}{4} = 12 \cdot \frac{5}{4}$ *Multiply by the reciprocal.*

$n = \frac{60}{4} = 15$

EXERCISES

Solve each equation.

51. $4a = \frac{1}{2}$
52. $\frac{3b}{4} = 1\frac{1}{2}$
53. $\frac{2m}{7} = 5$
54. $6g = \frac{4}{5}$
55. $\frac{5}{6}r = 9$
56. $\frac{s}{8} = 6\frac{1}{4}$
57. $6p = \frac{2}{3}$
58. $\frac{8j}{9} = 1\frac{5}{8}$

CHAPTER 5

Find the least common multiple (LCM).

1. 10 and 15 **30**
2. 4, 6, and 18 **36**
3. 9, 10, and 12 **180**
4. 6, 15, and 20 **60**

Add or subtract. Write the answer in simplest form.

5. $4\frac{1}{9} - 2\frac{4}{9}$ **$1\frac{2}{3}$**
6. $1\frac{7}{10} + 3\frac{3}{4}$ **$5\frac{9}{20}$**
7. $\frac{2}{3} - \frac{3}{8}$ **$\frac{7}{24}$**
8. $2\frac{1}{3} - \frac{5}{6}$ **$1\frac{1}{2}$**
9. $4 + 2\frac{2}{7}$ **$6\frac{2}{7}$**
10. $\frac{1}{12} + \frac{5}{6}$ **$\frac{11}{12}$**
11. $\frac{3}{8} + \frac{3}{4}$ **$1\frac{1}{8}$**
12. $\frac{5}{6} - \frac{2}{5}$ **$\frac{13}{30}$**
13. On Saturday, Cecelia ran $3\frac{3}{7}$ miles. On Sunday, she ran $4\frac{5}{6}$ miles. How much farther did Cecelia run on Sunday than on Saturday? **$1\frac{17}{42}$ miles**
14. Michael studied social studies for $\frac{3}{4}$ of an hour, Spanish for $1\frac{1}{2}$ hours, and math for $1\frac{1}{4}$ hours. How many hours did Michael spend studying all three subjects? **$3\frac{1}{2}$ hours**
15. Quincy needs $6\frac{1}{3}$ feet of rope to tie down the things he is hauling in his truck. He finds a 9 foot long rope in his garage. How much extra rope does Quincy have? **$2\frac{2}{3}$ feet**

Find the reciprocal.

16. $\frac{3}{5}$ **$\frac{5}{3}$**
17. $\frac{7}{11}$ **$\frac{11}{7}$**
18. $\frac{5}{9}$ **$\frac{9}{5}$**
19. $\frac{1}{8}$ **$\frac{8}{1}$, or 8**

Multiply or divide. Write the answer in simplest form.

20. $\frac{3}{7} \cdot \frac{4}{9}$ **$\frac{4}{21}$**
21. $1\frac{3}{8} \cdot \frac{6}{11}$ **$\frac{3}{4}$**
22. $2\frac{1}{4} \cdot 2\frac{2}{3}$ **6**
23. $\frac{7}{8} \div 2$ **$\frac{7}{16}$**
24. $3\frac{1}{3} \div 1\frac{5}{12}$ **$2\frac{6}{17}$**
25. $\frac{4}{5} \cdot 1\frac{1}{3}$ **$1\frac{1}{15}$**
26. $3\frac{1}{8} \div 1\frac{1}{4}$ **$2\frac{1}{2}$**
27. $\frac{3}{8} \cdot \frac{2}{3}$ **$\frac{1}{4}$**

Evaluate the expression $n \cdot \frac{1}{4}$ for each value of n. Write the answer in simplest form.

28. $n = \frac{7}{8}$ **$\frac{7}{32}$**
29. $n = \frac{2}{5}$ **$\frac{1}{10}$**
30. $n = \frac{8}{9}$ **$\frac{2}{9}$**
31. $n = \frac{4}{11}$ **$\frac{1}{11}$**
32. Twenty-four students tried out for the cheerleading squad. Only $\frac{5}{6}$ of the students will be chosen. How many students will be chosen for the squad? **20 students**
33. A recipe for granola bars require $1\frac{1}{2}$ cups of flour. How much flour is needed to make a triple batch of granola bars? **$4\frac{1}{2}$ cups**

Solve each equation. Write the solution in simplest form.

34. $3r = \frac{9}{10}$ **$r = \frac{3}{10}$**
35. $n + 3\frac{1}{6} = 12$ **$n = 8\frac{5}{6}$**
36. $5\frac{5}{6} = x - 3\frac{1}{4}$ **$x = 9\frac{1}{12}$**
37. $\frac{2}{5}t = 9$ **$t = 22\frac{1}{2}$**
38. $\frac{4}{5}m = 7$ **$m = 8\frac{3}{4}$**
39. $y - 15\frac{3}{5} = 2\frac{1}{3}$ **$y = 17\frac{14}{15}$**
40. Jessica purchased a bag of cat food. She feeds her cat 1 cup of cat food each day. After 7 days, she has fed her cat $\frac{2}{3}$ of the food in the bag. How many cups of food were in the bag of cat food when Jessica bought it? **$10\frac{1}{2}$ cups**

Chapter Test

Organizer

Objective: Assess students' mastery of concepts and skills in Chapter 5.

Online Edition

Resources

Assessment Resources

Chapter 5 Tests
- Free Response (Levels A, B, C)
- Multiple Choice (Levels A, B, C)
- Performance Assessment

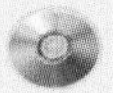

***IDEA Works!* CD-ROM**
Modified Chapter 5 Test

Test & Practice Generator
One-Stop Planner®

Organizer

Objective: Provide opportunities to learn and practice common test-taking strategies.

Online Edition

Resources

 ***CRCT Prep* Workbook**

 ***CRCT Prep* CD-ROM**

 ***CRCT Practice* Online**

go.hrw.com
KEYWORD: MR7 TestPrep

This test tackler focuses on how to correctly fill in a grid when answering a gridded-response item. Students often solve the test item correctly, but improper completion of the answer grid results in an incorrect response. This strategy involves students reviewing the rules for how to fill in a grid and then looking at filled-in grids and identifying why the response was marked as incorrect.

Gridded Response: Write Gridded Responses

When responding to a test item that has an answer grid, you must fill out the grid correctly, or the item will be marked as incorrect.

EXAMPLE 1

Gridded Response: Simplify the expression (8 × 3) − 5 × (6 − 3).

$(8 \times 3) - 5 \times (6 - 3)$

$24 - 5 \times 3$ *Perform operations within parentheses.*

$24 - 15$ *Multiply.*

9 *Subtract.*

The expression simplifies to 9.

- Use a pencil to write your answer in the answer boxes at the top of the grid.
- The boxes can be answered starting in the far left column, or in the far right column, but not in the middle.
- Write only one digit in each box. Do not leave a blank box in the middle of an answer.
- Shade the correct bubble below your written digit.

EXAMPLE 2

Gridded Response: Evaluate $2\frac{1}{4} + 1\frac{1}{4} + 3\frac{3}{4}$.

$2\frac{1}{4} + 1\frac{1}{4} + 3\frac{3}{4}$

$6\frac{5}{4}$ *Add the fractions and then add the whole numbers.*

$6\frac{5}{4} = 6 + 1\frac{1}{4} = 7\frac{1}{4}$ or 7.25 or $\frac{29}{4}$ *Simplify.*

- You cannot fill in mixed numbers. You must fill in the answer as an improper fraction or a decimal.
- Use a pencil to write your answer in the answer boxes at the top of the grid.
- Write only one digit or symbol in each box. On some grids, the fraction bar and the decimal point have a special box. If so, write your fraction or decimal around it correctly. Do not leave a blank box in the middle of an answer.
- Shade the correct bubble below your written digit.

Test Tackler

When filling out a grid be sure to use a pencil and completely fill in the bubbles directly below each digit or symbol you wrote.

Read each sample and then answer the questions that follow.

4		/	2	5

Sample A
A student divided two fractions and got $\frac{4}{25}$ as a result. Then the student filled in the grid as shown.

1. What error did the student make when filling in the grid?
2. Explain how to fill in the answer correctly.

	2	.	9	

Sample B
A student solved the equation $x + 3.1 = 5$, and found that $x = 2.9$. This answer is displayed in the grid below.

3. What error did the student make when filling in the grid?
4. Explain how to fill in the answer correctly.

Sample C
A student correctly simplified the expression $6\frac{7}{8} + 1\frac{3}{8} - 2\frac{5}{8}$. Then the student filled in the grid as shown.

5. What answer does the grid show?
6. Explain why you cannot grid a mixed number.
7. Write the answer $5\frac{5}{8}$ in two forms that could be entered in the grid correctly.

Sample D
A student wrote the standard form of the decimal one and twenty-five hundredths and then filled in the grid as shown.

8. What error did the student make when filling in the grid?
9. Explain how to fill in the answer correctly.

Remind students that they can also write their answer in the grid by placing the last digit of the answer in the box on the right. Reassure students that it is okay for the first box to be blank as long as the last box is filled and there are no blanks in between numbers.

Answers

1. There is a blank before the fraction bar. Blanks cannot be used in the middle of an answer.
2. Fill in the answer, starting from the left or right, leaving no space in the middle of an answer.
3. The answer is centered in the grid, and the decimal point is missing.
4. Possible answers: Write the 2 as the first digit, and then place the decimal point in the next box. Then place the 9 in the next box.
5. The student gridded the number $\frac{55}{8}$.
6. Possible answers: You cannot use a blank in the middle of an answer to represent the space between the whole number and the fraction, and without a blank, the answer is read as a fraction, not a mixed number.
7. 5.625; $\frac{45}{8}$
8. You cannot place the decimal point in the same box with a number, and you cannot shade two bubbles in the same column.
9. Possible answers: Write the 1 in the first column and the decimal point in the second column. Write the 2 and the 5 in the third and fourth columns, respectively. Remember to shade each bubble below the written digits and the decimal point.

Organizer

Objective: Provide review and practice for Chapters 1–5 and standardized tests.

Online Edition

Resources

Assessment Resources
Chapter 5 Cumulative Test

CRCT Prep **Workbook**

CRCT Prep **CD-ROM**

CRCT Practice **Online**

go.hrw.com
KEYWORD: MR7 TestPrep

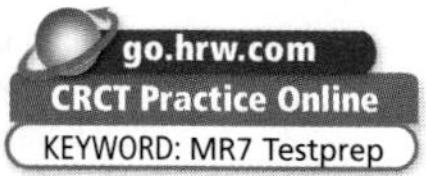

CRCT Prep

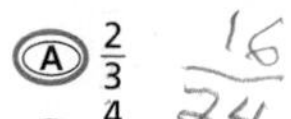

Cumulative Assessment, Chapters 1–5

Multiple Choice

1. Which number is less than $\frac{3}{4}$?
   - (A) $\frac{2}{3}$
   - (B) $\frac{4}{5}$
   - (C) $\frac{5}{6}$
   - (D) $\frac{9}{10}$

2. Mr. Ledden's briefcase has a mass of 9.4 kilograms on Earth. How much would his briefcase weigh on Jupiter?

Gravitational Pull of Planets (Compared with Earth)	
Planet	**Gravitational Pull**
Mercury	0.38
Venus	0.91
Mars	0.38
Jupiter	2.54
Saturn	0.93
Neptune	1.2

   - (F) 8.554 kg
   - (G) 11.28 kg
   - (H) 11.94 kg
   - (J) 23.876 kg

3. Brandon's family is planning a trip from Dallas to San Antonio. Dallas is about 272 miles from San Antonio. If Brandon's dad drives an average of 60 miles per hour, about how long will the trip take?
   - (A) 3 hours
   - (B) 5 hours
   - (C) 6 hours
   - (D) 7 hours

4. What is the value of 5^4?
   - (F) 9
   - (G) 20
   - (H) 625
   - (J) 1,000

5. A recipe calls for $\frac{1}{4}$ cup of sugar and $\frac{2}{3}$ cup of flour. How much more flour than sugar is needed for this recipe?
   - (A) $\frac{1}{7}$ cup
   - (B) $\frac{5}{12}$ cup
   - (C) $\frac{1}{2}$ cup
   - (D) $\frac{3}{4}$ cup

6. Maggie needs $15\frac{3}{8}$ yards of blue rope, $24\frac{1}{3}$ yards of white rope, and $8\frac{3}{4}$ yards of red rope. About how many yards of rope does she need in all?
   - (F) 38 yards
   - (G) 45 yards
   - (H) 48 yards
   - (J) 55 yards

7. Let d represent the number of dogs that Max walks in 1 day. Which expression shows the number of dogs Max walks in 7 days?
   - (A) $7 + d$
   - (B) $d - 7$
   - (C) $7d$
   - (D) $\frac{d}{7}$

8. Charlie eats $\frac{5}{8}$ of a pizza. One-fifth of the pizza he eats is covered with mushrooms. How much of Charlie's pizza is covered with mushrooms?
   - (F) $\frac{1}{8}$ pizza
   - (G) $\frac{5}{13}$ pizza
   - (H) $\frac{1}{5}$ pizza
   - (J) $3\frac{1}{8}$ pizza

9. Which of the following sets of decimals is ordered from least to greatest?
   - (A) 3.8, 3.89, 3.08, 3.9
   - (B) 3.89, 3.8, 3.9, 3.08
   - (C) 3.08, 3.89, 3.8, 3.9
   - (D) 3.08, 3.8, 3.89, 3.9

Test Prep Doctor

For item 6, students may try to find a common denominator before adding the lengths. Remind them the question asks for an estimate, not an exact amount. A good estimate is 15 + 24 + 9 = 48.

Answers

16. The tank should be $1\frac{2}{3}$ feet long and $1\frac{1}{4}$ feet wide.
17. $\frac{1}{6}b = \frac{5}{6}$; $b = 5$ bows; Lucy can make 5 bows out of her ribbon.
18. See 4-Point Response work sample.

10. Samantha gets to choose a number for her soccer jersey. She picks a number that is divisible by 3, 5, and 9, but not by 2, 4, or 6. Which of the following can be Samantha's jersey number?

Ⓕ 15   Ⓗ 30

Ⓖ 27   Ⓙ 45

11. A theater has 145 rows of seats. There are 12 seats in each row. The sixth grade class from Brookpark Middle School has 168 students and 15 chaperones that are attending a play next week. How many rows will they need to reserve for the upcoming play?

Ⓐ 14 rows   Ⓒ 16 rows

Ⓑ 15 rows   Ⓓ 17 rows

Underline key words given in the test question so you know for certain what the question is asking.

12. What is the least common denominator for the following fractions: $\frac{4}{5}$, $\frac{3}{4}$, and $\frac{1}{10}$?

Ⓕ 20   Ⓗ 50

Ⓖ 40   Ⓙ 100

13. During a walk-a-thon, Brian walks $3\frac{1}{4}$ kilometers, and Stacey walks $2\frac{7}{8}$ kilometers. How many more kilometers does Brian walk than Stacy?

Ⓐ $\frac{3}{8}$ Ⓒ $1\frac{1}{8}$

Ⓑ $\frac{7}{8}$ Ⓓ $\frac{7}{4}$

14. What is the reciprocal of $6\frac{1}{7}$?

Ⓕ $\frac{7}{43}$ Ⓗ $\frac{7}{6}$

Ⓖ $\frac{6}{7}$ Ⓙ 6

15. Natalie lives $\frac{1}{6}$ mile from school. Peter lives $\frac{3}{10}$ mile from school. How many miles further does Peter live from the school than Natalie?

Ⓐ $\frac{1}{20}$ Ⓒ $\frac{2}{15}$

Ⓑ $\frac{1}{30}$ Ⓓ $\frac{6}{60}$

STANDARDIZED TEST PREP

Short Response

16. Jane is building a tank for her pet snake. The tank's minimum length should equal two-thirds of the snake's length, and the tank's width should be equal to half the snake's length. Jane's snake is $2\frac{1}{2}$ feet long. Calculate and explain how to find the dimensions of the tank.

17. Lucy has $\frac{5}{6}$ yard of ribbon to wrap gifts for her friends. The bow on each gift requires $\frac{1}{6}$ yard of ribbon. Write an equation to determine how many b bows Lucy can make. Solve and interpret your answer.

Extended Response

18. Garrett attends a summer day camp for 6 hours each day. The circle graph below shows what fraction of each day he spends doing different activities.

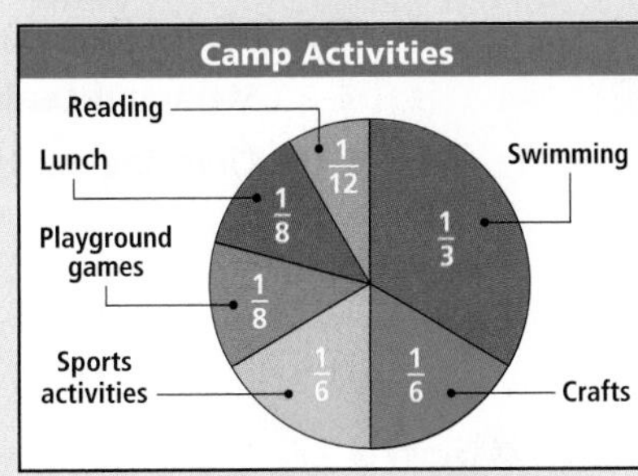

a. How long does Garrett spend doing each activity? Write the activities in order from longest to shortest.

b. Sports activities and playground games are all held on the camp fields. What fraction of the day does Garrett spend on the fields? Write your answer in simplest form.

c. Lunch and crafts are held in the cafeteria. How many hours does Garrett spend in the cafeteria during a 5-day week at day camp? Write your answer in simplest form, and show the work necessary to determine the correct answer.

CRCT Prep

Short Response Rubric

Items 16–17

2 Points = The student's answer is an accurate and complete execution of the task or tasks.

1 Point = The student's answer contains attributes of an appropriate response but is flawed.

0 Points = The student's answer contains no attributes of an appropriate response.

Extended Response Rubric

Item 18

4 Points = The student demonstrates a thorough understanding of all concepts and all work is shown correctly.

3 Points = The student demonstrates a basic understanding of all concepts, but the work shows some flaws reflecting inattentive execution of mathematical procedures or some misunderstanding of the underlying mathematics.

2 Points = The student demonstrates only a partial understanding of the concepts or procedures embodied in the tasks. The approach may be correct, but the work shows a misunderstanding of one or more important concepts.

1 Point = The student demonstrates a very limited understanding of the concepts or procedures embodied in the tasks. The response may show some understanding but exhibits many flaws or is incomplete.

0 Points = The student provides no response at all or a completely incorrect or uninterpretable response.

Student Work Samples for Item 18

4-Point Response

a. Swimming: $\frac{1}{3}(6) = 2$ hr
Crafts/Sports: $\frac{1}{6}(6) = 1$ hr
Playground/Lunch: $\frac{1}{8}(6) = \frac{3}{4}$ hr = 45 min.
Reading: $\frac{1}{12}(6) = \frac{1}{2}$ hr = 30 min.

b. $\frac{1}{6} + \frac{1}{8} = \frac{4}{24} + \frac{3}{24} = \frac{7}{24}$ day

c. 1 hr + $\frac{3}{4}$ hr = $1\frac{3}{4}$ hr $1\frac{3}{4}(5) = 8\frac{3}{4}$
$8\frac{3}{4}$ hr or 8 hr 45min.

The student answered parts A, B, and C correctly. The student showed all the steps in part C.

3-Point Response

a. Swimming – $\frac{1}{3}(6) = 2$ hours
Crafts – $\frac{1}{6}(6) = 1$ hour
Sports – $\frac{1}{6}(6) = 1$ hour
Playground – $\frac{1}{8}(6) = \frac{3}{4}$ hour
Lunch – $\frac{1}{8}(6) = \frac{3}{4}$ hour
Reading – $\frac{1}{12}(6) = \frac{1}{2}$ hour

b. 1 hour + $\frac{3}{4}$ hour = $1\frac{3}{4}$ hour
$1\frac{3}{4} \div 6 = \frac{6}{4} \cdot \frac{1}{6} = \frac{1}{4}$ day

c. 1 hour + $\frac{3}{4}$ hour = $1\frac{3}{4}$ hour
$1\frac{3}{4} \cdot 5 = \frac{6}{4} \times 5 = \frac{30}{4} = 7\frac{1}{2}$ hours

The student correctly answered part A. The student incorrectly wrote $1\frac{3}{4}$ as $\frac{6}{4}$, resulting in incorrect calculations for parts B and C.

2-Point Response

a. Swimming, Crafts, Sports, Playground, Lunch, Reading

b. $\frac{1}{6} + \frac{1}{8} = \frac{2}{14} = \frac{1}{7}$ day

c. $\frac{1}{7} \times 5 = \frac{5}{7}$ hr

The list is in the correct order but the time spent doing each activity was omitted. The student incorrectly added fractions in part **b** and did not understand part **c**.

CHAPTER 6

Collecting and Displaying Data

Section 6A	Section 6B
Organizing Data	**Displaying and Interpreting Data**
6-1 Make a Table	**6-4 Bar Graphs**
6-2 Hands-On Lab Collect Data to Explore Mean	**6-4 Technology Lab** Create Bar Graphs
6-2 Mean, Median, Mode, and Range	**6-5 Line Plots, Frequency Tables, and Histograms**
6-3 Additional Data and Outliers	**6-5 Hands-On Lab** Use a Survey to Collect Data
	6-6 Ordered Pairs
	6-7 Line Graphs
	6-8 Misleading Graphs
	6-9 Stem-and-Leaf Plots
	6-10 Choosing an Appropriate Display

Pacing Guide for 45-Minute Classes

Chapter 6

Countdown to Testing Weeks 12, 13

DAY 1	DAY 2	DAY 3	DAY 4	DAY 5
6-1 Lesson	6-2 Hands-On Lab	6-2 Lesson	6-3 Lesson	Ready to Go On? Focus on Problem Solving 6-4 Lesson
DAY 6	**DAY 7**	**DAY 8**	**DAY 9**	**DAY 10**
6-4 Lesson 6-4 Technology Lab	6-5 Lesson	6-5 Hands-On Lab 6-6 Lesson	6-6 Lesson 6-7 Lesson	6-7 Lesson 6-8 Lesson
DAY 11	**DAY 12**	**DAY 13**	**DAY 14**	**DAY 15**
6-8 Lesson 6-9 Lesson	6-9 Lesson 6-10 Lesson	6-10 Lesson Ready to Go On? Multi-Step Test Prep	Chapter 6 Review	Chapter 6 Test

Pacing Guide for 90-Minute Classes

Chapter 6

DAY 1	DAY 2	DAY 3	DAY 4	DAY 5
6-1 Lesson 6-2 Hands-On Lab	6-2 Lesson 6-3 Lesson	Ready to Go On? Focus on Problem Solving 6-4 Lesson 6-4 Technology Lab	6-5 Lesson 6-5 Hands-On Lab 6-6 Lesson	6-6 Lesson 6-7 Lesson 6-8 Lesson
DAY 6	**DAY 7**	**DAY 8**		
6-8 Lesson 6-9 Lesson 6-10 Lesson	6-10 Lesson Ready to Go On? Multi-Step Test Prep Chapter 6 Review	Chapter 6 Test		

ONGOING ASSESSMENT and INTERVENTION

	DIAGNOSE	PRESCRIBE
Assess Prior Knowledge	**Before Chapter 6**	
	Diagnose readiness for the chapter.	Prescribe intervention.
	Are You Ready? SE p. 291	***Are You Ready? Intervention*** Skills 1, 4, 5, 26, 61
Formative Assessment	**Before Every Lesson**	
	Diagnose readiness for the lesson.	Prescribe intervention.
	Warm Up TE, every lesson	**Skills Bank** SE pp. 749–761 **Reteach** CRB, Chapters 1–6
	During Every Lesson	
	Diagnose understanding of lesson concepts.	Prescribe intervention.
	Think and Discuss SE, every lesson **Write About It** SE, lesson exercises **Journal** TE, lesson exercises	***Questioning Strategies*** Chapter 6 **Reading Strategies** CRB, every lesson ***Success for ELL*** pp. 87–106
	After Every Lesson	
	Diagnose mastery of lesson concepts.	Prescribe intervention.
	Lesson Quiz TE, every lesson **Test Prep** SE, every lesson ***Test and Practice Generator***	**Reteach** CRB, every lesson **Problem Solving** CRB, every lesson **Test Prep Doctor** TE, lesson exercises ***Homework Help* Online**
	Before Chapter 6 Testing	
	Diagnose mastery of concepts in the chapter.	Prescribe intervention.
	Ready to Go On? SE pp. 306, 336 **Focus on Problem Solving** SE p. 307 **Multi-Step Test Prep** SE p. 337 **Section Quizzes** AR pp. 106–107 ***Test and Practice Generator***	***Ready to Go On? Intervention*** **Scaffolding Questions** TE p. 337
	Before High Stakes Testing	
	Diagnose mastery of benchmark concepts.	Prescribe intervention.
	CRCT Prep SE pp. 344–345 ***CRCT Prep* CD-ROM**	***CRCT Prep Workbook***
Summative Assessment	**After Chapter 6**	
	Check mastery of chapter concepts.	Prescribe intervention.
	Multiple-Choice Tests (Forms A, B, C) **Free-Response Tests (Forms A, B, C)** **Performance Assessment** AR pp. 108–121 ***Test and Practice Generator***	**Reteach** CRB, every lesson ***Lesson Tutorial Videos*** Chapter 6
	Check mastery of benchmark concepts.	Prescribe intervention.
	CRCT	***CRCT Prep Workbook***

KEY: **SE** = *Student Edition* **TE** = *Teacher's Edition* **CRB** = *Chapter Resource Book* **AR** = *Assessment Resources* Available online Available on CD-ROM

CHAPTER 6

Supporting the Teacher

Chapter 6 Resource Book

Practice A, B, C
pp. 3–5, 11–13, 19–21, 27–29, 36–38, 45–47, 53–55, 62–64, 70–72, 78–80

Reading Strategies ELL
pp. 9, 17, 25, 34, 43, 51, 60, 68, 76, 84

Puzzles, Twisters, and Teasers
pp. 10, 18, 26, 35, 44, 52, 61, 69, 77, 85

Reteach
pp. 6, 14, 22, 30–31, 39–40, 48, 56–57, 65, 73, 81

Problem Solving
pp. 8, 16, 24, 33, 42, 50, 59, 67, 75, 83

Challenge
pp. 7, 15, 23, 32, 41, 49, 58, 66, 74, 81

Parent Letter pp. 1–2

Transparencies

Lesson Transparencies, Volume 1 .... Chapter 6
- Teaching Tools
- Warm Ups
- Problem of the Day
- Teaching Transparencies
- Lesson Quizzes

Know-It Notebook .... Chapter 6
- Additional Examples
- Vocabulary
- Chapter Review
- Big Ideas

Alternate Openers: Explorations .... pp. 44–53

Countdown to CRCT .... pp. 23–26

Teacher Tools

Power Presentations®
Complete PowerPoint® presentations for Chapter 6 lessons

Lesson Tutorial Videos® SPANISH
Holt authors Ed Burger and Freddie Renfro present tutorials to support the Chapter 6 lessons.

One-Stop Planner® SPANISH
Easy access to all Chapter 6 resources and assessments, as well as software for lesson planning, test generation, and puzzle creation

IDEA Works!®
Key Chapter 6 resources and assessments modified to address special learning needs

Lesson Plans .... pp. 44–53

Questioning Strategies .... Chapter 6

Solutions Key .... Chapter 6

Interdisciplinary Posters and Worksheets .... Chapter 6

TechKeys

Lab Resources

Project Teacher Support

Parent Resources 

Workbooks

Homework and Practice Workbook SPANISH
Teacher's Guide .... pp. 22–27

Know-It Notebook
Teacher's Guide .... Chapter 6

Problem Solving Workbook SPANISH
Teacher's Guide .... pp. 22–27

CRCT Prep
Teacher's Guide

Technology Highlights for the Teacher

 **Power Presentations**

Dynamic presentations to engage students. Complete PowerPoint® presentations for every lesson in Chapter 6.

2-1 Solving One-Step Equations

Isolate a variable by using inverse operations which "undo" operations on the variable.

An equation is like a balanced scale. To keep the balance, perform the same operation on both sides.

Inverse Operations	
Operation	**Inverse Operation**
Addition	Subtraction
Subtraction	Addition

 **One-Stop Planner** SPANISH

Easy access to Chapter 6 resources and assessments. Includes lesson-planning, test-generation, and puzzle-creation software.

 **Premier Online Edition** SPANISH

Chapter 6 includes Tutorial Videos, Lesson Activities, Lesson Quizzes, Homework Help, and Chapter Project.

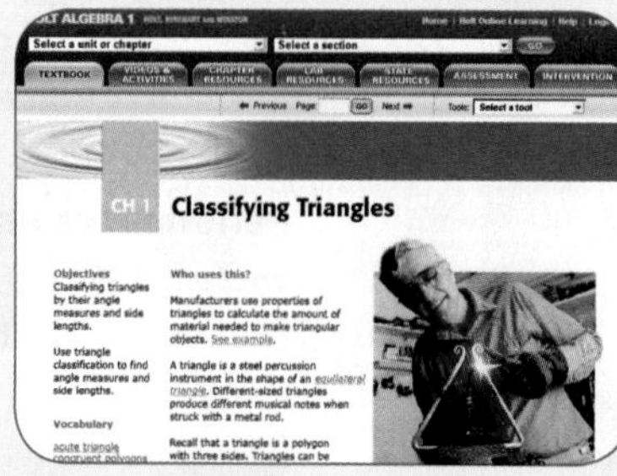

KEY: **SE** = *Student Edition* **TE** = *Teacher's Edition*  English Language Learners  Spanish version available  Available online  Available on CD-ROM

Reaching All Learners

Resources for All Learners

Hands-On Lab Activities	Chapter 6
Technology Lab Activities	Chapter 6
Homework and Practice Workbook SPANISH	pp. 44–53
Know-It Notebook SPANISH	Chapter 6
Problem Solving Workbook SPANISH	pp. 44–53

DEVELOPING LEARNERS

Practice A	CRB, every lesson
Reteach	CRB, every lesson
Inclusion	TE pp. 323, 327
Questioning Strategies	Chapter 6
Modified Chapter 6 Resources	*IDEA Works!*
***Homework Help* Online**	

ON-LEVEL LEARNERS

Practice B	CRB, every lesson
Puzzles, Twisters, and Teasers	CRB, every lesson
Multiple Representations	TE p. 295
Cognitive Strategies	TE p. 323

ADVANCED LEARNERS

Practice C	CRB, every lesson
Challenge	CRB, every lesson
Extension	TE pp. 293, 337, 338, 339
Critical Thinking	TE pp. 309, 331

English Language Learners

ENGLISH LANGUAGE LEARNERS

Are You Ready? Vocabulary	SE p. 291
Vocabulary Connections	SE p. 292
Lesson Vocabulary	SE, every lesson
Vocabulary Review	SE p. 340
English Language Learners	TE pp. 293, 299, 303, 320, 323, 347
Reading Strategies	CRB, every lesson
Success for English Language Learners	pp. 87–106
Multilingual Glossary	

Reaching All Learners Through...

Inclusion	TE pp. 323, 327
Diversity	TE p. 299
Kinesthetic Experience	TE p. 319
Concrete Manipulatives	TE p. 309
Multiple Representations	TE p. 295
Cognitive Strategies	TE p. 323
Cooperative Learning	TE pp. 303, 315, 327, 334
Critical Thinking	TE pp. 309, 331
Test Prep Doctor	TE pp. 301, 305, 311, 317, 325, 329, 344
Common Error Alert	TE p. 334
Scaffolding Questions	TE p. 337

Technology Highlights for Reaching All Learners

Lesson Tutorial Videos 

Starring Holt authors Ed Burger and Freddie Renfro! Live tutorials to support every lesson in Chapter 6.

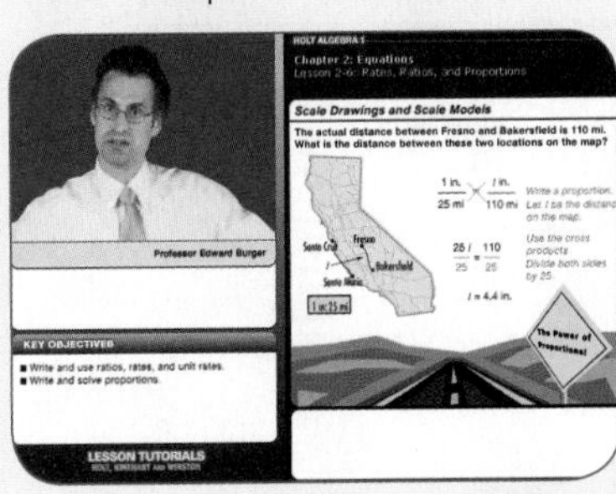

Multilingual Glossary

Searchable glossary includes definitions in English, Spanish, Vietnamese, Chinese, Hmong, Korean, and 4 other languages.

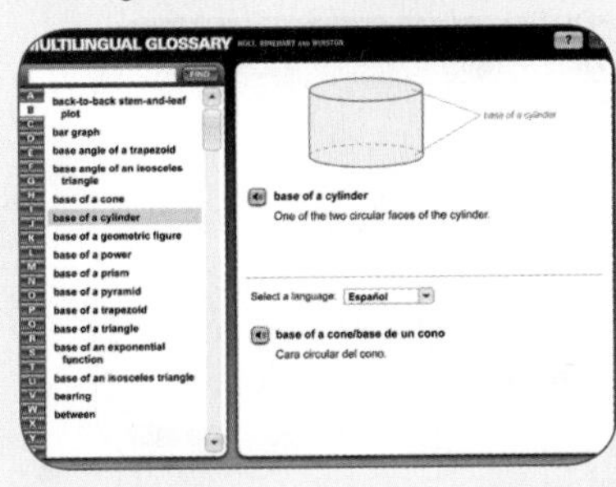

Online Interactivities

Interactive tutorials provide visually engaging alternative opportunities to learn concepts and master skills.

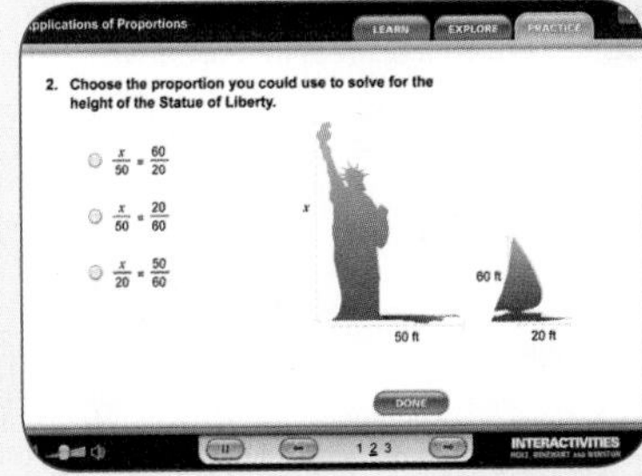

KEY: **SE** = *Student Edition* **TE** = *Teacher's Edition* **CRB** = *Chapter Resource Book* SPANISH Spanish version available  Available online  Available on CD-ROM

Ongoing Assessment

Assessing Prior Knowledge

Determine whether students have the prerequisite concepts and skills for success in Chapter 6.

Are You Ready? SPANISH .... SE p. 291

Warm Up .... TE, every lesson

Test Preparation

Provide review and practice for Chapter 6 and standardized tests.

Multi-Step Test Prep .... SE p. 337

Study Guide: Review .... SE pp. 340–341

Standardized Test Prep .... SE pp. 344–345

Countdown to CRCT Transparencies .... pp. 23–26

CRCT Prep Workbook

***CRCT Prep* CD-ROM**

IDEA Works!

Alternative Assessment

Assess students' understanding of Chapter 6 concepts and combined problem-solving skills.

Chapter 6 Project .... SE p. 290

Performance Assessment .... AR pp. 120–121

Portfolio Assessment .... AR p. xxxiv

Daily Assessment

Provide formative assessment for each day of Chapter 6.

Questioning Strategies .... Chapter 6

Think and Discuss .... SE, every lesson

Write About It .... SE, lesson exercises

Journal .... TE, lesson exercises

Lesson Quiz .... TE, every lesson

Modified Lesson Quizzes .... *IDEA Works!*

Weekly Assessment

Provide formative assessment for each week of Chapter 6.

Focus on Problem Solving .... SE p. 307

Multi-Step Test Prep .... SE p. 337

Ready to Go On? SPANISH .... SE pp. 306, 336

Chapter 6 Test .... SE p. 343

Cumulative Assessment .... SE pp. 344–345

Test and Practice Generator SPANISH ... *One-Stop Planner*

Formal Assessment

Provide summative assessment of Chapter 6 mastery.

Section Quizzes SPANISH .... AR pp. 106–107

Chapter Test (Levels A, B, C) SPANISH .... AR pp. 108–119
- Multiple Choice
- Free Response

Cumulative Test SPANISH .... AR pp. 122–125

Test and Practice Generator SPANISH ... *One-Stop Planner*

Modified Chapter 6 Test .... *IDEA Works!*

Technology Highlights for Ongoing Assessment

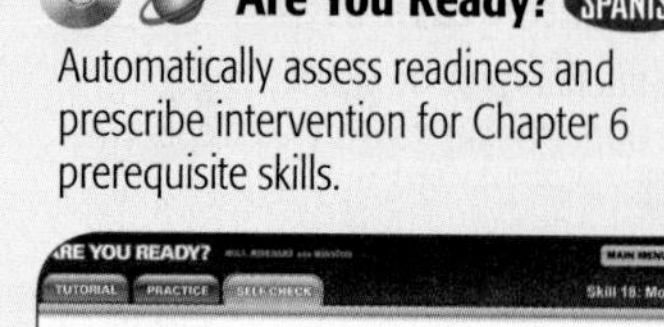

Are You Ready? SPANISH

Automatically assess readiness and prescribe intervention for Chapter 6 prerequisite skills.

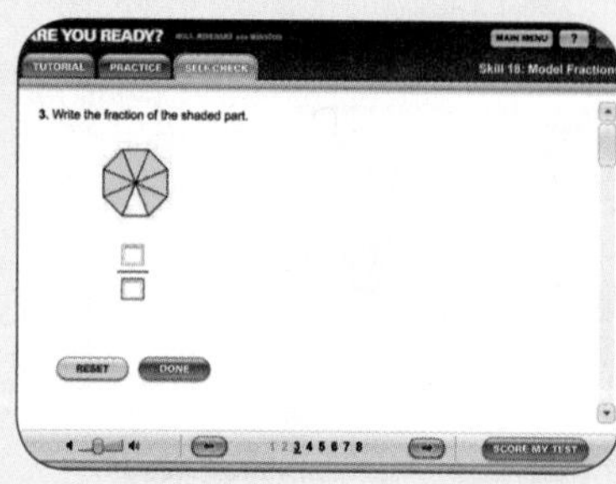

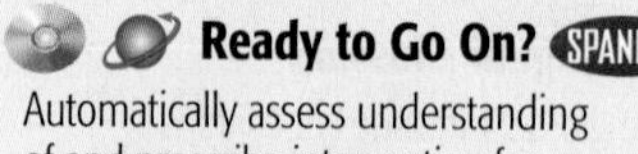

Ready to Go On? SPANISH

Automatically assess understanding of and prescribe intervention for Sections 6A and 6B.

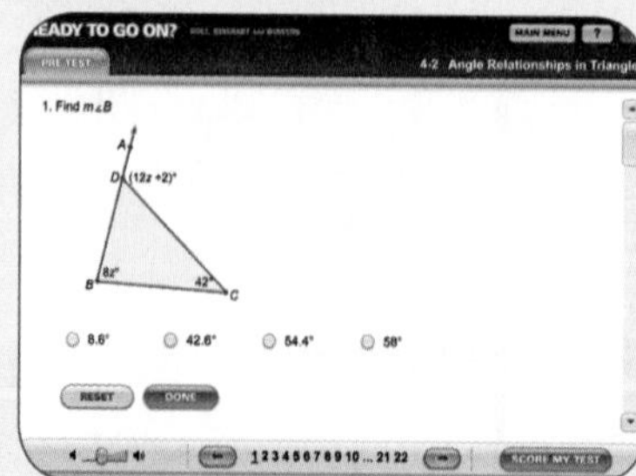

Test and Practice Generator SPANISH

Use Chapter 6 problem banks to create assessments and worksheets to print out or deliver online. Includes dynamic problems.

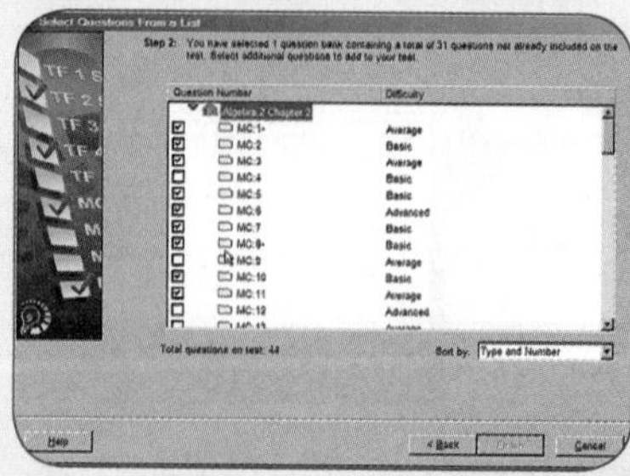

KEY: **SE** = *Student Edition* **TE** = *Teacher's Edition* **AR** = *Assessment Resources* SPANISH Spanish version available  Available online  Available on CD-ROM

Formal Assessment

Three levels (A, B, C) of multiple-choice and free-response chapter tests are available in the *Assessment Resources.*

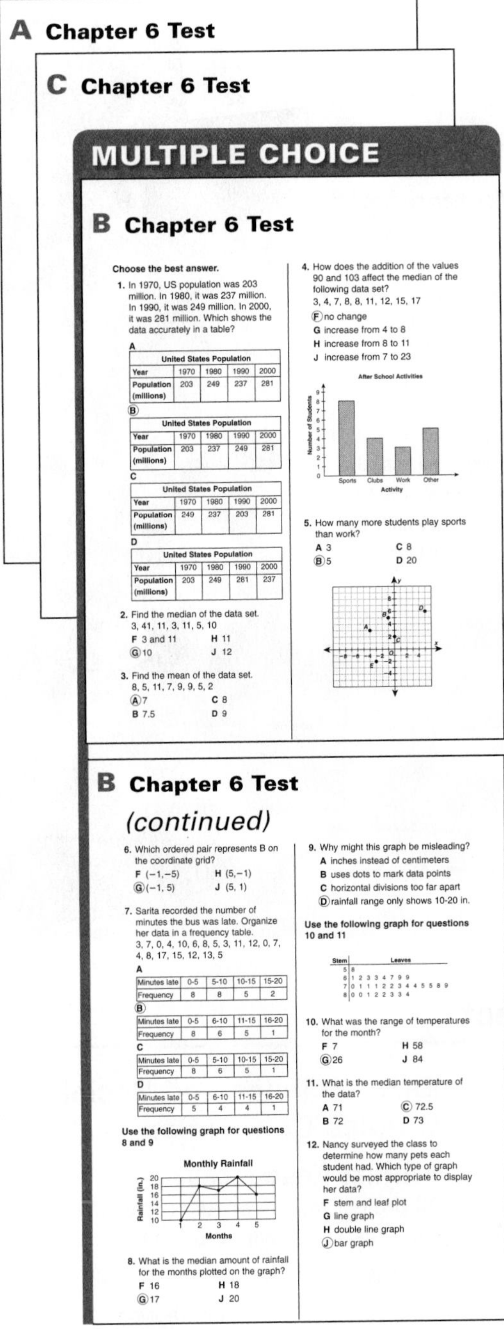

A Chapter 6 Test

C Chapter 6 Test

MULTIPLE CHOICE

B Chapter 6 Test

Choose the best answer.

1. In 1970, US population was 203 million. In 1980, it was 237 million. In 1990, it was 249 million. In 2000, it was 281 million. Which shows the data accurately in a table?

A

United States Population				
Year	1970	1980	1990	2000
Population (millions)	203	249	237	281

(B)

United States Population				
Year	1970	1980	1990	2000
Population (millions)	203	237	249	281

C

United States Population				
Year	1970	1980	1990	2000
Population (millions)	249	237	203	281

D

United States Population				
Year	1970	1980	1990	2000
Population (millions)	203	249	281	237

2. Find the median of the data set.
3, 41, 11, 3, 11, 5, 10
F 3 and 11 H 11
(G) 10 J 12

3. Find the mean of the data set.
8, 5, 11, 7, 9, 9, 5, 2
(A) 7 C 8
B 7.5 D 9

4. How does the addition of the values 90 and 103 affect the median of the following data set?
3, 4, 7, 8, 8, 11, 12, 15, 17
(F) no change
G increase from 4 to 8
H increase from 8 to 11
J increase from 7 to 23

After School Activities

5. How many more students play sports than work?
A 3 C 8
(B) 5 D 20

B Chapter 6 Test

(continued)

6. Which ordered pair represents B on the coordinate grid?
F (−1,−5) H (5,−1)
(G) (−1, 5) J (5, 1)

7. Sarita recorded the number of minutes the bus was late. Organize her data in a frequency table.
3, 7, 0, 4, 10, 6, 8, 5, 3, 11, 12, 0, 7, 4, 8, 17, 15, 12, 13, 5

A

Minutes late	0-5	5-10	10-15	15-20
Frequency	8	8	5	2

(B)

Minutes late	0-5	6-10	11-15	16-20
Frequency	8	6	5	1

C

Minutes late	0-5	5-10	10-15	15-20
Frequency	8	6	5	1

D

Minutes late	0-5	6-10	11-15	16-20
Frequency	5	4	4	1

Use the following graph for questions 8 and 9

Monthly Rainfall

8. What is the median amount of rainfall for the months plotted on the graph?
F 16 H 18
(G) 17 J 20

9. Why might this graph be misleading?
A inches instead of centimeters
B uses dots to mark data points
C horizontal divisions too far apart
(D) rainfall range only shows 10-20 in.

Use the following graph for questions 10 and 11

Stem	Leaves
5	8
6	1 2 3 3 4 7 9 9
7	0 1 1 1 2 2 3 4 4 5 5 8 9
8	0 0 1 2 2 3 3 4

10. What was the range of temperatures for the month?
F 7 H 58
(G) 26 J 84

11. What is the median temperature of the data?
A 71 (C) 72.5
B 72 D 73

12. Nancy surveyed the class to determine how many pets each student had. Which type of graph would be most appropriate to display her data?
F stem and leaf plot
G line graph
H double line graph
(J) bar graph

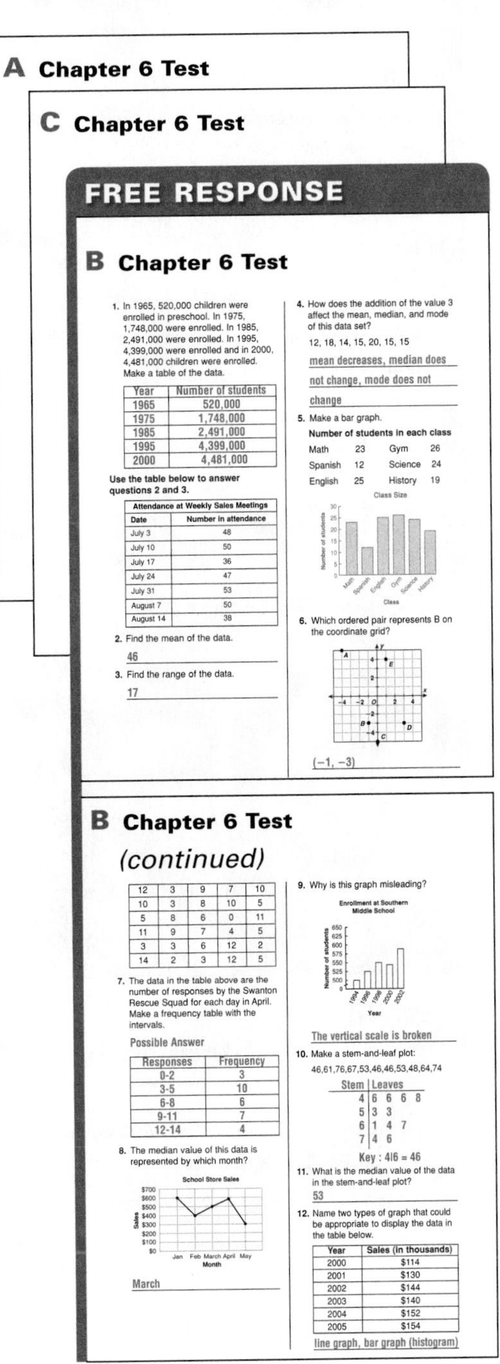

A Chapter 6 Test

C Chapter 6 Test

FREE RESPONSE

B Chapter 6 Test

1. In 1965, 520,000 children were enrolled in preschool. In 1975, 1,748,000 were enrolled. In 1985, 2,491,000 were enrolled. In 1995, 4,399,000 were enrolled and in 2000, 4,481,000 children were enrolled. Make a table of the data.

Year	Number of students
1965	520,000
1975	1,748,000
1985	2,491,000
1995	4,399,000
2000	4,481,000

Use the table below to answer questions 2 and 3.

Attendance at Weekly Sales Meetings	
Date	Number in attendance
July 3	48
July 10	50
July 17	36
July 24	47
July 31	53
August 7	50
August 14	38

2. Find the mean of the data.
46

3. Find the range of the data.
17

4. How does the addition of the value 3 affect the mean, median, and mode of this data set?
12, 18, 14, 15, 20, 15, 15
mean decreases, median does not change, mode does not change

5. Make a bar graph.
Number of students in each class
Math 23 Gym 26
Spanish 12 Science 24
English 25 History 19

Class Size

6. Which ordered pair represents B on the coordinate grid?
(−1, −3)

B Chapter 6 Test

(continued)

12	3	9	7	10
10	3	8	10	5
5	8	6	0	11
11	9	7	4	5
3	3	6	12	2
14	2	3	12	5

7. The data in the table above are the number of responses by the Swanton Rescue Squad for each day in April. Make a frequency table with the intervals.

Possible Answer

Responses	Frequency
0-2	3
3-5	10
6-8	6
9-11	7
12-14	4

8. The median value of this data is represented by which month?

School Store Sales

March

9. Why is this graph misleading?

Enrollment at Southern Middle School

The vertical scale is broken

10. Make a stem-and-leaf plot:
46,61,76,67,53,46,46,53,48,64,74

Stem	Leaves
4	6 6 6 8
5	3 3
6	1 4 7
7	4 6

Key : 4|6 = 46

11. What is the median value of the data in the stem-and-leaf plot?
53

12. Name two types of graph that could be appropriate to display the data in the table below.

Year	Sales (in thousands)
2000	$114
2001	$130
2002	$144
2003	$140
2004	$152
2005	$154

line graph, bar graph (histogram)

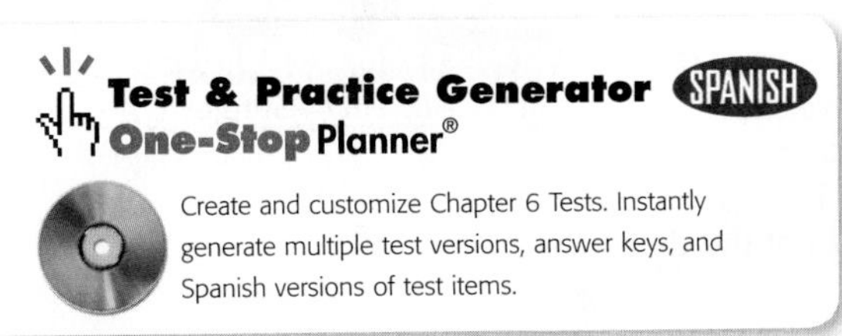

Test & Practice Generator
SPANISH
One-Stop Planner®
Create and customize Chapter 6 Tests. Instantly generate multiple test versions, answer keys, and Spanish versions of test items.

CHAPTER 6

Why Learn This?

Tell students that weather statistics are collected every day. For example, the high and low temperatures, the amount of precipitation, and the time of sunrise and sunset are recorded daily. Meteorologists compare this data to past weather and also use it to predict future weather.

Using Data

To begin the study of this chapter, have students:

- Describe what is meant by *average high temperature.* The average high temperature for each month is the average of the highest recorded temperatures for each day of the month.
- Identify which national park has the highest average high temperature during July. Badlands, SD Which has the lowest? Crater Lake, OR
- Find the difference in the average high temperatures of the national park with the highest and the national park with the lowest average high temperatures during June. 32°C–19°C = 13°C

On page 344, students will find cumulative CRCT practice.

CHAPTER 6

Collecting and Displaying Data

go.hrw.com
Chapter Project Online
KEYWORD: MR7 Ch6

National Park	Average High Temperatures (°C)		
	Jun	Jul	Aug
Badlands, SD	27	33	32
Big Bend, TX	32	31	31
Crater Lake, OR	19	25	24
Everglades, FL	31	32	32

Career Meteorologist

Weather affects our daily activities, and weather information is useful and often necessary. Businesses such as farms, ski resorts, and airlines need to know weather conditions.

This information comes from meteorologists, people who study and forecast the weather. They gather data such as temperature, wind speed, and rainfall. They then study this data and make predictions.

The table lists the average daily high temperatures during the summer in some popular national parks.

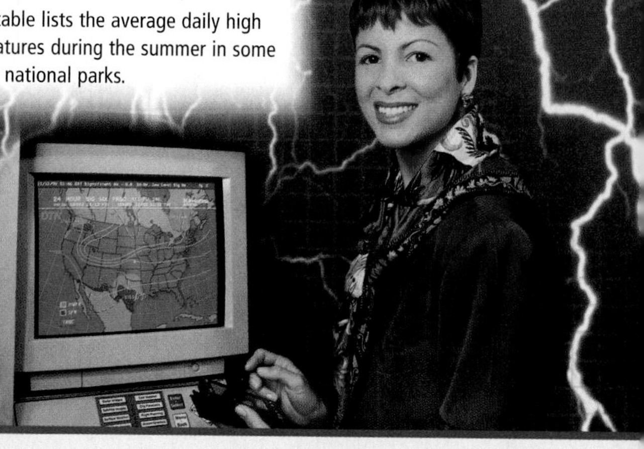

PROBLEM SOLVING

Problem Solving Project

Understand, Plan, Solve, and Look Back

Have students:

- Complete the National Park Climate worksheet to learn about the temperature conditions in our national parks.
- Make a table comparing the high temperatures of the five parks they most want to visit. Then use the table to create a graph.
- Take a poll of their class or of the whole school to discover how many different national parks the students have visited. Then have students create a graph of the data they collected.

Earth Science and Social Studies Connection

Project Resources

All project resources for teachers and students are provided online.

Materials:

- National Park Climate worksheet, thermometers

ARE YOU READY?

Vocabulary

Choose the best term from the list to complete each sentence.

horizontally
place value
quotients
sum
vertically

1. The answer to an addition problem is called the __?__. sum
2. The __?__ of the 6 in 5,672 is hundreds. place value
3. When you move __?__, you move left or right. horizontally
   When you move __?__, you move up or down. vertically

Complete these exercises to review skills you will need for this chapter.

Place Value

Write the digit in the tens place of each number.

4. 718 1
5. 989 8
6. 55 5
7. 7,709 0

Compare and Order Whole Numbers

Order the numbers from least to greatest.

8. 40, 32, 51, 78, 26, 43, 27
   26, 27, 32, 40, 43, 51, 78
9. 132, 150, 218, 176, 166 132, 150, 166, 176, 218
10. 92, 91, 84, 92, 87, 90
    84, 87, 90, 91, 92, 92
11. 23, 19, 33, 27, 31, 31, 28, 18
    18, 19, 23, 27, 28, 31, 31, 33

Find the greatest number in each set.

12. 452, 426, 502, 467, 530, 512
    530
13. 711, 765, 723, 778, 704, 781 781
14. 143, 122, 125, 137, 140, 118, 139
    143
15. 1,053; 1,106; 1,043; 1,210; 1,039; 1,122 1,210

Write Fractions as Decimals

Write each fraction as a decimal.

16. $\frac{1}{4}$ 0.25
17. $\frac{5}{8}$ 0.625
18. $\frac{1}{6}$ $0.1\overline{6}$
19. $\frac{2}{5}$ 0.4
20. $\frac{5}{6}$ $0.8\overline{3}$
21. $\frac{1}{2}$ 0.5
22. $\frac{3}{4}$ 0.75
23. $\frac{9}{11}$ $0.\overline{81}$

Locate Points on a Number Line

Name the point on the number line that corresponds to each given value.

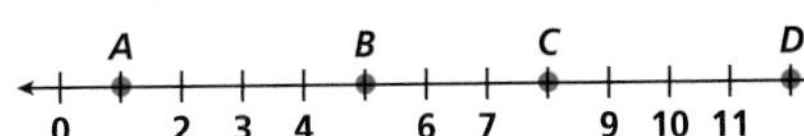

24. 5 B
25. 12 D
26. 8 C
27. 1 A

ARE YOU READY? CHAPTER 6

Organizer

Objective: Assess students' understanding of prerequisite skills.

Prerequisite Skills

Place Value
Compare and Order Whole Numbers
Write Fractions as Decimals
Locate Points on a Number Line

Assessing Prior Knowledge

INTERVENTION 

Diagnose and Prescribe

Use this page to determine whether intervention is necessary or enrichment is appropriate.

Resources

 ***Are You Ready? Intervention and Enrichment* Worksheets**

 ***Are You Ready?* CD-ROM**

 ***Are You Ready?* Online**

my.hrw.com

ARE YOU READY?
Diagnose and Prescribe

NO INTERVENE

Prerequisite Skill	*Are You Ready? Intervention*, Chapter 6 — Worksheets	CD-ROM	Online
Place Value	Skill 1	Activity 1	Diagnose and Prescribe Online
Compare and Order Whole Numbers	Skills 4 & 5	Activities 4 & 5	
Write Fractions as Decimals	Skill 26	Activity 26	
Locate Points on a Number Line	Skill 61	Activity 61	

***Are You Ready? Enrichment*, Chapter 6**

 **Worksheets**

 **CD-ROM**

Online

CHAPTER 6 Study Guide: Preview

Organizer

Objective: Help students organize the new concepts they will learn in Chapter 6.

Online Edition
Multilingual Glossary

Resources

PuzzlePro®
One-Stop Planner®

Multilingual Glossary Online

go.hrw.com
KEYWORD: MR7 Glossary

Answers to Vocabulary Connections

Possible answers:

1. A bar graph uses a straight stripe or band to display data.
2. A coordinate grid has numbered horizontal and vertical lines.
3. An ordered pair has two numbers in an arrangement that defines one unique point.
4. The range of a set of numbers is the difference between the greatest and least values.
5. A stem-and-leaf plot is a way of displaying data. It is made up of a column of stems, which are generally the tens digits, and a column of leaves, which are generally the ones digits.

CHAPTER 6 Study Guide: Preview

Where You've Been

Previously, you

- described characteristics of data such as the shape of the data and the middle number.
- graphed a given set of data using an appropriate graphical representation.
- used tables of related number pairs to make line graphs.

In This Chapter

You will study

- using mean, median, mode, and range to describe data.
- solving problems by collecting, organizing, and displaying data.
- drawing and comparing different graphical representations of the same data.

Where You're Going

You can use the skills learned in this chapter

- to recognize misuses of graphical information and evaluate conclusions based on data analysis.
- to display data correctly for projects in social studies and science.that involve fractions.

Key Vocabulary/Vocabulario

bar graph	gráfica de barras
coordinate grid	plano cartesiano
line graph	gráfica lineal
mean	media
median	mediana
mode	moda
ordered pair	par ordenado
outlier	valor atípico
range	rango (en esta dística)
stem-and-leaf plot	tabla arborescente

Vocabulary Connections

To become familiar with some of the vocabulary terms in the chapter, consider the following. You may refer to the chapter, the glossary, or a dictionary if you like.

1. A *bar* can be a straight stripe or band. What do you think a **bar graph** uses to display data?
2. A *grid* is a network of uniformly spaced horizontal and perpendicular lines. What do you think a **coordinate grid** looks like?
3. *Ordered* means "to be arranged." The word *pair* can mean "two things designed for use together." What do you think an **ordered pair** is made up of?
4. A *range* can mean the distance between possible extremes. If you are looking for the **range** of a set of numbers, what do you think you are looking for?
5. The *stem* is the main trunk of a plant. The *leaves* are the outgrowth from the stem. How do you think a **stem-and-leaf plot** is made?

Grade 6 CRCT GPS

M6D1. **Students will pose questions, collect data, represent and analyze the data, and interpret results.** **a.** Formulate questions that can be answered by data. Students should collect data by using samples from a larger population (surveys), or by conducting experiments. **b.** Using data, construct frequency distributions, frequency tables, and graphs. **d.** Use tables and graphs to examine variation that occurs within a group and variation that occurs between groups. **e.** Relate the data analysis to the context of the questions posted.	M6P1. **Students will solve problems (using appropriate technology).** M6P2. **Students will reason and evaluate mathematical arguments.** M6P4. **Students will make connections among mathematical ideas and to other disciplines.** M6P5. **Students will represent mathematics in multiple ways.**

Georgia Mathematics Performance Standards* **statements are written out completely on pp. GA28–GA35.

Reading Strategy: Read and Interpret Graphics

Figures, diagrams, charts, and graphs are used to illustrate data. Knowing how to understand these visual aids will help you learn the important facts and details of a problem.

Chart

Gustavo's Gift Wrap Table	
Gift Size	Paper Needed (yd²)
Small	$\frac{11}{12}$
Medium	$1\frac{5}{9}$
Large	$2\frac{2}{3}$
X-large	$3\frac{1}{9}$

Read and understand each column head and each row head.

- **Title:** Gustavo's Gift Wrap Table
- **Gift Size:** Small, Medium, Large, and X-large
- **Paper Needed (yd²):** Tells how much paper is needed to wrap the given gift size.

Graph

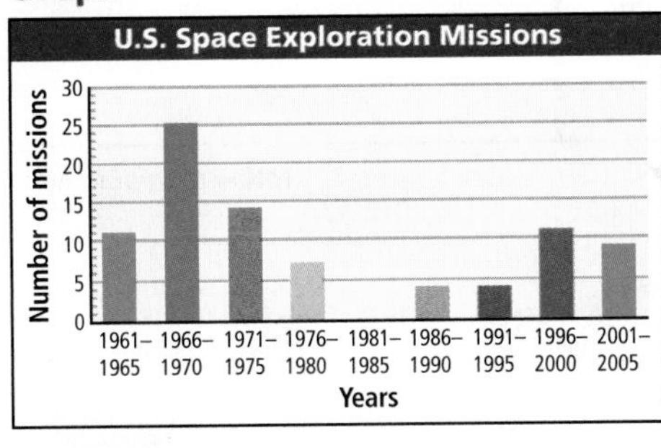

The titles of the graph describe what information is being graphed. Read the label on each axis.

- **Title:** U.S. Space Exploration Missions
- ***x*-axis:** Years (given as 5-year intervals)
- ***y*-axis:** Number of missions

Try This

Look up each exercise in your textbook and answer the following questions.

1. Lesson 5-5, Exercise 32: What type of graph is shown? How many minutes long is "Winter"? Explain.
2. Lesson 5-10, Exercise 36: What is the title of the circle graph? What types of bagels are listed?

Reading and Writing Math

Organizer

Objective: Help students apply strategies to understand and retain key concepts.

Online Edition

Resources

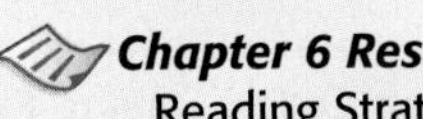

Chapter 6 Resource Book
Reading Strategies

ENGLISH LANGUAGE LEARNERS

Reading Strategy: Read and Interpret Graphics

Discuss The results of a poll to choose a number between 1 and 20 are in a box. Have students discuss how they would create a system to rank each number choice.

Extend Provide multiple opportunities to collect and represent data relating to topics chosen by the students.

Answers to *Try This*

1. Pictograph, 8 min 45 s; each CD represents 1 minute. There are $8\frac{3}{4}$ CDs, and $\frac{3}{4}$ of a CD is 45 s.
2. favorite bagels; sesame, plain, poppy, raisin

Grade 6 CRCT GPS

Standards	6-1	LAB 6-2	6-2	6-3	6-4	LAB 6-4	6-5	LAB 6-5	6-6	6-7	6-8	6-9	6-10
M6D1.a								★					
M6D1.b					★	★	★	★		★			★
M6D1.d					★								
M6D1.e				★									
M6P1	★				★						★	★	★
M6P2											★		
M6P4	★		★	★		★	★		★	★			
M6P5	★	★	★		★		★			★		★	★

SECTION 6A Organizing Data

One-Minute Section Planner

Lesson	Materials	MiC and Lab Resources
Lesson 6-1 Problem Solving Skill: Make a Table • Use tables to record and organize data. ☐ CRCT ☑ SAT-10 ☑ ITBS ☑ CTBS ☑ NAEP	Media sources	**MiC:** ***Picturing Numbers*** pp. 1, 5
6-2 Hands-On Lab Collect Data to Explore Mean • Collect data and use counters to find the mean. **Lesson 6-2** Mean, Median, Mode, and Range • Find the range, mean, median, and mode of a data set. ☐ CRCT ☑ SAT-10 ☑ ITBS ☑ CTBS ☑ NAEP	Counters (MK)	**MiC:** ***Picturing Numbers*** pp. 5, 25 ***Hands-On Lab Activities*** 6-2
Lesson 6-3 Additional Data and Outliers • Learn the effect of additional data and outliers. ☑ CRCT ☑ SAT-10 ☐ ITBS ☑ CTBS ☑ NAEP	Magazines or newspapers containing data sets with outliers	**MiC:** ***Picturing Numbers*** pp. 26–27

MK = *Manipulatives Kit*

Mathematics in Context

The unit ***Picturing Numbers*** from the *Mathematics in Context* © 2006 series can be used with Section 6A. See Section Planner above for suggestions for integrating *MiC* with *Holt Mathematics*.

Section Overview

Make a Table

Lesson 6-1

 Making a table helps you to organize and interpret data.

At 1 P.M., the temperature was 72°F. At 2 P.M. it was 74°F. At 3 P.M., it was 76°F. At 4 P.M., it was 73°F.

Time (P.M.)	Temperature (°F)
1	72
2	74
3	76
4	73

Measures of Central Tendency

Lesson 6-2

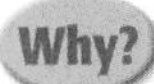 The mean, median, and mode are measures used to represent values of a data set.

Consider the following data set: **9, 2, 2, 4, 8, 2, 8.**

Mean

The **mean (average)** is the sum of all the items, divided by the number of items in the set.

$9 + 2 + 2 + 4 + 8 + 2 + 8 = 35$

$35 \div 7 = 5$

The mean is 5.

Median

The **median** is the middle value when the data are in numerical order or the mean of the two middle values if there is an even number of items.

2, 2, 2, <u>4</u>, 8, 8, 9

The median is 4.

Mode

The **mode** is the value or values that occur most often. There may be more than one mode for a data set. If all values occur an equal number of times, the data set has no mode.

The number 2 occurs most often. The mode is 2.

Additional Data and Outliers

Lessons 6-3

 Data values that are not close to most other values in the data set can greatly change the mean.

Add the value 47 to the data set above to form the new data set: **9, 2, 2, 4, 8, 2, 8, 47.** Find the mean, median, and mode of the new data set.

$9 + 2 + 2 + 4 + 8 + 2 + 8 + 47 = 82$

$82 \div 8 = 10.25$

The mean is 10.25.

2, 2, 2, <u>4</u>, <u>8</u>, 8, 9, 47

The mean of 4 and 8 is 6.
The median is 6.

9, 2, 2, 4, 8, 2, 8, 47

The number 2 still occurs most often.
The mode is 2.

In this case, the mean is not very representative of the data set because it is greater than all the data values except 47. The mean best represents a data set when the values are close and there are not outliers.

6-1 Organizer

Pacing: Traditional 1 day
Block $\frac{1}{2}$ day

Objective: Students use tables to record and organize data.

Online Edition
Tutorial Videos

Countdown to CRCT Week 12

Power Presentations with PowerPoint®

Warm Up

Write the values in simplest form.

1. $\frac{1}{3} + \frac{5}{8}$ $\frac{23}{24}$ **2.** $\frac{7}{8} \div \frac{1}{3}$ $2\frac{5}{8}$

Problem of the Day

If February 1 falls on a Tuesday, then March 1 falls on what day of the week? Tuesday or Wednesday, depending on whether or not it is a leap year

Also available on transparency

Power Presentations with PowerPoint®

Additional Examples

Example 1

Use the audience data to make a table. Then use your table to describe how attendance changed over time.

On May 1, there were 275 people.
On May 2, there were 302 people.
On May 3, there were 322 people.
Answers see p. A4.

Also available on transparency

Georgia Performance Standards

M6P1.c Apply and adapt a variety of appropriate strategies to solve problems.

M6P4.c Recognize and apply mathematics in contexts outside of mathematics.

M6P5.a Create and use representations to organize, record, and communicate mathematical ideas.

6-1 Make a Table

Problem Solving Strategy

Learn to use tables to record and organize data.

Georgia Performance Standards

M6P1.c Apply and adapt a variety of appropriate strategies to solve problems. Also, M6P4.c, M6P5.a.

Weather forecasters collect data about weather. By organizing and interpreting this data, they can often warn people of severe weather before it happens. This advance warning can save lives.

This satellite image shows a hurricane approaching Florida's coastline.

One way to organize data is to make a table. By looking at a table, you may see patterns and relationships.

EXAMPLE 1 *Weather Application*

Use the data about Hurricane Mitch to make a table. Then use your table to describe how the hurricane's strength changed over time.

On October 24, 1998, Hurricane Mitch's wind speed was 90 mi/h. On October 26, its wind speed was 130 mi/h. On October 27, its wind speed was 150 mi/h. On October 31, its wind speed was 40 mi/h. On November 1, its wind speed was 30 mi/h.

Date (1998)	Wind Speed
October 24	90 mi/h
October 26	130 mi/h
October 27	150 mi/h
October 31	40 mi/h
November 1	30 mi/h

Make a table. Write the dates in order so that you can see how the hurricane's strength changed over time.

From the table, you can see that Hurricane Mitch became stronger from October 24 to October 27 and then weakened from October 27 to November 1.

LINK — Weather

The National Weather Service estimated that Mitch's wind speed reached 180 mi/h. This made Mitch a Category 5 hurricane, which is the strongest type.

go.hrw.com
Web Extra!
KEYWORD: MR7 Hurricane

1 Introduce

Alternate Opener

EXPLORATION

6-1 Make a Table

The table shows the number of medals awarded to the top 13 medal-winning countries during the 2002 Winter Olympics.

1. Compute the total number of medals won by each country.

Country	Gold	Silver	Bronze	Total
Germany	12	16	7	
USA	10	13	11	
Norway	11	7	6	
Canada	6	3	8	
Austria	2	4	10	
Russia	6	6	4	
Italy	4	4	4	
France	4	5	2	
Switzerland	3	2	6	
China	2	2	4	
Netherlands	3	5	0	
Finland	4	2	1	
Sweden	0	2	4	

Think and Discuss

2. **Explain** why the table is set up the way it is.
3. **Describe** a different way to organize this data.

2 Teach

Guided Instruction

In this lesson, students learn to use tables to record and organize data. Explain to students how the data in the Examples are easier to describe when organized in the tables than when in paragraph form.

Explorations and answers are provided in *Alternate Openers: Explorations Transparencies.*

EXAMPLE 2 **Organizing Data in a Table**

Use the temperature data to make a table. Then use your table to find a pattern in the data and draw a conclusion.

At 10 A.M., the temperature was 62°F. At noon, it was 65°F. At 2 P.M., it was 68°F. At 4 P.M., it was 70°F. At 6 P.M., it was 66°F.

Time	Temperature (°F)
10 A.M.	62
Noon	65
2 P.M.	68
4 P.M.	70
6 P.M.	66

The temperature rose until 4 P.M., and then it dropped. One conclusion is that the high temperature on this day was at least 70°F.

Possible answers to *Think and Discuss*

1. By using a table, you can easily line up data and reduce the number of words so you can notice the patterns in data.
2. so you can see how the temperature changed throughout the day

Think and Discuss

GPS M6P2.c, M6P3.b

1. **Tell** how a table helps you organize data.
2. **Explain** why the data in Example 2 was arranged from earliest to latest time instead of from lowest to highest temperature.

Power Presentations with PowerPoint®

Additional Examples

Example 2

Use the temperature data to make a table. Then use your table to find a pattern in the data and draw a conclusion.

At 3 A.M., the temperature was 53°F. At 5 A.M., it was 52°F. At 7 A.M., it was 50°F. At 9 A.M., it was 53°F. At 11 A.M., it was 57°F.

Answers see p. A4.

Also available on transparency

6-1 Exercises

Georgia Performance Standards

M6P3.a, M6P5.a

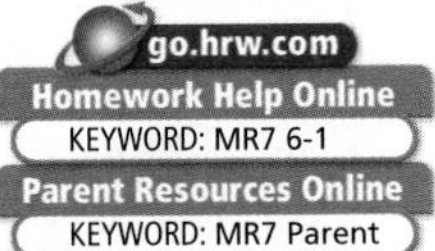

go.hrw.com
Homework Help Online
KEYWORD: MR7 6-1
Parent Resources Online
KEYWORD: MR7 Parent

GUIDED PRACTICE

See Example 1

1. On Monday, the high temperature was 72°F. On Tuesday, the high was 75°F. On Wednesday, the high was 68°F. On Thursday, the high was 62°F. On Friday, the high was 55°F. Use this data to make a table.

See Example 2

2. Use your table from Exercise 1 to find a pattern in the data and draw a conclusion. Possible answer: The daily high peaked on Tuesday and then dropped for the remainder of the week. The temperature will continue to drop over the weekend.

INDEPENDENT PRACTICE

See Example 1

3. On his first math test, Joe made a grade of 70. On the second test, Joe made a grade of 75. On the third test, Joe made a grade of 80. On the fourth test, Joe made a grade of 85. On the fifth test, Joe made a grade of 90. Use this data to make a table.

See Example 2

4. Use your table from Exercise 3 to find a pattern in the data and draw a conclusion.

6-1 Exercises

Assignment Guide

If you finished Example 1 assign:
Average 1, 8–17
Advanced 3, 8–17

If you finished Example 2 assign:
Average 1–5, 8–17
Advanced 3–4, 6–17

Answers

1, 3–4. See p. A4.

3 Close

Summarize

Give students an unorganized set of data and have them organize it in a table. For example, you could list the number of sixth-grade students enrolled in your school in the past 5 years.

If you use the sixth-grade enrollment example, students may organize the data by year and describe the trends, if any, in enrollment.

Reaching All Learners

Through Multiple Representations

Have students gather data about their classmates. Ideas for the data include: the number of bottles of water consumed weekly, the amount of time spent on a computer, on a phone, or watching TV, the number of people in their family, or the number of pets they own. Have students organize their data in the tables and present the data to the class. Discuss how tables can be presented in a horizontal or vertical format.

Georgia Performance Standards

M6P3.a Organize and consolidate their mathematical thinking through communication.

M6P5.a Create and use representations to organize, record, and communicate mathematical ideas.

and INTERVENTION 

Diagnose **Before** the Lesson
6-1 Warm Up, TE p. 294

Monitor **During** the Lesson
6-1 Know-It Notebook
6-1 Questioning Strategies

Assess **After** the Lesson
6-1 Lesson Quiz, TE p. 296

Answers

5, 9. See p. A4.

6-1 Lesson Quiz

1. Humans have the following approximate heart rates at the ages given: newborn, 135 beats per minute (bpm); 2 years old, 110 bpm; 6 years old, 95 bpm; 10 years old, 87 bpm; 20 years old, 71 bpm; 40 years old, 72 bpm; and 60 years old, 74 bpm. Use this data to make a table. See p. A4.
2. Use the data from problem 1 to estimate how many times per minute an 8-year-old's heart beats. 91

Also available on transparency 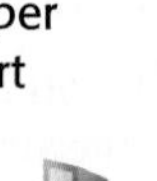

PRACTICE AND PROBLEM SOLVING

Extra Practice p. 724

6. Possible answer: The table on the left would be useful when you are interested in how temperature changes over time. The table on the right would be useful if you wanted to know when it would be a certain temperature.

7. Jeffery is in 6th grade. Victoria is in 7th, and Arthur is in 8th.

5. **Multi-Step** For ice-skating on a frozen pond to be safe, the ice should be at least 7 inches thick. Use the data below to make a table, and estimate the date on which it first became safe to ice-skate.
On December 3, the ice was 1 in. thick. On December 18, the ice was 2 in. thick. On January 3, the ice was 5 in. thick. On January 18, the ice was 11 in. thick. On February 3, the ice was 17 in. thick.

6. **Write About It** The tables below were made using identical data that have been organized differently. When might each table be useful?

Time	Temperature (°F)
6 A.M.	55
10 A.M.	68
2 P.M.	75

Time	Temperature (°F)
2 P.M.	75
10 A.M.	68
6 P.M.	62

7. **Challenge** Arthur, Victoria, and Jeffrey are in the sixth, seventh, and eighth grades, although not necessarily in that order. Victoria is not in eighth grade. The sixth-grader is in choir with Arthur and in band with Victoria. Which student is in which grade? Use a yes/no table like the one at right to help you answer this question.

	Arthur	Victoria	Jeffrey
6th			
7th			
8th		No	

CRCT PREP • GPS SUPPORT • SPIRAL REVIEW

8. **Multiple Choice** In 1999, an earthquake that measured 7.4 on the Richter scale occurred in Turkey. In 2001, an earthquake that measured 7.9 on the Richter scale occurred in India. In 2003, an earthquake that measured 6.5 on the Richter scale occurred in Iran. Which shows the data accurately in a table?

(A)

Country	Turkey	India	Iran
Measure	7.4	6.5	7.9

(B)

Country	Turkey	India	Iran
Measure	7.9	7.4	6.5

(C)

Country	Turkey	India	Iran
Measure	6.5	7.4	7.9

(D) (circled)

Country	Turkey	India	Iran
Measure	7.4	7.9	6.5

9. **Short Response** Make a table to show the following data: Ty builds model cars. He built 2 the first week, 5 the second week, 8 the third week, and 11 the fourth week. Use your table to find a pattern in the data and draw a conclusion.

Find each value. (Lesson 1-3)

10. 5^3 125
11. 3^4 81
12. 2^6 64
13. 6^3 216

Write two phrases for each expression. (Lesson 2-2)

14. $b + 13$ *b* plus 13; 13 added to *b*
15. $(2)(12)$ 2 times 12; 2 multiplied by 12
16. $26 - c$ 26 minus *c*; *c* less than 26
17. $m \div 3$ *m* divided by 3, the quotient of *m* and 3

CHALLENGE 6-1

PROBLEM SOLVING 6-1

LESSON 6-1 Problem Solving
Problem Solving Skill: Make a Table

Complete each activity and answer each question.

1. In January, the normal temperature in Atlanta, Georgia, is 41°F. In February, the normal temperature in Atlanta is 45°F. In March, the normal temperature in Atlanta is 54°F, and in April, it is 62°F. Atlanta's normal temperature in May is 69°F. Use this data to complete the table at right.

Atlanta Normal Temperatures

Month	Temperature (°F)
January	41
February	45
March	54
April	62
May	69

2. Use your table from Exercise 1 to find a pattern in the data and draw a conclusion about the temperature in June.
Pattern: The normal temperature in Atlanta increases each month from January to May. Possible conclusion: Atlanta's normal temperature in June is higher than 69°F.
3. In what other ways could you organize the data in a table?
Possible answers: by temperature from lowest to highest, or from highest to lowest

Circle the letter of the correct answer.

4. In which month given does Atlanta have the highest temperature?
A February
B March
C April
(D) May
5. In which month given does Atlanta have the lowest temperature?
(F) January
G February
H March
J April
6. Which of these statements about Atlanta's temperature data from January to May is true?
(A) It is always higher than 40°F.
B It is always lower than 60°F.
C It is hotter in March than in April.
D It is cooler in February than in January.
7. Between which two months in Atlanta does the normal temperature change the most?
F January and February
(G) February and March
H March and April
J April and May

RETEACH 6-1

LESSON 6-1 Reteach
Problem Solving Skill: Make a Table

You can make a table to organize data. Then you can use the table to see patterns and draw conclusions.

During the week-long book fair, 324 books were sold. On Monday, 45 books were sold. On Tuesday, students bought 58 books. On Wednesday, 79 books were sold. Sixty-two books were sold on Thursday, and students bought 51 books on Friday.

Day	Books Sold
Monday	45
Tuesday	58
Wednesday	79
Thursday	62
Friday	51

To make a table, arrange the information in order by days so you can see patterns over time. Remember to make headings for each column of the table.

From the table, you can see that the number of books sold increased from Monday to Wednesday, and decreased from Wednesday to Friday.

Use the data to make a table. Then use the table to find a pattern in the data and draw a conclusion.

1. During the championship series, the school basketball team earned 24 points in the first game, 28 points in the second game, 33 points in the third game, 42 points in the fourth game, and 49 points in the last game.
The team earned more points each time that it played a game. The team earned at least 24 points each game.

Game	Points Earned
1	24
2	28
3	33
4	42
5	49

2. In the sixth grade, 18 students study Spanish, 35 students study French, 11 students study Latin, and 5 students study no foreign language at all.
Most of the sixth grade students study French as a foreign language.

Foreign Language	Students
French	35
Spanish	18
Latin	11
None	5

PRACTICE 6-1

LESSON 6-1 Practice B
Problem Solving Skill: Make a Table

Complete each activity and answer each question.

1. Pizza Express sells different-sized pizzas. The jumbo pizza has 20 slices. The extra large has 16 slices. The large has 12 slices. There are 8 slices in a medium, and 6 slices in a small. A personal-sized pizza has 4 slices. Use this data to complete the table at right, from largest to smallest pizza.

Pizza Express Pizza Sizes

Size	Slices
Jumbo	20
Extra large	16
Large	12
Medium	8
Small	6
Personal	4

2. What pattern do you see in the table's data?
The first 4 sizes decrease by 4 slices each; the last 3 sizes decrease by 2 slices each.
3. A plain large pizza at Pizza Express costs $13.75. A large pizza with one topping costs $14.20. A 2-topping large pizza costs $14.65, and a 3-topping large pizza costs $15.10. If you want 4 toppings on your large pizza, it will cost you $15.55. Use this data to complete the table at right.

Pizza Express Pizza Prices

Large Pizza	Price
Plain	$13.75
1 Topping	$14.20
2 Toppings	$14.65
3 Toppings	$15.10
4 Toppings	$15.55

4. What pattern do you see in the table's data?
The price increases by $0.45 for each additional topping.
5. How much does each slice of a 1-topping large pizza from Pizza Express cost? Round your answer to the nearest hundredth of a dollar.
$1.18 per slice
6. You and three friends buy two large pizzas from Pizza Express. One pizza has pepperoni and onions, and one pizza is plain. If you equally share the total price, how much will you each pay? How many slices will you each get?
$7.10 each; 6 slices each

Collect Data to Explore Mean

Use with Lesson 6-2

Georgia Performance Standards
M6P5.b, M6P5.c

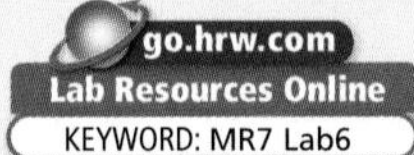

go.hrw.com
Lab Resources Online
KEYWORD: MR7 Lab6

You can use counters to find a single number that describes an entire set of data. Consider the set of data in the table.

2	5	4	3	6

First use counters to make stacks that match the data.

Now move some of the counters so that all of the stacks are the same height.

All of the stacks have 4 counters. The set of data can be described by the number 4. It is the *mean* (average) of the set of data.

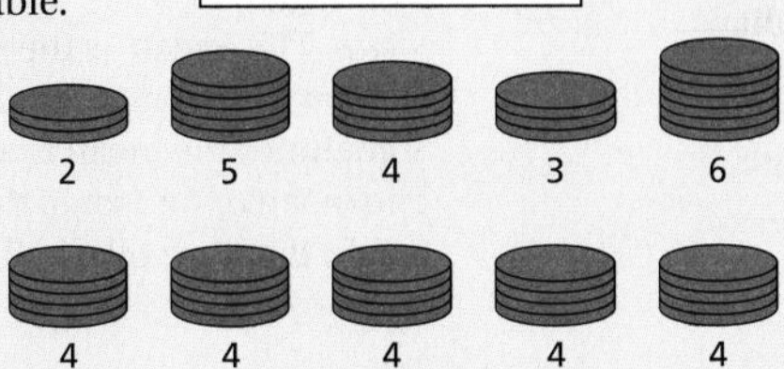

Activity

1. Ella surveys five people to find out how many brothers and sisters they have.
2. She collects the data and records the results.
3. Use counters to show the data.
4. Move counters so that all of the stacks are the same height. The mean is 2.

Number of Siblings				
2	3	1	1	3

2 3 1 1 3

2 2 2 2 2

Think and Discuss

1. Suppose one of the people surveyed had 8 brothers and sisters instead of 3. How would this change the mean? **The mean would increase to 3.**
2. All of the students in a classroom have 3 textbooks. What is the mean of the set of data? How do you know? **3; all of the stacks would have 3 counters**

Try This

1. Collect data by surveying four friends to find out how many pets they have. Use counters to find the mean of the set of data. **Check students' work.**

Teacher to Teacher

I love this activity. I let my students do this activity with multi-link cubes because they stay together well. Tall stacks can be moved around so students can compare their heights. Students really enjoy this activity, and it makes the concept of mean very easy to grasp. I think they understand the concept of mean better after this activity.

Organizer

Use with Lesson 6-2

Pacing:
Traditional 1 day
Block $\frac{1}{2}$ day

Objective: Collect data and use counters to find the mean of a set of data.

Materials: Counters

Online Edition

Resources

Hands-On Lab Activities
Lab 6-2 Recording Sheet

Teach

Discuss

Have students discuss how using counters to represent data is similar to creating a pictograph and a bar graph.

Close

Key Concept

Finding the mean of a set of data is like finding a common level among stacks of chips.

Assessment

1. Use counters to represent the data set. Rearrange the counters to find the mean of the data.

CDs Recycled				
3	1	4	1	6

mean = 3

Georgia Performance Standards

M6P5.b Select, apply, and translate among mathematical representations to solve problems.

M6P5.c Use representations to model and interpret physical, social, and mathematical phenomena.

6-2 Organizer

Pacing: Traditional 1 day
Block $\frac{1}{2}$ day

Objective: Students find the range, mean, median, and mode of a data set.

Hands-On Lab
In *Hands-On Lab Activities*

Online Edition
Tutorial Videos, Interactivities

Countdown to CRCT Week 12

Power Presentations with PowerPoint®

Warm Up

Order the numbers from least to greatest.

1. 8, 6, 25, 7, 4, 12   4, 6, 7, 8, 12, 25

2. 60, 11, 27, 45, 32   11, 27, 32, 45, 60

Divide.

3. 720 ÷ 4   180   **4.** 760 ÷ 10   76

Problem of the Day

Ms. Red, Ms. Blue, and Ms. Green attended a holiday party. They each wore a different-colored dress, red, blue, or green. Ms. Red said to the lady wearing the blue dress, "Did you notice that none of us is wearing a dress with the color that corresponds to our name?" Who wore which color dress?
Ms. Red: green; Ms. Blue: red; Ms. Green: blue

Also available on transparency

6-2 Mean, Median, Mode, and Range

Learn to find the mean, median, mode, and range of a data set.

Vocabulary
mean
median
mode
range

Players on a volleyball team measured how high they could jump. The results in inches are recorded in the table.

13	23	21	20	21	24	18

One way to describe this data set is to find the *mean.* The **mean** is the sum of all the items divided by the number of items in the set. Sometimes the mean is also called the *average.* The mean of this set of data is the average height that the volleyball team could jump.

EXAMPLE 1 Finding the Mean of a Data Set

Georgia Performance Standards
M6P4.c Recognize and apply mathematics in contexts outside of mathematics. Also, M6P5.b, M6P5.c.

Find the mean of each data set.

A

Heights of Vertical Jumps (in.)						
13	23	21	20	21	24	18

$13 + 23 + 21 + 20 + 21 + 24 + 18 = 140$ *Add all values.*
$140 \div 7 = 20$ *Divide the sum by the number of items.*

The mean is 20 inches.

B

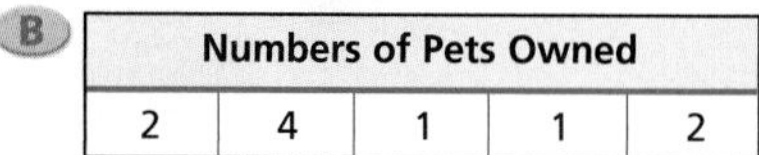

Numbers of Pets Owned				
2	4	1	1	2

$2 + 4 + 1 + 1 + 2 = 10$ *Add all values.*
$10 \div 5 = 2$ *Divide the sum by the number of items.*

The mean is 2. The average number of pets that these five people own is 2.

Check

Move the chips so that each stack has the same number.

The mean is 2.

1 Introduce

Alternate Opener

EXPLORATION

6-2 Mean, Median, Mode, and Range

The table shows an ordered list of all the times in the men's 1,500-meter speed-skating competition in the 2002 Winter Olympics. The fastest time was 1:43.95, or 1 minute 43.95 seconds. Notice that all of the times are only seconds apart.

1:43.95	1:44.57	1:45.26	1:45.34	1:45.41	1:45.51	1:45.63	1:45.82
1:45.86	1:45.97	1:45.98	1:46.00	1:46.04	1:46.29	1:46.38	1:46.40
1:46.75	1:46.99	1:47.04	1:47.21	1:47.26	1:47.63	1:47.64	1:47.72
1:47.78	1:47.83	1:48.02	1:48.13	1:48.20	1:48.27	1:48.40	1:48.57
1:48.58	1:48.76	1:49.24	1:49.42	1:49.45	1:49.50	1:49.57	1:50.15
1:50.26	1:50.70	1:51.02	1:51.02	1:51.81	1:52.01	1:52.87	

1. How many seconds behind the winner was the second-place skater? the third-place skater?
2. Find the range. (Subtract the fastest time from the slowest time.)
3. Find the median. (The median is the number in the middle of the data set.)
4. Find the mean. (The mean is the average of all the times.)

Think and Discuss

5. **Discuss** how you found the median.
6. **Explain** how the mean compares with the median.

Motivate

To give students a meaningful context for studying data, discuss how report card grades are figured. Explain that when teachers add a student's scores and divide by the number of scores, they are finding the *average*, or *mean*, score for that student. Tell students that *range*, *median*, and *mode* are other statistics that can be used to help describe data such as test scores.

Explorations and answers are provided in *Alternate Openers: Explorations Transparencies.*

Georgia Performance Standards

M6P4.c Recognize and apply mathematics in contexts outside of mathematics.

M6P5.b Select, apply, and translate among mathematical representations to solve problems.

M6P5.c Use representations to model and interpret physical, social, and mathematical phenomena.

Some other descriptions of a set of data are called the *median, mode,* and *range.*

- The **median** is the middle value when the data are in numerical order, or the mean of the two middle values if there are an even number of items.
- The **mode** is the value or values that occur most often. There may be more than one mode for a data set. When all values occur an equal number of times, the data set has no mode.
- The **range** is the difference between the least and greatest values in the set.

EXAMPLE 2 Finding the Mean, Median, Mode, and Range of a Data Set

Find the mean, median, mode, and range of each data set.

NFL Career Touchdowns			
Marcus Allen	145	Franco Harris	100
Jim Brown	126	Walter Payton	125

mean: $\frac{145 + 126 + 100 + 125}{4}$ *Add all values. Divide the sum by the number of items.*

$= 124$

Write the data in numerical order: 100, 125, 126, 145

median: 100, (125, 126), 145 *There are an even number of items, so find the mean of the two middle values.*

$\frac{125 + 126}{2} = 125.5$

mode: none *No value occurs most often.*

range: $145 - 100 = 45$ *Subtract least value from greatest value.*

The mean is 124 touchdowns; the median is 125.5 touchdowns; there is no mode; and the range is 45 touchdowns.

Think and Discuss GPS M6P2.b, M6P3.b

1. **Describe** what you can say about the values in a data set if the set has a small range.
2. **Tell** how many modes are in the following data set. Explain your answer. 15, 12, 13, 15, 12, 11
3. **Describe** how adding 20 inches to the data set in Example 1A would affect the mean.

Power Presentations with PowerPoint®

Additional Examples

Example 1

Find the mean of each data set.

A. depths of puddles (in.)
5 8 3 5 4 2 1
mean: 4 in.

B. number of points scored
96 75 84 7
mean: 65.5 points

Example 2

Find the mean, median, mode, and range of the data set.

Car Wash Totals			
6th grade	12	7th grade	11
8th grade	14	9th grade	15

mean = 13, median = 13, no mode, range = 4

Also available on transparency

Answers to *Think and Discuss*

1. Possible answer: If the set of data has a small range, then there is not very much difference between the values of the individual items.
2. Two modes; the values 12 and 15 both occur twice, which is more than any other values occur.
3. Possible answer: Adding 20 to a data set that has a mean of 20 will not change the mean.

2 Teach

Guided Instruction

In this lesson, students learn to find the range, mean, median, and mode of a set of data. First teach them to find these values for a set containing an odd number of items, and then teach them to find the median for a set containing an even number of items. Be sure to discuss the three possibilities for mode: one, more than one, and none. Help students to understand that range, mean, median, and mode are ways to summarize or describe a data set.

Reaching All Learners

Through Diversity

Have students gather data about the populations of 10 other cities in the state and find the range, mean, median, and mode for the data. Have students explain which measure of central tendency best summarizes the data and why.

3 Close

Summarize

ENGLISH LANGUAGE LEARNERS

Have students write brief definitions of new vocabulary in the lesson: *range, mean, median,* and *mode.*

Possible answer: For a given set of data, the range is the difference between the least and greatest values. The mean is the sum of all the items, divided by the number of items. The median is the middle value when the data are in numerical order. The mode is the value or values that occur most often.

6-2 Exercises

Assignment Guide

If you finished Example 1 assign:
Average 1, 19–26
Advanced 3, 19–26

If you finished Example 2 assign:
Average 1–14, 19–26
Advanced 3–5, 9–14, 16–26

Homework Quick Check

Quickly check key concepts.
Exercises: 4, 6, 10, 12

Answers

7.

State	Mean Score
Connecticut	509
Maine	500
Massachusetts	513
New Hampshire	519
Rhode Island	500
Vermont	508

range = 19, mean = 508.2, median = 508.5, mode = 500

Georgia Performance Standards

M6P1.c Apply and adapt a variety of appropriate strategies to solve problems.

M6P5.a Create and use representations to organize, record, and communicate mathematical ideas.

6-2 Exercises

M6P1.c, M6P5.a

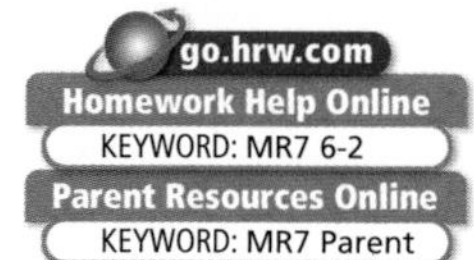

GUIDED PRACTICE

See Example 1 Find the mean of the data set.

1.

Number of Petals	13	24	35	18	15	27

mean = 22

See Example 2 Find the mean, median, mode, and range of the data set.

2.

Heights of Students (in.)	51	67	63	52	49	48	48

mean = 54, median = 51, mode = 48, range = 19

INDEPENDENT PRACTICE

See Example 1 Find the mean of the data set.

3.

Numbers of Books Read	6	4	10	5	6	8

mean = 6.5

See Example 2 Find the mean, median, mode, and range of each data set.

4.

Ages of Students (yr)	14	16	15	17	16	12

mean = 15, median = 15.5, mode = 16, range = 5

5.

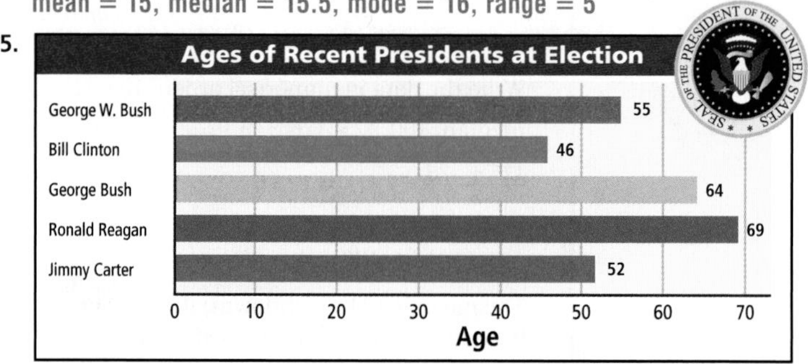

mean = 57.2, median = 55, no mode, range = 23

PRACTICE AND PROBLEM SOLVING

CRCT GPS
Extra Practice p. 724

6. Frank has 3 nickels, 5 dimes, and 2 quarters. Find the range, mean, median, and mode of the values of Frank's coins. range = 20 cents, mean = 11.5 cents, median = 10 cents, mode = 10 cents

7. **Education** For the six New England states, the mean scores on the math section of the SAT one year were as follows: Connecticut, 509; Maine, 500; Massachusetts, 513; New Hampshire, 519; Rhode Island, 500; and Vermont, 508. Create a table using this data. Then find the range, mean, median, and mode. range = 19, mean = 508.2, median = 508.5, mode = 500

8. **Critical Thinking** Gina spent \$4, \$5, \$7, \$7, and \$6 over the past 5 days buying lunch. Is the mean, median, mode, or range the most useful way to describe this data set? Explain.

8. mean, \$5.80, or median, \$6; they are close to most of the data.

RETEACH 6-2

LESSON 6-2 **Reteach**
Mean, Median, Mode, and Range

You can find the mean, median, mode, and range to describe a set of data.

Terry's Test Scores	76	81	94	81	78

The **mean** or average is the sum of the items divided by the number of items.
76 + 81 + 94 + 81 + 78 = 410 First, find the sum of the values.
410 ÷ 5 = 82 Then divide the sum by the number of values in the set of data.
The mean is 82 points.

The **median** is the middle value of an ordered set of data. If there are two middle values, the median is the mean of those two values.
76, 78, **81**, 81, 94 Put the values in order first.
The median is 81 points.

The **mode** is the value that occurs most often in a set of data.
The mode is 81 points.

The **range** is the difference between the greatest and least values in the set of data.
94 − 76 = 18 Use subtraction to find the range.
The range is 18 points.

Find the mean, median, mode, and range of each set of values.

1. 23, 78, 45, 22
mean: 42
median: 34
mode: no mode
range: 56

2. 102, 79, 82, 103, 79
mean: 89
median: 82
mode: 79
range: 24

3. 56, 99, 112, 112, 56
mean: 87
median: 99
mode: 56, 112
range: 56

PRACTICE 6-2

LESSON 6-2 **Practice B**
Mean, Median, Mode, and Range

Find the mean of each data set.

1.

Brian's Math Test Scores	86	90	93	85	79	92

mean: 87.5

2.

Heights of Basketball Players (in.)	72	75	78	72	73

mean: 74 in.

Find the mean, median, mode, and range of each data set.

3.

School Sit-Up Records (sit-ups per minute)	31	28	30	31	30

mean: 30 sit-ups; median: 30 sit-ups; mode: 30 and 31 sit-ups; range: 3 sit-ups

4.

Team Heart Rates (beats per min)	70	68	70	72	68	66

mean: 69 bpm; median: 69 bpm; mode: 68 and 70 bpm; range: 6 bpm

5.

Daily Winter Temperatures (°F)	45	50	47	52	53	45	51

mean: 49°F; median: 50°F; mode: 45°F; range: 8°F

6. Anita has two sisters and three brothers. The mean of all their ages is 6 years. What will their mean age be 10 years from now? Twenty years from now?
16 years; 26 years

7. In a class of 28 sixth graders, all but one of the students are 12 years old. Which two data measurements are the same for the student's ages? What are those measurements?
the median and mode; 12 years

Find each missing value.

9. 3, 5, 7, 9, ■; mean: 7 **11**

10. 15, 17, ■, 28, 30; mean: 23 **25**

11. 10, 9, ■, 4, 8, 8, 4, 7; mode: 4 **4**

12. 7, 2, ■, 15, 20, 8, 14, 29; median: 13 **12**

13. 50, 100, 75, 60, ■, 25, 105, 40; median: 65 **70**

14. 14, 8, 17, 21, ■, 11, 3, 13; range: 20 **23**

15. **Critical Thinking** Find the set of 5 items of data that has a range of 9, a mean of 11, a median of 12, and a mode of 15. **6, 7, 12, 15, 15**

16. **What's the Error?** Joey says that the mean of the set of data is 23.5. Describe Joey's error. **Joey found the median instead of the mean.**

Numbers of Flowers in Bouquets	25	20	21	22	25	25

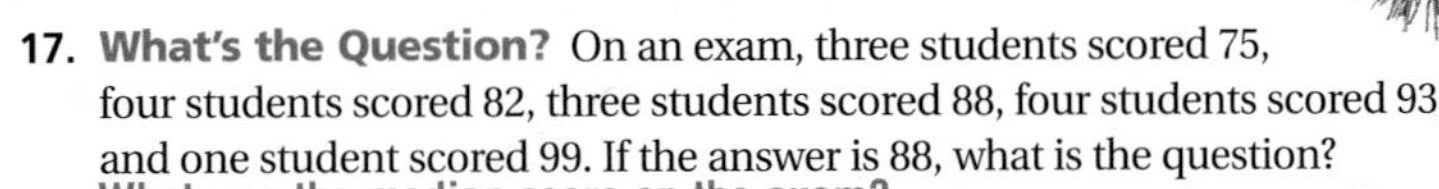

17. **What's the Question?** On an exam, three students scored 75, four students scored 82, three students scored 88, four students scored 93, and one student scored 99. If the answer is 88, what is the question? **What was the median score on the exam?**

18. **Challenge** In the Super Bowls from 1997 to 2002, the winning team won by a mean of $12\frac{1}{6}$ points. By how many points did the Green Bay Packers win in 1997? **14**

Year	Super Bowl Champion	Points Won By
2002	New England Patriots	3
2001	Baltimore Ravens	27
2000	St. Louis Rams	7
1999	Denver Broncos	15
1998	Denver Broncos	7
1997	Green Bay Packers	■

CRCT Prep • GPS Support • Spiral Review

19. **Multiple Choice** Over 5 days, Pedro jogged 6.5 miles, 5 miles, 2 miles, 2 miles, and 4.5 miles. Find the mean distance that Pedro jogged.

(A) 2 miles (B) 3.5 miles **(C) 4 miles** (D) 4.75 miles

20. **Multiple Choice** Which value is NOT always a number in the data set it represents?

(F) Mode **(G) Mean** (H) Least value (J) Greatest value

21. **Gridded Response** The mean of 12, 15, 20 and x is 18. Find the value of x. **25**

Tell whether each number is divisible by 2, 3, or 5. (Lesson 4-1)

22. 155 **5** **23.** 14 **2** **24.** 99 **3** **25.** 2,345 **5**

26. Make a table to show the number of days in each month of a non-leap year. (Lesson 6-1)

Ongoing Assessment and Intervention

***Diagnose Before* the Lesson**
6-2 Warm Up, TE p. 298

***Monitor During* the Lesson**
6-2 Know-It Notebook
6-2 Questioning Strategies

***Assess After* the Lesson**
6-2 Lesson Quiz, TE p. 301

Answers

26.

Numbers of Days in Each Month	
Month	**Days**
January	31
February	28
March	31
April	30
May	31
June	30
July	31
August	31
September	30
October	31
November	30
December	31

Test Prep Doctor In Exercise 19, if the student's choice was **A,** perhaps mode was confused with mean. If the choice was **B** or **D,** remind the student of the steps involved in finding the mean.

Journal

Have students explain the first step in determining the median of a data set.

Power Presentations with PowerPoint®

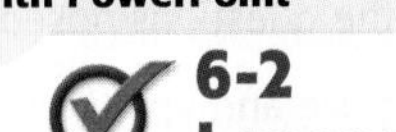

6-2 Lesson Quiz

Use the following data set:
18, 20, 56, 47, 30, 18, 21.

1. Find the range. **38**
2. Find the mean. **30**
3. Find the median. **21**
4. Find the mode. **18**
5. Bonnie ran a mile in 8 minutes, 8 minutes, 7 minutes, 9 minutes, and 8 minutes. What was her mean time? **8 minutes**

Also available on transparency

PROBLEM SOLVING 6-2

LESSON 6-2 **Problem Solving**
Mean, Median, Mode, and Range

Write the correct answer.

1. Use the table at right to find the mean, median, mode, and range of the data set.
mean: 4 wins; median: 4 wins; mode: 3 and 5 wins; range: 2 wins

World Series Winners

Team	Number of Wins
Baltimore Orioles	3
Boston Red Sox	5
Detroit Tigers	4
Minnesota Twins	3
Pittsburgh Pirates	5

2. When you use the data for only 2 of the teams in the table, the mean, median, and mode for the data are the same. Which teams are they?
Orioles and Twins or Pirates and Red Sox

Circle the letter of the correct answer.

3. The states that border the Gulf of Mexico are Alabama, Florida, Louisiana, Mississippi, and Texas. What is the mean for the number of letters in those states' names?
A 7 letters
(B) 7.8 letters
C 8 letters
D 8.7 letters

4. There are 5 whole numbers in a data set. The mean of the data is 10. The median and mode are both 9. The least number in the data set is 7, and the greatest is 14. What are the numbers in the data set?
F 7, 7, 9, 11, and 14
G 7, 7, 9, 9, and 14
(H) 7, 9, 9, 11, and 14
J 7, 9, 9, 14, and 14

5. If the mean of two numbers is 2.5, what is true about the data?
A Both numbers are greater than 5.
B One of the numbers is less than 2.
C One of the numbers is 2.5.
(D) The sum of the data is not divisible by 2.

6. Tom wants to find the average height of the students in his class. Which measurement should he find?
F the range
(G) the mean
H the median
J the mode

CHALLENGE 6-2

LESSON 6-2 **Challenge**
Speedy Data

Match each set of data with its description.

Mammal Speeds	
Antelope	54 mi/h
Cheetah	65 mi/h
Greyhound	42 mi/h
Horse	43 mi/h

C, H, M, N

Insect Speeds	
Bumble bee	11 mi/h
Honey bee	7 mi/h
Hornet	13 mi/h
Horsefly	9 mi/h

D, G, J, N

Fish Speeds	
Bluefin tuna	47 mi/h
Bonefish	40 mi/h
Sailfish	69 mi/h
Swordfish	40 mi/h

B, E, L, O

Bird Speeds	
Crane	42 mi/h
Goose	42 mi/h
Mallard	40 mi/h
Swan	44 mi/h

A, F, K, P

Range Descriptions	
A Range	4 mi/h
B Range	29 mi/h
C Range	23 mi/h
D Range	6 mi/h

Mean Descriptions	
E Mean	49 mi/h
F Mean	42 mi/h
G Mean	10 mi/h
H Mean	51 mi/h

Median Descriptions	
J Median	10 mi/h
K Median	42 mi/h
L Median	43.5 mi/h
M Median	48.5 mi/h

Mode Descriptions	
N Mode	none
O Mode	40 mi/h
P Mode	42 mi/h
Q Mode	44 mi/h

6-3 Organizer

Pacing: Traditional 1 day
Block $\frac{1}{2}$ day

Objective: Students learn the effect of additional data and outliers.

Online Edition
Tutorial Videos, Interactivities

Countdown to CRCT Week 12

Warm Up

Use the numbers to answer the questions.

146, 161, 114, 178, 150, 134, 172, 131, 128

1. What is the greatest number? 178
2. What is the least number? 114
3. How can you find the median? Order the numbers and find the middle value.

Problem of the Day

Ms. Green has 6 red gloves and 10 blue gloves in a box. She closes her eyes and picks some gloves. What is the least number of gloves Ms. Green will have to pick to ensure 2 gloves of the same color? 3

Also available on transparency

M6D1.e Relate the data analysis to the context of the questions posed.

M6P4.c Recognize and apply mathematics in contexts outside of mathematics.

6-3 Additional Data and Outliers

Learn the effect of additional data and outliers.

Vocabulary
outlier

The mean, median, and mode may change when you add data to a data set.

USA's Jim Shea in Men's Skeleton at the 2002 Winter Olympics

M6D1.e Relate the data analysis to the context of the questions posed. Also, M6P4.c.

EXAMPLE 1 Sports Application

A **Find the mean, median, and mode of the data in the table.**

U.S. Winter Olympic Medals Won								
Year	2002	1998	1994	1992	1988	1984	1980	1976
Medals	34	13	13	11	6	8	12	10

mean = 13.375 mode = 13 median = 11.5

B **The United States also won 8 medals in 1972 and 5 medals in 1968. Add this data to the data in the table and find the mean, median, and mode.**

mean = 12 *The mean decreased by 1.375.*
modes = 8, 13 *There is an additional mode.*
median = 10.5 *The median decreased by 1.*

An **outlier** is a value in a set that is very different from the other values.

EXAMPLE 2 Social Studies Application

In 2001, 64-year-old Sherman Bull became the oldest person to reach the top of Mount Everest. Other climbers to reach the summit that day were 33, 31, 31, 32, 33, and 28 years old. Find the mean, median, and mode without and with Bull's age, and explain the changes.

Data without Bull's age: mean ≈ 31.3 modes = 31, 33 median = 31.5

Data with Bull's age: mean = 36 modes = 31, 33 median = 32

When you add Bull's age, the mean increases by 4.7, the modes stay the same, and the median increases by 0.5. The mean is the most affected by the outlier.

Helpful Hint

Sherman Bull's age is an outlier because he is much older than the others in the group.

1 Introduce

Alternate Opener

EXPLORATION

6-3 Additional Data and Outliers

Casey Fitzrandolph won the men's 500-meter speed-skating competition in the 2002 Olympics with a time of **69.23 seconds.** The table lists the top 32 times in the 500-meter race.

69.23	69.26	69.47	69.49	69.59	69.60	69.60	69.81
69.86	69.89	70.10	70.11	70.28	70.32	70.33	70.44
70.57	70.75	70.84	70.88	70.97	71.27	71.39	71.54
71.96	72.07	72.49	72.58	72.64	72.69	72.93	74.81

1. Find the range, which is the difference between the fastest and the slowest time.
2. Find the median, which is the number in the middle of the data set.
3. Find the mean with a calculator.
4. The table excluded three more times. These times are 108.46, 117.41, and 133.57. Calculate the range, median, and mean including these three additional times.

Think and Discuss

5. **Discuss** why the last three times in number 4 were excluded from the table above.
6. **Describe** how the additional three times affect the range, median, and mean.

Motivate

Give students the following list of CD prices. Have them describe the data set and tell you anything that they notice about the data set.

$13, $11, $15, $15, $29, $15, $12, $16

Possible answer: The mode is $15. Most of the prices are from $11 to $16, but one is much higher, $29.

Explorations and answers are provided in *Alternate Openers: Explorations Transparencies.*

Sometimes one or two data values can greatly affect the mean, median, or mode. When one of these values is affected like this, you should choose a different value to best describe the data set.

EXAMPLE 3 Describing a Data Set

The Seawells are shopping for a DVD player. They found ten DVD players with the following prices:

$175, $180, $130, $150, $180, $500, $160, $180, $150, $160

What are the mean, median, and mode of this data set? Which one best describes the data set?

mean = $196.50 mode = $180 median = $167.50

The median price is the best description of the prices. Most of the DVD players cost *about* $167.50.

The mean is higher than most of the prices because of the $500 player, and the mode is higher because of the three players that cost $180 each.

Some data sets do not contain numbers. For example, the circle graph shows the results of a survey to find people's favorite color.

When it does not contain numbers, the only way to describe the data set is with the mode. You cannot find a mean or a median for a set of colors.

The mode for this data set is blue. Most people in this survey chose blue as their favorite color.

Favorite Colors

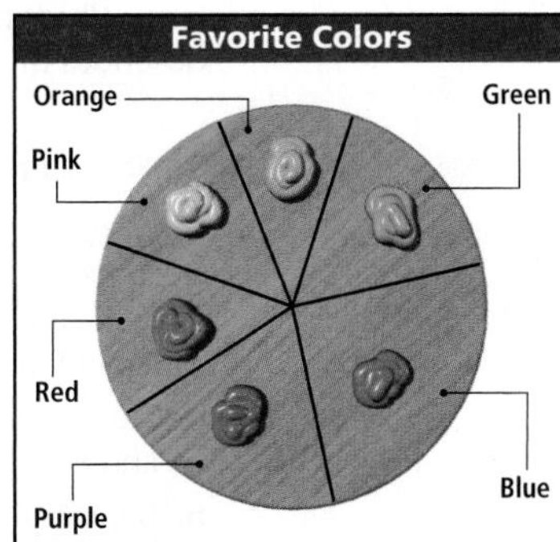

Possible answers to *Think and Discuss*

1. The mean will be greater than it would have been without the outlier with a large value. An outlier with a small value will make the mean less than it would have been without the outlier.
2. because with the outlier of 39° the mean will be too low
3. results of a survey to find people's favorite singer or any data set with nonnumeric data

Think and Discuss GPS M6P2.c, M6P3.a

1. **Explain** how an outlier with a large value will affect the mean of a data set. What is the effect of a small outlier value?
2. **Explain** why the mean would not be a good description of the following high temperatures that occurred over 7 days: 72°F, 73°F, 70°F, 68°F, 70°F, 71°F, and 39°F.
3. **Give an example** of a data set that could be described only by its mode.

Power Presentations with PowerPoint®

Additional Examples

Example 1

A. Find the mean, median, and mode of the data in the table.

EMS Football Games Won					
Year	'98	'99	'00	'01	'02
Games	11	5	7	5	7

mean = 7; modes = 5, 7; median = 7

B. EMS also won 13 games in 1997 and 8 games in 1996. Add this data to the data in the table and find the mean, median, and mode.

mean = 8; modes = 5, 7; median = 7

Example 2

Ms. Gray is 25 years old. She took a class with students who were 55, 52, 59, 61, 63, and 58 years old. Find the mean, median, and mode with and without Ms. Gray's age.

with:

mean ≈ 53.3; no mode; median = 58

without:

mean = 58; no mode; median = 58.5

Example 3

The Yorks found 8 pairs of skates with the following prices: $35, $42, $75, $40, $47, $34, $45, and $40. What are the mean, median, and mode of this data set? Which statistic best describes the data set?

mean = $44.75 mode = $40

median = $41

The median price is the best description of the prices.

Also available on transparency

2 Teach

Guided Instruction

In this lesson, students learn the effect of additional data and outliers. First teach them how adding data to an existing set of data can change the mean, median, and mode. Then teach students how an outlier can affect the mean, median, and mode of a data set. Have them determine which measure of central tendency best describes a given data set.

Reaching All Learners

Through Cooperative Learning

Have groups do research (for example, in newspapers and magazines) to find data sets with outliers. You may want to choose a particular data set to save time. Have students find the mean, median, and mode of the data and determine which is the best description of the data set. Then ask students to find the mean, median, and mode without including the outliers.

3 Close

ENGLISH LANGUAGE LEARNERS

Summarize

Have the students explain what an *outlier* is and how it can affect a set of data.

Possible answer: An outlier is a value in a set that is very different from the other values. It can affect the mean of a set of data by making it much higher or lower than it would have been without the outlier.

6-3 Exercises

Assignment Guide

If you finished Example 1 assign:
Average 1, 12–17
Advanced 4, 12–17

If you finished Example 2 assign:
Average 1–2, 7–8, 12–17
Advanced 4–5, 7, 9, 12–17

If you finished Example 3 assign:
Average 1–9, 12–17
Advanced 4–17

Homework Quick Check

Quickly check key concepts.
Exercises: 4, 6, 8

Math Background

A group of five workers with annual incomes of $22,000, $35,000, $40,000, $48,000, and $60,000 have a mean income of $41,000 and a median income of $40,000. The inclusion of an individual with annual income of $1,500,000 increases the median only to $44,000 but inflates the mean to over $280,000.

Income data presented by the United States Census Bureau is based upon a much larger data set than six individuals. Nevertheless, incomes that are outliers significantly skew the mean. Therefore the median income is the standard *average* used to report income in the United States.

Answers

1–2, 5. See p. A4.

Georgia Performance Standards

M6P3.a Organize and consolidate their mathematical thinking through communication.

M6P3.c Analyze and evaluate the mathematical thinking and strategies of others.

6-3 Exercises

M6P3.a, M6P3.c

GUIDED PRACTICE

See Example 1

1. Sports The graph shows how many times some countries have won the Davis Cup in tennis from 1900 to 2000.

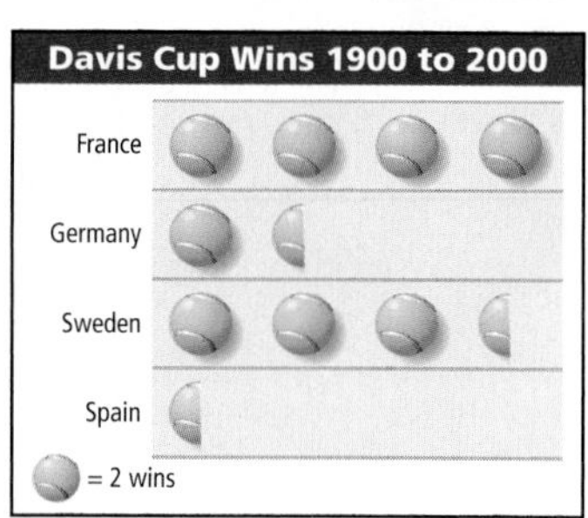

a. Find the mean, median, and mode of the data.

b. The United States won 31 Davis Cups between 1900 and 2000. Add this number to the data in the graph and find the mean, median, and mode.

See Example 2

2. In 1998, 77-year-old John Glenn became the oldest person to travel into space. Other astronauts traveling on that same mission were 43, 37, 38, 46, 35, and 42 years old. Find the mean, median, and mode of all their ages with and without Glenn's age, and explain the changes.

See Example 3

3. Kate read books that were 240, 450, 180, 160, 195, 170, 240, and 165 pages long. What are the mean, median, and mode of this data set? Which one best describes the data set? mean = 225, median = 187.5, mode = 240; median

INDEPENDENT PRACTICE

See Example 1

4. History The table shows the ages of the 10 youngest signers of the Declaration of Independence.

Ages of 10 Youngest Signers of Declaration of Independence

Age	26	29	30	31	33	34
Number Of Signers	//	/	/	/	///	//

a. Find the mean, median, and mode of the data. mean ≈ 30.9, median = 32, mode = 33

b. Benjamin Franklin was 70 years old when he signed the Declaration of Independence. Add his age to the data in the table and find the mean, median, and mode. mean ≈ 34.5, median = 33, mode = 33

See Example 2

5. Geography The map shows the population densities of several states along the Atlantic coast. Find the mean, median, and mode of the data with and without Maine's population density, and explain the changes.

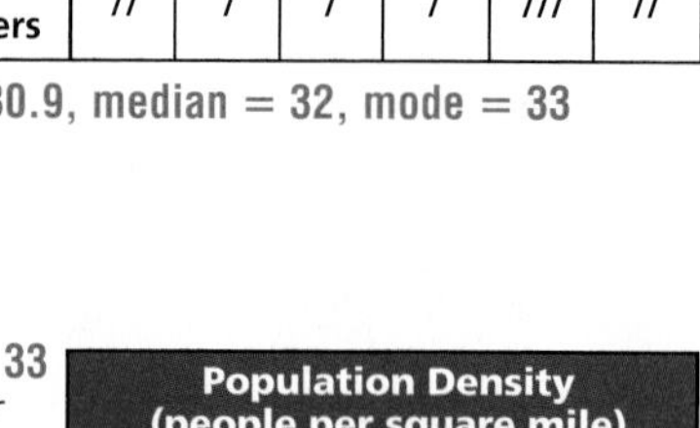

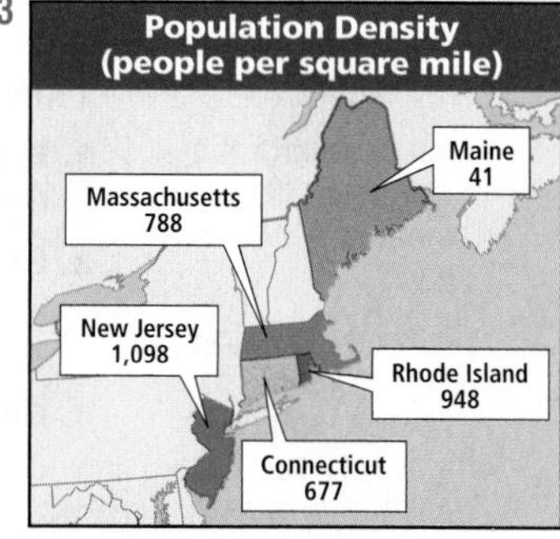

See Example 3

6. The passengers in a van are 16, 19, 17, 18, 15, 14, 32, 32, and 41 years old. What are the mean, median, and mode of this data set? Which one best describes the data set? mean = 22.7, median = 18, mode = 32; mean

Extra Practice p. 724

RETEACH 6-3

LESSON 6-3 Reteach
Additional Data and Outliers

An **outlier** is a value in a set of data that is much greater or much less than the other values.

Number of Minutes Spent on Homework

Mon	Tue	Wed	Thurs	Fri
47	42	45	46	10

The outlier is 10 minutes, because it is much less than the other values in the set.

An outlier may affect the mean, median, or mode.

Data without Friday's value: mean = 45 median = 45.5 no mode
Data with Friday's value: mean = 38 median = 45 no mode

When Friday's value is included, the mean decreases by 7 minutes, the median decreases by 0.5 minutes, and the mode stays the same. The mean is most affected by the outlier because it is less than every value except for the outlier itself.

Find the mean, median, and mode for the set of data with and without the outlier.

1. 22, 25, 48, 26, 21, 27, 26, 29

With outlier: mean: 28; median: 26; mode: 26

Without outlier: mean: 25.1; median: 26; mode: 26

When an outlier affects the mean, median, or mode, choose a value that best describes the data.

In the example above, the median best describes the data because 45 minutes is closer to most of the data values in the set.

Find the mean, median, and mode. Then decide which best describes the set of data.

2. 16, 12, 14, 17, 81, 18, 13, 19, 14, 19

mean: 22.3; median: 16.5; mode: 14 and 19. The median best describes the data.

PRACTICE 6-3

LESSON 6-3 Practice B
Additional Data and Outliers

Use the table to answer Exercises 1–2.

Population Densities

State	People (per mi²)
Idaho	16
Nevada	18
New Mexico	15
North Dakota	9
South Dakota	10

1. The table shows population data for some of the least-crowded states. Find the mean, median, and mode of the data.

mean: 13.6; median: 15;
mode: none

2. Alaska has the lowest population density of any state. Only about 1 person per square mile lives there. Add this number to the data in the table and find the mean, median, and mode.

mean: 11.5; median: 12.5;
mode: none

Use the table to answer Exercises 3–4.

State Counties

State	Number of Counties
Illinois	102
Iowa	99
North Carolina	100
Tennessee	95
Virginia	95

3. The table shows some of the states with the most counties. Find the mean, median, and mode of the data.

mean: 98.2; median: 99;
mode: 95

4. With 254 counties, Texas has more counties than any other state. Add this number to the data in the table and find the mean, median, and mode.

mean: $124.1\overline{6}$; median: 99.5;
mode: 95

5. In Exercise 1, which measurement best describes the data? Why is Alaska's population density an outlier for that data set?

the mean; because it is much lower than the other data

6. In Exercise 4, why is the number of counties in Texas an outlier for the data set? Which measurement best describes the data set with Texas included?

because Texas has many more counties; the median

Earth Science LINK

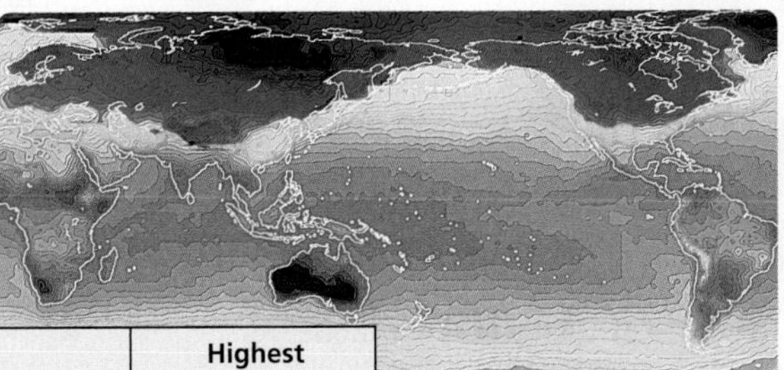

On September 13, 1922, the temperature in El Azizia, Libya, reached 136°F, the record high for the planet. (*Source: The World Almanac and Book of Facts*)

This satellite map shows the world's surface temperature. The dark blue areas are coldest, and the deep red areas are hottest.

Continent	Highest Temperature (°F)
Africa	136
Antarctica	59
Asia	129
Australia	128
Europe	122
North America	134
South America	120

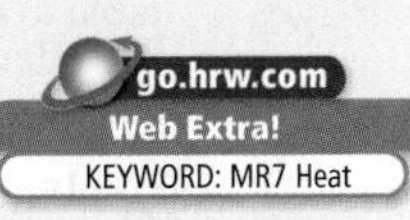

7. What are the mean, median, and mode of the highest recorded temperatures on each continent? mean ≈ 118.29, median = 128, no mode

8. a. Which temperature is an outlier? 59°

b. What are the mean, median, and mode of the temperatures if the outlier is not included?

9. **What's the Error?** A student stated that the median temperature would rise to 120.6°F if a new record high of 75°F were recorded in Antarctica. Explain the error. How would the median temperature actually be affected if a high of 75°F were recorded in Antarctica?
The mean of the data would rise to 120.6°F. The median would remain unchanged.

10. **Write About It** Is the data in the table best described by the mean, median, or mode? Explain. Possible answer: median; Antarctica's temperature of 59°F lowers the mean.

11. **Challenge** Suppose a new high temperature were recorded in Europe, and the new mean temperature became 120°F. What is Europe's new high temperature? 134°F

8b. mean ≈ 128.17, median = 128.5, no mode

CRCT PREP • GPS SUPPORT • SPIRAL REVIEW

12. **Multiple Choice** Which value will change the most when 16 is added to the data set 0, 1, 4, 0, 3, 4, 2, and 1?

Ⓐ Mean Ⓑ Median Ⓒ Mode Ⓓ Outlier

13. **Gridded Response** The table shows the speeds, in miles per hour, of certain animals. Which speed is an outlier? 70

Animal	House cat	Rabbit	Cheetah	Reindeer	Zebra	Elk	Elephant
Speed (mi/h)	30	35	70	32	40	45	25

Solve each equation. Check your answer. (Lesson 5-5)

14. $\frac{1}{2} + m = 2$ $m = 1\frac{1}{2}$ or $\frac{3}{2}$

15. $n - \frac{4}{5} = \frac{1}{10}$ $n = \frac{9}{10}$

16. $\frac{1}{3} + x = \frac{2}{3}$ $x = \frac{1}{3}$

17. Find the median, mode, and range of the animal speeds in Exercise 13. (Lesson 6-2)
median = 35; no mode; range = 45

CHALLENGE 6-3

LESSON 6-3 Challenge
Outer Space Outlier

You have been chosen to train as an astronaut! The statisticians at NASA are not happy, because you are a major outlier for their data. Use the information below to find how you will affect their astronaut data. Some answers depend on student ages. Sample answers are given for age 12.

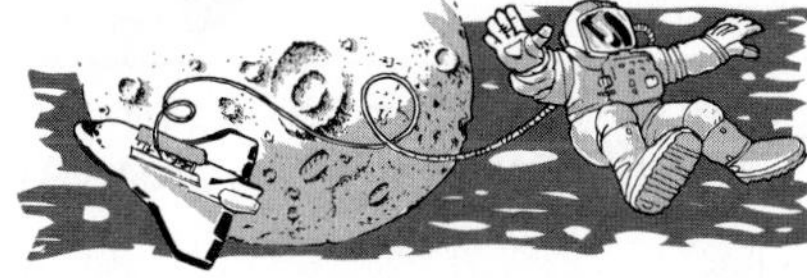

Youngest Astronauts

In 1970, Russian astronaut Gherman S. Titov became the youngest person to travel into space. He was 25 years old at liftoff. The ages of some of the other youngest astronauts of all time were 26, 29, 28, 27, 26, and 28.

Data Without Your Age:	Data With Your Age:
Mean age: 27	Mean age: 25.125
Median age: 27	Median age: 26.5
Mode age: 26 and 28	Mode age: 26 and 28

Oldest Astronauts

In 1998, American astronaut John H. Glenn became the oldest person to travel into space. He was 77 years old at liftoff. The ages of some of the other oldest astronauts of all time were 54, 59, 61, 56, 58, and 55.

Data Without Your Age:	Data With Your Age:
Mean age: 60	Mean age: 54
Median age: 58	Median age: 57
Mode age: no mode	Mode age: no mode

PROBLEM SOLVING 6-3

LESSON 6-3 Problem Solving
Additional Data and Outliers

Use the table to answer the questions.

Successful Films in the U.S.

Film	U.S. Earnings for first release (million $)
E.T. the Extra-Terrestrial	400
Forrest Gump	330
Independence Day	305
Jurassic Park	357
The Lion King	313

1. Find the mean, median, and mode of the earnings data.
mean: $341 million; median: $330 million; mode: none

2. *Titanic* earned more money in the United States than any other film—a total of $600 million! Add this figure to the data and find the mean, median, and mode. Round your answer for the mean to the nearest whole million.
mean: $384 million; median: $343.5 million; mode: none

Circle the letter of the correct answer.

3. In Canada, people watch TV an average of 74 minutes each day. In Germany, people watch an average of 68 minutes a day. In France it is 67 minutes a day, in Spain it is 91 minutes a day, and in Ireland it is 74 minutes a day. Find the mean, median, and mode of the data.
   - A mean: 74 min.; median: 74 min.; mode: 74 min.
   - B mean: 74 min.; median: 74.8 min.; mode: 74 min.
   - C mean: 74.8 min.; median: 74 min.; mode: 24 min.
   - Ⓓ mean: 74.8 min.; median: 74 min.; mode: 74 min.

4. People in the United States watch more television than in any other country. Americans watch an average of 118 minutes a day! Add this number to the data and find the mean, median, and mode.
   - Ⓕ mean: 82 min.; median: 74 min.; mode: 74 min.
   - G mean: 82 min.; median: 74 min.; mode: 118 min.
   - H mean: 82 min.; median: 91 min.; mode: 74 min.
   - J mean: 74.8 min.; median: 82 min.; mode: 74 min.

5. In Exercise 2, which data measurement changed the least with the addition of *Titanic*'s earnings?
   - A the range
   - Ⓒ the median
   - B the mean
   - D the upper extreme

6. In Exercise 4, which measurements best describe the data?
   - F mean and median
   - G range and mean
   - Ⓗ median and mode
   - J range and mode

ONGOING ASSESSMENT and INTERVENTION

***Diagnose Before* the Lesson**
6-3 Warm Up, TE p. 302

***Monitor During* the Lesson**
6-3 Know-It Notebook
6-3 Questioning Strategies

***Assess After* the Lesson**
6-3 Lesson Quiz, TE p. 305

Interdisciplinary LINK

Earth Science

Exercises 7–11 require students to use the table of record high temperatures of continents in the world. Students study weather in middle school Earth science programs such as *Holt Science and Technology*.

For Exercise 13, remind students that an outlier is a piece of data that is far greater or less than the other data in the set.

Journal

Have students give an example of a data set with an outlier. Have them find the mean, median, and mode of the data without and with the outlier and explain how the outlier changes these measures of central tendency.

6-3 Lesson Quiz

At the college bookstore, your brother buys 6 textbooks at the following prices: $21, $58, $68, $125, $36, and $140.

1. Find the mean. $74.67

2. Find the median. $63

3. Find the mode. none

4. Your brother signs up for an additional class, and the textbook costs $225. Recalculate the mean, including the extra book. $96.14

Also available on transparency

Organizer

Objective: Assess students' mastery of concepts and skills in Lessons 6-1 through 6-3.

Resources

Assessment Resources
Section 6A Quiz

Test & Practice Generator
One-Stop Planner®

INTERVENTION

Resources

***Ready to Go On? Intervention and Enrichment* Worksheets**

***Ready to Go On?* CD-ROM**

***Ready to Go On?* Online**

my.hrw.com

Answers

1.

Year	Attendance
Five years ago	220
Four years ago	235
Three years ago	250
Two years ago	242
Last year	258

7. See p. A4.

CHAPTER 6

SECTION 6A

READY TO GO ON?

Quiz for Lessons 6-1 Through 6-3

6-1 Make a Table

1. The local dance studio holds a spring recital each year. Five years ago, 220 people attended the recital. Four years ago, 235 people attended. Three years ago, 250 people attended. Two years ago, 242 people attended. Last year, 258 people attended. Use the attendance data to make a table. Then use your table to describe how attendance changed over time.
The attendance increased for 2 years, decreased for a year, and then increased again.

6-2 Mean, Median, Mode, and Range

Find the mean, median, mode, and range of each data set.

2.

Distance (mi)					
5	6	4	7	3	5

mean = 5, median = 5, mode = 5, range = 4

3.

Test Scores				
78	80	85	92	90

mean = 85, median = 85, no mode, range = 14

4.

Ages of Students (yr)							
11	13	12	12	12	13	9	14

mean = 12, median = 12, mode = 12, range = 5

5.

Number of Pages in Each Book						
145	119	156	158	125	128	135

mean = 138, median = 135, no mode, range = 39

Ready to Go On?

6-3 Additional Data and Outliers

6. The table shows the number of people who attended each monthly meeting from January to May.

Number of People Attending				
Jan	Feb	Mar	Apr	May
27	26	32	30	30

a. Find the mean, median, and mode of the attendances. mean = 29; median = 30; mode = 30

b. In June, 39 people attended the meeting, and in July, 26 people attended the meeting. Add this data to the table and find the mean, median, and mode with the new data. mean = 30, median = 30, modes = 26 and 30

7. The four states with the longest coastlines are Alaska, Florida, California, and Hawaii. Alaska's coastline is 6,640 miles. Florida's coastline is 1,350 miles. California's coastline is 840 miles, and Hawaii's coastline is 750 miles. Find the mean, median, and mode of the lengths with and without Alaska's, and explain the changes.

8. The daily snowfall amounts for the first ten days of December are listed below.

2 in., 5 in., 0 in., 0 in., 15 in., 1 in., 0 in., 3 in., 1 in., 4 in.

What are the mean, median, and mode of this data set? Which one best describes the data set? mean = 3.1 in., median = 1.5 in., mode = 0 in.; median

READY TO GO ON?

Diagnose and Prescribe

NO INTERVENE

YES ENRICH

Ready to Go On? Intervention	*Ready to Go On? Intervention,* Section 6A: Worksheets	CD-ROM	Online
Lesson 6-1	6-1 Intervention	Activity 6-1	Diagnose and Prescribe Online
Lesson 6-2	6-2 Intervention	Activity 6-2	
Lesson 6-3	6-3 Intervention	Activity 6-3	

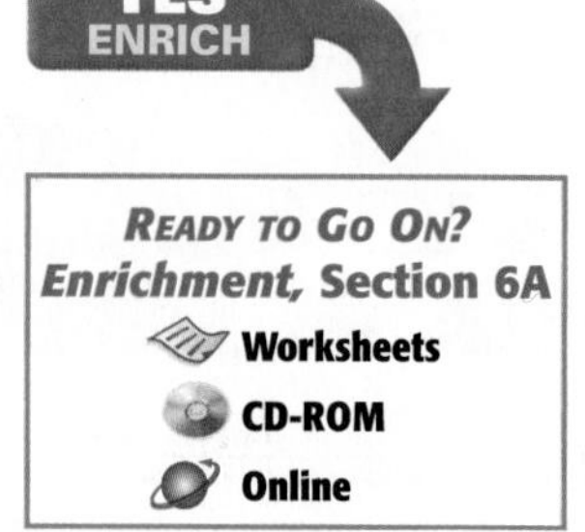

Focus on Problem Solving

Make a Plan

• Prioritize and sequence information

Some problems give you a lot of information. Read the entire problem carefully to be sure you understand all of the facts. You may need to read it over several times, perhaps aloud so that you can hear yourself say the words.

Then decide which information is most important (prioritize). Is there any information that is absolutely necessary to solve the problem? This information is important.

Finally, put the information in order (sequence). Use comparison words like *before, after, longer, shorter,* and so on to help you. Write the sequence down before you try to solve the problem.

Read the problems below and answer the questions that follow.

1. The compact disc (CD) was invented 273 years after the piano. The tape recorder was invented in 1898. Thomas Edison invented the phonograph 21 years before the tape recorder and 95 years before the compact disc. What is the date of each invention?
   - **a.** Which invention's date can you use to find the dates of all the others?
   - **b.** Can you solve the problem without this date? Explain.
   - **c.** List the inventions in order from earliest invention to latest invention.

2. Jon recorded the heights of his family members. There are 4 people in Jon's family, including Jon. Jon's mother is 2 inches taller than Jon's father. Jon is 56 inches tall. Jon's sister is 4 inches taller than Jon and 5 inches shorter than Jon's father. What are the heights of Jon and his family members?
   - **a.** Whose height can you use to find the heights of all the others?
   - **b.** Can you solve the problem without this height? Explain.
   - **c.** List Jon's family members in order from shortest to tallest.

Answers

1. piano: 1699
   phonograph: 1877
   tape recorder: 1898
   CD: 1972
2. Jon: 56 in.
   Jon's sister: 60 in.
   Jon's father: 65 in.
   Jon's mother: 67 in.

2. **a.** Jon's height
   b. If the height of any one of the family members were given instead, you could find the heights of all of the family members. But without at least one height, the problem could not be solved.
   c. Jon, Jon's sister, Jon's father, Jon's mother

Possible strategy:

Position the family members' heights relative to each other on a vertical number line, using tick marks to show inches. Use Jon's height to find the heights of the other family members.

Focus on Problem Solving

Organizer

Objective: Focus on making a plan to solve the problem.

Online Edition

Resources

Chapter 6 Resource Book
Reading Strategies

Problem Solving Process

This page focuses on the second step of the problem-solving process: **Make a Plan**

Discuss

Have students discuss their answers for parts **a–c** for each problem and then discuss the strategies they used to order the information.

Possible answers:

1. **a.** the tape recorder's invention date
   b. If the invention date of any of the other inventions were given instead, you could still find the other dates, but without at least one date, the problem could not be solved.
   c. piano, phonograph, tape recorder, CD

Possible strategy:

Use a timeline to position the inventions relative to each other. Label the time elapsed between inventions. Use the fact that the tape recorder was invented in 1898 to find the other information.

SECTION 6B

Displaying and Interpreting Data

One-Minute Section Planner

Lesson	Materials	MiC and Lab Resources
Lesson 6-4 Bar Graphs • Display and analyze data in bar graphs. **6-4 Technology Lab** Create Bar Graphs • Use a spreadsheet program to create bar graphs. ☑ CRCT ☑ SAT-10 ☑ ITBS ☑ CTBS ☑ NAEP	Graph paper, connecting cubes, spreadsheet software	**MiC:** ***Picturing Numbers*** pp. 1–7, 13–17 **MiC:** ***Fraction Times*** pp. 2–9 ***Hands-On Lab Activities*** 6-4 ***Technology Lab Activities*** 6-4
Lesson 6-5 Line Plots, Frequency Tables, and Histograms • Organize data in line plots, frequency tables, and histograms. **6-5 Hands-On Lab** Use a Survey to Collect Data • Use a survey to collect and organize data in a table. ☑ CRCT ☑ SAT-10 ☑ ITBS ☑ CTBS ☑ NAEP	Graph paper	**MiC:** ***Picturing Numbers*** p. 5 **MiC:** ***Take a Chance*** pp. 20–23 ***Hands-On Lab Activities*** 6-5
Lesson 6-6 Ordered Pairs • Graph ordered pairs on a coordinate grid. ☐ CRCT ☑ SAT-10 ☑ ITBS ☐ CTBS ☑ NAEP	Graph paper, road maps	**MiC:** ***Figuring All the Angles*** p. 9 ***Hands-On Lab Activities*** 6-6
Lesson 6-7 Line Graphs • Display and analyze data in line graphs. ☑ CRCT ☑ SAT-10 ☑ ITBS ☐ CTBS ☑ NAEP	Graph paper, line graphs from media resources	**MiC:** ***Picturing Numbers*** pp. 32–38 ***Technology Lab Activities*** 6-7
Lesson 6-8 Misleading Graphs • Recognize misleading graphs ☐ CRCT ☑ SAT-10 ☑ ITBS ☑ CTBS ☑ NAEP	Graph paper	**MiC:** ***Picturing Numbers*** pp. 16–17
Lesson 6-9 Stem-and-Leaf Plots • Make and analyze stem-and-leaf plots. ☐ CRCT ☑ SAT-10 ☑ ITBS ☐ CTBS ☑ NAEP		
Lesson 6-10 Choosing an Appropriate Display • Choose an appropriate way to display data. ☑ CRCT ☐ SAT-10 ☑ ITBS ☑ CTBS ☑ NAEP	Graph paper	**MiC:** ***Picturing Numbers*** All sections ***Hands-On Lab Activities*** 6-10

MK = *Manipulatives Kit*

Mathematics in Context

The units ***Picturing Numbers, Fraction Times, Take a Chance,*** and ***Figuring All the Angles*** from the *Mathematics in Context* © 2006 series can be used with Section 6B. See Section Planner above for suggestions for integrating *MiC* with *Holt Mathematics*.

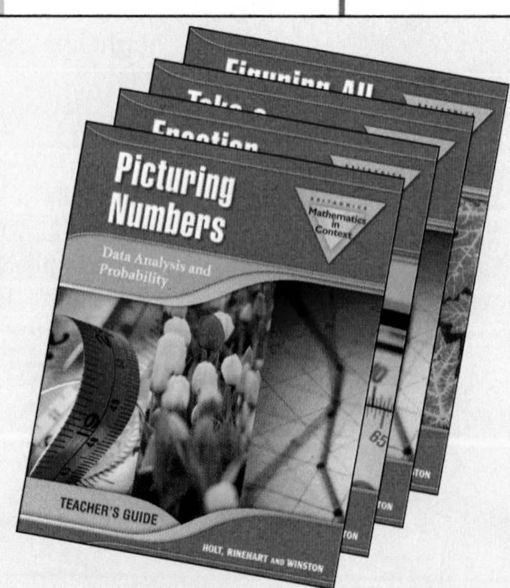

Section Overview

Bar Graphs, Line Plots, Frequency Tables, and Histograms *Lessons 6-4, 6-5*

Why? Data is easier to interpret when it is organized into a table or a graph.

A **bar graph** is used to display countable data that are grouped in categories.

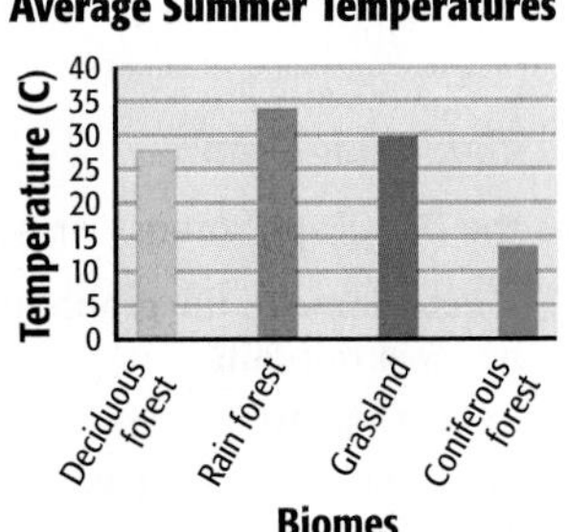

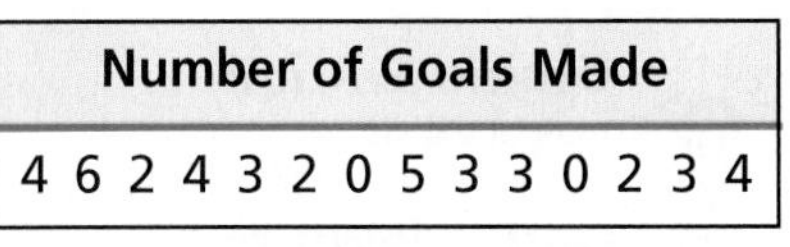

Number of Goals Made
4 6 2 4 3 2 0 5 3 3 0 2 3 4

A **line plot** uses a number line and X's or other symbols to show frequencies of values.

Data Item	Tally	Frequency
Item 1	|||	33
Item 2	||||	47
Item 3	||	29
Item 4	~~||||~~	5

A **frequency table** tells the number of times something occurs.

A **histogram** is a bar graph that shows the frequency of occurrences within each interval.

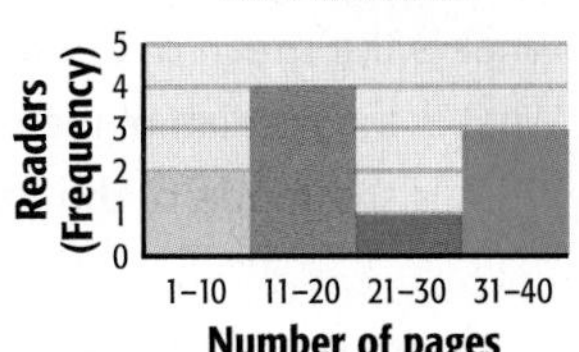

Ordered Pairs, Line Graphs, and Stem-and-Leaf Plots *Lessons 6-6 through 6-10*

Why? Choosing an appropriate data display depends on the data and the purpose.

Ordered Pairs

Each point on a coordinate grid can be located by using an ordered pair of numbers, such as (**3**, **2**).

- The starting point is (0, 0).
- The first number tells how to move **horizontally**.
- The second number tells how to move **vertically**.

A **stem-and-leaf plot** arranges data by place value.

Stems	Leaves
1	1 2 3
2	2 2 3 6 7
3	1 1 3 3 8 9
4	7 8
5	4 6 9

Key: 3|8 means 38

A **line graph** displays a set of data using line segments. Data that shows change over time is best displayed in a line graph.

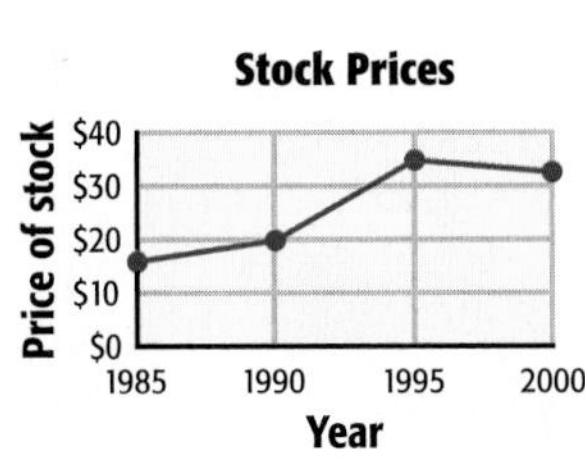

Line graphs that display two sets of data are called **double-line graphs.** Double-line graphs are often used to compare the two data sets.

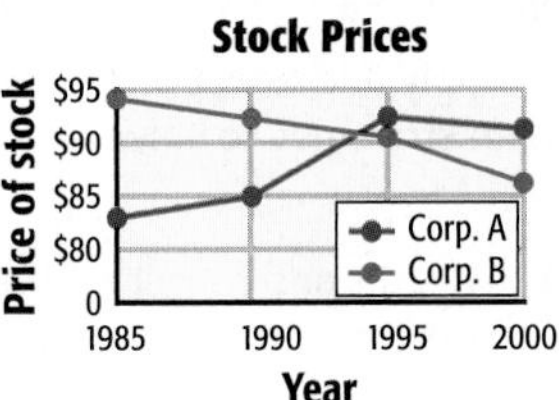

6-4 Organizer

Pacing: Traditional 1 day
Block $\frac{1}{2}$ day

Objective: Students display and analyze data in bar graphs.

GPS M6D1.b
Hands-On Lab
In *Hands-On Lab Activities*

Online Edition
Tutorial Videos

Countdown to CRCT Week 12

Power Presentations with PowerPoint®

Warm Up

Use the following data set.

45 55 58 63 63 37 76 46 34

1. What is the mean of the data? 53
2. What is the median of the data? 55
3. What is the mode of the data? 63

Problem of the Day

The distance around the bases is 4 × 90 feet. How many runs does a baseball team need to score before the scoring base runners have covered a mile? (1 mile = 5,280 feet)
15 runs

Also available on transparency

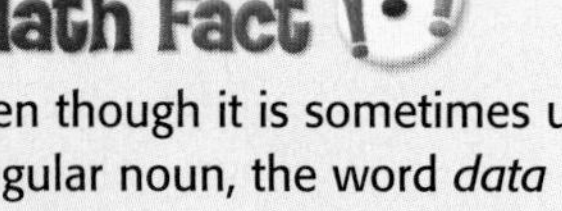

Even though it is sometimes used as a singular noun, the word *data* is actually the plural of the Latin word *datum*, which means "a gift".

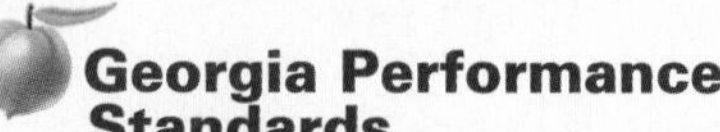

M6D1.b Using data, construct frequency distributions, frequency tables, and graphs.

M6P1.a Build new mathematical knowledge through problem solving.

M6P1.c Apply and adapt a variety of appropriate strategies to solve problems.

M6P1.d Monitor and reflect on the process of mathematical problem solving.

M6P5.b Select, apply, and translate among mathematical representations to solve problems.

6-4 Bar Graphs

Deciduous Forest
Tundra
Rain Forest
Savannah

Learn to display and analyze data in bar graphs.

Vocabulary
bar graph
double-bar graph

A biome is a large region characterized by a specific climate. There are ten land biomes on Earth. Some are pictured at right. Each gets a different amount of rainfall.

A *bar graph* can be used to display and compare data about rainfall. A **bar graph** displays data with vertical or horizontal bars.

Georgia Performance Standards
M6D1.b Using data, construct graphs. Also, M6P1.a, M6P1.c, M6P1.d, M6P5.b.

EXAMPLE 1 Reading a Bar Graph

Use the bar graph to answer each question.

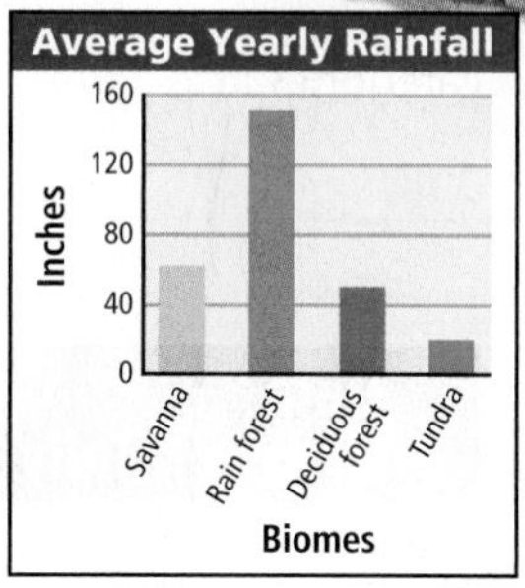

Average Yearly Rainfall
Inches: 0, 40, 80, 120, 160
Savanna, Rain forest, Deciduous forest, Tundra
Biomes

A **Which biome in the graph has the most rainfall?**

Find the highest bar.

The rain forest has the most rainfall.

B **Which biomes in the graph have an average yearly rainfall less than 40 inches?**

Find the bar or bars whose heights measure less than 40.

The tundra has an average yearly rainfall less than 40 inches.

EXAMPLE 2 Making a Bar Graph

Use the given data to make a bar graph.

Coal Reserves (billion metric tons)		
Asia	Europe	Africa
695	404	66

Step 1: Find an appropriate scale and interval. The scale must include all of the data values. The interval separates the scale into equal parts.

Step 2: Use the data to determine the lengths of the bars. Draw bars of equal width. The bars cannot touch.

Step 3: Title the graph and label the axes.

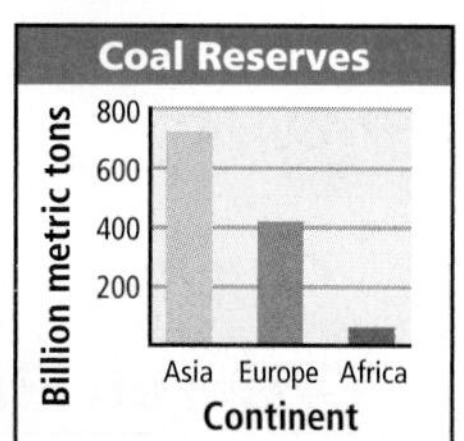

1 Introduce

Alternate Opener

EXPLORATION

Bar Graphs

The bar graph shows the medal totals of the four countries that won the most medals at the 2002 Winter Olympic Games.

Top Four Medal-Winning Countries at 2002 Winter Olympic Games
Number of medals: 0, 4, 8, 12, 16, 20, 24, 28, 32, 36
Gold, Silver, Bronze, Total
Germany, USA, Norway, Canada

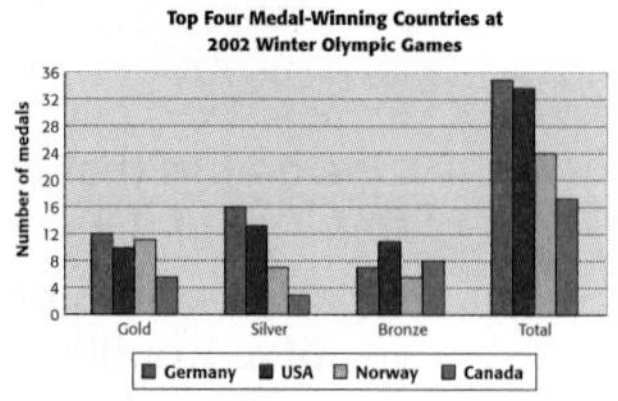

1. Name the country that won
 a. the most gold medals.
 b. the most silver medals.
 c. the most bronze medals.
 d. the most medals overall.
2. What is the total number of medals won by each country?

Think and Discuss

3. **Explain** a different way to display the data.
4. **Discuss** information that is not shown by the bar graph.

Motivate

Have students discuss places where they have seen graphs and what the graphs represent. Possible answers: newspapers, magazines, television; stock performance, survey results Explain that this lesson focuses on *bar graphs,* which display data with vertical or horizontal bars.

Explorations and answers are provided in *Alternate Openers: Explorations Transparencies.*

A **double-bar graph** shows two sets of related data.

EXAMPLE 3 **PROBLEM SOLVING APPLICATION**

Make a double-bar graph to compare the data in the table.

Life Expectancies in Atlantic South America				
	Brazil	Argentina	Uruguay	Paraguay
Male (yr)	59	71	73	70
Female (yr)	69	79	79	74

1 Understand the Problem

You are asked to use a graph to compare the data given in the table. You will need to use all of the information given.

2 Make a Plan

You can make a double-bar graph to display the two sets of data.

3 Solve

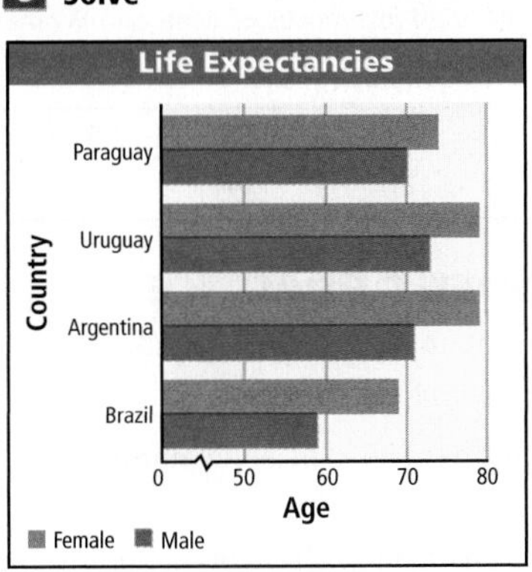

Determine appropriate scales for both sets of data.

Use the data to determine the lengths of the bars. Draw bars of equal width. Bars should be in pairs. Use a different color for male ages and female ages.

Title the graph and label both axes.

Include a key to show what each bar represents.

4 Look Back

You could make two separate graphs, one of male ages and one of female ages. However, it is easier to compare the two data sets when they are on the same graph.

Reading Math

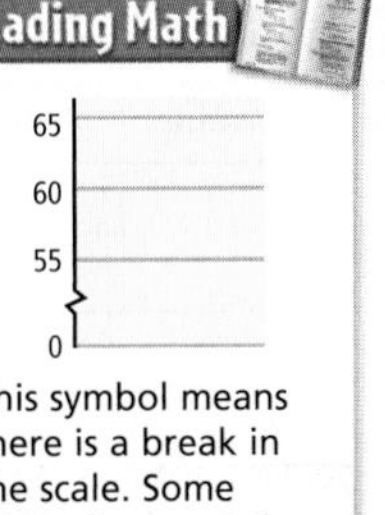

This symbol means there is a break in the scale. Some intervals were left out because they were not needed for the graph.

Answers to *Think and Discuss*

1. Possible answers: least and greatest value; values that are less than or greater than a given value
2. countable data that are grouped in categories
3. The key lets you know which color bar represents males and which color represents females.

Think and Discuss GPS M6D1.c, M6P3.b

1. **Give** comparisons you can make by looking at a bar graph.
2. **Describe** the kind of data you would display in a bar graph.
3. **Tell** why the graph in Example 3 needs a key.

Power Presentations with PowerPoint®

Additional Examples

Example 1

Use the bar graph to answer each question.

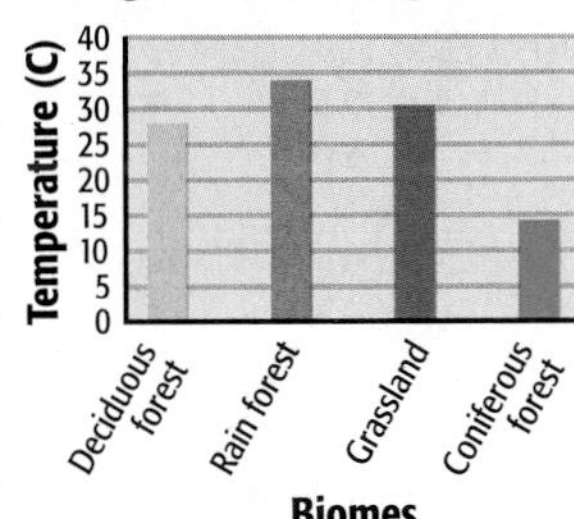

A. Which biome in the graph has the least average summer temperature?

B. Which biomes in the graph have an average summer temperature of 30°C or greater?

Example 2

Use the data to make a bar graph.

Magazine Subscriptions Sold		
Grade 6	Grade 7	Grade 8
258	597	374

Example 3

Make a double-bar graph to compare the data in the table.

Club Memberships			
Club	Art	Music	Science
Boys	12	6	16
Girls	8	14	4

Answers see p. A4.

Also available on transparency

2 Teach

Guided Instruction

In this lesson, students learn to display and analyze data in bar graphs. First teach students to read a bar graph. Then teach them to make bar graphs and double-bar graphs, given sets of data. Have students think of other examples of when a double-bar graph would be appropriate.

Teaching Tip **Critical Thinking** Ask students why a double bar graph might be better than two separate bar graphs for comparing similar data. Help them to see that a double bar graph is often easier to use when comparing two data sets because the corresponding bars are not only closer together, but also use the same scale.

Reaching All Learners

Through Concrete Manipulatives

Some students may benefit from building double-bar graph bars with connecting cubes before drawing the graphs on paper. Give these students cubes in two colors, one for each set of data. Allow students to construct the bars for each data set separately and to then combine them to make the double-bar graph. Students can refer to the connecting cube model as they draw their graphs on paper. To represent large numbers, cubes could be 10's or 100's.

3 Close

Summarize

Review the difference between a bar graph and a double-bar graph, and review the parts of each.

6-4 Exercises

Assignment Guide

If you finished Example 1 assign:
Average 1–2, 16–21
Advanced 5–6, 16–21

If you finished Example 2 assign:
Average 1–3, 16–21
Advanced 5–7, 16–21

If you finished Example 3 assign:
Average 1–10, 16–21
Advanced 5–21

Homework Quick Check

Quickly check key concepts.
Exercises: 6, 8, 10

Math Background

Studying and constructing bar graphs is a way for students to begin their approach to ordered pairs and coordinate graphing. In a vertical bar graph, the location of a bar corresponds to the *x*-coordinate of a point, and the height of a bar corresponds to the *y*-coordinate of a point. This connection between data presentation and coordinate graphing will be carried one step further in Lesson 6-7, in which line graphs are studied.

Answers

3–4, 7–8. See pp. A4–A5.

Georgia Performance Standards

M6D1.d Use tables and graphs to examine variation that occurs within a group and variation that occurs between groups.

M6P2.c Develop and evaluate mathematical arguments and proofs.

M6P5.a Create and use representations to organize, record, and communicate mathematical ideas.

6-4 Exercises

M6D1.d, M6P2.c, M6P5.a

go.hrw.com
Homework Help Online
KEYWORD: MR7 6-4
Parent Resources Online
KEYWORD: MR7 Parent

GUIDED PRACTICE

See Example 1 **Use the bar graph to answer each question.**

1. Which color was the least common among the cars in the parking lot? **green**
2. Which colors appeared more than ten times in the parking lot? **black, white, red**

Cars in the Parking Lot
Number: 0, 10, 20
Black White Red Green
Color

See Example 2

3. Use the given data to make a bar graph.

Students in Mr. Jones's History Classes			
Period 1	28	Period 6	22
Period 2	27	Period 7	7

See Example 3

4. Make a bar graph to compare the data in the table.

Total:
M=100
W=100

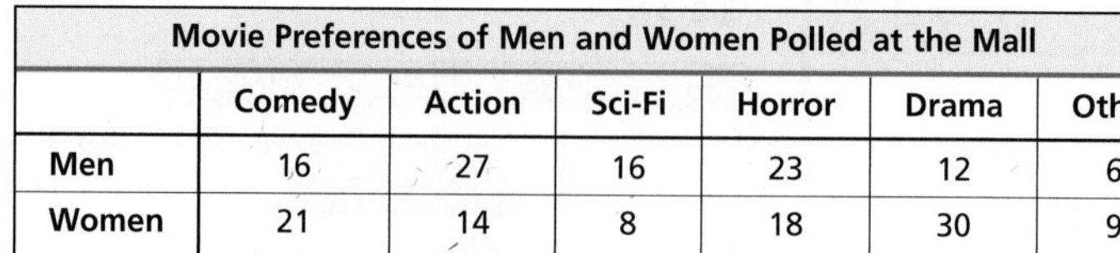

Movie Preferences of Men and Women Polled at the Mall						
	Comedy	Action	Sci-Fi	Horror	Drama	Other
Men	16	27	16	23	12	6
Women	21	14	8	18	30	9

INDEPENDENT PRACTICE

See Example 1 **Use the bar graph to answer each question.**

5. Which fruit was liked the best? **orange**
6. Which fruits were liked by equal numbers of people? **banana, apple**

Favorite Fruits
Number of people: 0, 4, 8, 12, 16, 20
Banana Apple Orange Grapes
Type of fruit

See Example 2

7. Use the given data to make a bar graph.

Days with Rainfall			
January	14	March	16
February	12	April	23

See Example 3

8. Make a bar graph to compare the data in the table.

Heart Rates Before and After Exercise (beats per minute)						
	Jason	Jamal	Ray	Tonya	Peter	Brenda
Before	60	62	61	65	64	65
After	131	140	128	140	135	120

RETEACH 6-4

LESSON 6-4 **Reteach**
Bar Graphs (continued)

A double-bar graph shows two sets of related data.

To make a double-bar graph, choose a scale and an interval for the scale. Then draw bars to match the data. The bars for the same grade should touch, but bars for different grades should not touch.

Middle School Students			
Grade	6	7	8
Boys	34	29	25
Girls	28	31	22

Because there are two bars for each grade, make a key to show which bars represent girls and which bars represent boys.

Your graph should have a title and its axes should be labeled.

Middle School Students
Number of Students: 0, 5, 10, 15, 20, 25, 30, 35, 40, 45, 50
6 7 8
Grade
Key: Boys Girls

Make a double-bar graph to match the data below. Then answer the question.

3.

Movie Tickets Sold			
	Fri	Sat	Sun
Adult	136	118	98
Student	84	102	154

Movie Tickets Sold
Tickets Sold: 0, 20, 40, 60, 80, 100, 120, 140, 160
Fri Sat Sun
Day
Key: Adult Student

4. On which day was the number of adult tickets sold about the same as the number of student tickets sold?

The number of adult tickets sold was about the same as the number of student tickets sold on Saturday.

PRACTICE 6-4

LESSON 6-4 **Practice B**
Bar Graphs

Use the bar graph to answer each question.

1. In which country did people spend the most money on toys in 2000?
   the United States
2. In which two countries did people spend the same amount of money on toys in 2000? How much did they each spend?
   France and Germany; $3 million each
3. In which country did people spend $9 million on toys in 2000?
   Japan

Top Toy-Buying Countries, 2000
Country: France, Germany, Japan, United Kingdom, United States
0 5 10 15 20 25 30 35 40
Money Spent (millions)

Make a bar graph to compare the data in the table.

Female Groups with the Most Top 10 and Top 20 Hits

Top 10		Top 20	
The Supremes	20	The Supremes	24
The Pointer Sisters	7	The Pointer Sisters	13
TLC	9	TLC	11
En Vogue	5	En Vogue	7
Spice Girls	4	Spice Girls	7

Female Groups with the Most Top 10 and Top 20 Hits
Number of Hits: 0, 5, 10, 15, 20, 25
The Supremes, The Pointer Sisters, TLC, En Vogue, Spice Girls
Artist
Key: Top 10 Top 20

PRACTICE AND PROBLEM SOLVING

Extra Practice p. 724

Social Studies Use the bar graph for Exercises 9–12.

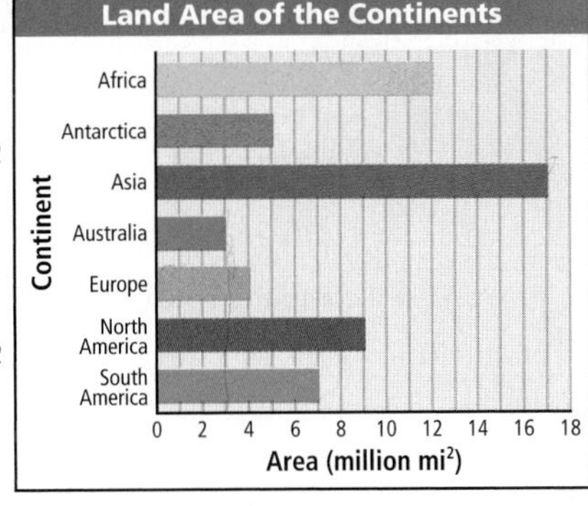

9. What is the range of the land area of the continents? **14 million mi^2**
10. What is the mode of the land area of the continents? **no mode**
11. What is the mean of the land area of the continents? **≈ 8.14 million mi^2**
12. What is the median of the land area of the continents? **7 million mi^2**

13. The basketball coach divided the team into two practice squads, the Blue Squad and the Green Squad. The table shows the scores from 6 weeks of practice games.
    a. Draw a double bar graph.
    b. Find the mean score and range for each squad.
    c. Which squad would you pick to play in an upcoming tournament? Explain your reasoning.

13b. Blue: mean = 47.3, range = 26; Green: mean = 47.3, range = 16

Scores of Practice Games

	Blue	Green
Week 1	62	40
Week 2	40	44
Week 3	42	44
Week 4	54	48
Week 5	36	52
Week 6	50	56

14. **Write About It** Explain how you would make a bar graph of the five most populated cities in the United States.

13c. Possible answer: The green squad. Their performance is more consistent, and their scores have steadily increased over time.

15. **Challenge** Create a bar graph displaying the number of A's, B's, C's, D's, and F's in Ms. Walker's class if the grades were the following: 81, 87, 80, 75, 77, 98, 52, 78, 75, 82, 74, 95, 76, 52, 76, 53, 86, 77, 90, 83, 96, 83, 74, 67, 90, 65, 69, 93, 68, and 76.

Grading System

A	90–100
B	80–89
C	70–79
D	60–69
F	0–59

CRCT Prep • GPS Support • Spiral Review

Use the bar graph for Exercises 16 and 17.

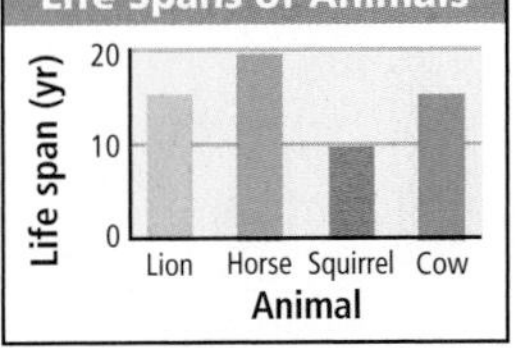

16. **Multiple Choice** Which animal has the longest life span?
    Ⓐ Lion **Ⓑ Horse** Ⓒ Squirrel Ⓓ Cow
17. **Multiple Choice** Which two animals have the same life span?
    Ⓕ Lion and horse Ⓖ Squirrel and cow Ⓗ Horse and squirrel **Ⓙ Lion and cow**

Find each sum or difference. Write the answer in simplest form. (Lessons 5-2 and 5-3)

18. $\frac{1}{7} + \frac{1}{4}$ **$\frac{11}{28}$**
19. $\frac{1}{2} - \frac{3}{10}$ **$\frac{1}{5}$**
20. $1\frac{3}{4} + 2\frac{1}{8}$ **$3\frac{7}{8}$**
21. $8\frac{2}{5} - 6\frac{1}{15}$ **$2\frac{1}{3}$**

CHALLENGE 6-4

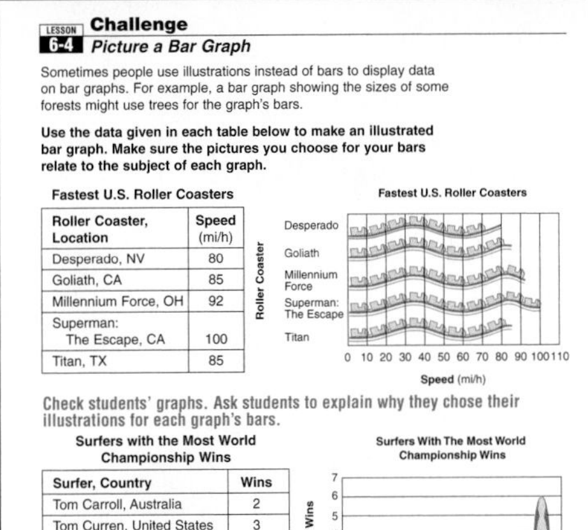

LESSON 6-4 **Challenge**
Picture a Bar Graph

Sometimes people use illustrations instead of bars to display data on bar graphs. For example, a bar graph showing the sizes of some forests might use trees for the graph's bars.

Use the data given in each table below to make an illustrated bar graph. Make sure the pictures you choose for your bars relate to the subject of each graph.

Fastest U.S. Roller Coasters

Roller Coaster, Location	Speed (mi/h)
Desperado, NV	80
Goliath, CA	85
Millennium Force, OH	92
Superman: The Escape, CA	100
Titan, TX	85

Check students' graphs. Ask students to explain why they chose their illustrations for each graph's bars.

Surfers with the Most World Championship Wins

Surfer, Country	Wins
Tom Carroll, Australia	2
Tom Curren, United States	3
Damien Hardman, Australia	2
Mark Richards, Australia	4
Kelly Slater, United States	6

PROBLEM SOLVING 6-4

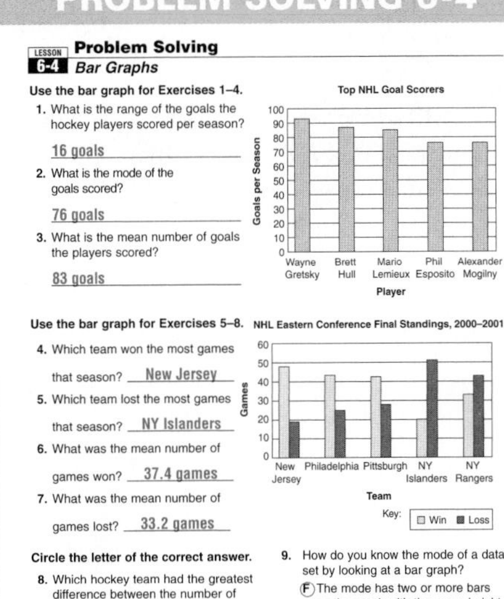

LESSON 6-4 **Problem Solving**
Bar Graphs

Use the bar graph for Exercises 1–4.

1. What is the range of the goals the hockey players scored per season? **16 goals**
2. What is the mode of the goals scored? **76 goals**
3. What is the mean number of goals the players scored? **83 goals**

Use the bar graph for Exercises 5–8.

4. Which team won the most games that season? **New Jersey**
5. Which team lost the most games that season? **NY Islanders**
6. What was the mean number of games won? **37.4 games**
7. What was the mean number of games lost? **33.2 games**

Circle the letter of the correct answer.

8. Which hockey team had the greatest difference between the number of games won and lost?
   A New Jersey
   Ⓑ New York Islanders
   C Philadelphia
   D Pittsburgh
9. How do you know the mode of a data set by looking at a bar graph?
   Ⓕ The mode has two or more bars on the graph with the same height.
   G The mode has the tallest bar.
   H The mode has the lowest bar.
   J The bar for the mode is in the middle of the graph.

Ongoing Assessment and Intervention

***Diagnose Before* the Lesson**
6-4 Warm Up, TE p. 308

***Monitor During* the Lesson**
6-4 Know-It Notebook
6-4 Questioning Strategies

***Assess After* the Lesson**
6-4 Lesson Quiz, TE p. 311

Answers

13a, 14–15. See p. A5.

For Exercise 17, remind students that care should be taken when selecting an answer. A student choosing **A** might have based the decision on the first word, *lion*.

Journal

Have students think of and describe a situation in which a double-bar graph would be used to represent data. Have them come up with data and make the graph.

Power Presentations with PowerPoint®

6-4 Lesson Quiz

Use the bar graph to answer each question.

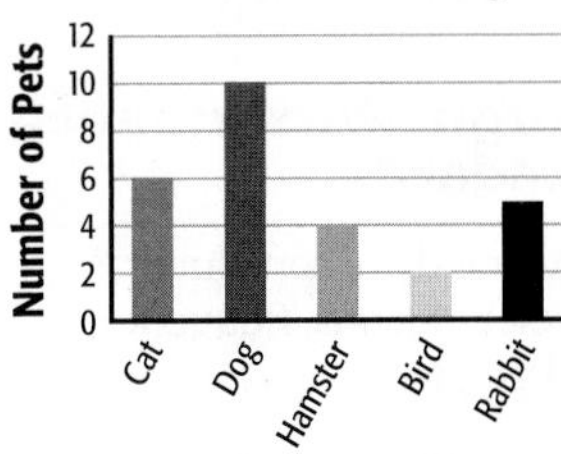

1. Which animal was least popular among students? bird
2. Which pet was more popular to twice as many students as rabbits were? dog
3. Make a bar graph of this data.
   Number of Daily Servings
   Grains = 6 Fruit = 2
   Meat = 2 Milk = 3
   Vegetables = 3

See p. A5.

Also available on transparency

Organizer

Use with Lesson 6-4

Pacing:
Traditional $\frac{1}{2}$ day
Block $\frac{1}{4}$ day

Objective: Use a spreadsheet program to create bar graphs.

Materials: Spreadsheet software

Online Edition

Resources

Technology Lab Activities
Lab 6-4 Recording Sheet

Teach

Discuss

Have students discuss how to create bar graphs from a data set without the use of a computer.

Close

Key Concept

Spreadsheet programs create bar graphs quicker and more accurately than using a pencil and paper.

Assessment

1. What pattern do you see in the projected population from 2000 to 2035?
2. How can you change the title of the graph?
3. In Excel®, what is the difference between the **Bar** option and the **Column** option in the **Chart Type** screen?

Georgia Performance Standards

M6D1.b Using data, construct frequency distributions, frequency tables, and graphs.

M6P4.c Recognize and apply mathematics in contexts outside of mathematics.

Create Bar Graphs

Use with Lesson 6-4

Georgia Performance Standards
M6D1.b, M6P4.c

go.hrw.com
Lab Resources Online
KEYWORD: MR7 Lab6

You can use a computer spreadsheet to draw bar graphs. The Chart Wizard icon, [icon], on a spreadsheet menu looks like a bar graph. The Chart Wizard allows you to create different types of graphs.

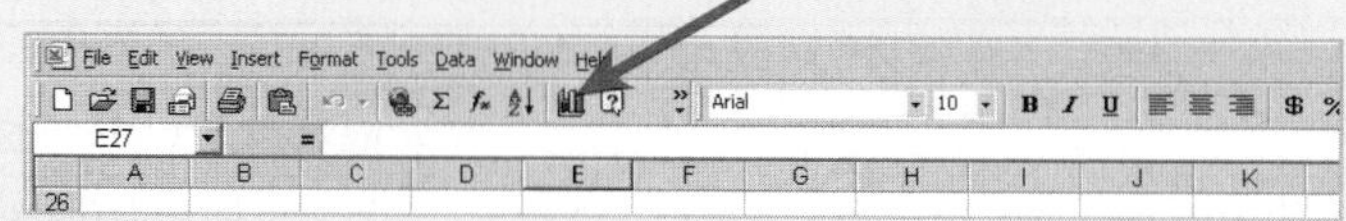

Activity

In a study conducted in December 2001 at Texas A&M University, the population of Texas through 2035 was projected. Make a bar graph of this data.

Texas Population	
Year	Population
2000	20,851,820
2005	23,207,929
2010	25,897,018
2015	28,971,283
2020	32,427,282
2025	36,273,829
2030	40,538,290
2035	45,283,746

1. Type the titles *Year* and *Population* into cells A1 and B1. Then type the data into columns A (year) and B (population).
2. Select the cells containing the titles and the data. Do this by placing your pointer in A1, clicking and holding the mouse button, and dragging the pointer down to B9.
3. Click the Chart Wizard icon. Highlight **Column** to make a vertical bar graph. Click **Next**.

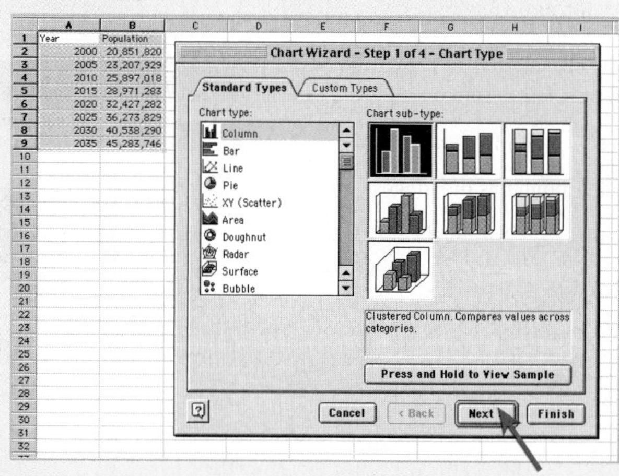

Answers to *Assessment*

1. The populations will increase steadily every 5 years.
2. Go to **Chart Options**. Select the **Titles** tab, and change the **Chart Title**.
3. Selecting **Column** yields a vertical bar graph; selecting **Bar** yields a horizontal bar graph.

4. The next screen shows where the data from the graph comes from. Click **Next**.

5. Title your graph and both axes. Click the **Legend** tab. Click the box next to **Show Legend** to turn off the key. (You would need a key if you were making a double-bar graph.) Click **Next** when you are finished.

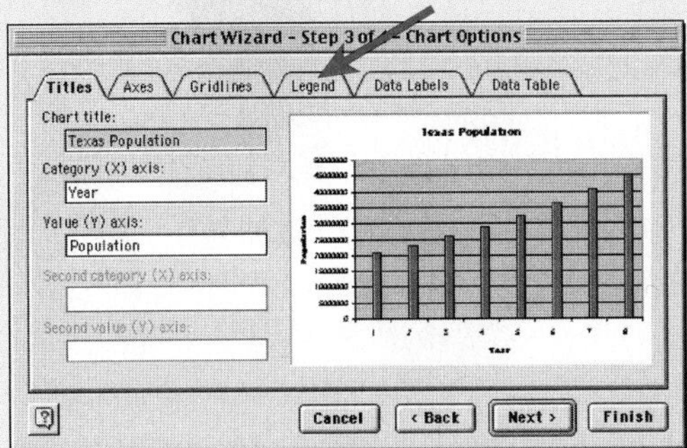

6. The next screen asks you where you want to place your chart. Click **Finish** to place it in your spreadsheet.

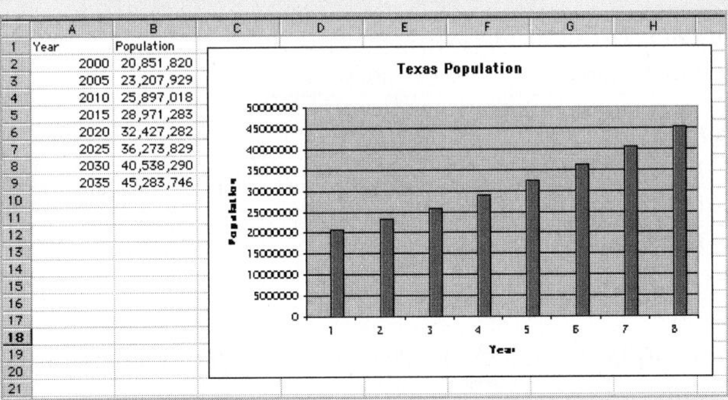

Think and Discuss

1. Do you think the population of Texas will be 32,427,282 in the year 2020 as shown in the graph? Explain. **Possible answer: Probably not; the number is only a projection and cannot be assumed to be completely accurate.**

Try This

1. Redraw the bar graph in the activity to show the population of Texas as 39,000,000 in 2035 and 33,000,000 in 2040.

2. Find the number of Texas counties that begin with the letter *A*, *B*, *C*, or *D*. Make a bar graph of the data.

Answers to *Try This*

1.

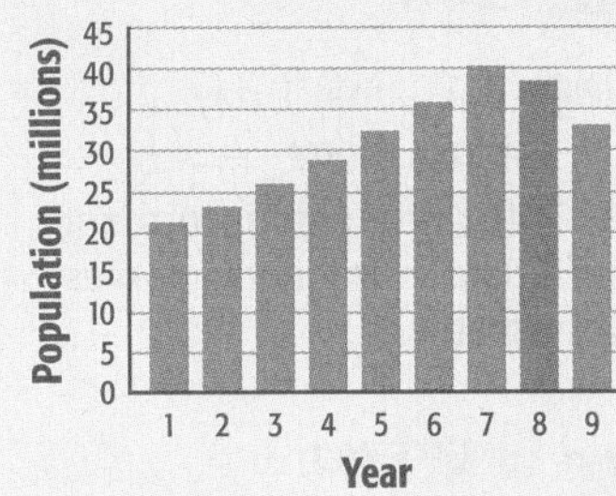

2.

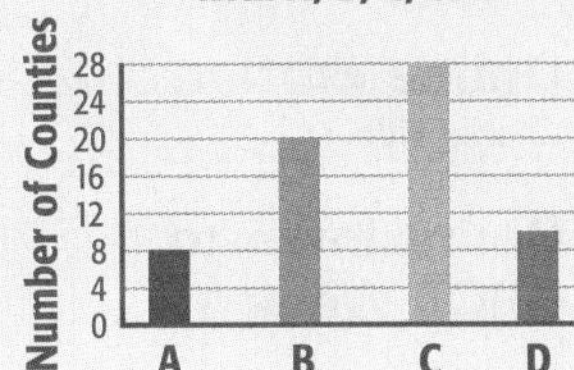

6-5 Organizer

Pacing: Traditional 1 day
Block $\frac{1}{2}$ day

Objective: Students record and organize data in frequency tables and histograms.

GPS M6D1.b
Hands-On Lab
In *Hands-On Lab Activities*

Online Edition
Tutorial Videos

Countdown to CRCT Week 12

Power Presentations with PowerPoint®

Warm Up

Create a bar graph of the data.

Favorite rides at fair:
Ferris wheel = 5, loop the loop = 4, merry-go-round = 3, bumper cars = 7, sit and spin = 9

Problem of the Day

A set of 7 numbers has a mean of 36, a median of 37, a mode of 37, and a range of 6. What could the 7 numbers be? Possible answer: 33, 33, 36, 37, 37, 37, 39

Answers in Chapter 6 Resource Book

Also available on transparency

Math Humor

What kind of a message do you send to a snake? A histogram

6-5 Line Plots, Frequency Tables, and Histograms

Learn to organize data in line plots, frequency tables, and histograms.

Vocabulary
line plot
frequency table
histogram

Your fingerprints are unlike anyone else's. Even identical twins have slightly different fingerprint patterns.

All fingerprints have one of three patterns: whorl, arch, or loop.

Whorl

Arch

Loop

EXAMPLE 1 Making a Tally Table

Each student in Mrs. Choe's class recorded their fingerprint pattern. Which type do most students in Mrs. Choe's class have?

whorl	loop	loop	loop	loop	arch	loop
whorl	arch	loop	arch	loop	arch	whorl

Make a *tally table* to organize the data.

Step 1: Make a column for each fingerprint pattern.

Step 2: For each fingerprint, make a tally mark in the appropriate column.

Number of Fingerprint Patterns		
Whorl	**Arch**	**Loop**
|||	||||	卌 ||

Most students in Mrs. Choe's class have a loop fingerprint pattern.

Reading Math
A group of four tally marks with a line through it means five.
卌 = 5
卌 卌 = 10

A **line plot** uses a number line and *x*'s or other symbols to show frequencies of values.

EXAMPLE 2 Making a Line Plot

Students in Mr. Lee's class each ran several miles in a week. Make a line plot of the data.

Number of Miles Run												
8	3	5	6	7	8	5	5	3	6	10	7	5

Step 1: Draw a number line.

Step 2: For each student, use an *x* on the number line to represent how many miles he or she ran.

```
        X
        X
X       X   X   X   X
X       X   X   X   X       X
<+---+---+---+---+---+---+---+>
 3   4   5   6   7   8   9   10
```
Number of miles run

Georgia Performance Standards
M6D1.b Using data, construct frequency distributions, frequency tables, and graphs. Also, M6P4.c, M6P5.a, M6P5.b.

A **frequency table** tells the number of times an event, category, or group occurs.

1 Introduce

Alternate Opener

EXPLORATION

6-5 Line Plots, Frequency Tables, and Histograms

Below are the top 50 women's times at the 2002 Olympic biathlon.

20:41.4	20:57.0	21:20.4	21:24.1	21:27.9	21:32.1	21:35.7	21:44.2
21:50.3	21:55.6	21:57.0	22:01.7	22:11.9	22:14.9	22:17.7	22:19.7
22:20.6	22:25.8	22:27.3	22:29.9	22:32.1	22:33.5	22:37.7	22:39.9
22:41.1	22:44.7	22:45.5	22:58.3	23:00.0	23:03.5	23:03.8	23:05.0
23:06.6	23:09.4	23:10.0	23:11.2	23:11.3	23:14.2	23:14.6	23:14.7
23:18.0	23:18.9	23:24.6	23:26.5	23:36.8	23:36.9	23:37.4	23:40.9
23:44.1	23:48.7						

1. Complete the *frequency table.*

Time (min)	20:00.0–20:59.9	21:00.0–21:59.9	22:00.0–22:59.9	23:00.0–23:59.9
Frequency	2			

2. Use the numbers in the frequency table to complete the *histogram.*

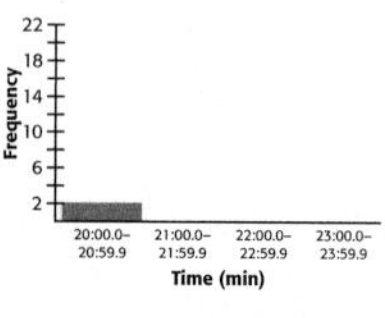

Think and Discuss

3. **Explain** how you completed the histogram in number 2.

Motivate

Using the photos in the lesson opener, have students determine which type of fingerprint pattern they have. Determine which type most students in the class have.

Explorations and answers are provided in *Alternate Openers: Explorations Transparencies.*

Georgia Performance Standards

M6D1.b Using data, construct frequency distributions, frequency tables, and graphs.

M6P4.c Recognize and apply mathematics in contexts outside of mathematics.

M6P5.a Create and use representations to organize, record, and communicate mathematical ideas.

M6P5.b Select, apply, and translate among mathematical representations to solve problems.

EXAMPLE 3 **Making a Frequency Table with Intervals**

Use the data in the table to make a frequency table with intervals.

Number of Representatives per State in the U.S. House of Representatives												
7	1	6	4	52	6	6	1	1	23	11	2	2
20	10	5	4	6	7	2	8	10	16	8	5	9
1	3	2	2	13	3	31	12	1	19	6	5	21
2	6	1	9	30	3	1	11	9	3	9		

Step 1: Choose equal intervals.

Step 2: Find the number of data values in each interval. Write these numbers in the "Frequency" row.

Number of Representatives per State in the U.S. House of Representatives									
Number	0–5	6–11	12–17	18–23	24–29	30–35	36–41	42–47	48–53
Frequency	22	18	3	4	0	2	0	0	1

This table shows that 22 states have between 0 and 5 representatives, 18 states have between 6 and 11 representatives, and so on.

A **histogram** is a bar graph that shows the number of data items that occur within each interval.

EXAMPLE  **Making a Histogram**

Use the frequency table in Example 3 to make a histogram.

Step 1: Choose an appropriate scale and interval.

Step 2: Draw a bar for the number of states in each interval. The bars should touch but not overlap.

Step 3: Title the graph and label the axes.

Number of Representatives by State

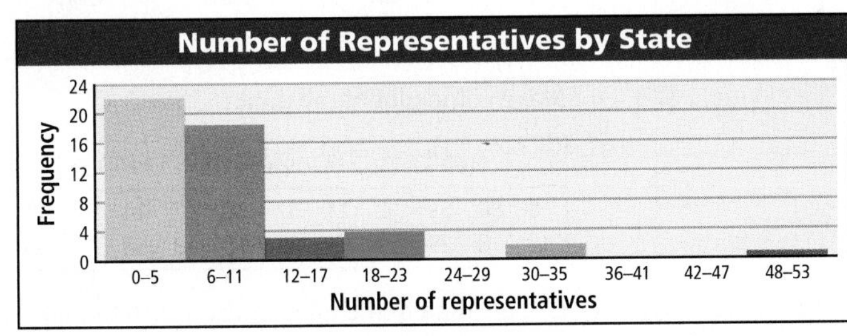

Answers to *Think and Discuss*

1. Possible answer: A histogram can be used to display data that has been collected in categories or by events.

Think and Discuss 

1. Describe a data set that can appropriately be displayed using a histogram.

Power Presentations with PowerPoint®

Additional Examples

Example 

Students in Mr. Ray's class recorded their fingerprint patterns. Which type of pattern do most students in Mr. Ray's class have?

whorl loop whorl loop
arch arch loop whorl
loop arch whorl arch
arch whorl arch loop
arch

Example 

Students collected tennis balls for a project. The number of balls collected by the students is recorded in the table. Make a line plot of the data.

Balls Collected					
10	14	11	16	11	10
14	10	15	15	10	11

Example 

Use the data in the table to make a frequency table with intervals.

Pages Read Last Weekend				
12	15	40	19	7
5	22	34	37	18

Example 

Use the frequency table from Additional Example 3 to make a histogram.

Answers see p. A5.

Also available on transparency

2 Teach

Guided Instruction

In this lesson, students learn to record and organize data in frequency tables and histograms. Teach students to make a tally table. Then teach them to make a frequency table with intervals, and a histogram. You can add your class's data to the data for Mrs. Choe's class, or you can have your students create new tally tables based on their data. Discuss how histograms are different from bar graphs. Histograms compare data in intervals; bar graphs compare data in categories.

Reaching All Learners

Through Cooperative Learning

Have students work in groups to find data that they are interested in and can display using a frequency table. Ideas can include the number of Super Bowls won by the teams in the NFL and the number of Olympic medals won by different countries. Have students make a frequency table with intervals and a histogram to represent the data. Have groups present their data to the class.

3 Close

Summarize

Review the procedures for completing a frequency table based on intervals. Then review how an interval-based frequency table is related to a histogram.

6-5 Exercises

Assignment Guide

If you finished Example 1 assign:
Average 1, 17–25
Advanced 5, 17–25

If you finished Example 2 assign:
Average 1–2, 10, 17–25
Advanced 5–6, 10, 17–25

If you finished Example 3 assign:
Average 1–3, 10–11, 17–25
Advanced 5–7, 10–11, 17–25

If you finished Example 4 assign:
Average 1–12, 17–25
Advanced 5–11, 14–25

Homework Quick Check

Quickly check key concepts.
Exercises: 6, 8, 10, 12

Math Background

A tally was originally a stick on which notches were made with a sharp object to indicate numbers. The tallies we use in a frequency table today correspond to the notches on a tally stick. The word *tally* has the same root as the word *tailor*. The connection between the two is the idea of cutting: a tally originally cut notches onto a stick, and a tailor cuts cloth.

Evidence of civilizations keeping numerical records on a stick can be traced as far back as 1350 B.C.E.

Answers

1–8. See p. A5.

Georgia Performance Standards

M6P1.b Solve problems that arise in mathematics and in other contexts.

M6P3.c Analyze and evaluate the mathematical thinking and strategies of others.

6-5 Exercises

M6P1.b, M6P3.c

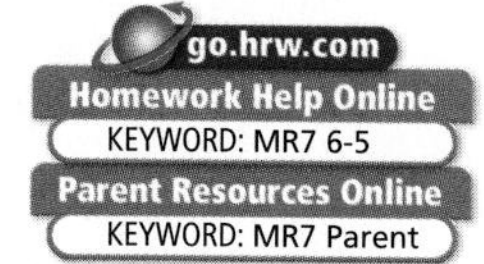

GUIDED PRACTICE

See Example 1

1. Each student in the band recorded the type of instrument he or she plays. The results are shown in the box. Make a tally table to organize the data. Which instrument do the fewest students play?

trumpet	tuba	French horn	drums	trombone
drums	trombone	trombone	trumpet	trumpet
trumpet	French horn	trumpet	French horn	French horn

See Example 2

2. Make a line plot of the data.

Length of Each U.S. Presidency (yr)																			
8	4	8	8	8	4	8	4	0	4	4	1	3	4	4	4	4	8	4	0	4
4	4	4	4	8	4	8	2	6	4	12	8	8	2	6	5	3	4	8	4	8

See Example 3

3. Use the data in the table in Exercise 2 to make a frequency table with intervals.

See Example 4

4. Use your frequency table from Exercise 3 to make a histogram.

INDEPENDENT PRACTICE

See Example 1

5. Students recorded the type of pet they own. The results are shown in the box. Make a tally table. Which type of pet do most students own?

cat	cat	bird	dog	dog
dog	bird	dog	bird	fish
bird	cat	fish	dog	cat
fish	hamster	cat	hamster	dog

See Example 2

6. Make a line plot of the data.

Number of Olympic Medals Won by 27 Countries													
8	88	59	12	11	57	38	17	14	28	28	26	25	23
18	8	29	34	14	17	13	13	58	12	97	10	9	

See Example 3

7. Use the data in the table in Exercise 6 to make a frequency table with intervals.

See Example 4

8. Use your frequency table from Exercise 7 to make a histogram.

9. histogram; it would show the test scores in intervals instead of having to list every single score on a bar graph.

PRACTICE AND PROBLEM SOLVING

CRCT GPS
Extra Practice p. 725

9. Critical Thinking Would a bar graph or a histogram be more appropriate to display the state test scores for an entire sixth grade class? Explain.

RETEACH 6-5

LESSON 6-5 **Reteach**
Line Plots, Frequency Tables, and Histograms

Julie picked the following cards from a deck.

You can make a tally table to organize the data. Make a row for the numbers. Then for each card, make a tally mark in the appropriate column.

Julie's Cards				
2	3	4	5	6
II	II	III	I	II

1. Make a tally table to organize the data.

Rolls of a Number Cube						
2	3	6	5	1	4	1
3	3	5	1	6	1	4

Rolls of a Number Cube					
1	2	3	4	5	6
IIII	I	III	II	II	II

A line plot gives a visual picture of data. To make a line plot of Julie's data, draw a number line. Then use an X to represent each tally mark in the tally table.

Julie's Cards

2. Make a line plot for the tally table you made Exercise 1.

Roll of a Number Cube

PRACTICE 6-5

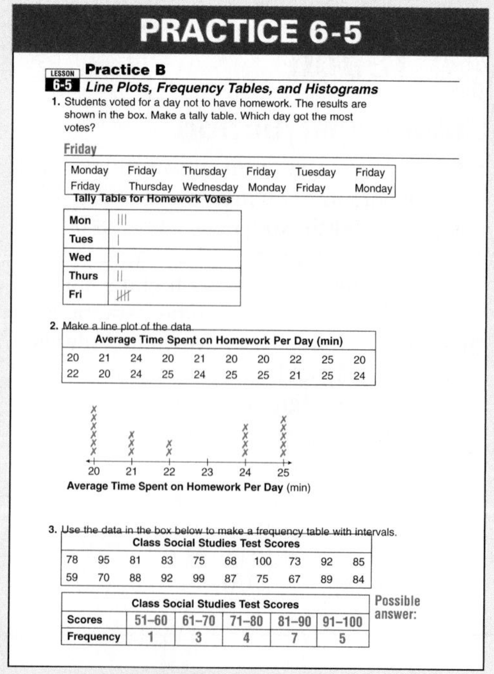
LESSON 6-5 **Practice B**
Line Plots, Frequency Tables, and Histograms

1. Students voted for a day not to have homework. The results are shown in the box. Make a tally table. Which day got the most votes?

Friday

Monday	Friday	Thursday	Friday	Tuesday	Friday
Friday	Thursday	Wednesday	Monday	Friday	Monday

Tally Table for Homework Votes

Mon	III
Tues	I
Wed	I
Thurs	II
Fri	~~IIII~~

2. Make a line plot of the data.

Average Time Spent on Homework Per Day (min)									
20	21	24	20	21	20	20	22	25	20
22	20	24	25	24	25	25	21	25	24

Average Time Spent on Homework Per Day (min)

3. Use the data in the box below to make a frequency table with intervals.

Class Social Studies Test Scores									
78	95	81	83	75	68	100	73	92	85
59	70	88	92	99	87	75	67	89	84

Class Social Studies Test Scores					
Scores	51–60	61–70	71–80	81–90	91–100
Frequency	1	3	4	7	5

Possible answer:

LINK Social Studies

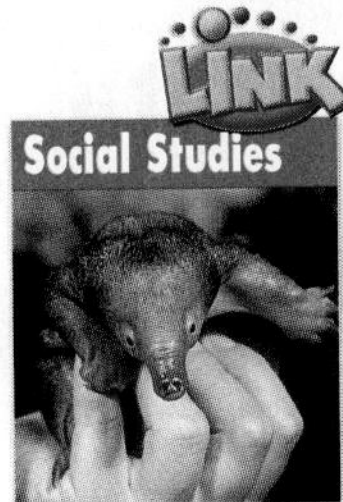

Echidnas are egg-laying mammals found only in Australia and New Guinea. A baby echidna is called a puggle.

10. **Multi-Step** Gather data on the number of pairs of shoes your classmates own. Make two line plots of the data, one for the boys and one for the girls. Compare the data. **Check students' work.**

11. **Social Studies** The map shows the populations of Australia's states and territories. Use the data to make a frequency table with intervals.

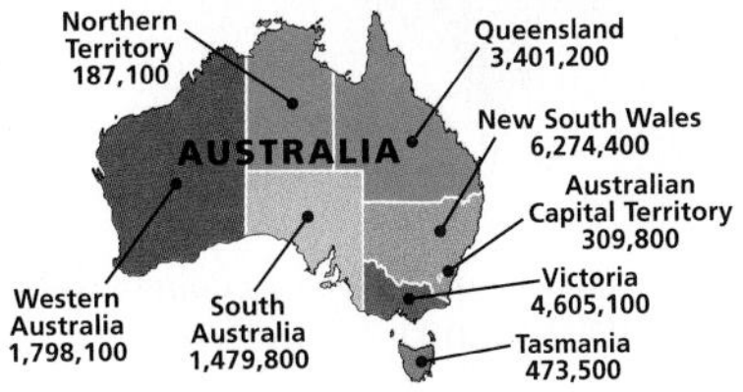

12. **Social Studies** Use your frequency table from Exercise 11 to make a histogram.

AUSTRALIA
Northern Territory 187,100
Queensland 3,401,200
New South Wales 6,274,400
Australian Capital Territory 309,800
Victoria 4,605,100
Tasmania 473,500
South Australia 1,479,800
Western Australia 1,798,100

13. **Critical Thinking** Can a frequency table have intervals of 0–5, 5–10, and 10–15? Why or why not? **No; intervals cannot contain the same values.**

14. **What's the Error?** Reading from the line plot, Kathryn says that there are 10 campers who are three years old. What is Kathryn's error?

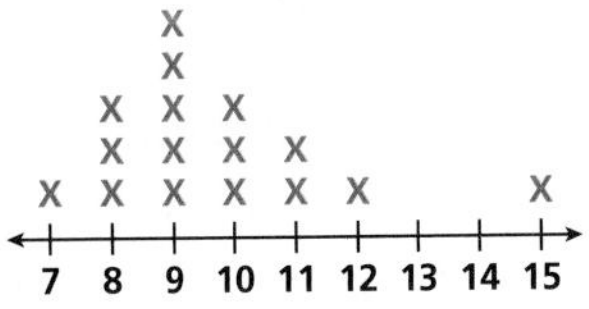

Age	7	8	9	10	11	12	13	14	15
	X	XXX	XXXXX	XXX	XX	X			X

Ages of campers

15. **Write About It** Choose one of the histograms you made for this lesson and redraw it using different intervals. How did the histogram change? Explain.

16. **Challenge** Can you find the mean, median, and mode price using this frequency table? If so, find them. If not, explain why not.

Cost of Video Game Rentals at Different Stores				
Price	$2.00–$2.99	$3.00–$3.99	$4.00–$4.99	$5.00–$5.99
Frequency	5	12	8	5

15. Kathryn read the line plot incorrectly; there are 3 ten-year-old campers, not 10 three-year-old campers.

16. You cannot find them. You do not know the actual data points, only the ranges they fall in.

CRCT Prep • GPS Support • Spiral Review

17. **Multiple Choice** Emily is making a histogram for the data 12, 24, 56, 7, 34, 75, 34, 86, 34, 78, and 96. Which is the most appropriate first interval?

Ⓐ 0–5   (B) 0–10 (circled)   Ⓒ 0–50   Ⓓ 0–100

18. **Short Response** Use the data in the table to make a frequency table with three-goal intervals. How many times were 6–8 goals scored? **3; For table see p. A5.**

Number of Goals Scored Each Game
3 5 2 5 4 7 1 0 6 4 8 5 3 2 4 5 9

Write each decimal in expanded form and word form. (Lesson 3-1)

19. 1.23
20. 0.45
21. 26.07
22. 80.002 **80 + 0.002; eighty and two-thousandths**

Find the outlier in each data set. (Lesson 6-3)

23. 3, 6, 19, 4, 2, and 5 **19**
24. 564, 514, 723, and 573 **723**
25. 34, 37, 41, 9, and 34 **9**

CHALLENGE 6-5

LESSON 6-5 **Challenge**
Write Often

What letter is used more than any other letter in the English language? e

The box below contains the six English letters that are used most often. Use the box to complete the tally table at the bottom of the page. Your completed table will show the answer to the question.

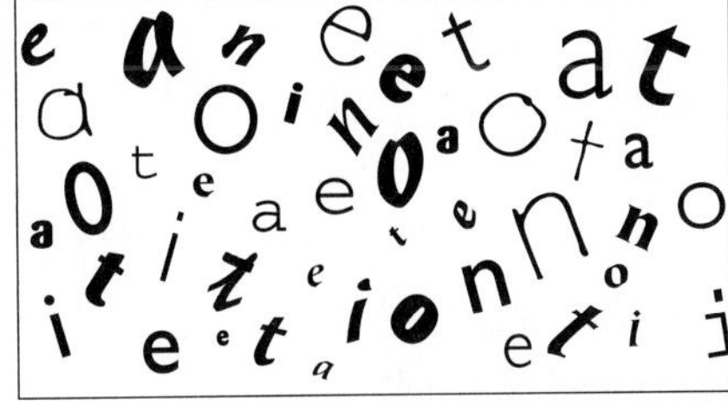

Tally Table for the Number of Letters	
A	𝍸 III
E	𝍸 𝍸
I	𝍸 I
N	𝍸
O	𝍸 II
T	𝍸 IIII

PROBLEM SOLVING 6-5

LESSON 6-5 **Problem Solving**
Line Plots, Frequency Tables, and Histograms

The sixth grade class voted on their favorite ice cream flavors. The results of the vote are shown below.

chocolate	vanilla	strawberry	vanilla	vanilla
vanilla	chocolate	vanilla	chocolate	strawberry
chocolate	strawberry	vanilla	vanilla	chocolate

1. Use the data to make a tally table. How many students voted in all?
   15 students
2. Which flavor got the most votes?
   vanilla

Ice Cream Flavor Votes

Flavor	Number of Votes
Chocolate	𝍸
Vanilla	𝍸 II
Strawberry	III

Use the histogram for Exercises 3–5.

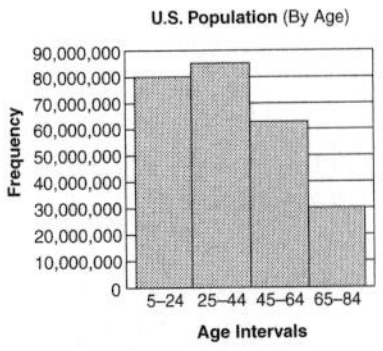

U.S. Population (By Age)
Frequency: 0, 10,000,000, 20,000,000, 30,000,000, 40,000,000, 50,000,000, 60,000,000, 70,000,000, 80,000,000, 90,000,000
Age Intervals: 5–24, 25–44, 45–64, 65–84

3. How many years make up each age interval on the histogram?
   20 years
4. Which range of ages on the histogram has the highest population?
   25–44
5. Which range of ages has the lowest population?
   65–84

Circle the letter of the correct answer.

6. Which of the following cannot be used to make a frequency table with intervals?
   A histogram
   B tally table
   C line plot
   Ⓓ double-bar graph

7. Which question can be answered by using the histogram above?
   A How many people in the United States are younger than 5 years?
   B What is the mean age of all people in the United States?
   C How many people in the United States are older than 84 years old?
   Ⓓ How many people in the United States are age 25 to 64?

Ongoing Assessment and Intervention

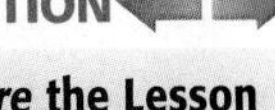

***Diagnose Before* the Lesson**
6-5 Warm Up, TE p. 314

***Monitor During* the Lesson**
6-5 Know-It Notebook
6-5 Questioning Strategies

***Assess After* the Lesson**
6-5 Lesson Quiz, TE p. 317

Answers

11–12. See p. A5.

14. Possible answer: Kathryn confused the number of campers with the age of the campers.

18. See p. A5.

19. 1 + 0.2 + 0.03; one and twenty-three hundredths

20. 0.4 + 0.05; forty-five hundredths

21. 20 + 6 + 0.07; twenty-six and seven-hundredths

Test Prep Doctor For Exercise 18, remind students to look for all instances in which 6, 7, or 8 goals were scored.

Journal

Have students explain why a histogram is more appropriate than a bar graph for displaying the data in Example 4.

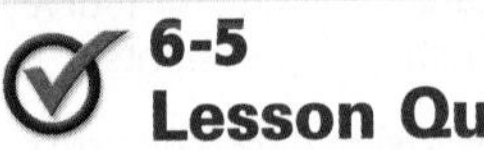

Power Presentations with PowerPoint®

6-5 Lesson Quiz

1. Students listed the number of days they spent on vacation in one year. Make a tally table with intervals of 5.

   2, 18, 5, 15, 7, 10, 1, 10, 4, 16, 7, 11, 17, 3, 8, 14, 13, 10

2. Use your tally table from problem 1 to make a frequency table.

Answers on p. A5.

Also available on transparency

Organizer

Use with Lesson 6-5

Pacing:
Traditional $\frac{1}{2}$ day
Block $\frac{1}{4}$ day

Objective: Use a survey to collect and display data.

Materials: Pencil and paper

Resources

Hands-On Lab Activities
Lab 6-5 Recording Sheet

Teach

Discuss

Have students discuss the importance of asking the same questions each time. Ask students why it is important that the first question they ask is whether the person has been surveyed by any other team.

Close

Key Concept

A properly conducted survey will yield dependable data.

Assessment

1. Explain why members of the survey team should ask the same set of questions.
2. When someone says that they have already answered the survey questions, what could be the result of asking the questions again?

M6D1.a Formulate questions that can be answered by data. Students should collect data by using samples from a larger population (surveys), or by conducting experiments.

M6D1.b Using data, construct frequency distributions, frequency tables, and graphs.

Use a Survey to Collect Data

Use with Lesson 6-5

Georgia Performance Standards
M6D1.a, M6D1.b

go.hrw.com
Lab Resources Online
KEYWORD: MR7 Lab6

You can use a survey to collect data. In this lab, you will split into teams and ask your classmates how long it takes them to get to school.

Work in teams of 2 or 3 students. Each team will survey students as they arrive at school, but the teams will work in different locations:

- Half the teams should survey students outside as they get off the school buses.
- The other teams should survey students as they enter their homerooms.

Each team should follow the steps below for their survey.

Activity

1. Ask students if they have been surveyed by any other team. If not, ask them what time they left their house that morning. Try to get 10 to 15 responses.
2. After you've finished surveying, calculate the time between when each student left the house and the time that first period of school starts. Record your data in a table like the one at right.
3. Calculate the mean travel time for the students you surveyed.

Time Student Left Home	Total Time Spent Getting to First Period (min)
6:57 A.M.	33
7:05 A.M.	25

Think and Discuss

1. Do you think the mean times will be longer for the bus teams or for the homeroom teams? Explain why.
2. As a class, find the mean time of all the students surveyed by the bus teams. Then find the mean time of all the students surveyed by the homeroom teams. Do the results match your prediction from problem **1**? **Check students' answers.**
3. Do you think the bus mean or the homeroom mean is a more accurate estimate of the average time students take to get to school? Why?

Try This

1. Draw a histogram to display your team's data. **Check students' answers.**
2. Think of something you'd like to know about the students in your school and write a survey question to find the answer. Explain how you would conduct the survey to get accurate results. **Check students' answers.**

Answers to *Assessment*

1. Possible answer: The data from the survey is more consistent when the set of questions does not vary.
2. Possible answer: The outcome of the survey would not be fair. It would be like voting twice in an election.

Answers to *Try This*

1. Possible answer: The mean times from the bus teams will be higher. The homeroom mean will include students who walk or ride with their parents, and their travel time will be shorter that that of students who ride the bus.
2. Possible answer: The homeroom mean is a better estimate. The bus mean only includes students who ride the bus, but the homeroom mean includes students who traveled by bus or car or who walked.

6-6 Ordered Pairs

Learn to graph ordered pairs on a coordinate grid.

Vocabulary

coordinate grid

ordered pair

Georgia Performance Standards

M6P4.c Recognize and apply mathematics in contexts outside of mathematics.

Cities, towns, and neighborhoods are often laid out on a grid. This makes it easier to map and find locations.

A **coordinate grid** is formed by horizontal and vertical lines and is used to locate points.

Each point on a coordinate grid can be located by using an **ordered pair** of numbers, such as (4, 6). The starting point is (0, 0).

San Diego, CA. Image courtesy of spaceimaging.com.

- The first number tells how far to move horizontally from (0, 0).
- The second number tells how far to move vertically.

EXAMPLE 1 Identifying Ordered Pairs

Name the ordered pair for each location.

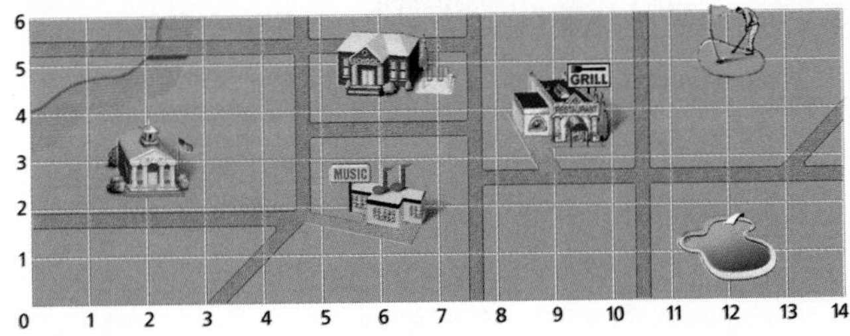

A library

Start at (0, 0). Move right 2 units and then up 3 units.

The library is located at (2, 3).

B school

Start at (0, 0). Move right 6 units and then up 5 units.

The school is located at (6, 5).

C pool

Start at (0, 0). Move right 12 units and up 1 unit.

The pool is located at (12, 1).

Georgia LINK Social Studies

Savannah is considered to be the first planned city in the U.S. The streets are laid out in a grid with 22 public squares placed throughout the city.

Organizer 6-6

Pacing: Traditional 1 day
Block $\frac{1}{2}$ day

Objective: Students graph ordered pairs on a coordinate grid.

Hands-On Lab
In *Hands-On Lab Activities*

Online Edition
Tutorial Videos, Interactivities

Countdown to CRCT Week 13

Power Presentations with PowerPoint®

Warm Up

24 35 47 67 36 22 80 41

Use the set of data above to find:

1. the mean 44 **2.** the median 38.5

Problem of the Day

What is the largest 6-digit number with each digit different and no digit a prime number? 986,410

Also available on transparency

Additional Examples

Example 1

Name the ordered pair for each location.

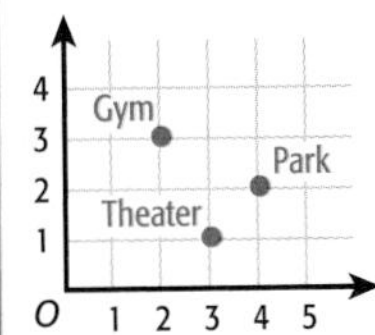

A. Gym (2, 3)
B. Theater (3, 1)
C. Park (4, 2)

Also available on transparency

1 Introduce

Alternate Opener

EXPLORATION

6-6 Ordered Pairs

The table shows the number of faces and vertices of the five regular polyhedrons.

Faces	4	8	20	6	12
Vertices	4	6	12	8	20

This data can be represented on a graph using *ordered pairs*. Each ordered pair is composed of the number of faces and the number of vertices of the polyhedron.

1. Plot and label the remaining ordered pairs. First find the number of faces on the horizontal line. From the number of faces, move up to find the number of vertices on the vertical line.

Think and Discuss

2. Explain how to plot ordered pairs.
3. Discuss what the point (6, 8) means.

2 Teach

Guided Instruction

In this lesson, students learn to graph ordered pairs on a coordinate grid. First teach students to name the ordered pairs for given locations, and then teach them to graph points on the grid, given the ordered pairs.

Explorations and answers are provided in *Alternate Openers: Explorations Transparencies.*

Georgia Performance Standards

M6P4.c Recognize and apply mathematics in contexts outside of mathematics.

Power Presentations with PowerPoint®

Additional Examples

Example 2

Graph and label each point on a coordinate grid.

A. $L(3, 5)$ **B.** $M(4, 0)$

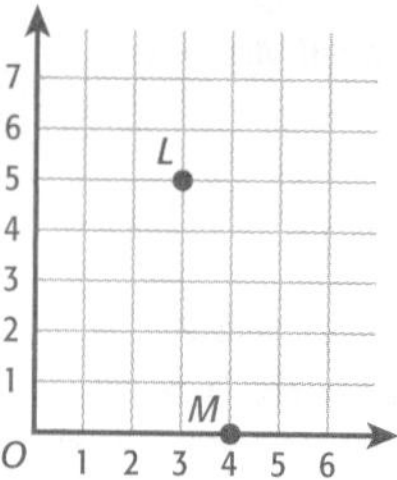

Also available on transparency

6-6 Exercises

Assignment Guide

If you finished Example 1 assign:
Average 1–6, 29–34, 39–47
Advanced 11–16, 29–34, 39–47

If you finished Example 2 assign:
Average 1–26, 39–47
Advanced 11–32, 37–47

Homework Quick Check

Quickly check key concepts.
Exercises: 14, 16, 18, 22, 28, 30

Answers

7–10. See p. A5.

EXAMPLE 2 Graphing Ordered Pairs

Graph and label each point on a coordinate grid.

A $Q\left(4\frac{1}{2}, 6\right)$

Start at (0, 0).
Move right $4\frac{1}{2}$ units.
Move up 6 units.

B $S(0, 4)$

Start at (0, 0).
Move right 0 units.
Move up 4 units.

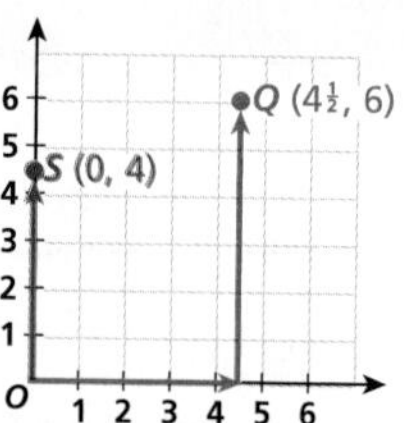

Possible answers to *Think and Discuss*

1. at (0, 0), in the bottom left corner
2. Start at (0, 0). Move $2\frac{1}{2}$ units right and then 8 units up.

Think and Discuss GPS M6P1.b, M6P3.b

1. Tell what point is the starting location when you are graphing on a coordinate grid.

2. Describe how to graph $(2\frac{1}{2}, 8)$ on a coordinate grid.

6-6 Exercises

Georgia Performance Standards
M6P3.a, M6P3.d

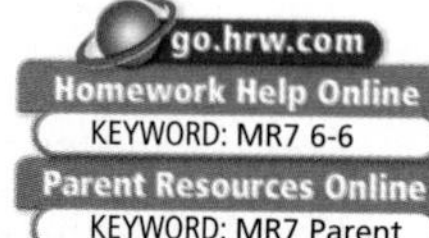

GUIDED PRACTICE

See Example 1 Name the ordered pair for each location.

1. school (2, 3) 2. store (0, 7)
3. hospital (7, 6) 4. mall (9, 1)
5. office (4, 5) 6. hotel (11, 4)

Store, Hospital, Office, Hotel, School, Mall

See Example 2 Graph and label each point on a coordinate grid.

7. $T\left(3\frac{1}{2}, 4\right)$ 8. $S(2, 8)$
9. $U(5, 5)$ 10. $V\left(4\frac{1}{2}, 1\right)$

INDEPENDENT PRACTICE

See Example 1 Name the ordered pair for each location.

11. diner (3, 0) 12. library (6, 6)
13. store (1, 4) 14. bank (10, 4)
15. theater (11, 7) 16. town hall (1, 7)

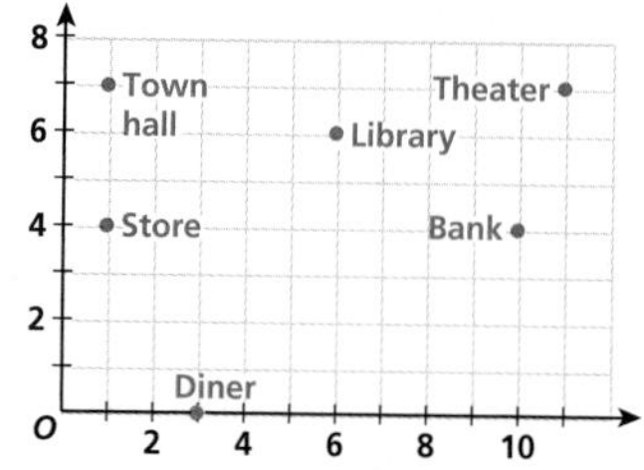

Georgia Performance Standards

M6P3.a Organize and consolidate their mathematical thinking through communication.

M6P3.d Use the language of mathematics to express mathematical ideas precisely.

Reaching All Learners

Through Kinesthetic Experience

Set up desks in rows and columns representing locations on a coordinate grid system, and have students take a seat at a desk. Call out ordered pairs for desks in the arrangement, and ask students to stand when the ordered pair that names their seat is called.

3 Close

Summarize

ENGLISH LANGUAGE LEARNERS

Review the terms *coordinate grid* and *ordered pair*. Have students explain how the terms are related.

Possible answer: Ordered pairs are used to name locations on a coordinate grid. The first number in an ordered pair tells how far to move horizontally from (0, 0). The second number tells how far to move vertically from (0, 0).

See Example 2 Graph and label each point on a coordinate grid.

17. $P(5\frac{1}{2}, 1)$ 18. $R(2, 4)$ 19. $Q(3\frac{1}{2}, 2)$

20. $V(6, 5)$ 21. $X(1\frac{1}{2}, 3)$ 22. $Y(7, 4)$

PRACTICE AND PROBLEM SOLVING

Extra Practice p. 725

Use the coordinate grid for Exercises 23–35.

Name the point found at each location.

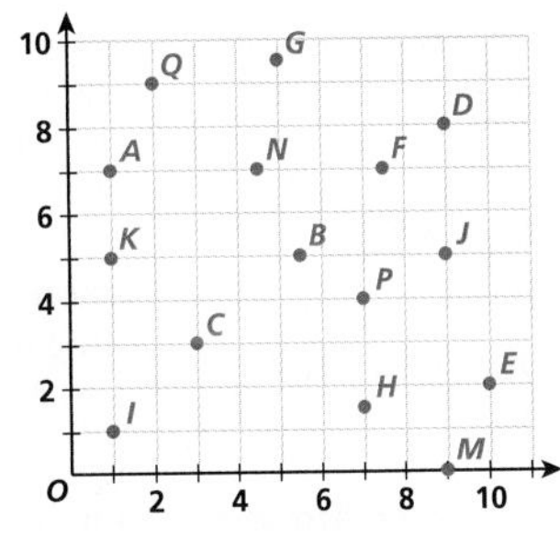

23. (1, 7) **A** 24. $(5, 9\frac{1}{2})$ **G** 25. (3, 3) **C**

26. $(4\frac{1}{2}, 7)$ **N** 27. (7, 4) **P** 28. $(7\frac{1}{2}, 7)$ **F**

Give the ordered pair for each point.

29. D **(9, 8)** 30. H **$(7, 1\frac{1}{2})$** 31. K **(1, 5)**

32. Q **(2, 9)** 33. M **(9, 0)** 34. B **$(5\frac{1}{2}, 5)$**

35. **Multi-Step** The coordinates of points B, J, and M in the coordinate grid above form three of the corners of a rectangle. What are the coordinates of the fourth corner? Explain how you found your answer. **$(5\frac{1}{2}, 0)$**

36. **Write About It** Explain the difference between the points (3, 2) and (2, 3).

37. **What's the Question?** If the answer is "Start at (0, 0) and move 3 units to the right," what is the question? **Possible answer: How do you graph the point (3, 0)?**

38. **Challenge** Locate and graph points that can be connected to form your initials. What are the ordered pairs for these points? **Possible answer: LYN; L: (1, 4), (1, 1), and (3, 1); Y(4, 4), (5, 3),(6, 4), and (5, 1); N:(7, 1), (7, 4), (9,1) and (9,4).**

CRCT Prep • GPS Support • Spiral Review

Use the coordinate grid for Exercises 39 and 40.

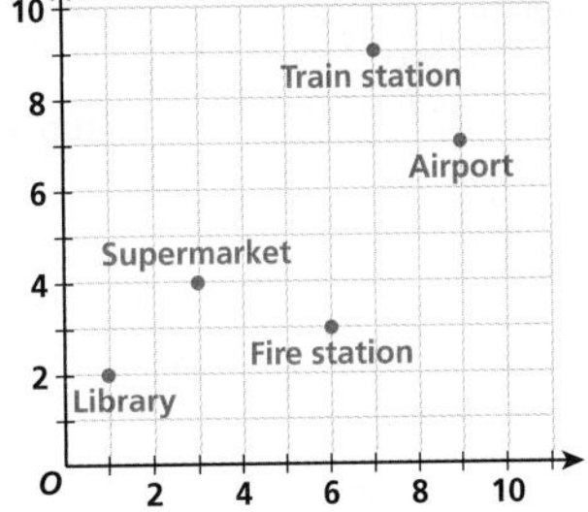

39. **Multiple Choice** At which ordered pair is the airport located?

Ⓐ (7, 9) Ⓑ (3, 4) Ⓒ (6, 3) **Ⓓ (9, 7)**

40. **Multiple Choice** Which location is at (1, 2)?

Ⓕ Airport Ⓗ Supermarket

Ⓖ Library Ⓙ Train station

Write each expression in exponential form. (Lesson 1-3)

41. $3 \times 3 \times 3 \times 5 \times 5$ **$3^3 \times 5^2$** 42. $7 \times 7 \times 4 \times 4$ **$7^2 \times 4^2$** 43. $2 \times 2 \times 3 \times 3 \times 5$ **$2^2 \times 3^2 \times 5$**

Find each product. Write each answer in simplest form. (Lesson 5-7)

44. $\frac{2}{3} \cdot \frac{1}{5}$ **$\frac{2}{15}$** 45. $\frac{3}{7} \cdot \frac{1}{4}$ **$\frac{3}{28}$** 46. $\frac{2}{9} \cdot \frac{3}{8}$ **$\frac{1}{12}$** 47. $\frac{1}{4} \cdot \frac{6}{7}$ **$\frac{3}{14}$**

ONGOING ASSESSMENT and INTERVENTION

Diagnose ***Before*** the Lesson
6-6 Warm Up, TE p. 319

Monitor ***During*** the Lesson
6-6 Know-It Notebook
6-6 Questioning Strategies

Assess ***After*** the Lesson
6-6 Lesson Quiz, TE p. 321

Answers

17-22, 35-36. See p. A5.

Power Presentations with PowerPoint®

6-6 Lesson Quiz

Give the ordered pair for each point.

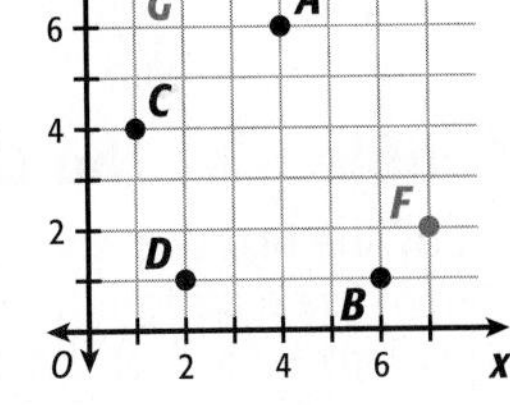

1. A (4, 6)
2. B (6, 1)
3. C (1, 4)
4. D (2, 1)

Graph and label each point on a coordinate grid.

5. $F(7, 2)$ 6. $G(1, 7)$

Answers on p. A5.

Also available on transparency

RETEACH 6-6

LESSON 6-6 Reteach
Ordered Pairs

A coordinate grid is formed by horizontal and vertical lines and is used to locate points.

An ordered pair names the location of a point by using two numbers.

The ordered pair (2, 5) gives the location of point A on the coordinate grid.

The first number, 2, tells the horizontal distance from the starting point (0, 0).

The second number, 5, tells the vertical distance.

To find the ordered pair for point B, start at (0, 0). Then move 6 units right and $3\frac{1}{2}$ units up. The coordinates of point B are $(6, 3\frac{1}{2})$.

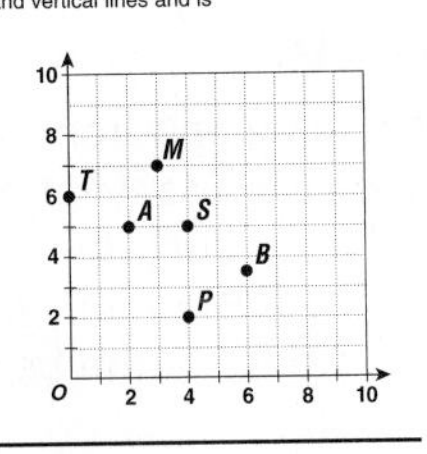

Give the ordered pair for each point shown on the coordinate grid above.

1. P **(4, 2)** 2. T **(0, 6)** 3. M **(3, 7)** 4. S **(4, 5)**

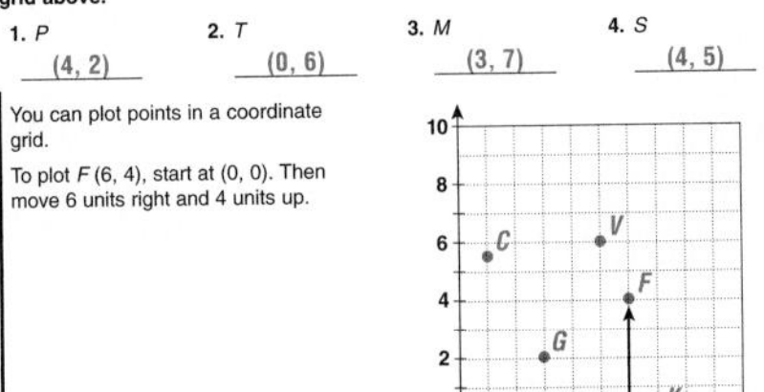

You can plot points in a coordinate grid.

To plot $F(6, 4)$, start at (0, 0). Then move 6 units right and 4 units up.

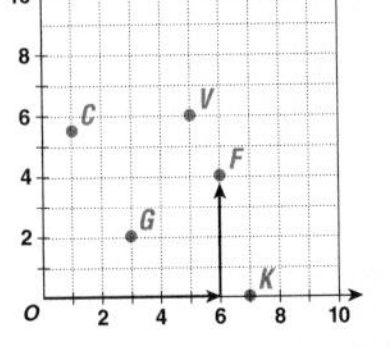

Plot each point in the coordinate grid above.

5. $V(5, 6)$ 6. $G(3, 2)$ 7. $K(7, 0)$ 8. $C(1, 5\frac{1}{2})$

PRACTICE 6-6

LESSON 6-6 Practice B
Ordered Pairs

Name the ordered pair for each location on the grid.

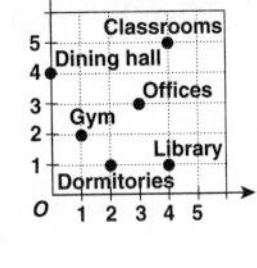

1. gym **(1, 2)**
2. dining hall **(0, 4)**
3. offices **(3, 3)**
4. library **(4, 1)**
5. classrooms **(4, 5)**
6. dormitories **(2, 1)**

Graph and label each point on the coordinate grid.

7. $A(5, 1\frac{1}{2})$
8. $B(2, 2)$
9. $C(1, 3)$
10. $D(4, 3)$
11. $E(5, 5)$
12. $F(2, 4)$

13. On a map of his neighborhood, Mark's house is located at point (7, 3). His best friend, Cheryl, lives 2 units west and 1 unit south of him. What ordered pair describes the location of Cheryl's house on their neighborhood map?
(5, 2)

14. Quan used a coordinate grid map of the zoo during his visit. Starting at (0, 0), he walked 3 units up and 4 units to the right to reach the tiger cages. Then he walked 1 unit down and 1 unit left to see the pandas. Describe the directions Quan should walk to get back to his starting point.
walk 2 units down and 3 units to the left

CHALLENGE 6-6
PROBLEM SOLVING 6-6

LESSON 6-6 Problem Solving
Ordered Pairs

Use the coordinate grid to answer each question.

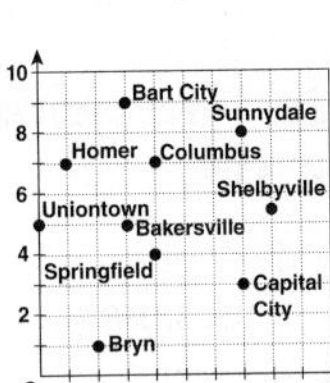

1. What city is located at point (4, 4) on the map?
Springfield

2. Which city is located at point $(8, 5\frac{1}{2})$ on the map?
Shelbyville

3. Which city's location is given by an ordered pair that includes a 0?
Uniontown

4. What ordered pair describes the location of Capital City?
(7, 3)

5. If you started at (0, 0) and moved 1 unit north and 2 units east, which city would you reach?
Bryn

6. Which two cities on the map are both located 4 units to the right of (0, 0)?
Springfield and Columbus

Circle the letter of the correct answer.

7. If you started in Bart City and moved 2 units south and 2 units west, which city would you reach?
A Columbus
B Sunnydale
Ⓒ Homer
D Bakersville

8. Starting at (0, 0), which of the following directions would lead you to Capital City?
Ⓕ Go 7 units east and 3 units north.
G Go 5 units north and 3 units east.
H Go 3 unit east and 7 units north.
J Go 8 units east and 6 units north.

6-7 Organizer

Pacing: Traditional 1 day
Block $\frac{1}{2}$ day

Objective: Students display and analyze data in line graphs.

GPS M6D1.b
Technology Lab
In *Technology Lab Activities*

Online Edition
Tutorial Videos

Countdown to CRCT Week 13

Power Presentations with PowerPoint®

Warm Up

Describe how to graph each point on a coordinate grid.

1. (4, 5) right 4, up 5
2. (0, 2) up 2
3. (3, 0) right 3

Problem of the Day

Study the first two columns to determine a pattern to help fill in the blank square at the bottom.

4	49	6
11	134	12
7	85	6

Also available on transparency

Math Humor

When the student dropped her graph on the floor, the teacher sent her to the principal's office for stepping over the line.

Georgia Performance Standards

M6D1.b Using data, construct frequency distributions, frequency tables, and graphs.

M6P4.c Recognize and apply mathematics in contexts outside of mathematics.

M6P5.a Create and use representations to organize, record, and communicate mathematical ideas.

M6P5.b Select, apply, and translate among mathematical representations to solve problems.

6-7 Line Graphs

Learn to display and analyze data in line graphs.

Vocabulary
line graph
double-line graph

Georgia Performance Standards

M6D1.b Using data, construct frequency distributions, frequency tables, and graphs. Also, M6P4.c, M6P5.a, M6P5.b.

A New England Dame School, 1713

The first permanent English settlement in the New World was founded in 1607. It contained 104 colonists. Population increased quickly as more and more immigrants left Europe for North America.

The table shows the estimated population of English American colonies from 1650 to 1700.

Population of American Colonies

Year	1650	1670	1690	1700
Population	50,400	111,900	210,400	250,900

Data that shows change over time is best displayed in a *line graph*. A **line graph** displays a set of data using line segments.

Caution!

Because time passes whether or not the population changes, time is *independent* of population. Always put the independent quantity on the horizontal axis.

EXAMPLE 1 Making a Line Graph

Use the data in the table above to make a line graph.

Step 1: Place *years* on the horizontal axis and *population* on the vertical axis. Label the axes.

Step 2: Determine an appropriate scale and interval for each axis.

Step 3: Mark a point for each data value. Connect the points with straight lines.

Step 4: Title the graph.

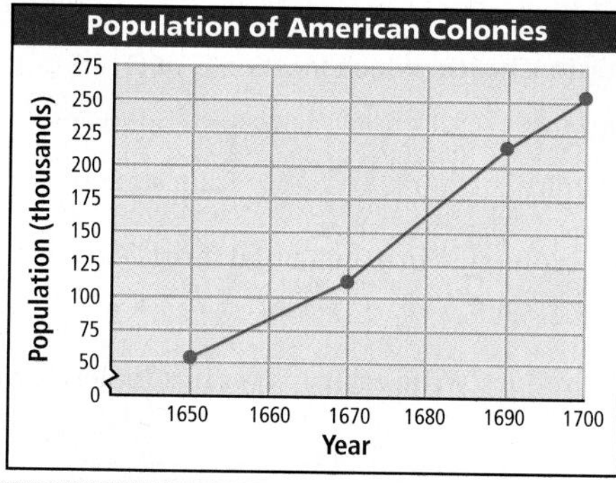

1 Introduce

Alternate Opener

EXPLORATION

6-7 Line Graphs

Luis works at a record store. His manager asked him to graph the number of CDs returned each day during one week.

Day	Sun	Mon	Tue	Wed	Thu	Fri	Sat
CDs Returned	10	3	2	4	7	11	14

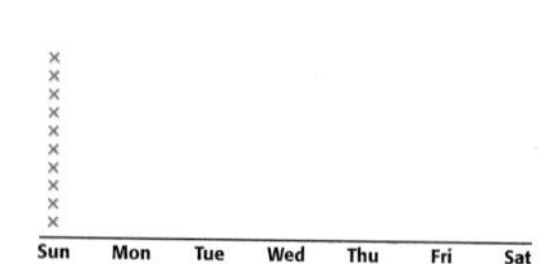

1. Complete the line plot.
2. Draw a vertical line to the left of Sun (Sunday) to form the *y*-axis. Number this line from 1 to 14.
3. Delete all the ×'s in each stack except the one at the top.
4. Connect the ×'s with line segments. You have constructed a *line graph*.

Think and Discuss

5. **Explain** how to construct a line graph.
6. **Discuss** some advantages of displaying data on a line graph rather than in a table.

Motivate

Display a line graph from a magazine or newspaper. Discuss what the graph shows, what is shown along the horizontal axis, and what is shown along the vertical axis. Explain that line graphs are the best graphs to show change over time.

Explorations and answers are provided in *Alternate Openers: Explorations Transparencies*.

EXAMPLE 2 Reading a Line Graph

Use the line graph to answer each question.

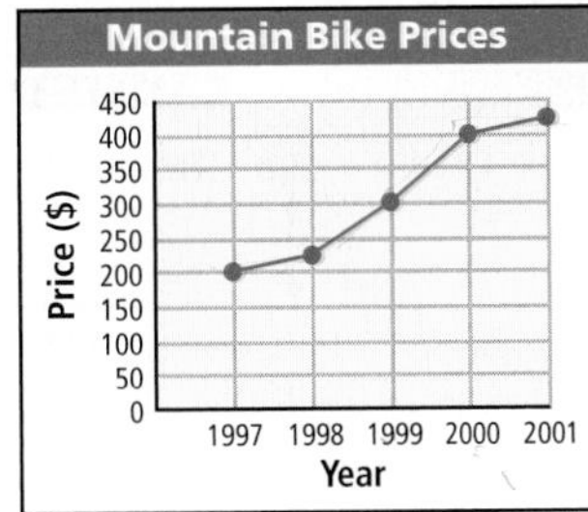

A In which year did mountain bikes cost the least? 1997

B About how much did mountain bikes cost in 1999? about $300

C Did mountain bike prices increase or decrease from 1997 through 2001? They increased.

Line graphs that display two sets of data are called **double-line graphs**.

EXAMPLE 3 Making a Double-Line Graph

Use the data in the table to make a double-line graph.

Life Expectancy in the United States							
	1970	1975	1980	1985	1990	1995	2000
Male (yr)	67	69	70	71	72	73	74
Female (yr)	71	77	77	78	79	79	80

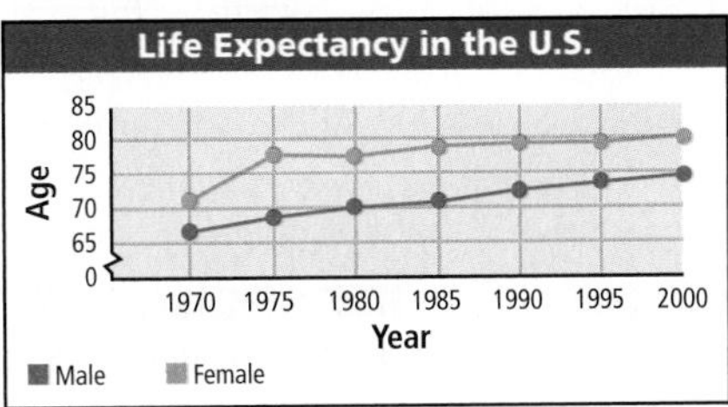

Step 1: Determine an appropriate scale and interval.

Step 2: Mark a point for each male value and connect the points.

Step 3: Mark a point for each female value and connect the points.

Step 4: Title the graph and label both axes. Include a key.

Answers to *Think and Discuss*

1. when the data show change over a period of time
2. Possible answer: You could look for a trend in the data, for example, increasing or decreasing, and then use that information to predict what will happen in the future.
3. so you can tell which line represents males and which represents females

Helpful Hint

Use different colors of lines to connect the male and female values so you will easily be able to tell the data apart.

Think and Discuss

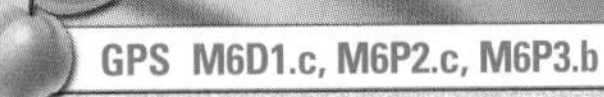

1. **Explain** when it would be helpful to use a line graph instead of a bar graph to display data.
2. **Describe** how you might use a line graph to make predictions.
3. **Tell** why the graph in Example 3 needs a key.

Power Presentations with PowerPoint®

Additional Examples

Example 1

Use the data in the table to make a line graph.

Population of New Hampshire	
Year	Population
1650	1,300
1670	1,800
1690	4,200
1700	5,000

Example 2

Use the line graph to answer each question.

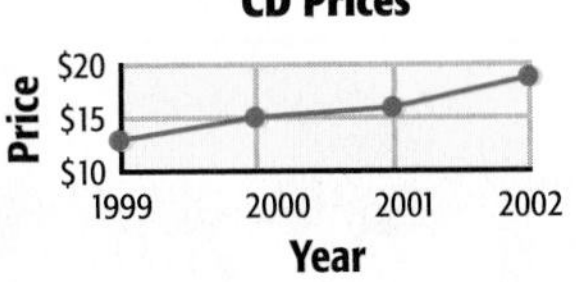

A. In which year did CDs cost the most? 2002

B. About how much did CDs cost in 2000? about $15

C. Did CD prices increase or decrease from 1999 through 2002? increase

Example 3

Use the data in the table to make a double-line graph.

Stock Prices				
	1985	1990	1995	2000
Corp. A	$16	$20	$34	$33
Corp. B	$38	$35	$31	$21

Answers see p. A6.

Also available on transparency

2 Teach

Guided Instruction

In this lesson, students display and analyze data in line graphs. First teach students to make a line graph, given data in a table. Then have students answer questions about a given line graph. Next, teach students to make a double-line graph, given data in a table.

Inclusion Discuss why line graphs are better than bar graphs when representing data that show change over time. On a line graph, you can estimate values for times that fall between the given times.

Through Cognitive Strategies

Discuss with students various examples of things that have increased over time (e. g., DVD sales) and some things that have decreased over time (e. g., VHS sales). Have students research to find data to support the trends discussed (or data that disputes the trends discussed), and create line graphs of the data.

3 Close

ENGLISH LANGUAGE LEARNERS

Summarize

Have students write brief descriptions for *line graphs* and *double-line graphs*. Have students give an example of data that would best be represented by a line graph.

Possible answer: Line graphs represent data values as points connected by lines. A double-line graph shows two sets of data. You could show in a line graph how the number of houses in a given town changes over the course of several years.

6-7 Exercises

Assignment Guide

If you finished Example 1 assign:
Average 1, 15–21
Advanced 6, 15–21

If you finished Example 2 assign:
Average 1–4, 15–21
Advanced 6–8, 15–21

If you finished Example 3 assign:
Average 1–8, 12–21
Advanced 6–21

Homework Quick Check

Quickly check key concepts.
Exercises: 6, 8, 12

Math Background

When you are deciding whether to display data using a line graph or a bar graph, it is sometimes unclear which to choose. The general choice of a line graph to show change over time and a bar graph to show noncontinuous data is a good rule of thumb, but cannot be followed in every instance. For example, if a graph is to show tourist population at a beach resort over the four seasons of a year, a bar graph would be a better choice, even though the graph shows change over time.

Answers

1, 5–6. See p. A6.

Georgia Performance Standards

M6P1.b Solve problems that arise in mathematics and in other contexts.

M6P3.a Organize and consolidate their mathematical thinking through communication.

6-7 Exercises

M6P1.b, M6P3.a

go.hrw.com
Homework Help Online
KEYWORD: MR7 6-7
Parent Resources Online
KEYWORD: MR7 Parent

GUIDED PRACTICE

See Example 1

1. Use the data in the table to make a line graph.

School Enrollment				
Year	2000	2001	2002	2003
Students	2,000	2,500	2,750	3,500

See Example 2

Use the line graph to answer each question.

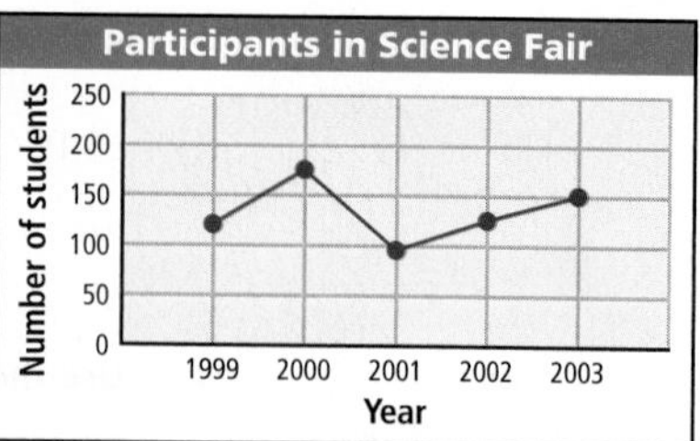

2. In which year did the most students participate in the science fair? **2000**
3. About how many students participated in 2002? **125**
4. Did the number of students increase or decrease from 2000 to 2001? **decrease**

See Example 3

5. Use the data in the table to make a double-line graph.

	January	February	March	April	May
Stock A	$10	$12	$20	$25	$22
Stock B	$8	$8	$12	$20	$30

INDEPENDENT PRACTICE

See Example 1

6. Use the data in the table to make a line graph.

Winning Times in the Iditarod Dog Sled Race							
Year	1995	1996	1997	1998	1999	2000	2001
Time (hr)	219	222	225	222	231	217	236

See Example 2

Use the line graph to answer each question.

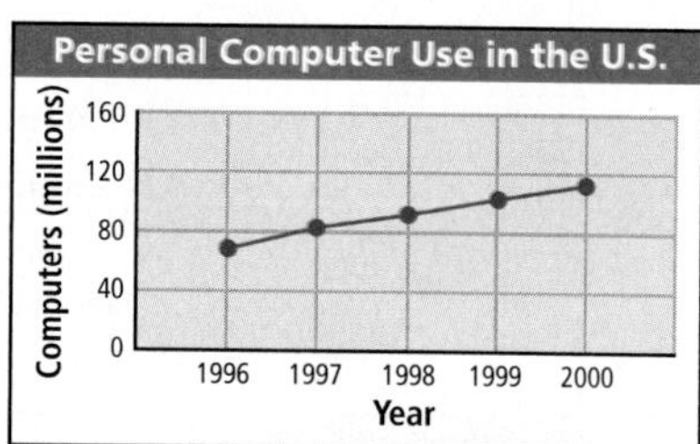

7. About how many personal computers were in use in the United States in 1996? **70 million**
8. When was the number of personal computers in use about 105 million? **1999**

RETEACH 6-7

LESSON 6-7 **Reteach**
Line Graphs

A line graph shows change over time.

You can represent data by making a line graph.

Stock Sales (millions)

Mon	Tue	Wed	Thurs	Fri
1.5	2.0	2.25	1.75	0.5

To make a line graph, make "days" the horizontal axis and "sales" the vertical axis. Label the axes.

Then determine an appropriate scale and interval for each axis.

Think of the data in the table as ordered pairs. Mark a point for each ordered pair. Then connect the points with straight segments.

Make sure your line graph has a title.

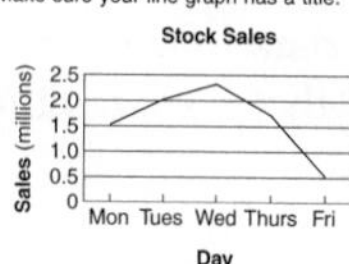

Use the data in the table to make a line graph.

1. Millie's Savings Account

Jan	Feb	March	April	May
30	40	35	45	25

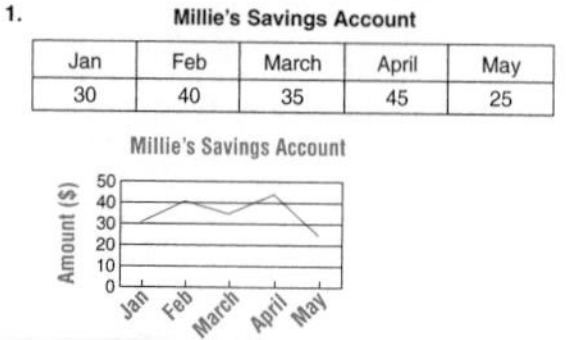

PRACTICE 6-7

LESSON 6-7 **Practice B**
Line Graphs

Use the line graph to answer each question.

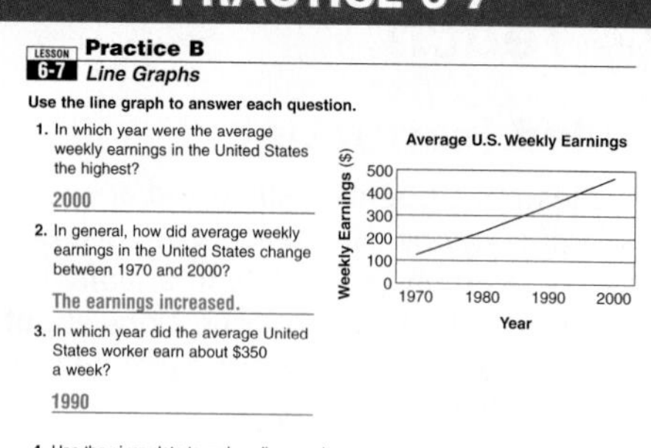

1. In which year were the average weekly earnings in the United States the highest?
   2000
2. In general, how did average weekly earnings in the United States change between 1970 and 2000?
   The earnings increased.
3. In which year did the average United States worker earn about $350 a week?
   1990
4. Use the given data to make a line graph.

U.S. Minimum Wage	
Year	**Hourly Rate**
1970	$1.60
1980	$3.10
1990	$3.80
2000	$5.15

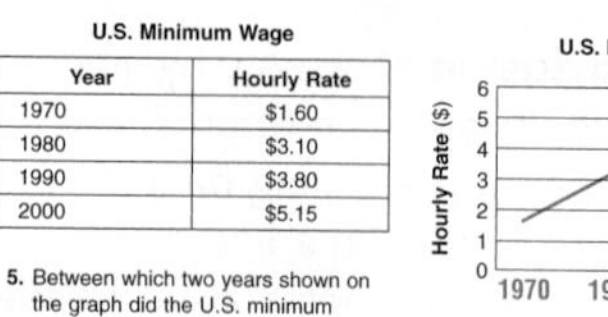

5. Between which two years shown on the graph did the U.S. minimum wage change the least?
   1980 and 1990
6. How has the hourly minimum wage changed in the U.S. since 1970?
   It has increased.

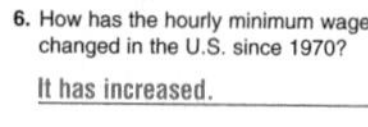

See Example 3

9. Use the data in the table to make a double-line graph.

Soccer Team's Total Fund-Raising Sales						
Day	0	1	2	3	4	5
Team A	$0	$100	$225	$300	$370	$450
Team B	$0	$50	$100	$150	$200	$250

CRCT GPS

Extra Practice p. 725

PRACTICE AND PROBLEM SOLVING

Use the line graph for Exercises 10 and 11.

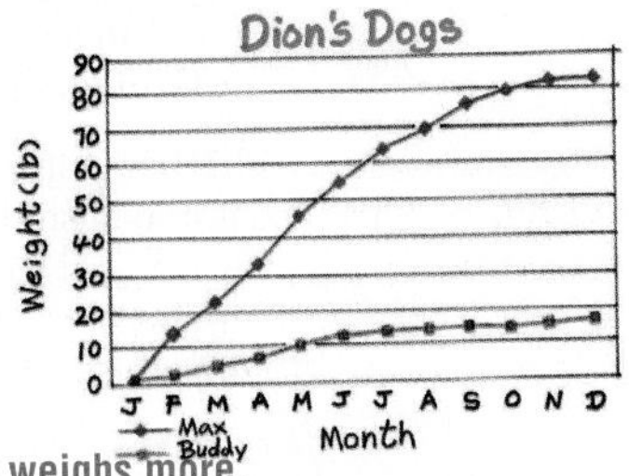

Dion's Dogs

90, 80, 70, 60, 50, 40, 30, 20, 10, 0

Weight (lb)

J F M A M J J A S O N D

Month

Max
Buddy

10. **Life Science** Estimate the difference in the dogs' weights in March. about 17 pounds

11. **Life Science** One of Dion's dogs is a Great Dane, and the other is a Jack Russell Terrier. Which dog is probably the Great Dane? Justify your answer.
Max is probably the Great Dane because he weighs more.

LINK Life Science

Larger dogs usually have shorter life spans than smaller dogs. Great Danes live an average of 8.4 years, and Jack Russell terriers live an average of 13.6 years.

12. **Life Science** The table shows the weights in pounds for Sara Beth's two pets. Use the data to make a line graph that is similar to Dion's.

	Jan	Feb	Mar	Apr	May	Jun	Jul	Aug	Sep	Oct	Nov	Dec
Ginger	3	9	15	21	24	25	26	25	26	27	26	28
Toto	4	8	13	17	24	26	27	29	25	26	28	28

13. **Write About It** You have a bowl of soup for lunch. Draw a line graph that could represent the changes in the soup's temperature during lunch. Explain.

14. **Challenge** Describe a situation that this graph could represent.
Possible answer: the speed of a runner in a 1-mile race

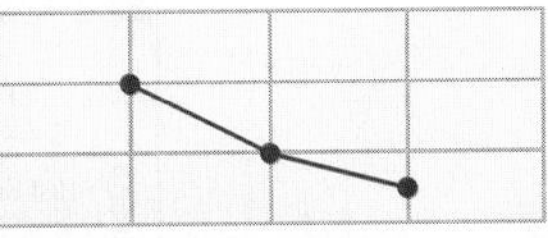

CRCT PREP • GPS SUPPORT • SPIRAL REVIEW

15. **Multiple Choice** Which type of graph would you use to display two sets of data that change over time?

Ⓐ Bar graph Ⓑ Pictograph ⓒ Double-line graph Ⓓ Line graph

16. **Short Response** Use the graph from Exercises 10 and 11. Did Max's weight increase or decrease between September and October? Explain. Increase; It went up from about 78 lb to 80 lb.

Solve each equation. (Lesson 2-7)

17. $5s = 90$ $s = 18$
18. $4g = 128$ $g = 32$
19. $8m = 120$ $m = 15$
20. $17a = 544$ $a = 32$

21. A survey of 100 people found that 48 of the people have had 0 speeding tickets, 34 have had 1 ticket, 10 have had 2 tickets, 2 have had 3 tickets, and 3 have had 4 or more tickets. Create a bar graph to display the data. (Lesson 6-4)

ONGOING ASSESSMENT and INTERVENTION

Diagnose **Before** the Lesson
6-7 Warm Up, TE p. 322

Monitor **During** the Lesson
6-7 Know-It Notebook
6-7 Questioning Strategies

Assess **After** the Lesson
6-7 Lesson Quiz, TE p. 325

Answers

9, 12–13, 21. See p. A6.

TEST PREP DOCTOR In Exercise 16, remind students to use the legend for the double-line graph to correctly identify the line that relates to Max's weight.

Journal

Have students make up and solve a word problem for the graphs they made for Exercise 8.

Power Presentations with PowerPoint®

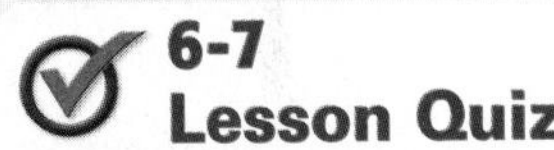

6-7 Lesson Quiz

1. **Use the data to make a line graph.** See p. A6.

Number of Aluminum Cans Collected				
Mon	Tue	Wed	Thu	Fri
100	150	200	125	175

Use the line graph to answer each question.

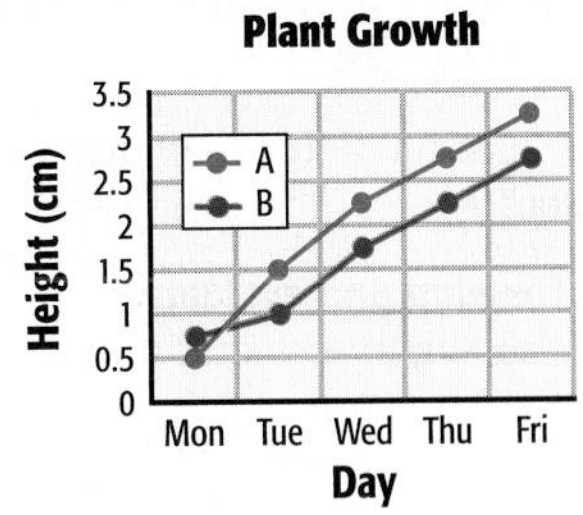

2. Which plant was taller on Tuesday? A
3. Which plant grew more between Thursday and Friday? Each grew the same amount.
4. Which plant grew the most in one week? A

Also available on transparency

CHALLENGE 6-7

LESSON 6-7 **Challenge**
A Trendy Park

Because line graphs show changes over time, you can use them to make predictions based on trends, or patterns. United States park rangers make line graphs to look for trends. They count the number of people who visit their parks each month. Then the park rangers analyze the data on line graphs to look for trends and predict how many visitors to expect each month in the coming years. This data helps the rangers schedule workers and provide services for their visitors.

Great Smoky Mountains National Park in Tennessee and North Carolina receives more visitors each year than any other national park. Imagine you are a park ranger there. Use the line graph below to identify trends and make predictions about the number of visitors the park will receive in the future.

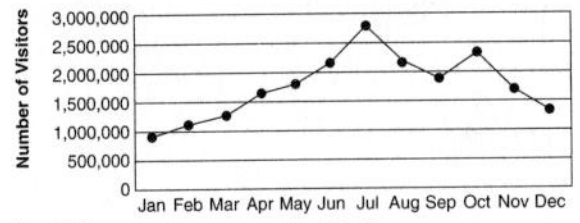

Visitors At Great Smoky Mountains National Park, 2000

Number of Visitors: 3,000,000; 2,500,000; 2,000,000; 1,500,000; 1,000,000; 500,000; 0

Jan Feb Mar Apr May Jun Jul Aug Sep Oct Nov Dec

Month

Possible answers:

1. In which month next year should you plan for the most visitors at your park? July
2. What can you expect next year at the park between October and January?
Each month the number of visitors will decrease.
3. You are in charge of deciding how many rangers should be scheduled to work at Great Smoky Mountains National Park each month next year. How will the number of park rangers you schedule change each month from January to June?
Each month, I will schedule more park rangers to work than the month before.
4. Which month next year would be best for you to take time off from your park ranger job and go on your own vacation? Explain.
January; because that is the month when the park has the least amount of visitors.

PROBLEM SOLVING 6-7

LESSON 6-7 **Problem Solving**
Line Graphs

Use the line graphs to answer each question.

U.S. Farm Population

35, 30, 25, 20, 15, 10, 5, 0

1900 1920 1940 1960 1980 2000

Year

Size of U.S. Farms

Average Farm Size (acres): 500, 450, 400, 350, 300, 250, 200, 150, 100, 50, 0

1900 1920 1940 1960 1980 2000

Year

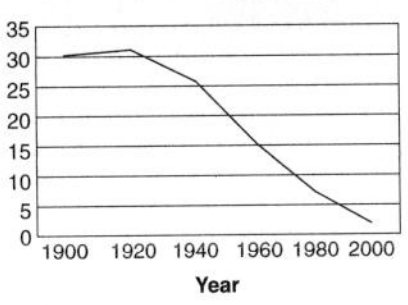

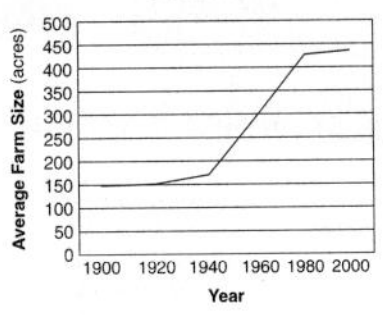

1. In which year was the U.S. farm population the highest? the lowest?
1920; 2000
2. In which year was the size of the average U.S. farm the largest? the smallest?
2000; 1900
3. In general, how has the U.S. farm population changed in the last 100 years?
The population has decreased.
4. In general, how has the size of the average U.S. farm changed in the last 100 years?
The average size has increased.

Circle the letter of the correct answer.

5. How many people lived on farms in the United States in 1940?
A 31 million
B 30 million
ⓒ 26 million
D 15 million
6. How many acres did the average farm in the United States cover in 1980?
F 150 acres
G 300 acres
H 400 acres
Ⓙ 426 acres
7. Between which two years did the U.S. farm population increase?
Ⓐ 1900 and 1920
B 1920 and 1940
C 1940 and 1960
D 1960 and 1980
8. Between which two years did the average size of farms in the United States change the least?
Ⓕ 1900 and 1920
G 1920 and 1940
H 1960 and 1980
J 1980 and 2000

6-8 Organizer

Pacing: Traditional 1 day
Block $\frac{1}{2}$ day

Objective: Students recognize misleading graphs.

Online Edition
Tutorial Videos, Interactivities

Countdown to CRCT Week 13

Power Presentations with PowerPoint®

Warm Up

Use the data below to answer each question.

20 21 23 24 27 33 34 35 36
38 40 41 42 43 46 52 53

1. What is the median? 36
2. What is the mode? none
3. What is the range? 33

Problem of the Day

Nine students in a group found that their mean score was 86 for the first math test. On the next test, each student in the group scored 7 points higher than on the first test. What was their mean score for the two tests? 89.5

Also available on transparency

The bankrupt restaurant was like a statistician waiting for data. There were lots of empty tables.

M6P1.b Solve problems that arise in mathematics and in other contexts.

M6P2.c Develop and evaluate mathematical arguments and proofs.

6-8 Misleading Graphs

Learn to recognize misleading graphs.

M6P2.c Develop and evaluate mathematical arguments. Also, M6P1.b.

Data can be displayed in many different ways. Sometimes people who make graphs choose to display data in a misleading way.

This bar graph was created by a group of students who believe their school should increase support of the football team. How could this bar graph be misleading?

At a glance, you might conclude that about three times as many students prefer football to basketball. But if you look at the values of the bars, you can see that only 20 students chose football over basketball.

EXAMPLE 1 Misleading Bar Graphs

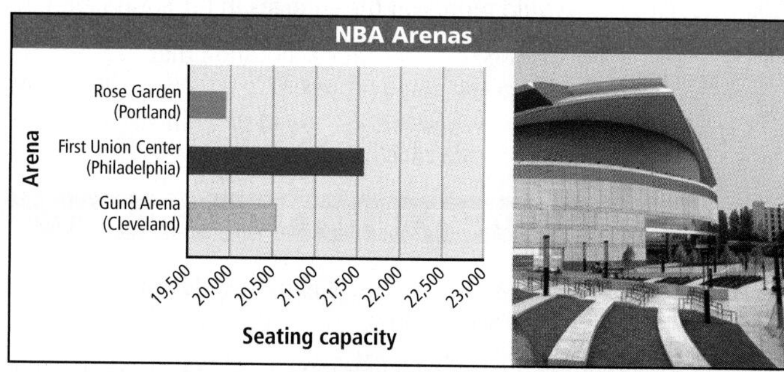

A **Why is this bar graph misleading?**
Because the lower part of the horizontal scale is missing, the differences in seating capacities are exaggerated.

B **What might people believe from the misleading graph?**
People might believe that the First Union Center holds 2–4 times as many people as Gund Arena and the Rose Garden. In reality, the First Union Center holds only one to two thousand more people than the other two arenas.

1 Introduce

Alternate Opener

EXPLORATION

Misleading Graphs

The graph shows the total number of medals won by four countries at the 2002 Winter Olympics.

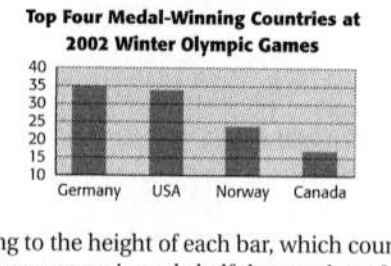

Top Four Medal-Winning Countries at 2002 Winter Olympic Games
(bar graph: 10, 15, 20, 25, 30, 35, 40; Germany, USA, Norway, Canada)

1. According to the height of each bar, which country appears to have won approximately half the number of medals won by the United States?
2. Look at the numbers on the left to estimate the number of medals won by each country.
3. Use the estimates in number 2 to determine whether the answer to number 1 is accurate.

Think and Discuss

4. **Discuss** how the graph is misleading.
5. **Explain** how you could modify the graph to represent the data more accurately.

Motivate

Show students the graph at the beginning of the lesson (Teaching Transparency). Discuss how the graph is misleading and what information people might believe from the graph. The scale does not begin at zero, and people might believe that 3 times as many students prefer football to basketball.

Explorations and answers are provided in *Alternate Openers: Explorations Transparencies.*

EXAMPLE 2 Misleading Line Graphs

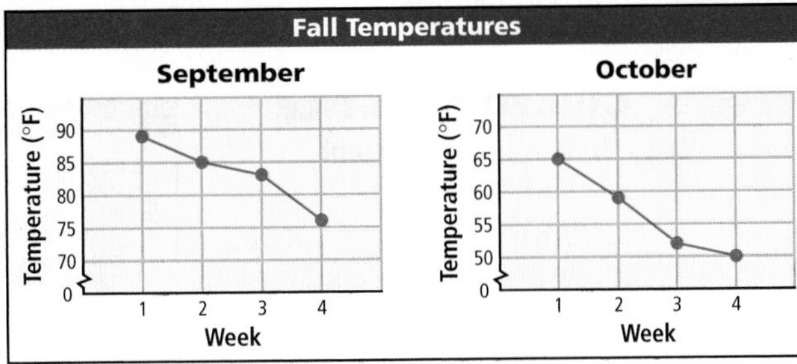

A **Why are these line graphs misleading?**

If you look at the scale for each graph, you will notice that the September graph goes from 75°F to 90°F and the October graph goes from 50°F to 65°F.

B **What might people believe from these misleading graphs?**

People might believe that the temperatures in October were about the same as the temperatures in September. In reality, the temperatures in September were 20–30 degrees higher.

C **Why is this line graph misleading?**

The scale does not have equal intervals. So, for example, an increase from 35 sit-ups to 40 sit-ups looks greater than an increase from 30 sit-ups to 35 sit-ups.

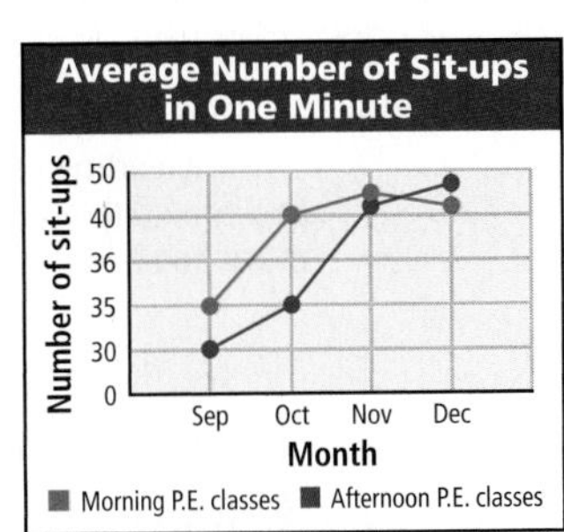

Possible answers to *Think and Discuss*

1. in advertising, to try to convince consumers to buy one product instead of another
2. The PE teacher may have made the graph as a way to convince the school principal to do away with afternoon PE classes.
3. Change the scale on the number of sit-ups to increments of 5.

Think and Discuss

1. **Give an example** of a situation in which you think someone would intentionally try to make a graph misleading.
2. **Tell** who might have made the misleading graph in Example 2C.
3. **Tell** how you could change the graph in Example 2C so that it is not misleading.

Power Presentations with PowerPoint®

Additional Examples

Example 1

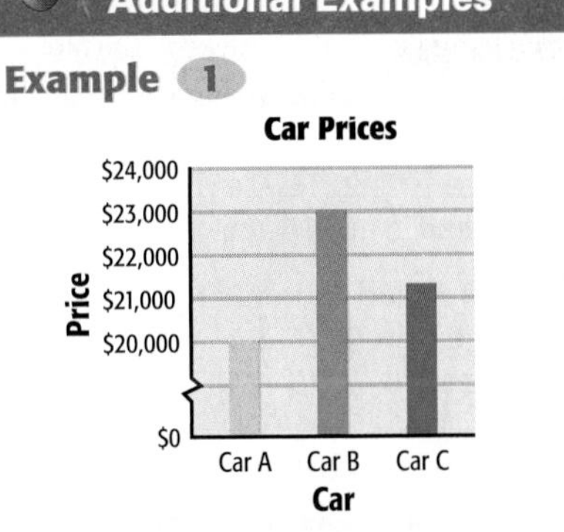

A. Why is this bar graph misleading.

B. What might people believe from the misleading graph?

Example 2

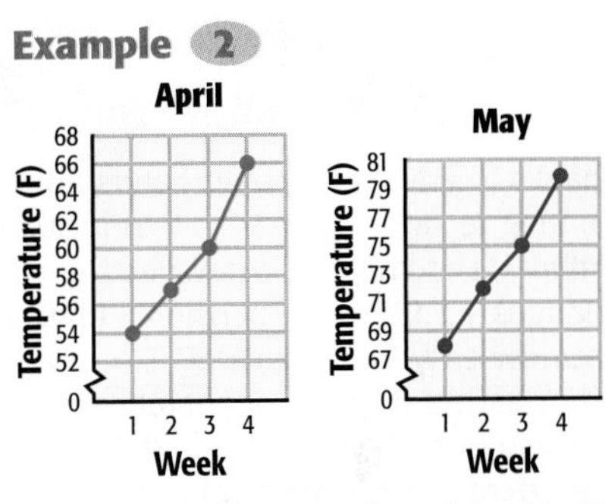

A. Why are these graphs misleading?

B. What might people believe from these misleading graphs?

C. Explain why this graph is misleading.

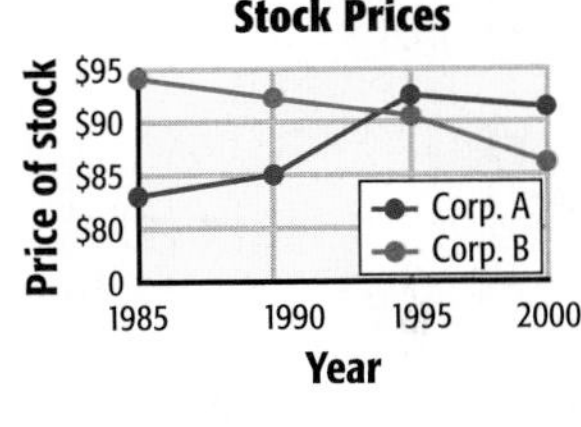

Answers see p. A6.

Also available on transparency

2 Teach

Guided Instruction

In this lesson, students learn to recognize misleading graphs. First teach students to analyze a misleading bar graph. Then teach them to analyze line graphs that are misleading. Emphasize the importance of analyzing scales to decide whether graphs are misleading.

Inclusion Have students describe how they could change the graphs in Examples 1 and 2 to make them less misleading.

Reaching All Learners

Through Cooperative Learning

Have students work in groups of four to make misleading graphs and graphs that are not misleading. Have each group decide on a set of data to graph. Half of the group then graphs the data in a way that is misleading, while the other half graphs it in a way that is not misleading. Have groups present both graphs to the class and see if the rest of the class can identify and explain which graph is misleading.

3 Close

Summarize

Review with students that graphs can be misleading, whether intentional or not. Remind students to carefully analyze all graphs before making conclusions about the data presented.

6-8 Exercises

Assignment Guide

If you finished Example 1 assign:
Average 1–2, 16–24
Advanced 5–6, 16–24

If you finished Example 2 assign:
Average 1–9, 16–24
Advanced 5–9, 13–24

Homework Quick Check

Quickly check key concepts.
Exercises: 6, 8

Math Background

Thanks to advances in computers and printing technology, graphs that include artwork, shading, color, perspective changes, and three-dimensional effects are now easy to produce. While they often have a pleasing appearance, they are also potentially misleading. The important thing to remember is that every graph must be examined with a critical eye.

More information on this issue can be found in Stephen M. Kosslyn's *Elements of Graph Design*.

Answers

1. Possible answer: The years for the top bar represent 40 years, but the other columns only represent 10 years.
3. Possible answer: Kerry does not begin biking from home.
5. The vertical axis begins at 430 rather than zero.
9. See p. A6.

Georgia Performance Standards

M6P3.a Organize and consolidate their mathematical thinking through communication.

M6P4.c Recognize and apply mathematics in contexts outside of mathematics.

6-8 Exercises

M6P3.a, M6P4.c

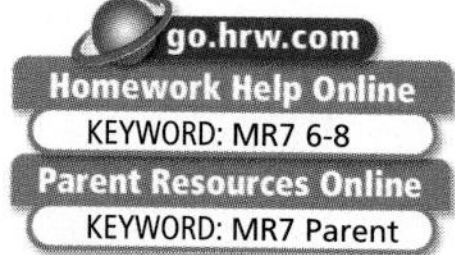

GUIDED PRACTICE

See Example 1

1. Why is this bar graph misleading?
2. What might people believe from the misleading graph?
that the community center had more volunteers in the past than now

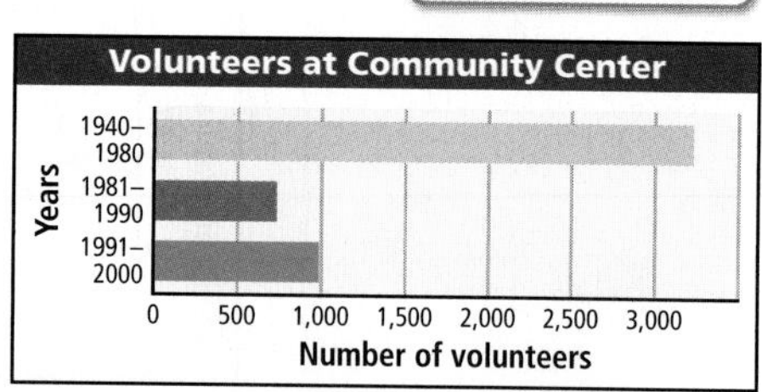

See Example 2

3. Why is this line graph misleading?
4. What might people believe from the misleading graph?
It appears that Kerry biked farther in the 30-minute period when actually she did not.

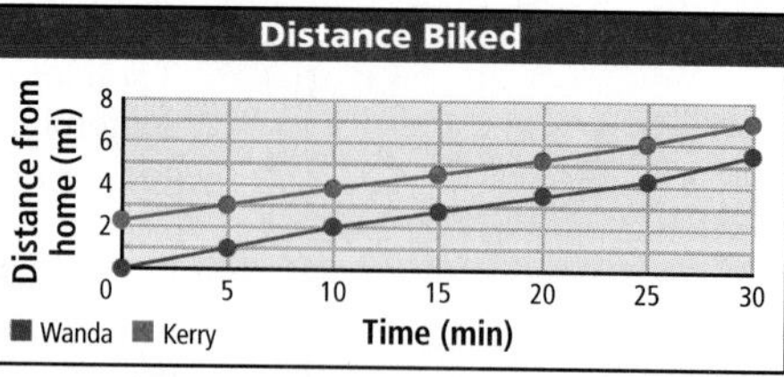

INDEPENDENT PRACTICE

See Example 1

5. Why is this bar graph misleading?
6. What might people believe from the misleading graph?
that the sixth graders have read 7 times more books than the seventh graders

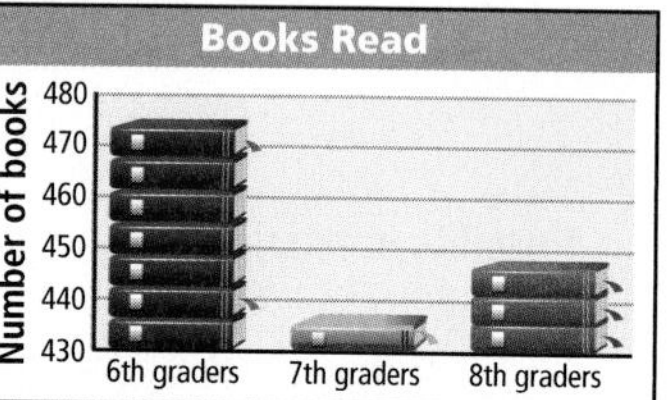

See Example 2

7. Why is this line graph misleading?
the yearly increments changed
8. What might people believe from the misleading graph?
Possible answer: The minimum wage is not increasing at as fast of a rate as it was several years ago

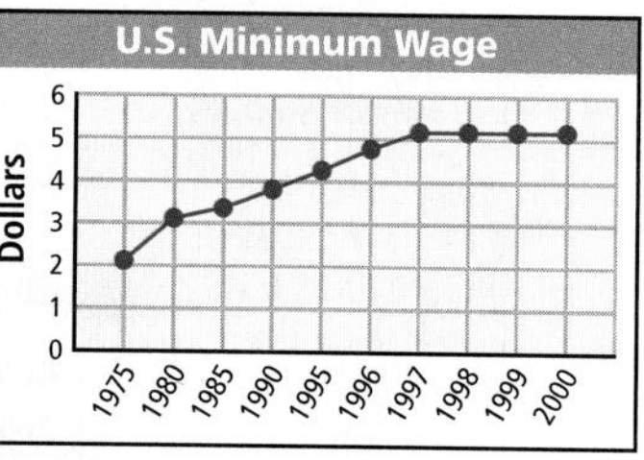

PRACTICE AND PROBLEM SOLVING

Extra Practice p. 725

9. **Critical Thinking** In a survey, people were asked which teeth-whitening product they found worked best. The results stated that 1,007 people chose strips, 995 people chose paste, and 998 chose paint. Make two bar graphs, one to show that the strips are significantly more effective than the paste or paint, and the other to show that the paste is the most effective.

RETEACH 6-8

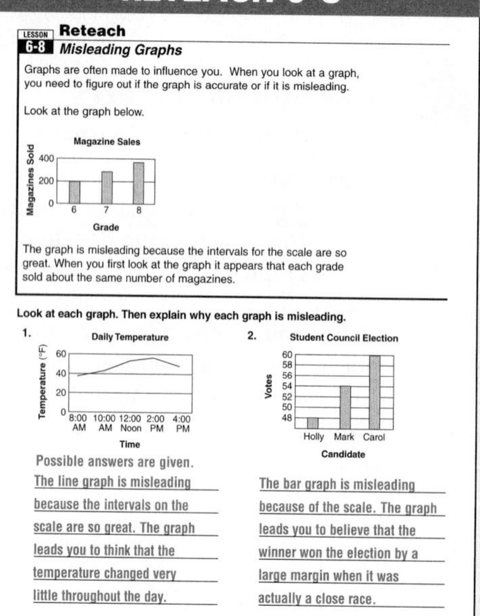

LESSON 6-8 **Reteach**
Misleading Graphs

Graphs are often made to influence you. When you look at a graph, you need to figure out if the graph is accurate or if it is misleading.

Look at the graph below.

Magazine Sales

The graph is misleading because the intervals for the scale are so great. When you first look at the graph it appears that each grade sold about the same number of magazines.

Look at each graph. Then explain why each graph is misleading.

1. Daily Temperature

Possible answers are given.
The line graph is misleading because the intervals on the scale are so great. The graph leads you to think that the temperature changed very little throughout the day.

2. Student Council Election

The bar graph is misleading because of the scale. The graph leads you to believe that the winner won the election by a large margin when it was actually a close race.

PRACTICE 6-8

LESSON 6-8 **Practice B**
Misleading Graphs

Use the graph to answer each question. Possible answers are given.

1. Why is this bar graph misleading?
Because the lower part of the vertical scale is missing, the differences in grades are exaggerated.
2. What might people believe from the misleading graph?
There are 4 times as many students in the 8th grade than the 6th grade.

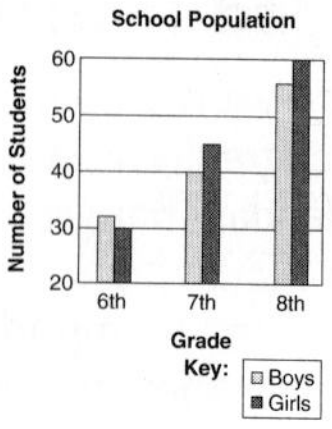

School Population
Number of Students
60
50
40
30
20
6th
7th
8th
Grade
Key: Boys Girls

Use the graph to answer each question.

3. Why is this line graph misleading?
Because there is a break in the vertical scale, the differences in attendance seem greater than they really are.
4. What might people believe from the misleading graph?
In some months, 3 times more people attended soccer games than lacrosse games.

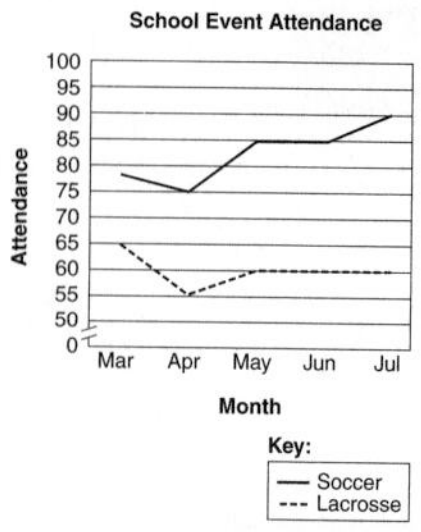

School Event Attendance
Attendance
100
95
90
85
80
75
70
65
60
55
50
0
Mar
Apr
May
Jun
Jul
Month
Key: Soccer Lacrosse

A research company has developed a cholesterol medication. The table shows the mean monthly cholesterol levels for patients who have been taking the medication for 5 months.

Mean Cholesterol Level	
Month	**Cholesterol**
1	300
2	275
3	240
4	230
5	210

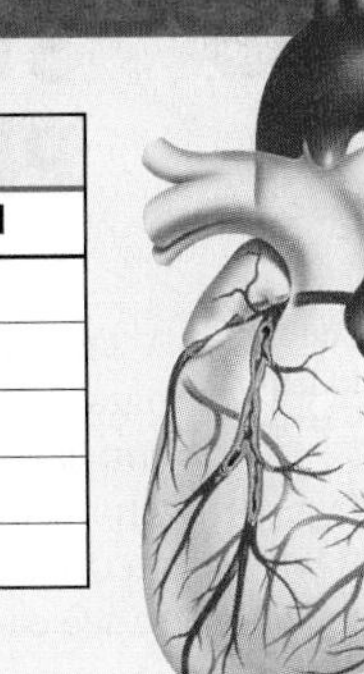
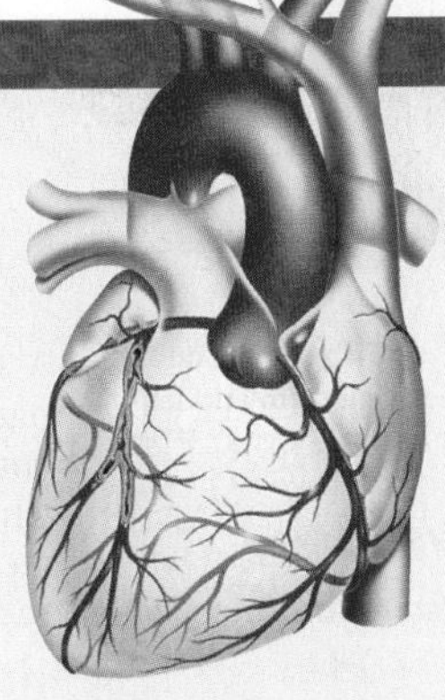

A heart with coronary artery disease, caused by buildup of fatty deposits

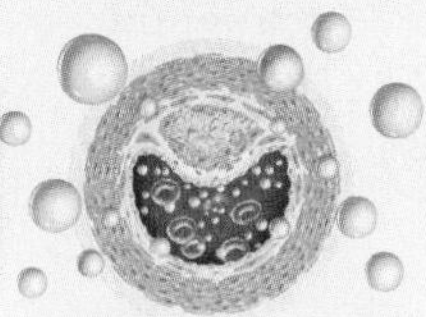
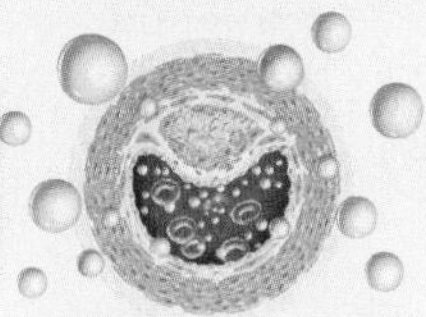

An artery that has been narrowed by high levels of blood cholesterol

10. What kind of graph would you make to display this data? Why?

11. Make a graph that suggests the medication greatly reduces cholesterol levels. Explain how your graph does this.

12. Make a graph that suggests the medication has little effect on cholesterol levels. Explain how your graph does this.

13. **What's the Question?** Look at the entries in the table. If the answer is 90, what is the question? What is the range of the data in the table?

14. **Write About It** Suppose you saw your graph from Exercise 11 in an advertisement. What do you think it might be an advertisement for? Explain. for a competitor's drug

15. **Challenge** What additional information could the research company gather and use to make a double-line graph that shows how its medication affects cholesterol levels?

CRCT Prep • GPS Support • Spiral Review

16. Multiple Choice Which statement is supported by the information in the bar graph?

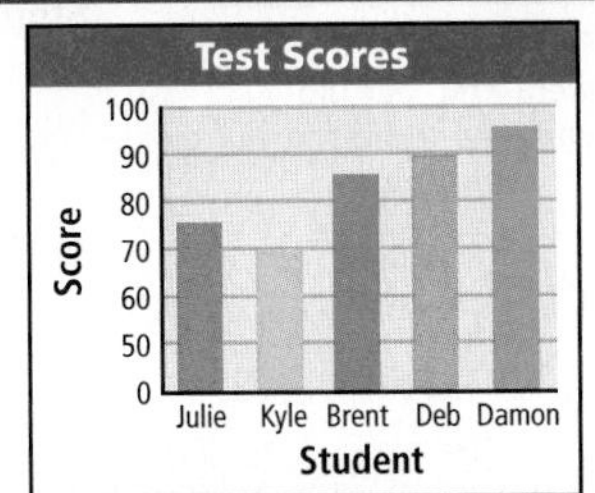

(A) Damon scored twice as high as Kyle on the test.
(B) Kyle scored the highest on the test.
(C) Brent scored twice as high as Julie on the test.
(D) Deb scored the second-highest on the test.

17. Short Response What might readers believe from the misleading line graph? Explain how to redraw the graph so that it is not as misleading.

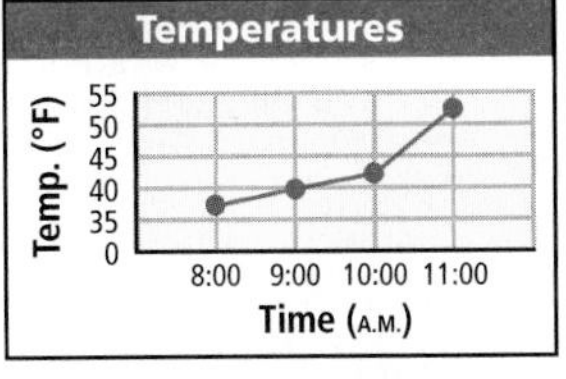

Evaluate each expression. (Lesson 1-4)

18. $6 \times 2^3 + 17 - 3 \times 2$ **59**

19. $85 - (44 + 33) \div 7 + (62 - 12)$ **124**

Plot each point on a coordinate grid. (Lesson 6-6)

20. $A(3, 5)$ **21.** $B(6, 2)$ **22.** $C(0, 4)$ **23.** $D(1, 0)$ **24.** $E(5.5, 7)$

Ongoing Assessment and Intervention

***Diagnose Before* the Lesson**
6-8 Warm Up, TE p. 326

***Monitor During* the Lesson**
6-8 Know-It Notebook
6-9 Questioning Strategies

***Assess After* the Lesson**
6-9 Lesson Quiz, TE p. 329

Answers

10. Possible answer: line graph; because you easily see the changes from month to month

11–12, 15, 17, 20–24. See p. A6.

For Exercise 17, remind students that the size of the intervals in the vertical scale must be uniform. The scale begins at zero, but the first interval is 35, and all others are 5. Because of this, the relationship between the bars on the graph will be distorted.

Journal

Have students write about a situation in which they might want to use a misleading graph.

CHALLENGE 6-8

LESSON 6-8 Challenge
Graph Detective

You are a police detective in Capital City. A gang of criminals there is distributing misleading graphs to convince people that your city does not need to hire more police officers. It's your job to catch these graph crooks.

Search the graphs below for evidence of misleading displays of data. Then use your detective skills to explain why each graph is misleading.

Possible answers:

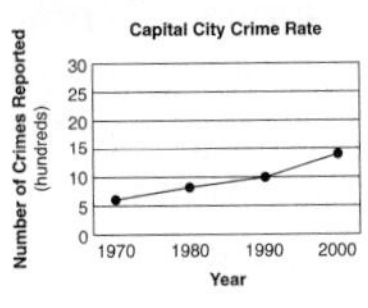

Why is this line graph misleading?

The intervals on the y-axis are so large, it looks like the crime rate has changed very little.

What might people believe from this misleading graph?

The city's crime rate is low and has not changed very much since 1970, so the city does not need to hire more police officers.

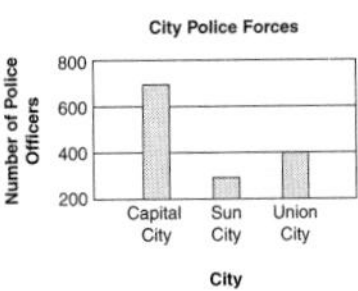

Why is this bar graph is misleading?

Because the lower part of the vertical scale is missing, the differences in the cities' police forces are exaggerated.

What might people believe from this misleading graph?

Capital City has 5 times as many police officers as Sun City and $2\frac{1}{2}$ times as many as Union City, so Capital City does not need to hire more police officers.

PROBLEM SOLVING 6-8

LESSON 6-8 Problem Solving
Misleading Graphs

Use the graphs to answer each question. Possible answers:

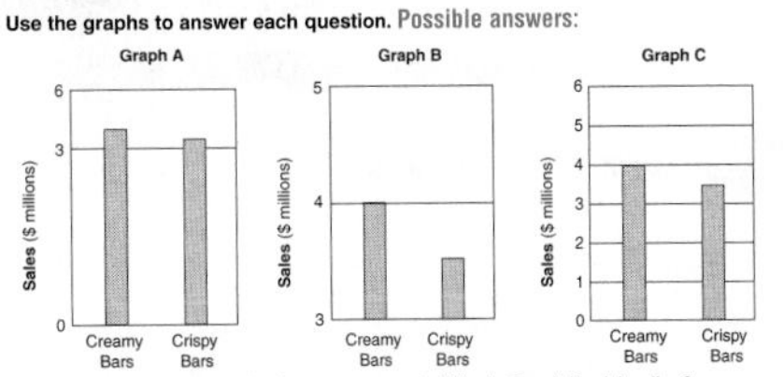

Graph A — Sales ($ millions): 0, 3, 6; Creamy Bars, Crispy Bars
Graph B — Sales ($ millions): 3, 4, 5; Creamy Bars, Crispy Bars
Graph C — Sales ($ millions): 0, 1, 2, 3, 4, 5, 6; Creamy Bars, Crispy Bars

1. Why is Graph A misleading?

The vertical scale intervals are not equal, which makes the data look closer than it actually is.

2. Why is Graph B misleading?

The lower part of the vertical scale is missing; differences in sales are exaggerated.

3. What might people believe from reading Graph A?

About the same number of Crispy Bars and Creamy Bars were sold.

4. What might people believe from reading Graph B?

Creamy Bar sales were twice the sales of Crispy Bar sales.

Circle the letter of the correct answer.

5. Which of the following information is different on all three graphs above?
(A) the vertical scale
B the Crispy Bars sales data
C the Creamy Bars sales data
D the horizontal scale

6. Which of the following is a way that graphs can be misleading?
F breaks in scales
G uneven scales
H missing parts of scales
(J) all of the above

7. Which graph do you think was made by the company that sells Crispy Bars?
(A) Graph A
B Graph B
C Graph C
D all of the graphs

8. If you were writing a newspaper article about candy bar sales, which graph would be best to use?
F Graph A
G Graph B
(H) Graph C
J all of the above

Power Presentations with PowerPoint®

6-8 Lesson Quiz

1. Why might this line graph be misleading?

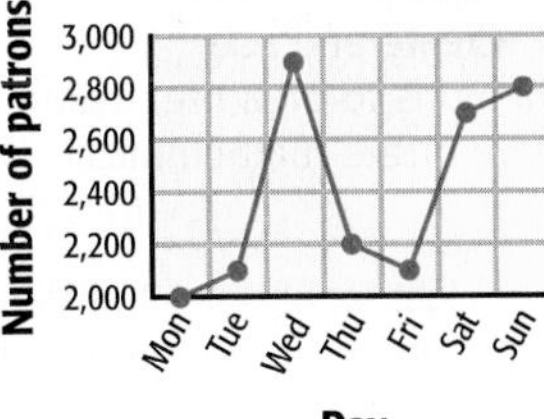

The scale does not start at zero.

2. What might people believe from the graph? Possible answer: that there were hardly any visitors on Monday

Also available on transparency

6-9 Organizer

Pacing: Traditional 1 day
Block $\frac{1}{2}$ day

Objective: Students make and analyze stem-and-leaf plots.

Online Edition
Tutorial Videos

Countdown to CRCT Week 13

Power Presentations with PowerPoint®

Warm Up

A set of data ranges from 12 to 86. What intervals would you use to display this data in a histogram with four intervals? Possible answer: 10–29, 30–49, 50–69, 70–89

Problem of the Day

What is the least number that can be divided evenly by each of the numbers 1 through 12? 27,720

Also available on transparency

Math Fact

The stem-and-leaf plot was invented by Professor Jon Tukey, of Princeton University, in the 1960s.

6-9 Stem-and-Leaf Plots

Learn to make and analyze stem-and-leaf plots.

Vocabulary
stem-and-leaf plot

Georgia Performance Standards

M6P5.a Create and use representations to organize, record, and communicate mathematical ideas. Also, M6P1.b, M6P5.b.

A **stem-and-leaf plot** shows data arranged by place value. You can use a stem-and-leaf plot when you want to display data in an organized way that allows you to see each value.

The Explorer Scouts had a competition to see who could build the highest card tower. The table shows the number of levels reached by each scout.

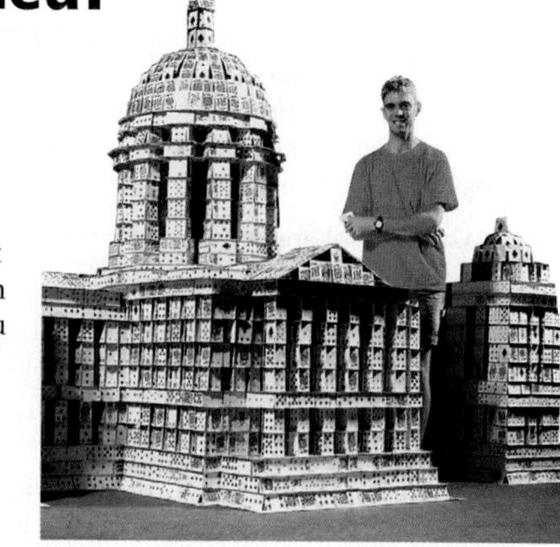

Bryan Berg and his card model of the Iowa State Capitol

Number of Card-Tower Levels									
12	23	31	50	14	17	25	44	51	20
23	18	35	15	19	15	23	42	21	13

EXAMPLE 1 Creating Stem-and-Leaf Plots

Use the data in the table above to make a stem-and-leaf plot.

Step 1: Group the data by tens digits.

Step 2: Order the data from least to greatest.

Step 3: List the tens digits of the data in order from least to greatest. Write these in the "stems" column.

Step 4: For each tens digit, record the ones digits of each data value in order from least to greatest. Write these in the "leaves" column.

Step 5: Title the graph and add a key.

12 13 14 15 15 17 18 19
20 21 23 23 23 25
31 35
42 44
50 51

Helpful Hint

To write 42 in a stem-and-leaf plot, write each digit in a separate column.

4 | 2
Stem Leaf

Number of Card Tower Levels

Stems	Leaves
1	2 3 4 5 5 7 8 9
2	0 1 3 3 3 5
3	1 5
4	2 4
5	0 1

Key: 1|5 means 15

Georgia Performance Standards

M6P1.b Solve problems that arise in mathematics and in other contexts.

M6P5.a Create and use representations to organize, record, and communicate mathematical ideas.

M6P5.b Select, apply, and translate among mathematical representations to solve problems.

1 Introduce

Alternate Opener

EXPLORATION

6-9 Stem-and-Leaf Plots

The table shows the times in seconds and hundredths of seconds for the women's 500-meter speed-skating competition in the 2002 Winter Olympics.

74.75	74.94	75.19	75.37	75.39	75.64	75.64	76.17	76.20	76.31
76.37	76.42	76.62	76.73	76.73	76.86	76.92	77.10	77.37	77.60
77.60	77.71	78.26	78.63	78.79	78.89	79.28	79.45	79.45	

You can organize the data by seconds and hundredths of seconds. Notice how the times are grouped using different colors.

1. Complete the *stem-and-leaf plot.* The stems represent seconds and the leaves represent hundredths of seconds. Notice how the colors correspond to the colors used in the table.

Stems	Leaves
74	75 94
75	
76	
77	
78	
79	

Key: 74 | 75 means 74.75

Think and Discuss

2. **Explain** what it means in this case for a stem to have the most number of leaves.
3. **Explain** what it means in this case for a stem to have the least number of leaves.

2 Teach

Guided Instruction

In this lesson, students make and analyze stem-and-leaf plots. Teach students to make a stem-and-leaf plot, given a set of unordered data. Then teach students to analyze a stem-and-leaf plot to identify least and greatest values, mean, median, mode, and range.

Explorations and answers are provided in *Alternate Openers: Explorations Transparencies.*

EXAMPLE 2 Reading Stem-and-Leaf Plots

Find the least value, greatest value, mean, median, mode, and range of the data.

Stems	Leaves
5	8
6	8 9
7	2 4 8
8	0 4 5 6 8
9	0 0 2 3 6 7 8
10	
11	7

Key: 5|8 means 58

The least stem and least leaf give the least value, 58.

The greatest stem and greatest leaf give the greatest value, 117.

Use the data values to find the mean.
$(58 + \ldots + 117) \div 19 = 85$

The median is the middle value in the table, 86.

To find the mode, look for the number that occurs most often in a row of leaves. Then identify its stem. The mode is 90.

The range is the difference between the greatest and least value.
$117 - 58 = 59$

Caution!

If a stem has no leaves, there are no data points with that stem. In the stem-and-leaf plot in Example 2, there are no data values between 100 and 109.

Answers to *Think and Discuss*

1. 2 | 5, where 2 is the stem and 5 is a leaf

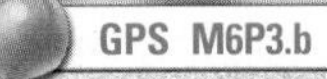

Think and Discuss

GPS M6P3.b

1. Describe how to show 25 on a stem-and-leaf plot.

Power Presentations with PowerPoint®

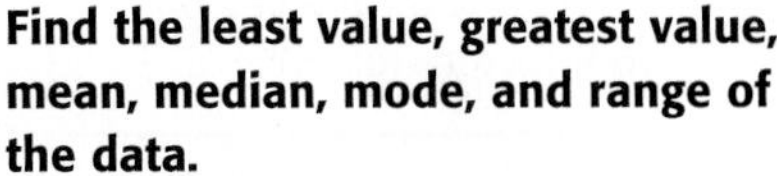

Additional Examples

Example 1

Use the data to make a stem-and-leaf plot.

75 86 83 91 94 88 84 99 79 86

Answers see p. A6.

Example 2

Find the least value, greatest value, mean, median, mode, and range of the data.

Stems	Leaves
4	0 0 1 5 7
5	1 1 2 4
6	3 3 3 5 9 9
7	0 4 4
8	3 6 7
9	1 4

Key: 4|0 means 40

least: 40; greatest: 94; mean: 64; median: 63; mode: 63; range: 54

Also available on transparency

6-9 Exercises

Georgia Performance Standards

M6P3.c, M6P4.c

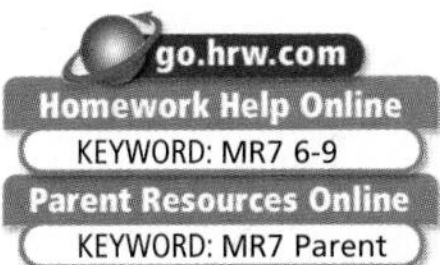

go.hrw.com
Homework Help Online
KEYWORD: MR7 6-9
Parent Resources Online
KEYWORD: MR7 Parent

GUIDED PRACTICE

See Example 1

1. Use the data in the table to make a stem-and-leaf plot.

Daily High Temperatures (°F)	45	56	40	39	37	48	51

See Example 2

Find each value of the data.

Stems	Leaves
1	0 2
2	
3	2
4	1 4

Key: 1|0 means 10

2. smallest value 10
3. largest value 44
4. mean 27.8
5. median 32
6. mode no mode
7. range 34

INDEPENDENT PRACTICE

See Example 1

8. Use the data in the table to make a stem-and-leaf plot.

Heights of Plants (cm)	30	12	27	28	15	47	37	28	40	20

6-9 Exercises

Assignment Guide

If you finished Example 1 assign:
Average 1, 17, 20–28
Advanced 8, 17, 20–28

If you finished Example 2 assign:
Average 1–8, 15–16, 20–28
Advanced 8–14, 17–28

Answers

1, 8. See p. A6.

Reaching All Learners

Through Critical Thinking

Have students work in groups to make a stem-and-leaf plot for which all of the following are true:

- range = 35
- mode = 25
- median = 30

Possible answer:

Stems	Leaves
2	5 5 8
3	0 2 5
4	
5	
6	0

Key: 2|5 means 25

3 Close

Summarize

Have students find the least and greatest values, median, mode, and range for the stem-and-leaf plot in Example 1. Then have students tell how they would find the mean of the data.

Smallest = 12; largest = 51; median = 22; mode = 23; range = 39; Possible answer: Add all the numbers and divide by the number of numbers.

Georgia Performance Standards

M6P3.c Analyze and evaluate the mathematical thinking and strategies of others.

M6P4.c Recognize and apply mathematics in contexts outside of mathematics.

ONGOING ASSESSMENT and INTERVENTION

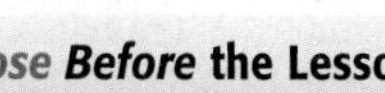

***Diagnose Before* the Lesson**
6-9 Warm Up, TE p. 330

***Monitor During* the Lesson**
6-9 Know-It Notebook
6-9 Questioning Strategies

***Assess After* the Lesson**
6-9 Lesson Quiz, TE p. 332

Answers

17, 19. See p. A6.

Power Presentations with PowerPoint®

6-9 Lesson Quiz

1. Make a stem-and-leaf plot of the data. See p. A7.

42 36 40 31 29 49 21 28 52
27 22 35 30 46 34 34

Find each value using the stem-and-leaf plot.

2. What is the least value? 21

3. What is the mean? 34.75

4. What is the median? 34

5. What is the mode? 34

Also available on transparency

See Example 2 **Find each value of the data.**

9. least value 41
10. greatest value 68
11. mean 52
12. median 51
13. mode 42
14. range 27

Stems	Leaves
4	1 2 2
5	1 3
6	7 8

Key: 4|1 means 41

PRACTICE AND PROBLEM SOLVING

Extra Practice p. 725

For Exercises 15 and 16, write the letter of the stem-and-leaf plot described.

A.

Stems	Leaves
1	0 3 4
2	0 0 1 1 1 3
3	4 5 9
4	8

Key: 1|0 means 10

B.

Stems	Leaves
1	6
2	2 3
3	0 1 4
4	1 4 8

Key: 1|6 means 16

C.

Stems	Leaves
1	4
2	
3	6
4	3 6 8

Key: 1|4 means 14

15. The data set has a mode of 21. A

16. The data set has a median of 31. B

Use the table for Exercises 17 and 18.

Cars with Only One Passenger					
82	103	95	125	88	94
89	92	94	99	87	80
109	101	100	83	124	81

17. Karla recorded the number of cars with only one passenger that came through a toll booth each day. Use Karla's data to make a stem-and-leaf plot.

18. What's the Error? Karla's classmate looked at the stem-and-leaf plot and said that the mean number of cars with only one passenger is 4. Explain Karla's classmate's error. What is the correct mean?

18. It must be incorrect because it is significantly smaller than all of the numbers in the data set. The classmate found the mode of the leaves only. The mean is ≈ 95.9.

19. Challenge Josh is the second youngest of 4 teenage boys, all 2 years apart in age. Josh's mother is 3 times as old as Josh is, and she is 24 years younger than her father. Make a stem-and-leaf plot to show the ages of Josh, his brothers, his mother, and his grandfather.

CRCT PREP • GPS SUPPORT • SPIRAL REVIEW

20. Multiple Choice What is the value of 1|2 in the stem-and-leaf plot?

Stems	Leaves
1	0 1 2 3
2	7 9 9 9

Key: 1|0 means 1,000

Ⓐ 12 Ⓒ 100,002
Ⓑ 1,200 Ⓓ 100,200

21. Gridded Response What is the median of the data in Exercise 20? 2,500

Order the numbers from least to greatest. (Lesson 1-1)

22. 3,673,809; 3,708,211; 3,671,935
3,671,935; 3,673,809; 3,708,211

23. 2,004,801; 225,971; 298,500,004
225,971; 2,004,801; 298,500,004

Find the reciprocal. (Lesson 5-9)

24. 6 $\frac{1}{6}$ **25.** $\frac{4}{7}$ $\frac{7}{4}$ **26.** $\frac{2}{9}$ $\frac{9}{2}$ **27.** $\frac{1}{5}$ 5 **28.** $\frac{9}{8}$ $\frac{8}{9}$

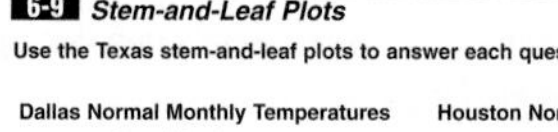

CHALLENGE 6-9
PROBLEM SOLVING 6-9

LESSON 6-9 **Problem Solving**
Stem-and-Leaf Plots

Use the Texas stem-and-leaf plots to answer each question.

Dallas Normal Monthly Temperatures

Stem	Leaves
4	3 7 8
5	6 7
6	6 7
7	3 7
8	1 5 5

Key: 4 | 3 = 43°F

Houston Normal Monthly Temperatures

Stem	Leaves
5	0 4 4
6	1 1 8
7	0 5 8
8	0 2 3

Key: 5 | 0 = 50°F

1. Which city's temperature data has a mode of 85°F?
Dallas

2. Which city's temperature data has a range of 33°F?
Houston

3. Which city has the lowest data value? What is that value?
Dallas; 43°F

4. Which city has the highest data value? What is that value?
Dallas; 85°F

Circle the letter of the correct answer.

5. Which city's temperature data has a mean of 68°F?
A Dallas
Ⓑ Houston
C both Dallas and Houston
D neither Dallas nor Houston

6. Which city's temperature data has a median of 69°F?
F Dallas
Ⓖ Houston
H both Dallas and Houston
J neither Dallas nor Houston

7. What do the data values 54°F and 61°F represent for the plots above?
A the ranges of normal temperatures in Dallas and Houston
Ⓑ the mode of normal temperatures for Houston
C the mean and median normal temperatures for Dallas
D the lowest normal temperatures for Dallas and Houston

8. Which of the following would be the best way to display the Dallas and Houston temperature data?
Ⓕ on a line graph
G in a tally table
H on a bar graph
J on a coordinate plane

RETEACH 6-9

CHAPTER 6-9 **Reteach**
Stem-and-Leaf Plots

You can use place value to make a stem-and-leaf plot.

Points Earned in Games During Basketball Season						
27	16	34	29	48	12	33
20	18	42	51	27	32	41

Write the numbers in order from least to greatest.

12 16 18 20 27 27 29 32 33 34 41 42 48 51

List the tens digits in order from least to greatest in the first, or stem, column. Then, for each tens digit, record the ones digit for each data value in order from least to greatest in the second, or leaves, column.

Points Earned

Stem	Leaves
1	2 6 8
2	0 7 7 9
3	2 3 4
4	1 2 8
5	1

Key: 1 | 2 = 12

Make sure your graph has a title and a key.

Use the data to make a stem-and-leaf plot.

1.

Valerie's Test Scores				
62	84	93	88	89
76	68	81	91	88

Valerie's Test Scores

Stem	Leaves
6	2 8
7	6
8	1 4 8 8 9
9	1 3

Key: 6 | 2 = 62

2. What is the range?
The range is 31 points.

3. What is the median?
The median is 86 points.

4. What is the mode?
The mode is 88 points.

PRACTICE 6-9

LESSON 6-9 **Practice B**
Stem-and-Leaf Plots

Complete each activity and answer the questions.

1. Use the data in the table to complete the stem-and-leaf plot below.

Richmond, Virginia, Monthly Normal Temperatures (°F)											
Jan	Feb	Mar	April	May	June	July	Aug	Sep	Oct	Nov	Dec
37	39	48	57	74	78	77	76	70	59	50	40

Stem	Leaves
3	7 9
4	0 8
5	0 7 9
6	
7	0 4 6 7 8

Key: 1 | 2 = 12°F

Find each value of the data.

2. least value 61
3. greatest value 98
4. mean $79.\overline{4}$
5. median 82
6. mode 82
7. range 37

Stem	Leaves
6	1 4
7	1 6
8	2 2
9	0 1 8

Key: 6 | 5 = 65

8. Look at the stem-and-leaf plot you made for Exercise 1. How many months in Richmond have a normal temperature above 70°F?
4 months

9. How would you display a data value of 100 on the stem-and-leaf plot above?
Use 10 for the stem and 0 for the leaf.

6-10 Choosing an Appropriate Display

Learn to choose an appropriate way to display data.

M6D1.c Choose appropriate graphs to be consistent with the nature of the data. Also, M6P1.b, M6P5.b, M6P5.c.

A neighborhood community center offers programs for people of all ages. Its recent brochure includes a bar graph that shows the number of people, by age, enrolled in various programs.

Depending on the data to be displayed, some types of graphs are more useful than others.

Common Uses of Data Displays			
	You can use a line plot to show how often each number occurs.		You can use a bar graph to display and compare data in separate categories.
	You can use a line graph to show how data change over a period of time.		You can use a stem-and-leaf plot to show how often data values occur and how they are distributed.

EXAMPLE 1 **Choosing an Appropriate Data Display**

A **The table shows the number of miles of coastline for states bordering the Gulf of Mexico. Which graph would be more appropriate to show the data—a bar graph or a line graph? Draw the more appropriate graph.**

State	AL	FL	LA	MS	TX
Miles of Coastline	33	770	397	44	367

Think: Is the information in the table describing a change over time? Is the information in the table divided into different categories?

The table shows the number of miles of coastline in different states. The data should be displayed in separate categories. So a bar graph is more appropriate than a line graph.

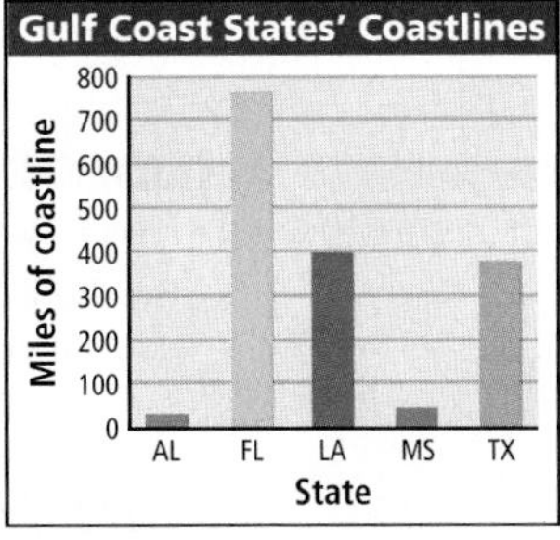

Organizer 6-10

Pacing: Traditional 1 day
Block $\frac{1}{2}$ day

Objective: Choose an appropriate way to display data.

GPS M6D1.c
Hands-On Lab
In *Hands-On Lab Activities*

Online Edition
Tutorial Videos

Countdown to CRCT Week 13

Power Presentations with PowerPoint®

Warm Up

Find the mean, median, and mode of each data set without the outlier.

1. 14, 11, 51, 12, 13, 11 mean: 12.2, median: 12, mode: 11
2. 52, 50, 11, 49, 52, 50 mean: 50.6, median: 50, mode: 50, 52
3. 99, 96, 98, 95, 97, 31 mean: 97, median: 97, modes: none

Problem of the Day

These are *rits:* 24042, 383, and 4994. These are not *rits:* 39239, 28, and 5505. Which of these are *rits:* 39883, 4040, and 101? Why? 101 is a *rit* because it is the same forward and backward.

Also available on transparency

1 Introduce

Alternate Opener

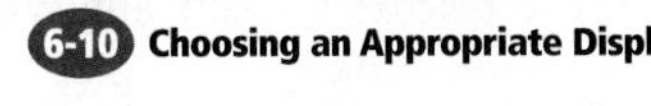

EXPLORATION

6-10 Choosing an Appropriate Display

The graphs shown below are not labeled. Match each of the descriptions with the graph that most likely represents the data.

1. The population of a town over the course of several years
2. The areas of the five Great Lakes
3. The test scores of the students in a Spanish class

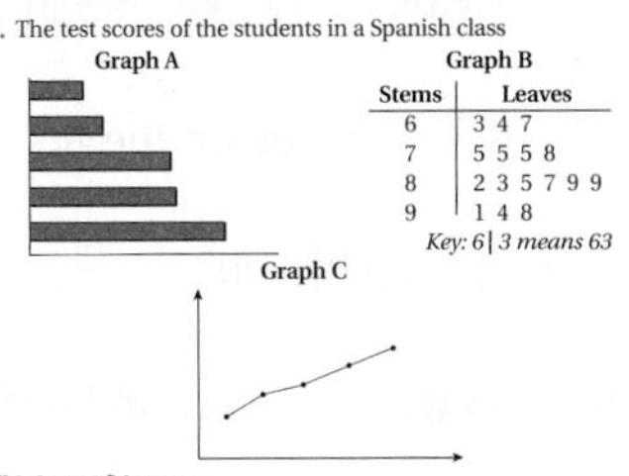

Think and Discuss

4. **Explain** how you decided which graph matches each description.
5. **Explain** what you would need to do to complete Graph A.

2 Teach

Guided Instruction

In this lesson, students learn to choose an appropriate way to display data. Use the table to review the different types of graphs. Help students differentiate between the graphs and discuss when it is appropriate to use each type. Show how the examples fit the descriptions of the appropriate use of each type of graph. Create examples of line and stem-and-leaf plots, and compare them.

Explorations and answers are provided in *Alternate Openers: Explorations Transparencies.*

Georgia Performance Standards

M6D1.c Choose appropriate graphs to be consistent with the nature of the data (categorical or numerical). Graphs should include pictographs, histograms, bar graphs, line graphs, circle graphs, and line plots.

M6P1.b Solve problems that arise in mathematics and in other contexts.

M6P5.b Select, apply, and translate among mathematical representations to solve problems.

M6P5.c Use representations to model and interpret physical, social, and mathematical phenomena.

Power Presentations with PowerPoint®

Additional Examples

Example 1

A. A table shows the miles jogged by five boxers. Which graph would be more appropriate to show the data—a line plot or a line graph? Draw the more appropriate graph. line plot

Boxer	Al	Bo	Max	Jo	Ty
Miles	12	17	10	18	17

B. The table shows the height of some plants. Which graph would be more appropriate to show the data—a bar graph or a stem-and-leaf plot? Draw the more appropriate graph. stem-and-leaf plot

Height of Plants (ft)					
11	27	14	35	11	26

Answers see p. A7.

Also available on transparency

B The table shows the lengths of some animals. Which graph would be more appropriate to show the data—a stem-and-leaf plot or a line graph? Draw the more appropriate graph.

Lengths of Animals (in.)					
70	43	42	50	35	32
32	45	61	35	40	30

Think: The table shows a number of different lengths. It does not show data changing over time.

A stem-and-leaf plot shows how often data values occur. So a stem-and-leaf plot is more appropriate than a line graph.

Lengths of Animals (in.)

Stems	Leaves
3	0 2 2 5 5
4	0 2 3 5
5	0
6	1
7	0

Key: 3|2 means 32

Possible answers to *Think and Discuss*
1. when you want to show a child's height over time
2. A line plot with a range of 40, from 30 to 70, can be used to display the data.

Think and Discuss

GPS M6P1.c, M6P1.d

1. **Describe** a situation when a line graph would be a more appropriate choice than a bar graph to show data.
2. **Describe** another type of graph that could be used to display the data shown in the table in Example 1B.

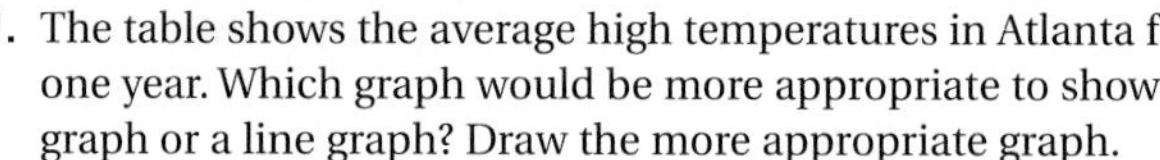

6-10 Exercises

Georgia Performance Standards
M6P3.a, M6P4.c

go.hrw.com
Homework Help Online
KEYWORD: MR7 6-10
Parent Resources Online
KEYWORD: MR7 Parent

GUIDED PRACTICE

See Example 1

1. The table shows the average high temperatures in Atlanta for six months of one year. Which graph would be more appropriate to show the data—a bar graph or a line graph? Draw the more appropriate graph. **line graph**

Month	Jan	Mar	May	Jul	Sep	Nov
Temp. (°F)	54	63	81	88	83	62

1–2. For graphs, see p. A7.

INDEPENDENT PRACTICE

See Example 1

2. The table shows the percentages of students who bought a hot lunch from the school cafeteria. Which graph would be more appropriate to show the data—a bar graph or a line graph? Draw the more appropriate graph. **line graph**

September	30%	November	27%	January	45%
October	28%	December	27%	February	42%

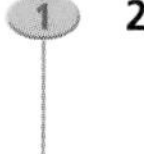

6-10 Exercises

Assignment Guide

If you finished Example 1 assign:
Average 1, 3–4, 8–14
Advanced 2, 5–14

Homework Quick Check

Quickly check key concepts.
Exercises: 2, 4

Georgia Performance Standards

M6P3.a Organize and consolidate their mathematical thinking through communication.

M6P4.c Recognize and apply mathematics in contexts outside of mathematics.

Reaching All Learners
Through Cooperative Learning

Have students work with partners or in small groups. Give each group a different type of data (such as stock prices, lengths of bridges, budget information, test scores, or data involving frequencies). Have students in each group work together to determine the best type of graph to display the data. Then have students create specific data for their data type and make a graph to show it, explaining why the graph best represents the data given.

3 Close

Summarize

Ask students to discuss the similarities and differences between the types of graphs. Ask which type of graph would best show the following data and why:

- how wins, losses, and ties compare to the total number of games circle graph
- prices of a gallon of gas on the first day of each month line graph
- heights of a group of adults stem-and-leaf plot
- how students got to school on Monday bar graph

PRACTICE AND PROBLEM SOLVING

3. **Social Studies** The table shows the U.S. population from 1900 through 2000.
   a. What graph would be most appropriate to show the data? Why?
   b. Make a graph of the data.

Year	Population
1900	76,094,000
1925	115,829,000
1950	152,271,417
1975	215,973,199
2000	281,421,906

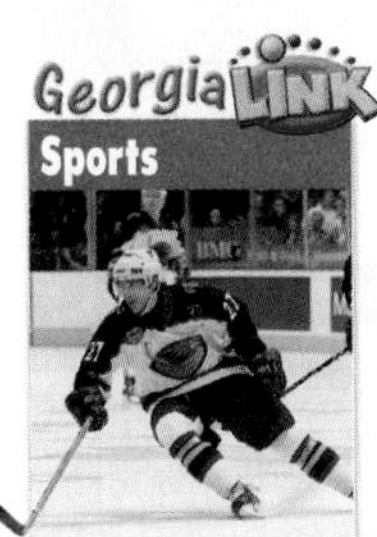

The Atlanta Thrashers hockey team played their first game on October 2, 1999. The team is named after the state bird of Georgia, the brown thrasher.

4. **Critical Thinking** The total wins that teams in the Western Conference of the National Hockey League had in a recent year are as follows: 48, 39, 38, 25, 20, 43, 40, 42, 36, 30, 43, 22, 29, 41, 28. Which graph would be more appropriate to show the data—a line plot or a bar graph? Draw the more appropriate graph. Then explain how to use the graph to find the median and mode.

5. **Write a Problem** Use the information in the table to write a problem that can be solved by drawing a graph. Tell which type of graph you would use.

6. **Write About It** Explain the similarities and differences between a bar graph and a line graph.

Animal	Life Span (yr)
Bear	40
Carp	100
Elephant	70
Tiger	22

7. **Challenge** The stem-and-leaf plot shows the number of hours 20 students spent studying over a two-week period. Make a line plot to show the data. What does the line plot show more clearly than a stem-and-leaf plot would?

Study Times

Stems	Leaves
1	5 6 6 6 7 7 9 9
2	0 0 1 1 1 1 2 2 3
3	5 7 9

Key: 1|5 means 15

CRCT PREP • GPS SUPPORT • SPIRAL REVIEW

8. **Multiple Choice** Which graph would be most appropriate to show the number of miles each student walked in one week for a charity walk-a-thon?

   (A) Circle graph (B) Stem-and-leaf plot (C) Line graph (D) Bar graph

9. **Extended Response** People leaving a gym were asked how long they exercised. The results in minutes are: 15, 10, 35, 35, 60, 65, 15, 60, 20, 35. Which type of graph would be most appropriate to show the data? Explain. Make a graph of the data. What is the median amount of time spent exercising?

Find the GCF of each set of numbers. (Lesson 4-3)

10. 4 and 16 **4**
11. 15 and 50 **5**
12. 15, 60, and 75 **15**
13. 4, 8, and 80 **4**

14. Ashlee spent 50 minutes washing and waxing her car. She spent $\frac{2}{5}$ of that time washing the car. How many minutes did Ashlee spend washing her car? (Lesson 5-6) **20 min.**

ONGOING ASSESSMENT and INTERVENTION

***Diagnose Before* the Lesson**
6-10 Warm Up, TE p. 333

***Monitor During* the Lesson**
6-10 Know-It Notebook
6-10 Questioning Strategies

***Assess After* the Lesson**
6-10 Lesson Quiz, TE p. 335

Answers

3–7, 9. See p. A7.

Power Presentations with PowerPoint®

6-10 Lesson Quiz

1. The table shows the weights of fish caught today. Which graph would be more appropriate to show the data—a bar graph or a line plot? line plot

Today's Catch (lbs)				
4	3	4	4	2

2. The table shows Dave's income for five days. Which graph would be more appropriate to show the data—a line plot or a line graph? line graph

Day	1	2	3	4	5
Pay	75	83	77	80	85

Also available on transparency

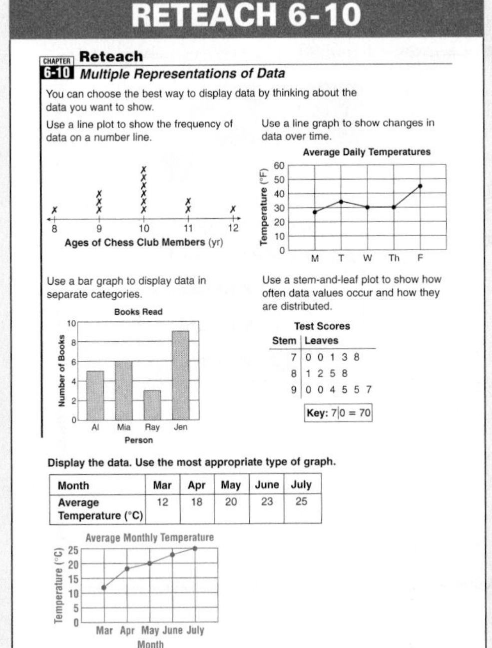

RETEACH 6-10

Reteach
CHAPTER 6-10 *Multiple Representations of Data*

You can choose the best way to display data by thinking about the data you want to show.

Use a line plot to show the frequency of data on a number line.

Use a line graph to show changes in data over time.

Use a bar graph to display data in separate categories.

Use a stem-and-leaf plot to show how often data values occur and how they are distributed.

Test Scores

Stem	Leaves
7	0 0 1 3 8
8	1 2 5 8
9	0 0 4 5 5 7

Key: 7|0 = 70

Display the data. Use the most appropriate type of graph.

Month	Mar	Apr	May	June	July
Average Temperature (°C)	12	18	20	23	25

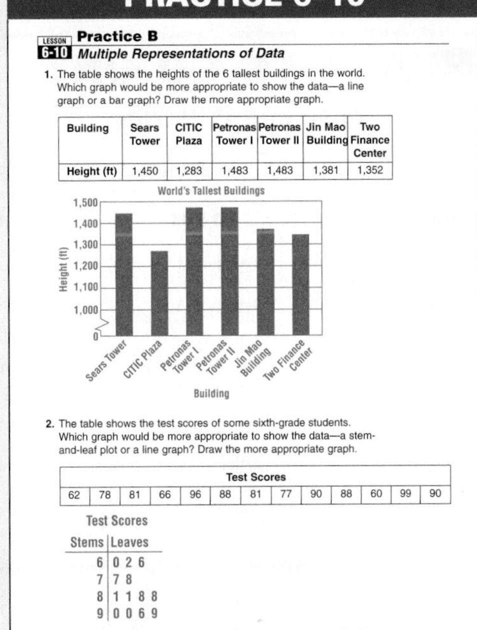

PRACTICE 6-10

Practice B
LESSON 6-10 *Multiple Representations of Data*

1. The table shows the heights of the 6 tallest buildings in the world. Which graph would be more appropriate to show the data—a line graph or a bar graph? Draw the more appropriate graph.

Building	Sears Tower	CITIC Plaza	Petronas Tower I	Petronas Tower II	Jin Mao Building	Two Finance Center
Height (ft)	1,450	1,283	1,483	1,483	1,381	1,352

2. The table shows the test scores of some sixth-grade students. Which graph would be more appropriate to show the data—a stem-and-leaf plot or a line graph? Draw the more appropriate graph.

Test Scores												
62	78	81	66	96	88	81	77	90	88	60	99	90

Test Scores

Stems	Leaves
6	0 2 6
7	7 8
8	1 1 8 8
9	0 0 6 9

CHALLENGE 6-10
PROBLEM SOLVING 6-10

Problem Solving
LESSON 6-10 *Multiple Representations of Data*

1. Write *line plot, stem-and-leaf plot, line graph,* or *bar graph* to describe the most appropriate way to show the height of a sunflower plant every week for one month.
   line graph

2. Write *line plot, stem-and-leaf plot, line graph,* or *bar graph* to describe the most appropriate way to show the number of votes received by each candidate running for class president
   bar graph

3. Write *line plot, stem-and-leaf plot, line graph,* or *bar graph* to describe the most appropriate way to show the test scores each student received on a math quiz.
   stem-and-leaf plot

4. Write *line plot, stem-and-leaf plot, line graph,* or *bar graph* to describe the most appropriate way to show the average time spent sleeping per day by 30 sixth-grade students.
   line plot

Circle the letter of the correct answer.

5. People leaving a restaurant were asked how much they spent for lunch. Here are the results of the survey to the nearest dollar: $8, $7, $9, $7, $10, $5, $8, $8, $12, $8. Which type of graph would be most appropriate to show the data?
   A bar graph
   B line graph
   (C) line plot
   D stem-and-leaf plot

6. People leaving a movie theater were asked their age. Here are the results of the survey to the nearest year: 12, 11, 13, 15, 22, 31, 40, 12, 17, 20, 33, 16, 12, 24, 19. Which type of graph would be most appropriate to show the data?
   F bar graph
   G line graph
   H line plot
   (J) stem-and-leaf plot

7. What is the median amount of money spent on lunch in Exercise 5?
   A $7
   (B) $8
   C $9
   D $12

8. What is the median age of the movie-goers in Exercise 6?
   F 15
   G 16
   (H) 17
   J 19

SECTION 6B

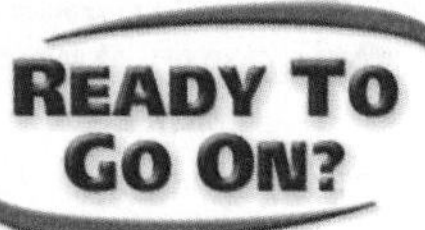

Organizer

Objective: Assess students' mastery of concepts and skills in Lessons 6-4 through 6-10.

Resources

Assessment Resources
Section 6B Quiz

Test & Practice Generator
One-Stop Planner®

INTERVENTION 

Resources

Ready to Go On? Intervention and Enrichment Worksheets

Ready to Go On? CD-ROM

Ready to Go On? Online

my.hrw.com

Answers

5–7, 9–10. See p. A7.

CHAPTER 6

SECTION 6B

Ready to Go On?

Quiz for Lessons 6-4 Through 6-10

6-4 Bar Graphs

The students in Ms. Bain's class voted on their favorite fruit juice. Use the bar graph to answer each question.

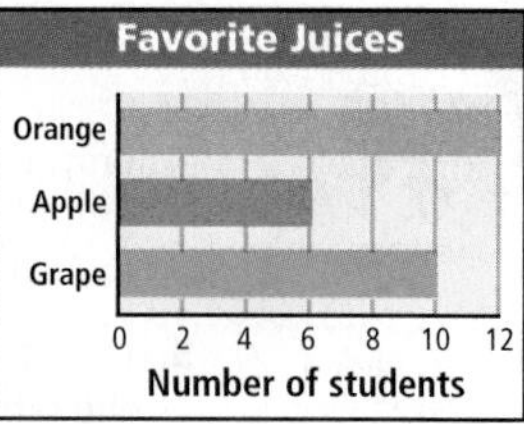

1. How many more students prefer orange juice than prefer grape juice? 2
2. How many students in all voted? 28

6-5 Line Plots, Frequency Tables, and Histograms

Shoppers leaving Midtown Mall were each asked to give their age. Use the line plot to answer each question.

Shoppers at Midtown Mall

Line plot (Ages of shoppers, 15–22): 15: X; 16: XXX; 18: X; 19: X; 20: XXXX; 21: XX; 22: XXX

3. What are the range and mode of the data? range = 7, mode = 20
4. How many of the shoppers surveyed were older than 20? 5

6-6 Ordered Pairs

Graph and label each point on a coordinate grid.

5. $A(4, 5)$
6. $B\left(0, 3\frac{1}{2}\right)$

Graphicworks	
Year	Numbers of Employees
2003	852
2004	1,098
2005	1,150
2006	1,150

6-7 Line Graphs

7. Use the data in the table to make a line graph.

6-8 Misleading Graphs

8. Bob drew a line graph of the Graphicworks data. For the vertical scale representing the number of employees, he used these intervals: 0; 800; 1,000; and 1,500. Explain why his graph is misleading.
Possible answer: The vertical scale does not have equal intervals.

6-9 Stem-and-Leaf Plots

9. Use the data in the line plot in problems 3 and 4 to make a stem-and-leaf plot.

6-10 Choosing an Appropriate Display

10. Would it also be appropriate to use a line graph to represent the data that is shown in the bar graph in problems 1 and 2? Explain.

READY TO GO ON? Diagnose and Prescribe

NO — INTERVENE

Ready to Go On? Intervention	Ready to Go On? Intervention, Section 6B — Worksheets	CD-ROM	Online
Lesson 6-4	6-4 Intervention	Activity 6-4	Diagnose and Prescribe Online
Lesson 6-5	6-5 Intervention	Activity 6-5	
Lesson 6-6	6-6 Intervention	Activity 6-6	
Lesson 6-7	6-7 Intervention	Activity 6-7	
Lesson 6-8	6-8 Intervention	Activity 6-8	
Lesson 6-9	6-9 Intervention	Activity 6-9	
Lesson 6-10	6-10 Intervention	Activity 6-10	

YES — ENRICH

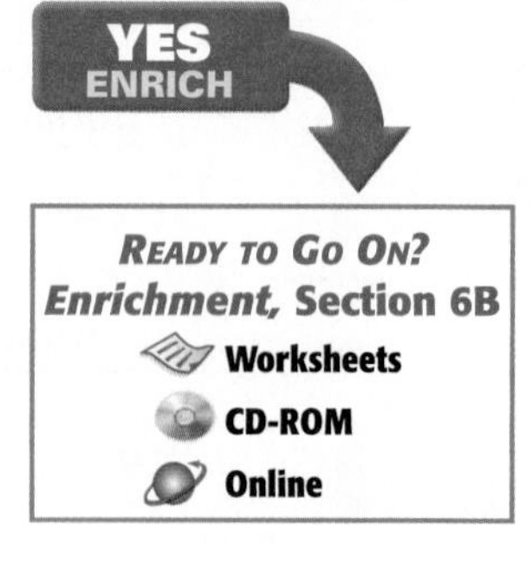

MULTI-STEP TEST PREP

Deet's Treats Trail mix at Deet's Treats is priced at $2 for 8 ounces. The trail mix is sold in 4-ounce and 8-ounce packages. The manager at the shop decides to put a graph on display to show the cost of trail mix. He asks three employees to each make a graph. Their graphs are shown at right.

1. For each graph, make a table that shows the data in the graph.
2. The manager wants to display the most appropriate graph for his customers to get detailed and accurate information about the trail mix. Explain in what ways, if any, the graphs are misleading.
3. To help clerks sell trail mix, create a table of prices for selling up to 4 pounds of trail mix. Explain your table. (*Hint:* 16 oz = 1 lb)
4. How many different ways can you purchase 4 pounds of trail mix when buying 4-ounce and 8-ounce packages? Explain.

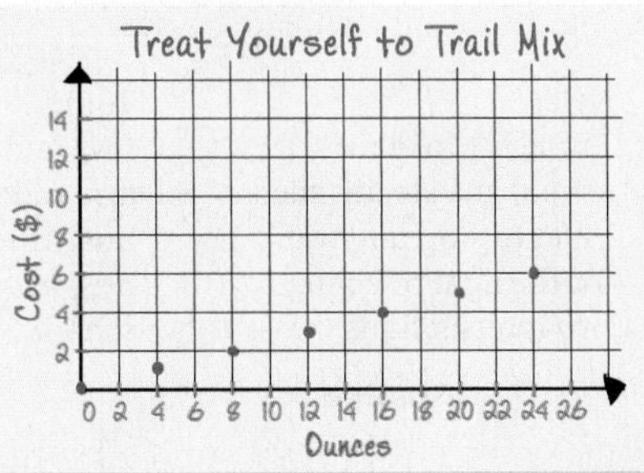

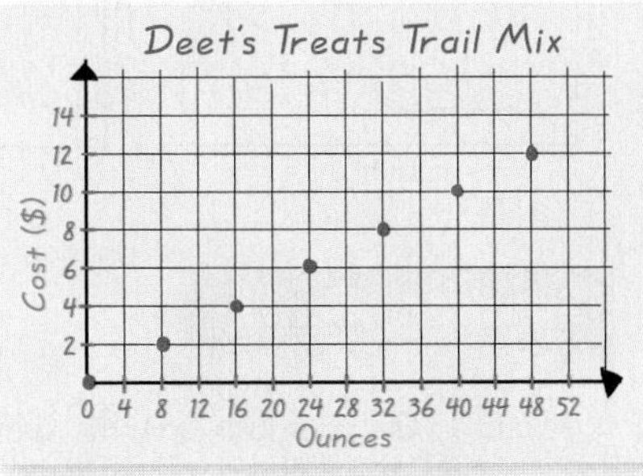

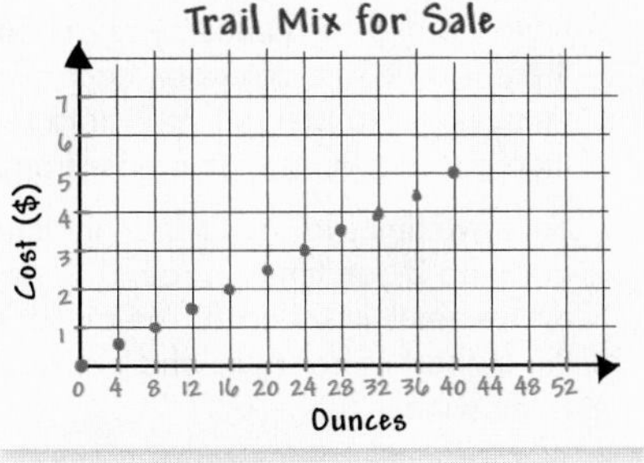

Multi-Step Test Prep

MULTI-STEP TEST PREP

CHAPTER 6

Organizer

Objective: Assess students' ability to apply concepts and skills in Chapter 6 in a real-world format.

Online Edition

Resources

Middle School Assessments
www.mathtekstoolkit.org

Problem	Text reference
1	Lesson 6-1
2	Lesson 6-8
3	Lesson 6-1
4	Lesson 6-1

Answers

1-4. See p. A7.

INTERVENTION

Scaffolding Questions

1. What does the horizontal axis show on each graph? the number of ounces What does the point (16, 4) mean on the Deet's Treats graph? 16 ounces of trail mix costs $4 What does each graph show about the cost of trail mix as the number of ounces increases? the cost increases
2. What is the cost of 16 ounces of trail mix on each graph? Treat Yourself: $4; Deet's Treats: $4; Trail Mix for Sale: $2 What can you conclude? Trail Mix for sale does not show the correct prices.
3. How many ounces are in one pound? 16 How many ounces of trail mix can a customer purchase with $2? 8 ounces With $4? 16 ounces
4. If a customer buys 24 ounces of trail mix, how can you find the number of 4-ounce packages she must buy? Divide 24 by 4. How can you find the number of 8-ounce packages? Divide 24 by 8. How can you find combinations of 4-ounce and 8-ounce packages? Start with 3 8-ounce packages and no 4-ounce packages. Then try two 8-ounce packages and find out how many 4-ounce packages are needed, etc.

Extension

1. What does 1 ounce of trail mix cost? $0.25
2. What would a customer pay for a quarter-pound of trail mix? $1
3. Find the cost of 96 ounces of trail mix. $24

Game Time

Organizer

Objective: Participate in games to practice and apply skills learned in Chapter 6.

 Online Edition

Resources

 ***Chapter 6 Resource Book***
Puzzles, Twisters & Teasers

A Thousand Words

Purpose: To apply the problem-solving skill of interpreting graphs to a story problem

Discuss Ask What will the graph look like when a student is not moving for a period of time? The graph will be a horizontal line. What happens to the graph as the student gets closer to school? As the student gets closer to school, he gets farther from home, so the distance increases and the graph rises from left to right.

Extend Have students write a scenario similar to those presented in the problem. Have them make several different graphs and challenge a classmate to determine which graph matches their scenario. Check students' work.

Spinnermeania

Purpose: To practice calculating mean, median, and mode in a game format

Discuss Discuss with students the range of answers they can expect for mean, median, and mode. What are the highest mean, median, and mode values possible? Are those values likely? The highest value possible for each measure is 10. To earn a mean, median, or mode of 10, the spinner would have to land on four 10's, which is not likely.

Extend Have students create a new spinner using ten numbers chosen randomly from 0 to 100. Have them play the game again using the new board. Check students' work.

Game Time

A Thousand Words

Did you ever hear the saying "A picture is worth a thousand words"? A graph can be worth a thousand words too!

Each of the graphs below tells a story about a student's trip to school. Read each story and think about what each graph is showing. Can you match each graph with its story?

Kyla:
I rode my bike to school at a steady pace. I had to stop and wait for the light to change at two intersections. B

Tom:
I walked to my bus stop and waited there for the bus. After I boarded the bus, it was driven straight to school. C

Megan:
On my way to school, I stopped at my friend's house. She wasn't ready yet, so I waited for her. Then we walked to school. A

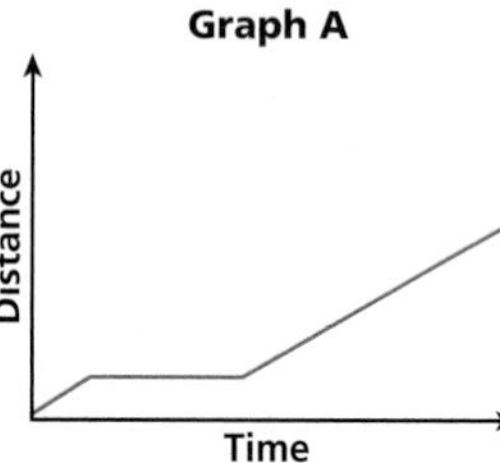

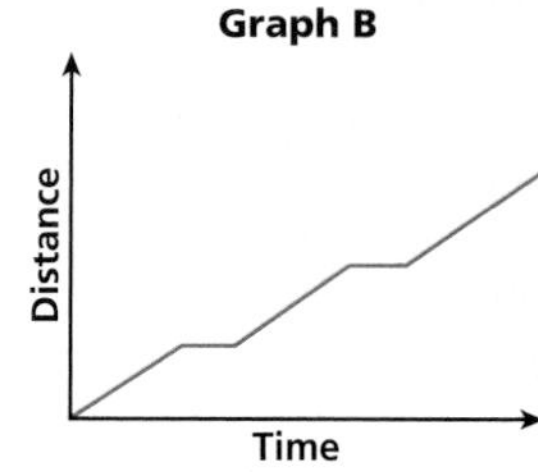

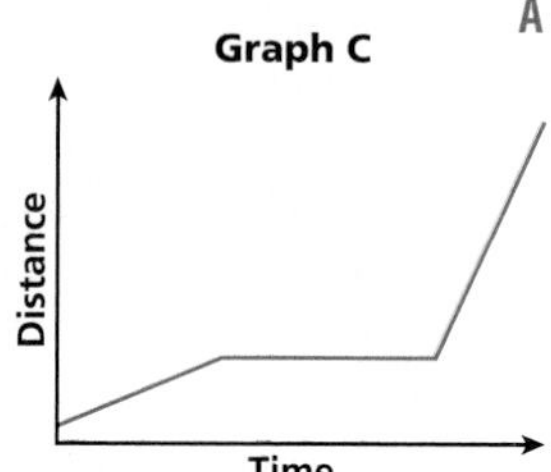

Spinnermeania

Round 1: On your turn, spin the spinner four times and record the results. After everyone has had a turn, find the mean, median, and mode of your results. For every category in which you have the highest number, you get one point. If there is a tie in a category, each player with that number gets a point. If your data set has more than one mode, use the greatest one.

Spin five times in round 2, eight times in round 3, ten times in round 4, and twelve times in round 5. The player with the highest score at the end of five rounds is the winner.

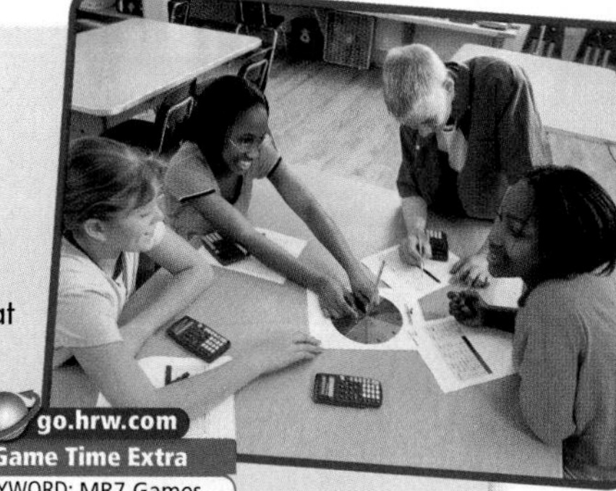

go.hrw.com
Game Time Extra
KEYWORD: MR7 Games

A complete copy of the rules and game pieces are available online.

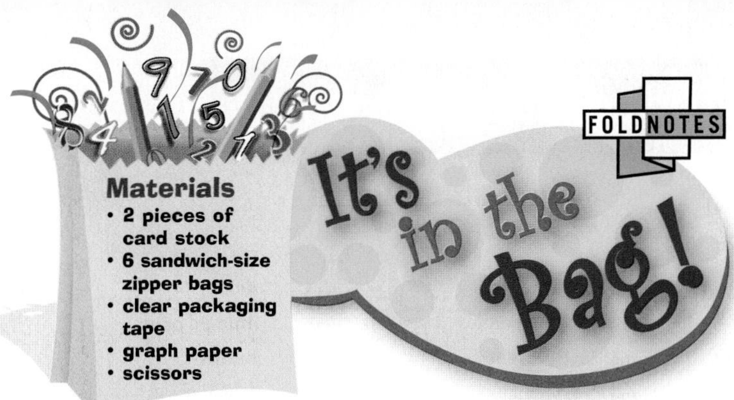

PROJECT **Graphing According to Me**

Create different types of graphs and make a zippered accordion book to hold them all.

Directions

1. Place one piece of card stock that is $6\frac{1}{2}$ inches by 7 inches next to one of the bags. The opening of the bag should be at the top, and there should be a small space between the card stock and the bag. Tape the card stock and bag together on the front and back sides. **Figure A**

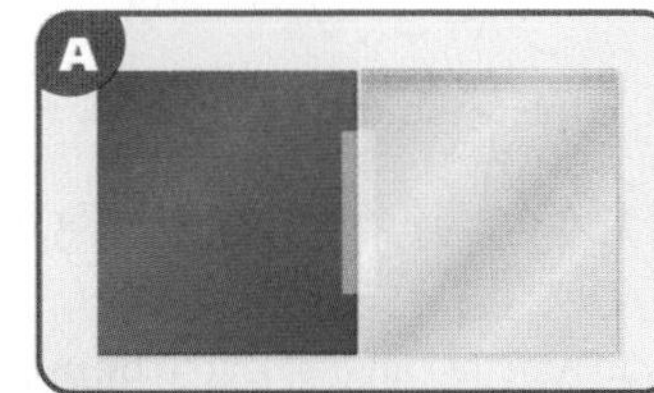

2. Lay another bag down next to the first, keeping a small space between them. Tape them together, front and back. **Figure B**

3. Continue with the rest of the bags. At the end of the chain, tape a second piece of card stock that is $6\frac{1}{2}$ inches by 7 inches to the last bag. **Figure C**

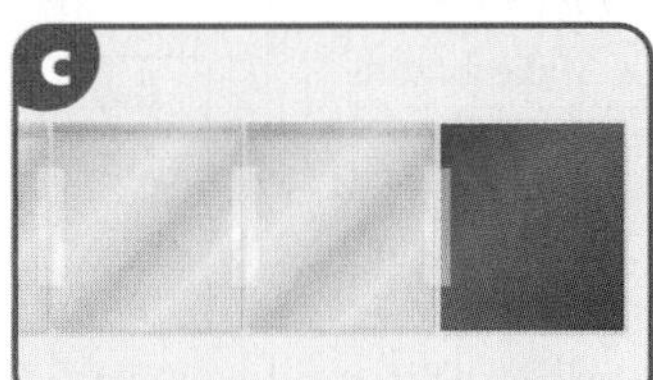

4. Fold the bags accordion-style, back and forth, with the two card stock covers on the front and back.

5. Cut out squares of graph paper so they will fit in the bags.

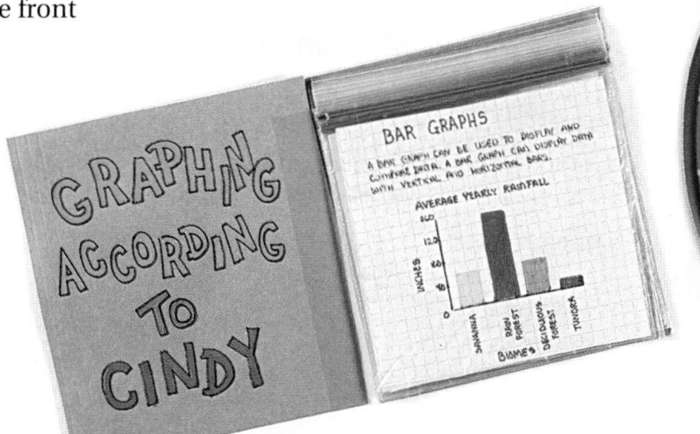

Taking Note of the Math

Write the number and title of the chapter on the cover. On each piece of graph paper, draw and label an example of one type of graph from the chapter. Store the graphs in the bags.

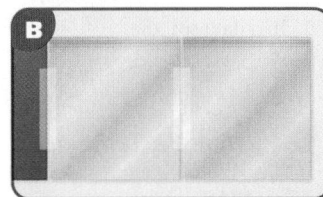

Organizer

Objective: Make an accordion-style book that holds examples of different types of graphs.

Materials: 2 pieces of card stock ($6\frac{1}{2}$ in. by 7 in.), 6 sandwich-size zipper bags, clear packaging tape, graph paper, scissors

Online Edition

Using the Page

Preparing the Materials
If necessary, start by having students trim the card stock to the appropriate size. To save time in the classroom, you can use a paper cutter and trim the card stock ahead of time.

Making the Project
As students tape the bags together, have them make sure that the bags will fold flat into an accordion-style booklet. Remind students that the book will fold more easily if they leave a small space between each bag and the next.

Extending the Project
Students can make longer accordion books. Have them use the extra bags to store several examples of misleading graphs.

There are lots of ways to extend and enhance this project. For example, you can have students use large freezer bags to make a version of the book that is suitable for classroom display. Another option is to have students use one of the bags to store their graphing supplies, including extra squares of graph paper. You might even have students punch holes along one side of the book while it is folded; by doing so, students can keep the book in a three-ring binder.

CHAPTER 6

Study Guide: Review

Organizer

Objective: Help students organize and review key concepts and skills presented in Chapter 6.

Online Edition
Multilingual Glossary

Resources

Multilingual Glossary Online

go.hrw.com
KEYWORD: MR7 Glossary

Lesson Tutorial Videos CD-ROM

Answers

1. histogram
2. ordered pair
3. mode
4.

Snake Lengths (ft)	
Anaconda	35 ft
Diamond python	21 ft
King cobra	19 ft
Boa constrictor	16 ft

5. Mean: 37; median: 38 mode: 39; range: 7

CHAPTER 6

Study Guide: Review

Study Guide: Review

Vocabulary

bar graph	308	histogram	315	mode	299
coordinate grid	319	line graph	322	ordered pair	319
double-bar graph	309	line plot	314	outlier	302
double-line graph	323	mean	298	range	299
frequency table	314	median	299	stem-and-leaf plot	330

Complete the sentences below with vocabulary words from the list above.

1. A(n) __?__ uses vertical or horizontal bars to show the number of items within each interval.
2. A point can be located by using a(n) __?__ of numbers such as (3, 5).
3. In a data set, the __?__ is the value or values that occur most often.

6-1 Make a Table (pp. 294–296)

EXAMPLE

■ **Make a table using the data.**

Monday it snowed 2 inches. Tuesday it snowed 3.5 inches. Thursday it snowed 4.25 inches.

Day	Snowfall
Mon	2 in.
Tue	3.5 in.
Thu	4.25 in.

EXERCISES

4. Make a table using the data on snake lengths.

An anaconda can be up to 35 ft long. A diamond python can be up to 21 ft long. A king cobra can be up to 19 ft long. A boa constrictor can be up to 16 ft long.

6-2 Mean, Median, Mode, and Range (pp. 298–301)

EXAMPLE

■ **Find the mean, median, mode, and range. 7, 8, 12, 10, 8**

mean: $7 + 8 + 8 + 10 + 12 = 45$

$45 \div 5 = 9$

median: 8

mode: 8

range: $12 - 7 = 5$

EXERCISES

Find the mean, median, mode, and range.

5.

Hours Worked Each Week						
32	39	39	38	36	39	36

6-3 Additional Data and Outliers (pp. 302–305)

GPS M6D1.e

EXAMPLE

- **Find the mean, median, and mode with and without the outlier.**

  10, 4, 7, 8, 34, 7, 7, 12, 5, 8 *The outlier is 34.*
  With: **mean** = 10.2, **mode** = 7, **median** = 7.5
  Without: **mean** ≈ 7.555, **mode** = 7, **median** = 7

EXERCISES

Find the mean, median, and mode of each data set with and without the outlier.

6. 12, 11, 9, 38, 10, 8, 12

7. 34, 12, 32, 45, 32

8. 16, 12, 15, 52, 10, 13

6-4 Bar Graphs (pp. 308–311)

GPS M6D1.b

EXAMPLE

- **Which grades have more than 200 students?** 6th grade and 8th grade

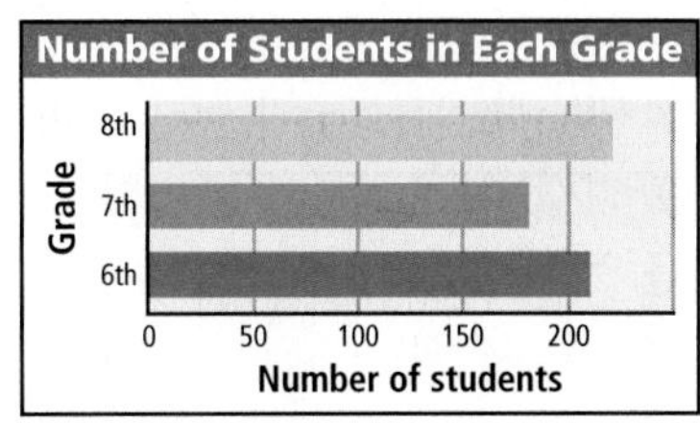

EXERCISES

Use the bar graph at left for Exercise 9.

9. Which grade has the most students?

10. Use the data to make a bar graph.

Test	Math	English	History	Science
Grade	95	85	90	80

6-5 Line Plots, Frequency Tables, and Histograms (pp. 314–317)

GPS M6D1.b

EXAMPLE

- **Make a frequency table with intervals.**

  Ages of people at Irene's birthday party: 37, 39, 18, 15, 13

Ages of People at Irene's Birthday Party				
Ages	13–19	20–26	27–33	34–40
Frequency	3	0	0	2

EXERCISES

11. Make a frequency table with intervals.

Points Scored					
6	4	5	4	7	10

12. Use the frequency table from Exercise 11 to make a histogram.

6-6 Ordered Pairs (pp. 319–321)

GPS M6P4.c

EXAMPLE

- **Name the ordered pair for *A*.**

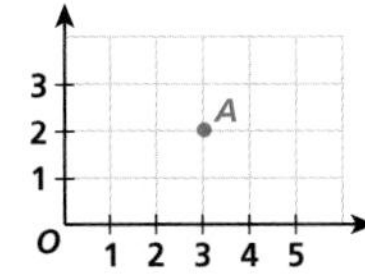

A is at (3, 2).

EXERCISES

Name the ordered pair for each location.

13. Bob's house

14. toy store

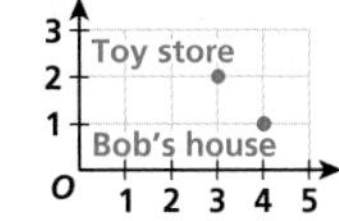

Study Guide: Review

Answers

6. With outlier: mean ≈ 14.29; median = 11; mode = 12; without outlier: mean ≈ 10.33; median = 10.5; mode = 12

7. With outlier: mean = 31; median = 32; mode = 32; without outlier: mean = 35.75; median = 33; mode = 32

8. With outlier: mean ≈ 19.67; median = 14; mode = none; without outlier: mean = 13.2; median = 13; mode = none

9. 8th grade

10.

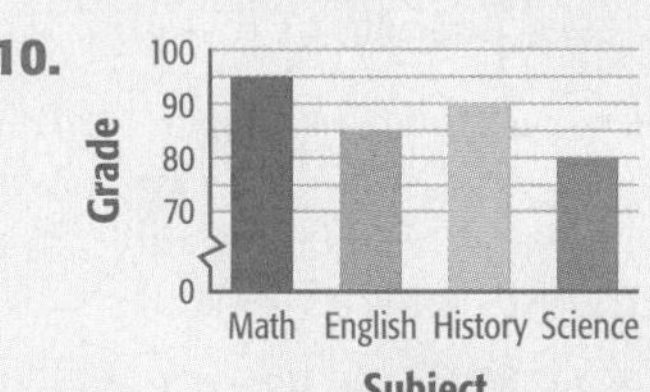

11.

Points Scored			
Points (Intervals)	1–4	5–8	9–12
Frequency	2	3	1

12.

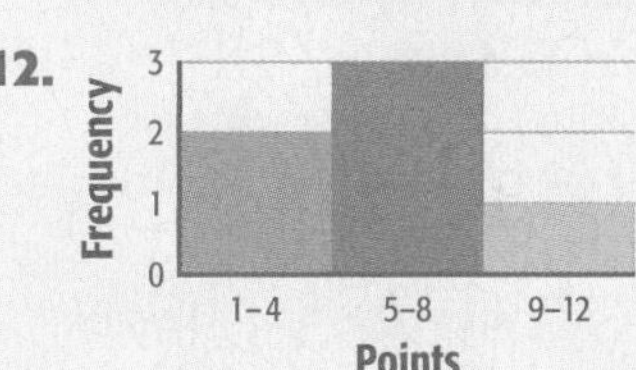

13. (4, 1)

14. (3, 2)

Answers

15.

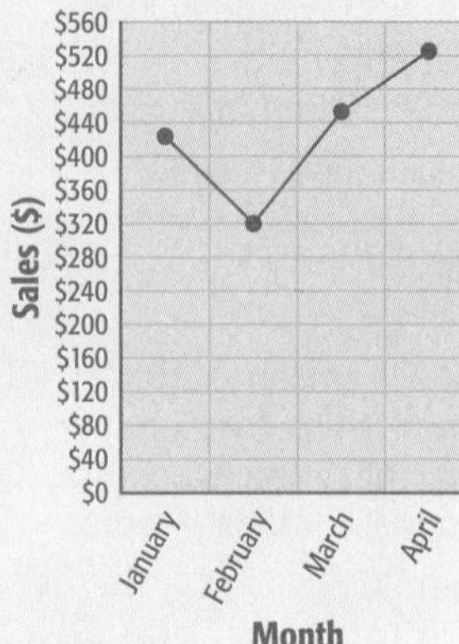

16. April

17. Sales decreased from January to February and then increased from February to April.

18. The scale starts out in increments of one mile and then it changes to 5 miles.

19. **Basketball Scores**

Stems	Leaves
2	0 2 6 8
3	4
4	0 4 6

Key: 2|0 means 20

20. smallest value: 20, largest value: 46, mean: 32.5, median: 31, mode: none, range: 26

21. line graph

Study Guide: Review

6-7 Line Graphs (pp. 322–325)

GPS M6D1.b

EXAMPLE

- **Use the temperature data to make a line graph.**

Day 1: 32°F; Day 2: 36°F; Day 3: 38°F; Day 4: 40°F; Day 5: 36°F

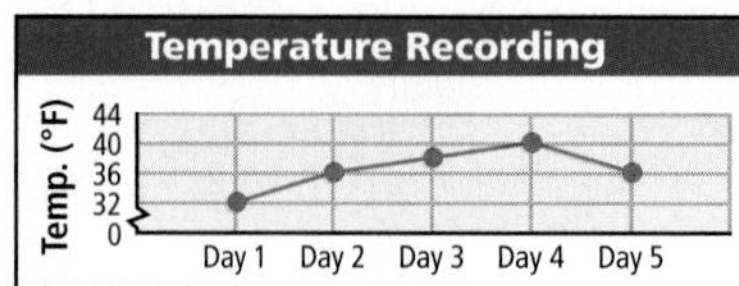

EXERCISES

15. Use the bookstore sales data to make a line graph.

Jan: $425; Feb: $320; Mar: $450; Apr: $530

Use your line graph from Exercise 15.

16. When were bookstore sales the greatest?

17. Describe the trend in bookstore sales over the four months.

6-8 Misleading Graphs (pp. 326–329)

GPS M6P2.c

EXAMPLE

- **Why is this graph misleading?**

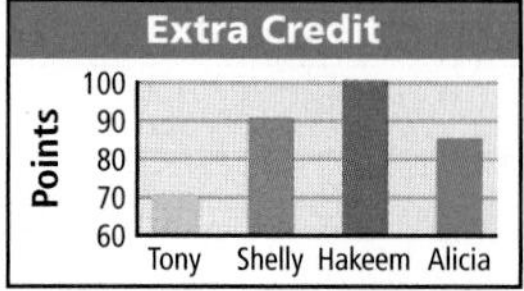

The lower part of the scale is missing.

EXERCISES

18. Explain why this graph is misleading.

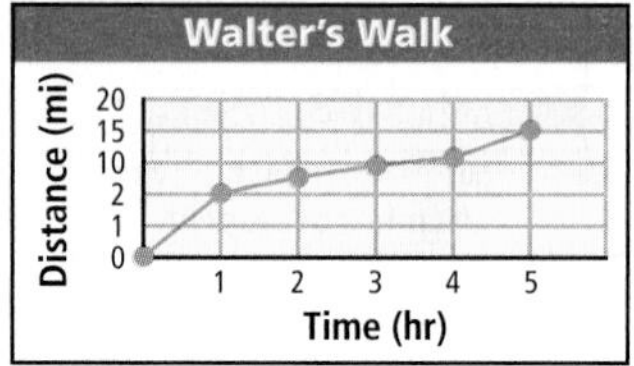

6-9 Stem-and-Leaf Plots (pp. 330–332)

EXAMPLE

- **Make a stem-and-leaf plot of the following test scores.**
80, 92, 88, 86, 85, 94

Stems	Leaves
8	0 5 6 8
9	2 4

Key: 8|0 means 80

EXERCISES

19. Make a stem-and-leaf plot of the following basketball scores.

22, 26, 34, 46, 20, 44, 40, 28

20. List the least value, greatest value, mean, median, mode, and range of the data from Exercise 19.

6-10 Choosing an Appropriate Display (pp. 333–335)

GPS M6D1.b

EXAMPLE

- **Which graph would be more appropriate to show time spent shopping—a stem-and-leaf plot or a line graph?**

Use a stem-and-leaf plot to see how often data values occur.

EXERCISES

21. Which graph would be more appropriate to show the number of books read over the school year by a class—a bar graph or a line graph?

1. Use the data about sound to make a table.

   The loudness of a sound is measured by the size of its vibrations. The unit of measurement is the decibel (dB). A soft whisper is 30 dB. Conversation is 60 dB. A loud shout is 100 dB. The pain threshold for humans is 130 dB. An airplane takeoff at 100 ft is 140 dB.

Use the bar graph for Exercises 2–4.

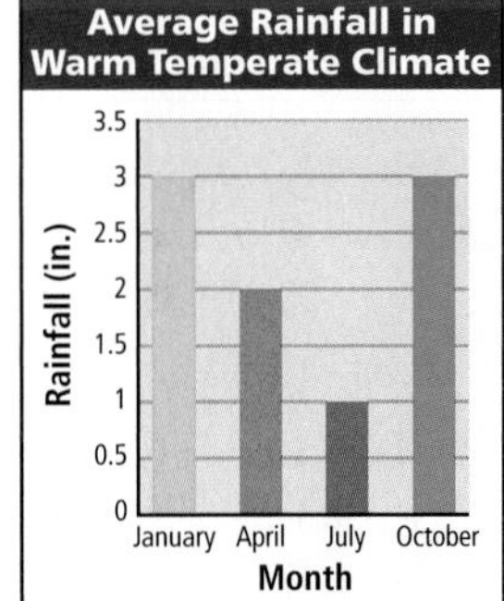

2. Find the mean, median, mode, and range of the rainfall amounts. mean = 2.25, median = 2.5, mode = 3, range = 2
3. Which month had the lowest average rainfall? July
4. Which months had rainfall amounts greater than 2 inches? January and October
5. The table shows the number of strawberries picked by customers at a pick-your-own strawberry patch. Organize the data in a line plot.

Number of Strawberries Picked							
28	33	35	27	35	28	35	29
30	27	30	35	28	27	31	32

Name the ordered pair for each point on the grid.

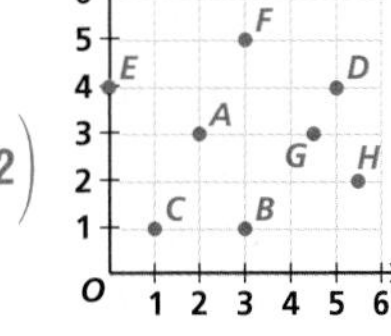

6. A (2, 3) 7. B (3, 1) 8. C (1, 1) 9. D (5, 4)

10. E (0, 4) 11. F (3, 5) 12. G $\left(4\frac{1}{2}, 3\right)$ 13. H $\left(5\frac{1}{2}, 2\right)$

Graph and label each point on a coordinate grid.

14. $T(3, 4)$ 15. $M\left(\frac{1}{2}, 6\right)$ 16. $P(5, 1)$ 17. $S\left(3\frac{1}{2}, 2\right)$ 18. $N(0, 5)$

19. Make a stem-and-leaf plot of the push-up data. Use your stem-and-leaf plot to find the mean, median, and mode of the data.

Number of Push-ups Performed						
35	33	25	45	52	21	18
41	27	35	40	53	24	38

20. The table shows the population of a small town over a 5-year period. Which graph would be more appropriate to show the data—a bar graph or a line graph? Draw the more appropriate graph.

Year	2002	2003	2004	2005
Population	852	978	1,125	1,206

Chapter Test

Organizer

Objective: Assess students' mastery of concepts and skills in Chapter 6.

Online Edition

Resources

Assessment Resources

Chapter 6 Tests
- Free Response (Levels A, B, C)
- Multiple Choice (Levels A, B, C)
- Performance Assessment

***IDEA Works!* CD-ROM**

Modified Chapter 6 Test

Answers

1.

Sound Data	
Sound	**Loudness**
Soft whisper	30 dB
Conversation	60 dB
Loud shout	100 dB
Pain threshold for humans	130 dB
Airplane takeoff at 100 ft	140 dB

5.

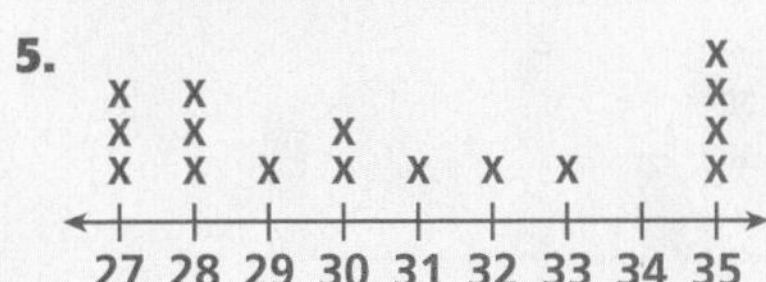

14–18.

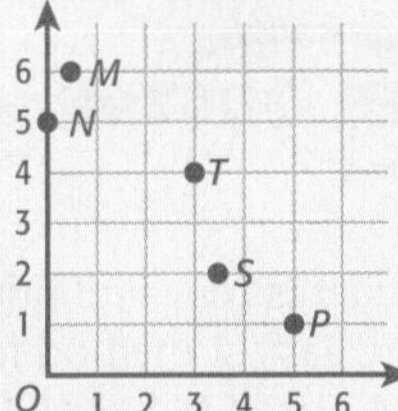

19.

Number of Push-ups Performed

Stems	Leaves
1	8
2	1 4 5 7
3	3 5 5 8
4	0 1 5
5	2 3

Key: 1|8 means 18

mean ≈ 34.79, median: 35, mode: 35

20.

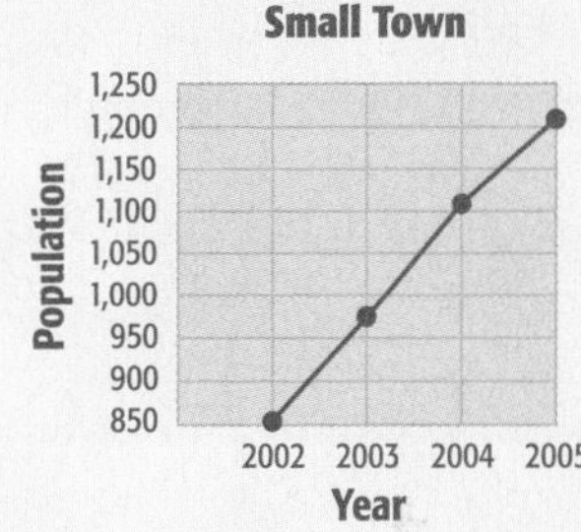

Organizer

Objective: Provide review and practice for Chapters 1–6 and standardized tests.

Online Edition

Resources

Assessment Resources
Chapter 6 Cumulative Test

***CRCT Prep* Workbook**

***CRCT Prep* CD-ROM**

***CRCT Practice* Online**

go.hrw.com
KEYWORD: MR7 TestPrep

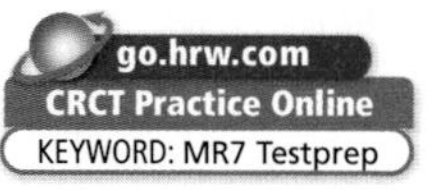

CRCT Prep

Cumulative Assessment, Chapters 1–6

Multiple Choice

1. The stem-and-leaf plot shows the ages of the volunteers who work at a local food bank. What is the median of this set of data?

Stems	Leaves
1	6
2	2 3
3	0 1 4
4	1 4 8

Key: 1|6 means 16

Ⓐ 37.5 (circled) Ⓒ 41
Ⓑ 38.1 Ⓓ 58

2. In a vacuum, light travels at a speed of 299,792,458 meters per second. Which of the following represents this rate in scientific notation?

Ⓕ 2.9×10^7 meters per second
Ⓖ 2.9×10^8 meters per second (circled)
Ⓗ 2.9×10^9 meters per second
Ⓙ 2.9×10^{10} meters per second

3. Harrison spends $3\frac{1}{2}$ hours a week working in his yard. He spends $1\frac{1}{3}$ hours pulling weeds. He spends the rest of the time mowing the yard. How much time does he spend mowing the yard?

Ⓐ $1\frac{1}{6}$ hours Ⓒ $2\frac{1}{3}$ hours
Ⓑ $2\frac{1}{6}$ hours (circled) Ⓓ $3\frac{1}{3}$ hours

4. Which value is equivalent to 4^4?

Ⓕ 8 Ⓗ 64
Ⓖ 16 Ⓙ 256 (circled)

5. Jamie is making a fruit salad. She needs $2\frac{1}{4}$ cups of crushed pineapple, $3\frac{3}{4}$ cups of sliced apples, $1\frac{1}{3}$ cups of mandarin oranges, and $2\frac{2}{3}$ cups of red grapes. How many cups total of fruit does she need for the fruit salad?

Ⓐ 6 cups Ⓒ 10 cups (circled)
Ⓑ 8 cups Ⓓ 12 cups

6. The line plot shows the ages of the number of participants in a science fair. Which of the following statements is NOT supported by the line plot?

Ages of Science Fair Participants

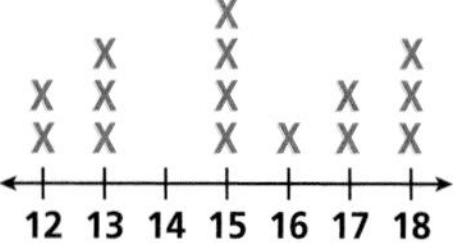

Ⓕ The range is 6.
Ⓖ The mean age of the participants in the science fair is 15.1.
Ⓗ The mode of the ages of the participants in the science fair is 16. (circled)
Ⓙ The median age of the participants in the science fair is 15.

7. What is the mode of the following data? 17, 13, 14, 13, 21, 18, 16, 19

Ⓐ 13 (circled) Ⓒ 16.5
Ⓑ 16 Ⓓ 16.375

Test Prep Doctor

For item 13, students may find prime factorization to be the easiest method for determining the LCM. The LCM has all factors of the three numbers, (5, 3, 2, 2, and 2). The LCM is $5 \times 3 \times 2 \times 2 \times 2 = 120$.

Answers

14. The vertical scale does not begin at 0.

Favorite Frozen Fruit Bars

Number of people: 0, 10, 20, 30, 40, 50
Mango, Berry, Strawberry banana, Lime

15a. range = 34; mean = 39; median = 39; mode = 55

b. range = 61; mean = 40.56; median = 39.5; mode = 55

16. See 4-Point Response work sample.

8. Which is a type of graph that uses bars and intervals to display data?

Ⓕ Stem-and-leaf plot

Ⓖ Histogram (circled)

Ⓗ Double-line graph

Ⓙ Line plot

9. Which equation has a solution of 8?

Ⓐ $2x = 18$	Ⓒ $x + 6 = 24$
Ⓑ $x - 4 = 12$	Ⓓ $\frac{x}{4} = 2$ (circled)

Read graphs and diagrams carefully. Look at the labels for important information.

Use the following data set for items 10 and 11.

4, 13, 7, 26, 6, 7, 3, 4, 2, 8, 10, 9

10. Which number in the data set is an outlier?

Ⓕ 3	Ⓗ 7
Ⓖ 6	Ⓙ 26 (circled)

11. What is the mean of the data set?

Ⓐ 7.0	Ⓒ 8.75
Ⓑ 8.25 (circled)	Ⓓ 9.5

12. Miguel has a piece of lumber that is 48.6 centimeters long. How many centimeters does he need to cut off if he wants the piece of lumber to measure 32.8 centimeters?

Ⓕ 15.2	Ⓗ 16.8
Ⓖ 15.8 (circled)	Ⓙ 17.2

13. What is the least common multiple of 5, 6, and 8?

Ⓐ 30	Ⓒ 60
Ⓑ 40	Ⓓ 120 (circled)

STANDARDIZED TEST PREP

Short Response

14. Look at the bar graph of favorite flavors of frozen fruit bars. Explain why the graph is misleading. Use the same data to make a graph that is not misleading.

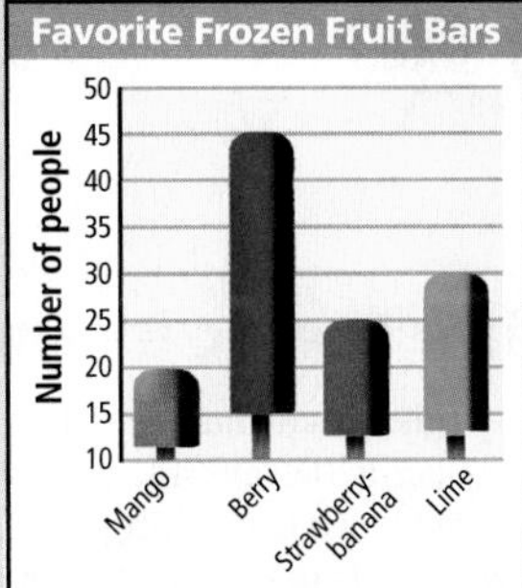

15.

Stems	Leaves
2	1 3 6
3	2 2 5 9
4	0 3
5	1 5 5 5

Key: 2|1 means 21

a. Find the range, mean, median, and mode of the data in the stem-and-leaf plot.

b. How does adding 82, 18, and 42 to the data change the range, mean, median, and mode?

Extended Response

16. The high temperature on Monday was 54°F. On Tuesday, it was 62°F. On Wednesday, it was 65°F. On Thursday, it was 60°F. On Friday, it was 62°F.

a. Organize this data in a table. Find the range, mean, median, and mode of the data.

b. Which graph would be more appropriate to show the data—a bar graph or a line graph? Explain.

c. Make a graph of the data.

CRCT Prep

Short Response Rubric

Items 14–15

2 Points = The student's answer is an accurate and complete execution of the task or tasks.

1 Point = The student's answer contains attributes of an appropriate response but is flawed.

0 Points = The student's answer contains no attributes of an appropriate response.

Extended Response Rubric

Item 16

4 Points = The student demonstrates a thorough understanding of all concepts and shows all work correctly.

3 Points = The student demonstrates a basic understanding of all concepts, but the work shows some flaws reflecting inattentive execution of mathematical procedures or some misunderstanding of the underlying mathematics.

2 Points = The student demonstrates only a partial understanding of the concepts or procedures embodied in the tasks. The approach may be correct, but the work shows a misunderstanding of one or more important concepts.

1 Point = The student demonstrates a very limited understanding of the concepts or procedures embodied in the tasks. The response may show some understanding but exhibits many flaws or is incomplete.

0 Points = The student provides no response at all or a completely incorrect or uninterpretable response.

Student Work Samples for Item 16

4-Point Response

a.

Daily Temperatures				
Mon	Tue	Wed	Thu	Fri
54°F	62°F	65°F	60°F	62°F

range = 11 mean = 60.6 median = 62 mode = 62

b. A line graph would be more appropriate for the data since the data is collected over time.

c. Daily Temperatures

Temperature (°F): 70, 60, 50, 40, 30, 20, 10

Mon Tue Wed Thu Fri

The answers are correct. All work shows a thorough understanding of the concepts.

3-Point Response

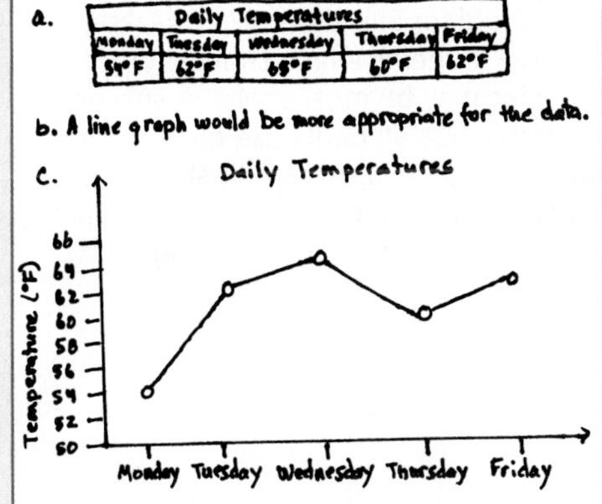

The answers are correct. However, part **a** was not answered completely, and the graph in part **c** does not begin at 0°.

2-Point Response

The work is adequate. The explanation for choosing the type of graph does not demonstrate an understanding of the selection criteria.

Problem Solving on Location

Organizer

Objective: To solve real-world problems involving fraction operations and data.

 Online Edition

Georgia's Scenic Byways

Reading Strategies

Help students use context clues to understand the meaning of any unfamiliar words. For example, if students do not know the word *byway*, ask them what must be true about a byway based on the information in the opening paragraph. Possible answer: They may be scenic; a motorist can drive on them.

Using Data Ask students to preview the information in the map before they solve the problems. Ask which byway is the longest. Cohutta-Chattahoochee Also ask students to identify the two byways that are almost the same length. South Fulton and Monticello Crossroads

Georgia Performance Standards

M6P1.c Apply and adapt a variety of appropriate strategies to solve problems.

M6P4.c Recognize and apply mathematics in contexts outside of mathematics.

M6P5.b Select, apply, and translate among mathematical representations to solve problems.

Problem Solving on Location

GEORGIA

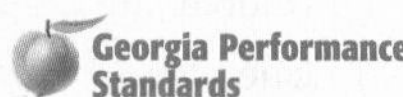

M6P1.c, M6P4.c, M6P5.a

Georgia's Scenic Byways

Several of Georgia's roads have been designated as scenic byways. Motorists on these roads can see everything from forests and waterfalls to historic farms and villages. The map shows the lengths of some of the state's most beautiful drives.

Cohutta–Chattahoochee 54 mi

Ridge and Valley $50\frac{7}{10}$ mi

Russell–Brasstown $40\frac{3}{5}$ mi

South Fulton $29\frac{1}{2}$ mi

Monticello Crossroads $28\frac{4}{5}$ mi

Altamaha 17 mi

Choose one or more strategies to solve each problem.

1. A visitor to Georgia wants to drive along two of the byways shown on the map. In how many different ways can she choose two of the routes? **15**
2. The state is considering putting new signs along the South Fulton route to mark it as a scenic byway. The signs would appear at the beginning and end of the route and every $\frac{1}{2}$ mile along the way. How many signs would be needed? **60**
3. A family passes a road sign on the Russell-Brasstown Byway. The sign says that Raven Cliff Falls is $7\frac{6}{10}$ miles ahead. The family decides to turn around and drive in the opposite direction around the loop. How many miles will they travel to Raven Cliff Falls? **$33\frac{1}{5}$ mi**

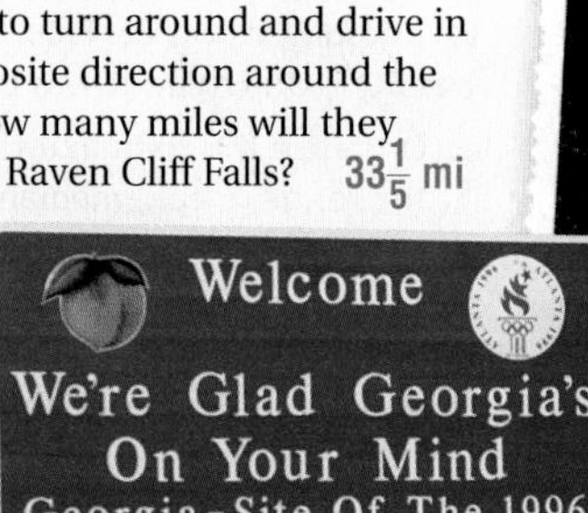

Welcome
We're Glad Georgia's On Your Mind
Georgia-Site Of The 1996 Olympic Games

Problem Solving Focus

For problem 3, focus on the second step of the Problem Solving Process: Make a Plan. Ask students which strategy or strategies may be most useful in solving the problem. If students use the strategy Draw a Diagram, ask them to share their diagrams with the entire class and explain how they used the diagrams to solve the problem.

Problem Solving Strategies

- Draw a Diagram
- Make a Model
- Guess and Test
- Work Backward
- Find a Pattern
- Make a Table
- Solve a Simpler Problem
- Use Logical Reasoning
- Act It Out
- Make an Organized List

Lighthouses

Georgia has a short coastline, but a long history of lighthouses. The state's first lighthouse was built in 1736 to guide ships into the port of Savannah. Since then, more than a dozen additional lighthouses have been built, but only a few remain standing today.

Choose one or more strategies to solve each problem.

1. The lamp in the St. Simons Island Lighthouse makes one complete turn each minute. The flash of a lighthouse lamp is the precise moment in its rotation when the lamp is pointing directly at you. If the lamp in the St. Simons Island Lighthouse flashes once per minute, how many times does the lamp flash between the hours of 6:00 P.M. and 6:00 A.M.? **720**

For 2 and 3, use the information in the graph.

2. The current Tybee Island Lighthouse, located at the mouth of the Savannah River, is the fourth lighthouse built at this site. The first lighthouse was $3\frac{1}{2}$ feet shorter than the second lighthouse. The second lighthouse was $6\frac{1}{2}$ feet shorter than the third lighthouse. The third lighthouse was 45 feet shorter than the current lighthouse. What was the height of the first lighthouse? **90 ft**

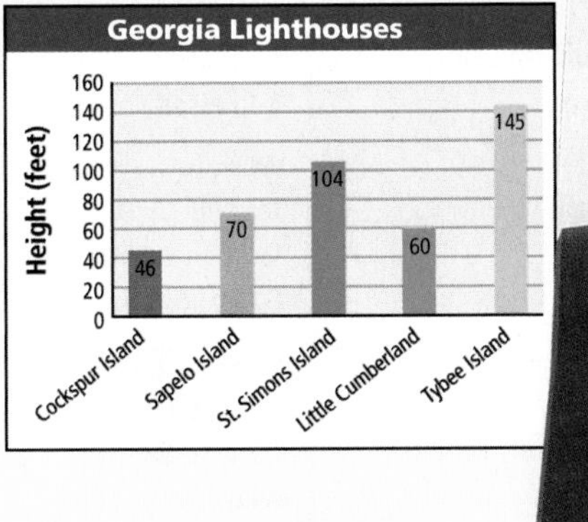

3. Among the lighthouses in the graph, the oldest was built in 1820. Its height is less than the mean (average) height of the lighthouses. Its height is greater than or equal to the median height of the lighthouses. Which lighthouse is the oldest? **Sapelo Island**

Lighthouses

Reading Strategies

ENGLISH LANGUAGE LEARNERS

Begin by asking students what they already know about lighthouses. This type of preview discussion can be especially helpful for ELL students, as it provides a natural setting in which to highlight some of the vocabulary that students may encounter while solving the problems.

Using Data Briefly discuss the bar graph showing the heights of lighthouses. Ask students if the data could have been presented in a bar graph with horizontal bars. Yes Then ask students why they think a graph with vertical bars was used. Possible answer: Vertical bars make sense when representing heights of objects.

Problem Solving Focus

For problem 2, focus on the final step in the Problem Solving Process: Look Back. In particular, ask students if their answer seems reasonable for the height of a lighthouse. Also, ask students to explain why it makes sense that the height of the first lighthouse turned out to be less than the height of the current lighthouse. Based on the information in the problem, each lighthouse was shorter than the one that came after it, so the first lighthouse was the shortest.

Discuss different strategies that could be used to solve problem 2. For example, some students may use the strategy Word Backward. Others might solve the problem using Draw a Diagram or Make an Organized List. After students have shared their strategies, ask them which one seemed most efficient for solving this problem.

CHAPTER 7

Proportional Relationships

Section 7A

Understanding Ratios and Proportions

- **7-1 Ratios and Rates**
- **7-2 Using Tables to Explore Equivalent Ratios and Rates**
- **7-3 Hands-On Lab** Explore Proportions
- **7-3 Proportions**
- **7-4 Similar Figures**
- **7-5 Indirect Measurement**
- **7-6 Hands-On Lab** Sketch Scale Drawings
- **7-6 Scale Drawings and Maps**

Section 7B

Understanding Percents

- **7-7 Hands-On Lab** Model Percents
- **7-7 Percents**
- **7-8 Percents, Decimals, and Fractions**
- **7-8 Technology Lab** Convert Between Percents, Decimals, and Fractions
- **7-9 Percent Problems**
- **7-10 Using Percents**
- **EXTENSION Simple Interest**

Pacing Guide for 45-Minute Classes

Chapter 7

Countdown to Testing Weeks 14, 15, 16

DAY 1	DAY 2	DAY 3	DAY 4	DAY 5
7-1 Lesson	7-2 Lesson	**7-3 Hands-On Lab** 7-3 Lesson	7-3 Lesson 7-4 Lesson	7-4 Lesson
DAY 6	**DAY 7**	**DAY 8**	**DAY 9**	**DAY 10**
7-5 Lesson	7-5 Lesson **7-6 Hands-On Lab**	7-6 Lesson	Ready to Go On? Focus on Problem Solving **7-7 Hands-On Lab**	7-7 Lesson
DAY 11	**DAY 12**	**DAY 13**	**DAY 14**	**DAY 15**
7-8 Lesson	**7-8 Technology Lab** 7-9 Lesson	7-9 Lesson 7-10 Lesson	7-10 Lesson Ready to Go On? Multi-Step Test Prep	EXTENSION
DAY 16	**DAY 17**			
Chapter 7 Review	Chapter 7 Test			

Pacing Guide for 90-Minute Classes

Chapter 7

DAY 1	DAY 2	DAY 3	DAY 4	DAY 5
7-1 Lesson 7-2 Lesson	**7-3 Hands-On Lab** 7-3 Lesson 7-4 Lesson	7-4 Lesson 7-5 Lesson	7-5 Lesson **7-6 Hands-On Lab** 7-6 Lesson	Ready to Go On? Focus on Problem Solving **7-7 Hands-On Lab** 7-7 Lesson
DAY 6	**DAY 7**	**DAY 8**	**DAY 9**	
7-8 Lesson **7-8 Technology Lab** 7-9 Lesson	7-9 Lesson 7-10 Lesson Ready to Go On? Multi-Step Test Prep	EXTENSION Chapter 7 Review	Chapter 7 Test	

ONGOING ASSESSMENT and INTERVENTION

	DIAGNOSE	PRESCRIBE
Assess Prior Knowledge	**Before Chapter 7**	
	Diagnose readiness for the chapter.	Prescribe intervention.
	Are You Ready? SE p. 349	***Are You Ready? Intervention*** Skills 19, 24–26, 40
Formative Assessment	**Before Every Lesson**	
	Diagnose readiness for the lesson.	Prescribe intervention.
	Warm Up TE, every lesson	**Skills Bank** SE pp. 749–761 **Reteach** CRB, Chapters 1–7
	During Every Lesson	
	Diagnose understanding of lesson concepts.	Prescribe intervention.
	Think and Discuss SE, every lesson **Write About It** SE, lesson exercises **Journal** TE, lesson exercises	***Questioning Strategies*** Chapter 7 **Reading Strategies** CRB, every lesson ***Success for ELL*** pp. 107–126
	After Every Lesson	
	Diagnose mastery of lesson concepts.	Prescribe intervention.
	Lesson Quiz TE, every lesson **Test Prep** SE, every lesson ***Test and Practice Generator***	**Reteach** CRB, every lesson **Problem Solving** CRB, every lesson **Test Prep Doctor** TE, lesson exercises ***Homework Help* Online**
	Before Chapter 7 Testing	
	Diagnose mastery of concepts in the chapter.	Prescribe intervention.
	Ready to Go On? SE pp. 378, 398 **Focus on Problem Solving** SE p. 379 **Multi-Step Test Prep** SE p. 399 **Section Quizzes** AR pp. 126–127 ***Test and Practice Generator***	***Ready to Go On? Intervention*** **Scaffolding Questions** TE p. 399
	Before High Stakes Testing	
	Diagnose mastery of benchmark concepts.	Prescribe intervention.
	Test Tackler SE pp. 408–409 **CRCT Prep** SE pp. 410–411 ***CRCT Prep* CD-ROM**	***CRCT Prep Workbook***
Summative Assessment	**After Chapter 7**	
	Check mastery of chapter concepts.	Prescribe intervention.
	Multiple-Choice Tests (Forms A, B, C) **Free-Response Tests (Forms A, B, C)** **Performance Assessment** AR pp. 128–141 ***Test and Practice Generator***	**Reteach** CRB, every lesson ***Lesson Tutorial Videos*** Chapter 7
	Check mastery of benchmark concepts.	Prescribe intervention.
	CRCT	***CRCT Prep Workbook***

KEY: **SE** = *Student Edition* **TE** = *Teacher's Edition* **CRB** = *Chapter Resource Book* **AR** = *Assessment Resources* Available online Available on CD-ROM

CHAPTER 7

Supporting the Teacher

Chapter 7 Resource Book

Practice A, B, C
pp. 3–5, 12–14, 20–22, 28–30, 36–38, 44–46, 52–54, 60–62, 68–70, 76–78

Reading Strategies ELL
pp. 10, 18, 26, 34, 42, 50, 58, 66, 74, 82

Puzzles, Twisters, and Teasers
pp. 11, 19, 27, 35, 43, 51, 59, 67, 75, 83

Reteach
pp. 6–7, 15, 23, 31, 39, 47, 55, 63, 71, 79

Problem Solving
pp. 9, 17, 25, 33, 41, 49, 57, 65, 73, 81

Challenge
pp. 8, 16, 24, 32, 40, 48, 56, 64, 72, 80

Parent Letter pp. 1–2

Transparencies

Lesson Transparencies, Volume 2 .... Chapter 7
- Warm Ups
- Problem of the Day
- Teaching Transparencies
- Lesson Quizzes

Know-It Notebook .... Chapter 7
- Additional Examples
- Vocabulary
- Chapter Review
- Big Ideas

Alternate Openers: Explorations .... pp. 54–63

Countdown to CRCT .... pp. 27–32

Teacher Tools

Power Presentations®
Complete PowerPoint® presentations for Chapter 7 lessons

Lesson Tutorial Videos® SPANISH
Holt authors Ed Burger and Freddie Renfro present tutorials to support the Chapter 7 lessons.

One-Stop Planner® SPANISH
Easy access to all Chapter 7 resources and assessments, as well as software for lesson planning, test generation, and puzzle creation

IDEA Works!®
Key Chapter 7 resources and assessments modified to address special learning needs

Lesson Plans .... pp. 54–63

Questioning Strategies .... Chapter 7

Solutions Key .... Chapter 7

Interdisciplinary Posters and Worksheets .... Chapter 7

TechKeys

Lab Resources

Project Teacher Support

Parent Resources  

Workbooks

Homework and Practice Workbook SPANISH
Teacher's Guide .... pp. 27–32

Know-It Notebook
Teacher's Guide .... Chapter 7

Problem Solving Workbook SPANISH
Teacher's Guide .... pp. 27–32

CRCT Prep
Teacher's Guide

Technology Highlights for the Teacher

 **Power Presentations**

Dynamic presentations to engage students. Complete PowerPoint® presentations for every lesson in Chapter 7.

2-1 Solving One-Step Equations

Isolate a variable by using inverse operations which "undo" operations on the variable.

An equation is like a balanced scale. To keep the balance, perform the same operation on both sides.

Inverse Operations	
Operation	**Inverse Operation**
Addition	Subtraction
Subtraction	Addition

One-Stop Planner SPANISH

Easy access to Chapter 7 resources and assessments. Includes lesson-planning, test-generation, and puzzle-creation software.

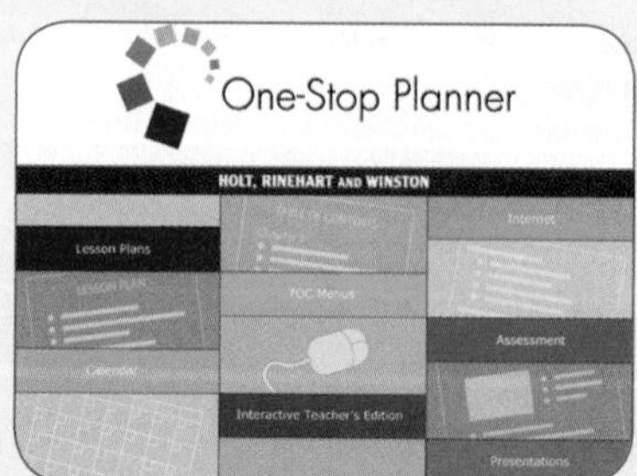

Premier Online Edition SPANISH

Chapter 7 includes Tutorial Videos, Lesson Activities, Lesson Quizzes, Homework Help, and Chapter Project.

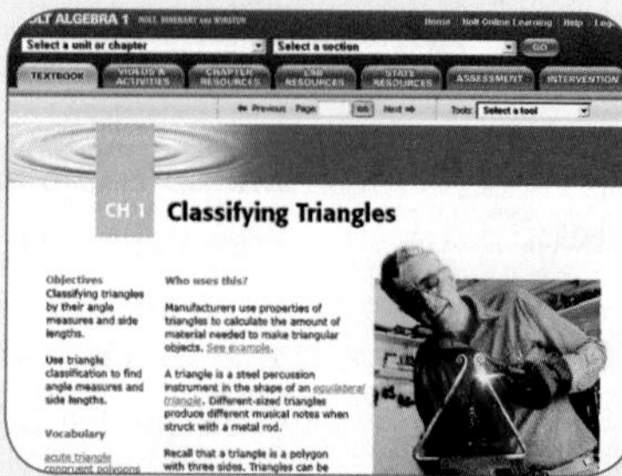

KEY: **SE** = *Student Edition* **TE** = *Teacher's Edition*  English Language Learners  Spanish version available  Available online  Available on CD-ROM

Reaching All Learners

Resources for All Learners

- ***Hands-On Lab Activities*** .... Chapter 7
- ***Technology Lab Activities*** .... Chapter 7
- ***Homework and Practice Workbook*** SPANISH .... pp. 54–63
- ***Know-It Notebook*** SPANISH .... Chapter 7
- ***Problem Solving Workbook*** SPANISH .... pp. 54–63

DEVELOPING LEARNERS

- **Practice A** .... CRB, every lesson
- **Reteach** .... CRB, every lesson
- **Inclusion** .... TE p. 367
- ***Questioning Strategies*** .... Chapter 7
- **Modified Chapter 7 Resources** .... *IDEA Works!*
- ***Homework Help* Online**

ON-LEVEL LEARNERS

- **Practice B** .... CRB, every lesson
- **Puzzles, Twisters, and Teasers** .... CRB, every lesson
- **Cooperative Learning** .... TE pp. 353, 386
- **Modeling** .... TE p. 357

ADVANCED LEARNERS

- **Practice C** .... CRB, every lesson
- **Challenge** .... CRB, every lesson
- **Extension** .... TE pp. 351, 399, 402, 403
- **Critical Thinking** .... TE p. 375

English Language Learners

ENGLISH LANGUAGE LEARNERS

- **Are You Ready? Vocabulary** .... SE p. 349
- **Vocabulary Connections** .... SE p. 350
- **Lesson Vocabulary** .... SE, every lesson
- **Vocabulary Review** .... SE p. 404
- **English Language Learners** .... TE pp. 351, 352, 353, 367, 375, 395
- **Reading Strategies** .... CRB, every lesson
- ***Success for English Language Learners*** .... pp. 107–126
- ***Multilingual Glossary***

Reaching All Learners Through...

- **Inclusion** .... TE p. 367
- **Diversity** .... TE pp. 371, 391
- **Kinesthetic Experience** .... TE p. 382
- **Concrete Manipulatives** .... TE p. 363
- **Cooperative Learning** .... TE pp. 353, 386
- **Modeling** .... TE p. 357
- **Graphic Organizers** .... TE p. 395
- **Critical Thinking** .... TE p. 375
- **Test Prep Doctor** .... TE pp. 355, 359, 365, 369, 377, 384, 388, 393, 397, 408, 409, 410
- **Common Error Alert** .... TE pp. 353, 357, 363, 375, 382, 386, 391, 395, 401
- **Scaffolding Questions** .... TE p. 399

Technology Highlights for Reaching All Learners

 **Lesson Tutorial Videos** 

Starring Holt authors Ed Burger and Freddie Renfro! Live tutorials to support every lesson in Chapter 7.

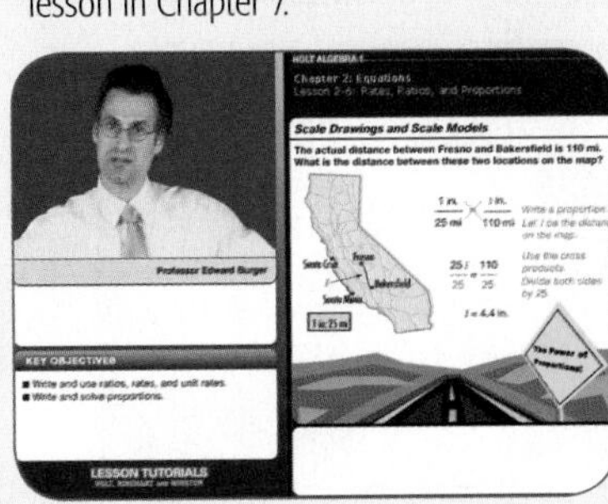

Multilingual Glossary

Searchable glossary includes definitions in English, Spanish, Vietnamese, Chinese, Hmong, Korean, and 4 other languages.

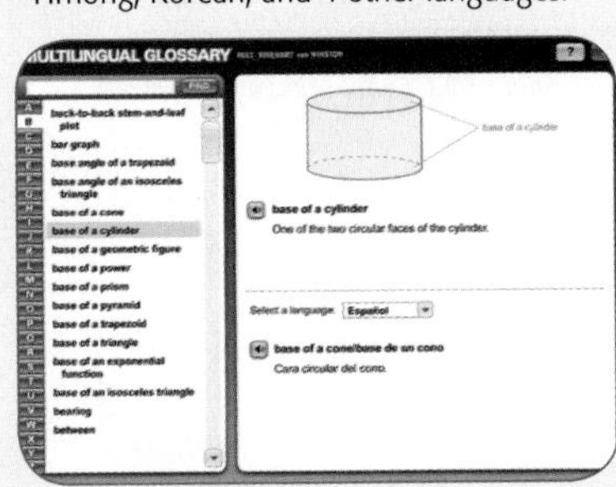

Online Interactivities

Interactive tutorials provide visually engaging alternative opportunities to learn concepts and master skills.

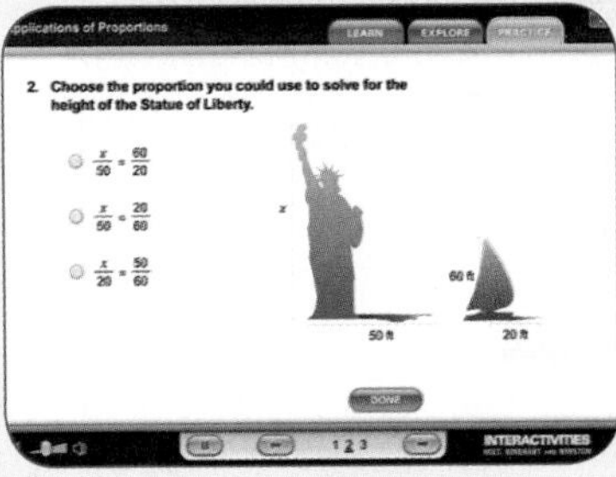

KEY: **SE** = *Student Edition* **TE** = *Teacher's Edition* **CRB** = *Chapter Resource Book* SPANISH Spanish version available  Available online  Available on CD-ROM

CHAPTER 7

Ongoing Assessment

Assessing Prior Knowledge

Determine whether students have the prerequisite concepts and skills for success in Chapter 7.

Are You Ready? SPANISH .... SE p. 349
Warm Up .... TE, every lesson

Test Preparation

Provide review and practice for Chapter 7 and standardized tests.

Multi-Step Test Prep .... SE p. 399
Study Guide: Review .... SE pp. 404–406
Test Tackler .... SE pp. 408–409
Standardized Test Prep .... SE pp. 410–411
Countdown to CRCT Transparencies .... pp. 27–32
CRCT Prep Workbook
***CRCT Prep* CD-ROM**
IDEA Works!

Alternative Assessment

Assess students' understanding of Chapter 7 concepts and combined problem-solving skills.

Chapter 7 Project .... SE p. 348
Performance Assessment .... AR pp. 140–141
Portfolio Assessment .... AR p. xxxiv

Daily Assessment

Provide formative assessment for each day of Chapter 7.

Questioning Strategies .... Chapter 7
Think and Discuss .... SE, every lesson
Write About It .... SE, lesson exercises
Journal .... TE, lesson exercises
Lesson Quiz .... TE, every lesson
Modified Lesson Quizzes .... *IDEA Works!*

Weekly Assessment

Provide formative assessment for each week of Chapter 7.

Focus on Problem Solving .... SE p. 379
Multi-Step Test Prep .... SE p. 399
Ready to Go On? SPANISH .... SE pp. 378, 398
Cumulative Assessment .... SE pp. 410–411
Test and Practice Generator SPANISH ... *One-Stop Planner*

Formal Assessment

Provide summative assessment of Chapter 7 mastery.

Section Quizzes SPANISH .... AR pp. 126–127
Chapter 7 Test .... SE p. 407
Chapter Test (Levels A, B, C) SPANISH .... AR pp. 128–139
• Multiple Choice • Free Response
Cumulative Test SPANISH .... AR pp. 142–145
Test and Practice Generator SPANISH ... *One-Stop Planner*
Modified Chapter 7 Test .... *IDEA Works!*

Technology Highlights for the Teacher

Are You Ready? SPANISH
Automatically assess readiness and prescribe intervention for Chapter 7 prerequisite skills.

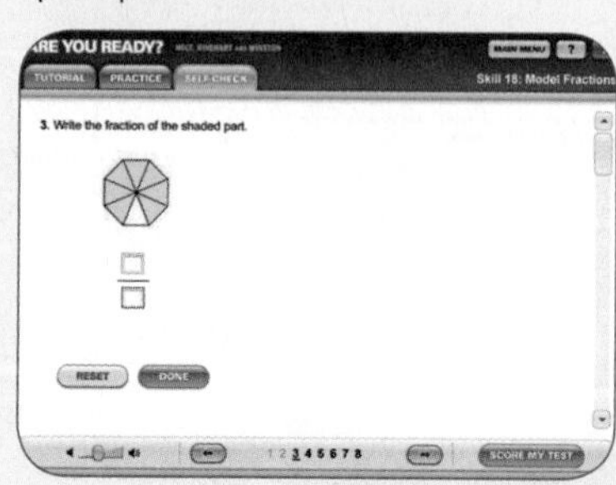

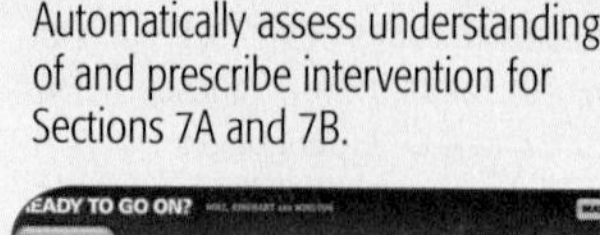

Ready to Go On? SPANISH
Automatically assess understanding of and prescribe intervention for Sections 7A and 7B.

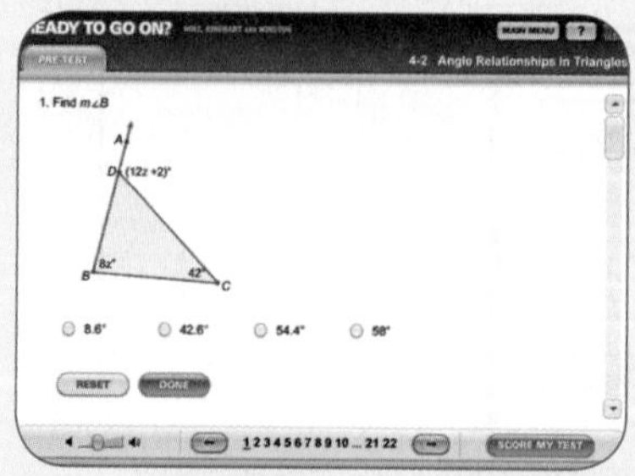

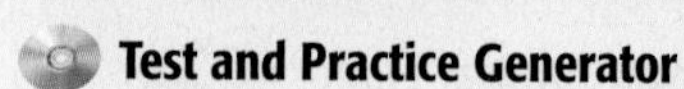

Test and Practice Generator SPANISH
Use Chapter 7 problem banks to create assessments and worksheets to print out or deliver online. Includes dynamic problems.

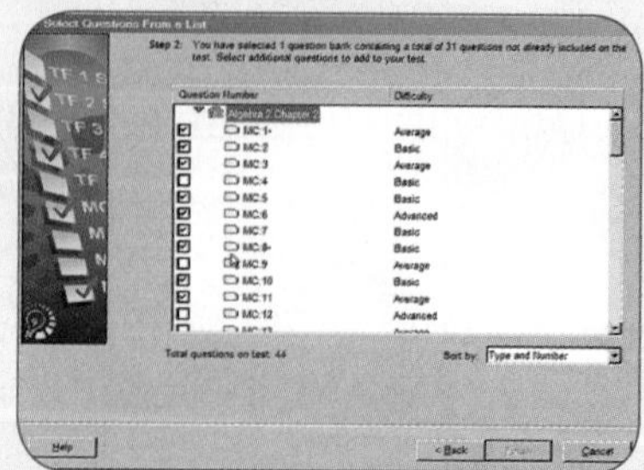

KEY: **SE** = *Student Edition* **TE** = *Teacher's Edition* **AR** = *Assessment Resources* SPANISH Spanish version available  Available online  Available on CD-ROM

CHAPTER
7

Formal Assessment

Three levels (A, B, C) of multiple-choice and free-response chapter tests are available in the *Assessment Resources.*

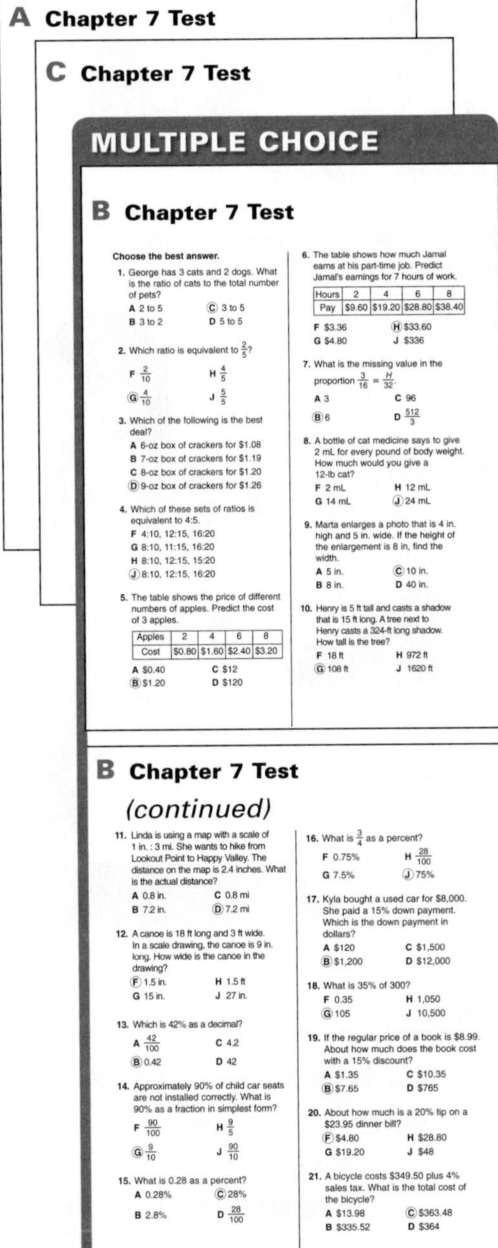

A Chapter 7 Test

C Chapter 7 Test

MULTIPLE CHOICE

B Chapter 7 Test

Choose the best answer.

1. George has 3 cats and 2 dogs. What is the ratio of cats to the total number of pets?
   A 2 to 5 (C) 3 to 5
   B 3 to 2 D 5 to 5

2. Which ratio is equivalent to $\frac{2}{5}$?
   F $\frac{2}{10}$ H $\frac{4}{5}$
   (G) $\frac{4}{10}$ J $\frac{5}{5}$

3. Which of the following is the best deal?
   A 6-oz box of crackers for $1.08
   B 7-oz box of crackers for $1.19
   C 8-oz box of crackers for $1.20
   (D) 9-oz box of crackers for $1.26

4. Which of these sets of ratios is equivalent to 4:5.
   F 4:10, 12:15, 16:20
   G 8:10, 11:15, 16:20
   H 8:10, 12:15, 15:20
   (J) 8:10, 12:15, 16:20

5. The table shows the price of different numbers of apples. Predict the cost of 3 apples.

Apples	2	4	6	8
Cost	$0.80	$1.60	$2.40	$3.20

   A $0.40 C $12
   (B) $1.20 D $120

6. The table shows how much Jamal earns at his part-time job. Predict Jamal's earnings for 7 hours of work.

Hours	2	4	6	8
Pay	$9.60	$19.20	$28.80	$38.40

   F $3.36 (H) $33.60
   G $4.80 J $336

7. What is the missing value in the proportion $\frac{3}{16} = \frac{H}{32}$.
   A 3 C 96
   (B) 6 D $\frac{512}{3}$

8. A bottle of cat medicine says to give 2 mL for every pound of body weight. How much would you give a 12-lb cat?
   F 2 mL H 12 mL
   G 14 mL (J) 24 mL

9. Marta enlarges a photo that is 4 in. high and 5 in. wide. If the height of the enlargement is 8 in, find the width.
   A 5 in. (C) 10 in.
   B 8 in. D 40 in.

10. Henry is 5 ft tall and casts a shadow that is 15 ft long. A tree next to Henry casts a 324-ft long shadow. How tall is the tree?
   F 18 ft H 972 ft
   (G) 108 ft J 1620 ft

B Chapter 7 Test

(continued)

11. Linda is using a map with a scale of 1 in. : 3 mi. She wants to hike from Lookout Point to Happy Valley. The distance on the map is 2.4 inches. What is the actual distance?
   A 0.8 in. C 0.8 mi
   B 7.2 in. (D) 7.2 mi

12. A canoe is 18 ft long and 3 ft wide. In a scale drawing, the canoe is 9 in. long. How wide is the canoe in the drawing?
   (F) 1.5 in. H 1.5 ft
   G 15 in. J 27 in.

13. Which is 42% as a decimal?
   A $\frac{42}{100}$ C 4.2
   (B) 0.42 D 42

14. Approximately 90% of child car seats are not installed correctly. What is 90% as a fraction in simplest form?
   F $\frac{90}{100}$ H $\frac{9}{5}$
   (G) $\frac{9}{10}$ J $\frac{90}{10}$

15. What is 0.28 as a percent?
   A 0.28% (C) 28%
   B 2.8% D $\frac{28}{100}$

16. What is $\frac{3}{4}$ as a percent?
   F 0.75% H $\frac{28}{100}$
   G 7.5% (J) 75%

17. Kyla bought a used car for $8,000. She paid a 15% down payment. Which is the down payment in dollars?
   A $120 C $1,500
   (B) $1,200 D $12,000

18. What is 35% of 300?
   F 0.35 H 1,050
   (G) 105 J 10,500

19. If the regular price of a book is $8.99. About how much does the book cost with a 15% discount?
   A $1.35 C $10.35
   (B) $7.65 D $765

20. About how much is a 20% tip on a $23.95 dinner bill?
   (F) $4.80 H $28.80
   G $19.20 J $48

21. A bicycle costs $349.50 plus 4% sales tax. What is the total cost of the bicycle?
   A $13.98 (C) $363.48
   B $335.52 D $364

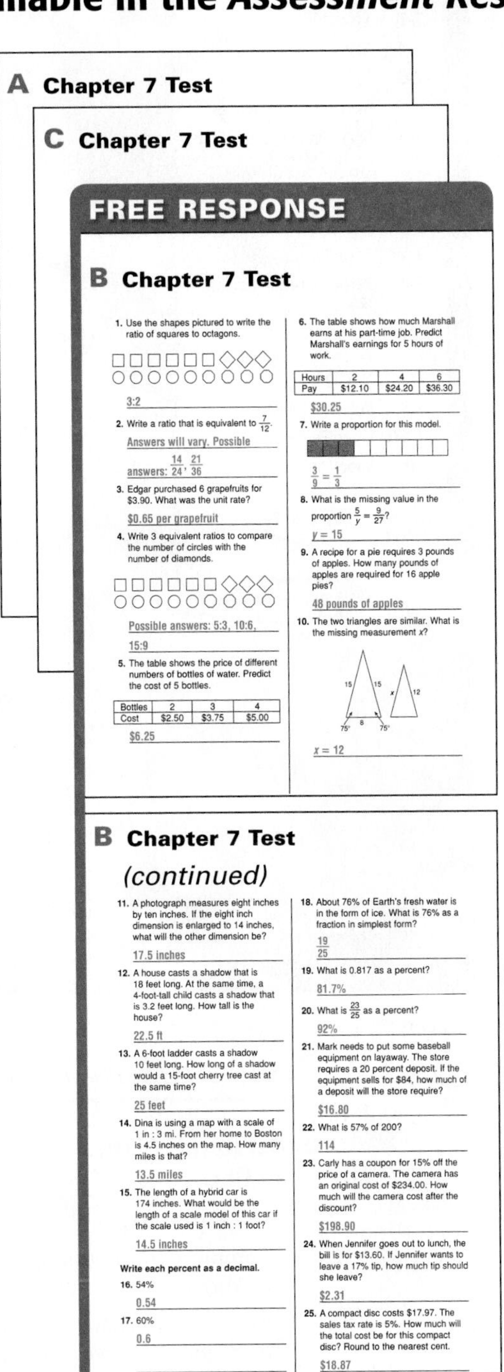

A Chapter 7 Test

C Chapter 7 Test

FREE RESPONSE

B Chapter 7 Test

1. Use the shapes pictured to write the ratio of squares to octagons.
   3:2

2. Write a ratio that is equivalent to $\frac{7}{12}$.
   Answers will vary. Possible answers: $\frac{14}{24}$, $\frac{21}{36}$

3. Edgar purchased 6 grapefruits for $3.90. What was the unit rate?
   $0.65 per grapefruit

4. Write 3 equivalent ratios to compare the number of circles with the number of diamonds.
   Possible answers: 5:3, 10:6, 15:9

5. The table shows the price of different numbers of bottles of water. Predict the cost of 5 bottles.

Bottles	2	3	4
Cost	$2.50	$3.75	$5.00

   $6.25

6. The table shows how much Marshall earns at his part-time job. Predict Marshall's earnings for 5 hours of work.

Hours	2	4	6
Pay	$12.10	$24.20	$36.30

   $30.25

7. Write a proportion for this model.
   $\frac{3}{9} = \frac{1}{3}$

8. What is the missing value in the proportion $\frac{5}{y} = \frac{9}{27}$?
   $y = 15$

9. A recipe for a pie requires 3 pounds of apples. How many pounds of apples are required for 16 apple pies?
   48 pounds of apples

10. The two triangles are similar. What is the missing measurement x?
   15, 15, 8, 75°, 75°; x, 12
   $x = 12$

B Chapter 7 Test

(continued)

11. A photograph measures eight inches by ten inches. If the eight inch dimension is enlarged to 14 inches, what will the other dimension be?
   17.5 inches

12. A house casts a shadow that is 18 feet long. At the same time, a 4-foot-tall child casts a shadow that is 3.2 feet long. How tall is the house?
   22.5 ft

13. A 6-foot ladder casts a shadow 10 feet long. How long of a shadow would a 15-foot cherry tree cast at the same time?
   25 feet

14. Dina is using a map with a scale of 1 in : 3 mi. From her home to Boston is 4.5 inches on the map. How many miles is that?
   13.5 miles

15. The length of a hybrid car is 174 inches. What would be the length of a scale model of this car if the scale used is 1 inch : 1 foot?
   14.5 inches

Write each percent as a decimal.

16. 54%
   0.54

17. 60%
   0.6

18. About 76% of Earth's fresh water is in the form of ice. What is 76% as a fraction in simplest form?
   $\frac{19}{25}$

19. What is 0.817 as a percent?
   81.7%

20. What is $\frac{23}{25}$ as a percent?
   92%

21. Mark needs to put some baseball equipment on layaway. The store requires a 20 percent deposit. If the equipment sells for $84, how much of a deposit will the store require?
   $16.80

22. What is 57% of 200?
   114

23. Carly has a coupon for 15% off the price of a camera. The camera has an original cost of $234.00. How much will the camera cost after the discount?
   $198.90

24. When Jennifer goes out to lunch, the bill is for $13.60. If Jennifer wants to leave a 17% tip, how much tip should she leave?
   $2.31

25. A compact disc costs $17.97. The sales tax rate is 5%. How much will the total cost be for this compact disc? Round to the nearest cent.
   $18.87

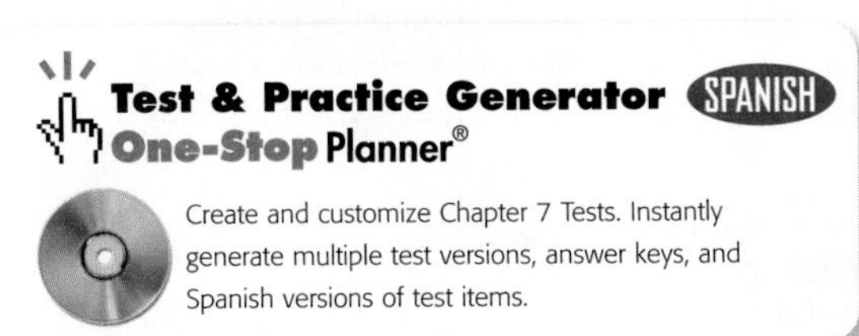
Test & Practice Generator
SPANISH
One-Stop Planner®
Create and customize Chapter 7 Tests. Instantly generate multiple test versions, answer keys, and Spanish versions of test items.

Why Learn This?

Tell students that a small sample is often used to gain information about a larger group. For example, a fisheries biologist may find the number of tagged fish in a sample of 100 fish. Then, since the total number of tagged fish is known, the fisheries biologist can use the fraction of tagged fish out of recaptured fish to estimate the total number of fish in the lake.

Using Data

To begin the study of this chapter, have students:

- Write a fraction to show the portion of the fish recaptured in Duck Lake that were tagged. $\frac{23}{96}$
- Write in simplest form the fraction of the fish recaptured in Los Dos Perros Lake that were tagged. $\frac{32}{40} = \frac{4}{5}$
- Use the information about Robyn Lake to fill in the tag, release, and recapture formula. $\frac{18}{26} = \frac{75}{x}$
- Use the information in the table and the tag, release, and recapture formula to estimate the total number of fish in each lake. Duck: 451; Los Dos Perros: 70; Robyn: 109

On page 410, students will find cumulative CRCT practice.

CHAPTER 7

Proportional Relationships

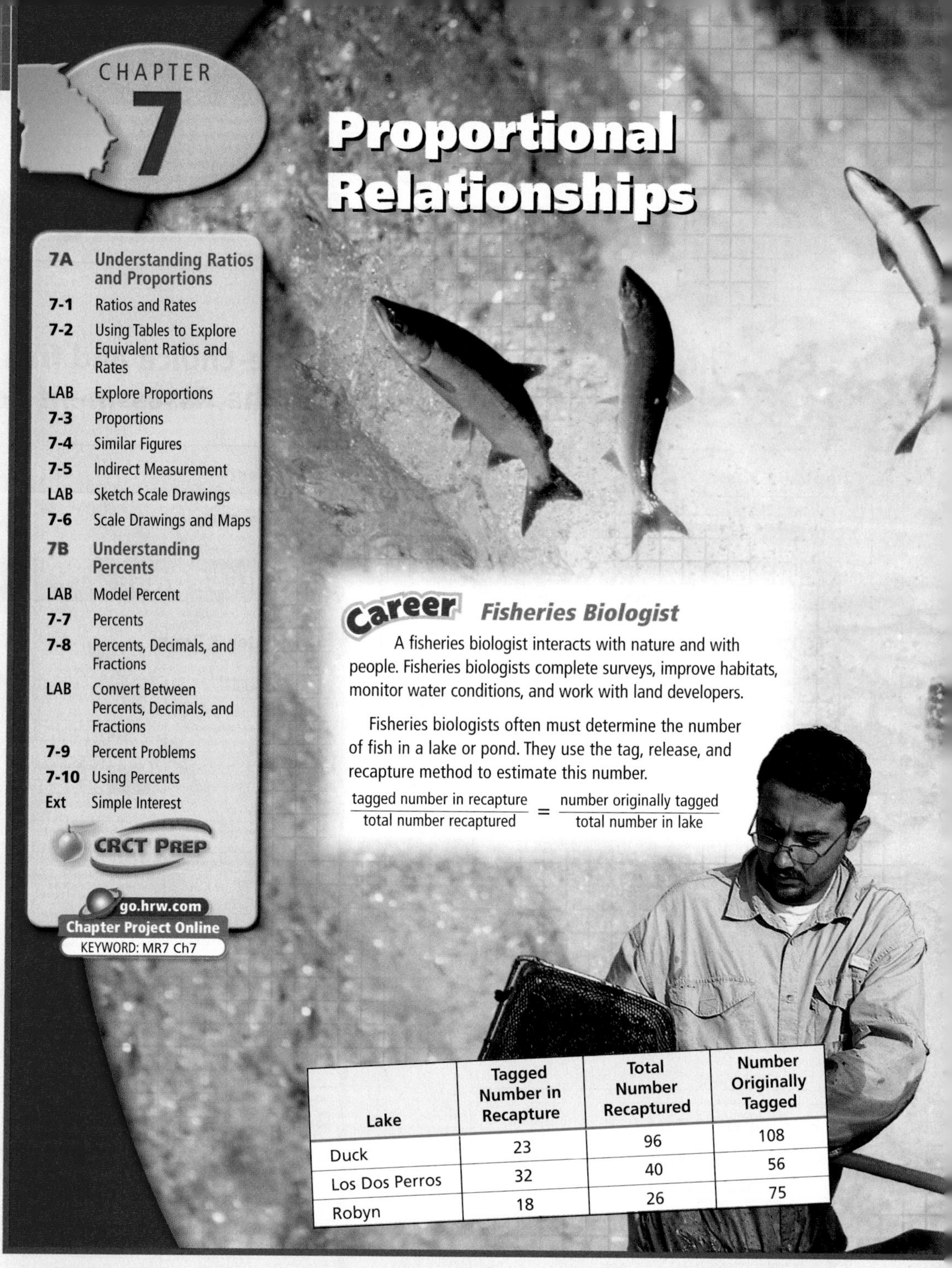

go.hrw.com
Chapter Project Online
KEYWORD: MR7 Ch7

Career *Fisheries Biologist*

A fisheries biologist interacts with nature and with people. Fisheries biologists complete surveys, improve habitats, monitor water conditions, and work with land developers.

Fisheries biologists often must determine the number of fish in a lake or pond. They use the tag, release, and recapture method to estimate this number.

$$\frac{\text{tagged number in recapture}}{\text{total number recaptured}} = \frac{\text{number originally tagged}}{\text{total number in lake}}$$

Lake	Tagged Number in Recapture	Total Number Recaptured	Number Originally Tagged
Duck	23	96	108
Los Dos Perros	32	40	56
Robyn	18	26	75

Problem Solving Project

Understand, Plan, Solve, and Look Back

Have students:

- Complete the Counting the Unknown worksheet.
- Examine the chart and explain what they observe. What does the data suggest about the number of fish in each lake? Is it easy to tell which lake has the most fish?
- Make up data for a new lake, exchange data with their classmates, and calculate the estimated populations.
- Think of other situations in nature where tagging and collecting specimens might be useful.

Life Science Connection

Project Resources

Materials:

- Counting the Unknown worksheet, paper bags or cans, Unifix® cubes, centimeter cubes, multiple colors of cardboard squares or other similar objects, marking pens

ARE YOU READY?

Vocabulary

Choose the best term from the list to complete each sentence.

1. A(n) __?__ is a three-sided polygon, and a(n) __?__ is a four-sided polygon. triangle; quadrilateral
2. A(n) __?__ is used to name a part of a whole. fraction
3. When two numbers have the same value, they are said to be __?__. equivalent
4. When writing 0.25 as a fraction, 25 is the __?__ and 100 is the __?__. numerator; denominator

angle
denominator
equivalent
fraction
numerator
pentagon
quadrilateral
triangle

Complete these exercises to review skills you will need for this chapter.

Simplify Fractions

Write each fraction in simplest form.

5. $\frac{6}{10}$ $\frac{3}{5}$ **6.** $\frac{9}{12}$ $\frac{3}{4}$ **7.** $\frac{8}{6}$ $1\frac{1}{3}$ or $\frac{4}{3}$

Write Equivalent Fractions

Write three equivalent fractions for each given fraction. Possible answers:

8. $\frac{4}{16}$ $\frac{1}{4}, \frac{2}{8}, \frac{3}{12}$ **9.** $\frac{5}{10}$ $\frac{1}{2}, \frac{10}{20}, \frac{25}{50}$ **10.** $\frac{5}{6}$ $\frac{10}{12}, \frac{15}{18}, \frac{20}{24}$

Compare Fractions

Compare. Write >, <, or =.

11. $\frac{3}{10} \bigcirc \frac{2}{5}$ < **12.** $1\frac{3}{4} \bigcirc 1\frac{5}{7}$ > **13.** $\frac{5}{8} \bigcirc \frac{1}{2}$ > **14.** $2\frac{11}{12} \bigcirc \frac{35}{12}$ =

Write Decimals as Fractions

Write each decimal as a fraction in simplest form.

15. 0.5 $\frac{1}{2}$ **16.** 0.35 $\frac{7}{20}$ **17.** 0.08 $\frac{2}{25}$ **18.** 0.12 $\frac{3}{25}$

Multiply Decimals

Multiply.

19. 0.42 · 10 4.2 **20.** 0.3 · 52 15.6 **21.** 20.5 · 0.25 5.125 **22.** 6.75 · 0.40 2.7

23. 9.8 · 0.2 1.96 **24.** 0.8 · 7.4 5.92 **25.** 0.52 · 0.64 0.3328 **26.** 0.75 · 8.9 6.675

ARE YOU READY? CHAPTER 7

Organizer

Objective: Assess students' understanding of prerequisite skills.

Prerequisite Skills

Simplify Fractions
Write Equivalent Fractions
Compare Fractions
Write Fractions as Decimals
Multiply Decimals

Assessing Prior Knowledge

INTERVENTION 

Diagnose and Prescribe

Use this page to determine whether intervention is necessary or enrichment is appropriate.

Resources

 ***Are You Ready? Intervention and Enrichment* Worksheets**

 ***Are You Ready?* CD-ROM**

 ***Are You Ready?* Online**

my.hrw.com

ARE YOU READY?

Diagnose and Prescribe

NO INTERVENE

Prerequisite Skill	*Are You Ready? Intervention,* Chapter 7 — Worksheets	CD-ROM	Online
Simplify Fractions	Skill 19	Activity 19	Diagnose and Prescribe Online
Write Equivalent Fractions	Skill 24	Activity 24	
Compare Fractions	Skill 25	Activity 25	
Write Fractions as Decimals	Skill 26	Activity 26	
Multiply Decimals	Skill 40	Activity 40	

***Are You Ready? Enrichment,* Chapter 7**
Worksheets
CD-ROM
Online

CHAPTER 7 Study Guide: Preview

Organizer

Objective: Help students organize the new concepts they will learn in Chapter 7.

Online Edition
Multilingual Glossary

Resources

***Multilingual Glossary* Online**

go.hrw.com
KEYWORD: MR7 Glossary

Answers to *Vocabulary Connections*

Possible answers:

1. Equivalent ratios name the same comparison.
2. No. You may measure objects or distances that provide values needed to calculate a distance indirectly.
3. A ratio comparing a number to 100.
4. Since a ratio is a relationship between two things, it will have two numbers.
5. You will show the ratio between a distance on the drawing to the corresponding actual distance.

CHAPTER 7

Study Guide: Preview

Where You've Been

Previously, you

- used fractions to represent situations involving division.
- generated equivalent fractions and decimals.
- used multiplication and division to find equivalent fractions.

In This Chapter

You will study

- using ratios to describe proportional situations.
- representing ratios and percents with concrete models, fractions, and decimals.
- using multiplication and division to solve problems involving equivalent ratios and rates.
- using ratios to make predictions in proportional situations.

Where You're Going

You can use the skills learned in this chapter

- to find discounts and sales tax on retail items at stores.
- to know how much of a tip to leave at restaurants.

Key Vocabulary/Vocabulario

corresponding angles	ángulos correspondientes (en polígonos)
equivalent ratios	razones equivalentes
indirect measurement	medición indirecta
percent	por ciento
proportion	proporción
rate	tasa
ratio	razón
scale drawing	dibujo a escala
similar	semejante
unit rate	tasa unitaria

Vocabulary Connections

To become familiar with some of the vocabulary terms in the chapter, consider the following. You may refer to the chapter, the glossary, or a dictionary if you like.

1. *Equivalent* can mean "equal in value." How do you think **equivalent ratios** are related?
2. *Indirect* means "not direct." Do you think you will use a ruler to find an **indirect measurement**?
3. *Percent* comes from *per* and the Latin word *centum,* meaning "hundred." What do you think **percent** means?
4. *Ratio* can mean "the relationship in quantity, amount, or size between two things." How many numbers do you think a **ratio** will have?
5. A *scale* shows the relationship in size between two or more things. If you are making a **scale drawing** of a room, what do you think you would include on the drawing to show the room's actual size?

Grade 6 CRCT GPS

M6N1.
Students will understand the meaning of the four arithmetic operations as related to positive rational numbers and will use these concepts to solve problems.

f. Use fractions, decimals, and percents interchangeably.
g. Solve problems involving fractions, decimals, and percents.

M6G1.
Students will further develop their understanding of plane figures.

c. Use the concepts of ratio, proportion and scale factor to demonstrate the relationships between similar plane figures.
d. Interpret and sketch simple scale drawings.
e. Solve problems involving scale drawings.

M6A1.
Students will understand the concept of ratio and use it to represent quantitative relationships.

M6A2.
Students will consider relationships between varying quantities.

a. Analyze and describe patterns arising from mathematical rules, tables, and graphs.
b. Use manipulatives or draw pictures to solve problems involving proportional relationships.
c. Use proportions ($a/b=c/d$) to describe relationships and solve problems, including percent problems.
g. Use proportional reasoning ($a/b=c/d$ and $y = kx$) to solve problems.

M6A3.
Students will evaluate algebraic expressions, including those with exponents, and solve simple one-step equations using each of the four basic operations.

***Georgia Mathematics Performance Standards* statements are written out completely on pp. GA28–GA35.**

Writing Strategy: Write a Convincing Explanation

You will see the Write About It icons throughout the book. These icons show exercises that require you to write a convincing explanation.

A convincing explanation should include

- a restatement of the question or problem.
- a complete solution to the problem.
- any work, definitions, diagrams, or charts needed to answer the problem.

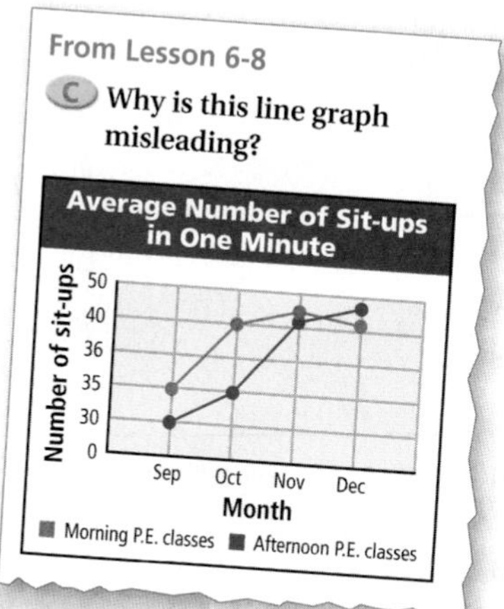

Step 1 **Restate the question.**
The graph is misleading because the scale does not have equal intervals.

Step 2 **Provide a complete solution to the problem with facts and an explanation.**
For example, an increase from 35 sit-ups to 40 sit-ups appears greater than an increase from 30 sit-ups to 35 sit-ups. By reading the scale, you know that this is incorrect. Therefore, the graph is misleading.

Use your textbook.

1. Write a convincing explanation to explain why there are two modes in the data set 4, 6, 1, 0, 4, 8, 9, 0.
2. Look at one of your previous Write About It exercises. Does your answer follow the method outlined above? If so, label the items that should be included. If not, rewrite the explanation.

Reading and Writing Math

Grade 6 CRCT GPS

Standards	7-1	7-2	LAB 7-3	7-3	7-4	7-5	LAB 7-6	7-6	LAB 7-7	7-7	7-8	LAB 7-8	7-9	7-10	Ext.
M6N1.f										★	★	★			
M6N1.g										★	★		★	★	★
M6G1.c					★	★		★							
M6G1.d							★								
M6G1.e								★							
M6A1	★	★	★												
M6A2.a		★													
M6A2.b			★												
M6A2.c				★	★	★		★					★		
M6A2.g				★	★	★		★					★		
M6A3															★

******Georgia Mathematics Process Standards* **are covered throughout the book. For a complete list,** **see pp. GA28–GA35.**

Reading and Writing Math

Organizer

Objective: Help students apply strategies to understand and retain key concepts.

Online Edition

Resources

Chapter 7 Resource Book
Reading Strategies

ENGLISH LANGUAGE LEARNERS

Writing Strategy: Write a Convincing Explanation

Discuss Have students discuss the importance of being given a clear explanation to a question. Remind them that math involves more than finding an answer, sometimes a clear explanation will convince others that an answer is correct when it was believed to be wrong.

Extend As students work through the chapter, have them practice writing explanations that are convincing by using the strategies taught on this page. Students can exchange explanations to share ideas for supporting arguments.

Answers to *Try This*

1. There are 2 modes in the data set because the values 0 and 4 both occur two times in the data set. The definition of mode is the value or values that occur most often in a data set. Because 0 and 2 both occur two times, which is the most often in the set, there are 2 modes.
2. Answers may vary.

SECTION **7A**

Understanding Ratios and Proportions

One-Minute Section Planner

Lesson	Materials	MiC and Lab Resources
Lesson 7-1 Ratios and Rates • Write ratios and rates and find unit rates. ☑ CRCT ☑ SAT-10 ☑ ITBS ☑ CTBS ☑ NAEP		**MiC:** ***Models You Can Count On*** pp. 40–46 **MiC:** ***More or Less*** pp. 1–5
Lesson 7-2 Using Tables to Explore Equivalent Ratios and Rates • Use a table to find equivalent ratios and rates. ☑ CRCT ☐ SAT-10 ☑ ITBS ☑ CTBS ☐ NAEP	Colored pencils (MK)	**MiC:** ***Models You Can Count On*** pp. 1–9
7-3 Hands-On Lab Explore Proportions • Use counters to model equivalent ratios. ☑ CRCT ☑ SAT-10 ☑ ITBS ☑ CTBS ☑ NAEP **Lesson 7-3** Proportions • Write and solve proportions.	Two-color counters (MK)	***Hands-On Lab Activities*** 7-3
Lesson 7-4 Similar Figures • Use ratios to identify similar figures. ☑ CRCT ☑ SAT-10 ☑ ITBS ☑ CTBS ☑ NAEP	Customary rulers (MK), protractors (MK), drawings of similar polygons	***Hands-On Lab Activities*** 7-4
Lesson 7-5 Indirect Measurement • Use proportions and similar figures to find unknown measures. ☑ CRCT ☑ SAT-10 ☑ ITBS ☑ CTBS ☑ NAEP		***Technology Lab Activities*** 7-5
7-6 Hands-On Lab Sketch Scale Drawings • Use a scale factor to produce similar figures. ☑ CRCT ☑ SAT-10 ☑ ITBS ☑ CTBS ☑ NAEP **Lesson 7-6** Scale Drawings and Maps • Read and use map scales and scale drawings.	Dot paper, maps, atlas	**MiC:** ***Figuring All the Angles*** pp. 10–11, 14–19 ***Hands-On Lab Activities*** 7-6

MK = *Manipulatives Kit*

Mathematics in Context

The units ***Models You Can Count On, More or Less,*** and ***Figuring All the Angles*** from the *Mathematics in Context* © 2006 series can be used with Section 7A. See Section Planner above for suggestions for integrating *MiC* with *Holt Mathematics.*

Section Overview

Ratios, Rates, and Proportions *Lessons 7-1, 7-2, 7-3*

Why? You can use ratios to compare quantities or describe rates.

A **ratio** is a comparison of two quantities that uses division. A ratio can be **written 3 ways.**

One molecule of water contains 2 hydrogen atoms and 1 oxygen atom. So the ratio of hydrogen to oxygen in water can be written the following ways:

$\frac{2}{1}$ 2 to 1 2:1

A **proportion** shows that two ratios are equivalent.

Cross products in a proportion are equal.

$\frac{2}{1} = \frac{6}{3}$ $\frac{2}{1} \times \frac{6}{3} \Rightarrow 2 \times 3 = 1 \times 6$

Similar Figures, Indirect Measurement, and Scale Drawings *Lessons 7-4, 7-5, 7-6*

Why? Indirect measurement is based on similar figures, which have proportional dimensions, and is used in many fields, such as construction.

Similar figures have the same shape, but not necessarily the same size.

For similar figures:

- Corresponding sides have lengths that are proportional.
- Corresponding angles are congruent.

A **scale** is a ratio between two sets of measurements.

A **scale drawing**, such as a map, is a drawing of a real object that is proportionally smaller or larger than the real object.

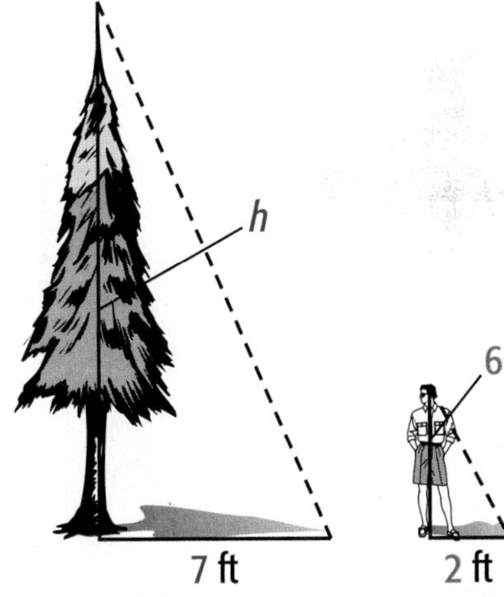

To find the height of the tree, use indirect measurement by solving a proportion.

$$\frac{6}{h} = \frac{2}{7}$$
$$2 \cdot h = 6 \cdot 7$$
$$h = 21$$

The height of the tree is 21 feet.

7-1 Ratios and Rates

Learn to write ratios and rates and to find unit rates.

Vocabulary
ratio
equivalent ratios
rate
unit rate

For a time, the Boston Symphony Orchestra was made up of 95 musicians.

Violins	29	Violas	12
Cellos	10	Basses	9
Flutes	5	Trumpets	3
Double reeds	8	Percussion	5
Clarinets	4	Harp	1
Horns	6	Trombones	3

You can compare the different groups by using ratios. A **ratio** is a comparison of two quantities using division.

Reading Math
Read the ratio $\frac{29}{12}$ as "twenty-nine to twelve."

For example, you can use a ratio to compare the number of violins with the number of violas. This ratio can be written in three ways.

Terms $\frac{29}{12}$ 29 to 12 29:12

Notice that the ratio of violins to violas, $\frac{29}{12}$, is different from the ratio of violas to violins, $\frac{12}{29}$. The order of the terms is important.

Ratios can be written to compare a part to a part, a part to the whole, or the whole to a part.

EXAMPLE 1 Writing Ratios

Use the table above to write each ratio.

Georgia Performance Standards
M6A1 Understand the concept of ratio and use it to represent quantitative relationships. Also, M6P4.a, M6P4.b, M6P4.c.

A flutes to clarinets

$\frac{5}{4}$ or 5 to 4 or 5:4 *Part to part*

B trumpets to total instruments

$\frac{3}{95}$ or 3 to 95 or 3:95 *Part to whole*

C total instruments to basses

$\frac{95}{9}$ or 95 to 9 or 95:9 *Whole to part*

Equivalent ratios are ratios that name the same comparison. You can find an equivalent ratio by multiplying or dividing both terms of a ratio by the same number.

7-1 Organizer

Pacing: Traditional 1 day
Block $\frac{1}{2}$ day

Objective: Students write ratios and rates and find unit rates.

Online Edition
Tutorial Videos, Interactivities

Countdown to CRCT Week 14

Power Presentations with PowerPoint®

Warm Up

Write each fraction in simplest form.

1. $\frac{2}{6}$ $\frac{1}{3}$
2. $\frac{4}{16}$ $\frac{1}{4}$
3. $\frac{25}{70}$ $\frac{5}{14}$
4. $\frac{6}{52}$ $\frac{3}{26}$

Problem of the Day

What three consecutive odd numbers are factors of 105? 3, 5, 7

Also available on transparency

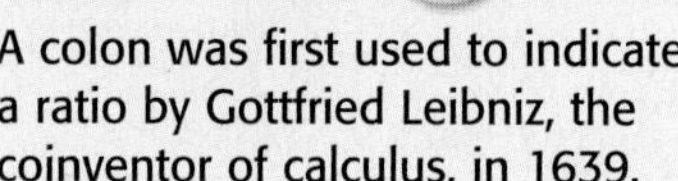

Math Fact

A colon was first used to indicate a ratio by Gottfried Leibniz, the coinventor of calculus, in 1639.

Georgia Performance Standards

M6A1 Students will understand the concept of ratio and use it to represent quantitative relationships.

M6P4.a Recognize and use connections among mathematical ideas.

M6P4.b Understand how mathematical ideas interconnect and build on one another to produce a coherent whole.

M6P4.c Recognize and apply mathematics in contexts outside of mathematics.

1 Introduce

Alternate Opener

EXPLORATION

7-1 Ratios and Rates

A TV network offers the numbers of shows each week shown in the table.

You can compare the numbers of TV shows by using ratios. A ***ratio*** is a comparison of two quantities that uses division. For example, the ratio of science fiction shows to drama shows is $\frac{3}{14}$, which can also be written 3:14 or 3 to 14.

Type of TV Show	Number of Shows
Comedy	14
Drama	14
Science fiction	3
Game show	7
Talk show	15
News	14
Morning show	10
Late-night show	5
Sports	6

Find each ratio.

1. comedy shows to game shows
2. game shows to news shows
3. morning shows to late-night shows
4. talk shows to sports shows

Think and Discuss

5. **Discuss** whether the ratios in numbers 1–4 compare part to part, part to whole, or whole to part.
6. **Discuss** whether order is important when calculating ratios. (*Hint:* Is $\frac{news}{sports}$ equivalent to $\frac{sports}{news}$?)

ENGLISH LANGUAGE LEARNERS

Motivate

Ask students if they have ever heard the terms *rate* and *ratios* and, if so, in what context.

Possible answers: win/loss ratios, heart rate, rate of pay, rate of speed, etc.

Explorations and answers are provided in *Alternate Openers: Explorations Transparencies.*

EXAMPLE 2 **Writing Equivalent Ratios**

Write three equivalent ratios to compare the number of stars with the number of moons in the pattern.

$\frac{\text{number of stars}}{\text{number of moons}} = \frac{4}{6}$ *There are 4 stars and 6 moons.*

$\frac{4}{6} = \frac{4 \div 2}{6 \div 2} = \frac{2}{3}$ *There are 2 stars for every 3 moons.*

$\frac{4}{6} = \frac{4 \cdot 2}{6 \cdot 2} = \frac{8}{12}$ *If you double the pattern, there will be 8 stars and 12 moons.*

So $\frac{4}{6}$, $\frac{2}{3}$, and $\frac{8}{12}$ are equivalent ratios.

A **rate** compares two quantities that have different units of measure.

Suppose a 2-liter bottle of soda costs $1.98.

$\text{rate} = \frac{\text{price}}{\text{number of liters}} = \frac{\$1.98}{2 \text{ liters}}$ $1.98 for 2 liters

When the comparison is to one unit, the rate is called a **unit rate**.

Divide both terms by the second term to find the unit rate.

$\text{unit rate} = \frac{\$1.98}{2} = \frac{\$1.98 \div 2}{2 \div 2} = \frac{\$0.99}{1}$ $0.99 for 1 liter

When the prices of two or more items are compared, the item with the lowest unit rate is the best deal.

EXAMPLE  ***Consumer Math Application***

A 2-liter bottle of soda costs $2.02. A 3-liter bottle of the same soda costs $2.79. Which is the better deal?

2-liter bottle		3-liter bottle	
$\frac{\$2.02}{2 \text{ liters}}$	*Write the rate.*	$\frac{\$2.79}{3 \text{ liters}}$	*Write the rate.*
$\frac{\$2.02 \div 2}{2 \text{ liters} \div 2}$	*Divide both terms by 2.*	$\frac{\$2.79 \div 3}{3 \text{ liters} \div 3}$	*Divide both terms by 3.*
$\frac{\$1.01}{1 \text{ liter}}$	*$1.01 for 1 liter*	$\frac{\$0.93}{1 \text{ liter}}$	*$0.93 for 1 liter*

The 3-liter bottle is the better deal.

Possible answers to *Think and Discuss*

1. because even though the terms are the same, they are in a different order
2. After the rate is written as a ratio, divide both terms by the lower term to find the unit rate.

Think and Discuss  GPS M6P1.d, M6P3.b

1. Explain why the ratio 2 boys:5 girls is different from the ratio 5 girls:2 boys.

2. Describe how to determine what number to divide by when finding a unit rate.

COMMON ERROR ALERT

Some students may think that the order of the terms in a ratio is unimportant. Explain that using the wrong order completely changes the meaning of the ratio.

Power Presentations with PowerPoint®

Additional Examples

Example 

Use the table to write each ratio.

Animals at the Vet	
Cats	5
Dogs	7
Rabbits	2

A. cats to rabbits $\frac{5}{2}$

B. dogs to total number of pets $\frac{7}{14}$

C. total number of pets to cats $\frac{14}{5}$

Example 2

Write three equivalent ratios to compare the number of diamonds to the number of spades in the pattern.

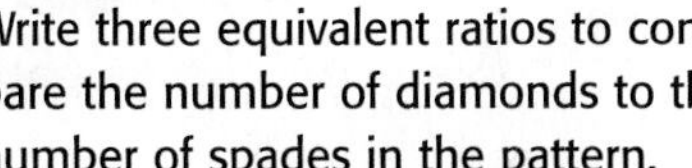

$\frac{3}{6}$, $\frac{1}{2}$, and $\frac{9}{18}$ are equivalent ratios.

Example 

A 3-pack of paper towels costs $2.79. A 6-pack costs $5.46. Which is the better deal?

The 6-pack is the better deal.

Also available on transparency

2 Teach

Guided Instruction

In this lesson, students learn to write ratios and rates and to find unit rates. First teach what a ratio is and the three ways to write ratios. Then teach students that a ratio can compare a part to a part, a part to the whole, or the whole to a part. Finally teach students to find equivalent ratios. Have students apply a unit rate in a consumer application.

Reaching All Learners

Through Cooperative Learning

Provide quantity pricing (e.g., 3 for $1.46) for several different items from two different grocery stores. Have students work to find the unit rates for the items and compare their findings with those of their classmates. Which store had the best unit rates for each item?

3 Close

ENGLISH LANGUAGE LEARNERS

Summarize

You may wish to review the terms *ratio*, *equivalent ratios*, *rate*, and *unit rate*. Have students explain how to find an equivalent ratio.

Possible answer: Multiply or divide both terms of a ratio by the same number to find an equivalent ratio.

7-1 Exercises

Assignment Guide

If you finished Example 1 assign:
Average 1–3, 32–41
Advanced 6–8, 32–41

If you finished Example 2 assign:
Average 1–4, 21–24, 32–41
Advanced 6–9, 21–24, 32–41

If you finished Example 3 assign:
Average 1–14, 20–41
Advanced 6–41

Homework Quick Check

Quickly check key concepts.
Exercises: 8, 10, 14, 20, 22

Answers

12–19. See p. A7.

Math Background

Ratio is an ancient topic in mathematics. For example, ratios were used in early Greek works in arithmetic, geometry, and music.

The word *ratio* comes from the Latin word *ratus,* which means "calculation." During the Middle Ages, the word *ratio* was used to mean "computation." During that time, the word *proportio* was used to indicate what we mean by a ratio today.

Georgia Performance Standards

M6P3.a Organize and consolidate their mathematical thinking through communication.

M6P5.a Create and use representations to organize, record, and communicate mathematical ideas.

M6P5.b Select, apply, and translate among mathematical representations to solve problems.

7-1 Exercises

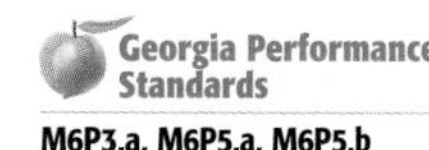

M6P3.a, M6P5.a, M6P5.b

go.hrw.com
Homework Help Online
KEYWORD: MR7 7-1
Parent Resources Online
KEYWORD: MR7 Parent

GUIDED PRACTICE

See Example 1 — Use the table to write each ratio.

Jacqueline's Software Collection	
Educational games	16
Word processing	2
Art programs	10
Arcade games	10
Music programs	3

1. music programs to art programs 3:10
2. arcade games to entire collection 10:41
3. entire collection to educational games 41:16

See Example 2

4. Write three equivalent ratios to compare the number of red hearts in the picture with the total number of hearts. Possible answer: $\frac{2}{9}$, $\frac{4}{18}$, $\frac{6}{27}$

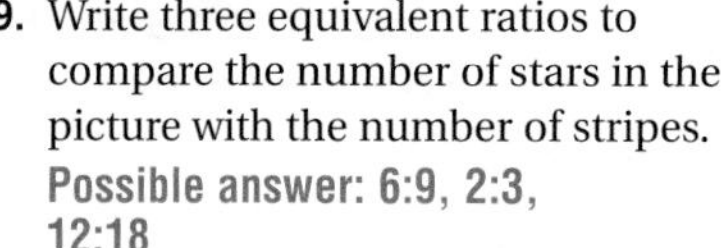

See Example 3

5. **Consumer Math** An 8-ounce bag of sunflower seeds costs $1.68. A 4-ounce bag of sunflower seeds costs $0.88. Which is the better deal? the 8-ounce bag

INDEPENDENT PRACTICE

See Example 1 — Use the table to write each ratio.

	Redbirds	Blue Socks
Left-Handed Batters	8	3
Right-Handed Batters	11	19

6. Redbirds to Blue Socks 19:22
7. right-handed Blue Socks to left-handed Blue Socks 19:3
8. left-handed Redbirds to total Redbirds $\frac{8}{19}$

See Example 2

9. Write three equivalent ratios to compare the number of stars in the picture with the number of stripes. Possible answer: 6:9, 2:3, 12:18

See Example 3

10. Gina charges $28 for 3 hours of swimming lessons. Hector charges $18 for 2 hours of swimming lessons. Which instructor offers a better deal? Hector
11. **Consumer Math** A 12-pound bag of dog food costs $12.36. A 15-pound bag of dog food costs $15.30. Which is the better deal? the 15 lb bag

PRACTICE AND PROBLEM SOLVING

Extra Practice p. 726

Write each ratio three different ways.

12. ten to seven
13. $\frac{24}{11}$
14. 4 to 30
15. $\frac{7}{10}$
16. 16 to 20
17. $\frac{5}{9}$
18. 50 to 79
19. one hundred to one hundred one
20. A florist can create 16 bouquets during an 8-hour work day. How many bouquets can the florist create per hour? 2

RETEACH 7-1

LESSON 7-1 Reteach
Ratios and Rates

A ratio is a comparison of two quantities by division.

To compare the number of times vowels are used to the number of time consonants are used in the word "mathematics," first find each quantity.

Number of times vowels are used: 4
Number of times consonants are used: 7

Then write the comparison as a ratio, using the quantities in the same order as they appear in the word expression. There are three ways to write a ratio.

$\frac{4}{7}$ 4 to 7 4:7

Write each ratio.

1. days in May to days in a year 31 to 365
2. sides of triangle to sides of a square 3 to 4

Equivalent ratios are ratios that name the same comparison. The ratio of inches in a foot to inches in a yard is $\frac{12}{36}$. To find equivalent ratios, divide or multiply the numerator and denominator by the same number.

$\frac{12}{36} = \frac{12 \div 3}{36 \div 3} = \frac{4}{12}$ $\frac{12}{36} = \frac{12 \cdot 2}{36 \cdot 2} = \frac{24}{72}$

So, $\frac{12}{36}$, $\frac{4}{12}$, and $\frac{24}{72}$ are equivalent ratios.

Write three equivalent ratios to compare each of the following.
Possible answers are given.

3. 8 triangles to 12 circles 2:3, 4:6, 6:9
4. 20 pencils to 25 erasers 4:5, 8:10, 12:15
5. 5 girls to 6 boys 10:12, 15:18, 20:24
6. 10 pants to 14 shirts 5:7, 15:21, 20:28

PRACTICE 7-1

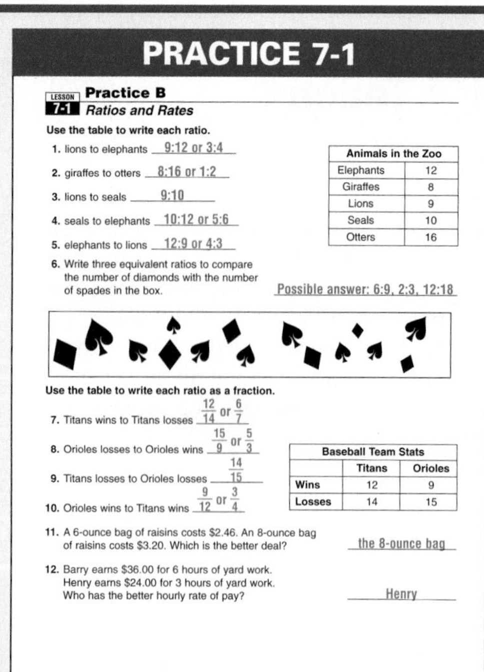

LESSON 7-1 Practice B
Ratios and Rates

Use the table to write each ratio.

Animals in the Zoo	
Elephants	12
Giraffes	8
Lions	9
Seals	10
Otters	16

1. lions to elephants 9:12 or 3:4
2. giraffes to otters 8:16 or 1:2
3. lions to seals 9:10
4. seals to elephants 10:12 or 5:6
5. elephants to lions 12:9 or 4:3
6. Write three equivalent ratios to compare the number of diamonds with the number of spades in the box. Possible answer: 6:9, 2:3, 12:18

Use the table to write each ratio as a fraction.

Baseball Team Stats	Titans	Orioles
Wins	12	9
Losses	14	15

7. Titans wins to Titans losses $\frac{12}{14}$ or $\frac{6}{7}$
8. Orioles losses to Orioles wins $\frac{15}{9}$ or $\frac{5}{3}$
9. Titans losses to Orioles losses $\frac{14}{15}$
10. Orioles wins to Titans wins $\frac{9}{12}$ or $\frac{3}{4}$
11. A 6-ounce bag of raisins costs $2.46. An 8-ounce bag of raisins costs $3.20. Which is the better deal? the 8-ounce bag
12. Barry earns $36.00 for 6 hours of yard work. Henry earns $24.00 for 3 hours of yard work. Who has the better hourly rate of pay? Henry

Use the diagram of an oxygen atom and a boron atom for Exercises 21–24. Find each ratio. Then give two equivalent ratios.

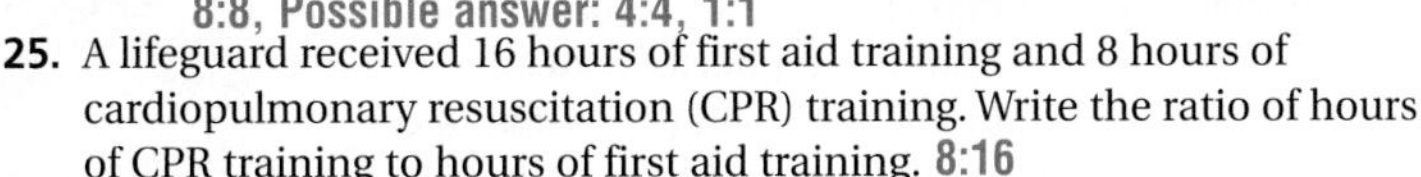

21. oxygen protons to boron protons 8:5, Possible answer: 16:10, 24:15
22. boron neutrons to boron protons 6:5, Possible answer: 12:10, 18:15
23. boron electrons to oxygen electrons 5:8, Possible answer: 10:16, 15:24
24. oxygen electrons to oxygen protons 8:8, Possible answer: 4:4, 1:1
25. A lifeguard received 16 hours of first aid training and 8 hours of cardiopulmonary resuscitation (CPR) training. Write the ratio of hours of CPR training to hours of first aid training. 8:16
26. **Critical Thinking** Cassandra has three pictures on her desk. The pictures measure 4 in. long by 6 in. wide, 24 mm long by 36 mm wide, and 6 cm long by 7 cm wide. Which photos have a length-to-width ratio equivalent to 2:3? 4×6 and 24×36
27. **Multi-Step** On which day did Alfonso run faster? Wednesday

Day	Distance (m)	Time (min)
Monday	1,020	6
Wednesday	1,554	9

28. **Earth Science** Water rushes over Niagara Falls at the rate of 180 million cubic feet every 30 minutes. How much water goes over the falls in 1 minute? 6 million ft^3
29. **What's the Question?** The ratio of total students in Mr. Avalon's class to students in the class who have a blue backpack is 3 to 1. The answer is 1:2. What is the question?
30. **Write About It** How are equivalent ratios like equivalent fractions?
31. **Challenge** There are 36 performers in a dance recital. The ratio of men to women is 2:7. How many men are in the dance recital? 8 men

CRCT Prep • GPS Support • Spiral Review

32. **Multiple Choice** Which ratio is equivalent to $\frac{1}{20}$?

Ⓐ 9:180 (circled) B 180 to 9 C 4 to 100 D 100:4

33. **Short Response** A 24-ounce box of raisins costs $4.56. A 15-ounce box of raisins costs $3.15. Which is the better deal? Explain. The 24-ounce box is the better deal. The unit price of the 24-ounce box is $0.19. The unit price of the 15-ounce box is $0.21.

Find the GCF of each set of numbers. (Lesson 4-3)

34. 12, 36 12
35. 15, 24 3
36. 18, 24, 42 6
37. 5, 14, 17 1

Solve each equation. Write the solution in simplest form. (Lesson 5-5)

38. $g + \frac{3}{10} = \frac{2}{5}$ $g = \frac{1}{10}$
39. $m - \frac{1}{2} = \frac{1}{9}$ $m = \frac{11}{18}$
40. $\frac{2}{3} = p + \frac{1}{6}$ $p = \frac{1}{2}$
41. $h - \frac{1}{4} = \frac{5}{12}$ $h = \frac{2}{3}$

Ongoing Assessment and Intervention

Diagnose **Before** the Lesson
7-1 Warm Up, TE p. 352

Monitor **During** the Lesson
7-1 Know-It Notebook
7-1 Questioning Strategies

Assess **After** the Lesson
7-1 Lesson Quiz, TE p. 355

Answers

29. Possible answer: What is the ratio of students with blue backpacks to students without blue backpacks?
30. You can find equivalent ratios just like you find equivalent fractions: Divide or multiply both terms by the same number.

Test Prep Doctor In Exercise 32, students need to remember that a ratio can be written in three forms. When changing a ratio from a fraction to another form, the numerator is written first, on the left. Therefore, choices **B** and **D** can be eliminated because the first number in the correct ratio should be much smaller than the second number.

Journal

Have students define *ratio,* and have them give examples of and explain how to find equivalent ratios.

Power Presentations with PowerPoint®

7-1 Lesson Quiz

Use the table to write each ratio.

Flower Bulbs Planted	
Crocuses	20
Tulips	9
Daffodils	17
Lilies	5

1. tulips to daffodils 9:17
2. crocuses to total number of bulbs 20:51
3. total bulbs to lilies 51:5
4. A dozen eggs cost $1.25 at one market. At a competing market, $1\frac{1}{2}$ dozen eggs cost $2.00. Which is the better buy? eggs from the first market

Also available on transparency

CHALLENGE 7-1

LESSON 7-1 Challenge
The Golden Ratio

For centuries, people all over the world have considered a certain rectangle to be one of the most beautiful shapes. Which of these rectangles do you find the most attractive?

A B C D E F

If you are like most people, you chose rectangle B. Why? It's a golden rectangle, of course! In a golden rectangle, the ratio of the length to the width is called the **golden ratio**—about 1.6 to 1.

Golden Ratio

$\frac{\ell}{w} = \frac{1.6}{1}$ $w = 1$ in. $\ell = 1.6$ in.

The golden ratio pops up all over the place—in music, sculptures, the Egyptian pyramids, seashells, paintings, pinecones, and of course in rectangles.

To create your own golden rectangle, just write a ratio equivalent to the golden ratio. This will give you the length and width of another golden rectangle.

Use a ruler to draw a new golden rectangle in the space below. Then draw several non-golden rectangles around it. Now conduct a survey of your family and friends to see if they choose the golden rectangle as their favorite.

PROBLEM SOLVING 7-1

LESSON 7-1 Problem Solving
Ratios and Rates

Use the table to answer each question.

Atomic Particles of Elements

Element	Protons	Neutrons	Electrons
Gold	79	118	79
Iron	26	30	26
Neon	10	10	10
Platinum	78	117	78
Silver	47	61	47
Tin	50	69	50

1. What is the ratio of gold protons to silver protons?
79:47
2. What is the ratio of gold neutrons to platinum protons?
118:78 or 59:39
3. What are two equivalent ratios of the ratio of neon protons to tin protons?
Possible answer: 10:50 and 1:5
4. What are two equivalent ratios of the ratio of iron protons to iron neutrons?
Possible answer: 26:30 and 13:15

Circle the letter of the correct answer.

5. A ratio of one element's neutrons to another element's electrons is equivalent to 3 to 5. What are those two elements?
Ⓐ iron neutrons to tin electrons (circled)
B gold neutrons to tin electrons
C tin neutrons to gold electrons
D neon neutrons to iron electrons
6. The ratio of two elements' protons is equivalent to 3 to 1. What are those two elements?
F gold to tin
G neon to tin
Ⓗ platinum to iron (circled)
J silver to gold
7. Which element in the table has a ratio of 1 to 1, no matter what parts you are comparing in the ratio?
A iron
Ⓑ neon (circled)
C tin
D silver
8. If the ratio for any element is 1:1, which two parts is the ratio comparing?
F protons to neutrons
G electrons to neutrons
Ⓗ protons to electrons (circled)
J neutrons to electrons

7-2 Organizer

Pacing: Traditional 1 day
Block $\frac{1}{2}$ day

Objective: Students use a table to find equivalent ratios and rates.

Online Edition
Tutorial Videos

Countdown to CRCT Week 14

Power Presentations with PowerPoint®

Warm Up

Find the unit rate.

1. 16 miles in 4 hours 4 mi/h
2. 3 oranges for \$2.40 \$0.80 per orange
3. 3 bottles for 93¢ 31¢ per bottle
4. 6 DVDs for \$36.60 \$6.10 per DVD

Problem of the Day

There are 4 ounces in a gill. There are 4 gills in a pint. There are 8 pints in a gallon. How many ounces are the same as the total of 3 gallons, 3 pints, 3 gills, and 3 ounces? 447

Also available on transparency

Julius Caesar used a calendar system that made March (*Martius* in Latin) the first month of the year. This is why September, October, November, and December contain prefixes meaning *seven, eight, nine,* and *ten.*

Georgia Performance Standards

M6A1 Students will understand the concept of ratio and use it to represent quantitative relationships.

M6A2.a Analyze and describe patterns arising from mathematical rules, tables, and graphs.

M6P4.a Recognize and use connections among mathematical ideas.

M6P4.b Understand how mathematical ideas interconnect and build on one another to produce a coherent whole.

M6P5.b Select, apply, and translate among mathematical representations to solve problems.

7-2 Using Tables to Explore Equivalent Ratios and Rates

Learn to use a table to find equivalent ratios and rates.

Georgia Performance Standards

M6A1 Understand the concept of ratio and use it to represent quantitative relationships. Also, M6A2.a, M6P4.a, M6P4.b, M6P5.b.

Mrs. Kennedy's students are painting a mural in their classroom. They mixed yellow and blue paints for a green background and found that the ratio of the amount of yellow to the amount of blue is 3 to 2.

Now they need to make more green paint, using the same ratio as before.

Use a table to find ratios equivalent to 3 to 2.

Reading Math

Finding equivalent ratios is sometimes referred to as "scaling up" or "scaling down."

	Original ratio	3 · 2 / 2 · 2	3 · 3 / 2 · 3	3 · 4 / 2 · 4
Pints of yellow	3	6	9	12
Pints of blue	2	4	6	8

You can increase amounts but keep them in the same ratio by multiplying both the numerator and denominator of the ratio by the same number.

The ratios 3 to 2, 6 to 4, 9 to 6, and 12 to 8 are equivalent.

You can also decrease amounts in the same ratio by dividing the numerator and denominator by the same number.

EXAMPLE  1 **Making a Table to Find Equivalent Ratios**

Use a table to find three equivalent ratios.

Helpful Hint

Multiplying by 2, 3, and 4 will give you three equivalent ratios, but there are many other equivalent ratios that are correct.

A $\frac{8}{3}$

Original ratio	8 · 2 / 3 · 2	8 · 3 / 3 · 3	8 · 4 / 3 · 4
8	16	24	32
3	6	9	12

Multiply the numerator and the denominator by 2, 3, and 4.

The ratios $\frac{8}{3}$, $\frac{16}{6}$, $\frac{24}{9}$, and $\frac{32}{12}$ are equivalent.

1 Introduce

Alternate Opener

EXPLORATION

7-2 Using Tables to Explore Equivalent Ratios and Rates

McMillans Restaurant is celebrating its 50th anniversary by offering 3 hamburgers for \$2.

1. Sue makes this table for quick reference at the drive-up window. Complete the table.

Number of Hamburgers	3	6	9		15		21
Total Cost (\$)	2	4					

2. The weekend goal is to sell 1,200 hamburgers. How much money will the restaurant receive if it reaches its goal of 1,200 hamburgers? Complete the table to help you answer this question.

Number of Hamburgers Sold	300	600	900	1,200
Amount Received (\$)	200			

Think and Discuss

3. **Describe** any patterns you notice in the table for Exercise 1.
4. **Explain** how you could find the amount of money the restaurant would receive if it sold 1,500 hamburgers.

Motivate

Ask the class how many wheels are on a skateboard. Make a table showing how many wheels are needed to make different numbers of skateboards. Have them predict the number of wheels needed for 85 boards and the number of boards needed for 124 wheels. 340 wheels, 31 boards

Explorations and answers are provided in *Alternate Openers: Explorations Transparencies.*

Use a table to find three equivalent ratios.

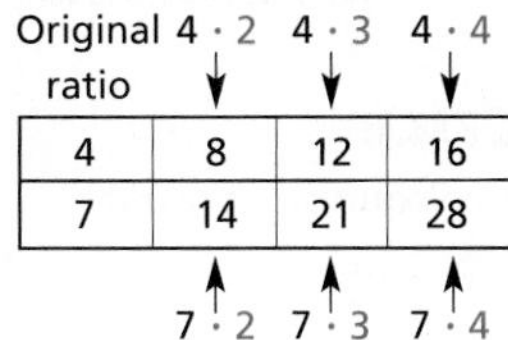

B 4 to 7

Original ratio: 4 · 2, 4 · 3, 4 · 4

4	8	12	16
7	14	21	28

7 · 2, 7 · 3, 7 · 4

Multiply the numerator and the denominator by 2, 3, and 4.

The ratios 4 to 7, 8 to 14, 12 to 21, and 16 to 28 are equivalent.

C 40:16

Original ratio: 40 ÷ 2, 40 ÷ 4, 40 ÷ 8

40	20	10	5
16	8	4	2

16 ÷ 2, 16 ÷ 4, 16 ÷ 8

Divide the numerator and the denominator by 2.

The ratios 40:16, 20:8, 10:4, and 5:2 are equivalent.

Ratios in tables can be used to make estimates or predictions.

EXAMPLE 2 ***Entertainment Application***

A group of 10 friends is in line to see a movie. The table shows how much different groups will pay in all. Predict how much the group of 10 will pay.

Number in Group	3	5	6	12
Amount Paid ($)	15	25	30	60

$6 < 10 < 12$; therefore, the group will pay between $30 and $60.

Use the amount paid by the group of 5. *The only factor of 10 in the table is 5.*

$2 \cdot 5 = 10$
$2 \cdot \$25 = \$50$ *Multiply the numerator and denominator by the same factor, 2.*

A group of 10 friends would pay $50.00.

Possible answers to *Think and Discuss*

1. Check to see that each part of the ratio has been correctly multiplied or divided by the same factors.
2. Check to see that the number to the left of the colon is the numerator in the ratio when written as a fraction.

Think and Discuss GPS M6P1.d, M6P3.b

1. When you have multiplied or divided a ratio to find equivalent ratios, how can you be sure that all the ratios you have written are correct?

2. If two ratios have colons and you rewrite the ratios as fractions, how can you be sure that you have written the numerator and denominator in the correct order?

COMMON ERROR ALERT

Some students may forget to set up the ratio properly. Remind them that the term to the left of the word *to* is the numerator or first term in the ratio, the term to the right is the denominator or last term in the ratio.

Power Presentations with PowerPoint®

Additional Examples

Example 1

Use a table to find three equivalent ratios. Possible answers:

A. $\frac{6}{7}$ $\frac{12}{14}$ $\frac{18}{21}$ $\frac{24}{28}$

B. $\frac{3}{5}$ $\frac{6}{10}$ $\frac{9}{15}$ $\frac{12}{20}$

C. $\frac{48}{36}$ $\frac{24}{18}$ $\frac{16}{12}$ $\frac{12}{9}$

Example 2

Several groups of friends are going to take a shuttle bus to the park. The table shows how much the different groups will pay in all. Predict how much a group of 15 friends will pay. $30

Number in Group	6	12	18
Bus Fare	12	24	36

Also available on transparency

2 Teach

Guided Instruction

In this lesson, students learn to use a table to find equivalent ratios and rates. Review how to find equivalent fractions by multiplying or dividing the numerator and denominator by the same number. Also review the three different ways of writing ratios. Demonstrate how a table can be used to show equivalent ratios, as in Example 1. Then have students apply the concept to the application in Example 2.

Reaching All Learners

Through Modeling

Have students work in groups to design a beaded friendship bracelet. First, have them create a two-color pattern that will be repeated along the bracelet. Next, write the ratio of one color to the other from the pattern they created. Then, draw and label a table with the colors in the first column and the original ratio in the second column. Then, use the table to produce four equivalent ratios.

3 Close

Summarize

Show students the following table:

Roses	4	6	10	16
Cost	$6	$9	$15	$24

Have students use the table to predict the cost of a dozen roses. more than $15 but less than $24 Then have students find the cost of a dozen roses and explain how they found it. $18; Possible answer: 6 roses cost $9, so multiply 6 by 2 and $9 by 2.

7-2 Exercises

Assignment Guide

If you finished Example 1 assign:
Average 1–8, 31–34
Advanced 10–17, 31–34

If you finished Example 2 assign:
Average 1–22, 31–34
Advanced 10–34

Homework Quick Check

Quickly check key concepts.
Exercises: 12, 16, 18, 20, 22

Answers

Possible Answers:

1.

2	7
4	14
6	21
16	56

2.

7	12
14	24
28	48
56	96

3.

96	48
48	24
24	12
12	6

4–8, 10–17. See p. A7–A8.

7-2 Exercises

Georgia Performance Standards
M6P3.a, M6P3.c, M6P5.b

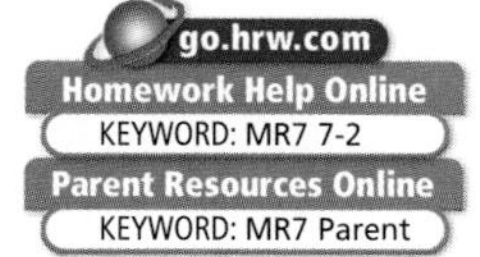

GUIDED PRACTICE

See Example 1

Use a table to find three equivalent ratios.

1. $\frac{2}{7}$
2. 7 to 12
3. 96:48
4. $\frac{3}{5}$
5. 5 to 8
6. $\frac{9}{4}$
7. 24 to 16
8. 25:26

See Example 2

9. **Sports** Leo runs laps around a track. The table shows how long it takes him to run different numbers of laps. Predict how long it will take Leo to run 7 laps. **35 min**

Number of Laps	2	4	6	8	10
Time (min)	10	20	30	40	50

INDEPENDENT PRACTICE

See Example 1

Use a table to find three equivalent ratios.

10. 6:5
11. 5 to 8
12. $\frac{12}{4}$
13. 6 to 7
14. $\frac{13}{20}$
15. 11:25
16. 5 to 18
17. $\frac{51}{75}$

See Example 2

18. Lee Middle School orders 15 textbooks for every 12 students. The table shows how many textbooks the school orders for certain numbers of students. Predict the number of textbooks that the school would order for 72 students. **90 textbooks**

Students	12	24	48	96	192
Textbooks	15	30	60	120	240

PRACTICE AND PROBLEM SOLVING

CRCT GPS
Extra Practice p. 726

19. **Biology** Brown bats vary in length from 3 to 6 inches and have wing spans from 8 to 16 inches. Write a ratio in simplest form of a bat's wing span to the bat's body length. $\frac{8}{3}$

20. Buy-A-Lot Market has tomatoes on sale. The table shows some sale prices. Predict how much a restaurant owner will pay for 25 pounds of tomatoes at the rate shown in the table. **\$9.75**

Amount (lb)	30	20	15	10	5
Cost (\$)	11.70	7.80	5.85	3.90	1.95

Complete each table to find the missing ratios.

21.

6	12	18	
5	10		20

24; 15

22.

96	48	24	
48	24		6

12; 12

Georgia Performance Standards

M6P3.a Organize and consolidate their mathematical thinking through communication.

M6P3.c Analyze and evaluate the mathematical thinking and strategies of others.

M6P5.b Select, apply, and translate among mathematical representations to solve problems.

RETEACH 7-2

LESSON 7-2 **Reteach**
Using Tables to Explore Equivalent Ratios and Rates

You can use a table to find ratios equivalent to $\frac{1}{4}$.
Write the numerator in the top box for the original ratio.
Write the denominator in the bottom box for the original ratio.
Then multiply the numerator and the denominator by 2, 3, and 4.

Original ratio	$1 \cdot 2$	$1 \cdot 3$	$1 \cdot 4$
1	2	3	4
4	8	12	16
	$1 \cdot 2$	$1 \cdot 3$	$1 \cdot 4$

Use each new numerator and denominator to write an equivalent ratio.

So, the ratios $\frac{2}{8}$, $\frac{3}{12}$, and $\frac{4}{16}$ are equivalent to $\frac{1}{4}$.

1. **Use the table to find three ratios equivalent to $\frac{2}{5}$.** Possible answers are given.

2	4	6	8
5	10	15	20

Equivalent ratios: $\frac{2}{5}$, $\frac{4}{10}$, $\frac{6}{15}$, and $\frac{8}{20}$

You can use a table to find ratios equivalent to 3 to 8.
Write the first number in the top box for the original ratio.
Write the second number in the bottom box for the original ratio.
Then multiply both numbers by 2, 3, and 4.

Original ratio	$3 \cdot 2$	$3 \cdot 3$	$3 \cdot 4$
3	6	9	12
8	16	24	32
	$8 \cdot 2$	$8 \cdot 3$	$8 \cdot 4$

Use each new top number and bottom number to write an equivalent ratio.

So, the ratios 6 to 16, 9 to 24, and 12 to 32 are equivalent to 3 to 8.

2. **Use the table to find three ratios equivalent to 4 to 10.** Possible answers are given.

4	8	12	16
10	20	30	40

Equivalent ratios: 4 to 10, 8 to 20, 12 to 30, and 16 to 40

PRACTICE 7-2

LESSON 7-2 **Practice B**
Using Tables to Explore Equivalent Ratios and Rates

Use a table to find three equivalent ratios. Possible answers are given.

1. 4 to 7
   8 to 14; 12 to 21; 16 to 28
2. $\frac{10}{3}$
   $\frac{20}{6}$; $\frac{30}{9}$; $\frac{40}{12}$
3. 2:5
   4:10; 6:15; 8:20
4. 8 to 9
   16 to 18; 24 to 27; 32 to 36
5. 3 to 15
   6 to 30; 9 to 45; 12 to 60
6. $\frac{30}{90}$
   $\frac{15}{45}$; $\frac{10}{30}$; $\frac{6}{18}$
7. 1:3
   2:6; 3:9; 4:12
8. $\frac{7}{2}$
   $\frac{14}{4}$; $\frac{21}{6}$; $\frac{28}{8}$

9. Britney does sit-ups every day. The table shows how long it takes her to do different numbers of sit-ups.

Number of Sit-Ups	10	30	50	200	220
Time (min)	2	6	10	40	44

How long do you predict it will take Britney to do 120 sit-ups?

24 minutes

10. The School Supply Store has markers on sale. The table shows some sale prices.

Number of Markers	12	8	6	4	2
Cost (\$)	9.00	6.00	4.50	3.00	1.50

How much do you predict you would pay for 10 markers?

\$7.50

President Lyndon Baines Johnson, often referred to as LBJ, was born in Stillwater, Texas, in 1908. President Johnson had no vice president from November 1963 to January 1965.

Multiply and divide each ratio to find two equivalent ratios. Possible answers:

23. 36:48 72:96, 3:4 **24.** $\frac{4}{60}$ $\frac{8}{120}, \frac{1}{15}$ **25.** $\frac{128}{48}$ $\frac{32}{11}, \frac{256}{88}$ **26.** 15:100 30:200, 3:20

27. Multi-Step Lyndon Johnson was elected president in 1964. The ratio of the number of votes he received to the number of votes that Barry Goldwater received was about 19:12. About how many votes were cast for both candiates? about 70,000,000

Candidates	Number of Votes
Lyndon Johnson	43,121,085
Barry Goldwater	▒

28. What's the Error? A student said that 3:4 is equivalent to 9:16 and 18:64. What did the student do wrong? Correct the ratios so they are equivalent.

29. Write About It If Daniel drives the same distance each day, will he be able to complete a 4,500-mile trip in 2 weeks? Explain how you solved the problem.

Days	Distance (mi)
3	1,020
5	1,700
9	3,060

29. Possible answer: Yes he drives 340 mi/day. In 14 days (2 weeks) he will drive 4,760 miles, which is more than 4,500 miles.

30. Challenge The table shows the regular and sale prices of CDs at Bargain Blast. How much money will you save if you buy 10 CDs on sale? $13

Number of CDs	Regular Price ($)	Sale Price ($)
2	17.00	14.40
3	25.50	21.60
6	51.00	42.40

CRCT Prep • GPS Support • Spiral Review

31. Multiple Choice Which ratio is NOT equivalent to 3 to 7?

Ⓐ 9:21 Ⓑ 36:77 Ⓒ 45:105 Ⓓ 54:126

32. Short Response The table shows the distances traveled and the numbers of gallons of gas used on four automobile trips. Predict the number of gallons of gas that would be used for a trip of 483 miles. 21 gal

Distance (mi)	552	414	276	138
Gas Used (gal)	24	18	12	6

33. In 2005, the heights of the world's tallest buildings were 509, 452, 452, 442, 421, and 415 meters. Find the mean, median, mode, and range of the data set. (Lesson 6-2) 94; 448.5; 447; 452

34. Javier saved $65, $82, $58, $74, $65, and $72 each month from his part-time job for six months. The next month he worked full-time and saved $285. Find the mean, median, and mode of the amounts saved with and without the full-time savings. (Lesson 6-3)

Ongoing Assessment and Intervention

Diagnose **Before** the Lesson
7-2 Warm Up, TE p. 356

Monitor **During** the Lesson
7-2 Know-It Notebook
7-2 Questioning Strategies

Assess **After** the Lesson
7-2 Lesson Quiz, TE p. 359

Answers

28. The student did not multiply both parts of the ratio by the same number. To scale up the ratio 3:4, the student should have multiplied $3 \cdot 3 = 9$ and $4 \cdot 3 = 12$, and $3 \cdot 6$ and $4 \cdot 6$. The equivalent ratios are 3:4, 9:12, and 18:24.

34. with full-time savings:
mean ≈ 100.14; median = 72; mode = 65, 72
without full-time savings:
mean ≈ 69.33; median = 68.5; mode = 65, 72

Test Prep Doctor In Exercise 32, encourage students to simplify the last ratio in the table by dividing the numerator and denominator by 6. The result will be a ratio of 23 to 1. Dividing 483 by 23 provides the correct answer of 21 gallons.

Journal

Have students explain how the word *to* is used when writing a ratio.

CHALLENGE 7-2

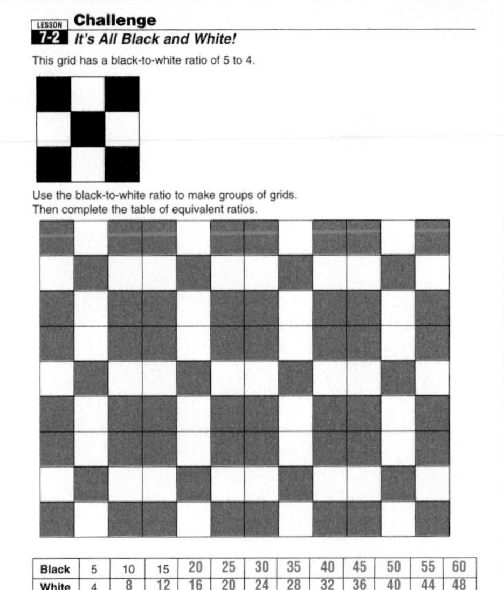

LESSON 7-2 **Challenge**
It's All Black and White!

This grid has a black-to-white ratio of 5 to 4.

Use the black-to-white ratio to make groups of grids. Then complete the table of equivalent ratios.

Black	5	10	15	20	25	30	35	40	45	50	55	60
White	4	8	12	16	20	24	28	32	36	40	44	48

PROBLEM SOLVING 7-2

LESSON 7-2 **Problem Solving**
Using Tables to Explore Equivalent Ratios and Rates

Use the table to answer the questions.

School Outing Student-to-Parent Ratios

Number of Students	8	16	24	32	40	48	56	64	72
Number of Parents	2	4	6	8	10	12	14	16	18

1. Each time some students go on a school outing, their teachers invite students' parents to accompany them. Predict how many parents will accompany 88 students.
22 parents

2. Next week 112 students will go to the Science Museum. Their teachers invited some of the students' parents to go with them. How many parents do you predict will go with the students to the Science Museum?
24 parents

Circle the letter of the correct answer.

3. Tanya's class of 28 students will be going to the Nature Center. How many parents do you predict Tanya's teacher will invite to accompany them?
A 5 parents
Ⓑ 7 parents
C 9 parents
D 11 parents

4. Some students will be going on an outing to the local police station. Their teachers invited 13 parents to accompany them. How many students do you predict will be going on the outing?
F 49 students
G 50 students
H 51 students
Ⓙ 52 students

5. In June, all of the students in the school will be going on their annual picnic. If there are 416 students in the school, what do you predict the number of parents accompanying them on the picnic will be?
A 52 parents
B 78 parents
Ⓒ 104 parents
D 156 parents

6. On Tuesday, all of the sixth-grade students will be going to the Space Museum. Their teachers invited 21 parents to accompany them. How many sixth graders do you predict will be going to the Space Museum?
F 80 sixth graders
G 82 sixth graders
Ⓗ 84 sixth graders
J 86 sixth graders

Power Presentations with PowerPoint®

7-2 Lesson Quiz

Use a table to find three equivalent ratios. Possible answers.

1. $\frac{1}{3}$ $\frac{2}{6}, \frac{3}{9}, \frac{4}{12}$

2. $\frac{9}{4}$ $\frac{18}{8}, \frac{27}{12}, \frac{36}{16}$

3. $\frac{12}{60}$ $\frac{6}{30}, \frac{2}{10}, \frac{1}{5}$

4. Fred is saving for a new sound system. The table shows some amounts he could save in different numbers of weeks. Predict the amount of his savings after 10 weeks. $125

Weeks	4	8	12
Savings	50	100	150

Also available on transparency

Organizer

Use with Lesson 7-3

Pacing:
Traditional 1 day
Block $\frac{1}{2}$ day

Objective: Use counters to model equivalent ratios.

Materials: Color counters

Online Edition

Countdown to CRCT Week 14

Resources

Hands-On Lab Activities
Lab 7-3 Recording Sheet

Teach

Discuss

Have students discuss how color counters can be used to represent a ratio, and then an equivalent ratio.

Close

Key Concept

Color counters provide concrete examples of ratios and equivalent ratios.

Assessment

Represent each ratio using two-color counters.

1. 3 red counters to 4 yellow counters

2. 5 red counters to 3 yellow counters

Write the ratio represented by the counters.

3. 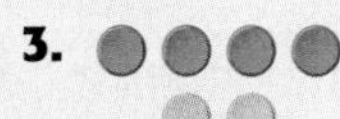

Georgia Performance Standards

M6A1 Students will understand the concept of ratio and use it to represent quantitative relationships.

M6A2.b Use manipulatives or draw pictures to solve problems involving proportional relationships.

M6P5.b Select, apply, and translate among mathematical representations to solve problems.

M6P5.c Use representations to model and interpret physical, social, and mathematical phenomena.

Explore Proportions

Use with Lesson 7-3

Georgia Performance Standards
M6A1, M6A2.b, M6P5.b, M6P5.c

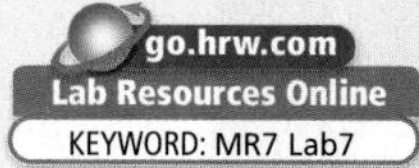

You can use counters to model equivalent ratios.

Activity 1

Find three ratios that are equivalent to $\frac{6}{12}$.

1. Show 6 red counters and 12 yellow counters.
2. Separate the red counters into two equal groups. Then separate the yellow counters into two equal groups.
3. Write the ratio of red counters in each group to yellow counters in each group.

$$\frac{3 \text{ red counters}}{6 \text{ yellow counters}} = \frac{3}{6}$$

4. Now separate the red counters into three equal groups. Then separate the yellow counters into three equal groups.
5. Write the ratio of red counters in each group to yellow counters in each group.

$$\frac{2 \text{ red counters}}{4 \text{ yellow counters}} = \frac{2}{4}$$

6. Now separate the red counters into six equal groups. Then separate the yellow counters into six equal groups.
7. Write the ratio of red counters in each group to yellow counters in each group.

$$\frac{1 \text{ red counter}}{2 \text{ yellow counters}} = \frac{1}{2}$$

The three ratios you wrote are equivalent to $\frac{6}{12}$.

$$\frac{6}{12} = \frac{3}{6} = \frac{2}{4} = \frac{1}{2}$$

When you write an equation showing equivalent ratios, that equation is called a *proportion.*

Answers to *Assessment*

1. 

2. 

3. 4 red counters to 2 yellow counters

Think and Discuss

1. How do the models show that the ratios are equivalent?
The number of counters is the same in each model.

Try This

Use models to determine whether the ratios form a proportion.

1. $\frac{1}{3}$ and $\frac{4}{12}$ **yes**
2. $\frac{3}{4}$ and $\frac{6}{9}$ **no**
3. $\frac{4}{10}$ and $\frac{2}{5}$ **yes**

Activity 2

Write a proportion in which one of the ratios is $\frac{1}{3}$.

1. You must find a ratio that is equivalent to $\frac{1}{3}$. First show one red counter and three yellow counters.

2. Show one more group of one red counter and three yellow counters.

3. Write the ratio of red counters to yellow counters for the two groups.

$$\frac{\text{2 red counters}}{\text{6 yellow counters}} = \frac{2}{6}$$

4. The two ratios are equivalent. Write the proportion $\frac{1}{3} = \frac{2}{6}$.

You can find more equivalent ratios by adding more groups of one red counter and three yellow counters. Use your models to write proportions.

$$\frac{\text{3 red counters}}{\text{9 yellow counters}} = \frac{3}{9}$$

$$\frac{3}{9} = \frac{1}{3}$$

$$\frac{\text{4 red counters}}{\text{12 yellow counters}} = \frac{4}{12}$$

$$\frac{4}{12} = \frac{1}{3}$$

Think and Discuss

1. The models above show that $\frac{1}{3}$, $\frac{2}{6}$, $\frac{3}{9}$, and $\frac{4}{12}$ are equivalent ratios. Do you see a pattern in this list of ratios? **Every time the first term increases by 1, the second term increases by 3.**
2. Use counters to find another ratio that is equivalent to $\frac{1}{3}$.
Possible answer: $\frac{5}{15}$ is equivalent to $\frac{1}{3}$.

Try This

Use counters to write a proportion containing each given ratio. **Possible answers:**

1. $\frac{1}{4}$ $\frac{1}{4} = \frac{3}{12}$
2. $\frac{1}{5}$ $\frac{1}{5} = \frac{2}{10}$
3. $\frac{3}{7}$ $\frac{3}{7} = \frac{6}{14}$
4. $\frac{1}{6}$ $\frac{1}{6} = \frac{3}{18}$
5. $\frac{4}{9}$ $\frac{4}{9} = \frac{8}{18}$

7-3 Organizer

Pacing: Traditional 1 day
Block $\frac{1}{2}$ day

Objective: Students write and solve proportions.

Online Edition
Tutorial Videos, Interactivities

Countdown to CRCT Week 14

Warm Up

Use the table to write each ratio.

Brown bears	3
Giraffes	2
Monkeys	17
Polar bears	4

1. giraffes to monkeys 2:17
2. polar bears to all bears 4:7
3. monkeys to all animals 17:26
4. all animals to all bears 26:7

Problem of the Day

A carpenter can build one doghouse in one day. How many doghouses can 12 carpenters build in 20 days? 240

Also available on transparency

7-3 Proportions

Learn to write and solve proportions.

Vocabulary
proportion

M6A2.c Use proportions to describe relationships and solve problems. Also, M6A2.g, M6P4.a, M6P4.b, M6P5.c.

Have you ever heard water called H_2O? H_2O is the scientific formula for water. One molecule of water contains two hydrogen atoms (H_2) and one oxygen atom (O). No matter how many molecules of water you have, hydrogen and oxygen will always be in the ratio 2 to 1.

Water Molecules	1	2	3	4
$\frac{\text{Hydrogen}}{\text{Oxygen}}$	$\frac{2}{1}$	$\frac{4}{2}$	$\frac{6}{3}$	$\frac{8}{4}$

Reading Math

Read the proportion $\frac{2}{1} = \frac{4}{2}$ as "two is to one as four is to two."

Notice that $\frac{2}{1}$, $\frac{4}{2}$, $\frac{6}{3}$, and $\frac{8}{4}$ are equivalent ratios.

A **proportion** is an equation that shows two equivalent ratios.

$\frac{2}{1} = \frac{4}{2}$ $\frac{4}{2} = \frac{8}{4}$ $\frac{2}{1} = \frac{6}{3}$

EXAMPLE 1 Modeling Proportions

Write a proportion for the model.

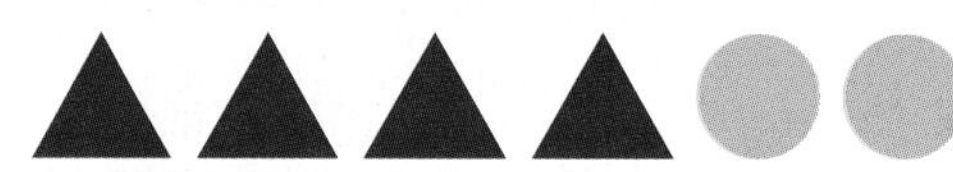

First write the ratio of triangles to circles.

$$\frac{\text{number of triangles}}{\text{number of circles}} = \frac{4}{2}$$

Next separate the triangles and the circles into two equal groups.

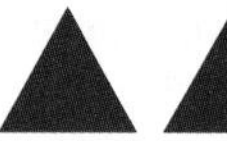

Now write the ratio of triangles to circles in each group.

$$\frac{\text{number of triangles in each group}}{\text{number of circles in each group}} = \frac{2}{1}$$

A proportion shown by the model is $\frac{4}{2} = \frac{2}{1}$.

Georgia Performance Standards

M6A2.c Use proportions (a/b=c/d) to describe relationships and solve problems, including percent problems.

M6A2.g Use proportional reasoning (a/b=c/d and y = kx) to solve problems.

M6P4.a Recognize and use connections among mathematical ideas.

M6P4.b Understand how mathematical ideas interconnect and build on one another to produce a coherent whole.

M6P5.c Use representations to model and interpret physical, social, and mathematical phenomena.

1 Introduce

Alternate Opener

An automobile assembly line finishes 3 cars every 2 hours.

1. Use the diagram to determine how many cars are finished each hour.
2. Use the diagram to determine approximately how long it takes to finish 1 car.
3. If it takes 2 hours to finish 3 cars, how many hours does it take to finish
   a. 6 cars? b. 9 cars? c. 12 cars?
   d. 4 cars? e. 8 cars? f. 16 cars?

Think and Discuss

4. **Discuss** how you used the diagram to solve numbers 1 and 2.
5. **Explain** how you solved numbers 3a–3f.

Motivate

To review how to express ratios as fractions and how to find equivalent ratios, pose this problem:

Ethan is mixing orange juice. For every 1 can of frozen concentrate, he adds 3 cans of water. What is the ratio of concentrate to water? Give the ratio as a fraction. Write an equivalent ratio to show how much water Ethan will need if he uses 3 cans of concentrate. $\frac{1}{3}$; $\frac{1}{3} = \frac{3}{9}$; He will need 9 cans of water. This will get students ready to learn about *proportions*.

Explorations and answers are provided in *Alternate Openers: Explorations Transparencies.*

CROSS PRODUCTS

Cross products in proportions are equal.

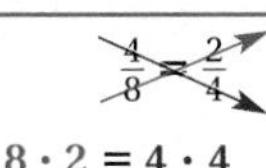 $\frac{4}{8}$ $\frac{2}{4}$	$\frac{3}{5}$ $\frac{9}{15}$	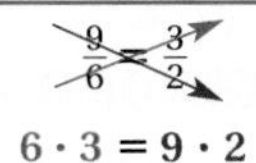 $\frac{9}{6}$ $\frac{3}{2}$	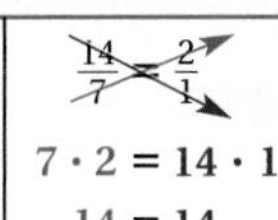 $\frac{14}{7}$ $\frac{2}{1}$
$8 \cdot 2 = 4 \cdot 4$	$5 \cdot 9 = 3 \cdot 15$	$6 \cdot 3 = 9 \cdot 2$	$7 \cdot 2 = 14 \cdot 1$
$16 = 16$	$45 = 45$	$18 = 18$	$14 = 14$

EXAMPLE 2 Using Cross Products to Complete Proportions

Find the missing value in the proportion $\frac{3}{4} = \frac{n}{16}$.

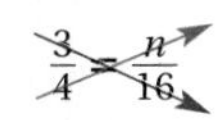

$\frac{3}{4} \times \frac{n}{16}$ — *Find the cross products.*

$4 \cdot n = 3 \cdot 16$ — *The cross products are equal.*

$4n = 48$ — *n is multiplied by 4.*

$\frac{4n}{4} = \frac{48}{4}$ — *Divide both sides by 4 to undo the multiplication.*

$n = 12$

EXAMPLE 3 *Measurement Application*

Caution!

In a proportion, the units must be in the same order in both ratios.

$\frac{tsp}{lb} = \frac{tsp}{lb}$

or $\frac{lb}{tsp} = \frac{lb}{tsp}$

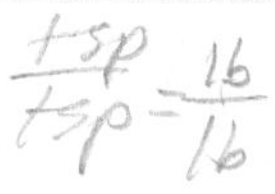

The label from a bottle of pet vitamins shows recommended dosages. What dosage would you give an adult dog that weighs 15 lb?

Pet Vitamins

- **Adult dogs:** 1 tsp per 20 lb body weight
- **Puppies, pregnant dogs, or nursing dogs:** 1 tsp per 10 lb body weight
- **Cats:** 1 tsp per 12 lb body weight

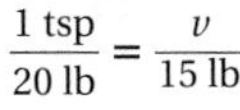

$\frac{1 \text{ tsp}}{20 \text{ lb}} = \frac{v}{15 \text{ lb}}$ — *Let v be the amount of vitamins for a 15 lb dog.*

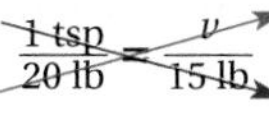

$\frac{1 \text{ tsp}}{20 \text{ lb}} \times \frac{v}{15 \text{ lb}}$ — *Write a proportion.*

$20 \cdot v = 1 \cdot 15$ — *The cross products are equal.*

$20v = 15$ — *v is multiplied by 20.*

$\frac{20v}{20} = \frac{15}{20}$ — *Divide both sides by 20 to undo the multiplication.*

$v = \frac{3}{4}$ tsp — *Write your answer in simplest form.*

You should give $\frac{3}{4}$ tsp of vitamins to a 15 lb dog.

Possible answers to *Think and Discuss*

1. No; the cross products (32 and 98) are not equal.
2. $\frac{3}{5} = \frac{6}{10}$; I know it is a proportion because $\frac{3}{5}$ and $\frac{6}{10}$ are equivalent ratios, and also because $5 \times 6 = 3 \times 10$.

Think and Discuss

GPS M6P3.b, M6P3.d

1. **Tell** whether $\frac{7}{8} = \frac{4}{14}$ is a proportion. How do you know?
2. **Give an example** of a proportion. Tell how you know that it is a proportion.

COMMON ERROR ALERT

Some students may try to cancel the numerator on one side of the equation with the denominator on the other side of the equation, as when multiplying fractions, instead of *cross multiplying*. Stress that they can't cancel across the equal sign.

Power Presentations with PowerPoint®

Additional Examples

Example 1

Write a proportion for the model.

♥♥♥♥☆☆☆☆☆☆☆☆

♥♥☆☆☆☆

♥♥☆☆☆☆

A proportion shown by the model is $\frac{4}{8} = \frac{2}{4}$.

Example 2

Find the missing value in the proportion.

$\frac{5}{6} = \frac{n}{18}$ $\quad n = 15$

Example 3

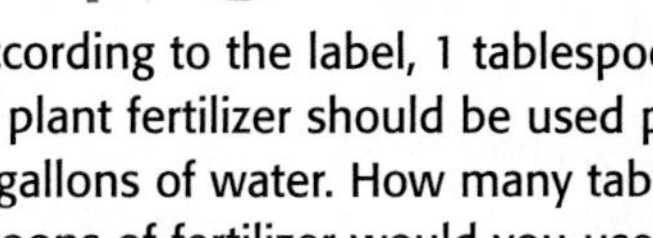

According to the label, 1 tablespoon of plant fertilizer should be used per 6 gallons of water. How many tablespoons of fertilizer would you use for 4 gallons of water?

You would use $\frac{2}{3}$ tbsp of fertilizer.

Also available on transparency

2 Teach

Guided Instruction

In this lesson, students write and solve proportions. Teach students the format for writing proportions as equivalent ratios, and have them practice doing this. Then teach them to use cross products to find missing values in proportions. Have students use cross products to find missing values in a measurement context.

Teaching Tip

Concrete Manipulatives You may wish to allow students to use two-color counters to model some of the proportions in the lesson.

Reaching All Learners

Through Curriculum Integration

Science The lesson opener deals with H_2O. Use the table to show equivalent ratios based on the number of water molecules, and write two or three proportions based on the equivalent ratios in the table.

You may want to create another table for a different molecule, such as ammonia (NH_3), and have the students write proportions based on the equivalent ratios in the table for ammonia.

3 Close

Summarize

Review the fact that a *proportion* is an equation that shows two equivalent ratios. Demonstrate how to find a missing value in a proportion by using cross products.

7-3 Exercises

Assignment Guide

If you finished Example 1 assign:
Average 1, 27–36
Advanced 7, 27–36

If you finished Example 2 assign:
Average 1–5, 13–16, 27–36
Advanced 7–11, 17–20, 27–36

If you finished Example 3 assign:
Average 1–10, 16–36
Advanced 7–36

Homework Quick Check

Quickly check key concepts.
Exercises: 10, 16, 20, 22

Math Background

The statement that cross products in a proportion are equal is true because you are multiplying both sides of the proportion by the denominators of the fractions. Consider the following demonstration:

For real numbers *a*, *b*, *c*, and *d*,

$\frac{a}{b} = \frac{c}{d}$,

$\frac{a}{b} = \frac{ad}{bd}$, and $\frac{c}{d} = \frac{cb}{db}$.

Since the fractions to the right of the equal signs have the same denominator, they are equal if and only if their numerators are equal (i.e., if and only if $ad = cb$).

Georgia Performance Standards

M6P1.a Build new mathematical knowledge through problem solving.

M6P3.a Organize and consolidate their mathematical thinking through communication.

M6P3.c Analyze and evaluate the mathematical thinking and strategies of others.

7-3 Exercises

Georgia Performance Standards
M6P1.a, M6P3.a, M6P3.c

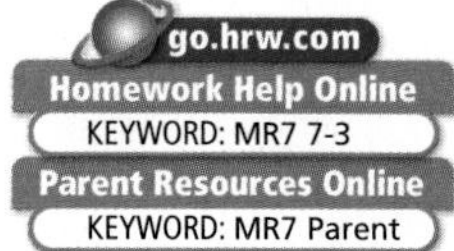

GUIDED PRACTICE

See Example 1

1. Write a proportion for the model. Possible answer: $\frac{6}{3} = \frac{2}{1}$

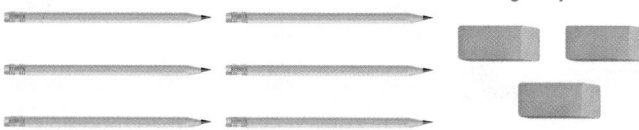

See Example 2

Find the missing value in each proportion.

2. $\frac{12}{9} = \frac{n}{3}$ 4
3. $\frac{t}{5} = \frac{28}{20}$ 7
4. $\frac{1}{c} = \frac{6}{12}$ 2
5. $\frac{6}{7} = \frac{30}{b}$ 35

See Example 3

6. Ursula is entering a bicycle race for charity. Her mother pledges $0.75 for every 0.5 mile she bikes. If Ursula bikes 17.5 miles, how much will her mother donate? $26.25

INDEPENDENT PRACTICE

See Example 1

7. Write a proportion for the model. Possible answer: $\frac{12}{9} = \frac{4}{3}$

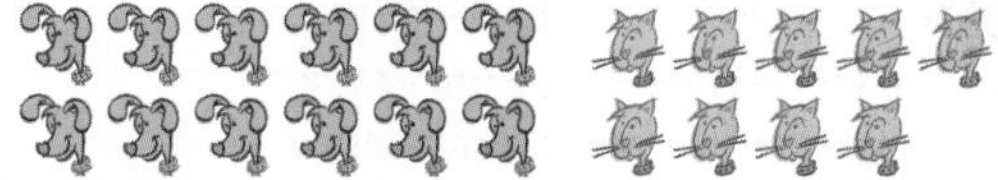

See Example 2

Find the missing value in each proportion.

8. $\frac{3}{2} = \frac{24}{d}$ 16
9. $\frac{p}{40} = \frac{3}{8}$ 15
10. $\frac{6}{14} = \frac{x}{7}$ 3
11. $\frac{5}{p} = \frac{7}{77}$ 55

See Example 3

12. According to Ty's study guidelines, how many minutes of science reading should he do if his science class is 90 minutes long? 30 minutes

Ty's Study Guidelines

Class	Reading Time
Literature	35 minutes for every 50 minutes of class time
Science	20 minutes for every 60 minutes of class time
History	30 minutes for every 55 minutes of class time

PRACTICE AND PROBLEM SOLVING

CRCT GPS
Extra Practice p. 726

Find the value of *p* in each proportion.

13. $\frac{18}{6} = \frac{6}{p}$ 2
14. $\frac{4}{p} = \frac{48}{60}$ 5
15. $\frac{p}{10} = \frac{15}{50}$ 3
16. $\frac{3}{5} = \frac{12}{p}$ 20
17. $\frac{21}{15} = \frac{p}{5}$ 7
18. $\frac{3}{6} = \frac{p}{8}$ 4
19. $\frac{15}{5} = \frac{9}{p}$ 3
20. $\frac{6}{p} = \frac{4}{28}$ 42

21. **Patterns** Given that the first term in a sequence is $\frac{7}{2}$, the second term is $\frac{14}{4}$, the fourth term is $\frac{28}{8}$, and the fifth term is $\frac{35}{10}$, find the value of the third term. $\frac{21}{6}$

RETEACH 7-3

LESSON 7-3 **Reteach**
Proportions

A proportion is an equation that shows two equivalent ratios.

$\frac{3}{4} = \frac{9}{12}$ is an example of a proportion.

$3 \cdot 12 = 36$ and $4 \cdot 9 = 36$. The cross products of proportions are equal.

You can use cross products to find the missing value in a proportion.

$\frac{3}{x} = \frac{12}{48}$

$12 \cdot x = 3 \cdot 48$ To find *x*, first find the cross products.

$12x = 144$

Think: $144 \div 12 = x$ Then use a related math sentence to solve the equation.

$x = 12$

So, $\frac{3}{12} = \frac{12}{48}$.

Find the cross products to solve each proportion.

1. $\frac{x}{8} = \frac{3}{4}$ $x \cdot 4 = 8 \cdot 3$ $x = 6$
2. $\frac{2}{3} = \frac{x}{6}$ $2 \cdot 6 = 3 \cdot x$ $x = 4$
3. $\frac{2}{5} = \frac{4}{x}$ $2 \cdot x = 5 \cdot 4$ $x = 10$
4. $\frac{6}{x} = \frac{1}{3}$ $6 \cdot 3 = x \cdot 1$ $x = 18$
5. $\frac{3}{8} = \frac{12}{x}$ $x = 32$
6. $\frac{3}{5} = \frac{6}{x}$ $x = 10$
7. $\frac{x}{8} = \frac{2}{16}$ $x = 1$
8. $\frac{2}{9} = \frac{4}{x}$ $x = 18$
9. $\frac{3}{4} = \frac{15}{x}$ $x = 20$
10. $\frac{1}{2} = \frac{x}{30}$ $x = 15$
11. $\frac{x}{5} = \frac{24}{30}$ $x = 4$
12. $\frac{25}{35} = \frac{5}{x}$ $x = 7$

PRACTICE 7-3

LESSON 7-3 **Practice B**
Proportions

Find the missing value in each proportion.

1. $\frac{24}{8} = \frac{n}{2}$ $n = 6$
2. $\frac{4}{9} = \frac{20}{n}$ $n = 45$
3. $\frac{n}{36} = \frac{5}{6}$ $n = 30$
4. $\frac{n}{5} = \frac{4}{10}$ $n = 2$
5. $\frac{3}{9} = \frac{2}{n}$ $n = 6$
6. $\frac{6}{n} = \frac{3}{7}$ $n = 14$
7. $\frac{5}{3} = \frac{n}{6}$ $n = 10$
8. $\frac{9}{6} = \frac{6}{n}$ $n = 4$
9. $\frac{2}{130} = \frac{1}{n}$ $n = 65$

Write a proportion for each model.

10.

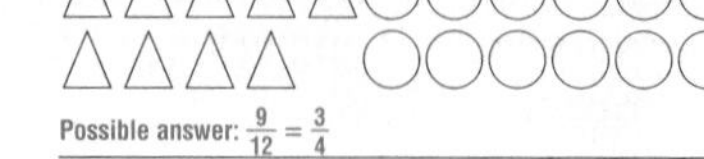

Possible answer: $\frac{9}{12} = \frac{3}{4}$

11. Possible answer: $\frac{16}{4} = \frac{4}{1}$

12. Shane's neighbor pledged $1.25 for every 0.5 miles that Shane swims in the charity swim-a-thon. If Shane swims 3 miles, how much money will his neighbor donate?

$7.50

13. Barbara's goal is to practice piano 20 minutes for every 5 minutes of lessons she takes. If she takes a 20 minute piano lesson this week, how many minutes should she practice this week?

80 minutes

Social Studies LINK

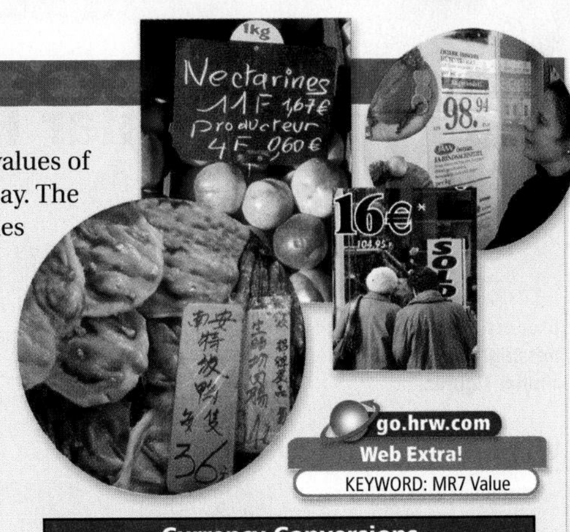

The value of the U.S. dollar as compared to the values of currencies from other countries changes every day. The graph shows the recent value of various currencies compared to the U.S. dollar. Use the graph for Exercises 22–26.

22. What is the value of 9.72 European euros in U.S. dollars? **$7.87**

23. **Multi-Step** You have $100 in U.S. dollars. Determine how much money this is in euros, Canadian dollars, renminbi, shekels, and Mexican pesos.

24. **What's the Error?** A student set up the proportion $\frac{1}{8.10} = \frac{x}{30}$ to determine the value of 30 U.S. dollars in China. Why is this proportion incorrect? Write the correct proportion, and find the missing value.

25. **Write About It** Which is worth more: five U.S. dollars or five Canadian dollars? Why?

26. **Challenge** A dime is worth about how many Mexican pesos?

about 1.06 pesos

go.hrw.com
Web Extra!
KEYWORD: MR7 Value

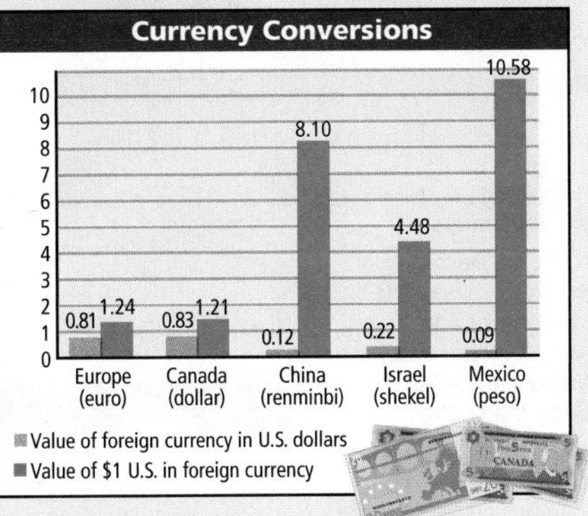

CRCT Prep • GPS Support • Spiral Review

27. **Multiple Choice** A recipe calls for 4 cups of sugar and 16 cups of water. If the recipe is reduced, how many cups of water should be used with 1 cup of sugar?

Ⓐ 0.25 cups　Ⓑ 1.6 cups　**(C) 4 cups** (circled)　Ⓓ 16 cups

28. **Multiple Choice** Li mixes 3 units of red paint with 8 units of white paint to get pink. How many units of red paint should she mix with 12 units of white paint to get the same pink shade?

Ⓕ $2\frac{3}{4}$　Ⓖ 3　Ⓗ $3\frac{1}{4}$　**(J) $4\frac{1}{2}$** (circled)

Compare. Write <, >, or =. (Lesson 4-7)

29. $\frac{4}{7}$ ▪ $\frac{7}{10}$ **<**　**30.** $\frac{3}{5}$ ▪ $\frac{14}{15}$ **<**　**31.** $\frac{9}{27}$ ▪ $\frac{6}{18}$ **=**　**32.** $\frac{45}{18}$ ▪ $\frac{18}{9}$ **>**

Write each ratio two different ways. (Lesson 7-1)

33. 4:9 **4 to 9, $\frac{4}{9}$**　**34.** eight to eleven **8:11, $\frac{8}{11}$**　**35.** $\frac{6}{13}$ **6:13, 6 to 13**　**36.** 7:5 **7 to 5, $\frac{7}{5}$**

CHALLENGE 7-3

LESSON 7-3 **Challenge**
Patriotic Proportions

On August 21, 1959, President Eisenhower signed an order that established the official proportions of the United States flag. No matter what size the flag is, it must match those proportions to be used officially.

Official Proportions for the United States Flag	
Width of flag	1
Length of flag	$1\frac{9}{10}$
Width of union	$\frac{7}{13}$
Length of union	$\frac{19}{25}$
Width of each stripe	$\frac{1}{13}$

The union is the blue area.
The 50 stars represent the 50 states.

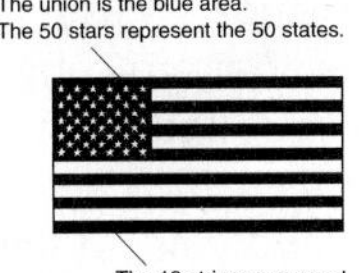

The 13 stripes represent the first 13 states.

Use the official proportions to find the missing dimension of each flag.

1. Length of flag = 10 feet; Width of flag = **$5\frac{5}{19}$ feet**
2. Width of flag = 57 yards; Length of flag = **$108\frac{3}{10}$ yards**
3. Width of flag = 13 centimeters; Width of Union = **7 centimeters**
4. Width of flag = 260 inches; Width of each stripe = **20 inches**
5. Length of flag = 25 meters; Length of Union = **10 meters**

Choose a width in inches for a United States flag. Then use a ruler to draw your flag with the official proportional length in the space below.

Check students' flag widths and lengths for the correct width-to-length ratio of 1 inch to 1.9 inches.

PROBLEM SOLVING 7-3

LESSON 7-3 **Problem Solving**
Proportions

Write the correct answer.

1. For most people, the ratio of the length of their head to their total height is 1:7. Use proportions to test your measurements and see if they match this ratio.
Answers should test the 1:7 head to height ratio measurements.

2. The ratio of an object's weight on Earth to its weight on the Moon is 6:1. The first person to walk on the Moon was Neil Armstrong. He weighed 165 pounds on Earth. How much did he weigh on the Moon?
27.5 pounds

3. It has been found that the distance from a person's eye to the end of the fingers of his outstretched hand is proportional to the distance between his eyes at a 10:1 ratio. If the distance between your eyes is 2.3 inches, what should the distance from your eye to your outstretched fingers be?
23 inches

4. Chemists write the formula of ordinary sugar as $C_{12}H_{22}O_{11}$, which means that the ratios of 1 molecule of sugar are always 12 carbon atoms to 22 hydrogen atoms to 11 oxygen atoms. If there are 4 sugar molecules, how many atoms of each element will there be?
48 carbon, 88 hydrogen, 44 oxygen

Circle the letter of the correct answer.

5. A healthy diet follows the ratio for meat to vegetables of 2.5 servings to 4 servings. If you eat 7 servings of meat a week, how many servings of vegetables should you eat?
A 28 servings　C 14 servings
B 17.5 servings　**(D) 11.2 servings** (circled)

6. A 150-pound person will burn 100 calories while sitting still for 1 hour. Following this ratio, how many calories will a 100-pound person burn while sitting still for 1 hour?
F $666\frac{2}{3}$ calories　H $6\frac{2}{3}$ calories
(G) $66\frac{2}{3}$ calories (circled)　J 6 calories

7. Recently, 1 U.S. dollar was worth 1.58 in euros. If you exchanged $25 at that rate, how many euros would you get?
(A) 39.50 euros (circled)
B 15.82 euros
C 26.58 euros
D 23.42 euros

8. Recently, 1 U.S. dollar was worth 0.69 English pound. If you exchanged 500 English pounds, how many dollars would you get?
F 345 U.S. dollars
(G) 725 U.S. dollars (circled)
H 500.69 U.S dollars
J 499.31 U.S. dollars

Ongoing Assessment and Intervention

***Diagnose Before* the Lesson**
7-3 Warm Up, TE p. 362

***Monitor During* the Lesson**
7-3 Know-It Notebook
7-3 Questioning Strategies

***Assess After* the Lesson**
7-3 Lesson Quiz, TE p. 365

Interdisciplinary LINK

Social Studies

Exercises 22–26 involve comparing the value of the U.S. dollar with values of currencies from other countries. Students learn more about these other countries in middle school social studies programs, such as Holt, Rinehart & Winston's *People, Places, and Change*.

Answers

23–25. See p. A8.

Test Prep Doctor In Exercise 28, students will benefit from recognizing the proportional situation in this problem. Point out how to properly set up the proportion, red units over white units, $\frac{3}{8} = \frac{x}{12}$.

Journal

Have students write an explanation of how proportions and ratios are related. Have them write a proportion with a missing value and use cross products to solve the proportion.

Power Presentations with PowerPoint®

7-3 Lesson Quiz

1. Write a proportion for the model.
□□□□□□◇◇　**$\frac{2}{6} = \frac{1}{3}$**

Find the missing value in each proportion.

2. $\frac{9}{5} = \frac{45}{x}$　**$x = 25$**

3. $\frac{p}{36} = \frac{5}{6}$　**$p = 30$**

4. The label on a bottle of salad dressing states that there are 3 grams of fat per tablespoon. If you use 3 tablespoons, how many grams of fat would you be getting? **9 g**

Also available on transparency

7-4 Organizer

Pacing: Traditional 1 day
Block $\frac{1}{2}$ day

Objective: Students use ratios to identify similar figures.

GPS M6G1.c, M6A2.g
Hands-On Lab
In *Hands-On Lab Activities*

Online Edition
Tutorial Videos, Interactivities

Countdown to CRCT Week 14

Power Presentations with PowerPoint®

Warm Up

Fill in the missing value.

1. ▢ c = 2 qt — 8
2. 180 in. = ▢ yd — 5
3. 3 tons = ▢ lb — 6,000
4. ▢ min = 2,760 s — 46

Problem of the Day

How many 8 in. by 10 in. rectangular tiles would be needed to cover a 16 ft by 20 ft floor? 576

Also available on transparency

Math Humor

A class in Texas and a class in California did the same science fair experiment. Their results were so similar that the judges knew the sides must have been corresponding.

Georgia Performance Standards

M6G1.c Use the concepts of ratio, proportion and scale factor to demonstrate the relationships between similar plane figures.

M6A2.c Use proportions (a/b=c/d) to describe relationships and solve problems, including percent problems.

M6A2.g Use proportional reasoning (a/b=c/d and y = kx) to solve problems.

M6P1.c Apply and adapt a variety of appropriate strategies to solve problems.

M6P1.d Monitor and reflect on the process of mathematical problem solving.

7-4 Similar Figures

Learn to use proportions to find missing measures in similar figures.

Vocabulary
corresponding sides
corresponding angles
similar

Georgia Performance Standards

M6G1.c Use the concepts of ratio, proportion and scale factor to demonstrate the relationships between similar plane figures. Also, M6A2.c, M6A2.g, M6P1.c, M6P1.d.

Matching sides of two or more polygons are called **corresponding sides**, and matching angles are called **corresponding angles**.

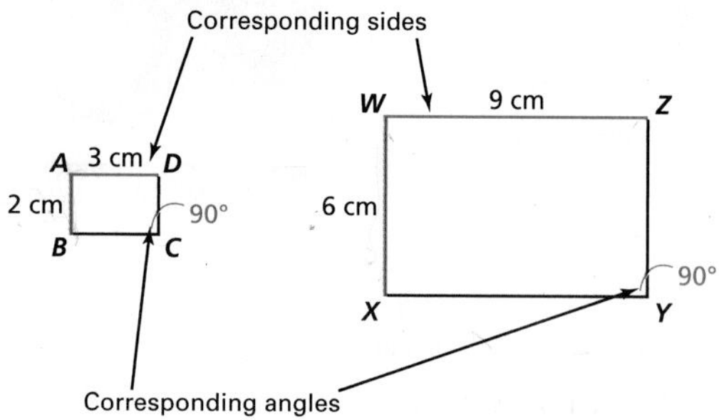

Similar figures have the same shape but not necessarily the same size.

SIMILAR FIGURES

Two figures are similar if
- the measures of the corresponding angles are equal.
- the ratios of the lengths of the corresponding sides are proportional.

In the rectangles above, one proportion is $\frac{AB}{WX} = \frac{AD}{WZ}$, or $\frac{2}{6} = \frac{3}{9}$.

EXAMPLE 1 Finding Missing Measures in Similar Figures

The two triangles are similar. Find the missing length x and the measure of $\angle A$.

$\frac{8}{12} = \frac{6}{x}$ — *Write a proportion using corresponding side lengths.*

$12 \cdot 6 = 8 \cdot x$ — *The cross products are equal.*

$72 = 8x$ — *x is multiplied by 8.*

$\frac{72}{8} = \frac{8x}{8}$ — *Divide both sides by 8 to undo the multiplication.*

$9 \text{ cm} = x$

Angle A corresponds to angle B, and the measure of $\angle B = 65°$. The measure of $\angle A = 65°$.

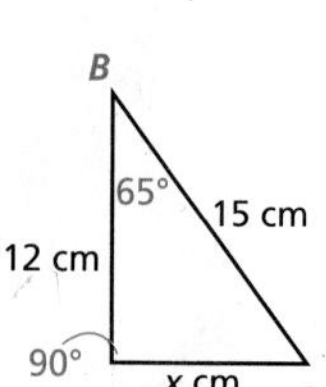

1 Introduce

Alternate Opener

EXPLORATION

7-4 Similar Figures

Similar rectangles have the same shape but may be different sizes.

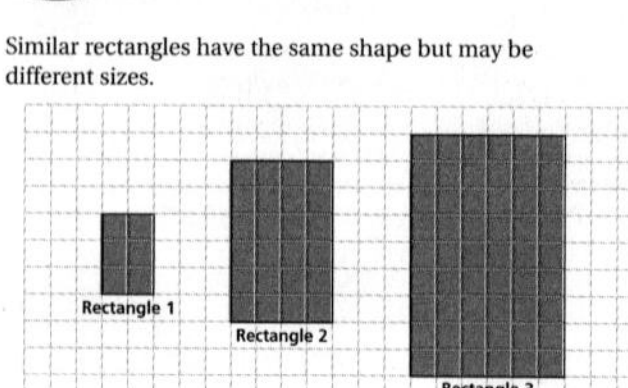

Determine the length and width of each rectangle and find each ratio.

	Ratio 1	Ratio 2
1.	length of rectangle 1 / length of rectangle 2 =	width of rectangle 1 / width of rectangle 2 =
2.	length of rectangle 2 / length of rectangle 3 =	width of rectangle 2 / width of rectangle 3 =
3.	length of rectangle 1 / length of rectangle 3 =	width of rectangle 1 / width of rectangle 3 =

Think and Discuss

4. **Describe** the pattern between ratio 1 and ratio 2.
5. **Explain** why the three rectangles are similar.

Motivate

Have students use a protractor to draw two angles that are congruent to each other. Ask how they know the angles are congruent. Their measures are the same. Then draw and label two pairs of line segments, a 1-inch and a 2-inch, and a 3-inch and a 6-inch. Ask students whether the lengths of these segments can form a proportion. yes; $\frac{1}{2} = \frac{3}{6}$ Remind students to measure carefully because measurements will never be exact. Protractors and rulers are provided in the Manipulatives Kit.

Explorations and answers are provided in *Alternate Openers: Explorations Transparencies*.

EXAMPLE 2 **PROBLEM SOLVING APPLICATION**

***The Boating Party* was painted by American artist Mary Cassatt. This reduction is similar to the actual painting. The height of the actual painting is 90.2 cm. To the nearest centimeter, what is the width of the actual painting?**

Understand the Problem

The **answer** will be the width of the actual painting.

List the **important information:**

- The actual painting and the reduction above are similar.
- The reduced painting is 4.6 cm tall and 6 cm wide.
- The actual painting is 90.2 cm tall.

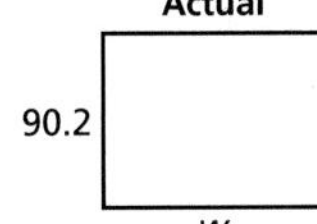

2 Make a Plan

Draw a diagram to represent the situation.

Use the corresponding sides to write a proportion.

Solve

$\frac{4.6 \text{ cm}}{90.2 \text{ cm}} = \frac{6 \text{ cm}}{w \text{ cm}}$ *Write a proportion.*

$90.2 \cdot 6 = 4.6 \cdot w$ *The cross products are equal.*

$541.2 = 4.6w$ *w is multiplied by 4.6.*

$\frac{541.2}{4.6} = \frac{4.6w}{4.6}$ *Divide both sides by 4.6 to undo the multiplication.*

$118 \approx w$ *Round to the nearest centimeter.*

The width of the actual painting is about 118 cm.

4 Look Back

Estimate to check your answer. The ratio of the heights is about 5:90, or 1:18. The ratio of the widths is about 6:120, or 1:20. Since these ratios are close to each other, 118 cm is a reasonable answer.

Remember!

The symbol ≈ means "is approximately equal to."

Think and Discuss GPS M6P3.b, M6P4.c

1. **Name** two items in your classroom that appear to be similar figures.
2. **Describe** how similar figures are different from congruent figures.

Power Presentations with PowerPoint®

Additional Examples

Example 1

The two triangles are similar. Find the missing length y and the measure of $\angle D$.

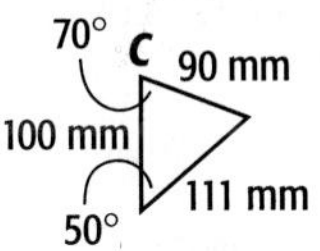

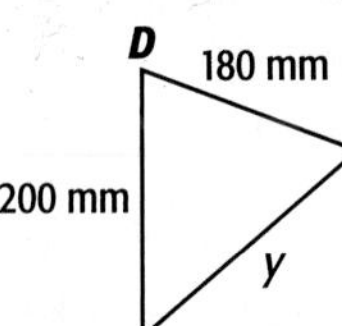

$y = 222$ mm $\quad m\angle D = 70°$

Example 2

This reduction is similar to a picture that Katie painted. The height of the actual painting is 54 centimeters. What is the width of the actual painting?

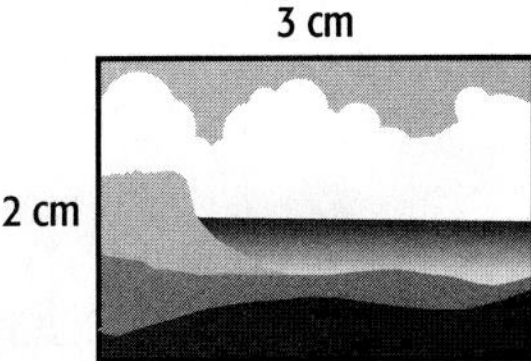

81 cm

Also available on transparency

2 Teach

Guided Instruction

In this lesson, students learn to use ratios to identify similar figures. Define the terms *similar*, *corresponding sides*, and *corresponding angles*. Teach students to use a proportion to find the length of a missing side, given two similar polygons. Then have students apply the concept in a problem-solving context.

Reaching All Learners

Through Inclusion

Have students cut out drawings of similar polygons (Teaching Tools) and have them explore the proportionality of corresponding sides. They can place the cutout figures on top of each other to prove that the corresponding angles are congruent. If time is limited, use this as a reinforcing activity to be completed at home or when time allows.

3 Close

Summarize

ENGLISH LANGUAGE LEARNERS

Have the students discuss how the new vocabulary terms in the lesson (*similar*, *corresponding sides*, and *corresponding angles*) relate to each other.

Possible answer: Two figures are similar if they have the same shape. Corresponding sides of similar figures are proportional. Corresponding angles of similar figures are congruent.

7-4 Exercises

Assignment Guide

If you finished Example 1 assign:
Average 1, 8, 16–23
Advanced 3, 9, 16–23

If you finished Example 2 assign:
Average 1–4, 7–23
Advanced 3–23

Homework Quick Check

Quickly check key concepts.
Exercises: 4, 8, 10

Answers

5. sides: $\overline{AC}$ and $\overline{XY}$; $\overline{XW}$ and $\overline{AB}$; $\overline{BC}$ and $\overline{WY}$; angles: X and A; W and B; Y and C
6. sides: $\overline{KJ}$ and $\overline{ST}$; $\overline{KL}$ and $\overline{SR}$; $\overline{LM}$ and $\overline{RU}$; $\overline{JM}$ and $\overline{TU}$; angles: S and K; L and R; J and T; M and U

Math Background

As with congruence, triangles can be proven similar without having to prove that all pairs of corresponding angles are congruent and all pairs of corresponding sides are in proportion.

If either of the following situations occurs, you can conclude that two triangles are similar: All corresponding sides have lengths that are proportional, or two pairs of corresponding angles are congruent.

Georgia Performance Standards

M6P3.a Organize and consolidate their mathematical thinking through communication.

M6P3.c Analyze and evaluate the mathematical thinking and strategies of others.

M6P5.b Select, apply, and translate among mathematical representations to solve problems.

7-4 Exercises

Georgia Performance Standards
M6P3.a, M6P3.c, M6P5.b

go.hrw.com
Homework Help Online
KEYWORD: MR7 7-4
Parent Resources Online
KEYWORD: MR7 Parent

GUIDED PRACTICE

See Example 1

1. The two triangles are similar. Find the missing length x and the measure of $\angle G$.

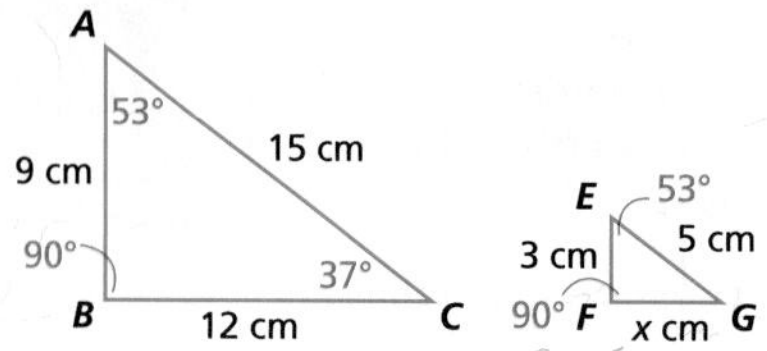

See Example 2

2. Pat's school photo package includes one large photo and several smaller photos. The large photo is similar to the photo at right. If the height of the large photo is 10 in., what is its width?

INDEPENDENT PRACTICE

See Example 1

3. The two triangles are similar. Find the missing length n and the measure of $\angle M$.

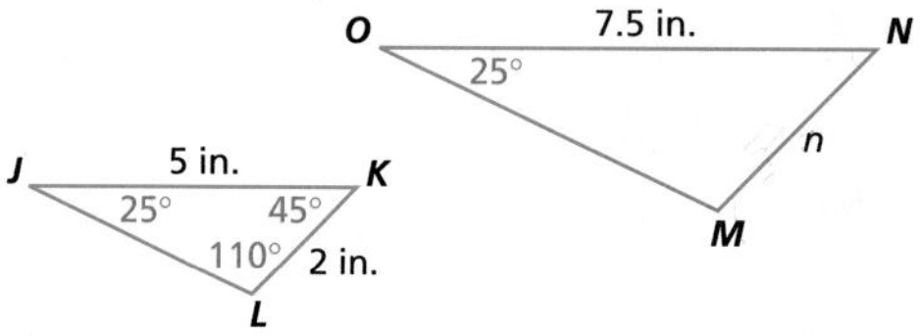

See Example 2

4. LeJuan swims in a pool that is similar to an Olympic-sized pool. LeJuan's pool is 30 m long by 8 m wide. The length of an Olympic-sized pool is 50 m. To the nearest meter, what is the width of an Olympic-sized pool?

PRACTICE AND PROBLEM SOLVING

CRCT GPS
Extra Practice p. 726

Name the corresponding sides and angles for each pair of similar figures.

5.

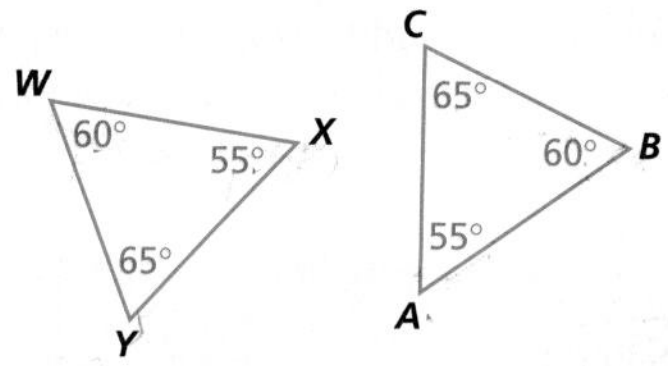

6.

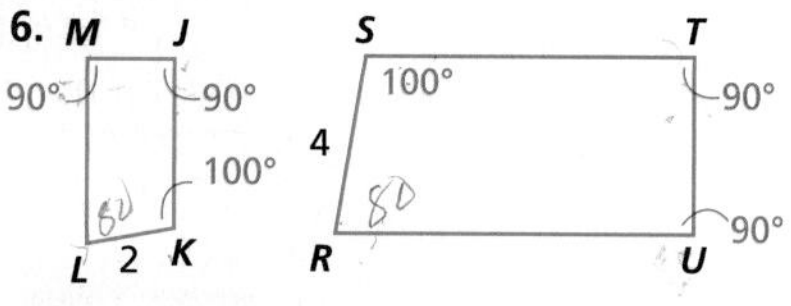

7. **Critical Thinking** The ratio of the lengths of two similar paintings is $\frac{100}{32}$. If the length of one painting is 100 cm, is the length of the other less than or greater than 100 cm? Explain.

RETEACH 7-4

LESSON 7-4 **Reteach**
Similar Figures

Two figures are similar if they have the same shape but are different sizes.

Similar figures have corresponding sides and corresponding angles. Corresponding sides are proportional. Corresponding angles are congruent.

Look at the similar triangles below.

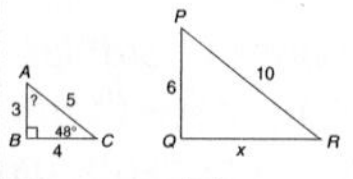

$\overline{AB}$ corresponds to $\overline{PQ}$. $\angle A$ corresponds to $\angle P$.
$\overline{BC}$ corresponds to $\overline{QR}$. $\angle B$ corresponds to $\angle Q$.
$\overline{AC}$ corresponds to $\overline{PR}$. $\angle C$ corresponds to $\angle R$.

What is the length of $\overline{QR}$?

$\frac{AB}{BC} = \frac{PQ}{QR}$	Set up a proportion.
$\frac{3}{4} = \frac{6}{x}$	Substitute the values.
$3 \cdot x = 4 \cdot 6$	The cross products are equal.
$3x = 24$	x is multiplied by 3.
$\frac{3x}{3} = \frac{24}{3}$	Divide both sides by 3.
$x = 8$	

So, the length of $\overline{QR}$ is 8 units.

Find each missing length.

1.

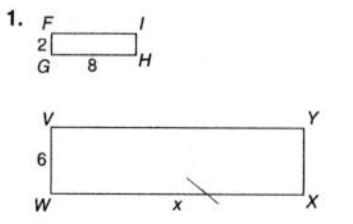

$x = 24$ units

2.

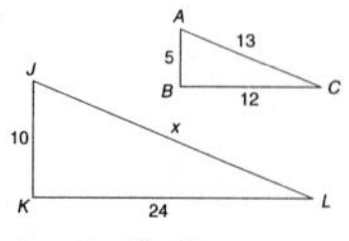

$x = 26$ units

PRACTICE 7-4

LESSON 7-4 **Practice B**
Similar Figures

Write the correct answers.

1. The two triangles are similar. Find the missing length x and the measure of $\angle A$. $x = 18$ ft; $m\angle A = 80°$

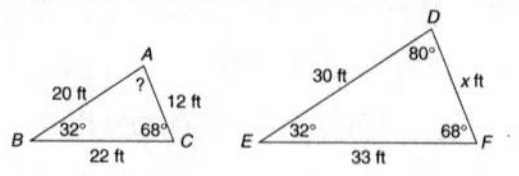

2. The two triangles are similar. Find the missing length x and the measure of $\angle J$. $x = 8$m; $m\angle J = 23°$

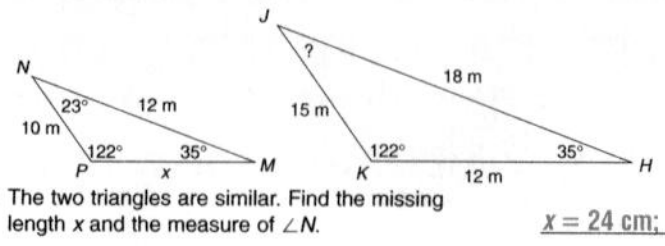

3. The two triangles are similar. Find the missing length x and the measure of $\angle N$. $x = 24$ cm; $m\angle N = 53°$

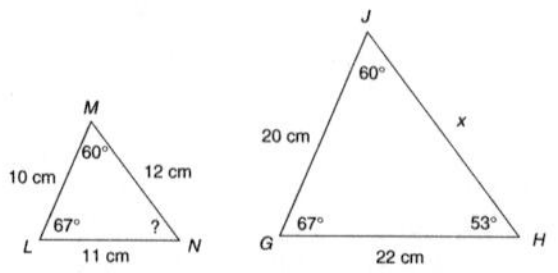

4. Juanita planted two flower gardens in similar square shapes. What are the measures of all the angles in each garden? Explain how you know.

They are all 90°; All squares have all right angles.

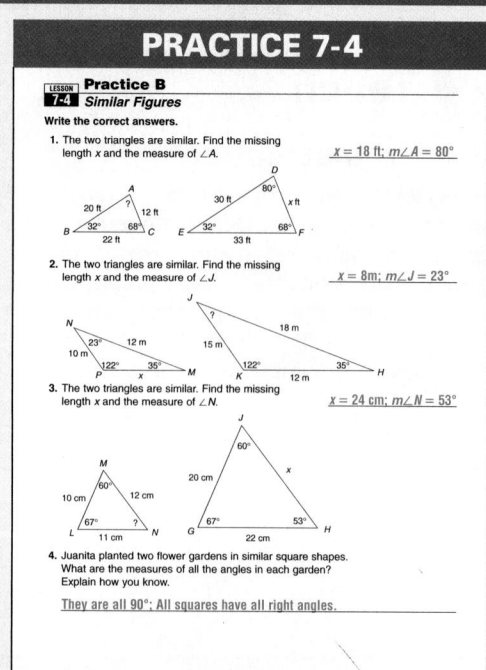

The figures in each pair are similar. Find the unknown measures.

8. 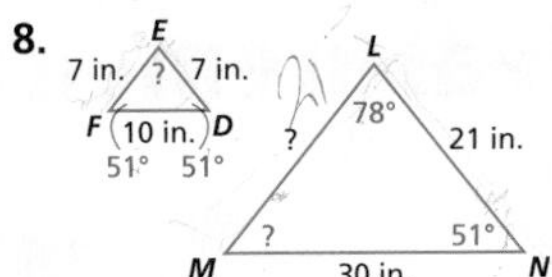

9. 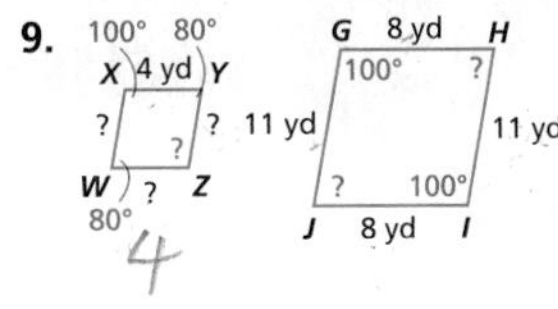

Tell whether the figures in each pair are similar. Explain your answers.

10. 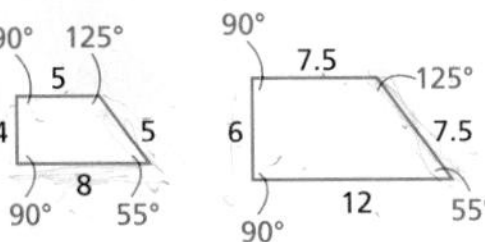

11. 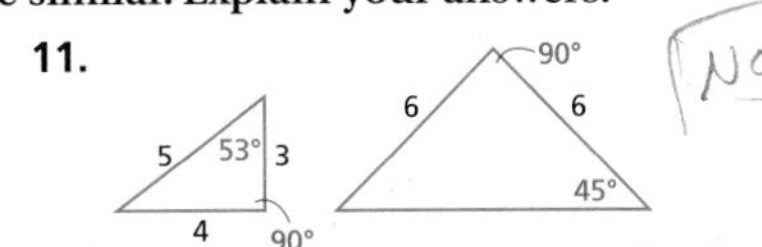

12. Graphic Art Lenny sketches designs for billboards. The sketch and the billboard are similar. If the height of the billboard is 30 ft, what is the width to the nearest foot of the billboard? **50 feet**

13. What's the Error? A student drew two rectangles with dimensions 10 in. by 9 in. and 5 in. by 3 in. The student said that the rectangles are similar. What's the error?

13. The lengths of the sides are not proportional, because $\frac{10}{5}$ does not equal $\frac{9}{3}$.

14. Write About It Are all triangles that have one 90° angle similar? Explain your answer.

14. No; All right triangles have one angle that measures 90 degrees, but not all right triangles have the same angle measures for the other angles.

15. Challenge Draw two similar rectangles whose sides are in a ratio of 5:2.

CRCT Prep • GPS Support • Spiral Review

16. Multiple Choice The triangles are similar. Find the missing angle measure.

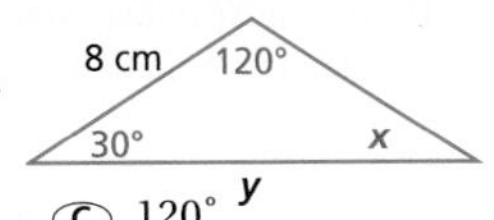

Ⓐ 30° (circled) Ⓑ 60° Ⓒ 120° Ⓓ 180°

17. Multiple Choice Use the similar triangles in Exercise 16. Find the missing length y.

Ⓕ 4 cm Ⓖ 12 cm (circled) Ⓗ 18 cm Ⓙ 24 cm

Identify the property that is illustrated by each equation. (Lesson 1-5)

18. $3 + (4 + 5) = (3 + 4) + 5$ **Associative Property**

19. $19(24) = 19(20) + 19(4)$ **Distributive Property**

20. $(2)(13) = (13)(2)$ **Commutative Property**

Find the value of n in each proportion. (Lesson 7-3)

21. $\frac{n}{7} = \frac{30}{42}$ **5**

22. $\frac{4}{n} = \frac{16}{8}$ **2**

23. $\frac{1}{9} = \frac{n}{6.3}$ **0.7**

Ongoing Assessment and Intervention

***Diagnose Before* the Lesson**
7-4 Warm Up, TE p. 366

***Monitor During* the Lesson**
7-4 Know-It Notebook
7-4 Questioning Strategies

***Assess After* the Lesson**
7-4 Lesson Quiz, TE p. 369

Answers

8. $m\angle E = 78°$, $m\angle M = 51°$; the length of $\overline{ML}$ is 21 in.

9–11, 15. See p. A8.

Test Prep Doctor In Exercise 17, students may find it helpful to carefully redraw the triangles, rotating one 180° so the corresponding sides can be more easily identified. Then, use a proportion to solve for y.

Journal

Have students write an explanation for the following statement: If two figures are congruent, they must also be similar.

Power Presentations with PowerPoint®

7-4 Lesson Quiz

These two triangles are similar.

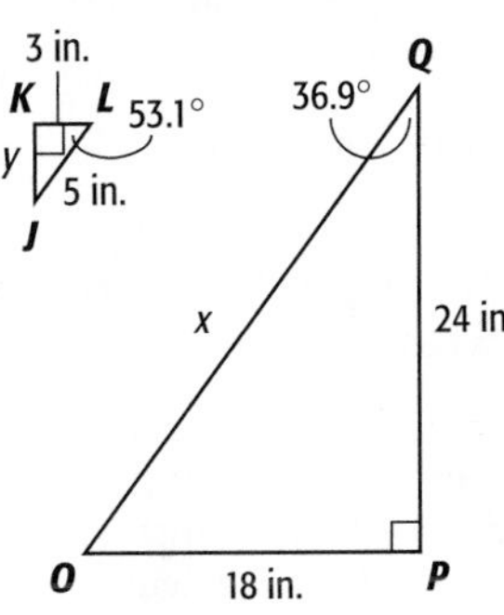

1. Find the missing length x. **30 in.**

2. Find the measure of $\angle J$. **36.9°**

3. Find the missing length y. **4 in.**

4. Find the measure of $\angle P$. **90°**

5. Susan is making a wood deck from plans for an 8 ft by 10 ft deck. However, she is going to increase its size proportionally. If the length is to be 15 ft, what will the width be? **12 ft**

Also available on transparency

Challenge 7-4

Lesson 7-4 Challenge
You Won't Believe Your Eyes!

Answer each question by looking at the drawings below. Then use what you know about similar and congruent figures to verify your answers.

1. 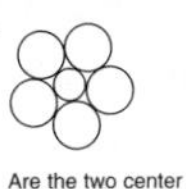
Are the two line segments congruent? **yes**

2. 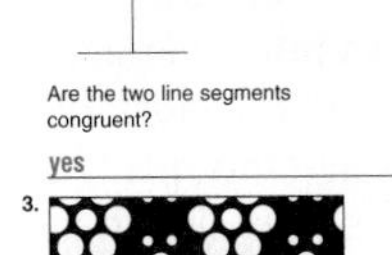
Are the two center circles similar or congruent? **congruent**

3. 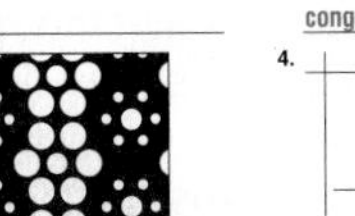
Are any of these circles similar? **yes; all the circles**

4. Are any of these line segments congruent? **yes; horizontal lines**

5. 
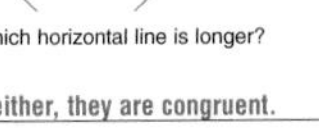
Which horizontal line is longer? **Neither, they are congruent.**

6. 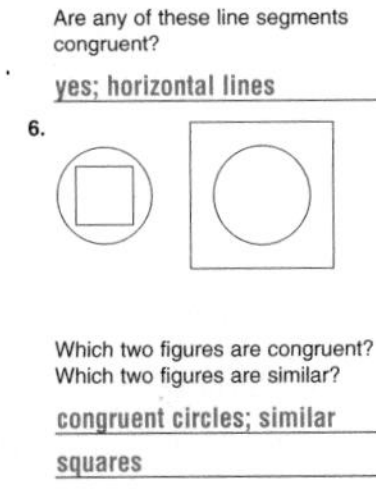
Which two figures are congruent? Which two figures are similar? **congruent circles; similar squares**

Problem Solving 7-4

Lesson 7-4 Problem Solving
Similar Figures

Write the correct answe

1. The map at right shows the dimensions of the Bermuda Triangle, a region of the Atlantic Ocean where many ships and airplanes have disappeared. If a theme park makes a swimming pool in a similar figure, and the longest side of the pool is 0.5 mile long, about how long would the other sides of the pool have to be? **0.403 mile**

2. Completed in 1883, *The Battle of Gettysburg* is 410 feet long and 70 feet tall. A museum shop sells a print of the painting that is similar to the original. The print is 2.05 feet long. How tall is the print? **0.35 ft**

3. *Panorama of the Mississippi* was 12 feet tall and 5,000 feet long! If you wanted to make a copy similar to the original that was 2 feet tall, how many feet long would the copy have to be? **$833\frac{1}{3}$ feet**

Circle the letter of the correct answer.

4. Two tables shaped like triangles are similar. The measure of one of the larger table's angles is 38°, and another angle is half that size. What are the measures of all the angles in the smaller table?
A 19°, 9.5°, and 61.5°
Ⓑ 38°, 19°, and 123°
C 38°, 38°, and 104°
D 76°, 38°, and 246°

5. Two rectangular gardens are similar. The area of the larger garden is 8.28 m², and its length is 6.9 m. The smaller garden is 0.6 m wide. What is the smaller garden's length and area?
F length = 6.9 m; area = 2.07 m²
G length = 3.45 m; area = 4.14 m²
H length = 3.45 m; area = 1.97 m²
Ⓙ length = 3.45 m; area = 2.07 m²

6. Which of the following is not always true if two figures are similar?
A They have the same shape.
Ⓑ They have the same size.
C Their corresponding sides have proportional lengths.
D Their corresponding angles are

7. Which of the following figures are always similar?
F two rectangles
G two triangles
Ⓗ two squares
J two pentagons

7-5 Organizer

Pacing: Traditional 1 day
Block $\frac{1}{2}$ day

Objective: Students use proportions and similar figures to find unknown measures.

Technology Lab
In Technology Lab Activities

Online Edition
Tutorial Videos

Countdown to CRCT Week 15

Warm Up

Find the missing value in each proportion.

1. $\frac{6}{t} = \frac{18}{45}$ $t = 15$
2. $\frac{k}{19} = \frac{20}{76}$ $k = 5$
3. $\frac{6}{8} = \frac{42}{n}$ $n = 56$
4. $\frac{21}{11} = \frac{x}{44}$ $x = 84$

Problem of the Day

Bryce, Kate, and Annie have drawn rectangles. Each side of Bryce's rectangle is twice the size of one side of Kate's. The same side of Kate's rectangle is congruent to one side of Annie's. One side of Annie's rectangle is congruent to one side of Bryce's. Which two rectangles could be congruent? Annie's and Kate's

Also available on transparency

Georgia Performance Standards

M6G1.c Use the concepts of ratio, proportion and scale factor to demonstrate the relationships between similar plane figures.

M6A2.c Use proportions (a/b=c/d) to describe relationships and solve problems, including percent problems.

M6A2.g Use proportional reasoning (a/b=c/d and y = kx) to solve problems.

M6P1.b Solve problems that arise in mathematics and in other contexts.

7-5 Indirect Measurement

Learn to use proportions and similar figures to find unknown measures.

Vocabulary
indirect measurement

Georgia Performance Standards

M6G1.c Use the concepts of ratio, proportion and scale factor to demonstrate the relationships between similar plane figures. Also, M6A2.c, M6A2.g, M6P1.b.

Residents of Maine spent 14 days in 1999 building this enormous snowman. How could you measure the height of this snowman?

One way to find a height that you cannot measure directly is to use similar figures and proportions. This method is called **indirect measurement**.

Suppose that on a sunny day, the snowman cast a shadow that was 228 feet long. A 6-foot-tall person standing by the snowman cast a 12-foot-long shadow.

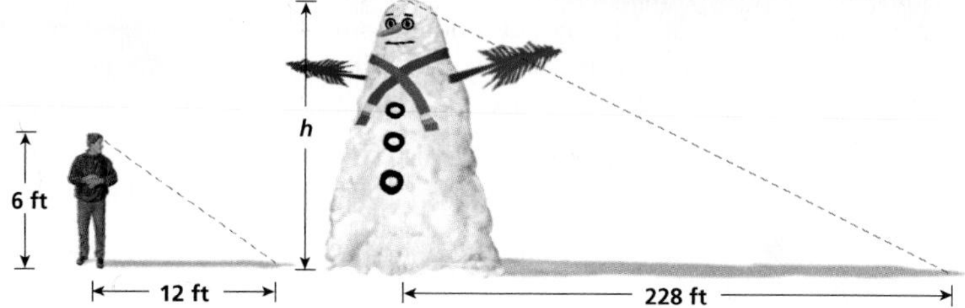

Both the person and the snowman form 90° angles with the ground, and their shadows are cast at the same angle. This means we can form two similar triangles and use proportions to find the missing height.

EXAMPLE 1 Using Indirect Measurement

Use the similar triangles above to find the height of the snowman.

$\frac{6}{h} = \frac{12}{228}$	*Write a proportion using corresponding sides.*
$12 \cdot h = 6 \cdot 228$	*The cross products are equal.*
$12h = 1{,}368$	*h is multiplied by 12.*
$\frac{12h}{12} = \frac{1{,}368}{12}$	*Divide both sides by 12 to undo the multiplication.*
$h = 114$	

The snowman was 114 feet tall.

1 Introduce

Alternate Opener

EXPLORATION

7-5 Indirect Measurement

The heights of very tall structures can be measured indirectly using similar figures and proportions. This method is called *indirect measurement.*

Augustine and Carmen want to measure the height of the school's flagpole. To do this, they go outside and hold a meterstick upright. The meterstick casts a shadow that measures 50 cm.

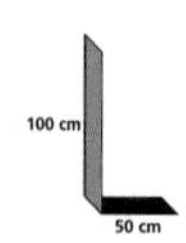

1. If the shadow of the flagpole measures 6 meters, how tall is the flagpole? To answer this question, follow these steps:
   a. Draw a sketch of the flagpole and its shadow next to the sketch of the meterstick and its shadow.
   b. Label the height of the flagpole x.
   c. Write the proportion $\frac{\text{height of flagpole}}{\text{shadow of flagpole}} = \frac{\text{height of meterstick}}{\text{shadow of meterstick}}$, and substitute the values for the given measurements.
   d. Solve the proportion for x.

Think and Discuss

2. **Explain** how you solved the proportion for x in number **1d**.
3. **Explain** whether you could have solved the problem by writing the proportion as $\frac{\text{shadow of flagpole}}{\text{height of flagpole}} = \frac{\text{shadow of meterstick}}{\text{height of meterstick}}$.

2 Teach

Guided Instruction

In this lesson, students learn to use proportions and similar figures to find unknown measures. Teach the indirect measurement method. Have students solve the question presented in the lesson opener and then a similar question. (Teaching Transparency) Teach students to use cross products to check each solution.

Explorations and answers are provided in *Alternate Openers: Explorations Transparencies.*

EXAMPLE 2 *Measurement Application*

Georgia LINK
Measurement

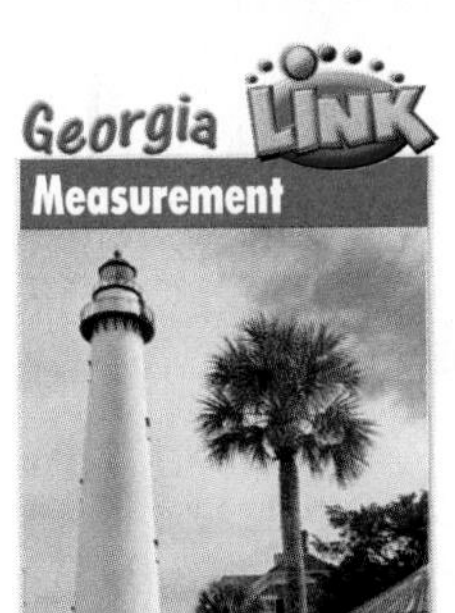

The St. Simons Island Lighthouse can shine a light up to 23 miles out to sea.

A lighthouse casts a shadow that is 36 m long when a meterstick casts a shadow that is 3 m long. How tall is the lighthouse?

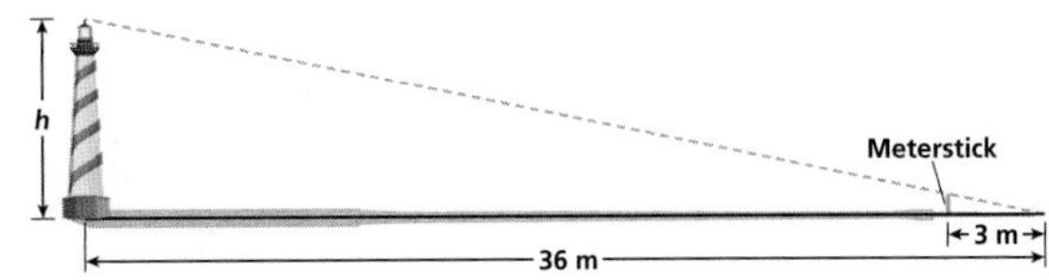

$\frac{h}{1} = \frac{36}{3}$	*Write a proportion using corresponding sides.*
$1 \cdot 36 = 3 \cdot h$	*The cross products are equal.*
$36 = 3h$	*h is multiplied by 3.*
$\frac{36}{3} = \frac{3h}{3}$	*Divide both sides by 3 to undo the multiplication.*
$12 = h$	

The lighthouse is 12 m tall.

Think and Discuss

1. **Name** two items for which it would make sense to use indirect measurement to find their heights.
2. **Name** two items for which it would **not** make sense to use indirect measurement to find their heights.

Possible answers to *Think and Discuss*
1. a flagpole, a tall tree
2. a pencil, a can of soup

7-5 Exercises

M6P3.a, M6P4.c, M6P5.b

go.hrw.com
Homework Help Online
KEYWORD: MR7 7-5
Parent Resources Online
KEYWORD: MR7 Parent

GUIDED PRACTICE

See Example 1

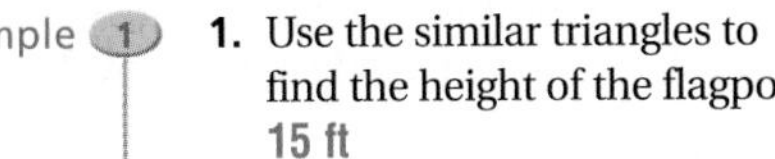

1. Use the similar triangles to find the height of the flagpole. **15 ft**

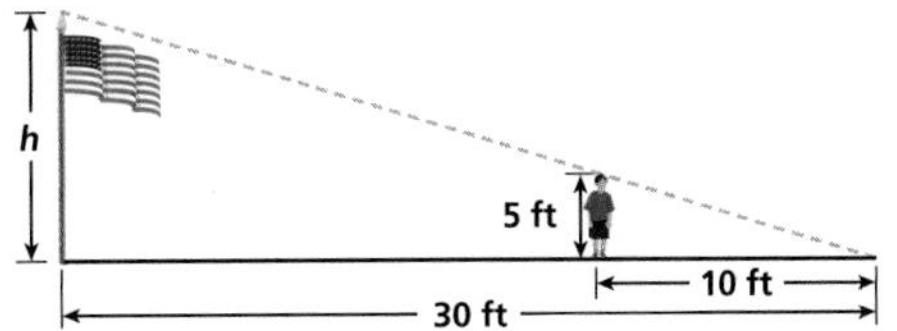

See Example 2

2. A tree casts a shadow that is 26 ft long. At the same time, a 3-foot-tall sunflower casts a shadow that is 4 ft long. How tall is the tree? **19.5 ft**

Power Presentations with PowerPoint®

Additional Examples

Example 1

Use the similar triangles to find the height of the tree.

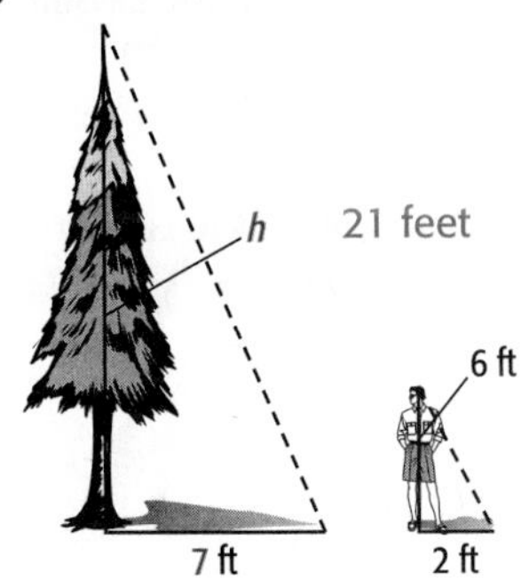

Example 2

A rocket casts a shadow that is 91.5 feet long. A 4-foot model rocket casts a shadow that is 3 feet long. How tall is the rocket? 122 feet

Also available on transparency

7-5 Exercises

Assignment Guide

If you finished Example 1 assign:
Average 1, 5, 10–18
Advanced 3, 6, 10–18

If you finished Example 2 assign:
Average 1–5, 8–18
Advanced 3–18

Homework Quick Check

Quickly check key concepts.
Exercises: 4, 6, 8

3 Close

Summarize

You may wish to review the teaching examples, explaining step by step what each number represents in each proportion.

Reaching All Learners

Through Diversity

Have students do research to find heights of various landmarks around the world. (You may wish to assign a different landmark to each student.) Then have them write an indirect measurement problem about their landmarks. (Model how to write such a problem.) Display these problems on a bulletin board and have students solve some of the problems written by the other students.

Georgia Performance Standards

M6P3.a Organize and consolidate their mathematical thinking through communication.

M6P4.c Recognize and apply mathematics in contexts outside of mathematics.

M6P5.b Select, apply, and translate among mathematical representations to solve problems.

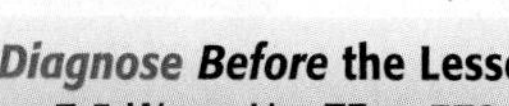

ONGOING ASSESSMENT and INTERVENTION

Diagnose ***Before*** **the Lesson**
7-5 Warm Up, TE p. 370

Monitor ***During*** **the Lesson**
7-5 Know-It Notebook
7-5 Questioning Strategies

Assess ***After*** **the Lesson**
7-5 Lesson Quiz, TE p. 372

Power Presentations with PowerPoint®

7-5 Lesson Quiz

1. Use the similar triangles to find the height of the post. **20 ft**

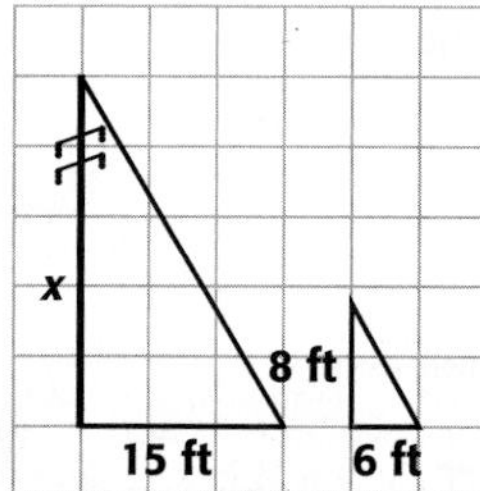

2. On a sunny afternoon, a goalpost casts a 75 ft shadow. A 6.5 ft football player next to the goal post has a shadow 19.5 ft long. How tall is the goalpost? **25 feet**

Also available on transparency

INDEPENDENT PRACTICE

See Example 1

3. Use the similar triangles to find the height of the lamppost. **18 ft**

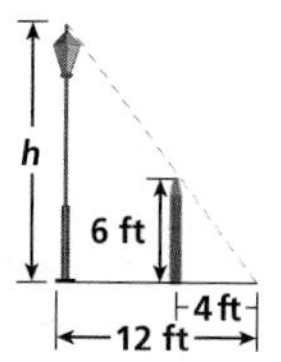

See Example 2

4. The Eiffel Tower casts a shadow that is 328 feet long. A 6-foot-tall person standing by the tower casts a 2-foot-long shadow. How tall is the Eiffel Tower? **984 ft**

PRACTICE AND PROBLEM SOLVING

CRCT GPS
Extra Practice p. 726

Find the unknown heights.

5. 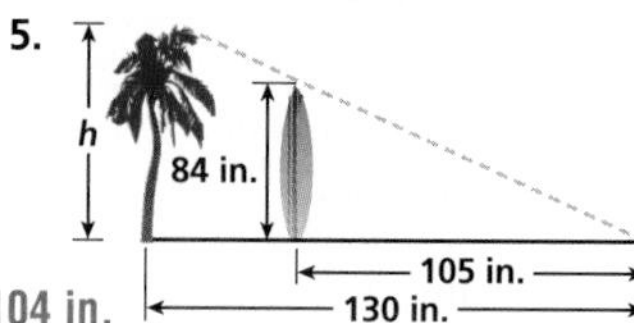

104 in.

6. 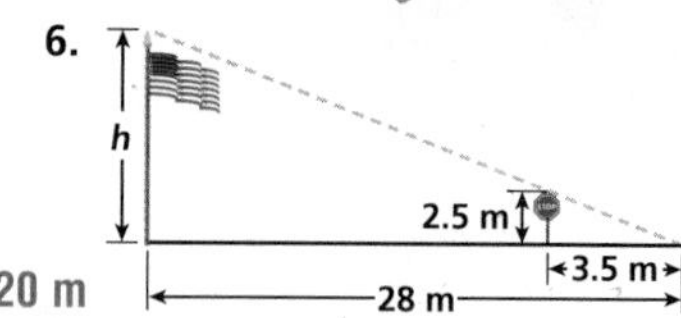

20 m

7. A statue casts a shadow that is 360 m long. At the same time, a person who is 2 m tall casts a shadow that is 6 m long. How tall is the statue? **120 m**

8. **Write About It** How are indirect measurements useful?

8. Possible answer: Using indirect measurements allows you to find the heights of tall objects that would otherwise be difficult to measure.

9. **Challenge** A 5.5-foot-tall girl stands so that her shadow lines up with the shadow of a telephone pole. The tip of her shadow is even with the tip of the pole's shadow. If the length of the pole's shadow is 40 feet and the girl is standing 27.5 feet away from the pole, how tall is the telephone pole? **17.6 ft**

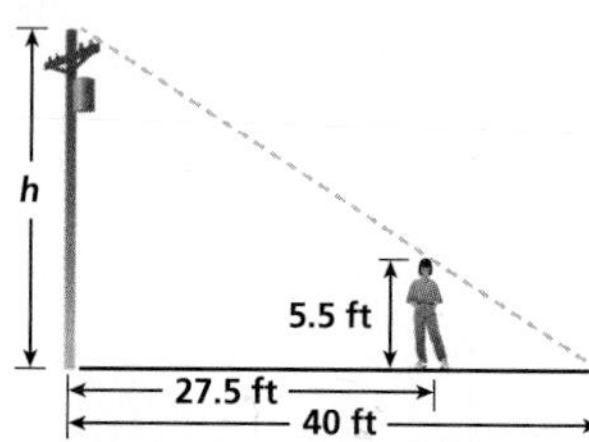

CRCT PREP • GPS SUPPORT • SPIRAL REVIEW

10. **Multiple Choice** An 18-foot-tall telephone pole casts a shadow that is 28.8 feet long. At the same time, a woman casts a shadow that is 8.8 feet long. How tall is the woman?

Ⓐ 4.4 feet **Ⓑ 5.5 feet** Ⓒ 14.08 feet Ⓓ 158.4 feet

11. **Gridded Response** A 4-foot-tall girl casts a shadow that is 7.2 feet long. A nearby tree casts a shadow that is 25.56 feet long. How tall, in feet, is the tree? **14.2**

Estimate by rounding to the indicated place value. (Lesson 3-2)

12. 4.325 − 1.895; tenths **2.4**
13. 5.121 − 0.1568; tenths **4.9**
14. 7.592 + 9.675; hundredths **17.27**

Solve each equation. Write the solution in simplest form. (Lesson 5-5)

15. $x - 1\frac{1}{4} = 7$ **$\frac{33}{4}$ or $8\frac{1}{4}$**
16. $4\frac{1}{3} = x + \frac{5}{6}$ **$\frac{21}{6}$ or $3\frac{1}{2}$**
17. $x - 8\frac{1}{2} = \frac{3}{10}$ **$\frac{88}{10}$ or $8\frac{4}{5}$**
18. $6\frac{2}{3} = 4\frac{1}{6} + x$ **$\frac{17}{6}$ or $2\frac{5}{6}$**

CHALLENGE 7-5
PROBLEM SOLVING 7-5

LESSON 7-5 **Problem Solving**
Indirect Measurement

Use the table to answer each question.

1. The Petronas Towers in Malaysia are the tallest buildings in the world. On a sunny day, the Petronas Towers cast shadows that are 4,428 feet long. A 6-foot-tall person standing by one building casts an 18-foot-long shadow. How tall are the Petronas Towers?
1,476 feet

2. The Sears Tower in Chicago is the tallest building in the United States. On a sunny day, the Sears Tower casts a shadow that is 2,908 feet long. A 5-foot-tall person standing by the building casts a 10-foot-long shadow. How tall is the Sears Tower?
1,454 feet

3. The world's tallest man cast a shadow that was 535 inches long. At the same time, a woman who was 5 feet 4 inches tall cast a shadow that was 320 inches long. How tall was the world's tallest man in feet and inches?
8 feet 11 inches

4. Hoover Dam on the Colorado River casts a shadow that is 2,904 feet long. At the same time, an 18-foot-tall flagpole next to the dam casts a shadow that is 72 feet long. How tall is Hoover Dam?
726 feet

Circle the letter of the correct answer.

5. An NFL goalpost casts a shadow that is 170 feet long. At the same time, a yardstick casts a shadow that is 51 feet long. How tall is an NFL goalpost?
A 100 feet
B 56 2/3 feet
Ⓒ 10 feet
D 1 foot

6. A gorilla casts a shadow that is 600 centimeters long. A 92-centimeter-tall chimpanzee casts a shadow that is 276 centimeters long. What is the height of the gorilla in meters?
F 0.2 meter
Ⓖ 2 meters
H 20 meters
J 200 meters

7. A 6-foot-tall man casts a shadow that is 30 feet long. If a boy standing next to the man casts a shadow that is 12 feet long, how tall is the boy?
A 2.2 feet **Ⓒ 2.4 feet**
B 5 feet D 2 feet

8. An ostrich is 108 inches tall. If its shadow is 162 inches, and an emu standing next to it casts a 90-inch shadow, how tall is the emu?
F 162 inches **Ⓗ 60 inches**
G 90 inches J 194.4 inches

RETEACH 7-5

LESSON 7-5 **Reteach**
Indirect Measurement

If you cannot measure a length directly, you can use indirect measurement. Indirect measurement uses similar figures and proportions to find lengths.

The small tree is 8 feet high and it casts a 12-foot shadow. The large tree casts a 36-foot shadow.

8 ft
12 ft

The triangles formed by the trees and the shadows are similar. So, their heights are proportional.

To find the height of the large tree, first set up a proportion. Use a variable to stand for the height of the large tree.

x
36 ft

$\frac{8}{12} = \frac{x}{36}$	Write a proportion using corresponding sides.
$8 \cdot 36 = 12 \cdot x$	The cross products are equal.
$12x = 288$	x is multiplied by 12.
$\frac{12x}{12} = \frac{288}{12}$	Divide both sides by 12.
$x = 24$	

So, the height of the tall tree is 24 feet.

Use indirect measurement to find the missing heights.

1. x; 75 ft; 6 ft; 3 ft
150 feet

2. 15 ft; 25 ft; h; 10 ft
6 feet

PRACTICE 7-5

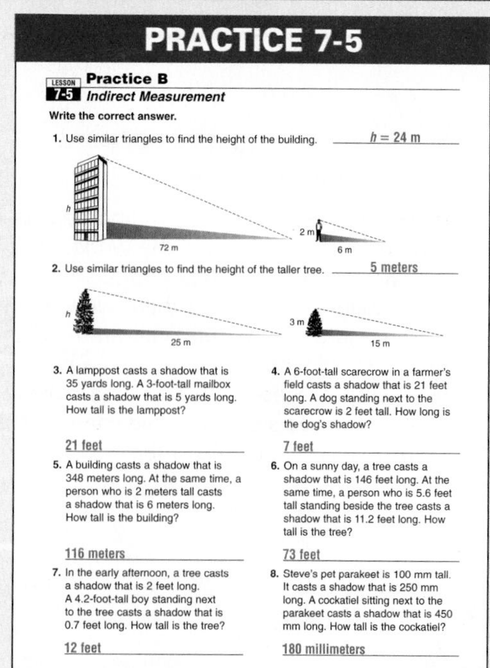

LESSON 7-5 **Practice B**
Indirect Measurement

Write the correct answer.

1. Use similar triangles to find the height of the building. **h = 24 m**

h; 72 m; 2 m; 6 m

2. Use similar triangles to find the height of the taller tree. **5 meters**

h; 25 m; 3 m; 15 m

3. A lamppost casts a shadow that is 35 yards long. A 3-foot-tall mailbox casts a shadow that is 5 yards long. How tall is the lamppost?
21 feet

4. A 6-foot-tall scarecrow in a farmer's field casts a shadow that is 21 feet long. A dog standing next to the scarecrow is 2 feet tall. How long is the dog's shadow?
7 feet

5. A building casts a shadow that is 348 meters long. At the same time, a person who is 2 meters tall casts a shadow that is 6 meters long. How tall is the building?
116 meters

6. On a sunny day, a tree casts a shadow that is 146 feet long. At the same time, a person who is 5.6 feet tall standing beside the tree casts a shadow that is 11.2 feet long. How tall is the tree?
73 feet

7. In the early afternoon, a tree casts a shadow that is 2 feet long. A 4.2-foot-tall boy standing next to the tree casts a shadow that is 0.7 feet long. How tall is the tree?
12 feet

8. Steve's pet parakeet is 100 mm tall. It casts a shadow that is 250 mm long. A cockatiel sitting next to the parakeet casts a shadow that is 450 mm long. How tall is the cockatiel?
180 millimeters

Sketch Scale Drawings

Use with Lesson 7-6

go.hrw.com
Lab Resources Online
KEYWORD: MR7 Lab7

REMEMBER

- Similar figures are exactly the same shape, but they may be different sizes.

Georgia Performance Standards

M6G1.d, M6P2.c

You can use a *scale factor* to sketch scale drawings. A *scale drawing* is a drawing of an object that is proportionally smaller or larger than the object. A *scale factor* is the ratio that describes how much a figure is enlarged or reduced.

Activity

Draw triangle A on graph paper with height 1 and base 3 as shown.

To draw a similar triangle using a scale factor of 3, draw another triangle whose sides are 3 times as long as the corresponding sides of the original.

To find the height of the new triangle, multiply the height of triangle A by 3.
height = 1 × 3 = 3; the new height will be 3 units.

To find the base of the new triangle, multiply the base of triangle A by 3.
base = 3 × 3 = 9; the new base will be 9 units.

Label the new figure triangle B.

For every 1 unit of length on the original triangle, the second triangle has 3 units of length.

Think and Discuss

1. How does knowing the scale factor help you find the dimensions of a similar figure? It helps you find how many units the new figure will be compared to the original.
2. If you use a scale factor of $\frac{3}{2}$, will the new figure be larger or smaller than the original? Explain.
It will be larger; for every 2 units on the original, the new figure will be 3 units.

Try This

Use the given scale factor to draw a figure similar to triangle A.

1. 4 **2.** $\frac{1}{2}$ **3.** 2 **4.** $\frac{3}{2}$

Organizer

Use with Lesson 7-6

Pacing:
Traditional 1 day
Block $\frac{1}{2}$ day

Objective: Use a scale factor to produce similar figures.

Materials: Graph paper

Online Edition

Countdown to CRCT Week 15

Resources

Hands-On Lab Activities
Lab 7-6 Recording Sheet

Teach

Discuss

Have students discuss what they would do if they were given a 6 in. square and were asked to draw a square half that size, or twice that size.

Close

Key Concept

Scale drawings accurately represent objects without being drawn full size.

Assessment

Use a square with a height of 4 and the given scale factor to draw a similar figure.

1. scale factor: 2

2. scale factor: $\frac{1}{4}$

Answers to *Try This*

1.

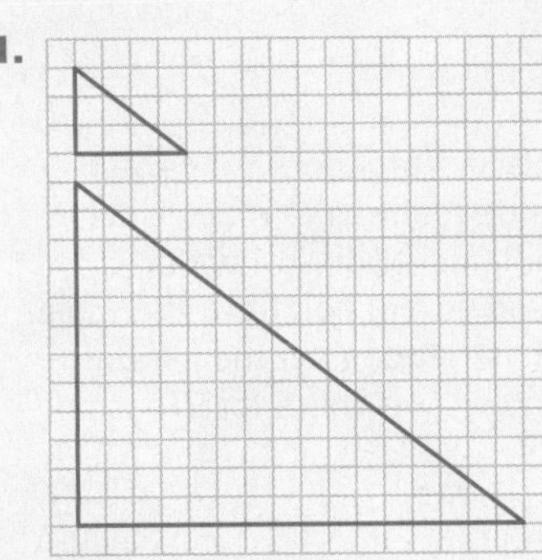

2–4. See p. A8.

Answers to *Assessment*

1.

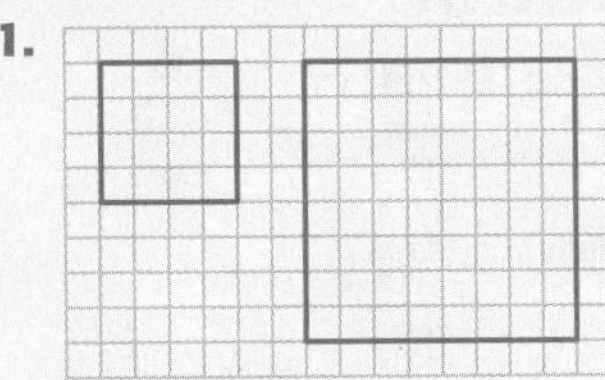

2.

Georgia Performance Standards

M6G1.d Interpret and sketch simple scale drawings.

M6P2.c Develop and evaluate mathematical arguments and proofs.

7-6 Organizer

Pacing: Traditional 1 day
Block $\frac{1}{2}$ day

Objective: Students read and use map scales and scale drawings.

GPS M6G1.c, M6G1.e
Hands-On Lab
In *Hands-On Lab Activities*

Online Edition
Tutorial Videos, Interactivities

Countdown to CRCT Week 15

Power Presentations with PowerPoint®

Warm Up

Find the unknown heights.

1. A tower casts a 56 ft shadow. A 5 ft girl next to it casts a 3.5 ft shadow. How tall is the tower? 80 ft
2. A 50 ft silo casts a 10 ft shadow. The barn next to the silo casts a shadow that is 4 ft long. How tall is the barn? 20 ft

Problem of the Day

Hal runs 4 miles in 32 minutes. Julie runs 5 miles more than Hal runs. If Julie runs at the same rate as Hal, for how many minutes will Julie run? 72 minutes

Also available on transparency

Math Humor

What do you call people who are in favor of tractors? Protractors

Georgia Performance Standards

M6G1.c Use the concepts of ratio, proportion and scale factor to demonstrate the relationships between similar plane figures.

M6G1.e Solve problems involving scale drawings.

M6A2.c Use proportions (a/b=c/d) to describe relationships and solve problems, including percent problems.

M6A2.g Use proportional reasoning (a/b=c/d and y = kx) to solve problems.

M6P4.c Recognize and apply mathematics in contexts outside of mathematics.

7-6 Scale Drawings and Maps

Learn to read and use map scales and scale drawings.

Vocabulary
scale drawing
scale

Georgia Performance Standards

M6G1.e Solve problems involving scale drawings. Also, M6G1.c, M6A2.c, M6A2.g, M6P4.c.

The map of Yosemite National Park shown above is a *scale drawing*. A **scale drawing** is a drawing of a real object that is proportionally smaller or larger than the real object. In other words, measurements on a scale drawing are in proportion to the measurements of the real object.

A **scale** is a ratio between two sets of measurements. In the map above, the scale is 1 in:2 mi. This ratio means that 1 inch on the map represents 2 miles in Yosemite National Park.

EXAMPLE 1 Finding Actual Distances

On the map, the distance between El Capitan and Panorama Cliff is 2 inches. What is the actual distance?

$\frac{1 \text{ in.}}{2 \text{ mi}} = \frac{2 \text{ in.}}{x \text{ mi}}$ *Write a proportion using the scale. Let x be the actual number of miles from El Capitan to Panorama Cliff.*

$2 \cdot 2 = 1 \cdot x$ *The cross products are equal.*

$4 = x$

The actual distance from El Capitan to Panorama Cliff is 4 miles.

Helpful Hint

In Example 1, think "1 inch is 2 miles, so 2 inches is how many miles?" This approach will help you set up proportions in similar problems.

1 Introduce

Alternate Opener

EXPLORATION

7-6 Scale Drawings and Maps

A *scale* is a ratio between two sets of measurements. For example, the scale 2 in:1 mi means that 2 inches on a scale drawing represents 1 mile.

1. Each letter of the Hollywood sign measures 50 ft tall and 30 ft wide. Use the rectangles below to sketch a scale drawing of the Hollywood sign. The side lengths of each square inside each rectangle represent 10 ft.

2. If the total width of the Hollywood sign is approximately 450 ft, what is the approximate distance between each pair of neighboring letters?

Think and Discuss

3. **Explain** how you found the answer in number 2.
4. **Discuss** other examples of scale drawings.

Motivate

Have a class discussion about maps. Ask students to name features of maps, such as roads, mountains, bodies of water, towns/cities, and so on. Point out the scale on a map and ask students if they know what it is and what it is there for. (Teaching Transparency)

Explorations and answers are provided in *Alternate Openers: Explorations Transparencies.*

EXAMPLE 2 *Astronomy Application*

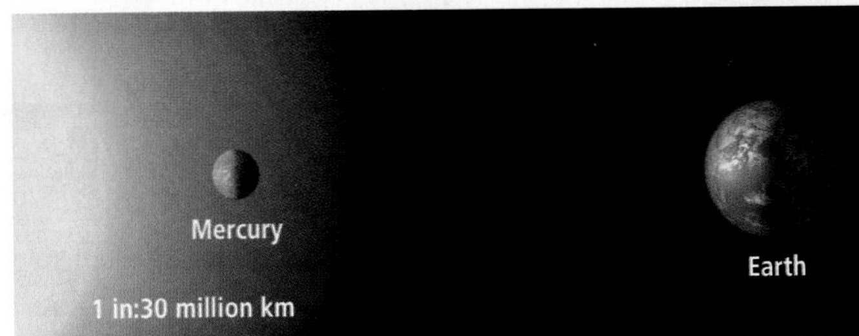

A What is the actual distance from Mercury to Earth?

Use your inch ruler to measure the distance from the center of Mercury to the center of Earth on the drawing. Mercury and Earth are about 3 inches apart.

$\frac{1 \text{ in.}}{30 \text{ million km}} = \frac{3 \text{ in.}}{x \text{ million km}}$ *Write a proportion. Let x be the actual distance from Mercury to Earth.*

$30 \cdot 3 = 1 \cdot x$ *The cross products are equal.*

$90 = x$

The actual distance from Mercury to Earth is about 90 million km.

B The actual distance from Mercury to Venus is 50 million kilometers. How far apart should Mercury and Venus be drawn?

$\frac{1 \text{ in.}}{30 \text{ million km}} = \frac{x \text{ in.}}{50 \text{ million km}}$ *Write a proportion. Let x be the distance from Mercury to Venus on the drawing.*

$30 \cdot x = 1 \cdot 50$ *The cross products are equal.*

$30x = 50$ *x is multiplied by 30.*

$\frac{30x}{30} = \frac{50}{30}$ *Divide both sides by 30 to undo the multiplication.*

$x = 1\frac{2}{3}$

Mercury and Venus should be drawn $1\frac{2}{3}$ inches apart.

Think and Discuss  GPS M6P3.b, M6P4.c

1. **Give an example** of when you would use a scale drawing.
2. **Suppose** that you are going to make a scale drawing of your classroom with a scale of 1 inch:3 feet. Select a distance in your classroom and measure it. What will this distance be on your drawing?

Some students may confuse the order of the measurements in the scale. The distance on the drawing always precedes the actual distance.

Power Presentations with PowerPoint®

Additional Examples

Example 1

The scale on a map is 4 in:1 mi. On the map, the distance between two towns is 20 in. What is the actual distance? 5 miles

Example 2

A. If a drawing of the planets was made using the scale 1 in:30 million km, the distance from Mars to Jupiter on the drawing would be about 18.3 in. What is the actual distance from Mars to Jupiter?

The actual distance from Mars to Jupiter is about 549 million km.

B. The actual distance from Earth to Mars is about 78 million kilometers. How far apart should they be drawn?

Earth and Mars should be $2\frac{3}{5}$ inches apart on the drawing.

Also available on transparency

Answers to *Think and Discuss*

1. Possible answer: to draw the floor plan of a house
2. Possible answer: The distance from the door to the teacher's desk is 9 feet. So on my scale drawing that distance should be 3 inches.

2 Teach

Guided Instruction

In this lesson, students learn to read and use map scales and scale drawings. Teach students to set up proportions using a map scale and a given map distance to find the actual distance. Then teach students to determine the map distance, given an actual distance.

Critical Thinking Point out that map scales vary depending on the size of the area being mapped and the size of a map. An inch on an 11 × 17 inch map of a small town would represent a smaller distance than an inch on an 11 × 17 inch map of a state or country.

Reaching All Learners
Through Curriculum Integration

Social Studies Give each student a map or atlas. Have them use the map's scale to calculate actual distances between cities or other landmarks. Have students show how they wrote and solved each proportion to find each distance.

3 Close

ENGLISH LANGUAGE LEARNERS

Summarize

You may wish to have students explain the terms *scale* and *scale drawing.* Ask how a scale on a map is used to find actual distances.

Possible answers: A scale is a ratio between two sets of measurements, and a scale drawing is a drawing of a real object that is similar to the real object. You can set up a proportion using a map scale and a measured distance on the map to find the actual distance.

7-6 Exercises

Assignment Guide

If you finished Example 1 assign:
Average 1, 8, 16–27
Advanced 4, 8, 16–27

If you finished Example 2 assign:
Average 1–6, 8–27
Advanced 4–27

Homework Quick Check

Quickly check key concepts.
Exercises: 6, 8, 10, 12

Answers

7b–7c. See p. A8.

Math Background

The mathematical problem of mapping Earth lies in the fact that its surface is curved and the surface of a map is flat. There is no way to maintain both the correct shapes of the various objects on Earth and the relative sizes of those objects when making a world map. For this reason, maps historically have made some parts of the world appear larger than they actually are (e.g., Europe) while making other parts appear smaller than they actually are (e.g., Africa). More recent mapmakers have sought to correct this distortion of relative size, but as a result they have created maps in which the shapes of continents do not resemble their true shapes.

Georgia Performance Standards

M6P1.b Solve problems that arise in mathematics and in other contexts.

M6P3.a Organize and consolidate their mathematical thinking through communication.

M6P5.c Use representations to model and interpret physical, social, and mathematical phenomena.

7-6 Exercises

M6P1.b, M6P3.a, M6P5.c

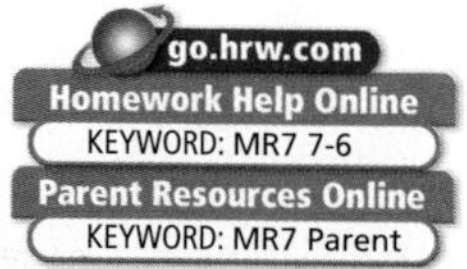

GUIDED PRACTICE

See Example 1

1. On the map, the distance between the post office and the fountain is 6 cm. What is the actual distance? **300 ft**

Scale: 1 cm:50 ft

See Example 2

2. What is the actual length of the car? **4.4 m**
3. The actual height of the car is 1.6 meters. Is the car's height in the drawing correct? **No; the height should be about 2 cm**

Scale: 1 cm:0.8 m

INDEPENDENT PRACTICE

See Example 1

4. On the map of California, Los Angeles is 1.25 inches from Malibu. Find the actual distance from Los Angeles to Malibu. **25 miles**

See Example 2

5. Riverside, California, is 50 miles from Los Angeles. On the map, how far should Riverside be from Los Angeles? **2.5 inches**

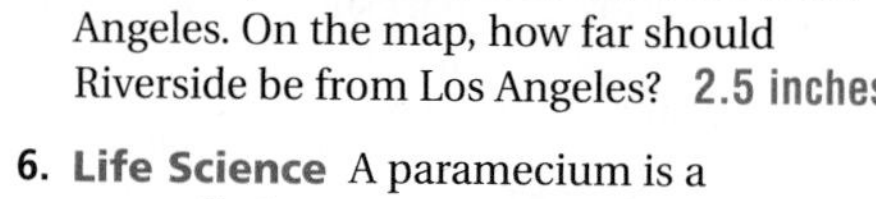

Scale: 1 in:20 mi

6. **Life Science** A paramecium is a one-celled organism. The scale drawing at right is larger than an actual paramecium. Find the actual length of the paramecium. **0.009375 inches**

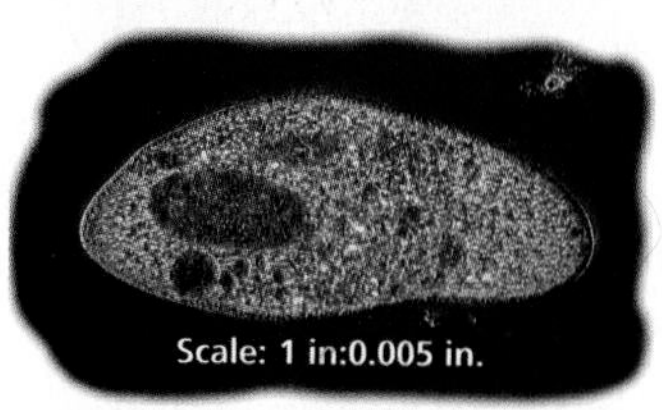
Scale: 1 in:0.005 in.

PRACTICE AND PROBLEM SOLVING

Extra Practice p. 726

7. Suppose you are asked to make a scale drawing of a room. The room has four walls. The lengths of the walls are as follows: north wall, 8 ft; west wall, 12 ft; south wall, 20 ft; slanted east wall, 17 ft. The scale for the drawing is 1 in:4 ft.
   a. Use the actual lengths of the walls to find the lengths in the drawing.
   b. Sketch the room and label each wall. What shape does the room resemble?
   c. Mark a 2.5 ft wide window on the west wall, and a 3.5 ft wide door on the south wall. Give the width of each on the scale drawing.

7. north wall: 2 in.; west wall: 3 in.; south wall: 5 in.; east wall: 4.25 in.

8. **Hobbies** A popular scale used in model trains is called HO. The scale for HO is 1 ft:87 ft. If a model train is 3 feet long, how long is the actual train? **261 ft**

RETEACH 7-6

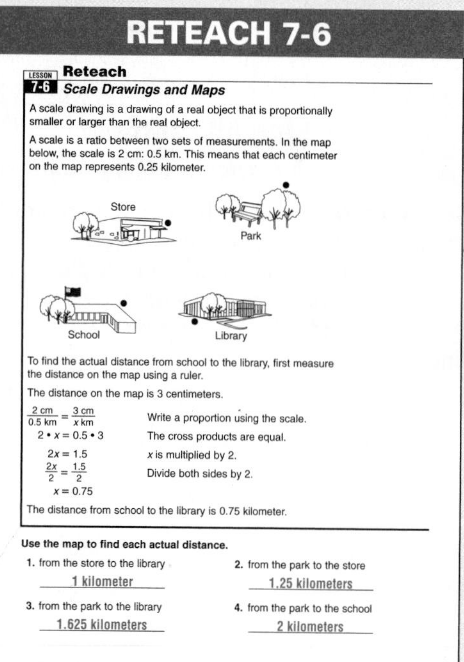

LESSON 7-6 **Reteach**
Scale Drawings and Maps

A scale drawing is a drawing of a real object that is proportionally smaller or larger than the real object.

A scale is a ratio between two sets of measurements. In the map below, the scale is 2 cm: 0.5 km. This means that each centimeter on the map represents 0.25 kilometer.

To find the actual distance from school to the library, first measure the distance on the map using a ruler.

The distance on the map is 3 centimeters.

$\frac{2 \text{ cm}}{0.5 \text{ km}} = \frac{3 \text{ cm}}{x \text{ km}}$	Write a proportion using the scale.
$2 \cdot x = 0.5 \cdot 3$	The cross products are equal.
$2x = 1.5$	x is multiplied by 2.
$\frac{2x}{2} = \frac{1.5}{2}$	Divide both sides by 2.
$x = 0.75$	

The distance from school to the library is 0.75 kilometer.

Use the map to find each actual distance.

1. from the store to the library **1 kilometer**
2. from the park to the store **1.25 kilometers**
3. from the park to the library **1.625 kilometers**
4. from the park to the school **2 kilometers**

PRACTICE 7-6

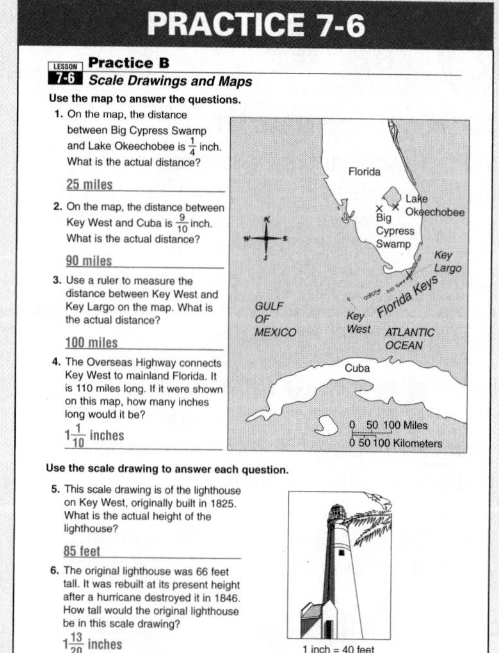

LESSON 7-6 **Practice B**
Scale Drawings and Maps

Use the map to answer the questions.

1. On the map, the distance between Big Cypress Swamp and Lake Okeechobee is $\frac{1}{4}$ inch. What is the actual distance? **25 miles**
2. On the map, the distance between Key West and Cuba is $\frac{9}{10}$ inch. What is the actual distance? **90 miles**
3. Use a ruler to measure the distance between Key West and Key Largo on the map. What is the actual distance? **100 miles**
4. The Overseas Highway connects Key West to mainland Florida. It is 110 miles long. If it were shown on this map, how many inches long would it be? **$1\frac{1}{10}$ inches**

Use the scale drawing to answer each question.

5. This scale drawing is of the lighthouse on Key West, originally built in 1825. What is the actual height of the lighthouse? **85 feet**
6. The original lighthouse was 66 feet tall. It was rebuilt at its present height after a hurricane destroyed it in 1846. How tall would the original lighthouse be in this scale drawing? **$1\frac{13}{20}$ inches**

1 inch = 40 feet

Social Studies 

Texas is the second largest state in the country and is the largest state in the lower 48 states. It is more than 1,120 kilometers across. There is even a ranch in Texas that is larger than Rhode Island!

AMARILLO, FORT WORTH, DALLAS, EL PASO, AUSTIN, HOUSTON, SAN ANTONIO, CORPUS CHRISTI

Scale: 1 cm:119 km

9. What is the distance in kilometers from Houston to Dallas? 357 km
10. What is the distance in kilometers from Corpus Christi to San Antonio? 226.1 km
11. Name two cities on the map that are more than 200 kilometers apart.
    Possible answer: Corpus Christi and Amarillo
12. Wichita Falls is about 480 kilometers from San Antonio.
    a. About how far apart should these two cities be on the map? about 4 cm
    b. What else would you need to know to be able to place Wichita Falls on the map? Possible answer: You would have to know which direction Wichita Falls is from San Antonio.
13. **Write a Problem** Write a problem using the map and its scale. Possible answer: About how far is Fort Worth from Dallas?
14. **Write About It** Explain how to find the actual distance between two cities if you know the distance on a map and the scale of the map. Write a proportion using the map distance and the scale. Solve the proportion.
15. **Challenge** If you drive at a constant speed of 100 kilometers per hour, about how long will it take you to drive from Amarillo to San Antonio? about 7 hours

CRCT Prep • GPS Support • Spiral Review

16. **Multiple Choice** The distance between towns A and C on a map is 13 centimeters. What is the actual distance between towns B and C?

5 cm — Town A, Town B, Town C

Scale: 1 cm:30 km

Ⓐ 0.27 kilometers Ⓑ 150 kilometers Ⓒ 240 kilometers Ⓓ 390 kilometers

17. **Gridded Response** Tanya has a 1 in:32 in. scale model car. The length of the model car is 2 inches. What is the actual length of the car? 64 in.

Find each sum or difference. (Lesson 3-3)

18. 8.3 − 6.7 1.6 19. 25.6 + 12.8 38.4 20. 14 − 5.9 8.1 21. 8.62 − 4.75 3.87 22. 15.75 + 9.38 25.13

Find the missing value in each proportion. (Lesson 7-3)

23. $\frac{9}{15} = \frac{x}{5}$ $x = 3$ 24. $\frac{b}{20} = \frac{3}{15}$ $b = 4$ 25. $\frac{1}{7} = \frac{6}{k}$ $k = 42$ 26. $\frac{8}{3} = \frac{a}{9}$ $a = 24$ 27. $\frac{p}{4} = \frac{11}{44}$ $p = 1$

Challenge 7-6

LESSON 7-6 Challenge
Solar System String

Distances in outer space are usually measured in millions of miles. Understanding or comparing such huge measurements can be difficult, and it is impossible to map or draw them in their actual scale. Here's an activity that can help you understand the vast scale of our solar system. Identify the 1-millimeter mark on your ruler. This tiny distance represents 1,000,000 miles in space! You will use it as the scale for your model: 1 millimeter = 1 million miles.

Make a scale model of our solar system.

1. Cut a piece of string 4 meters long. Tape a small piece of paper at one end of the string and label it "Sun."
2. From the sun, measure 3.6 cm. Tape a "Mercury" label there.
3. From Mercury, measure another 3.1 cm. Tape a "Venus" label there.
4. From Venus, measure another 2.6 cm. Tape an "Earth" label there.
5. From Earth, measure another 4.9 mm. Tape a "Mars" label there.
6. From Mars, measure another 34.2 cm. Tape a "Jupiter" label there.
7. From Jupiter, measure another 40.2 cm. Tape a "Saturn" label there.
8. From Saturn, measure another 89.8 cm. Tape a "Uranus" label there.
9. From Uranus, measure another 1,010 mm. Tape a "Neptune" label there.
10. From Neptune, measure another 88.1 cm. Tape a "Pluto" label there.

Now use the scale and your model to find the actual distance of each planet from Earth. For example, the distance from Earth to the sun on the string measures 93 mm, so the actual distance is 93 million miles.

Earth to Mercury: 57 million miles
Earth to Venus: 26 million miles
Earth to Mars: 49 million miles
Earth to Jupiter: 391 million miles
Earth to Saturn: 793 million miles
Earth to Uranus: 1,691 million miles
Earth to Neptune: 2,701 million miles
Earth to Pluto: 3,582 million miles

Problem Solving 7-6

LESSON 7-6 Problem Solving
Scale Drawings and Maps

Write the correct answer.

1. About how many kilometers long is the northern border of California along Oregon? about 300 kilometers
2. What is the distance in kilometers from Los Angeles to San Francisco? about 600 kilometers
3. How many kilometers would you have to drive to get from San Diego to Sacramento? about 800 kilometers
4. At its longest point, about how many kilometers long is Death Valley National Park? about 250 kilometers
5. Approximately what is the distance, in kilometers, between Redwood National Park and Yosemite National Park? about 500 kilometers

Redwood National Park, Sacramento, Yosemite National Park, San Francisco, Monterey, Death Valley National Park, Pacific Ocean, Bakersfield, Palm Springs, Los Angeles, San Diego
0 50 100 Miles
0 50 100 Kilometers

Circle the letter of the correct answer.

6. Which of the following two cities in California are about 200 kilometers apart?
   Ⓐ San Diego and Los Angeles
   B Monterey and Los Angeles
   C San Francisco and Fresno
   D Palm Springs and Bakersfield
7. Joshua Tree National Park is about 200 kilometers from Sequoia National Park. How many centimeters should separate those parks on this map?
   F 220 cm Ⓗ 2 cm
   G 22 cm J 0.22 cm

Ongoing Assessment and Intervention 

Diagnose ***Before*** **the Lesson**
7-6 Warm Up, TE p. 374

Monitor ***During*** **the Lesson**
7-6 Know-It Notebook
7-6 Questioning Strategies

Assess ***After*** **the Lesson**
7-6 Lesson Quiz, TE p. 377

Interdisciplinary 

Social Studies

Exercises 9–15 involve using a scale to determine actual distances represented on a map. Students learn to read maps and use scales in middle school social studies programs, such as Holt, Rinehart & Winston's *People, Places, and Change.*

Test Prep Doctor In Exercise 16, remind students to read the problem carefully. Students choosing **B** may have found the distance between town A and town B. Students choosing **D** may have found the distance between town A and town C. Students choosing **A** have divided by 30 instead of multiplying.

Journal

Have students write about how the scale on a map is useful. If the scale is 1 in. = 5 mi, what does this mean, and how can this information be used?

Power Presentations with PowerPoint®

7-6 Lesson Quiz

On a map of the Great Lakes, 2 cm = 45 km. Find the actual distance of the following, given their distances on the map.

1. Detroit to Cleveland = 12 cm 270 km
2. Duluth to Nipigon = 20 cm 450 km
3. Buffalo to Syracuse = 10 cm 225 km
4. Sault Ste. Marie to Toronto = 33 cm 742.5 km

Also available on transparency

Organizer

Objective: Assess students' mastery of concepts and skills in Lessons 7-1 through 7-6.

Resources

Assessment Resources
Section 7A Quiz

Test & Practice Generator
One-Stop Planner®

INTERVENTION 

Resources

Ready to Go On? Intervention and Enrichment **Worksheets**

Ready to Go On? **CD-ROM**

Ready to Go On? **Online**

my.hrw.com

(14) $\frac{1\text{cm}}{8\text{ft}} = \frac{1.8\text{cm}}{x}$
$x = 8(1.8) = 14.4\text{ft}$

SECTION 7A

Quiz for Lessons 7-1 Through 7-6

7-1 Ratios and Rates

Use the table to write each ratio.

Types of CDs in Mark's Music Collection			
Classical	4	Jazz	3
Country	9	Pop	14
Dance	8	Rock	10

1. classical CDs to rock CDs **4:10**
2. country to total CDs **9:48**
3. A package containing 6 pairs of socks costs $6.89. A package containing 4 pairs of socks costs $4.64. Which is the better deal? **the 6-pair pack of socks**

7-2 Using Tables to Explore Equivalent Ratios and Rates

Use a table to find three equivalent ratios. **Possible answers:**

4. $\frac{21}{30}$ **$\frac{7}{10}, \frac{14}{20}, \frac{28}{40}$**
5. 15:6 **5:2, 10:4, 20:8**
6. 3 to 101 **6 to 202, 9 to 303, 12 to 404**
7. The table shows the wait time for different groups at a restaurant. Predict how long a group of 8 will wait. **24 min**

Number in Group	1	2	5	7	10
Wait Time (min)	3	6	15	21	30

Ready to Go On?

7-3 Proportions

Find the missing value in each proportion.

8. $\frac{1}{4} = \frac{n}{12}$ **$n = 3$**
9. $\frac{3}{n} = \frac{15}{25}$ **$n = 5$**
10. $\frac{n}{4} = \frac{18}{6}$ **$n = 12$**
11. $\frac{10}{4} = \frac{5}{n}$ **$n = 2$**

7-4 Similar Figures

$\frac{6}{24} = \frac{n}{22.8}$

12. The two triangles are similar. Find the missing length n and the measure of $\angle R$. **$n = 5.7$ cm; $m\angle R = 30°$**

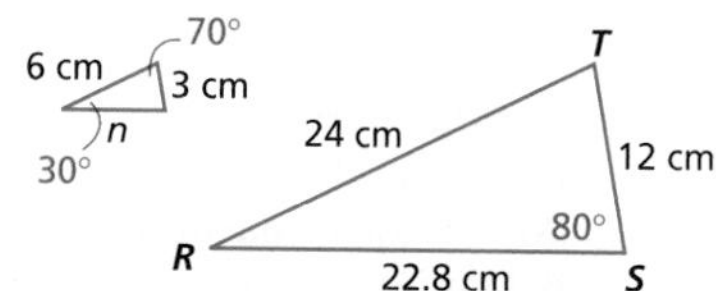

7-5 Indirect Measurement

13. A tree casts a shadow that is 18 feet long. At the same time, a 5-foot-tall person casts a shadow that is 3.6 feet long. How tall is the tree? **about 25 feet tall**

7-6 Scale Drawings and Maps

Use the scale drawing and a metric ruler to answer each question.

14. What is the actual length of the kitchen? **20 ft** (1.8cm)
15. What are the actual length and width of bedroom 1? **~~20 ft by 12 ft~~** (1.9cm, 1.1cm) 15.2 x 8.8 ft

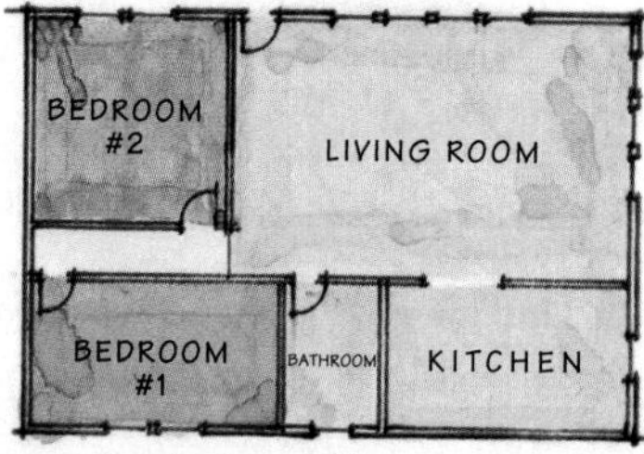

Scale: 1cm:8ft

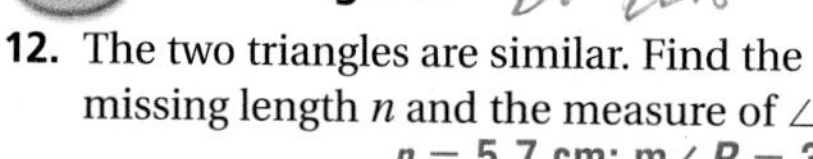

READY TO GO ON?
Diagnose and Prescribe

NO INTERVENE

YES ENRICH

Ready to Go On? Intervention	*Ready to Go On? Intervention,* Section 7A		
	Worksheets	CD-ROM	Online
Lesson 7-1	7-1 Intervention	Activity 7-1	Diagnose and Prescribe Online
Lesson 7-2	7-2 Intervention	Activity 7-2	
Lesson 7-3	7-3 Intervention	Activity 7-3	
Lesson 7-4	7-4 Intervention	Activity 7-4	
Lesson 7-5	7-5 Intervention	Activity 7-5	
Lesson 7-6	7-6 Intervention	Activity 7-6	

Ready to Go On? Enrichment, Section 7A
- Worksheets
- CD-ROM
- Online

Focus on Problem Solving

Make a Plan

- **Estimate or find an exact answer**

Sometimes an estimate is all you need to solve a problem, and sometimes you need to find an exact answer.

One way to decide whether you can estimate is to see if you can rewrite the problem using the words *at most, at least,* or *about.* For example, suppose Laura has $30. Then she could spend *at most* $30. She would not have to spend *exactly* $30. Or, if you know it takes 15 minutes to get to school, you must leave your house *at least* (not exactly) 15 minutes before school starts.

Read the problems below. Decide whether you can estimate or whether you must find the exact answer. How do you know?

1. Alex is a radio station disc jockey. He is making a list of songs that should last no longer than 30 minutes total when played in a row. His list of songs and their playing times are given in the table. Does Alex have the right amount of music?

Song Title	Length (min)
Color Me Blue	4.5
Hittin' the Road	7.2
Stand Up, Shout	2.6
Top Dog	3.6
Kelso Blues	4.3
Smile on Me	5.7
A Long Time Ago	6.4

2. For every 10 minutes of music, Alex has to play 1.5 minutes of commercials. If Alex plays the songs on the list, how much time does he need to allow for commercials?

3. If Alex must play the songs on the list and the commercials in 30 minutes, how much music time does he need to cut to allow for commercials?

Focus on Problem Solving

Organizer

Objective: To focus on making a plan to solve a problem.

Online Edition

Resources

Chapter 7 Resource Book
Reading Strategies

Problem Solving Process

This page focuses on the second step of the problem-solving process: **Make a Plan.**

Discuss

Have students rewrite each problem and use the words *at most, at least,* or *exactly* to determine whether they can estimate or whether they must find an exact answer.

Possible answers:

1. Alex's songs should last *at most* 30 minutes, but they can last less than 30 minutes, so you can estimate.
2. Alex has to play *exactly* 1.5 minutes of commercials for every 10 minutes of music, so you need an exact answer.
3. Alex must know *exactly* how many minutes of music must be cut in order for the songs and commercials to last *exactly* 30 minutes, so you need an exact answer.

Answers

1. No; by rounding the length of each song to the nearest minute you find that Alex has about 35 minutes of music, which is over 30 minutes by about 5 minutes.
2. $\frac{1.5}{10} = \frac{x}{34.3}$; $x = 5.145$ minutes
3. Alex must play songs and commercials for exactly 30 minutes. For every 11.5 minutes of air time there should be 1.5 minutes of commercials. Solving the proportion $\frac{11.5}{1.5} = \frac{30}{x}$ indicates that there should be about 3.9 minutes of commercials for 30 minutes of airtime. Since Alex's song list already exceeds 30 minutes by 4.3 minutes, Alex needs to cut 3.9 + 4.3 = 8.2 minutes of music.

SECTION 7B

Understanding Percent

One-Minute Section Planner

Lesson	Materials	MiC and Lab Resources
7-7 Hands-On Lab Model Percents • Use a 10-by-10 grid to model a percent. **Lesson 7-7** Percents • Write percents as decimals and fractions. ☑ CRCT ☐ SAT-10 ☑ ITBS ☐ CTBS ☑ NAEP	10-by-10 grids, graph paper, number cubes (MK)	***Hands-On Lab Activities*** 7-7
Lesson 7-8 Percents, Decimals, and Fractions • Write decimals and fractions as percents. **7-8 Technology Lab** Convert Between Percents, Decimals, and Fractions • Use a calculator to quickly change between fractions, decimals, and percents. ☑ CRCT ☐ SAT-10 ☑ ITBS ☐ CTBS ☑ NAEP	Graphing calculators	**MiC:** ***Models You Can Count On*** pp. 18–20 **MiC:** ***More or Less*** pp. 11–12 **MiC:** ***Picturing Numbers*** pp. 12, 15 **MiC:** ***Take A Chance*** pp. 13–17 **MiC:** ***Fraction Times*** pp. 14–20, 25–29, 33–39 ***Technology Lab Activities*** 7-8
Lesson 7-9 Percent Problems • Find the missing value in a percent problem. ☑ CRCT ☐ SAT-10 ☐ ITBS ☐ CTBS ☑ NAEP		***Technology Lab Activities*** 7-9
Lesson 7-10 Using Percents • Solve percent problems that involve discounts, tips, and sales tax. ☑ CRCT ☐ SAT-10 ☐ ITBS ☐ CTBS ☑ NAEP	Advertisements using percent	**MiC:** ***More or Less*** pp. 13–15 ***Technology Lab Activities*** 7-10
Extension Simple Interest • Find simple interest. ☑ CRCT ☐ SAT-10 ☐ ITBS ☐ CTBS ☑ NAEP		**MiC:** ***More or Less*** pp. 14–15, 18–19, 22–23, 26–31 **MiC:** ***Models You Can Count On*** pp. 20–21

MK = *Manipulatives Kit*

Mathematics in Context

The units ***More or Less, Models You Can Count On, Picturing Numbers, Take a Chance,*** and ***Fraction Times*** from the *Mathematics in Context* © 2006 series can be used with Section 7B. See Section Planner above for suggestions for integrating *MiC* with *Holt Mathematics*.

Section Overview

Professional Development

Percents, Decimals, and Fractions

Lessons 7-7, 7-8

Why? In calculations, percents are changed to decimals and fractions.

A percent is a ratio of a number to 100.

Percents to Decimals	Percents to Fractions
$45\% = \frac{45}{100} = 0.45$	$65\% = \frac{65 \div 5}{100 \div 5} = \frac{13}{20}$

Decimals to Percents	Fractions to Percents
$0.27 = \frac{27}{100} = 27\%$	$\frac{3}{5} = \frac{3 \times 20}{5 \times 20} = \frac{60}{100} = 60\%$

Percent Problems

Lesson 7-9

Statistics, such as those in sport, are sometimes reported as percents.

Three Types of Percent Problems

20% of 80 is ■.	■ % of 80 is 16.	20% of ■ is 16.
$0.20 \cdot 80 = x$	$x \cdot 80 = 16$	$0.20 \cdot x = 16$
$x = 0.20 \cdot 80$	$80x = 16$	$0.20x = 16$
$x = 16$	$x = \frac{16}{80} = \frac{1}{5} = 20\%$	$x = \frac{16}{0.20} = 80$
20% of 80 is 16.	20% of 80 is 16.	20% of 80 is 16.

Using Percents

Lesson 7-10

Percents are used in calculating discounts, tips, and sales tax.

Common Uses of Percents	
Discounts	A **discount** is an amount that is subtracted from the regular price of an item. discount = regular price • discount rate
Tips	A **tip** is an amount added to a bill. tip = total bill • tip rate
Sales Tax	**Sales tax** is an amount added to the price of an item. sales tax = purchase price • sales tax rate

Organizer

Use with Lesson 7-7

Pacing:
Traditional 1 day
Block $\frac{1}{2}$ day

Objective: Use a 10-by-10 grid to model a percent.

Materials: Graph paper

Online Edition
Fraction/Decimal Grids

Countdown to CRCT Week 15

Resources

Hands-On Lab Activities
Lab 7-7 Recording Sheet

Teach

Discuss

Have students discuss the similarities between modeling decimals on a decimal grid and modeling percents on a 10-by-10 grid.

Close

Key Concept

A percent can be modeled on a 10-by-10 grid to show the ratio of a number to 100.

Assessment

Model each percent on a 10-by-10 grid.

1. 16%
2. 45%
3. 25%

Georgia Performance Standards

M6P5.a Create and use representations to organize, record, and communicate mathematical ideas.

M6P5.b Select, apply, and translate among mathematical representations to solve problems.

M6P5.c Use representations to model and interpret physical, social, and mathematical phenomena.

Model Percents

Use with Lesson 7-7

Georgia Performance Standards
M6P5.a, M6P5.b, M6P5.c

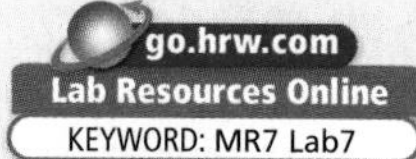

go.hrw.com
Lab Resources Online
KEYWORD: MR7 Lab7

A *percent* shows the ratio of a number to 100. You can model percents by using a 10-by-10 grid on graph paper.

Activity

1 Model 55% on a 10-by-10 grid.

Write 55% as a ratio comparing 55 to 100.

$55\% = \frac{55}{100}$

Since there are 100 squares in a 10 × 10 grid, shade in 55 squares.

$\frac{\text{number of squares shaded}}{\text{total number of squares}} = \frac{55}{100} = 55\%$

The model represents 55%.

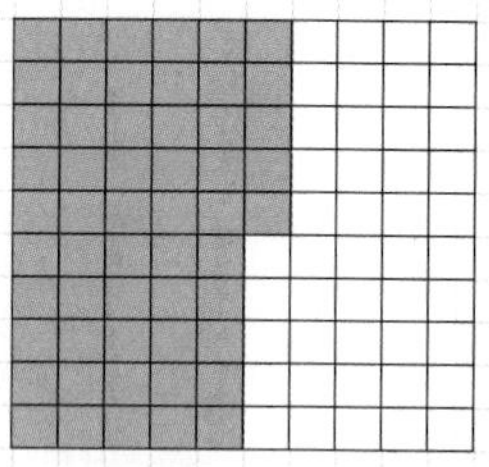

2 What percent of grid A is shaded?

Find the number of squares shaded in grid A. Compare it with the total number of squares.

$\frac{\text{number of squares shaded}}{\text{total number of squares}} = \frac{42}{100}$

Since 42 out of 100 squares are shaded, the grid models 42%.

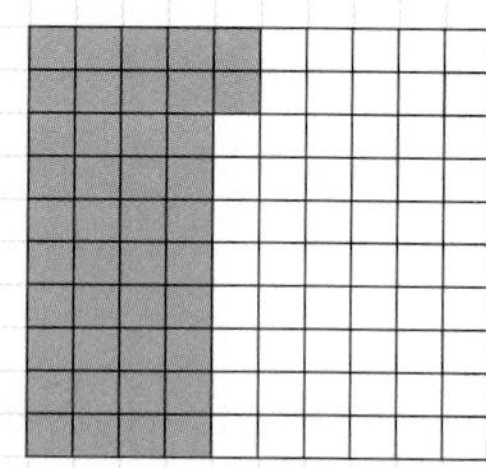

Grid A

Think and Discuss

1. Shade in $\frac{3}{4}$ of a 10-by-10 grid. What percent of the grid is shaded? Explain. **75%; 75 squares out of 100 squares are shaded.**
2. How can equivalent ratios help you find your answer to **1?**
3. How would you model 105%? 0.5%? Explain your answer. **shade an entire 10 × 10 grid and 5 squares of another 10 × 10 grid, this is 105%; shade half a square; this is $\frac{1}{2}$ or 0.5%**

Try This

Model each percent on a 10-by-10 grid.

1. 50%
2. 68%
3. 4%
4. 91%
5. 100%

Answers to *Assessment*

1.

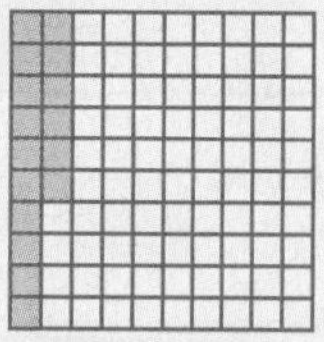

2.

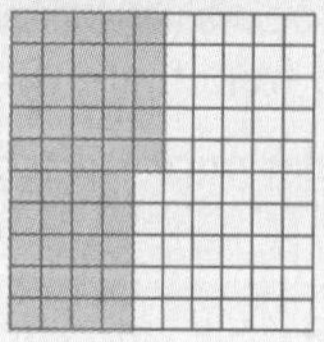

3.

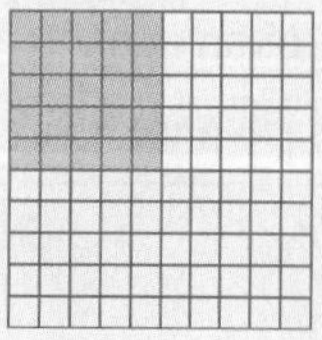

Answers to *Think and Discuss*

1–2. See p. A8.

Answers to *Try This*

1–5. See p. A8.

7-7 Percents

Learn to write percents as decimals and as fractions.

Vocabulary

percent

Georgia Performance Standards

M6N1.f Use fractions, decimals, and percents interchangeably. Also, M6N1.g, M6P1.b, M6P5.a, M6P5.c.

Most states charge sales tax on items you purchase. Sales tax is a percent of the item's price. A **percent** is a ratio of a number to 100.

You can remember that *percent* means "per hundred." For example, 8% means "8 per hundred," or "8 out of 100."

If a sales tax rate is 8%, the following statements are true:

- For every $1.00 you spend, you pay $0.08 in sales tax.
- For every $10.00 you spend, you pay $0.80 in sales tax.
- For every $100 you spend, you pay $8 in sales tax.

At a sales tax rate of 8%, the tax on this guitar and amplifier would be $36.56.

Because *percent* means "per hundred," 100% means "100 out of 100." This is why 100% is often used to mean "all" or "the whole thing."

EXAMPLE 1 Modeling Percents

Use a 10-by-10-square grid to model 8%.

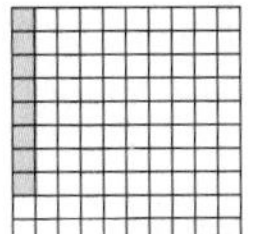

A 10-by-10-square grid has 100 squares.

8% means "8 out of 100," or $\frac{8}{100}$.

Shade 8 squares out of 100 squares.

EXAMPLE 2 Writing Percents as Fractions

Write 40% as a fraction in simplest form.

$40\% = \frac{40}{100}$ *Write the percent as a fraction with a denominator of 100.*

$\frac{40 \div 20}{100 \div 20} = \frac{2}{5}$ *Write the fraction in simplest form.*

Written as a fraction, 40% is $\frac{2}{5}$.

1 Introduce

Alternate Opener

EXPLORATION

7-7 Percents

Percent means "per one hundred." The decimal grid shows 50%, or 50 out of 100.

Use the decimal grid to show a model of each percent. Then write the percent as a fraction in simplest form.

1. 25% = ____ 2. 75% = ____ 3. 80% = ____

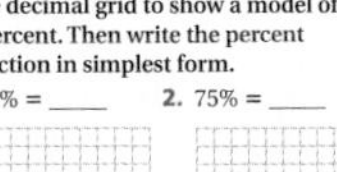

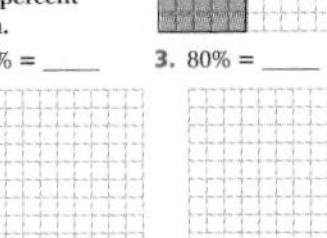

Determine the percent modeled by each decimal grid, and then write it as a fraction in simplest form.

4. 5. 6.

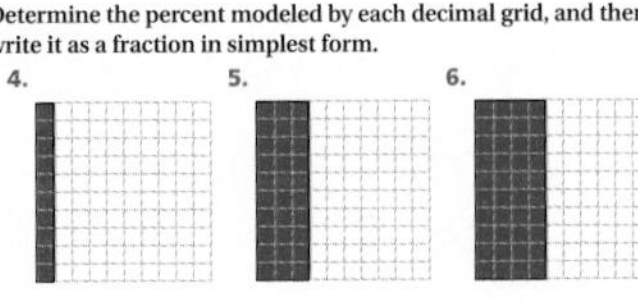

Think and Discuss____

7. **Explain** how to write a percent as a fraction.

Motivate

Ask students to give you examples of ways they have seen percents used. If necessary, show them what the percent symbol (%) looks like. Possible answers: chance of rain; real juice content of drinks; sales signs in stores; grades on tests

Explorations and answers are provided in *Alternate Openers: Explorations Transparencies.*

Organizer 7-7

Pacing: Traditional 1 day
Block $\frac{1}{2}$ day

Objective: Students write percents as decimals and as fractions.

GPS M6N1.g **Hands-On Lab**
In *Hands-On Lab Activities*

Online Edition
Tutorial Videos, Interactivities

Countdown to CRCT Week 15

Power Presentations with PowerPoint®

Warm Up

Write each fraction as a decimal.

1. $\frac{3}{4}$ 0.75 2. $\frac{9}{10}$ 0.9

Write each decimal as a fraction.

3. 0.375 $\frac{3}{8}$ 4. 0.05 $\frac{1}{20}$

Problem of the Day

Wally wanted to change the scale of a drawing from 1 in. = 2 ft to 1 in. = 10 ft. The scale height of a building in the first drawing is 25 in. How high is the building in the new drawing? 5 in.

Also available on transparency

Math Humor

Coach: You're not giving 100%.
Player: I am! I give 50% when I'm on offense and 50% when I'm on defense.

Georgia Performance Standards

M6N1.f Use fractions, decimals, and percents interchangeably.

M6N1.g Solve problems involving fractions, decimals, and percents.

M6P1.b Solve problems that arise in mathematics and in other contexts.

M6P5.a Create and use representations to organize, record, and communicate mathematical ideas.

M6P5.c Use representations to model and interpret physical, social, and mathematical phenomena.

When changing from a percent to a decimal, some students may divide 100 by the percent instead of the other way around. Remind them to divide by the denominator.

Power Presentations with PowerPoint®

Additional Examples

Example 1

Use a 10-by-10-square grid to model 17%.

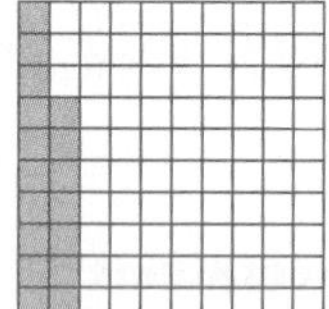

Example 2

Write 35% as a fraction in simplest form. $\frac{7}{20}$

Example 3

Janell has 20% body fat. Write 20% as a fraction in simplest form. $\frac{1}{5}$

Example 4

Write 56% as a decimal. 0.56

Example 5

Water made up 85% of the fluids that Kirk drank yesterday. Write 85% as a decimal. 0.85

Also available on transparency

EXAMPLE 3 *Life Science Application*

Up to 55% of the heat lost by your body can be lost through your head. Write 55% as a fraction in simplest form.

$55\% = \frac{55}{100}$ *Write the percent as a fraction with a denominator of 100.*

$\frac{55 \div 5}{100 \div 5} = \frac{11}{20}$ *Write the fraction in simplest form.*

Written as a fraction, 55% is $\frac{11}{20}$.

EXAMPLE 4 Writing Percents as Decimals

Remember!

To divide by 100, move the decimal point two places to the left.

$24 \div 100 = 0.24$

Write 24% as a decimal.

$24\% = \frac{24}{100}$ *Write the percent as a fraction with a denominator of 100.*

Write the fraction as a decimal.

$$\begin{array}{r} 0.24 \\ 100\overline{)24.00} \\ -\underline{200} \\ 400 \\ -\underline{400} \\ 0 \end{array}$$

Written as a decimal, 24% is 0.24.

EXAMPLE 5 *Earth Science Application*

The water frozen in glaciers makes up almost 75% of the world's fresh water supply. Write 75% as a decimal.

$75\% = \frac{75}{100}$ *Write the percent as a fraction with a denominator of 100.*

$75 \div 100 = 0.75$ *Write the fraction as a decimal.*

Written as a decimal, 75% is 0.75.

Answers to Think and Discuss

1. Possible answer: A store has a 25% off sale.
2. 5 cents; 50 cents; 500 cents, or $5.00
3. Convert the percent to a fraction with a denominator of 100, and then simplify the fraction.
4. 100% written as a decimal and as a fraction is 1 because 1.00 = 1 and $\frac{100}{100} = 1$.

Think and Discuss

GPS M6P3.b, M6P4.c

1. **Give an example** of a situation in which you have seen percents.
2. **Tell** how much sales tax you would have to pay on $1, $10, and $100 if your state had a 5% sales tax rate.
3. **Explain** how to write a percent as a fraction.
4. **Write** 100% as a decimal and as a fraction.

2 Teach

Guided Instruction

In this lesson, students learn to write percents as decimals and as fractions. Teach students to use a 10-by-10 grid (Teaching Tools) to model a percent as a part of 100. Then teach students to write percents as fractions and as decimals. Examples 3 and 5 provide real-world settings for the use of percents.

Reaching All Learners

Through Kinesthetic Experience

Have students work in pairs to model percents and write them as decimals and fractions. Give each pair a set of 10-by-10 grids (Teaching Tools) and two number cubes (Manipulatives Kit). One student rolls one, then the other, number cube and writes the numbers rolled as a percent. For example, if you roll a 5 and a 6, write this as 56%. The other student shades a grid to model the percent and writes the percent as a decimal and as a fraction. The first student checks the other's work. Students continue, taking turns.

3 Close

Summarize

Model a percent using a 10-by-10 grid (Teaching Tools), and show the percent as an equivalent decimal and fraction.

7-7 Exercises

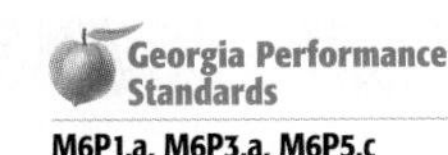
Georgia Performance Standards
M6P1.a, M6P3.a, M6P5.c

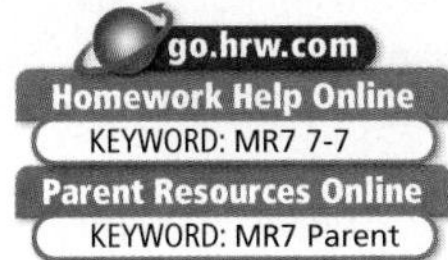
go.hrw.com
Homework Help Online
KEYWORD: MR7 7-7
Parent Resources Online
KEYWORD: MR7 Parent

GUIDED PRACTICE

See Example 1 — **Use a 10-by-10-square grid to model each percent.**

1. 45%
2. 3%
3. 61%

See Example 2 — **Write each percent as a fraction in simplest form.**

4. 25% $\frac{1}{4}$
5. 80% $\frac{4}{5}$
6. 54% $\frac{27}{50}$

See Example 3

7. **Social Studies** Belize is a country in Central America. Of the land in Belize, 92% is made up of forests and woodlands. Write 92% as a fraction in simplest form. $\frac{23}{25}$

See Example 4 — **Write each percent as a decimal.**

8. 72% 0.72
9. 4% 0.04
10. 90% 0.9

See Example 5

11. About 64% of the runways at airports in the United States are not paved. Write 64% as a decimal. 0.64

INDEPENDENT PRACTICE

See Example 1 — **Use a 10-by-10-square grid to model each percent.**

12. 14%
13. 98%
14. 36%
15. 28%

See Example 2 — **Write each percent as a fraction in simplest form.**

16. 20% $\frac{1}{5}$
17. 75% $\frac{3}{4}$
18. 11% $\frac{11}{100}$
19. 72% $\frac{18}{25}$
20. 5% $\frac{1}{20}$
21. 64% $\frac{16}{25}$
22. 31% $\frac{31}{100}$
23. 85% $\frac{17}{20}$

See Example 3

24. Nikki must answer 80% of the questions on her final exam correctly to pass her class. Write 80% as a fraction in simplest form. $\frac{4}{5}$

See Example 4 — **Write each percent as a decimal.**

25. 44% 0.44
26. 13% 0.13
27. 29% 0.29
28. 51% 0.51
29. 60% 0.6
30. 92% 0.92
31. 7% 0.07
32. 87% 0.87

See Example 5

33. Brett was absent 2% of the school year. Write 2% as a decimal. 0.02

PRACTICE AND PROBLEM SOLVING

Extra Practice p. 727

Write each percent as a fraction in simplest form and as a decimal.

34. 23% $\frac{23}{100}$, 0.23
35. 1% $\frac{1}{100}$, 0.01
36. 49% $\frac{49}{100}$, 0.49
37. 70% $\frac{7}{10}$, 0.7
38. 10% $\frac{1}{10}$, 0.1
39. 37% $\frac{37}{100}$, 0.37
40. 85% $\frac{17}{20}$, 0.85
41. 8% $\frac{2}{25}$, 0.08
42. 63% $\frac{63}{100}$, 0.63
43. 75% $\frac{3}{4}$, 0.75
44. 94%
45. 100% 1, 1
46. 0% 0, 0
47. 52% 0.52, $\frac{13}{25}$
48. 12% $\frac{3}{25}$, 0.12
49. Model 15%, 52%, 71%, and 100% using different 10-by-10 grids. Then write each percent as a fraction in simplest form.

RETEACH 7-7

LESSON 7-7 **Reteach**
Percents

A percent is a ratio of a number to 100. Percent means "per hundred."

To write 38% as a fraction, write a fraction with a denominator of 100.

$\frac{38}{100}$

Then write the fraction in simplest form.

$\frac{38}{100} = \frac{38 \div 2}{100 \div 2} = \frac{19}{50}$

So, 38% = $\frac{19}{50}$.

Write each percent as a fraction in simplest form.

1. 43% $\frac{43}{100}$
2. 72% $\frac{18}{25}$
3. 88% $\frac{22}{25}$
4. 35% $\frac{7}{20}$

To write 38% as a decimal, first write it as fraction.

38% = $\frac{38}{100}$

$\frac{38}{100}$ means "38 divided by 100."

```
      0.38
100)38.00
   -300
    800
   -800
      0
```

So, 38% = 0.38.

Write each percent as a decimal.

5. 64% 0.64
6. 92% 0.92
7. 73% 0.73
8. 33% 0.33

PRACTICE 7-7

LESSON 7-7 **Practice B**
Percents

Write each percent as a fraction in simplest form.

1. 30% $\frac{3}{10}$
2. 42% $\frac{21}{50}$
3. 18% $\frac{9}{50}$
4. 35% $\frac{7}{20}$
5. 100% $\frac{1}{1}$ or 1
6. 29% $\frac{29}{100}$
7. 56% $\frac{14}{25}$
8. 70% $\frac{7}{10}$
9. 25% $\frac{1}{4}$

Write each percent as a decimal.

10. 19% 0.19
11. 45% 0.45
12. 3% 0.03
13. 80% 0.8
14. 24% 0.24
15. 6% 0.06

Order the percents from least to greatest.

16. 89%, 42%, 91%, 27% — 27%, 42%, 89%, 91%
17. 2%, 55%, 63%, 31% — 2%, 31%, 55%, 63%
18. Sarah correctly answered 84% of the questions on her math test. What fraction of the test questions did she answer correctly? Write your answer in simplest form. $\frac{21}{25}$
19. Chloe swam 40 laps in the pool, but this was only 50% of her total swimming workout. How many more laps does she still need to swim? 40 more laps

7-7 Exercises

Assignment Guide

If you finished Example 1 assign:
Average 1–3, 51, 58–64
Advanced 12–15, 51, 58–64

If you finished Example 2 assign:
Average 1–6, 50–51, 58–64
Advanced 12–23, 58–64

If you finished Example 3 assign:
Average 1–7, 49–51, 58–64
Advanced 12–24, 58–64

If you finished Example 4 assign:
Average 1–10, 34–51, 58–64
Advanced 12–32, 58–64

If you finished Example 5 assign:
Average 1–11, 22–64
Advanced 12–64

Homework Quick Check

Quickly check key concepts.
Exercises: 22, 26, 38, 40, 50

Answers

1–3, 12–15, 44, 49. See p. A8.

Math Background

The percent symbol, %, has evolved over time. Manuscripts are available from the fifteenth century showing percent symbolized as "per $\overset{o}{c}$," which is an abbreviation of the Latin phrase *per cento.* By the middle of the seventeenth century, percent had begun to be symbolized by "per $\frac{o}{o}$." Following this, the word *per* was dropped, leaving only the symbol $\frac{o}{o}$. The modern form of the symbol is a direct descendant of $\frac{o}{o}$.

Georgia Performance Standards

M6P1.a Build new mathematical knowledge through problem solving.

M6P3.a Organize and consolidate their mathematical thinking through communication.

M6P5.c Use representations to model and interpret physical, social, and mathematical phenomena.

ONGOING ASSESSMENT and INTERVENTION

Diagnose **Before** the Lesson
7-7 Warm Up, TE p. 381

Monitor **During** the Lesson
7-7 Know-It Notebook
7-7 Questioning Strategies

Assess **After** the Lesson
7-7 Lesson Quiz, TE p. 384

Answers

50. $\frac{15}{100} = \frac{3}{20}$

51. See p. A8.

53. No; $\frac{1}{10}$ is equivalent to 10%, and only 9% play Top 40.

54. 1; the sum of the percents would be 100%, which is equivalent to 1.

56. 6% is equal to $\frac{6}{100}$, or $\frac{3}{50}$, which is smaller than $\frac{1}{6}$.

TEST PREP DOCTOR In Exercise 58, students remembering to move the decimal point two places to the left will avoid the intermediate step of writing the percent as a fraction and converting the fraction to a decimal.

Journal

Have students write three different percents, including percents with both 1 and 2 digits. For each percent, have them draw and shade a 10-by-10-square grid to model it, then have them write it as a decimal and as a fraction in simplest form. For one of the percents, have them explain why all three forms are equivalent.

Power Presentations with PowerPoint®

7-7 Lesson Quiz

Write each percent as a fraction in simplest form.

1. 52% $\frac{13}{25}$

2. 29% $\frac{29}{100}$

Write each percent as a decimal.

3. 17% 0.17

4. 86% 0.86

5. A store clerk has an 8% sales increase. Write the increase as a fraction in simplest form and as a decimal. $\frac{2}{25}$, 0.08

Also available on transparency

Music LINK

The circle graph shows the percent of radio stations around the world that play each type of music listed. Use the graph for Exercises 50–57.

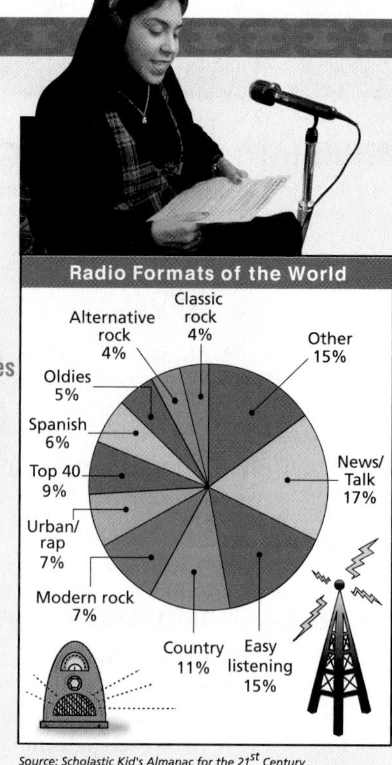

Source: Scholastic Kid's Almanac for the 21st Century

50. What fraction of the radio stations play easy listening music? Write this fraction in simplest form.

51. Use a 10-by-10-square grid to model the percent of radio stations that play country music. Then write this percent as a decimal. 11% = 0.11

52. Which type of music makes up $\frac{1}{20}$ of the graph? Oldies

53. Someone reading the graph said, "More than $\frac{1}{10}$ of the radio stations play top 40 music." Do you agree with this statement? Why or why not?

54. Suppose you converted all of the percents in the graph to decimals and added them. Without actually doing this, tell what the sum would be. Explain.

55. **Write a Problem** Write a question about the circle graph that involves changing a percent to a fraction. Then answer your question.

56. **Write About It** How does the percent of radio stations that play Spanish music compare with the fraction $\frac{1}{6}$? Explain.

57. **Challenge** Name a fraction that is greater than the percent of radio stations that play Spanish music but less than the percent of radio stations that play urban/rap music. Possible answer: $\frac{61}{1000}$

55. Possible answer: What fraction of the radio stations play country music? $\frac{11}{100}$

CRCT PREP • GPS SUPPORT • SPIRAL REVIEW

58. **Multiple Choice** Which decimal is equivalent to 85%?

Ⓐ 85.0　　Ⓑ 8.5　　Ⓒ 0.85　　Ⓓ 0.085

59. **Multiple Choice** Which term describes a number compared to 100?

Ⓕ Rate　　Ⓖ Ratio　　Ⓗ Percent　　Ⓙ Proportion

Evaluate each expression. (Lesson 1-4)

60. $45 \div 5 + 2 - 10$ 1　**61.** $25 - 4 \times 2$ 17　**62.** $18 - 7 \times 2 + 8$ 12　**63.** $48 - 9 \times 3 - 11$ 10

64. The Sears Tower in Chicago casts a shadow 580 feet long. At the same time, a 5-foot-tall boy casts a 2-foot shadow. What is the height of the Sears Tower? (Lesson 7-5) 1,450 ft

CHALLENGE 7-7

LESSON 7-7 **Challenge**
Per State

To show a percent, you can shade a 10-by-10 grid in any design that you want. For each percent below, try to shade the grid to look like the state it describes.

1. California has the largest population of any state. About 12% of all Americans live in California. 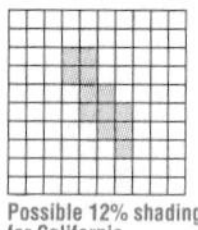
Possible 12% shading for California

2. Florida is the top tourist state. About 26% of all visitors to the United States choose Florida for their vacations. 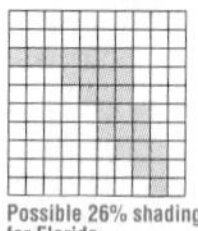
Possible 26% shading for Florida

3. Nevada is the fastest-growing state. Its population has grown about 66% in the last ten years. 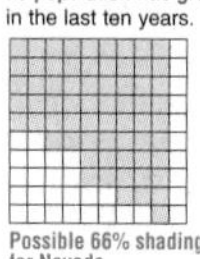
Possible 66% shading for Nevada

4. Alaska is the largest state. It makes up about 15% of the total area of the United States. 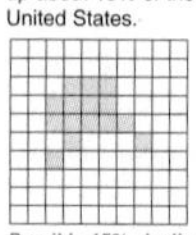
Possible 15% shading for Alaska

5. Washington produces the most apples. About 50% of all the apples grown in the U.S. come from Washington. 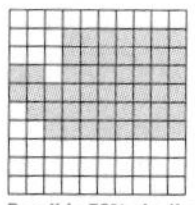
Possible 50% shading for Washington

6. Texas is the top oil-producing state. About 21% of all the oil produced in the United States comes from Texas. 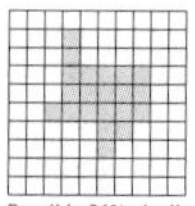
Possible 21% shading for Texas

PROBLEM SOLVING 7-7

LESSON 7-7 **Problem Solving**
Percents

Use the circle graph to answer each question. Write fractions in simplest form.

1. What fraction of the total 2000 music sales in the United States were rock recordings?
$\frac{1}{4}$

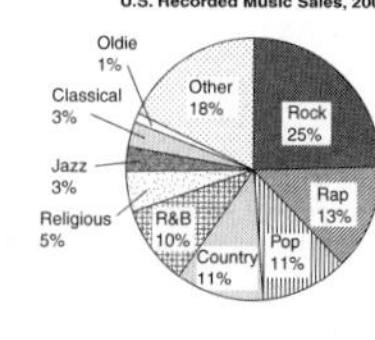

2. On this grid, model the percent of total United States music sales that were rap recordings. Then write that percent as a decimal.
0.13

Circle the letter of the correct answer.

3. What kind of music made up $\frac{1}{20}$ of the total U.S. music recording sales?
A Oldie　C Jazz
B Classical　Ⓓ Religious

4. What fraction of the United States music sales were country recordings?
F $\frac{110}{100}$　H $\frac{1}{10}$
Ⓖ $\frac{11}{100}$　J $\frac{1}{100}$

5. What fraction of all United States recording sales did jazz and classical music make up together?
A $\frac{6}{10}$　C $\frac{1}{5}$
Ⓑ $\frac{3}{50}$　D $\frac{11}{100}$

6. What kind of music made up $\frac{1}{10}$ of the total music recording sales in the United States in 2000?
F Pop　Ⓗ R&B
G Jazz　J Oldies

7-8 Percents, Decimals, and Fractions

Learn to write decimals and fractions as percents.

Georgia Performance Standards

M6N1.g Solve problems involving fractions, decimals, and percents. Also, M6N1.f, M6P4.a, M6P4.b, M6P4.c.

Percents, decimals, and fractions appear in newspapers, on television, and on the Internet. To fully understand the data you see in your everyday life, you should be able to change from one number form to another.

"Oh yes, a one-half of one percent allowance increase is quite a bit."

EXAMPLE 1 **Writing Decimals as Percents**

Write each decimal as a percent.

Method 1: Use place value.

A 0.3

$0.3 = \frac{3}{10}$ — *Write the decimal as a fraction.*

$\frac{3 \cdot 10}{10 \cdot 10} = \frac{30}{100}$ — *Write an equivalent fraction with 100 as the denominator.*

$\frac{30}{100} = 30\%$ — *Write the numerator with a percent symbol.*

B 0.43

$0.43 = \frac{43}{100}$ — *Write the decimal as a fraction.*

$\frac{43}{100} = 43\%$ — *Write the numerator with a percent symbol.*

Method 2: Multiply by 100.

C 0.7431

$0.7431 \cdot 100$ — *Multiply by 100.*

74.31% — *Add the percent symbol.*

D 0.023

$0.023 \cdot 100$ — *Multiply by 100.*

2.3% — *Add the percent symbol.*

Organizer 7-8

Pacing: Traditional 1 day
Block $\frac{1}{2}$ day

Objective: Students write decimals and fractions as percents.

Online Edition
Tutorial Videos, Interactivities

Countdown to CRCT Week 16

Power Presentations with PowerPoint®

Warm Up

Write each percent as a fraction in simplest form.

1. 37% $\frac{37}{100}$ **2.** 78% $\frac{39}{50}$

Write each percent as a decimal.

3. 59% 0.59 **4.** 7% 0.07

Problem of the Day

Jennifer gave Karen 50% of her comic books. Karen gave Jack 50% of the books she got from Jennifer. Jack gave Lucas 50% of the books he got from Karen. Lucas got 4 comic books. What percent of Jennifer's comic books does Lucas have? 12.5%

Also available on transparency

Math Humor

The student was so unfamiliar with football that he thought a quarterback was a 25-cent refund.

1 Introduce

Alternate Opener

EXPLORATION

7-8 Percents, Decimals, and Fractions

To report what percent of their fund-raising goal has been reached, a charity uses the number-line model below.

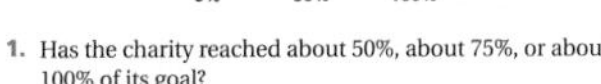

1. Has the charity reached about 50%, about 75%, or about 100% of its goal?

Complete each number-line model by writing percents above the line and the corresponding fractions below the line.

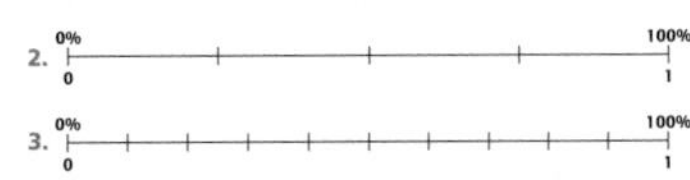

Think and Discuss

4. **Explain** how you matched percents with fractions in numbers 2 and 3.
5. **Explain** how you could label the number lines with decimals.

Motivate

Have students explain how to convert from a percent to a fraction and from a percent to a decimal. Have them hypothesize how to do the opposite, changing a fraction or decimal to a percent.

Explorations and answers are provided in *Alternate Openers: Explorations Transparencies.*

Georgia Performance Standards

M6N1.f Use fractions, decimals, and percents interchangeably.

M6N1.g Solve problems involving fractions, decimals, and percents.

M6P4.a Recognize and use connections among mathematical ideas.

M6P4.b Understand how mathematical ideas interconnect and build on one another to produce a coherent whole.

M6P4.c Recognize and apply mathematics in contexts outside of mathematics.

COMMON ERROR ALERT

When writing decimals as percents, students may simply drop the decimal point and write a percent symbol. For example, they may think that 0.3 = 3% and 0.435 = 435%. Reinforce the idea of multiplying by 100 and *moving* the decimal point two spaces right rather than simply ignoring the decimal point.

Power Presentations with PowerPoint®

Additional Examples

Example 1

Write each decimal as a percent.

A. 0.7 70%
B. 0.16 16%
C. 0.4118 41.18%
D. 0.067 6.7%

Example 2

Write each fraction as a percent.

A. $\frac{9}{25}$ 36%
B. $\frac{3}{20}$ 15%

Example 3

One year, $\frac{7}{25}$ of people with home offices were self-employed. What percent of people with home offices were self-employed?

28% of people with home offices were self-employed.

Also available on transparency

EXAMPLE 2 Writing Fractions as Percents

Write each fraction as a percent.

Method 1: Write an equivalent fraction with a denominator of 100.

Helpful Hint

When the denominator is a factor of 100, it is often easier to use method 1. When the denominator is not a factor of 100, it is usually easier to use method 2.

A $\frac{4}{5}$

$\frac{4 \cdot 20}{5 \cdot 20} = \frac{80}{100}$ *Write an equivalent fraction with a denominator of 100.*

$\frac{80}{100} = 80\%$ *Write the numerator with a percent symbol.*

Method 2: Use division to write the fraction as a decimal.

B $\frac{3}{8}$

$8\overline{)3.000}$ = 0.375 *Divide the numerator by the denominator.*

0.375 = 37.5% *Multiply by 100 by moving the decimal point right two places. Add the percent symbol.*

EXAMPLE 3 *Earth Science Application*

About $\frac{39}{50}$ of Earth's atmosphere is made up of nitrogen. About what percent of the atmosphere is nitrogen?

$\frac{39}{50}$

$\frac{39 \cdot 2}{50 \cdot 2} = \frac{78}{100}$ *Write an equivalent fraction with a denominator of 100.*

$\frac{78}{100} = 78\%$ *Write the numerator with a percent symbol.*

About 78% of Earth's atmosphere is made up of nitrogen.

Answers to *Think and Discuss*

1. Possible answer: multiplying by 100, because it is easier to move the decimal point two places right
2. decimal: 0.3; fraction: $\frac{3}{10}$
3. Possible answer: Write an equivalent fraction with a denominator of 100 and write the numerator with a percent symbol. Divide the numerator by the denominator, multiply by 100 by moving the decimal point two places right, and add a percent symbol.

Common Equivalent Fractions, Decimals, and Percents

Fraction	$\frac{1}{5}$	$\frac{1}{4}$	$\frac{1}{3}$	$\frac{2}{5}$	$\frac{1}{2}$	$\frac{3}{5}$	$\frac{2}{3}$	$\frac{3}{4}$	$\frac{4}{5}$
Decimal	0.2	0.25	$0.\overline{3}$	0.4	0.5	0.6	$0.\overline{6}$	0.75	0.8
Percent	20%	25%	$33.\overline{3}$%	40%	50%	60%	$66.\overline{6}$%	75%	80%

Think and Discuss

1. **Tell** which method you prefer for converting decimals to percents—using equivalent fractions or multiplying by 100. Why?
2. **Give** two different ways to write three-tenths.
3. **Explain** how to write fractions as percents using two different methods.

2 Teach

Guided Instruction

In this lesson, students learn to write decimals and fractions as percents. Teach them two methods for writing a decimal as a percent–one using place value and one involving multiplying by 100. Then teach students to use equivalent fractions or division to change a fraction to a percent. Discuss the table of common equivalent fractions, decimals, and percents.

Reaching All Learners

Through Cooperative Learning

Have students work in pairs to divide the following list into sets of three equivalent numbers:

$\frac{1}{4}$, 75%, 0.40, $\frac{1}{8}$, 40%, 0.50, $\frac{2}{5}$, 25%, 0.75, $\frac{1}{2}$, 12.5%, 0.25, $\frac{3}{4}$, 50%, and 0.125.

Have students trade with another pair to check results.

$\frac{1}{4}$, 25%, 0.25
75%, 0.75, $\frac{3}{4}$
0.40, 40%, $\frac{2}{5}$
$\frac{1}{8}$, 12.5%, 0.125
0.50, $\frac{1}{2}$, 50%

3 Close

Summarize

Review each of the two methods presented for changing decimals to percents and fractions to percents. Have students discuss the advantages of each method.

7-8 Exercises

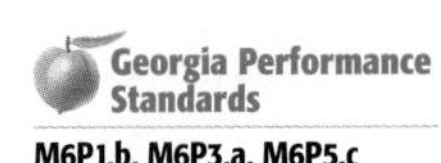

M6P1.b, M6P3.a, M6P5.c

go.hrw.com
Homework Help Online
KEYWORD: MR7 7-8
Parent Resources Online
KEYWORD: MR7 Parent

GUIDED PRACTICE

See Example 1 Write each decimal as a percent.

1. 0.39 39% 2. 0.125 12.5% 3. 0.8 80% 4. 0.112 11.2%

See Example 2 Write each fraction as a percent.

5. $\frac{11}{25}$ 44% 6. $\frac{7}{8}$ 87.5% 7. $\frac{7}{10}$ 70% 8. $\frac{1}{2}$ 50% 9. $\frac{7}{10}$ 70%

See Example 3 10. Patti spent $\frac{3}{4}$ of her allowance on a new backpack. What percent of her allowance did she spend? 75%

INDEPENDENT PRACTICE

See Example 1 Write each decimal as a percent.

11. 0.6 60% 12. 0.55 55% 13. 0.34 34% 14. 0.308 30.8% 15. 0.62 62%

See Example 2 Write each fraction as a percent.

16. $\frac{3}{5}$ 60% 17. $\frac{3}{10}$ 30% 18. $\frac{24}{25}$ 96% 19. $\frac{9}{20}$ 45% 20. $\frac{17}{20}$ 85%

21. $\frac{1}{8}$ 12.5% 22. $\frac{11}{16}$ 68.75% 23. $\frac{37}{50}$ 74% 24. $\frac{2}{5}$ 40% 25. $\frac{18}{45}$ 40%

See Example 3 26. About $\frac{1}{125}$ of the people in the United States have the last name *Johnson.* What percent of people in the United States have this last name? 0.8%

PRACTICE AND PROBLEM SOLVING

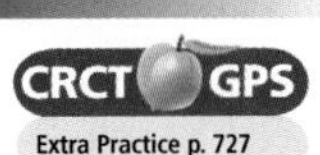

Extra Practice p. 727

Write each decimal as a percent and a fraction.

27. 0.04 4%, $\frac{1}{25}$ 28. 0.32 32%, $\frac{8}{25}$ 29. 0.45 45%, $\frac{9}{20}$ 30. 0.59 59%, $\frac{59}{100}$ 31. 0.01 1%, $\frac{1}{100}$

32. 0.81 81%, $\frac{81}{100}$ 33. 0.6 60%, $\frac{3}{5}$ 34. 0.39 39%, $\frac{39}{100}$ 35. 0.14 14%, $\frac{7}{50}$ 36. 0.62 62%, $\frac{31}{50}$

Write each fraction as a percent and as a decimal. Round to the nearest hundredth, if necessary.

37. $\frac{4}{5}$ 80%, 0.8 38. $\frac{1}{3}$ 33.33%, 0.33 39. $\frac{5}{6}$ 83.33%, 0.83 40. $\frac{7}{12}$ 58.33%, 0.58 41. $\frac{17}{50}$ 34%, 0.34

42. $\frac{2}{30}$ 6.67%, 0.07 43. $\frac{1}{25}$ 4%, 0.04 44. $\frac{8}{11}$ 72.73%, 0.73 45. $\frac{4}{15}$ 26.67%, 0.27 46. $\frac{22}{35}$ 63%, 0.63

Compare. Write <, >, or =.

47. 70% ■ $\frac{3}{4}$ < 48. $\frac{5}{8}$ ■ 6.25% > 49. 0.2 ■ $\frac{1}{5}$ = 50. 1.25 ■ $\frac{1}{8}$ >

51. 0.7 ■ 7% > 52. $\frac{9}{10}$ ■ 0.3 > 53. 37% ■ $\frac{3}{7}$ < 54. $\frac{17}{20}$ ■ 0.85 =

55. **Language Arts** The longest word in all of Shakespeare's plays is *honorificabilitudinitatibus.* About what percent of the letters in this word are vowels? About what percent of the letters are consonants? about 48%; about 52%

RETEACH 7-8

LESSON 7-8 **Reteach**
Percents, Decimals, and Fractions

You can write decimals as percents.

To write 0.5 as a percent, multiply the decimal by 100%.

0.5 • 100% = 50%

To multiply a number by 100, move the decimal point two places to the right.

0.50

So, 0.5 = 50%.

Write each decimal as a percent.

1. 0.8 80% 2. 0.64 64% 3. 0.075 7.5% 4. 0.29 29%

You can solve a proportion to write a fraction as a percent.

To write $\frac{3}{4}$ as a percent, first set up a proportion.

$\frac{3}{4} = \frac{x}{100}$

3 • 100 = 4 • x The cross products are equal.

300 = 4x x is multiplied by 4.

$\frac{4x}{4} = \frac{300}{4}$ Divide both sides by 4.

x = 75

So, $\frac{3}{4} = \frac{75}{100}$

$\frac{75}{100}$ = 75%, So, $\frac{3}{4}$ = 75%.

Write each fraction as a percent.

5. $\frac{4}{5}$ 80% 6. $\frac{9}{10}$ 90% 7. $\frac{1}{8}$ 12.5% 8. $\frac{7}{25}$ 28%

9. $\frac{1}{4}$ 25% 10. $\frac{5}{6}$ 83.3% 11. $\frac{3}{4}$ 75% 12. $\frac{1}{5}$ 20%

PRACTICE 7-8

LESSON 7-8 **Practice B**
Percents, Decimals, and Fractions

Write each decimal as a percent.

1. 0.03 3% 2. 0.92 92% 3. 0.18 18%

4. 0.49 49% 5. 0.7 70% 6. 0.09 9%

7. 0.26 26% 8. 0.11 11% 9. 1.0 100%

Write each fraction as a percent.

10. $\frac{2}{5}$ 40% 11. $\frac{1}{5}$ 20% 12. $\frac{7}{10}$ 70%

13. $\frac{1}{20}$ 5% 14. $\frac{1}{50}$ 2% 15. $\frac{4}{50}$ 8%

Compare. Write <, >, or =.

16. 60% < $\frac{2}{3}$ 17. 0.4 = $\frac{2}{5}$

18. 0.5 > 5% 19. $\frac{1}{100}$ < 0.03

20. $\frac{7}{9}$ > 72% 21. $\frac{3}{10}$ < 35%

22. Bradley completed $\frac{3}{5}$ of his homework. What percent of his homework does he still need to complete? 40%

23. After reading a book for English class, 100 students were asked whether or not they enjoyed it. Nine twenty-fifths of the students did not like the book. How many students liked the book? 64 students

7-8 Exercises

Assignment Guide

If you finished Example 1 assign:
Average 1–4, 67–75
Advanced 11–14, 65, 67–75

If you finished Example 2 assign:
Average 1–9, 62, 67–75
Advanced 11–25, 67–75

If you finished Example 3 assign:
Average 1–18, 28–75
Advanced 11–75

Homework Quick Check

Quickly check key concepts.
Exercises: 14, 18, 28, 34, 40

Math Background

Another method of writing a fraction as a percent is to use a proportion. For example, to write $\frac{4}{5}$ as a percent, use the proportion $\frac{4}{5} = \frac{x}{100}$, since *percent* means "per hundred." Solving for x yields the percent.

$\frac{4}{5} = \frac{x}{100}$

$5x = 400$

$x = 80$

So $\frac{4}{5}$ is 80%.

Georgia Performance Standards

M6P1.b Solve problems that arise in mathematics and in other contexts.

M6P3.a Organize and consolidate their mathematical thinking through communication.

M6P5.c Use representations to model and interpret physical, social, and mathematical phenomena.

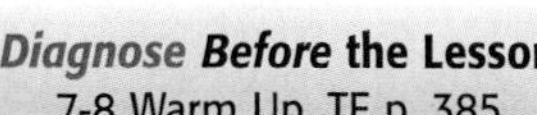

ONGOING ASSESSMENT and INTERVENTION

***Diagnose Before* the Lesson**
7-8 Warm Up, TE p. 385

***Monitor During* the Lesson**
7-8 Know-It Notebook
7-8 Questioning Strategies

***Assess After* the Lesson**
7-8 Lesson Quiz, TE p. 389

COMMON ERROR ALERT

Students may be confused about Exercises 56–61. You may wish to help students by telling them to convert each number to the same form before comparing and ordering.

Answers

64. What percent of the students prefer neither Monday nor Tuesday for their test day?

65. To express 0.8 as a percent, you multiply by 100 by moving the decimal point two places to the right and adding the percent symbol, making it 80%, not 8%.

TEST PREP DOCTOR Students having difficulty with Exercise 68 may find it useful to convert $\frac{2}{3}$ to a percent. The fact that the sum of the two percents is 100% will indicate that choice **H** is correct.

Journal

Have students explain which method of changing decimals to percents and fractions to percents they prefer and why.

Power Presentations with PowerPoint®

7-8 Lesson Quiz

Write each decimal as a percent.

1. 0.26 **26%**

2. 0.419 **41.9%**

Write each fraction as a percent.

3. $\frac{1}{5}$ **20%**

4. $\frac{9}{16}$ **56.25%**

5. About $\frac{1}{16}$ of all the students at a local high school own their own car. What percent is this? **6.25%**

Also available on transparency

LINK Entertainment

This photo from 1953 shows one of the first color television cameras.

go.hrw.com Web Extra! KEYWORD: MR7 TV

Order the numbers from least to greatest.

56. 45%, $\frac{21}{50}$, 0.43 **$\frac{21}{50}$, 0.43, 45%**
57. $\frac{7}{8}$, 90%, 0.098 **0.098, $\frac{7}{8}$, 90%**
58. 0.7, 26%, $\frac{1}{4}$ **$\frac{1}{4}$, 26%, 0.7**

59. 38%, $\frac{7}{25}$, 0.21 **0.21, $\frac{7}{25}$, 38%**
60. $\frac{9}{20}$, 14%, 0.125 **0.125, 14%, $\frac{9}{20}$**
61. 0.605, 17%, $\frac{5}{9}$ **17%, $\frac{5}{9}$, 0.605**

62. Entertainment About 97 million households in the United States have at least one television. Use the table below to answer the questions that follow.

Television in the United States	
Fraction of households with at least one television	$\frac{49}{50}$
Percent of households with three televisions	38%
Fraction of television owners with basic cable	$\frac{2}{3}$

a. About what percent of television owners have basic cable? **about 67%**

b. Write a decimal to express the percent of television owners who have three televisions. **0.38**

63. Multi-Step A record-company official estimates that 3 out of every 100 albums released become hits. What percent of albums do not become hits? **97%**

12/25 = 48%
5/25 = 20%

64. What's the Question? Out of 25 students, 12 prefer to take their test on Monday, and 5 prefer to take their test on Tuesday. The answer is 32%. What is the question?

65. Write About It Explain why 0.8 is equal to 80% and not 8%.

66. Challenge The dimensions of a rectangle are 0.5 yard and 24% of a yard. What is the area of the rectangle? Write your answer as a fraction in simplest form. **$\frac{3}{25}$ square yard**

24/100 = 6/25 / 6/25 · 1/2 = 3/25 sq yd

CRCT PREP • GPS SUPPORT • SPIRAL REVIEW

67. Multiple Choice Which expression is NOT equal to half of n?

Ⓐ $0.5n$ Ⓑ $\frac{n}{2}$ Ⓒ $n \div 2$ **Ⓓ 5% of n**

68. Multiple Choice Approximately $\frac{2}{3}$ of U.S. homeowners own a cell phone. What percent of homeowners do NOT own a cell phone?

Ⓕ 0.67% Ⓖ 2.3% **Ⓗ 33.3%** Ⓙ 66.7%

Add or subtract. Write each answer in simplest form. (Lesson 5-2)

69. $\frac{1}{2} + \frac{3}{4}$ **$1\frac{1}{4}$ or $\frac{5}{4}$**
70. $\frac{2}{3} - \frac{1}{5}$ **$\frac{7}{15}$**
71. $\frac{2}{5} + \frac{1}{2}$ **$\frac{9}{10}$**
72. $\frac{8}{9} - \frac{1}{6}$ **$\frac{13}{18}$**

The scale for blueprints of a house is 2 in:3 ft. Use the scale to determine the related actual lengths. (Lesson 7-6)

73. porch length: 2 in. **3 ft**
74. bedroom wall: 5 in. **7.5 ft**
75. window: 1.5 in. **2.25 ft**

CHALLENGE 7-8

LESSON 7-8 Challenge
Trash or Treasure?

People in the United States produce about 208 million tons of garbage every year! We recycle about 56 million tons of that garbage, or about 27% of the total.

Complete the chart at right. Then display the percents on the circle graph below. Remember to give your graph a title. Label each section of the graph with the material and the percent of the total garbage recycled that each section represents. You may wish to color each section differently or add illustrations.

United States Recycling

Material	Total Garbage Recycled	
	Fraction	Percent
Metals	$\frac{1}{10}$	10%
Yard Waste	$\frac{17}{100}$	17%
Glass	$\frac{3}{50}$	6%
Paper	$\frac{29}{50}$	58%
Plastics	$\frac{1}{50}$	2%
All Other Materials	$\frac{7}{100}$	7%

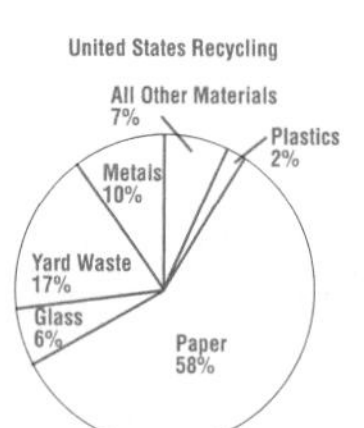

PROBLEM SOLVING 7-8

LESSON 7-8 Problem Solving
Percents, Decimals, and Fractions

Write the correct answer.

1. Deserts cover about $\frac{1}{7}$ of all the land on Earth. About what percent of Earth's land is made up of deserts?
about 14%

2. The Sahara is the largest desert in the world. It covers about 3% of the total area of Africa. What decimal expresses this percent?
0.03

3. Cactus plants survive in deserts by storing water in their thick stems. In fact, water makes up $\frac{3}{4}$ of the saguaro cactus's total weight. What percent of its weight is water?
75%

4. Daytime temperatures in the Sahara can reach 130°F! At night, however, the temperature can drop by 62%. What decimal expresses this percent?
0.62

Circle the letter of the correct answer.

5. The desert nation of Saudi Arabia is the world's largest oil producer. About $\frac{1}{4}$ of all the oil imported to the United States is shipped from Saudi Arabia. What percent of our nation's oil is that?
A 20%
B 22%
Ⓒ 25%
D 40%

6. About $\frac{2}{5}$ of all the food produced on Earth is grown on irrigated cropland. What percent of the world's food production relies on irrigation? What is the percent written as a decimal?
F 40%; 40.0
G 40%; 4.0
Ⓗ 40%; 0.4
J 40%; 0.04

7. About $\frac{3}{25}$ of all the freshwater in the United States is used for drinking, washing, and other domestic purposes. What percent of our fresh water resources is that?
A 3%
B 25%
Ⓒ 12%
D $\frac{1}{5}$

8. Factories and other industrial users account for about $\frac{23}{50}$ of the total water usage in the United States. Which of the following show that amount as a percent and decimal?
Ⓕ 46% and 0.46
G 23% and 0.23
H 50% and 0.5
J 46% and 4.6

Convert Between Percents, Decimals, and Fractions

Use with Lesson 7-8

M6N1.f, M6P1.c

go.hrw.com
Lab Resources Online
KEYWORD: MR7 Lab7

You can use your calculator to quickly change between percents, decimals, and fractions.

Activity

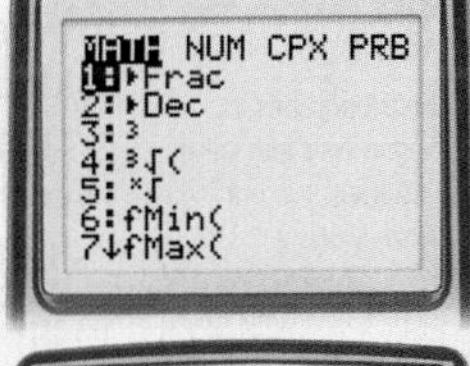

1. To write a decimal as a fraction on a graphing calculator, use the **FRAC** command from the **MATH** menu.

   Find the fraction equivalent of 0.225 by pressing 0.225 MATH 1 ENTER.

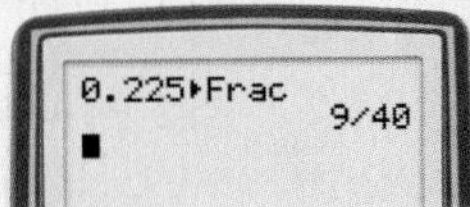

2. To write a percent as a fraction, first write the percent as a fraction whose denominator is 100. Then use the **FRAC** command to find the simplest form of the fraction.

   Find the fraction equivalent of 65% by pressing 65 ÷ 100 MATH 1 ENTER.

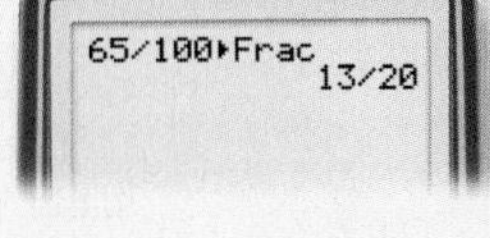

3. To write a fraction as a percent, multiply the fraction by 100.

   Find the percent equivalent of $\frac{11}{25}$ by pressing 11 ÷ 25 × 100 ENTER.

   $\frac{11}{25} = 44\%$

Think and Discuss

1. Use the **FRAC** command on a graphing calculator to find the fraction equivalent of 0.1428571429 by pressing 0.1428571429 MATH 1 ENTER. Describe what happens. **Possible answer: Some graphing calculators cannot convert decimals with more than 4 digits to fractions. Others will accept decimal approximations for common fractions and will return $\frac{1}{7}$ in this case.**

Try This

Write each percent as a fraction.

1. 57.5% $\frac{23}{40}$
2. 32.5% $\frac{13}{40}$
3. 3.25% $\frac{13}{400}$
4. 1.65% $\frac{33}{2,000}$
5. 81.25% $\frac{13}{16}$

Write each fraction as a percent.

6. $\frac{7}{40}$ 17.5%
7. $\frac{3}{8}$ 37.5%
8. $\frac{19}{25}$ 76%
9. $\frac{3}{16}$ 18.75%
10. $\frac{17}{20}$ 85%

Teacher to Teacher

Dianne Shaver
Round Rock, Texas

Many students need more work with the benchmark fractions at the concrete and connecting level before this lab will be meaningful. You may want to have students use benchmarks to estimate their answers before finding the answers using the calculators.

Using fraction bars to represent fractions helps students connect to percents because they are already familiar with the percent bars shown on computers when downloading, or installing software.

Organizer

Use with Lesson 7-8

Pacing:
Traditional 1 day
Block $\frac{1}{2}$ day

Objective: Use a calculator to quickly change between fractions, decimals, and percents

Materials: Graphing calculator

Online Edition
Scientific Calculator, TechKeys

Resources

Technology Lab Activities
Lab 7-8 Recording Sheet

Teach

Discuss

Have students discuss situations in and out of school when they might need to quickly change between fractions, decimals, and percents.

Close

Key Concept

A calculator is a valuable tool for changing between fractions, decimals, and percents.

Assessment

1. What keystrokes are needed to convert the fraction $\frac{3}{26}$ to a decimal?
2. What keystrokes are needed to convert the decimal 0.082 to a fraction?
3. What keystrokes are needed to convert the percent 32.4% to a fraction?

Answers to *Assessment*

1–3. See p. A9.

Georgia Performance Standards

M6N1.f Use fractions, decimals, and percents interchangeably.

M6P1.c Apply and adapt a variety of appropriate strategies to solve problems.

7-9 Organizer

Pacing: Traditional 1 day
Block $\frac{1}{2}$ day

Objective: Students find the missing value in a percent problem.

GPS M6N1.g, M6A2.c
Technology Lab
In *Technology Lab Activities*

Online Edition
Tutorial Videos, Interactivities

Countdown to CRCT Week 16

Power Presentations with PowerPoint®

Warm Up

Write each decimal as a percent and fraction.

1. 0.38 — 38%, $\frac{19}{50}$
2. 0.06 — 6%, $\frac{3}{50}$
3. 0.2 — 20%, $\frac{1}{5}$

Problem of the Day

Lucky Jim won $16,000,000 in a lottery. Every year for 10 years he spent 50% of what was left. How much did Lucky Jim have after 10 years? **$15,625**

Also available on transparency

Math Humor

What does a house full of happy cats smell like? Purr scent

Georgia Performance Standards

M6N1.g Solve problems involving fractions, decimals, and percents.

M6A2.c Use proportions (a/b=c/d) to describe relationships and solve problems, including percent problems.

M6A2.g Use proportional reasoning (a/b=c/d and y = kx) to solve problems.

M6P4.a Recognize and use connections among mathematical ideas.

M6P4.b Understand how mathematical ideas interconnect and build on one another to produce a coherent whole.

7-9 Percent Problems

Learn to find the missing value in a percent problem.

Georgia Performance Standards

M6A2.c Use proportions to describe relationships and solve problems, including percent problems. Also, M6N1.g, M6A2.g, M6P4.a, M6P4.b.

The frozen-yogurt stand in the mall sells 420 frozen-yogurt cups per day, on average. Forty-five percent of the frozen-yogurt cups are sold to teenagers. On average, how many frozen-yogurt cups are sold to teenagers each day?

To answer this question, you will need to find 45% of 420.

To find the percent one number is of another, use this proportion:

$$\frac{\%}{100} = \frac{\text{is}}{\text{of}}$$

Because you are looking for 45% of 420, 45 replaces the percent sign and 420 replaces "of." The first denominator, 100, always stays the same. The "is" part is what you have been asked to find.

EXAMPLE 1 Consumer Math Application

How many frozen-yogurt cups are sold to teenagers each day?

First estimate your answer. Think: 45% = $\frac{45}{100}$, which is close to $\frac{50}{100}$, or $\frac{1}{2}$.
So about $\frac{1}{2}$ of the 420 yogurt cups are sold to teenagers.

$\frac{1}{2} \cdot 420 = 210$ ← *This is the estimate.*

Now solve:

$\frac{45}{100} = \frac{y}{420}$ — *Let y represent the number of yogurt cups sold to teenagers.*

$100 \cdot y = 45 \cdot 420$ — *The cross products are equal.*

$100y = 18{,}900$ — *y is multiplied by 100.*

$\frac{100y}{100} = \frac{18{,}900}{100}$ — *Divide both sides of the equation by 100 to undo the multiplication.*

$y = 189$

Since 189 is close to your estimate of 210, 189 is a reasonable answer.
About 189 yogurt cups per day are sold to teenagers.

Helpful Hint

Think: "45 out of 100 is how many out of 420?"

1 Introduce

Alternate Opener

EXPLORATION

7-9 Percent Problems

You can use a number line to find the percent of a number.

0 125 250 375 500
0% 100%

Use the number-line model above to complete each problem.

1. $\frac{125}{500}$ = ____% 2. $\frac{250}{500}$ = ____% 3. $\frac{375}{500}$ = ____%

0 640
0% 100%

Label the number-line model above to find each percent of 640.

4. 50% of 640 is ____.
5. 25% of 640 is ____.
6. 75% of 640 is ____.

Think and Discuss

7. **Discuss** what it means to find 100% of a number. (*Hint:* What is 100% of 640?)
8. **Explain** how you can use number-line models to solve percent problems.

Motivate

Review estimation with students. Ask them why it can be a good idea to estimate an answer before solving a problem. Possible answer: so you will know if the answer you get is reasonable Also review some common decimal to fraction equivalencies.

Explorations and answers are provided in *Alternate Openers: Explorations Transparencies.*

EXAMPLE 2 *Technology Application*

Heather is downloading a file from the Internet. So far, she has downloaded 75% of the file. If 30 minutes have passed since she started, how long will it take her to download the rest of the file?

$\frac{\%}{100} = \frac{\text{is}}{\text{of}}$

$\frac{75}{100} = \frac{30}{m}$ *75% of the file has downloaded, so 30 minutes **is** 75% **of** the total time needed.*

$100 \cdot 30 = 75 \cdot m$ *The cross products are equal.*

$3{,}000 = 75m$ *m is multiplied by 75.*

$\frac{3{,}000}{75} = \frac{75m}{75}$ *Divide both sides by 75 to undo the multiplication.*

$40 = m$

The time needed to download the entire file is 40 min. So far, the file has been downloading for 30 min. Because $40 - 30 = 10$, the remainder of the file will be downloaded in 10 min.

Instead of using proportions, you can also multiply to find a percent of a number.

Possible answers to *Think and Discuss*

1. You must find the remaining minutes. So, you subtract the time it took for 75% of the files to download (30 min) from the amount of time it should take 100% of the files to download (40 min).

EXAMPLE 3 Multiplying to Find a Percent of a Number

Find 20% of 150.

$20\% = 0.20$ *Write the percent as a decimal.*

$0.20 \cdot 150$ *Multiply using the decimal.*

30

So 30 is 20% of 150.

Check

Use a model to check the answer.

0%	10%	20%	30%	40%	50%	60%	70%	80%	90%	100%
0	15	30	45	60	75	90	105	120	135	150

2. when you want to find the amount of discount when you know the regular price and the percent of discount, for instance, finding the amount of money saved when saving 5% off the regular price of $50

Think and Discuss

GPS M6P1.d, M6P3.b

1. **Explain** why you must subtract 30 from 40 in Example 2.
2. **Give an example** of a time when you would need to find a percent of a number.

COMMON ERROR ALERT

Some students may multiply by the percent instead of by the equivalent decimal when finding percent of a number (e.g., multiply 5 × 25 to find 5% of 25). Explain that the percent must be written as a decimal or fraction before computing with it.

Power Presentations with PowerPoint®

Additional Examples

Example 

There are 560 students in Ella's school. If 35% of the students participate in after-school sports, how many students participate in after-school sports?

196 students participate in after-school sports.

Example 

Johan is 25% of the way through his exercises. If he has exercised for 20 minutes so far, how much longer does he have to work out?

He still has another 60 min to go.

Example 

Find 36% of 50. 18

Also available on transparency

Teaching Tip **Math Connections** In Example 3, the *of* in each problem can be replaced with ×. So 20% of 150 means 20% × 150, and 5% of 90 means 5% × 90.

2 Teach

Guided Instruction

In this lesson, students learn to find the missing value in a percent problem. Teach students to set up a proportion to answer questions involving percent. Then teach them to multiply by a decimal to find a percent of a given number.

Reaching All Learners

Through Diversity

Have students do research to find real data about population percents and write problems involving the percents. Have students exchange problems to solve.

Possible answer:

47% of the people in Smithville are males. The population of Smithville is 100,000. How many males live in Smithville?

Answer: Find 47% of 100,000.
0.47 × 100,000 = 47,000
47,000 males live in Smithville.

3 Close

Summarize

Review the proportion presented in the lesson opener:

$$\frac{\%}{100} = \frac{\text{is}}{\text{of}}$$

Have students tell you what replaces %, *of,* and *is* in the proportion.

The number before the percent sign replaces %, the total number replaces *of,* and the number that is the percentage of the total replaces *is.*

7-9 Exercises

Assignment Guide

If you finished Example 1 assign:
Average 1, 19–30, 38–45
Advanced 9–10, 19–29, 33, 38–45

If you finished Example 2 assign:
Average 1–2, 19–30, 38–45
Advanced 9–12, 19–28, 38–45

If you finished Example 3 assign:
Average 1–26, 33–35, 38–45
Advanced 9–45

Homework Quick Check
Quickly check key concepts.
Exercises: 12, 14, 20, 26

Math Background

The proportion shown on the first page of the lesson can be rewritten using variables and cross products to assume one of the forms shown below:

Given $\frac{A}{100} = \frac{C}{B}$,

$\frac{A}{100} \cdot B = C$, $\frac{100}{A} \cdot C = B$, and $\frac{100}{B} \cdot C = A$.

Students can then substitute for two of the three unknown quantities and solve for the third quantity. This method allows students to find a missing percent (A), the percent of a number (C), or a number when a percent of it is known (B).

Georgia Performance Standards

M6P3.a Organize and consolidate their mathematical thinking through communication.

M6P3.c Analyze and evaluate the mathematical thinking and strategies of others.

M6P5.c Use representations to model and interpret physical, social, and mathematical phenomena.

7-9 Exercises

M6P3.a, M6P3.c, M6P5.c

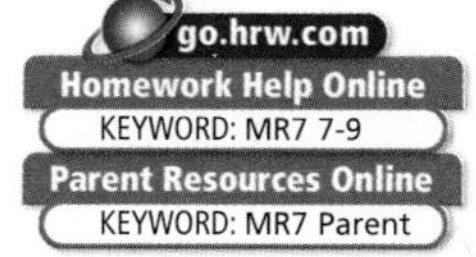

GUIDED PRACTICE

See Example 1
1. Members of the drama club sold T-shirts for their upcoming musical. Of the 80 T-shirts sold, 55% were size medium. How many of the T-shirts sold were size medium? **44 T-shirts**

See Example 2
2. Loni has read 25% of a book. If she has been reading for 5 hours, how many more hours will it take her to complete the book? **15 hours**

See Example 3
3. Find 12% of 56. **6.72**
4. Find 65% of 240. **156**
5. Find 2% of 20. **0.4**
6. Find 85% of 115. **97.75**
7. Find 70% of 54. **37.8**
8. Find 85% of 355. **301.75**

INDEPENDENT PRACTICE

See Example 1
9. Tamara collects porcelain dolls. Of the 24 dolls that she has, 25% have blond hair. How many of her dolls have blond hair? **6 dolls**
10. Mr. Green has a garden. Of the 40 seeds he planted, 35% were vegetable seeds. How many vegetable seeds did he plant? **14 seeds**

See Example 2
11. Kevin has mowed 40% of the lawn. If he has been mowing for 20 minutes, how long will it take him to mow the rest of the lawn? **30 minutes**
12. Maggie ordered a painting. She paid 30% of the total cost when she ordered it, and she will pay the remaining amount when it is delivered. If she has paid $15, how much more does she owe? **$35**

See Example 3
13. Find 22% of 130. **28.6**
14. Find 78% of 350. **273**
15. Find 28% of 65. **18.2**
16. Find 9% of 50. **4.5**
17. Find 45% of 210. **94.5**
18. Find 54% of 602. **325.08**

PRACTICE AND PROBLEM SOLVING

Extra Practice p. 727

Find the percent of each number.

19. 6% of 38 **2.28**
20. 20% of 182 **36.4**
21. 13% of 40 **5.2**
22. 32% of 205 **65.6**
23. 14% of 88 **12.32**
24. 98% of 105 **102.9**
25. 78% of 52 **40.56**
26. 31% of 345 **106.95**
27. 62% of 50 **31**
28. 10% of 50 **5**
29. 1.5% of 800 **12**
30. 0.3% of 9 **0.027**
31. **Geometry** The width of a rectangular room is 75% of the length of the room. The room is 12 feet long.
    a. How wide is the room? **9 feet**
    b. The area of a rectangle is the product of the length and the width. What is the area of the room? **108 square feet**
32. **Multi-Step** Marissa is shopping and finds a sales rack with items that are 25% off. If Marissa likes a shirt on the rack that originally cost $15, how much will she pay for the shirt before tax? **$11.25**

RETEACH 7-9

LESSON 7-9 **Reteach**
Percent Problems

You can use proportions to solve percent problems.

To find 25% of 72, first set up a proportion.

$\frac{25}{100} = \frac{x}{72}$

$25 \cdot 72 = 100 \cdot x$ Next, find cross products.

$1{,}800 = 100x$

$\frac{100x}{100} = \frac{1{,}800}{100}$ Then solve the equation.

$x = 18$

So, 18 is 25% of 72.

Use a proportion to find each number.

1. Find 3% of 75. **2.25**
2. Find 15% of 85. **12.75**
3. Find 20% of 50. **10**
4. Find 6% of 90. **5.4**

You can use multiplication to solve percent problems.

To find 9% of 70, first write the percent as a decimal.

9% = 0.09

Then multiply using the decimal.

$0.09 \cdot 70 = 6.3$

So, 9% of 70 = 6.3.

Use multiplication to find each number.

5. Find 80% of 48. **38.4**
6. Find 6% of 30. **1.8**
7. Find 40% of 120. **48**
8. Find 20% of 98. **19.6**
9. Find 70% of 70. **49**
10. Find 35% of 120. **42**
11. Find 9% of 50. **4.5**
12. Find 40% of 150. **60**

PRACTICE 7-9

LESSON 7-9 **Practice B**
Percent Problems

Find the percent of each number.

1. 8% of 40 **3.2**
2. 105% of 80 **84**
3. 35% of 300 **105**
4. 13% of 66 **8.58**
5. 64% of 50 **32**
6. 51% of 445 **226.95**
7. 14% of 56 **7.84**
8. 98% of 72 **70.56**
9. 24% of 230 **55.2**
10. 35% of 225 **78.75**
11. 44% of 89 **39.16**
12. 3% of 114 **3.42**
13. 70% of 68 **47.6**
14. 1.5% of 300 **4.5**
15. 85% of 240 **204**
16. 47% of 13 **6.11**
17. 20% of 522 **104.4**
18. 2.5% of 400 **10**
19. Jenna ordered 28 shirts for her soccer team. Seventy-five percent of those shirts were size large. How many large shirts did Jenna order? **21 large shirts**
20. Douglas sold 125 sandwiches to raise money for his boy scout troop. Eighty percent of those sandwiches were sold in his neighborhood. How many sandwiches did Douglas sell in his neighborhood? **100 sandwiches**
21. Samuel has run for 45 minutes. If he has completed 60% of his run, how many minutes will Samuel run in all? **75 minutes**

Georgia LINK Technology

The Advanced Technology Development Center at Georgia Tech helps new high-tech businesses start and grow in Georgia.

33. **Chemistry** Glucose is a type of sugar. A glucose molecule is composed of 24 atoms. Hydrogen atoms make up 50% of the molecule, carbon atoms make up 25% of the molecule, and oxygen atoms make up the other 25%. How many of each atom are in a molecule of glucose?

34. **Technology** Students were asked in a school survey about how they use their computers. The circle graph shows the results. 289 students

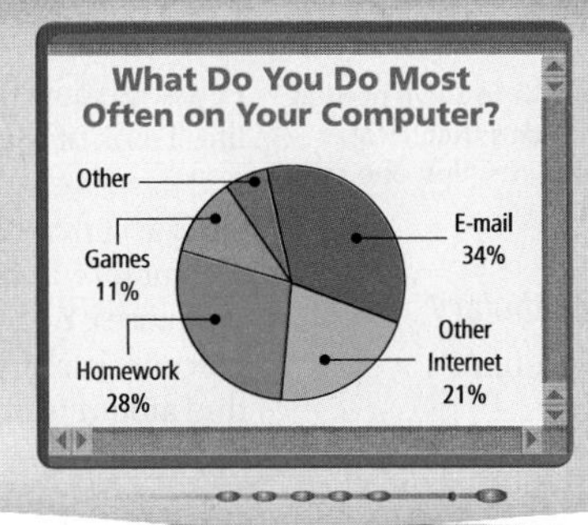

   a. If there are 850 students in the school, how many spend most of their computer time using e-mail?
   b. Fifty-one students selected "other." What percent of the school population does this represent? 6%
   c. Which choices were selected by more than 200 students? E-mail, homework
   d. How many more students chose Internet than chose playing games? 85

35. **What's the Error?** To find 80% of 130, a student set up the proportion $\frac{80}{100} = \frac{130}{x}$. Explain the error. Write the correct proportion, and find the missing value.

36. **Write About It** Suppose you were asked to find 48% of 300 and your answer was 6.25. Would your answer be reasonable? How do you know? What is the correct answer?

37. **Challenge** Mrs. Peterson makes ceramic figurines. She recently made 25 figurines. Of those figurines, 16 are animals. What percent of the figurines are NOT animals? 36%

33. 12 atoms of hydrogen, 6 atoms of carbon, and 6 atoms of oxygen

CRCT Prep • GPS Support • Spiral Review

38. **Multiple Choice** Which of the following amounts is greatest?

   Ⓐ 45% of 200 Ⓑ 50% of 150 Ⓒ 60% of 190 Ⓓ 100% of 110

39. **Short Response** If Sara orders 8 sports magazines and 12 health magazines on sale, how much will she save compared to the regular price? Explain.

Magazine Type	Original Price	Sale
Sports	8 for $60	Save 60%
Health	12 for $72	Save 30%

Write each decimal as a fraction or mixed number. (Lesson 4-4)

40. 0.25 $\frac{1}{4}$ 41. 0.78 $\frac{39}{50}$ 42. 1.4 $1\frac{2}{5}$ 43. 0.99 $\frac{99}{100}$ 44. 5.36 $5\frac{9}{25}$

45. About $\frac{7}{8}$ of the flowers in Monica's garden are snapdragons. What percent of the flowers in the garden are snapdragons? (Lesson 7-8) 87.5%

CHALLENGE 7-9

LESSON 7-9 Challenge
Pet Percentages

The United States Census Bureau counts all the people in the United States—but they do not count our pets! So, veterinarians use the percents shown in the table below to estimate pet populations. Their estimated U.S. pet population data is based on the 2000 census, which counted about 106 million households in the United States.

U.S. Pet Census, 2000

Pet	Percent of all Households	Estimated U.S. Pet Population
Dogs	53%	56,180,000
Cats	60%	63,600,000
Birds	13%	13,780,000
Horses	4%	4,240,000

Use the percents to estimate the number of pets that your class owns altogether, and the number of pets that your school owns altogether. Let each student in your class and each student in your school represent 1 household.

My Class and School Pet Population

Pet	Estimated Class Pet Population	Estimated School Pet Population
Dogs	15.9	106
Cats	18	120
Birds	3.9	26
Horses	1.2	8

Answers will vary depending on the number of students in the class and the number of students in the school. Example answers are given for a 30-student class and a 200-student school.

PROBLEM SOLVING 7-9

LESSON 7-9 Problem Solving
Percent Problems

In 2000, the population of the United States was about 280 million people.
Use this information to answer each question.

1. About 20% of the total United States population is 14 years old or younger. How many people is that? 56 million people
2. About 6% of the total United States population is 75 years old or older. How many people is that? 16.8 million people
3. About 50% of Americans live in states that border the Atlantic or Pacific Ocean. How many people is that? 140 million people
4. About 12% of all Americans live in California. What is the population of California? 33.6 million people
5. About 7.5% of all Americans live in the New York City metropolitan area. What is the population of that region? 21 million people
6. About 12.3% of all Americans have Hispanic ancestors. What is the Hispanic American population here? 34.44 million people

Circle the letter of the correct answer.

7. Males make up about 49% of the total population of the United States. How many males live here?
   A 1,372 million C 13.72 million
   Ⓑ 137.2 million D 1.372 million
8. About 75% of all Americans live in urban areas. How many Americans live in or near large cities?
   F 70 milliom Ⓗ 210 million
   G 200 million J 420 million
9. About 7.4% of all Americans live in Texas. What is the population of Texas?
   A 74 million C 7.4 million
   Ⓑ 20.72 million D 2.072 million
10. Between 1990 and 2000, the population of the United States grew by about 12%. What was the U.S. population in 1990?
   Ⓕ 250 million H 313.6 million
   G 33.6 million J 268 million

Ongoing Assessment and Intervention

***Diagnose Before* the Lesson**
7-9 Warm Up, TE p. 390

***Monitor During* the Lesson**
7-9 Know-It Notebook
7-9 Questioning Strategies

***Assess After* the Lesson**
7-9 Lesson Quiz, TE p. 393

Answers

35. The student set up the proportion for "80% of what number is 130?" instead of "what is 80% of 130?" The proportion should be $\frac{80}{100} = \frac{x}{130}$. The correct answer is 104.

36. Possible answer: No, the answer is not reasonable because 48% is close to half, and 6.25 is not anywhere close to half of 300; 144.

39. $57.60;
   60% of $60 = $36.00
   30% of $72 = $21.60
   Total savings = $57.60

Test Prep Doctor In Exercise 38, remind students to convert percents to fractions or decimals, and then the word *of* can be replaced with the symbol for multiplication.

Journal

Have students think of and write real-world situations in which percents are used.

Power Presentations with PowerPoint®

7-9 Lesson Quiz

1. Find 28% of 310. 86.8
2. Find 70% of 542. 379.4
3. Martha is taking a 100-question test. She has completed 60% of the test in 45 minutes. How much longer will it take her to finish the test? 30 min
4. Crystal has a collection of 72 pennies. If 25% of them are Canadian, how many Canadian pennies does she have? 18

Also available on transparency

7-10 Organizer

Pacing: Traditional 1 day
Block $\frac{1}{2}$ day

Objective: Students solve percent problems that involve discounts, tips, and sales tax.

GPS M6N1.g **Technology Lab**
In *Technology Lab Activities*

Online Edition
Tutorial Videos

Countdown to CRCT Week 16

Power Presentations with PowerPoint®

Warm Up

Find the percent of each number.

1. 75% of 300 225
2. 93% of 56 52.08
3. 32% of 128 40.96
4. 9% of 60 5.4

Problem of the Day

A chessboard is 8 squares wide by 8 squares long. Each player has 8 pawns, 1 king, and 7 other pieces. At the start of a game, all the pieces are on the board, 1 piece per square. What percent of the total number of squares have a chess piece? 50%

Also available on transparency

7-10 Using Percents

Learn to solve percent problems that involve discounts, tips, and sales tax.

Vocabulary
discount
tip
sales tax

Georgia Performance Standards

M6N1.g Solve problems involving fractions, decimals, and percents. Also, M6P4.a, M6P4.b, M6P4.c.

Percents show up often in daily life. Think of examples that you have seen of percents—sales at stores, tips in restaurants, and sales tax on purchases. You can estimate percents such as these to find amounts of money.

Common Uses of Percents	
Discounts	A **discount** is an amount that is subtracted from the regular price of an item. discount = price • discount rate total cost = price − discount
Tips	A **tip** is an amount added to a bill for service. tip = bill • tip rate total cost = bill + tip
Sales tax	**Sales tax** is an amount added to the price of an item. sales tax = price • sales tax rate total cost = price + sales tax

EXAMPLE 1 Finding Discounts

A music store sign reads "10% off the regular price." If Nichole wants to buy a CD whose regular price is $14.99, about how much will she pay for her CD after the discount?

Remember!
To multiply by 0.10, move the decimal point one place left.

Step 1: First round $14.99 to $15.

Step 2: Find 10% of $15 by multiplying 0.10 • $15. (*Hint:* Moving the decimal point one place left is a shortcut.)

10% of 15 = 0.10 • $15 = $1.50

The approximate discount is $1.50. Subtract this amount from $15.00 to estimate the cost of the CD.

$15.00 − $1.50 = $13.50

Nichole will pay about $13.50 for the CD.

Georgia Performance Standards

M6N1.g Solve problems involving fractions, decimals, and percents.

M6P4.a Recognize and use connections among mathematical ideas.

M6P4.b Understand how mathematical ideas interconnect and build on one another to produce a coherent whole.

M6P4.c Recognize and apply mathematics in contexts outside of mathematics.

1 Introduce

Alternate Opener

EXPLORATION

7-10 Using Percents

Stores that go out of business often offer big discounts on purchases. In such situations, 50% off sales are common.

Estimate the discount for each item at 50% off. Then calculate the actual discount.

	Item	Price	Estimated Discount	Actual Discount
1.	Shirt	$39.95		
2.	DVD player	$288.99		
3.	Speakers	$239.95		
4.	TV	$1,035.29		
5.	MP3 player	$247.99		

Think and Discuss

6. **Discuss** the estimation strategies you used.
7. **Explain** whether a one-time 50% discount is equivalent to two consecutive 25% discounts. (*Hint:* Use $100.00 as the base amount.)

Motivate

Ask students to explain what sales tax is and what, if any, strategies they use to figure out how much tax they will have to pay when they buy something at the store. Then discuss tips and how to figure out how much of a tip to leave at a restaurant.

Explorations and answers are provided in *Alternate Openers: Explorations Transparencies.*

When estimating percents, use percents that you can calculate mentally.

- You can find 10% of a number by moving the decimal point one place to the left.
- You can find 1% of a number by moving the decimal point two places to the left.
- You can find 5% of a number by finding one-half of 10% of the number.

EXAMPLE 2 Finding Tips

Leslie's lunch bill is $13.95. She wants to leave a tip that is 15% of the bill. About how much should her tip be?

Step 1: First round $13.95 to $14.

Step 2: Think: 15% = 10% + 5%

10% of $14 = 0.10 · $14 = $1.40

Step 3: 5% = 10% ÷ 2

= $1.40 ÷ 2 = $0.70

Step 4: 15% = 10% + 5%

= $1.40 + $0.70 = $2.10

Leslie should leave about $2.10 as a tip.

EXAMPLE 3 Finding Sales Tax

Marc is buying a scooter for $79.65. The sales tax rate is 6%. About how much will the total cost of the scooter be?

Step 1: First round $79.65 to $80.

Step 2: Think: 6% = 6 · 1%

1% of $80 = 0.01 · $80 = $0.80

Step 3: 6% = 6 · 1%

= 6 · $0.80 = $4.80

The approximate sales tax is $4.80. Add this amount to $80 to estimate the total cost of the scooter.

$80 + $4.80 = $84.80

Marc will pay about $84.80 for the scooter.

Possible answers to *Think and Discuss*

1. When you are buying something, you can use the estimate to check that you are being charged the correct sales tax or given the correct discount.
2. Round the cost of the item to the nearest dollar, and then multiply by the sales tax rate.

Think and Discuss GPS M6P1.d, M6P3.b

1. **Tell** when it would be useful to estimate the percent of a number.
2. **Explain** how to estimate to find the sales tax of an item.

COMMON ERROR ALERT

When finding the price after a discount, students may multiply by the discount rate and neglect to subtract that amount from the original price. Explain that a *discount* is the amount saved, and the *sale price* is the final cost after subtracting the discount.

Power Presentations with PowerPoint®

Additional Examples

Example 

A clothing store is having a 10% off sale. If Angela wants to buy a sweater whose regular price is $19.95, about how much will she pay for the sweater after the discount?

Angela will pay about $18 for the sweater.

Example 

Ben's dinner bill is $7.85. He wants to leave a tip that is 15% of the bill. About how much should his tip be?

Ben should leave about $1.20 as a tip.

Example 

Ann is buying a $29.75 dog bed. The sales tax rate is 7%. About how much will the total cost be?

Ann will pay about $32.10 for the dog bed.

Also available on transparency

2 Teach

Guided Instruction

In this lesson, students learn to solve percent problems that involve discounts, tips, and sales tax. Define the new vocabulary for the lesson, and then teach students to compute each. Explain that it's a good idea when making purchases to estimate the total price after sales tax or discount to be sure you are charged the correct amount. (Teaching Transparency)

Teaching Tip **Graphic Organizers** You may wish to have students make a personal "tip chart" showing 15% and 20% tips for various amounts.

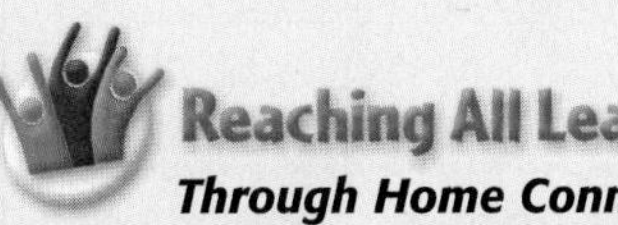

Reaching All Learners
Through Home Connection

Have students use examples of percents from the advertising flyers in newspapers. Have them use the original prices and the percent of discount to find the sale prices.

3 Close

ENGLISH LANGUAGE LEARNERS

Summarize

Have students explain how *discounts* are different from *sales tax* and *tips*.

Possible answer: Discounts are subtracted from the price of an item. Sales tax and tips are added to the total cost.

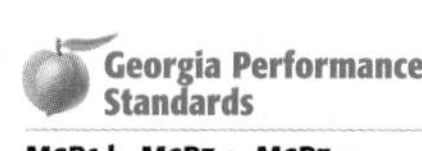

7-10 Exercises

Assignment Guide

If you finished Example 1 assign:
Average 1, 18–27
Advanced 4, 15, 18–27

If you finished Example 2 assign:
Average 1–2, 18–27
Advanced 4–7, 18–27

If you finished Example 3 assign:
Average 1–12, 16–27
Advanced 4–27

Homework Quick Check

Quickly check key concepts.
Exercises: 6, 8, 10, 12

Answers

11. Yes; the total cost with tax is $31.92. $32.50 is greater than $31.92.

Math Background

Taxation is one of the oldest applications of arithmetic. Records of it are found in the histories of people from around the globe. The word *tax* is derived from the Latin word *taxare,* which means "to estimate or evaluate."

Tipping is a widely varying phenomenon. In some areas, it is standard practice to tip a certain percentage of a bill. On the other hand, there are establishments and cultures in which tipping is either expressly forbidden or considered unnecessary. A person traveling in a place with a different culture is advised to become acquainted with the conventions of tipping there.

Georgia Performance Standards

M6P1.b Solve problems that arise in mathematics and in other contexts.

M6P3.a Organize and consolidate their mathematical thinking through communication.

M6P3.c Analyze and evaluate the mathematical thinking and strategies of others.

7-10 Exercises

Georgia Performance Standards
M6P1.b, M6P3.a, M6P3.c

go.hrw.com
Homework Help Online
KEYWORD: MR7 7-10
Parent Resources Online
KEYWORD: MR7 Parent

GUIDED PRACTICE

See Example 1

1. Norine wants to buy a beaded necklace that is on sale for 10% off the marked price. If the marked price is $8.49, about how much will the necklace cost after the discount? **about $7.65**

See Example 2

2. Alice and Wagner ordered a pizza to be delivered. The total bill was $12.15. They want to give the delivery person a tip that is 20% of the bill. About how much should the tip be? **about $2.40**

See Example 3

3. A bicycle sells for $139.75. The sales tax rate is 8%. About how much will the total cost of the bicycle be? **about $151.20**

INDEPENDENT PRACTICE

See Example 1

4. Peter has a coupon for 15% off the price of any item in a sporting goods store. He wants to buy a pair of sneakers that are priced at $36.99. About how much will the sneakers cost after the discount? **about $31.45**
5. All DVDs are discounted 25% off the original price. The DVD that Marissa wants to buy was originally priced at $24.98. About how much will the DVD cost after the discount? **about $18.75**

See Example 2

6. Michael's breakfast bill came to $7.65. He wants to leave a tip that is 15% of the bill. About how much should he leave for the tip? **about $1.20**
7. Betty and her family went out for dinner. Their bill was $73.82. Betty's parents left a tip that was 15% of the bill. About how much was the tip that they left? **about $11.10**

See Example 3

8. A computer game costs $36.85. The sales tax rate is 6%. About how much will the total cost be for this computer game? **about $39.22**
9. Irene is buying party supplies. The cost of her supplies is $52.75. The sales tax rate is 5%. About how much will the total cost of her party supplies be? **about $55.65**

PRACTICE AND PROBLEM SOLVING

Extra Practice p. 727

10. **Multi-Step** Lenny, Robert, and Katrina went out for lunch. The items they ordered are listed on the receipt. The sales tax rate was 7%, and they left a tip that was 15% of the total bill. How much did the three friends spend in all? **$27.49**

**** Thank you ****

Chicken Sandwich - 1	$5.95
Hamburger - 1	$4.75
Roast Beef Sandwich - 1	$7.35
Milk - 2	$2.40
Iced Tea - 1	$1.89

11. Jackie has $32.50 to buy a new pair of jeans. The pair she likes costs $38 but is marked "20% off ticketed price." The sales tax rate is 5%. Does Jackie have enough money to buy the jeans? Explain.

RETEACH 7-10

LESSON 7-10 **Reteach**
Using Percents

There are many uses for percents.

Common Uses of Percents

Discounts	A **discount** is an amount that is subtracted from the regular price of an item. discount = regular price • discount rate
Tips	A **tip** is an amount added to a bill. tip = total bill • tip rate
Sales Tax	**Sales tax** is an amount added to the price of an item. sales tax = purchase price • sales tax rate

Rachel is buying a sweater that costs $42. The sales tax rate is 5%. About how much will the total cost of the sweater be?

You can use fractions to find the amount of sales tax.

First round $42 to $40.

Think: 5% is equal to $\frac{1}{20}$.

So, the amount of tax is about $\frac{1}{20} \cdot \$40$.

The tax is about $2.00.

Then find the sum of the price of the sweater and the tax.

$42 + $2.00 = $44.00

Rachel will pay about $44.00 for the sweater.

Solve each problem. Estimates may vary.

1. About how much would you pay for a meal that costs $29.75 if you left a 15% tip?
   $34.50
2. About how much do you save if a book whose regular price is $25.00 is on sale for 10% off?
   $2.50
3. About how much would you pay for a box of markers whose price is $5.99 with a sales tax rate of 9.5%?
   $6.60

PRACTICE 7-10

LESSON 7-10 **Practice B**
Using Percents

Write the correct answer.

1. Carl and Rita ate breakfast at the local diner. Their bill came to $11.48. They gave their waitress a tip that was 25% of the bill. How much money did they give the waitress for her tip?
   $2.87
2. The school's goal for the charity fundraiser was $3,000. They exceeded the goal by 22%. How much money for charity did the school raise at the event?
   $3,660
3. Rob had a 15% off coupon for the sporting goods store. He bought a tennis racket that had a regular ticket price of $94.00. How much did Rob spend on the racket after using his coupon?
   $79.90
4. Lisa's family ordered sandwiches to be delivered. The total bill was $21.85. They gave the delivery person a tip that was 20% of the bill. How much did they tip the delivery person?
   $4.37
5. A portable CD player costs $118.26. The sales tax rate is 7%. About how much will it cost to buy the CD player?
   $126.54
6. Kathy bought two CDs that each cost $14.95. The sales tax rate was 5%. About how much did Kathy pay in all?
   $31.40
7. Tom bought $65.86 worth of books at the book fair. He got a 12% discount since he volunteered at the fair. About how much did Tom's books cost after the discount?
   $57.96
8. Sawyer bought a T-shirt for $12.78 and shorts for $17.97. The sales tax rate was 6%. About how much money did Sawyer spend altogether?
   $32.60
9. Melody buys a skateboard that costs $79.81 and a helmet that costs $26.41. She uses a 45% off coupon on the purchase. If Melody pays with a $100 bill, about how much change should she get back?
   $41.58
10. Bruce saved $35.00 to buy a new video game. The game's original price was $42.00, but it was on sale for 30% off. The sales tax rate was 5%. Did Bruce have enough money to buy the game? Explain.
    Yes; with the discount and sales tax, the total cost was $30.87.

12. Evan buys a bike that is on sale for 20% off the original price of $95. His brother Kyle buys the same bike at a different store on sale for 15% off the original price of $90. Who paid more? Explain. Kyle; Evan paid $76, and Kyle paid $76.50.

13. **Multi-Step** An electronics store is going out of business. The sign on the door reads "All items on sale for 60% off the ticketed price." A computer has a ticketed price of $649, and a printer has a ticketed price of $199. What is the total cost of both items after the discount? $339.20

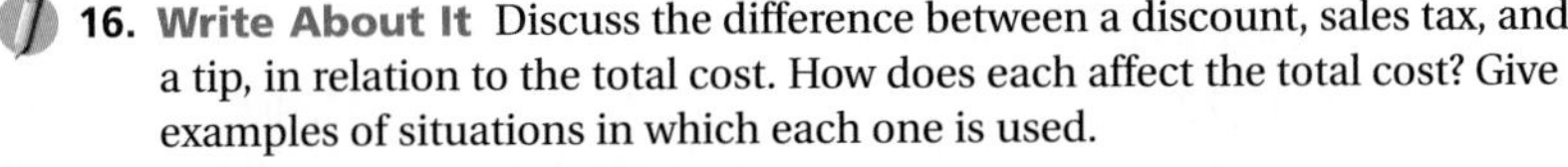

14. **Social Studies** Use the table.

State	Sales Tax Rate
Georgia	4%
Kentucky	6%
New York	4%
North Carolina	4.5%

a. A shirt costs $18.95. Will the shirt cost more after sales tax in Georgia or in Kentucky? About how much more? Kentucky; about $0.38

b. A video game in North Carolina costs $59.75. The same video game in New York costs $60. After sales tax, in which state will the video game cost less? How much less? New York; $0.04 less than in North Carolina

15. **What's the Error?** The original price of an item was $48.65. The item was discounted 40%. A customer calculated the price after the discount to be $19.46. What's the error? Give the correct price after the discount.

16. **Write About It** Discuss the difference between a discount, sales tax, and a tip, in relation to the total cost. How does each affect the total cost? Give examples of situations in which each one is used.

17. **Challenge** Suppose a jacket is discounted 50% off the original price and then discounted an additional 20%. Is this the same as discounting the jacket 70% off the original price? Explain.

CRCT Prep • GPS Support • Spiral Review

18. **Multiple Choice** Electric City is offering a 20% discount on all radios. Pedro would like to buy a radio that was originally priced at $36.50. What is the total cost after the discount?

(A) $7.30 (B) $16.50 (C) $29.20 (D) $36.70

19. **Extended Response** Ann is researching the price of a CD. At Music Place, the CD that Ann wants was originally priced at $15.96 but is discounted 25%. At Awesome Sound, the CD was originally priced at $12.99 but is discounted 10%. What is the sale price of each CD? Which is the better deal? Explain.

Determine whether the given value of the variable is a solution. (Lesson 2-4)

20. $2x + 3 = 10$ for $x = 4$ no
21. $5(b - 3) = 25$ for $b = 8$ yes
22. $18 = 3a - 9$ for $a = 3$ no

Find 20% of each number. (Lesson 7-9)

23. 15 3
24. 50 10
25. 65 13
26. 200 40
27. 3,000 600

CHALLENGE 7-10

LESSON 7-10 Challenge
Shop Smart

The Sport Zone and Sport City are both competing for customers by offering big discounts. To be a smart customer, you need to decide which store is offering the better price on each item.

For each item, write the store offering the best deal and the price you will pay there to the nearest whole cent.

	The Sport Zone	Sport City	
1.			The Sport Zone; $118.99
2.			Sport City; $30.30
3.			The Sport Zone; $15.50
4.			Sport City; $42.20

PROBLEM SOLVING 7-10

LESSON 7-10 Problem Solving
Using Percents

Use the table to answer each question.

Federal Income Tax Rates, 2001

Single Income	Tax Rate	Married Joint Income	Tax Rate
$0 to $27,050	15%	$0 to $45,200	15%
$27,051 to $65,550	27.5%	$45,201 to $109,250	27.5%
$65,551 to $136,740	30.5%	$109,251 to $166,500	30.5%
$136,741 to $297,350	35.5%	$166,501 to $297,350	35.5%
More than $297,350	39.1%	More than $297,350	31.5%

1. If a single person makes $25,000 a year, how much federal income tax will he or she have to pay?

$3,750

2. If a married couple makes $148,000 together, how much federal income tax will they have to pay?

$45,140

3. The average salary for a public school teacher in the United States is $42,898. If two teachers are married, what is the average amount of federal income taxes they have to pay together?

$23,593.90

4. In 2002 President George W. Bush received an annual salary of $400,000. Vice President Dick Cheney got $186,300. How much federal income tax do they each have to pay on their salary?

Bush: $126,000;
Cheney: $66,136.50

Circle the letter of the correct answer.

5. Members of the U.S. Congress each earn $145,100 a year. How much federal income tax does each pay on their salary?

(A) $51,510.50 C $21,765
B $44,255.50 D $39,902.50

6. A married couple each working a minimum-wage job will earn an average of $21,424 together a year. How much income tax will they pay?

F $5,891.60 H $321.36
(G) $3,213.60 J $6,534.32

7. The average American with a college degree earns $33,365 a year. About how much federal income tax does he or she have to pay at a single rate?

A $5,004.75 C $10,176.33
(B) $9,175.38 D $11,844.58

8. The governor of New York makes $179,000 a year. How much federal income tax does that governor have to pay at a single rate?

(F) $63,545 H $49,225
G $54,595 J $26,850

Ongoing Assessment and Intervention

***Diagnose Before* the Lesson**
7-10 Warm Up, TE p. 396

***Monitor During* the Lesson**
7-10 Know-It Notebook
7-10 Questioning Strategies

***Assess After* the Lesson**
7-10 Lesson Quiz, TE p. 399

Answers

15–17, 19. See p. A9.

Test Prep Doctor In Exercises 18 and 19, students sometimes forget that finding a price after a discount involves two calculations. First, find the amount of the discount. Then, subtract the discount from the original price.

Journal

Have students estimate and solve the problem below. Have them explain each step in their solution.

Tom's Toys is having a 25% off sale. The regular price of a badminton set is $39.80. How much will the set cost after the discount, including 6% sales tax? $31.64

Power Presentations with PowerPoint®

7-10 Lesson Quiz

1. Sean's new jeans are priced at $29.97, but the sale sign reads, "Take 15% off." About how much will the jeans cost after the discount? about $25.50
2. The bill for a family dinner comes to $56.78. About how much would a 20% tip be? about $11.50
3. The price on a book is $12.99. If sales tax is 4%, about how much will its total cost be? about $13.50
4. Megan wants a new bike. She is happy to see a sign that reads, "All bikes 10% off." If the original price of the bike was $159.90 and sales tax is 6%, about how much will the total cost of the bike be? about $150

Also available on transparency

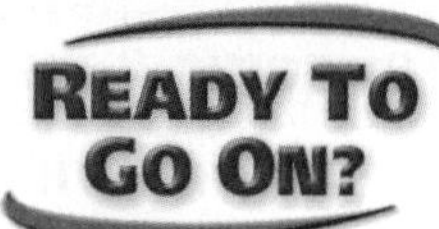

Organizer

Objective: Assess students' mastery of concepts and skills in Lessons 7-7 through 7-10.

Resources

Assessment Resources
Section 7B Quiz

INTERVENTION

Resources

***Ready to Go On? Intervention and Enrichment* Worksheets**

***Ready to Go On?* CD-ROM**

***Ready to Go On?* Online**

SECTION 7B

Quiz for Lessons 7-7 Through 7-10

7-7 Percents

Write each percent as a fraction in simplest form.

1. 60% $\frac{3}{5}$
2. 15% $\frac{3}{20}$
3. 75% $\frac{3}{4}$

Write each percent as a decimal.

4. 34% 0.34
5. 77% 0.77
6. 6% 0.06
7. About 71% of Earth's surface is covered with water. Write 71% as a decimal. 0.71

7-8 Percents, Decimals, and Fractions

Write each fraction as a percent.

8. $\frac{9}{20}$ 45%
9. $\frac{2}{3}$ $66.\overline{6}\%$
10. $\frac{21}{50}$ 42%

Write each decimal as a percent.

11. 0.28 28%
12. 0.9 90%
13. 0.02 2%
14. Mike's baseball team won $\frac{17}{20}$ of its games. What percent of the games did Mike's baseball team win? 85%

7-9 Percent Problems

Use the circle graph for problems 15 and 16.

In a survey, 300 students were asked how they contact their friends.

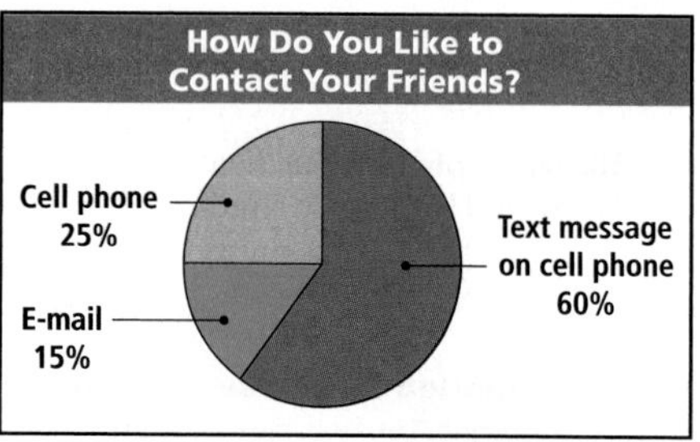

15. How many students said they use text messaging? 180
16. How many students said they use a cell phone? 75
17. Find 40% of 80. 32
18. Find 5% of 30. 1.5

7-10 Using Percents

19. Max and Dan order a pizza. The total bill is $11.60. If they give the delivery person a tip that is 20% of the bill, how much is the tip? $2.32
20. Mia wants to buy a poster that is 10% off the marked price. If the marked price is $15.99, about how much will the poster cost with the discount? $14.40

Ready to Go On?

READY TO GO ON? Diagnose and Prescribe

NO INTERVENE

Ready to Go On? Intervention	*Ready to Go On? Intervention*, Section 7B Worksheets	CD-ROM	Online
Lesson 7-7	7-7 Intervention	Activity 7-7	Diagnose and Prescribe Online
Lesson 7-8	7-8 Intervention	Activity 7-8	
Lesson 7-9	7-9 Intervention	Activity 7-9	
Lesson 7-10	7-10 Intervention	Activity 7-10	

YES ENRICH

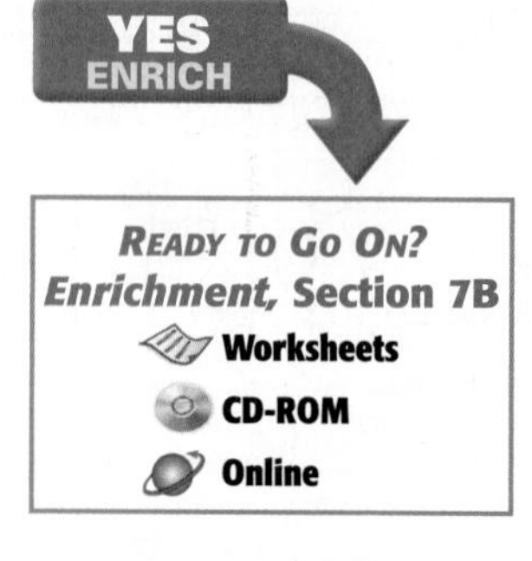

MULTI-STEP TEST PREP

Secret Recipe The ingredients for Sal's famous Old-timer's lemonade are given in the graph below.

Sal's Old-timer's lemonade is so popular that many others have tried to copy the recipe. The graphs at right show some competitors' attempts to copy Sal's recipe. All of the bar graphs are drawn to the same scale.

1. In Sal's recipe, what is the ratio of lemon juice to simple syrup? What is the ratio of simple syrup to water? 2:1; 1:5
2. How much simple syrup should you use to make a batch of Sal's recipe that contains 16 ounces of lemon juice? 8 ounces
3. Which of the competitor's recipes taste identical to Sal's recipe? Explain.
4. Sal poured 1 cup of his Old-timer's lemonade for himself. How much of his glass, in ounces, is lemon juice? simple syrup? water? Explain. (*Hint:* 1 cup = 8 ounces)
5. What fraction of Sal's Old-timer's lemonade is lemon juice? Show how to write this as a percent.

$\frac{2}{8} = \frac{1}{4} = 0.25 = 25\%$

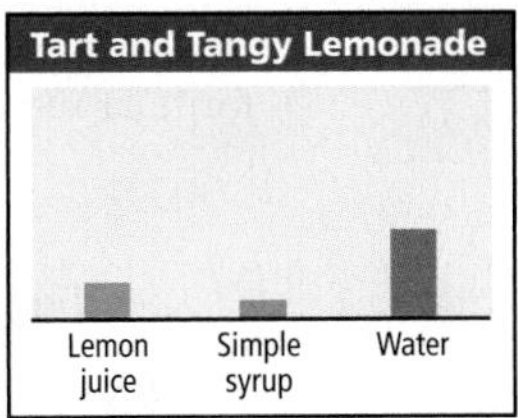

Multi-Step Test Prep

MULTI-STEP TEST PREP

CHAPTER 7

Organizer

Objective: Assess students' ability to apply concepts and skills in Chapter 7 in a real-world format.

Online Edition

Resources

Middle School Assessments
www.mathtekstoolkit.org

Problem	Text reference
1	Lesson 7-1
2	Lesson 7-3
3	Lesson 7-3
4	Lesson 7-3
5	Lesson 7-8

Answers

3. Sweet and Sour and Tart and Tangy; the ratio of lemon juice to simple syrup to water is the same as in Sal's recipe (2 to 1 to 5).
4. 2 ounces lemon juice, 1 ounce simple syrup, 5 ounces water. 1 cup equals 8 ounces. The ratio of lemon juice to syrup to water is 2 to 1 to 5, so 2 parts must be lemon juice, 1 part must be syrup, and 5 parts must be water.

INTERVENTION

Scaffolding Questions

1. How does the length of the bar representing lemon juice compare to the length of the bar representing simple syrup? It is twice as long. How can you write this relationship as a ratio? 2:1
2. What proportion can you use to solve this problem? $\frac{2}{1} = \frac{16}{x}$ How do you solve this proportion? Set cross products equal; $2x = 16$; $x = 8$.
3. What must be true in order for two recipes to taste the same? The ratios of the ingredients must be the same. Are the ingredients of Yellow Birdie in the same ratio as those of Sal's recipe? Why or why not? No; to match Sal's recipe, the amount of syrup should be half the amount of lemon juice.
4. How many ounces are in a cup? 8 ounces Suppose there are 2 ounces of lemon juice. How many ounces of syrup and water are there? How many ounces of liquid are there altogether? 1 ounce syrup; 5 ounces water; 8 ounces altogether
5. If there are 8 ounces of lemonade, how much of that is lemon juice? 2 ounces How can you express this as a fraction? $\frac{2}{8}$ or $\frac{1}{4}$

Extensions

1. How much water do you need to make a batch of Sal's recipe if you use 40 ounces of lemon juice? 100 ounces
2. How much lemonade do you make in this case? 160 ounces (20 cups)

Chapter 7 Extension

Pacing: Traditional 1 day
Block $\frac{1}{2}$ day

Objective: Students find simple interest.

Online Edition

Countdown to CRCT Week 14

Using the Extension

In Lesson 7-10, students solved percent problems that involved discounts, tips, and sales tax. In this extension, students find simple interest.

EXTENSION Simple Interest

Learn to find simple interest.

Vocabulary
interest
principal
simple interest

Georgia Performance Standards

M6N1.g Solve problems involving fractions, decimals, and percents. Also, M6A3, M6P1.b, M6P3.a, M6P4.c.

When you save money in a savings account, you earn money that the bank adds to your account. The added money is called **interest**. The original amount you put into the account is the **principal**. Interest is a percentage of the principal.

One type of interest is called *simple interest*. **Simple interest** is a fixed percentage of the original principal and is often paid over a certain time period. For example, simple interest may be paid once per year or several times per year. In this section, we will assume that simple interest is paid once per year.

Simple Interest

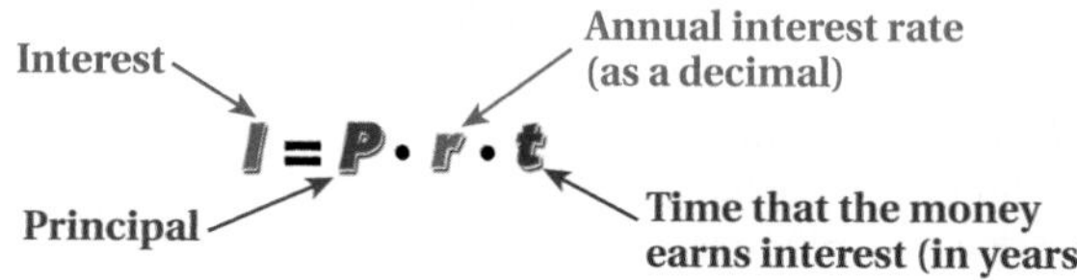

Note that interest rates are usually given as percents, but you must convert the rates to decimals when you use the simple interest formula above.

EXAMPLE 1 Finding Simple Interest

Alyssa put $250 in a savings account at a simple interest rate of 6% per year.

A If she does not add money to or take money from her account, how much interest will she have earned at the end of 3 years?

$I = P \cdot r \cdot t$ *P = $250, r = 0.06, t = 3 years*

$I = 250 \cdot 0.06 \cdot 3$ *Multiply.*

$I = \$45$

Alyssa will earn $45 in interest in 3 years.

B How much money will be in her account after 3 years?

To find the total amount in Alyssa's account after three years, add the interest to the principal.

$$\$250 + \$45 = \$295$$

Alyssa will have $295 in her account after 3 years.

Georgia Performance Standards

M6N1.g Solve problems involving fractions, decimals, and percents.

M6A3 Students will evaluate algebraic expressions, including those with exponents, and solve simple one-step equations using each of the four basic operations.

M6P1.b Solve problems that arise in mathematics and in other contexts.

M6P3.a Organize and consolidate their mathematical thinking through communication.

M6P4.c Recognize and apply mathematics in contexts outside of mathematics.

1 Introduce

Motivate

Money doesn't grow on trees, but it can grow if you save and invest wisely. Earning simple interest on your money is one way to make your money grow.

2 Teach

Guided Instruction

In this extension, students find simple interest. Define *interest, principal,* and *simple interest.* Show students the formula for simple interest, $I = Prt$. Have students find simple interest using the formula. Then have students add the interest to the principal to get the new balance.

EXTENSION Exercises

1. Tamara put $425 in a savings account at a simple interest rate of 7% per year. How much interest will she have earned after 5 years? **$148.75**

2. Jerome put $75 in a savings account at a simple interest rate of 3% per year. How much interest will Jerome have earned after 1 year? How much money will he have in his account after 1 year? **$2.25; $77.25**

Use the equation $I = P \cdot r \cdot t$ to find the missing amount.

3. principal = $320
   interest rate = 5% per year
   time = 2 years
   interest = ■ **$32**

4. principal = $150
   interest rate = 2% per year
   time = 7 years
   interest = ■ **$21**

5. principal = ■ **$250**
   interest rate = 4% per year
   time = 3 years
   interest = $30

6. principal = $456
   interest rate = 6% per year
   time = ■ **4 years**
   interest = $109.44

7. principal = $100
   interest rate = ■ per year **3%**
   time = 5 years
   interest = $15

8. principal = $750
   interest rate = ■ per year **4%**
   time = 10 years
   interest = $300

9. Mr. Bruckner is saving to go on a vacation. He put $340 in a savings account at a simple interest rate of 4% per year. How much money will he have in the savings account after 2 years? **$367.20**

10. When you borrow money, the amount borrowed is the principal. Instead of receiving interest, you pay interest on the principal. Kendra borrowed $1,500 from the bank to buy a home computer. The bank is charging her a simple interest rate of 7% per year. How much interest will Kendra owe the bank after 1 year? **$105.00**

11. Mr. Pei paid $7,500 in interest over 20 years at 1% per year on a loan. How much money did he borrow? **$37,500**

12. Hunter put $165 in a savings account at a simple interest rate of 6% per year. Nicholas put $145 in a savings account at a simple interest rate of 7% per year. Who will have earned more interest after 3 years? How much more? **Nicholas; $0.75 more**

13. **Write About It** Explain the difference between principal and interest.

14. **Write About It** Would you prefer a high or low interest rate when you are borrowing money? When you are saving money? Explain.

15. **Challenge** Madison put $200 in a savings account at an interest rate of 5%. Each year the interest is added to the principal, and then the new amount of interest is calculated. If Madison does not add money to or take money out of the account, how much will she have after 3 years? **$231.53**

Teaching Tip

Number Sense Make sure that the students convert the interest rate to a decimal when they use the simple interest formula.

3 Close

Summarize

Review the terms *interest, principal,* and *simple interest.* Have the students tell what each of the variables represents in the formula for simple interest, $I = Prt$.

I = interest earned, P = principal, r = interest rate per year written as a decimal, and t = time in years.

COMMON ERROR ALERT

In Exercise 5, some students may multiply the interest by the number of years by the interest rate to get the principal. Remind students that they need to substitute the given values into the formula $I = Prt$ and then solve for P.

Additional Examples

Example 1

Ricardo put $300 into a savings account at a simple interest rate of 7% per year.

A. If he does not add money to or take money from his account, how much interest will he have earned at the end of 2 years? $42

B. How much money will be in his account after 2 years? $342

Also available on transparency

Answers

13. The principal is the amount of money you originally have or borrow, and interest is the amount of money you earn or have to pay on the principal after a specified number of years at a certain rate.

14. When you borrow money, you want a low interest rate because you will have to pay back less. When you are saving money, you want a high interest rate because that way you will earn more money.

Game Time

Organizer

Objective: Participate in games to practice and apply skills learned in Chapter 7.

Online Edition

Resources

Chapter 7 Resource Book
Puzzles, Twisters & Teasers

The Golden Rectangle

Purpose: To apply the skill of writing proportions to identifying golden rectangles

Discuss Show students how to test a 3-by-5-inch index card to see whether it approximates a golden rectangle. Let $\ell = 3$ in. and $w = 5$ in. Ask: What proportion can you write to test the rectangle? $\frac{3}{5} = \frac{5}{8}$ Is the proportion true? no Have students write each fraction as a decimal to show that the ratios are nearly equal. $0.60 \approx 0.625$

Extend Have students measure visually appealing rectangles in their environment (e.g., flags, windows, notebook paper) to determine whether they approximate golden rectangles. Check students' work.

Triple Play

Purpose: To practice finding equivalent fractions, decimals, and percents in a game format.

Discuss After a student wins the game, have the winner show each set of cards to the other players so they can verify that each set shows an equivalent fraction, decimal, and percent.

Extend For each set of three cards, have students create an additional card showing a fraction strip representing the fraction. Have them repeat the game, with four cards now needed to create a set.

Example: fourth card for the set 0.1, 10%, $\frac{1}{10}$:

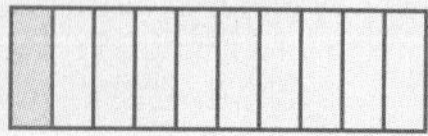

Game Time

The Golden Rectangle

Which rectangle do you find most visually pleasing?

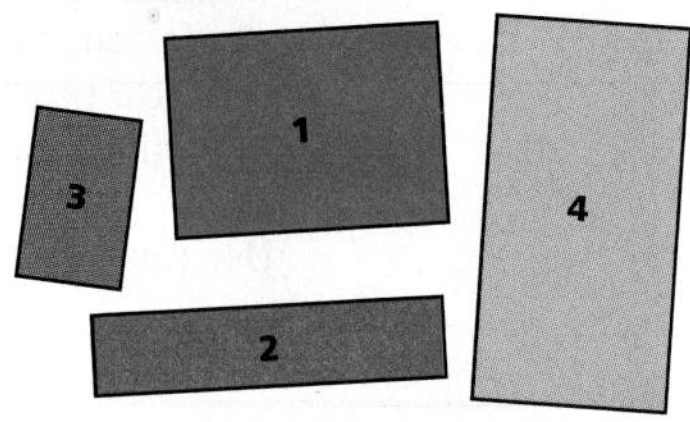

Did you choose rectangle 3? If so, you agree with artists and architects throughout history. Rectangle 3 is a golden rectangle. Golden rectangles are said to be the most pleasing to the human eye.

In a golden rectangle, the ratio of the length of the longer side to the length of the shorter side is approximately equal to 1.6. In other words,

$$\frac{\text{length of longer side}}{\text{length of shorter side}} \approx \frac{1.6}{1}$$

Measure the length and width of each rectangle below. Which could be golden rectangles? Are they the most pleasing to your eye?

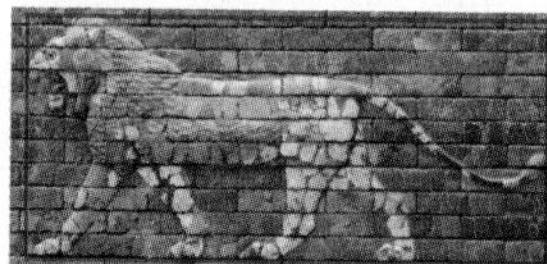

Triple Play

Number of players: 3–5

Deal five cards to each player. Place the remaining cards in a pile facedown. At any time, you may remove *triples* from your hand. A *triple* is a fraction card, a decimal card, and a percent card that are all equivalent.

On your turn, ask any other player for a specific card. For example, if you have the $\frac{3}{5}$ card, you might ask another player if he or she has the 60% card. If so, he or she must give it to you, and you repeat your turn. If not, take the top card from the deck, and your turn is over.

The first player to get rid of his or her cards is the winner.

go.hrw.com
Game Time Extra
KEYWORD: MR7 Games

A complete copy of the rules and game pieces are available online.

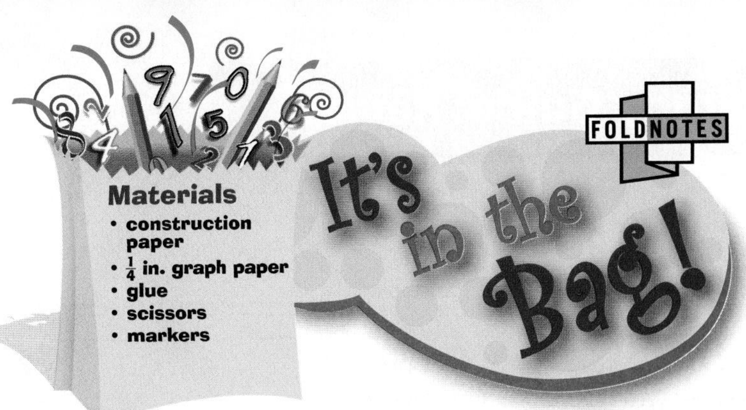

PROJECT Double-Door Fractions, Decimals, and Percents

Open the door to fractions, decimals, and percents by making this handy converter.

Directions

1. Cut the construction paper to $6\frac{1}{2}$ inches by $8\frac{1}{2}$ inches. Fold it in half lengthwise and then unfold it. Fold the top and bottom edges to the middle crease to make a double door. **Figure A**

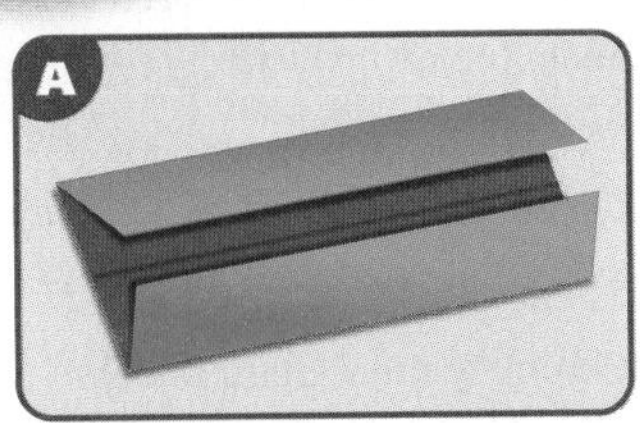

2. Cut a strip of graph paper that is 2 inches wide by $8\frac{1}{2}$ inches long. Make a percent number line along the middle of the strip. Include 0%, 5%, 10%, and so on, up to 100%. **Figure B**

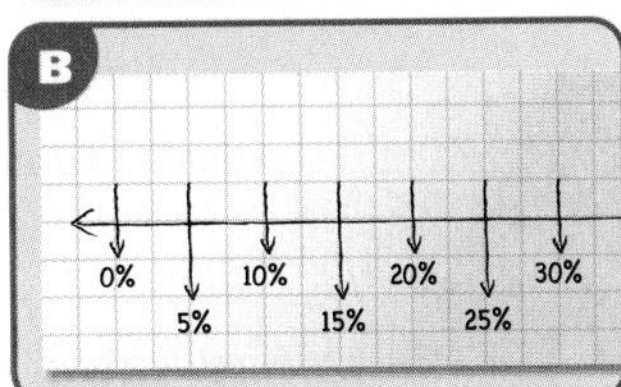

3. Cut two 1-by-$8\frac{1}{2}$-inch strips of graph paper. On one strip, make a fraction number line that includes $\frac{0}{20}$, $\frac{1}{20}$, and so on, up to $\frac{20}{20}$. Write the fractions in simplest form. On the other strip, make a decimal number line that includes 0.0, 0.05, 0.1, and so on, up to 1. **Figure C**

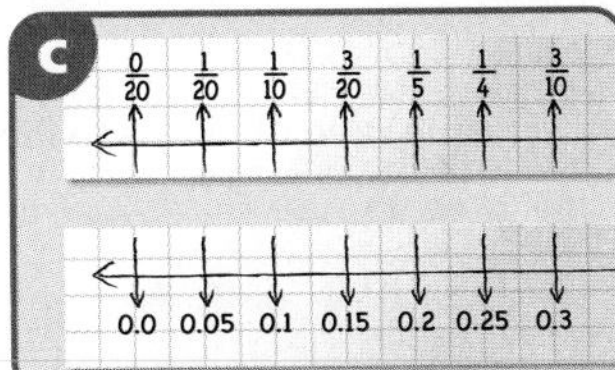

4. Glue the percent number line along the center fold of the construction paper. **Figure D**

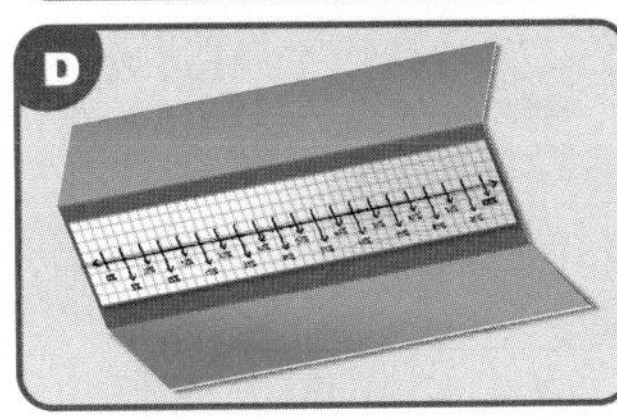

5. Close the double doors. Glue the remaining number lines to the outside of the doors, making sure the number lines match up.

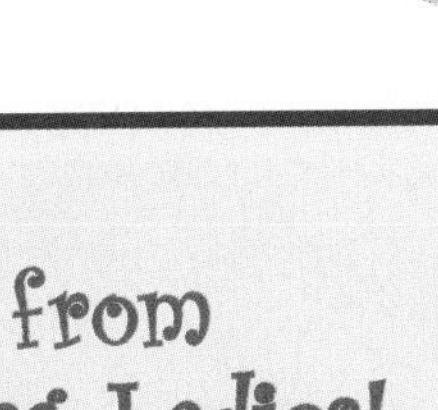

Putting the Math into Action

Team up with a classmate. Use your double-door converters to quiz each other on equivalent fractions, decimals, and percents.

Organizer

Objective: Make a fraction, decimal, and percent converter.

Materials: construction paper, $\frac{1}{4}$ in. graph paper, scissors, glue stick, markers

Online Edition

Using the Page

Preparing the Materials
You can use construction paper, decorative paper, scraps of wallpaper, or pieces of card stock for this project.

Making the Project
Remind students that their three number lines should all be the same length. Also, encourage them to check that equivalent fractions, decimals, and percents fall in the same places along all the number lines.

Extending the Project
Have students make another converter that includes thirds and sixths as well as their equivalent decimals and percents.

Tips from the Bag Ladies!

This project is great for visual and kinesthetic learners, but all students will benefit from making the converters. Students really have to think about equivalent fractions, decimals, and percents to ensure that their number lines match up properly. If students are having trouble making the number lines, you might suggest that they let every three squares along the strip represent 10% of the line. This makes for a number line that is just the right size to fit on the construction paper.

CHAPTER 7 Study Guide: Review

Organizer

Objective: Help students organize and review key concepts and skills presented in Chapter 7.

Online Edition
Multilingual Glossary

Countdown to CRCT Week 16

Resources

Multilingual Glossary **Online**

go.hrw.com
KEYWORD: MR7 Glossary

Lesson Tutorial Videos **CD-ROM**

Answers

1. discount
2. percent
3. corresponding angles
4. Possible answers: 2:4; 3:6; 6:12
5. 12 oz for $2.64
6. Possible answers:

3	6	9	12
10	20	30	40

7. Possible answers:

5	10	15	20
21	42	63	84

8. Possible answers:

15	30	45	60
7	14	21	28

9. $47.25

CHAPTER 7 Study Guide: Review

Study Guide: Review

Vocabulary

corresponding angles	366	ratio	352
corresponding sides	366	sales tax	394
discount	394	scale	374
equivalent ratios	352	scale drawing	374
indirect measurement	370	similar	366
percent	381	tip	394
proportion	362	unit rate	353
rate	353		

Complete the sentences below with vocabulary words from the list above.

1. A(n) __?__ is an amount subtracted from the regular price of an item.
2. A __?__ is a ratio of a number to 100.
3. In similar figures, __?__ have the same measure.

7-1 Ratios and Rates (pp. 352–355)

GPS M6A1

EXAMPLE

■ **Write the ratio of hearts to diamonds.**

♥♥♥♥

♦♦♦♦♦♦♦♦ $\frac{\text{hearts}}{\text{diamonds}} = \frac{4}{8}$

EXERCISES

4. Write three equivalent ratios for 4:8.
5. Which is the better deal—an 8 oz package of pretzels for $1.92 or a 12 oz package of pretzels for $2.64?

7-2 Using Tables to Explore Equivalent Ratios and Rates (pp. 356–359)

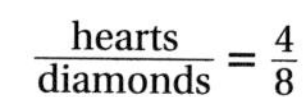
GPS M6A1, M6A2.a

EXAMPLE

■ **Use a table to find three ratios equivalent to 6:7.**

6	12	18	24
7	14	21	28

Multiply the numerator and denominator by 2, 3, and 4.

The ratios 6:7, 12:14, 18:21, and 24:28 are equivalent.

EXERCISES

Use a table to find three equivalent ratios.

6. $\frac{3}{10}$ 7. 5 to 21 8. 15:7

9. The table below shows the cost of canoeing for different-sized groups. Predict how much a group of 9 will pay.

Number in Group	2	4	8	10
Cost ($)	10.50	21	42	52.50

7-3 Proportions (pp. 362–365)

GPS M6A2.c, M6A2.g

EXAMPLE

- **Find the value of n in $\frac{5}{6} = \frac{n}{12}$.**

$6 \cdot n = 5 \cdot 12$ *Cross products are equal.*

$\frac{6n}{6} = \frac{60}{6}$ *Divide both sides by 6.*

$n = 10$

EXERCISES

Find the value of n in each proportion.

10. $\frac{3}{5} = \frac{n}{15}$ **11.** $\frac{1}{n} = \frac{3}{9}$

12. $\frac{7}{8} = \frac{n}{16}$ **13.** $\frac{n}{4} = \frac{8}{16}$

7-4 Similar Figures (pp. 366–369)

GPS M6G1.c, M6A2.c, M6A2.g

EXAMPLE

- **The triangles are similar. Find b.**

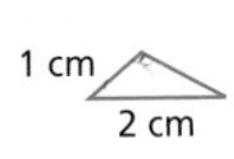

$\frac{1}{32} = \frac{2}{b}$ *Write a proportion.*

$32 \cdot 2 = 1 \cdot b$ *Cross products are equal.*

$64 \text{ cm} = b$

EXERCISES

14. The shapes are similar. Find n and $m\angle A$.

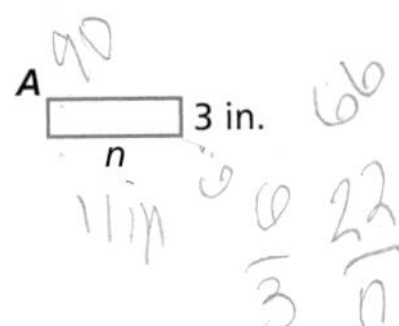

7-5 Indirect Measurement (pp. 370–372)

GPS M6G1.c, M6A2.c, M6A2.g

EXAMPLE

- **A tree casts a 12 ft shadow when a 6 ft man casts a 4 ft shadow. How tall is the tree?**

$\frac{h}{6} = \frac{12}{4}$ *Write a proportion.*

$6 \cdot 12 = 4 \cdot h$ *The cross products are equal.*

$\frac{72}{4} = \frac{4h}{4}$ *Divide both sides by 4.*

$18 = h$ The tree is 18 ft tall.

EXERCISES

15. Find the height of the building.

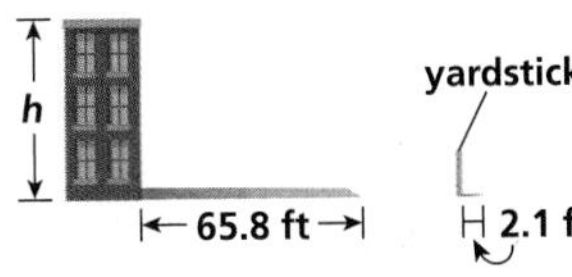

7-6 Scale Drawings and Maps (pp. 374–377)

GPS M6G1.c, M6G1.e, M6A2.c, M6A2.g

EXAMPLE

- **Find the actual distance from A to B.**

A ← 3 cm → B

Scale: 1 cm:35 m

$\frac{1 \text{ cm}}{35 \text{ m}} = \frac{3 \text{ cm}}{x \text{ m}}$ *Write a proportion.*

$35 \cdot 3 = 1 \cdot x$ *Cross products are equal.*

$105 = x$

The actual distance is 105 m.

EXERCISES

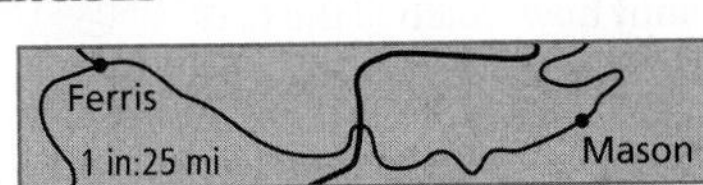

16. Find the actual distance from Ferris to Mason.

17. Renfield is 75 mi from Mason. About how far apart should Renfield and Mason be on the map?

Study Guide: Review

Answers

10. $n = 9$

11. $n = 3$

12. $n = 14$

13. $n = 2$

14. $n = 11$ inches; $m\angle A = 90°$

15. 94 ft

16. 43.75 miles

17. 3 inches

Answers

18. $\frac{3}{4}$
19. $\frac{3}{50}$
20. $\frac{3}{10}$
21. 0.08
22. 0.65
23. 0.2
24. 89.6%
25. 70%
26. 5.7%
27. 12%
28. 70%
29. 25%
30. 87.5%
31. 80%
32. 6.25%
33. 12
34. 5.94
35. 117 tickets
36. about $19.00
37. about $4.35
38. about $1.08

Study Guide: Review

7-7 Percents (pp. 381–384)

GPS M6N1.f, M6N1.g

EXAMPLE

- **Write 48% as a fraction in simplest form.**

  $48\% = \frac{48}{100}$ $\quad \frac{48 \div 4}{100 \div 4} = \frac{12}{25}$

- **Write 16% as a decimal.**

  $16\% = \frac{16}{100}$ $\quad 16 \div 100 = 0.16$

EXERCISES

Write each as a fraction in simplest form.

18. 75% **19.** 6% **20.** 30%

Write each percent as a decimal.

21. 8% **22.** 65% **23.** 20%

7-8 Percents, Decimals, and Fractions (pp. 385–388)

GPS M6N1.f, M6N1.g

EXAMPLE

- **Write 0.365 as a percent.**

  0.365 = 36.5% *Multiply by 100.*

- **Write $\frac{3}{5}$ as a percent.**

  $\frac{3 \cdot 20}{5 \cdot 20} = \frac{60}{100} = 60\%$

EXERCISES

Write each decimal or fraction as a percent.

24. 0.896 **25.** 0.70 **26.** 0.057

27. 0.12 **28.** $\frac{7}{10}$ **29.** $\frac{3}{12}$

30. $\frac{7}{8}$ **31.** $\frac{4}{5}$ **32.** $\frac{1}{16}$

7-9 Percent Problems (pp. 390–393)

GPS M6N1.g, M6A2.c, M6A2.g

EXAMPLE

- **Find 30% of 85.**

  30% = 0.30 *Write 30% as a decimal.*

  0.30 · 85 = 25.5 *Multiply.*

EXERCISES

33. Find 25% of 48.

34. Find 33% of 18.

35. A total of 325 tickets were sold for the school concert, and 36% of these were sold to students. How many tickets were sold to students?

7-10 Using Percents (pp. 394–397)

GPS M6N1.g

EXAMPLE

- **A DVD costs $24.98. The sales tax is 5%. About how much is the tax?**

  Step 1: Round $24.98 to $25.

  Step 2: 5% = 5 · 1%
  1% of $25 = 0.01 · $25 = $0.25

  Step 3: 5% = 5 · 1%
  = 5 · $0.25 = $1.25

  The tax is about $1.25.

EXERCISES

36. A sweater is marked 40% off the original price. The original price was $31.75. About how much is the sweater after the discount?

37. Barry and his friends went out for lunch. The bill was $28.68. About how much should they leave for a 15% tip?

38. Ana is purchasing a book for $17.89. The sales tax rate is 6%. About how much will she pay in sales tax?

Use the table to write each ratio.

Types of Videos in Richard's Collection			
Comedy	5	Cartoon	7
Drama	6	Exercise	3
Music	3	Documentary	2

1. three equivalent ratios to compare dramas to documentaries **6:2, 12:4, 3:1**
2. documentaries to total videos **2:26**
3. music videos to exercise videos **3:3**
4. Which is a better deal—5 videos for $29.50 or 3 videos for $17.25? **3 videos for $17.25**

Find the value of n in each proportion.

5. $\frac{5}{6} = \frac{n}{24}$ **$n = 20$** 6. $\frac{8}{n} = \frac{12}{3}$ **$n = 2$** 7. $\frac{n}{10} = \frac{3}{6}$ **$n = 5$** 8. $\frac{3}{9} = \frac{4}{n}$ **$n = 12$**
9. A cocoa recipe calls for 4 tbsp cocoa mix to make an 8 oz serving. How many tbsp of cocoa mix are needed to make a 15 oz serving? **$7\frac{1}{2}$ tbsp**
10. A 3-foot-tall mailbox casts a shadow that is 1.8 feet long. At the same time, a nearby street lamp casts a shadow that is 12 feet long. How tall is the street lamp? **20 ft**
11. The table shows the time it takes Jenny to swim laps. Predict how long it will take her to swim 14 laps. **10.5 min**

Number of Laps	4	8	12	16
Time (min)	3	6	9	12

Chapter Test

Use the scale drawing for Problems 12 and 13.

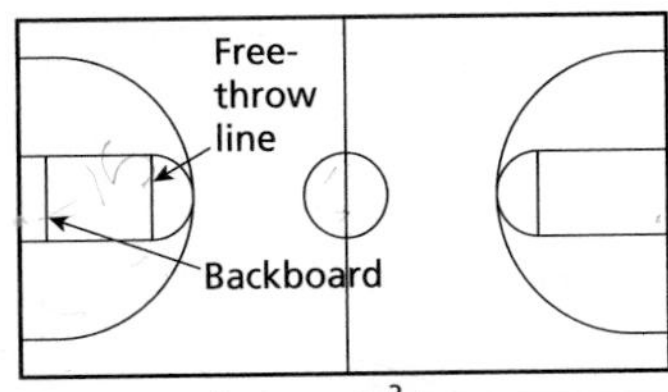

Scale:1 cm:$15\frac{2}{3}$ft

12. The length of the court in the drawing is 6 cm. How long is the actual court? **94 ft**
13. The free-throw line is always 15 feet from the backboard. Is the distance between the backboard and the free-throw line correct in the drawing? Explain.

Write each percent as a fraction in simplest form and as a decimal.

14. 66% **$\frac{33}{50}$, 0.66** 15. 90% **$\frac{9}{10}$, 0.9** 16. 5% **$\frac{1}{20}$, 0.05** 17. 18% **$\frac{9}{50}$, 0.18**

Write each decimal or fraction as a percent.

18. 0.546 **54.6%** 19. 0.092 **9.2%** 20. $\frac{14}{25}$ **56%** 21. $\frac{1}{8}$ **12.5%**

Find each percent.

22. 55% of 218 **119.9** 23. 30% of 310 **93** 24. 25% of 78 **19.5**
25. A bookstore sells paperback books at 20% off the listed price. If Brandy wants to buy a paperback book whose listed price is $12.95, about how much will she pay for the book after the discount? **about $10.40**

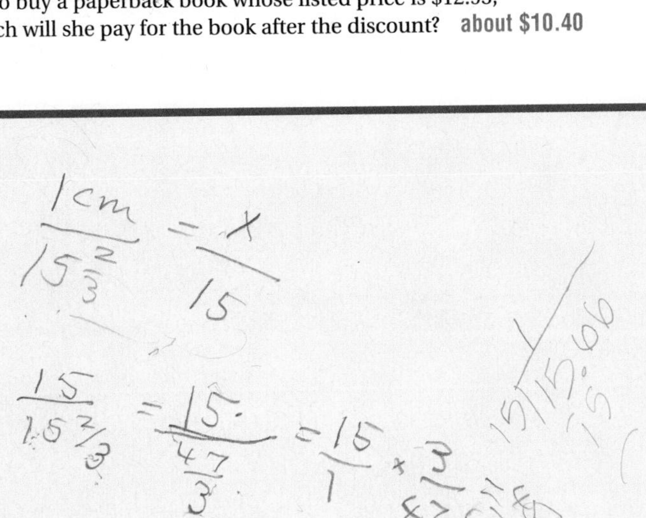

Organizer

Objective: Assess students' mastery of concepts and skills in Chapter 7.

 Online Edition

Resources

 ***Assessment Resources***

Chapter 7 Tests
- Free Response (Levels A, B, C)
- Multiple Choice (Levels A, B, C)
- Performance Assessment

 ***IDEA Works!* CD-ROM**
Modified Chapter 7 Test

Answers

13. Yes; the distance from the backboard to the free-throw line is correct. It should be a little less than 1 cm, and it is.

Organizer

Objective: Provide opportunities to learn and practice common test-taking strategies.

 Online Edition

Resources

 *CRCT Prep* Workbook

 *CRCT Prep* CD-ROM

 *CRCT Practice* Online

go.hrw.com
KEYWORD: MR7 TestPrep

 This test tackler explains how extended-response test items are scored and demonstrates how to write a response that is deserving of full credit. Students need to be aware that a grader scores responses to these types of questions, and points are awarded based on the completeness and correctness of their answer. It may help for students to understand that the scoring guides, or rubrics, are designed so that different graders will arrive at the same score for a given student response.

Standardized Test Strategies

Extended Response: Write Extended Responses

When you answer an extended-response test item, you need to explain your reasoning clearly. Extended-response items are scored using a 4-point scoring rubric like the one shown below.

EXAMPLE

Extended Response Amber tracks her math test scores. Her goal is to have a 92% average. Her 10 test scores are 94, 76, 90, 98, 91, 93, 88, 90, 89, and 85. Find the range, mean, median, and mode of the data set. If her lowest score is dropped, will she meet her goal? Explain your answer.

Here is an example of a 4-point response according to the scoring rubric at right.

Scoring Rubric

4 points: The student correctly answers all parts of the question, shows all work, and provides a complete and correct explanation.

3 points: The student answers all parts of the question, shows all work, and provides a complete explanation that demonstrates understanding, but the student makes minor errors in computation.

2 points: The student does not answer all parts of the question but shows all work and provides a complete and correct explanation for the parts answered, or the student correctly answers all parts of the question but does not show all work or does not provide an explanation.

1 point: The student gives incorrect answers and shows little or no work or explanation, or the student does not follow directions.

0 points: The student gives no response.

Test Tackler

4-point response:

Range: $98 - 76 = 22$
The range is 22.
Mean:

$$\frac{94 + 76 + 90 + 98 + 91 + 93 + 88 + 90 + 89 + 85}{10} = \frac{894}{10} = 89.4$$

The mean is 89.4.

Median: There are an even number of values in this set. The two middle numbers are 90 and 90. The median is 90.

Mode: The value that occurs most often is 90. The mode is 90.

When the lowest score, 76, is dropped, the average is $\frac{894 - 76}{9} = \frac{818}{9} = 90.9$*. This value is less than 92. Even if the lowest score is dropped, Amber will not meet her goal.*

The student correctly calculates and shows how to find the range, mean, median, and mode of this data set.

The student correctly answers the questions and shows how the answer is calculated.

Once you have answered an extended-response test item, double-check to make sure that you answered all of the different parts.

Read each test item and use the scoring rubric to answer the questions that follow.

Item A
Extended Response Use the table below to identify a pattern and find the next three terms. Is this sequence arithmetic? Explain.

Position	Value of Term
1	4
2	7
3	10
4	13
5	16
n	■

1. What needs to be included in a response that would receive 4 points?
2. Write a response that would receive full credit.

Item B
Extended Response Draw a polygon that has three congruent sides. What is true about the measures of the angles of this polygon? Find the measurement of each angle. Classify the type of polygon you drew. Explain your answer.

Kim wrote this response:

Each angle measures 60°.
This is an equilateral triangle.

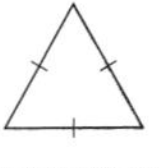

3. Score Kim's response. Explain your scoring decision.
4. Rewrite Kim's response so that it receives full credit.

Item C
Extended Response Look at the graph. Why is this graph misleading? Explain your answer. What might someone believe from this graph? What changes would you make to the graph so it is not misleading?

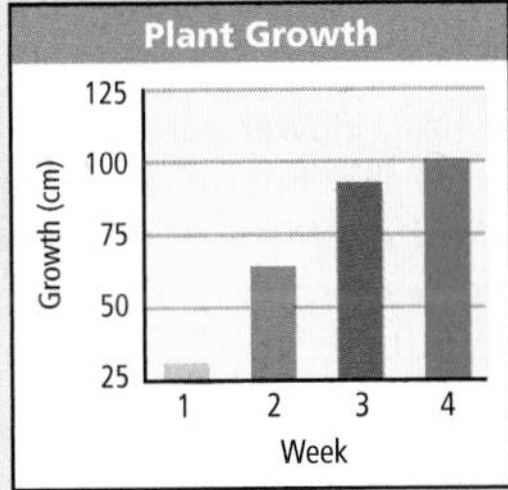

5. What needs to be included in a response that would receive 4 points?
6. Write a response that would receive full credit.

Item D
Extended Response The ages of the employees at a discount store are shown below. Find the mean, median, and mode of the data set. Which one bests describes the data set? Explain your answer.

68	32	16	23	21
17	28	20	39	38
21	22	17	23	37

7. Should the response shown receive a score of 4 points? Why or why not?

The mean is 28.
The modes are 17 and 23.
The median is 22.
The best descriptor is the mode because there is more than one.

8. Correct or add any information, if necessary, for the response to receive full credit.

Test Tackler

Point out to students that many times extended response questions have several steps. For instance, test items A, B, and C have three parts. Remind students to answer each part of the question.

Answers

Possible answers:

1. A 4-point response needs to include a pattern that generates the terms in the table, the next three terms, and an explanation as to why the sequence is or is not arithmetic.
2. A pattern would be $3n + 1$. The next three terms are: 19, 22, and 25. The sequence is arithmetic because the difference between each term and the next is 3.
3. This response is a 3 because there is not a full explanation of the answer.
4. The measures of the angles of this polygon are the same because the length of the sides are congruent. Since there are 180° in a triangle, find the measurement of each angle as follows: $180 \div 3 = 60$. Each angle measures 60°. This triangle can be classified as an equilateral acute triangle.
5. To receive a score of 4 points, each question needs to be correctly answered and fully explained using complete sentences.
6. This graph is misleading because the scale does not start at zero. Someone might believe that in week 2, the plant had a huge plant growth. To fix this graph, start the scale at zero and use intervals of 5 instead of 25.
7. This response should not receive a score of 4 because part of the answer is incorrect and the explanations are not complete.
8. The mean is 28. Calculate this by adding up the values and dividing by 15, the number of ages in the table.
$\frac{422}{15} = 28.1 \approx 28$
The modes are 17, 21, and 23. The mode is the value or values that occur most often. The median is the middle number when the values are placed in numerical order. The median of this data set is 23. The median best describes this data set because most of the numbers are around 23. The mean is too large because of the outlier 68.

Organizer

Objective: Provide review and practice for Chapters 1–7 and standardized tests.

 Online Edition

Resources

 ***Assessment Resources***
Chapter 7 Cumulative Test

 ***CRCT Prep* Workbook**

 ***CRCT Prep* CD-ROM**

 ***CRCT Practice* Online**

go.hrw.com
KEYWORD: MR7 TestPrep

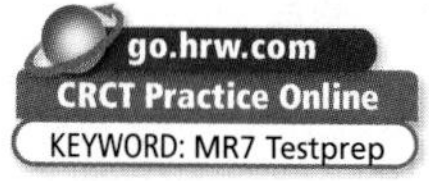

Cumulative Assessment, Chapters 1–7

Multiple Choice

1. Janet has a flower garden with 6 rose bushes, 7 lilac bushes, and 5 azaleas. Which of the following shows the ratio of lilac bushes to the total number of plants in Janet's garden?

Ⓐ 7:11 Ⓒ 11:18
Ⓑ 7:18 Ⓓ 18:5

2. Jenny lives in Paris, Kentucky. She wants to visit Paris, France, this summer. The distance between the two cities is 6.715×10^3 kilometers. What is this distance in standard form?

Ⓕ 67.15 kilometers
Ⓖ 671.5 kilometers
Ⓗ 6,715 kilometers
Ⓙ 67,150 kilometers

3. Carina rode her exercise bike 30 minutes on Monday, 45 minutes on Tuesday, 30 minutes on Wednesday, 60 minutes on Thursday, and 50 minutes on Friday. Find the mean amount of time that Carina rode her bike in these 5 days.

Ⓐ 30 minutes Ⓒ 45 minutes
Ⓑ 43 minutes Ⓓ 215 minutes

4. The sixth grade chorus is going to a competition. There are 116 students in the sixth grade chorus. If each bus holds 35 students, how many buses will be needed to take the students to the competition?

Ⓕ 5 buses Ⓗ 3 buses
Ⓖ 4 buses Ⓙ 2 buses

5. Which of the following is NOT an example of a proportion?

Ⓐ $\frac{3}{4} = \frac{9}{12}$ Ⓒ $\frac{1}{3} = \frac{15}{42}$
Ⓑ $\frac{5}{9} = \frac{45}{81}$ Ⓓ $\frac{7}{8} = \frac{35}{40}$

6. On the map the distance between point R and point T is 1.125 inches. Find the actual distance between point R and point T.

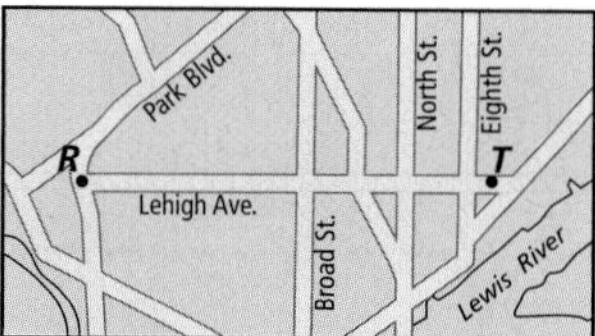

Scale: 1 in:10 mi

Ⓕ 10 miles Ⓗ 12.5 miles
Ⓖ 11.25 miles Ⓙ 15 miles

7. Esperanza has a puppy that weighs $3\frac{1}{4}$ pounds. In 3 months, the puppy should weigh 3 times as much as it weighs now. How much weight should the puppy gain in the next 3 months?

Ⓐ $6\frac{1}{2}$ pounds
Ⓑ $6\frac{3}{4}$ pounds
Ⓒ $8\frac{1}{4}$ pounds
Ⓓ $9\frac{3}{4}$ pounds

8. Which value is greatest?

Ⓕ $\frac{5}{6}$ Ⓗ 80%
Ⓖ 0.7 Ⓙ $\frac{6}{7}$

CRCT Prep

TEST PREP DOCTOR

For item 2, students may not remember that the exponent in scientific notation indicates the number of times the decimal point will be moved to the right.

Answers

14a. [Diagram: 105 ft, 15 ft, h, 75 ft]

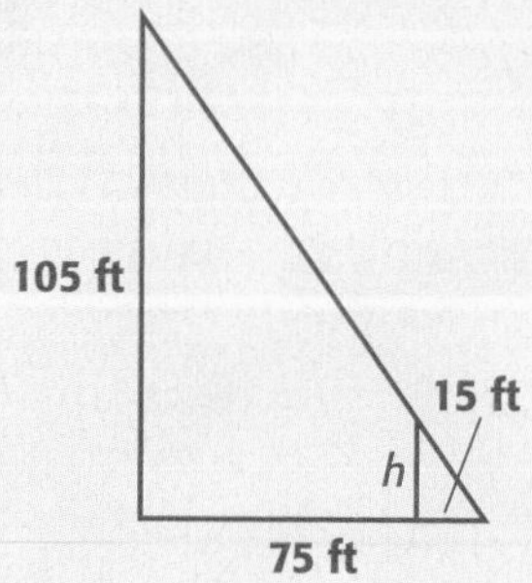

14b. $\frac{h}{15} = \frac{105}{75}$

$75h = 1{,}575$

$\frac{75h}{75} = \frac{1{,}575}{75}$

$h = 21$

The young tree is 21 ft tall.

15. Package A–unit price is $\frac{15.50}{10} = \$1.55$

Package B–unit price is $\frac{20.50}{15} = \$1.37$

Package C–unit price is $\frac{55.50}{20} = \$1.28$

Package C, with the lowest unit price, is the best deal.

16. \$205.50 discount; \$479.50 sale price

17. See 4-Point Response work sample.

9. Max earns $7.25 per hour working for a florist. His weekly paycheck is $108.75 before taxes. If h equals the number of hours worked, which expression can be used to find the number of hours Max works each week?

Ⓐ $7.25 + h = 108.75$

Ⓑ $\frac{7.25}{h} = 108.75$

Ⓒ $108.75 - h = 7.25$

Ⓓ $7.25h = 108.75$

Estimate your answer before solving the problem. You can often use your estimate to eliminate some of the answer choices.

10. A school is making music kits with 72 recorders, 96 kazoos, and 60 whistles. Each kit has the same number of each instrument. What is the greatest number of kits that can be made?

Ⓕ 6 Ⓗ 15

Ⓖ 12 Ⓙ 30

11. Find the value of $40 \div (3 + 5) \times 2$.

Ⓐ 2.5 Ⓒ 10

Ⓑ 5 Ⓓ 40

12. Write $2\frac{3}{4} + \frac{1}{3}$ as an improper fraction.

Ⓕ $\frac{12}{7}$ Ⓗ $3\frac{1}{12}$

Ⓖ $\frac{16}{7}$ Ⓙ $\frac{37}{12}$

13. Ms. Chavez is ordering art supplies. She orders enough pencils for every student and then adds 20% more for extras. If she has 210 students, how many pencils does she need to order?

Ⓐ 42 Ⓒ 420

Ⓑ 252 Ⓓ 630

STANDARDIZED TEST PREP

Short Response

14. One of the oldest living oak trees is 105 feet tall. One sunny day it casts a shadow that is 75 feet long. At the same time, a younger oak tree casts a shadow that is 15 feet long.

a. Draw a picture to explain how to find the height of the younger tree.

b. Use your picture to write a proportion to find the height of the younger tree. Solve the proportion. Show your work.

15. Chrissy is shopping for T-shirts for the pep club. Package A is 10 shirts for $15.50. Package B is 15 shirts for $20.50. Package C is 20 shirts for $25.50. Find the unit price for each package. Which T-shirt package is the best deal? Explain your reasoning and show your work.

16. A computer is marked 30% off the original price. The computer originally cost $685. Find the amount of the discount and the sale price of the computer.

Extended Response

17. A small purple rectangle is 8 millimeters wide and 18 millimeters tall. A larger purple rectangle is 18 millimeters wide and 25 millimeters tall.

a. Are the two purple rectangles similar? Explain your answer.

b. A third rectangle is similar to the smaller purple rectangle. The width of the third rectangle is 14 millimeters. Let x represent the height of the third rectangle. Write an equation that could be used to find x.

c. Find the height of the third rectangle. Show your work.

CRCT Prep

Short Response Rubric

Items 14–16

2 Points = The student's answer is an accurate and complete execution of the task or tasks.

1 Point = The student's answer contains attributes of an appropriate response but is flawed.

0 Points = The student's answer contains no attributes of an appropriate response.

Extended Response Rubric

Item 17

4 Points = The student demonstrates a thorough understanding of all concepts and shows all work correctly.

3 Points = The student demonstrates a basic understanding of all concepts, but the work shows some flaws reflecting inattentive execution of mathematical procedures or some misunderstanding of the underlying mathematics.

2 Points = The student demonstrates only a partial understanding of the concepts or procedures embodied in the tasks. The approach may be correct, but the work shows a misunderstanding of one or more important concepts.

1 Point = The student demonstrates a very limited understanding of the concepts or procedures embodied in the tasks. The response may show some understanding but exhibits many flaws or is incomplete.

0 Points = The student provides no response at all or a completely incorrect or uninterpretable response.

Student Work Samples for Item 17

4-Point Response

a. No. Corresponding angles are congruent, but corresponding sides aren't proportional. $\frac{8}{18} \neq \frac{18}{25}$

b. $\frac{8}{18} = \frac{14}{x}$

c. $8x = 18 \cdot 14$

$8x = 252$

$x = 31.5$mm

The student demonstrated an understanding of similar figures and proportions.

3-Point Response

a. No. Side lengths are not proportional.

b. $\frac{8}{18} = \frac{x}{14}$

c. $8(14) = 18x$

$112 = 18x$

$x = 6.22$ mm

The student gave a correct answer for part **a**, but did not correctly set up a proportion to answer parts **b** and **c.**

2-Point Response

a. no, they don't look the same

b. $\frac{8}{14} = \frac{x}{18}$

c. $14x = 144$

$x = 10.29$

It's 10.29 ft high

The student gave an answer to part **a** that demonstrated an understanding of similar figures. The equation in part **b** was incorrectly written.

CHAPTER 8

Geometric Relationships

Section 8A — **Lines and Angles**

- **8-1 Building Blocks of Geometry**
- **8-2 Measuring and Classifying Angles**
- **8-3 Angle Relationships**
- **8-4 Classifying Lines**
- **8-4 Hands-On Lab** Parallel Line Relationships

Section 8B — **Polygons**

- **8-5 Hands-On Lab** Classify Triangles
- **8-5 Triangles**
- **8-5 Technology Lab** Angles in Triangles
- **8-6 Quadrilaterals**
- **8-7 Polygons**
- **8-8 Geometric Patterns**

Section 8C — **Polygon Relationships**

- **8-9 Congruence**
- **8-10 Transformations**
- **8-10 Hands-On Lab** Transformations in the Coordinate Plane
- **8-11 Line Symmetry**
- **8-11 Hands-On Lab** Create Tessellations

Pacing Guide for 45-Minute Classes

Chapter 8 — Countdown to Testing Weeks 17, 18, 19

DAY 1	DAY 2	DAY 3	DAY 4	DAY 5
8-1 Lesson	8-2 Lesson	8-3 Lesson	8-4 Lesson	8-4 Hands-On Lab Ready to Go On? Focus on Problem Solving
DAY 6	**DAY 7**	**DAY 8**	**DAY 9**	**DAY 10**
8-5 Hands-On Lab 8-5 Lesson	8-5 Lesson 8-5 Hands-On Lab	8-6 Lesson	8-7 Lesson	8-8 Lesson
DAY 11	**DAY 12**	**DAY 13**	**DAY 14**	**DAY 15**
Ready to Go On? Focus on Problem Solving 8-9 Lesson	8-9 Lesson 8-10 Lesson	8-10 Lesson 8-10 Hands-On Lab	8-11 Lesson	8-11 Hands-On Lab Ready to Go On? Multi-Step Test Prep
DAY 16	**DAY 17**			
Chapter 8 Review	Chapter 8 Test			

Pacing Guide for 90-Minute Classes

Chapter 8

DAY 1	DAY 2	DAY 3	DAY 4	DAY 5
8-1 Lesson 8-2 Lesson	8-3 Lesson 8-4 Lesson	8-4 Hands-On Lab Ready to Go On? Focus on Problem Solving 8-5 Hands-On Lab 8-5 Lesson	8-5 Lesson 8-5 Hands-On Lab 8-6 Lesson	8-7 Lesson 8-8 Lesson
DAY 6	**DAY 7**	**DAY 8**	**DAY 9**	
Ready to Go On? Focus on Problem Solving 8-9 Lesson 8-10 Lesson	8-10 Lesson 8-10 Hands-On Lab 8-11 Lesson	8-11 Hands-On Lab Ready to Go On? Multi-Step Test Prep Chapter 8 Review	Chapter 8 Test	

ONGOING ASSESSMENT and INTERVENTION

	DIAGNOSE	PRESCRIBE
Assess Prior Knowledge	**Before Chapter 8**	
	Diagnose readiness for the chapter.	Prescribe intervention.
	Are You Ready? SE p. 413	***Are You Ready? Intervention*** Skills 69, 76, 81
Formative Assessment	**Before Every Lesson**	
	Diagnose readiness for the lesson.	Prescribe intervention.
	Warm Up TE, every lesson	**Skills Bank** SE pp. 749–761 **Reteach** CRB, Chapters 1–8
	During Every Lesson	
	Diagnose understanding of lesson concepts.	Prescribe intervention.
	Think and Discuss SE, every lesson **Write About It** SE, lesson exercises **Journal** TE, lesson exercises	***Questioning Strategies*** Chapter 8 **Reading Strategies** CRB, every lesson ***Success for ELL*** pp. 127–148
	After Every Lesson	
	Diagnose mastery of lesson concepts.	Prescribe intervention.
	Lesson Quiz TE, every lesson **Test Prep** SE, every lesson ***Test and Practice Generator***	**Reteach** CRB, every lesson **Problem Solving** CRB, every lesson **Test Prep Doctor** TE, lesson exercises ***Homework Help* Online**
	Before Chapter 8 Testing	
	Diagnose mastery of concepts in the chapter.	Prescribe intervention.
	Ready to Go On? SE pp. 434, 454, 470 **Focus on Problem Solving** SE p. 435, 455 **Multi-Step Test Prep** SE p. 471 **Section Quizzes** AR pp. 146–148 ***Test and Practice Generator***	***Ready to Go On? Intervention*** **Scaffolding Questions** TE p. 471
	Before High Stakes Testing	
	Diagnose mastery of benchmark concepts.	Prescribe intervention.
	CRCT Prep SE pp. 478–479 ***CRCT Prep* CD-ROM**	***CRCT Prep Workbook***
Summative Assessment	**After Chapter 8**	
	Check mastery of chapter concepts.	Prescribe intervention.
	Multiple-Choice Tests (Forms A, B, C) **Free-Response Tests (Forms A, B, C)** **Performance Assessment** AR pp. 149–162 ***Test and Practice Generator***	**Reteach** CRB, every lesson ***Lesson Tutorial Videos*** Chapter 8
	Check mastery of benchmark concepts.	Prescribe intervention.
	CRCT	***CRCT Prep Workbook***

KEY: **SE** = *Student Edition* **TE** = *Teacher's Edition* **CRB** = *Chapter Resource Book* **AR** = *Assessment Resources*  Available on CD-ROM  Available online

CHAPTER 8

Supporting the Teacher

Chapter 8 Resource Book

Practice A, B, C
pp. 3–5, 11–13, 20–22, 29–31, 37–39, 46–48, 54–56, 62–64, 70–72, 78–80, 87–89

Reading Strategies ELL
pp. 9, 18, 27, 35, 44, 52, 60, 68, 76, 85, 93

Puzzles, Twisters, and Teasers
pp. 10, 19, 28, 36, 45, 53, 61, 69, 77, 86, 94

Reteach
pp. 6, 14–15, 23–24, 32, 40–41, 49, 57, 65, 73, 81–82, 90

Problem Solving
pp. 8, 17, 26, 34, 43, 51, 59, 67, 75, 84, 92

Challenge
pp. 7, 16, 25, 33, 42, 50, 58, 66, 74, 83, 91

Parent Letter pp. 1–2

Transparencies

Lesson Transparencies, Volume 2 .... Chapter 8
- Warm Ups
- Problem of the Day
- Teaching Transparencies
- Lesson Quizzes

Know-It Notebook .... Chapter 8
- Additional Examples
- Vocabulary
- Chapter Review
- Big Ideas

Alternate Openers: Explorations .... pp. 64–74

Countdown to CRCT .... pp. 33–38

Teacher Tools

Power Presentations®
Complete PowerPoint® presentations for Chapter 8 lessons

Lesson Tutorial Videos® SPANISH
Holt authors Ed Burger and Freddie Renfro present tutorials to support the Chapter 8 lessons.

One-Stop Planner® SPANISH
Easy access to all Chapter 8 resources and assessments, as well as software for lesson planning, test generation, and puzzle creation

IDEA Works!®
Key Chapter 8 resources and assessments modified to address special learning needs

Lesson Plans .... pp. 64–74

Questioning Strategies .... Chapter 8

Solutions Key .... Chapter 8

Interdisciplinary Posters and Worksheets .... Chapter 8

TechKeys

Lab Resources

Project Teacher Support

Parent Resources

Workbooks

Homework and Practice Workbook SPANISH
Teacher's Guide .... pp. 32–37

Know-It Notebook
Teacher's Guide .... Chapter 8

Problem Solving Workbook SPANISH
Teacher's Guide .... pp. 32–37

CRCT Prep Workbook
Teacher's Guide

Technology Highlights for the Teacher

Power Presentations

Dynamic presentations to engage students. Complete PowerPoint® presentations for every lesson in Chapter 8.

2-1 Solving One-Step Equations

Isolate a variable by using inverse operations which "undo" operations on the variable.

An equation is like a balanced scale. To keep the balance, perform the same operation on both sides.

Inverse Operations	
Operation	**Inverse Operation**
Addition	Subtraction
Subtraction	Addition

One-Stop Planner SPANISH

Easy access to Chapter 8 resources and assessments. Includes lesson-planning, test-generation, and puzzle-creation software.

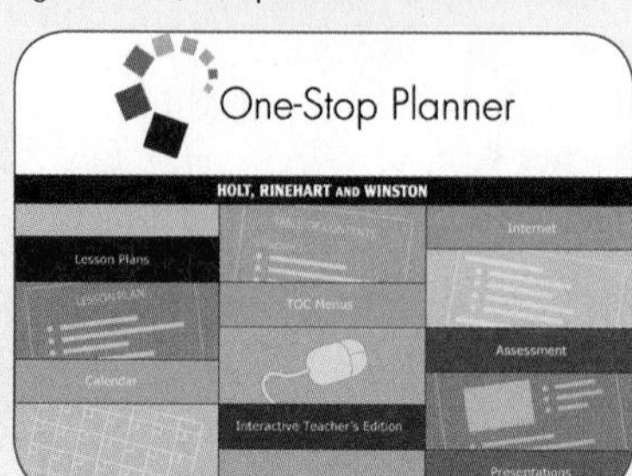

Premier Online Edition SPANISH

Chapter 8 includes Tutorial Videos, Lesson Activities, Lesson Quizzes, Homework Help, and Chapter Project.

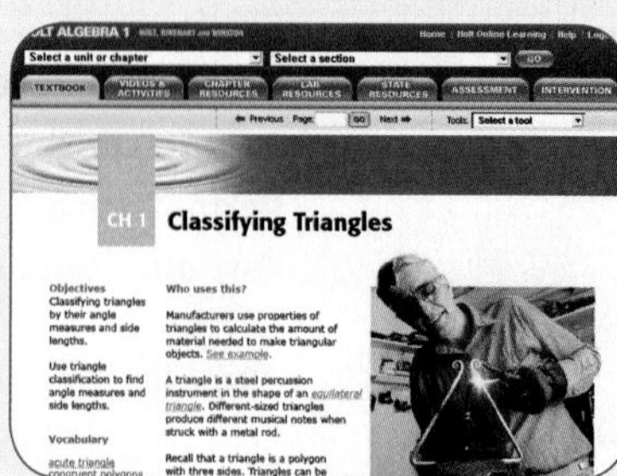

KEY: **SE** = *Student Edition* **TE** = *Teacher's Edition*  English Language Learners  Spanish version available  Available on CD-ROM  Available online

Reaching All Learners

Resources for All Learners

Hands-On Lab Activities .... Chapter 8
Technology Lab Activities .... Chapter 8
Homework and Practice Workbook SPANISH .... pp. 64–74
Know-It Notebook SPANISH .... Chapter 8
Problem Solving Workbook SPANISH .... pp. 64–74

DEVELOPING LEARNERS

Practice A .... CRB, every lesson
Reteach .... CRB, every lesson
Inclusion .... TE pp. 417, 425, 438
Questioning Strategies .... Chapter 8
Modified Chapter 8 Resources .... *IDEA Works!*
***Homework Help* Online**

ON-LEVEL LEARNERS

Practice B .... CRB, every lesson
Puzzles, Twisters, and Teasers .... CRB, every lesson
Multiple Representations .... TE pp. 429, 451
Cognitive Strategies .... TE pp. 417, 429

ADVANCED LEARNERS

Practice C .... CRB, every lesson
Challenge .... CRB, every lesson
Extension .... TE pp. 415, 471, 472, 473
Critical Thinking .... TE p. 447

English Language Learners

ENGLISH LANGUAGE LEARNERS

Are You Ready? Vocabulary .... SE p. 413
Vocabulary Connections .... SE p. 414
Lesson Vocabulary .... SE, every lesson
Vocabulary Review .... SE p. 474
English Language Learners .... TE pp. 415, 417, 421, 425, 447, 460, 481
Reading Strategies .... CRB, every lesson
Success for English Language Learners .... pp. 127–148
Multilingual Glossary

Reaching All Learners Through...

Inclusion .... TE pp. 417, 425, 438
Visual Cues .... TE p. 421
Kinesthetic Experience .... TE pp. 443, 460
Concrete Manipulatives .... TE pp. 425, 460
Multiple Representations .... TE pp. 429, 451
Cognitive Strategies .... TE pp. 417, 429
Cooperative Learning .... TE p. 457
Modeling .... TE pp. 438, 451
Critical Thinking .... TE p. 447
Test Prep Doctor .... TE pp. 419, 423, 427, 431, 440, 445, 449, 453, 462, 467, 478
Common Error Alert .... TE pp. 443, 447
Scaffolding Questions .... TE p. 471

Technology Highlights for Reaching All Learners

Lesson Tutorial Videos SPANISH

Starring Holt authors Ed Burger and Freddie Renfro! Live tutorials to support every lesson in Chapter 8.

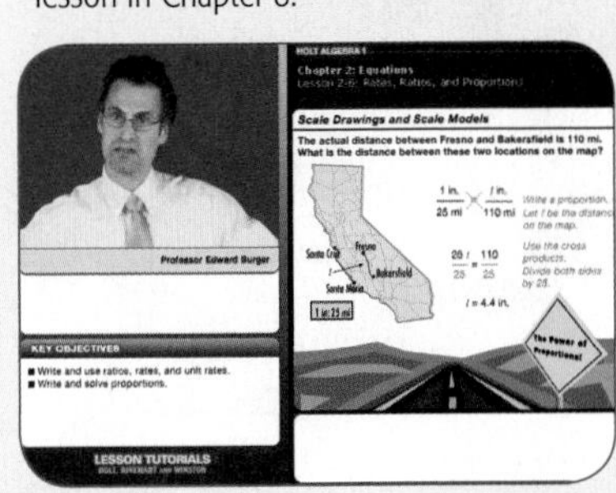

Multilingual Glossary

Searchable glossary includes definitions in English, Spanish, Vietnamese, Chinese, Hmong, Korean, and 4 other languages.

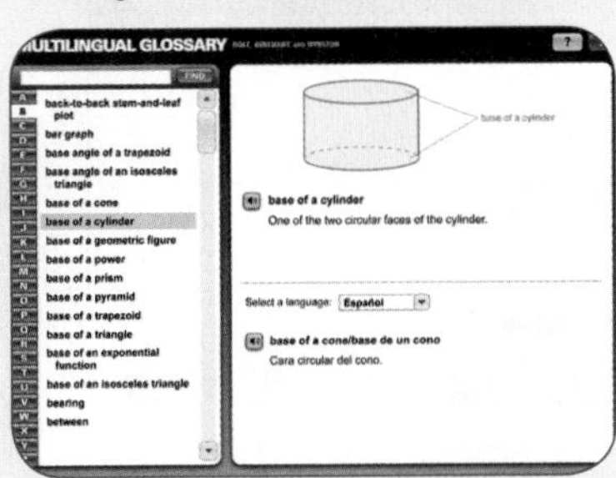

Online Interactivities

Interactive tutorials provide visually engaging alternative opportunities to learn concepts and master skills.

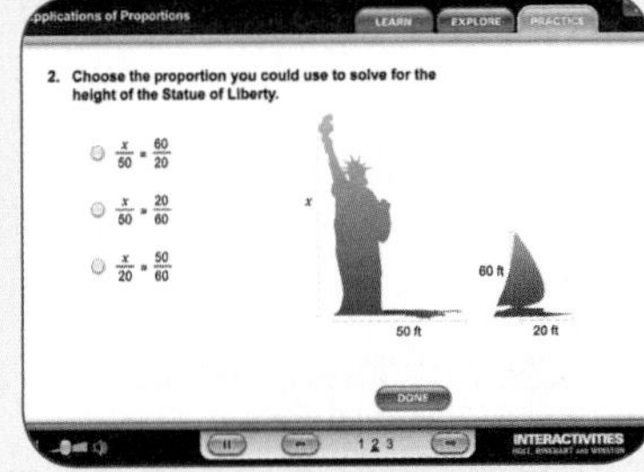

KEY: **SE** = *Student Edition* **TE** = *Teacher's Edition* **CRB** = *Chapter Resource Book* SPANISH Spanish version available  Available on CD-ROM 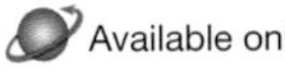 Available online

Ongoing Assessment

Assessing Prior Knowledge

Determine whether students have the prerequisite concepts and skills for success in Chapter 8.

Are You Ready? SPANISH .... SE p. 413

Warm Up .... TE, every lesson

Test Preparation

Provide review and practice for Chapter 8 and standardized tests.

Multi-Step Test Prep .... SE p. 471

Study Guide: Review .... SE pp. 474–476

CRCT Prep .... SE pp. 478–479

Countdown to CRCT Transparencies .... pp. 33–38

CRCT Prep Workbook

***CRCT Prep* CD-ROM**

IDEA Works!

Alternative Assessment

Assess students' understanding of Chapter 8 concepts and combined problem-solving skills.

Chapter 8 Project .... SE p. 412

Performance Assessment SPANISH .... AR pp. 161–162

Portfolio Assessment SPANISH .... AR p. xxxiv

Daily Assessment

Provide formative assessment for each day of Chapter 8.

Questioning Strategies .... Chapter 8

Think and Discuss .... SE, every lesson

Write About It .... SE, lesson exercises

Journal .... TE, lesson exercises

Lesson Quiz .... TE, every lesson

Modified Lesson Quizzes .... *IDEA Works!*

Weekly Assessment

Provide formative assessment for each week of Chapter 8.

Focus on Problem Solving .... SE pp. 435, 454

Multi-Step Test Prep .... SE p. 471

Ready to Go On? SPANISH .... SE pp. 434, 453, 470

Cumulative Assessment .... SE pp. 478–479

Test and Practice Generator SPANISH .... *One-Stop Planner*

Formal Assessment

Provide summative assessment of Chapter 8 mastery.

Section Quizzes SPANISH .... AR pp. 146–148

Chapter 8 Test .... SE p. 477

Chapter Test (Levels A, B, C) SPANISH .... AR pp. 149–160
- Multiple Choice
- Free Response

Cumulative Test SPANISH .... AR pp. 163–166

Test and Practice Generator SPANISH .... *One-Stop Planner*

Modified Chapter 8 Test .... *IDEA Works!*

Technology Highlights for Ongoing Assessment

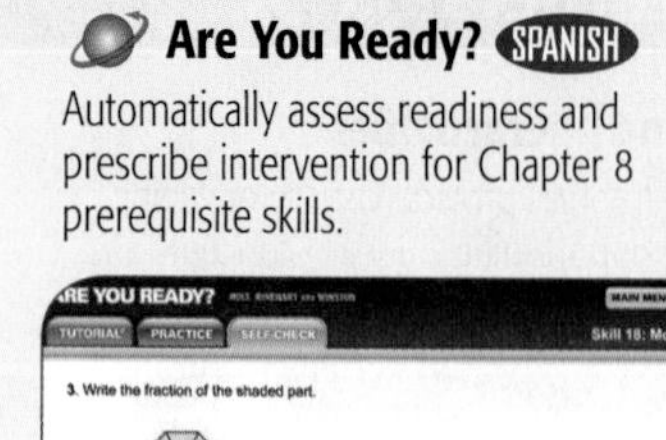

Are You Ready? SPANISH

Automatically assess readiness and prescribe intervention for Chapter 8 prerequisite skills.

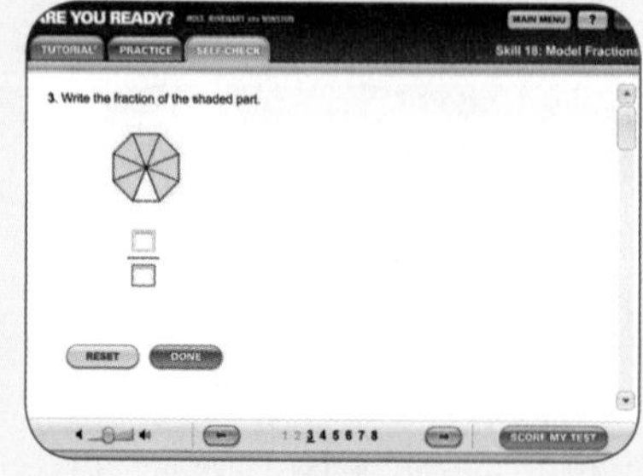

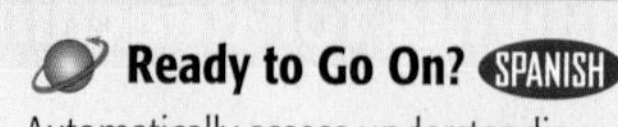

Ready to Go On? SPANISH

Automatically assess understanding of and prescribe intervention for Sections 8A, 8B, and 8C.

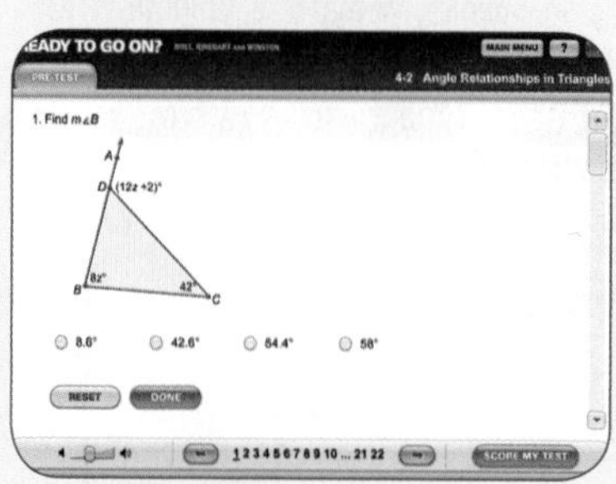

Test and Practice Generator SPANISH

Use Chapter 8 problem banks to create assessments and worksheets to print out or deliver online. Includes dynamic problems.

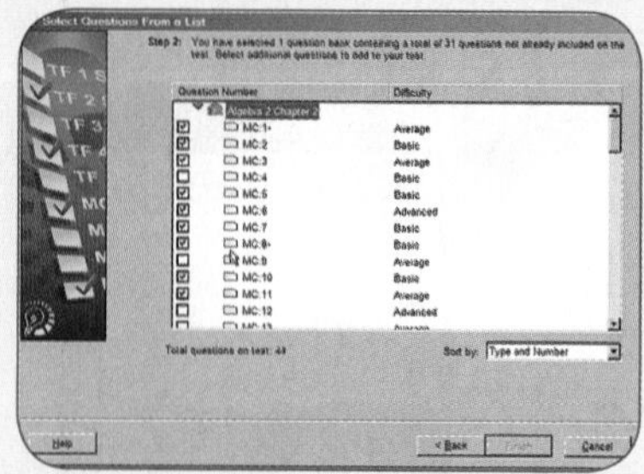

KEY: **SE** = *Student Edition* **TE** = *Teacher's Edition* **AR** = *Assessment Resources*   Spanish version available   Available on CD-ROM  Available online

Formal Assessment

Three levels (A, B, C) of multiple-choice and free-response chapter tests are available in the *Assessment Resources.*

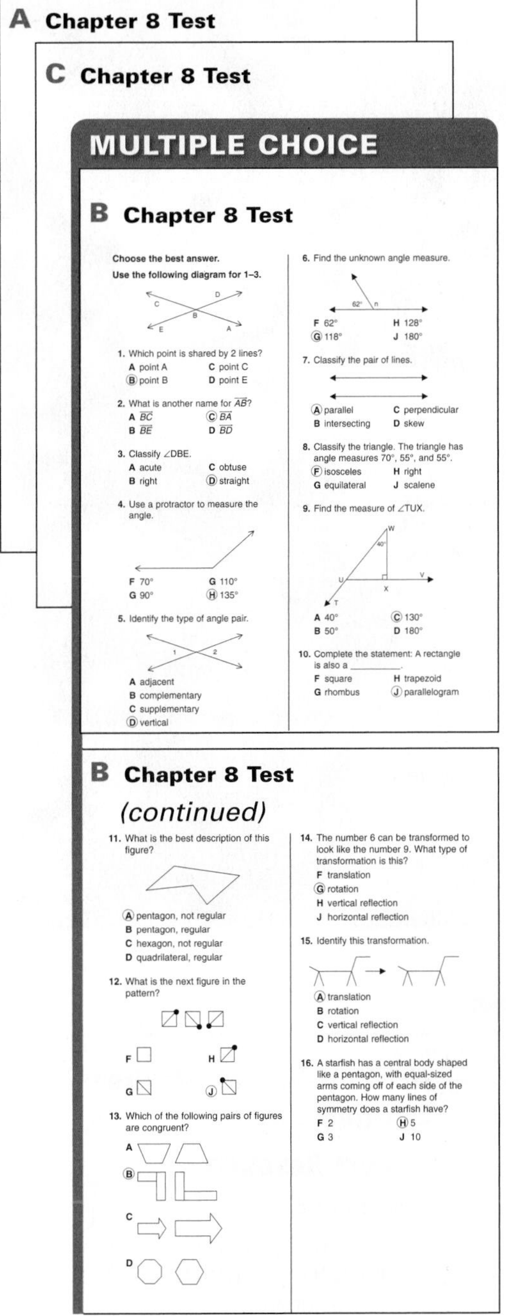

A Chapter 8 Test

C Chapter 8 Test

MULTIPLE CHOICE

B Chapter 8 Test

Choose the best answer.
Use the following diagram for 1–3.

1. Which point is shared by 2 lines?
A point A C point C
(B) point B D point E

2. What is another name for $\overleftrightarrow{AB}$?
A $\overrightarrow{BC}$ (C) $\overleftrightarrow{BA}$
B $\overrightarrow{BE}$ D $\overrightarrow{BD}$

3. Classify ∠DBE.
A acute C obtuse
B right (D) straight

4. Use a protractor to measure the angle.
F 70° G 110°
G 90° (H) 135°

5. Identify the type of angle pair.
A adjacent
B complementary
C supplementary
(D) vertical

6. Find the unknown angle measure.
F 62° H 128°
(G) 118° J 180°

7. Classify the pair of lines.
(A) parallel C perpendicular
B intersecting D skew

8. Classify the triangle. The triangle has angle measures 70°, 55°, and 55°.
(F) isosceles H right
G equilateral J scalene

9. Find the measure of ∠TUX.
A 40° (C) 130°
B 50° D 180°

10. Complete the statement: A rectangle is also a ______.
F square H trapezoid
G rhombus (J) parallelogram

B Chapter 8 Test (continued)

11. What is the best description of this figure?
(A) pentagon, not regular
B pentagon, regular
C hexagon, not regular
D quadrilateral, regular

12. What is the next figure in the pattern?
F H
G (J)

13. Which of the following pairs of figures are congruent?
A
(B)
C
D

14. The number 6 can be transformed to look like the number 9. What type of transformation is this?
F translation
(G) rotation
H vertical reflection
J horizontal reflection

15. Identify this transformation.
(A) translation
B rotation
C vertical reflection
D horizontal reflection

16. A starfish has a central body shaped like a pentagon, with equal-sized arms coming off of each side of the pentagon. How many lines of symmetry does a starfish have?
F 2 (H) 5
G 3 J 10

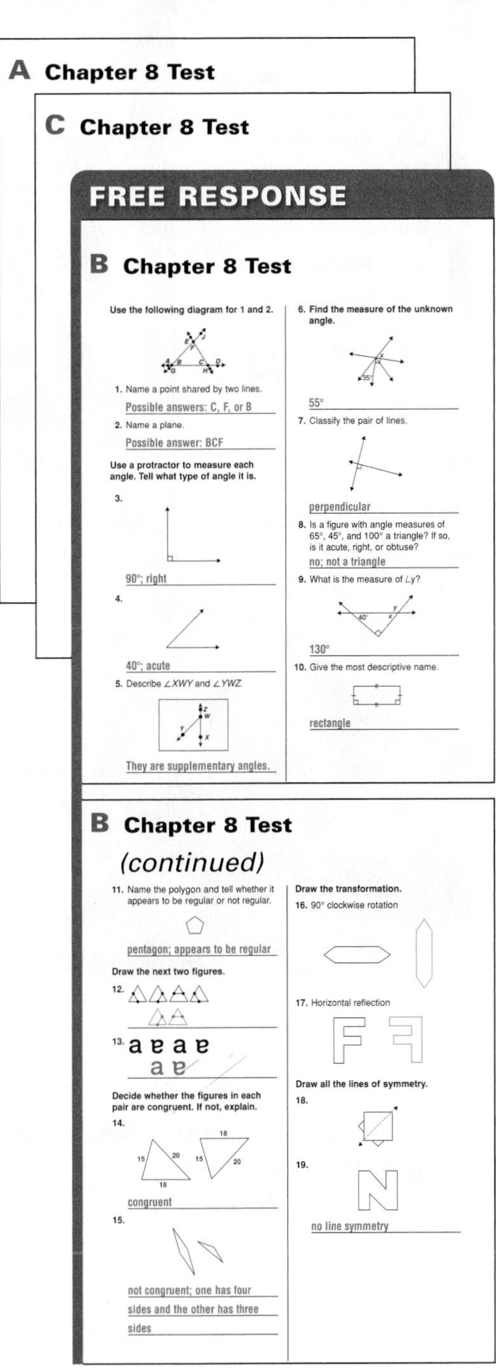

A Chapter 8 Test

C Chapter 8 Test

FREE RESPONSE

B Chapter 8 Test

Use the following diagram for 1 and 2.

1. Name a point shared by two lines.
Possible answers: C, F, or B

2. Name a plane.
Possible answer: BCF

Use a protractor to measure each angle. Tell what type of angle it is.

3. 90°; right

4. 40°; acute

5. Describe ∠XWY and ∠YWZ.
They are supplementary angles.

6. Find the measure of the unknown angle.
55°

7. Classify the pair of lines.
perpendicular

8. Is a figure with angle measures of 65°, 45°, and 100° a triangle? If so, is it acute, right, or obtuse?
no; not a triangle

9. What is the measure of ∠y?
130°

10. Give the most descriptive name.
rectangle

B Chapter 8 Test (continued)

11. Name the polygon and tell whether it appears to be regular or not regular.
pentagon; appears to be regular

Draw the next two figures.

12.

13. a ɐ a ɐ

Decide whether the figures in each pair are congruent. If not, explain.

14. congruent

15. not congruent; one has four sides and the other has three sides

Draw the transformation.

16. 90° clockwise rotation

17. Horizontal reflection

Draw all the lines of symmetry.

18.

19. no line symmetry

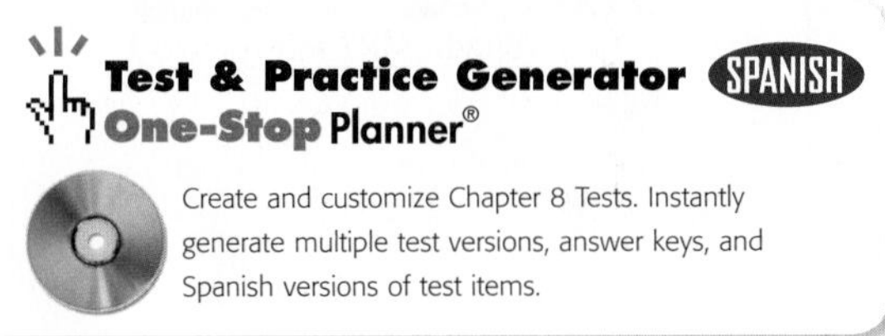

Test & Practice Generator SPANISH
One-Stop Planner®

Create and customize Chapter 8 Tests. Instantly generate multiple test versions, answer keys, and Spanish versions of test items.

CHAPTER 8

Why Learn This?

Tell students that the language of geometry is essential in describing real-world objects. For example, the shapes of classroom objects, such as desktops, floor tiles, blackboards, and book covers can be described as types of plane figures. Students are likely to be familiar with basic figures, such as triangles, circles, and quadrilaterals. Other names are needed to describe more complex figures.

Using Data

To begin the study of this chapter, have students:

- Sketch an example of a nonagon. Check students' sketches. Possible answers:

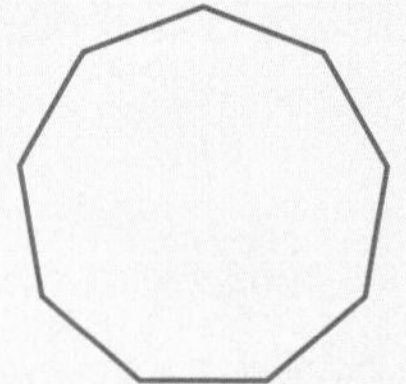

- Find the total number of sides in a heptagon and hexagon. 13
- Name a common object shaped like a regular octagon. stop sign

On page 478, students will find cumulative CRCT practice.

CHAPTER 8

Geometric Relationships

go.hrw.com
Chapter Project Online
KEYWORD: MR7 Ch8

Name of Figure	Number of Sides
Pentagon	5
Hexagon	6
Heptagon	7
Octagon	8
Nonagon	9
Decagon	10
Undecagon	11
Dodecagon	12

Career *Artist*

Artists help us to see our world in new ways. They use their creativity in many different kinds of careers. Artists might design graphics for Web sites, draw cartoons, design textiles and furniture, paint murals, or even illustrate courtroom scenes. Artists work with many materials, such as different kinds of paints, paper, stone, metal, stained glass, and tile. The table shows some geometric figures that an artist might use in a design.

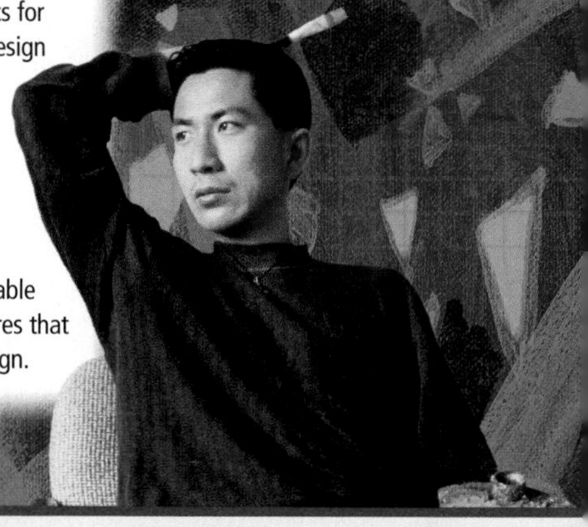

Problem Solving Project

Understand, Plan, Solve, and Look Back

Have students:

- Complete the Tile Artistry worksheet to solve problems using polygons.
- Discover the similarities between regular and irregular polygons that have the same number of sides.
- Use or create a set of polygon pieces. Have students copy and/or create figures.

Art and Social Studies Connection

Project Resources

Materials:

- Tile Artistry worksheet, ruler, compass, tiling materials, overhead projector, polygon pieces

ARE YOU READY?

Vocabulary

Choose the best term from the list to complete each sentence.

clockwise
counterclockwise
horizontal
protractor
quadrilateral
ruler
triangle
vertical

1. A closed figure with three sides is a __?__, and a closed figure with four sides is a __?__. triangle; quadrilateral
2. A __?__ is used to measure and draw angles. protractor
3. 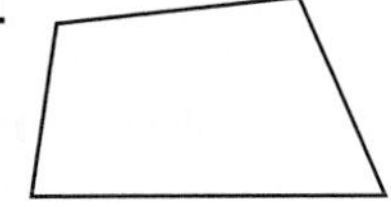
The arrow inside the circle is moving __?__. clockwise
4. 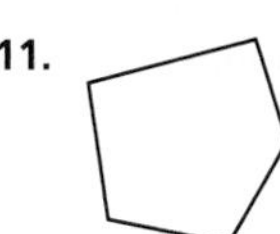
A line that extends left to right is __?__. horizontal

Complete these exercises to review skills you will need for this chapter.

Graph Ordered Pairs

Use the coordinate plane for problems 5–8. Write the ordered pair for each point.

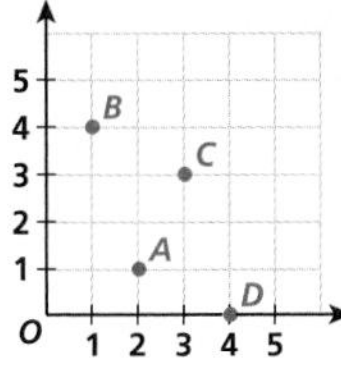

5. A (2, 1)
6. B (1, 4)
7. C (3, 3)
8. D (4, 0)

Identify Polygons

Tell how many sides and angles each figure has.

9. 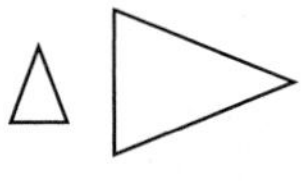 4 sides, 4 angles
10. 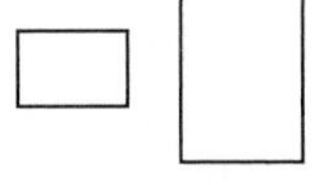 8 sides, 8 angles
11. 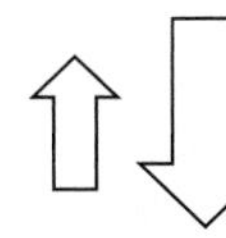 5 sides, 5 angles

Identify Congruent Figures

Which two figures are exactly the same size and shape but in different positions? B

12. A B C D

ARE YOU READY? CHAPTER 8

Organizer

Objective: Assess students' understanding of prerequisite skills.

Prerequisite Skills

Graph Ordered Pairs
Identify Polygons
Identify Congruent Figures

Assessing Prior Knowledge

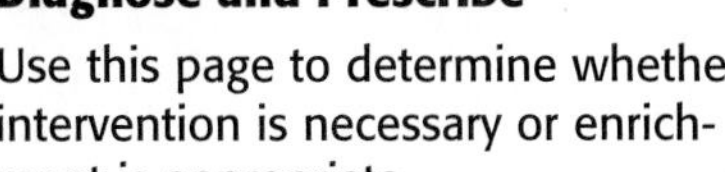

Diagnose and Prescribe

Use this page to determine whether intervention is necessary or enrichment is appropriate.

Resources

 *Are You Ready? Intervention and Enrichment* Worksheets

 *Are You Ready?* CD-ROM

 *Are You Ready?* Online

my.hrw.com

ARE YOU READY?

Diagnose and Prescribe

NO INTERVENE

Prerequisite Skill	*Are You Ready? Intervention*, Chapter 8 — Worksheets	CD-ROM	Online
Graph Ordered Pairs	Skill 69	Activity 69	Diagnose and Prescribe Online
Identify Polygons	Skill 76	Activity 76	
Identify Congruent Figures	Skill 81	Activity 81	

YES ENRICH

CHAPTER 8 Study Guide: Preview

Organizer

Objective: Help students organize the new concepts they will learn in Chapter 8.

Online Edition
Multilingual Glossary

Resources

PuzzlePro®
One-Stop Planner®

***Multilingual Glossary* Online**

go.hrw.com
KEYWORD: MR7 Glossary

Answers to *Vocabulary Connections*

Possible answers:

1. If two figures are congruent, they look the same.
2. If two lines are parallel, they are alongside each other.
3. According to this information, a polygon includes many angles.
4. A quadrilateral has four sides.

CHAPTER 8

Study Guide: Preview

Where You've Been

Previously, you

- defined geometric shapes.
- identified congruent and similar figures.
- located points on a coordinate plane.

In This Chapter

You will study

- measuring angles.
- using angle measurements to classify angles as acute, obtuse, or right.
- identifying relationships involving angles in triangles and quadrilaterals.
- using congruence and similarity to solve problems.
- transforming figures on the coordinate plane and describing the transformation.

Where You're Going

You can use the skills learned in this chapter

- to solve problems and create geometric proofs by using angle and line relationships in geometry.
- to use transformations to create patterns in art class.

Key Vocabulary/Vocabulario

angle	ángulo
congruent	congruente
line symmetry	simetría axial
parallel lines	líneas paralelas
perpendicular lines	rectas perpendiculares
polygon	polígono
quadrilateral	cuadrilátero
rotation	rotación
transformation	transformación
vertex	vértice

Vocabulary Connections

To become familiar with some of the vocabulary terms in the chapter, consider the following. You may refer to the chapter, the glossary, or a dictionary if you like.

1. *Congruent* comes from the Latin word *congruere* meaning "to agree, correspond." If two figures are **congruent**, do you think they look the same or different?
2. *Parallel* comes from the Greek words *para* meaning "alongside" and *allenon* meaning "one another." If two lines are **parallel** where do you think they are located in relation to each other?
3. *Polygon* comes from the Greek words *polus* meaning "many" and *gonia* meaning "angle." According to this information, what do you think a shape called a **polygon** includes?
4. *Quadrilateral* comes from the Latin words *quadri* meaning "four" and *latus* meaning "sides." How many sides do you think a **quadrilateral** has?

Study Guide: Preview

Grade 6 CRCT GPS

M6M2.
Students will use appropriate units of measure for finding length, perimeter, area and volume and will express each quantity using the appropriate unit.

a. Measure length to the nearest half, fourth, eighth and sixteenth of an inch.
b. Select and use units of appropriate size and type to measure length, perimeter, area and volume.

M6G1.
Students will further develop their understanding of plane figures.

a. Determine and use lines of symmetry.

M6A2.
Students will consider relationships between varying quantities.

a. Analyze and describe patterns arising from mathematical rules, tables, and graphs.

M6A3.
Students will evaluate algebraic expressions, including those with exponents, and solve simple one-step equations using each of the four basic operations.

M6P1.
Students will solve problems (using appropriate technology).

M6P2.
Students will reason and evaluate mathematical arguments.

M6P3.
Students will communicate mathematically.

M6P4.
Students will make connections among mathematical ideas and to other disciplines.

M6P5.
Students will represent mathematics in multiple ways.

***Georgia Mathematics Performance Standards* statements are written out completely on pp. GA28–GA35.**

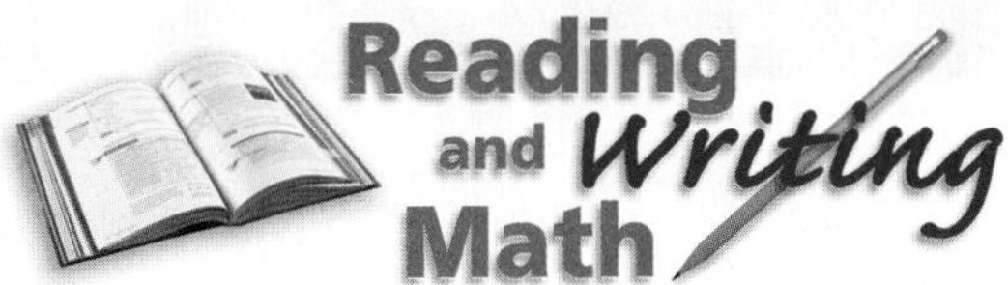

Reading Strategy: Read Problems for Understanding

It is important to read word problems carefully to make sure you understand the problem and identify all the parts of the problem that need to be answered.

Following these steps can help you understand and answer problems:

1. Read through the problem once.
2. Identify what you are supposed to answer and what skills are needed.
3. Read the problem again carefully and identify key information.
4. Make a plan to solve and answer ALL parts of the problem.
5. Solve.

Lesson 7-9 Percent Problems

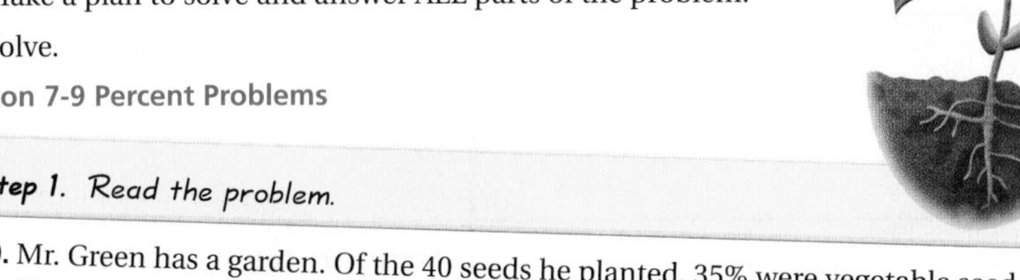

Step 1. *Read the problem.*

10. Mr. Green has a garden. Of the 40 seeds he planted, 35% were vegetable seeds. How many vegetable seeds did he plant?

Step 2.	*What are you supposed to answer, and what skills are needed?*	• *Find how many vegetable seeds were planted in the garden.* • *Find the percent of a number.*
Step 3.	*Identify the key information.*	• *There were a total of 40 seeds planted.* • *The vegetable seeds make up 35% of the total number of seeds.*
Step 4.	*Make a plan to solve and answer all parts of the problem.*	• *Write 35% as a fraction.* • *Set up a proportion and solve for the unknown value.* • *Check your answer by making sure the cross products are equal.*
Step 5.	*Solve.*	

Try This

Read the problem for understanding. Use the steps above to answer the following question.

1. A garden has the shape of a square. The distance around the garden is 200 meters. What is the length of one side of the garden?

Reading and Writing Math

Reading and Writing Math

Organizer

Objective: Help students apply strategies to understand and retain key concepts.

Online Edition

Resources

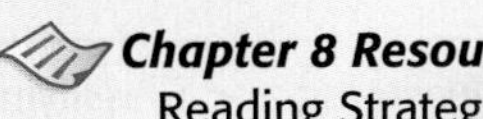
Chapter 8 Resource Book
Reading Strategies

Reading Strategy: Read Problems for Understanding

ENGLISH LANGUAGE LEARNERS

Discuss Have students discuss what could happen if they are not understood by others or if they don't understand what others are saying.

Encourage students to find different ways to state a word problem.

Extend Reading for understanding is important in and out of math class. Make reading a part of some assigned projects to encourage the development of good reading skills.

Answers to *Try This*

1. One side of the square garden is 50 feet.

Grade 6 CRCT GPS

Standards	8-1	8-2	8-3	8-4	LAB 8-4	LAB 8-5	8-5	LAB 8-5	8-6	8-7	8-8	8-9	8-10	LAB 8-10	8-11	LAB 8-11
M6M2.a												★★				
M6M2.b						★										
M6G1.a															★	
M6A2.a										★						
M6A3			★				★									
M6P1			★	★				★		★		★		★	★	
M6P2					★	★		★	★		★	★				★
M6P3	★	★	★	★					★	★			★			★
M6P4	★	★		★			★				★	★		★		
M6P5						★		★					★			

SECTION 8A

Lines and Angles

One-Minute Section Planner

Lesson	Materials	MiC and Lab Resources
Lesson 8-1 Building Blocks of Geometry • Describe figures by using the terms of . ☐ CRCT ☑ SAT-10 ☑ ITBS ☑ CTBS ☑ NAEP	Index cards	
Lesson 8-2 Measuring and Classifying Angles • Name, measure, draw, and classify angles. ☐ CRCT ☑ SAT-10 ☑ ITBS ☑ CTBS ☑ NAEP	Protractors (MK), straight-edges (MK)	**MiC:** ***Figuring All the Angles*** pp. 14–19, 38–43
Lesson 8-3 Angle Relationships • Understand relationships of angles. ☑ CRCT ☑ SAT-10 ☑ ITBS ☑ CTBS ☑ NAEP	Protractors (MK), angle templates	***Hands-On Lab Activities*** 8-3 ***Technology Lab Activities*** 8-3
Lesson 8-4 Classifying Lines • Classify the different types of lines. **8-4 Hands-On Lab** Parallel Line Relationships • Use a compass, a straightedge, and a protractor to explore parallel line relationships. ☐ CRCT ☑ SAT-10 ☑ ITBS ☑ CTBS ☑ NAEP	Compasses (MK), straight-edges (MK), protractors (MK)	**MiC:** ***Figuring All the Angles*** p. 8 ***Hands-On Lab Activities*** 8-4 ***Technology Lab Activities*** 8-4

MK = *Manipulatives Kit*

Mathematics in Context

The unit ***Figuring All the Angles*** from the *Mathematics in Context* © 2006 series can be used with Section 8A. See Section Planner above for suggestions for integrating *MiC* with *Holt Mathematics*.

Section Overview

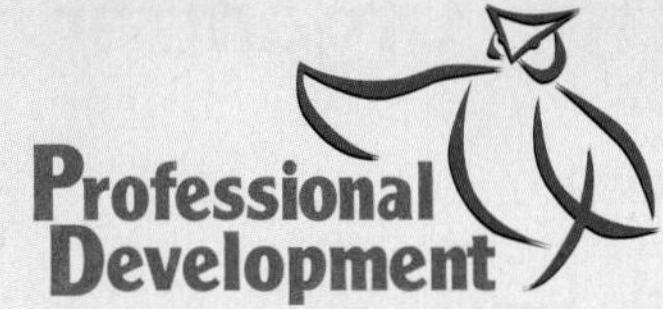

Points, Lines, and Planes — Lesson 8-1

Why? Points, lines, and planes are the foundation of geometry.

A **line** is a straight path that extends without end in opposite directions. $\overleftrightarrow{PQ}$ and $\overleftrightarrow{NR}$ are lines.

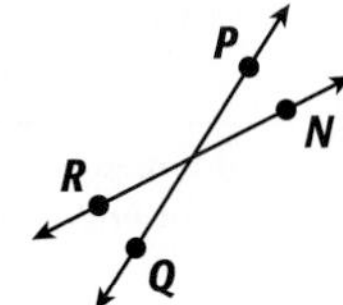

A **point** is an exact location. *P, Q, R, M,* and *N* are points.

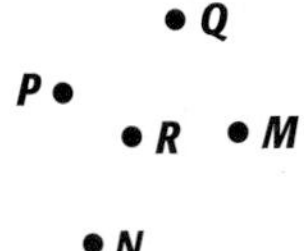

Line **segments** and **rays** are parts of lines. $\overline{PQ}$ is a line segment. $\overrightarrow{RS}$ is a ray.

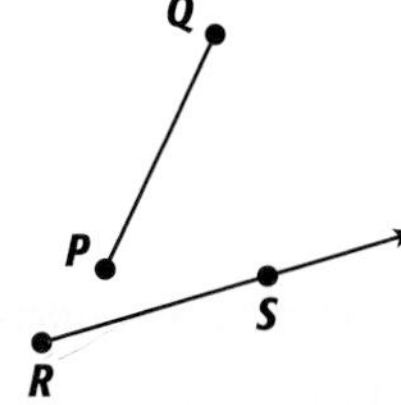

A **plane** is a flat surface that extends without end in all directions. Plane *MNP* is a plane.

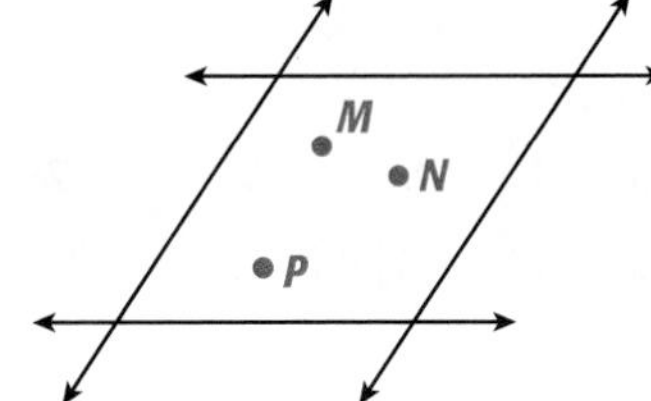

Angles and Angle Relationships — Lessons 8-2, 8-3

Many geometric figures contains angles.

An **angle** is formed by two rays with a common end-point, called the **vertex**.

acute angle < 90° < obtuse angle < 180°
straight angle = 180°   right angle = 90°

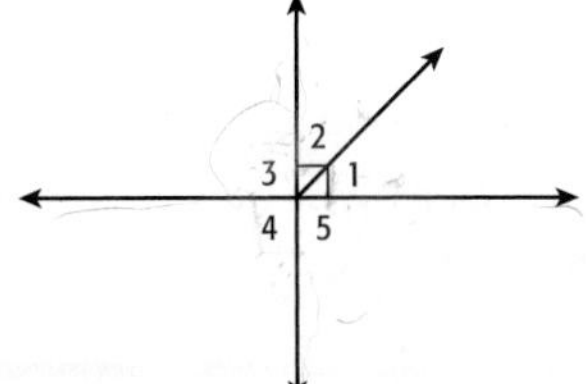

Complementary Angles	Supplementary Angles	Adjacent Angles	Vertical Angles
∠1 and ∠2	∠3 and ∠4 ∠4 and ∠5	∠1 and ∠2 ∠3 and ∠4 ∠4 and ∠5	∠3 and ∠5

Classfy Lines — Lessons 8-4

Parallel and perpendicular lines are used in construction, among other applications.

Intersecting lines are lines that cross at one common point.

Line *YZ* intersects line *WX*.

$\overleftrightarrow{YZ}$ intersects $\overleftrightarrow{WX}$.

Parallel lines are lines in the same plane that never intersect.

Line *AB* is parallel to line *ML*.

$\overleftrightarrow{AB} \parallel \overleftrightarrow{ML}$

Perpendicular lines intersect to form 90° angles, or right angles.

Line *RS* is perpendicular to line *TU*. $\overleftrightarrow{RS}$ ⊥ $\overleftrightarrow{TU}$

Skew lines are lines that lie in different planes. They are neither parallel nor intersecting.

Line *AB* and line *ML* are skew.

$\overleftrightarrow{AB}$ and $\overleftrightarrow{ML}$ are skew.

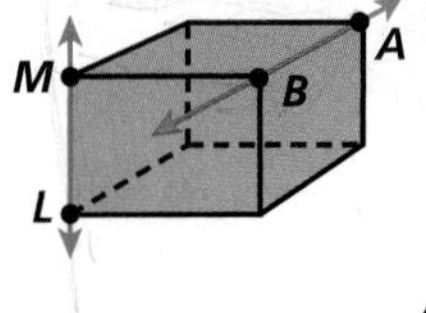

8-1 Organizer

Pacing: Traditional 1 day
Block $\frac{1}{2}$ day

Objective: Students describe figures by using the terms of geometry.

Online Edition
Tutorial Videos, Interactivities

Countdown to CRCT Week 17

Power Presentations with PowerPoint®

Warm Up

Solve.

1. $x + 1\frac{1}{3} = 5$ $3\frac{2}{3}$ **2.** $2\frac{1}{2} = 2x$ $1\frac{1}{4}$

3. $x - 7\frac{2}{3} = 6\frac{1}{3}$ 14 **4.** $\frac{x}{3} = \frac{4}{5}$ $2\frac{2}{5}$

Problem of the Day

Draw a clock face that includes the numerals 1–12. Draw two lines that do not intersect and that separate the clock face into three parts so that the sums of the numbers on each part are the same.

Also available on transparency

Math Humor

What did the circle say to the line?
I'll be around if you need me.

Georgia Performance Standards

M6P3.d Use the language of mathematics to express mathematical ideas precisely.

M6P4.a Recognize and use connections among mathematical ideas.

M6P4.b Understand how mathematical ideas interconnect and build on one another to produce a coherent whole.

8-1 Building Blocks of Geometry

Learn to describe figures by using the terms of geometry.

Vocabulary
point
line
plane
line segment
ray

Georgia Performance Standards

M6P3.d Use the language of mathematics to express mathematical ideas precisely. Also, M6P4.a, M6P4.b.

The building blocks of geometry are *points, lines,* and *planes.*

A **point** is an exact location.	• *P* *A point is named by a capital letter.*	point *P*, *P*
A **line** is a straight path that extends without end in opposite directions.	*A line is named by two points on the line.*	line *AB*, $\overleftrightarrow{AB}$, line *BA*, $\overleftrightarrow{BA}$
A **plane** is a flat surface that extends without end in all directions.	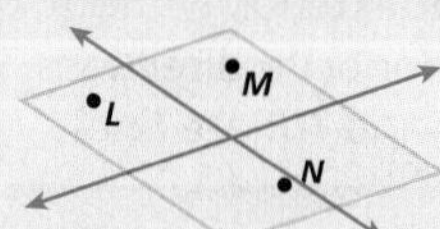 *A plane is named by three points on the plane that are not on the same line.*	plane *LMN*, plane *MLN*, plane *NLM*

EXAMPLE 1 Identifying Points, Lines, and Planes

Use the diagram to name each geometric figure.

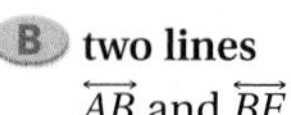

A three points
A, C, and *D*
Five points are labeled: points A, B, C, D, and E.

B two lines
$\overleftrightarrow{AB}$ and $\overleftrightarrow{BE}$
You can also write $\overleftrightarrow{BA}$ and $\overleftrightarrow{EB}$.

C a point shared by two lines
point *B*
Point B is a point on $\overleftrightarrow{AB}$ and $\overleftrightarrow{BE}$.

D a plane
plane *ADC*
Use any three points in the plane that are not on the same line. Write the three points in any order.

1 Introduce

Alternate Opener

EXPLORATION

8-1 Building Blocks of Geometry

Geometry can be used to describe the physical world around us. Check the box of the geometry term that each real-world item represents.

		Point	Line Segment	Plane
1.	A freckle			
2.	A strand of hair			
3.	A poster			
4.	A pixel on your calculator screen			
5.	A period at the end of a sentence			
6.	A guitar string			
7.	The minute hand of a clock			
8.	A computer screen			

Think and Discuss

9. **Describe** the characteristics of the items that you classified as *points* in the table above.
10. **Describe** the characteristics of the items that you classified as *line segments* in the table above.

Motivate

Ask students to give examples of symbols that are used instead of words (e.g., pictures on men's and women's restrooms). Have them explain why symbols are sometimes used instead of words. Explain that in this lesson, symbols are used to name lines, line segments, and rays.

Explorations and answers are provided in *Alternate Openers: Explorations Transparencies.*

Line segments and *rays* are parts of lines. Use points on a line to name line segments and rays.

A **line segment** is made of two endpoints and all the points between the endpoints.		line segment *XY*, $\overline{XY}$, line segment *YX*, $\overline{YX}$
	A line segment is named by its endpoints.	
A **ray** has one endpoint. From the endpoint, the ray extends without end in one direction only.	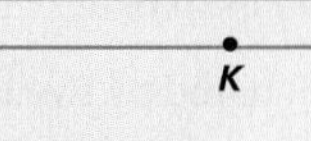	ray *JK*, $\overrightarrow{JK}$
	A ray is named by its endpoint first followed by another point on the ray.	

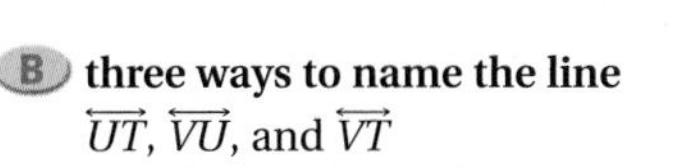

EXAMPLE 2 **Identifying Line Segments and Rays**

Use the diagram to give a possible name to each figure.

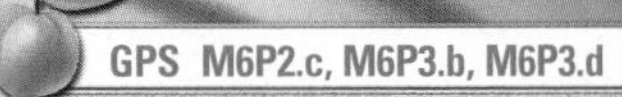

A **three different line segments**

$\overline{TU}$, $\overline{UV}$, and $\overline{TV}$

You can also write $\overline{UT}$, $\overline{VU}$, and $\overline{VT}$.

B **three ways to name the line**

$\overleftrightarrow{UT}$, $\overleftrightarrow{VU}$, and $\overleftrightarrow{VT}$

You can also write $\overleftrightarrow{TU}$, $\overleftrightarrow{UV}$, and $\overleftrightarrow{TV}$.

C **six rays**

$\overrightarrow{TU}$, $\overrightarrow{TV}$, $\overrightarrow{VT}$, $\overrightarrow{VU}$, $\overrightarrow{UV}$, and $\overrightarrow{UT}$

D **another name for ray *TU***

$\overrightarrow{TV}$

T is still the endpoint. V is another point on the ray.

Possible answers to *Think and Discuss*

1. plane; point; line segment
2. $\overrightarrow{XY}$ is a ray with endpoint *X* that passes through point *Y*; $\overleftrightarrow{XY}$ is a line that passes through points *X* and *Y*.
3. $\overline{AB}$ is a line segment with endpoints *A* and *B*; $\overleftrightarrow{AB}$ is a line that passes through points *A* and *B*.

Think and Discuss GPS M6P2.c, M6P3.b, M6P3.d

1. **Name** the geometric figure suggested by each of the following: a page of a book; a dot (also called a *pixel*) on a computer screen; the path of a jet across the sky.
2. **Explain** how $\overrightarrow{XY}$ is different from $\overleftrightarrow{XY}$.
3. **Explain** how $\overline{AB}$ is different from $\overleftrightarrow{AB}$.

Power Presentations with PowerPoint®

Additional Examples

Example 1

Use the diagram to name each geometric figure.

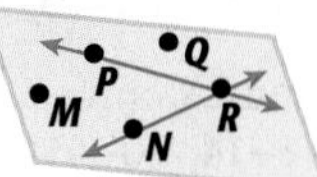

A. three points

M, *N*, and *P* (also *Q* and *R*)

B. two lines

$\overleftrightarrow{PR}$ and $\overleftrightarrow{NR}$ or $\overleftrightarrow{RP}$ and $\overleftrightarrow{RN}$

C. a location shared by two lines

point *R*

D. a plane

plane *QRM*

Example 2

Use the diagram to give a possible name to each figure.

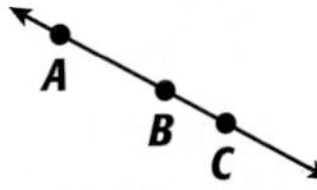

A. three different line segments

$\overline{AB}$, $\overline{BC}$, $\overline{AC}$, or $\overline{BA}$, $\overline{CB}$, $\overline{CA}$

B. three ways to name the line

$\overleftrightarrow{AB}$, $\overleftrightarrow{BC}$, $\overleftrightarrow{AC}$ or $\overleftrightarrow{BA}$, $\overleftrightarrow{CB}$, $\overleftrightarrow{CA}$

C. six different rays

$\overrightarrow{AB}$, $\overrightarrow{AC}$, $\overrightarrow{BC}$, $\overrightarrow{CB}$, $\overrightarrow{CA}$, $\overrightarrow{BA}$

D. another name for ray *AB*

$\overrightarrow{AC}$

Also available on transparency

2 Teach

Guided Instruction

ENGLISH LANGUAGE LEARNERS

In this lesson, students learn to describe figures by using the terms of geometry. Use the diagrams to teach students the meanings of *point*, *line*, *plane*, *line segment*, and *ray* (Teaching Transparency). Point out that when naming a ray the order of the points *does* matter—the endpoint is always listed first.

Teaching Tip **Inclusion** Remind students that line segments have two endpoints, rays have one endpoint, and lines have no endpoints.

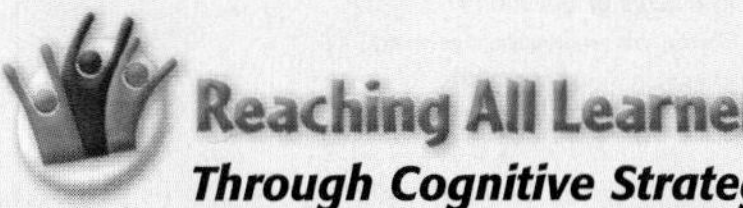

Reaching All Learners

Through Cognitive Strategies

Have students work with a partner to play a geometry memory game. Give each pair a set of ten index cards. On five of the cards, have students write the terms *point*, *line*, *plane*, *line segment*, and *ray* (one per card). On the other five cards, have them draw pictures representing each term (again, one per card). Have students mix the cards, place them face down, and take turns turning over pairs of cards to make a match. This continues until all matches have been made. (These cards can be kept and added to as students progress through the chapter.)

3 Close

Summarize

Draw a diagram like the one shown in Example 1, and have volunteers identify a *point*, a *line*, a *plane*, a *line segment*, and a *ray* on the diagram.

8-1 Exercises

Assignment Guide

If you finished Example 1 assign:
Average 1–4, 15–19, 31–41
Advanced 8–11, 15–19, 31–41

If you finished Example 2 assign:
Average 1–14, 20–41
Advanced 8–41

Homework Quick Check

Quickly check key concepts.
Exercises: 10, 12, 14

Answers

Possible answers:

13. $\overrightarrow{WX}$, $\overrightarrow{XY}$, $\overrightarrow{YZ}$, $\overrightarrow{ZY}$, $\overrightarrow{YW}$, and $\overrightarrow{ZX}$

20–24. See p. A9.

Math Background

When Euclid wrote *The Elements* he began with definitions of the terms *point* and *line*. To define a point, Euclid wrote "that which has no part."

In modern developments of geometry as a logical system, one must begin with undefined terms. When your students encounter geometry in high school, the terms *point*, *line*, and *plane* will be treated as undefined terms. These terms will then form the basis for defining more-complicated geometric figures.

Georgia Performance Standards

M6P1.a Build new mathematical knowledge through problem solving.

M6P3.a Organize and consolidate their mathematical thinking through communication.

M6P3.c Analyze and evaluate the mathematical thinking and strategies of others.

M6P3.d Use the language of mathematics to express mathematical ideas precisely.

8-1 Exercises

M6P1.a, M6P3.a, M6P3.c, M6P3.d

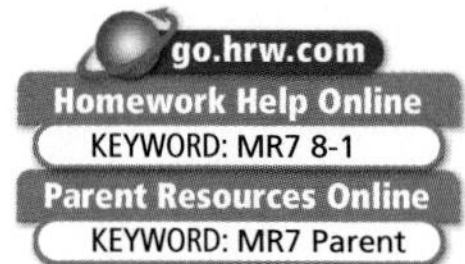

GUIDED PRACTICE

See Example 1

Use the diagram to name each geometric figure.

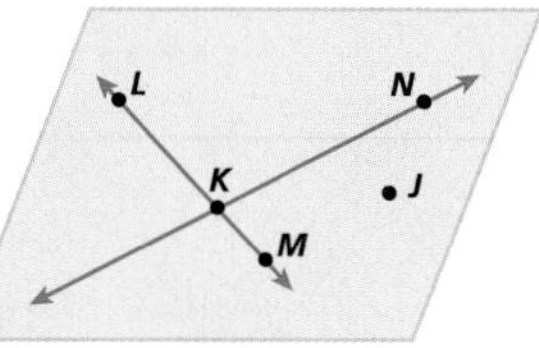

1. two points Possible answer: *M* and *N*
2. a line Possible answer: $\overleftrightarrow{KN}$
3. a point shared by two lines *K*
4. a plane Possible answer: *JKL*

See Example 2

Use the diagram to give a possible name to each figure.

5. two different ways to name the line $\overleftrightarrow{AC}$ and $\overleftrightarrow{AB}$
6. four rays $\overrightarrow{AC}$, $\overrightarrow{BC}$, $\overrightarrow{BA}$ and $\overrightarrow{CA}$
7. another name for $\overrightarrow{AC}$ $\overrightarrow{AB}$

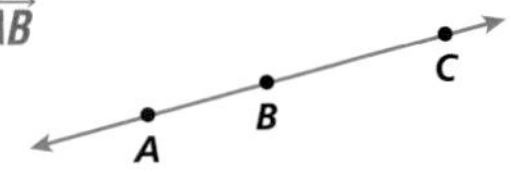

INDEPENDENT PRACTICE

See Example 1

Use the diagram to name each geometric figure.

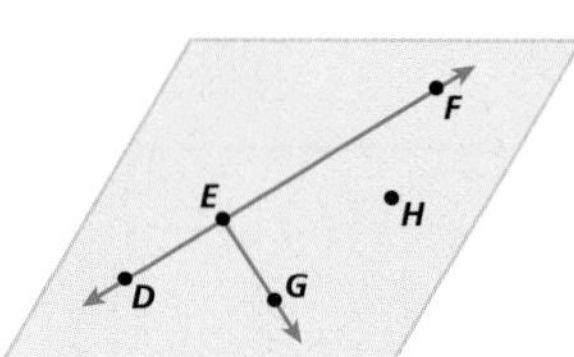

8. three points Possible answer: *D*, *E*, and *F*
9. two lines Possible answer: $\overleftrightarrow{DF}$; $\overrightarrow{ED}$
10. a point shared by a line and a ray *E*
11. a plane Possible answer: *FGH*

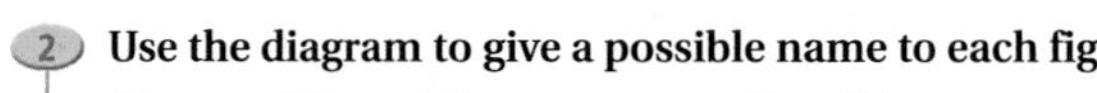

See Example 2

Use the diagram to give a possible name to each figure.

12. two different line segments Possible answer: $\overline{WX}$ and $\overline{YZ}$
13. six rays
14. another name for $\overrightarrow{YX}$ $\overrightarrow{YW}$

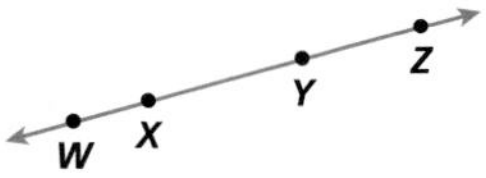

PRACTICE AND PROBLEM SOLVING

Extra Practice p. 728

Use the diagram to find a name for each geometric figure described.

15. a point shared by three lines *C*
16. two points on the same line Possible answer: *C* and *F*
17. two rays $\overrightarrow{CA}$ and $\overrightarrow{CB}$
18. another name for $\overrightarrow{AD}$ $\overrightarrow{AC}$
19. two different names for the same line $\overleftrightarrow{BC}$ and $\overleftrightarrow{CB}$

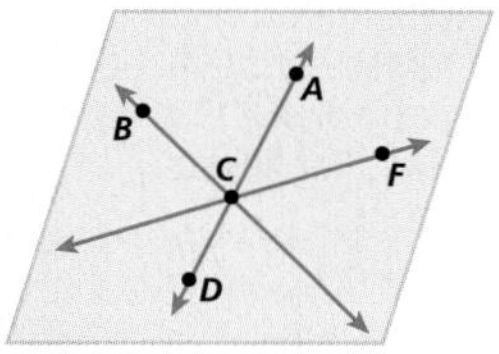

Draw each geometric figure.

20. $\overrightarrow{RS}$
21. $\overline{LM}$
22. $\overleftrightarrow{AB}$
23. $\overrightarrow{XY}$ on $\overrightarrow{YX}$
24. $\overrightarrow{JK}$ and $\overrightarrow{JH}$ on the same line

RETEACH 8-1

LESSON 8-1 **Reteach**
Building Blocks of Geometry

Here are terms that can help you understand geometry.

A point is an exact location. A point has no size.

•*A* point *A* or *A* — Use a capital letter to name a point.

A line is a straight path that extends without end in opposite directions. A line has infinite length, but no width.

A *B* $\overleftrightarrow{AB}$ or $\overleftrightarrow{BA}$ — Two points name a line.

A plane is a flat surface that extends without end in all directions. A plane has infinite length and width, but no depth.

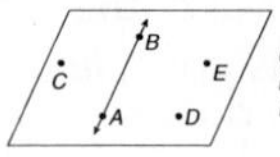

CDE *EDC*
DEC *CED*
ECD *DCE*
A plane is named by 3 points on the plane that are not on a line.

A line segment has two endpoints. The length of a line segment can be measured.

J *K* $\overline{JK}$ or $\overline{KJ}$ — A line segment is named by its endpoints.

X *Y* $\overrightarrow{XY}$

A ray has one endpoint and extends without end in one direction. A ray is named by its endpoint first and another point on the ray.

Use the diagram to name each geometric figure. Possible answers are given.

1. two points *R, S*
2. two lines $\overleftrightarrow{PQ}$ and $\overleftrightarrow{RQ}$
3. a plane *STU*
4. two line segments $\overline{PQ}$ and $\overline{QR}$
5. two rays $\overrightarrow{QP}$ and $\overrightarrow{QR}$
6. a point shared by two lines *Q*

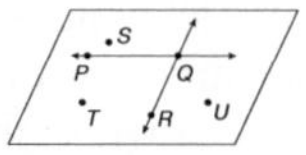

PRACTICE 8-1

LESSON 8-1 **Practice B**
Building Blocks of Geometry

Use the diagram to name each geometric figure. Possible answers are given.

1. two points *A* and *B*
2. a plane plane *ABD*
3. a line segment $\overline{BD}$
4. a point shared by two lines *A*
5. a line $\overleftrightarrow{CD}$

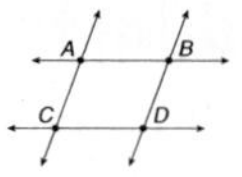

Use the diagram to give a possible name to each figure. Possible answers are given.

6. two different ways to name the line
line *XY* and $\overleftrightarrow{XY}$
7. four different names for rays
ray *PY*, ray *PX*, $\overrightarrow{PY}$, and $\overrightarrow{PX}$
8. another name for $\overline{QP}$
$\overline{PQ}$ 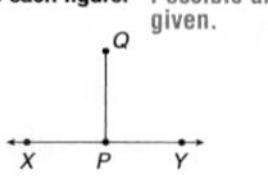
9. Is the following statement always true, sometimes true, or never true? Explain your reasoning. A line is longer than a line segment.
It is always true, because a line segment only extends between two endpoints, but a line extends without end in opposite directions.
10. Using endpoints as your basis, explain how a line, a line segment, and a ray are different.
A line has no endpoints, a ray has one endpoint, and a line segment has two endpoints.

Geography LINK

Mapmakers often include a *legend* on the maps they create. The legend explains what each symbol or location on the map represents.

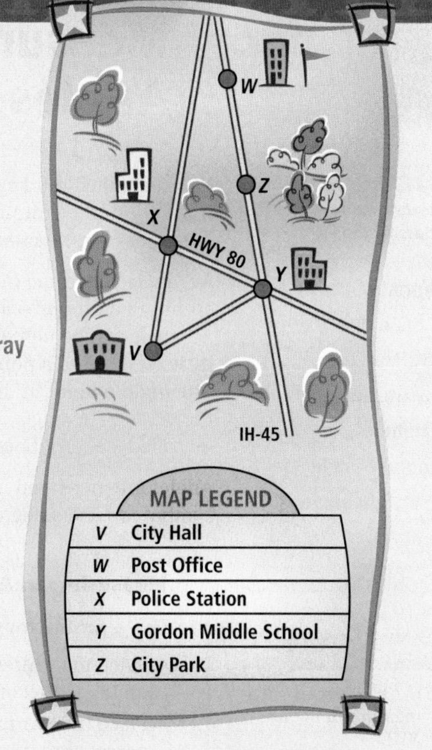

25. Name the geometric figure suggested by each part of the map.
    a. City Hall and Gordon Middle School **points**
    b. Highway 80 **line**
    c. the section of the road from the park to the post office **line segment**
    d. the road from City Hall past the police station **ray**
26. A student rides her bike from Gordon Middle School to City Hall. She then rides to the city park, first passing through the intersection near the police station and then passing by the school. List the segments on the map that represent her route. $\overline{YV}, \overline{VX}, \overline{XY}, \overline{YZ}$
27. **Critical Thinking** Name a line segment, a ray, and a line that include the same two locations on the map, but do not include the city park. $\overline{XY}, \overrightarrow{XY}, \overleftrightarrow{XY}$
28. **What's the Error?** A student described the road from Gordon Middle School to City Hall as $\overrightarrow{VY}$. What was the student's error?
29. **Write About It** Explain why the road from City Hall that goes past the police station suggests a ray named $\overrightarrow{VX}$ rather than a ray named $\overrightarrow{XV}$.
30. **Challenge** What are all the possible names for the line suggested by IH-45? $\overleftrightarrow{YZ}, \overleftrightarrow{YW}, \overleftrightarrow{ZY}, \overleftrightarrow{ZW}, \overleftrightarrow{WY}$, and $\overleftrightarrow{WZ}$

28. Since the road has endpoints as Y and V, the student should have described the road as $\overline{VY}$.

CRCT Prep • GPS Support • Spiral Review

31. **Multiple Choice** Which figure is NOT found in the diagram?

    (A) Line (circled)   (C) Line segment
    (B) Point   (D) Ray

    F R M T

32. **Gridded Response** How many endpoints does a ray have? **1**

Find the value of *k* in each equation. (Lesson 2-8)

33. $\frac{k}{3} = 7$ **$k = 21$**
34. $\frac{k}{11} = 4$ **$k = 44$**
35. $20 = \frac{k}{5}$ **$k = 100$**
36. $21 = \frac{k}{7}$ **$k = 147$**

Write each improper fraction as a mixed number. (Lesson 4-6)

37. $\frac{13}{4}$ **$3\frac{1}{4}$**
38. $\frac{70}{9}$ **$7\frac{7}{9}$**
39. $\frac{41}{3}$ **$13\frac{2}{3}$**
40. $\frac{75}{6}$ **$12\frac{1}{2}$**
41. $\frac{81}{7}$ **$11\frac{4}{7}$**

CHALLENGE 8-1

LESSON 8-1 Challenge
Points of Light

Astronomers have divided the sky into 88 constellations, or groups of stars. To map these constellations, astronomers use a point for each star and draw imaginary lines between the points. One of the easiest groups of stars to see is called the Big Dipper. The Big Dipper is not officially a constellation. It is only part of a large constellation called Ursa Major, or Great Bear.

Imagine the stars of Ursa Major are labeled as shown below. Follow these instructions to make a star map of Ursa Major.

1. Use line segments to connect points *A–G* in alphabetical order, and then draw $\overline{DG}$.
2. Use line segments to connect points *G–L* in alphabetical order, and then draw $\overline{FJ}$.
3. Use line segments to connect points *M–O* in alphabetical order. Then draw $\overline{EM}$ and $\overline{MP}$.
4. Label the star grouping formed by the 7 points *A–G* as the "Big Dipper."
5. Then label each point of the Big Dipper with its proper star name: *A*: Alkaid; *B*: Mizar; *C*: Alioth; *D*: Megrez; *E*: Phecda; *F*: Merak; *G*: Dubhe

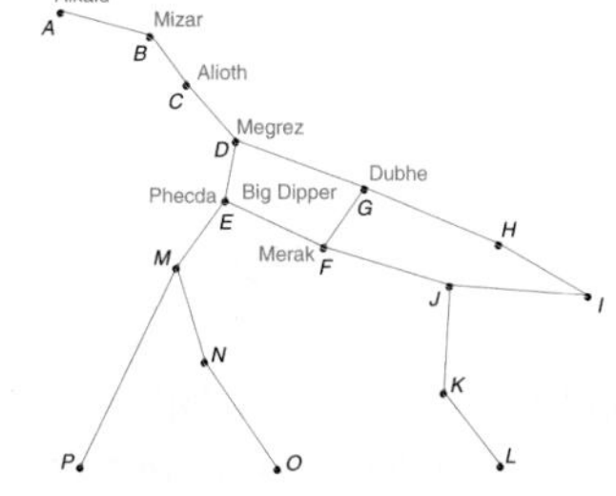

PROBLEM SOLVING 8-1

LESSON 8-1 Problem Solving
Building Blocks of Geometry

Place your hand down flat on a sheet of paper. Draw a point at the tip of your thumb, the tip of your middle finger, and the tip of your pinky.

1. Label the thumb point *A*, the middle finger point *B*, and the pinky point *C*. **Check students' drawings.**
2. Name all the planes you possibly can with points *A*, *B*, and *C*. **plane *ABC***
3. Draw and name all the lines you can make with points *A*, *B*, and *C*. $\overleftrightarrow{AB}$, $\overleftrightarrow{AC}$, and $\overleftrightarrow{BC}$
4. Name all the line segments possible using points *A*, *B*, and *C*. $\overline{AB}$, $\overline{AC}$, and $\overline{BC}$
5. Name all the rays possible using points *A*, *B*, and *C*. $\overrightarrow{AB}, \overrightarrow{AC}, \overrightarrow{BA}, \overrightarrow{BC}, \overrightarrow{CA}$, and $\overrightarrow{CB}$
6. Choose one line that you drew. Give all the different possible names for that line. **Possible answer: $\overleftrightarrow{AB}$, $\overleftrightarrow{BA}$, line *AB*, and line *BA***

Circle the letter of the correct answer.

7. Which of the following has exactly one endpoint?
   A $\overline{OP}$
   B $\overleftrightarrow{AB}$
   C $\overline{TR}$
   D $\overrightarrow{SM}$ (circled)
8. Which of the following is a straight path that extends without end in opposite directions?
   F a point
   G a line (circled)
   H a ray
   J a line segment
9. Which statement is false?
   A An infinite number of lines can be drawn through one point.
   B Exactly one line can be drawn between two points.
   C A line contains exactly one ray. (circled)
   D If points *A* and *B* are on a line, then line segment *AB* and line segment *BA* are the same.
10. Why is the false statement in Exercise 9 not true?
    F Any point on a line defines another ray on the line. (circled)
    G A line contains exactly two rays.
    H A line contains exactly five rays.
    J A line does not contain any rays.

Ongoing Assessment and Intervention

Diagnose Before the Lesson
8-1 Warm Up, TE p. 416

Monitor During the Lesson
8-1 Know-It Notebook
8-1 Questioning Strategies

Assess After the Lesson
8-1 Lesson Quiz, TE p. 419

Interdisciplinary LINK

Geography

Exercises 25–30 involve reading and interpreting a map. Students learn to work with maps in middle school social studies programs, such as Holt, Rinehart, and Winston's *People, Places, and Change.*

Answers

29. See p. A9.

TEST PREP DOCTOR In Exercise 31, students may find that sketching each answer choice reproduces part of the given drawing, except for choice **A.**

Journal

Have students draw a diagram. Then have them name four points, two lines, two line segments, three rays, and a plane shown in the diagram.

Power Presentations with PowerPoint®

8-1 Lesson Quiz

Use the diagram to name each geometric figure.

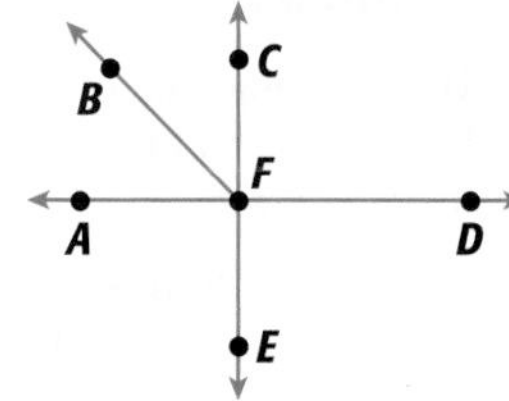

1. three points **Possible answer: *A, B, C***
2. two lines **Possible answer: $\overleftrightarrow{AD}$, $\overleftrightarrow{CE}$**
3. a point shared by a line and a ray **Possible answer: *F***
4. a plane **Possible answer: plane *AEC***

Also available on transparency

8-2 Organizer

Pacing: Traditional 1 day
Block $\frac{1}{2}$ day

Objective: Students learn to name, measure, draw, and classify angles.

Online Edition
Tutorial Videos, Interactivities

Countdown to CRCT Week 17

Power Presentations with PowerPoint®

Warm Up

1. Draw two points. Label one point *A* and the other point *B*.
2. Draw a line through points *A* and *B*.
3. Draw a ray with *A* as an endpoint and *C* as a point on the ray.
4. Name all the rays in your drawing. $\overrightarrow{AB}$, $\overrightarrow{BA}$, and $\overrightarrow{AC}$

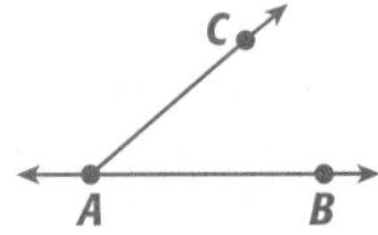

Problem of the Day

The measure of Jack's angle is twice that of Amy's and half that of Nate's. The sum of the measures of all the angles is equal to 105°. What is the measure of each student's angle?
Jack's angle: 30°; Nate's angle: 60°; Amy's angle: 15°

Also available on transparency

Georgia Performance Standards

M6P3.d Use the language of mathematics to express mathematical ideas precisely.

M6P4.a Recognize and use connections among mathematical ideas.

M6P4.b Understand how mathematical ideas interconnect and build on one another to produce a coherent whole.

M6P4.c Recognize and apply mathematics in contexts outside of mathematics.

8-2 Measuring and Classifying Angles

Learn to name, measure, draw, and classify angles.

Vocabulary
angle
vertex
acute angle
right angle
obtuse angle
straight angle

You can adjust the *angle* that a treadmill makes with the ground in order to have an easier or more intense workout.

An **angle** is formed by two rays with a common endpoint, called the **vertex**. An angle can be named by its vertex or by its vertex and a point from each ray. The middle point in the name must be the vertex. The angle of the treadmill can be called $\angle F$, $\angle EFG$, or $\angle GFE$.

Angles are measured in degrees. Use the symbol ° to show degrees.

EXAMPLE 1 Measuring an Angle with a Protractor

Reading Math
m$\angle XYZ$ is read "the measure of angle *XYZ*."

Use a protractor to measure the angle.

- Place the center point of the protractor on the vertex of the angle.
- Place the protractor so that ray *YZ* passes through the 0° mark.
- Using the scale that starts with 0° along ray *YZ*, read the measure where ray *YX* crosses.
- The measure of $\angle XYZ$ is 75°. Write this as m$\angle XYZ$ = 75°.

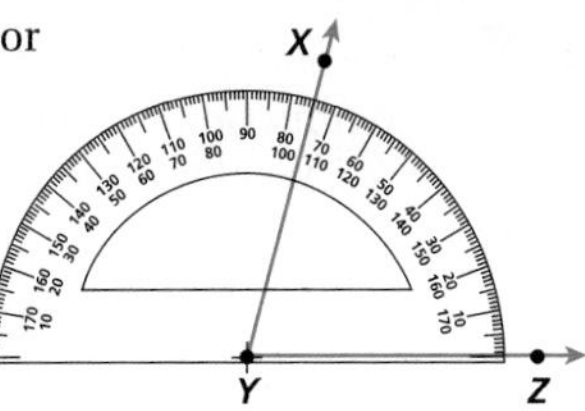

EXAMPLE 2 Drawing an Angle with a Protractor

Georgia Performance Standards
M6P3.d Use the language of mathematics to express mathematical ideas precisely. Also, M6P4.a, M6P4.b, M6P4.c.

Use a protractor to draw an angle that measures 150°.

- Draw a ray on a sheet of paper.
- Place the center point of the protractor on the endpoint of the ray.
- Place the protractor so that the ray passes through the 0° mark.
- Make a mark at 150° above the scale on the protractor.
- Draw a ray from the endpoint of the first ray through the mark at 150°.

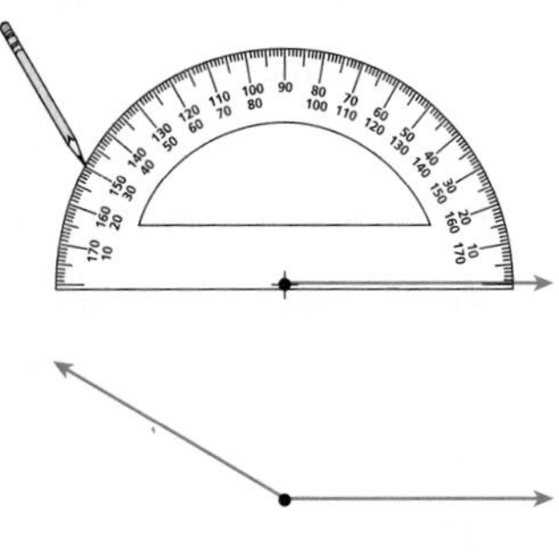

1 Introduce

Alternate Opener

EXPLORATION

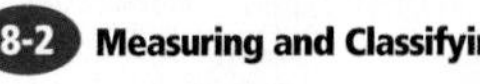

8-2 Measuring and Classifying Angles

An angle is formed by two rays that have a common endpoint. Right angles measure 90° and are shaped like a letter L. You can estimate an angle measure by comparing the angle with a right angle.

Estimate the measure of each angle. Then measure the angle with a protractor.

		Estimate	Actual
1.			
2.			
3.			
4.			

Think and Discuss
5. **Discuss** how you estimated the angle measures.

Motivate

Ask students to brainstorm real-world examples of angles. Possible answers: hands of a clock, blades of a pair of scissors, wheelchair ramp, etc. Then tell students that they will learn how to describe and classify all of these angles more precisely.

Explorations and answers are provided in *Alternate Openers: Explorations Transparencies.*

You can classify an angle by its measure.

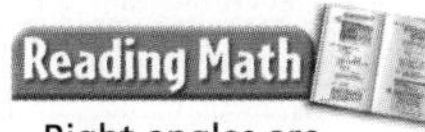

Right angles are usually marked with a ⅂ symbol.

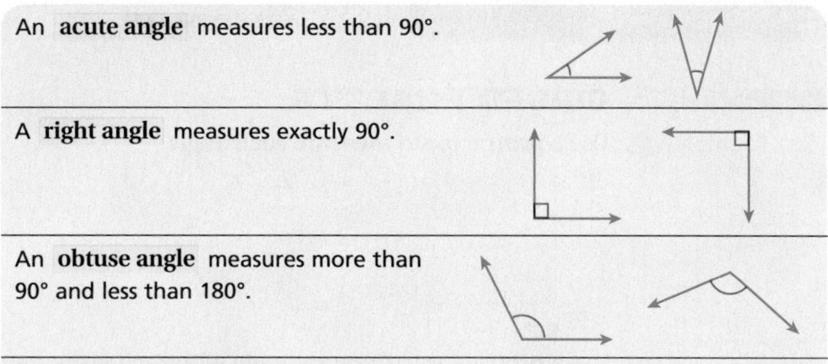

An **acute angle** measures less than 90°.

A **right angle** measures exactly 90°.

An **obtuse angle** measures more than 90° and less than 180°.

A **straight angle** measures exactly 180°.

EXAMPLE 3 Classifying Angles

Classify each angle as acute, right, obtuse, or straight.

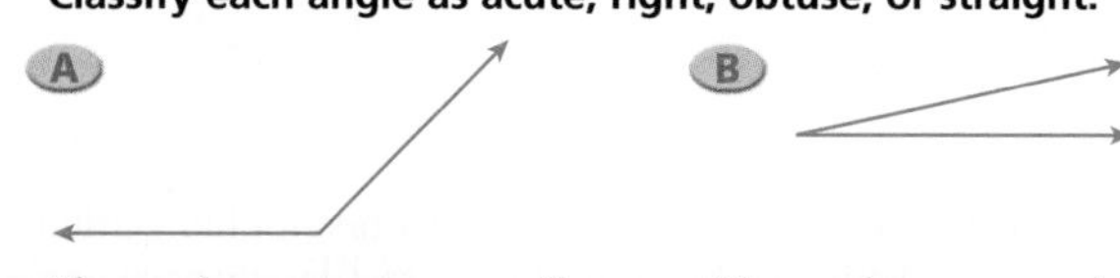

A The angle measures more than 90° and less than 180°, so it is an obtuse angle.

B The angle measures less than 90°, so it is an acute angle.

EXAMPLE 4 *Architectural Application*

An architect designed this floor plan for a five-sided room of a house. Classify ∠A, ∠B, and ∠D in the floor plan.

∠A	right angle	*The angle is marked as a right angle.*
∠B	obtuse angle	*The angle measures more than 90° and less than 180°.*
∠D	acute angle	*The angle measures less than 90°.*

Answers to *Think and Discuss*

1. The vertex is written in the middle of the name of an angle, so the vertex is point *Y*.
2. Possible answers: the corner of a window, the corner of a desk

3a. straight angle
b. right angle
c. acute angle
d. obtuse angle

Think and Discuss GPS M6P1.d, M6P3.b, M6P3.d

1. Explain how you know which point is the vertex of ∠XYZ.

2. Give an example of a right angle in your classroom.

3. Tell what type of angle is suggested by each of the following.

a. an open book lying flat
b. the corner of a sheet of paper
c. the point of a pencil
d. the hands of a clock at 12:25

Power Presentations with PowerPoint®

Additional Examples

Example 1

Use a protractor to measure the angle. Tell what type of angle it is.

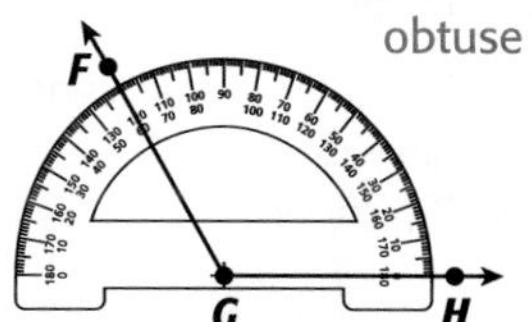

m∠FGH = 120°

Example 2

Use a protractor to draw an angle that measures 80°.

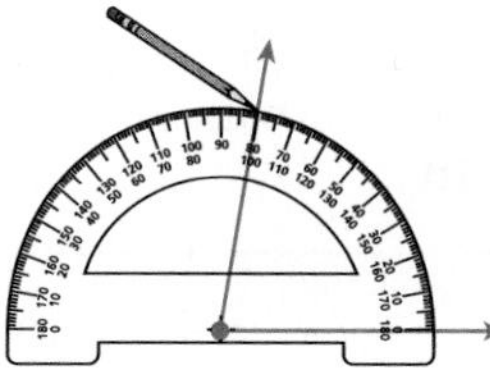

Example 3

Classify each angle as acute, right, obtuse, or straight.

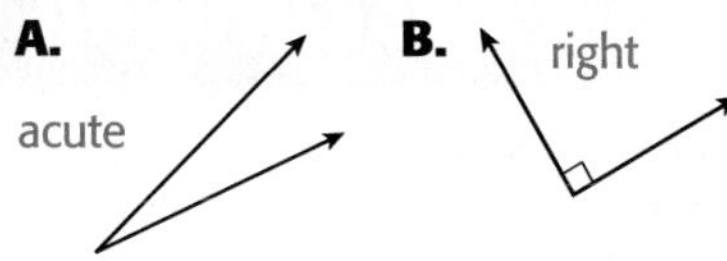

Example 4

A welder used this piece of metal on his project. Classify ∠X, ∠Y, and ∠Z.

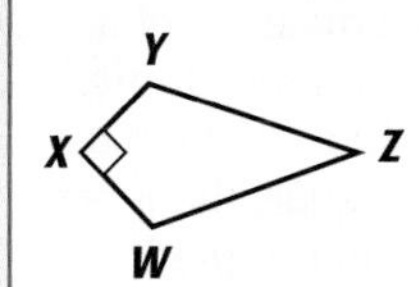

∠X: right,
∠Y: obtuse,
∠Z: acute

Also available on transparency

2 Teach

Guided Instruction

In this lesson, students learn to measure, draw, and classify angles. First, show students how to measure and draw angles using a protractor. Then teach them to identify acute, right, obtuse, and straight angles.

Teaching Tip

Language Arts Tell students that the word *acute* comes from a Latin word meaning "sharp." This may help students remember that acute angles look sharper or pointier than the other types of angles.

ENGLISH LANGUAGE LEARNERS

Reaching All Learners

Through Visual Cues

Have students do research to find examples of geometric art. Have them measure and classify the angles they see in these examples. Encourage students to create their own geometric artwork, and discuss the angles that they used.

3 Close

Summarize

Display examples of acute, right, obtuse, and straight angles. Have students classify the angles. Then review the steps to measure an angle: place the center of the protractor over the vertex of the angle; line up one ray and a 0° mark; read the measure from that 0° mark to where the other ray crosses the scale.

8-2 Exercises

Assignment Guide

If you finished Example 1 assign:
Average 1–3, 34–44
Advanced 12–14, 34–44

If you finished Example 2 assign:
Average 1–7, 24–25, 34–44
Advanced 12–19, 26, 34–44

If you finished Example 3 assign:
Average 1–10, 24–29, 34–44
Advanced 12–22, 24–28, 34–44

If you finished Example 4 assign:
Average 1–11, 15–23, 30–44
Advanced 12–44

Homework Quick Check

Quickly check key concepts.
Exercises: 16, 18, 20, 22

Answers

4–7, 15–19. See p. A9.

Math Background

The measurement system for angles shown in this lesson comes from the division of a circle into 360 equal parts, or degrees.

In some areas of mathematics, instead of degrees, angles are measured in radians. To find the radian measure of an angle, place the angle's vertex at the center of a circle of radius 1. The radian measure of the angle equals the length of the arc of the circle intercepted by the angle. For example, because a circle of radius 1 has circumference 2π, a 90° angle has a radian measure of $\frac{2\pi}{4} = \frac{\pi}{2}$.

Georgia Performance Standards

M6P3.a Organize and consolidate their mathematical thinking through communication.

M6P3.c Analyze and evaluate the mathematical thinking and strategies of others.

M6P5.a Create and use representations to organize, record, and communicate mathematical ideas.

8-2 Exercises

M6P3.a, M6P3.c, M6P5.a

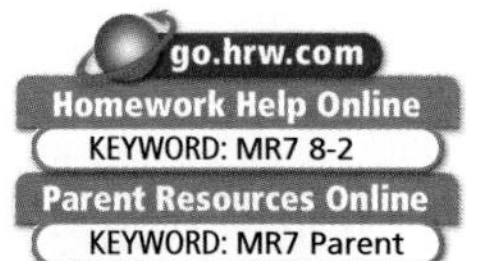

GUIDED PRACTICE

See Example 1 — Use a protractor to measure each angle.

1. 90°
2. 135°
3. 60°

See Example 2 — Use a protractor to draw an angle with each given measure.

4. 55°
5. 135°
6. 20°
7. 190°

See Example 3 — Classify each angle as acute, right, obtuse, or straight.

8. obtuse
9. acute
10. acute

See Example 4 — 11. Kendra is planning a flower bed for her garden, which is shown in the figure. Classify each angle of the flower bed. ∠*G* acute; ∠*H* obtuse; ∠*J* right; ∠*K* obtuse; ∠*L* obtuse

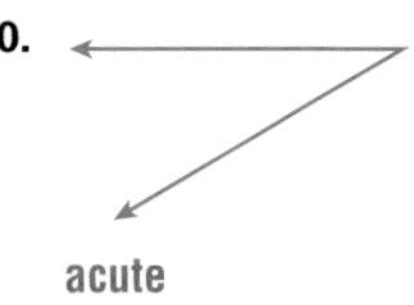

INDEPENDENT PRACTICE

See Example 1 — Use a protractor to measure each angle.

12. 40°
13. 35°
14. 180°

See Example 2 — Use a protractor to draw an angle with each given measure.

15. 150°
16. 38°
17. 90°
18. 72°
19. 45°

See Example 3 — Classify each angle as acute, right, obtuse, or straight.

20. acute
21. acute
22. obtuse

See Example 4 — 23. The figure shows the shape of a ceramic tile. Classify each of the tile's angles.
∠*A* obtuse; ∠*B* obtuse; ∠*C* acute; ∠*D* obtuse; ∠*E* obtuse; ∠*F* acute

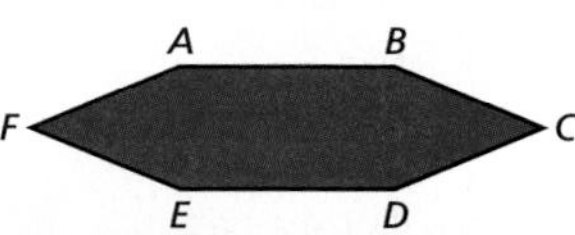

RETEACH 8-2

LESSON 8-2 **Reteach**
Measuring and Classifying Angles

An angle is formed by two rays with a common endpoint, called the vertex.

You can name an angle in different ways.

By its vertex ∠*B* OR By its vertex and one point from each ray. ∠*ABC*, ∠*CBA* Vertex letter in the middle.

Give three ways to name each angle.

1. ∠*Q*, ∠*PQR*, ∠*RQP*
2. ∠*M*, ∠*GMZ*, ∠*ZMG*

You can use a protractor to measure an angle.

To measure the angle, place the center point of the protractor on the vertex, *K*. Make sure that the protractor is placed so that $\overrightarrow{KL}$ passes through 0°. The measure of the angle is where $\overrightarrow{KJ}$ crosses the protractor.

The measure of the angle is 60 degrees.

Write m∠*K* = 60°.

Use a protractor to measure each angle.

3. m∠*Y* = 120°
4. m∠*L* = 60°

PRACTICE 8-2

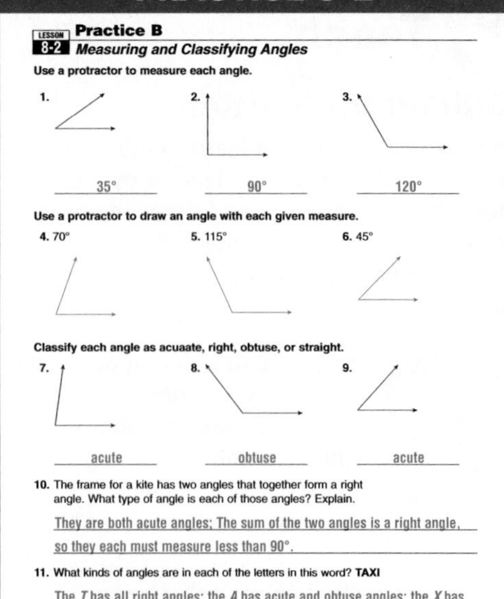
LESSON 8-2 **Practice B**
Measuring and Classifying Angles

Use a protractor to measure each angle.

1. 35°
2. 90°
3. 120°

Use a protractor to draw an angle with each given measure.

4. 70°
5. 115°
6. 45°

Classify each angle as acuaate, right, obtuse, or straight.

7. acute
8. obtuse
9. acute

10. The frame for a kite has two angles that together form a right angle. What type of angle is each of those angles? Explain.
They are both acute angles; The sum of the two angles is a right angle, so they each must measure less than 90°.

11. What kinds of angles are in each of the letters in this word? **TAXI**
The *T* has all right angles; the *A* has acute and obtuse angles; the *X* has acute and obtuse angles; and the *I* has one straight angle.

PRACTICE AND PROBLEM SOLVING

CRCT GPS Extra Practice p. 728

Use a protractor to draw each angle.

24. an acute angle whose measure is less than 45°
25. an obtuse angle whose measure is between 100° and 160°
26. a right angle

Georgia LINK History

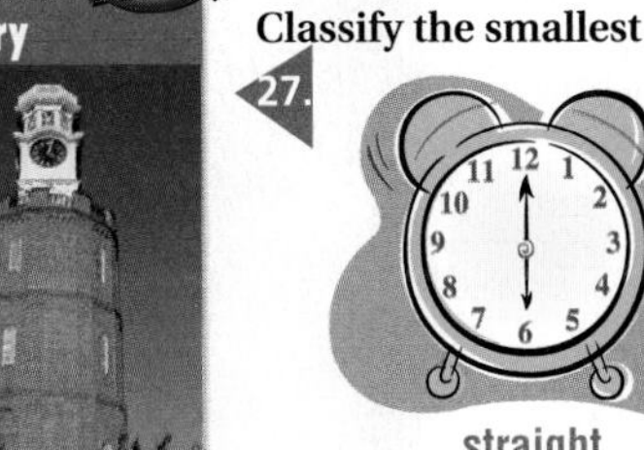

The clock tower in Rome, Georgia, was originally built as a water tower in 1871. The clock, built in Waltham, Massachusetts, was added to the top a year later.

Classify the smallest angle formed by the hands on each clock.

27.  straight
28.  obtuse
29.  acute

30. **Critical Thinking** Can two acute angles that share a vertex form a right angle? Justify your answer with a diagram.
31. **What's the Error?** A student wrote that the measure of this angle is 156°. Explain the error the student may have made, and give the correct measure of the angle. How can the student avoid making the same mistake again?

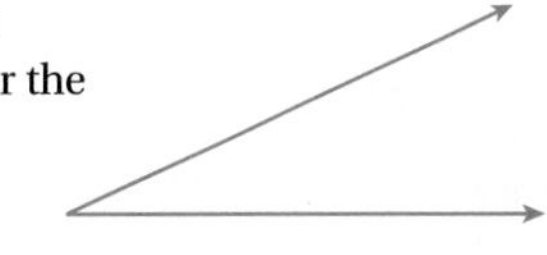

32. **Write About It** Describe how an acute angle and an obtuse angle are different.

33. **Challenge** How many times during the day do the hands of a clock form a straight angle? 24

CRCT Prep • GPS Support • Spiral Review

34. **Multiple Choice** The figure shows a plan for a skateboard ramp. What type of angle is $\angle B$?

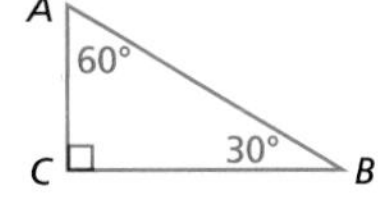

Ⓐ Acute Ⓑ Right Ⓒ Obtuse Ⓓ Straight

35. **Multiple Choice** Which of the following is another name for $\angle PQR$?

Ⓕ $\angle P$ Ⓖ $\angle RQP$ Ⓗ $\angle PRQ$ Ⓙ $\angle QPR$

Write each decimal as a percent and a fraction. (Lesson 7-8)

36. 0.09 9%; $\frac{9}{100}$
37. 0.4 40%; $\frac{2}{5}$
38. 0.65 65%; $\frac{13}{20}$
39. 0.9 90%; $\frac{9}{10}$
40. 0.76 76%; $\frac{19}{25}$

Find the percent of each number. (Lesson 7-9)

41. 12% of 30 3.6
42. 30% of 60 18
43. 65% of 110 17.5
44. 82% of 360 295.2

CHALLENGE 8-2

LESSON 8-2 Challenge
I'll Meet You in 30°

No one knows for sure when people invented clocks to measure time. The first clocks were probably sundials, which measure time by the sun's shadow moving around a circle. Although today's clocks no longer use the sun to measure time, many people still use a circle to display time. A circle has 360°, and a clock face has 12 hours marked. So, each hour on the clock represents 30° of the circle.

Write the time shown on each clock below. Then use a protractor to measure each angle formed by the clock's hands and tell what kind of angle it is.

1.  3:00; 90°; right angle
2.  11:25; 180°; straight angle
3.  9:05; 120°; obtuse angle
4.  5:10; 90°; right angle
5.  8:00; 120°; obtuse angle
6. 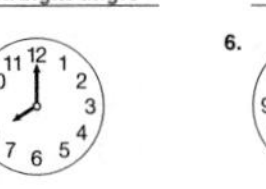 4:30; 60°; acute angle
7. 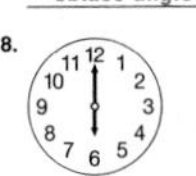 2:35; 150°; obtuse angle
8.  6:00; 180°; straight angle
9.  10:50; 30°; acute angle

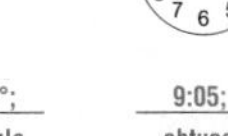
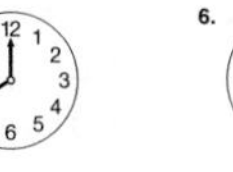
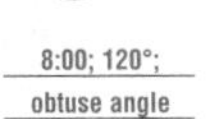
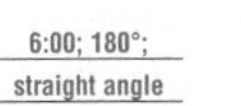

PROBLEM SOLVING 8-2

LESSON 8-2 Problem Solving
Measuring and Classifying Angles

Write the correct answer.

1. When a patient is lying flat in a hospital bed, what type of angle does the patient's body form? What is the measurement of that angle?
straight angle; 180°
2. When a patient is sitting straight up in a hospital bed, the upper body has been raised to what angle? What type of angle is that?
90° angle; right angle
3. Most hospital beds have a setting for the Fowler position. In this position, the patient's upper body is raised to form a 60° to 70° angle from a flat position. What types of angles are these?
They are both acute.
4. What are the greatest and least differences between the straight-up position and the Fowler position in a hospital bed?
least: 20°; greatest: 30°

Circle the letter of the correct answer.

5. Medical technicians often set the handles of crutches so that the patient's elbow is at a 30° angle. What type of angle is this?
Ⓐ acute angle
B right angle
C obtuse angle
D straight angle
6. By law, wheelchair ramps in public places cannot be greater than 5 degrees. Which type of angle does a wheelchair ramp in public form with the ground?
Ⓕ acute angle
G right angle
H obtuse angle
J straight angle
7. Physical therapists use a goniometer to measure the extension of a sitting patient's knee. Resting is 90°, and full extension is 180°. What angle does the goniometer measure if the patient's knee is at $\frac{1}{2}$ extension?
A 45°
B 90°
Ⓒ 135°
D 0°
8. The Q-angle is measured between two points on a patient's hip joint and one point on the knee joint. A normal Q-measure from men is 14° plus or minus 3 degrees. What type of angle is any normal Q-angle for men?
F straight
G obtuse
H right
Ⓙ acute

Ongoing Assessment and INTERVENTION

Diagnose Before the Lesson
8-2 Warm Up, TE p. 420

Monitor During the Lesson
8-2 Know-It Notebook
8-2 Questioning Strategies

Assess After the Lesson
8-2 Lesson Quiz, TE p. 423

Answers

24. Possible answer:

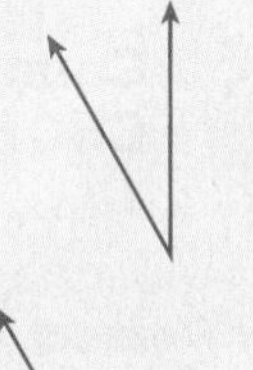

25. Possible answer:

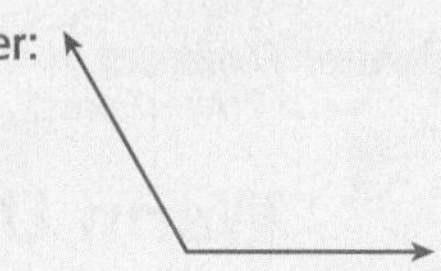

26, 30-32. See p. A9.

Test Prep Doctor In Exercise 35, students should remember that an angle named with three letters must have the letter that names the vertex in the middle of the other two letters. This eliminates choices **H** and **J.** Choice **F** can be eliminated because *P* is not the vertex of the given angle.

Journal

Have students draw examples of an acute, a right, and an obtuse angle. Have students use a protractor to measure each angle.

Power Presentations with PowerPoint®

8-2 Lesson Quiz

Use a protractor to draw an angle with the given measure. Tell what type of angle it is.

1. 140° Check student drawings; obtuse.
2. 20° Check student drawings; acute.
3. Draw a right angle. Check student drawings.
4. Is the angle shown closer to 30° or 120°? 30°

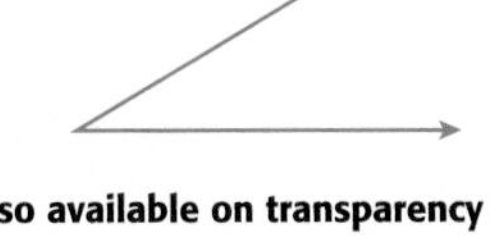

Also available on transparency

8-3 Organizer

Pacing: Traditional 1 day
Block $\frac{1}{2}$ day

Objective: Students understand relationships of angles.

Hands-On Lab
In *Hands-On Lab Activities*

Technology Lab
In *Technology Lab Activities*

Online Edition
Tutorial Videos, Interactivities

Countdown to CRCT Week 17

Power Presentations with PowerPoint®

Warm Up

Identify the type of angle.

1. 70° acute **2.** 90° right
3. 140° obtuse **4.** 180° straight

Problem of the Day

A line forms an angle of 57° with the vertical axis. What angle does the line form with the horizontal axis?
33° or 147°

Also available on transparency

Math Humor

Two wrongs don't make a right, but

- two rights make a straight angle,
- two writes make a second draft, and
- two Wrights make an airplane.

Georgia Performance Standards

M6A3 Students will evaluate algebraic expressions, including those with exponents, and solve simple one-step equations using each of the four basic operations.

M6P1.b Solve problems that arise in mathematics and in other contexts.

M6P3.d Use the language of mathematics to express mathematical ideas precisely.

8-3 Angle Relationships

Learn to understand relationships of angles.

Vocabulary
congruent
vertical angles
adjacent angles
complementary angles
supplementary angles

Georgia Performance Standards
M6A3 Evaluate algebraic expressions, including those with exponents, and solve simple one-step equations using each of the four basic operations. Also, M6P1.b, M6P3.d.

Angle relationships play an important role in many sports and games. Miniature-golf players must understand angles to know where to aim the ball. In the miniature-golf hole shown, m∠1 = m∠2, m∠3 = m∠4, and m∠5 = m∠6.

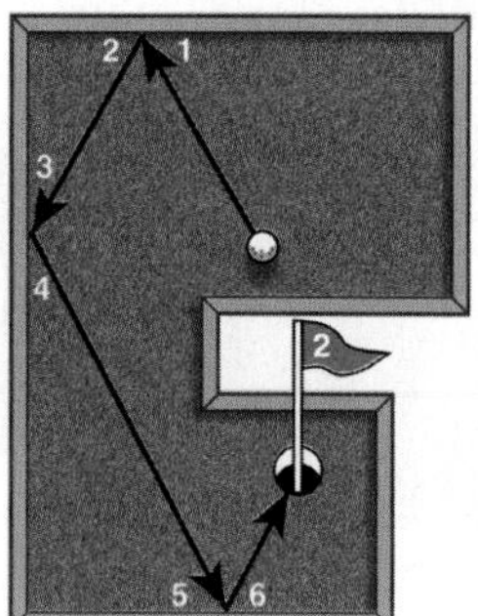

When angles have the same measure, they are said to be **congruent**.

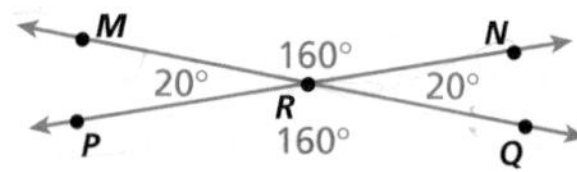

Vertical angles are formed opposite each other when two lines intersect. Vertical angles have the same measure, so they are always congruent.

∠*MRP* and ∠*NRQ* are vertical angles.
∠*MRN* and ∠*PRQ* are vertical angles.

Adjacent angles are side by side and have a common vertex and ray. Adjacent angles may or may not be congruent.

∠*MRN* and ∠*NRQ* are adjacent angles. They share vertex *R* and $\overrightarrow{RN}$.
∠*NRQ* and ∠*QRP* are adjacent angles. They share vertex *R* and $\overrightarrow{RQ}$.

EXAMPLE 1 Identifying Types of Angle Pairs

Identify the type of each angle pair shown.

A

∠1 and ∠2 are opposite each other and are formed by two intersecting lines.
They are vertical angles.

B

∠3 and ∠4 are side by side and have a common vertex and ray.
They are adjacent angles.

1 Introduce

Alternate Opener

EXPLORATION

8-3 Angle Relationships

The line segments in some letters, symbols, and numbers form angles.

Numbers 1–5 describe types of angle pairs. Determine which marked angle pairs in the figures apply to each description, and then check the appropriate boxes.

		Z	X	F	↗	4
1.	Congruent angles: same measure					
2.	Vertical angles: opposite each other when two lines intersect					
3.	Adjacent angles: side by side with a common vertex and ray					
4.	Complementary angles: sum equals 90°					
5.	Supplementary angles: sum equals 180°					

Think and Discuss

6. Discuss other examples of vertical angles in the real world.

Motivate

To introduce angle relationships, draw two intersecting lines as below.

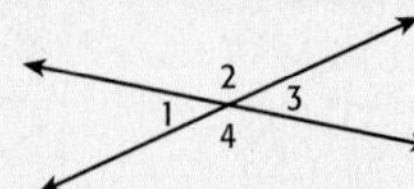

Ask students to tell you what they notice about the angles. For example, ∠1 and ∠3 are opposite each other, and so are ∠4 and ∠2; ∠1 and ∠2 are side by side and have a common vertex and ray, and so do ∠2 and ∠3, ∠3 and ∠4, and ∠4 and ∠1.

Explorations and answers are provided in *Alternate Openers: Explorations Transparencies*.

Complementary angles are two angles whose measures have a sum of 90°.

$65° + 25° = 90°$
$\angle LMN$ and $\angle NMP$ are complementary.

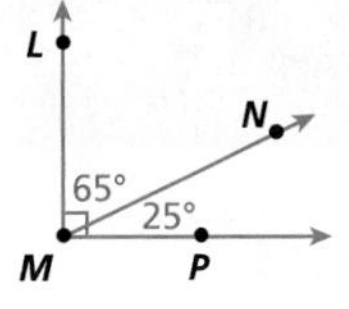

Supplementary angles are two angles whose measures have a sum of 180°.

$65° + 115° = 180°$
$\angle GHK$ and $\angle KHJ$ are supplementary.

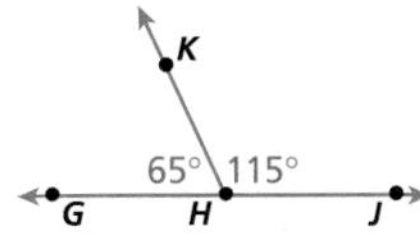

EXAMPLE 2 Identifying an Unknown Angle Measure

Find each unknown angle measure.

A The angles are complementary.

$$55° + a = 90°$$
$$-55° \quad -55°$$
$$a = 35°$$

The sum of the measures is 90°.

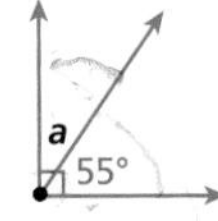

B The angles are supplementary.

$$75° + b = 180°$$
$$-75° \quad -75°$$
$$b = 105°$$

The sum of the measures is 180°.

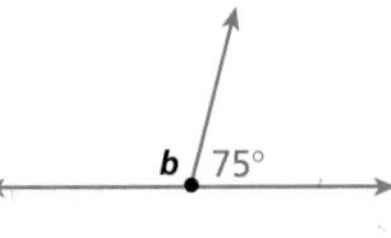

C The angles are vertical angles.

$c = 51°$ *Vertical angles are congruent.*

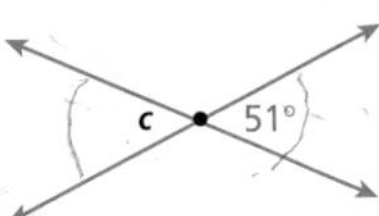

D Angles JGF and KGH are congruent.

$$d + e + 136° = 180°$$
$$-136° \quad -136°$$
$$d + e = 44°$$
$$d = 22° \text{ and } e = 22°$$

The sum of the measures is 180°. Each angle measures half of 44°.

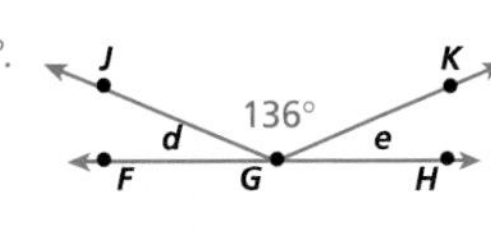

Think and Discuss

GPS M6P1.d, M6P3.b

1. **Give** the measure of $\angle 2$ if $\angle 1$ and $\angle 2$ are vertical angles and $m\angle 1 = 40°$.
2. **Give** the measure of $\angle 3$ if $\angle 3$ and $\angle 4$ are supplementary and $m\angle 4 = 150°$.
3. **Tell** whether the angles in Example 1B are supplementary or complementary.

Answers to *Think and Discuss*

1. $m\angle 2 = 40°$
2. $m\angle 3 = 30°$
3. supplementary

Power Presentations with PowerPoint®

Additional Examples

Example 1

Identify the type of each angle pair shown.

A.

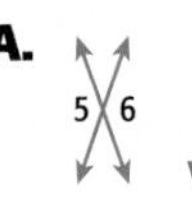

vertical

B.

adjacent

Example 2

Find each unknown angle measure.

A. The angles are complementary.
$m\angle 1 = 19°$

B. The angles are supplementary.
$m\angle 2 = 55°$

C. The angles are vertical angles.
$m\angle 3 = 82°$

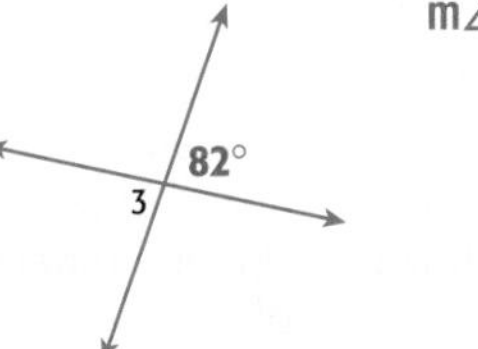

D. $\angle JKL$ and $\angle MKN$ are congruent.

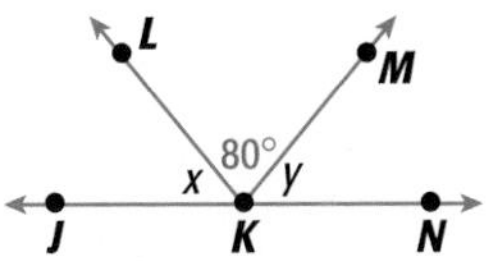

$m\angle JKL = 50°$ and $m\angle MKN = 50°$

Also available on transparency

2 Teach

Guided Instruction

In this lesson, students learn to describe relationships of angles. Explain the term *congruent*, and show students examples of *vertical* and *adjacent* angles. Then show students examples of *complementary* and *supplementary* angles, and teach how to find the measure of an unknown angle, given the measure of its complementary or supplementary angle.

Inclusion Remind students that complementary angles and supplementary angles do not have to be adjacent.

Reaching All Learners

Through Concrete Manipulatives

Give each pair of students a protractor and two strips of cardboard fastened at the center so they intersect (provided in the Manipulatives Kit). Show students that the fastener is the vertex of the angles formed by the lines on the strips of cardboard. Have students move the strips to make vertical angles of varying sizes. Have pairs measure one angle and use what they know to calculate the measures of the remaining angles. Repeat with other sets of angles.

3 Close

ENGLISH LANGUAGE LEARNERS

Summarize

Review the new vocabulary in the lesson: *congruent, vertical angles, adjacent angles, complementary angles*, and *supplementary angles*. Have students volunteer to draw examples of each.

Check students' drawings.

8-3 Exercises

Assignment Guide

If you finished Example 1 assign:
Average 1–2, 29–38
Advanced 5–6, 29–38

If you finished Example 2 assign:
Average 1–4, 9–38
Advanced 5–38

Homework Quick Check

Quickly check key concepts.
Exercises: 10, 12, 14, 18, 22

Math Background

If ∠1 and ∠2 are supplementary, then m∠1 + m∠2 = 180°. If ∠2 and ∠3 are supplementary, then m∠2 + m∠3 = 180°. Therefore, m∠1 + m∠2 = m∠2 + m∠3. Subtracting m∠2 from each side, m∠1 = m∠3. So, if two angles are supplementary to the same angle, their measures are equal. In a similar fashion, it can be shown that complements of equal angles are equal.

Georgia Performance Standards

M6P1.b Solve problems that arise in mathematics and in other contexts.

M6P3.a Organize and consolidate their mathematical thinking through communication.

M6P5.b Select, apply, and translate among mathematical representations to solve problems.

8-3 Exercises

M6P1.b, M6P3.a, M6P5.b

GUIDED PRACTICE

See Example 1 **Identify the type of each angle pair shown.**

1.

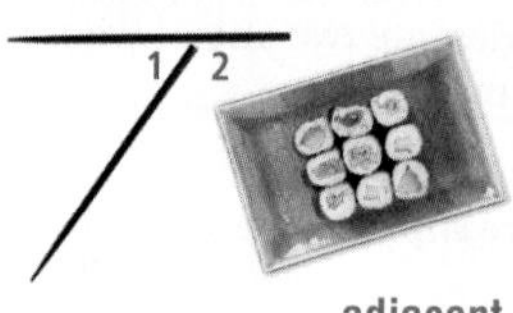

adjacent

2.

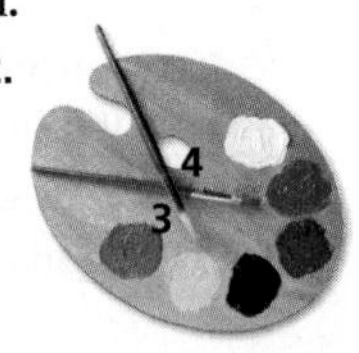

vertical

See Example 2 **Find each unknown angle measure.**

3. The angles are complementary.

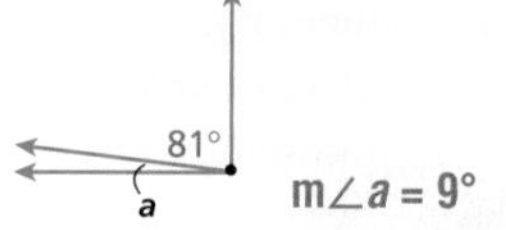

m∠*a* = 9°

4. The angles are supplementary.

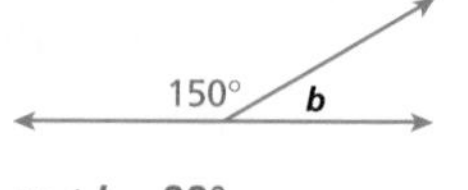

m∠*b* = 30°

INDEPENDENT PRACTICE

See Example 1 **Identify the type of each angle pair shown.**

5.

adjacent

6. vertical

See Example 2 **Find each unknown angle measure.**

7. The angles are vertical angles.

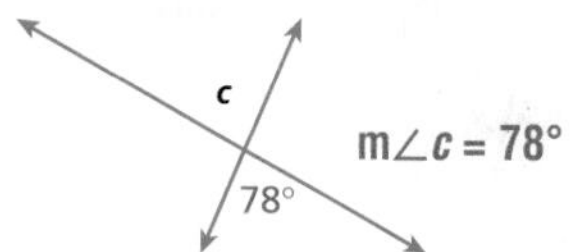

m∠*c* = 78°

8. The angles are supplementary.

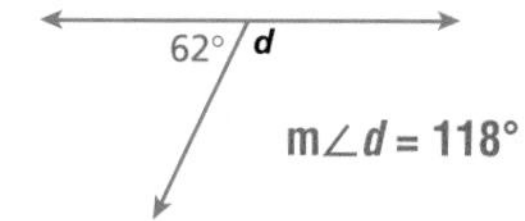

m∠*d* = 118°

PRACTICE AND PROBLEM SOLVING

Extra Practice p. 728

Use the figure for Exercises 9–12.

9. Which angles are not adjacent to ∠3? angles 1, 5, 6, 7, and 8
10. Name all the pairs of vertical angles that include ∠8. ∠6 and ∠8
11. If the m∠6 is 72°, what are the measures of ∠5, ∠7, and ∠8? 108°, 108°, 72°
12. What is the sum of the measures of ∠1, ∠2, ∠3, and ∠4? 360°

RETEACH 8-3

LESSON 8-3 **Reteach**
Angle Relationships

When two lines intersect, two pairs of opposite angles, called vertical angles, are formed. Vertical angles are congruent.

∠ABC and ∠DBF are vertical angles.
∠ABD and ∠CBF are vertical angles.

Adjacent angles have a common side and vertex.

∠PQR and ∠PQS are adjacent angles.

Identify the type of each angle pair shown.

1. adjacent angles
2. vertical angles

If the sum of the measures of two angles is 90°, then the angles are complementary angles.

∠F and ∠G are complementary angles.

If the sum of the measures of two angles is 180°, then the angles are supplementary angles.

∠J and ∠K are supplementary angles.

Identify the type of each angle pair shown.

3. supplementary angles
4. complementary angles

PRACTICE 8-3

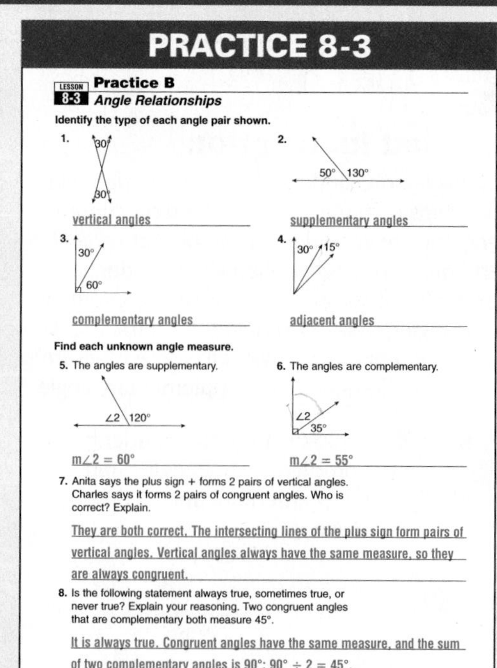

LESSON 8-3 **Practice B**
Angle Relationships

Identify the type of each angle pair shown.

1. vertical angles
2. supplementary angles
3. complementary angles
4. adjacent angles

Find each unknown angle measure.

5. The angles are supplementary. m∠2 = 60°
6. The angles are complementary. m∠2 = 55°

7. Anita says the plus sign + forms 2 pairs of vertical angles. Charles says it forms 2 pairs of congruent angles. Who is correct? Explain.

They are both correct. The intersecting lines of the plus sign form pairs of vertical angles. Vertical angles always have the same measure, so they are always congruent.

8. Is the following statement always true, sometimes true, or never true? Explain your reasoning. Two congruent angles that are complementary both measure 45°.

It is always true. Congruent angles have the same measure, and the sum of two complementary angles is 90°; 90° ÷ 2 = 45°.

Use the figure for Exercises 13–15.

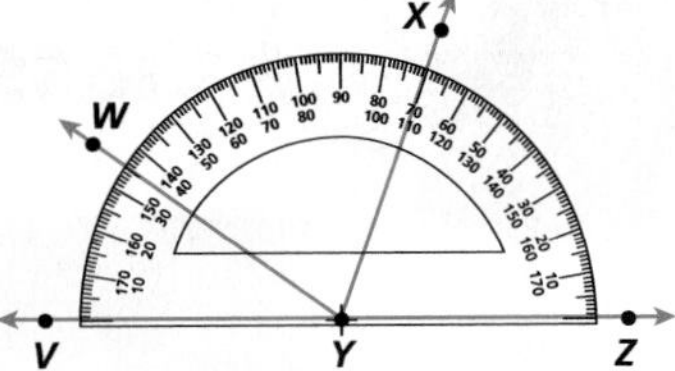

13. Find the measure of $\angle VYW$. 35°

14. Find the measure of $\angle XYZ$. 70°

15. **Multi-Step** Use the measures of $\angle VYW$ and $\angle XYZ$ to find the measure of $\angle WYX$. 75°

Find the measure of the angle that is complementary to each given angle. Use a protractor to draw both angles.

16. 47° 43° 17. 62° 28° 18. 55° 35° 19. 31° 59°

Find the measure of the angle that is supplementary to each given angle. Use a protractor to draw both angles.

20. 75° 105° 21. 102° 78° 22. 136° 44° 23. 81° 99°

24. Angles A and B are complementary. If the measure of angle A equals the measure of angle B, what is the measure of each angle? 45°

25. Angles C and D are each complementary to angle F. How are angle C and angle D related? angles C and D are congruent angles

26. **Write a Problem** Draw a pair of adjacent supplementary angles. Write a problem in which the measure of one of the angles must be found.

27. **Write About It** Two angles are supplementary to the same angle. Explain the relationship between the measures of these angles.

27. The angles will have the same measure, because they are supplementary to the same angle.

28. **Challenge** The measure of angle A is 38°. Angle B is complementary to angle A. Angle C is supplementary to angle B. What is the measure of angle C? 128°

CRCT Prep • GPS Support • Spiral Review

29. **Multiple Choice** Which type of angles are always congruent?

(A) Adjacent (B) Complementary (C) Supplementary (D) Vertical

30. **Multiple Choice** Angle J and angle K are supplementary. What is the measure of $\angle K$ if the measure of $\angle J$ is 75°?

(F) 15° (G) 25° (H) 105° (J) 150°

Find the missing value in each proportion. (Lesson 7-3)

31. $\frac{n}{6} = \frac{5}{15}$ $n = 2$ 32. $\frac{2}{m} = \frac{0.8}{3.6}$ $m = 9$ 33. $\frac{1}{8} = \frac{p}{2}$ $p = 0.25$ 34. $\frac{30}{8} = \frac{15}{s}$ $s = 4$

Classify each angle as acute, right, obtuse, or straight. (Lesson 8-2)

35. straight 36. right 37. acute 38. obtuse

CHALLENGE 8-3

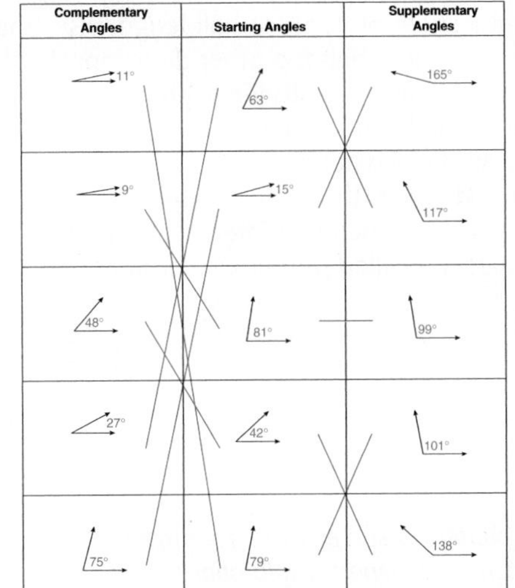

Challenge
8-3 *Angle Partners*

Measure all the angles in the chart below. Then draw lines to match each starting angle with its complementary and supplementary angles.

Complementary Angles	Starting Angles	Supplementary Angles
11°	63°	165°
9°	15°	117°
48°	81°	99°
27°	42°	101°
75°	79°	138°

PROBLEM SOLVING 8-3

Problem Solving
8-3 *Angle Relationships*

Use the two compass roses to answer questions 1-6.

Cardinal Directions

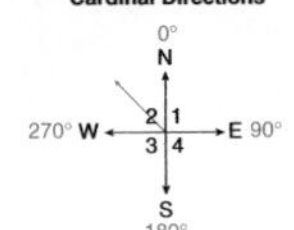

Intermediate Directions

315° NW, 45° NE, 5, 6, 7, 8, SW 225°, SE 135°

1. Which angles formed by the cardinal directions are vertical angles?
$\angle 1$ and $\angle 3$; $\angle 2$ and $\angle 4$

2. Which angles formed by the intermediate directions are vertical angles?
$\angle 5$ and $\angle 7$; $\angle 6$ and $\angle 8$

3. Draw the northwest directional ray on the cardinal compass rose. Describe the adjacent angles formed by the new ray. Possible answer:
complementary angles

4. North on a compass is 0°, and east is 90°. Use this information to label the degrees for each direction on the two compass roses above.

Circle the letter of the correct answer.

5. Which angles formed by the cardinal directions are supplementary to $\angle 2$?
A $\angle 1$
B $\angle 1$ and $\angle 3$
C $\angle 3$ and $\angle 4$
(D) $\angle 1$, $\angle 3$ and $\angle 4$

6. Which angles formed by the intermediate directions are supplementary to $\angle 6$?
F $\angle 5$
G $\angle 5$ and $\angle 7$
H $\angle 7$ and $\angle 8$
(J) $\angle 5$, $\angle 7$ and $\angle 8$

7. Angles A and B are complementary. $\angle B$ is twice as large as $\angle A$. What are the measurements for each angle?
A $\angle A = 45°$; $\angle B = 90°$
(B) $\angle A = 30°$; $\angle B = 60°$
C $\angle A = 60°$; $\angle B = 120°$
D $\angle A = 90°$; $\angle B = 180°$

8. $\angle 1$ and $\angle 2$ are complementary. $\angle 2$ and $\angle 3$ are supplementary. The measure of $\angle 1$ is 45°. What is the measure of $\angle 3$?
F 45°
G 270°
H 90°
(J) 135°

Ongoing Assessment and Intervention

***Diagnose Before* the Lesson**
8-3 Warm Up, TE p. 424

***Monitor During* the Lesson**
8-3 Know-It Notebook
8-3 Questioning Strategies

***Assess After* the Lesson**
8-3 Lesson Quiz, TE p. 427

Answers

16. 17. 18. 19.

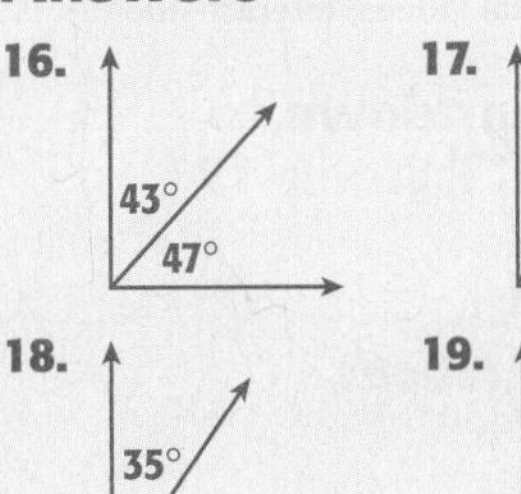

20–23, 26. See p. A9.

Test Prep Doctor In Exercise 30, students having difficulty remembering the meaning of *supplementary angles* can relate the term to *straight angles.* Both begin with the letter *s* and have meanings that involve 180°. Students choosing **A** are confusing *supplementary* and *complementary.*

Journal

Have students explain the methods used to compute the measures of complementary and supplementary angles.

Power Presentations with PowerPoint®

8-3 Lesson Quiz

1. Identify the type of angle pair shown. adjacent

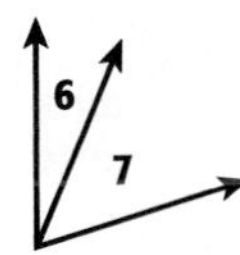

Find each unknown angle measure.

2. The angles are vertical angles. $d = 130°$

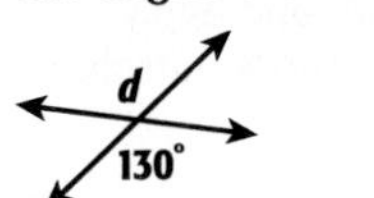

3. The angles are supplementary. $x = 45°$

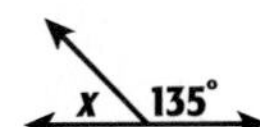

Also available on transparency

8-4 Organizer

Pacing: Traditional 1 day
Block $\frac{1}{2}$ day

Objective: Students classify the different types of lines.

Hands-On Lab
In *Hands-On Lab Activities*

Technology Lab
In *Technology Lab Activities*

Online Edition
Tutorial Videos, Interactivities

Countdown to CRCT Week 17

Power Presentations with PowerPoint®

Warm Up

Give the complement of each angle.

1. 80° 10° **2.** 64° 26°
3. 15° 75° **4.** 48° 42°

Problem of the Day

Draw three points that are not in a straight line. Label them *A, B,* and *C.* How many different lines can you draw that contain two of the points? Name the lines.
3; $\overleftrightarrow{AB}$, $\overleftrightarrow{AC}$, $\overleftrightarrow{BC}$

Also available on transparency

Math Fact

Another word that is sometimes used to describe skew lines is *noncoplanar,* which means that they cannot lie in the same plane.

Georgia Performance Standards

M6P1.b Solve problems that arise in mathematics and in other contexts.

M6P3.d Use the language of mathematics to express mathematical ideas precisely.

M6P4.c Recognize and apply mathematics in contexts outside of mathematics.

8-4 Classifying Lines

Learn to classify the different types of lines.

Vocabulary
parallel lines
perpendicular lines
skew lines

Georgia Performance Standards

M6P4.c Recognize and apply mathematics in contexts outside of mathematics. Also, M6P1.b, M6P3.d.

The photograph of the houses and the table below show some of the ways that lines can relate to each other. The yellow lines are intersecting. The purple lines are *parallel.* The green lines are *perpendicular.* The white lines are *skew.*

Reading Math

The red arrows on the lines show that the lines are parallel.

Intersecting lines are lines that cross at one common point.	W, Y, X, Z	Line *YZ* intersects line *WX*. $\overleftrightarrow{YZ}$ intersects $\overleftrightarrow{WX}$.
Parallel lines are lines in the same plane that never intersect.	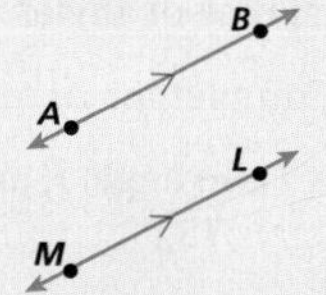	Line *AB* is parallel to line *ML*. $\overleftrightarrow{AB} \parallel \overleftrightarrow{ML}$
Perpendicular lines intersect to form 90° angles, or right angles.	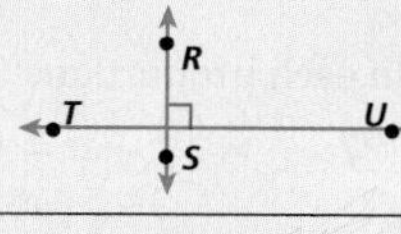	Line *RS* is perpendicular to line *TU*. $\overleftrightarrow{RS} \perp \overleftrightarrow{TU}$
Skew lines are lines that lie in different planes. They are neither parallel nor intersecting.	M, B, A, L	Line *AB* and line *ML* are skew. $\overleftrightarrow{AB}$ and $\overleftrightarrow{ML}$ are skew.

1 Introduce

Alternate Opener

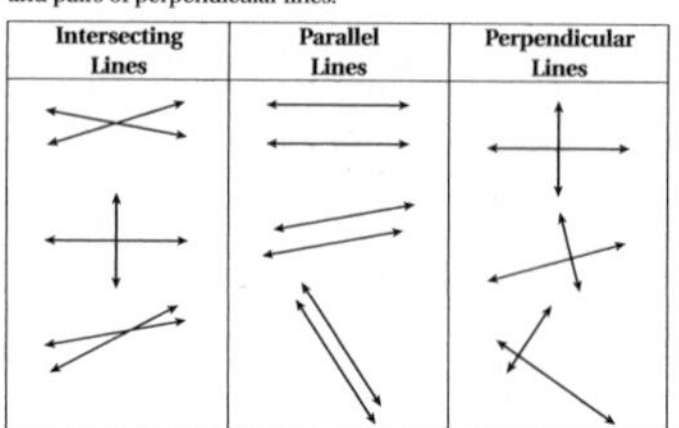

EXPLORATION

8-4 Classifying Lines

The table shows pairs of intersecting lines, pairs of parallel lines, and pairs of perpendicular lines.

Intersecting Lines	Parallel Lines	Perpendicular Lines

1. Draw your own examples of intersecting lines, parallel lines, and perpendicular lines.

Think and Discuss

2. **Describe** how you can tell if two lines are parallel.
3. **Discuss** what makes perpendicular lines different from other lines that intersect.

Motivate

Fold a sheet of paper in half lengthwise, and then fold it in half the other direction. Unfold the paper and ask students what they notice about the lines formed. They intersect. Ask the students what kinds of angles are formed where the lines intersect. right angles Explain that lines that intersect to form right angles are called *perpendicular* lines.

Explorations and answers are provided in *Alternate Openers: Explorations Transparencies.*

EXAMPLE 1 Classifying Pairs of Lines

Classify each pair of lines.

A

The lines are in the same plane. They do not appear to intersect.
They are parallel.

B

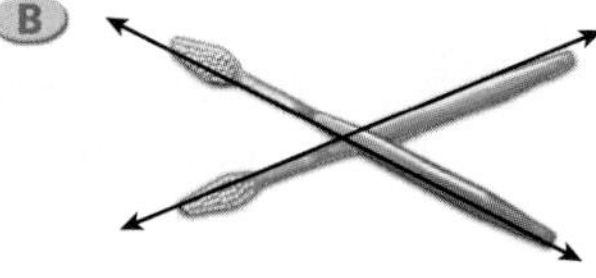

The lines cross at one common point.
They are intersecting.

C

The lines intersect to form right angles.
They are perpendicular.

D

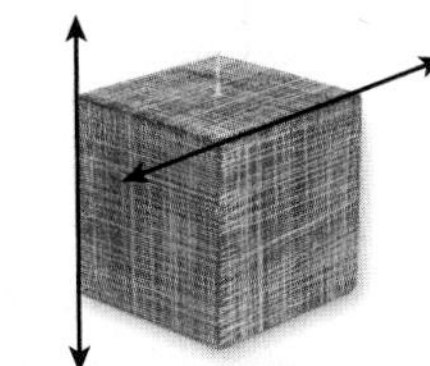

The lines are in different planes and are not parallel or intersecting.
They are skew.

EXAMPLE 2 *Physical Science Application*

The particles in a transverse wave move up and down as the wave travels to the right. What type of line relationship does this represent?

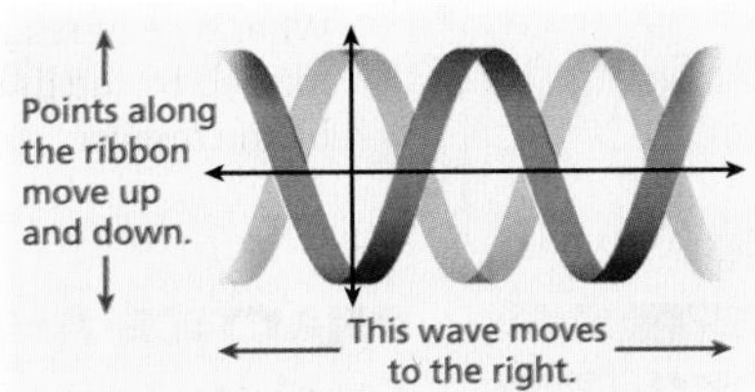
Points along the ribbon move up and down.
This wave moves to the right.

The direction that the particles move forms a right angle with the direction that the wave is traveling. The lines are perpendicular.

Think and Discuss

GPS M6P2.c, M6P3.b

1. **Give an example** of intersecting, parallel, perpendicular, and skew lines or line segments in your classroom.
2. **Determine** whether two lines must be parallel if they do not intersect. Explain.

Possible answers to *Think and Discuss*

1. intersecting, lines between the ceiling tiles; parallel, the top and bottom of the door; perpendicular, the top corner of the window; skew, the line where the wall and the ceiling meet in front of the room and the line where the wall and the floor meet on the right side of the room
2. No; two lines that don't intersect are skew if they do not and cannot lie in the same plane.

COMMON ERROR ALERT

Students may confuse intersecting and perpendicular lines. Remind them that perpendicular lines are a special kind of intersection.

Power Presentations with PowerPoint®

Additional Examples

Example 1

Classify each pair of lines.

A.

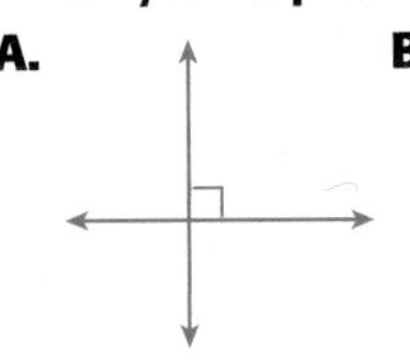

perpendicular

B.

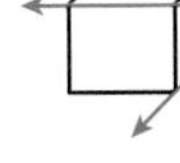

skew

C.

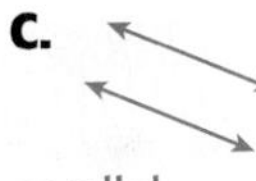

parallel

D.

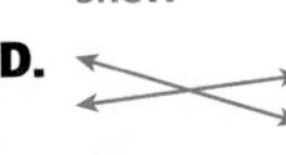

intersecting

Example 2

The handrails on an escalator are in the same plane. What type of line relationship do they represent?

The lines are parallel.

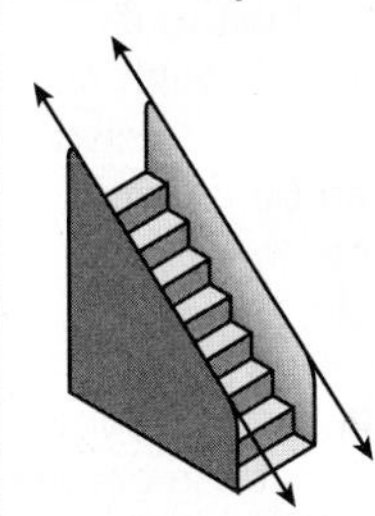

Also available on transparency

2 Teach

Guided Instruction

In this lesson students learn to classify different types of lines. Show students the photo in the lesson opener, which provides a real context for illustrating intersecting, parallel, perpendicular, and skew lines. Have students work through the examples to practice classifying pairs of lines. Have students think of other examples for each type of line relationship.

Teaching Tip **Multiple Representations** Understanding the concept of skew lines calls for thinking in three dimensions. You may wish to use yardsticks to show students a three-dimensional model of skew lines.

Reaching All Learners
Through Cognitive Strategies

Give students old street maps on which they can identify several examples of parallel, intersecting, and perpendicular lines. Have students write questions about the line relationships they find on the map and exchange maps and questions with other students.

Possible answers: What street is perpendicular to Main Street? What street intersects Stagecoach Boulevard? What street runs parallel to Alcove Drive?

3 Close

Summarize

Ask students these questions to review the new vocabulary in the lesson:

- What do you call lines that intersect to form 90° angles? perpendicular
- What do you call lines in the same plane that never intersect? parallel
- What do you call lines that do not lie in the same plane and never intersect? skew

8-4 Exercises

Assignment Guide

If you finished Example 1 assign:
Average 1–2, 8–10, 24–36
Advanced 4–6, 8–10, 24–36

If you finished Example 2 assign:
Average 1–9, 12–36
Advanced 4–36

Homework Quick Check
Quickly check key concepts.
Exercises: 8, 12, 16, 18

Answers

11a, b. See p. A9.

Math Background

Based on our experiences in the real world, it seems reasonable to assume that parallel lines exist. This assumption is made explicit in Euclid's fifth postulate, now known as the Parallel Postulate. This postulate, set forth as a statement to be accepted without proof, offers the idea that through any point not on a given line, there exists exactly one line that can be drawn parallel to the given line.

In the nineteenth century, mathematicians came to realize that new geometries could be created that use alternative versions of the Parallel Postulate. These are known as non-Euclidean geometries.

Georgia Performance Standards

M6P3.a Organize and consolidate their mathematical thinking through communication.

M6P3.c Analyze and evaluate the mathematical thinking and strategies of others.

M6P5.b Select, apply, and translate among mathematical representations to solve problems.

8-4 Exercises

Georgia Performance Standards
M6P3.a, M6P3.c, M6P5.b

go.hrw.com
Homework Help Online
KEYWORD: MR7 8-4
Parent Resources Online
KEYWORD: MR7 Parent

GUIDED PRACTICE

See Example 1 Classify each pair of lines.

1. intersecting

2. perpendicular

See Example 2

3. Jamal dropped a fishing line from a pier, as shown in the drawing. What type of relationship is formed by the lines? perpendicular

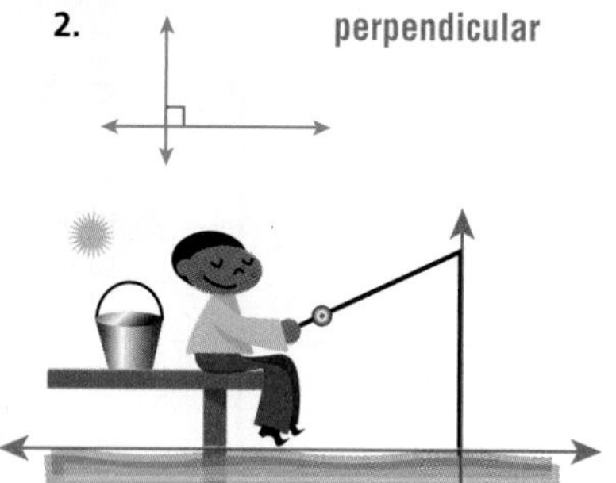

INDEPENDENT PRACTICE

See Example 1 Classify each pair of lines.

4. parallel

5. skew

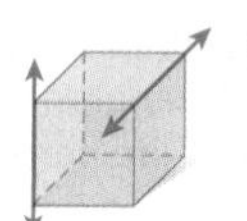

6. perpendicular

See Example 2

7. The drawing shows where an archaeologist found two fossils. What type of relationship is formed by the lines suggested by the fossils? skew

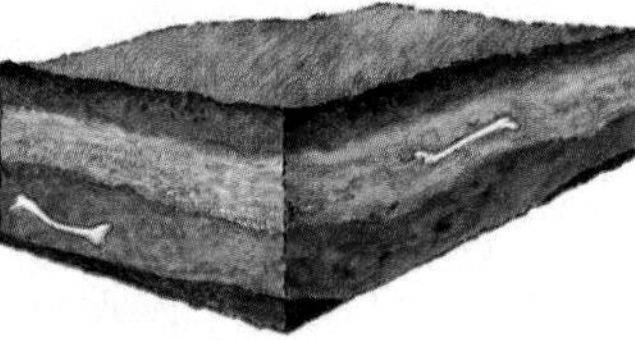

PRACTICE AND PROBLEM SOLVING

CRCT GPS
Extra Practice p. 728

Describe each pair of lines as parallel, skew, intersecting, or perpendicular.

8. intersecting

9. parallel

10. skew

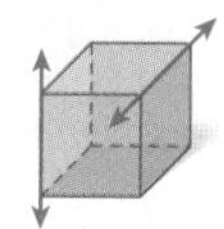

11. Capitol Street intersects 1st, 2nd, and 3rd Avenues, which are parallel to each other. West Street and East Street are perpendicular to 2nd Avenue.
   a. Draw a map showing the six streets.
   b. Suppose East and West Streets were perpendicular to Capitol Street rather than 2nd Avenue. Draw a map showing the streets.

RETEACH 8-4

LESSON 8-4 Reteach
Classifying Lines

Some lines have relationships.

Intersecting lines cross each other at one point.

$\overleftrightarrow{AB}$ intersects $\overleftrightarrow{CD}$.

Perpendicular lines intersect to form right angles.

$\overleftrightarrow{JK} \perp \overleftrightarrow{MN}$

Parallel lines lie in the same plane but never intersect.

$\overleftrightarrow{PQ} \parallel \overleftrightarrow{RS}$

Skew lines lie in different planes and do not intersect.

$\overleftrightarrow{FG}$ and $\overleftrightarrow{VW}$ are skew.

Classify each pair of lines.

1. parallel
2. skew
3. perpendicular
4. intersecting

PRACTICE 8-4

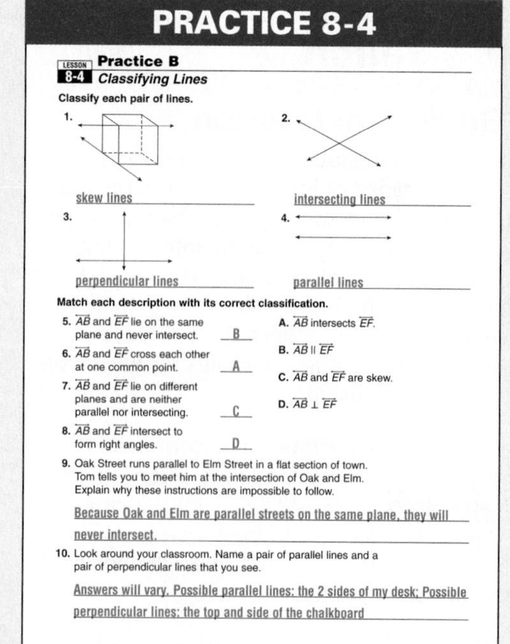

LESSON 8-4 Practice B
Classifying Lines

Classify each pair of lines.

1. skew lines
2. intersecting lines
3. perpendicular lines
4. parallel lines

Match each description with its correct classification.

5. $\overleftrightarrow{AB}$ and $\overleftrightarrow{EF}$ lie on the same plane and never intersect. B
6. $\overleftrightarrow{AB}$ and $\overleftrightarrow{EF}$ cross each other at one common point. A
7. $\overleftrightarrow{AB}$ and $\overleftrightarrow{EF}$ lie on different planes and are neither parallel nor intersecting. C
8. $\overleftrightarrow{AB}$ and $\overleftrightarrow{EF}$ intersect to form right angles. D

A. $\overleftrightarrow{AB}$ intersects $\overleftrightarrow{EF}$.
B. $\overleftrightarrow{AB} \parallel \overleftrightarrow{EF}$
C. $\overleftrightarrow{AB}$ and $\overleftrightarrow{EF}$ are skew.
D. $\overleftrightarrow{AB} \perp \overleftrightarrow{EF}$

9. Oak Street runs parallel to Elm Street in a flat section of town. Tom tells you to meet him at the intersection of Oak and Elm. Explain why these instructions are impossible to follow.
Because Oak and Elm are parallel streets on the same plane, they will never intersect.

10. Look around your classroom. Name a pair of parallel lines and a pair of perpendicular lines that you see.
Answers will vary. Possible parallel lines: the 2 sides of my desk; Possible perpendicular lines: the top and side of the chalkboard

The lines in the figure intersect to form a rectangular box.

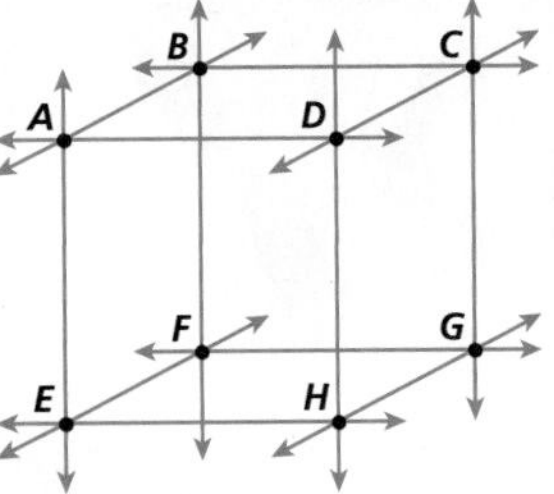

12. Name all the lines that are parallel to $\overleftrightarrow{AD}$. $\overleftrightarrow{BC}$, $\overleftrightarrow{FG}$, and $\overleftrightarrow{EH}$

13. Name all the lines that are perpendicular to $\overleftrightarrow{FG}$. $\overleftrightarrow{BF}$, $\overleftrightarrow{GH}$, $\overleftrightarrow{EF}$, $\overleftrightarrow{CG}$

14. Name a pair of lines that are skew. Possible answer: $\overleftrightarrow{AD}$ and $\overleftrightarrow{GH}$

15. Name all the lines that are not parallel to and do not intersect $\overleftrightarrow{DH}$. $\overleftrightarrow{AB}$, $\overleftrightarrow{EF}$, $\overleftrightarrow{FG}$, $\overleftrightarrow{BC}$

Tell whether each statement is *always, sometimes,* or *never* true.

16. Intersecting lines are parallel. never

17. Intersecting lines are perpendicular. sometimes

18. Perpendicular lines are intersecting. always

19. Parallel lines are skew. never

20. **Critical Thinking** Use *parallel, perpendicular, skew,* or a combination of these terms to describe the lines on a sheet of graph paper. Explain your answer. parallel and perpendicular; some lines on the graph paper will never intersect, and other lines intersect at right angles

21. **What's the Error?** A student drew two lines and claimed that the lines were both parallel and intersecting. Explain the error.

22. **Write About It** Explain the similarities and differences between perpendicular and intersecting lines.

23. **Challenge** Lines *x*, *y*, and *z* are in a plane. If lines *x* and *y* are parallel and line *z* intersects line *x*, does line *z* intersect line *y*? Explain. Yes; line *z* will intersect both lines *x* and *y* if it intersects line *x*.

CRCT Prep • GPS Support • Spiral Review

24. **Multiple Choice** Which types of lines never intersect when they are in the same plane?

(A) Intersecting (B) Parallel (C) Perpendicular (D) Skew

25. **Multiple Choice** Main Street and Elm Street meet at a 90° angle. Which term best describes the streets?

(F) Intersecting (G) Parallel (H) Perpendicular (J) Skew

26. **Extended Response** A student draws two lines on the same plane. He claims the lines are skew lines. Is he correct? Explain. What are the possible line types that the student drew? No, skew lines cannot be on the same plane; parallel lines, intersecting lines.

Graph and label each point on a coordinate grid. (Lesson 6-6)

27. $A(3, 4)$ 28. $B(1, 5)$ 29. $C(7, 1)$ 30. $D\left(8\frac{1}{2}, 5\right)$ 31. $E\left(2, 3\frac{1}{2}\right)$

Find the measure of the angle that is complementary to each given angle. (Lesson 8-3)

32. 14° 76° 33. 57° 33° 34. 80° 10° 35. 63° 27° 36. 21° 69°

CHALLENGE 8-4

LESSON 8-4 Challenge
Capital Streets

Washington, D.C., became the capital of the United States in 1800. The city's planners designed wide streets reaching out from two main centers—the White House and the Capitol Building. The President works and lives in the White House, and Congress works in the Capitol.

The map below shows the section of Washington, D.C, where the White House and Capitol are located. Use the following clues to label the streets on the map. Then name all the pairs of perpendicular streets on the map.

1. Madison Drive, Jefferson Drive, and Independence Avenue are parallel streets. Madison Drive is north of Jefferson Drive and Jefferson Drive is north of Independence Avenue.
2. 14th Street and 3rd Street are parallel streets. 14th Street is west of 3rd Street.
3. Pennsylvania Avenue intersects 14th Street near the White House.
4. The National Mall lies between Madison Drive to the north and Jefferson Drive to the south.

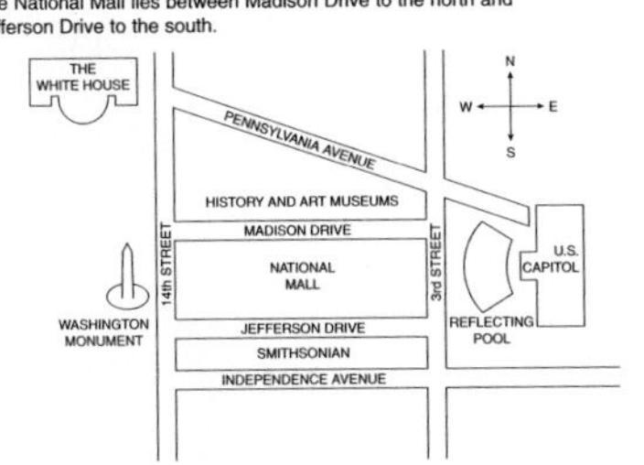

14th ⊥ Madison; 14th ⊥ Jefferson; 14th ⊥ Independence;
3rd ⊥ Madison; 3rd ⊥ Jefferson; 3rd ⊥ Independence

PROBLEM SOLVING 8-4

LESSON 8-4 Problem Solving
Classifying Lines

Use the map to answer each question.

1. The area where the borders of Utah, Colorado, Arizona, and New Mexico meet is sometimes called the Four Corners. What kind of lines are formed where the borders meet?
perpendicular lines
2. Which borderlines on the map are skew lines?
none
3. What kinds of lines are suggested by the eastern and western borders of New Mexico?
parallel lines

Circle the letter of the correct answer.

4. Which three states' borderlines intersect near the Grand Canyon?
A Utah, Arizona, and Idaho
B Idaho, Arizona, and Oregon
(C) Nevada, Utah, and Arizona
D Utah, Wyoming, and Idaho
5. Which two western states seem to have congruent borderlines?
(F) Colorado and Wyoming
G Oregon and Nevada
H New Mexico and Nevada
J Utah and Idaho
6. Which of the following do not appear to be parallel to the western borderline of Nevada?
(A) the western borderline of California
B the western borderline of Wyoming
C the eastern borderline of Montana
D the eastern borderline of Arizona
7. Which of these western states do not have borderlines that intersect near Great Salt Lake?
F Utah and Nevada
G Utah and Idaho
H Utah and Wyoming
(J) Utah and Colorado

Ongoing Assessment and Intervention

Diagnose ***Before*** **the Lesson**
8-4 Warm Up, TE p. 428

Monitor ***During*** **the Lesson**
8-4 Know-It Notebook
8-4 Questioning Strategies

Assess ***After*** **the Lesson**
8-4 Lesson Quiz, TE p. 431

Answers

21. By definition, parallel lines do not intersect. It is impossible to draw lines that are both parallel and intersecting.

22, 27–31. See p. A9.

Test Prep Doctor In Exercise 24, students can eliminate choices **A** and **C** because they name lines that intersect. Choice **D** can be eliminated because skew lines are never in the same plane.

Journal

Have students draw and label intersecting, parallel, and perpendicular lines and write a brief explanation of each. Also have students explain how they drew skew lines on their paper.

Power Presentations with PowerPoint®

8-4 Lesson Quiz

1. Sketch a pair of perpendicular lines.

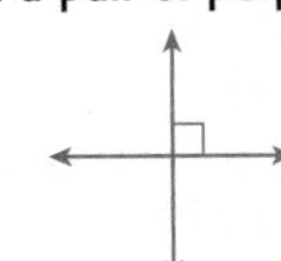

2. Sketch a pair of parallel lines.

Use the figure to classify the lines.

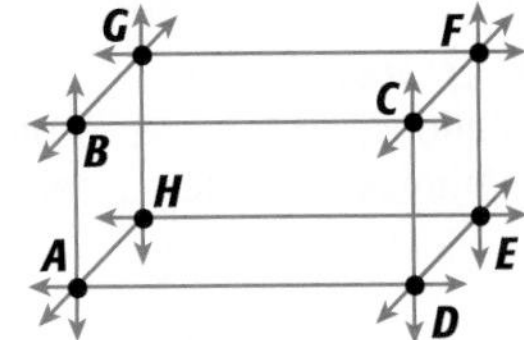

3. $\overleftrightarrow{AD}$ and $\overleftrightarrow{BC}$ parallel
4. $\overleftrightarrow{AD}$ and $\overleftrightarrow{CF}$ skew
5. $\overleftrightarrow{AB}$ and $\overleftrightarrow{BG}$ perpendicular

Also available on transparency

Organizer

Use with Lesson 8-4

Pacing:
Traditional $\frac{1}{2}$ day
Block $\frac{1}{4}$ day

Objective: Use a compass, a straightedge, and a protractor to explore parallel line relationships.

Materials: Compass, straightedge, protractor

Online Edition

Countdown to CRCT Week 17

Resources

Hands-On Lab Activities
Lab 8-4 Recording Sheet

Teach

Discuss

Remind the students how to use a compass and a protractor and provide some time for students to practice drawing geometric figures.

Close

Key Concept

A strong foundation in geometry is based on an understanding of parallel lines and their relationships.

Assessment

Draw each figure using the tool given.

1. 52° angle; protractor
2. Line segment $\overline{CD}$; straightedge
3. Point P and two lines that intersect at P; straightedge

Georgia Performance Standards

M6P2.a Recognize reasoning and proof as fundamental aspects of mathematics.

M6P2.b Make and investigate mathematical conjectures.

M6P5.a Create and use representations to organize, record, and communicate mathematical ideas.

Parallel Line Relationships

Use with Lesson 8-4

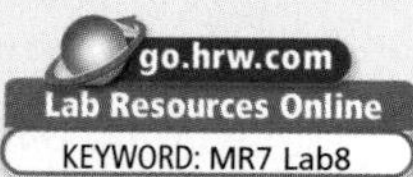

Georgia Performance Standards
M6P2.a, M6P2.b, M6P5.a

Parallel lines are in the same plane and never intersect. You can use a straightedge and protractor to draw parallel lines.

Activity

1. Draw a line on your paper. Label two points A and B.

Use your protractor to measure and mark a 90° angle at each point.

Draw rays with endpoints A and B through the marks you made with the protractor.

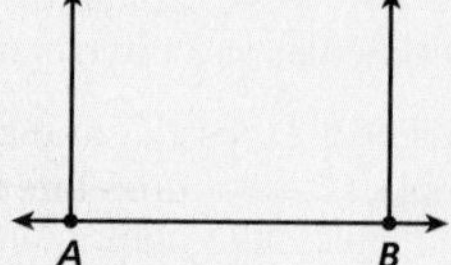

Place the point of your compass on point A, and draw an arc through the ray.

Use the same compass opening to draw an arc through the ray at point B.

Label the points of intersection X and Y.

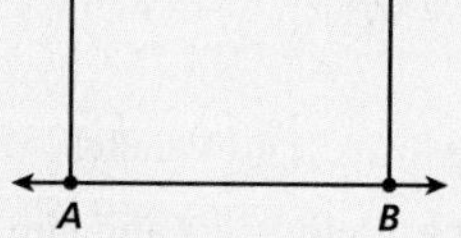

Now use your straightedge to draw a line through X and Y.

Use the symbol for parallel lines to indicate that $\overleftrightarrow{AB}$ is parallel to $\overleftrightarrow{XY}$.

$\overleftrightarrow{AB} \parallel \overleftrightarrow{XY}$

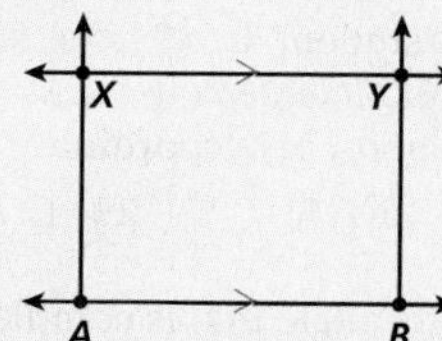

Answers to *Assessment*

1. Check students' work.
2. Check students' work.
3. Check students' work.

When a pair of parallel lines is intersected by a third line, the angles formed have special relationships.

2 Draw a pair of parallel lines and a third line that intersects them. Label the angles 1 through 8, as shown.

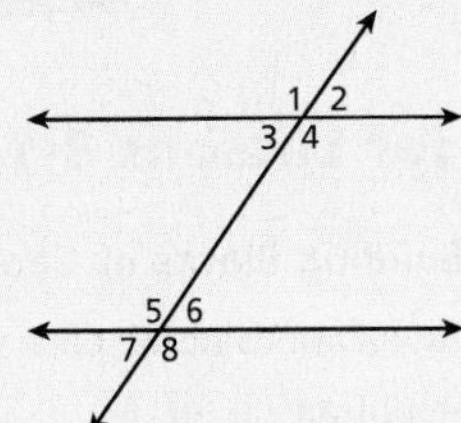

Angles inside the parallel lines are called *interior angles.* The interior angles here are angles 3, 4, 5, and 6.

Angles outside the parallel lines are called *exterior angles.* The exterior angles here are angles 1, 2, 7, and 8.

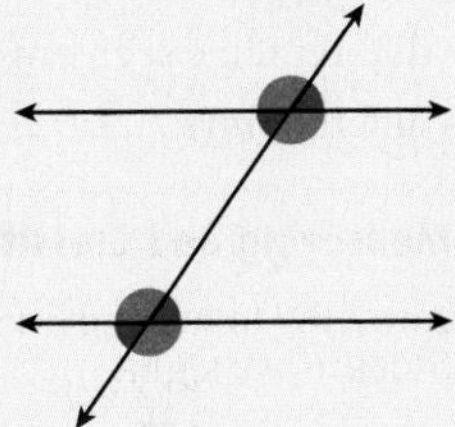

Measure each angle, and write its measurement inside the angle.

Shade angles with the same measure with the same color.

The interior angles with the same measure are called *alternate interior angles.* They are angles 3 and 6 and angles 4 and 5.

The exterior angles with the same measure are called *alternate exterior angles.* They are angles 1 and 8 and angles 2 and 7.

Angles in the same position when the third line intersects the parallel lines are called *corresponding angles.*

Think and Discuss

1. Name three pairs of corresponding angles. **1 and 5, 2 and 6, 3 and 7, or 4 and 8**
2. Tell the relationship between the measure of interior angles and the measure of exterior angles. **The sum of the measures of an interior angle and an adjacent exterior angle at the same intersection is 180°.**

Try This

Follow the steps to construct and label the diagram.

1. Draw a pair of parallel lines, and draw a third line intersecting them where one angle measures 75°.
2. Label each angle on the diagram using the measure you know.

Answers to *Try This*

1.

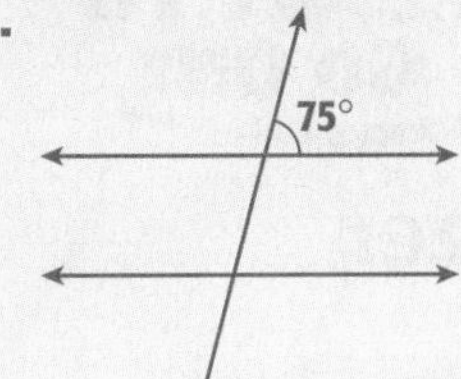

2.

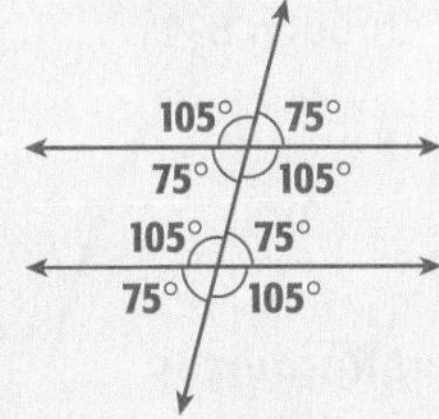

Organizer

Objective: Assess students' mastery of concepts and skills in Lessons 8-1 through 8-4.

Resources

Assessment Resources
Section 8A Quiz

Test & Practice Generator

INTERVENTION

Resources

Ready to Go On? Intervention and Enrichment **Worksheets**

Ready to Go On? **CD-ROM**

Ready to Go On? **Online**

my.hrw.com

Answers

11.

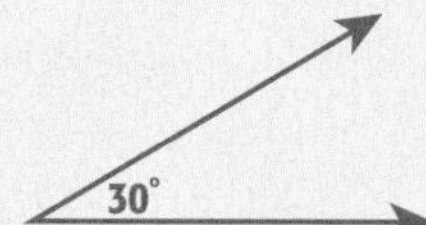

SECTION 8A

Quiz for Lessons 8-1 Through 8-4

8-1 Building Blocks of Geometry

Use the diagram to name each geometric figure. Possible answers:

1. three points L, M, N
2. two lines $\overleftrightarrow{NO}$; $\overleftrightarrow{NM}$
3. a point shared by two lines N
4. a plane MOL
5. two different line segments $\overline{NM}$; $\overline{NO}$
6. two different rays $\overrightarrow{MN}$; $\overrightarrow{NO}$

8-2 Measuring and Classifying Angles

Use a protractor to measure each angle. Then classify each angle as acute, right, obtuse, or straight.

7. 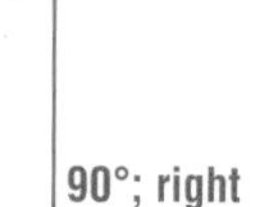

8. 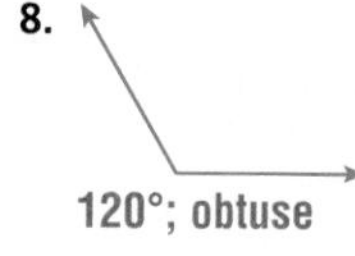

9. 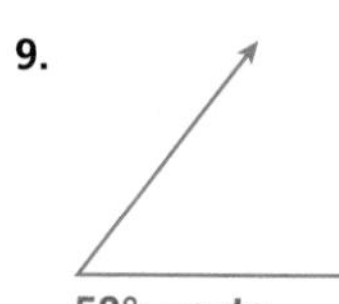

10. 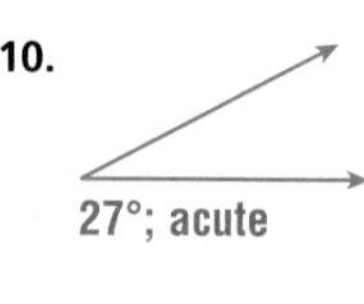

11. The quarterback of a football team throws a long pass, and the angle the path of the ball makes with the ground is 30°. Draw an angle with this measurement.

Ready to Go On?

8-3 Angle Relationships

12. If two angles are supplementary and one angle measures 97°, what is the measure of the other angle? 83°

Find each unknown angle measure.

13. $a = 45°$ 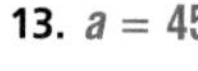 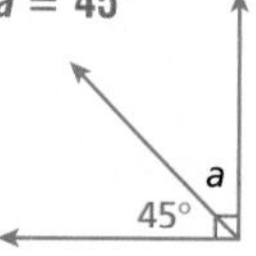

14. 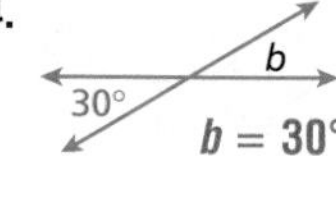

15. 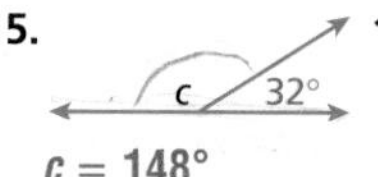

16. 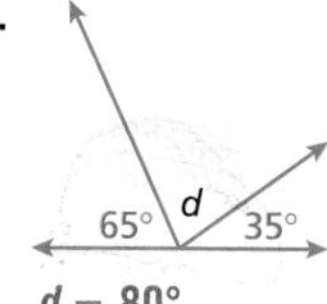

8-4 Classifying Lines

Classify each pair of lines.

17. 
parallel

18. 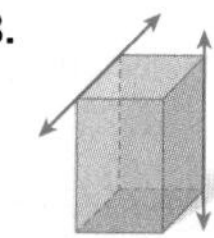
skew

19. perpendicular

20. 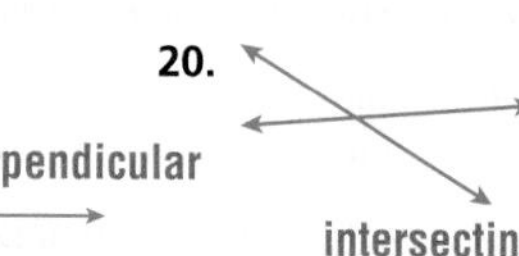
intersecting

READY TO GO ON? Diagnose and Prescribe

NO INTERVENE

YES ENRICH

Ready to Go On? Intervention	*Ready to Go On? Intervention,* Section 8A Worksheets	CD-ROM	Online
Lesson 8-1	8-1 Intervention	Activity 8-1	Diagnose and Prescribe Online
Lesson 8-2	8-2 Intervention	Activity 8-2	
Lesson 8-3	8-3 Intervention	Activity 8-3	
Lesson 8-4	8-4 Intervention	Activity 8-4	

***Ready to Go On? Enrichment,* Section 8A**
Worksheets
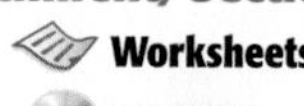
CD-ROM
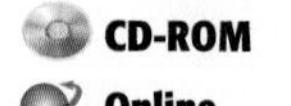
Online

Focus on Problem Solving

Solve

• **Eliminate answer choices**

Sometimes, when a problem has multiple answer choices, you can eliminate some of the choices to help you solve the problem.

For example, a problem reads, "The missing shape is not a red triangle." If one of the answer choices is a red triangle, you can eliminate that answer choice.

Read each problem, and look at the answer choices. Determine whether you can eliminate any of the answer choices before solving the problem. Then solve.

Smileys are letters and symbols that look like faces if you turn them around. When you write an e-mail to someone, you can use smileys to show how you are feeling.

Smileys	
Symbol	**Meaning**
:-(	Frown
:-D	Laugh
:-)	Smile
:-o	Shout
;-)	Wink

For 1–3, use the table.

1 Dora made a pattern with smileys. Which smiley will she probably use next?
:-D :-) :-D :-) :-D :-) :-D :-) :-D ■

Ⓐ :-D Ⓒ :-)
Ⓑ :-) Ⓓ :-D

2 Troy made a pattern with smileys. Identify a pattern. Which smiley is missing?
:-(;-) :-o :-(;-) :-o :-(■ :-o

Ⓕ :-(Ⓗ ;-)
Ⓖ :-o Ⓙ ;-)

3 To end an e-mail, Mya typed four smileys in a row. The shout is first. The wink is between the frown and the smile. The smile is not last. In which order did Mya type the smileys?

Ⓐ :-o :-(;-) :-) Ⓒ :-) ;-) :-o :-(
Ⓑ :-o :-) ;-) :-(Ⓓ :-o ;-) :-(:-)

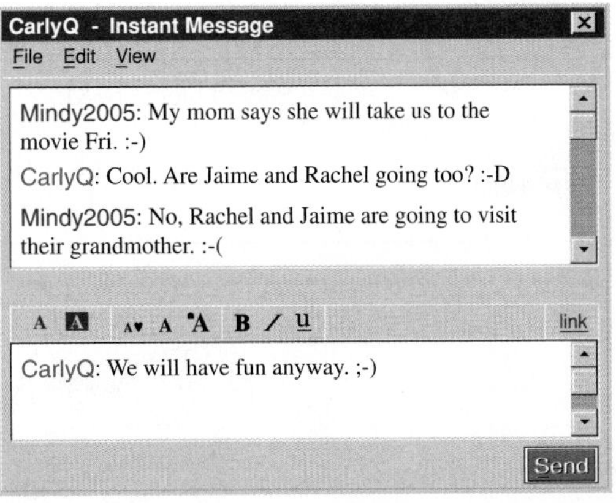

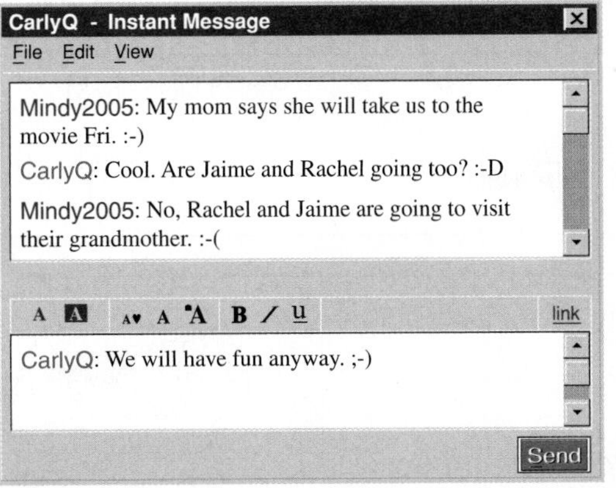

Answers

1. C
2. J
3. B

Focus on Problem Solving

Organizer

Objective: Focus on solving a problem by eliminating answer choices.

Online Edition

Resources

Chapter 8 Resource Book
Reading Strategies

Problem Solving Process

This page focuses on the third step of the problem-solving process: **Solve.**

Discuss

Have students discuss which answers can be eliminated immediately and why. Then identify the pattern when possible to help solve the problem.

1. Eliminate **B** and **D** because green always precedes red, and **B** and **D** are blue.
smileys: laugh, smile, laugh, smile, laugh . . .
colors: red, blue, green, red, blue, green, red . . .
2. Eliminate **F** and **H** because there are never two of the same color in a row.
smileys: frown, wink, shout, frown, wink, shout, frown . . .
colors: red, blue, red, blue, red . . .
3. Eliminate **A** and **D** because the smile is not last, and eliminate **C** because the shout is first.

SECTION
8A Polygons

One-Minute Section Planner

Lesson	Materials	MiC and Lab Resources
8-5 Hands-On Lab Classify Triangles • Use a ruler to classify triangles by the length of their sides. **Lesson 8-5** Triangles • Classify triangles and solve problems involving angle and side measures of triangles. **8-5 Technology Lab** Angles in Triangles • Use geometry software to explore the angles in a triangle. ☑ CRCT ☑ SAT-10 ☑ ITBS ☑ CTBS ☑ NAEP	Protractors (MK), straightedges (MK), geoboards (MK), metric rulers (MK), dot paper, geometry software	***Hands-On Lab Activities*** 8-5 ***Technology Lab Activities*** 8-5
Lesson 8-6 Quadrilaterals • Identify, classify, and compare quadrilaterals. ☐ CRCT ☑ SAT-10 ☑ ITBS ☑ CTBS ☑ NAEP	Cut-out quadrilaterals, geoboards (MK), rulers (MK), graph paper, scissors	**MiC:** ***Figuring All the Angles*** p. 35
Lesson 8-7 Polygons • Identify regular and not regular polygons, and find the angle measures of regular polygons. ☑ CRCT ☑ SAT-10 ☑ ITBS ☑ CTBS ☑ NAEP		**MiC:** ***Figuring All the Angles*** p. 35 **MiC:** ***Reallotment*** pp. 1–3 ***Hands-On Lab Activities*** 8-7
Lesson 8-8 Geometric Patterns • Recognize, describe, and extend geometric patterns.. ☐ CRCT ☐ SAT-10 ☑ ITBS ☑ CTBS ☑ NAEP	Pattern blocks (MK)	***Hands-On Lab Activities*** 8-8

MK = *Manipulatives Kit*

Mathematics in Context

The units ***Figuring All the Angles*** and ***Reallotment*** from the *Mathematics in Context* © 2006 series can be used with Section 8B. See Section Planner above for suggestions for integrating *MiC* with *Holt Mathematics*.

Section Overview

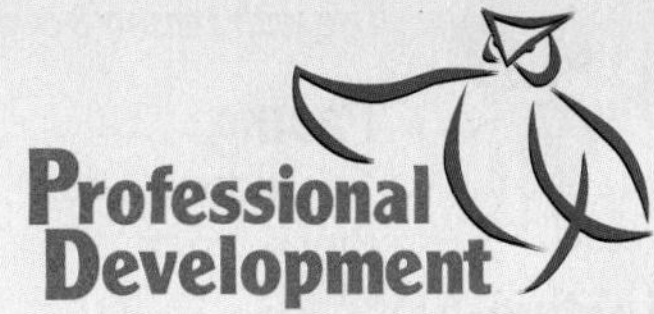

Triangles — *Lesson 8-5*

Why? Triangles are often used in construction to provide structural support.

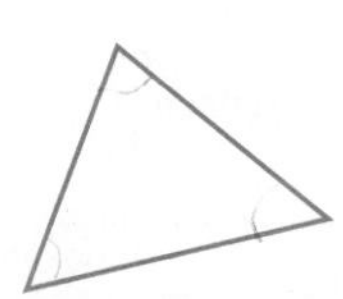
Acute triangle

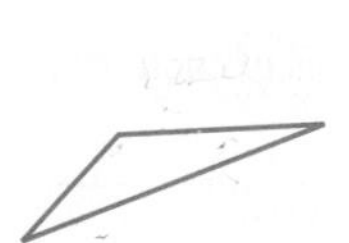
Obtuse triangle

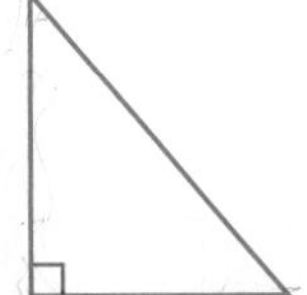
Right triangle

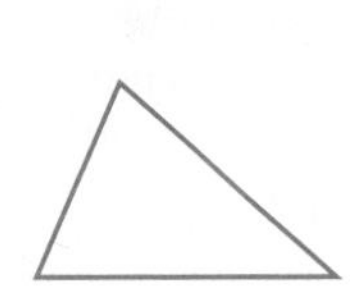
Scalene triangle

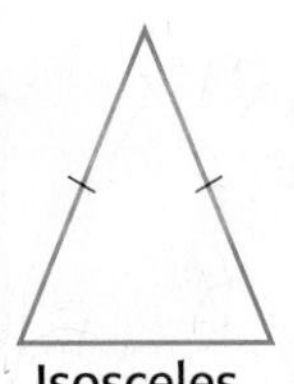
Isosceles triangle

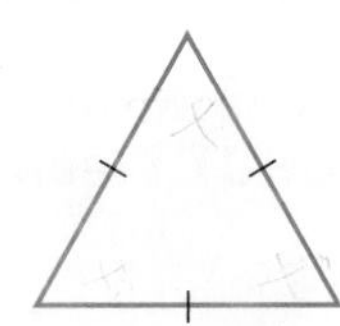
Equilateral triangle

> The sum of the measures of the angles in any triangle is 180°.

Quadrilaterals and Polygons — *Lessons 8-6, 8-7*

Polygons are used in many architectural designs.

Quadrilaterals

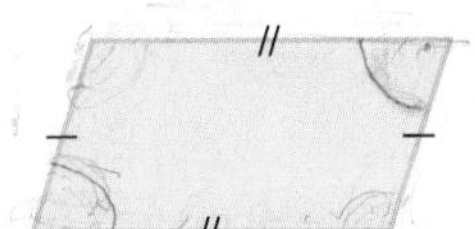
Parallelogram
Opposite sides are parallel and congruent. Opposite angles are congruent.

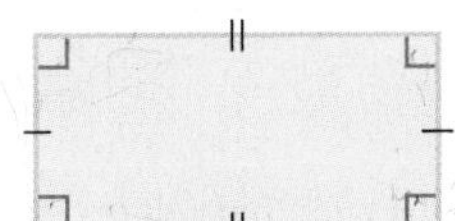
Rectangle
Parallelogram with four right angles

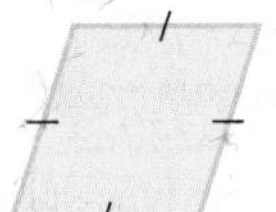
Rhombus
Parallelogram with four congruent sides

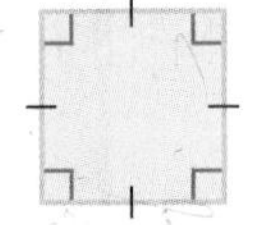
Square
Rectangle with four congruent sides

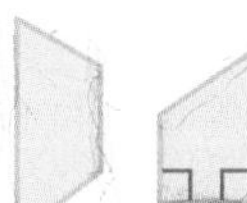
Trapezoid
Quadrilateral with exactly two parallel sides; may have two right angles.

Polygons

Name	Triangle	Quadrilateral	Pentagon	Hexagon	Octagon
Sides and Angles	3	4	5	6	8
Regular					
Not Regular					

Geometric Patterns — *Lessons 8-8*

Many designs and works of art involve geometric patterns.

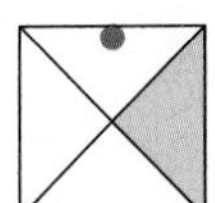
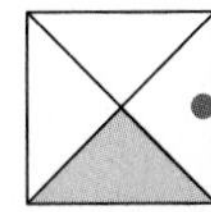
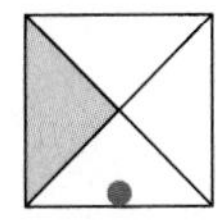
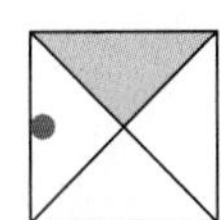

Perfect squares, such as 2^2, 3^2, and 4^2 are also called square numbers because they can be modeled as a square array.

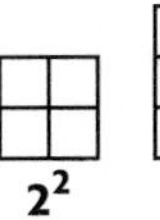
2^2

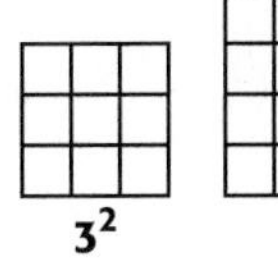
3^2

4^2

Organizer

Use with Lesson 8-5

Pacing:
Traditional $\frac{1}{2}$ day
Block $\frac{1}{4}$ day

Objective: Use a ruler to classify triangles by the length of their sides.

Materials: Metric ruler

Online Edition

Countdown to CRCT Week 18

Resources

Hands-On Lab Activities
Lab 8-5 Recording Sheet

Teach

Discuss

Have students describe how metric measurements should be made and recorded.

Have the class decide whether to record measurements in millimeters or centimeters.

Close

Key Concept

Using the lengths of a triangle's sides is one way of classifying triangles.

Assessment

1. Draw and label three types of triangles defined by the lengths of their sides. Check students' work.

Use with Lesson 8-5

Classify Triangles

Georgia Performance Standards
M6M2.b, M6P2.a, M6P2.b, M6P2.d

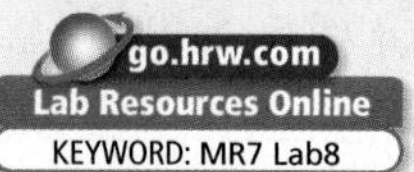

REMEMBER
- A triangle is a polygon with three sides and three angles.

A triangle can be classified by its sides as either *equilateral, isosceles,* or *scalene.*

Activity

Use a centimeter ruler to measure the sides of each triangle. Sketch each triangle and label the length of each side.

Type of Triangle	Examples	Nonexamples
Equilateral		
Isosceles		
Scalene		

Think and Discuss

1. For each type of triangle, find a rule that relates the side lengths to the type of triangle.

Try This

Measure each triangle and classify it as equilateral, isosceles, or scalene. Justify your answer.

1. 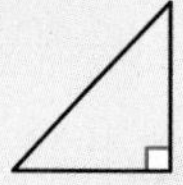

2. 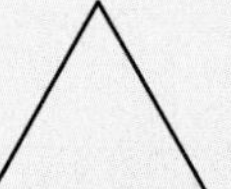

3. 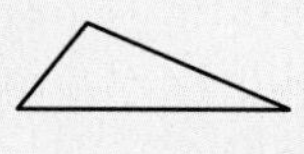

4. 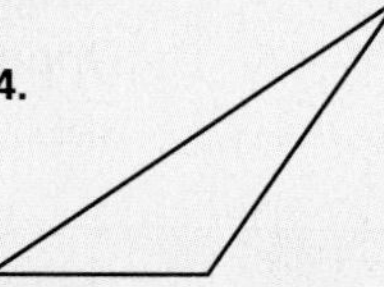

Possible answers to *Think and Discuss*

1. Equilateral triangles: In each of these triangles, all sides are equal in length.
   Isosceles triangles: In each of these triangles, two sides are equal in length.
   Scalene triangles: In each of these triangles, none of the sides are equal in length.

Answers to *Try This*

1. Isosceles; two sides are equal.
2. Equilateral; all sides are equal.
3. Scalene; no sides are equal.
4. Scalene; no sides are equal.

Georgia Performance Standards

M6M2.b Select and use units of appropriate size and type to measure length, perimeter, area and volume.

M6P2.a Recognize reasoning and proof as fundamental aspects of mathematics.

M6P2.b Make and investigate mathematical conjectures.

M6P2.d Select and use various types of reasoning and methods of proof.

8-5 Triangles

Learn to classify triangles and solve problems involving angle and side measures of triangles.

Vocabulary

acute triangle
obtuse triangle
right triangle
scalene triangle
isosceles triangle
equilateral triangle

Georgia Performance Standards

M6A3 Evaluate algebraic expressions, including those with exponents, and solve simple one-step equations using each of the four basic operations. Also, M6P4.c, M6P5.a.

A triangle is a closed figure with three line segments and three angles. Triangles can be classified by the measures of their angles. An **acute triangle** has only acute angles. An **obtuse triangle** has one obtuse angle. A **right triangle** has one right angle.

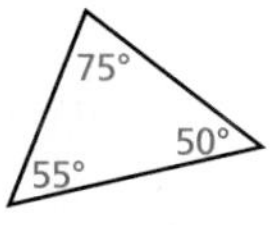

Acute triangle

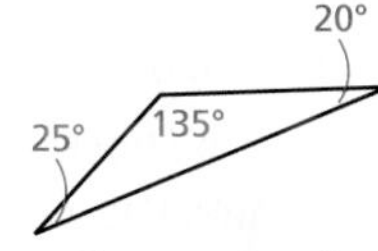

Obtuse triangle

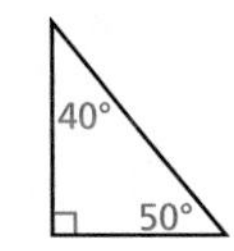

Right triangle

To decide whether a triangle is acute, obtuse, or right, you need to know the measures of its angles.

The sum of the measures of the angles in any triangle is 180°. You can see this if you tear the corners from a triangle and arrange them around a point on a line.

By knowing the sum of the measures of the angles in a triangle, you can find unknown angle measures.

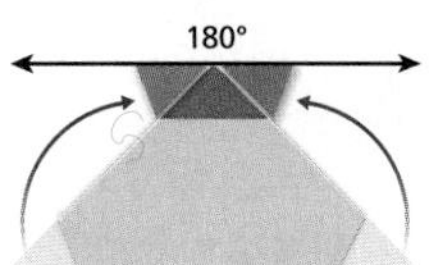

EXAMPLE 1 *Sports Application*

Boat sails are often shaped like triangles. The measure of $\angle A$ is 70°, and the measure of $\angle B$ is 45°. Classify the triangle.

To classify the triangle, find the measure of $\angle C$ on the sail.

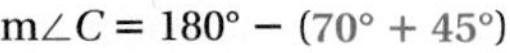

$m\angle C = 180° - (70° + 45°)$
$m\angle C = 180° - 115°$ — *Subtract the sum of the known angle measures from 180°.*
$m\angle C = 65°$

So the measure of $\angle C$ is 65°. Because $\triangle ABC$ has only acute angles, the boat sail is an acute triangle.

You can use what you know about vertical, adjacent, complementary, and supplementary angles to find the missing measures of angles.

Organizer 8-5

Pacing: Traditional 1 day
Block $\frac{1}{2}$ day

Objective: Students classify triangles and solve problems involving angle and side measures of triangles.

Online Edition
Tutorial Videos, Interactivities

Countdown to CRCT Week 18

Power Presentations with PowerPoint®

Warm Up

1. What are two angles whose sum is 90°? complementary angles
2. What are two angles whose sum is 180°? supplementary angles
3. A part of a line between two points is called a ________. segment
4. Two lines that intersect at 90° are ________. perpendicular

Problem of the Day

Find the total number of shaded triangles in each figure. 3, 6, 10

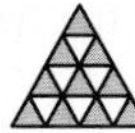

Also available on transparency

Math Humor

The scalene triangle confused everyone on the baseball field. When it stood on a different base, it had a different height.

1 Introduce

Alternate Opener

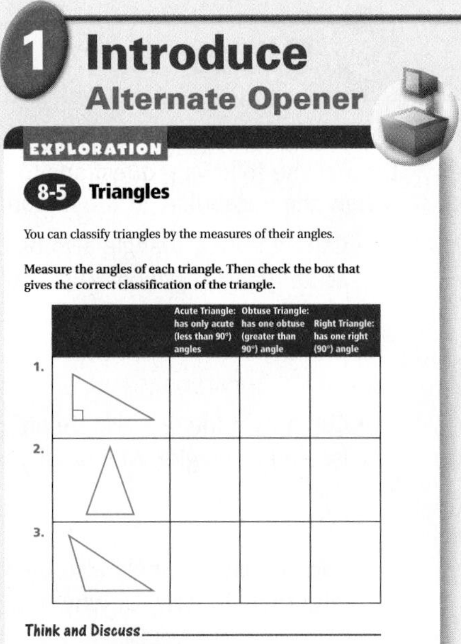

EXPLORATION

8-5 Triangles

You can classify triangles by the measures of their angles.

Measure the angles of each triangle. Then check the box that gives the correct classification of the triangle.

	Acute Triangle: has only acute (less than 90°) angles	Obtuse Triangle: has one obtuse (greater than 90°) angle	Right Triangle: has one right (90°) angle
1.			
2.			
3.			

Think and Discuss

4. **Find** the sum of the angle measures in each triangle.
5. **Make** a generalization about the sum of the angle measures in a triangle.

Motivate

Have each student use a straightedge to draw a triangle. Have students measure the angles in their triangles and count the number of right, acute, and obtuse angles. Have them measure the sides of their triangles, and note how many sides (if any) are congruent. Students can refer back to these drawings as you teach the different types of triangles. Straightedges, protractors, and rulers are provided in the Manipulatives Kit.

Explorations and answers are provided in *Alternate Openers: Explorations Transparencies.*

Georgia Performance Standards

M6A3 Students will evaluate algebraic expressions, including those with exponents, and solve simple one-step equations using each of the four basic operations.

M6P4.c Recognize and apply mathematics in contexts outside of mathematics.

M6P5.a Create and use representations to organize, record, and communicate mathematical ideas.

Power Presentations with PowerPoint®

Additional Examples

Example 1

Sara designed this triangular trophy. The measure of $\angle E$ is 38°, and the measure of $\angle F$ is 52°. Classify the triangle.

right triangle

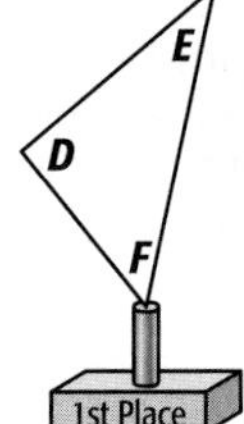

Example 2

Use the diagram to find the measure of each indicated angle.

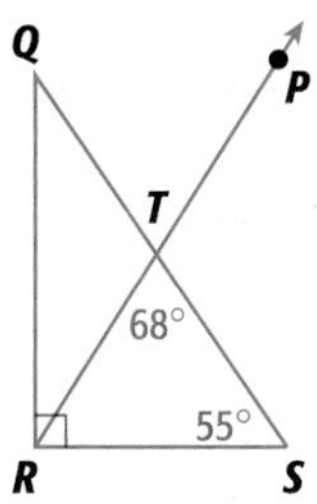

A. $\angle QTR$ 112°

B. $\angle QRT$ 33°

Example 3

Classify the triangle. The sum of the lengths of the sides is 19.5 in.

equilateral

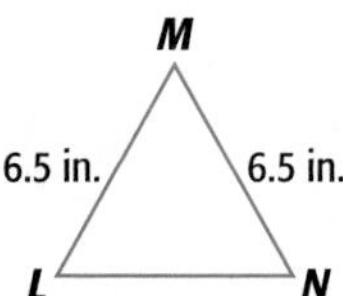

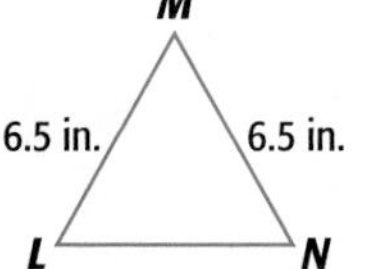

Also available on transparency

EXAMPLE 2 **Using Properties of Angles to Label Triangles**

Use the diagram to find the measure of each indicated angle.

Remember!

Vertical angles are congruent. The sum of the measures of complementary angles is 90°. The sum of the measures of supplementary angles is 180°.

A $\angle BDE$

$\angle BDE$ and $\angle ADC$ are vertical angles, so $m\angle BDE = m\angle ADC$.

$m\angle ADC = 180° - (30° + 35°)$

$= 180° - 65°$

$= 115°$

$m\angle BDE = 115°$

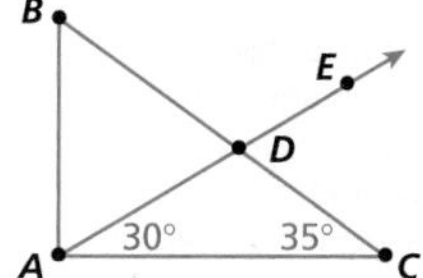

B $\angle ADB$

The sum of $m\angle BDE$ and $m\angle ADB$ is 180°.

$m\angle ADB = 180° - 115°$

$= 65°$

$m\angle ADB = 65°$

Triangles can be classified by the lengths of their sides. A **scalene triangle** has no congruent sides. An **isosceles triangle** has at least two congruent sides. An **equilateral triangle** has three congruent sides. You can use tick marks to show congruent sides.

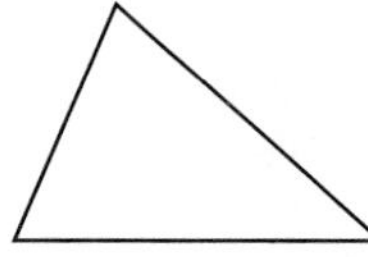

Scalene triangle

Isosceles triangle

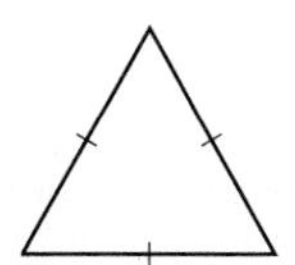

Equilateral triangle

EXAMPLE 3 **Classifying Triangles by Lengths of Sides**

Classify the triangle. The perimeter of the triangle is 7.8 cm.

$a + (3.8 + 2) = 7.8$

$a + 5.8 = 7.8$

$a + 5.8 - 5.8 = 7.8 - 5.8$

$a = 2$

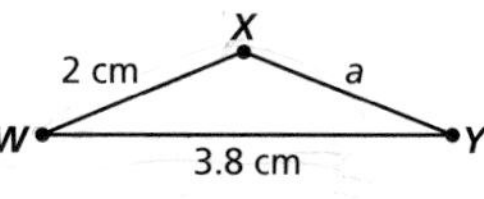

Side a is 2 centimeters long. Because $\triangle WXY$ has at least two sides, but not three, that are the same length, it is an isosceles triangle.

Answers to Think and Discuss

1. Possible answer: The sum of the angle measures in a triangle is 180°. Two obtuse angles would measure greater than 180°.
2. No; a right triangle has one 90° angle. In an acute triangle, all three angles measure less than 90°.

Think and Discuss GPS M6P2.c, M6P3.b

1. Explain why a triangle cannot have two obtuse angles.

2. Tell whether a right triangle can also be an acute triangle. Explain.

2 Teach

Guided Instruction

In this lesson, students learn to classify triangles and solve problems involving angle and side measures of triangles. First teach students to use angles to classify triangles and to use the sum of the measures of the angles in a triangle to find the measure of an unknown angle. Then teach them to classify triangles by the lengths of the sides. Have students classify the acute, obtuse, and right triangles as scalene, isosceles, or equilateral, and vice versa.

Teaching Tip **Inclusion** Remind students that a triangle needs only one obtuse angle to be an obtuse triangle, but three acute angles to be an acute triangle.

Reaching All Learners

Through Modeling

Have students use geoboards (Manipulatives Kit) to model acute, right, obtuse, scalene, isosceles, and equilateral triangles. Have them draw their triangles on dot paper and classify each according to measures of angles and lengths of sides.

3 Close

Summarize

Discuss the following questions to review the vocabulary in the lesson:

- Can an obtuse triangle also be an acute triangle? Why or why not? No; obtuse triangles have two acute angles, but acute triangles must have three acute angles.
- Can a right triangle also be an isosceles triangle? Why or why not? Yes; if the right triangle has two sides that are equal lengths
- Can an acute triangle also be a scalene triangle? Why or why not? Yes; if the sides are all different lengths

8-5 Exercises

Georgia Performance Standards
M6P1.c, M6P2.a, M6P2.b

go.hrw.com
Homework Help Online
KEYWORD: MR7 8-5
Parent Resources Online
KEYWORD: MR7 Parent

GUIDED PRACTICE

See Example 1

1. Three stars form a triangular constellation. Two of the angles measure 20° and 50°. Classify the triangle. **obtuse triangle**

See Example 2

Use the diagram to find the measure of each indicated angle.

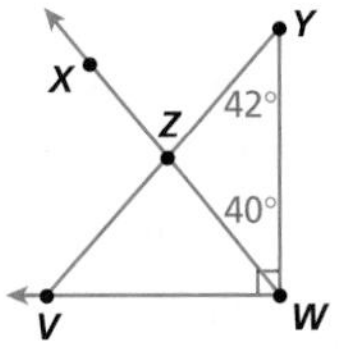

2. ∠*XZV* **98°**

3. ∠*VZW* **82°**

See Example 3

Classify each triangle using the given information.

4. The perimeter of the triangle is 24 cm. **equilateral**

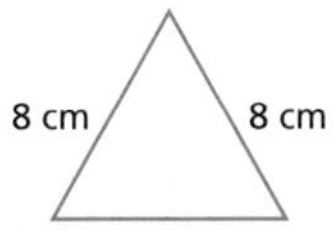

5. The perimeter of the triangle is 30 ft. **isosceles**

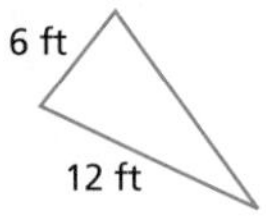

INDEPENDENT PRACTICE

See Example 1

6. Interstate highways connecting towns *R*, *S*, and *T* form a triangle. Two of the angles measure 40° and 42°. Classify the triangle. **obtuse triangle**

See Example 2

Use the diagram to find the measure of each indicated angle.

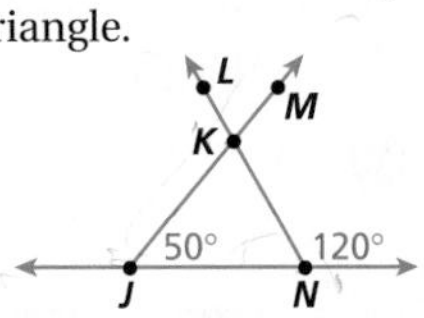

7. ∠*KNJ* **60°**

8. ∠*LKM* **70°**

See Example 3

Classify each triangle using the given information.

9. The perimeter of the triangle is 10.5 in. **scalene**

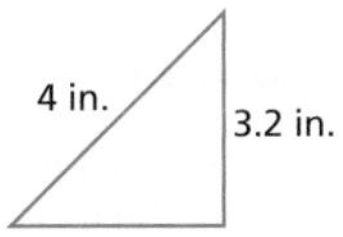

10. The perimeter of the triangle is 231 km. **scalene**

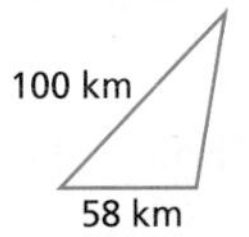

PRACTICE AND PROBLEM SOLVING

CRCT GPS
Extra Practice p. 729

If the angles can form a triangle, classify it as acute, obtuse, or right.

11. 45°, 90°, 45° **yes, right**
12. 51°, 88°, 41° **yes, acute**
13. 71°, 40°, 59° **no**
14. 55°, 102°, 33° **no**
15. 37°, 40°, 103° **yes, obtuse**
16. 90°, 30°, 50° **no**

17. Find a triangle in your classroom or at home. Describe the triangle and classify it. Explain your classification. **Check students' work.**

RETEACH 8-5

LESSON 8-5 **Reteach**
Triangles

You can classify triangles by the measures of their angles.

An acute triangle has only acute angles.
A right triangle has one right angle.
An obtuse triangle has one obtuse angle.

To classify the triangle below by its angles, you first need to find the measure of all the angles.

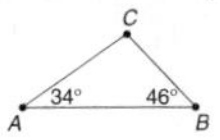

The sum of the angles of a triangle is 180°.

To find the unknown angle, first find the sum of the two known angles.

34 + 46 = 80

Then subtract the sum from 180.

180 − 80 = 100

The difference is the measure of the third angle.

The measures of the angles are 34°, 46°, and 100°. So the triangle is obtuse.

Find each unknown angle. Then classify each triangle.

1.
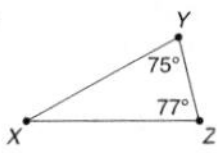

28°, acute

2.
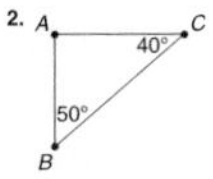

90°, right

3.
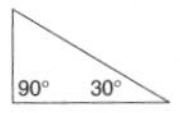

60°, right

4.
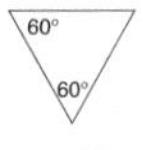

60°, acute

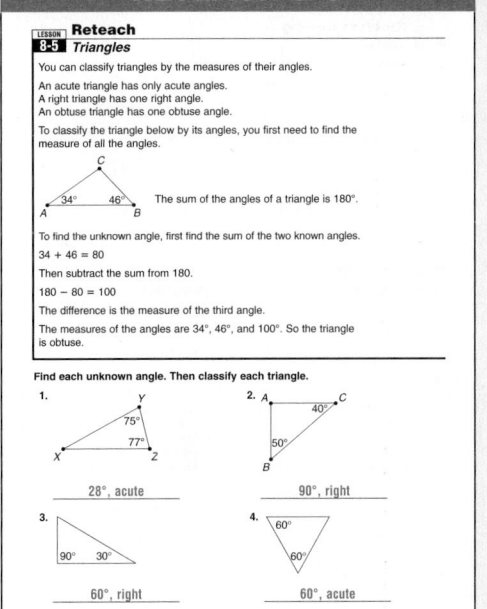

PRACTICE 8-5

LESSON 8-5 **Practice B**
Triangles

Use the diagram to find the measure of each indicated angle.

1. ∠*CBD* 90°
2. ∠*DAC* 45°
3. ∠*ABC* 90°
4. ∠*EBA* 90°
5. ∠*ACB* 45°

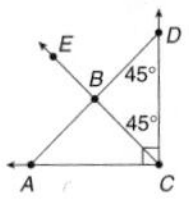

Classify each triangle using the given information.

6. The perimeter of the triangle is 30 in.

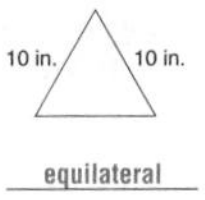

equilateral

7. The perimeter of the triangle is 15 cm.

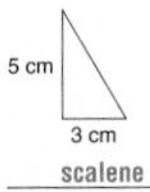

scalene

8. The perimeter of the triangle is 22 ft.

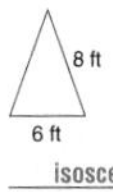

isosceles

9. The angles of a triangular sail measure 90°, 30°, and 60°. Its sides measure approximately 2 feet, 3.5 feet, and 4 feet. Classify the triangular shape of the sail in two different ways.

It is a right triangle; It is a scalene triangle.

10. Two angles in one triangle are congruent to two angles in another triangle. What can you conclude about the third angle in both triangles?

They are congruent.

8-5 Exercises

Assignment Guide

If you finished Example 1 assign:
Average 1, 11–16, 29–39
Advanced 6, 11–16, 29–39

If you finished Example 2 assign:
Average 1–3, 11–16, 29–39
Advanced 6–8, 11–16, 29–39

If you finished Example 3 assign:
Average 1–13, 18–39
Advanced 6–39

Homework Quick Check

Quickly check key concepts.
Exercises: 6, 8, 12, 18

Math Background

Although isosceles and equilateral triangles are defined in terms of side lengths, it turns out that their angles have special properties as well. In an isosceles triangle, the angles opposite the congruent sides are congruent. In an equilateral triangle, all three angles are congruent and measure 60°.

Students can explore each of these propositions by folding paper or by using protractors. In a high school Geometry course, where the first result is known as the Isosceles Triangle Theorem, both propositions are easily proven.

Georgia Performance Standards

M6P1.c Apply and adapt a variety of appropriate strategies to solve problems.

M6P2.a Recognize reasoning and proof as fundamental aspects of mathematics.

M6P2.b Make and investigate mathematical conjectures.

ONGOING ASSESSMENT and INTERVENTION

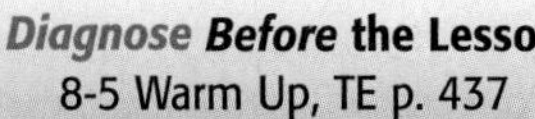

***Diagnose Before* the Lesson**
8-5 Warm Up, TE p. 437

***Monitor During* the Lesson**
8-5 Know-It Notebook
8-5 Questioning Strategies

***Assess After* the Lesson**
8-5 Lesson Quiz, TE p. 440

Answers

Possible answers 21–24:

21. (triangle with sides 5, 7, 6)

22.

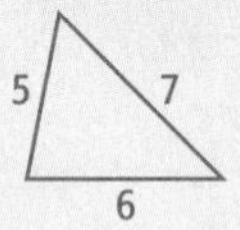

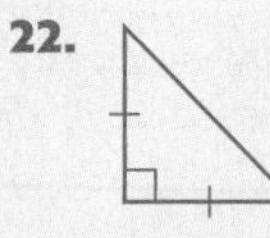

23.

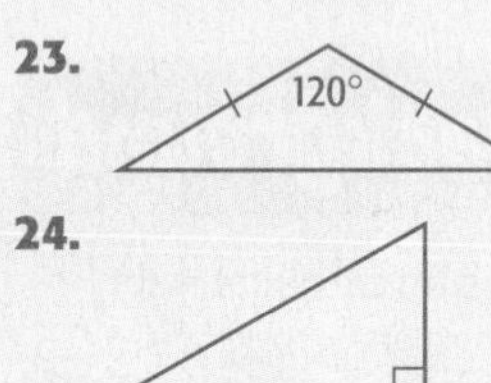

24. (right triangle)

27, 36–39. See p. A9.

TEST PREP DOCTOR In Exercise 29, students who remember that right angles have a measure of 90° and that the sum of the angles in a triangle is 180° should be able to determine that the sum of the other angles in the triangle is 90°.

Journal

Have students draw examples of the six types of triangles presented in the lesson. For each triangle, have students explain why it is that type of triangle.

Power Presentations with PowerPoint®

8-5 Lesson Quiz

If the angles can form a triangle, classify the triangle as acute, obtuse, or right.

1. 37°, 53°, 90° right
2. 65°, 110°, 25° not a triangle
3. 61°, 78°, 41° acute
4. 115°, 25°, 40° obtuse

The lengths of three sides of a triangle are given. Classify the triangle.

5. 12, 16, 25 scalene
6. 10, 10, 15 isosceles

Also available on transparency

In 2002, the U.S. Postal Service released the "Greetings From America" stamp series. Each of the 50 states was represented by a special stamp.

The lengths of two sides are given for $\triangle ABC$. Use the sum of the lengths of the three sides to calculate the length of the third side and classify each triangle.

18. $AB = 7$ cm; $BC = 7$ cm; sum = 15.9 cm **1.9 cm, isosceles**

19. $AB = 1\frac{1}{6}$ ft; $BC = 1\frac{1}{6}$ ft; sum = $3\frac{1}{2}$ ft **$1\frac{1}{6}$ ft, equilateral**

20. Social Studies Some triangular stamps are made by dividing a rectangle into two parts. Classify the triangle that is made by cutting on a line that connects one corner of a rectangle to the opposite corner. **right triangle**

Draw an example of each triangle described.

21. a scalene acute triangle
22. an isosceles right triangle
23. an isosceles obtuse triangle
24. a scalene right triangle

25. Critical Thinking Use a centimeter ruler to measure each side of triangle A. Add the lengths of any two sides and compare the sum to the length of the third side. Add a different pair of lengths and compare the sum to the third side. Do the same for triangles B and C. How does the sum of the lengths of any two sides of a triangle compare to the length of the third side?

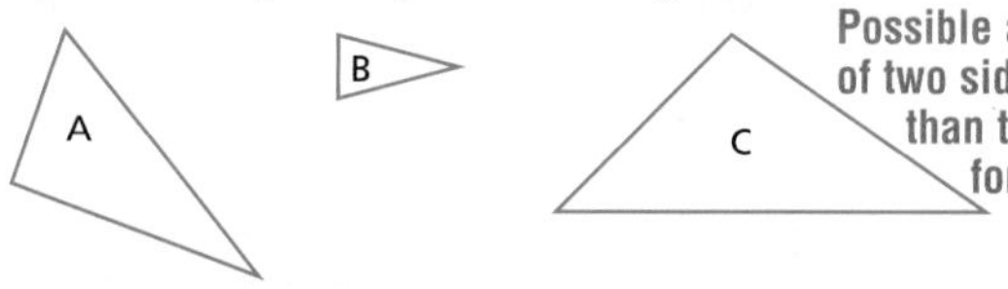

Possible answer: The sum of two sides must be greater than the third side to form a triangle.

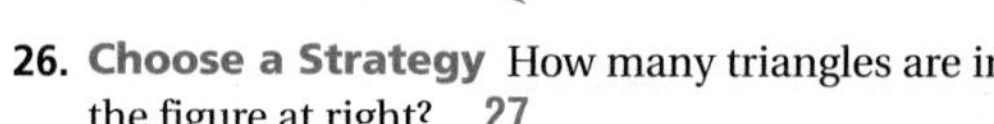

26. Choose a Strategy How many triangles are in the figure at right? **27**

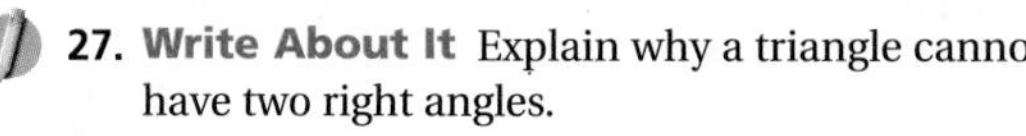

27. Write About It Explain why a triangle cannot have two right angles.

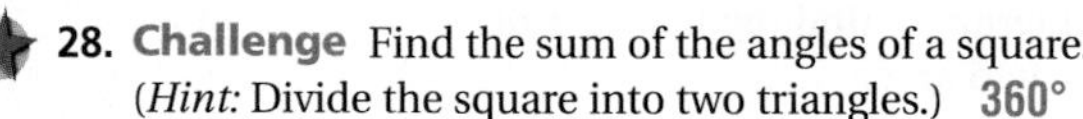

28. Challenge Find the sum of the angles of a square. (*Hint:* Divide the square into two triangles.) **360°**

CRCT PREP • GPS SUPPORT • SPIRAL REVIEW

29. Multiple Choice A triangle has one right angle. What could the measures of the other two angles be?

Ⓐ 20° and 70° Ⓑ 30° and 15° Ⓒ 60° and 120° Ⓓ 90° and 100°

30. Multiple Choice The lengths of two sides of a triangle are 54 meters and 45 meters. The sum of the three sides is 126 meters. Find the missing third side.

Ⓕ 27 m Ⓖ 72 m Ⓗ 81 m Ⓙ 99 m

Write each percent as a decimal. (Lesson 7-7)

31. 12% **0.12** **32.** 55% **0.55** **33.** 3% **0.03** **34.** 47% **0.47** **35.** 76% **0.76**

Draw each geometric figure. (Lesson 8-1)

36. $\overleftrightarrow{CD}$ **37.** $\overrightarrow{GM}$ **38.** $\overline{XY}$ **39.** point A

CHALLENGE 8-5

LESSON 8-5 Challenge
Square Legs

About 2,400 years ago a Greek philosopher and mathematician named Pythagoras proved a very important rule for triangles. Today people all over the world study and use this rule named in his honor—the Pythagorean Theorem. It states the relationship between the side lengths of a right triangle.

Pythagoras

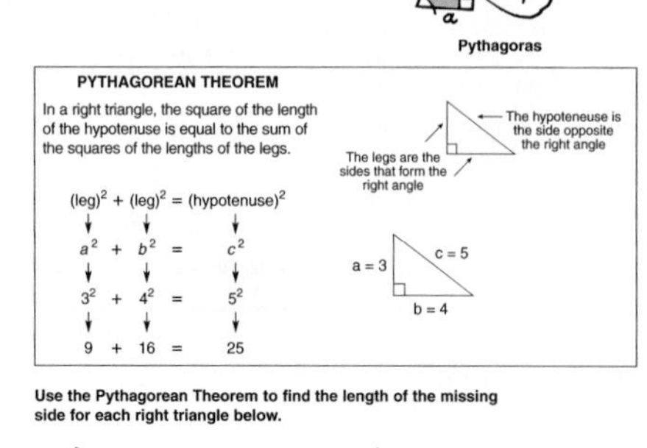

PYTHAGOREAN THEOREM
In a right triangle, the square of the length of the hypotenuse is equal to the sum of the squares of the lengths of the legs.
The hypoteneuse is the side opposite the right angle
The legs are the sides that form the right angle
(leg)² + (leg)² = (hypotenuse)²
a² + b² = c²
3² + 4² = 5²
9 + 16 = 25
a = 3
c = 5
b = 4

Use the Pythagorean Theorem to find the length of the missing side for each right triangle below.

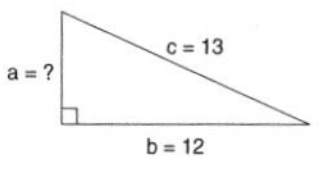

a = ?, c = 13, b = 12 — $a = 5$

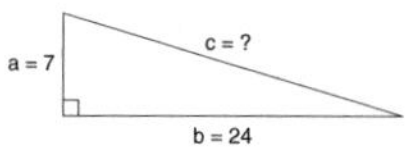

a = 7, c = ?, b = 24 — $c = 25$

PROBLEM SOLVING 8-5

LESSON 8-5 Problem Solving
Triangles

Use the triangle diagram to answer each question.

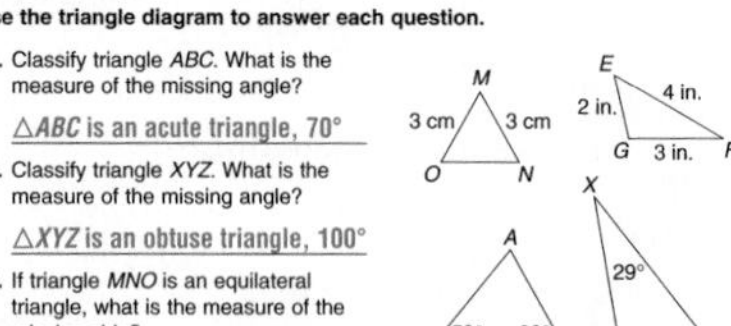

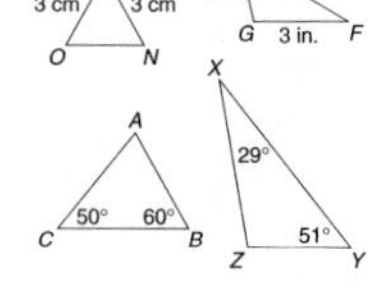

1. Classify triangle *ABC*. What is the measure of the missing angle?
   $\triangle ABC$ is an acute triangle, 70°
2. Classify triangle *XYZ*. What is the measure of the missing angle?
   $\triangle XYZ$ is an obtuse triangle, 100°
3. If triangle *MNO* is an equilateral triangle, what is the measure of the missing side?
   $\overline{ON} = 3$ cm

Circle the letter of the correct answer.

4. What is the complement of $\angle XYZ$?
   Ⓐ 39°
   B 51°
   C 129°
   D 309°
5. Classify triangle *EFG*.
   Ⓕ scalene triangle
   G isosceles triangle
   H equilateral triangle
   J right triangle
6. Which of the following statements is always true?
   A A right triangle is a scalene triangle.
   Ⓑ An equilateral triangle is an isosceles triangle.
   C An isosceles triangle is an obtuse triangle.
   D A right triangle is an acute triangle.
7. Which of the following is not true of all right triangles?
   F The sum of the measures of the angles is 180°.
   Ⓖ Two of its angles are supplementary angles.
   H At least two of its angles are acute.
   J The side with the greatest length is opposite the right angle.

Angles in Triangles

Use with Lesson 8-5

Georgia Performance Standards
M6P1.c, M6P2.a, M6P2.b

go.hrw.com
Lab Resources Online
KEYWORD: MR7 Lab8

The sum of the angle measures is the same for any triangle. You can use geometry software to find this sum and to check that the sum is the same for many different triangles.

Activity

1. Use the geometry software to make triangle *ABC*. Then use the angle measure tool to measure $\angle B$.

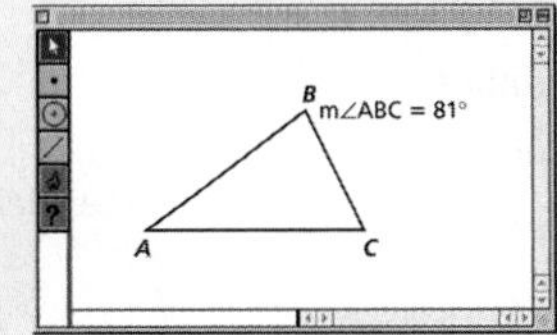

2. Use the angle measure tool to measure $\angle C$ and $\angle A$. Then use the calculator tool to add the measures of the three angles. Notice that the sum is 180°.

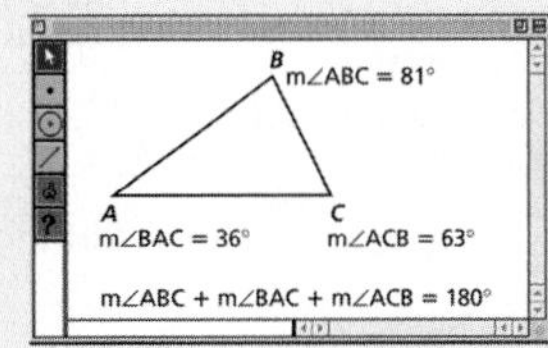

3. Select vertex *A* and drag it around to change the shape of triangle *ABC*. Watch the angle sum. Change the shape of the triangle again and then again. Be sure to make acute and obtuse triangles.

   Notice that the sum of the angle measures is always 180°, regardless of the triangle's shape.

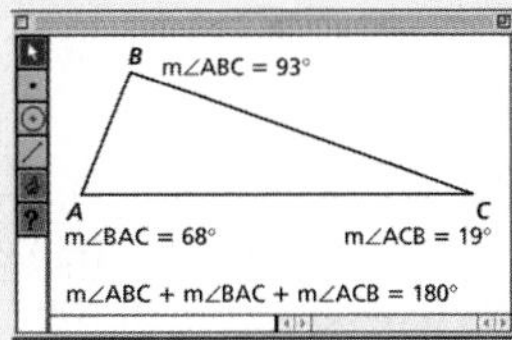

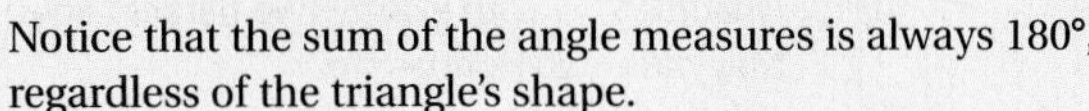

Think and Discuss

1. Can you use geometry software to draw a triangle with two obtuse angles? Explain. **No, the sum of the angles cannot be greater than 180°.**

Try This

Solve. Then use geometry software to check each answer.

1. In triangle *ABC*, $m\angle B = 49.15°$ and $m\angle A = 113.75°$. Find $m\angle C$. $m\angle C = 17.1°$
2. Use geometry software to construct an acute triangle *XYZ*. Give the measures of its angles, and check that their sum is 180°. **Check students' work.**

Organizer

Use with Lesson 8-5

Pacing:
Traditional $\frac{1}{2}$ day
Block $\frac{1}{4}$ day

Objective: Use geometry software to explore the angles in a triangle.

Materials: Geometry software

Online Edition
TechKeys

Countdown to CRCT Week 18

Resources

Technology Lab Activities
Lab 8-5 Recording Sheet

Teach

Discuss

Have students become familiar with the basic tools of the geometry software. The drawing tools and the measuring tools are all that are needed for this lab. Specific instructions may vary, depending on the software used. The instructions given are for Geometer's Sketch Pad.

Close

Key Concept

Geometry software is superior to pencil and paper in demonstrating the unchanging sum of the angles of any triangle.

Assessment

1. If two angles of a triangle measure 26° and 105°, what is the measure of the third angle? 49°

Georgia Performance Standards

M6P1.c Apply and adapt a variety of appropriate strategies to solve problems.

M6P2.a Recognize reasoning and proof as fundamental aspects of mathematics.

M6P2.b Make and investigate mathematical conjectures.

8-6 Organizer

Pacing: Traditional 1 day
Block $\frac{1}{2}$ day

Objective: Students identify, classify, and compare quadrilaterals.

Online Edition
Tutorial Videos, Interactivities

Countdown to CRCT Week 18

Power Presentations with PowerPoint®

Warm Up

The lengths of three sides of a triangle are given. Classify the triangle.

1. 12, 12, 12 equilateral
2. 18, 10, 14 scalene
3. 15, 15, 26 isosceles

Problem of the Day

How many different rectangles are in the figure?

1		2
5	4	3

10; if the rectangles are marked 1–5 clockwise from upper left, they are 1; 2; 3; 4; 5; 1-2; 3-4; 4-5; 3-5; 1-2-3-4-5.

Also available on transparency

Math Fact

The figure formed by joining the consecutive midpoints of the sides of a quadrilateral is a parallelogram.

Georgia Performance Standards

M6P2.c Develop and evaluate mathematical arguments and proofs.

M6P2.d Select and use various types of reasoning and methods of proof.

M6P3.d Use the language of mathematics to express mathematical ideas precisely.

8-6 Quadrilaterals

Learn to identify, classify, and compare quadrilaterals.

Vocabulary
quadrilateral
parallelogram
rectangle
rhombus
square
trapezoid

Georgia Performance Standards
M6P3.d Use the language of mathematics to express mathematical ideas precisely. Also, M6P2.c, M6P2.d.

A **quadrilateral** is a plane figure with four sides and four angles.

Five special types of quadrilaterals and their properties are shown in the table below. The tick marks on two or more sides of a figure indicate that the sides are congruent.

	Properties
Parallelogram	Opposite sides are parallel and congruent. Opposite angles are congruent.
Rectangle	Parallelogram with four right angles
Rhombus	Parallelogram with four congruent sides
Square	Rectangle with four congruent sides
Trapezoid	Quadrilateral with exactly two parallel sides. May have two right angles

EXAMPLE 1 Naming Quadrilaterals

Give the most descriptive name for each figure.

A

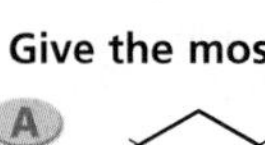

The figure is a quadrilateral, a parallelogram, and a rhombus.

Rhombus is the most descriptive name.

B

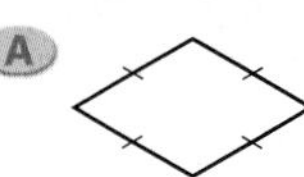

The figure is a quadrilateral and a trapezoid.

Trapezoid is the most descriptive name.

1 Introduce

Alternate Opener

EXPLORATION

8-6 Quadrilaterals

Find a real-world example for each quadrilateral.

	Quadrilateral	Example
1.	Parallelogram	
2.	Rhombus	
3.	Rectangle	
4.	Trapezoid	

Think and Discuss
5. **Discuss** how all the quadrilaterals are similar.
6. **Explain** what is special about the rectangle.

Motivate

Have students examine a set of cut-out quadrilaterals: parallelogram, rectangle, rhombus, square, and trapezoid. Have students name similarities and differences between the figures.

Possible answers: They all have four sides. Some have all right angles. Some have parallel sides. Some have all equal sides.

Explorations and answers are provided in *Alternate Openers: Explorations Transparencies.*

Give the most descriptive name for each figure.

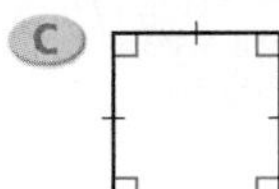

C The figure is a quadrilateral, parallelogram, rectangle, rhombus, and square.

Square is the most descriptive name.

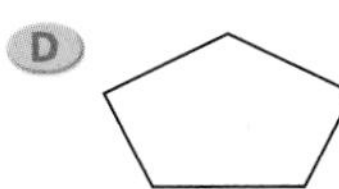

D This figure is a plane figure, but it has more than 4 sides.

The figure is not a quadrilateral.

You can draw a diagram to classify quadrilaterals based on their properties.

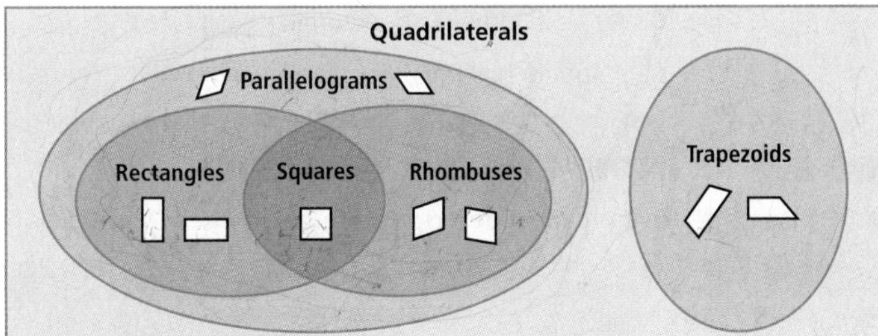

Answers to *Think and Discuss*

1. All squares are rhombuses because they have four congruent sides. Not every rhombus is a square, because the angles in a rhombus do not have to be right angles.
2. Possible answer: Both have four sides. A rectangle has two sets of parallel sides and four right angles. A trapezoid has only one set of parallel sides and may have two right angles.

EXAMPLE 2 Classifying Quadrilaterals

Complete each statement.

A A rhombus that is a rectangle is also a __?__.

A rhombus has four congruent sides, and the opposite sides are parallel. If it is a rectangle, it has four right angles, which makes it a square.

B A square can also be called a __?__, __?__, and __?__.

A square has opposite sides that are parallel; it can be called a parallelogram.

A square has four congruent sides; it can be called a rhombus.

A square has four right angles; it can be called a rectangle.

Think and Discuss

GPS M6P2.c, M6P3.b

1. **Tell** whether all squares are rhombuses and whether all rhombuses are squares.
2. **Compare** a trapezoid with a rectangle.

COMMON ERROR ALERT

Students may be confused by the fact that some quadrilaterals can be described by more than one name. Give students several examples of these quadrilaterals to illustrate the point.

Power Presentations with PowerPoint®

Additional Examples

Example 1

Give the most descriptive name for each figure.

A. 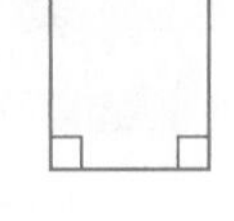 trapezoid

B. 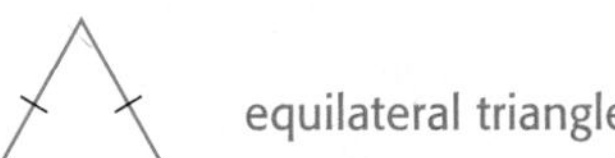 rectangle

C.  equilateral triangle

D.  rhombus

Example 2

Complete each statement.

A. A rectangle can also be called a __?__. parallelogram

B. A parallelogram cannot be a __?__. trapezoid

Also available on transparency

2 Teach

Guided Instruction

In this lesson, students learn to identify, classify, and compare quadrilaterals. Show students the chart illustrating the types of quadrilaterals and describing the properties of each (Teaching Transparency). Teach students to find the most descriptive name for a given quadrilateral, and have students complete statements comparing quadrilaterals.

Teaching Tip **Kinesthetic Experience** Have students use geoboards (Manipulatives Kit) to model each quadrilateral as you define each type.

Reaching All Learners

Through Diversity

Have students provide examples or drawings of the different types of quadrilaterals they may find in their homes. These could include clocks, mirrors, pictures cut out from magazines, patterns on bedspreads, etc. Ask them to give all the possible names for each quadrilateral.

3 Close

Summarize

Display a parallelogram, rectangle, rhombus, square, and trapezoid. Have students use the most descriptive name to classify each figure. Ask students what all of these figures are called. quadrilaterals

8-6 Exercises

Assignment Guide

If you finished Example 1 assign:
Average 1–3, 13–15, 34–39
Advanced 7–9, 13–15, 34–39

If you finished Example 2 assign:
Average 1–19, 25–39
Advanced 7–39

Homework Quick Check

Quickly check key concepts.
Exercises: 8, 12, 14, 16, 18

Math Background

A theorem states that a line segment joining the midpoints of two sides of a triangle is parallel to the third side and equal to one-half the length of the third side. This theorem can be used to prove the math fact of this lesson.

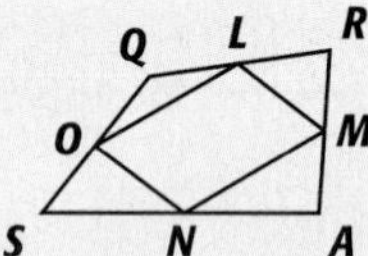

Draw diagonal $\overline{QA}$. Because $\overline{LM}$ joins the midpoints of two sides of a triangle, $\overline{LM} \parallel \overline{QA}$ and $LM = \frac{1}{2}QA$. Because $\overline{ON}$ joins the midpoints of two sides of a triangle, $\overline{ON} \parallel \overline{QA}$ and $ON = \frac{1}{2}QA$. So, $\overline{LM} \parallel \overline{ON}$ and $LM = ON$. In a similar manner, it can be shown that $\overline{LO} \parallel \overline{MN}$ and $LO = MN$. Therefore, $LMNO$ is a parallelogram.

Answers

13–15. See p. A9.

Georgia Performance Standards

M6P2.c Develop and evaluate mathematical arguments and proofs.

M6P2.d Select and use various types of reasoning and methods of proof.

M6P3.a Organize and consolidate their mathematical thinking through communication.

M6P3.c Analyze and evaluate the mathematical thinking and strategies of others.

8-6 Exercises

M6P2.c, M6P2.d, M6P3.a, M6P3.c

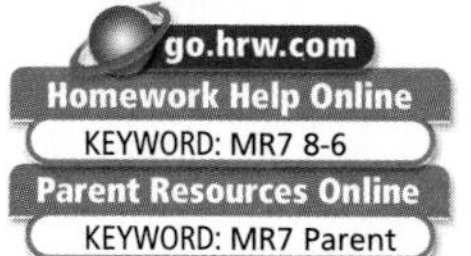

GUIDED PRACTICE

See Example 1 **Give the most descriptive name for each figure.**

1. 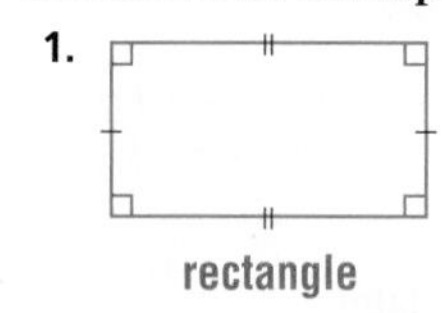 rectangle
2.  trapezoid
3. 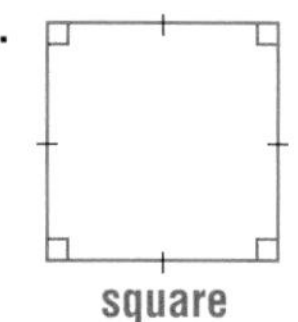 square

See Example 2 **Complete each statement.**

4. A trapezoid is also a __?__. quadrilateral
5. All __?__ are also rectangles. squares
6. A square has four __?__ angles. right

INDEPENDENT PRACTICE

See Example 1 **Give the most descriptive name for each figure.**

7. 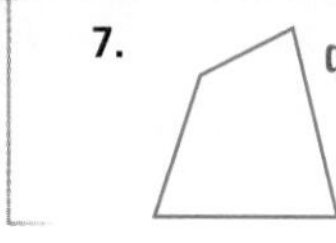 quadrilateral
8.  rhombus
9. 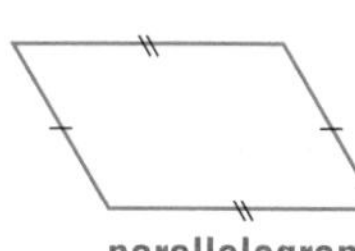 parallelogram

See Example 2 **Complete each statement.**

10. A rhombus with four right angles is a __?__. square
11. A parallelogram cannot be a __?__. trapezoid
12. A quadrilateral with four congruent sides and no right angles can be called a __?__ and a __?__. rhombus, parallelogram

PRACTICE AND PROBLEM SOLVING

CRCT GPS
Extra Practice p. 729

Give all of the possible names for each figure. Circle the most exact name.

13. 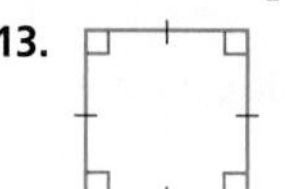
14. 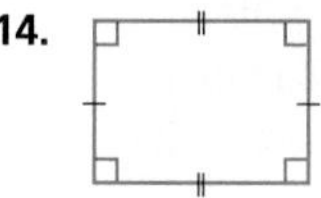
15. 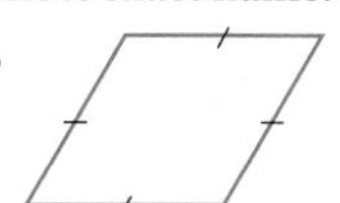

Determine if the given statements are *sometimes*, *always*, or *never* true.

16. A square is a rectangle. always
17. A trapezoid is a parallelogram. never
18. A rhombus is a square. sometimes
19. A parallelogram is a quadrilateral. always
20. A rectangle is a rhombus. sometimes
21. Four-sided figures are parallelograms. sometimes
22. A rectangle is a square. sometimes
23. A trapezoid has one right angle. never sometimes

RETEACH 8-6

LESSON 8-6 **Reteach**
Quadrilaterals

A quadrilateral is a plane figure with four sides and four angles.

There are special types of quadrilaterals.

parallelogram rectangle rhombus square trapezoid

A parallelogram has opposite sides that are parallel and congruent. Opposite angles are also congruent.

A rectangle is a parallelogram that has four right angles.

A rhombus is a parallelogram with four congruent sides.

A square is a rectangle with four congruent sides.

A trapezoid is a quadrilateral with exactly two parallel sides.

The best description for the figure below is rectangle because it is a parallelogram with four right angles.

Give the best name for each figure.

1. trapezoid
2. square
3. parallelogram
4. rhombus
5. rectangle
6. trapezoid

PRACTICE 8-6

LESSON 8-6 **Practice B**
Quadrilaterals

Give the most descriptive name for each figure.

1. rhombus
2. trapezoid
3. parallelogram
4. quadrilateral
5. square
6. rectangle

Complete each statement.

7. All rectangles are also parallelograms.
8. A rhombus is sometimes a square.
9. All trapezoids are also quadrilaterals.
10. A quadrilateral is any plane figure with four straight sides and four angles.
11. A quadrilateral with two sets of parallel lines, but does not have 90° angles is called a rhombus.
12. Devon made a table top in the shape of a quadrilateral. All of its angles measure 90°. What could the shape of Devon's table top be?
    a rectangle or a square
13. The perimeter of a rhombus is 64 inches. What is the length of each side of the rhombus? Explain.
    16 inches, All four sides of a rhombus are congruent, and $64 \div 4 = 16$.
14. Explain why a trapezoid is a quadrilateral, but a quadrilateral is not always a trapezoid.
    A trapezoid has four sides, always making it a quadrilateral. A quadrilateral can,but not always, have two parallel sides, thus a quatrilateral is not always a trapezoid.

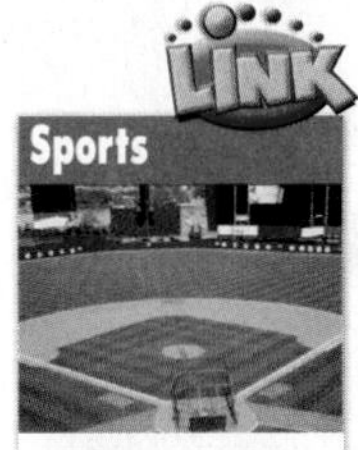

Sports

The first baseball game played at Shea Stadium was on April 17, 1964. In September 1974, the Mets played a 25-inning game, almost three times the length of a regulation game.

go.hrw.com
Web Extra!
KEYWORD: MR7 Baseball

Draw each quadrilateral as described. If it is not possible to draw, explain why.

24. a rectangle that is also a square

25. a rhombus that is also a trapezoid **not possible: A rhombus has two pairs of parallel sides, and a trapezoid only has one pair.**

26. a parallelogram that is not a rectangle

27. a square that is not a rhombus **not possible: A square has four congruent sides. It must always be a rhombus.**

28. **Sports** A baseball diamond is in the shape of a square. The distance from home plate to first base is 90 ft. What is the distance around the baseball diamond? **360 ft**

29. A rectangular picture frame is 3 in. wider than it is tall. The total length of the four sides of the frame is 38 in.

   a. The dimensions of the frame could be 10 in. by 13 in. because one dimension is 3 in. longer than the other. Explain how you know the frame is not 10 in. by 13 in.

   b. **Critical Thinking** How can you use your answer from part **a** to find the dimensions of the frame?

   c. Using parts **a** and **b,** what are the dimensions of the frame? **8 in. by 11 in.**

30. Anika drew a quadrilateral. Then she drew a line segment connecting one pair of opposite corners. She saw that she had divided the original quadrilateral into two right isosceles triangles. Classify the quadrilateral she began with. **square**

31. **What's the Error?** A student said that any quadrilateral with two right angles and a pair of parallel sides is a rectangle. What is the error in the statement?

32. **Write About It** Explain why a square is also a rectangle and a rhombus.

33. **Challenge** Part of a quadrilateral is hidden. What are the possible types of quadrilaterals that the figure could be?
trapezoid, parallelogram, rectangle, rhombus, square

CRCT Prep • GPS Support • Spiral Review

34. **Multiple Choice** Which quadrilateral is NOT a parallelogram?

   Ⓐ Rectangle   Ⓑ Rhombus   Ⓒ Square   **Ⓓ Trapezoid**

35. **Short Response** List all of the names for the figure. Which is the most descriptive? **Quadrilateral, parallelogram, rhombus; *rhombus* is the most descriptive.**

Use the pattern to write the first five terms of the sequence. (Lesson 1-7)

36. Start with 6; add 5. **6, 11, 16, 21, 26**

37. Start with 2; multiply by 3. **2, 6, 18, 54, 162**

Tell whether each statement is *always, sometimes,* or *never* true. (Lesson 8-4)

38. Perpendicular lines are intersecting lines. **always**

39. Skew lines are on the same plane. **never**

CHALLENGE 8-6

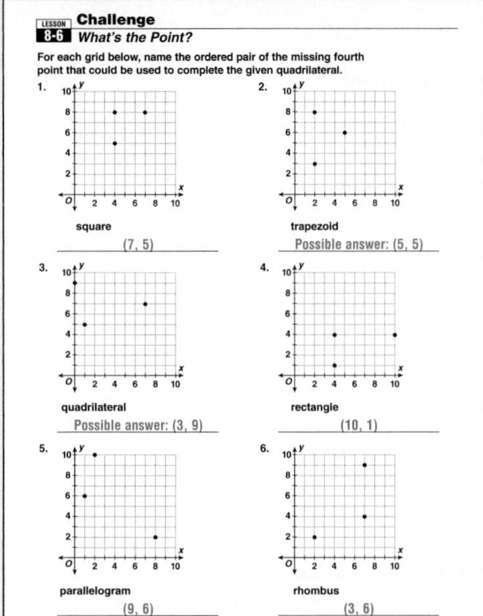

LESSON 8-6 **Challenge**
What's the Point?

For each grid below, name the ordered pair of the missing fourth point that could be used to complete the given quadrilateral.

1. square (7, 5)
2. trapezoid Possible answer: (5, 5)
3. quadrilateral Possible answer: (3, 9)
4. rectangle (10, 1)
5. parallelogram (9, 6)
6. rhombus (3, 6)

PROBLEM SOLVING 8-6

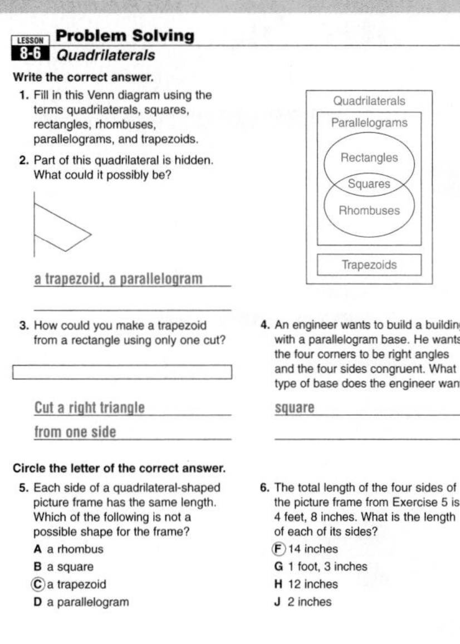

LESSON 8-6 **Problem Solving**
Quadrilaterals

Write the correct answer.

1. Fill in this Venn diagram using the terms quadrilaterals, squares, rectangles, rhombuses, parallelograms, and trapezoids.

2. Part of this quadrilateral is hidden. What could it possibly be?
a trapezoid, a parallelogram

3. How could you make a trapezoid from a rectangle using only one cut?
Cut a right triangle from one side

4. An engineer wants to build a building with a parallelogram base. He wants the four corners to be right angles and the four sides congruent. What type of base does the engineer want?
square

Circle the letter of the correct answer.

5. Each side of a quadrilateral-shaped picture frame has the same length. Which of the following is not a possible shape for the frame?
A a rhombus
B a square
C a trapezoid
D a parallelogram

6. The total length of the four sides of the picture frame from Exercise 5 is 4 feet, 8 inches. What is the length of each of its sides?
F 14 inches
G 1 foot, 3 inches
H 12 inches
J 2 inches

Ongoing Assessment and Intervention

Diagnose ***Before*** **the Lesson**
8-6 Warm Up, TE p. 442

Monitor ***During*** **the Lesson**
8-6 Know-It Notebook
8-6 Questioning Strategies

Assess ***After*** **the Lesson**
8-6 Lesson Quiz, TE p. 445

Answers

24, 26. See p. A9.

29. a. If the frame is 10 in. by 13 in., the total length of the sides is 46 in., not 38 in.

b. Possible answer: The dimensions, 10 in. by 13 in., were too long, so try shorter lengths. Try 9 in. and 12 in., since 12 in. is 3 in. more than 9 in. This is also too large, so you can try shorter lengths.

31–32. See p. A9.

Test Prep Doctor In Exercise 34, some students might benefit from making a sketch of each figure to help in identifying the correct choice, as long as they remember that a parallelogram has two pairs of parallel sides.

Journal

Have students write brief descriptions and draw pictures of the five types of quadrilaterals discussed in this lesson.

Power Presentations with PowerPoint®

8-6 Lesson Quiz

Complete each statement.

1. A quadrilateral with four right angles is a ___?___. square or rectangle

2. A parallelogram with four right angles and four congruent sides is a ___?___. square

3. A figure with 4 sides and 4 angles is a ___?___. quadrilateral

4. Give the most descriptive name for this quadrilateral. trapezoid

Also available on transparency

8-7 Organizer

Pacing: Traditional 1 day
Block $\frac{1}{2}$ day

Objective: Students identify regular and not regular polygons and find the angle measures of regular polygons.

Hands-On Lab
In *Hands-On Lab Activities*

Online Edition
Tutorial Videos

Countdown to CRCT Week 18

Power Presentations with PowerPoint®

Warm Up

True or false?

1. Some trapezoids are parallelograms. false
2. Some figures with 4 right angles are squares. true
3. Some quadrilaterals have only one right angle. true

Problem of the Day

Four square tables pushed together can seat either 8 or 10 people. How many people could 12 square tables pushed together seat?

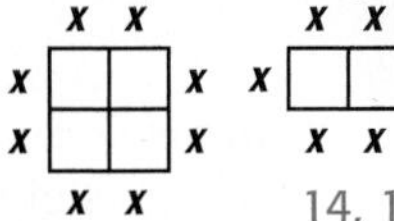

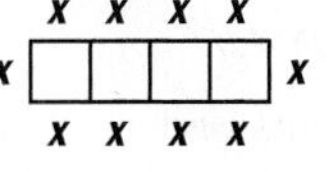

14, 16, or 26 people

Also available on transparency

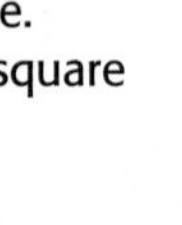

8-7 Polygons

Learn to identify regular and not regular polygons and to find the angle measures of regular polygons.

Vocabulary
polygon
regular polygon

Triangles and quadrilaterals are examples of polygons. A **polygon** is a closed plane figure formed by three or more line segments. A **regular polygon** is a polygon in which all sides are congruent and all angles are congruent.

Polygons are named by the number of their sides and angles.

Remember!
An equilateral triangle has three congruent sides.

	Triangle	Quadrilateral	Pentagon	Hexagon	Octagon
Sides and Angles	3	4	5	6	8
Regular					
Not Regular					

EXAMPLE 1 Identifying Polygons

Tell whether each shape is a polygon. If so, give its name and tell whether it appears to be regular or not regular.

Georgia Performance Standards
M6A2.a Analyze and describe patterns arising from mathematical rules and tables. Also, M6P1.c, M6P1.d, M6P3.d.

A

There are 4 sides and 4 angles.
quadrilateral
The sides and angles appear to be congruent.
regular

B

There are 4 sides and 4 angles.
quadrilateral
All 4 sides do not appear to be congruent.
not regular

The sum of the interior angle measures in a triangle is 180°, so the sum of the interior angle measures in a quadrilateral is 360°.

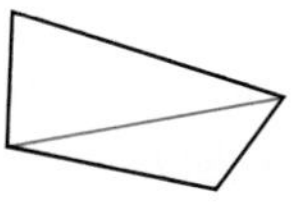

Georgia Performance Standards

M6A2.a Analyze and describe patterns arising from mathematical rules, tables, and graphs.

M6P1.c Apply and adapt a variety of appropriate strategies to solve problems.

M6P1.d Monitor and reflect on the process of mathematical problem solving.

M6P3.d Use the language of mathematics to express mathematical ideas precisely.

1 Introduce

Alternate Opener

EXPLORATION

8-7 Polygons

In a *regular polygon,* all sides are congruent and all angles are congruent.

Name each polygon and determine whether it is regular. Use number 1 as an example.

	Polygon	Name	Regular?
1.		Triangle	no
2.			
3.			
4.			
5.			
6.			

Think and Discuss
7. **Explain** how you classified each polygon in numbers 2–6.

Motivate

Have students draw closed plane figures with 3, 4, 5, 6, and 8 sides. Have students identify the figures they can name. They should at least be able to name *triangle* and *quadrilateral.* Tell them that in this lesson they will learn the names of 5-, 6-, and 8-sided polygons.

Explorations and answers are provided in *Alternate Openers: Explorations Transparencies.*

EXAMPLE 2 PROBLEM SOLVING APPLICATION

A stop sign is in the shape of a regular octagon. What is the measure of each angle of the stop sign?

1 Understand the Problem

The **answer** will be the measure of each angle in a regular octagon. List the **important information:**

- A regular octagon has 8 congruent sides and 8 congruent angles.

2 Make a Plan

Make a table to look for a pattern using regular polygons.

3 Solve

Draw some regular polygons and divide each into triangles.

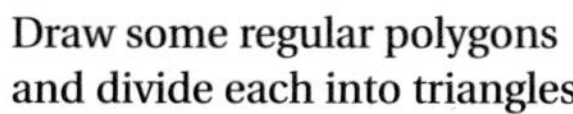
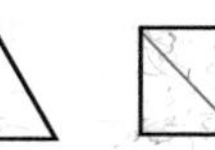

Polygon	Sides	Triangles	Sum of Angle Measures
Triangle	3	1	1 × 180° = 180°
Quadrilateral	4	2	2 × 180° = 360°
Pentagon	5	3	3 × 180° = 540°
Hexagon	6	4	4 × 180° = 720°

The number of triangles is always 2 fewer than the number of sides.
An octagon can be divided into 8 − 2 = 6 triangles.
The sum of the interior angle measures in an octagon is 6 × 180° = 1,080°.
So the measure of each angle is 1,080° ÷ 8 = 135°.

÷ by # of sides

4 Look Back

Each angle in a regular octagon is obtuse. 135° is a reasonable answer, because an obtuse angle is between 90° and 180°.

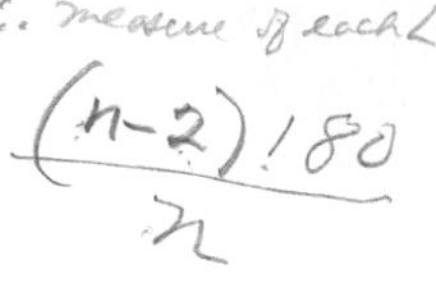

Reading Math

The prefixes in the names of the polygons tell you how many sides and angles there are.

tri- = three
quad- = four
penta- = five
hexa- = six
octa- = eight

∴ measure of each ∠ = $\frac{(n-2)180}{n}$

Answers to *Think and Discuss*

1. acute; obtuse; right
2. Possible answer: the front of a small birdhouse; a stop sign

Think and Discuss GPS M6P3.b

1. **Classify** the angles in each figure: a regular triangle, a regular hexagon, and a rectangle.
2. **Name** an object that is in the shape of a pentagon and an object that is in the shape of an octagon.

COMMON ERROR ALERT

Some students may not understand the reasoning for finding the sums of angle measures in various polygons. Help them to see that the sum of the interior angles of the polygon is the same as the sum of all the angles in all the triangles in the polygon's interior.

Power Presentations with PowerPoint®

Additional Examples

Example 1

Tell whether each shape is a polygon. If so, give its name and tell whether it appears to be regular or not regular.

A.

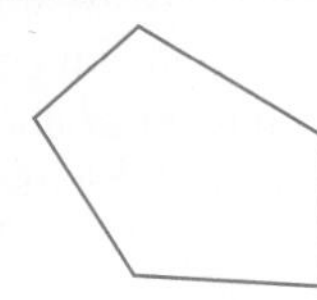

polygon
pentagon
not regular

B.

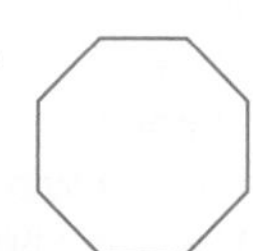

polygon
octagon
regular

Example 2

Malcolm designed a wall hanging that was a regular 9-sided polygon (called a *nonagon*). What is the measure of each angle of the nonagon? 140°

Also available on transparency

2 Teach

Guided Instruction

In this lesson, students learn to identify regular and not regular polygons and to find the angle measures of regular polygons. First teach the difference between regular and not regular polygons and the names for 5-, 6-, and 8-sided polygons. (Teaching Transparency). Then teach students to find the sum of the measures of the interior angles of an octagon.

Language Arts Direct students' attention to the Reading Math box explaining the polygon prefixes. ENGLISH LANGUAGE LEARNERS

Reaching All Learners

Through Critical Thinking

Have students research the names of other polygons. Have them find the sum of the angle measures for each polygon and the measure of each angle if the polygon is regular (to the nearest tenth of a degree).

Possible answers:
7-sided: heptagon; 900°; 128.6°
10-sided: decagon; 1,440°; 144°
11-sided: undecagon; 1,620°; 147.3°
12-sided: dodecagon; 1,800°; 150°
15-sided: pentadecagon; 2,340°; 156°

3 Close

Summarize

Review the polygons in the lesson. Ask students to tell you the difference between a polygon that is regular and one that is not regular.

A regular polygon has all congruent sides and all congruent angles. A polygon that is not regular does not have all congruent sides and all congruent angles.

8-7 Exercises

Assignment Guide

If you finished Example 1 assign:
Average 1–3, 9–14, 24–30
Advanced 5–7, 9–14, 24–30

If you finished Example 2 assign:
Average 1–4, 9–30
Advanced 5–30

Homework Quick Check
Quickly check key concepts.
Exercises: 10, 12, 14, 16, 18

Math Background

If you extend a side of a polygon past a vertex, you will form an exterior angle. The sum of the measures of the interior and exterior angle at that vertex is 180°. For a polygon with n sides, the sum of all the interior and exterior angle pairs is $180n$. The sum of the measures of the interior angles of a polygon with n sides is $180(n - 2)$. Thus, the sum of the exterior angles, one at each vertex, of a polygon of n sides is $180n - 180(n - 2) = 180n - 180n + 360 = 360$.

Georgia Performance Standards

M6P2.c Develop and evaluate mathematical arguments and proofs.

M6P2.d Select and use various types of reasoning and methods of proof.

M6P3.a Organize and consolidate their mathematical thinking through communication.

M6P3.c Analyze and evaluate the mathematical thinking and strategies of others.

8-7 Exercises

M6P2.c, M6P2.d, M6P3.a, M6P3.c

GUIDED PRACTICE

See Example 1

Tell whether each shape is a polygon. If so, give its name and tell whether it appears to be regular or not regular.

1. polygon, hexagon, regular
2. polygon, quadrilateral, not regular
3. polygon, triangle, regular

See Example 2

4. A carpenter is building a deck around a hot tub in the shape of a regular hexagon. What is the measure of each angle of the hexagon? 120°

INDEPENDENT PRACTICE

See Example 1

Tell whether each shape is a polygon. If so, give its name and tell whether it appears to be regular or not regular.

5. 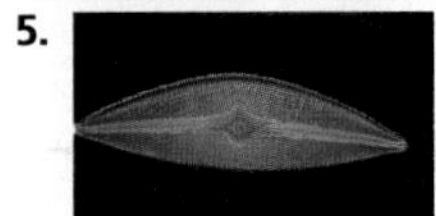
not a polygon

6. polygon, triangle, regular

7. 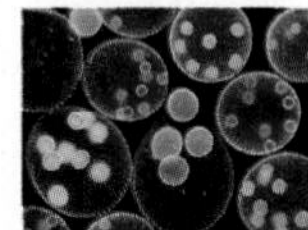
not a polygon

See Example 2

8. Janet made a sign for her room in the shape of a regular pentagon. What is the measure of each angle of the pentagon? 108°

PRACTICE AND PROBLEM SOLVING

CRCT GPS
Extra Practice p. 729

Explain why each shape is NOT a polygon.

9. 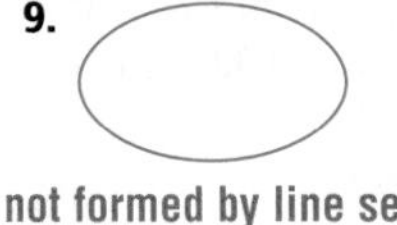
not formed by line segments

10. not a closed figure

11. not formed by line segments

Name each polygon.

12. octagon

13. hexagon

14. pentagon

15. Lucy drew a regular decagon (ten-sided figure). What is the sum of the interior angle measures? What is the measure of each angle? 1,440°; 144°

RETEACH 8-7

LESSON 8-7 **Reteach**
Polygons

A polygon is a closed plane figure formed by three or more line segments.

Polygons are named by the number of their sides and angles.

Sides and Angles	3	4	5	6	8
Polygon	triangle	quadrilateral	pentagon	hexagon	octagon

A regular polygon has all congruent sides and angles.

Each angle is 90 degrees.
Each side is 3 centimeters long.

If the angles and the sides are not all congruent, then the polygon is not regular.

Name each polygon and tell whether it is regular or not regular.

1. quadrilateral, regular

2. quadrilateral, not regular

To find the angle measures of a regular hexagon, first divide the polygon into triangles by drawing connecting segments from one vertex to all of its nonadjacent vertices.

There are 4 triangles.

Next, multiply the number of triangles by 180.

$4 \cdot 180 = 720$ The sum of the angle measures of a triangle is 180°.
Divide the product by 6, the number of sides, to find the measure of each angle.

$\frac{720}{6} = 120$ All of the angles of a regular polygon are congruent.
Each angle is 120°.

Find the angle measure of each regular polygon.

3. regular quadrilateral 90°
4. regular pentagon 108°

PRACTICE 8-7

LESSON 8-7 **Practice B**
Polygons

Name each polygon and tell whether it appears to be *regular* or *not regular*.

1. triangle; not regular
2. hexagon; regular
3. octagon; regular
4. quadrilateral; regular
5. pentagon; not regular
6. quadrilateral; not regular

7. The public swimming pool is in the shape of a regular hexagon. Each side of the pool measures 5 feet. What is the distance around the entire pool?

30 feet

8. In the space below, draw a regular quadrilateral. Now draw one diagonal of that quadrilateral. Describe the two polygons that are formed.

They are both triangles.

Classify each of the following polygons as either *always* regular, *sometimes* regular, or *never* regular.

		Always	Sometimes	Never
16.	Equilateral triangle	? ✓	?	?
17.	Trapezoid	?	?	? ✓
18.	Right triangle	?	?	? ✓
19.	Parallelogram	?	? ✓	?

Critical Thinking A *diagonal* is a line segment that connects two nonadjacent vertices of a polygon. One diagonal is shown in each figure.

20. a. How many diagonals does a rectangle have? **2**

b. How many diagonals does a pentagon have? **5**

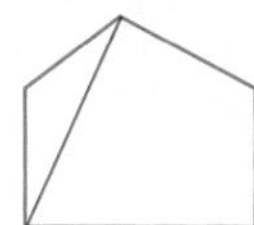

21. What's the Error? A student said a rectangle is never a regular polygon because the lengths of all the sides are not congruent. What error did the student make? Explain why a rectangle is sometimes a regular polygon.

22. Write About It What polygon is formed when two equilateral triangles are placed side by side, with one upside down? Draw examples, and explain whether the polygon formed by the two triangles is regular.

23. Challenge A figure is formed by placing 6 equilateral triangle tiles around a regular hexagon tile. The distance around the regular hexagon is 60 cm. A snail moves along the sides of the figure. How far will the snail travel until it gets back to its starting point? **120 cm**

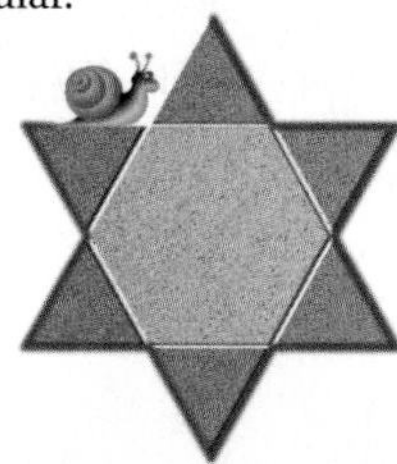

CRCT Prep • GPS Support • Spiral Review

24. Multiple Choice Which quadrilateral is regular?

Ⓐ Triangle Ⓑ Trapezoid **Ⓒ Square** Ⓓ Rhombus

25. Gridded Response What is the measure, in degrees, of each angle of a regular pentagon? **108**

Solve each equation. (Lesson 3-9)

26. $5.5 = 5c$ **$c = 1.1$** **27.** $d + 4.96 = 9$ **$d = 4.04$** **28.** $j - 12.5 = 39.04$ **$j = 51.54$** **29.** $\frac{x}{2.4} = 3.5$ **$x = 8.4$**

30. Can the angles with measurements 34°, 53°, and 93° form a triangle? If so, classify the triangle as acute, obtuse, or right. (Lesson 8-5) **yes; obtuse**

CHALLENGE 8-7

LESSON 8-7 **Challenge**
Sign Language

Traffic signs are symbols used to convey information. In the United States, certain shapes are used only for certain traffic signs. As a result, you can often understand the message of a traffic sign simply by classifying its geometric shape.

Tell whether each traffic sign below is a polygon. If it is, name the polygon that best describes its shape, and tell whether it appears to be *regular* or *not regular*.

1. 

yes, octagon, regular

2. 

not a polygon

3. 

yes, triangle, regular

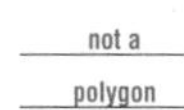

4. 
yes, pentagon, not regular

5. 

yes, quadrilateral, not regular

6. 

not a polygon

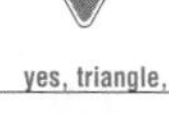

7. 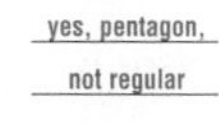

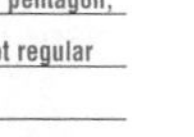
yes, trapezoid, not regular

8. 
yes, quadrilateral, regular

9. 

yes, triangle, not regular

PROBLEM SOLVING 8-7

LESSON 8-7 **Problem Solving**
Polygons

Write the correct answer.

1. Name each polygon in this figure.
1, 2, 4, 5, and 6 are triangles; 3 is a parallelogram; 7 is a square (some students may name the entire figure a square)

2. How could you use the sum of the angles inside a triangle to find the sum of the angles inside a heptagon?
Five triangles are needed to fill a heptagon; 5 × 180° = 900°. So, the sum of the angles inside a heptagon is 900°.

3. How could you use the sum of the angles inside a triangle to find the sum of the angles inside a decagon?
Eight triangles are needed to fill a decagon; 8 × 180° = 1,440°. So, the sum of the angles inside a decagon is 1,440°.

4. In the space below, draw a rectangle and a parallelogram with side lengths congruent to the rectangle's. Now draw the diagonals for each of those polygons. What new polygons are formed by the diagonals in each quadrilateral?

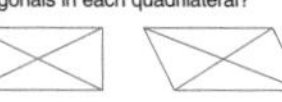

triangles

5. In Exercise 4, what is true of the diagonals in the rectangle that isn't true of the diagonals of the parallelogram?
The diagonals in the rectangle are congruent.

Circle the letter of the correct answer.

6. The perimeter of a regular hexagon is $13\frac{1}{2}$ inches. What is the length of each side?
A $2\frac{7}{10}$ inches C $3\frac{3}{4}$ inches
Ⓑ $2\frac{1}{4}$ inches D $1\frac{11}{16}$ inches

7. Which of the following statements is sometimes false?
Ⓕ A plane figure is a polygon.
G Each side of a polygon intersects exactly two other sides.
H A polygon is a closed figure.
J A polygon has straight sides.

Ongoing Assessment and Intervention

***Diagnose Before* the Lesson**
8-7 Warm Up, TE p. 446

***Monitor During* the Lesson**
8-7 Know-It Notebook
8-7 Questioning Strategies

***Assess After* the Lesson**
8-7 Lesson Quiz, TE p. 449

Answers

21. A square is always a rectangle, and a square has congruent sides and angles, so it is a regular polygon.

22. Possible answer: Two equilateral triangles form a rhombus. It is not regular because not all angles are congruent.

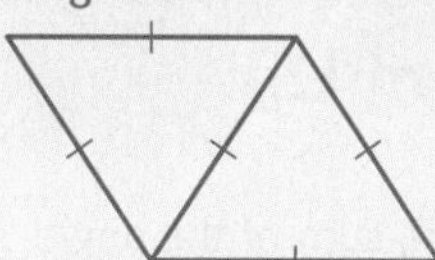

Test Prep Doctor In Exercise 25, students might make a sketch of a pentagon and draw two diagonals to create three triangles. When the sum of the angles in all three triangles is divided by the number of angles in a pentagon, the result will be the measure of each angle of a regular pentagon.

Journal

Have students explain the difference between polygons that are regular and polygons that are not regular.

Power Presentations with PowerPoint®

8-7 Lesson Quiz

1. Name each polygon and tell whether it appears to be regular or not regular.

nonagon, regular; octagon, not regular

2. What is the measure of each angle in a regular dodecagon (12-sided figure)? **150°**

Also available on transparency

(n-2)180 = 10(180) = 1800
1800/12 = 150

8-8 Organizer

Pacing: Traditional 1 day
Block $\frac{1}{2}$ day

Objective: Students recognize, describe, and extend geometric patterns.

Hands-On Lab
In *Hands-On Lab Activities*

Online Edition
Tutorial Videos

Countdown to CRCT Week 19

Power Presentations with PowerPoint®

Warm Up

Divide.

1. What is the sum of the angle measures in a quadrilateral? 360°
2. What is the sum of the angle measures in a hexagon? 720°
3. What is the measure of each angle in a regular octagon? 135°

Problem of the Day

Which three letters come next in the following series: *W, T, L, C, N, I, . . .?*
T, F, S; the letters are the initial letters of the words in the question.

Also available on transparency

Georgia Performance Standards

M6P2.d Select and use various types of reasoning and methods of proof.

M6P4.c Recognize and apply mathematics in contexts outside of mathematics.

8-8 Geometric Patterns

Learn to recognize, describe, and extend geometric patterns.

Georgia Performance Standards

M6P2.d Select and use various types of reasoning and methods of proof. Also, M6P4.c.

Native American art often involves geometric patterns. The patterns are based on the shape, color, size, position, or number of geometric figures.

This blanket has a geometric pattern. The first row with a complete figure has a parallelogram with a horse in its center. The next row has two parallelograms with cows in the centers. This pattern continues. If the weaver wanted to make a longer blanket, the next row would be two parallelograms with pictures of cows.

This Navajo blanket was made in the late seventeenth century.

EXAMPLE 1 Extending Geometric Patterns

Identify a possible pattern. Use the pattern to draw the next figure.

A

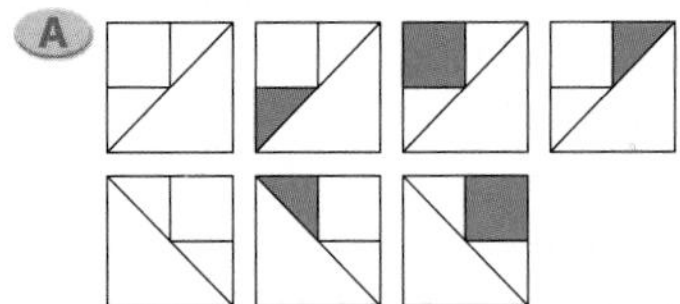

The small shapes within the figure are shaded one at a time from bottom to top. Then the figure is rotated and the top triangle is shaded.

So the next figure might look like this:

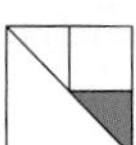

B

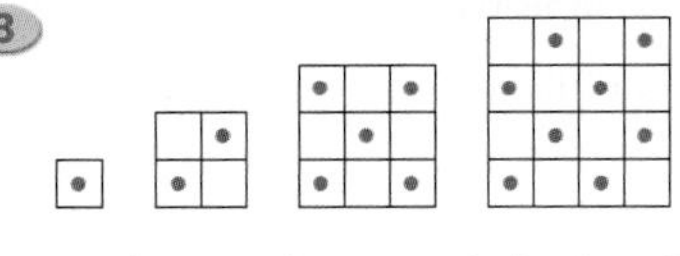

The figures from left to right are a 1 × 1 square, a 2 × 2 square, a 3 × 3 square, and a 4 × 4 square.

So the next figure might look like this:

Remember!

Perfect squares, such as 2^2, 3^2, and 4^2, are also called "square numbers" because they can be modeled as a square array.

1 Introduce

Alternate Opener

EXPLORATION

8-8 Geometric Patterns

Look for a pattern, and draw the next three figures in the sequence.

1. 

2. 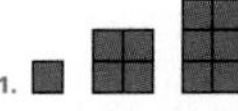 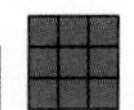

3. 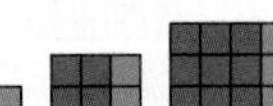

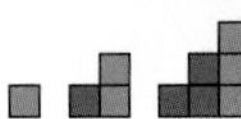

Think and Discuss

4. **Explain** how the sequence in number 2 is built on the sequence in number 1.
5. **Describe** in words the sequence in number 3.

Motivate

Discuss possible rules for each number pattern below, and have students find the next two numbers in each pattern.

Possible answers:

1, 3, 5, 7, 9, . . . Add 2; 11, 13.

5, 10, 15, 20, 25, . . . Add 5; 30, 35.

4, 14, 9, 19, 14, 24, . . . Add 10, and then subtract 5; 19, 29.

Have students make up other patterns.

Explorations and answers are provided in *Alternate Openers: Explorations Transparencies.*

EXAMPLE 2 Completing Geometric Patterns

Identify a possible pattern. Use the pattern to draw the missing figure.

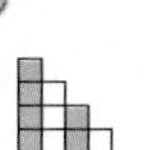 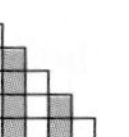 ? 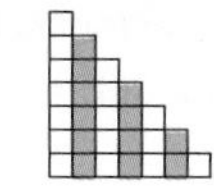

The first figure from the bottom row to the top has 4 squares and then 3, 2, and 1 square. The next figure has 5 squares in the bottom row and then 4, 3, 2, and 1.

So the missing figure might look like this:

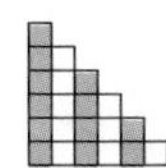

 ?  

Each figure is an equilateral triangle. The first figure has 3 red triangles along the base. The third figure has 5 red triangles, and the last figure has 6.

So the missing figure might look like this:

EXAMPLE 3 *Art Application*

Dan is painting a clay pot. Identify a pattern in Dan's design and tell what the finished pot might look like.

The pattern from bottom to top is narrow stripe, wide stripe, narrow stripe, wide stripe. The color pattern from bottom to top is blue, green, yellow, blue, green.

If this pattern is followed, the finished pot might look like the pot at left.

Possible answers to *Think and Discuss*

1. Each figure has one more square in the bottom row than the one to its left. So the fifth figure will have the following number of squares from the bottom row to the top 8, 7, 6, 5, 4, 3, 2, and finally 1.

Think and Discuss

GPS M6P1.d, M6P3.b

1. **Explain** how you can use a pattern to find the number of squares in the next, or fifth, figure in Example 2A.
2. **Tell** how you can use a pattern to find the number of small red triangles in the sixth figure in Example 2B.

Power Presentations with PowerPoint®

Additional Examples

Example 1

Identify a possible pattern. Use the pattern to draw the next figure.

A.  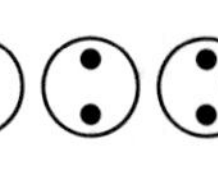  

B.  

Example 2

Identify a possible pattern. Use the pattern to draw the missing figure.

A. 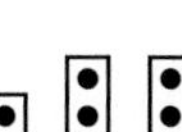 ? 

B. ? 

Example 3

Travis is painting a platter. Identify a pattern that Travis is using and draw what the finished platter might look like.

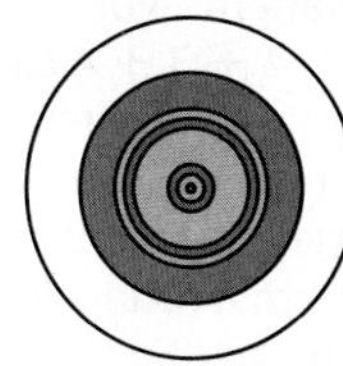 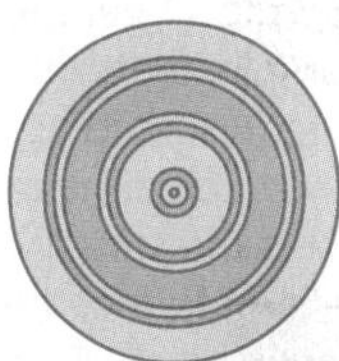

Also available on transparency

2. The third figure has 5 more than the second, and the fourth has 6 more than the third. So the fifth figure would have 7 more red triangles than the fourth, and the sixth figure would have 8 more than the fifth.

2 Teach

Guided Instruction

In this lesson, students learn to recognize, describe, and extend geometric patterns. Teach students to describe patterns, to use the descriptions to extend the patterns, and to identify missing elements in the patterns. Encourage students to give other possible ways to identify each pattern, because there is not just one way to describe a pattern.

Teaching Tip **Multiple Representations** Point out patterns that are different from those that simply repeat (e.g., A, B, A, B , . . .). Example 2 illustrates the concept of a growing pattern.

Reaching All Learners
Through Modeling

Have students build geometric patterns with pattern blocks (Manipulatives Kit). Ask them to draw and describe their patterns. If time allows, share patterns with the class, and have students tell what figure might come next in the pattern.

3 Close

Summarize

Have students make patterns that follow a given rule. For example, each figure is twice as wide as the figure to its left, or each figure has one more triangle than the one before it.

Check students' patterns.

8-8 Exercises

Assignment Guide

If you finished Example 1 assign:
Average 1, 7–9, 13–24
Advanced 4, 7–9, 13–24

If you finished Example 2 assign:
Average 1–2, 7–9, 13–24
Advanced 4–5, 7–9, 13–24

If you finished Example 3 assign:
Average 1–6, 10–24
Advanced 4–24

Homework Quick Check

Quickly check key concepts.
Exercises: 4, 6, 10

Answers

1–5, 7–9. See p. A10.

Math Background

A formula for the sum of the first n counting numbers can be found with the help of geometric patterns. For example, the sum of $1 + 2 + 3 + 4$ can be represented as a pattern of squares (below left). The diagram on the right shows the sum twice. The two copies of the sum fit together to form a rectangle containing $4 \cdot 5 = 20$ squares. So the sum equals $\frac{4 \cdot 5}{2} = 10$.

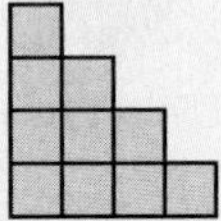
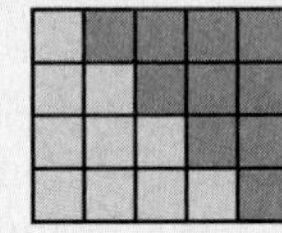

Because this approach works for any value of n, the sum of the first n counting numbers equals $\frac{n(n+1)}{2}$.

Georgia Performance Standards

M6P1.a Build new mathematical knowledge through problem solving.

M6P2.d Select and use various types of reasoning and methods of proof.

M6P3.a Organize and consolidate their mathematical thinking through communication.

M6P4.c Recognize and apply mathematics in contexts outside of mathematics.

8-8 Exercises

Georgia Performance Standards
M6P1.a, M6P2.d, M6P3.a, M6P4.c

go.hrw.com
Homework Help Online
KEYWORD: MR7 8-8
Parent Resources Online
KEYWORD: MR7 Parent

GUIDED PRACTICE

See Example 1 **Identify a possible pattern. Use the pattern to draw the next figure.**

1. 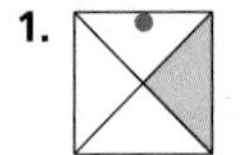 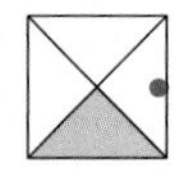 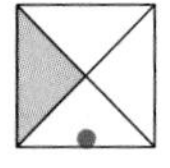 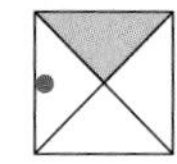

See Example 2 **Identify a possible pattern. Use the pattern to draw the missing figure.**

2.   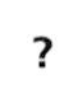 ? 

See Example 3

3. Oscar is making a beaded necklace. Identify a pattern in Oscar's design. Then tell which five beads Oscar will probably use next.

INDEPENDENT PRACTICE

See Example 1 **Identify a possible pattern. Use the pattern to draw the next figure.**

4. 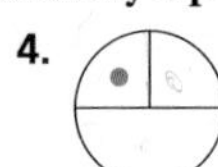 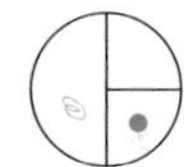 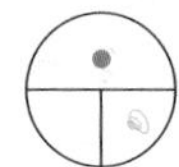 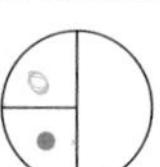 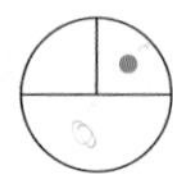

See Example 2 **Identify a possible pattern. Use the pattern to draw the missing figure.**

5.  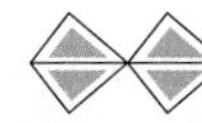  ? 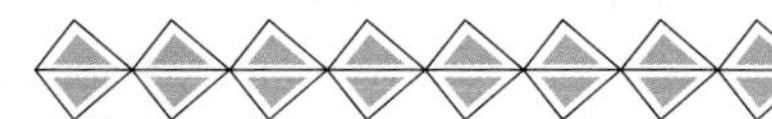

See Example 3

6. Tamara is planting flowers in her garden. She makes groups of purple flowers and groups of pink flowers.

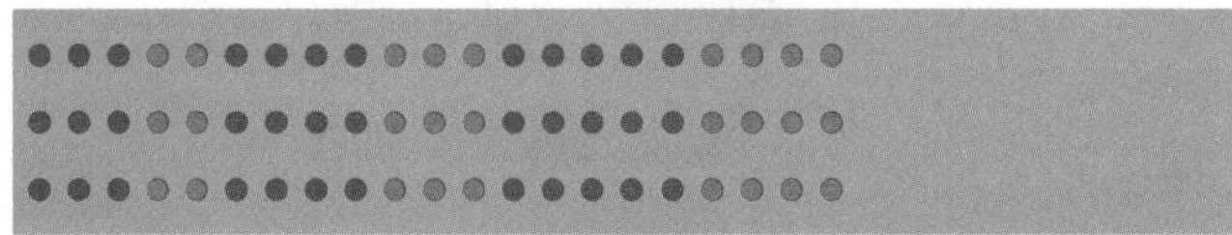

If she continues this pattern, how many flowers might Tamara plant in the next group of purple flowers? How many flowers might she plant in the next group of pink flowers? **18 purple flowers; 15 pink flowers**

PRACTICE AND PROBLEM SOLVING

CRCT GPS
Extra Practice p. 729

Draw the next figure in the pattern.

7. 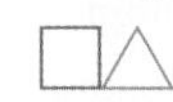 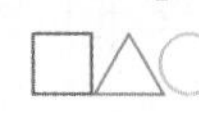 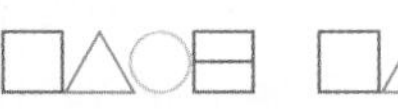 

8.  

9.

RETEACH 8-8

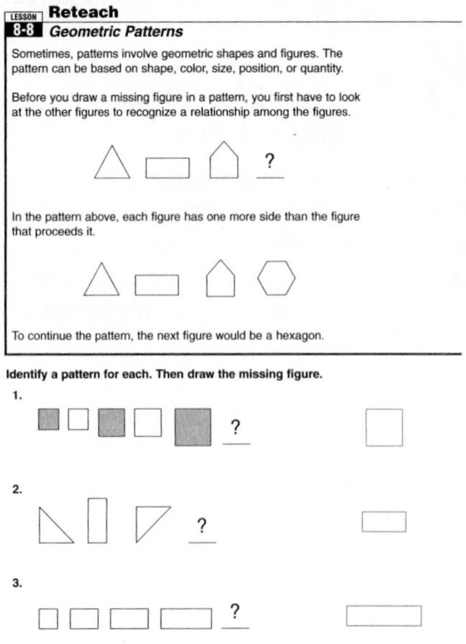

LESSON 8-8 **Reteach**
Geometric Patterns

Sometimes, patterns involve geometric shapes and figures. The pattern can be based on shape, color, size, position, or quantity.

Before you draw a missing figure in a pattern, you first have to look at the other figures to recognize a relationship among the figures.

?

In the pattern above, each figure has one more side than the figure that proceeds it.

To continue the pattern, the next figure would be a hexagon.

Identify a pattern for each. Then draw the missing figure.

1. 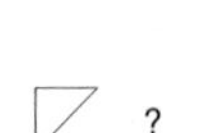  ?

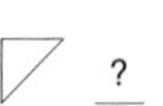

2. ?

3.  ?

PRACTICE 8-8

LESSON 8-8 **Practice B**
Geometric Patterns

Identify a possible pattern. Use the pattern to draw the next figure.

1.

Pattern: A bottom row is added to each figure with 1 more dot than the row above it.

2. 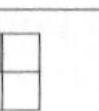 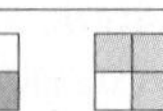

Pattern: One more square is shaded than the figure before it.

3.  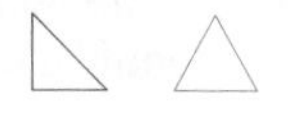

Pattern: Repeating groups of 1 right triangle, 1 equilateral triangle, and 1 scalene triangle

4. 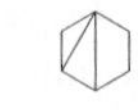 

Pattern: One more diagonal is drawn from the same vertex in each hexagon in the pattern.

5. Use triangles to create a geometric pattern. Describe your pattern.

Accept all geometric patterns using triangles. Students' descriptions should match their patterns.

Social Studies LINK

In South Africa, Ndebele people paint their houses with brightly colored patterns made up of geometric shapes.

10. Look at the shapes found on the wall surrounding the Ndebele house. Identify a possible pattern that was used to paint the top band of the wall. Use the pattern to draw the shapes hidden by the Ndebele people. (You do not need to include color in the pattern.)

11. **Write About It** Look closely at the Ndebele house. Draw four geometric figures you see painted on the house. Then use those figures to make a pattern. Describe your pattern.

12. **Challenge** Look at the designs below, which were made using an African motif. Identify a possible pattern. If the pattern continues, how many motifs will be in the sixth design? If there are 45 motifs, what will the design number be? **28 motifs; Design 8**

Design 1   Design 2   Design 3

go.hrw.com
Web Extra!
KEYWORD: MR7 Patterns

CRCT Prep • GPS Support • Spiral Review

13. **Multiple Choice** Identify a possible pattern in the image. Use the pattern to determine the missing figure.

Ⓐ 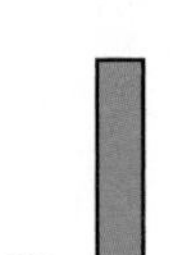 Ⓑ  ⓒ (circled) 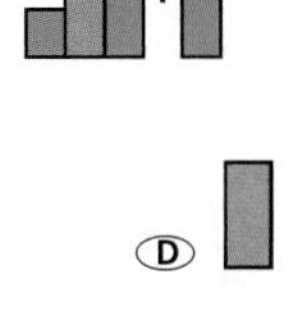 Ⓓ

14. **Short Response** Determine the next figure in the pattern. Draw the figure. Explain your answer.

Find each value. (Lesson 1-3)

15. 9^2 **81** **16.** 2^6 **64** **17.** 3^3 **27** **18.** 1^{12} **1** **19.** 4^5 **1,024**

Write the prime factorization of each number. (Lesson 4-2)

20. 38 $2 \cdot 19$ **21.** 50 $2 \cdot 5^2$ **22.** 120 $2^3 \cdot 3 \cdot 5$ **23.** 214 $2 \cdot 107$ **24.** 75 $3 \cdot 5^2$

Ongoing Assessment and Intervention

Diagnose **Before** the Lesson
8-8 Warm Up, TE p. 450

Monitor **During** the Lesson
8-8 Know-It Notebook
8-8 Questioning Strategies

Assess **After** the Lesson
8-8 Lesson Quiz, TE p. 453

Answers

10. Possible answer: A pattern is triangle, white stripe, upside down triangle, white stripe, triangle, etc.

11. Check that students' work includes figures from the house.

14. The dot moves around the figure from corner-to-corner in a clockwise direction.

Test Prep Doctor In Exercise 14, it might help some students to think of each figure as a frame in a strip of movie film. Have them imagine how the "action" (the changing position of the dot) progresses as they move from frame to frame.

Journal

Have students make up their own geometric patterns and describe each pattern that they make. Encourage them to make both repeating and growing patterns.

CHALLENGE 8-8

LESSON 8-8 **Challenge**
Polygon Patterns

Look for patterns to complete this chart and discover two rules for polygons.

Regular Polygon	Number of Sides, *n*	Number of Triangles to Fill	Sum of the Interior Angles
Triangle	$n = 3$	1	1(180°) = 180°
Quadrilateral	$n = 4$	2	2(180°) = 360°
Pentagon	$n = 5$	3	3(180°) = 540°
Hexagon	$n = 6$	4	4(180°) = 720°

1. Use the patterns to write an expression for the number of triangles needed to fill any regular polygon.
$n - 2$

2. Use the patterns to write an expression for the sum of all the angles inside any regular polygon.
$(n - 2)180°$

3. Using these expressions, how many triangles are needed to fill any regular octagon? What is the sum of a regular octagon's interior angles?
6; 1,080°

PROBLEM SOLVING 8-8

LESSON 8-8 **Problem Solving**
Geometric Patterns

Complete this chart and look for patterns. Then answer the questions. Possible answers are given for 1–4.

	Number of Points on the Line	Draw and Label the Line and Points	Number of Different Line Segments in the Line
	2	A B	1
1.	3	A B C	3
2.	4	A B C D	6
3.	5	A B C D E	10
4.	6	A B C D E F	15

Circle the letter of the correct answer.

5. If $n =$ the number of points on a line, which of the following expressions shows the number of different line segments on that line?
A $2n - 3$
Ⓑ $(n^2 - n) \div 2$
C $(n \div 2) \cdot 5$
D $10n \div 2$

6. Using the pattern in the table and your answer to Exercise 5, how many different line segments will be on a line if there are 10 points on the line?
F 17 line segments
G 25 line segments
Ⓗ 45 line segments
J 50 line segments

Power Presentations with PowerPoint®

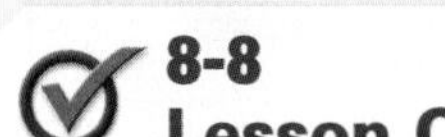

8-8 Lesson Quiz

Identify a possible pattern. Use the pattern to draw the next figure.

Possible answer: 

Also available on transparency

Organizer

Objective: Assess students' mastery of concepts and skills in Lessons 8-5 through 8-8.

Resources

Assessment Resources
Section 8B Quiz

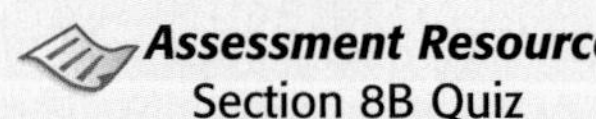

Test & Practice Generator
One-Stop Planner®

INTERVENTION

Resources

Ready to Go On? Intervention and Enrichment Worksheets

Ready to Go On? CD-ROM

Ready to Go On? Online

my.hrw.com

Answers

17–20. See p. A10.

CHAPTER 8

READY TO GO ON?

SECTION 8B

Quiz for Lessons 8-5 Through 8-8

8-5 Triangles

Use the diagram for problems 1 and 2.

1. Find m∠*SUV*. 58°
2. Classify triangle *STR* by its angles and by its sides. acute isosceles triangle

If the angles can form a triangle, classify it as acute, obtuse, or right.

3. 15°, 60°, 95° no
4. 47°, 51°, 82° acute
5. 94°, 76°, 10° obtuse
6. 78°, 102°, 20° no

8-6 Quadrilaterals

Give the most descriptive name for each figure.

7. rectangle
8. trapezoid
9. rhombus
10. square

8-7 Polygons

11. Nina cuts a regular hexagon out of poster board. What is the measure of each angle of the hexagon? 120°
12. The perimeter of an equilateral triangle is 186 centimeters. What is the length of one side of the triangle? 62 cm

Name each polygon, and tell whether it appears to be regular or not regular.

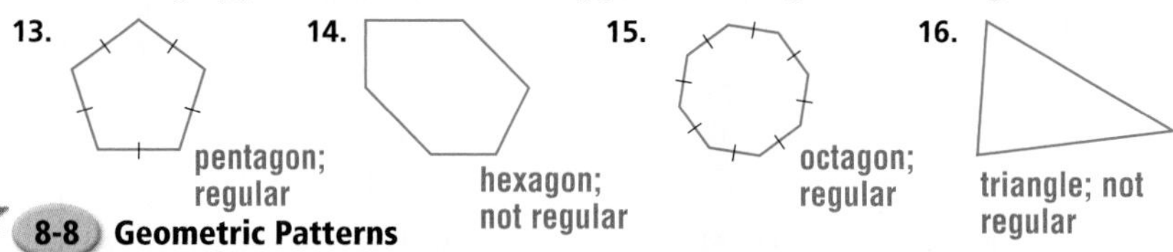

13. pentagon; regular
14. hexagon; not regular
15. octagon; regular
16. triangle; not regular

8-8 Geometric Patterns

Identify a possible pattern. Use the pattern to draw the missing figure.

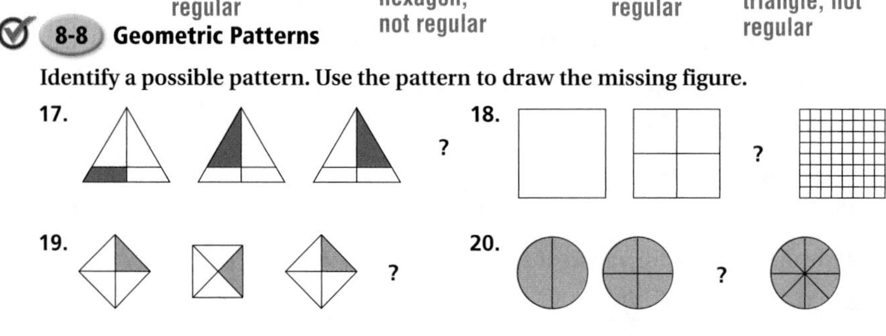

17. ?
18. ?
19. ?
20. ?

Ready to Go On?

READY TO GO ON?

Diagnose and Prescribe

NO INTERVENE

Ready to Go On? Intervention	*Ready to Go On? Intervention*, Section 8B Worksheets	CD-ROM	Online
Lesson 8-5	8-5 Intervention	Activity 8-5	Diagnose and Prescribe Online
Lesson 8-6	8-6 Intervention	Activity 8-6	
Lesson 8-7	8-7 Intervention	Activity 8-7	
Lesson 8-8	8-8 Intervention	Activity 8-8	

YES ENRICH

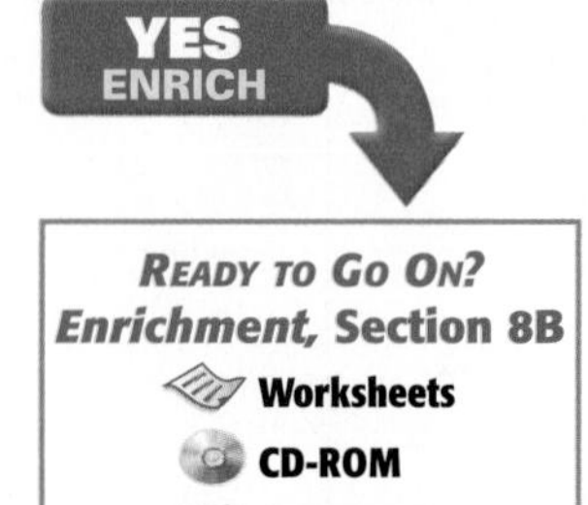

Focus on Problem Solving

Make a Plan

- **Draw a diagram**

Sometimes a problem seems difficult because it is described in words only. You can draw a diagram to help you picture the problem. Try to label all the information you are given on your diagram. Then use the diagram to solve the problem.

Read each problem. Draw a diagram to help you solve the problem. Then solve.

1. Bob used a ruler to draw a quadrilateral. First he drew a line 3 in. long and labeled it $\overline{AB}$. From *B*, he drew a line 2 in. long and labeled the endpoint *C*. From *A*, he drew a line $2\frac{1}{2}$ in. long and labeled the endpoint *D*. What is the length of $\overline{CD}$ if the perimeter of Bob's quadrilateral is $12\frac{1}{2}$ in?

2. Karen has a vegetable garden that is 12 feet long and 10 feet wide. She plans to plant tomatoes in one-half of the garden. She will divide the other half of the garden equally into three beds, where she'll grow cabbage, pumpkin, and radishes.
   a. What are the possible whole number dimensions of the tomato bed?
   b. What fraction of the garden will Karen use to grow cabbage?

3. Pam draws three parallel lines that are an equal distance apart. The two outside lines are 8 cm apart. How far apart is the middle line from the outside lines?

4. Jan connected the following points on a coordinate grid: (2, 4), (4, 6), (6, 6), (6, 2), (3, 2), and (2, 4).
   a. What figure did Jan draw?
   b. How many right angles does the figure have?

5. Triangle *ABC* is isoceles. The measure of angle *B* is equal to the measure of angle *C*. The measure of angle *B* equals 50°. What is the measure of angle *A*?

Focus on Problem Solving

Organizer

Objective: Focus on making a plan to solve the problem by drawing a diagram.

Online Edition

Resources

Chapter 8 Resource Book
Reading Strategies

Problem Solving Process

This page focuses on the second step of the problem-solving process:
Make a Plan.

Discuss

For problems 1–5, have students identify what must be labeled in each diagram.

1. names of vertices; side lengths
2. length and width of garden; length and width of each bed
3. distance between outside lines
4. names of points
5. measures of ∠B and ∠C

Answers

1. 5 inches

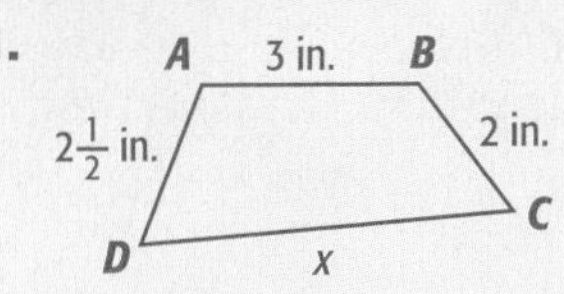

2.

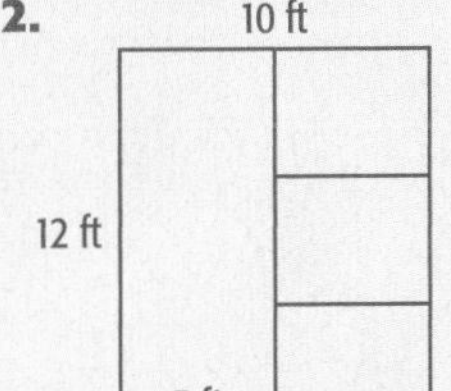

or

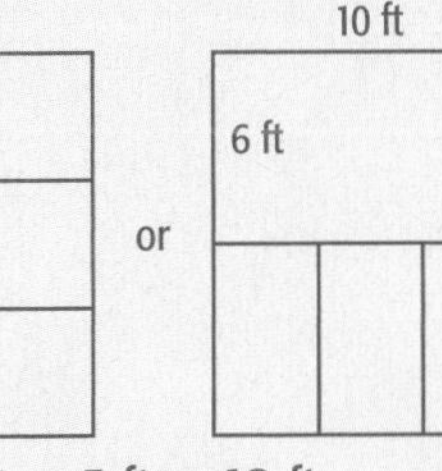

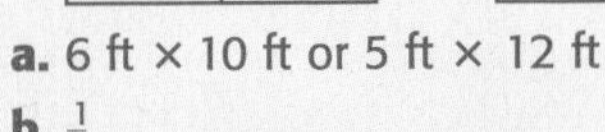

a. 6 ft × 10 ft or 5 ft × 12 ft

b. $\frac{1}{6}$

3. 4 cm

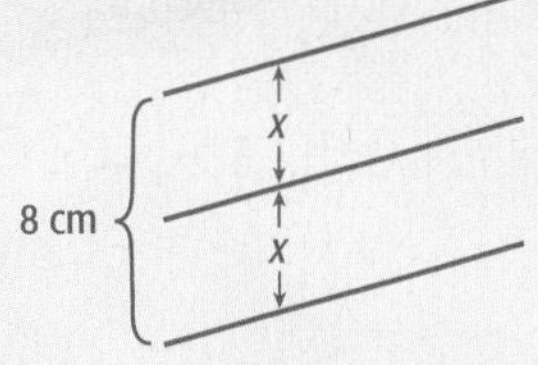

4. a. pentagon
   b. 2

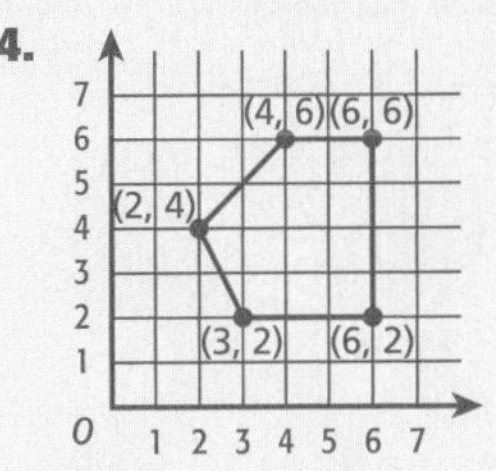

5. 80°

A, B, C; 50°, 50°

SECTION 8C

Polygon Relationships

One-Minute Section Planner

Lesson	Materials	MiC and Lab Resources
Lesson 8-9 Congruence • Identify congruent figures and use congruence to solve problems. ☐ SAT-10 ☐ ITBS ☑ CTBS ☑ NAEP	Customary rulers (MK), graph paper, straightedges (MK), scissors	**MiC:** ***Reallotment*** pp. 4–6
Lesson 8-10 Transformations • Use translations, reflections, and rotations to transform geometric shapes. **8-10 Hands-On Lab** Transformations in the Coordinate Plane • Use graph paper to record the coordinates of transformed objects. ☐ SAT-10 ☑ ITBS ☑ CTBS ☑ NAEP	Graph paper, pattern blocks (MK)	**MiC:** ***Figuring All the Angles*** pp. 26–30, 33–34 ***Hands-On Lab Activities*** 8-10 ***Technology Lab Activities*** 8-10
Lesson 8-11 Line Symmetry • Identify line symmetry. **8-11 Hands-On Lab** Create Tessellations • Use paper, scissors, and tape to make shapes that tessellate. ☐ SAT-10 ☑ ITBS ☑ CTBS ☑ NAEP	Paper, scissors, tape	**MiC:** ***Reallotment*** pp. 4–6 ***Hands-On Lab Activities*** 8-11

MK = *Manipulatives Kit*

Mathematics in Context

The units ***Figuring All the Angles*** and ***Reallotment*** from the *Mathematics in Context* © 2006 series can be used with Section 8C. See Section Planner above for suggestions for integrating *MiC* with *Holt Mathematics*.

Section Overview

Congruence — *Lesson 8-9*

Why? Manufacturers use congruent figures in mass production.

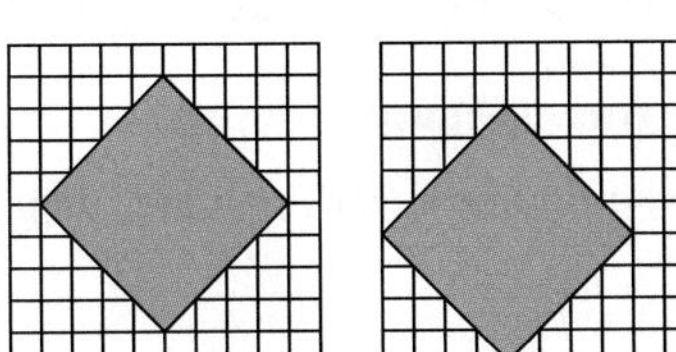

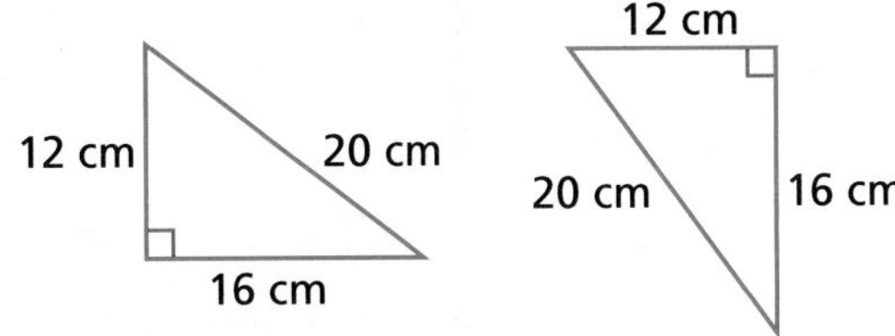

Congruent figures have the same shape and size.

Transformations — *Lesson 8-10*

Transformations can be used to alter the size, shape, or position of geometric figures.

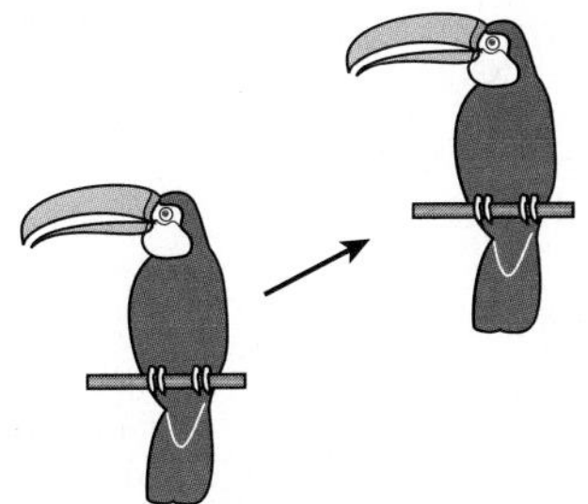

Translation

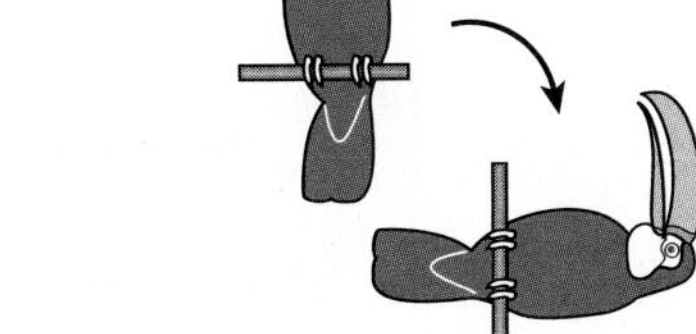

Rotation

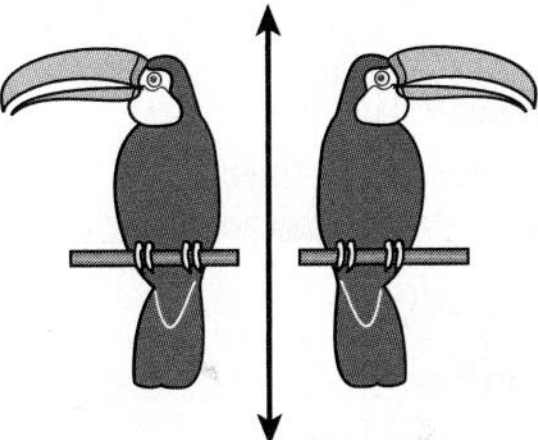

Reflection

Line Symmetry and Tesellations — *Lessons 8-11, 8-11 Hands-On Lab*

Tessellations are used in works of art.

A figure has line symmetry if it can be folded or reflected so that the two parts of the figures match, or are congruent. The line of reflection is called the line of symmetry.

A tessellation is a repeating arrangement of one or more shapes that completely cover a plane with no gaps and no overlaps.

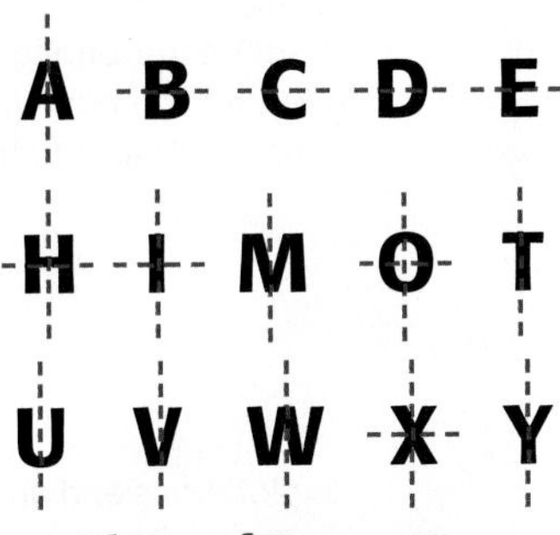

Lines of Symmetry

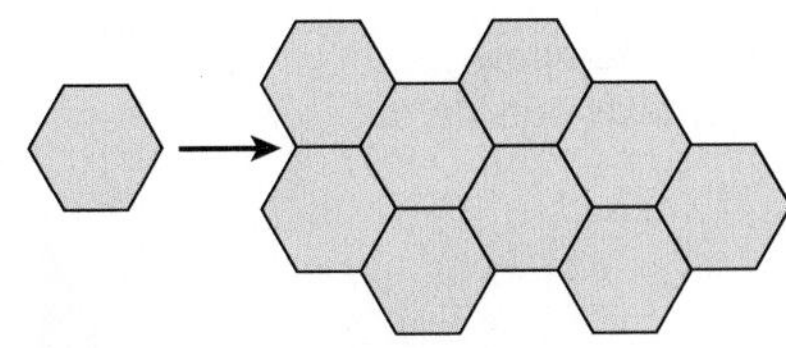

Tessellation

8-9 Organizer

Pacing: Traditional 1 day
Block $\frac{1}{2}$ day

Objective: Students identify congruent figures and use congruence to solve problems.

Online Edition
Tutorial Videos, Interactivities

Countdown to CRCT Week 19

Power Presentations with PowerPoint®

Warm Up

1. $\frac{3}{4} - \frac{1}{3}$ $\frac{5}{12}$ **2.** $3\frac{1}{2} \times 2\frac{2}{3}$ $9\frac{1}{3}$

Problem of the Day

The sum of two decimals is 9.3; their difference is 4.3, and their product is 17.00. What are they? **2.5, 6.8**

Also available on transparency

Power Presentations with PowerPoint®

Additional Examples

Example 1

Decide whether the figures are congruent. If not, explain.

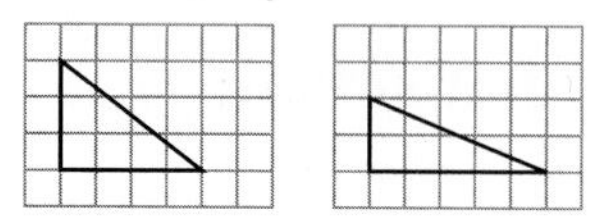

No; the triangles are not the same size.

Also available on transparency

Georgia Performance Standards

M6P1.b Solve problems that arise in mathematics and in other contexts.

M6P2.c Develop and evaluate mathematical arguments and proofs.

M6P4.c Recognize and apply mathematics in contexts outside of mathematics.

8-9 Congruence

Learn to identify congruent figures and to use congruence to solve problems.

You know that angles that have the same measure are congruent. Figures that have the same shape and same size are also congruent.

You can use stencils to decorate pages of a scrapbook. The stencil helps you draw congruent figures.

Georgia Performance Standards

M6P2.c Develop and evaluate mathematical arguments and proofs. Also, M6P1.b, M6P4.c.

EXAMPLE 1 Identifying Congruent Figures

Decide whether the figures in each pair are congruent. If not, explain.

A

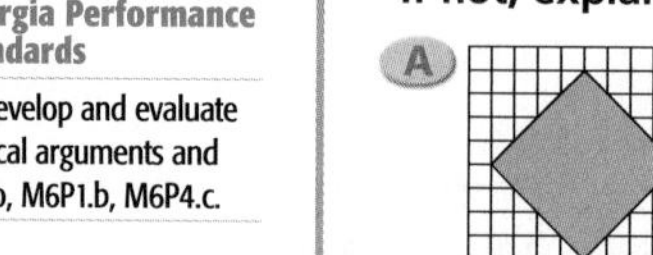

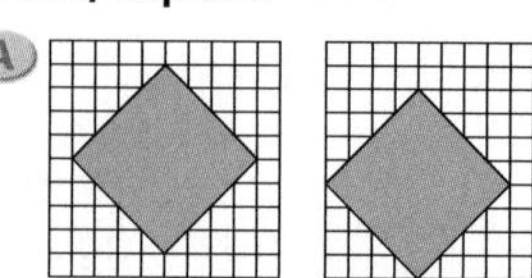

The figures are congruent.

These figures have the same shape and size.

B

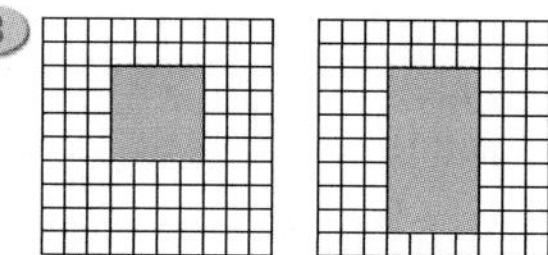

The figures are not congruent.

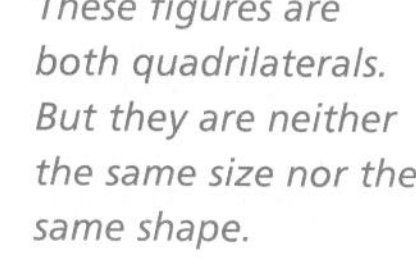

These figures are both quadrilaterals. But they are neither the same size nor the same shape.

C

12 cm 20 cm 16 cm | 12 cm 20 cm 16 cm

The triangles are congruent.

Each triangle has a 12 cm side, a 16 cm side, and a 20 cm side.

D

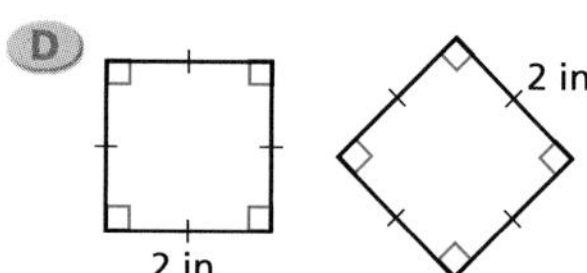

The figures are congruent.

Each figure is a square. Each side of each square measures 2 inches.

1 Introduce

Alternate Opener

EXPLORATION

8-9 Congruence

Congruent figures are exactly the same shape and size.

1. Connect two congruent figures with a line. Two congruent rectangles have been connected for you to use as a guide.

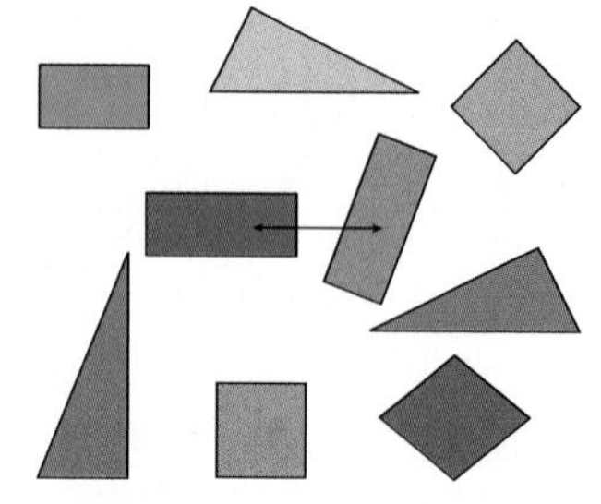

2. Measure the sides and angles of each pair of connected figures to be sure that they are congruent.

Think and Discuss

3. **Give examples** of congruent figures that occur in the real world.

2 Teach

Guided Instruction

In this lesson, students learn to identify congruent figures and to use congruence to solve problems. Explain that congruent figures need not be oriented in the same way. Have students draw the figures in Examples 1A and 1B on graph paper and cut them out to test congruence. Discuss reasons for needing to know whether figures are congruent, as illustrated in Example 2.

Explorations and answers are provided in *Alternate Openers: Explorations Transparencies.*

EXAMPLE 2 *Consumer Application*

Landra needs a ground cloth that is congruent to the tent floor. Which ground cloth should she buy?

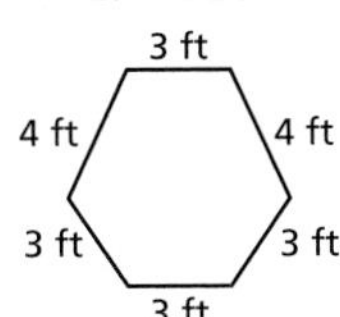

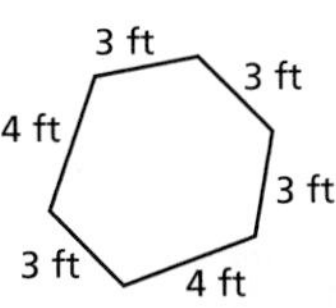

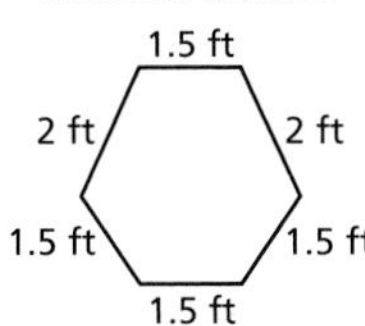

Which ground cloth is the same size and shape as the tent floor?
Both cloths are hexagons. Only Cloth A is the same size as the floor.

Cloth A is congruent to the tent floor.

Possible answers to *Think and Discuss*

1. No; two figures may look like they are the same size, but you cannot be certain unless you measure the corresponding parts of the figures.
2. If the lengths and widths of two rectangles are equal, then the rectangles are congruent.

Think and Discuss GPS M6P2.c, M6P3.b

1. **Explain** whether you can determine that figures are congruent just by looking at them.
2. **Tell** what information you would need to know about two rectangles to determine whether they are congruent.

Power Presentations with PowerPoint®

Additional Examples

Example 2

Jodi needs a sleeping pad that is congruent to her sleeping bag. Which pad should she buy?

Sleeping bag

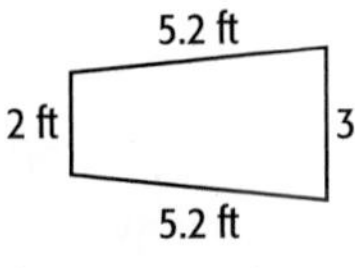

Sleeping pad A

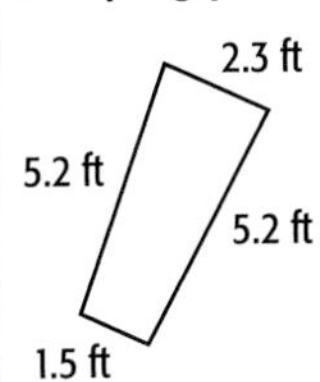

Sleeping pad B

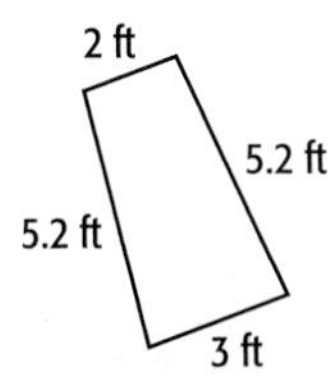

sleeping pad B

Also available on transparency

8-9 Exercises

Georgia Performance Standards
M6M2.a, M6P2.c, M6P3.a

go.hrw.com
Homework Help Online
KEYWORD: MR7 8-9
Parent Resources Online
KEYWORD: MR7 Parent

GUIDED PRACTICE

See Example 1
Decide whether the figures in each pair are congruent. If not, explain.

1.

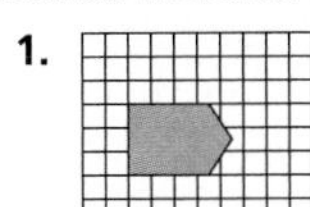

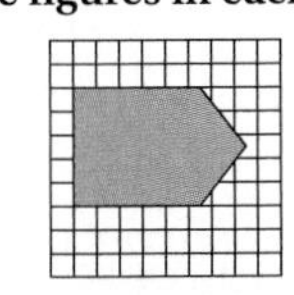

not congruent; different sizes

2.

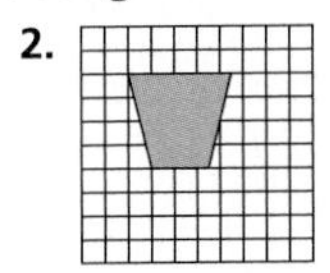

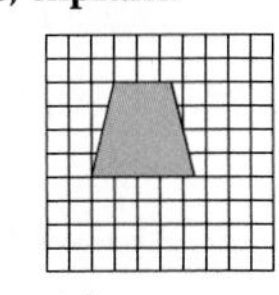

congruent

See Example 2
3. Which quadrilateral is congruent to the bottom of the box? Figure A

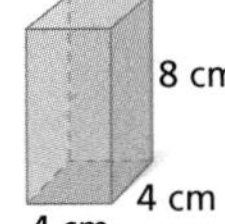

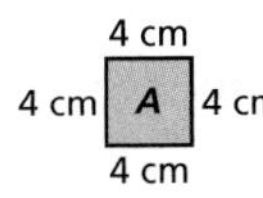

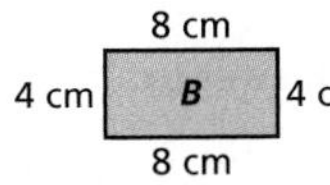

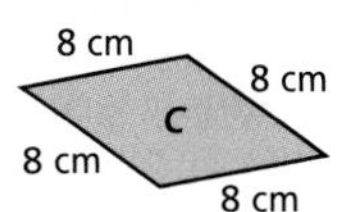

8-9 Exercises

Assignment Guide

If you finished Example 1 assign:
Average 1–2, 11–20
Advanced 4–5, 11–20

If you finished Example 2 assign:
Average 1–6, 8–20
Advanced 4–20

Homework Quick Check

Quickly check key concepts.
Exercises: 4, 6

Reaching All Learners
Through Cooperative Learning

Give groups of students sheets of graph paper. The student leader of each group draws a triangle, a quadrilateral, and a pentagon on his or her paper. Then the other group members draw figures that are congruent. Have the group discuss why some, if any, of the figures are not congruent. This continues until each group member has had a chance to be the leader.

3 Close

Summarize

Ask students how they can tell whether two figures are congruent.

Possible answer: Two figures are congruent if they are the same shape and the same size.

Georgia Performance Standards

M6M2.a Measure length to the nearest half, fourth, eighth and sixteenth of an inch.

M6P2.c Develop and evaluate mathematical arguments and proofs.

M6P3.a Organize and consolidate their mathematical thinking through communication.

ONGOING ASSESSMENT

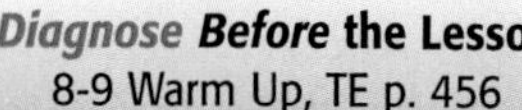
and INTERVENTION

Diagnose **Before** the Lesson
8-9 Warm Up, TE p. 456

Monitor **During** the Lesson
8-9 Know-It Notebook
8-9 Questioning Strategies

Assess **After** the Lesson
8-9 Lesson Quiz, TE p. 458

Answers

7–8. See p. A10.

Power Presentations with PowerPoint®

8-9 Lesson Quiz

True or false?

1. If two figures have sides of the same length, they are congruent. false
2. Congruent figures have angle measures that are equal. true
3. Decide whether the figures are congruent. If not, explain.

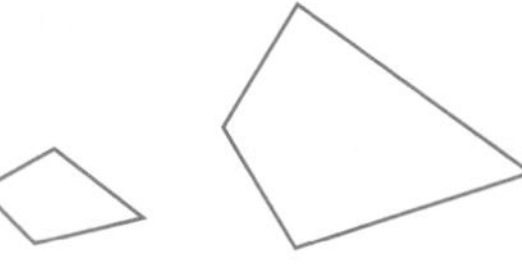

No; both are quadrilaterals, but they are not the same size or shape.

Also available on transparency

INDEPENDENT PRACTICE

See Example 1 Decide whether the figures in each pair are congruent. If not, explain.

4. 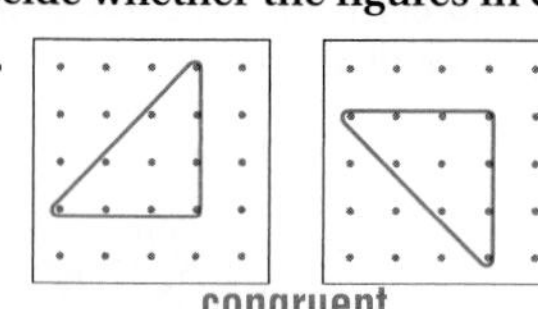 congruent

5. 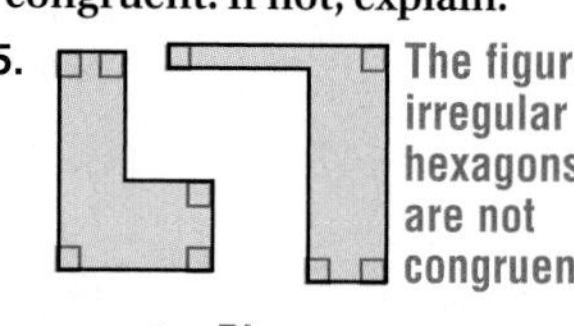 The figures are irregular hexagons that are not congruent.

See Example 2 **6.** Which puzzle piece will fit into the empty space? Piece a

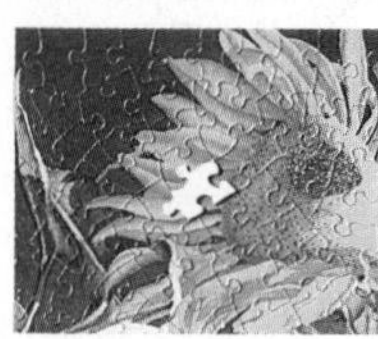

a.  b. 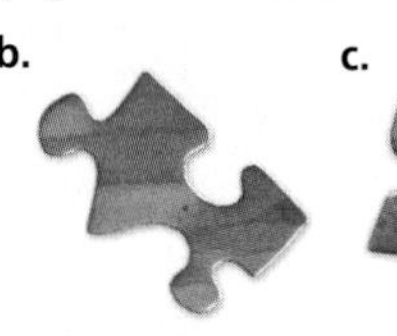 c. 

PRACTICE AND PROBLEM SOLVING

CRCT GPS
Extra Practice p. 730

7. Copy the dot grid. Then draw three figures congruent to the given figure. The figures can have common sides but should not overlap.

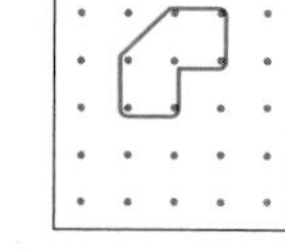

8. **Measurement** Use an inch ruler to draw two congruent rectangles with side lengths that are longer than 2 in. and shorter than 6 in. Label each side length.

9. **Write About It** Explain how to tell whether two polygons are congruent.

9. Possible answer: You can measure the sides and angles to make sure they are the same size and shape.

10. **Challenge** Two quadrilaterals have side lengths 2 cm, 2 cm, 5 cm, and 5 cm. Are the two quadrilaterals congruent? Explain.
Not necessarily; one may be a rectangle with 90° angles, and one may be a parallelogram with angles less than and greater than 90°.

CRCT PREP • GPS SUPPORT • SPIRAL REVIEW

11. **Multiple Choice** Squares *ABCD* and *WXYZ* are congruent. The length of $\overline{AB}$ is 5 in. What is the length of $\overline{WX}$?

Ⓐ 5 in. (circled) Ⓑ 9 in. Ⓒ 20 in. Ⓓ 25 in.

12. **Multiple Choice** Hexagons *FGHJKL* and *RSTWXY* are congruent and regular. The length of $\overline{FG}$ is 7 km. Find the perimeter of hexagon *RSTWXY*.

Ⓕ 7 km Ⓖ 35 km Ⓗ 42 km (circled) Ⓙ 49 km

Solve each equation. Check your answers. (Lesson 2-7)

13. $9y = 81$ $y = 9$ **14.** $70 = 10x$ $x = 7$ **15.** $64 = 8n$ $n = 8$ **16.** $60 = 12m$ $m = 5$

Multiply. Write each answer in simplest form. (Lesson 5-7)

17. $\frac{2}{3} \cdot \frac{4}{7}$ $\frac{8}{21}$ **18.** $\frac{1}{5} \cdot \frac{3}{8}$ $\frac{3}{40}$ **19.** $\frac{3}{4} \cdot \frac{1}{2}$ $\frac{3}{8}$ **20.** $\frac{4}{5} \cdot \frac{1}{3}$ $\frac{4}{15}$

CHALLENGE 8-9
PROBLEM SOLVING 8-9

LESSON 8-9 Problem Solving
Congruence

Write the correct answer.

1. Similar figures have the same shape but may have different sizes. How are similar figures different from congruent figures?
Congruent figures must have the same shape and size.
2. Pentagon A and Pentagon B are congruent regular polygons. If the total length of the sides of Pentagon B is 68.5 feet, what is the length of each side of Pentagon A?
13.7 feet
3. Is the following statement always true, sometimes true, or never true? Two congruent figures are similar figures. Explain.
Always true; Possible answer: Congruent figures have the same shape, which is the definition of similar figures.
4. Draw a figure congruent to this line segment. Explain how you drew your congruent figure.
A B
I measured the line segment and drew mine the same length.

Circle the letter of the correct answer.

5. Which word makes this statement true? Corresponding parts of congruent figures are ______.
A not regular
(B) congruent
C polygons
D horizontal
6. If two angles of a right triangle are congruent, what are the measures of each angle in the triangle?
F 35°, 55°, and 90°
(G) 45°, 45°, and 90°
H 50°, 50°, and 90°
J 55°, 55°, and 90°
7. Which of the following polygons do not always have all congruent sides?
A a square
B an equilateral triangle
C a rhombus
(D) a pentagon
8. If ∠A of rectangle *ABCD* is congruent to ∠X of triangle *XYZ*, which of these statements is true?
F Rectangle *ABCD* is also a square.
(G) Triangle *XYZ* is a right triangle.
H Rectangle *ABCD* is a regular polygon.
J Triangle *XYZ* is an acute triangle.

RETEACH 8-9

LESSON 8-9 Reteach
Congruence

Two figures are congruent if they have the same size and shape.

Look at the two figures.

They are congruent because they are both triangles and they are the same size.

Now look at these two figures.

These figures are not congruent. They are both rectangles but they are not the same size.

Decide whether the figures in each pair are congruent. If not, explain.

1. The figures are congruent.
2. The figures are not congruent; they are not the same shape.
3. The figures are congruent.

PRACTICE 8-9

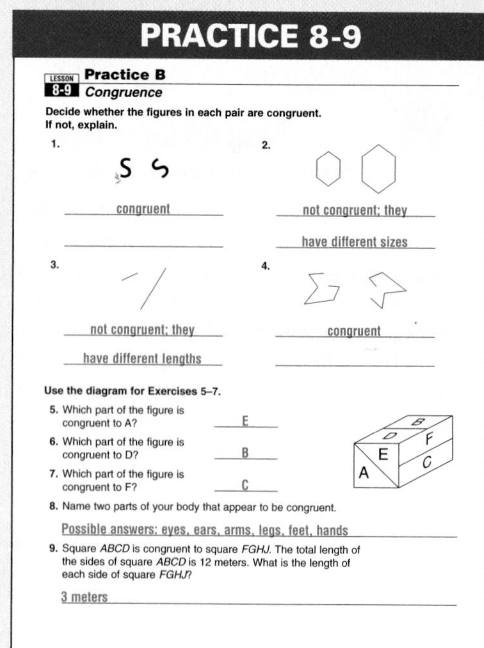

LESSON 8-9 Practice B
Congruence

Decide whether the figures in each pair are congruent. If not, explain.

1. congruent
2. not congruent; they have different sizes
3. not congruent; they have different lengths
4. congruent

Use the diagram for Exercises 5–7.

5. Which part of the figure is congruent to A? E
6. Which part of the figure is congruent to D? B
7. Which part of the figure is congruent to F? C
8. Name two parts of your body that appear to be congruent.
Possible answers: eyes, ears, arms, legs, feet, hands
9. Square *ABCD* is congruent to square *FGHJ*. The total length of the sides of square *ABCD* is 12 meters. What is the length of each side of square *FGHJ*?
3 meters

8-10 Transformations

Learn to use translations, reflections, and rotations to transform geometric shapes.

Vocabulary
- transformation
- translation
- rotation
- reflection
- line of reflection

Georgia Performance Standards

M6P5.a Create and use representations to organize and communicate mathematical ideas. Also, M6P3.d, M6P5.b.

A rigid **transformation** moves a figure without changing its size or shape. So the original figure and the transformed figure are always congruent.

The illustrations of the alien show three transformations: a *translation*, a *rotation*, and a *reflection*. Notice the transformed alien does not change in size or shape.

A **translation** is the movement of a figure along a straight line.

Only the location of the figure changes with a translation.

A **rotation** is the movement of a figure around a point. A point of rotation can be on or outside a figure.

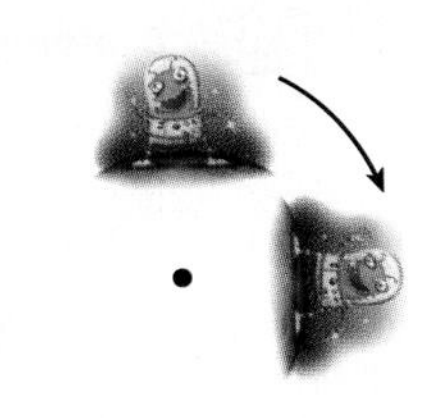

The location and position of a figure can change with a rotation.

When a figure flips over a line, creating a mirror image, it is called a **reflection**. The line the figure is flipped over is called the **line of reflection**.

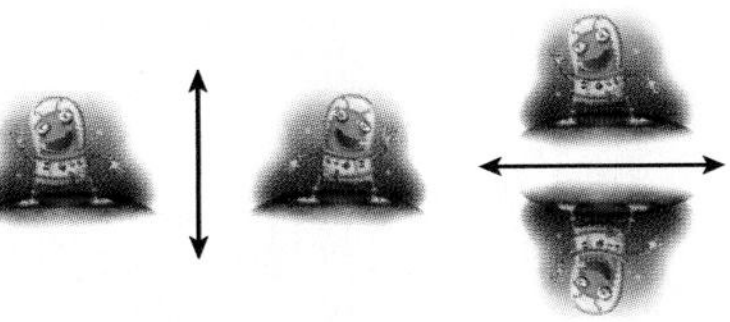

The location and position of a figure change with a reflection.

EXAMPLE 1 Identifying Transformations

Tell whether each is a translation, rotation, or reflection.

A

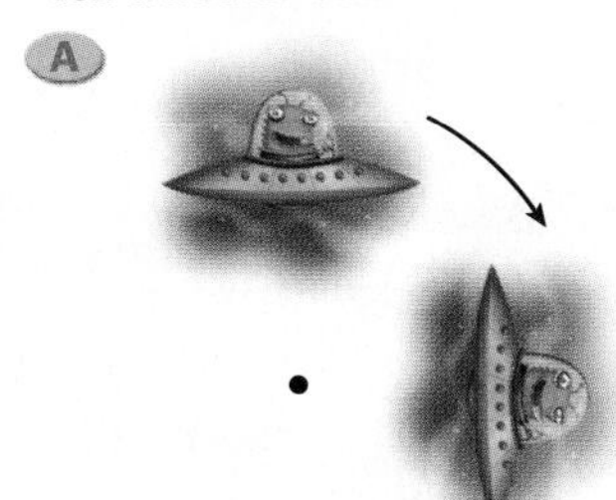

The figure moves around a point.

It is a rotation.

Organizer 8-10

Pacing: Traditional 1 day
Block $\frac{1}{2}$ day

Objective: Students use translations, reflections, and rotations to transform geometric shapes.

Hands-On Lab
In *Hands-On Lab Activities*

Technology Lab
In *Technology Lab Activities*

Online Edition
Tutorial Videos, Interactivities

Countdown to CRCT Week 19

Power Presentations with PowerPoint®

Warm Up

Find the supplement of each angle.

1. 35° 145° **2.** 95° 85°

Problem of the Day

Imagine that each figure is folded so that point A lies on point B. What figures would be formed?

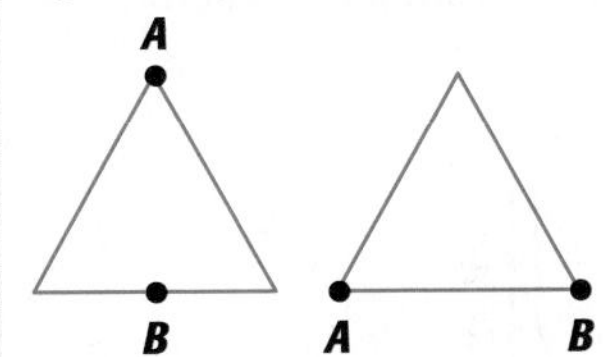

trapezoid, right triangle

Also available on transparency

1 Introduce

Alternate Opener

EXPLORATION

8-10 Transformations

The green triangle is a *reflection* of the blue triangle across the solid vertical line.

1. Reflect the green triangle across the horizontal line, and then reflect the resulting triangle across the vertical line.

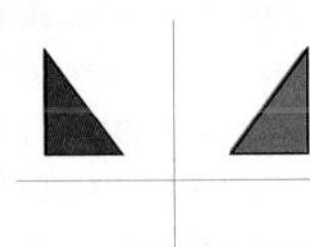

The orange triangle is a *translation* of the yellow triangle down and to the right.

2. Translate the orange triangle up and to the right.

Think and Discuss

3. Define *reflection* in your own words.
4. Define *translation* in your own words.

Motivate

To introduce students to transformations, show them the pictures on the Teaching Transparency, and have them explain the relationship between the figures in each.

Possible answers: The triangles are on the same line as each other. The hearts are mirror images of each other. The cat heads are turned in different directions.

Explorations and answers are provided in *Alternate Openers: Explorations Transparencies.*

Georgia Performance Standards

M6P3.d Use the language of mathematics to express mathematical ideas precisely.

M6P5.a Create and use representations to organize, record, and communicate mathematical ideas.

M6P5.b Select, apply, and translate among mathematical representations to solve problems.

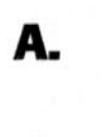

Additional Examples

Example 1

Tell whether each is a translation, rotation, or reflection.

A.

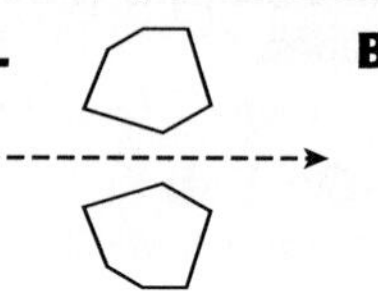

reflection

B.

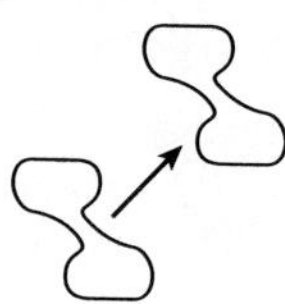

translation

C.

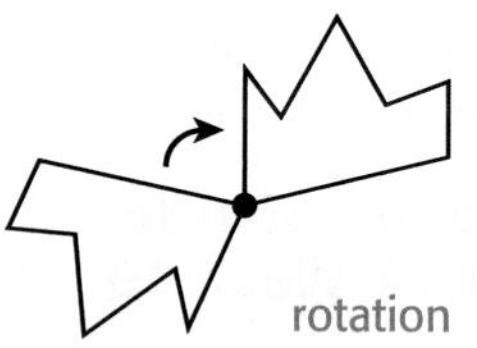

rotation

Example 2

Draw each transformation.

A. Draw a 180° rotation about the point shown.

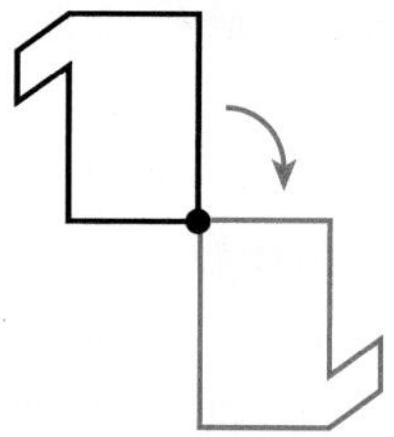

B. Draw a horizontal reflection.

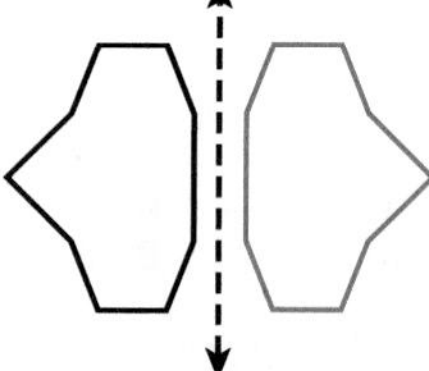

Also available on transparency

Tell whether each is a translation, rotation, or reflection.

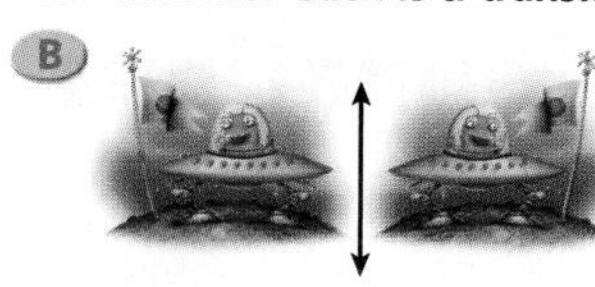

B

The figure is flipped over a line.

It is a reflection.

C

The figure is moved along a line.

It is a translation.

A full turn is a 360° rotation. So a $\frac{1}{4}$ turn is 90°, and a $\frac{1}{2}$ turn is 180°.

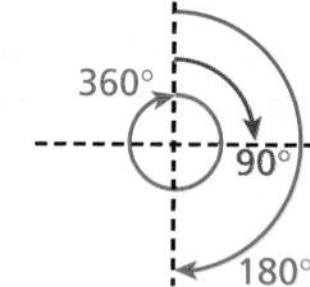

EXAMPLE 2 Drawing Transformations

Draw each transformation.

A

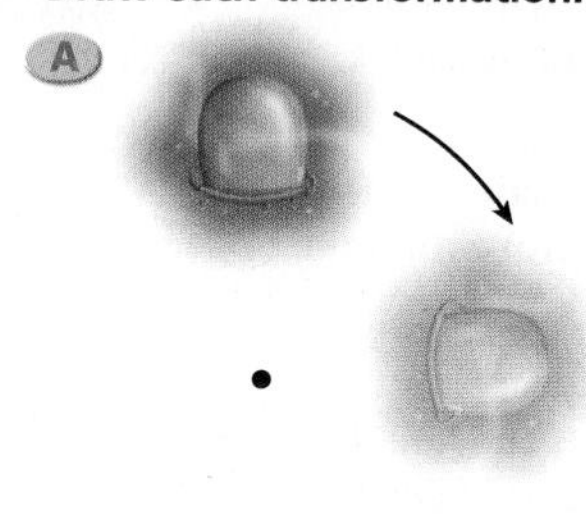

Draw a 90° clockwise rotation about the point shown.

Trace the figure and the point of rotation.

Place your pencil on the point of rotation.

Rotate the figure clockwise 90°.

Trace the figure in its new location.

B

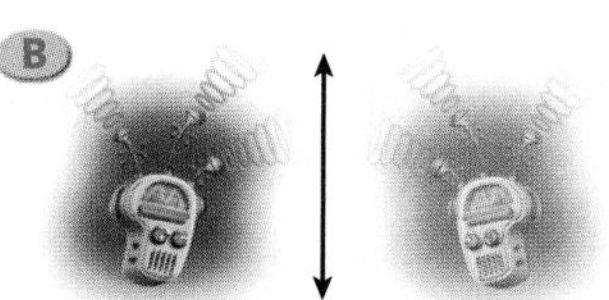

Draw a horizontal reflection.

Trace the figure and the line of reflection.

Fold along the line of reflection.

Trace the figure in its new location.

Answers to *Think and Discuss*

1. Possible answers: wallpaper designs, reflections in a mirror, reflections of buildings or trees in a lake
2. Possible answer: any figure rotated 360° about any point

Think and Discuss

1. **Give examples** of reflections that occur in the real world.
2. **Name** a figure that can be rotated so that it will land on top of itself.

2 Teach

Guided Instruction

In this lesson, students learn to use translations, reflections, and rotations to transform geometric shapes. Teach students first to identify transformations and then to draw transformations.

Kinesthetic Experience Have students trace and cut out the figures shown in the examples so they can physically perform the transformations shown.

Review the meaning of *clockwise* and *counterclockwise* for Example 2.

Reaching All Learners

Through Concrete Manipulatives

Have each student draw some unusual plane figures on graph paper. Then have them translate, rotate, and reflect each figure.

Have students mount their drawings on poster board and label each transformation.

3 Close

English Language Learners

Summarize

Review the vocabulary from the lesson. In a rigid *transformation,* a figure is moved without changing its size or shape. In a *rotation,* a figure is turned around a point. In a *reflection,* a mirror image is created across a line. In a *translation,* a figure is moved along a line. Provide examples of each.

8-10 Exercises

Georgia Performance Standards

M6P1.b, M6P1.c, M6P3.a, M6P3.d

GUIDED PRACTICE

See Example 1 Tell whether each is a translation, rotation, or reflection.

1. 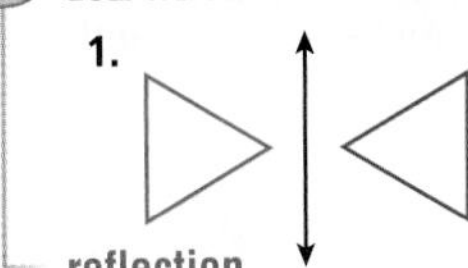
reflection

2. 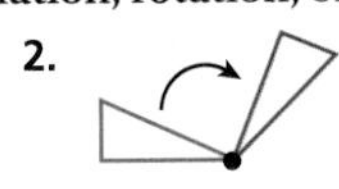
rotation

3. 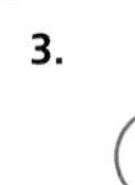
translation

See Example 2 Draw each transformation.

4. Draw a 180° clockwise rotation about the point shown.

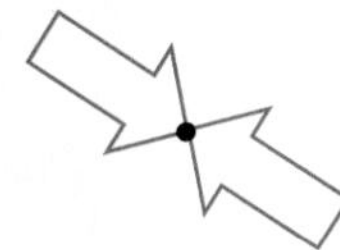

5. Draw a horizontal reflection across the line.

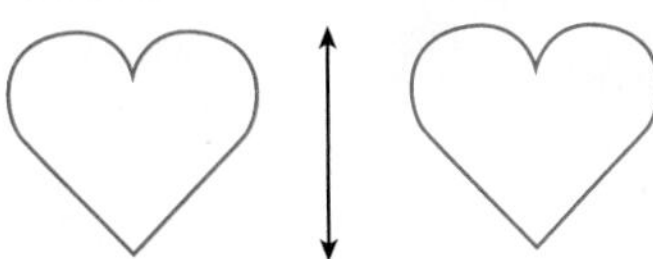

INDEPENDENT PRACTICE

See Example 1 Tell whether each is a translation, rotation, or reflection.

6. 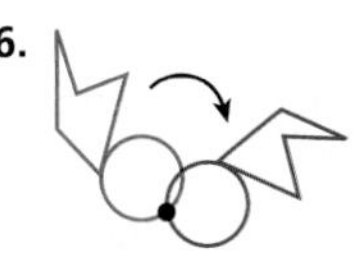
rotation

7. 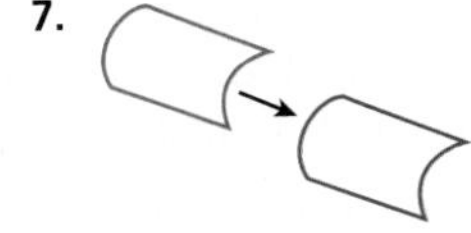
translation

8. 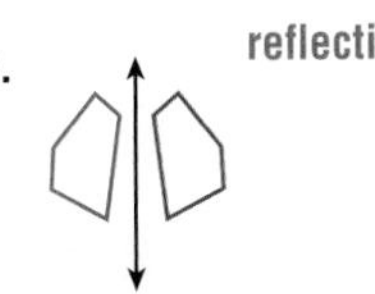
reflection

See Example 2 Draw each transformation.

9. Draw a vertical reflection across the line.

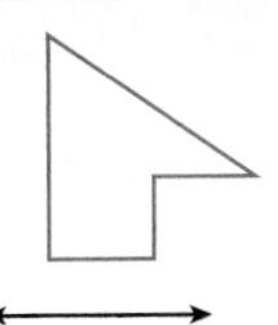

10. Draw a 90° counterclockwise rotation about the point.

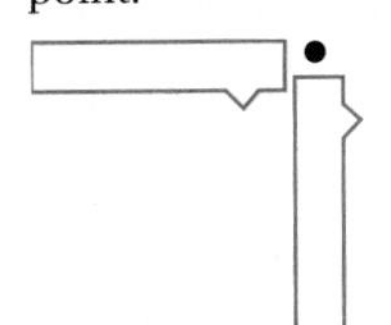

11. Draw a translation.

Possible answer:

12. Draw a translation.

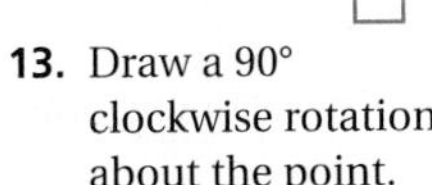

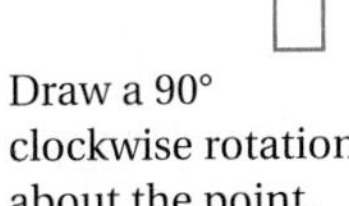

13. Draw a 90° clockwise rotation about the point.

14. Draw a horizontal reflection across the line.

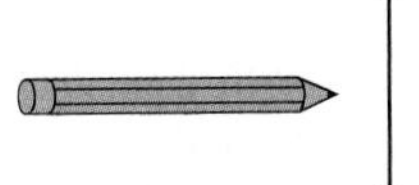

RETEACH 8-10

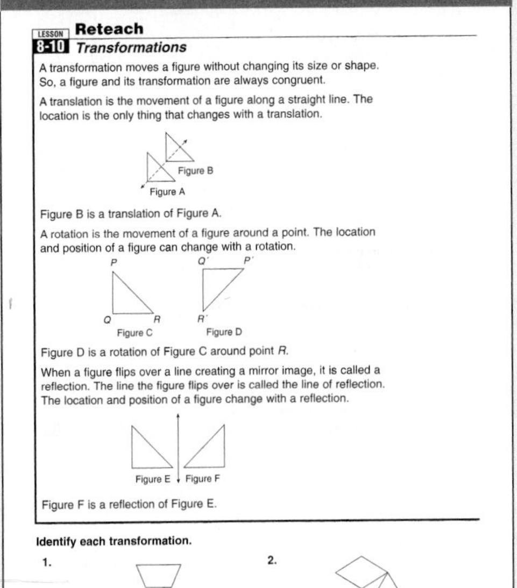

LESSON 8-10 **Reteach**
Transformations

A transformation moves a figure without changing its size or shape. So, a figure and its transformation are always congruent.

A translation is the movement of a figure along a straight line. The location is the only thing that changes with a translation.

Figure B
Figure A

Figure B is a translation of Figure A.

A rotation is the movement of a figure around a point. The location and position of a figure can change with a rotation.

P Q′ P′
Q R R′
Figure C Figure D

Figure D is a rotation of Figure C around point *R*.

When a figure flips over a line creating a mirror image, it is called a reflection. The line the figure flips over is called the line of reflection. The location and position of a figure change with a reflection.

Figure E Figure F

Figure F is a reflection of Figure E.

Identify each transformation.

1. translation

2. rotation or reflection

PRACTICE 8-10

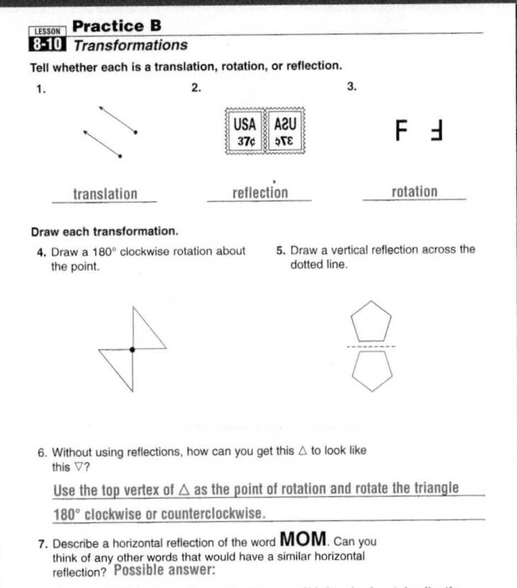

LESSON 8-10 **Practice B**
Transformations

Tell whether each is a translation, rotation, or reflection.

1. translation
2. reflection
3. rotation

Draw each transformation.

4. Draw a 180° clockwise rotation about the point.

5. Draw a vertical reflection across the dotted line.

6. Without using reflections, how can you get this △ to look like this ▽?

Use the top vertex of △ as the point of rotation and rotate the triangle 180° clockwise or counterclockwise.

7. Describe a horizontal reflection of the word MOM. Can you think of any other words that would have a similar horizontal reflection? Possible answer:

The word MOM will look exactly the same if it is a horizontal reflection left or right. Other possible words: TOOT, HAH

8-10 Exercises

Assignment Guide

If you finished Example 1 assign:
Average 1–3, 15, 21–30
Advanced 6–8, 15, 21–30

If you finished Example 2 assign:
Average 1–11, 16–30
Advanced 6–30

Homework Quick Check

Quickly check key concepts.
Exercises: 6, 8, 10

Answers

9, 12–14. See p. A10.

Math Background

You can combine two or more transformations to form a *composition*. An example of a composition is the glide reflection. A glide reflection is created by reflecting a figure across a given line and then translating the resulting figure along that same line.

An example of a transformation that changes size (but not shape) is a dilation. When a geometric figure undergoes a dilation, the resulting figure is similar to the original figure.

Georgia Performance Standards

M6P1.b Solve problems that arise in mathematics and in other contexts.

M6P1.c Apply and adapt a variety of appropriate strategies to solve problems.

M6P3.a Organize and consolidate their mathematical thinking through communication.

M6P3.d Use the language of mathematics to express mathematical ideas precisely.

ONGOING ASSESSMENT and INTERVENTION

Diagnose **Before** the Lesson
8-10 Warm Up, TE p. 459

Monitor **During** the Lesson
8-10 Know-It Notebook
8-10 Questioning Strategies

Assess **After** the Lesson
8-10 Lesson Quiz, TE p. 462

Answers

16. horizontally: A, H, I, M, O, T, U, V, W, X, Y; vertically: B, C, D, E, H, I, O, X

17.

19–20. See p. A10.

TEST PREP DOCTOR In Exercise 22, some students may find it helpful to associate a reflection in a mirror with a geometric reflection. It could be said that in both cases the objects appear to be facing their reflection.

Journal

Have students create a design using transformations. Have them explain what kinds of transformations they used.

Power Presentations with PowerPoint®

8-10 Lesson Quiz

1. Tell whether the figure is translated, rotated, or reflected. rotated

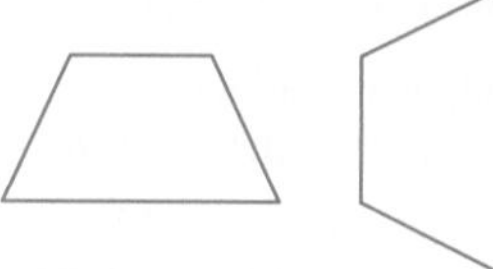

2. Draw a vertical reflection of the first figure in problem 1.

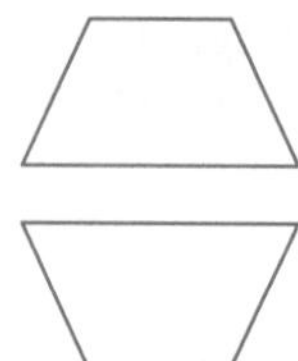

Also available on transparency

PRACTICE AND PROBLEM SOLVING

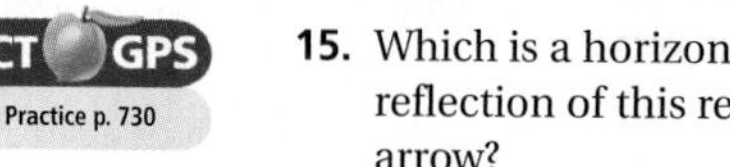

CRCT GPS Extra Practice p. 730

15. Which is a horizontal reflection of this red arrow?

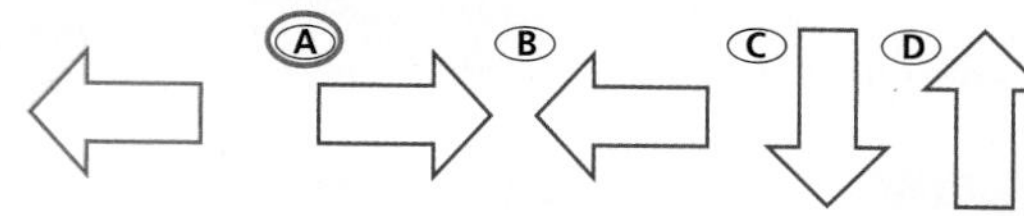

Ⓐ Ⓑ Ⓒ Ⓓ

16. Language Arts Which letters in the alphabet can be horizontally reflected and still look the same? Which letters can be vertically reflected and still look the same?

LINK Hobbies

In a game of chess, each player has 318,979,564,000 possible ways to make the first four moves.

Use the chessboard for Exercises 17–20.

Hobbies Chess is a game of skill that is played on a board divided into 64 squares. Each chess piece is moved differently.

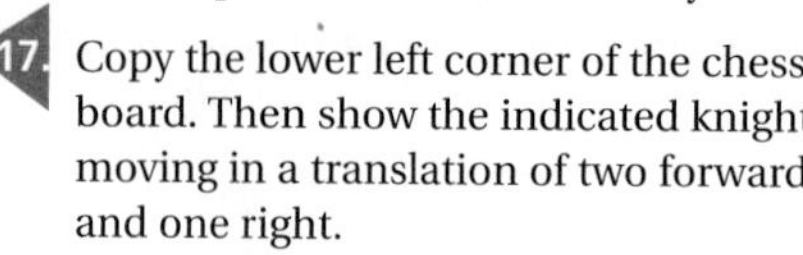

17. Copy the lower left corner of the chessboard. Then show the indicated knight moving in a translation of two forward and one right.

Knight

King

Pawn

18. Choose a Strategy If the knight, king, and pawn are placed in a straight line, how many ways can they be arranged?

Ⓐ 3 Ⓑ 4 Ⓒ 6 Ⓓ 12

19. Write About It Draw one of the chess pieces. Then draw a translation, rotation, and reflection of that piece. Describe each transformation.

20. Challenge Draw one of the chess pieces rotated 90° clockwise around the vertex of a square and then horizontally reflected.

CRCT PREP • GPS SUPPORT • SPIRAL REVIEW

21. Multiple Choice What is the movement of a figure about a point?

Ⓐ Translation Ⓑ Tessellation Ⓒ Reflection Ⓓ Rotation

22. Short Response Tell whether the picture shows a rotation, translation, or reflection. Explain.
Reflection; the figure is flipped.

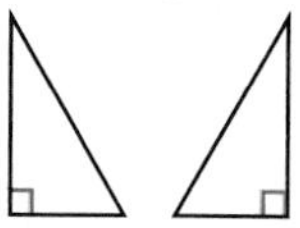

Write each phrase as a numerical or algebraic expression. *(Lesson 2-2)*

23. 19 times 3 19×3

24. the quotient of g divided by 6 $g \div 6$

25. the sum of 5 and 9 $5 + 9$

Write each decimal as a fraction or mixed number. *(Lesson 4-4)*

26. 0.9 $\frac{9}{10}$

27. 6.71 $6\frac{71}{100}$

28. 0.20 $\frac{1}{5}$

29. 2.88 $2\frac{22}{25}$

30. 0.55 $\frac{11}{20}$

CHALLENGE 8-10

LESSON 8-10 **Challenge**
Rotation Ride

The Ferris wheel shown below is turning clockwise around its rotation point at the center of the wheel. For each person on the Ferris wheel, describe how many degrees he or she must rotate to be able to get off the ride.

Carlos, Jenna, Ben, Mei, Darius, Sarah, Mindy, Paul

1. Darius	90°	**2.** Jenna	225°
3. Paul	0°	**4.** Sarah	315°
5. Mei	270°	**6.** Ben	135°
7. Mindy	45°	**8.** Carlos	180°

PROBLEM SOLVING 8-10

LESSON 8-10 **Problem Solving**
Transformations

Write the correct answer.

1. If the rotation point of a circle is its center, how will all rotations affect the circle?
The circle will never change.

2. What transformation could make an arrow pointing east become an arrow pointing north?
a 90° counterclockwise rotation

3. What transformation could make the number 9 become the number 6?
a vertical and a horizontal reflection or a 180° rotation

4. What transformation could make the letter P look like the letter b?
a vertical reflection

5. On the coordinate plane at right, graph Triangle A with vertices (3, 1), (6, 1), and (3, 5). Then graph Triangle B with vertices (3, 6), (6, 6), and (3, 10). What transformation best describes the change from Triangle A to Triangle B?
vertical translation

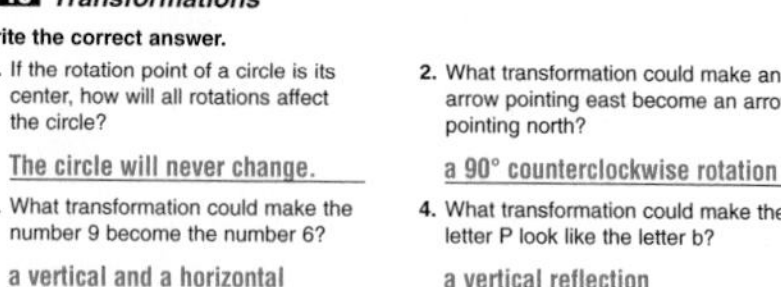

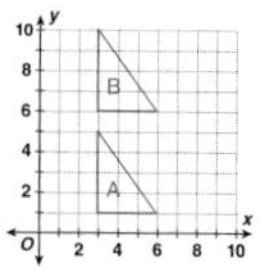

Circle the letter of the correct answer.

6. Which transformation best describes the figure on the right?

A 90° clockwise rotation
B horizontal reflection
Ⓒ 90° counterclockwise rotation
D horizontal translation

7. Which transformation best describes the figure on the left?

Ⓕ horizontal reflection
G 180° counterclockwise rotation
H 90° counterclockwise rotation
J horizontal translation

Transformations in the Coordinate Plane

Use with Lesson 8-10

Georgia Performance Standards
M6P1.c, M6P4.a, M6P4.b

Activity

1. Draw the first quadrant of a coordinate plane on graph paper.

   Place a red pattern block on the coordinate plane so the endpoints are on (1, 1), (1, 6), (3, 5), and (3, 2). Trace around the figure and label it Figure A.

   Move the figure so that its endpoints are on (5, 1), (5, 6), (7, 5), and (7, 2). Trace around the figure and label it Figure B.

   Describe the shape, size, and position of Figure B compared with those of Figure A.

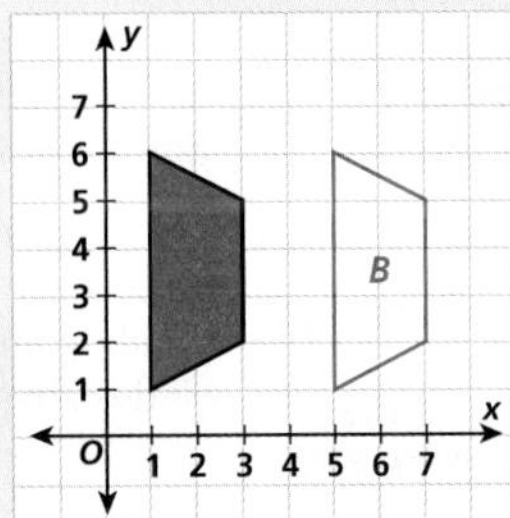

One kind of transformation when only the location of a figure changes is called a *translation*.

2. Draw the first quadrant of a coordinate plane on graph paper.

   Place an orange pattern block on the coordinate plane so the endpoints are on (3, 3), (3, 5), (5, 5), and (5, 3). Trace around the figure and label it Figure C.

   Draw Figure D so that its endpoints are on (3, 1), (3, 5), (7, 5), and (7, 1).

   Describe the shape, size, and position of Figure C compared with those of Figure D.

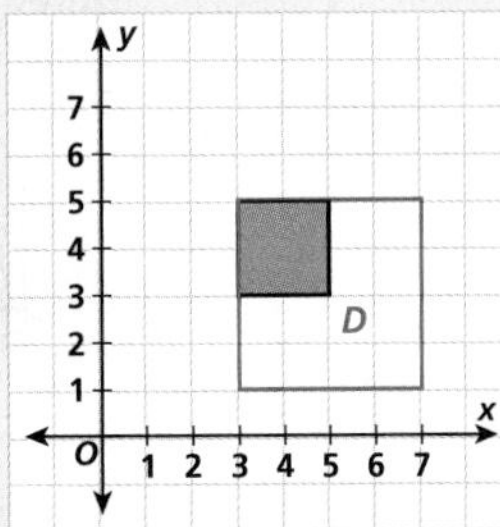

When a figure changes size but keeps the same shape, the transformation is called a *dilation*.

Think and Discuss

1. Which transformation results in a figure that is congruent? similar?
   translation; dilation

Try This

Draw each transformation.

1. a translation 2 units down

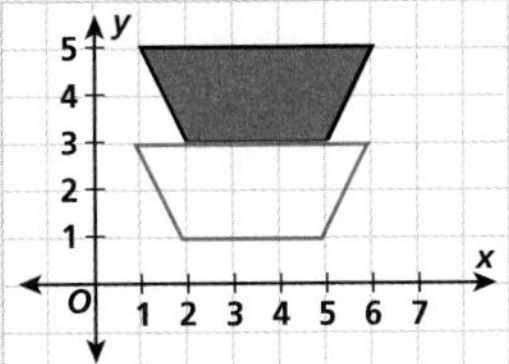

2. a dilation 2 times as big

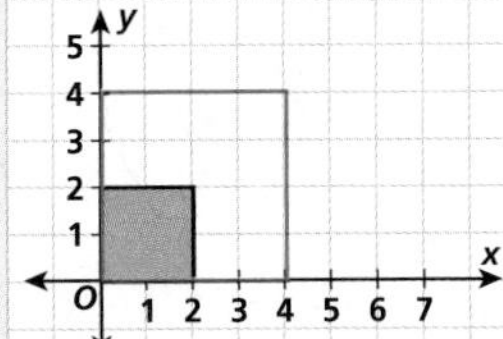

3. a translation 6 units left

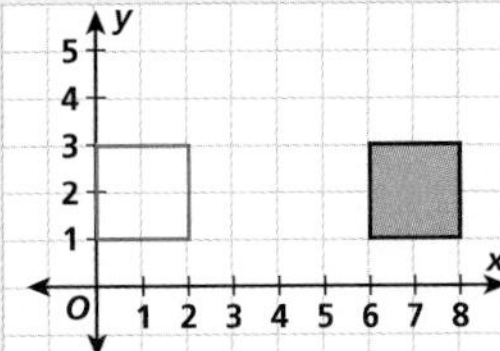

Answers to *Assessment*

1.

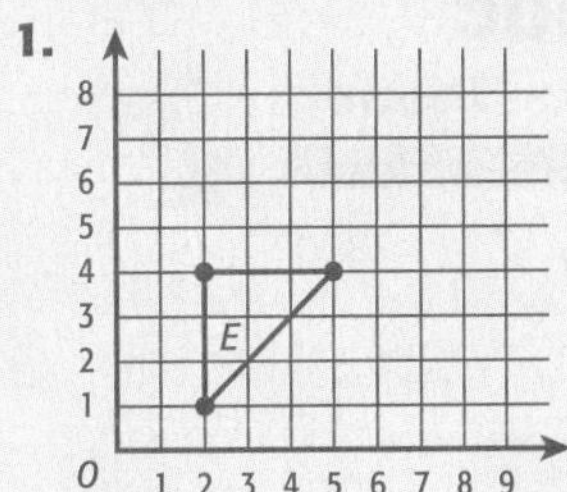

2. Possible answer: Figure E is a right isosceles triangle. The congruent sides in figure E are 3 units long.

Organizer

Use with Lesson 8-10

Pacing:
Traditional $\frac{1}{2}$ day
Block $\frac{1}{4}$ day

Objective: Use graph paper to record the coordinates of transformed objects.

Materials: Graph paper, pattern blocks

Online Edition

Countdown to CRCT Week 19

Resources

Hands-On Lab Activities
Lab 8-10 Recording Sheet

Teach

Discuss

Have students discuss similarities between using a coordinate grid in class and NASA controlling a remote probe on another planet.

Close

Key Concept

Graphing transformations provide an initial exposure to more formal geometric transformations that will be studied in high school.

Assessment

1. Locate and connect the following points on a coordinate grid. Label the figure E. (2, 1), (2, 4), (5, 4)
2. Describe the shape and size of the figure.

Georgia Performance Standards

M6P1.c Apply and adapt a variety of appropriate strategies to solve problems.

M6P4.a Recognize and use connections among mathematical ideas.

M6P4.b Understand how mathematical ideas interconnect and build on one another to produce a coherent whole.

8-11 Organizer

Pacing: Traditional 1 day
Block $\frac{1}{2}$ day

Objective: Students identify line symmetry.

GPS M6G1.b
Hands-On Lab
In Hands-On Lab Activities

Online Edition
Tutorial Videos, Interactivities

Countdown to CRCT Week 19

Power Presentations with PowerPoint®

Warm Up

True or false?

1. In a vertical reflection, the original figure is flipped over a line of symmetry. false
2. In a translation, the original figure slides along a straight line and is flipped. false
3. In rotation, a figure is moved around a point. true

Problem of the Day

Name four plane figures that can be rotated 180° around a center point and look the same after the rotation as they did before. Possible answer: rectangle, square, parallelogram, regular hexagon

Also available on transparency

Georgia Performance Standards

M6G1.a Determine and use lines of symmetry.

M6P1.b Solve problems that arise in mathematics and in other contexts.

8-11 Line Symmetry

Learn to identify line symmetry.

Vocabulary
line symmetry
line of symmetry

Georgia Performance Standards
M6G1.a Determine and use lines of symmetry. Also, M6P1.b.

A figure has **line symmetry** if it can be folded or reflected so that the two parts of the figure match, or are congruent. The line of reflection is called the **line of symmetry**.

You can draw a line of symmetry on this windmill. The shape of the building and the position of the blades are symmetrical.

EXAMPLE 1 Identifying Lines of Symmetry

Determine whether each dashed line appears to be a line of symmetry.

A

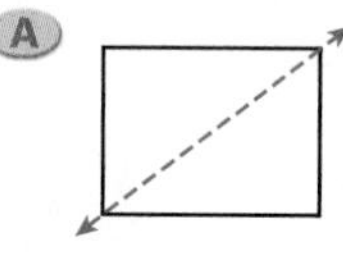

The two parts of the figure are congruent, but they do not match exactly when folded or reflected across the line.

The line does not appear to be a line of symmetry.

B

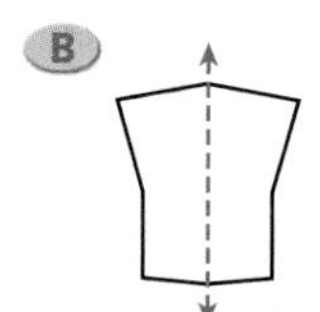

The two parts of the figure appear to match exactly when folded or reflected across the line.

The line appears to be a line of symmetry.

Some figures have more than one line of symmetry.

EXAMPLE 2 Finding Multiple Lines of Symmetry

Find all of the lines of symmetry in each regular polygon.

A

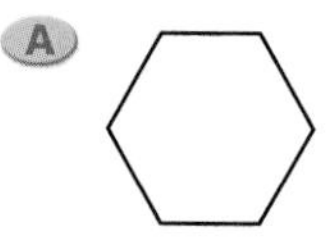

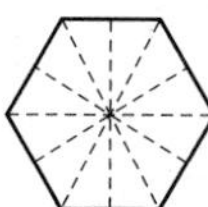

Trace each figure and cut it out.
Fold the figure in half in different ways.
Count the lines of symmetry.

6 lines of symmetry

1 Introduce

Alternate Opener

EXPLORATION

8-11 Line Symmetry

A figure has *line symmetry* if you can draw a line through it to form two congruent shapes that are reflections of each other.

Draw as many lines of symmetry through each figure as possible. Then give the total number of lines drawn in each.

		How Many Lines of Symmetry?
1.		
2.		
3.		
4.		

Think and Discuss

5. **Discuss** the characteristics of the figures that have more than one line of symmetry.
6. **Discuss** the characteristics of the figures that have only one line of symmetry.

Motivate

Have each student fold a piece of paper in half and cut an unusual shape from it. Then have them unfold the shapes they cut out. Ask students to tell you what they notice about the parts of the shape on either side of the fold line. They are identical mirror images of each other. Explain that the fold line is a *line of symmetry*.

Explorations and answers are provided in *Alternate Openers: Explorations Transparencies.*

Find all of the lines of symmetry in each regular polygon.

B

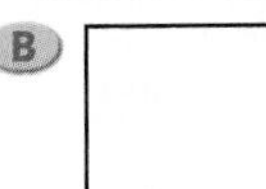

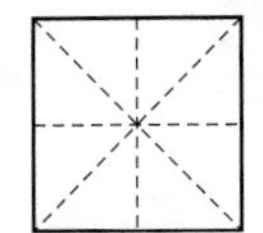

4 lines of symmetry

C

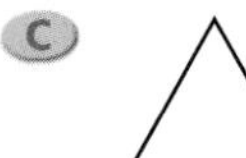

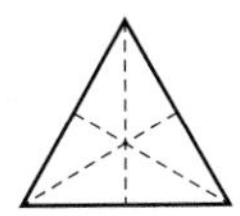

Count the lines of symmetry.

3 lines of symmetry

EXAMPLE 3 ***Social Studies Application***

Find all of the lines of symmetry in each flag design.

A Antigua and Barbuda

1 line of symmetry

B Macedonia

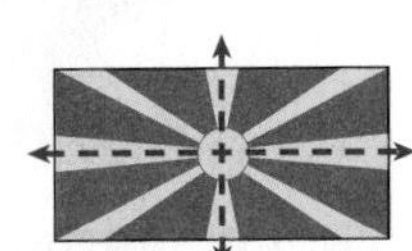

2 lines of symmetry

C Norway

1 line of symmetry

D Lesotho

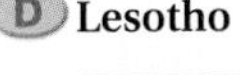

There are no lines of symmetry.

Possible answers to *Think and Discuss*

1. If a figure is reflected over a line that touches it, the line of reflection becomes the line of symmetry for the resulting figure.
2. No, only regular hexagons have six lines of symmetry.
3. a rectangular chalkboard; two lines of symmetry

Think and Discuss GPS M6P2.c, M6P4.c

1. **Explain** how you can use your knowledge of reflection to create a figure that has a line of symmetry.
2. **Determine** whether all hexagons have six lines of symmetry.
3. **Name** objects with line symmetry in your classroom. Tell how many lines of symmetry each of these objects has.

Power Presentations with PowerPoint®

Additional Examples

Example 1

Determine whether each dashed line appears to be a line of symmetry.

A.

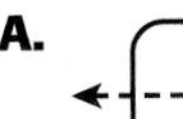

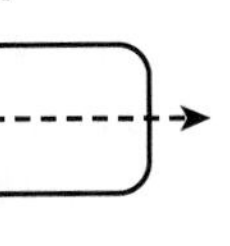

yes

B.

no

Example 2

Find all the lines of symmetry in each regular polygon.

A.

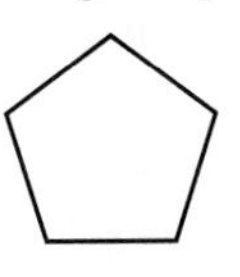

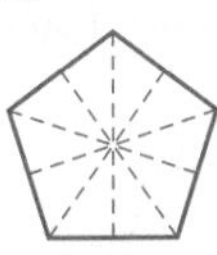

B.

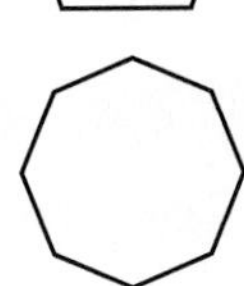

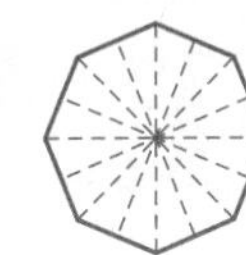

Example 3

Find all the lines of symmetry in each flag design.

A. Alaska

none

B. Arizona

C. Colorado

D. New Mexico

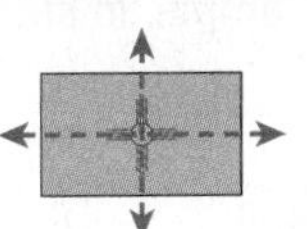

Also available on transparency

2 Teach

Guided Instruction

In this lesson, students learn to identify lines of symmetry. Teach students how to determine whether a given line dividing a figure is a line of symmetry. Explain that figures can have zero, one, or more than one line of symmetry. Have students find multiple lines of symmetry in polygons and find symmetry in flags.

Reaching All Learners

Through Curriculum Integration

Social Studies Have students research flags from other countries. Have them categorize the flags as having zero, one, or two lines of symmetry.

3 Close

Summarize

Have the students write a brief definition of *line symmetry* and draw an example of a figure with its line or lines of symmetry drawn.

Possible answer: A figure has line symmetry if a line can divide it into two parts that match when the figure is folded along the line. Check students' drawings.

8-11 Exercises

Assignment Guide

If you finished Example 1 assign:
Average 1–3, 18, 21–28
Advanced 9–11, 18, 21–28

If you finished Example 2 assign:
Average 1–6, 18, 21–28
Advanced 9–14, 18, 21–28

If you finished Example 3 assign:
Average 1–17, 21–28
Advanced 9–28

Homework Quick Check

Quickly check key concepts.
Exercises: 10, 16

Math Background

The study of mathematics includes the study of rotational symmetry in addition to the study of line symmetry. When a figure can be rotated about a point between 0° and 360°, and the resulting figure matches the original figure point for point, the figure has rotational symmetry. For example, a square has 90° rotational symmetry about the point where its diagonals meet.

Rotational symmetry abounds in nature, for example, in snowflakes and flower petals.

Answers

17. See p. A10.

Georgia Performance Standards

M6P1.a Build new mathematical knowledge through problem solving.

M6P3.a Organize and consolidate their mathematical thinking through communication.

M6P4.c Recognize and apply mathematics in contexts outside of mathematics.

8-11 Exercises

Georgia Performance Standards
M6P1.a, M6P3.a, M6P4.c

GUIDED PRACTICE

See Example 1 Determine whether each dashed line appears to be a line of symmetry.

1. 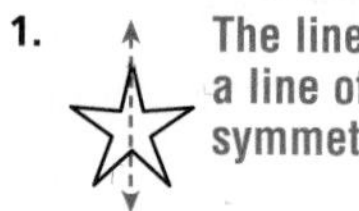 The line is a line of symmetry.
2. 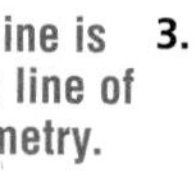 The line is not a line of symmetry.
3. The line is a line of symmetry.

See Example 2 Find all of the lines of symmetry in each regular polygon.

4. 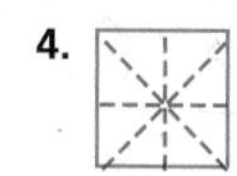 4 lines of symmetry
5. 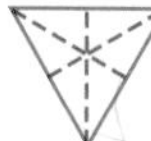 3 lines of symmetry
6. 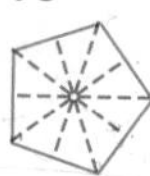 5 lines of symmetry

See Example 3 Find all of the lines of symmetry in each design.

7. 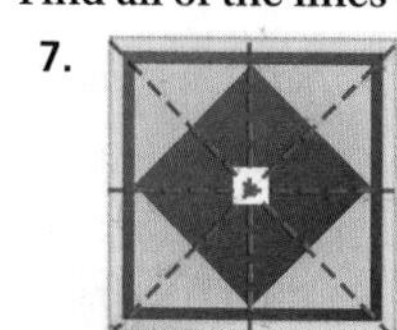 4 lines of symmetry
8. 3 lines of symmetry

INDEPENDENT PRACTICE

See Example 1 Determine whether each dashed line appears to be a line of symmetry.

9. 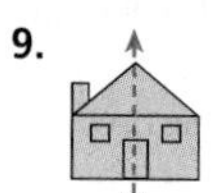 The line is not a line of symmetry.
10. 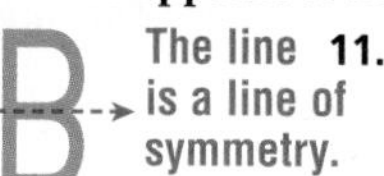 The line is a line of symmetry.
11.  The line is not a line of symmetry.

See Example 2 Find all of the lines of symmetry in each regular polygon.

12. 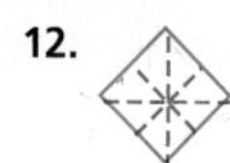 4 lines of symmetry
13. 8 lines of symmetry
14. 7 lines of symmetry

See Example 3 Find all of the lines of symmetry in each object.

15. 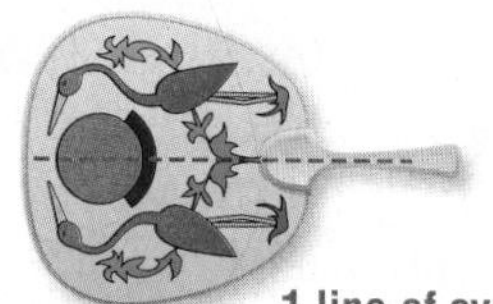 1 line of symmetry
16. no lines of symmetry

PRACTICE AND PROBLEM SOLVING

Extra Practice p. 730

17. How many lines of symmetry does an equilateral triangle have? an isosceles triangle? a scalene triangle? Draw diagrams to support your answer.

RETEACH 8-11

LESSON 8-11 **Reteach**
Line Symmetry

A figure has line symmetry if it can be folded or reflected so that the two overlapping parts of the figure are congruent. The line of reflection is called the line of symmetry.

To figure out if a dashed line is a line of symmetry, test to see if the two parts match exactly when folded or reflected across the line.

The two parts match, so the line is a line of symmetry.

Decide if each line is a line of symmetry.

1. no
2. yes

To find all of the lines of symmetry in the regular octagon, first trace the polygon and cut it out.

Then fold the polygon in half in different ways to find the lines of symmetry.

A regular octagon has 8 lines of symmetry.

Find all of the lines of symmetry in each figure. Write how many lines of symmetry each figure has.

3. 1 line
4. 4 lines

PRACTICE 8-11

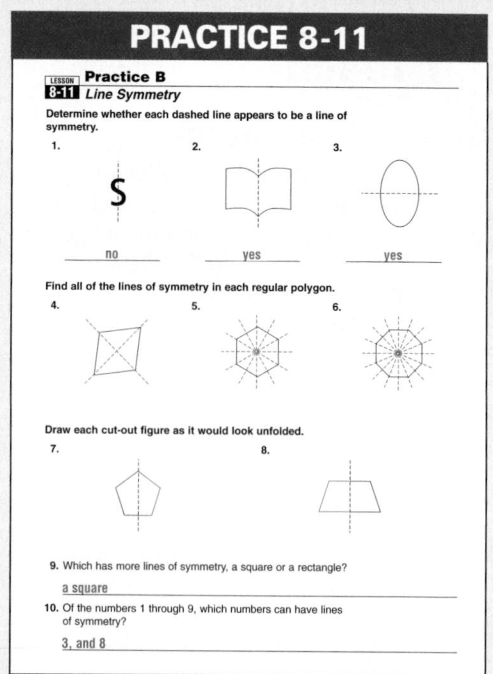
LESSON 8-11 **Practice B**
Line Symmetry

Determine whether each dashed line appears to be a line of symmetry.

1. no
2. yes
3. yes

Find all of the lines of symmetry in each regular polygon.

4.
5.
6.

Draw each cut-out figure as it would look unfolded.

7.
8.

9. Which has more lines of symmetry, a square or a rectangle?
a square

10. Of the numbers 1 through 9, which numbers can have lines of symmetry?
3, and 8

Music LINK

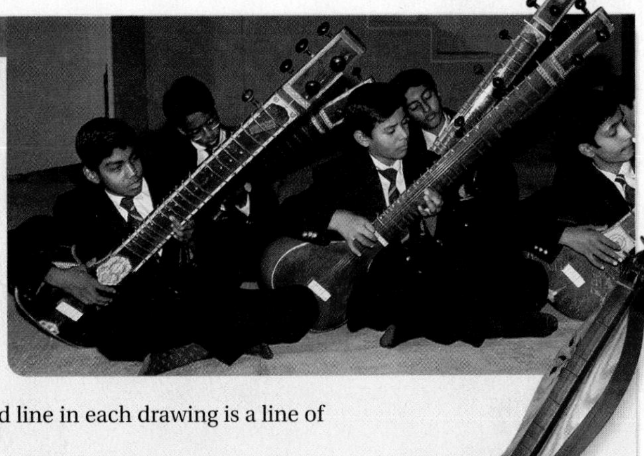

Many cultures play music on unique instruments. You might hear the sun drum or turtle drum in Native American music. In music made by people from the Appalachian Mountains, you might hear the strains of a dulcimer. The photo shows young musicians playing sitars, instruments heard in north Indian classical music.

18. Determine whether the dashed line in each drawing is a line of symmetry.

a.

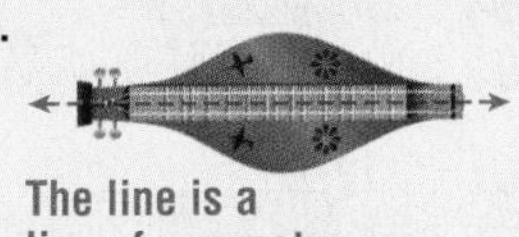

The line is a line of symmetry.

b.

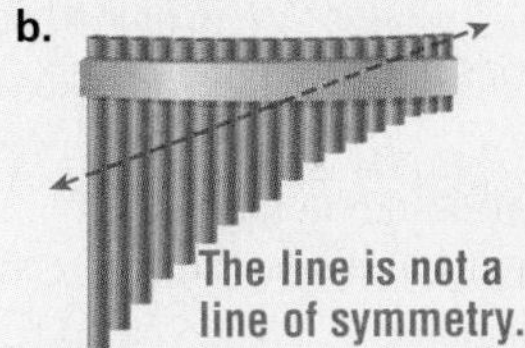

The line is not a line of symmetry.

19. **Write About It** The turtle drum is a regular octagon. How can you find all of the lines of symmetry in a regular polygon?

20. **Challenge** A student drew a drum in the shape of an octagon on a grid. What are the coordinates of the vertices of the unfolded half of the drum drawing if the fold shown is a line of symmetry? (5,4), (6, 3), (6, 2), (5, 1)

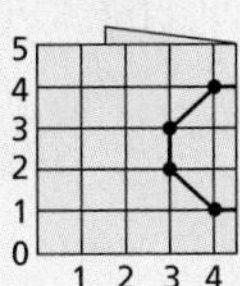

CRCT Prep • GPS Support • Spiral Review

21. **Multiple Choice** How many lines of symmetry are in a rectangle that is NOT a square?

Ⓐ 1  Ⓑ 2 Ⓒ 4  Ⓓ 6

22. **Short Response** Draw the lines of symmetry in the figure.

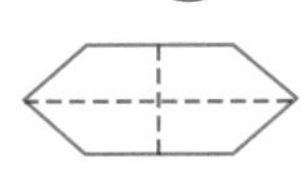

Compare. Write <, >, or =. (Lesson 1-1)

23. 4,897,204 ▒ 4,895,190 >

24. 133,099,588 ▒ 133,099,600 <

Find each sum or difference. (Lesson 3-3)

25. 30 − 5.32 24.68

26. 80.37 + 15.125 95.495

27. 100 − 25.65 74.35

28. 200.6 + 62.78 263.38

CHALLENGE 8-11

LESSON 8-11 Challenge
Alphabetical Symmetry

Tell whether each capital letter has a horizontal line of symmetry, a vertical line of symmetry, both, or neither. Draw the lines of symmetry to illustrate.

A	B	C	D
vertical	horizontal	horizontal	horizontal
E	F	G	H
horizontal	neither	neither	both
I	J	K	L
both	neither	horizontal	neither
M	N	O	P
vertical	neither	both	neither
Q	R	S	T
neither	neither	neither	vertical
U	V	W	X
vertical	vertical	vertical	both
Y	Z		
vertical	neither		

PROBLEM SOLVING 8-11

LESSON 8-11 Problem Solving
Line Symmetry

Write the correct answer.

1. Do your body and face appear to have a vertical line of symmetry or a horizontal line of symmetry?
   vertical
2. Which letter of the alphabet has an infinite, or endless, number of lines of symmetry?
   the letter o
3. Ted says the diagonals of a rectangle are also its lines of symmetry. Do you agree? Explain.
   No, because when folded or reflected along a diagonal, the two parts of the rectangle do not match.
4. Using the digits 0 through 9 and not repeating any digits, write a 3-digit number that has a horizontal line of symmetry.
   3-digit numbers only choices are: 083, 038, 803, 830, 308, 380
5. Draw a line of symmetry for this word.
   DOCK
6. Draw the lines of symmetry for this star.

Circle the letter of the correct answer.

7. How many lines of symmetry does this hexagon have?
   A 4
   B 8
   Ⓒ 6
   D 2 
8. How many lines of symmetry does this flower have?
   F 3
   Ⓖ 4
   H 5
   J 6 
9. How many lines of symmetry does a square have?
   A 0
   B 2
   Ⓒ 4
   D 6
10. How many lines of symmetry does a regular pentagon have?
    F 1
    G 2
    H 4
    Ⓙ 5

Ongoing Assessment and Intervention

Diagnose ***Before*** **the Lesson**
8-11 Warm Up, TE p. 464

Monitor ***During*** **the Lesson**
8-11 Know-It Notebook
8-11 Questioning Strategies

Assess ***After*** **the Lesson**
8-11 Lesson Quiz, TE p. 467

Interdisciplinary LINK

Music

Exercises 18–20 focus on some unique instruments from various cultures.

Answers

19. Possible answer: Trace the figure and cut it out. Fold the figure in half in as many ways as possible. If the halves match, then each fold line is a line of symmetry.

Test Prep Doctor In Exercise 21, students can visualize folding a rectangle so that the halves match up.

Journal

Have students describe how they determine whether a figure has zero, one, or two lines of symmetry.

Power Presentations with PowerPoint®

8-11 Lesson Quiz

Does the described figure have line symmetry?

1. right isosceles triangle yes

2. rectangle yes

Do the following capital letters of the alphabet have line symmetry? If so, is the line of symmetry horizontal or vertical?

3. H yes, vertical and horizontal

4. R no

Also available on transparency

Organizer

Use with Lesson 8-11

Pacing:
Traditional 1 day
Block $\frac{1}{2}$ day

Objective: Use paper, scissors, and tape to make shapes that tessellate.

Materials: Paper, scissors, tape

Online Edition

Resources

Hands-On Lab Activities
Lab 8-11 Recording Sheet

Teach

Discuss

Help students to understand the basic shapes that tessellate. Then show them how a piece can be cut from one side of a basic tessellating shape and translated to the opposite side to create a new shape that also tessellates.

Close

Key Concept

From the basic shapes that tessellate, an infinite number of designs that still tessellate can be created.

Assessment

1. Create a unique design from a 3 × 5 card that is then used to tessellate a sheet of paper. Check student's work.

Georgia Performance Standards

M6P2.a Recognize reasoning and proof as fundamental aspects of mathematics.

M6P2.c Develop and evaluate mathematical arguments and proofs.

M6P3.d Use the language of mathematics to express mathematical ideas precisely.

Hands-On LAB 8-11

Create Tessellations

Use with Lesson 8-11

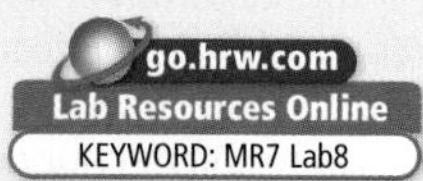

go.hrw.com
Lab Resources Online
KEYWORD: MR7 Lab8

Georgia Performance Standards
M6P2.a, M6P2.c, M6P3.d

A repeating arrangement of one or more shapes that completely covers a plane, with no gaps or overlaps, is called a *tessellation*. You can make your own tessellations using paper, scissors, and tape.

Activity

1. Start with a square.

   Use scissors to cut out a shape from one side of the square.

   Translate the shape you cut out to the opposite side of the square and tape the two pieces together.

   Trace this new shape to form at least two rows of a tessellation. You will need to translate, rotate, or reflect the shape.

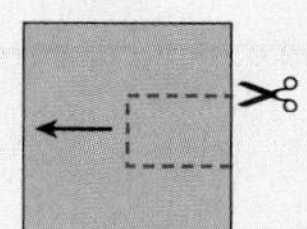

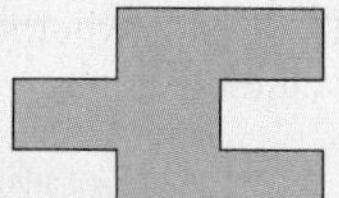

2. Start again with a square.

   Use scissors to cut out shapes and move them to the opposite sides of the square.

   Trace this new shape to form at least two rows of a tessellation. You will need to translate, rotate, or reflect the shape.

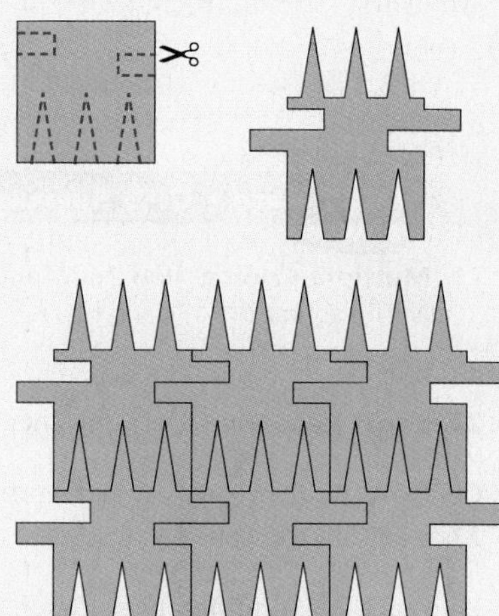

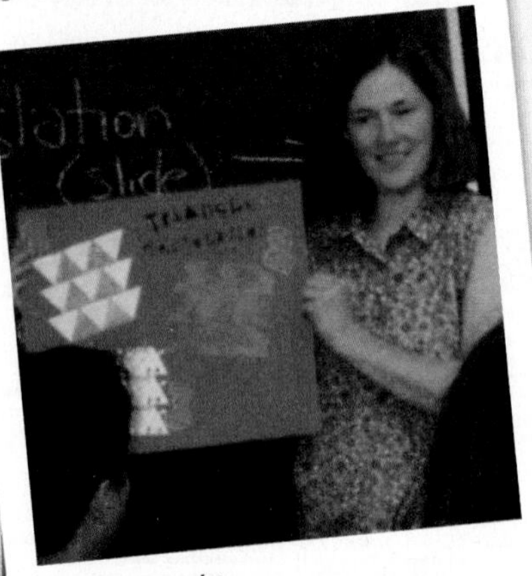

Kendra Vaught
San Gabriel, California

Teacher to Teacher

When we work through the activity, I like to highlight the vocabulary and reinforce it for my ELD students. Once they have successfully made their original template and traced it a few times, I challenge them to color it creatively and see whether they can make a picture.

When they have done the translation, we go through the same process with the rotations. When the projects are finished, they look great on the bulletin board. I like to challenge them to tell me the rule that polygons must satisfy to make a successful tessellation. (The sum of the angles must equal 360°.)

❸ You can base a tessellating shape on other polygons.

Try starting with a hexagon.

Use scissors to cut out a shape from one side of the hexagon. Translate the shape to the opposite side of the hexagon.

Try repeating these steps on other sides of the hexagon.

Trace the new shape to form a tessellation. You will need to translate, rotate, or reflect the shape.

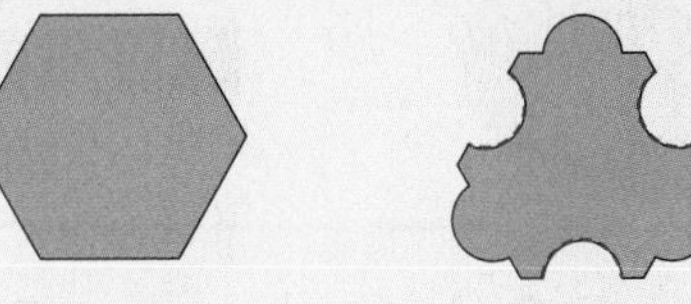

Answers to *Try This*

1.
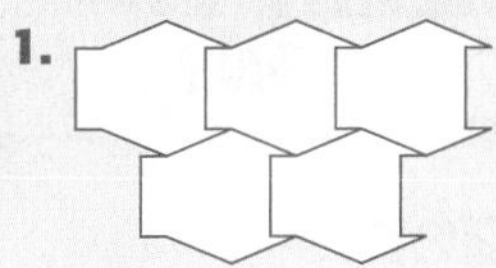

2.
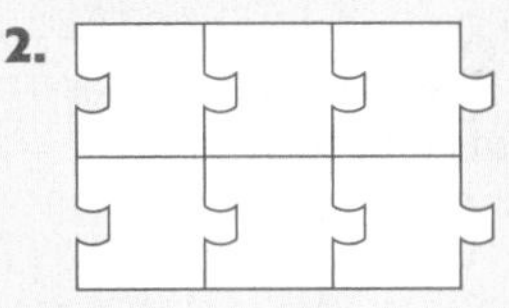

3.
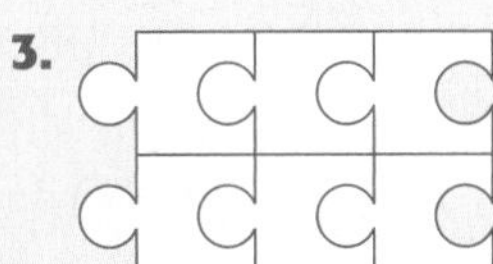

Think and Discuss

1. Tell whether you can make a tessellation out of circles. No. Circles have no edges that allow them to fit together.
2. Tell whether any polygon can make a tessellation. No. Some polygons do not fit together without leaving gaps.

Try This

Make each tessellation shape described. Then form two rows of a tessellation. Check students' work.

1. 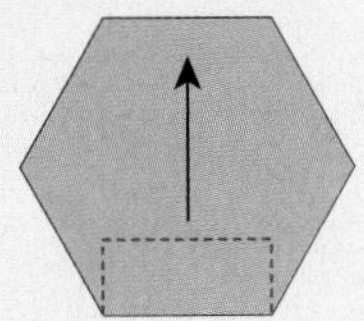

2. 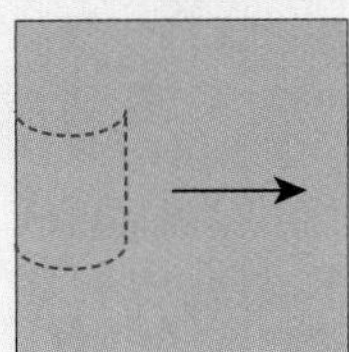

3. 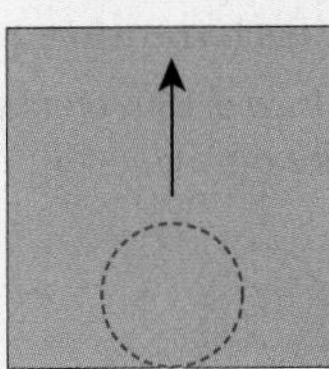

Tell whether each shape can be used to form a tessellation.

4. 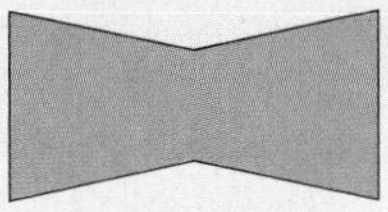 yes

5.  no

6. 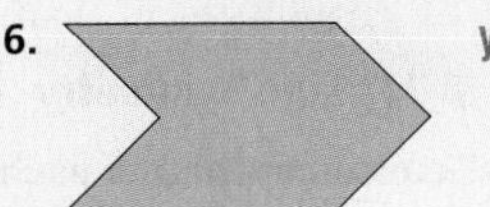 yes

7. Cut out a polygon, and then change it by cutting out a part of one side. Translate the cut-out part to the opposite side. Can your shape form a tessellation? Make a drawing to show your answer. Check students' work.

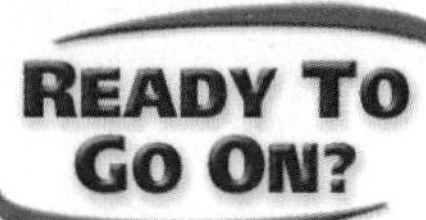

Organizer

Objective: Assess students' mastery of concepts and skills in Lessons 8-9 through 8-11.

Resources

 ***Assessment Resources***
Section 8C Quiz

 **Test & Practice Generator**
One-Stop Planner®

INTERVENTION

Resources

 ***Ready to Go On? Intervention and Enrichment* Worksheets**

 ***Ready to Go On?* CD-ROM**

 ***Ready to Go On?* Online**

my.hrw.com

Answers

6.

SECTION 8C

Ready to Go On?

Quiz for Lessons 8-9 Through 8-11

8-9 Congruence

Decide whether the figures in each pair are congruent. If not, explain.

1. 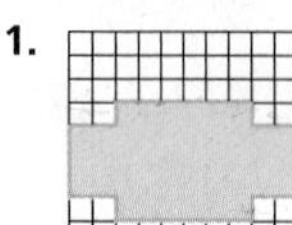 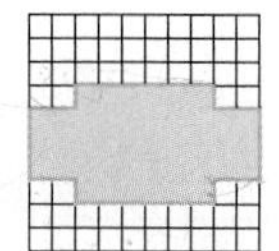 yes

2. 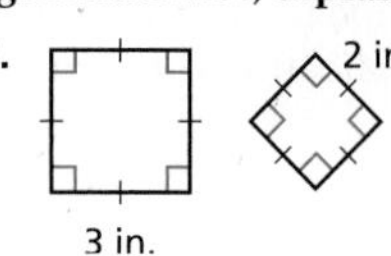

no; different sizes

3. Marcus needs a lid for his box. Which lid should he buy? Lid A

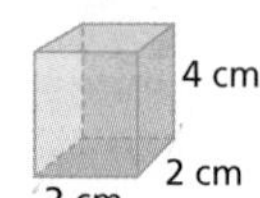

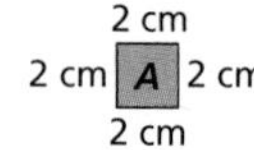

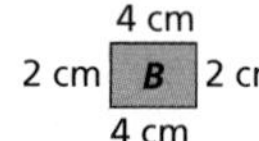

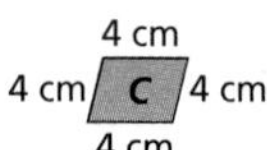

8-10 Transformations

Tell whether each is a translation, rotation, or reflection.

4.  rotation

5. 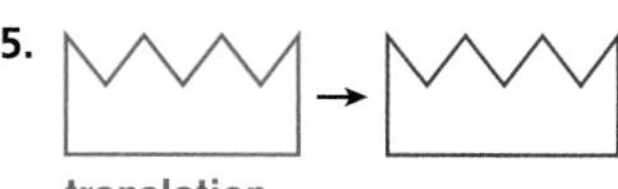 translation

Draw each transformation.

6. Draw a 180° clockwise rotation about the point.

7. Draw a translation.

8-11 Line Symmetry

Determine whether each dashed line appears to be a line of symmetry.

8. 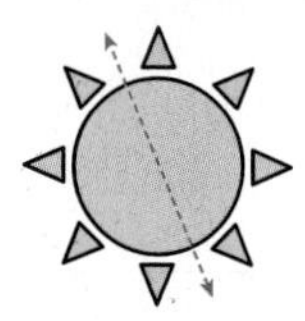 yes

9. 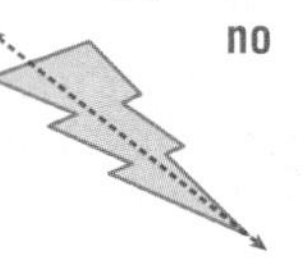 no

10. 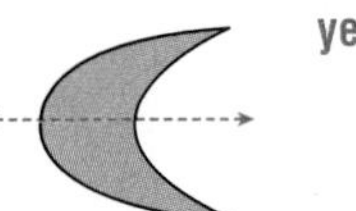 yes

READY TO GO ON? Diagnose and Prescribe

NO INTERVENE

Ready to Go On? Intervention	*Ready to Go On? Intervention*, Section 8C Worksheets	CD-ROM	Online
Lesson 8-9	8-9 Intervention	Activity 8-9	Diagnose and Prescribe Online
Lesson 8-10	8-10 Intervention	Activity 8-10	
Lesson 8-11	8-11 Intervention	Activity 8-11	

YES ENRICH

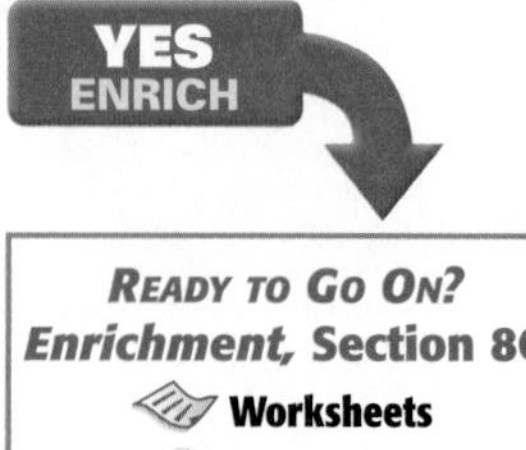

***Ready to Go On? Enrichment*, Section 8C**
Worksheets
CD-ROM
Online

MULTI-STEP TEST PREP

Tonya's Tiles Tonya makes and sells ceramic tiles in the shapes shown at right. She is creating a database that includes information about the tiles.

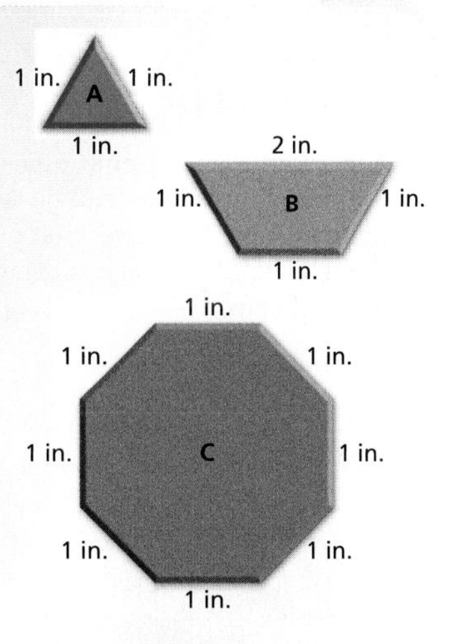

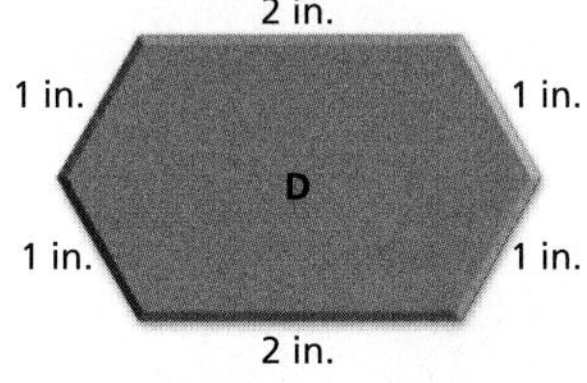

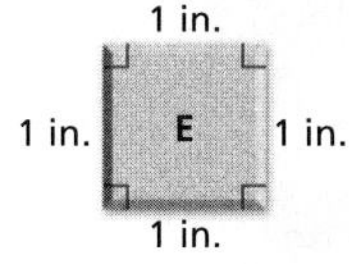

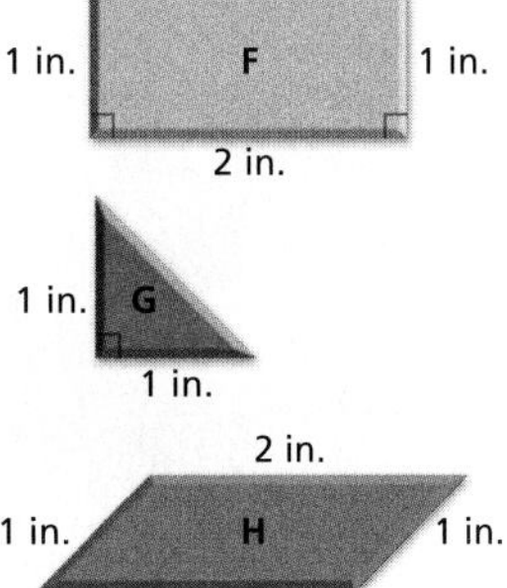

1. The database includes a description of each tile. Describe each tile by classifying its shape as specifically as possible.
2. The database also includes information about symmetry. Give the number of lines of symmetry for each tile.
3. Tonya wants to provide information about the angles in some of the tiles. In tile G, the two acute angles have the same measure. What is the measure of each acute angle? Explain.
4. Tile C is a regular polygon. What is the measure of each of its angles? Explain how you know the answer.
5. A customer wants to use tiles A and B to create a long strip with the following pattern.

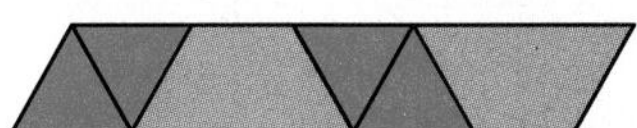

Draw the next five tiles in the pattern.

6. The customer wants the top and bottom edges of the strip to each be 25 inches long. How many of each type of tile will the customer need?

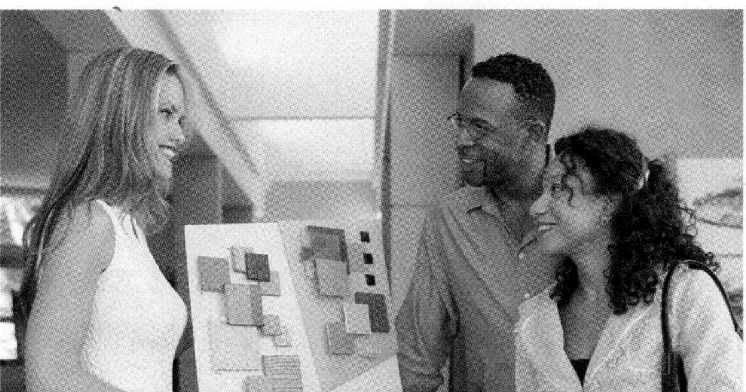

Multi-Step Test Prep

MULTI-STEP TEST PREP

CHAPTER 8

Organizer

Objective: Assess students' ability to apply concepts and skills in Chapter 8 in a real-world format.

PREMIER **Online Edition**

Resources

Middle School Assessments
www.mathtekstoolkit.org

Problem	Text Reference
1	Lesson 8-7
2	Lesson 8-11
3	Lesson 8-5
4	Lesson 8-7
5	Lesson 8-8
6	Lesson 8-8

Answers

1. A: Equilateral triangle; B: Trapezoid; C: Regular Octagon; D: Hexagon; E: Square; F: Rectangle; G; Right Isosceles Triangle; H: Parallelogram
2. A: 3; B: 1; C: 8; D: 2; E: 4; F: 2; G: 1; H: 0
3. 45°; The sum of the angle measures in the triangle is 180° and one angle is a right angle (90°), so the two acute angles must add up to 90°. Since they have the same measure, each must measure 45°.

4–6. See p. A10.

INTERVENTION

Scaffolding Questions

1. What do you notice about the sides of tile A? They are congruent. How can you use this to classify the triangle? It is equilateral. How can you classify tile G by its angles? by its sides? acute triangle; isosceles triangle
2. What is a line of symmetry? a line that divides a figure into two halves that are mirror images of each other Which of the tiles has no line of symmetry? tile H
3. What is the sum of the angle measures in the triangle? 180° What can you say about the measure of the right angle? It is 90°. What does that tell you about the measures of the other two angles? They must add up to 90°
4. How can you find the sum of the measures of the octagon's angles? Draw lines from one vertex to all the other vertices to divide the figure into triangles. Then add the angle measures of all the triangles.
5. How can you describe the pattern using the letter names of the tiles? A A B A A B...
6. How long are the top and bottom edges of the portion of the strip shown in the figure? 5 in.

Extension

1. A customer uses tiles A and H in an alternating pattern (A H A H A H...) to make a long strip. How many of each tile does he need if the top and bottom edges of the strip are to be 35 inches long? 14 of each tile

Game Time

Organizer

Objective: Participate in games to practice and apply skills learned in Chapter 8.

 **Online Edition**

Resources

Chapter 8 Resource Book
Puzzles, Twisters & Teasers

Tangrams

Purpose: To apply knowledge of geometry to visualizing and creating shapes

Discuss Ask students to describe the shapes that make up the tangram puzzle. two large isosceles triangles; one medium-sized isosceles triangle; two small isosceles triangles; one square; one parallelogram. What fraction of the area of the square made from all of the tangram pieces is one large isosceles triangle? $\frac{1}{4}$ What fraction of the large isosceles triangle's area is the medium-sized isosceles triangle? $\frac{1}{2}$

Extend Have students make a figure using all seven tangram pieces. Have them trace around their shape to form an outline. Then have them challenge a classmate to re-create the shape using only the outline. Check students' work.

Game Time

Tangrams

A tangram is an ancient Chinese puzzle. The seven shapes that make this square can be arranged to make many other figures. Copy the shapes that make this square, and then cut them apart. See if you can arrange the pieces to make the figures below.

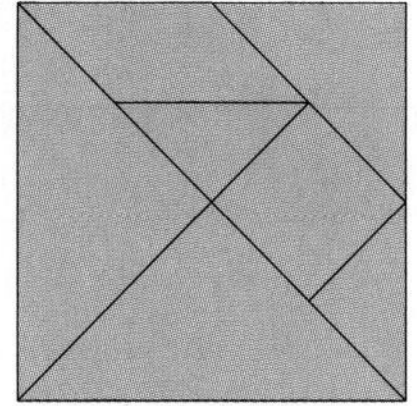

A complete copy of Tangram puzzle pieces is available online.

go.hrw.com
Game Time Extra
KEYWORD: MR7 Games

Answers

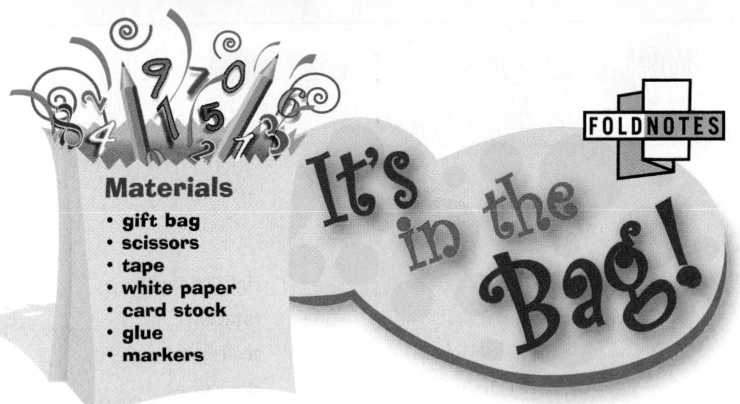

PROJECT Geometry Grab Bag

Use a recycled gift bag to make a journal for your geometry notes.

Directions

1. Cut away the sides and bottom of the bag. This will leave two rectangles with handles attached. **Figure A**

2. Place the two halves of the bag face down and tape them together as shown, leaving a small space between them. This will form the covers of your journal. **Figure B**

3. Cut several sheets of white paper and the card stock so that they are all the same size and slightly smaller than the covers of the journal. Staple them together, with a piece of card stock on the top and bottom of the stack. **Figure C**

4. Glue the top piece of card stock to the inside front cover. Glue the bottom piece of card stock to the inside back cover.

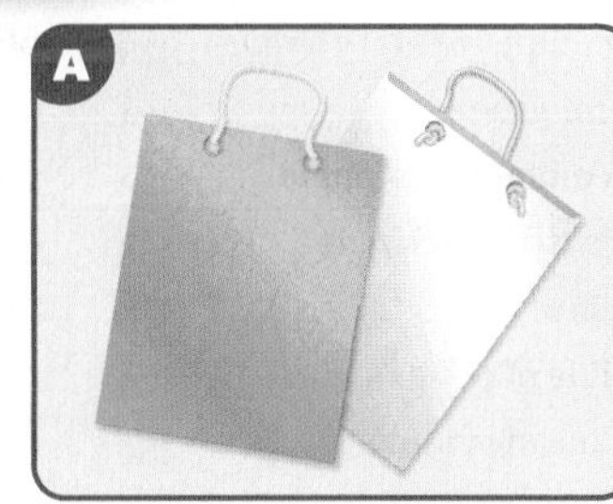

A

B

C

Taking Note of the Math

Write the number and title of the chapter on the front of the journal. Then use the pages of the journal to take notes on angles, polygons, and transformations.

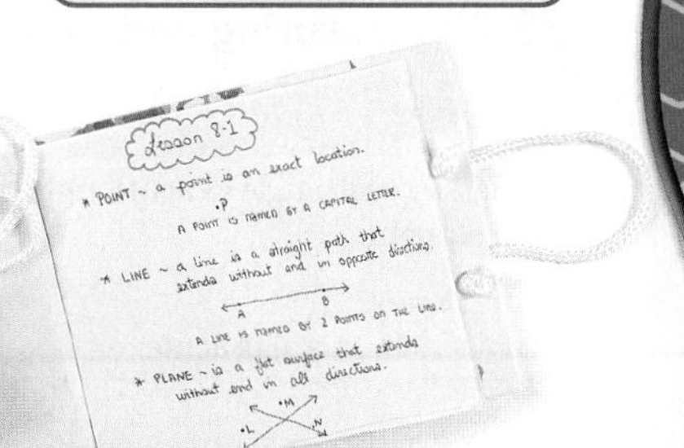

Organizer

Objective: Make a journal in which students can take notes on angles, polygons, and transformations.

Materials: Gift bag, scissors, tape, white paper, card stock, glue, markers

Online Edition

Using the Page

Preparing the Materials
Small gift bags tend to work best, but students can also make the journal out of small shopping bags.

Making the Project
Encourage students to get as many pages as possible out of their sheets of white paper. For example, they may be able to cut the sheets in half and then trim them to size so that each sheet results in two pages of the journal.

Extending the Project
Have students include some sheets of graph paper in their journals. Then ask students to use the graph-paper pages to record examples of congruent figures and/or tessellations.

Instead of stapling the pages together and then gluing the card stock to the bag, you can have students assemble the journal, punch holes along the edge, and attach everything with brass fasteners. The advantage of making the journal this way is that students can add additional pages later on.

Students can use the leftover sections of the bag to make pockets for the inside front and back covers. Then they can use the pockets to store assignments or index cards.

CHAPTER 8 Study Guide: Review

Organizer

Objective: Help students organize and review key concepts and skills presented in Chapter 8.

Online Edition
Multilingual Glossary

Resources

PuzzlePro®
One-Stop Planner®

***Multilingual Glossary* Online**
go.hrw.com
KEYWORD: MR7 Glossary

Lesson Tutorial Videos
CD-ROM

Test & Practice Generator
One-Stop Planner®

Answers

1. trapezoid
2. polygon
3. Possible answer: $\overleftrightarrow{ED}$, $\overleftrightarrow{AD}$
4. acute
5. obtuse
6. acute
7. straight

CHAPTER 8

Study Guide: Review

Vocabulary

Complete the sentences below with vocabulary words from the list above.

1. A quadrilateral with exactly two parallel sides is called a(n) __?__.
2. A(n) __?__ is a closed plane figure formed by three or more line segments.

8-1 Building Blocks of Geometry (pp. 416–419)

GPS M6P3.d

EXAMPLE

- **Use the diagram.**

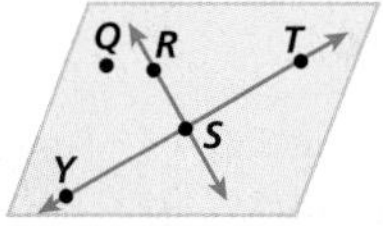

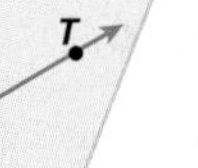

Name a line. $\overleftrightarrow{RS}$
Name a line segment. $\overline{ST}$

EXERCISES

Use the diagram.

3. Name two lines.

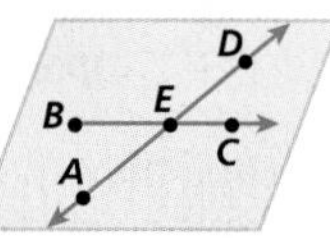

8-2 Measuring and Classifying Angles (pp. 420–423)

GPS M6P3.d

EXAMPLE

- **Classify each angle as acute, right, obtuse, or straight.**

$m\angle A = 80°$
$80° < 90°$, so $\angle A$ is acute.

EXERCISES

Classify each angle as acute, right, obtuse, or straight.

4. $m\angle x = 60°$
5. $m\angle x = 100°$
6. $m\angle x = 45°$
7. $m\angle x = 180°$

8-3 Angle Relationships (pp. 424–427)

GPS M6A3

EXAMPLE

- **Find the unknown angle measure.**

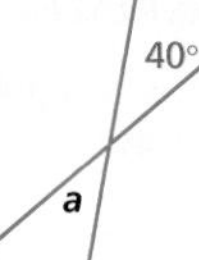

m∠a = 40° *Vertical angles are congruent.*

EXERCISES

Find each unknown angle measure.

8. 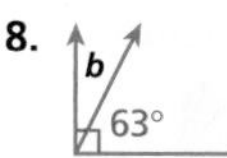

9. 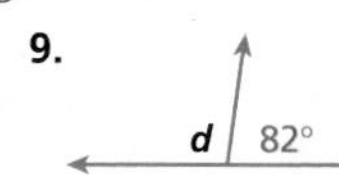

8-4 Classifying Lines (pp. 428–431)

GPS M6P4.c

EXAMPLE

- **Classify each pair of lines.**

The red lines are parallel.
The blue lines are perpendicular.

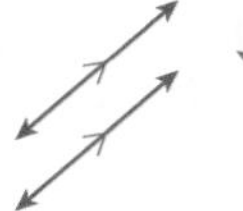

EXERCISES

Classify each pair of lines.

10. 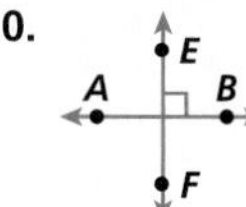

11. 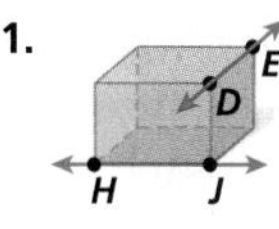

8-5 Triangles (pp. 437–440)

GPS M6A3

EXAMPLE

- **Classify the triangle using the given information.**

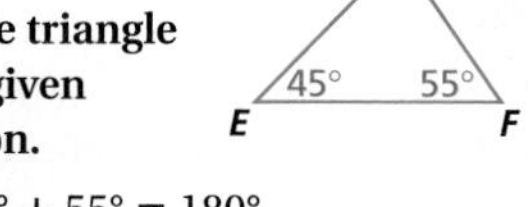

m∠G + 45° + 55° = 180°
m∠G = 80°, so △EFG is an acute triangle.

EXERCISES

Classify the triangle using the given information.

12. 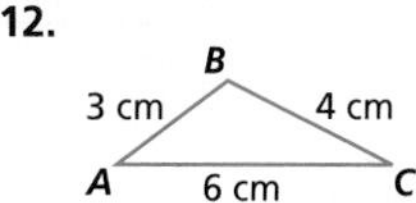

8-6 Quadrilaterals (pp. 442–445)

GPS M6P3.d

EXAMPLE

- **Give the most exact name for the figure.**

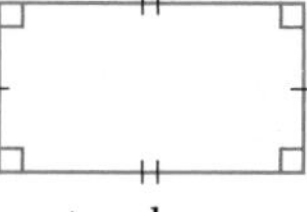

The most exact name is rectangle.

EXERCISES

Give the most exact name for the figure.

13. 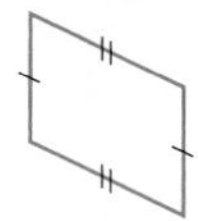

8-7 Polygons (pp. 446–449)

GPS M6A2.a

EXAMPLE

- **Name the polygon and tell whether it appears to be regular or not regular.**

It is a regular octagon.

EXERCISES

Name each polygon and tell whether it appears to be regular or not regular.

14. 

15. MAIN STREET

Study Guide: Review

Answers

8. b = 27°
9. d = 98°
10. perpendicular
11. skew
12. obtuse scalene
13. parallelogram
14. triangle; not regular
15. rectangle; not regular

Answers

16. Add 1 shaded and 1 white triangle each time.

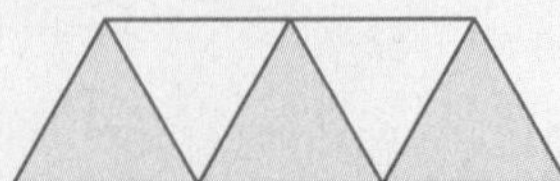

17. not congruent; different sizes

18. congruent

19. translation

20.

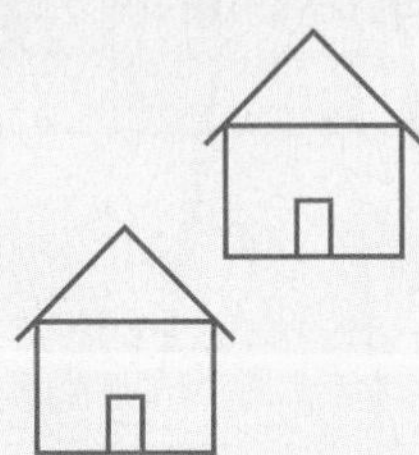

21.

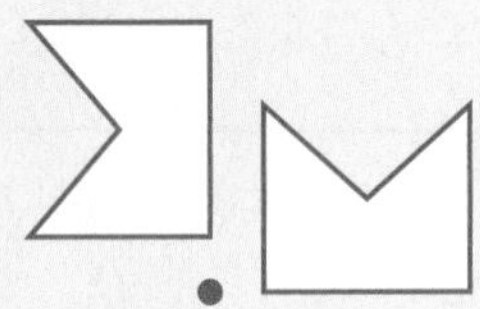

22. The line is a line of symmetry.

Study Guide: Review

8-8 Geometric Patterns (pp. 450–453)

GPS M6P2.d

EXAMPLE

- **Identify a possible pattern. Use the pattern to draw the missing figure.**

 ?  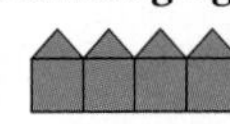 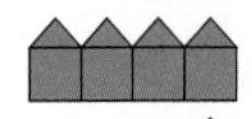

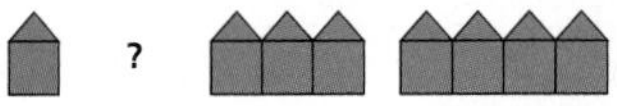

The missing figure might be 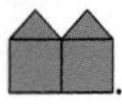 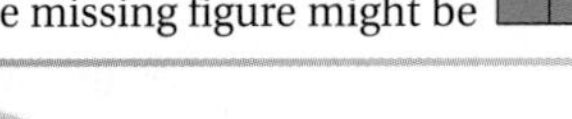.

EXERCISES

Identify a possible pattern. Use the pattern to draw the missing figure.

16. 

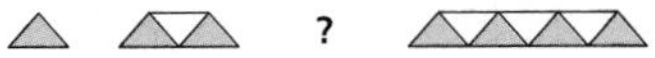

8-9 Congruence (pp. 456–458)

GPS M6P2.c

EXAMPLE

- **Decide whether the figures are congruent. If not, explain.**

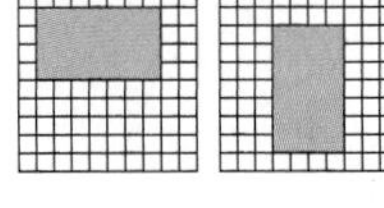

These figures are congruent.

EXERCISES

Decide whether the figures in each pair are congruent. If not, explain.

17. 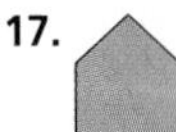 

18. 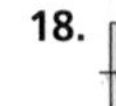 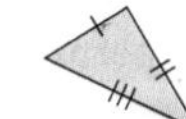

8-10 Transformations (pp. 459–462)

GPS M6P5.a

EXAMPLE

- **Tell whether the transformation is a translation, rotation, or reflection.**

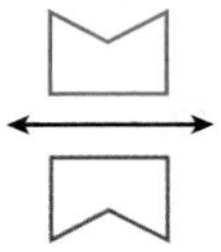

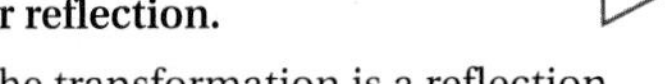

The transformation is a reflection.

- **Draw the transformation.**

Draw a horizontal reflection.

EXERCISES

Tell whether the transformation is a translation, rotation, or reflection.

19. 

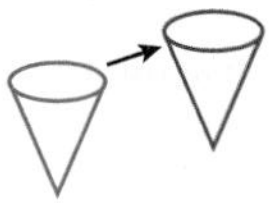

Draw each transformation.

20. Draw a translation. 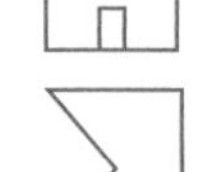

21. Draw a 90° clockwise rotation about the point. 

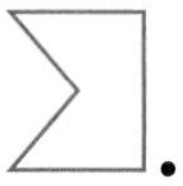

8-11 Line Symmetry (pp. 464–467)

GPS M6G1.a

EXAMPLE

- **Determine whether the dashed line appears to be a line of symmetry.**

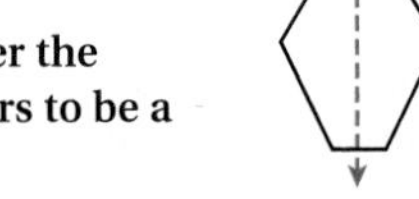

The line appears to be a line of symmetry.

EXERCISES

Determine whether the dashed line appears to be a line of symmetry.

22. 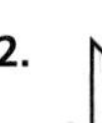 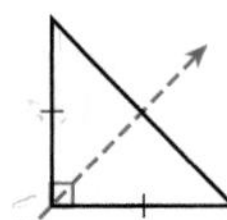

Classify each pair of angles or lines.

1. 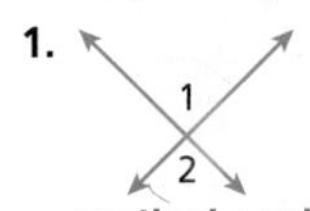
vertical angles

2. 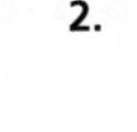 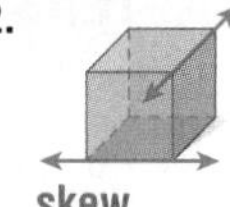
skew

3. 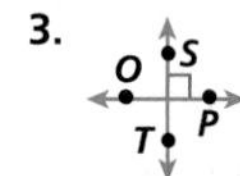
perpendicular

Classify the triangles by angle and side measures. Possible answers given.

4. 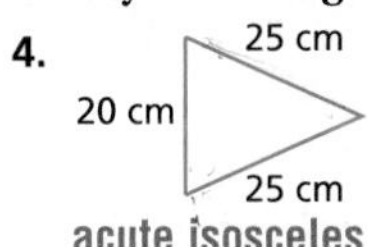

acute isosceles

5. 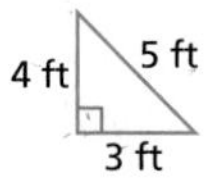 4 ft, 5 ft, 3 ft
right scalene

6. 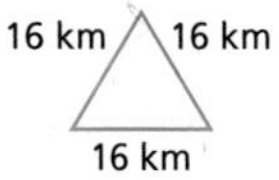 16 km, 16 km, 16 km
acute equilateral

Find the unknown angle measure.

7. 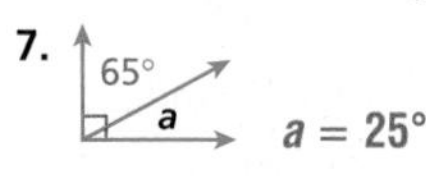

$a = 25°$

8. 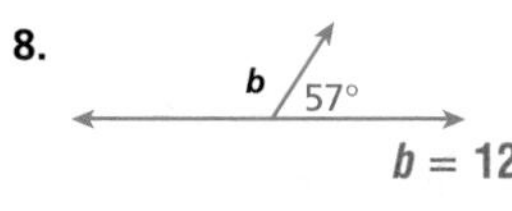

$b = 123°$

9. 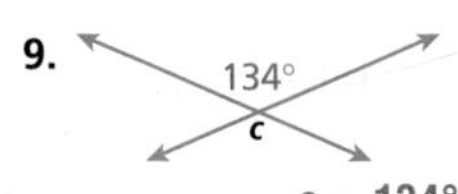

$c = 134°$

10. Triangle ABC has sides of equal length. The measure of $\angle A$ is 60°, and the measure of $\angle B$ is 60°. What is the measure of $\angle C$? Classify the triangle based on the measures of the angles and lengths of the sides.
$\angle C$ is 60°; the triangle is an acute, equilateral triangle.

Draw each transformation.

11. Reflect across the line.
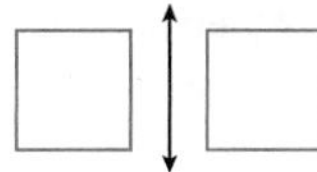

12. Rotate 270° clockwise about the point.

13. Translate $\frac{3}{4}$ in. right.
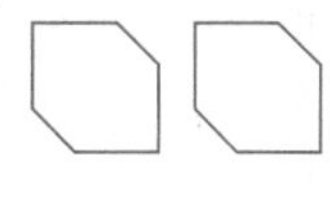

Determine whether each dashed line appears to be a line of symmetry.

14. 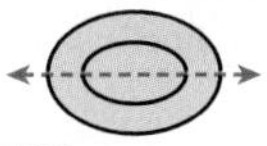 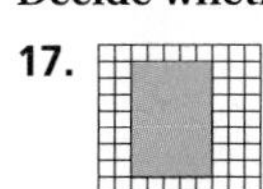
yes

15. 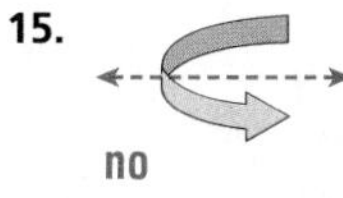
no

16.  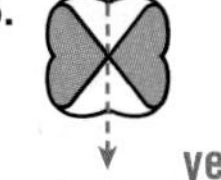
yes

Decide whether the figures in each pair are congruent. If not, explain.

17. 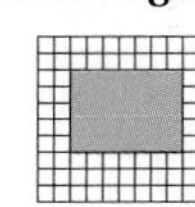 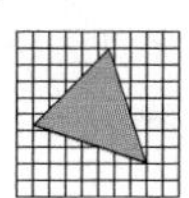
congruent

18. 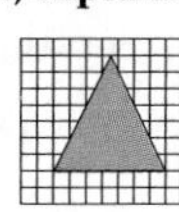 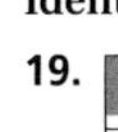
congruent

Identify a possible pattern. Use your pattern to draw the next figure.

19. 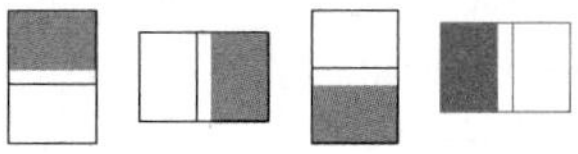 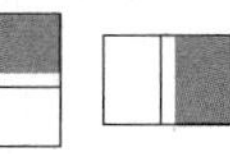  
rotate 90° clockwise

20. 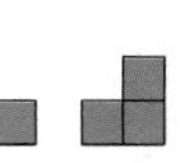 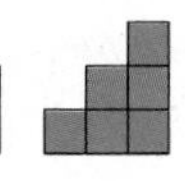 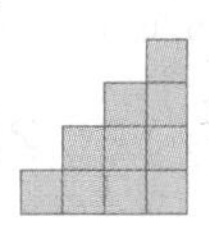
increase the number of squares to the right by 1

Chapter Test

CHAPTER TEST
CHAPTER 8

Organizer

Objective: Assess students' mastery of concepts and skills in Chapter 8.

 Online Edition

Resources

 ***Assessment Resources***

Chapter 8 Tests
- Free Response (Levels A, B, C)
- Multiple Choice (Levels A, B, C)
- Performance Assessment

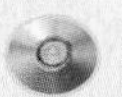 ***IDEA Works!* CD-ROM**
Modified Chapter 8 Test

Organizer

Objective: Provide review and practice for Chapters 1–8 and standardized tests.

 Online Edition

Resources

 ***Assessment Resources***
Chapter 8 Cumulative Test

 ***CRCT Prep* Workbook**

 ***CRCT Prep* CD-ROM**

 ***CRCT Practice* Online**

go.hrw.com
KEYWORD: MR7 TestPrep

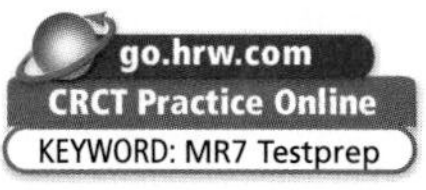

CRCT Prep

CUMULATIVE ASSESSMENT, CHAPTERS 1–8

Multiple Choice

1. Which of the following is an example of an obtuse angle?

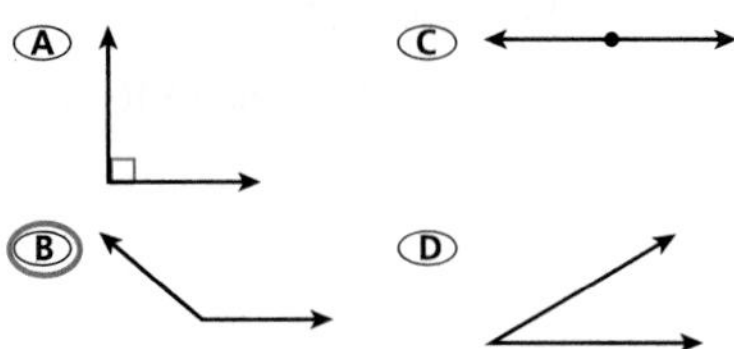

Ⓐ Ⓑ Ⓒ Ⓓ

2. Hillary buys 6 flower bouquets for table decorations. Each bouquet costs \$16. The sales tax is 6.5%. What is the total cost of her purchase?

Ⓕ \$17.03 Ⓗ \$101.70
Ⓖ \$95.94 Ⓙ \$102.24

3. Two angles are complementary. If the measure of one angle is 36°, what is the measure of the second angle?

Ⓐ 36° Ⓒ 64°
Ⓑ 54° Ⓓ 144°

4. Steve, Ashley, and Jeremy work at the same restaurant. Steve works every 4 days. Ashley works every 6 days. Jeremy works every 3 days. If on May 1 they are all working at the restaurant, what is the next date that the three of them will work together?

Ⓕ May 6 Ⓗ May 18
Ⓖ May 12 Ⓙ May 24

5. Terri is $60\frac{1}{2}$ inches tall. Steve is $65\frac{1}{4}$ inches tall. What is the difference, in inches, in their heights?

Ⓐ $4\frac{1}{4}$ Ⓒ $4\frac{3}{4}$
Ⓑ $4\frac{1}{2}$ Ⓓ $5\frac{1}{4}$

6. In the figure below, which of the following angle pairs are NOT adjacent?

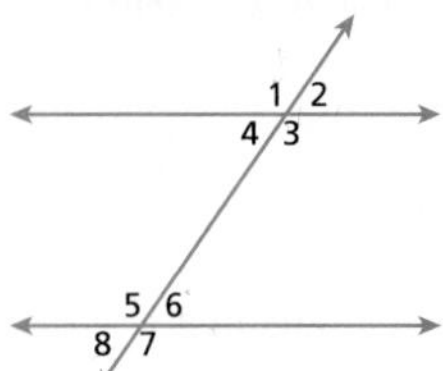

Ⓕ ∠1 and ∠2 Ⓗ ∠1 and ∠3
Ⓖ ∠5 and ∠8 Ⓙ ∠6 and ∠7

7. Reggie is a long-distance runner. His daily $2\frac{1}{2}$-hour practice is divided evenly into three areas: warm-up, running, and cool-down. How many minutes does Reggie spend warming up and cooling down each day at practice?

Ⓐ 100 min Ⓒ 60 min
Ⓑ 75 min Ⓓ 50 min

8. The arrow is being reflected over the black line. Which of the following correctly shows the arrow after it is reflected over the black line?

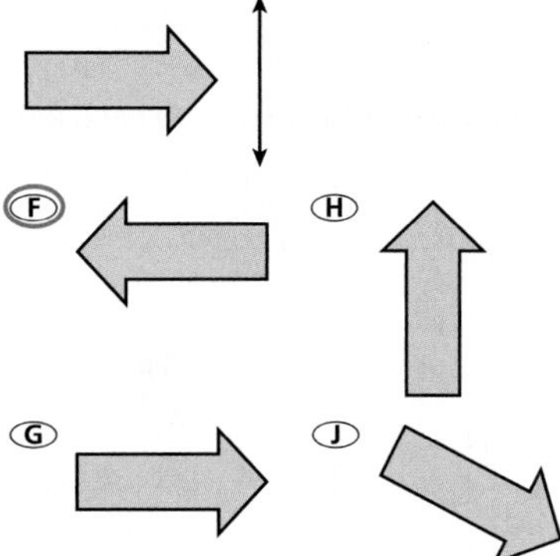

For item 4, students may benefit from using a number line and drawing three arrows that start at 1 and arc over every 3, 4, and 6 days. The arrows all converge on 12, which represents May 12.

Answers

13. The figure is a pentagon.

My drawing is congruent to the given figure because my drawing is the same size and shape of the original pentagon.

14. The mean distance is more than the median distance. To find the mean, I found the sum of all the distances and then divided the sum by 10.
$3234 \div 10 = 323.4$
To find the median, I ordered the data, took the two middle distances, and found the mean of those two values. The mean of 330 and 334 is 332.

15a. $\angle JKM = 60°$; $\angle KLM = 30°$; $\angle KML = 120°$; $\angle KMJ = 60°$

b. Triangle *KML* is an obtuse angle because is has one obtuse angle. Triangle *JKM* is an acute triangle because all of its angles are less than 90°.

16. See 4-Point Response work sample.

9. Shown below is a map of specific areas at Boone Park. Which of the following is located at the point (7, 6) on the map?

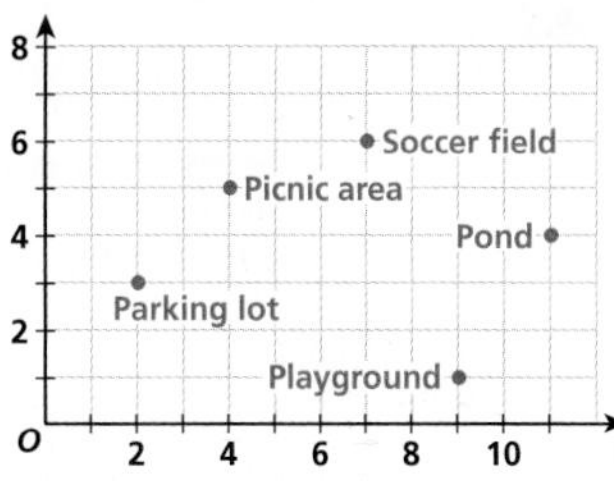

Ⓐ Playground　　Ⓒ Pond

Ⓑ Parking lot　　Ⓓ Soccer field

10. What is the most descriptive name for the figure below?

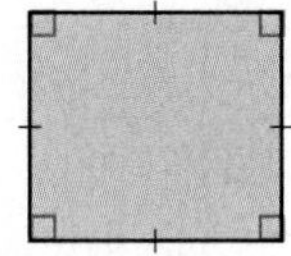

Ⓕ Rhombus　　Ⓗ Square

Ⓖ Rectangle　　Ⓙ Parallelogram

Draw a picture to help in problem solving situations involving plane figures. Be sure to accurately label your drawings.

11. The distance around a square flower box is 128.4 inches. How many inches long is one side of the flower box?

Ⓐ 32.1　　Ⓒ 64.2

Ⓑ 42.8　　Ⓓ 256.8

12. There are 120 students trying out for the school play. Only 5% of those trying out will have a speaking part. Write this percent as a fraction in lowest terms.

Ⓕ $\frac{6}{120}$　　Ⓗ $\frac{120}{6}$

Ⓖ $\frac{1}{20}$　　Ⓙ 20

STANDARDIZED TEST PREP

Short Response

13. Identify the figure shown.

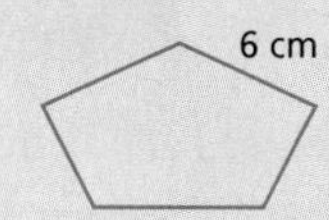

Draw a figure that is congruent to this figure. Explain why your figure is congruent to the given figure.

14. The table shows ten distances hit by a baseball player.

Distances (ft)				
334	360	350	343	330
320	265	327	335	270

Is the mean distance of this player's hits more than or less than the median distance? Explain how you found your answer.

15. Triangle *JKL* is a right triangle.

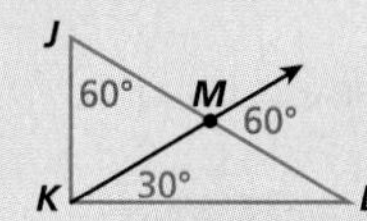

a. What are the angle measurements of ∠*JKM*, ∠*KLM*, ∠*KML*, and ∠*KMJ*?

b. Name two other triangles. Classify these triangles by their angles. Explain your classifications.

Extended Response

16. A student draws a trapezoid on a coordinate grid. The coordinates are *A* (3, 1), *B* (2, 2), *C* (2, 3), and *D* (3, 4).

a. Plot these points on a grid and connect the points.

b. Draw a line that passes through points *A* and *D*. Reflect the trapezoid over that line, label the points on the new trapezoid, and give the new coordinates.

c. What new plane figure is created? Does this new figure have line symmetry? Explain your answer.

CRCT Prep

Short Response Rubric

Items 13–15

2 Points = The student's answer is an accurate and complete execution of the task or tasks.

1 Point = The student's answer contains attributes of an appropriate response but is flawed.

0 Points = The student's answer contains no attributes of an appropriate response.

Extended Response Rubric

Item 16

4 Points = The student demonstrates a thorough understanding of all concepts and shows all work correctly.

3 Points = The student demonstrates a basic understanding of all concepts, but the work shows some flaws reflecting inattentive execution of mathematical procedures or some misunderstanding of the underlying mathematics.

2 Points = The student demonstrates only a partial understanding of the concepts or procedures embodied in the tasks. The approach may be correct, but the work shows a misunderstanding of one or more important concepts.

1 Point = The student demonstrates a very limited understanding of the concepts or procedures embodied in the tasks. The response may show some understanding but exhibits many flaws or is incomplete.

0 Points = The student provides no response at all or a completely incorrect or uninterpretable response.

Student Work Samples for Item 16

4-Point Response

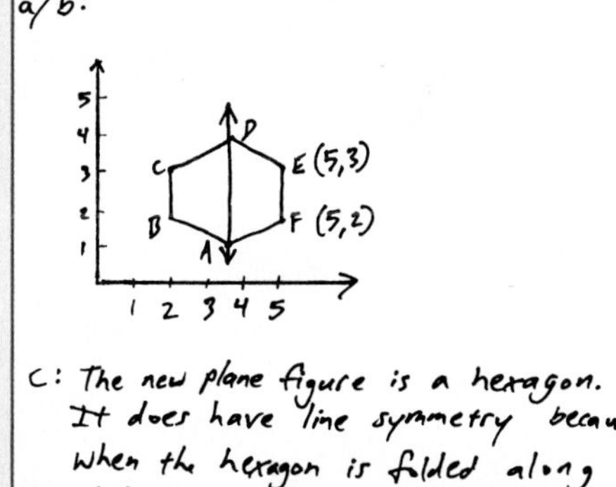

The student drew the figures correctly for parts **a** and **b.** The answer to part **c** is correct, and the explanation is adequate.

3-Point Response

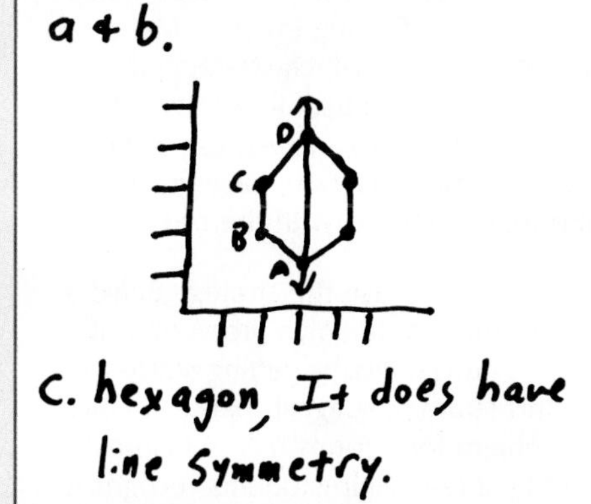

The student drew the figure correctly but did not label all points. The answer to part **c** is correct, but the explanation is incomplete.

2-Point Response

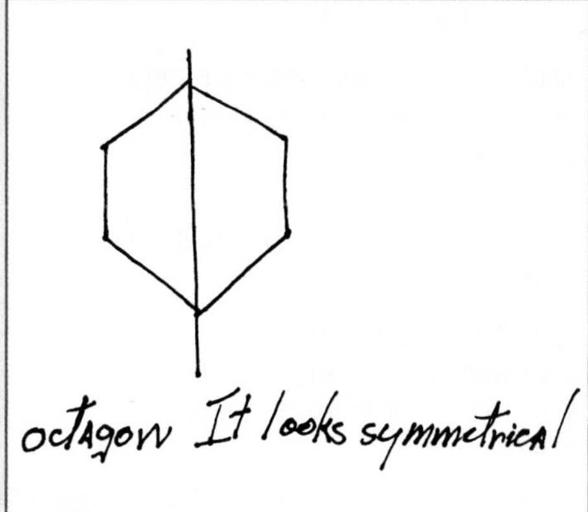

The drawing for parts **a** and **b** shows an understanding of the concepts. An incorrect name is used in part **c,** and an unsatisfactory explanation is given.

Problem Solving on Location

Organizer

Objective: To solve real-world problems involving ratios, proportions, percents, and geometric figures.

 Online Edition

Wesleyan College

Reading Strategies

Ask students to rewrite the question in problem 1 as a statement that tells them what they must find. Find the number of faculty members at the meeting.

Using Data Ask students to summarize the important data in problem 1 in their own words. Possible answer: The ratio of faculty members to students is 11:1 and there are 84 people altogether.

Problem Solving on Location

GEORGIA

Georgia Performance Standards

M6P1.c, M6P4.c, M6P5.a

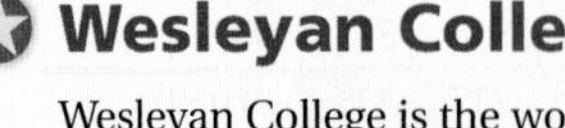

Wesleyan College

Wesleyan College is the world's oldest college for women. Classes began in 1839 with a total enrollment of about 100 students. Today, the 200-acre campus in Macon, Georgia, welcomes nearly 600 students who study everything from art to zoology.

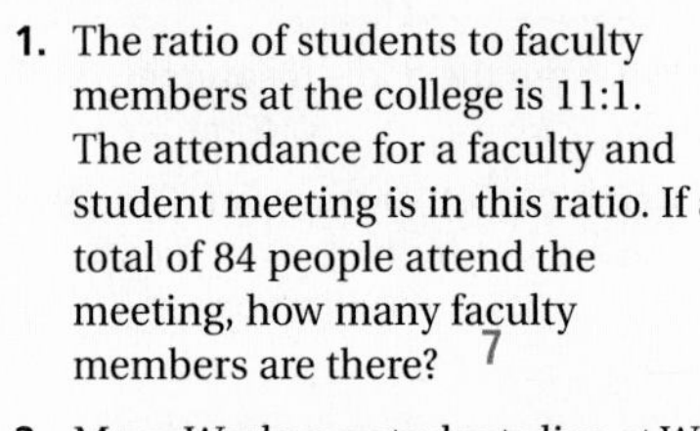

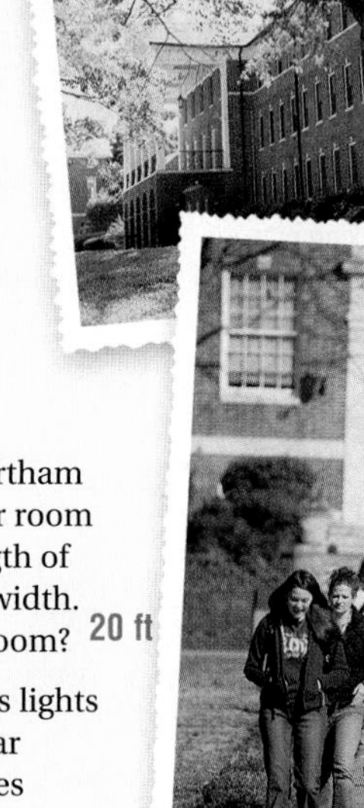

Choose one or more strategies to solve each problem.

1. The ratio of students to faculty members at the college is 11:1. The attendance for a faculty and student meeting is in this ratio. If a total of 84 people attend the meeting, how many faculty members are there? 7
2. Many Wesleyan students live at Wortham Hall. The perimeter of a rectangular room at Wortham Hall is 72 feet. The length of the room is 4 feet greater than the width. What is the length of the meeting room? 20 ft
3. A student living at Jones Hall strings lights around the ceiling of her rectangular room. To attach the lights, she places tacks in the corners of the room and around the edge one foot apart. How many tacks does she need if the room is 16 feet long and 12 feet wide? 56

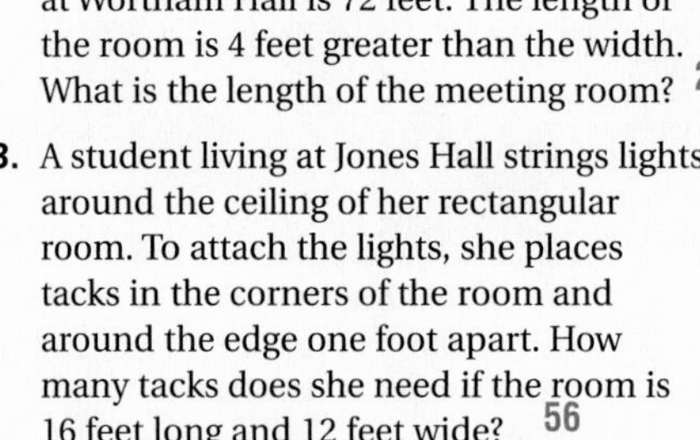

Problem Solving Focus

For problem 3, focus on the second step in the Problem Solving Process: Make a Plan. Ask students which strategy or strategies might be useful in solving this problem. If students suggest using the strategy Draw a Diagram, have volunteers share their diagrams with the class.

Discuss how to use the strategy Solve a Simpler Problem to solve problem 3. If students have difficulty getting started with this strategy, suggest that they solve the problem for a room that measures 3 feet by 2 feet. Help students recognize that the number of tacks can be found by adding the length and the width and then multiplying by 2.

Georgia Performance Standards

M6P1.c Apply and adapt a variety of appropriate strategies to solve problems.

M6P4.c Recognize and apply mathematics in contexts outside of mathematics.

M6P5.a Create and use representations to organize, record, and communicate mathematical ideas.

Problem Solving Strategies

Draw a Diagram
Make a Model
Guess and Test
Work Backward
Find a Pattern
Make a Table
Solve a Simpler Problem
Use Logical Reasoning
Act It Out
Make an Organized List

Atlanta's Skyscrapers

The Atlanta skyline is graced with nearly 200 high-rise buildings. The tallest, Bank of America Plaza, rises more than 1,000 feet above the downtown streets. In fact, it is the tallest building in any state capital.

Choose one or more strategies to solve the problem.

1. The 55-story Bank of America Plaza was built relatively quickly. It took 21 days to build 7 floors and 27 days to build 9 floors. At this rate, how long did it take to build all the floors of the skyscraper? **165 days**

For 2 and 3, use the information in the photograph.

2. The Marriot Marquis Hotel is 123 feet shorter than the BellSouth building, The BellSouth building is 46 feet shorter than the Westin Peachtree Plaza. How tall is the Marriot Marquis Hotel? **554 ft**

3. Only one of the skyscrapers labeled in the photo was built before 1980. The height if this building is less than 85% of the SunTrust Plaza. The building is greater than 92% of the height of 191 Peachtree Plaza. Which building was built before 1980? **Westin Peachtree Plaza**

Atlanta's Skyscrapers

Reading Strategies

English Language Learners

Having students work in small groups can be beneficial to all students while helping ELL students with unfamiliar vocabulary. Have students read the problems in small groups and ask them to discuss any vocabulary questions among themselves. If everyone in a group has the same question, they should share it with the entire class.

Using Data Have students preview the photo before using it to solve problems. Ask students how much taller SunTrust Plaza is compared to Westin Peachtree Plaza. 148 ft

Problem Solving Focus

For problem 3, focus on the strategy Use Logical Reasoning. Ask students how they used a sequence of logical steps to help them solve the problem. You may want to have students use a flowchart or other graphic organizer to present the steps in their logical processes.

CHAPTER 9

Measurement and Geometry

Section 9A

Customary and Metric Measurement

- 9-1 **Hands-On Lab** Select and Use Appropriate Measuring Tools
- 9-1 **Understanding Customary Units of Measure**
- 9-2 **Understanding Metric Units of Measure**
- 9-3 **Converting Customary Units**
- 9-4 **Converting Metric Units**
- 9-5 **Time and Temperature**

Section 9B

Measurement and Geometric Figures

- 9-6 **Finding Angle Measures in Polygons**
- 9-7 **Perimeter**
- 9-8A **Hands-On Lab** Explore Circumference
- 9-8 **Circle and Circumference**
- 9-8B **Hands-On Lab** Construct Circle Graphs

Pacing Guide for 45-Minute Classes

Chapter 9

Countdown to Testing Weeks 20, 21

DAY 1	DAY 2	DAY 3	DAY 4	DAY 5
9-1 Hands-On Lab	9-1 Lesson	9-2 Lesson	9-3 Lesson	9-4 Lesson
DAY 6	**DAY 7**	**DAY 8**	**DAY 9**	**DAY 10**
9-5 Lesson	Ready to Go On? Focus on Problem Solving 9-6 Lesson	9-6 Lesson 9-7 Lesson	9-7 Lesson 9-8A Hands-On Lab	9-8A Hands-On Lab 9-8 Lesson
DAY 11	**DAY 12**	**DAY 13**	**DAY 14**	
9-8 Lesson	9-8B Hands-On Lab Ready to Go On? Multi-Step Test Prep	Chapter 9 Review	Chapter 9 Test	

Pacing Guide for 90-Minute Classes

Chapter 9

DAY 1	DAY 2	DAY 3	DAY 4	DAY 5
9-1 Hands-On Lab 9-1 Lesson	9-2 Lesson 9-3 Lesson	9-4 Lesson 9-5 Lesson	Ready to Go On? Focus on Problem Solving 9-6 Lesson 9-7 Lesson	9-7 Lesson 9-8A Hands-On Lab 9-8 Lesson
DAY 6	**DAY 7**			
9-8 Lesson 9-8B Hands-On Lab Ready to Go On? Multi-Step Test Prep	Chapter 9 Review Chapter 9 Test			

ONGOING ASSESSMENT and INTERVENTION

Assess Prior Knowledge

Before Chapter 9

DIAGNOSE	PRESCRIBE
Diagnose readiness for the chapter.	Prescribe intervention.
Are You Ready? SE p. 483	 ***Are You Ready? Intervention*** Skills 15, 19, 27, 65

Formative Assessment

Before Every Lesson

DIAGNOSE	PRESCRIBE
Diagnose readiness for the lesson.	Prescribe intervention.
Warm Up TE, every lesson	**Skills Bank** SE pp. 749–761
	Reteach CRB, Chapters 1–9

During Every Lesson

DIAGNOSE	PRESCRIBE
Diagnose understanding of lesson concepts.	Prescribe intervention.
Think and Discuss SE, every lesson	***Questioning Strategies*** Chapter 9
Write About It SE, lesson exercises	**Reading Strategies** CRB, every lesson
Journal TE, lesson exercises	***Success for ELL*** pp. 149–164

After Every Lesson

DIAGNOSE	PRESCRIBE
Diagnose mastery of lesson concepts.	Prescribe intervention.
Lesson Quiz TE, every lesson	**Reteach** CRB, every lesson
Test Prep SE, every lesson	**Problem Solving** CRB, every lesson
Test and Practice Generator	**Test Prep Doctor** TE, lesson exercises
	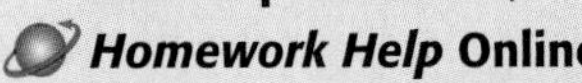 ***Homework Help* Online**

Before Chapter 9 Testing

DIAGNOSE	PRESCRIBE
Diagnose mastery of concepts in the chapter.	Prescribe intervention.
Ready to Go On? SE pp. 508, 526	***Ready to Go On? Intervention*** Chapter 9
Focus on Problem Solving SE p. 509	**Scaffolding Questions** TE p. 527
Multi-Step Test Prep SE p. 527	
Section Quizzes AR pp. 167–168	
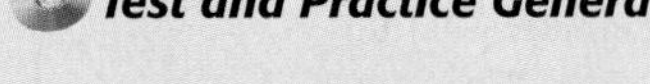 ***Test and Practice Generator***	

Before High Stakes Testing

DIAGNOSE	PRESCRIBE
Diagnose mastery of benchmark concepts.	Prescribe intervention.
Test Tackler SE pp. 534–535	***CRCT Prep Workbook***
CRCT Prep SE pp. 536–537	
***CRCT Prep* CD-ROM**	

Summative Assessment

After Chapter 9

DIAGNOSE	PRESCRIBE
Check mastery of chapter concepts.	Prescribe intervention.
Multiple-Choice Tests (Forms A, B, C)	**Reteach** CRB, every lesson
Free-Response Tests (Forms A, B, C)	***Lesson Tutorial Videos*** Chapter 9
Performance Assessment AR pp. 169–182	
Test and Practice Generator	
Check mastery of benchmark concepts.	Prescribe intervention.
CRCT	***CRCT Prep Workbook***

KEY: **SE** = *Student Edition* **TE** = *Teacher's Edition* **CRB** = *Chapter Resource Book* **AR** = *Assessment Resources* Available online Available on CD-ROM

Supporting the Teacher

Chapter 9 Resource Book

Practice A, B, C
pp. 3–5, 11–13, 19–21, 27–29, 35–37, 43–45, 51–53, 59–61

Reading Strategies ELL
pp. 9, 17, 25, 33, 41, 49, 57, 65

Puzzles, Twisters, and Teasers
pp. 10, 18, 26, 34, 42, 50, 58, 66

Reteach
pp. 6, 14, 22, 30, 38, 46, 54, 62

Problem Solving
pp. 8, 16, 24, 32, 40, 48, 56, 64

Challenge
pp. 7, 15, 23, 31, 39, 47, 55, 63

Parent Letter pp. 1–2

Transparencies

Lesson Transparencies, Volume 2 .... Chapter 9
- Warm Ups
- Problem of the Day
- Teaching Transparencies
- Lesson Quizzes

Know-It Notebook .... Chapter 9
- Additional Examples
- Vocabulary
- Chapter Review
- Big Ideas

Alternate Openers: Explorations .... pp. 75–82

Countdown to CRCT .... pp. 39–42

Teacher Tools

Power Presentations®
Complete PowerPoint® presentations for Chapter 9 lessons

Lesson Tutorial Videos® SPANISH
Holt authors Ed Burger and Freddie Renfro present tutorials to support the Chapter 9 lessons.

One-Stop Planner® SPANISH
Easy access to all Chapter 9 resources and assessments, as well as software for lesson planning, test generation, and puzzle creation

IDEA Works!®
Key Chapter 9 resources and assessments modified to address special learning needs

Lesson Plans .... pp. 75–82

Questioning Strategies .... Chapter 9

Solutions Key .... Chapter 9

Interdisciplinary Posters and Worksheets .... Chapter 9

TechKeys

Lab Resources

Project Teacher Support

Parent Resources 

Workbooks

Homework and Practice Workbook SPANISH
Teacher's Guide .... pp. 38–41

Know-It Notebook
Teacher's Guide .... Chapter 9

Problem Solving Workbook SPANISH
Teacher's Guide .... pp. 38–41

CRCT Prep
Teacher's Guide

Technology Highlights for the Teacher

 **Power Presentations**

Dynamic presentations to engage students. Complete PowerPoint® presentations for every lesson in Chapter 9.

2-1 Solving One-Step Equations

Isolate a variable by using inverse operations which "undo" operations on the variable.

An equation is like a balanced scale. To keep the balance, perform the same operation on both sides.

Inverse Operations	
Operation	**Inverse Operation**
Addition	Subtraction
Subtraction	Addition

 **One-Stop Planner** SPANISH

Easy access to Chapter 9 resources and assessments. Includes lesson-planning, test-generation, and puzzle-creation software.

 **Premier Online Edition** SPANISH

Chapter 9 includes Tutorial Videos, Lesson Activities, Lesson Quizzes, Homework Help, and Chapter Project.

KEY: **SE** = *Student Edition* **TE** = *Teacher's Edition*  English Language Learners  Spanish version available  Available online  Available on CD-ROM

Reaching All Learners

Resources for All Learners

Hands-On Lab Activities	Chapter 9
Technology Lab Activities	Chapter 9
Homework and Practice Workbook SPANISH	pp. 75–82
Know-It Notebook	Chapter 9
Problem Solving Workbook SPANISH	pp. 75–82

DEVELOPING LEARNERS

Practice A	CRB, every lesson
Reteach	CRB, every lesson
Inclusion	TE p. 521
Questioning Strategies	Chapter 9
Modified Chapter 9 Resources	*IDEA Works!*
Homework Help Online	

ON-LEVEL LEARNERS

Practice B	CRB, every lesson
Puzzles, Twisters, and Teasers	CRB, every lesson
Cooperative Learning	TE p. 511
Modeling	TE p. 515

ADVANCED LEARNERS

Practice C	CRB, every lesson
Challenge	CRB, every lesson
Extension	TE pp. 485, 527, 528, 529
Critical Thinking	TE p. 521

English Language Learners

ENGLISH LANGUAGE LEARNERS

Are You Ready? Vocabulary	SE p. 483
Vocabulary Connections	SE p. 484
Lesson Vocabulary	SE, every lesson
Vocabulary Review	SE p. 530
English Language Learners	TE pp. 500, 515, 521
Reading Strategies	CRB, every lesson
Success for English Language Learners	pp. 149–164
Multilingual Glossary	

Reaching All Learners Through...

Inclusion	TE p. 521
Diversity	TE p. 489
Kinesthetic Experience	TE p. 493
Concrete Manipulatives	TE p. 497
Cooperative Learning	TE p. 511
Modeling	TE p. 515
Graphic Organizers	TE p. 501
Critical Thinking	TE p. 521
Test Prep Doctor	TE pp. 491, 495, 499, 503, 507, 513, 517, 523, 534, 535, 536
Common Error Alert	TE pp. 489, 493, 497, 501, 505, 511, 521
Scaffolding Questions	TE p. 527

Technology Highlights for Reaching All Learners

Lesson Tutorial Videos SPANISH

Starring Holt authors Ed Burger and Freddie Renfro! Live tutorials to support every lesson in Chapter 9.

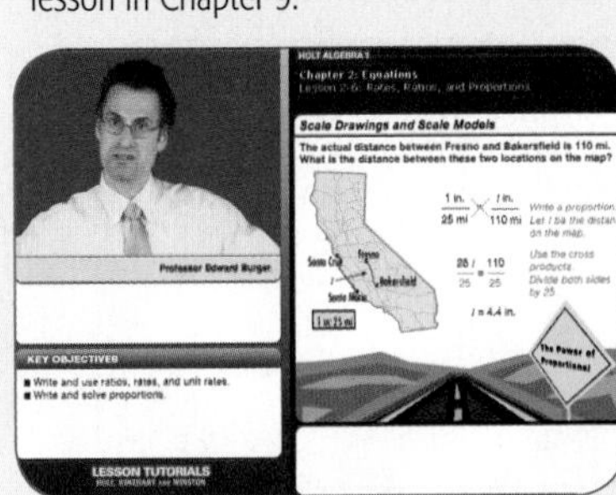

Multilingual Glossary

Searchable glossary includes definitions in English, Spanish, Vietnamese, Chinese, Hmong, Korean, and 4 other languages.

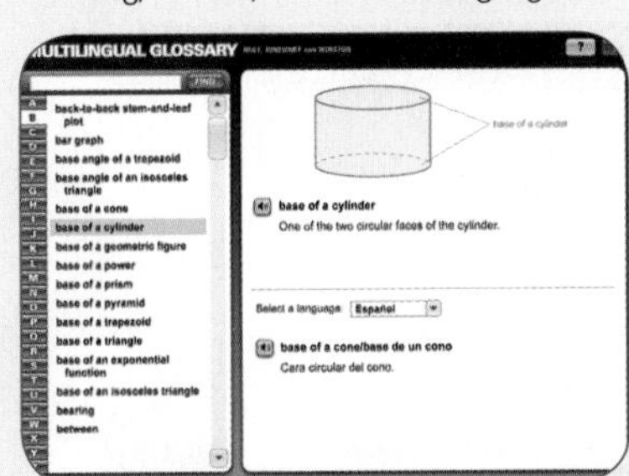

Online Interactivities

Interactive tutorials provide visually engaging alternative opportunities to learn concepts and master skills.

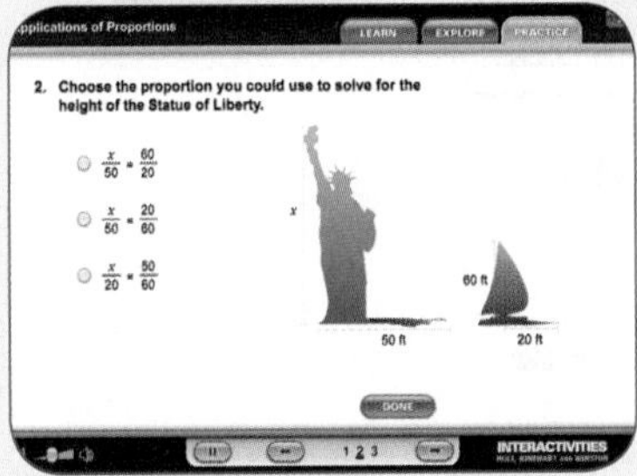

KEY: **SE** = *Student Edition* **TE** = *Teacher's Edition* **CRB** = *Chapter Resource Book*  Spanish version available  Available online  Available on CD-ROM

Ongoing Assessment

Assessing Prior Knowledge

Determine whether students have the prerequisite concepts and skills for success in Chapter 9.

Are You Ready? SPANISH .... SE p. 483

Warm Up .... TE, every lesson

Test Preparation

Provide review and practice for Chapter 9 and standardized tests.

Multi-Step Test Prep .... SE p. 527

Study Guide: Review .... SE pp. 530–532

Test Tackler .... SE pp. 534–535

CRCT Prep .... SE pp. 536–537

Countdown to CRCT Transparencies .... pp. 39–42

CRCT Prep Workbook

***CRCT Prep* CD-ROM**

IDEA Works!

Alternative Assessment

Assess students' understanding of Chapter 9 concepts and combined problem-solving skills.

Chapter 9 Project .... SE p. 482

Performance Assessment SPANISH .... AR pp. 181–182

Portfolio Assessment SPANISH .... AR p. xxxiv

Daily Assessment

Provide formative assessment for each day of Chapter 9.

Questioning Strategies .... Chapter 9

Think and Discuss .... SE, every lesson

Write About It .... SE, lesson exercises

Journal .... TE, lesson exercises

Lesson Quiz .... TE, every lesson

Modified Lesson Quizzes .... *IDEA Works!*

Weekly Assessment

Provide formative assessment for each week of Chapter 9.

Focus on Problem Solving .... SE p. 509

Multi-Step Test Prep .... SE p. 527

Ready to Go On? SPANISH .... SE pp. 508, 526

Cumulative Assessment .... SE pp. 536–537

Test and Practice Generator SPANISH .... *One-Stop Planner*

Formal Assessment

Provide summative assessment of Chapter 9 mastery.

Section Quizzes SPANISH .... AR pp. 167–168

Chapter 9 Test .... SE p. 533

Chapter Test (Levels A, B, C) SPANISH .... AR pp. 169–180
- Multiple Choice
- Free Response

Cumulative Test SPANISH .... AR pp. 183–186

Test and Practice Generator SPANISH .... *One-Stop Planner*

Modified Chapter 9 Test .... *IDEA Works!*

Technology Highlights for Ongoing Assessment

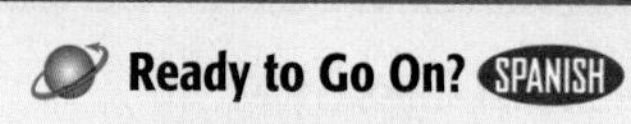

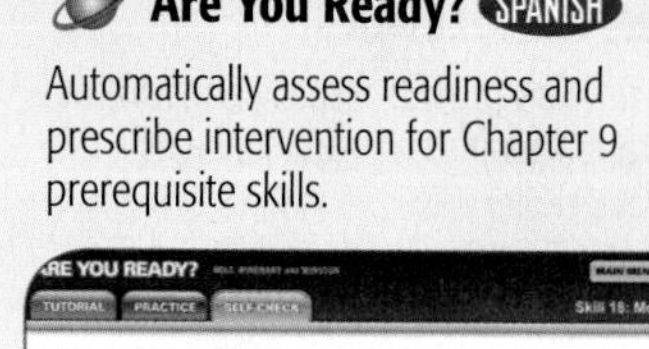

Are You Ready? SPANISH

Automatically assess readiness and prescribe intervention for Chapter 9 prerequisite skills.

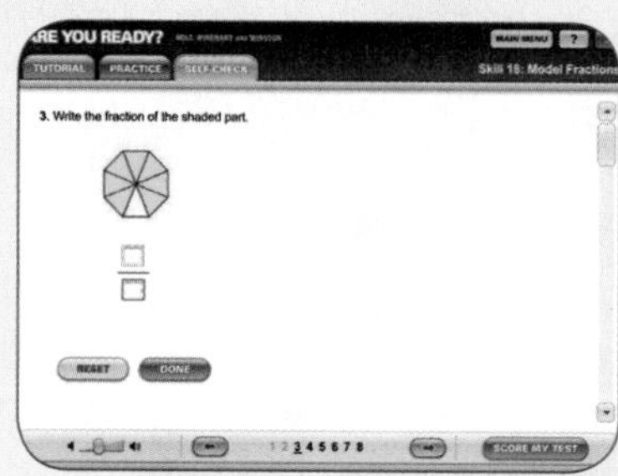

Ready to Go On? SPANISH

Automatically assess understanding of and prescribe intervention for Sections 9A and 9B.

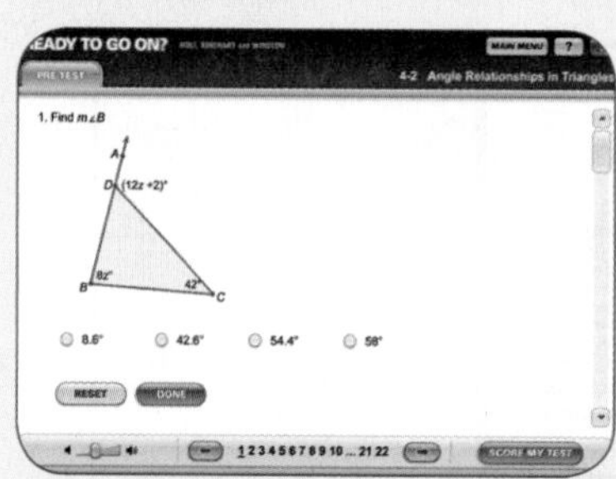

Test and Practice Generator SPANISH

Use Chapter 9 problem banks to create assessments and worksheets to print out or deliver online. Includes dynamic problems.

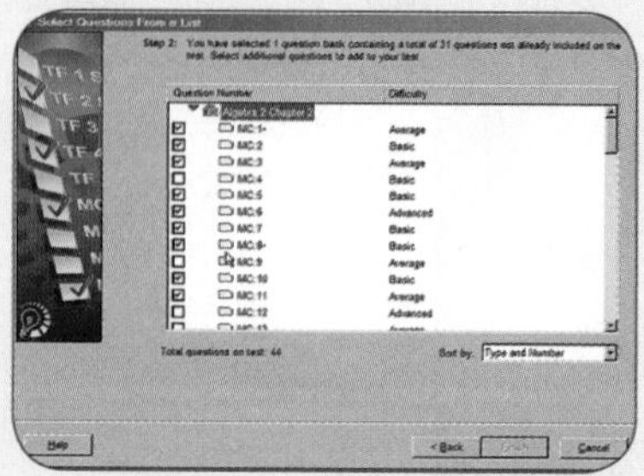

KEY: **SE** = *Student Edition* **TE** = *Teacher's Edition* **AR** = *Assessment Resources* SPANISH Spanish version available  Available online  Available on CD-ROM

Formal Assessment

Three levels (A, B, C) of multiple-choice and free-response chapter tests are available in the *Assessment Resources*.

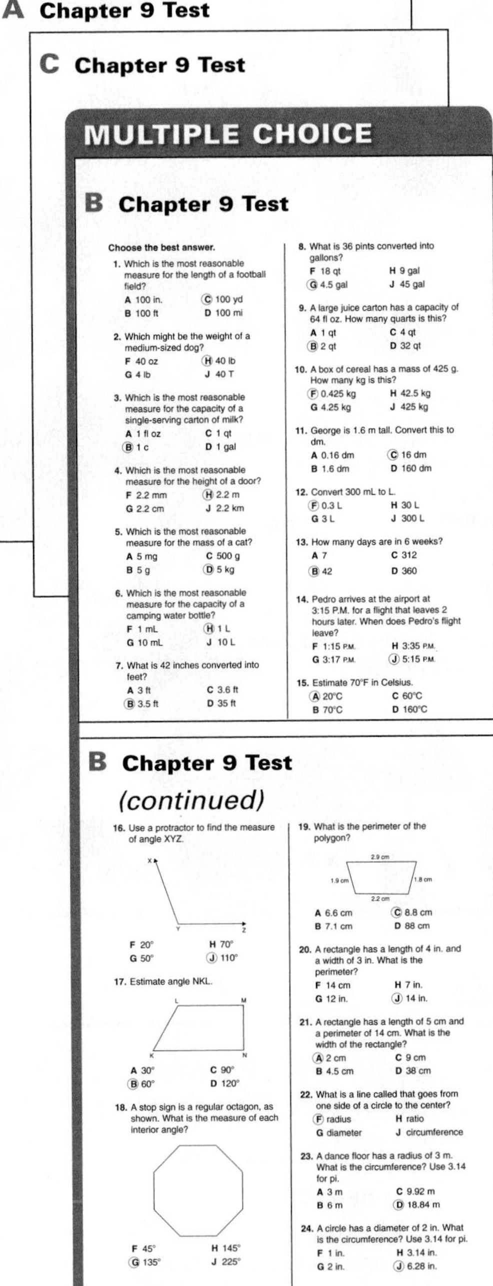

A Chapter 9 Test

C Chapter 9 Test

MULTIPLE CHOICE

B Chapter 9 Test

Choose the best answer.

1. Which is the most reasonable measure for the length of a football field?
A 100 in. (C) 100 yd
B 100 ft D 100 mi

2. Which might be the weight of a medium-sized dog?
F 40 oz (H) 40 lb
G 4 lb J 40 T

3. Which is the most reasonable measure for the capacity of a single-serving carton of milk?
A 1 fl oz C 1 qt
(B) 1 c D 1 gal

4. Which is the most reasonable measure for the height of a door?
F 2.2 mm (H) 2.2 m
G 2.2 cm J 2.2 km

5. Which is the most reasonable measure for the mass of a cat?
A 5 mg C 500 g
B 5 g (D) 5 kg

6. Which is the most reasonable measure for the capacity of a camping water bottle?
F 1 mL (H) 1 L
G 10 mL J 10 L

7. What is 42 inches converted into feet?
A 3 ft C 3.6 ft
(B) 3.5 ft D 35 ft

8. What is 36 pints converted into gallons?
F 18 qt H 9 gal
(G) 4.5 gal J 45 gal

9. A large juice carton has a capacity of 64 fl oz. How many quarts is this?
A 1 qt C 4 qt
(B) 2 qt D 32 qt

10. A box of cereal has a mass of 425 g. How many kg is this?
(F) 0.425 kg H 42.5 kg
G 4.25 kg J 425 kg

11. George is 1.6 m tall. Convert this to dm.
A 0.16 dm (C) 16 dm
B 1.6 dm D 160 dm

12. Convert 300 mL to L.
(F) 0.3 L H 30 L
G 3 L J 300 L

13. How many days are in 6 weeks?
A 7 C 312
(B) 42 D 360

14. Pedro arrives at the airport at 3:15 P.M. for a flight that leaves 2 hours later. When does Pedro's flight leave?
F 1:15 P.M. H 3:35 P.M.
G 3:17 P.M. (J) 5:15 P.M.

15. Estimate 70°F in Celsius.
(A) 20°C C 60°C
B 70°C D 160°C

B Chapter 9 Test (continued)

16. Use a protractor to find the measure of angle XYZ.
F 20° H 70°
G 50° (J) 110°

17. Estimate angle NKL.
A 30° C 90°
(B) 60° D 120°

18. A stop sign is a regular octagon, as shown. What is the measure of each interior angle?
F 45° H 145°
(G) 135° J 225°

19. What is the perimeter of the polygon?
A 6.6 cm (C) 8.8 cm
B 7.1 cm D 88 cm

20. A rectangle has a length of 4 in. and a width of 3 in. What is the perimeter?
F 14 cm H 7 in.
G 12 in. (J) 14 in.

21. A rectangle has a length of 5 cm and a perimeter of 14 cm. What is the width of the rectangle?
(A) 2 cm C 9 cm
B 4.5 cm D 38 cm

22. What is a line called that goes from one side of a circle to the center?
(F) radius H ratio
G diameter J circumference

23. A dance floor has a radius of 3 m. What is the circumference? Use 3.14 for pi.
A 3 m C 9.92 m
B 6 m (D) 18.84 m

24. A circle has a diameter of 2 in. What is the circumference? Use 3.14 for pi.
F 1 in. H 3.14 in.
G 2 in. (J) 6.28 in.

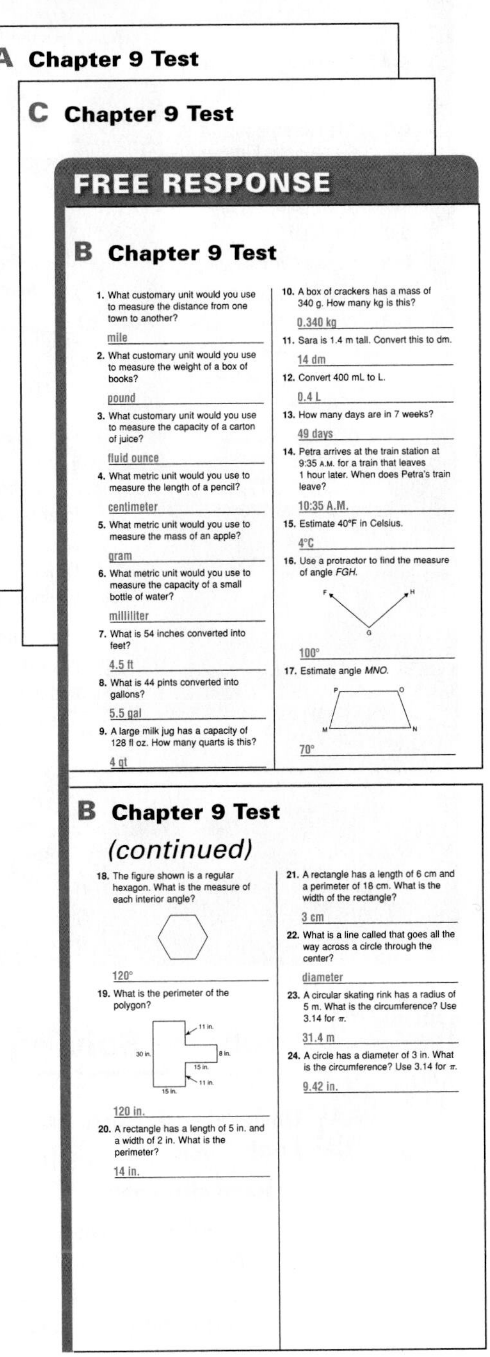

A Chapter 9 Test

C Chapter 9 Test

FREE RESPONSE

B Chapter 9 Test

1. What customary unit would you use to measure the distance from one town to another?
mile

2. What customary unit would you use to measure the weight of a box of books?
pound

3. What customary unit would you use to measure the capacity of a carton of juice?
fluid ounce

4. What metric unit would you use to measure the length of a pencil?
centimeter

5. What metric unit would you use to measure the mass of an apple?
gram

6. What metric unit would you use to measure the capacity of a small bottle of water?
milliliter

7. What is 54 inches converted into feet?
4.5 ft

8. What is 44 pints converted into gallons?
5.5 gal

9. A large milk jug has a capacity of 128 fl oz. How many quarts is this?
4 qt

10. A box of crackers has a mass of 340 g. How many kg is this?
0.340 kg

11. Sara is 1.4 m tall. Convert this to dm.
14 dm

12. Convert 400 mL to L.
0.4 L

13. How many days are in 7 weeks?
49 days

14. Petra arrives at the train station at 9:35 A.M. for a train that leaves 1 hour later. When does Petra's train leave?
10:35 A.M.

15. Estimate 40°F in Celsius.
4°C

16. Use a protractor to find the measure of angle FGH.
100°

17. Estimate angle MNO.
70°

B Chapter 9 Test (continued)

18. The figure shown is a regular hexagon. What is the measure of each interior angle?
120°

19. What is the perimeter of the polygon?
120 in.

20. A rectangle has a length of 5 in. and a width of 2 in. What is the perimeter?
14 in.

21. A rectangle has a length of 6 cm and a perimeter of 18 cm. What is the width of the rectangle?
3 cm

22. What is a line called that goes all the way across a circle through the center?
diameter

23. A circular skating rink has a radius of 5 m. What is the circumference? Use 3.14 for π.
31.4 m

24. A circle has a diameter of 3 in. What is the circumference? Use 3.14 for π.
9.42 in.

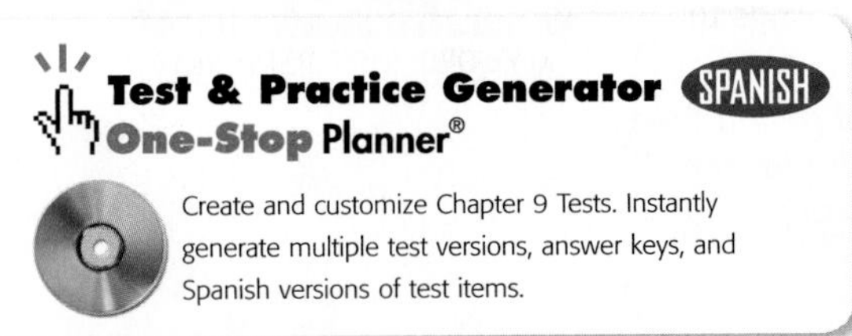

Test & Practice Generator SPANISH
One-Stop Planner®

Create and customize Chapter 9 Tests. Instantly generate multiple test versions, answer keys, and Spanish versions of test items.

CHAPTER 9

Why Learn This?

Tell students that the study of mathematics is essential to many career fields. *Pure* mathematicians study mathematical ideas and try to create and prove new rules about the way values and figures behave in certain situations. *Applied* mathematicians use the mathematical concepts discovered by pure mathematicians to evaluate and solve real-world situations. The study of π is of interest to both pure and applied mathematicians.

Using Data

To begin the study of this chapter, have students:

- Identify the value of π to the nearest hundredth. 3.14
- Use words to explain what π represents. In any circle, π is the ratio of the circumference to the diameter.

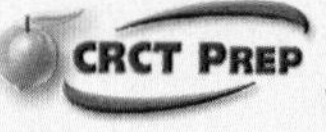

CRCT PREP On page 536, students will find cumulative CRCT practice.

CHAPTER 9

Measurement and Geometry

CRCT PREP

go.hrw.com
Chapter Project Online
KEYWORD: MR7 Ch9

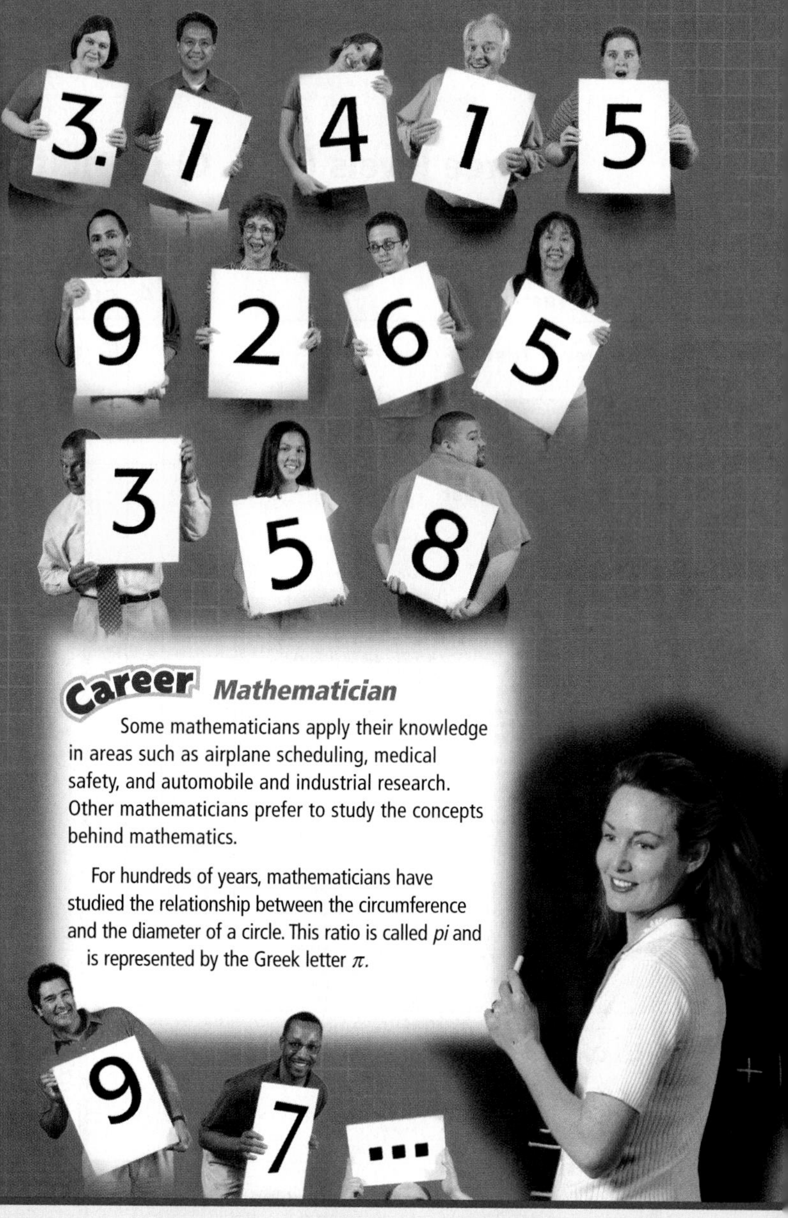

3.
1
4
1
5
9
2
6
5
3
5
8
9
7
...

Career *Mathematician*

Some mathematicians apply their knowledge in areas such as airplane scheduling, medical safety, and automobile and industrial research. Other mathematicians prefer to study the concepts behind mathematics.

For hundreds of years, mathematicians have studied the relationship between the circumference and the diameter of a circle. This ratio is called *pi* and is represented by the Greek letter π.

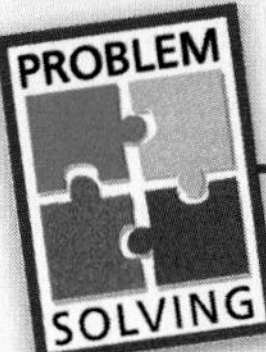

PROBLEM SOLVING

Problem Solving Project

Understand, Plan, Solve, and Look Back

Have students:

- Complete the Discovering *Pi* worksheet.
- Explain whether $A = \pi r^2$ can be used to find the exact area of a circle.
- Research ways to find the area of a circle without using the equation $A = \pi r^2$ and create drawings to demonstrate them.
- Research the history of *pi* and then make a wall chart to display the known decimal places of *pi*.

Social Studies and Geometry Connection

Project Resources

Materials:

- Discovering *Pi* worksheet, cans and other objects, strings, and rulers or other measuring devices

go.hrw.com
Project Teacher Support
KEYWORD: MR7 PSProject9

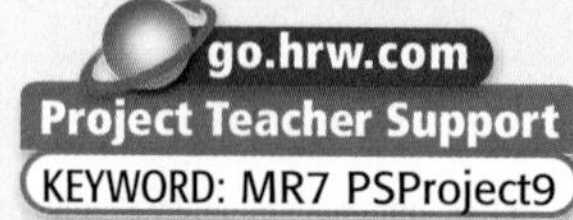

ARE YOU READY?

Vocabulary

Choose the best term from the list to complete each sentence.

1. If you find how heavy an object is, you are finding the ___?___. weight
2. A ___?___ is used to measure an angle. protractor
3. If you find the amount a container can hold when filled, you are finding the ___?___ of the container. capacity
4. A ___?___ is an equation that shows two equivalent ratios. proportion
5. A parallelogram with four right angles is a ___?___. rectangle

capacity
length
proportion
protractor
rectangle
temperature
weight

Complete these exercises to review skills you will need for this chapter.

Write and Read Decimals

Write each decimal in standard form.

6. 12 and 4 tenths 12.4
7. 150 and 18 hundredths 150.18
8. 1 thousand, 60 and 5 tenths 1,060.5

Simplify Fractions

Write each fraction in simplest form.

9. $\frac{8}{12}$ $\frac{2}{3}$
10. $\frac{4}{20}$ $\frac{1}{5}$
11. $\frac{6}{8}$ $\frac{3}{4}$
12. $\frac{8}{16}$ $\frac{1}{2}$

Write Ratios

Write each ratio three different ways.

13. Hearts to rectangles 5:4; 5 to 4; $\frac{5}{4}$
14. Rectangles to circles 4:3; 4 to 3; $\frac{4}{3}$

15. Triangles to squares 5:1; 5 to 1; $\frac{5}{1}$
16. Hexagons to triangles 3:5; 3 to 5; $\frac{3}{5}$

Solve Proportions

Solve for n.

17. $\frac{2}{n} = \frac{4}{10}$ $n = 5$
18. $\frac{3}{8} = \frac{6}{n}$ $n = 16$
19. $\frac{n}{7} = \frac{8}{14}$ $n = 4$
20. $\frac{5}{9} = \frac{n}{18}$ $n = 10$

ARE YOU READY? CHAPTER 9

Organizer

Objective: Assess students' understanding of prerequisite skills.

Prerequisite Skills

Write and Read Decimals
Simplify Fractions
Write Ratios
Solve Proportions

Assessing Prior Knowledge

INTERVENTION

Diagnose and Prescribe

Use this page to determine whether intervention is necessary or enrichment is appropriate.

Resources

Are You Ready? Intervention and Enrichment Worksheets

Are You Ready? CD-ROM

Are You Ready? Online

my.hrw.com

ARE YOU READY?

Diagnose and Prescribe

NO INTERVENE

Prerequisite Skill	*Are You Ready? Intervention*, Chapter 9 — Worksheets	CD-ROM	Online
Write and Read Decimals	Skill 15	Activity 15	Diagnose and Prescribe Online
Simplify Fractions	Skill 19	Activity 19	
Write Ratios	Skill 27	Activity 27	
Solve Proportions	Skill 65	Activity 65	

YES ENRICH

Are You Ready? Enrichment, Chapter 9
Worksheets
CD-ROM
Online

CHAPTER 9 Study Guide: Preview

Organizer

Objective: Help students apply strategies to understand and retain key concepts.

Online Edition
Multilingual Glossary

Resources

PuzzlePro®
One-Stop Planner®

***Multilingual Glossary* Online**

go.hrw.com
KEYWORD: MR7 Glossary

Answers to *Vocabulary Connections*

Possible answers:

1. Perimeter is the distance around a polygon.
2. The circumference of a circle is the distance around the circle.
3. The radius of a circle is the distance from the center of the circle to a point on the circle.
4. You will measure the length of a line segment that passes through the center of the circle with end-points on the circle.

CHAPTER 9

Study Guide: Preview

Where You've Been

Previously, you

- performed simple conversions within the metric system.
- used angle measurements to classify angles.
- classified polygons according to their sides.

In This Chapter

You will study

- converting measures within the same measurement system.
- identifying relationships involving angles in triangles and quadrilaterals.
- solving problems involving perimeter.
- describing the relationship between the radius, diameter, and circumference of a circle.

Where You're Going

You can use the skills learned in this chapter

- to understand the relationship between the perimeter and the area of a polygon.
- to determine how much fencing to buy to enclose an animal pen or garden.

Key Vocabulary/Vocabulario

center of a circle	centro (de un círculo)
circle	círculo
circumference	circunferencia
customary system	sistema imperial de medidas
diameter	diámetro
metric system	sistema métrico de medidas
perimeter	perímetro
pi	*pi*
radius	radio

Vocabulary Connections

To become familiar with some of the vocabulary terms in the chapter, consider the following. You may refer to the chapter, the glossary, or a dictionary if you like.

1. The word *perimeter* has the prefix *peri-*, which means "all around or surrounding," and the root *meter*, which is the basic unit of length in the metric system. What do you think the **perimeter** of an object is?
2. The word *circumference* has the prefix *circum-*, which means "around a circle." What do you think you will measure if you find the **circumference** of a circle?
3. The word *radius* is related to the word *radiate*, which means to move outward in all directions from the center. What do you think the **radius** of a circle is?
4. The word *diameter* has the prefix *dia-*, which means "across." What do you think you will measure if you find the **diameter** of a circle?

Grade 6 CRCT GPS

M6N1. Students will understand the meaning of positive and negative rational numbers and use them in computation.

M6M1. Students will convert from one unit to another within one system of measurement (customary or metric) by using proportional relationships.

M6M2. Students will use appropriate units of measure for finding length, perimeter, area and volume and will express each quantity using the appropriate unit.

M6A2. Students will consider relationships between varying quantities.

M6A3. Students will evaluate algebraic expressions, including those with exponents, and solve simple one-step equations using each of the four basic operations.

M6D1. Students will pose questions, collect data, represent and analyze the data, and interpret results.

****Georgia Mathematics Performance Standards*** **statements are written out completely on pp. GA28–GA35.**

Study Strategy: Use Multiple Representations

Math concepts can be explained using multiple representations. As you study, pay attention to any tables, lists, graphs, diagrams, symbols, and words used to describe a concept.

From Lesson 8-4

In this example, the concept of classifying lines is explained using words, diagrams, symbols, and examples.

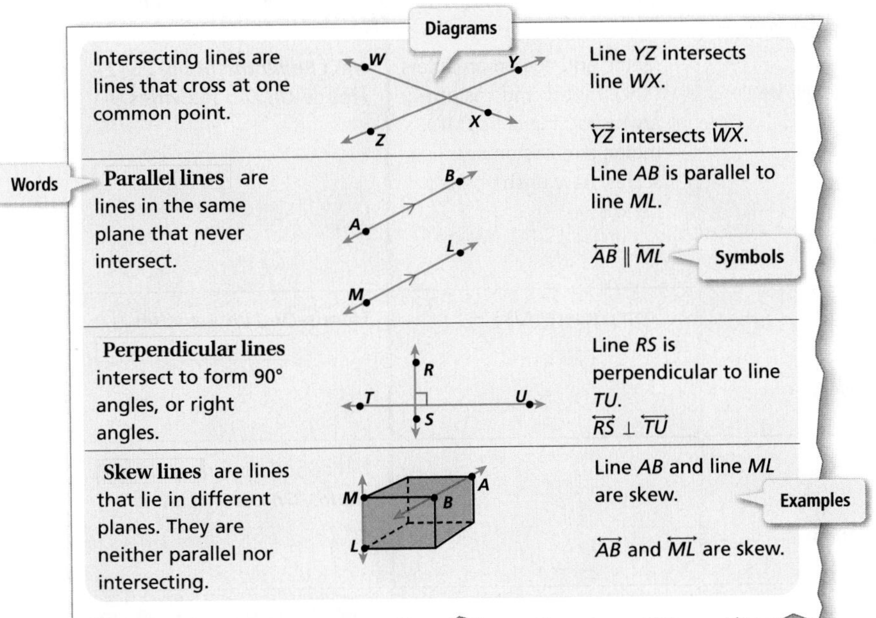

Diagrams
Intersecting lines are lines that cross at one common point.
W
Y
X
Z
Line YZ intersects line WX.
$\overleftrightarrow{YZ}$ intersects $\overleftrightarrow{WX}$.
Words
Parallel lines are lines in the same plane that never intersect.
B
A
L
M
Line AB is parallel to line ML.
$\overleftrightarrow{AB} \parallel \overleftrightarrow{ML}$
Symbols
Perpendicular lines intersect to form 90° angles, or right angles.
R
T
S
U
Line RS is perpendicular to line TU.
$\overleftrightarrow{RS} \perp \overleftrightarrow{TU}$
Skew lines are lines that lie in different planes. They are neither parallel nor intersecting.
M
B
A
L
Line AB and line ML are skew.
Examples
$\overleftrightarrow{AB}$ and $\overleftrightarrow{ML}$ are skew.

Try This

1. Classify one of the types of triangles in Lesson 8-5 using the four different representations shown above.
2. Review your notes from the previous chapter. Which different representations did you use to explain how to classify lines? Which representation do you prefer? Why?

Reading and Writing Math

Organizer

Objective: Help students apply strategies to understand and retain key concepts.

Online Edition

Resources

Chapter 9 Resource Book
Reading Strategies

Study Strategy: Use Multiple Representations

Discuss Have students discuss the benefits of stating a word problem in their own words, drawing a picture of a problem situation, or acting out a given situation by using classmates or manipulatives. All of these methods are examples of multiple representation.

Extend Using multiple representations when taking notes in other classes is an excellent way to improve retention of important concepts.

Answers to *Try This*

1. An isosceles triangle has two congruent sides.

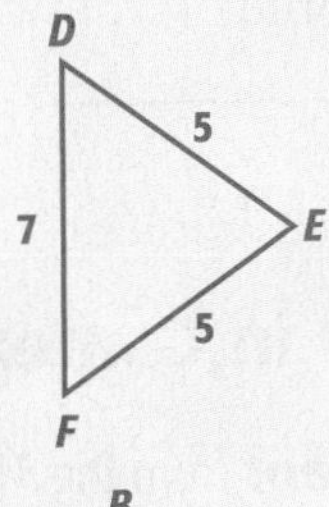

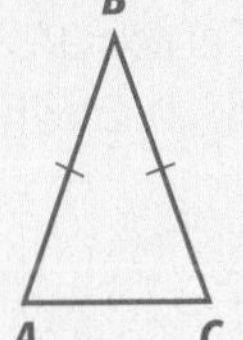

$\triangle ABC$ is isosceles because $\overline{AB} \cong \overline{BC}$.

2. Check students' work.

Grade 6 CRCT GPS

Standards	Lab 9-1	9-1	9-2	9-3	9-4	9-5	9-6	9-7	Lab 9-8A	9-8	Lab 9-8B
M6N1.g						★					
M6M1				★	★	★					
M6M2.a	★										
M6M2.b	★	★	★						★		
M6A2.a									★		
M6A3								★		★	
M6D1.a											★
M6D1.b											★

***Georgia Mathematics Process Standards* are covered throughout the book.**
For a complete list, see pp. GA28–GA35.

SECTION **9A**

Customary and Metric Measurement

One-Minute Section Planner

Lesson	Materials	MiC and Lab Resources
9-1 Hands-On Lab Select Appropriate Measuring Tools • Select and use appropriate customary or metric tools for measuring length, weight, or capacity. **Lesson 9-1** Understanding Customary Units of Measure • Understand and select appropriate customary units of measure. ☑ CRCT ☑ SAT-10 ☑ ITBS ☑ CTBS ☑ NAEP	Metric and customary rulers (MK), metric and customary measuring cups (MK), metric and customary scales, new unsharpened pencils	**MiC:** ***Reallotment*** pp. 25–27 ***Hands-On Lab Activities*** 9-1
Lesson 9-2 Understanding Metric Units of Measure • Understand and select approriate metric units of measure. ☑ CRCT ☑ SAT-10 ☑ ITBS ☑ CTBS ☑ NAEP	Metric rulers (MK)	***Hands-On Lab Activities*** 9-2
Lesson 9-3 Converting Customary Units • Convert customary units of measure. ☑ CRCT ☑ SAT-10 ☑ ITBS ☑ CTBS ☑ NAEP		**MiC:** ***Reallotment*** pp. 28–29 ***Hands-On Lab Activities*** 9-3
Lesson 9-4 Converting Metric Units • Convert metric units of measure. ☑ CRCT ☑ SAT-10 ☑ ITBS ☑ CTBS ☑ NAEP		**MiC:** ***Reallotment*** pp. 28–29 ***Hands-On Lab Activities*** 9-4
Lesson 9-5 Time and Temperature • Find measures of time and temperature. ☑ CRCT ☐ SAT-10 ☐ ITBS ☑ CTBS ☑ NAEP		

MK = *Manipulatives Kit*

Mathematics in Context

The unit ***Reallotment*** from the *Mathematics in Context* © 2006 series can be used with Section 9A. See Section Planner above for suggestions for integrating *MiC* with *Holt Mathematics*.

Section Overview

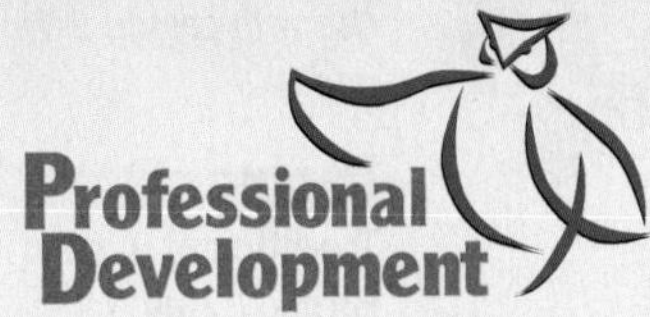

Customary Units of Measure

Lessons 9-1, 9-3

Why? Customary units of measure are commonly used in the United States.

Common Customary Measurements		
Length	**Weight**	**Capacity**
1 foot = 12 inches 1 yard = 36 inches 1 yard = 3 feet 1 mile = 5,280 feet 1 mile = 1,760 yards	1 pound = 16 ounces 1 ton = 2,000 pounds	1 cup = 8 fluid ounces 1 pint = 2 cups 1 quart = 2 pints 1 quart = 4 cups 1 gallon = 4 quarts 1 gallon = 16 cups 1 gallon = 128 fluid ounces

Proportions can be used to convert units within the customary system.

Convert 4 yards to feet.

$$\frac{1 \text{ yd}}{3 \text{ ft}} = \frac{4 \text{ yd}}{x \text{ ft}}$$
$$1 \cdot x = 3 \cdot 4$$
$$x = 12$$

So 4 yards is 12 feet.

Metric Units of Measure

Lessons 9-2, 9-4

Why? Metric units of measure are commonly used in science.

To **multiply** by the *n*th power of ten, move the decimal point *n* places right.

To **divide** by the *n*th power of ten, move the decimal point *n* places left.

	Unit	Abbreviation	Approximate Comparison
Length	**Kilo**meter	km	Length of 10 football fields
	Meter	m	Width of a door
	Centimeter	cm	Width of your little finger
	Millimeter	mm	Thickness of a dime
Mass	**Kilo**gram	kg	Mass of a textbook
	Gram	g	Mass of a small paperclip
Capacity	Liter	L	Filled bottle of sparkling water
	Milliliter	mL	Half-filled eyedropper

Time and Temperature

Lesson 9-5

Many real-world situations involve using measures of time or temperature.

Time	
1 year (yr) = 365 days 1 year = 12 months (mo) 1 year = 52 weeks 1 week = 7 days	1 day = 24 hours (hr) 1 hour = 60 minutes (min) 1 minute = 60 seconds (s)

Temperature Conversions	
To convert Celsius to Fahrenheit, use $F = \frac{9}{5}C + 32$.	To convert Fahrenheit to Celsius, use $C = \frac{5}{9}(F - 32)$.

Organizer

Use with Lesson 9-1 and 9-2

Pacing:
Traditional 1 day
Block $\frac{1}{2}$ day

Objective: Use an appropriate tool to make precise measurements.

Materials: Metric ruler, customary ruler, measuring cup, metric scale, customary scale

 **Online Edition**

Resources

 ***Hands-On Lab Activities***
Lab 9-1 Recording Sheet

Teach

Discuss

Have students discuss how accurately the thickness of a human hair can be measured using a 12-inch ruler.

Close

Key Concept

Different tools and different units of measure are available to measure lengths, weights, and volumes.

Assessment

Identify the more precise unit of measure.

1. sixteenth of an inch or eighth of an inch sixteenth of an inch
2. millimeter or kilometer millimeter

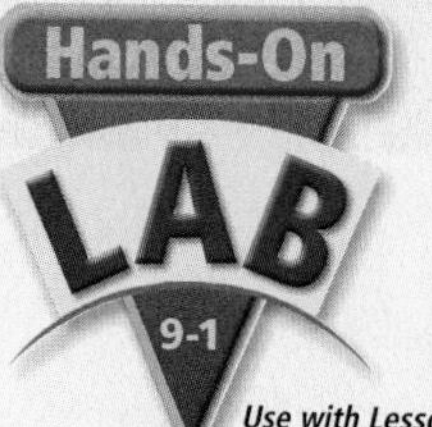

Select and Use Appropriate Measuring Tools

Use with Lessons 9-1 and 9-2

Georgia Performance Standards
M6M2.a, M6M2.b

Activity 1

1. Measure the length of a paper clip to the nearest inch. Select an inch or millimeter ruler to measure the length of the paper clip. 1 in.
2. Count the small markings from the first line on the left to the line that shows 1 inch. How many are there? 16

   Measure the paper clip to the nearest sixteenth of an inch. $1\frac{3}{16}$ in.
3. Measure a pencil to the nearest fourth of an inch. Then measure the pencil to the nearest eighth of an inch. Check students' measurements.
4. Now using the metric ruler, measure the length of this line segment to the nearest centimeter. 2 cm
5. Count the small markings from the first line on the left to the line that shows 1 centimeter. How many are there? 10
6. Each line shows 1 millimeter. How long is the line segment in millimeters? 23 mm
7. Measure a pencil to the nearest centimeter. Then measure the pencil to the nearest millimeter. Check students' measurements.

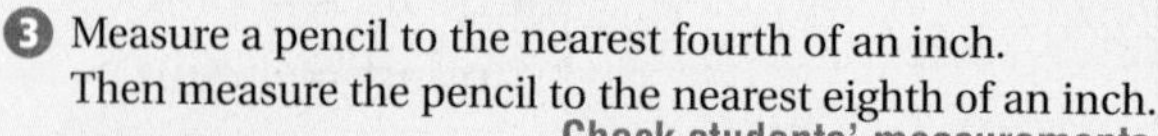

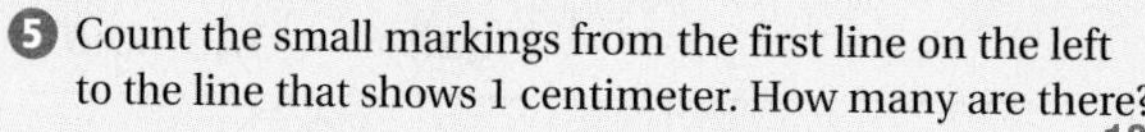

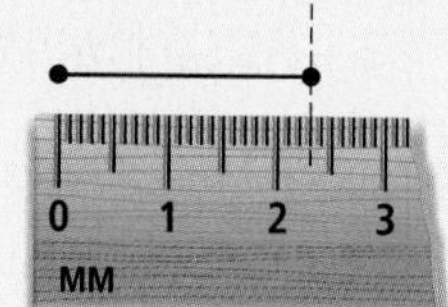

Think and Discuss

1. Name 5 items that would be appropriate to measure with a ruler. Check students' answers.
2. *Precision* is the level of detail an instrument can measure. The smaller the unit of measure on the instrument, the more precise the measurement will be. Is the measurement in 1 or 2 more precise? Explain.

Try This

Use a ruler to measure each object to the nearest sixteenth of an inch and to the nearest millimeter. 1–3. Check students' measurements.

1. your pinky
2. your desktop
3. your shoe

Georgia Performance Standards

M6M2.a Measure length to the nearest half, fourth, eighth and sixteenth of an inch.

M6M2.b Select and use units of appropriate size and type to measure length, perimeter, area and volume.

Jennifer Sawyer
Shawboro, North Carolina

Teacher to Teacher

Here is a way to get students interested in converting measurements through an interactive activity. Divide the class into groups of 2–4. Provide each group with a long strip of paper about 1 inch wide. Each group will mark a random length on the strip of paper and call the length "one unit." Then through folding, equally spaced units can be marked off to fill the strip. Any excess can be trimmed off the end. Students can measure three or four objects in the classroom using the ruler that they created and then also measure the objects in centimeters and inches, recording the measurements in a table. Meet as a group to discuss conversion factors.

Activity 2

1. Find the weight of a bunch of grapes.
Use a customary or metric scale to weigh the grapes.

What is the weight of the grapes in pounds? **$\frac{1}{2}$ lb**

What is the weight of the grapes in kilograms? **$\frac{1}{4}$ kg**

Pounds

Kilograms

2. What is the weight of your math book in pounds and in kilograms? **Check students' measurements.**

Think and Discuss

1. Which is heavier, 1 pound of grapes or 1 kilogram of grapes? **1 kg is heavier than 1 lb.**

Try This

Use a scale to measure each object in pounds and kilograms.

1. your shoe
2. 5 pencils
3. a tissue box

1–3 Check students' measurements.

Activity 3

1. Use a measuring cup that shows fluid ounces and milliliters. Fill the cup with water up to the 8 fluid ounces mark. About how many milliliters is this? **about 240 mL**
2. Fill a measuring cup with 150 milliliters of water. About how many fluid ounces is this? **about 5 fl oz**

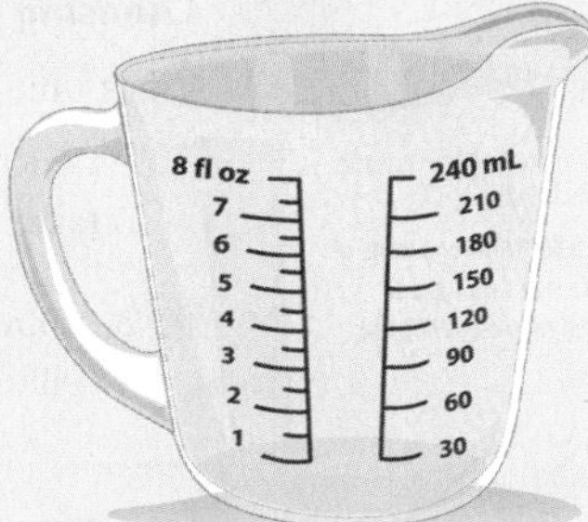

Think and Discuss

1. Explain how you can use a measuring cup and a metric scale to find the mass of 2 cups of water. **First find the mass of the empty measuring cup. Then find the mass of the cup with 2 cups of water. Then subtract the mass of the empty cup.**
2. About how many milliliters are in 2 cups? **about 470 mL**

Try This

1. Place 25 tablespoons of water in a measuring cup. How many fluid ounces is this? how many milliliters? **$12\frac{1}{2}$ fl oz; about 370 mL**
2. Find the mass of 2 cups of water. **Check students' measurement.**

Activity 1

Answers to *Think and Discuss*

2. A sixteenth of an inch is a smaller unit of measure than an inch, so the measurement in problem 2 is the more precise measurement.

9-1 Organizer

Pacing: Traditional 1 day
Block $\frac{1}{2}$ day

Objective: Students understand and select appropriate units of measure.

Online Edition
Tutorial Videos

Countdown to CRCT Week 20

Power Presentations with PowerPoint®

Warm Up

Simplify.

1. $\frac{2}{8}$ $\frac{1}{4}$
2. $\frac{6}{16}$ $\frac{3}{8}$
3. $\frac{4}{8}$ $\frac{1}{2}$
4. $\frac{12}{16}$ $\frac{3}{4}$

Problem of the Day

Maria rented an electric car at a rate of $40 per day and $0.15 per mile. She returned the car the same day, gave the rental clerk a $100 bill, and got $21.75 back in change. How far did Maria drive the car? 255 miles

Also available on transparency

Math Humor

What do "$x = 4$" and salt water have in common? Both can be called solutions.

9-1 Understanding Customary Units of Measure

Learn to understand and select appropriate customary units of measure.

Vocabulary
customary system

If you do not have an instrument, such as a ruler, scale, or measuring cup, you can estimate the length, weight, and capacity of an object by using a benchmark.

The **customary system** is the measurement system often used in the United States. It includes units of measurement for length, weight, and capacity.

Customary Units of Length

Unit	Abbreviation	Benchmark
Inch	in.	Width of your thumb
Foot	ft	Distance from your elbow to your wrist
Yard	yd	Width of a classroom door
Mile	mi	Total length of 18 football fields

EXAMPLE 1 Choosing Appropriate Units of Length

Georgia Performance Standards
M6M2.b Select and use units of appropriate size and type to measure length. Also, M6P1.b, M6P4.c.

What unit of measure provides the best estimate? Explain.

A **A table is about 4 __?__ long.**
A table is about 4 ft long.
Think: The length of a table is about 4 times the distance from your elbow to your wrist.

B **A ceiling is about 3 __?__ high.**
A ceiling is about 3 yd high.
Think: The height of a ceiling is about 3 times the width of a classroom door.

Customary Units of Weight

Unit	Abbreviation	Benchmark
Ounce	oz	A slice of bread
Pound	lb	A loaf of bread
Ton	T	A small car

EXAMPLE 2 Choosing Appropriate Units of Weight

What unit of measure provides the best estimate? Explain.

A **A female elephant can weigh up to 4 __?__.**
A female elephant can weigh up to 4 T.
Think: An elephant has a weight of about 4 small cars.

Georgia Performance Standards

M6M2.b Select and use units of appropriate size and type to measure length, perimeter, area and volume.

M6P1.b Solve problems that arise in mathematics and in other contexts.

M6P4.c Recognize and apply mathematics in contexts outside of mathematics.

1 Introduce

Alternate Opener

EXPLORATION

9-1 Understanding Customary Units of Measure

Different units of measure are used for measuring length, weight, and capacity. Capacity is the amount that a container can hold.

1. Decide whether each of the units of measure below is used to measure length, weight, or capacity. Write the name of the unit in the appropriate column of the table.

Pint Pound Inch Ton
Foot Quart Mile Gallon
Yard Ounce Cup Fluid Ounce

Length	Weight	Capacity

Think and Discuss

2. **Describe** an object that could be measured using yards.
3. **Explain** how you would decide whether to measure an object using inches or feet.

Motivate

Ask students how they think early societies measured objects. Discuss that people first used body parts and natural surroundings as measuring tools. Length was measured using the finger, hand, and forearm. An object's weight could be measured by balancing the object against a known amount of seeds or stones. Capacity was measured by filling gourds or vessels with seeds and then counting the seeds.

Explorations and answers are provided in *Alternate Openers: Explorations Transparencies.*

What unit of measure provides the best estimate? Explain.

B A remote control weighs about 5 __?__. *Think: A remote control has a weight of about 5 slices of bread.*

A remote control weighs about 5 oz.

Capacity deals with volume, or the amount a container can hold.

Customary Units of Capacity		
Unit	**Abbreviation**	**Benchmark**
Fluid Ounce	fl oz	A spoonful
Cup	c	A glass of juice
Pint	pt	A small bottle of salad dressing
Quart	qt	A small container of paint
Gallon	gal	A large container of milk

EXAMPLE 3 **Choosing Appropriate Units of Capacity**

What unit of measure provides the best estimate? Explain.

A bathtub holds about 50 __?__ of water. *Think: A bathtub holds about 50 large containers of milk.*

A bathtub holds about 50 gal of water.

Inch rulers are usually separated into sixteenths of an inch.

EXAMPLE 4 **Finding Measurements**

Measure the length of the golf tee to the nearest half, fourth, or eighth inch.

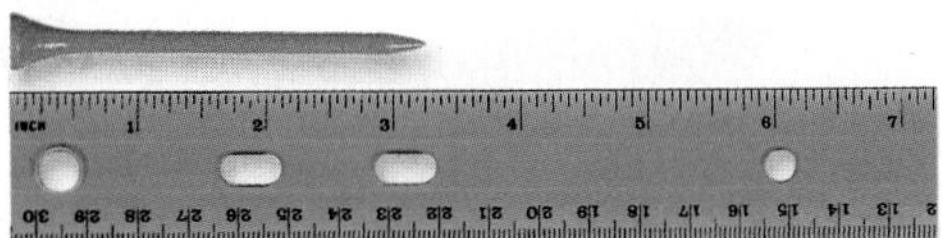

The golf tee is between $3\frac{1}{4}$ in. and $3\frac{3}{8}$ in. It is closer to $3\frac{1}{4}$ in.

The length of the golf tee is about $3\frac{1}{4}$ in.

Think and Discuss GPS M6P3.b

1. Give an example of when you might need to estimate the weight of an object.

2. Give an example of when you might need to estimate the capacity of a container.

Possible answers to *Think and Discuss:*

1. when buying vegetables, fruit, or meat
2. when you are cooking or filling a bowl with food

COMMON ERROR ALERT

Students sometimes confuse pints (pt) and quarts (qt). Have them associate the order of the units with the order of the alphabet. *P* comes before *Q* and pints come before quarts.

Power Presentations with PowerPoint®

Additional Examples

Example 1

What unit of measure provides the best estimate?

A. A doorway is about 7 ___ high. ft

B. A calculator is about 6 ___ long. in.

Example 2

What unit of measure provides the best estimate?

A. A loaf of bread weighs about 16 ___. oz

B. A bike could weigh 20 ___. lb

Example 3

What unit of measure provides the best estimate?

A large watercooler holds about 10 ___ of water. gal

Example 4

Measure the length of the line segment to the nearest half, fourth, or eighth of an inch. $1\frac{5}{8}$ in.

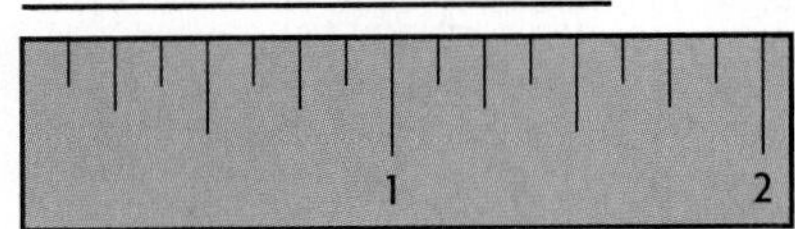

Also available on transparency

2 Teach

Guided Instruction

In this lesson, students learn to understand and select appropriate customary units of measure. Give each student a tape measure. Have each student measure the width of a thumb, the distance from elbow to wrist, and the width of a classroom door. Then have students use those benchmarks with Example 1. Discuss the benchmarks for capacity and weight. Then show students how to estimate the length of an object to the nearest half, fourth, or eighth inch.

Reaching All Learners

Through Diversity

Have students do research to find examples of benchmarks that were used by people before the customary system of measurement was developed. Have students make a table showing the benchmark and the unit of length, weight, or capacity for which it was used.

3 Close

Summarize

Ask students to explain how to choose a reasonable unit of length, weight, or capacity when given an object to measure.

Possible answer: Smaller units are used for smaller objects, and larger units are used for larger objects.

Then ask students to name the units of length, weight, and capacity from smallest to largest. length: inch, foot, yard, mile; weight: ounce, pound, ton; capacity: fluid ounce, cup, pint, quart, gallon

9-1 Exercises

Assignment Guide

If you finished Example 1 assign:
Average 1, 9–10, 15–16, 28–37
Advanced 5, 9–10, 15, 22, 28–37

If you finished Example 2 assign:
Average 1–2, 9–10, 13–16, 18, 28–37
Advanced 5–6, 9–10, 13–16, 22, 28–37

If you finished Example 3 assign:
Average 1–3, 9–18, 28–37
Advanced 5–7, 9–17, 22, 28–37

If you finished Example 4 assign:
Average 1–20, 25–37
Advanced 5–37

Homework Quick Check

Quickly check key concepts.
Exercises: 8, 12, 16, 20

Answers

9–14. Complete answers on p. A10.

19. Possible answer: when you need a more precise answer

9-1 Exercises

M6P2.c, M6P3.a, M6P5.a

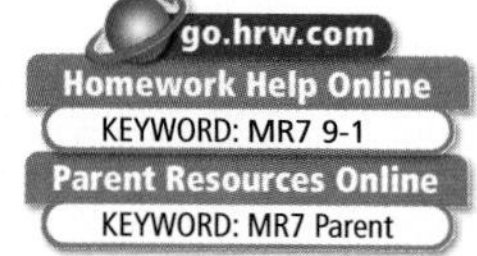

GUIDED PRACTICE

See Example 1 **What unit of measure provides the best estimate? Explain.**

1. A pencil is about 7 __?__ long. in.; about 7 widths of your thumb

See Example 2
2. A tube of toothpaste weighs about 8 __?__. oz; about 8 slices of bread

See Example 3
3. A swimming pool holds about 20,000 __?__ of water. gal; about 20,000 large containers of milk

See Example 4
4. Measure the length of the key to the nearest half, fourth, or eighth inch. about $2\frac{1}{4}$ in.

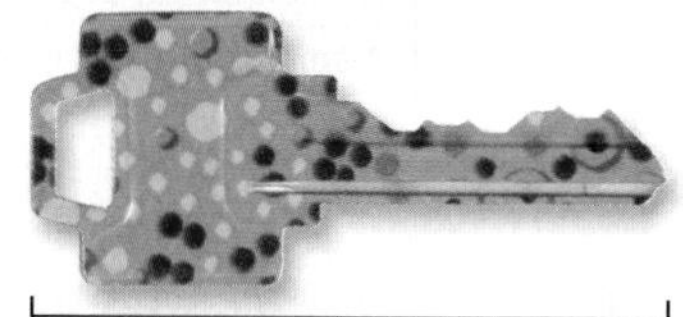

INDEPENDENT PRACTICE

See Example 1 **What unit of measure provides the best estimate? Explain.**

5. The distance from New York City to Boston is about 200 __?__. mi; about the total length of 3,600 football fields

See Example 2
6. A small dog weighs about 12 __?__. lb; about 12 loaves of bread

See Example 3
7. A pot for cooking soup holds about 10 __?__ of water. qt; about 10 small containers of paint

See Example 4
8. Measure the length of the green bean to the nearest half, fourth, or eighth inch. about $4\frac{1}{8}$ in.

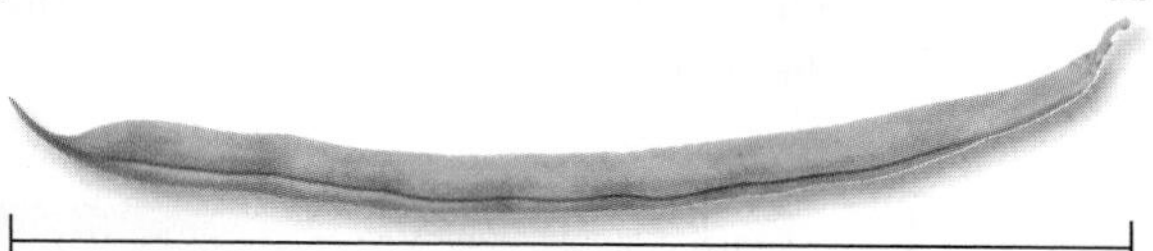

PRACTICE AND PROBLEM SOLVING

CRCT GPS
Extra Practice p. 731

Which unit of measure would you use for each? Justify your answer.

9. the height of a flagpole ft
10. the width of a CD case in.
11. the capacity of a car's gas tank gal
12. the capacity of a baby's bottle c
13. the weight of an egg oz
14. the weight of a chair lb

Use benchmarks to estimate each measure. Possible answers:

15. the width of your math textbook about 9 in.
16. the width of an armchair about 1 yd
17. the capacity of a flower pot about 1 qt
18. the weight of an alarm clock about 4 lb
19. **Critical Thinking** When would you choose to measure to the nearest eighth inch rather than the nearest fourth inch?

Georgia Performance Standards

M6P2.c Develop and evaluate mathematical arguments and proofs.

M6P3.a Organize and consolidate their mathematical thinking through communication.

M6P5.a Create and use representations to organize, record, and communicate mathematical ideas.

RETEACH 9-1

LESSON 9-1 **Reteach**
Understanding Customary Units of Measure

The customary system of measurement uses inches, feet, yards, and miles to measure length, width, distance, and height.
- Use inches to measure objects that are a few widths of your thumb.
- Use feet to measure objects that are a few times the distance from your shoulder to your elbow.
- Use yards to measure objects that are a few widths of a classroom door.
- Use miles to measure distances that are a few times the lengths of 18 football fields.

Write *inches*, *feet*, *yards*, or *miles*.

1. Your hand is about 3 __inches__ wide.
2. A grown man is about 2 __yards__ tall.

The customary system of measurement uses ounces, pounds, and tons to measure weight.
- Use ounces to measure objects that weigh as much as a few slices of bread.
- Use pounds to measure objects that weigh as much as a few loaves of bread.
- Use tons to measure objects that weigh as much as a few small cars.

Write *ounces*, *pounds*, or *tons*.

3. A feather weighs about 2 __ounces__.
4. A hippo weighs about 4 __tons__.

The customary system of measurement uses fluid ounces, cups, pints, quarts, and gallons to measure capacity.
- Use fluid ounces to measure objects that have a capacity of a few spoonfuls.
- Use cups to measure objects that have a capacity of a few glasses of juice.
- Use pints to measure objects that have a capacity of a few small bottles of salad dressing.
- Use quarts to measure objects that have a capacity of a few small containers of paint.
- Use gallons to measure objects that have a capacity of a few large containers of milk.

Write *fluid ounces*, *cups*, *pints*, *quarts*, or *gallons*.

5. Two teaspoons hold about 2 __fluid ounces__.
6. Five mugs hold about 5 __cups__.

PRACTICE 9-1

LESSON 9-1 **Practice B**
Understanding Customary Units of Measure

What unit of measure provides the best estimate? Justify your answer.

1. A pair of eyeglasses is about 5 __inches__ long because
they are about 5 times the width of my thumb.
2. A chalkboard is about 4 __yards__ long because
it is about 4 times the width of a classroom door.
3. A bottle of shampoo weighs about 12 __ounces__ because
it has a weight of about 12 slices of bread.
4. A cat weighs about 8 __pounds__ because
it has a weight of about 8 loaves of bread.
5. An eyedropper holds about 2 __fluid ounces__ because
it holds about 2 spoonfuls.
6. Ramon filled a watering can with water. What benchmark should he use for the capacity of the watering can?
a large container of milk
7. Estimate the length of the feather to the nearest half, fourth, or eighth inch.

4 inches

LINK History

Alfred the Great was one of the most famous Anglo-Saxon kings. He defended England from Viking raids and helped found the British Navy. He is the only English monarch to be awarded the label of "the Great."

Find the weight of the object to the nearest half, fourth, or eighth of a pound.

20.

$2\frac{3}{4}$ lb

21.

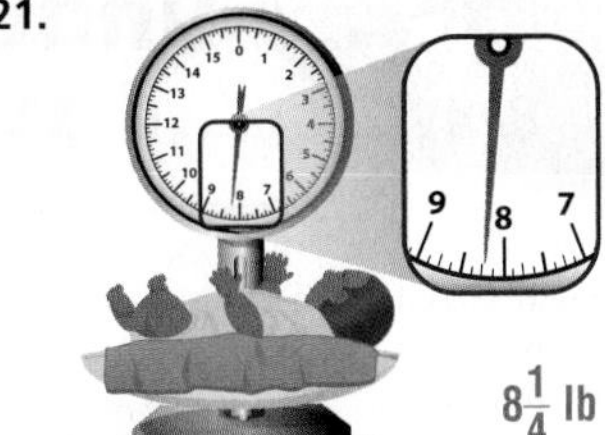

$8\frac{1}{4}$ lb

22. History The early Saxon kings of England wore a sash around their waist that they used as a benchmark for measuring length. The name of the sash eventually became the name of one of the customary units of length. What unit of length did the sash represent: the inch, foot, yard, or mile? Explain.

Find how much liquid is in each container to the nearest half, fourth, or eighth of a cup or quart.

23.

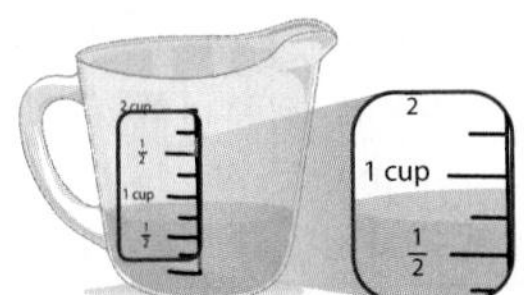

$\frac{3}{4}$ c

24.

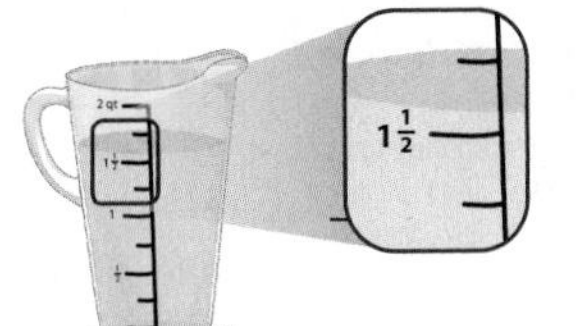

$1\frac{1}{2}$ qt

25. Write a Problem Write a problem that can be answered using a pen as a benchmark.

26. Write About It Make up your own personal benchmarks for an inch, a cup, and a pound.

27. Challenge Look up the words *rod, peck,* and *dram* in a dictionary. Tell what each one is and what it is used to measure.

CRCT Prep • GPS Support • Spiral Review

28. Multiple Choice Which is the best estimate for the width of a classroom?

Ⓐ 30 in.   Ⓑ 30 ft   Ⓒ 30 yd   Ⓓ 30 mi

29. Multiple Choice Madison needs to buy a turkey to feed 12 people. What weight turkey should she buy?

Ⓕ 16 lb   Ⓖ 16 oz   Ⓗ 16 c   Ⓘ 16 T

List all the factors of each number. (Lesson 4-2)

30. 24   1, 2, 3, 4, 6, 8, 12, 24   **31.** 45   1, 3, 5, 9, 15, 45   **32.** 56   1, 2, 4, 7, 8, 14, 28, 56   **33.** 80   1, 2, 4, 5, 8, 10, 16, 20, 40, 80

Two angles of a triangle are given. Classify the triangle. (Lesson 8-5)

34. 55°, 35°   right   **35.** 18°, 82°   acute   **36.** 47°, 26°   obtuse   **37.** 95°, 45°   obtuse

Ongoing Assessment and Intervention

Diagnose ***Before*** **the Lesson**
9-1 Warm Up, TE p. 488

Monitor ***During*** **the Lesson**
9-1 Know-It Notebook
9-1 Questioning Strategies

Assess ***After*** **the Lesson**
9-1 Lesson Quiz, TE p. 491

Answers

22, 25. See p. A10.

26. Possible answers: inch: the diameter of a quarter; cup: a glass of milk; pound: a box of spaghetti

27. Possible answers: *rod:* a unit of length equal to $5\frac{1}{2}$ yards; *peck:* a dry measure of capacity equal to 8 quarts; *dram:* a very small unit of weight equal to 0.0625 ounce

Test Prep Doctor If students have difficulty with Exercise 28, have them relate back to the benchmarks of thumb width for an inch, elbow to wrist for a foot, door width for a yard, and 18 football fields for a mile.

Journal

Have students describe how closely their own thumb and elbow-to-wrist dimensions compare to an inch and a foot, respectively.

CHALLENGE 9-1

LESSON 9-1 **Challenge**
Customary Classroom Challenge

Find objects in your classroom for each unit of measure. Estimate first. Then measure. Check students' work.

LENGTH, WIDTH, OR HEIGHT

Object	Estimate	Actual
Objects and estimates may vary.	______ inches	______ inches
	______ inches	______ inches
	______ feet	______ feet
	______ feet	______ feet
	______ yards	______ yards
	______ yards	______ yards

WEIGHT

Object	Estimate	Actual
	______ ounces	______ ounces
	______ ounces	______ ounces
	______ pounds	______ pounds
	______ pounds	______ pounds

CAPACITY

Object	Estimate	Actual
	____ fluid ounces	____ fluid ounces
	______ cups	______ cups
	______ pints	______ pints
	______ quarts	______ quarts

PROBLEM SOLVING 9-1

LESSON 9-1 **Problem Solving**
Understanding Customary Units of Measure

Use customary units of measure to answer each question.

1. Which unit of measure would be most appropriate to use for the capacity of a swimming pool?
   gallons
2. Which unit of measure would be most appropriate to use for the length of an insect?
   inches
3. Which unit of measure would be most appropriate to use for the weight of a television set?
   pounds
4. Which unit of measure would be most appropriate to use for the weight of a feather?
   ounces
5. Which unit of measure would be most appropriate to use for the distance between two cities?
   miles
6. Which unit of measure would be most appropriate to use for the capacity of a can of soup?
   cups

Circle the letter of the correct answer.

7. How long is a desk?
   A about 4 in.
   Ⓑ about 4 ft
   C about 4 yd
   D about 4 mi
8. How much does a bird weigh?
   Ⓕ about 3 oz
   G about 3 lb
   H about 3 T
   J about 30 T
9. How much does a can of soda hold?
   Ⓐ about 1 glass of juice
   B about 4 small bottles of salad dressing
   C about 8 large containers of milk
   D about 10 spoonfuls
10. How long is your math book?
   F about 3 times the distance from your shoulder to your elbow
   G about 5 times the width of a classroom door
   H about 8 times the total length of 18 football fields
   Ⓙ about 12 times the width of your thumb

Power Presentations with PowerPoint®

9-1 Lesson Quiz

What unit of measure provides the best estimate?

1. A row boat is 10 ___ long. ft
2. A skateboard is 30 ___ long. in.
3. A pair of earphones weighs 4 ___. oz
4. Drinking water is delivered in a 5___ bottle. gal
5. Estimate the length of the line to the nearest half, fourth, or eighth of an inch. 2 in.

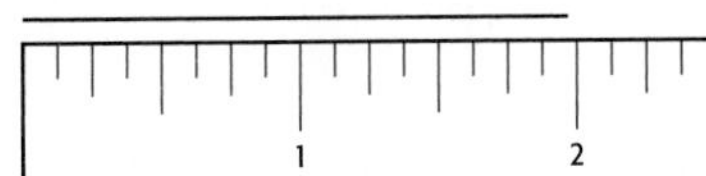

Also available on transparency

9-2 Organizer

Pacing: Traditional 1 day
Block $\frac{1}{2}$ day

Objective: Students understand and select appropriate metric units of measure.

GPS M6M2.a, M6M2.b
Hands-On Lab
In *Hands-On Lab Activities*

Online Edition
Tutorial Videos

Countdown to CRCT Week 20

Power Presentations with PowerPoint®

Warm Up

Multiply the following by 1,000.

1. 0.03 30 **2.** 4.02 4,020

Divide the following by 1,000.

3. 30 0.03 **4.** 487.1 0.4871

Problem of the Day

James said he was 5 ft 6 in. tall. His brother's height is 65 in. Who is the tallest and by how much?
James, by 1 in.

Also available on transparency

Math Humor

Which metric measurement can you use to measure how bad something smells? A scent-i-meter

Georgia Performance Standards

M6M2.b Select and use units of appropriate size and type to measure length, perimeter, area and volume.

M6P1.b Solve problems that arise in mathematics and in other contexts.

M6P4.c Recognize and apply mathematics in contexts outside of mathematics.

9-2 Understanding Metric Units of Measure

Learn to understand and select appropriate metric units of measure.

Vocabulary
metric system

The **metric system** of measurement is used almost everywhere in the world. Its advantage over the customary system is that all metric units are related by the decimal system.

The shortest Olympic track race is 100 meters. Use the length of your classroom as a benchmark. A classroom is about 10 meters long, so a 100-meter race is about the length of 10 classrooms.

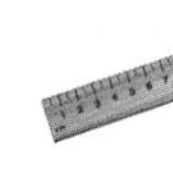

Metric Units of Length

Unit	Abbreviation	Relation to a Meter	Benchmark
Millimeter	mm	0.001 m	Thickness of a dime
Centimeter	cm	0.01 m	Width of a fingernail
Decimeter	dm	0.1 m	Width of a CD case
Meter	m	1 m	Width of a single bed
Kilometer	km	1,000 m	Distance around a city block

Georgia Performance Standards

M6M2.b Select and use units of appropriate size and type to measure length. Also, M6P1.b, M6P4.c.

EXAMPLE 1 Choosing Appropriate Units of Length

What unit of measure provides the best estimate? Explain.

A A TV remote control is about 19 __?__ long.

Think: A TV remote control is about 19 times the width of a fingernail.

A TV remote control is about 19 cm long.

B A school auditorium is about 40 __?__ long.

Think: An auditorium is about 40 times the width of a single bed.

A school auditorium is about 40 m long.

Metric Units of Mass

Unit	Abbreviation	Relation to a Gram	Benchmark
Milligram	mg	0.001 g	Very small insect
Gram	g	1 g	Large paper clip
Kilogram	kg	1,000 g	Textbook

1 Introduce

Alternate Opener

EXPLORATION

9-2 Understanding Metric Units of Measure

In the metric system, the basic unit of length is the meter. One meter (1 m) is about the width of a classroom doorway. Other metric units of length are based on the meter.

Unit	Fraction of a Meter	Decimal Part of a Meter
Millimeter	$\frac{1}{1,000}$ of a meter	0.001 m
Centimeter	$\frac{1}{100}$ of a meter	0.01 m
Decimeter	$\frac{1}{10}$ of a meter	0.1 m

1. Which of the units listed is the smallest? How do you know?
2. Which of the units listed is the largest? How do you know?
3. In the metric system, the basic unit of capacity is the liter (L). The prefixes *milli-*, *centi-*, and *deci-* are used in the same way to create other units of capacity. Complete the table.

Unit	Fraction of a Liter	Decimal Part of a Liter
Milliliter	__?__ of a liter	__?__
Centiliter	__?__ of a liter	__?__
Deciliter	__?__ of a liter	__?__

Think and Discuss

4. **Explain** which is longer, a stick that is 5 centimeters long or a stick that is 5 decimeters long.
5. **Explain** which holds more, a container with a capacity of 7 milliliters or a container with a capacity of 7 centiliters.

Motivate

Discuss whether students have ever traveled outside the United States. Tell students that the United States is the only major country in the world that does not use the metric system of measurement. Ask students to name as many metric units of measurement as they can.

Possible answers: millimeter, centimeter, decimeter, meter, kilometer, milliliter, liter, milligram, gram, kilogram

Explorations and answers are provided in *Alternate Openers: Explorations Transparencies.*

EXAMPLE 2 Choosing Appropriate Units of Mass

What unit of measure provides the best estimate? Explain.

A sandwich has a mass of about 400 __?__.

Think: A sandwich has a mass of about 400 paperclips.

A sandwich has a mass of about 400 g.

Metric Units of Capacity			
Unit	**Abbreviation**	**Relation to a Liter**	**Benchmark**
Milliliter	mL	0.001 L	Drop of water
Liter	L	1 L	Blender container

EXAMPLE 3 Choosing Appropriate Units of Capacity

What unit of measure provides the best estimate? Explain.

A bucket has a capacity of about 10 __?__.

Think: A bucket has a capacity of about 10 blender containers.

A bucket has a capacity of about 10 L.

EXAMPLE 4 Finding Measurements

Measure the length of the toothbrush to the nearest centimeter.

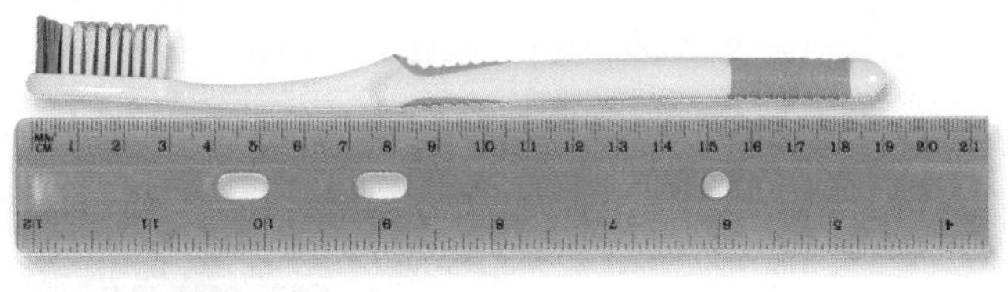

The toothbrush is between 18 and 19 cm. It is closer to 19 cm than 18 cm.

The length of the toothbrush is about 19 cm.

Think and Discuss

GPS M6P2.c

1. Explain how you would estimate the length of the board in your classroom using the toothbrush in Example 4 as a benchmark.

Possible answer to *Think and Discuss:*

1. Since the toothbrush is about 19 cm long, the estimated length of the board, measured in toothbrushes, will be multiplied by 19 to find the estimate in cm.

COMMON ERROR ALERT

At times students will confuse measurements with the prefix *milli* with the prefix *kilo.* Suggest they associate *milli* with the word *mini* and *kilo* with the word *colossal.*

Power Presentations with PowerPoint®

Additional Examples

Example 

What unit of measure provides the best estimate?

A. A ballpoint pen is about 14 ___ long. cm

B. A football field is about 100 ___ long. m

Example 

What unit of measure provides the best estimate?

An orange has a mass of about 600 ___. g

Example 

What unit of measure provides the best estimate?

An ice cream scoop holds about 100 ___. mL

Example 

Measure the length of the line to the nearest meter. 4 m

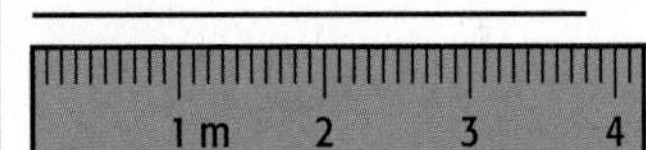

Also available on transparency

2 Teach

Guided Instruction

In this lesson, students learn to understand and select appropriate metric units of measure. A metric ruler shows the approximate metric length of each benchmark in Example 1. Have students use the benchmarks for Example 1. Discuss the benchmarks for capacity and mass, and show examples, if possible. Then show students how to estimate the length of an object to the nearest centimeter and millimeter.

Reaching All Learners

Through Kinesthetic Experience

Have students choose a metric benchmark and use it to estimate the distance between the fingertips of each hand when their arms are extended. Tell students that this distance is their approximate height. Then give each student a string that is about 3 meters long. Have students use their benchmarks and cut the string to the lengths of their estimates. Students can hold up the strings to test the accuracy of their estimates.

3 Close

Summarize

Have students name the metric units of length, capacity, and mass covered in this lesson and give a benchmark for each. Have students suggest items around the classroom that can be measured, and have the class agree on the appropriate metric unit of measurement for each item.

9-2 Exercises

Assignment Guide

If you finished Example 1 assign:
Average 1, 11–13, 23–32
Advanced 6, 11–13, 23–32

If you finished Example 2 assign:
Average 1–2, 11–15, 23–32
Advanced 6–7, 11–14, 18, 23–32

If you finished Example 3 assign:
Average 1–4, 11–18, 23–32
Advanced 6–9, 11–17, 19, 23–32

If you finished Example 4 assign:
Average 1–12, 18–32
Advanced 6–32

Homework Quick Check

Quickly check key concepts.
Exercises: 8, 10, 12, 18

9-2 Exercises

M6P2.c, M6P3.a, M6P3.c

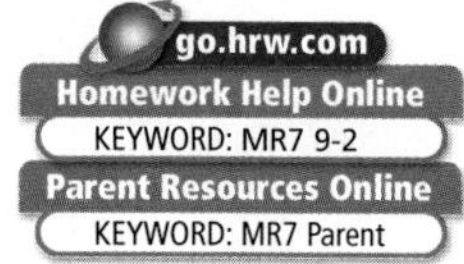

GUIDED PRACTICE

See Example 1 **What unit of measure provides the best estimate? Explain.**

1. The height of a doorknob from the floor is about 1 __?__. m; about the width of a single bed

See Example 2

2. A greeting card has a mass of about 28 __?__. mg; about 28 small insects

See Example 3

3. A kitchen sink holds about 20 __?__ of water. L; about 20 blender containers
4. A bowl holds about 350 __?__ of soup. mL; about 350 drops of water

See Example 4 **Estimate the length of the party favor to the nearest centimeter.**

5. about 7 cm

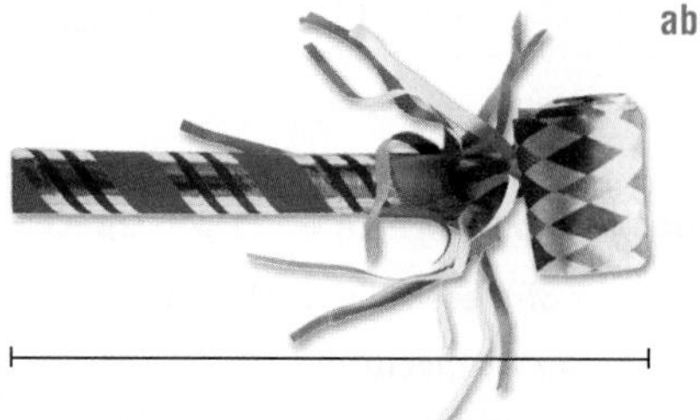

INDEPENDENT PRACTICE

See Example 1 **What unit of measure provides the best estimate? Explain.**

6. The width of a desk is about 10 __?__. dm; about the width of 10 CD cases

See Example 2

7. The mass of a packet of sugar is about 3 __?__. g; about 3 paper clips

See Example 3

8. A bathtub holds about 50 __?__ of water. L; about 50 blender containers
9. A cooking pot holds about 1.5 __?__. L; about 1.5 blender containers

See Example 4 **Estimate the length of the feather to the nearest centimeter.**

10. about 6 cm

PRACTICE AND PROBLEM SOLVING

CRCT GPS
Extra Practice p. 731

11. **Estimation** Felipe is estimating the length of his baseball bat using a benchmark. He gets an estimate of about 10 __?__. Which benchmark was Felipe most likely using: the width of his fist, the length of his foot, the distance from his elbow to his fingertip, or the length of his baseball cap? the width of his fist

Georgia Performance Standards

M6P2.c Develop and evaluate mathematical arguments and proofs.

M6P3.a Organize and consolidate their mathematical thinking through communication.

M6P3.c Analyze and evaluate the mathematical thinking and strategies of others.

RETEACH 9-2

LESSON 9-2 Reteach
Understanding Metric Units of Measure

The metric system of measurement uses millimeters, centimeters, decimeters, meters, and kilometers to measure length, width, distance, and height.
- Use millimeters to measure objects that are a few thicknesses of a dime.
- Use centimeters to measure objects that are a few widths of a fingernail.
- Use decimeters to measure objects that are a few widths of a CD case.
- Use meters to measure objects that are a few widths of a single bed.
- Use kilometers to measure distances that are a few distances around a city block.

Write millimeters, centimeters, decimeters, meters, or kilometers.

1. Your arm is about 3 decimeters long.
2. An ant is about 5 millimeters long.

The metric system of measurement uses milligrams, grams, and kilograms to measure mass.
- Use milligrams to measure objects that have a mass of a few very small insects.
- Use grams to measure objects that have a mass of a few large paper clips.
- Use kilograms to measure objects that have a mass of a few textbooks.

Write milligrams, grams, or kilograms.

3. A ruler has a mass of about 5 grams.
4. A kitten has a mass of about 2 kilograms.

The metric system of measurement uses milliliters and liters to measure capacity.
- Use milliliters to measure objects that have a capacity of a few drops of water.
- Use liters to measure objects that have a capacity of a few blender containers.

Write milliliters or liters.

5. A fish bowl has a capacity of about 7 liters.
6. A soup spoon has a capacity of about 20 millimeters.

PRACTICE 9-2

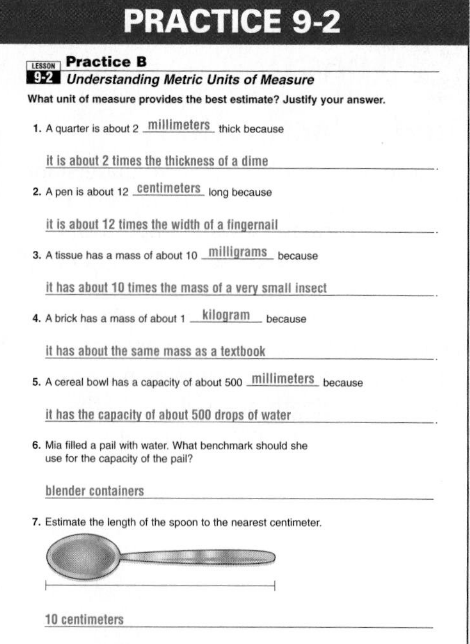

LESSON 9-2 Practice B
Understanding Metric Units of Measure

What unit of measure provides the best estimate? Justify your answer.

1. A quarter is about 2 millimeters thick because it is about 2 times the thickness of a dime.
2. A pen is about 12 centimeters long because it is about 12 times the width of a fingernail.
3. A tissue has a mass of about 10 milligrams because it has about 10 times the mass of a very small insect.
4. A brick has a mass of about 1 kilogram because it has about the same mass as a textbook.
5. A cereal bowl has a capacity of about 500 millimeters because it has the capacity of about 500 drops of water.
6. Mia filled a pail with water. What benchmark should she use for the capacity of the pail? blender containers
7. Estimate the length of the spoon to the nearest centimeter. 10 centimeters

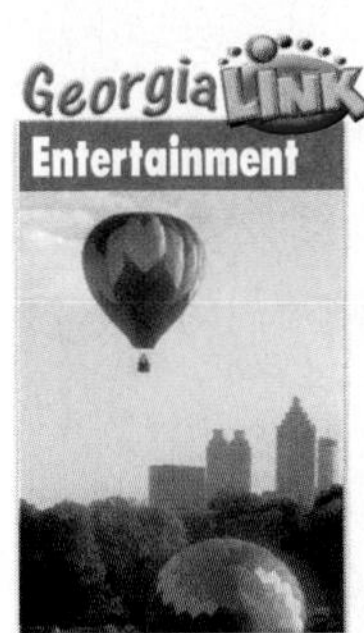

Each year, the Atlanta Dogwood Festival features a hot-air balloon race.

Which unit of measure would you use for each? Justify your answer.

12. the length of a movie screen m

13. the length of a walk around a campus km

14. the mass of a single flower g

15. the mass of a CD case kg

16. the capacity of a jug L

17. the capacity of a thimble mL

18. Multi-Step A shipment of DVD players contains 8 cartons. Each carton has 6 players in it. A single player weighs 1,500 g. All the players can be unpacked and placed on a shelf in the stockroom. A sign above the shelf reads "Maximum weight 80 __?__." What is the missing unit of measure on the sign above the shelf? kg

19. Physics An empty balloon weighs 4.5 g. A filled balloon weighs 5.3 g. Find the mass of the air in the balloon. Does air have mass? Explain.

20. What's the Error? Ellis made a travel brochure for his social studies project. He wrote that the common highway speed in Canada is 8,000 km per hour. What error did Ellis make? The speed should be 80 km per hour.

21. Write About It Measure the dimensions of a shoebox and estimate the mass of the box when it contains a pair of shoes. Describe which metric units of measure you used.

22. Challenge Jermaine is trying to limit the amount of fat in his diet to 50 g per day. At breakfast, Jermaine has one serving of milk, two servings of peanut butter, and a serving of apple, which has almost no fat. If his lunch and dinner contain the same amount of fat as his breakfast, is Jermaine likely to meet his goal for the day? Explain.

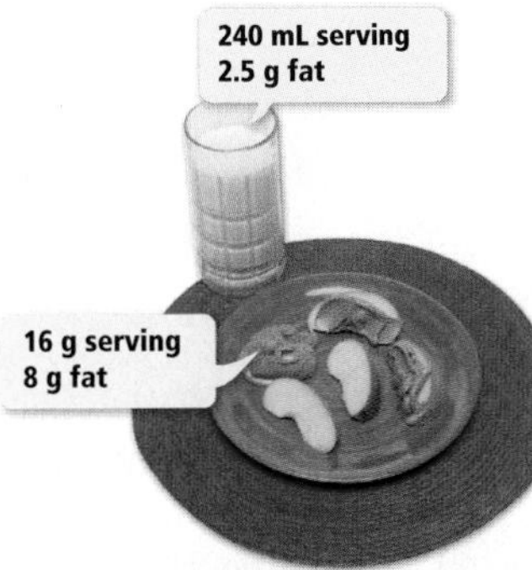

CRCT Prep • GPS Support • Spiral Review

23. Multiple Choice Which unit could NOT reasonably be used to measure something involving a home aquarium?

(A) A liter (B) A meter (C) A kilometer (circled) (D) A kilogram

24. Short Response What metric unit of measure provides the best estimate of the width of a bedroom window? Explain your answer.

Meter, the width of a bedroom window is about the width of a single bed.

Find the greatest common factor (GCF) of each set of numbers. (Lesson 4-3)

25. 16 and 24 8 **26.** 84 and 28 28 **27.** 48 and 112 16 **28.** 5, 10, and 105 5

Find the least common multiple (LCM). (Lesson 5-1)

29. 4 and 9 36 **30.** 6 and 11 66 **31.** 15 and 20 60 **32.** 2, 8, and 10 40

Ongoing Assessment and Intervention

***Diagnose Before* the Lesson**
9-2 Warm Up, TE p. 492

***Monitor During* the Lesson**
9-2 Know-It Notebook
9-2 Questioning Strategies

***Assess After* the Lesson**
9-2 Lesson Quiz, TE p. 495

Answers

19. Yes; possible answer: The balloon weighs 0.8 g more with the air.

21. You could measure the length, width, and height using centimeters or millimeters, capacity using liters, surface area using square centimeters, and mass using grams.

22. no; because breakfast has $2.5 + 2 \cdot 8$, or 18.5 g of fat, and $3 \cdot 18.5 > 50$

For Exercise 23, help students remember metric units of measure and some benchmarks associated with each unit. The benchmark for choice **C** is the distance around a city block, which is not appropriate for a home aquarium.

Journal

Have students select a familiar object, such as a tube of toothpaste, and estimate its metric length, mass, and volume.

Power Presentations with PowerPoint®

9-2 Lesson Quiz

Name the most appropriate unit of measure.

1. A door knob has a diameter of about 7 ___. cm

2. A ballpoint pen weighs about 3 ___. g

3. A gallon of milk is almost 4 ___. L

4. Paul estimated the weight of his infant sister to be 5 ___. kg

Also available on transparency

CHALLENGE 9-2

Lesson 9-2 Challenge
Metric Classroom Challenge

Find objects in your classroom for each unit of measure. Estimate first. Then measure. Check students' work.

LENGTH, WIDTH, OR HEIGHT

Object	Estimate	Actual
Objects and estimates may vary.	______ millimeters	______ millimeters
	______ centimeters	______ centimeters
	______ centimeters	______ centimeters
	______ decimeters	______ decimeters
	______ decimeters	______ decimeters
	______ meters	______ meters

WEIGHT

Object	Estimate	Actual
	______ milligrams	______ milligrams
	______ grams	______ grams
	______ grams	______ grams
	______ kilograms	______ kilograms

CAPACITY

Object	Estimate	Actual
	______ milliliters	______ milliliters
	______ milliliters	______ milliliters
	______ liters	______ liters
	______ liters	______ liters

PROBLEM SOLVING 9-2

Lesson 9-2 Problem Solving
Understanding Metric Units of Measure

Use metric units of measure to answer each question.

1. Which unit of measure would be most appropriate to use for the capacity of a swimming pool?
liters

2. Which unit of measure would be most appropriate to use for the length of an insect?
millimeters

3. Which unit of measure would be most appropriate to use for the weight of a television set?
kilograms

4. Which unit of measure would be most appropriate to use for the weight of a feather?
milligrams

5. Which unit of measure would be most appropriate to use for the distance between two cities?
kilometers

6. Which unit of measure would be most appropriate to use for the capacity of a can of soup?
millileters

Circle the letter of the correct answer.

7. How long is a desk?
A about 1.5 mm
B about 1.5 cm
(C) about 1.5 m
D about 1.5 km

8. What is the mass of a bird?
F about 9 mg
G about 90 mg
(H) about 90 g
J about 90 kg

9. What is the capacity of a can of soda?
A about 5 mL
(B) about 500 mL
C about 5 L
D about 500 L

10. How long is your math book?
(F) about 30 times the width of a fingernail
G about 10 times as thick as a dime
H about 5 times as wide as a single bed
J about 2 times the distance around a city block

9-3 Organizer

Pacing: Traditional 1 day
Block $\frac{1}{2}$ day

Objective: Students convert customary units of measure.

GPS M6M1, M6A2.g
Hands-On Lab
In *Hands-On Lab Activities*

Online Edition
Tutorial Videos

Countdown to CRCT Week 20

Power Presentations with PowerPoint®

Warm Up

List the first five multiples of the following numbers.

1. 3
3, 6, 9, 12, 15

2. 12
12, 24, 36, 48, 60

3. 36 36, 72, 108, 144, 180

4. 48 48, 96, 144, 192, 240

Problem of the Day

How much will it cost to build a fence that is 24 ft long, if it costs $20 to build a fence that is 15 ft long? $32

Also available on transparency

Math Humor

Big brother: How many feet are in 24 inches?

Little brother: 5

Big brother: That's wrong. It's only 2.

Little brother: My feet are smaller than yours.

Georgia Performance Standards

M6M1 Students will convert from one unit to another within one system of measurement (customary or metric) by using proportional relationships.

M6P1.c Apply and adapt a variety of appropriate strategies to solve problems.

M6P1.d Monitor and reflect on the process of mathematical problem solving.

9-3 Converting Customary Units

Learn to convert customary units of measure.

Georgia Performance Standards

M6M1 Convert from one unit to another within one system of measurement by using proportional relationships. Also, M6P1.c, M6P1.d.

Jacques Freitag is the first athlete to win gold medals at the International Association of Athletic Federations (IAAF) Youth, Junior, and Senior Championships. His personal best in the high jump is over 93 inches. How many feet is this?

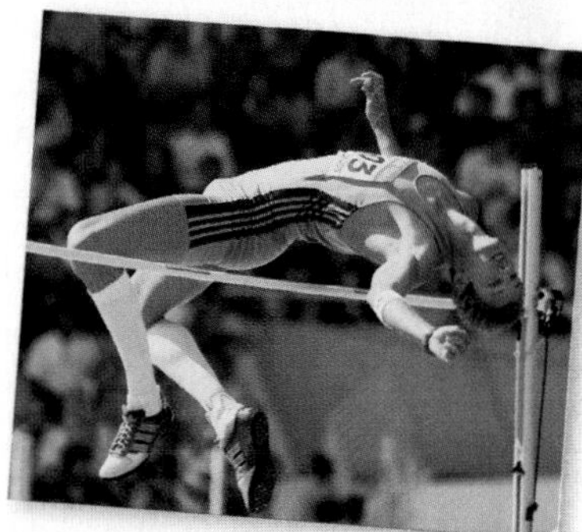

You can use the information in the table below to convert one customary unit to another.

Common Customary Measurements		
Length	**Weight**	**Capacity**
1 foot = 12 inch	1 pound = 16 ounces	1 cup = 8 fluid ounces
1 yard = 36 inches	1 ton = 2,000 pounds	1 pint = 2 cups
1 yard = 3 feet		1 quart = 2 pints
1 mile = 5,280 feet		1 quart = 4 cups
1 mile = 1,760 yards		1 gallon = 4 quarts
		1 gallon = 16 cups
		1 gallon = 128 fluid ounces

When you convert one unit of measure to another, you can multiply by a conversion factor.

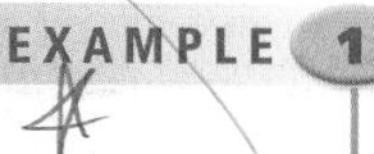

EXAMPLE 1 Using a Conversion Factor

Caution!
Write the unit you are converting *to* in the numerator and the unit you are converting *from* in the denominator.

A **Convert 93 inches to feet.**

Set up a conversion factor.

$93 \text{ in.} \times \frac{1 \text{ ft}}{12 \text{ in.}}$ *Think: inches to feet—1 ft = 12 in., so use $\frac{1 \text{ ft}}{12 \text{ in.}}$. Multiply 93 in. by the conversion factor. Cancel the common unit, in.*

93 in. = 7.75 ft

B **Convert 2 pounds to ounces.**

Set up a conversion factor.

$2 \text{ lb} \times \frac{16 \text{ oz}}{1 \text{ lb}} = 32 \text{ oz}$ *Think: ounces to pounds—16 oz = 1 lb, so use $\frac{16 \text{ oz}}{1 \text{ lb}}$. Multiply 2 lb by the conversion factor. Cancel the common unit, lb.*

2 lb = 32 oz

Another way to convert units is to use proportions.

1 Introduce

Alternate Opener

EXPLORATION

9-3 Converting Customary Units

One foot is equal to 12 inches. You can use this fact to explore the relationship between feet and inches.

1. Complete the table.

Feet	1	2	3	4	5	6	7	8
Inches	12	24						

2. Complete the table.

Feet								
Inches	108	120	132	144	156	168	180	192

3. If you are given a length in feet, how can you convert the length to inches?
4. If you are given a length in inches, how can you convert the length to feet?

Think and Discuss

5. **Describe** what you would do to convert 324 inches to feet.
6. **Explain** how you could use the above tables to convert 3.5 feet to inches.

Motivate

Show students gallon, quart, pint, and cup containers. Elicit that the relationships among the containers can be found by using the smaller containers to pour water into the larger containers and keeping track of how many smaller containers it takes to fill each larger container. Then use that method to demonstrate the relationship between a pint and a cup, between a quart and a pint, and between a gallon and a quart.

Explorations and answers are provided in *Alternate Openers: Explorations Transparencies.*

EXAMPLE 2 Converting Units of Measure by Using Proportions

Remember!

A proportion shows that two ratios are equivalent. Use a conversion factor for one of the ratios.

Convert 48 quarts to gallons.

48 qt = ▢ gal

$\frac{4 \text{ qt}}{1 \text{ gal}} = \frac{48 \text{ qt}}{x \text{ gal}}$ *1 gallon is 4 quarts. Write a proportion. Use a variable for the value you are trying to find.*

$4 \cdot x = 1 \cdot 48$ *The cross products are equal.*

$4x = 48$ *Divide both sides by 4 to undo the multiplication.*

$x = 16$

48 qt = 16 gal

EXAMPLE 3 PROBLEM SOLVING APPLICATION

PROBLEM SOLVING

The Washington Monument is about 185 yards tall. This height is almost equal to the length of two football fields. About how many feet is this?

1 Understand the Problem

The **answer** will be the height of the Washington Monument in feet.

List the **important information:**

- The height of the Washington Monument is about 185 yards.

2 Make a Plan

Make a table from the information to show the number of feet in 1, 2, and 3 yards. Then find the number of feet in n yards.

3 Solve

Yards	Feet
1	3
2	6
3	9
n	$3n$

Look for a pattern.

$1 \cdot 3 = 3$

$2 \cdot 3 = 6$

$3 \cdot 3 = 9$

$n \cdot 3 = 3n$

$185 \cdot 3 = 555$ so, the Washington Monument is about 555 ft tall.

4 Look Back

Round 185 to 200. Then multiply by 3.

$200 \cdot 3 = 600$

The answer is reasonable because 555 is close to 600.

Think and Discuss

GPS M6P3.b

1. Explain how to set up a proportion to convert miles to yards.

COMMON ERROR ALERT

Students sometimes mistakenly say that 2 quarts equal a gallon and 1,000 pounds equal a ton. Have students orally practice converting in customary units.

Power Presentations with PowerPoint®

Additional Examples

Example 1

A. Convert 9 yards to feet. 27 ft

B. Convert 10,000 pounds to tons. 5 tons

Example 2

Convert 3 quarts to cups. 12 cups

Example 3

The football goal posts are 30 feet tall. How many inches is this? 360 inches

Also available on transparency

Answers to *Think and Discuss*

1. Use the relationship of miles to yards to create a proportion.

$\frac{miles}{yards} = \frac{1 \text{ mi}}{1{,}760 \text{ yd}}$

Solve the proportion for yards when given a number of miles.

2 Teach

Guided Instruction

In this lesson, students learn to convert customary units of measure. Review with students the common customary measurement units for length, capacity, and weight. First, teach students how to convert by canceling units. Then teach how to convert by using proportions. In the Problem Solving Application, show students how to use a table to convert.

Reaching All Learners

Through Concrete Manipulatives

Have students measure several items in the classroom (rulers are available in the Manipulatives Kit). Have students set up a proportion for each item to determine an equivalent customary measure (e.g., door height is 84 in., and $\frac{12 \text{ in.}}{1 \text{ ft}} = \frac{84 \text{ in}}{x \text{ ft}}$). Students can then measure again using the new unit of measurement to check their answers.

3 Close

Summarize

You may wish to review some of the more common customary measurement equivalents and post them in the classroom for easy access. Then ask students to show two ways of finding the number of pounds in 88 ounces.

Possible answers: by canceling units:

$88 \cancel{oz} \times \frac{1 \text{ lb}}{16 \cancel{oz}} = 5.5 \text{ lb}$

by using a proportion:

$\frac{1 \text{ lb}}{16 \text{ oz}} = \frac{x \text{ lb}}{88 \text{ oz}}$; $16 \cdot x = 1 \cdot 88$; $x = 5.5$

9-3 Exercises

Assignment Guide

If you finished Example 1 assign:
Average 1–6, 51–59
Advanced 14–18, 36, 51–59

If you finished Example 2 assign:
Average 1–12, 40–41, 51–59
Advanced 14–25, 42–43, 51–59

If you finished Example 3 assign:
Average 1–28, 37–59
Advanced 14–59

Homework Quick Check

Quickly check key concepts.
Exercises: 16, 20, 26, 28, 34

9-3 Exercises

Georgia Performance Standards
M6P3.a, M6P3.c, M6P4.c

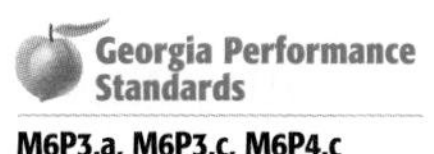

Homework Help Online
KEYWORD: MR7 9-3
Parent Resources Online
KEYWORD: MR7 Parent

GUIDED PRACTICE

See Example 1 **Convert.**

1. 9 ft = ■ in. 108
2. 10 pt = ■ qt 5
3. 14,000 lb = ■ T 7
4. 5 yd = ■ ft 15
5. 24 fl oz = ■ c 3
6. 4 lb = ■ oz 64

See Example 2

7. 32 qt = ■ gal 8
8. 9 lb = ■ oz 144
9. 36 in. = ■ ft 3
10. 2 yd = ■ in. 72
11. 11 qt = ■ pt 22
12. 6 T = ■ lb 12,000

See Example 3

13. **Biology** An adult male of average size normally has about 6 quarts of blood in his body. Approximately how many cups of blood does the average adult male have in his body? about 24 cups

INDEPENDENT PRACTICE

See Example 1 **Convert.**

14. 96 oz = ■ lb 6
15. 6 c = ■ fl oz 48
16. 3 mi = ■ ft 15,840
17. 4,000 lb = ■ T 2
18. 6 lb = ■ oz 96
19. 3,520 yd = ■ mi 2

See Example 2

20. 27 ft = ■ yd 9
21. 3 T = ■ lb 6,000
22. 16 qt = ■ gal 4
23. 48 oz = ■ lb 3
24. 3 yd = ■ in. 108
25. 10 pt = ■ c 20

See Example 3

26. **Architecture** The steel used to make the Statue of Liberty weighs about 125 tons. About how many pounds of steel were used to make the Statue of Liberty? about 250,000 pounds

PRACTICE AND PROBLEM SOLVING

Extra Practice p. 731

Compare. Use <, >, or =.

27. 18 ft ■ 220 in. <
28. 24 lb ■ 388 oz <
29. $\frac{1}{2}$ pt ■ 1 c =
30. 2 mi ■ 10,000 ft >
31. 12 pt ■ 3 gal <
32. 72 ft ■ 24 yd =
33. 9 c ■ 72 fl oz =
34. 30 yd ■ 93 ft <
35. 145 in. ■ 4 yd >

36. Linda cut off $1\frac{1}{2}$ feet of her hair to donate to an organization that makes wigs for children with cancer. How many inches of hair did Linda cut off? 18 in.

37. **Geography** Lake Superior is about 1,302 feet deep at its deepest point. What is this depth in yards? about 434 yards

38. **Multi-Step** A company produces 3 tons of cereal each week. How many 12-ounce cereal boxes can be filled each week? 8,000 boxes

39. **Sports** The width of a singles tennis court is 27 feet.
    a. How many yards wide is a singles tennis court? 9 yd
    b. How many inches wide is a singles tennis court? 324 in.

Georgia Performance Standards

M6P3.a Organize and consolidate their mathematical thinking through communication.

M6P3.c Analyze and evaluate the mathematical thinking and strategies of others.

M6P4.c Recognize and apply mathematics in contexts outside of mathematics.

RETEACH 9-3

LESSON 9-3 **Reteach**
Converting Customary Units

You can use the table below to convert customary units.

Length	Weight	Capacity
1 foot = 12 inches 1 yard = 36 inches 1 yard = 3 feet 1 mile = 5,280 feet 1 mile = 1,760 yards	1 pound = 16 ounces 1 ton = 2,000 pounds	1 cup = 8 fluid ounces 1 pint = 2 cups 1 quart = 2 pints 1 quart = 4 cups 1 gallon = 4 quarts 1 gallon = 128 fluid ounces

To figure out how many pounds are in 32 ounces, set up a proportion where the first ratio uses 16 ounces is 1 pound, and the second ratio uses a variable for the value you are trying to find.

$$\frac{16 \text{ ounces}}{1 \text{ pound}} = \frac{32 \text{ ounces}}{x \text{ pounds}}$$

Then solve the proportion.

$$\frac{16 \text{ ounces}}{1 \text{ pound}} = \frac{32 \text{ ounces}}{x \text{ pounds}}$$ First, find the cross products.

$16x = 32$

Think: $32 \div 16 = x$ Then, use a related math sentence to solve the equation.

$x = 2$

So, there are 2 pounds in 32 ounces.

Use the table above to set up a proportion. Then find each of the values.

1. the number of pounds in 80 ounces
   $\frac{1}{16} = \frac{x}{80}$
   5 pounds
2. the number of quarts in 6 gallons
   $\frac{4}{1} = \frac{x}{6}$
   24 quarts
3. the number of yards in 5 miles
   8,800 yards
4. the number of cups in 20 pints
   40 cups

PRACTICE 9-3

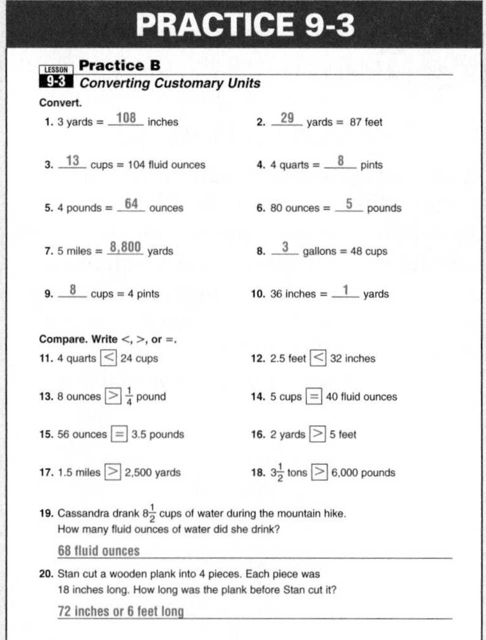

LESSON 9-3 **Practice B**
Converting Customary Units

Convert.

1. 3 yards = 108 inches
2. 29 yards = 87 feet
3. 13 cups = 104 fluid ounces
4. 4 quarts = 8 pints
5. 4 pounds = 64 ounces
6. 80 ounces = 5 pounds
7. 5 miles = 8,800 yards
8. 3 gallons = 48 cups
9. 8 cups = 4 pints
10. 36 inches = 1 yards

Compare. Write <, >, or =.

11. 4 quarts < 24 cups
12. 2.5 feet < 32 inches
13. 8 ounces > $\frac{1}{4}$ pound
14. 5 cups = 40 fluid ounces
15. 56 ounces = 3.5 pounds
16. 2 yards > 5 feet
17. 1.5 miles > 2,500 yards
18. $3\frac{1}{2}$ tons > 6,000 pounds

19. Cassandra drank $8\frac{1}{2}$ cups of water during the mountain hike. How many fluid ounces of water did she drink?
    68 fluid ounces

20. Stan cut a wooden plank into 4 pieces. Each piece was 18 inches long. How long was the plank before Stan cut it?
    72 inches or 6 feet long

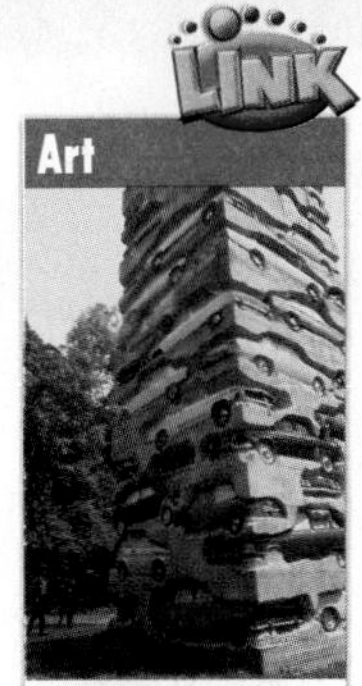

Long-Term Parking is 65 feet tall and stands in front of a parking lot in Paris.

Convert.

40. 108 in. = ▮ ft = ▮ yd **9; 3**

41. 10,560 ft = ▮ yd = ▮ mi **3,520; 2**

42. 12 qt = ▮ c = ▮ fl oz **48; 384**

43. 2 gal = ▮ qt = ▮ pt **8; 16**

44. **Art** In Paris, the sculpture *Long-Term Parking,* created by Armand Fernandez, contains 60 cars embedded in 3.5 million pounds of concrete. How many tons of concrete is this? **1,750 T**

45. **Multi-Step** If a half-gallon of milk sells for $1.60, what is the cost of a fluid ounce of milk? (Round your answer to the nearest cent.) **$0.03**

46. **Critical Thinking** Make a table to convert ounces to pounds. Write an expression for the number of ounces in n pounds. Then write an expression for the number of pounds in n ounces.

47. **Multi-Step** If you drink 14 quarts of water per week, on average, how many pints do you drink per day? **4 pints**

48. **What's the Error?** Sari said that she walked a total of 8,800 feet in a 5-mile walk-a-thon. Explain Sari's error.

49. **Write About It** Explain how to compare a length given in inches to a length given in feet.

50. **Challenge** In 1942, there were 15,000 troops on the ship *Queen Mary.* Each soldier was given 2 quarts of fresh water for the entire journey.

a. How many gallons of fresh water did the soldiers have in all? **7,500 gal**

b. **Estimation** If the journey took 5 days, about how many fluid ounces of fresh water should a soldier have rationed himself each day? **about 12 fl oz**

CRCT PREP • GPS SUPPORT • SPIRAL REVIEW

51. **Multiple Choice** Which of the following amounts is NOT equivalent to 1 gal?

Ⓐ 64 fl oz (circled) Ⓑ 16 c Ⓒ 8 pt Ⓓ 4 qt

52. **Multiple Choice** The world's largest ice cream sundae weighed about 55,000 pounds. How many tons did it weigh?

Ⓕ 2.7 T Ⓖ 27.5 T (circled) Ⓗ 275 T Ⓙ 2,750 T

Solve each equation. (Lessons 2-5, 2-6)

53. $6 + x = 15$ **$x = 9$**

54. $y - 17 = 29$ **$y = 46$**

55. $43 = 26 + d$ **$d = 17$**

56. $32 = w - 8$ **$w = 40$**

Give the most descriptive name for each figure. (Lesson 8-6)

57.

trapezoid

58.
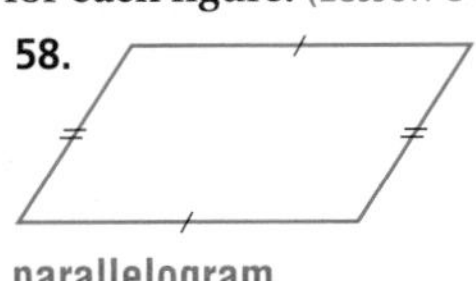
parallelogram

59.
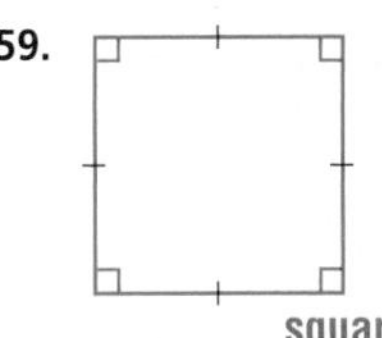
square

CHALLENGE 9-3

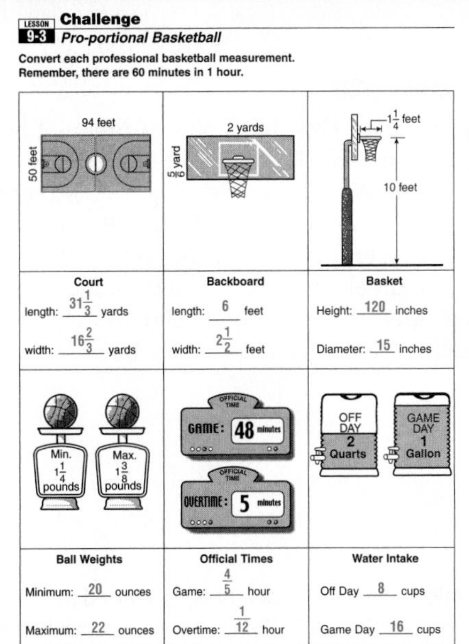
LESSON 9-3 **Challenge**

Pro-portional Basketball

Convert each professional basketball measurement. Remember, there are 60 minutes in 1 hour.

Court	Backboard	Basket
length: $31\frac{1}{3}$ yards	length: 6 feet	Height: 120 inches
width: $16\frac{2}{3}$ yards	width: $2\frac{1}{2}$ feet	Diameter: 15 inches
Ball Weights	**Official Times**	**Water Intake**
Minimum: 20 ounces	Game: $\frac{4}{5}$ hour	Off Day 8 cups
Maximum: 22 ounces	Overtime: $\frac{1}{12}$ hour	Game Day 16 cups

PROBLEM SOLVING 9-3

LESSON 9-3 **Problem Solving**

Converting Customary Units

Write the correct answer.

1. Each side of a professional baseball base must measure 15 inches. What is the base's side length in feet?
   $1\frac{1}{4}$ feet
2. In the NBA, any shot made from 22 feet or more from the basket is worth 3 points. How many yards from the basket is that?
   $7\frac{1}{3}$ yards
3. The maximum weight for a professional bowling ball is 16 pounds. What is the maximum weight in ounces?
   256 ounces
4. A professional hockey goal is 6 feet wide and 4 feet high. What is the area of the goal in square yards?
   $2\frac{2}{3}$ square yards
5. An NFL football field is 120 yards long. How many times would you have to run across the field to run 1 mile?
   $14\frac{2}{3}$ times
6. The official length for a marathon race is 26.2 miles. How many yards long is a marathon? How many feet?
   46,112 yards; 138,336 ft

Circle the letter of the correct answer.

7. The distance between bases in a professional baseball game is 90 feet. What is the distance between bases in inches?
   A 1,000 inches C 1,100 inches
   Ⓑ 1,080 inches D 10,800 inches
8. What is the area of a baseball diamond in square yards?
   F 300 square yards
   G 600 square yards
   Ⓗ 900 square yards
   J 8,100 square yards
9. An NFL football can be no less than $\frac{87}{96}$ feet long. What is the minimum length for an official football in inches?
   Ⓐ $10\frac{7}{8}$ inches C $\frac{87}{1152}$ inches
   B $1\frac{3}{32}$ inches D $2\frac{69}{96}$ inches
10. An official Olympic-sized swimming pool holds 880,000 gallons of water! How many fluid ounces of water is that?
   F 1,4080,000 fluid ounces
   G 7,040,000 fluid ounces
   Ⓗ 112,640,000 fluid ounces
   J 1,760,000 fluid ounces

ONGOING ASSESSMENT and INTERVENTION

***Diagnose Before* the Lesson**
9-3 Warm Up, TE p. 496

***Monitor During* the Lesson**
9-3 Know-It Notebook
9-3 Questioning Strategies

***Assess After* the Lesson**
9-3 Lesson Quiz, TE p. 499

Answers

46.

Oz	Lbs
1	$\frac{1}{16}$
2	$\frac{2}{16} = \frac{1}{8}$
3	$\frac{3}{16}$
n	$\frac{n}{16}$

48. Possible answer: Sari used an incorrect conversion factor. She used 1 mile = 1,760 feet instead of 1 mile = 5,280 feet. Sari walked a total of 26,400 feet in the Walk-a-Thon.

49. Possible answer: First, convert either the inches to feet or the feet to inches so that both lengths have the same unit. Then compare.

If students have difficulty with Exercise 52, review using a conversion factor or a proportion to solve the problem. In both cases, remembering the rule for division involving powers of ten will make 55,000 ÷ 2,000 much easier to evaluate.

Journal

Have students explain how they would convert gallons to pints.

Power Presentations with PowerPoint®

1. Convert 5 yards to inches.
   180 inches
2. Convert 16 tons to pounds.
   32,000 pounds
3. Convert 11 quarts to cups.
   44 cups
4. A project requires 288 inches of tape. How many yards is this?
   8 yards

Also available on transparency

9-4 Organizer

Pacing: Traditional 1 day
Block $\frac{1}{2}$ day

Objective: Students convert metric units of measure.

GPS M6M1, M6A2.g
Hands-On Lab
In *Hands-On Lab Activities*

Online Edition
Tutorial Videos

Countdown to CRCT Week 20

Power Presentations with PowerPoint®

Warm Up

Multiply the following by 1,000.

1. 0.0042 4.2 **2.** 38.705 38,705

Divide the following by 1,000.

3. 28,039 28.039 **4.** 0.8 0.0008

Problem of the Day

Richard needs to divide 180 feet of rope equally among the 30 members of his science class. How long will each piece of rope be? 6 feet

Also available on transparency

Math Humor

The exhausted runner said, "I'll never run that distance again. Now I know why they call it a killer-meter."

Georgia Performance Standards

M6M1 Students will convert from one unit to another within one system of measurement (customary or metric) by using proportional relationships.

M6P1.b Solve problems that arise in mathematics and in other contexts.

M6P4.c Recognize and apply mathematics in contexts outside of mathematics.

9-4 Converting Metric Units

Learn to convert metric units of measure.

Georgia Performance Standards

M6M1 Convert from one unit to another within one system of measurement by using proportional relationships. Also, M6P1.b, M6P4.c.

The first Tour de France was in 1903 and was 2,428 km long. It had only 6 stages. Compare that to the 2005 Tour de France, which had 21 stages and covered 3,607 km.

During the 2005 Tour de France, Lance Armstrong was the stage winner from Tours to Blois, which has a distance of 67.5 km. How many meters is this distance?

In the metric system, the value of each place is 10 times greater than the value of the place to its right. When you convert one unit of measure to another, you can multiply or divide by a power of 10.

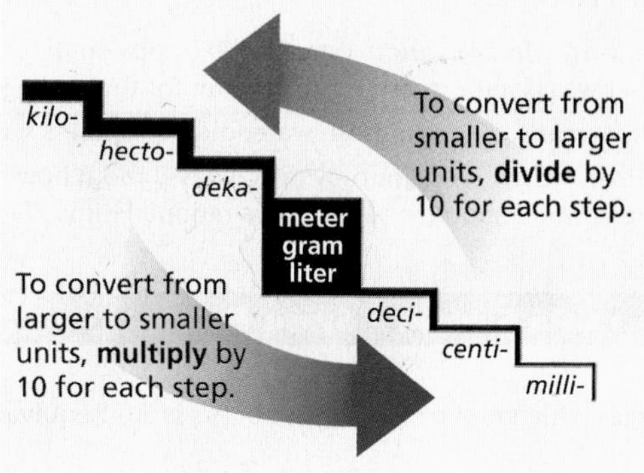

EXAMPLE 1 *Sports Application*

Helpful Hint

To decide whether to multiply or divide, think of a simpler model, such as your fingers and your hand.
fingers → hand
smaller unit → larger unit ÷ 5
hand → fingers
larger unit → smaller unit × 5

During the 2005 Tour de France, Lance Armstrong was the stage winner from Tours to Blois, which has a distance of 67.5 km. How many meters is this distance?

67.5 km = ▢ m — *Think: Kilometer to meter is going from a bigger unit to a smaller unit. A meter is 3 places to the right of a kilometer in the chart, so 10 · 10 · 10 or 10^3 = 1,000.*

67.5 km = (67.5 · 1,000) m — *1 km = 1,000 m. You are converting a bigger unit to a smaller unit, so multiply by 1,000.*

67.5 km = 67,500 m — *Move the decimal point 3 places to the right.*

1 Introduce

Alternate Opener

EXPLORATION

Converting Metric Units

Because the metric table is based on powers of 10, it is important to be able to multiply and divide quickly by powers of 10.

1. Complete the table by multiplying by 10, by 100, and by 1,000. You may use a calculator or any other method you wish. Look for patterns as you work.

Number	× 10	× 100	× 1,000
42			
3.8			
0.97			
0.065			

2. Complete the table by dividing by 10, by 100, and by 1,000. You may use a calculator or any other method you wish. Look for patterns as you work.

Number	÷ 10	÷ 100	÷ 1,000
512			
63.9			
4.05			
0.772			

Think and Discuss

3. **Describe** shortcuts for multiplying by 10, by 100, and by 1,000.
4. **Explain** shortcuts for dividing by 10, by 100, and by 1,000.

Motivate

ENGLISH LANGUAGE LEARNERS

Review the metric units of measurement by having students list as many units as they can. Then discuss the meanings of the prefixes *kilo-*, *centi-*, and *milli-*. Point out that the metric system was developed during the 1790s. Greek prefixes are used for metric units greater than 10 and Latin prefixes are used for metric units less than 1.

Explorations and answers are provided in *Alternate Openers: Explorations Transparencies.*

EXAMPLE 2 Using Powers of Ten to Convert Metric Units of Measure

Caution!

Make sure you are multiplying or dividing by the correct power of ten.

Convert.

A The width of a book is about 22 cm. 22 cm = ▮ mm

22 cm = (22 · 10) mm — *1 cm = 10 mm, bigger unit to smaller unit, so multiply by 10.*

22 cm = 220 mm — *Move the decimal point 1 place right.*

B A backpack has a mass of about 6 kg. 6 kg = ▮ g

6 kg = (6 · 1,000) g — *1 kg = 1,000 g, bigger unit to smaller unit, so multiply by 1,000.*

6 kg = 6,000 g — *Move the decimal point 3 places right.*

C A water bottle holds about 400 mL. 400 mL = ▮ L

400 mL = (400 ÷ 1,000) L — *1,000 mL = 1 L, smaller unit to bigger unit, so divide by 1,000.*

400 mL = 0.4 L — *Move the decimal point 3 places left.*

Metric Measurements		
Distance	Mass	Capacity
1 km = 1,000 m 1 m = 100 cm 1 cm = 10 mm	1 kg = 1,000 g 1 g = 1,000 mg	1 L = 1,000 mL

Convert metric measures by using a conversion factor or using proportions.

EXAMPLE 3 Converting Metric Units of Measure

Convert.

A Method 1: Use a conversion factor.

11 m = ▮ cm — *Think: 100 cm = 1 m so use $\frac{100\text{ cm}}{1\text{ m}}$.*

$11\not{m} \cdot \frac{100\text{ cm}}{1\not{m}} = 1{,}100\text{ cm}$ — *Multiply 11 m by the conversion factor. Cancel the common unit, m.*

B Method 2: Use proportions.

190 mL = ▮ L

$\frac{190\text{ mL}}{x\text{ L}} = \frac{1{,}000\text{ mL}}{1\text{ L}}$ — *Write a proportion.*

$1{,}000x = 190$ — *The cross products are equal. Divide both sides by 1,000 to undo the multiplication.*

$x = 0.19$ L

Possible answer to *Think and Discuss:*

1. In going from centimeters to the next smaller unit, millimeters, multiply 825 by 10.

Think and Discuss

GPS M6P3.b

1. Describe how to convert 825 cm to mm.

COMMON ERROR ALERT

Some students will think every metric conversion involves either multiplying or dividing by 10. Remind them that the conversions will involve a power of 10, either 10, 100, or 1,000. Have them refer to the conversion chart.

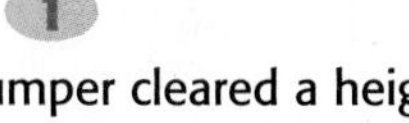

Power Presentations with PowerPoint®

Additional Examples

Example 1

The high-jumper cleared a height of 1.75 m. How many centimeters is this height? 175 cm

Example 2

Convert.

A. The CD case is 14 cm wide. 14 cm = ___ m 0.14

B. The ball of clay has a mass of 4 kg. 4 kg = ___ g 4,000

C. The bottle of water contains 0.8 L. 0.8 L = ___ mL 800 mL

Example 3

Convert.

A. Method 1: Cross out units. 16 m = ___ cm 1,600

B. Method 2: Use proportions. 450 g = ___ kg 0.45

Also available on transparency

2 Teach

Guided Instruction

In this lesson, students learn to convert metric units of measure. Show students that they can multiply or divide by powers of ten by moving the decimal point to the right for multiplication and to the left for division. Use the table of metric measures to show how to convert from a larger unit to a smaller unit and from a smaller unit to a larger unit. Also show students how to convert by canceling units or using proportions.

Reaching All Learners

Through Graphic Organizers

Have students copy the following diagram into their journal to help them remember how to convert between metric units.

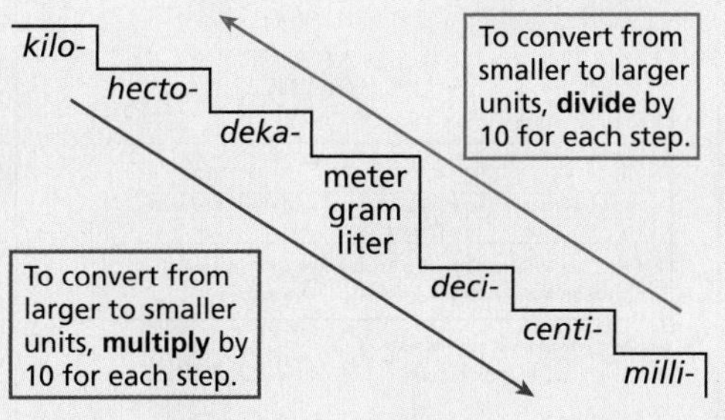

3 Close

Summarize

Name the metric units covered in the lesson. Outline the steps to follow to convert from a larger unit to a smaller unit and from a smaller unit to a larger unit. *Ask:*

How many centimeters are in 40 meters? 4,000 centimeters

How many grams are in 3 kilograms? 3,000 grams

How many liters are in 750 milliliters? 0.75 liter

9-4 Exercises

Assignment Guide

If you finished Example 1 assign:
Average 1, 40–48
Advanced 12, 40–48

If you finished Example 2 assign:
Average 1–5, 40–48
Advanced 12–15, 23, 40–48

If you finished Example 3 assign:
Average 1–27, 36–48
Advanced 12–48

Homework Quick Check

Quickly check key concepts.
Exercises: 14, 16, 20, 24, 26

Answers

24. No; 500 cm = 5 m, and Joanie will need 5.2 m to frame the picture.

9-4 Exercises

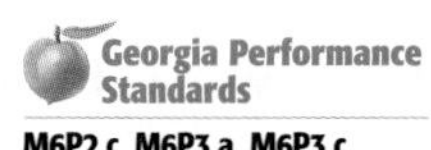

M6P2.c, M6P3.a, M6P3.c

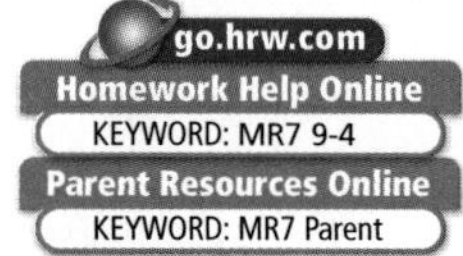

GUIDED PRACTICE

See Example 1

1. The length of a school hallway is 115 meters. How many kilometers long is the hallway? **0.115 km**

See Example 2

Convert.

2. The diameter of a ceiling fan is about 95 cm. 95 cm = ■ m **0.95**

3. A rock has a mass of about 852 g. 852 g = ■ kg **0.852**

4. A vase holds about 1.25 L of water. 1.25 L = ■ mL **1,250**

5. A sheet of paper has a mass of about 3.5 g. 3.5 g = ■ mg **3,500**

See Example 3

6. 3 kg = ■ g **3,000** **7.** 4.4 L = ■ mL **4,400** **8.** 1 kg = ■ mg **1,000,000**

9. 50 mm = ■ m **0.05** **10.** 21 km = ■ cm **2,100,000** **11.** 6 ml = ■ L **0.006**

INDEPENDENT PRACTICE

See Example 1

12. A juice container holds 300 milliliters. How many liters of juice are in the container? **0.3 L**

See Example 2

Convert.

13. A teacup holds about 110 mL. 110 mL = ■ L **0.110**

14. The distance around a school is about 825 m. 825 m = ■ km **0.825**

15. A chair has a mass of about 22.5 kg. 22.5 kg = ■ g **22,500**

16. A gas tank holds about 85 L. 85 L = ■ mL **85,000**

See Example 3

17. 2,460 m = ■ km **2.460** **18.** 842 mm = ■ cm **84.2** **19.** 9,680 mg = ■ g **9.68**

20. 25 cm = ■ mm **250** **21.** 782 g = ■ kg **0.782** **22.** 1.2 km = ■ m **1,200**

PRACTICE AND PROBLEM SOLVING

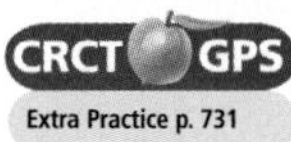

Extra Practice p. 731

23. **Multi-Step** There are 28 L of soup in a pot. Marshall serves 400 mL in each bowl. If he fills 16 bowls, how much soup is left in the pot? Write your answer two ways: as a number of liters and as a number of milliliters. **21.6 L; 21,600 mL**

24. **Multi-Step** Joanie wants to frame a rectangular picture that is 1.7 m by 0.9 m. Joanie has 500 cm of wood to use for a frame. Does Joanie have enough wood to frame the picture? Explain.

Convert.

25. $\frac{23{,}850 \text{ cm}}{x \text{ km}} = \frac{100{,}000 \text{ cm}}{1 \text{ km}}$ **$x = 0.23850$**

26. $\frac{350 \text{ L}}{x \text{ mL}} = \frac{1 \text{ L}}{1{,}000 \text{ mL}}$ **$x = 350{,}000$**

27. $7 \text{ km} \cdot \frac{1{,}000 \text{ m}}{\text{km}} =$ ■ m **7,000**

28. $9.5 \text{ L} \cdot \frac{1{,}000 \text{ mL}}{\text{L}} =$ ■ mL **9,500**

Georgia Performance Standards

M6P2.c Develop and evaluate mathematical arguments and proofs.

M6P3.a Organize and consolidate their mathematical thinking through communication.

M6P3.c Analyze and evaluate the mathematical thinking and strategies of others.

RETEACH 9-4

LESSON 9-4 **Reteach**
Converting Metric Units

There are patterns in powers of ten.

10 • 1 = 10 10 • 10 = 100 10 • 10 • 10 = 1,000

The number of times 10 is a factor equals the number of zeros in the power of ten.

You can use these patterns to multiply and divide by powers of ten. The number of zeros or the number of tens tells you how many places to move the decimal point.

If you are dividing by a power of ten, move the decimal point left.

7,345 ÷ 100 = 73.45

two zeros, two places

73.45 (2 1)

If you are multiplying by a power of ten, move the decimal point right.

23.4 • 10 • 10 • 10 = 23,400

three tens, three places

23,400 (1 2 3)

Multiply or divide.

1. 4.25 • 10 • 10 • 10 • 10 **42,500**

2. 1,347.8 ÷ • 10 • 10 **13.478**

3. 9.4 ÷ 1,000 **0.0094**

4. 18.05 • 100 **1,805**

The metric system uses powers of ten.

Each place value is 10 times as large as the place value to the right.						
1,000	100	10	1	0.1	0.01	0.001
thousands	hundreds	tens	ones	tenths	hundredths	thousandths
kilo	hecto	deka	meters	deci	centi	milli

2 m = ___ cm The centimeter unit is 2 places to the right of the meter.

2 m = 200 cm Move the decimal point 2 places to the right.

Use the chart to convert each measure.

5. 3.4 km = **3,400,000** mm

6. 7 dm = **0.007** hm

7. 4.32 dam = **43.2** m

8. 34.8 cm = **3.48** dm

PRACTICE 9-4

LESSON 9-4 **Practice B**
Converting Metric Units

Convert.

1. A large thermos holds about 1.5 liters. 1.5 L = **1,500** mL

2. A computer screen is about 30.75 wide. 30.75 cm = **307.5** mm

3. A beetle weighs about 0.68 g. 0.68 g = **680** mg

4. The distance from Dallas to Denver is 1,260 km. 1,260 km = **1,260,000** m

5. 50 cm = **500** mm

6. 3.6 L = **3,600** mL

7. 6.5 kg = **6,500** g

8. 0.9 km = **900** m

9. 1.42 m = **142** cm

10. 12.85 mL = **0.01285** L

Compare. Write <, >, or =.

11. 500 millimeters **<** 50 centimeters

12. 6.2 liters **>** 620 milliliters

13. 8.3 kilograms **=** 8,300 grams

14. 2.6 meters **<** 26,000 centimeters

15. An official hockey puck can weigh no more than 170 grams. What is the puck's maximum weight in kilograms?

0.17 kilograms

16. An official hockey puck is 2.54 centimeters thick. What is the official thickness of a hockey puck in millimeters?

25.4 millimeters

17. An official hockey goal is 46.45 meters tall. What is the height of a hockey goal in centimeters?

4,645 centimeters

18. Hockey pucks can be hit at speeds of up to 190 kilometers per hour! How many meters per hour is that?

190,000 meters per hour

Compare. Use <, >, or =.

29. 1,000 mm ■ 1 m   =   **30.** 5.2 kg ■ 60 g   >   **31.** 3 L ■ 6,000 mL   <

32. 2 g ■ 20,000 mg   <   **33.** 0.0065 m ■ 6.5 mm   =   **34.** 0.1 km ■ 10 mm   >

35. Multi-Step The St. Louis Gateway Arch in Missouri is about 19,200 centimeters tall. The San Jacinto Monument, outside of Houston, Texas, is about 174 m tall. Which structure is taller? by how much? Give your answer in meters. St. Louis Gateway Arch; 18 m

St. Louis Gateway Arch

San Jacinto Monument

36. Critical Thinking A *millimicron* is equal to one-billionth of a meter. How many millimicrons are there in 2.5 meters? 2,500,000,000

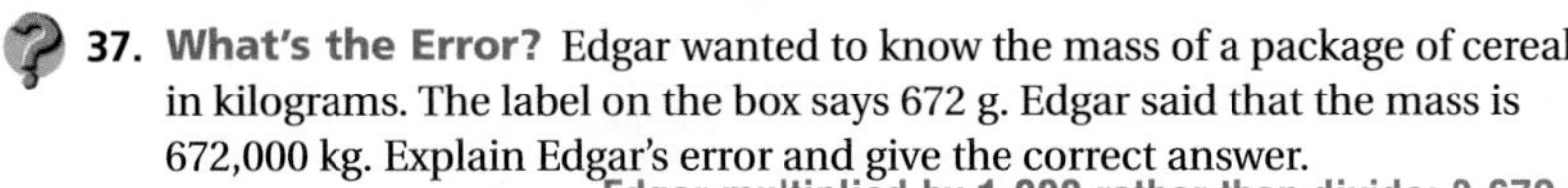

37. What's the Error? Edgar wanted to know the mass of a package of cereal in kilograms. The label on the box says 672 g. Edgar said that the mass is 672,000 kg. Explain Edgar's error and give the correct answer. Edgar multiplied by 1,000 rather than divide; 0.672 kg.

38. Write About It Amy ran a 1,000-meter race. Explain how to find the number of centimeters in 1,000 meters. 1m = 100 cm, therefore 1,000 m = 100 cm × 1,000 = 100,000 cm

39. Challenge The lemonade cooler at the class picnic holds 12.5 L. Each plastic cup holds 225 mL. How many cups can be filled from the cooler? If none of the lemonade is spilled, how many milliliters will be left in the cooler when all possible cups have been filled? 55 cups; 125 mL

CRCT Prep • GPS Support • Spiral Review

40. Multiple Choice Complete the statement with the most reasonable metric unit. A snail might crawl at a rate of about 0.01 __?__ per hour.

Ⓐ mm   **Ⓑ m** (circled)   Ⓒ mL   Ⓓ km

41. Extended Response Liza, Toni, and Kim used a metric scale to weigh some shells they collected at the beach. The masses of the shells were 29 g, 52 g, 18 g, 103 g, 154 g, and 96 g. What was the combined mass of the shells in kilograms? in milligrams? What is the difference in kilograms between the heaviest and lightest shells? 0.452 kg; 452,000 mg; 0.136 kg

If the angles can form a triangle, classify it as acute, obtuse, or right. (Lesson 8-5)

42. 49°, 41°, 90° right   **43.** 92°, 41°, 47° obtuse   **44.** 57°, 63°, 60° acute

Determine if the given statements are *sometimes, always,* or *never* true. (Lesson 8-6)

45. A rhombus is a square. sometimes   **46.** A square is a rhombus. always

47. A circle is a polygon. never   **48.** A polygon has fewer than 3 sides. never

CHALLENGE 9-4

LESSON 9-4 Challenge
Metric Animals

Write the most appropriate metric units for the measurements below.

	 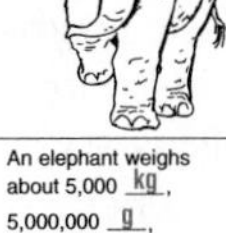	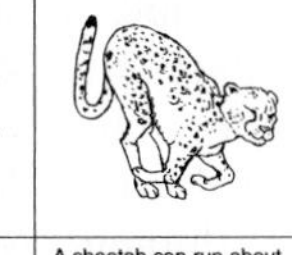
The teeth of a great white shark are about 12 __cm__, or 120 __mm__, long. That's probably longer than your hand!	An elephant weighs about 5,000 __kg__, 5,000,000 __g__, That's heavier than 5 cars piled on top of one another!	A cheetah can run about 110 __km__, or 110,000 __m__, per hour. That's faster than most cars driving on the highway!

A camel can drink about 225 __L__, or 225,000 __mL__, of water in one hour. That's enough water to fill a bathtub!	The midget spider weaves the tiniest web. At only 10 __mm__, or 1 __cm__, long, its web is smaller than your thumbnail!	The pygmy shrew is the smallest animal on Earth. It only weighs about 1.5 __g__, 0.0015 __kg__. That's less than a dime weighs!

PROBLEM SOLVING 9-4

LESSON 9-4 Problem Solving
Converting Metric Units

Write the correct answer.

1. The St. Gotthard Tunnel in Switzerland is the world's longest tunnel. It is 16.3 kilometers long. What is the tunnel's length in meters?
   16,300 meters

2. Ostriches are the world's heaviest birds. On average, they weigh 156,500 grams. How many kilograms does the average ostrich weigh?
   156.5 kilograms

3. The huge flower of the titam arum plant of Sumatra only lives for one day. During that time it grows 75 millimeters. What is the flower's height in centimeters?
   7.5 centimeters

4. The average male elephant drinks about 120,000 milliliters of water each day. How many liters of water do most male elephants drink each day?
   120 liters

Circle the letter of the correct answer.

5. The first successful steam locomotive pulled10,886.4 kilograms of iron. How many grams of iron did the locomotive pull?
   A 10.89 grams
   B 108.86 grams
   Ⓒ 10,886,400 grams
   D 108,864,000 grams

6. The track used by the first successful steam locomotive was 15.3 kilometers long. How many meters long was the track?
   F 0.153 meter
   G 1.53 meters
   H 153 meters
   Ⓙ 1,530 meters

7. About 2.03 meters of rain fall each year in a tropical rain forest. About how many centimeters of rainfall are there each year in a tropical rain forest?
   A 20.3 centimeters
   Ⓑ 203 centimeters
   C 2,030 centimeters
   D 20,300 centimeters

8. The top layer of trees in a tropical forest has trees that can reach 6,096 centimeters in height. How many meters tall are these trees?
   F 6.096 meters
   Ⓖ 60.96 meters
   H 609.6 meters
   J 609,600 meters

ONGOING ASSESSMENT and INTERVENTION

***Diagnose Before* the Lesson**
9-4 Warm Up, TE p. 500

***Monitor During* the Lesson**
9-4 Know-It Notebook
9-4 Questioning Strategies

***Assess After* the Lesson**
9-4 Lesson Quiz, TE p. 503

Test Prep Doctor For Exercise 40, help the students to understand that the distance is one one-hundredth of the selected unit, in one hour. Choice **A** represents a microscopic distance. Choice **B** represents 1 cm. Choice **C** is not a measure of length. Choice **D** represents 10 m.

Journal

Have students explain how they would convert millimeters to meters.

Power Presentations with PowerPoint®

9-4 Lesson Quiz

Convert.

1. A book is 24 cm long. 24 cm = ___ mm 240
2. The chain has a mass of 16 g. 16 g = ___ mg 16,000
3. The volume of the liquid was 12,000 mL. 12,000 mL = ___ L 12
4. Frank's paper airplane glided 78.9 m. Sarah's plane glided 85 m. How many more centimeters did Sarah's plane glide? 610 cm

Also available on transparency

9-5 Organizer

Pacing: Traditional 1 day
Block $\frac{1}{2}$ day

Objective: Students find measures of time and temperature.

Online Edition
Tutorial Videos

Countdown to CRCT Week 20

Warm Up

Convert each measurement to feet and inches.

1. 95 in. 7 ft 11 in.
2. 128 in. 10 ft 8 in.

Convert each measurement to meters.

3. 406 cm 4.06 m
4. 24,671 mm 24.671 m

Problem of the Day

The skateboard had rolled from the house to within 1.8 m of the street before Rick caught it. If the house is 16.9 m from the street, how far did the skateboard roll? 15.1 m

Also available on transparency

Math Humor

Joe: That carpenter took a 12-foot board and made this beautiful bench.

Sue: Wow, he's good at converting feet to benches.

Georgia Performance Standards

M6N1.g Solve problems involving fractions, decimals, and percents.

M6M1 Students will convert from one unit to another within one system of measurement (customary or metric) by using proportional relationships.

M6P1.b Solve problems that arise in mathematics and in other contexts.

9-5 Time and Temperature

Learn to find measures of time and temperature.

Georgia Performance Standards

M6M1 Convert from one unit to another by using proportional relationships. Also, M6N1.g, M6P1.b.

Jamie took a tour of London on a double-decker bus. The tour started at 11:45 A.M. and ended at 3:15 P.M. Jamie was on the bus for 3 hours 30 minutes.

You can use the information in the table below to convert one unit of time to another.

Time	
1 year (yr) = 365 days	1 day = 24 hours (hr)
1 year = 12 months (mo)	1 hour = 60 minutes (min)
1 year = 52 weeks	1 minute = 60 seconds (s)
1 week = 7 days	

EXAMPLE 1 Converting Time

Convert.

A 1 min 45 s = ■ s

1 minute 45 seconds

60 seconds + 45 seconds *Think: 1 minute = 60 seconds.*

105 seconds

1 min 45 s = 105 s

B 450 min = ■ hr

$450 \text{ min} \cdot \frac{1 \text{ hr}}{60 \text{ min}} = \frac{450}{60} \text{ hr}$ *Think: 1 hour = 60 minutes.*

$450 \text{ min} = 7\frac{1}{2} \text{ hr}$ *Write as a mixed number.*

C 6 weeks = ■ hr

$6 \text{ wk} \cdot \frac{7 \text{ days}}{1 \text{ wk}} \cdot \frac{24 \text{ hr}}{1 \text{ day}} = 1{,}008 \text{ hr}$ *Think: 1 week = 7 days and 1 day = 24 hours.*

6 weeks = 1,008 hr

The time between the start of an activity and the end of an activity is called the *elapsed time.*

1 Introduce

Alternate Opener

EXPLORATION

9-5 Time and Temperature

One hour is divided into 60 minutes. You can use proportional thinking to explore the relationship between hours and minutes.

1. How many minutes are there in 2 hours? in 3 hours?
2. How many minutes are there in $\frac{1}{2}$ hour? in $\frac{1}{4}$ hour?
3. Complete the table.

Hours	$\frac{1}{10}$	$\frac{1}{5}$	4	6		
Minutes					480	600

4. What fraction of an hour is 2 minutes?
5. In general, how can you convert any number of minutes to hours?
6. In general, how can you convert any number of hours to minutes?

Think and Discuss

7. **Explain** how to write 23 minutes as a fraction of an hour.
8. **Discuss** how you could write 72 minutes in terms of hours and minutes.

Motivate

Discuss how students might find the number of seconds they spend in school each day and the total amount of time they spend in school each week in hours and in minutes. Show students Celsius and Fahrenheit thermometers, and ask whether students know the freezing and boiling points on the two scales. 0°C, 32°F; 100°C, 212°F

Explorations and answers are provided in *Alternate Openers: Explorations Transparencies.*

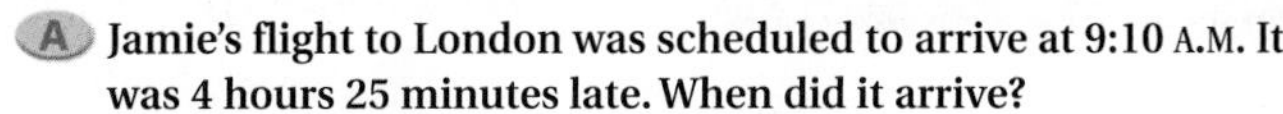

EXAMPLE 2 Finding Elapsed Time

A Jamie's flight to London was scheduled to arrive at 9:10 A.M. It was 4 hours 25 minutes late. When did it arrive?

Scheduled time: 9:10 A.M. *Think: 4 hours after 9:10 A.M. is 1:10 P.M. 25 minutes after 1:10 P.M. is 1:35 P.M.*

Arrival time: 1:35 P.M.

The flight arrived at 1:35 P.M.

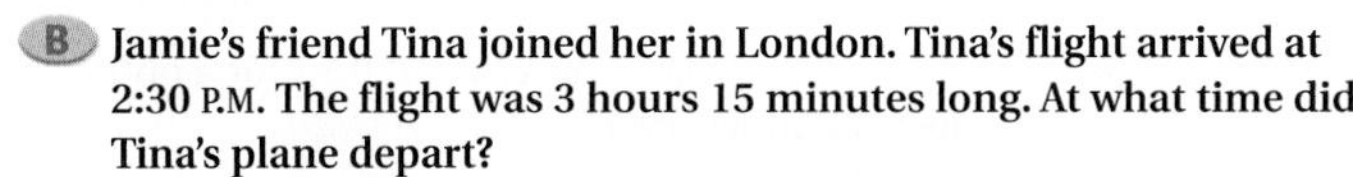

B Jamie's friend Tina joined her in London. Tina's flight arrived at 2:30 P.M. The flight was 3 hours 15 minutes long. At what time did Tina's plane depart?

Arrival time: 2:30 P.M. *Think: 3 hours before 2:30 P.M. is 11:30 A.M.*

Departure: 11:15 A.M. *15 minutes before 11:30 A.M. is 11:15 A.M.*

The plane departed at 11:15 A.M.

Celsius and Fahrenheit are the scales used to measure temperature. You can use these formulas to convert temperature.

Temperature Conversions	
To convert Celsius to Fahrenheit use $F = \frac{9}{5}C + 32$.	To convert Fahrenheit to Celsius use $C = \frac{5}{9}(F - 32)$.

EXAMPLE 3 Estimating Temperature

Estimate the temperature.

Remember!

Dividing by 2 is the same as multiplying by $\frac{1}{2}$.

A 20°C is about ▒°F.

$F = \frac{9}{5} \cdot C + 32$ *Use the formula.*

Round $\frac{9}{5}$ to 2, and 32 to 30.

$F = 2 \cdot 20 + 30$ *Use the order of operations.*

$F = 40 + 30$

$F = 70$

20°C is about 70°F.

B 50°F is about ▒°C.

$C = \frac{5}{9}(F - 32)$ *Use the formula.*

Round $\frac{5}{9}$ to $\frac{1}{2}$, and 32 to 30.

$C = \frac{1}{2}(50 - 30)$ *Use the order of operations.*

$C = \frac{1}{2}(20)$

$C = 10$

50°F is about 10°C.

Possible answers to *Think and Discuss:*

1. Multiply the minutes in an hour by the hours in a day and then by the days in a week.
2. Add 12 hours to that elapsed time since the elapsed time between 10:30 A.M. and 10:30 P.M. is 12 hours.

Think and Discuss GPS M6P3.b

1. **Explain** how to find the number of minutes in a week.
2. **Explain** how to find the elapsed time between 7:45 A.M. and 10:30 P.M. if you know the elapsed time between 7:45 A.M. and 10:30 A.M.

COMMON ERROR ALERT

Some students might misuse the parentheses when doing temperature conversions. Parentheses are only used in the formula converting to Celsius. There is no need for parentheses when converting to Fahrenheit.

Power Presentations with PowerPoint®

Additional Examples

Example 1

Convert.

A. 2 hr 5 min = ___ min 125

B. 195 min = ___ hr $3\frac{1}{4}$

C. 3 hr = ___ s 10,800

Example 2

Solve each equation.

A. Shawn was scheduled to arrive at 10:15 A.M. He was 1 hour and 55 minutes late. When did he arrive? 12:10 P.M.

B. Ty met his friends at 1:35 P.M. He had traveled for 2 hours and 45 minutes. At what time did Ty begin his trip? 10:50 A.M.

Example 3

Estimate the temperature.

A. 40°C is about ___ °F 110

B. 70°F is about ___ °C 20

Also available on transparency

2 Teach

Guided Instruction

In this lesson, students learn to convert measures of time and temperature. Review common units of time. Then have students find the equivalent times in Example 1. Use a clock to show how to solve elapsed-time problems. Have students apply the concept to the problems in Example 2. Discuss Celsius and Fahrenheit scales and formulas. Have students estimate before finding the equivalent temperatures in Example 3.

Reaching All Learners

Through Curriculum Integration

History Have students research the history of the Celsius and Fahrenheit scales. Ask students to write a paragraph about the history of each and tell how each is used today. Then ask students to give estimates for the equivalent temperatures on each scale for a cold day, room temperature, and a hot day.

Possible answers: cold day 0°C, 30°F; room temperature 20°C, 70°F; hot day 30°C, 90°F

3 Close

Summarize

Review the common units of time equivalencies. Ask: If a plane took off at 10:50 A.M. and landed at 1:20 P.M., how long was the flight in hours, in minutes, and in seconds? 2 hours, 30 minutes; 150 minutes; 9,000 seconds Then review how to estimate a Fahrenheit temperature given a Celsius temperature and vice versa. Ask: What is the Celsius temperature if the Fahrenheit temperature is 80°? about 25°C

9-5 Exercises

Assignment Guide

If you finished Example 1 assign:
Average 1–6, 23–24, 35–44
Advanced 12–17, 24–25, 35–44

If you finished Example 2 assign:
Average 1–8, 23–28, 35–44
Advanced 12–19, 23–27, 31, 35–44

If you finished Example 3 assign:
Average 1–11, 18–44
Advanced 12–44

Homework Quick Check

Quickly check key concepts.
Exercises: 18, 22, 24, 28

Georgia Performance Standards

M6P1.a Build new mathematical knowledge through problem solving.

M6P3.a Organize and consolidate their mathematical thinking through communication.

M6P3.c Analyze and evaluate the mathematical thinking and strategies of others.

9-5 Exercises

M6P1.a, M6P3.a, M6P3.c

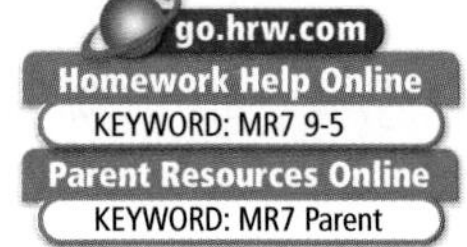

GUIDED PRACTICE

See Example 1

Convert.

1. 20 min = ▇ s **1,200**
2. 98 days = ▇ weeks **14**
3. 30 mo = ▇ yr **$2\frac{1}{2}$**
4. 3 min 25 s = ▇ s **205**
5. 8 hr = ▇ min **480**
6. 4,320 min = ▇ days **3**

See Example 2

7. A movie starts at 11:50 A.M. and runs for 2 hours 25 minutes. At what time does the movie end? **2:15 P.M.**
8. Nick drove to visit some friends. If he arrived at 1:30 P.M. and took 4 hours 10 minutes to get there, at what time did Nick start out? **9:20 P.M.**

See Example 3

Estimate the temperature.

9. 12°C is about ▇ °F **54**
10. 78°F is about ▇ °C **24**
11. 15°C is about ▇ °F **60**

INDEPENDENT PRACTICE

See Example 1

Convert.

12. 2 hr 25 min = ▇ min **145**
13. 96 hr = ▇ days **4**
14. 1 yr 6 mo = ▇ mo **18**
15. 7,200 s = ▇ hr **2**
16. 5 weeks 1 day = ▇ days **36**
17. 4,368 hr = ▇ weeks **26**

See Example 2

18. A bus arrived at its destination at 2:15 P.M. If the trip took 3 hours 50 minutes, at what time did the bus depart? **10:25 A.M.**
19. **Multi-Step** The school play lasts 1 hour 25 minutes, and there is a 15-minute intermission. The play started at 10:30 A.M. When will it end? **12:10 P.M.**

See Example 3

Estimate the temperature.

20. 56°F is about ▇ °C **13**
21. 84°C is about ▇ °F **198**
22. 75°F is about ▇ °C **22.5**

PRACTICE AND PROBLEM SOLVING

Extra Practice p. 732

Compare. Use <, >, or =.

23. 21 hr ▇ $\frac{5}{6}$ day **>**
24. 2 yr ▇ 104 weeks **=**
25. 80,000 s ▇ 1 day **<**
26. **Patterns** The sequence below shows the times that a radio station gives a traffic report. When will the radio station give the next traffic report?
11:18 A.M., 11:30 A.M., 11:42 A.M., 11:54 A.M., … **12:06 P.M.**
27. Which bus from Miami to Orlando would you take to spend the least amount of time on the bus? the greatest amount of time on the bus? **480; 470**
28. Bus 490 was delayed in traffic for 1 hour 15 minutes. At what time did the bus finally arrive? **12:35 A.M.**

Miami to Orlando Schedule		
Bus	**Depart**	**Arrive**
460	8:00 A.M.	2:45 P.M.
470	10:50 A.M.	5:45 P.M.
480	1:00 P.M.	7:40 P.M.
490	4:30 P.M.	11:20 P.M.

RETEACH 9-5

LESSON 9-5 **Reteach**
Time and Temperature

You can use the table below to convert units of time.

Time	
1 minute = 60 seconds	1 year = 52 weeks
1 hour = 60 minutes	1 year = 12 months
1 day = 24 hours	1 year = 365 days
1 week = 7 days	

To convert 1 minute 10 seconds to seconds, find the number of seconds in 1 minute. Then find the total number of seconds.

1 minute 10 seconds = 60 seconds + 10 seconds = 70 seconds
(60 seconds ↑ 1 minute)

Convert.

1. 1 hour 15 minutes = <u>75</u> minutes
2. 2 days 3 hours = <u>51</u> hours

You can find elapsed time by counting up or back.

Sue started to clean her room at 8:15 A.M. She spent 40 minutes cleaning. At what time did Sue finish?

Time Started		Time Spent		Time Finished	
8:15 A.M.	+	40 min	=	8:55 A.M.	Count up 40 minutes.

Solve.

3. Carlos started to wash the car at 3:15 P.M. He spent 1 hour 10 minutes washing the car. At what time did he finish? <u>4:25 P.M.</u>

You can estimate the temperature by using the rules below.

- To change from °C to °F, double the temperature and then add 30.
- To change from °F to °C, subtract 30 from the temperature and then divide by 2.

40°C	110°F
40 + 40 = 80	110 – 30 = 80
80 + 30 = 110	80 ÷ 2 = 40
40°C is about 110°F.	110°F is about 40°C.

Estimate the temperature.

4. 25°C is about <u>80</u> °F.
5. 60°F is about <u>15</u> °C.

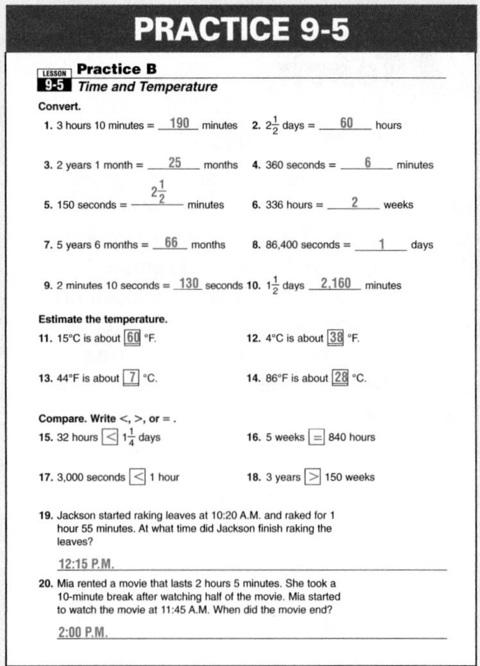

PRACTICE 9-5

LESSON 9-5 **Practice B**
Time and Temperature

Convert.

1. 3 hours 10 minutes = <u>190</u> minutes
2. $2\frac{1}{2}$ days = <u>60</u> hours
3. 2 years 1 month = <u>25</u> months
4. 360 seconds = <u>6</u> minutes
5. 150 seconds = <u>$2\frac{1}{2}$</u> minutes
6. 336 hours = <u>2</u> weeks
7. 5 years 6 months = <u>66</u> months
8. 86,400 seconds = <u>1</u> days
9. 2 minutes 10 seconds = <u>130</u> seconds
10. $1\frac{1}{2}$ days <u>2,160</u> minutes

Estimate the temperature.

11. 15°C is about [60] °F.
12. 4°C is about [38] °F.
13. 44°F is about [7] °C.
14. 86°F is about [28] °C.

Compare. Write <, >, or = .

15. 32 hours [<] $1\frac{1}{4}$ days
16. 5 weeks [=] 840 hours
17. 3,000 seconds [<] 1 hour
18. 3 years [>] 150 weeks
19. Jackson started raking leaves at 10:20 A.M. and raked for 1 hour 55 minutes. At what time did Jackson finish raking the leaves?
<u>12:15 P.M.</u>
20. Mia rented a movie that lasts 2 hours 5 minutes. She took a 10-minute break after watching half of the movie. Mia started to watch the movie at 11:45 A.M. When did the movie end?
<u>2:00 P.M.</u>

Social Studies 

The United States and Jamaica are the only two countries in the world that use the Fahrenheit scale for daily temperature readings. All the other countries in the world use the Celsius scale.

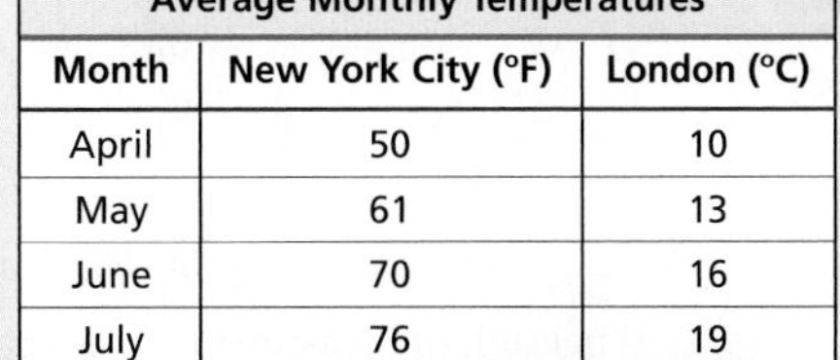

29. **Estimation** Diana, who lives in Paris, France, is going to Jamaica on vacation. She read that the temperature in Jamaica is 86°F. Estimate this temperature in degrees Celsius. **about 28°C**

30. **Multi-Step** The table shows the average monthly temperatures from April to July in degrees Fahrenheit for New York City and in degrees Celsius for London. In which months is the average monthly temperature in New York City higher than it is in London? **May, June, July**

Average Monthly Temperatures		
Month	New York City (°F)	London (°C)
April	50	10
May	61	13
June	70	16
July	76	19

31. Bobby's trip from Paris, Texas, to Paris, France, should have taken $10\frac{1}{2}$ hours, but it was 3 hours and 20 minutes longer. About how long was his trip? **about 14 hours**

32. **What's the Error?** David is going to Dublin, Ireland, in July. He read in a travel book that the average temperature in Dublin in July is 15°C. He estimated the temperature in degrees Fahrenheit by adding 30 to the Celsius temperature and then multiplying by 2. What did David do wrong?

33. **Write About It** How can it be Friday in one part of the United States and Saturday in another? **It can be 10 P.M. Friday on the west coast and 1:00 A.M. Saturday on the east coast.**

34. **Challenge** Below is a list of the daily high temperatures in Glasgow, Scotland, for one week. What was the mean high temperature in degrees Fahrenheit? 7°C, 12°C, 9°C, 10°C, 14°C, 10°C, 8°C **50°F**

CRCT Prep • GPS Support • Spiral Review

35. **Multiple Choice** Which measure is NOT equivalent to the others?

Ⓐ 8 hr Ⓑ 480 min **Ⓒ 28,000 s** Ⓓ $\frac{1}{3}$ day

36. **Multiple Choice** A flight departs at 11:35 A.M. The flight is 2 hours 45 minutes long, but it is delayed 30 minutes. What is the new arrival time?

Ⓕ 2:20 P.M. **Ⓖ 2:50 P.M.** Ⓗ 3:05 P.M. Ⓙ 3:15 P.M.

Compare. Write <, >, or =. (Lesson 3-1)

37. 9.17 ■ 9.107 **>** 38. 3.456 ■ 3.65 **<** 39. 0.051 ■ 0.052 **<** 40. 12.5 ■ 12.50 **=**

Evaluate 10.35 − w for each value of w. (Lesson 3-3)

41. $w = 4.8$ **5.55** 42. $w = 8.62$ **1.73** 43. $w = 0.903$ **9.447** 44. $w = 5.075$ **5.275**

ONGOING ASSESSMENT and INTERVENTION 

***Diagnose Before* the Lesson**
9-5 Warm Up, TE p. 504

***Monitor During* the Lesson**
9-5 Know-It Notebook
9-5 Questioning Strategies

***Assess After* the Lesson**
9-5 Lesson Quiz, TE p. 507

Answers

32. He should have multiplied by 2 and then added 30.

TEST PREP DOCTOR For Exercise 36, some students may find it easier to add the 30 min delay to the flight time and then add the flight time to the departure time.

Journal

Have students explain how to subtract 1 hour 45 minutes from 6 hours 10 minutes.

CHALLENGE 9-5

LESSON 9-5 Challenge
That's So Hot!

Estimate the temperatures of the following hottest places in the world.

The highest temperature ever recorded on the continent of Africa was 136°F, or about **53** °C.

The hottest temperature ever recorded on the continent of Antarctica was 59°F, or about **14.5** °C.

The hottest temperature ever recorded on the continent of Asia was 129°F, or about **49.5** °C.

The hottest temperature ever recorded on the continent of Australia was 128°F, or about **49** °C.

The highest temperature ever recorded on the continent of Europe was 50°C, or about **130** °F.

The hottest temperature ever recorded on the continent of North America was 57°C, or about **144** °F.

The hottest temperature ever recorded on the continent of South America was 49°C, or about **128** °F.

PROBLEM SOLVING 9-5

LESSON 9-5 Problem Solving
Time and Temperature

Use the schedule to answer the questions.

New York to Atlantic City Schedule		
Bus	Depart	Arrive
225	7:30 A.M.	10:00 A.M.
226	9:50 A.M.	12:10 P.M.
227	11:00 A.M.	1:35 P.M.
228	1:45 P.M.	4:40 P.M.
229	3:10 P.M.	5:40 P.M.
230	6:00 P.M.	8:35 P.M.

1. Which bus from New York to Atlantic City would you take to spend the least amount of time on the bus? **Bus 226**

2. Which bus would you take to spend the greatest amount of time on the bus? **Bus 228**

3. Bus 231 took the same amount of time as Bus 230 to travel from New York to Atlantic City. If bus 231 left New York at 7:10 P.M., at what time did it arrive in Atlantic City? **9:45 P.M.**

Circle the letter of the correct answer.

4. Which measure is equivalent to 2 weeks?
A 10 days
(B) 336 hours
C 2,016 minutes
D 120,000 seconds

5. Which measure is NOT equivalent to the others?
F $\frac{1}{4}$ day
G 6 hours
(H) 350 minutes
J 21,600 seconds

6. Which is the best estimate?
A 36°F is about 30°C.
B 36°F is about 24°C.
C 36°F is about 13°C.
(D) 36°F is about 3°C.

7. Which is the best estimate?
F 18°C is about 36°F.
G 11°C is about 20°F.
(H) 8°C is about 46°F.
G 3°C is about 0°F.

Power Presentations with PowerPoint®

9-5 Lesson Quiz

Convert.

1. 17 min = ___ s **1,020**
2. 49 days = ___ weeks **7**
3. 336 hr = ___ weeks **2**
4. Ray drove 3 hours and 10 minutes to visit friends. He started his trip at 9:45 A.M. What was his arrival time? **12:55 A.M.**

Estimate the temperature.

5. 20°C is about ___ °F **70**
6. 66°F is about ___ °C **18**

Also available on transparency

Organizer

Objective: Assess students' mastery of concepts and skills in Lessons 9-1 through 9-5.

Resources

 *Assessment Resources*
Section 9A Quiz

Test & Practice Generator
One-Stop Planner®

INTERVENTION

Resources

 *Ready to Go On? Intervention and Enrichment* Worksheets

 *Ready to Go On?* CD-ROM

 *Ready to Go On?* Online

my.hrw.com

CHAPTER 9

SECTION 9A

Ready to Go On?

Quiz for Lessons 9-1 Through 9-5

9-1 Understanding Customary Units of Measure

What unit of measure provides the best estimate? Explain.

1. A fishbowl can hold about 2 __?__ of water. qt; about 2 small containers of paint
2. A Columbian mammoth, which was about the same size as an elephant, lived in Mexico about 1.5 million years ago. A mammoth weighed about 10 __?__. T; about 10 small cars

9-2 Understanding Metric Units of Measure

What unit of measure provides the best estimate? Explain.

3. A cat has a mass of about 3 __?__. kg; about 3 textbooks
4. The length of an airport runway is about 3 __?__. km; about 3 times around a city block

Measure the length of each line to the nearest centimeter.

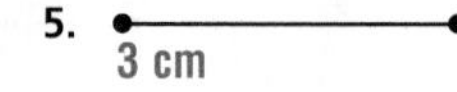

5. 3 cm
6. 6 cm

9-3 Converting Customary Units

Use the table for Exercises 7 and 8.

7. Convert Ty's length to feet and inches. 1 ft $9\frac{1}{2}$ in.
8. How many ounces does Ty weigh? 152 oz

Baby Ty Rodriguez	
Birth Date	July 8, 2005, 11:50 P.M.
Weight	9 lb 8 oz
Length	$21\frac{1}{2}$ in.

9-4 Converting Metric Units

Convert.

9. 8 m = ▒ cm 800
10. 12 kg = ▒ g 12,000
11. 2,000 mL = ▒ L 2

9-5 Time and Temperature

Convert.

12. 5 min 32 s = ▒ s 332
13. 3 days = ▒ min 4,320
14. 24 mo = ▒ yr 2
15. 330 s = ▒ h 5.5

Estimate the temperature.

16. 30°C is about ▒°F 90
17. 80°F is about ▒°C 25
18. 54°F is about ▒°C 12
19. What is the elapsed time between 8:45 P.M. and 12:15 A.M.? 3 hr 30 min
20. A train scheduled to arrive at 10:35 A.M. was delayed 3 hours 20 minutes. What time did it arrive? 1:55 P.M.

READY TO GO ON?

Diagnose and Prescribe

NO — INTERVENE

Ready to Go On? Intervention	*Ready to Go On? Intervention,* Section 9A — Worksheets	CD-ROM	Online
Lesson 9-1	9-1 Intervention	Activity 9-1	Diagnose and Prescribe Online
Lesson 9-2	9-2 Intervention	Activity 9-2	
Lesson 9-3	9-3 Intervention	Activity 9-3	
Lesson 9-4	9-4 Intervention	Activity 9-4	
Lesson 9-5	9-5 Intervention	Activity 9-5	

YES — ENRICH

Ready to Go On? Enrichment, Section 9A

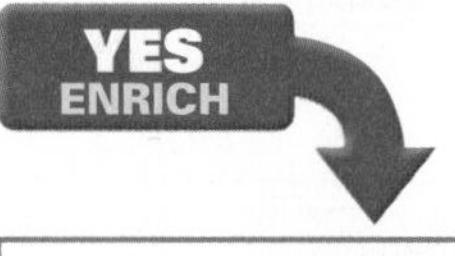
Worksheets
CD-ROM
Online

Focus on Problem Solving

Look Back

• Check that the question is answered.

Sometimes a problem requires you to go through a series of steps to find the answer. When you read a question, ask yourself what information you need to find in order to answer it. After you have solved the problem, reread the question to make sure you have answered it completely.

Read each problem and determine whether the given solution answers the question in the problem. If not, provide the correct answer.

1. The giant house spider has a leg span of 70 millimeters. The western black widow has a leg span of 4 centimeters. How many centimeters longer is the leg span of the giant house spider?
Solution: 3 centimeters

2. A recipe for fruit punch calls for 8 fluid ounces of pineapple juice. Daryl pours the required amount of pineapple juice into a bowl that holds 1 gallon. How many additional fluid ounces of liquid can the bowl hold?
Solution: 120 fluid ounces

3. The distance from Belleville to Cedar Falls is twice the distance from Appleton to Belleville. The distance from Cedar Falls to Donner is twice the distance from Belleville to Cedar Falls. What is the distance from Belleville to Donner?

2 km
Appleton Belleville Cedar Falls Donner

Solution: 8 kilometers

4. The 1939 film *Gone with the Wind* had a running time of 3 hours 50 minutes. The film was usually shown with one 15-minute intermission. An afternoon showing of the film started at 2:30 P.M. At what time did the film end?
Solution: 4 hr 5 min

5. A typical chicken egg weighs 2 ounces. A typical ostrich egg weighs 3 pounds. How many times greater is the weight of the ostrich egg than the chicken egg?
Solution: 48 ounces

Answers

1. Answered correctly.
2. Answered correctly.
3. 12 kilometers
4. 6:35 P.M.
5. 24 times as great

Focus on Problem Solving

Organizer

Objective: Focus on looking back to check that the question is answered.

Online Edition

Resources

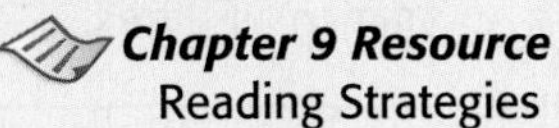

Chapter 9 Resource Book
Reading Strategies

Problem Solving Process

This page focuses on the last step of the problem-solving process: **Look Back**

Discuss

Have students discuss what information needs to be checked when they look back after finding a solution.

Possible answers:

1. The answer should be in centimeters.
2. The answer should be in fluid ounces.
3. The answer should be the distance from Belleville to Donner.
4. The answer should be about 4 hours after 2:30 P.M.
5. The answer should be "times as great."

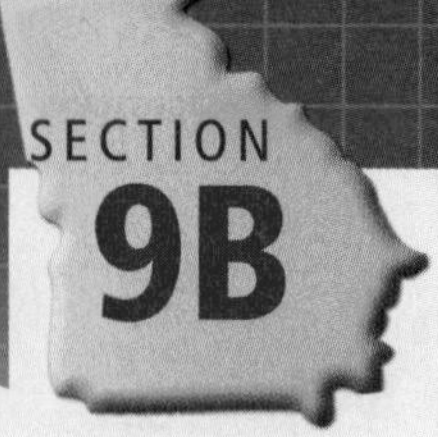

Measurement and Geometric Figures

One-Minute Section Planner

Lesson	Materials	MiC and Lab Resources
Lesson 9-6 Finding Angle Measures in Polygons • Find angle measures in polygons. ☐ CRCT ☐ SAT-10 ☐ ITBS ☑ CTBS ☑ NAEP		
Lesson 9-7 Perimeter • Find the perimeter and missing side lengths of a polygon. ☑ CRCT ☑ SAT-10 ☑ ITBS ☑ CTBS ☑ NAEP	Geoboards (MK), dot paper	**MiC: *Reallotment*** pp. 37–40 ***Hands-On Lab Activities*** 9-7 ***Technology Lab Activities*** 9-7
9-8A Hands-On Lab Explore Circumference • Use a compass, string, scissors, and a calculator to explore circumference. **Lesson 9-8** Circles and Circumference • Identify the parts of a circle and find the circumference of a circle. **9-8A Hands-On Lab** Construct Circle Graphs • Use a compass, straightedge, and protractor to construct circle graphs. ☑ CRCT ☑ SAT-10 ☐ ITBS ☐ CTBS ☑ NAEP	Circular objects, compasses (MK), straightedges (MK), rulers (MK), protractor (MK), string, scissors, calculators	**MiC: *Reallotment*** pp. 40–43 ***Hands-On Lab Activities*** 9-8

MK = *Manipulatives Kit*

Mathematics in Context

The unit ***Reallotment*** from the *Mathematics in Context* © 2006 series can be used with Section 9B. See Section Planner above for suggestions for integrating *MiC* with *Holt Mathematics*.

Section Overview

Angle Measures in Polygons

Lesson 9-6

Use a protractor to find the measure of $\angle ABC$. Then classify the angle.

- Place the center point of the protractor on the vertex of the angle.
- Read the measures where ray *BA* and ray *BC* cross.
- Ray *BA* crosses at 40°, and ray *BC* crosses at 120°.
- The measure of $\angle ABC$ is $120° - 40°$, or 80°. Write this as $m\angle ABC = 80°$.
- Since $80° < 90°$, the angle is acute.

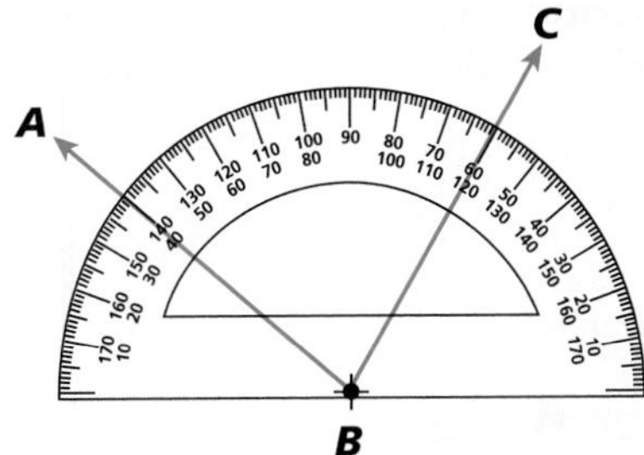

$m\angle ABC$ is $120° - 40° = 80°$

Finding Perimeter

Lesson 9-7

Why? You would need to find the perimeter of your backyard to know how much fencing is needed to enclose it.

The **perimeter** of a figure is the distance around it.

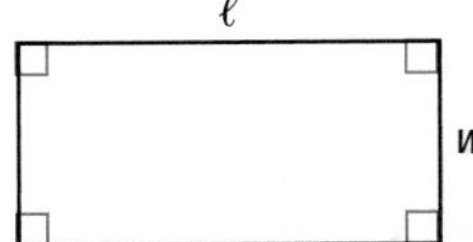

The formula for the **perimeter of a rectangle** is $P = 2\ell + 2w$.

Circles and Circumference

Lesson 9-8

The shape of a bicycle wheel is a circle. The size of tires and inner tubes are given by their diameters.

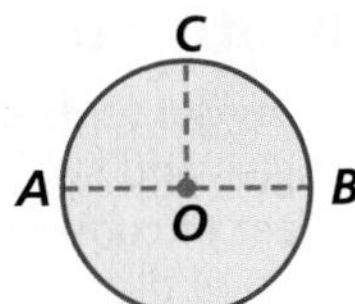

The circle is circle *O*.
$\overline{AB}$ is a diameter.
$\overline{OA}$, $\overline{OB}$, and $\overline{OC}$ are radii.

Circumference of a Circle
the distance around a circle
$C = \pi d$, or $C = 2\pi r$

Find the circumference of a circle with radius 5 cm.

$C = 2\pi r$
$C = 2\pi 5$
$C = 10\pi$ cm

Pi is the ratio of the circumference to the diameter, $\frac{C}{d}$, for any circle. This ratio is represented by the Greek letter π, which is read as "**pi**." $\frac{C}{d} = \pi$

The decimal representation of **pi** starts with 3.14159265 . . . and goes on forever without a repeating pattern. We approximate **pi** using either 3.14 or $\frac{22}{7}$.

9-6 Organizer

Pacing: Traditional 1 day
Block $\frac{1}{2}$ day

Objective: Students find angle measures in polygons.

Online Edition
Tutorial Videos

Countdown to CRCT Week 21

Power Presentations with PowerPoint®

Warm Up

Solve.

1. $n + 9 = 37$ $n = 28$

2. $6 = n - 20$ $n = 26$

3. $11n = 121$ $n = 11$

4. $7 = \frac{n}{7}$ $n = 49$

Problem of the Day

If a triangle has two angles that measure 41° and 117°, what is the measure of the third angle? 22°

Also available on transparency

Math Humor

Mark's two-year-old brother was crying by the open window. Mark asked, "What's wrong?" His brother said, "Polly gone."

9-6 Finding Angle Measures in Polygons

Learn to find angle measures in polygons.

Georgia Performance Standards

M6P1.b Solve problems that arise in mathematics and in other contexts.

All softball and baseball diamonds have a home plate. Home plate is in the shape of a pentagon.

You can use a protractor and your knowledge of angles in polygons to find the measures of the angles in home plate.

EXAMPLE 1 Subtracting to Find Angle Measures

Caution!

Ray *AB* can also be read as crossing at 140°, and ray *BC* can be read as crossing at 60°. The angle measure is still 80°. Make sure that you read the measures on the same scale.

Use a protractor to find the measure of $\angle ABC$. Then classify the angle.

- Place the center point of the protractor on the vertex of the angle.
- Read the measures where ray *AB* and ray *BC* cross.
- Ray *AB* crosses at 40°, and ray *BC* crosses at 120°.
- The measure of $\angle ABC$ is $120° - 40°$, or 80°. Write this as $m\angle ABC = 80°$.
- Since $80° < 90°$, the angle is acute.

Check

Use the other scale on the protractor to find the measure of $\angle ABC$.
$140° - 60° = 80°$

To estimate the measure of an angle, compare it with an angle whose measure you already know. A right angle has half the measure of a straight angle. A 45° angle has half the measure of a right angle.

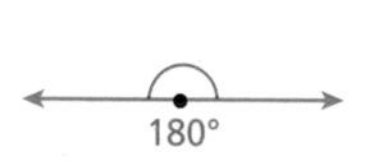

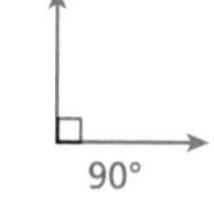

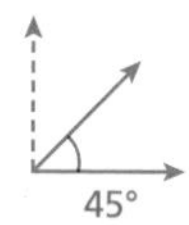

1 Introduce

Alternate Opener

EXPLORATION

9-6 Finding Angle Measures in Polygons

The figures show the measures of several angles.

45° 90° 135° 180°

You can use these angles as benchmarks to help you estimate the measures of other angles.

Estimate the measure of each angle.

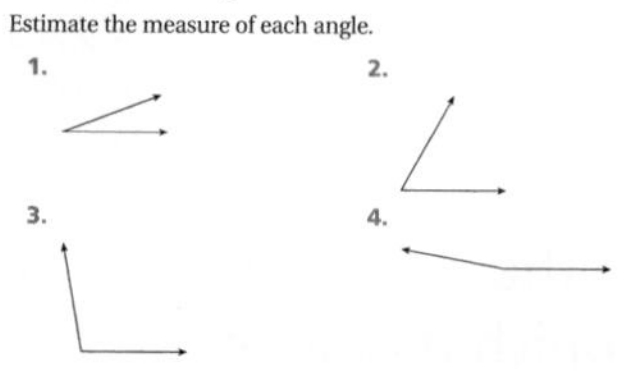

Think and Discuss

5. Explain how you could use the corner of an index card to help you estimate angle measures.

6. Describe how you could use the corner of an index card to draw a 135° angle. (*Hint:* Consider folding the corner of the card.)

Motivate

Show students objects that contain right angles and straight angles. The corner of a sheet of copy paper is a right angle and the edge of the sheet represents a straight angle. Fold the corner of the sheet in half and ask the class for the measure of the angle resulting from the fold. 45° Have them discuss how they would recognize angles that have measures less than 45° and greater than 45° without measuring them first.

Explorations and answers are provided in *Alternate Openers: Explorations Transparencies.*

Georgia Performance Standards

M6P1.b Solve problems that arise in mathematics and in other contexts.

EXAMPLE 2 Estimating Angle Measures

Estimate the measure of $\angle J$ in the parallelogram *JKLM*. Then use a protractor to check the reasonableness of your answer.

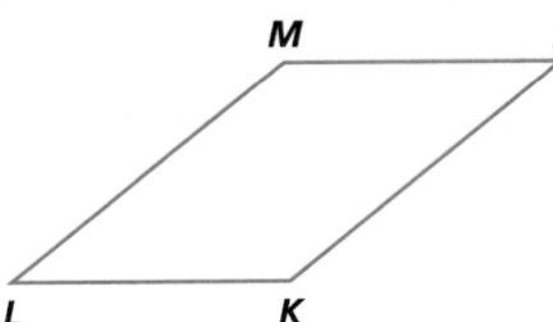

Think: The measure of the angle is close to 45°, but it is a little less. A good estimate would be about 35°.

Caution!

Use the scale on the protractor that starts with 0°.

Remember that in a parallelogram, opposite angles are congruent.

So use the angle opposite $\angle J$ to find its measure.

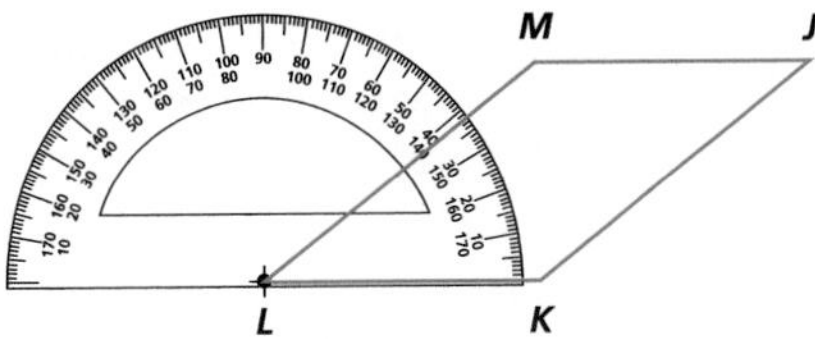

Use the protractor. The measure of the angle is 38°.

$m\angle J = 38°$, so the estimate of 35° is reasonable.

EXAMPLE 3 *Sports Application*

The shape of a softball home plate is shown at right. Find the measures of $\angle A$ and $\angle B$.

Use a protractor to measure $\angle A$. $\overrightarrow{AB}$ crosses at 60°, and $\overrightarrow{AE}$ crosses at 150°.

Subtract. 135° − 45° = 90°.

$\angle A = 90°$

Estimate the $m\angle B$.

It is greater than 90°, so it is obtuse. It looks as if the angle measure is 90° + 45°. So, $m\angle B$ is about 135°.

Use a protractor to measure $\angle B$.

$\angle B = 135°$

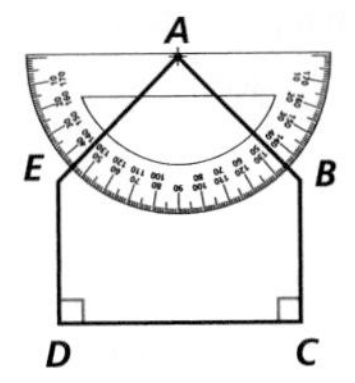

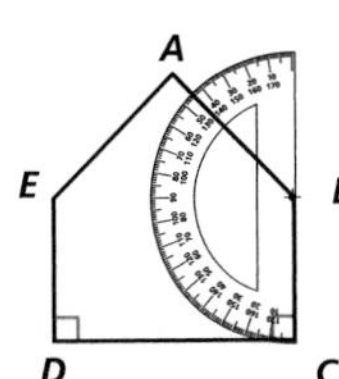

Answer to *Think and Discuss:*

1. $\angle J$ and $\angle K$ are supplementary. Therefore, $\angle K$ has a measure of 142°, and $\angle K$ and $\angle M$ are congruent.

Think and Discuss GPS M6P1.d

1. Explain how to find the measures of $\angle K$ and $\angle M$ in Example 2 without using a protractor once you know the measure of $\angle J$.

COMMON ERROR ALERT

Some students will read the wrong scale on the protractor when measuring an angle. Have them check for reasonableness. If their measurement is greater than 90°, the angle should appear obtuse. If their measurement is less than 90°, the angle should appear acute.

Power Presentations with PowerPoint®

Additional Examples

Example 1

Use the protractor to find the measure of $\angle XYZ$. Then classify the angle.

80°, acute angle

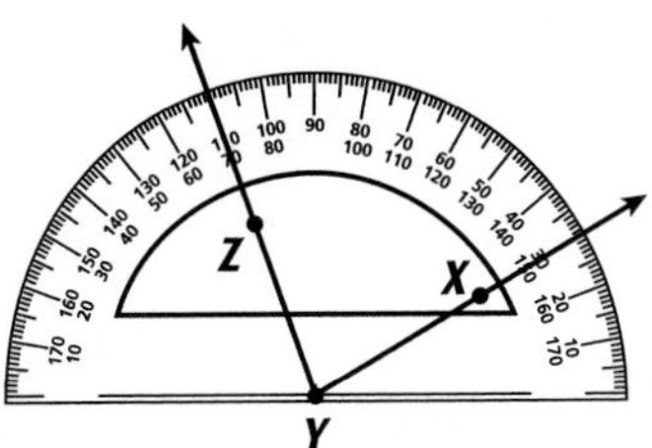

Example 2

Estimate the measure of $\angle K$ in parallelogram *JKLM* on page 511 in the student text. Then use a protractor to check the reasonableness of your answer. 145°

Example 3

A softball home plate is shown on page 511 in the student text. Find the measures of $\angle C$ and $\angle E$.

90°, 135°

Also available on transparency

2 Teach

Guided Instruction

In this lesson, students learn to find angle measures in polygons. First, teach them to use subtraction to find angle measures. Next, teach them to estimate angle measures using benchmarks of 45, 90, and 180 degrees. Then use a protractor to verify the angle measures.

Reaching All Learners

Through Cooperative Learning

Have students collect and label examples of polygons that are large enough to allow a protractor to be used to measure their angles. Have students exchange polygons in class so that they can estimate and measure the angles.

3 Close

Summarize

Ask students to explain how they know which scale to use when measuring angles with a protractor.

9-6 Exercises

Assignment Guide

If you finished Example 1 assign:
Average 1–3, 15, 22–28
Advanced 8–10, 16, 22–28

If you finished Example 2 assign:
Average 1–6, 15–16, 22–28
Advanced 8–13, 15–16, 22–28

If you finished Example 3 assign:
Average 1–12, 17–28
Advanced 8–28

Homework Quick Check

Quickly check key concepts.
Exercises: 8, 10, 12, 18

You may use the recording sheets in the Chapter 9 Resource Book for Exercises 1-16.

Georgia Performance Standards

M6P3.a Organize and consolidate their mathematical thinking through communication.

M6P3.c Analyze and evaluate the mathematical thinking and strategies of others.

M6P4.c Recognize and apply mathematics in contexts outside of mathematics.

9-6 Exercises

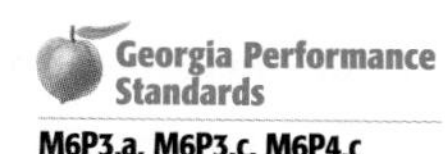

M6P3.a, M6P3.c, M6P4.c

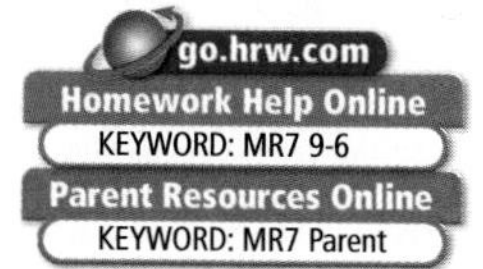

GUIDED PRACTICE

See Example 1

Use a protractor to find the measure of each angle. Then classify the angle.

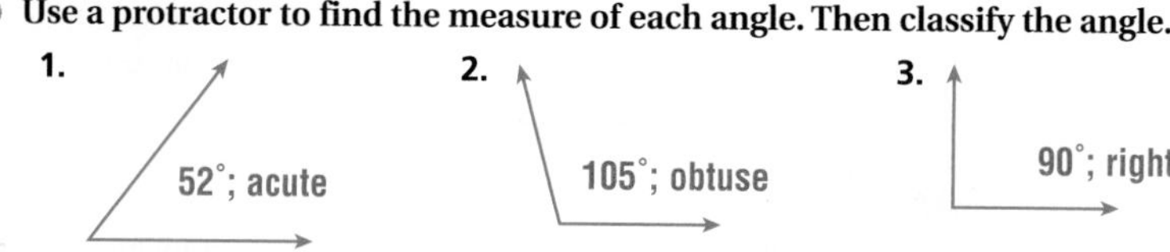

See Example 2

Estimate the measure of ∠A in each figure. Then use a protractor to check the reasonableness of your answer.

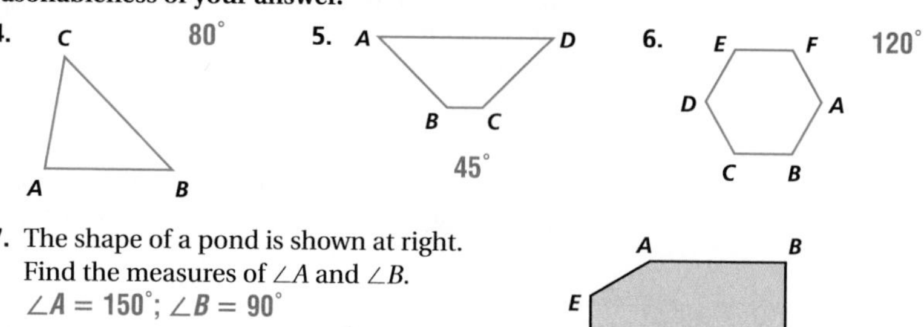

See Example 3

7. The shape of a pond is shown at right. Find the measures of ∠*A* and ∠*B*.
∠*A* = 150°; ∠*B* = 90°

A B E D C

INDEPENDENT PRACTICE

See Example 1

Use a protractor to find the measure of each angle. Then classify the angle.

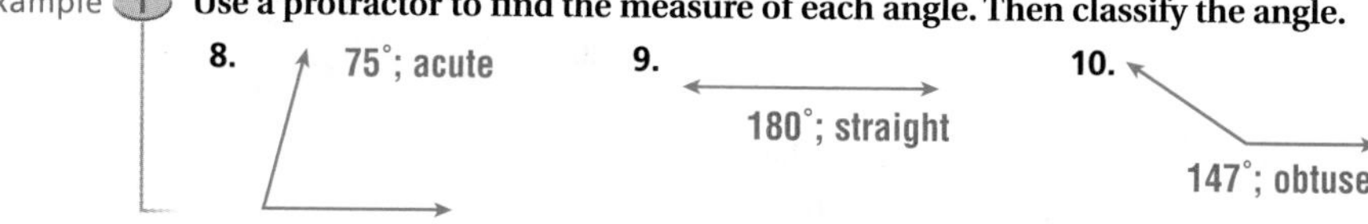

See Example 2

Estimate the measure of ∠A in each figure. Then use a protractor to check the reasonableness of your answer.

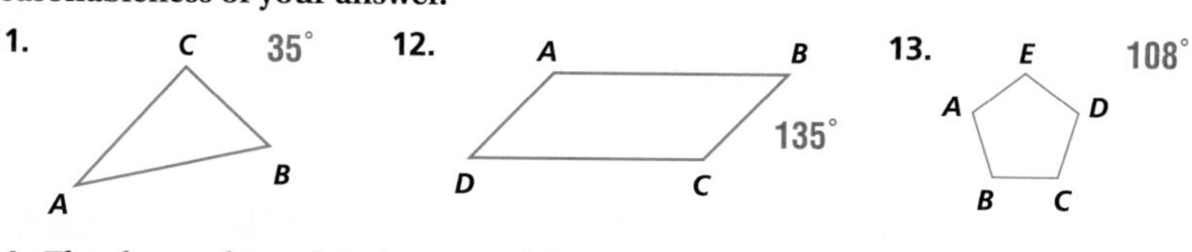

See Example 3

14. The shape of a park is shown at right. Find the measures of ∠*A* and ∠*B*.
∠*A* = 100°; ∠*B* = 80°

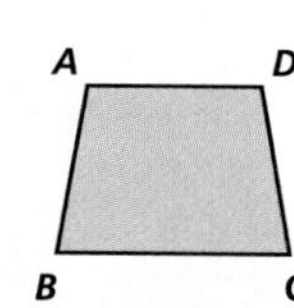

RETEACH 9-6

LESSON 9-6 Reteach
Finding Angle Measures in Polygons

You can subtract to find the measure of ∠ABC.

1. Place the center point of the protractor on the vertex of the angle.
2. Read the measures where ray AB and ray BC cross. Use the inside scale. 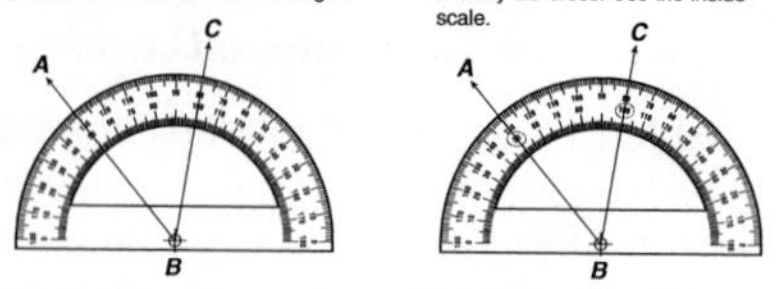
3. Write the measures where ray AB and ray BC cross. Ray AB crosses at 50°, and ray BC crosses at 100°.
4. Subtract to find the measure of ∠ABC. 100° − 50° = 50°.

Use a protractor to find the measure of each angle.

1.  40°
2. 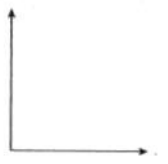 90°

You can estimate the measure of the angle. Use benchmarks of 45°, 90°, 135°, and 180°.

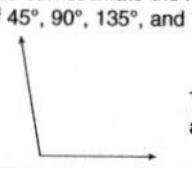

The measure of this angle is close to 90°, but a little more. A good estimate would be 100°.

Estimate the measure of the angle. Then use a protractor to check. Estimates will vary.

3. 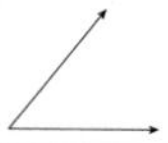 Estimate: ______
Actual: 50°

PRACTICE 9-6

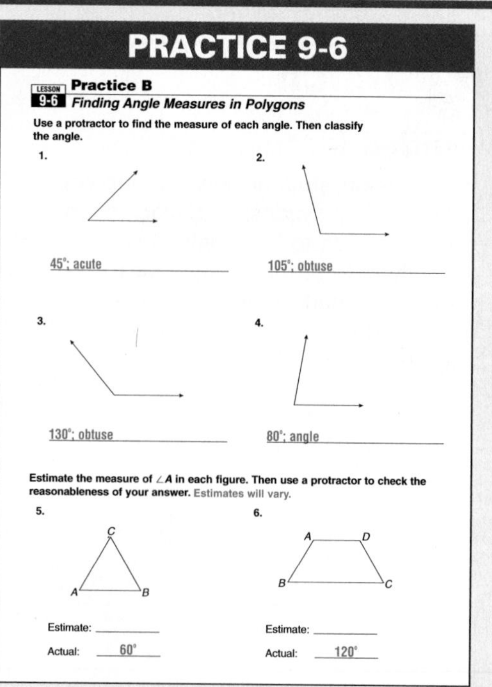

LESSON 9-6 Practice B
Finding Angle Measures in Polygons

Use a protractor to find the measure of each angle. Then classify the angle.

1. 45°; acute
2. 105°; obtuse
3. 130°; obtuse
4. 80°; angle

Estimate the measure of ∠A in each figure. Then use a protractor to check the reasonableness of your answer. Estimates will vary.

5. Estimate: ______
Actual: 60°
6. Estimate: ______
Actual: 120°

PRACTICE AND PROBLEM SOLVING

Extra Practice p. 732

Find the measure of the given angle and the measure of the angle that makes up its supplement.

15. 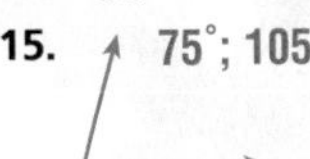 75°; 105°

16.  120; 60°

17. **Architecture** Most buildings are built at a 90° angle from the ground. The Leaning Tower of Pisa, in Pisa, Italy, is at an angle of approximately 84.5° from the ground. How many degrees is it leaning? 5.5°

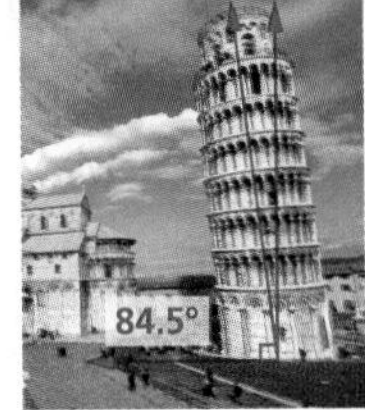

18. **Critical Thinking** Three angles form a 180° angle. If m∠3 = 80° and ∠1 and ∠2 are congruent, what is the measure of ∠1? 50°

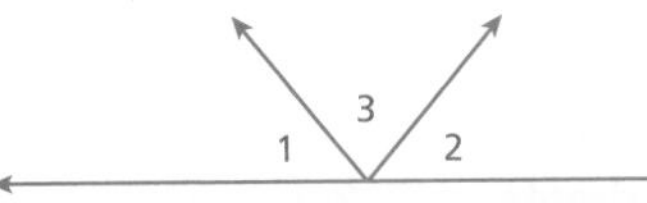

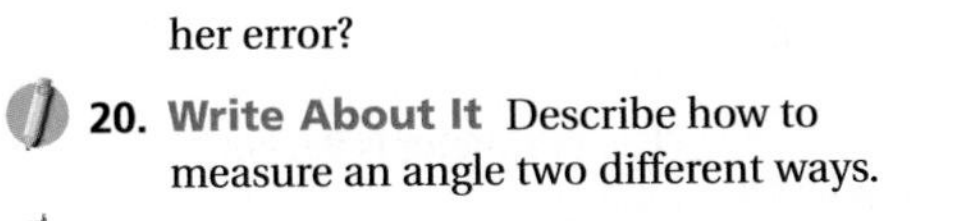

19. **What's the Error?** Loni said that the measurement of ∠J was 20°. What is her error?

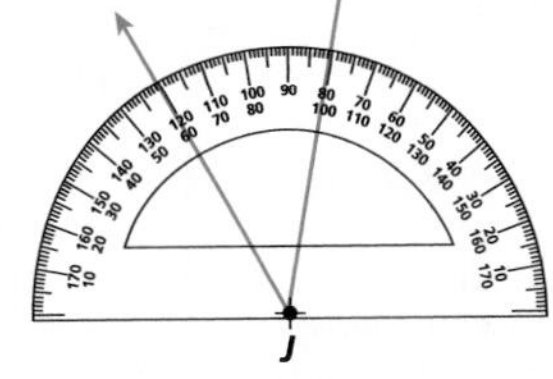

20. **Write About It** Describe how to measure an angle two different ways.

21. **Challenge** Another way to measure angles is in radians. 2π radians is equal to 360°. How many radians equal 90°? $\frac{1}{2}\pi$ radians

CRCT PREP • GPS SUPPORT • SPIRAL REVIEW

22. **Multiple Choice** Find the measure of ∠C to the nearest degree.

Ⓐ 30° Ⓑ 60° Ⓒ 75° Ⓓ 115°

23. **Short Response** Use a protractor to find the measure of ∠A. Classify the angle. Explain.
65°; acute; 65 < 90

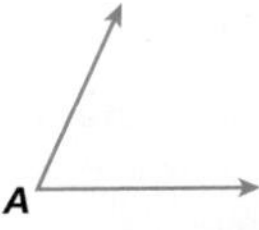

Convert. (Lesson 9-3)

24. 6 ft = ▒ in. 72
25. 8 qt = ▒ gal 2
26. 7 lb = ▒ oz 112
27. 4 qt = ▒ pt 8

28. Pete got into the pool to swim laps at 2:10 P.M. He got out of the pool at 3:25 P.M. How long was he in the pool? (Lesson 9-5) 1 hr 15 min

CHALLENGE 9-6

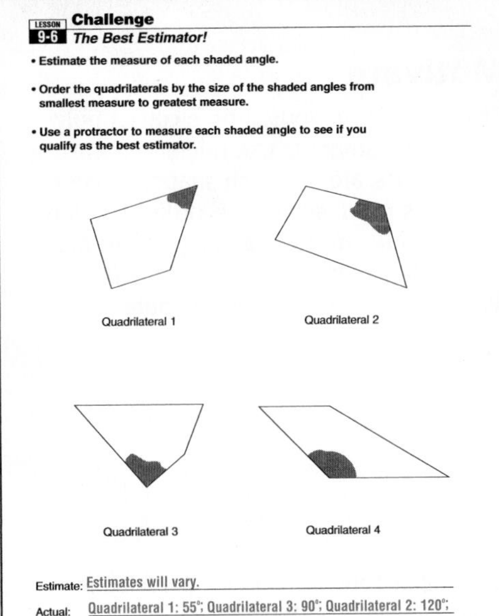

LESSON 9-6 **Challenge**
The Best Estimator!

- Estimate the measure of each shaded angle.
- Order the quadrilaterals by the size of the shaded angles from smallest measure to greatest measure.
- Use a protractor to measure each shaded angle to see if you qualify as the best estimator.

Quadrilateral 1 Quadrilateral 2

Quadrilateral 3 Quadrilateral 4

Estimate: Estimates will vary.
Actual: Quadrilateral 1: 55°; Quadrilateral 3: 90°; Quadrilateral 2: 120°; Quadrilateral 4: 135°

PROBLEM SOLVING 9-6

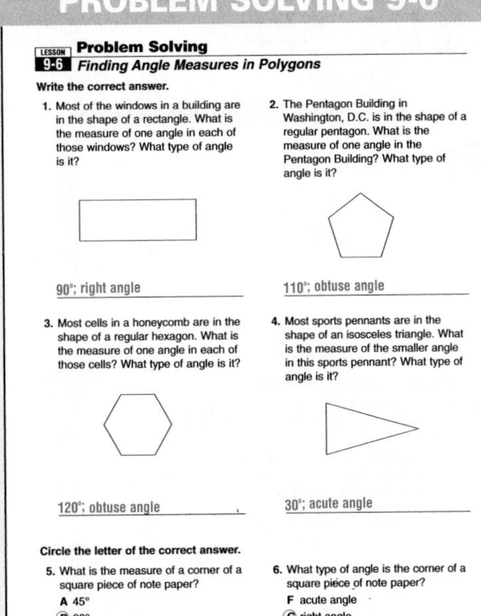

LESSON 9-6 **Problem Solving**
Finding Angle Measures in Polygons

Write the correct answer.

1. Most of the windows in a building are in the shape of a rectangle. What is the measure of one angle in each of those windows? What type of angle is it?
90°; right angle

2. The Pentagon Building in Washington, D.C. is in the shape of a regular pentagon. What is the measure of one angle in the Pentagon Building? What type of angle is it?
110°; obtuse angle

3. Most cells in a honeycomb are in the shape of a regular hexagon. What is the measure of one angle in each of those cells? What type of angle is it?
120°; obtuse angle

4. Most sports pennants are in the shape of an isosceles triangle. What is the measure of the smaller angle in this sports pennant? What type of angle is it?
30°; acute angle

Circle the letter of the correct answer.

5. What is the measure of a corner of a square piece of note paper?
A 45°
Ⓑ 90°
C 145°
D 180°

6. What type of angle is the corner of a square piece of note paper?
F acute angle
Ⓖ right angle
H obtuse angle
J straight angle

ONGOING ASSESSMENT and INTERVENTION

Diagnose **Before** the Lesson
9-6 Warm Up, TE p. 510

Monitor **During** the Lesson
9-6 Know-It Notebook
9-6 Questioning Strategies

Assess **After** the Lesson
9-6 Lesson Quiz, TE p. 513

Answers

19. She read 100 from one scale and 120 from the other scale and then found the difference.
20. The subtraction method can be used as in Example 1 of this lesson, or the protractor can be used in the conventional way with a ray of the angle placed at zero on the scale.

TEST PREP DOCTOR If students have difficulty determining the correct measure in Exercise 23, it might be due to reading the wrong scale on the protractor. Remind them that if the angle appears to be acute, then the reading on the protractor will not exceed 90°.

Journal

Have students explain the procedure for achieving an accurate measurement when using a protractor.

Power Presentations with PowerPoint®

9-6 Lesson Quiz

Solve each equation.

1. Use the protractor to find the measure of ∠ABC. Tell what type of angle it is. 120°, obtuse

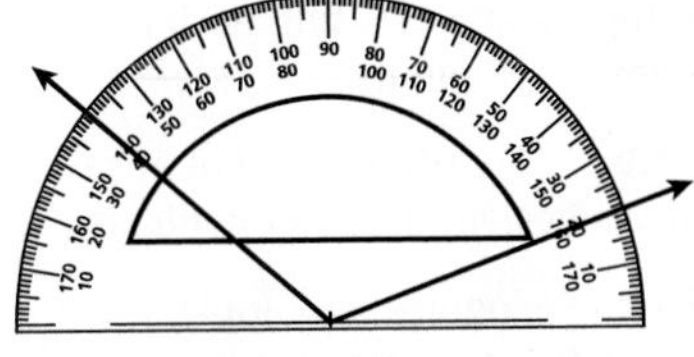

2. Estimate the measure of ∠B in the parallelogram for Exercise 12 on page 512 of the student text. Then use a protractor to check the reasonableness of your answer. 45°

Also available on transparency

9-7 Organizer

Pacing: Traditional 1 day
Block $\frac{1}{2}$ day

Objective: Students find the perimeter and missing side lengths of a polygon.

Hands-On Lab
In *Hands-On Lab Activities*

Technology Lab
In *Technology Lab Activities*

Online Edition
Tutorial Videos, Interactivities

Countdown to CRCT Week 21

Power Presentations with PowerPoint®

Warm Up

1. What figure has four equal sides and four right angles? square
2. What figure has eight sides? octagon
3. What figure has five sides pentagon

Problem of the Day

Find the greatest perimeter possible when 6 identical unit squares are arranged to form a closed figure. Adjacent squares must share an entire side. 14 units

Also available on transparency

9-7 Perimeter

Learn to find the perimeter and missing side lengths of a polygon.

Vocabulary
perimeter

One of the biggest finger paintings ever painted is *Ten Fingers, Ten Toes*. It is 8.53 meters wide and 10.66 meters long.

The **perimeter** of a figure is the distance around it. To find the perimeter of the painting, you can add the lengths of the sides.

$8.53 + 10.66 + 8.53 + 10.66 = 38.38$

The perimeter of the painting, is 38.38 meters.

Georgia Performance Standards

M6A3 Evaluate algebraic expressions and solve simple one-step equations using each of the four basic operations. Also, M6P1.b, M6P4.c.

EXAMPLE 1 Finding the Perimeter of a Polygon

Find the perimeter of the figure.

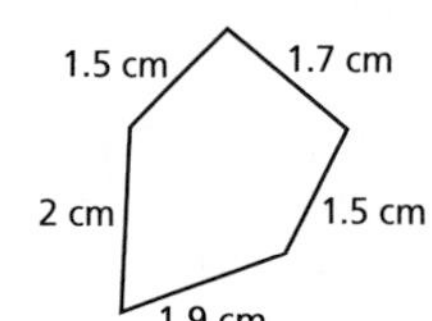

$1.5 + 1.7 + 1.5 + 1.9 + 2 = 8.6$

Add all the side lengths.

The perimeter is 8.6 cm.

PERIMETER OF A RECTANGLE

The opposite sides of a rectangle are equal in length. Find the perimeter of a rectangle by using the formula, in which ℓ is the length and w is the width.

$P = 2\ell + 2w$

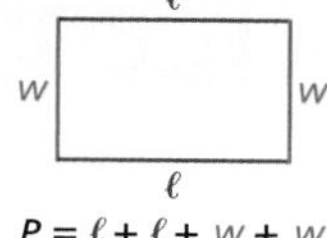

EXAMPLE 2 Using a Formula to Find Perimeter

Find the perimeter P of the rectangle.

$P = 2\ell + 2w$

$P = (2 \cdot 3) + (2 \cdot 2)$ *Substitute 3 for ℓ and 2 for w.*

$P = 6 + 4$ *Multiply.*

$P = 10$ *Add.*

The perimeter is 10 feet.

Georgia Performance Standards

M6A3 Students will evaluate algebraic expressions, including those with exponents, and solve simple one-step equations using each of the four basic operations.

M6P1.b Solve problems that arise in mathematics and in other contexts.

M6P4.c Recognize and apply mathematics in contexts outside of mathematics.

1 Introduce

Alternate Opener

EXPLORATION

Perimeter

Felicia is working with her dad to design a deck for their yard. They sketch the floor space on grid paper with the side length of each square representing 2 feet.

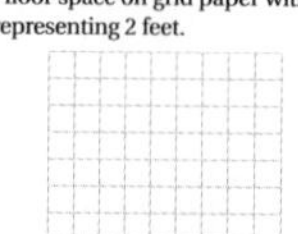

1. Label the dimensions in feet of the deck.
2. The final task in building the deck is to nail a trim piece all the way around the deck. Find the distance around the deck.
3. The distance around the deck is called the ***perimeter***. What are three other real-world situations in which you might want to find the perimeter?

Think and Discuss

4. **Discuss** your method for finding the perimeter of the deck.
5. **Explain** how you could write a formula for perimeter of a rectangle using ℓ for length and w for width.

Motivate

Give students various simple cutout polygons. Have students use rulers to measure the distance around each shape. Discuss strategies used, such as recording the length of each side and then adding to find the total distance around. Explain that the distance around a figure is its *perimeter*.

Explorations and answers are provided in *Alternate Openers: Explorations Transparencies.*

EXAMPLE 3 Finding Unknown Side Lengths and the Perimeter of a Polygon

Find each unknown measure.

A What is the length of side a if the perimeter equals 105 m?

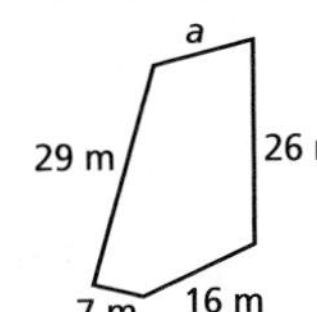

P = sum of side lengths

$105 = a + 26 + 16 + 7 + 29$ *Use the values you know.*

$105 = a + 78$ *Add the known lengths.*

$105 - 78 = a + 78 - 78$ *Subtract 78 from both sides.*

$27 = a$

Side a is 27 m long.

B What is the perimeter of the polygon?

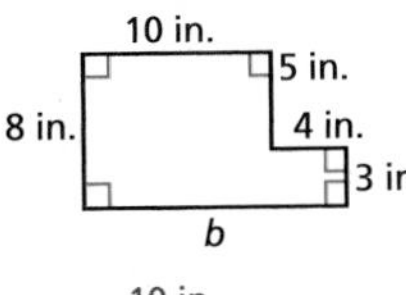

First find the unknown side length.

Find the sides opposite side b.

The length of side b = 10 + 4.

Side b is 14 in. long.

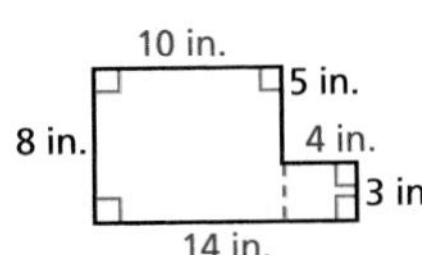

Find the perimeter.

$P = 14 + 8 + 10 + 5 + 4 + 3$

$P = 44$

The perimeter of the polygon is 44 in.

C The width of a rectangle is 12 cm. What is the perimeter of the rectangle if the length is 3 times the width?

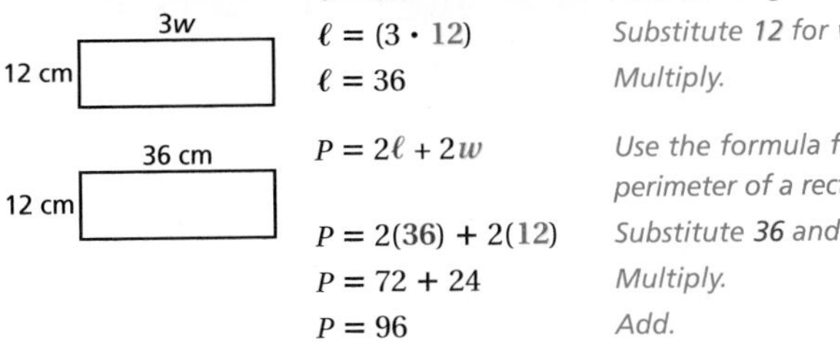

$\ell = 3w$ *Find the length.*

$\ell = (3 \cdot 12)$ *Substitute 12 for w.*

$\ell = 36$ *Multiply.*

$P = 2\ell + 2w$ *Use the formula for the perimeter of a rectangle.*

$P = 2(36) + 2(12)$ *Substitute 36 and 12.*

$P = 72 + 24$ *Multiply.*

$P = 96$ *Add.*

The perimeter of the rectangle is 96 cm.

Answers to *Think and Discuss:*

1. Possible answer: Multiply the length of the known side by 5.
2. $P = 4s$, where s is the length of each side

Think and Discuss

GPS M6P3.b

1. Explain how to find the perimeter of a regular pentagon if you know the length of one side.

2. Tell what formula you can use to find the perimeter of a square.

Power Presentations with PowerPoint®

Additional Examples

Example 1

Find the perimeter of the figure. 17.2 in.

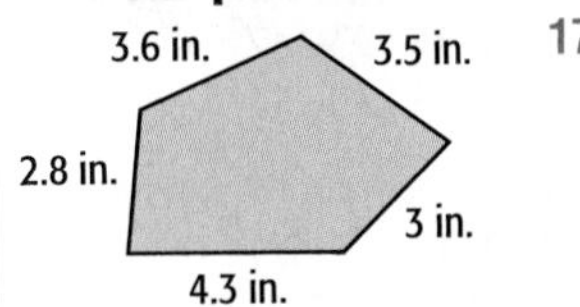

Example 2

Find the perimeter *P* of the rectangle. 30 cm

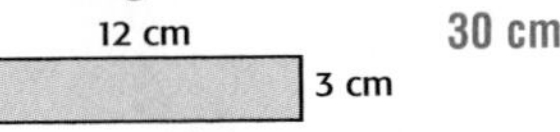

Example 3

Find each unknown measure.

A. What is the length of side a if the perimeter equals 1,471 mm? 293 mm

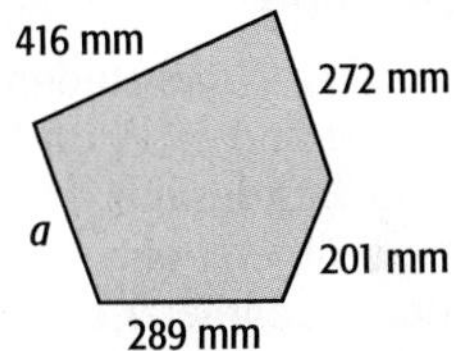

B. What is the perimeter of the polygon? 254 cm

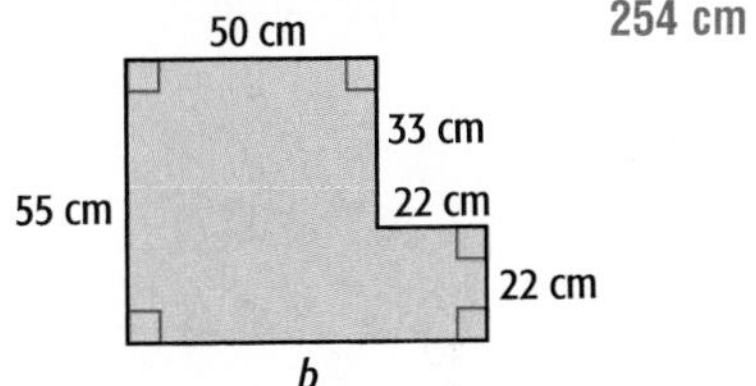

C. The width of a rectangle is 19 cm. What is the perimeter of the rectangle if the length is 4 times the width? 190 cm

Also available on transparency

2 Teach

Guided Instruction

In this lesson, students learn to find the perimeter and missing side lengths of a polygon. Teach students to find the perimeter of a figure by adding the lengths of all the sides. Then teach them to use a formula to find perimeter of a rectangle and to use an equation to find the length of a missing side.

Reaching All Learners

Through Modeling

Have each student make several polygons on a geoboard (provided in the Manipulatives Kit) and draw each polygon on dot paper. Have students measure the perimeter of each polygon. This activity reinforces the meaning of perimeter, maintains measuring skills, and requires the students to apply the correct fraction operation.

3 Close

ENGLISH LANGUAGE LEARNERS

Summarize

Review the term *perimeter* and have students explain how to find the perimeter of a polygon.

Possible answer: Measure each side of the polygon. Add the lengths of the sides to find the perimeter.

9-7 Exercises

Assignment Guide

If you finished Example 1 assign:
Average 1–2, 16, 23–32
Advanced 6–7, 19, 23–32

If you finished Example 2 assign:
Average 1–4, 16–17, 23–32
Advanced 6–10, 18–19, 23–32

If you finished Example 3 assign:
Average 1–14, 19–32
Advanced 6–32

Homework Quick Check
Quickly check key concepts.
Exercises: 6, 10, 12, 14

Math Background

The study of perimeter allows students to develop some simple and easily understandable formulas. Besides the formula in the text for the perimeter of a rectangle, a formula for the perimeter of a regular polygon can be stated as follows: $P = ns$, where n is the number of sides in the polygon and s is the length of each side.

9-7 Exercises

M6P3.a, M6P3.c, M6P5.c

go.hrw.com
Homework Help Online
KEYWORD: MR7 9-7
Parent Resources Online
KEYWORD: MR7 Parent

GUIDED PRACTICE

See Example 1 **Find the perimeter of each figure.**

1. 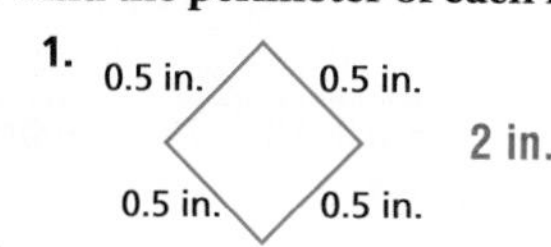

2 in.

2. 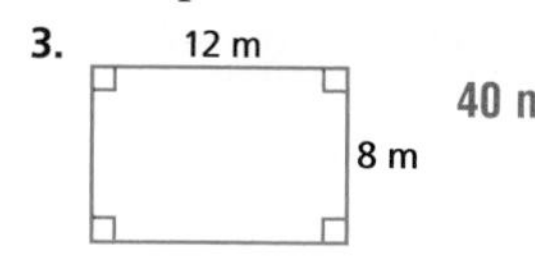

28 cm

See Example 2 **Find the perimeter P of each rectangle.**

3. 12 m, 8 m **40 m**

4. 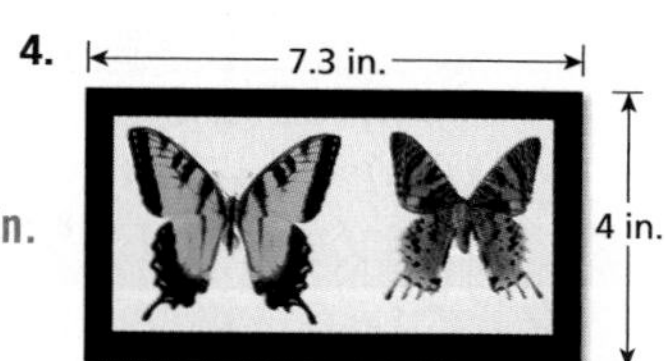

22.6 in.

See Example 3 **Find the unknown measure.**

5. What is the length of side b if the perimeter equals 21 yd? **7 yd**

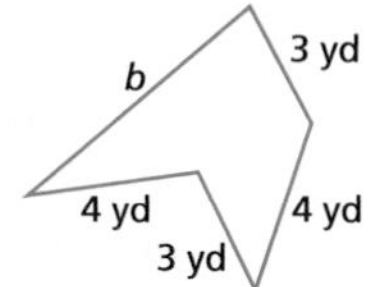

INDEPENDENT PRACTICE

See Example 1 **Find the perimeter of each figure.**

6. 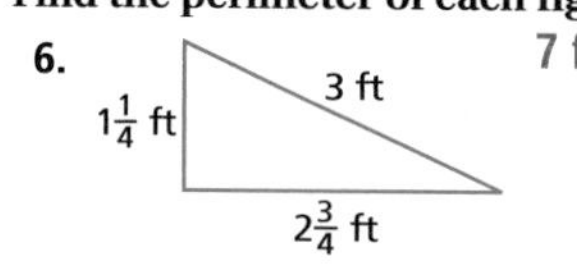

7 ft

7. regular octagon **96 in.**

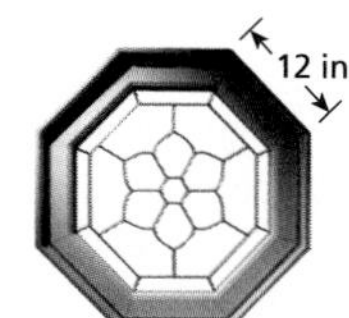

See Example 2 **Find the perimeter P of each rectangle.**

8. 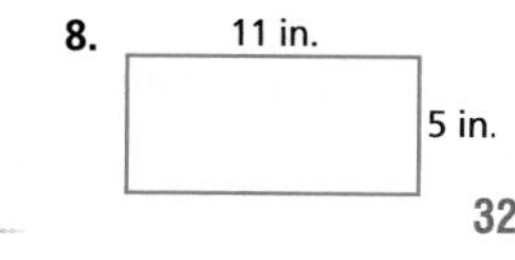

32 in.

9. 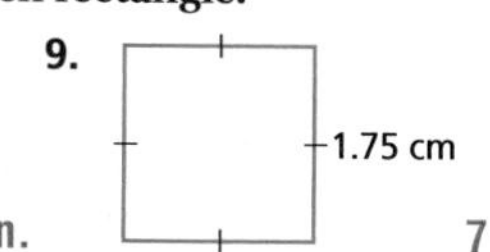

7 cm

10. 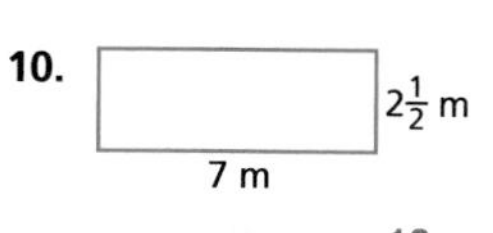

19 m

See Example 3 **Find each unknown measure.**

11. What is the perimeter of the polygon? **42 m**

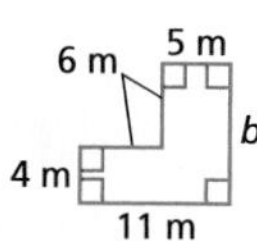

12. The width of a rectangle is 15 ft. What is the perimeter of the rectangle if the length is 5 ft longer than the width? **70 ft**

Georgia Performance Standards

M6P3.a Organize and consolidate their mathematical thinking through communication.

M6P3.c Analyze and evaluate the mathematical thinking and strategies of others.

M6P5.c Use representations to model and interpret physical, social, and mathematical phenomena.

RETEACH 9-7

LESSON 9-7 **Reteach**
Perimeter

The perimeter of a figure is the distance around it. To find the perimeter of a figure, find the sum of the lengths of its sides.

Look at the figure below. (4.2, 2.3, 3.4, 1.5)

The perimeter is the sum of the lengths of its sides.
$P = 2.3 + 1.5 + 3.4 + 4.2$
$= 11.4$
So, the perimeter of the figure is 11.4 units.

Find the perimeter of each figure.

1. (2, 2, 2, 3, 2, 4, 4, 7) **26 units**

2. (2, 1, 1, 3, 1, 1, 3, 3, 1, 2, 4, 2, 3, 3) **30 units**

If you know the perimeter of a figure, you can find the unknown length of a side.

The perimeter of the figure below is 94 units. (11, x, 18, 23, 20)

To find the missing length x first find the sum of the known lengths.
$23 + 18 + 20 + 11 = 72$
Then subtract the sum from the perimeter.
$94 - 72 = 22$ So, side x is 22 units long.

Find the missing length for each figure.

3. (5, 13, x) Perimeter = 30 units **x = 12 units**

4. (13, 2, 2, 2, 2, 2, 5, x) Perimeter = 34 units **x = 6 units**

PRACTICE 9-7

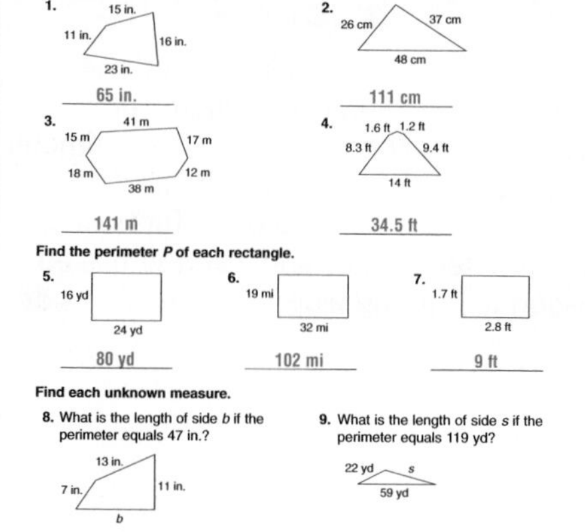

LESSON 9-7 **Practice B**
Perimeter

Find the perimeter of each figure.

1. (15 in., 11 in., 16 in., 23 in.) **65 in.**

2. (26 cm, 37 cm, 48 cm) **111 cm**

3. (41 m, 15 m, 17 m, 18 m, 12 m, 38 m) **141 m**

4. (1.6 ft, 1.2 ft, 8.3 ft, 9.4 ft, 14 ft) **34.5 ft**

Find the perimeter P of each rectangle.

5. (16 yd, 24 yd) **80 yd**

6. (19 mi, 32 mi) **102 mi**

7. (1.7 ft, 2.8 ft) **9 ft**

Find each unknown measure.

8. What is the length of side b if the perimeter equals 47 in.? (13 in., 7 in., 11 in., b) **b = 16 in.**

9. What is the length of side s if the perimeter equals 119 yd? (22 yd, s, 59 yd) **s = 38 yd**

10. Benjamin is putting a fence around his rectangular-shaped yard. The yard is 38 feet long and 27 feet wide. How many feet of fencing does Benjamin need to surround his entire yard? **130 ft of fencing**

11. If you drove from Bakersville to Salem and then to San Mateo, your entire 81-mile journey would form a triangle. The distance from Salem to San Mateo is 24 miles. The distance from Bakersville to San Mateo is 40 miles. How many miles is it from Salem to Baskerville? **17 miles**

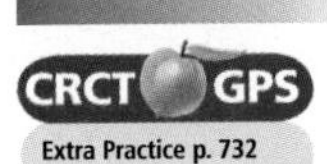
Extra Practice p. 732

PRACTICE AND PROBLEM SOLVING

Use the figure *ACDEFG* for Exercises 13–15.

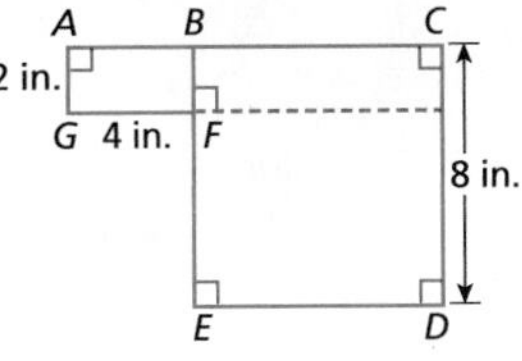

13. What is the length of side *FE*? **6 in.**
14. If the perimeter of rectangle *BCDE* is 34 in., what is the length of side *BC*? **9 in.**
15. Use your answer from Exercise 14 to find the perimeter of figure *ACDEFG*. **42 in.**

Find the perimeter of each figure.

16. a triangle with side lengths 6 in., 8 in., and 10 in. **24 in.**
17. a regular pentagon with side length $\frac{2}{5}$ km **2 km**
18. a regular dodecagon (12-sided figure) with side length 3m. **36 m**
19. **Sports** The diagram shows one-half of a badminton court.
    a. What are the dimensions of the whole court? **44 ft × 20 ft**
    b. What is the perimeter of the whole court? **128 ft**

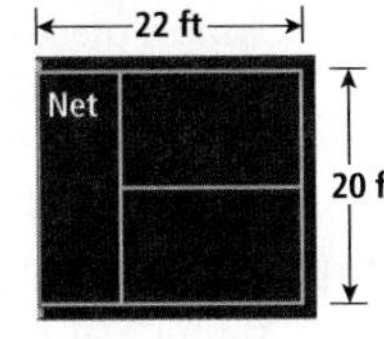

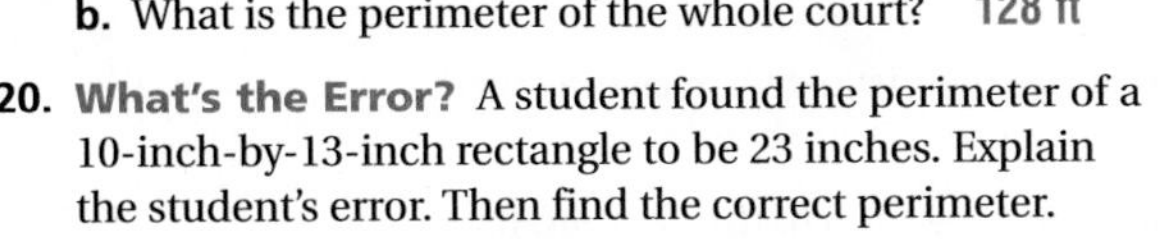

20. **What's the Error?** A student found the perimeter of a 10-inch-by-13-inch rectangle to be 23 inches. Explain the student's error. Then find the correct perimeter.
21. **Write About It** Explain how to find the unknown length of a side of a triangle that has a perimeter of 24 yd and two sides that measure 6 yd and 8 yd.
22. **Challenge** The perimeter of a regular octagon is 20 m. What is the length of one side of the octagon? **2.5 m**

CRCT PREP • GPS SUPPORT • SPIRAL REVIEW

23. **Multiple Choice** Find the perimeter of the figure.

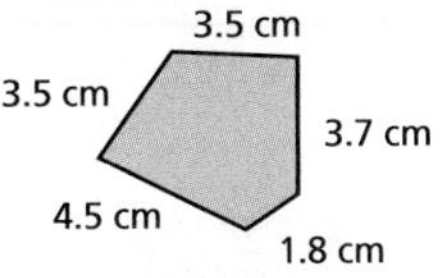

(A) 17 cm (C) 21 cm
(B) 19 cm (D) 25 cm

24. **Multiple Choice** The width of a rectangle is 16 m. What is the perimeter of the rectangle if the length is 2 times the width?

(F) 16 m (G) 32 m (H) 64 m (J) 96 m

Find each sum or difference. (Lesson 3-3)

25. 30 − 5.32 **24.68** 26. 80.31 + 15.125 **95.435** 27. 100 − 25.65 **74.35** 28. 200.6 + 1 **201.6**

Find the missing value in each proportion. (Lesson 7-3)

29. $\frac{9}{15} = \frac{x}{5}$ **$x = 3$** 30. $\frac{a}{20} = \frac{3}{15}$ **$a = 4$** 31. $\frac{1}{7} = \frac{6}{k}$ **$k = 42$** 32. $\frac{4}{5} = \frac{x}{5}$ **$x = 4$**

ONGOING ASSESSMENT and INTERVENTION

Diagnose **Before** the Lesson
9-7 Warm Up, TE p. 514

Monitor **During** the Lesson
9-7 Know-It Notebook
9-7 Questioning Strategies

Assess **After** the Lesson
9-7 Lesson Quiz, TE p. 517

Answers

20. The student did not multiply the length and width by 2 before adding. The correct perimeter is 46 inches.
21. Subtract the lengths of the known sides from the perimeter. The answer is the length of the third side.

In Exercise 24, students may find it helpful to sketch and label a figure.

Journal

Have students draw polygons and find their perimeters. Students should explain the steps they followed to find each perimeter.

CHALLENGE 9-7

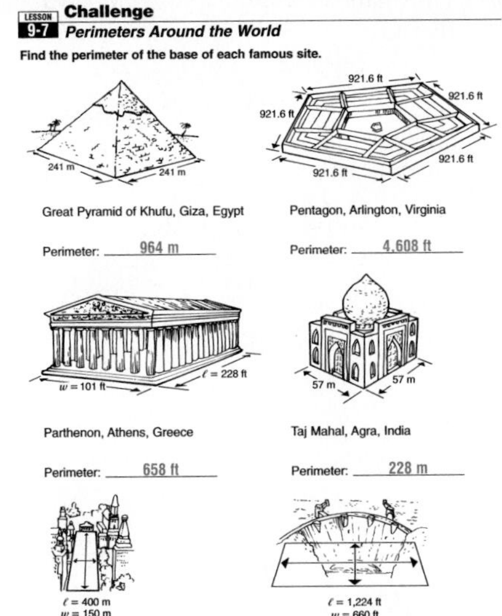

LESSON 9-7 **Challenge**
Perimeters Around the World

Find the perimeter of the base of each famous site.

Great Pyramid of Khufu, Giza, Egypt (241 m, 241 m) — Perimeter: 964 m

Pentagon, Arlington, Virginia (921.6 ft sides) — Perimeter: 4,608 ft

Parthenon, Athens, Greece (w = 101 ft, ℓ = 228 ft) — Perimeter: 658 ft

Taj Mahal, Agra, India (57 m, 57 m) — Perimeter: 228 m

Red Square, Moscow, Russia (ℓ = 400 m, w = 150 m) — Perimeter: 1,100 m

Hoover Dam, Arizona and Nevada (ℓ = 1,224 ft, w = 660 ft) — Perimeter: 3,768 ft

PROBLEM SOLVING 9-7

LESSON 9-7 **Problem Solving**
Perimeter

Write the correct answer.

1. Use a ruler to find the perimeter of your math textbook in inches. 39.5 inches
2. Use a ruler to find the perimeter of your desk in feet and inches. Answer depends on size of desk.
3. The world's largest flag weighs 3,000 pounds and requires at least 500 people to set up! This United States flag is 505 feet long and 255 feet wide. What is the perimeter of this United States flag? 1,520 feet
4. Students in Lisbon, Ohio, built the world's largest mousetrap in 1998. The mousetrap is 9 feet 10 inches long and 4 feet 5 inches wide—and it actually works! What is the perimeter of the mousetrap in feet and inches? 28 feet 6 inches

Circle the letter of the correct answer.

5. The giant ball dropped every New Year's Eve in New York City is covered with 504 crystal equilateral triangles. The average perimeter of each triangle is $15\frac{3}{4}$ inches. What is the average side length of each crystal triangle on the ball?
   A 5 inches
   B $5\frac{1}{8}$ inch
   (C) $5\frac{1}{4}$ inch
   D $5\frac{1}{2}$ inch
6. United States dollar bills are 2.61 inches wide and 6.14 inches long. Larger notes in circulation before 1919 measured 3.125 inches wide by 7.4218 inches long. What is the difference between the old and new dollar bill perimeters?
   (F) 3.5936 inches
   G 3.9536 inches
   H 4.0956 inches
   J 4.5936 inches
7. The perimeter of regular octagon-shaped swimming pool is 42 feet. What is the length of each side of the pool?
   A 5 feet
   (B) 5 feet 3 inches
   C 5 feet 2 inches
   D 5.2 feet
8. Each Scrabble® tile is 1.8 centimeters wide and 2.1 centimeters tall. If the tiles spell the word LOVE, what is the perimeter of the entire word?
   F 7.8 cm
   (G) 18.6 cm
   H 12 cm
   J 31.2 cm

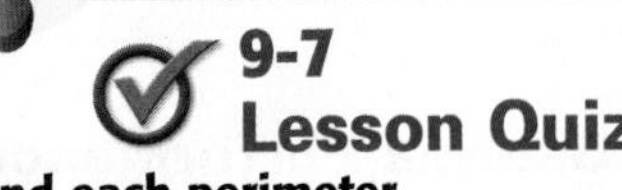

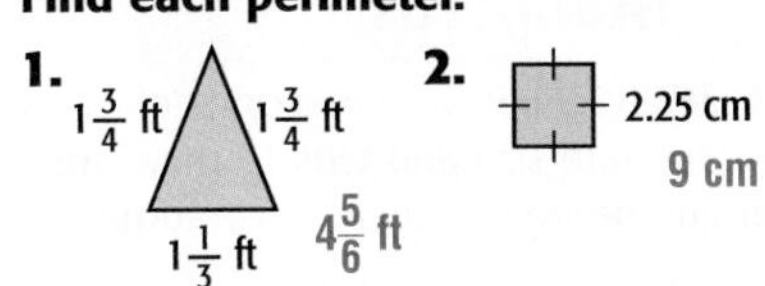

9-7 Lesson Quiz

Find each perimeter.

1. Triangle with sides $1\frac{3}{4}$ ft, $1\frac{3}{4}$ ft, $1\frac{1}{3}$ ft — **$4\frac{5}{6}$ ft**
2. Square with side 2.25 cm — **9 cm**
3. What is the perimeter of a polygon with side lengths of 15 cm, 18 cm, 21 cm, 32 cm, and 26 cm? **112 cm**
4. What is the perimeter of a rectangle with length 22 cm and width 8 cm? **60 cm**
5. The width of a rectangle is 12 in. What is the perimeter of the rectangle if the length is 7 in. longer than the width? **62 in.**

Also available on transparency

Organizer

Use with Lesson 9-8

Pacing:
Traditional 1 day
Block $\frac{1}{2}$ day

Objective: Use a compass, string, ruler, scissors, and a calculator to explore circles.

Materials: Compass, string, ruler, scissors, calculator

Online Edition

Countdown to CRCT Week 21

Resources

Hands-On Lab Activities
Lab 9-8A Recording Sheet

Teach

Discuss

Discuss with students items in the classroom that could be used to create circles with different diameters.

Georgia Performance Standards

M6M2.b Select and use units of appropriate size and type to measure length, perimeter, area and volume.

M6A2.a Analyze and describe patterns arising from mathematical rules, tables, and graphs.

M6P4.a Recognize and use connections among mathematical ideas.

M6P4.b Understand how mathematical ideas interconnect and build on one another to produce a coherent whole.

Explore Circumference

Use with Lesson 9-8

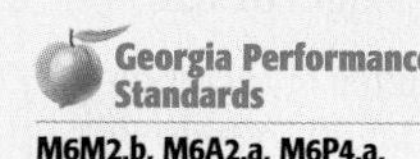

Georgia Performance Standards
M6M2.b, M6A2.a, M6P4.a, M6P4.b

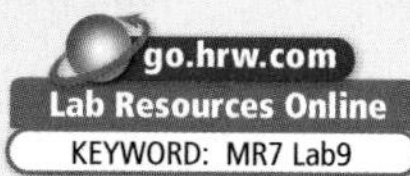

In this lab, you will measure objects to investigate the distance around a circle. The distance around a circle is called the *circumference*.

Activity 1

1. Choose a cylindrical object, such as a can or a mug. Tightly wrap a piece of string around the object, and mark the string where it meets itself. Measure this length on the string, and record it in a table like the one below as the circumference.

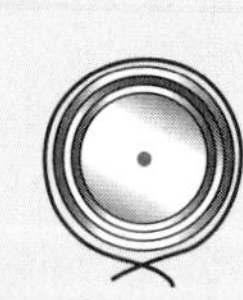

2. Using a ruler, measure the distance across the object through its center. Record this as the *diameter.*
3. Use a calculator to find the ratio of the circumference C to the diameter d. Round this value to the nearest hundredth, and record it in the table.
4. Repeat the process with three more cylindrical objects.

Possible answers:

	Object 1	Object 2	Object 3	Object 4
Circumference C	20 cm	15.2 cm	12.3 cm	5.7 cm
Diameter d	6.4 cm	4.5 cm	3.8 cm	2 cm
$\frac{C}{d}$	3.13	3.38	3.24	2.85

Think and Discuss

1. Describe what you notice about the ratio $\frac{C}{d}$ in your table. The ratio is always close to 3.

Try This

Find the ratio $\frac{C}{d}$ for each circle.

1. 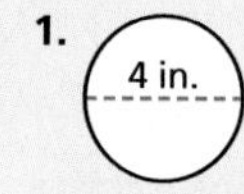

$C = 12.57$ in.
3.1425

2. 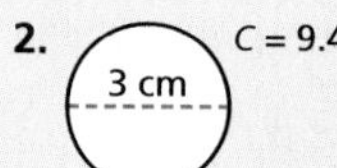

$C = 9.42$ cm
3.14

3. 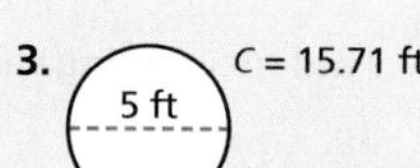

$C = 15.71$ ft
3.142

Close

Key Concept

The circumference of a circle is directly related to the diameter of the circle.

Assessment

1. How can you use string to measure a circle's circumference?
2. How can you measure a circle's diameter?
3. How do you draw a circle with a 2-inch radius?

Answers to *Assessment*

1. Wrap the string around the circle, and then unwrap the string and measure to the correct length.
2. Place the ruler so that it passes through the center, and measure from one side of the circle to the other side.
3. Open the compass so that the width between the points measures 2 inches on a ruler. Tighten the hinge and draw a circle.

The ratio of the circumference of a circle to its diameter is called *pi*, which is represented by the Greek letter π. As you saw in Activity 1, the value of π is close to 3. You can approximate π as 3.14 or $\frac{22}{7}$.

For any circle, $\frac{C}{d} = \pi$. You can solve this equation for C to give an equation for the circumference of a circle in terms of the diameter. The equation is $C = \pi d$.

Activity 2

1. Open your compass to a width of 4 cm. Use the compass to draw a circle with a radius of 4 cm. What is the diameter of the circle? **8 cm**

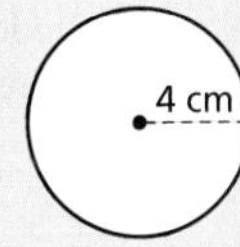

2. Use the equation $C = \pi d$ and the approximation $\pi \approx 3.14$ to predict the circumference of the circle. **25.12 cm**

3. Carefully lay a piece of string on top of the circle. Make sure the string matches the circle as closely as possible.

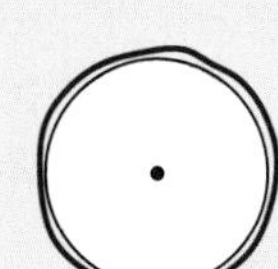

4. Mark the string where it meets itself, and measure this length.

5. Repeat the process, this time starting with a circle whose radius is 3.5 cm. Use the equation $C = \pi d$ to predict the circle's circumference, and then check the prediction by using a string to measure the circumference. **21.98 cm**

Think and Discuss

1. In each case, how did the length of the string compare with the circumference that you predicted? **The length of the string should be close to the calculated circumference.**
2. If you know the diameter of a circle, what should you do to find the circle's circumference? **Multiply by π.**
3. If you know the circumference of a circle, what should you do to find the circle's diameter? **Divide by π.**

Try This

Find the circumference of each circle. Use 3.14 for π.

1. 9 in. **28.26 in.**
2. 5 ft **15.7 ft**
3. 10 cm **31.4 cm**

9-8 Organizer

Pacing: Traditional 1 day
Block $\frac{1}{2}$ day

Objective: Students identify the parts of a circle and find the circumference of a circle.

GPS **M6A3**
Hands-On Lab
In *Hands-On Lab Activities*

Online Edition
Tutorial Videos

Countdown to CRCT Week 21

Power Presentations with PowerPoint®

Warm Up

The length and width of a rectangle are each multiplied by 5. Find how the perimeter and area of the rectangle change. The perimeter is multiplied by 5, and the area is multiplied by 25.

Problem of the Day

When using a calculator to find the width of a rectangle whose length one knew, a student accidentally multiplied by 20 when she should have divided by 20. The answer displayed was 520. What is the correct width? 1.3

Also available on transparency

Math Humor

Teacher: "Pi *r* squared. . ."
Student: "No, pie are round."

Georgia Performance Standards

M6A3 Students will evaluate algebraic expressions, including those with exponents, and solve simple one-step equations using each of the four basic operations.

M6P1.b Solve problems that arise in mathematics and in other contexts.

M6P4.c Recognize and apply mathematics in contexts outside of mathematics.

9-8 Circles and Circumference

Learn to identify the parts of a circle and to find the circumference of a circle.

Vocabulary
circle
center
radius (radii)
diameter
circumference
pi

Georgia Performance Standards
M6A3 Evaluate algebraic expressions and solve simple one-step equations using each of the four basic operations. Also, M6P1.b, M6P4.c.

The shape of a drum is a *circle*. A **circle** is the set of all points in a plane that are the same distance from a given point, called the **center**.

The length of the diameter is twice the length of the radius.

Like a polygon, a circle is a plane figure. But a circle is not a polygon because it is not made of line segments.

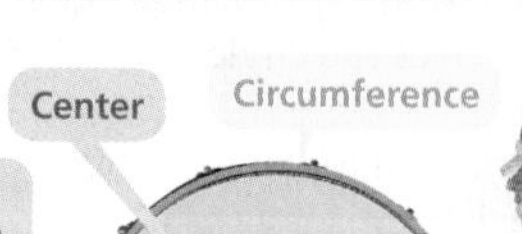

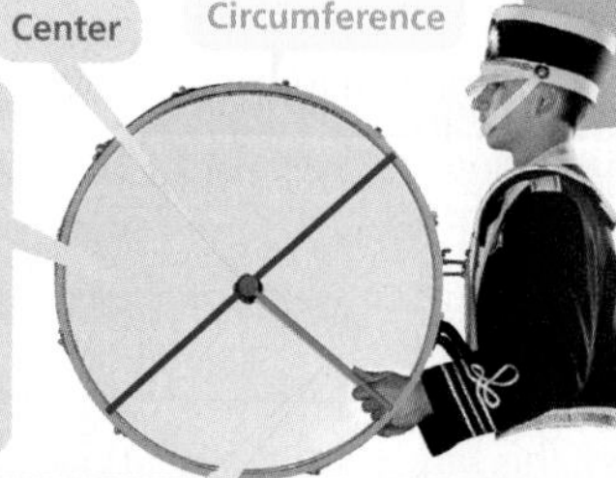

Diameter
A line segment that passes through the center of the circle and has both endpoints on the circle.

Radius (plural radii) A line segment with one endpoint at the center of the circle and the other endpoint on the circle.

EXAMPLE 1 **Naming Parts of a Circle**

Name the circle, a diameter, and three radii.

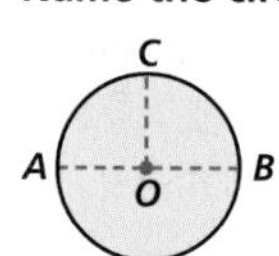

A circle is named by its center, so this is circle *O*.
$\overline{AB}$ is a diameter.
$\overline{OA}$, $\overline{OB}$, and $\overline{OC}$ are radii.

The distance around a circle is called the **circumference**.

The ratio of the circumference to the diameter, $\frac{C}{d}$, is the same for any circle. This ratio is represented by the Greek letter π, which is read " ***pi*** ."

$$\frac{C}{d} = \pi$$

The decimal representation of *pi* starts with 3.14159265 . . . and goes on forever without repeating. Most people approximate π using either 3.14 or $\frac{22}{7}$. To make multiplying by *pi* easier, you can round π to 3.

The formula for the circumference of a circle is $C = \pi d$, or $C = 2\pi r$.

1 Introduce

Alternate Opener

EXPLORATION

9-8 Circles and Circumference

People in ancient civilizations learned to estimate the distance around a circle (*circumference*) by multiplying the distance across (*diameter*) by three.

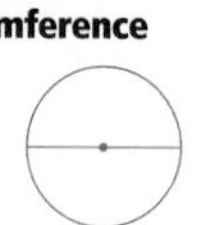

1. Does the distance around the circle above look like three times the diameter?
2. The table below contains actual measurements, to the nearest tenth of a centimeter, of two cans. Use a calculator to find the ratio $\frac{\text{circumference}}{\text{diameter}}$.

Object	Diameter (cm)	Circumference (cm)	Circumference / Diameter
Juice can	5.2	16.3	
Coffee can	15.7	49.3	

3. Are the $\frac{\text{circumference}}{\text{diameter}}$ ratios you found in number 2 reasonably close to 3?

Think and Discuss

4. **Discuss** whether the ratio $\frac{\text{circumference}}{\text{diameter}}$ changes according to the size of the circle.

Motivate

Have students name real-world items that are shaped like circles.

Possible answers: wheels, CDs, plates, clocks

Explain that, as for other plane figures, there are formulas for finding the distance around a circle.

Explorations and answers are provided in *Alternate Openers: Explorations Transparencies.*

Circumference of a Circle	
Words	**Formula**
The circumference of any circle is equal to π times the diameter, or 2π times the radius.	$C = \pi d$ or $C = 2\pi r$

EXAMPLE 2 **Architecture Application**

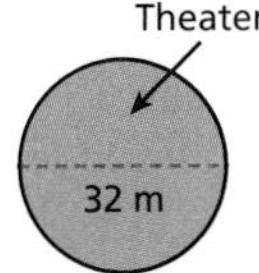

An architect is making a plan for a new circular theater. Find the circumference of the theater by rounding π to 3.

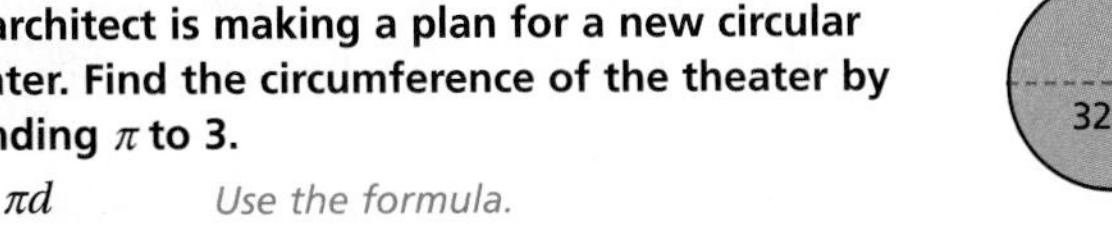

$C = \pi d$ *Use the formula.*

$C \approx 3 \cdot 32$ *Replace π with 3 and d with 32.*

$C \approx 96$ meters

The circumference of the circle is about 96 meters.

EXAMPLE 3 **Using the Formula for the Circumference of a Circle**

Find each missing value to the nearest hundredth. Use 3.14 for π.

A

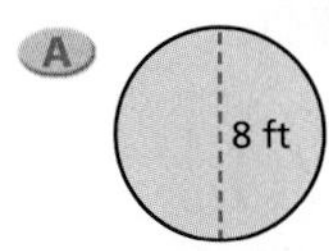

$d = 8$ ft; $C = ?$

$C = \pi d$ *Write the formula.*

$C \approx 3.14 \cdot 8$ *Replace π with 3.14 and d with 8.*

$C \approx 25.12$ ft

B

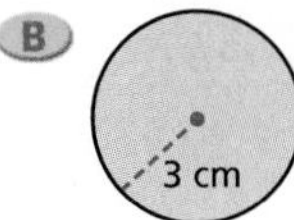

$r = 3$ cm; $C = ?$

$C = 2\pi r$ *Write the formula.*

$C \approx 2 \cdot 3.14 \cdot 3$ *Replace π with 3.14 and r with 3.*

$C \approx 18.84$ cm

C $C = 37.68$ in.; $d = ?$

$C = \pi d$ *Write the formula.*

$37.68 \approx 3.14d$ *Replace C with 37.68, and π with 3.14.*

$\frac{37.68}{3.14} \approx \frac{3.14d}{3.14}$ *Divide both sides by 3.14.*

$12.00 \text{ in.} \approx d$

Think and Discuss GPS M6P1.d, M6P2.c

1. **Explain** how to find the radius in Example 3C.
2. **Tell** whether rounding *pi* to 3 will result in an overestimation or an underestimation.
3. **Explain** why a circle is not a polygon.

Answers to *Think and Discuss:*

1. $12 \div 2 = 6$; the diameter is two times the length of the radius.
2. underestimation
3. Circles are not polygons because they are not made of line segments.

COMMON ERROR ALERT

When using the formulas for the circumference of a circle, some students may multiply the diameter by 2 or fail to multiply the radius by 2. Help the students to understand the formula $C = \pi d$ is used when the diameter is given. The formula $C = 2\pi r$ is used when the radius is given.

Power Presentations with PowerPoint®

Additional Examples

Example 1

Name the circle, a diameter, and three radii.

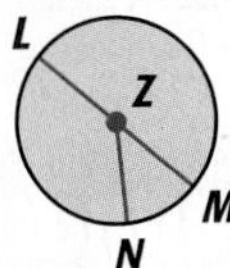

The circle is circle Z. $\overline{LM}$ is a diameter. $\overline{ZL}$, $\overline{ZM}$, and $\overline{ZN}$ are radii.

Example 2

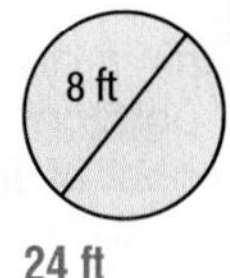

A skydiver is laying out a circular target for his next jump. Estimate the circumference of the target by rounding π to 3. **24 ft**

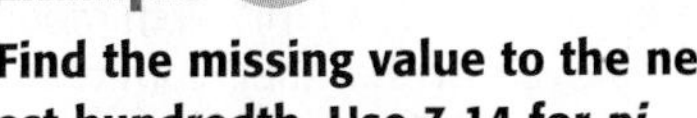

Example 3

Find the missing value to the nearest hundredth. Use 3.14 for *pi*.

A.

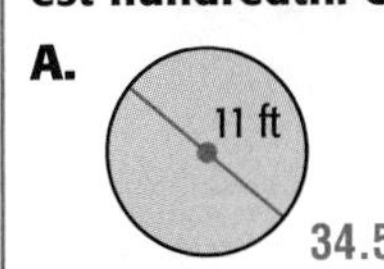

34.54 ft

$d = 11$ ft; $C = \square$

B.

5 cm

31.40 cm

$r = 5$ cm; $C = \square$

Also available on transparency

2 Teach

Guided Instruction

In this lesson, students learn to identify parts of a circle and find the circumference of a circle. Teach students parts of a circle (center, radius, diameter). Then teach the formulas for finding a circle's circumference.

Inclusion You may wish to use a CD to further illustrate the parts of a circle presented in the lesson.

Reaching All Learners

Through Critical Thinking

Use four circles to observe the influence of the different representations of pi. Provide students two circles with their diameters labeled, one in metric, and the other in customary units, as well as circles having their radii labeled, one in metric and the other in customary units. For each circle have students find the circumference using three different values for pi: 3.14, $\frac{22}{7}$, and the π button on a calculator.

3 Close

ENGLISH LANGUAGE LEARNERS

Summarize

Review the new vocabulary in the lesson: *circle, center, radius, diameter, circumference,* and *pi*. Discuss how the terms relate to each other.

9-8 Exercises

Assignment Guide

If you finished Example 1 assign:
Average 1, 22–32
Advanced 6, 22–32

If you finished Example 2 assign:
Average 1–3, 22–32
Advanced 6–8, 22–32

If you finished Example 3 assign:
Average 1–12, 17–32
Advanced 6–32

Homework Quick Check
Quickly check key concepts.
Exercises: 6, 8, 10, 12

Math Background

Around 225 B.C.E., the mathematician Archimedes inscribed regular polygons within a circle and circumscribed regular polygons about the circle. But as the number of sides in the regular polygons increase, the areas of the inscribed and circumscribed polygons move toward each other. In modern terminology, the two areas approach a limit. Archimedes was able to show that their common limit, the area of the circle, is πr^2.

Georgia Performance Standards

M6P1.b Solve problems that arise in mathematics and in other contexts.

M6P1.c Apply and adapt a variety of appropriate strategies to solve problems.

M6P3.a Organize and consolidate their mathematical thinking through communication.

9-8 Exercises

Georgia Performance Standards
M6P1.b, M6P1.c, M6P3.a

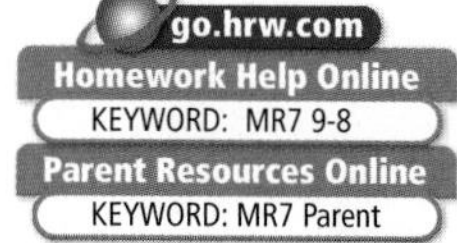

go.hrw.com
Homework Help Online
KEYWORD: MR7 9-8
Parent Resources Online
KEYWORD: MR7 Parent

GUIDED PRACTICE

See Example 1

1. Point G is the center of the circle. Name the circle, a diameter, and three radii.
circle G, diameter $\overline{EF}$, and radii $\overline{GF}$, $\overline{GE}$, and $\overline{GD}$

See Example 2

A builder is putting in a circular window. Find the circumference by rounding π to 3.

window

2. What is the circumference if the diameter is 8 feet? **24 ft**
3. What is the circumference if the radius is 2 feet? **12 ft**

See Example 3

Find each missing value to the nearest hundredth. Use 3.14 for π.

4. $C = ?$ $d = 10$ mm **31.4 mm**
5. $C = ?$ $r = 2$ in. **12.56 in.**

INDEPENDENT PRACTICE

See Example 1

6. Point P is the center of the circle. Name the circle, a diameter, and three radii.
circle P, diameter $\overline{RS}$, and radii $\overline{PR}$, $\overline{PS}$, and $\overline{PQ}$

See Example 2

A gardener is digging a circular pond and planting a circular herb garden around it. Find the circumference by rounding π to 3.

pond
garden

7. If the diameter of the pond is 5 yards, what is its circumference? **15 yd**
8. If the radius of the garden is 7 yards, what is its circumference? **42 yd**

See Example 3

Find each missing value to the nearest hundredth. Use 3.14 for π.

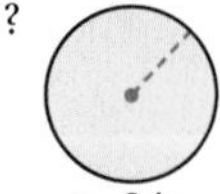

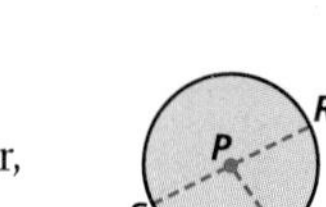

9. $C = ?$ $d = 1.5$ m **4.71 m**
10. $C = ?$ $r = 0.8$ cm **5.02 cm**
11. $d = ?$ $C = 1.57$ in. **0.5 in.**

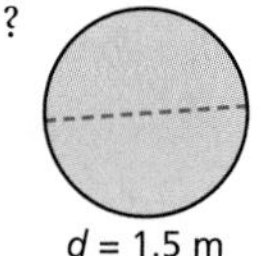

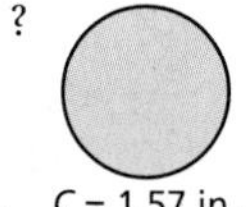

PRACTICE AND PROBLEM SOLVING

CRCT GPS
Extra Practice p. 732

Fill in the blanks. Use 3.14 for π and round to the nearest hundredth.

12. If $r = 7$ m, then $d =$ __?__, and $C =$ __?__. **14 m, 43.96 m**
13. If $d = 11.5$ ft, then $r =$ __?__, and $C =$ __?__. **5.75 ft, 36.11 ft**
14. If $C = 7.065$ cm, then $d =$ __?__, and $r =$ __?__. **2.25 cm, 1.13 cm**
15. If $C = 16.956$ in., then $d =$ __?__, and $r =$ __?__. **5.4 in., 2.7 in**

RETEACH 9-8

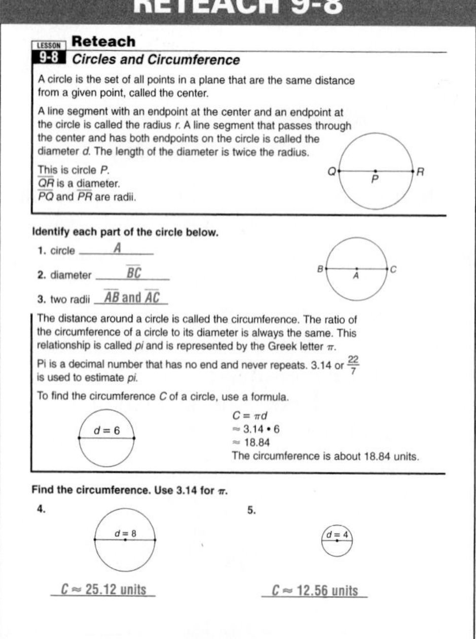

LESSON 9-8 Reteach
Circles and Circumference

A circle is the set of all points in a plane that are the same distance from a given point, called the center.

A line segment with an endpoint at the center and an endpoint at the circle is called the radius r. A line segment that passes through the center and has both endpoints on the circle is called the diameter d. The length of the diameter is twice the radius.

This is circle P.
$\overline{QR}$ is a diameter.
$\overline{PQ}$ and $\overline{PR}$ are radii.

Identify each part of the circle below.

1. circle __A__
2. diameter __$\overline{BC}$__
3. two radii __$\overline{AB}$ and $\overline{AC}$__

The distance around a circle is called the circumference. The ratio of the circumference of a circle to its diameter is always the same. This relationship is called *pi* and is represented by the Greek letter π.

Pi is a decimal number that has no end and never repeats. 3.14 or $\frac{22}{7}$ is used to estimate *pi*.

To find the circumference C of a circle, use a formula.

$C = \pi d$
$\approx 3.14 \cdot 6$
≈ 18.84
The circumference is about 18.84 units.

Find the circumference. Use 3.14 for π.

4. $d = 8$ __$C \approx 25.12$ units__
5. $d = 4$ __$C \approx 12.56$ units__

PRACTICE 9-8

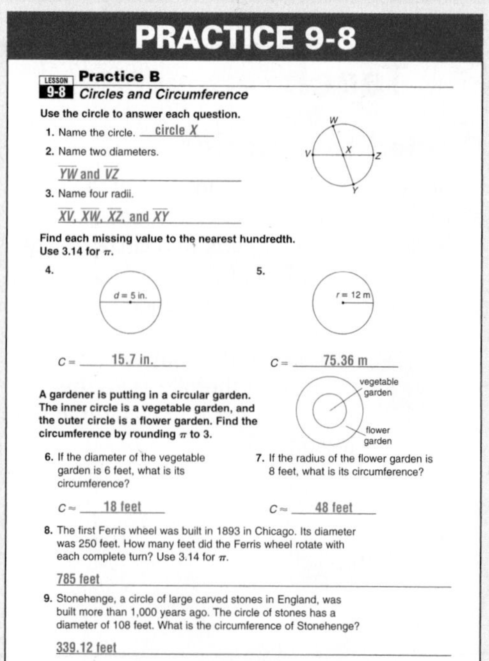

LESSON 9-8 Practice B
Circles and Circumference

Use the circle to answer each question.

1. Name the circle. __circle X__
2. Name two diameters. __$\overline{YW}$ and $\overline{VZ}$__
3. Name four radii. __$\overline{XV}$, $\overline{XW}$, $\overline{XZ}$, and $\overline{XY}$__

Find each missing value to the nearest hundredth. Use 3.14 for π.

4. $d = 5$ in. $C =$ __15.7 in.__
5. $r = 12$ m $C =$ __75.36 m__

A gardener is putting in a circular garden. The inner circle is a vegetable garden, and the outer circle is a flower garden. Find the circumference by rounding π to 3.

6. If the diameter of the vegetable garden is 6 feet, what is its circumference? $C \approx$ __18 feet__
7. If the radius of the flower garden is 8 feet, what is its circumference? $C \approx$ __48 feet__
8. The first Ferris wheel was built in 1893 in Chicago. Its diameter was 250 feet. How many feet did the Ferris wheel rotate with each complete turn? Use 3.14 for π. __785 feet__
9. Stonehenge, a circle of large carved stones in England, was built more than 1,000 years ago. The circle of stones has a diameter of 108 feet. What is the circumference of Stonehenge? __339.12 feet__

Performers like Patsy Rosales have learned to twirl multiple Hula Hoops around their bodies. The world record for most Hula Hoops kept in revolution is held by Yana Rodinova who kept 95 of them spinning.

16. **Measurement** Draw a circle. Name the center P and make the radius 2 in. long.
    a. Draw the diameter $\overline{AB}$ and give its length.
    b. Find the circumference. Use 3.14 for π. Round your answer to the nearest hundredth. **12.56 in.**

17. **History** The first Hula Hoop® was introduced in 1958. What is the circumference of a Hula Hoop with a 3 ft diameter? Use 3.14 for π. **9.42 ft**

Use the cylinders for Exercises 18 and 19.

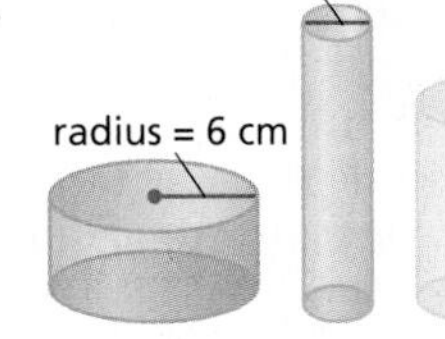

18. **Estimation** About how many times greater is the circumference of the top of the purple cylinder than the top of the blue cylinder?

19. **Choose a Strategy** If the circumference of the top of the yellow cylinder is 22.5 centimeters, which method can you use to find the radius?
    (A) Divide 22.5 by π.
    (B) Multiply 22.5 by π.
    (C) Divide 22.5 by π and then divide the quotient by 2.
    (D) Multiply 22.5 by π and then multiply the product by 2.

20. **Write About It** The circumference of a circle is 3.14 m. Explain how you can find the diameter and radius of the circle.

21. **Challenge** An Olympic outdoor archery target is made up of 10 equally spaced concentric circles. *Concentric* means that the center of each of the circles is the same. If the diameter of the biggest ring on the target is 122 cm and the diameter of the bullseye is 12.2 centimeters, what is the diameter of the fourth ring from the inside? **61 cm**

18. The purple cylinder's circumference is about three times greater than the blue cylinder.

CRCT Prep • GPS Support • Spiral Review

22. **Multiple Choice** A mini-DVD has a radius of 4 centimeters. Which expression can you use to find the circumference of the mini-DVD?
    (A) 4π **(B)** 8π (C) 16π (D) $2 \cdot 2 \cdot \pi \cdot 8$

23. **Short Response** The wheels on Ryan's bike are each about 2 feet in diameter. If Ryan rides his bike for 1 mile, about how many times will each wheel rotate? Use 3 for π. **880 revolutions**

Order the fractions from greatest to least. (Lesson 4-7)

24. $\frac{1}{2}, \frac{3}{8}, \frac{5}{8}$ **$\frac{5}{8}, \frac{1}{2}, \frac{3}{8}$**
25. $\frac{3}{4}, \frac{10}{12}, \frac{1}{12}$ **$\frac{10}{12}, \frac{3}{4}, \frac{1}{12}$**
26. $\frac{3}{10}, \frac{3}{5}, \frac{7}{10}$ **$\frac{7}{10}, \frac{3}{5}, \frac{3}{10}$**
27. $\frac{7}{16}, \frac{3}{4}, \frac{5}{8}$ **$\frac{3}{4}, \frac{5}{8}, \frac{7}{16}$**

Write each percent as a decimal. (Lesson 7-7)

28. 50% **0.50** 29. 5% **0.05** 30. 85% **0.85** 31. 100% **1** 32. 15% **0.15**

ONGOING ASSESSMENT and INTERVENTION

Diagnose ***Before*** **the Lesson**
9-8 Warm Up, TE p. 520

Monitor ***During*** **the Lesson**
9-8 Know-It Notebook
9-8 Questioning Strategies

Assess ***After*** **the Lesson**
9-8 Lesson Quiz, TE p. 523

Answers

16. a.

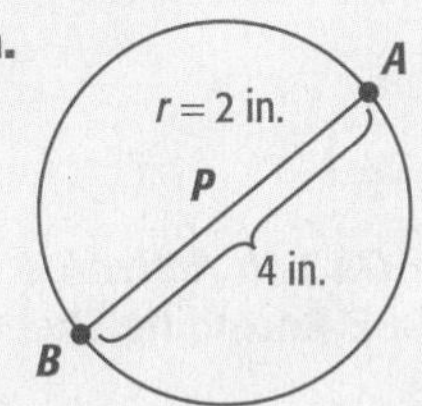

20. Use the formula for the circumference of a circle, $C = \pi d$. So $3.14 = 3.14d$, $d = 1$ in., and $r = 0.5$ in.

In Exercise 22, students choosing **A** might have confused radius with diameter. A choice of **C** indicates that the radius was squared when it should have been multiplied by 2. A student unfamiliar with the formulas for the circumference of a circle might have chosen **D**.

Journal

Have students use a compass to draw a circle. Have students label the center, a radius, and a diameter on the circle. Have students also find the circumference of the circle.

CHALLENGE 9-8

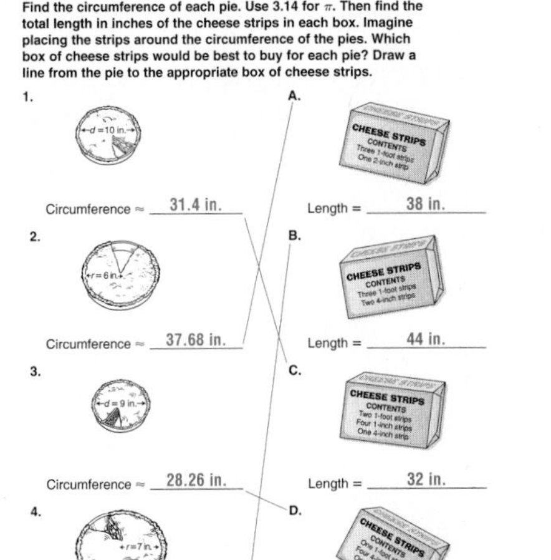

LESSON 9-8 **Challenge**
Cheesy Pies

Have you ever seen strips of cheese placed around the edge of an apple pie? I am sure you will agree that "cheesy pies" sound very tasty indeed.

Find the circumference of each pie. Use 3.14 for π. Then find the total length in inches of the cheese strips in each box. Imagine placing the strips around the circumference of the pies. Which box of cheese strips would be best to buy for each pie? Draw a line from the pie to the appropriate box of cheese strips.

1. $d = 10$ in. Circumference ≈ **31.4 in.**
2. $r = 6$ in. Circumference ≈ **37.68 in.**
3. $d = 9$ in. Circumference ≈ **28.26 in.**
4. $r = 7$ in. Circumference ≈ **43.96 in.**

A. CHEESE STRIPS CONTENTS: Three 1-foot strips, One 2-inch strip. Length = **38 in.**
B. CHEESE STRIPS CONTENTS: Three 1-foot strips, Two 4-inch strips. Length = **44 in.**
C. CHEESE STRIPS CONTENTS: Two 1-foot strips, Four 1-inch strips, One 4-inch strip. Length = **32 in.**
D. CHEESE STRIPS CONTENTS: One 1-foot strip, Four 4-inch strips, One 1-inch strip. Length = **29 in.**

PROBLEM SOLVING 9-8

LESSON 9-8 **Problem Solving**
Circles and Circumference

Use the table to answer each question. Use 3.14 for π.

Official U.S. Coin Sizes

Coin	**Diameter** (rounded to nearest mm)
Penny	19
Nickel	21
Dime	18
Quarter	24
Half Dollar	31
Dollar	27

1. Which coin has the smallest radius? How long is that coin's radius?
   dime; 9 mm
2. What is the circumference of a nickel?
   65.94 mm
3. What is the circumference of a quarter?
   75.36 mm
4. Which coin has a greater circumference, a dollar or half dollar? What is the difference in their circumferences?
   half dollar; 12.56 mm
5. If you rolled a dollar coin on its edge, how far would it go with each complete turn?
   84.78 mm
6. Which U.S. coins will fit in a vending machine coin slot that is 2 centimeters wide?
   penny and dime

Circle the letter of the correct answer.

7. A dime has 118 ridges evenly spaced along its circumference. About how wide is each ridge?
   A about 0.24 mm
   (B) about 0.48 mm
   C about 0.15 mm
   D about 0.08 mm
8. The engraved words "United States of America" run about one-half the circumference of all U.S. coins. On which coin will the words run about 38 mm?
   F penny **(H)** quarter
   G dime J half dollar
9. You have two coins with a total circumference of 116.18 mm. How much money do you have?
   A $0.02 **(C)** $0.11
   B $0.06 D $0.35
10. You have three coins with a total circumference of 216.66 mm. How much money do you have?
    F $0.15 H $0.30
    G $0.25 **(J)** $0.55

Power Presentations with PowerPoint®

9-8 Lesson Quiz

Find the circumference of each circle. Use 3.14 for π.

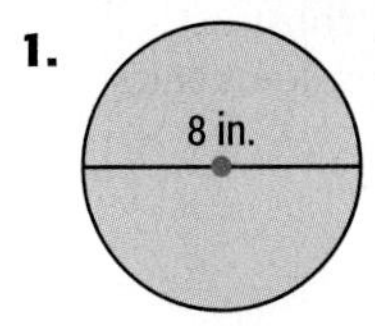

1. $C = 25.12$ in. 2. $C = 18.84$ in.

3. Find the circumference of a circle with a diameter of 20 feet. Use 3.14 for π. **62.8 ft**

Also available on transparency

Organizer

Use with Lesson 9-8

Pacing:
Traditional 1 day
Block $\frac{1}{2}$ day

Objective: Use a compass, straightedge, and protractor to construct circle graphs.

Materials: Compass, straightedge, and protractor

Online Edition

Countdown to CRCT Week 21

Resources

Hands-On Lab Activities
Lab 9-8B Recording Sheet

Teach

Discuss

Have students practice using the compass and protractor to construct circles and angles.

Construct Circle Graphs

Use with Lesson 9-8

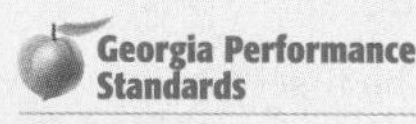

Georgia Performance Standards
M6D1.a, M6D1.b

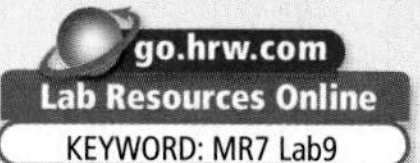

go.hrw.com
Lab Resources Online
KEYWORD: MR7 Lab9

REMEMBER
The sum of the measures of the angles in any circle is 360°.

A circle graph shows parts of a whole. If you think of a complete circle as 100%, you can express sections of a circle graph as percents.

- Ms. Shipley's class earned \$400 at the school fair. What fraction of the \$400 did the class earn at the bake sale? $\frac{1}{2}$
- What percent of the \$400 did the class earn at the bake sale? **50%**

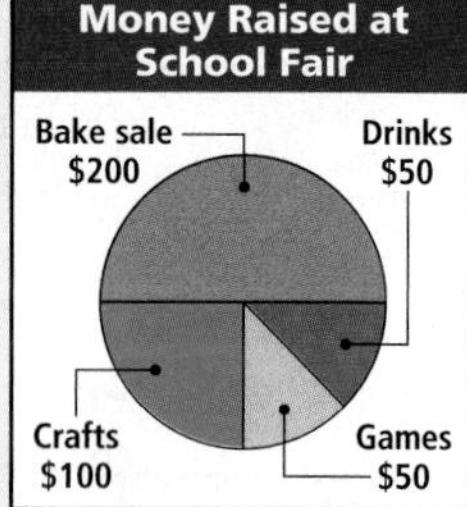

Activity

At Mazel Middle School, students were surveyed about their favorite types of TV programs. Make a circle graph to represent the results.

Students' Favorite Programs	
Type of Program	**Number of Students**
Science	25
Cooking	15
Sports	50
Sitcoms	150
Movies	60
Cartoons	200

1. Find the total number of students surveyed.

$$25 + 15 + 50 + 150 + 60 + 200 = 500$$

2. Find the percent of the total represented by students who like science programs.

$$\frac{25}{500} = 5\%$$

3. Since there are 360° in a circle, multiply 5% by 360°. This will give you an angle measure in degrees.

$$0.05 \cdot 360° = 18°$$

4. Use a compass to draw a circle. Mark the center and use a straightedge to draw a line from the center to the edge of the circle.

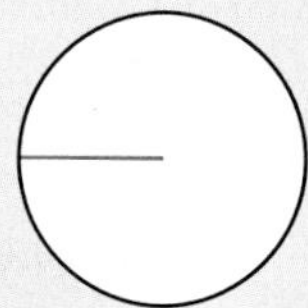

Close

Key Concept

Sections of a circle can represent percents if the whole circle represents 100%.

Assessment

Use the compass to draw a circle with the given radius. Mark the center and label it *C*. Use a straightedge to draw a radius.

1. $r = \frac{3}{8}$ in.

Use a protractor to draw angles with the given measurements.

2. 32°

3. 115°

Answers to *Assessment*

1.

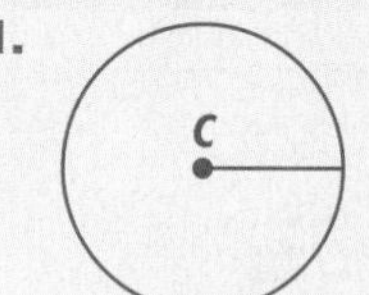

2.

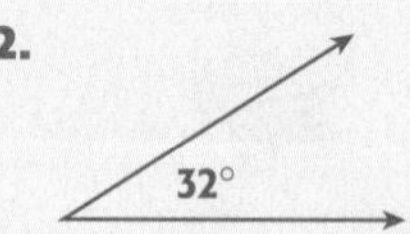

3.

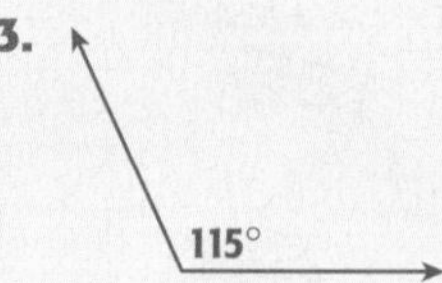

Georgia Performance Standards

M6D1.a Formulate questions that can be answered by data. Students should collect data by using samples from a larger population (surveys), or by conducting experiments.

M6D1.b Using data, construct frequency distributions, frequency tables, and graphs.

5. Use your protractor to draw an angle measuring 18°. The vertex of the angle will be the center of the circle, and one side will be the line that you drew. The section formed represents the percent of students who prefer science programs.

6. Repeat 2 through 5 for each type of program. Label each section, and give the graph a title.

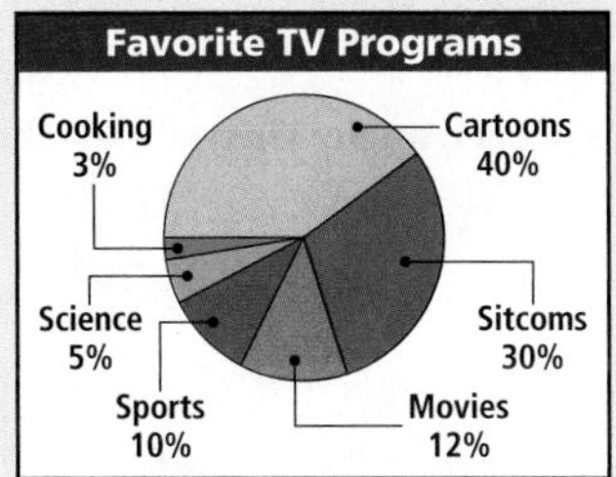

Think and Discuss

1. Looking at your circle graph, discuss five pieces of information you have learned about the TV habits of students at Mazel Middle School.
2. What does the whole circle represent? **all of the students surveyed**
3. Why do you need to know that there are 360° in a circle?
4. How does the size of each section of your circle graph relate to the percent that it represents?
   Larger percentages have larger sections; smaller percentages have smaller sections.

Try This

1. People at a mall were surveyed about their favorite pets. Make a circle graph to display the results of the survey. Round to the nearest tenth.

Favorite Pets	
Type of Pet	**Number of People**
Dog	225
Fish	150
Bird	112
Cat	198
Other	65

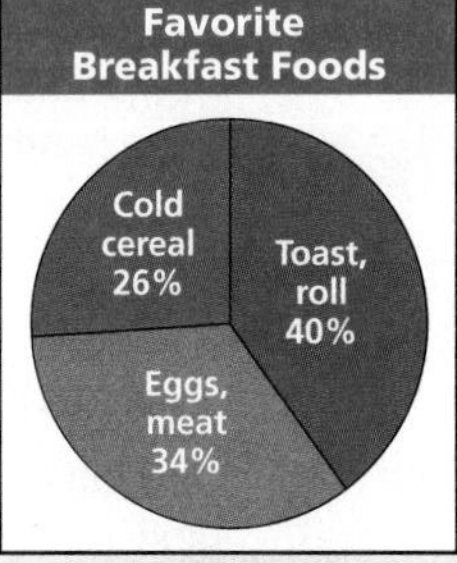

2. Collect data from your classmates about their favorite colors. Use the data to make a circle graph with no more than five sections.
   Check students' work.
3. The circle graph shows the results of a survey about what people in the United States like to eat for breakfast. If this survey included 1,500 people, how many people said they like to eat cereal for breakfast? **390**

Answers to *Think and Discuss*

1. Possible answer: The most popular kind of TV show is cartoons and the least popular is cooking shows. 4 out of 10 students like cartoons the best, 3 out of 10 students like sitcoms the best, and 1 out of 10 like sports the best.
3. To find the number of degrees each section should have, you must multiply the percent the section represents by the total number of degrees in a circle.

Answers to *Try This*

1. 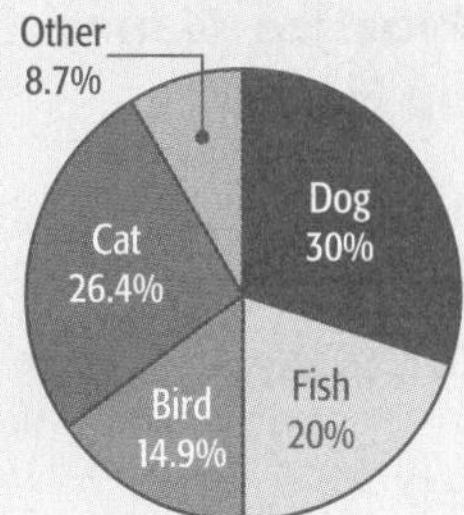

Organizer

Objective: Assess students' mastery of concepts and skills in Lessons 9-6 through 9-8.

Resources

Assessment Resources
Section 9B Quiz

INTERVENTION 

Resources

***Ready to Go On? Intervention and Enrichment* Worksheets**

***Ready to Go On?* CD-ROM**

***Ready to Go On?* Online**

my.hrw.com

Answers

9. circle D; $\overline{DH}$ and $\overline{DG}$ are radii; $C = 9.42$ in.
10. circle I; $\overline{IG}$ and $\overline{IF}$ are radii; $C = 51.81$ km
11. circle K; $\overline{KJ}$, $\overline{KM}$, and $\overline{KL}$ are radii; $C = 131.88$ cm

SECTION 9B

Ready to Go On?

Quiz for Lessons 9-6 Through 9-8

9-6 Finding Angle Measures in Polygons

Use a protractor to find the measure of each angle. Then classify the angle.

1. 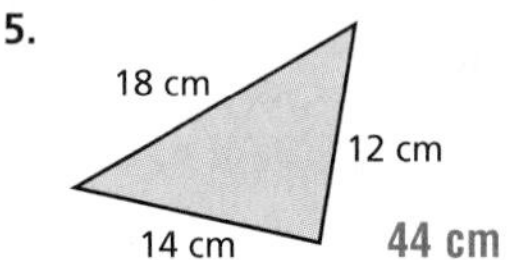 45°; acute
2. 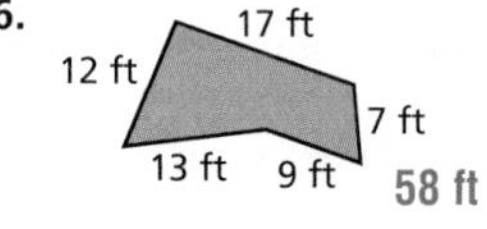 120°; obtuse
3. 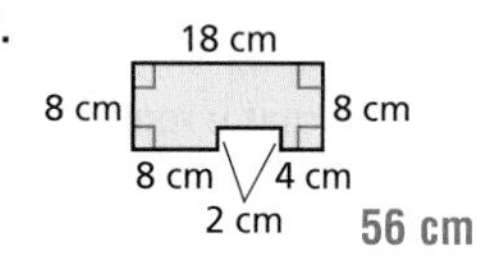 90°; right

4. A garden plot is shown at right. Find the measures of $\angle A$ and $\angle B$. $\angle A = 85°$; $\angle B = 95°$

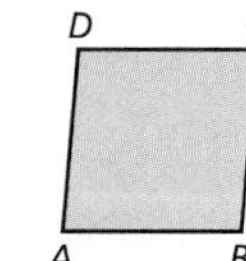

9-7 Perimeter

Find the perimeter of each figure.

5. 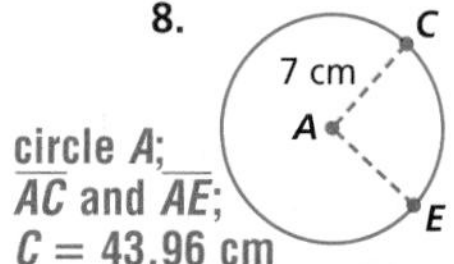

44 cm

6. 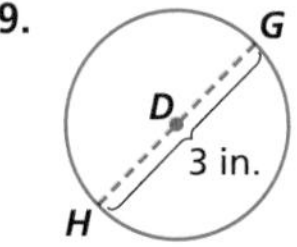

58 ft

7. 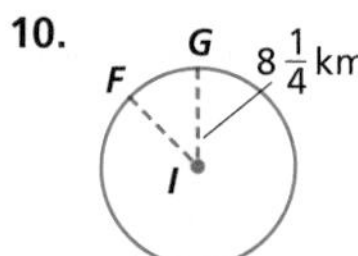

56 cm

9-8 Circles and Circumference

Name the circle and two radii, and then find the circumference for each circle. Use 3.14 for π and round to the nearest hundredth.

8.
circle A; $\overline{AC}$ and $\overline{AE}$; $C = 43.96$ cm

9.

10.

11. 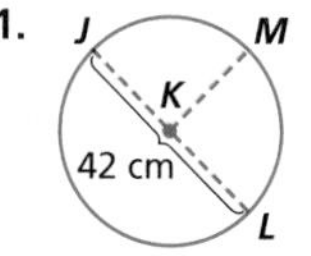

12. An architect is making a plan for a new circular playground. Find the circumference of the playground by rounding π to 3. 192 m

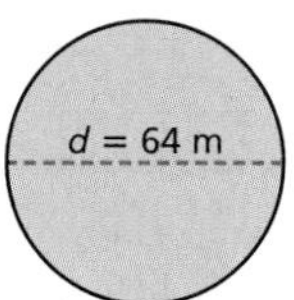

Find each missing value to the nearest hundredth. Use 3.14 for π.

13. $r = 9$ in.; $C =$ ___?___ 56.52 in.
14. $d = 20$ m; $C =$ ___?___ 62.8 m
15. $C = 37.68$ ft; $d =$ ___?___ 12 ft

READY TO GO ON?
Diagnose and Prescribe

NO — INTERVENE

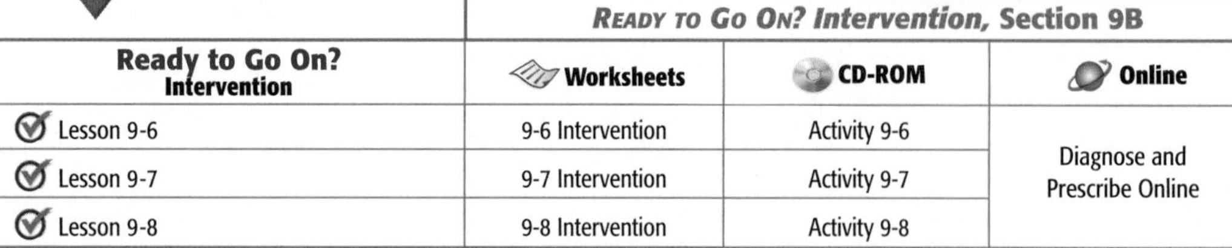

Ready to Go On? Intervention	*Ready to Go On?* Intervention, Section 9B — Worksheets	CD-ROM	Online
Lesson 9-6	9-6 Intervention	Activity 9-6	Diagnose and Prescribe Online
Lesson 9-7	9-7 Intervention	Activity 9-7	
Lesson 9-8	9-8 Intervention	Activity 9-8	

YES — ENRICH

***Ready to Go On?* Enrichment, Section 9B**

 Worksheets

 CD-ROM

 Online

MULTI-STEP TEST PREP

Fenced In The Midland Botanical Gardens has a rectangular bed of dahlias and a circular bed of tulips. The garden's landscaper has decided to install new fences around both of the flower beds.

1. The length of the dahlia bed is 3 feet longer than its width. What is the perimeter of the dahlia bed?
2. The new fence for the dahlia bed is available in sections that are each 18 inches long. How many sections should the landscaper order? Explain.
3. What is the circumference of the tulip bed to the nearest meter? Round *pi* to 3.
4. The new fence for the tulip bed is available in sections that are each 44 cm long. How many sections should the landscaper order? Explain.
5. The landscaper can install one section of a fence in 6 minutes. How long will it take to install the fences for both beds? Will the landscaper be able to complete the job in less than 5 hours? Why or why not?

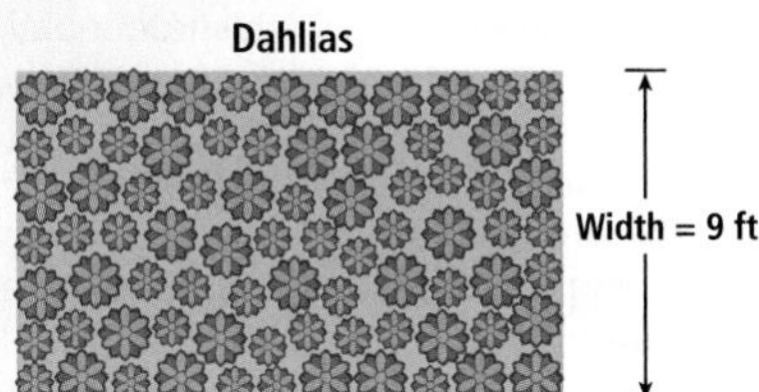

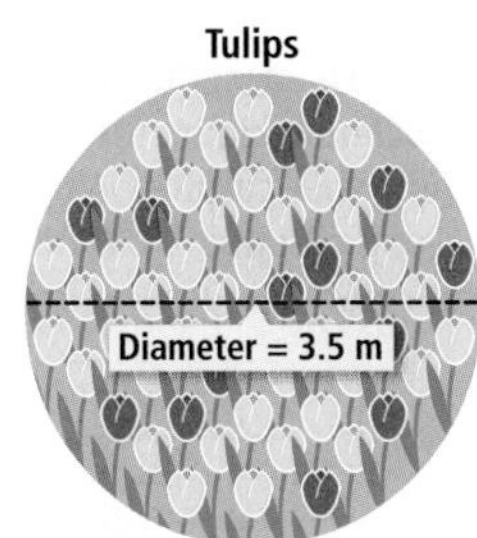

Multi-Step Test Prep

INTERVENTION

Scaffolding Questions

1. What is the length of the dahlia bed? 12 ft How can you find the perimeter of the bed? Use $P = 2\ell + 2w$.
2. What should you do first in order to solve this problem? Possible answer: Convert the perimeter to inches. How can you convert 42 ft to inches? $42 \text{ ft} \cdot \frac{12 \text{ in.}}{1 \text{ ft}} = 504 \text{ in.}$ How can you find the number of fence sections needed? Divide 504 in. by 18 in.
3. What is the formula for finding the circumference of a circle? $C = \pi d$ What is the diameter in this case? 3.5 m
4. What should you do first in order to solve this problem? Possible answer: Convert the circumference to centimeters. How can you convert 11 m to centimeters? $11 \text{ m} \cdot \frac{100 \text{ cm}}{1 \text{ m}} = 1{,}100 \text{ cm}$ How can you find the number of fence sections needed? Divide 1,100 cm by 44 cm.
5. How many fence sections will be installed altogether? 53 How can you find the total time it will take to install them? Multiply $53 \times 6 \text{ min} = 318 \text{ min}$. How do you convert 318 min to hours? $318 \text{ min} \cdot \frac{1 \text{ hr}}{60 \text{ min}} = 5.3 \text{ hr}$

Extension

The landscaper begins installing the fences at 10:30 A.M. At what time will the job be finished? 3:48 P.M.

Organizer

Objective: Assess students' ability to apply concepts and skills in Chapter 9 in a real-world format.

Online Edition

Resources

Middle School Assessments
www.mathtekstoolkit.org

Problem	Text reference
1	Lesson 9-7
2	Lesson 9-7
3	Lesson 9-8
4	Lesson 9-8
5	Lesson 9-5

Answers

1. 42 ft
2. 28 sections. The perimeter is 42 ft, which can be converted to 504 in., and $504 \div 18 = 28$
3. 11 m
4. 25 sections. The circumference is 11 m, which can be converted to 1,100 cm, and $1{,}100 \div 44 = 25$
5. 318 minutes. This can be converted to 5.3 hours, so the landscaper will not be able to complete the job in less than 5 hours.

Game Time

Organizer

Objective: Participate in games to practice and apply skills learned in Chapter 9.

Online Edition

Resources

Chapter 9 Resource Book
Puzzles, Twisters & Teasers

Logic Puzzle

Purpose: To apply problem-solving skills to a logic puzzle

Discuss Ask students to explain how the chart works. How can you use the chart to solve the puzzle? Use each clue to place *O*'s and *X*'s in the appropriate squares. When a row or column of squares has 4 *X*'s, the fifth square must contain an *O*. Clues sometimes give information in a way that is not straightforward. What can you conclude about Angela's choice of restaurant, using clues 1 and 3? Angela did not choose tacos, because she did not participate on Friday.

Extend Have students construct a chart and solve the following logic problem: Four boys are going to sports practice. Their names are Mike, Kurt, Paul, and Andy. Each one plays a different sport (baseball, soccer, basketball, or tennis) and has a different color of hat (black, red, blue, or white). Paul does not like to wear red and carries an orange ball. The boy with the blue hat is carrying a racket. Kurt does not play soccer. Mike uses a bat and wears a black hat. The soccer player wears a red hat.

Mike: baseball, black
Kurt: tennis, blue
Paul: basketball, white
Andy: soccer, red
Check students' charts.

Game Time

Logic Puzzle

Each day from Monday through Friday, Mayuri, Naomi, Brett, Thomas, and Angela took turns picking a restaurant for lunch. They ate at restaurants that serve either Chinese food, hamburgers, pizza, seafood, or tacos. Use the clues below to determine which student picked the restaurant on each day and which restaurant the student picked.

1. Angela skipped Friday's lunch to play in a basketball game.
2. Brett picked the restaurant on Wednesday.
3. The students ate tacos on Friday.
4. Naomi is allergic to seafood and volunteered to pick the first restaurant.
5. Thomas picked a hamburger restaurant on the day before another student chose a pizza restaurant.

You can use a chart like the one below to help you solve this puzzle. Place an *O* in a square for something that is true and an *X* in a square for something that cannot be true. Remember that when you place an *O* in a square, you can put *X*'s in the rest of the squares in that row and column. The information from the first two clues has been entered for you.

		Student					Restaurant				
		Mayuri	Naomi	Brett	Thomas	Angela	Seafood	Pizza	Hamburger	Chinese	Tacos
Day	Monday	X	0	X	X	X	X	X	X	0	X
	Tuesday	X	X	X	0	X	X	X	0	X	X
	Wednesday	X	X	O	X	X	X	0	X	X	X
	Thursday	X	X	X	X	0	0	X	X	X	X
	Friday	0	X	X	X	X	X	X	X	X	0
Restaurant	Seafood	X	X	X	X	0					
	Pizza	X	X	0	X	X					
	Hamburgers	X	X	X	0	X					
	Chinese	X	0	X	X	X					
	Tacos	0	X	X	X	X					

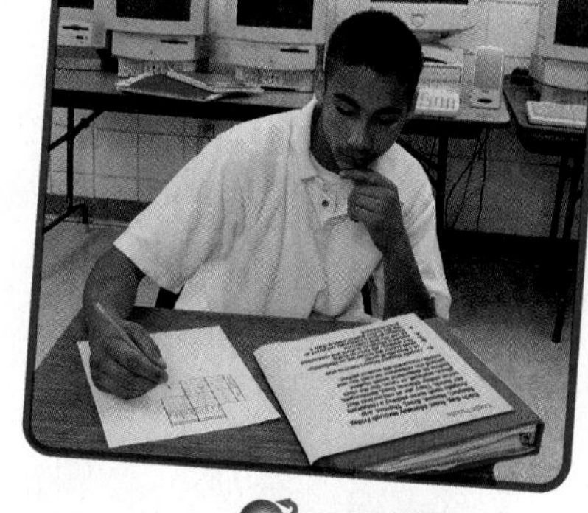

A copy of a blank logic puzzle chart is available online.

go.hrw.com
Game Time Extra
KEYWORD: MR7 Games

Answers

Mayuri: tacos, Friday
Naomi: Chinese, Monday
Brett: pizza, Wednesday
Thomas: hamburgers, Tuesday
Angela: seafood, Thursday

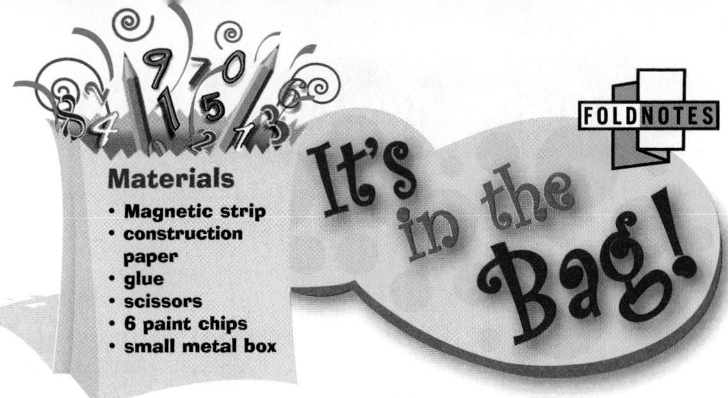

Perfectly Packaged Perimeters

This metal box stores magnetic vocabulary tiles and small squares that you can use to create a variety of shapes.

Directions

1. Glue construction paper onto the magnetic strip.
2. Write vocabulary words from this chapter on the magnetic strip. Then cut the words apart to form magnetic vocabulary tiles. **Figure A**
3. Cut the paint chips into smaller squares, each approximately $1\frac{1}{4}$ inches by $1\frac{1}{4}$ inches.
4. Glue a small piece of construction paper onto the lid of the metal box. Label it with the number and title of the chapter. **Figure B**
5. Store the vocabulary tiles and the small squares in the metal box.

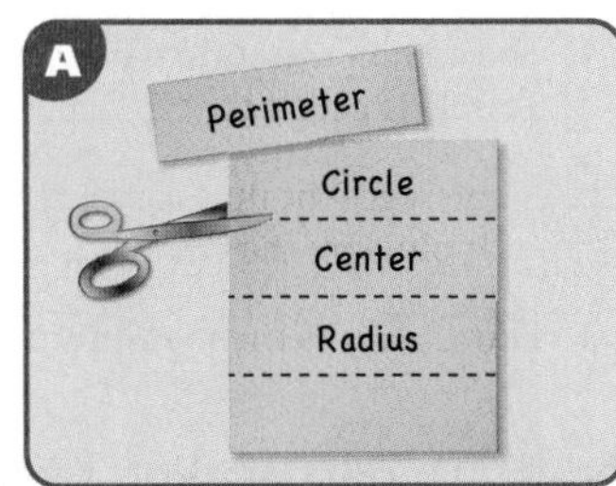

Putting the Math into Action

Place the vocabulary tiles on the outside of the box or on another metal surface to review key terms from the chapter. Arrange the small squares to form shapes with various perimeters. What is the greatest perimeter you can make?

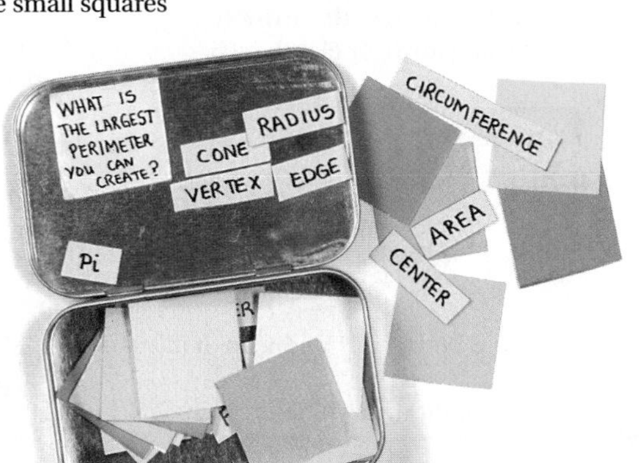
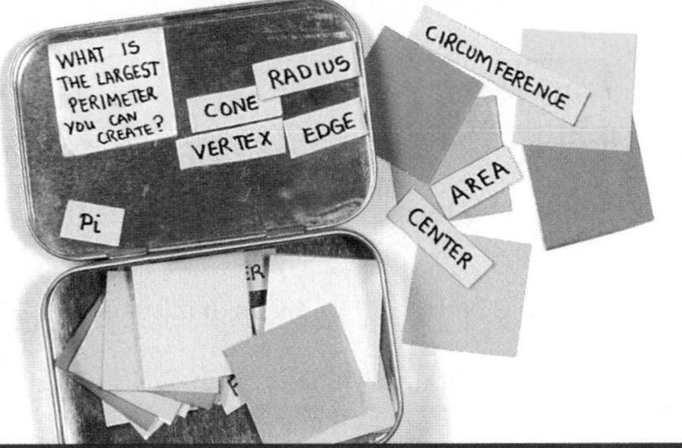

Flexible magnetic strips are available in rolls at hardware and home-improvement stores. If paint chips are not available, you can have students cut out 1-inch squares from card stock, empty cereal boxes, or pieces of recycled cardboard.

We sometimes have students make activity cards by writing problems and challenges on the backs of business cards. The cards are just the right size to store in the metal box along with everything else.

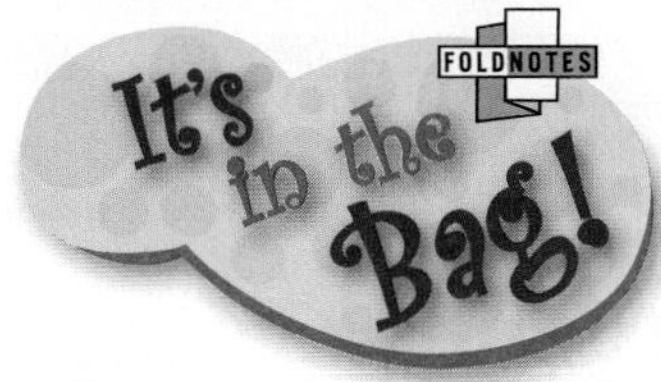

Organizer

Objective: Make a box that stores magnetic vocabulary tiles and small squares that can be used to create a variety of shapes.

Materials: magnetic strip, construction paper, glue, scissors, 6 paint chips, small metal box

Online Edition

Using the Page

Preparing the Materials
Several days before you begin the project, ask students to save any small metal containers that are used to package mints, teas, and other foods.

Making the Project
Remind students to write their vocabulary words on the magnetic strip before cutting it apart into rectangular tiles. This will ensure that the words fit on the magnetic tiles.

Extending the Project
Have pairs of students pool the squares that they made from the paint chips. Challenge the teams to arrange all of their squares into the shapes with the greatest possible perimeter and the least possible perimeter.

CHAPTER 9 **Study Guide: Review**

Organizer

Objective: Help students organize and review key concepts and skills presented in Chapter 9.

Online Edition
Multilingual Glossary

Resources

***Multilingual Glossary* Online**

go.hrw.com
KEYWORD: MR7 Glossary

Lesson Tutorial Videos
CD-ROM

Answers

1. perimeter, circumference
2. diameter
3. customary system
4. in.; about seven widths of your thumb
5. mi; about 800 times 18 football fields
6. lb; about 2 loaves of bread
7. fl oz; about a spoonful
8. $1\frac{1}{8}$ in.

CHAPTER 9

Study Guide: Review

Study Guide: Review

Vocabulary

center	520	metric system	492
circle	520	perimeter	514
circumference	520	*pi*	520
customary system	488	radius (radii)	520
diameter	520		

Complete the sentences below with vocabulary words from the list above.

1. The distance around a polygon is called the __?__, and the distance around a circle is called the __?__.
2. A line segment that passes through the center of a circle and has both endpoints on the circle is a __?__.
3. The __?__ is the measurement system often used in the United States.

9-1 Understanding Customary Units of Measure (pp. 488–491)

GPS M6M2.b

EXAMPLE

- **What unit of measure provides the best estimate? Explain.**

A desk is about 3 __?__ long.

Think: The length of a desk is about 3 times the distance from your shoulder to your elbow.

A desk is about 3 ft long.

Measure the length of the arrow to the nearest half, fourth, or eighth inch.

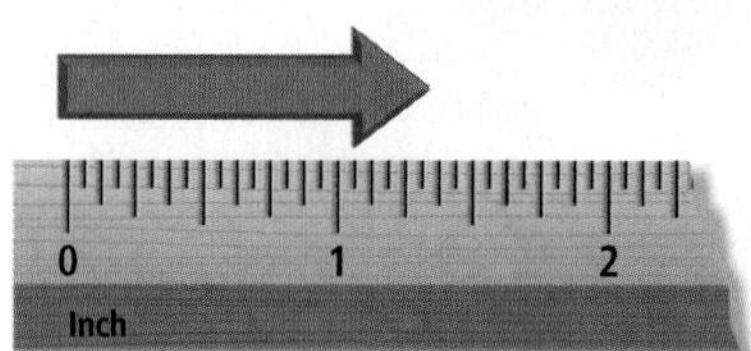

The arrow is between $1\frac{1}{4}$ and $1\frac{3}{8}$ in. It is closer to $1\frac{3}{8}$.
The length of the arrow is about $1\frac{3}{8}$ in.

EXERCISES

What unit of measure provides the best estimate? Explain.

4. A crayon is about 5 __?__ long.
5. The distance from Denver, CO, to Dallas, TX, is about 800 __?__.
6. A bunch of bananas weighs about 2 __?__.
7. An eyedropper holds about 1 __?__ of liquid.
8. Measure the length of the arrow to the nearest half, fourth, or eighth inch.

9-2 Understanding Metric Units of Measure (pp. 492–495)

GPS M6M2.b

EXAMPLE

- **What unit of measure provides the best estimate? Explain.**

A sofa is about 3 __?__ long.

Think: The length of a sofa is about 3 times the width of a single bed.

A sofa is about 3 m long.

Measure the length of the arrow to the nearest centimeter.

The arrow is between 2 and 3 cm. It is closer to 2 cm.

The length of the arrow is about 2 cm.

EXERCISES

What unit of measure provides the best estimate? Explain.

9. A paper clip is about 32 __?__ long.
10. A grain of rice has a mass of about 5 __?__.
11. A laptop computer has a mass of about 2 __?__.
12. A large pitcher has a capacity of about 2 __?__.
13. Measure the length of the arrow to the nearest centimeter.

9-3 Converting Customary Units (pp. 496–499)

GPS M6M1

EXAMPLE

- **Convert 5 yards to feet.**

Set up a conversion factor.

$5\,\cancel{yd} \times \frac{3\text{ ft}}{1\,\cancel{yd}}$ *Think: yards to feet— 3 ft = 1 yd, so use $\frac{3\text{ ft}}{\text{yd}}$.*

5 yd = 15 ft *Multiply 5 yd by the conversion factor. Cancel the common unit, yd.*

EXERCISES

Convert.

14. 3 mi to feet
15. 18 ft to yards
16. 3 qt to cups
17. 48 c to gal
18. 128 oz to pounds
19. 8,000 lb to tons
20. $\frac{64\text{ oz}}{x\text{ lb}} = \frac{16\text{ oz}}{1\text{ lb}}$
21. $\frac{12\text{ ft}}{x\text{ in.}} = \frac{1\text{ ft}}{12\text{ in.}}$
22. $\frac{8\text{ pt}}{x\text{ qt}} = \frac{2\text{ pt}}{1\text{ qt}}$
23. $\frac{3\text{ ft}}{1\text{ yd}} = \frac{x\text{ ft}}{33\text{ yd}}$
24. The Golden Gate Bridge, in San Francisco, has a tower height of 750 ft. How many yards tall is this?

9-4 Converting Metric Units (pp. 500–503)

GPS M6M1

EXAMPLE

- **Convert.**

29 cm = ▒ m

$29\,\cancel{cm} \cdot \frac{1\text{ m}}{100\,\cancel{cm}} = 0.29\text{ m}$ *Cancel the common unit, cm.*

EXERCISES

Convert.

25. 3.2 L = ▒ mL
26. 7 mL = ▒ L
27. 342 m = ▒ km
28. 42 g = ▒ kg
29. 51 mm = ▒ m
30. 71 km = ▒ m

Study Guide: Review

Answers

9. mm; about 32 times the thickness of a dime
10. mg; about 5 times the mass of a very small insect
11. kg; about two textbooks
12. L; about two blender containers
13. 2 cm
14. 15,840 ft
15. 54 yd
16. 12 c
17. 3 gal
18. 8 lb
19. 4 T
20. 4 lb
21. 144 in.
22. 4 qt
23. 99 ft
24. 250 yd
25. 3,200 mL
26. 0.007 L
27. 0.342 km
28. 0.042 kg
29. 0.051 m
30. 71,000 m

Answers

31. 1 hr
32. 59,400 s
33. 105 days
34. 105°
35. 33.9 in.
36. 6 ft
37. 31.4 ft
38. 9 m
39. 50.24 cm
40. 11 ft

Study Guide: Review

9-5 Time and Temperature (pp. 504–507)

GPS M6M1, M6N1.g

EXAMPLE

■ **Convert.**

14 hours = ■ minutes

$14 \cancel{h} \cdot \frac{60 \text{ min}}{1 \cancel{h}} = 840$ min *1 hour = 60 minutes*

EXERCISES

Convert.

31. 3,600 seconds = ■ hours

32. 990 minutes = ■ seconds

33. 15 weeks = ■ days

9-6 Finding Angle Measures in Polygons (pp. 510–513)

GPS M6P1.b

EXAMPLE

■ **Use a protractor to find the measure of ∠*ABC*. Then classify the angle.**

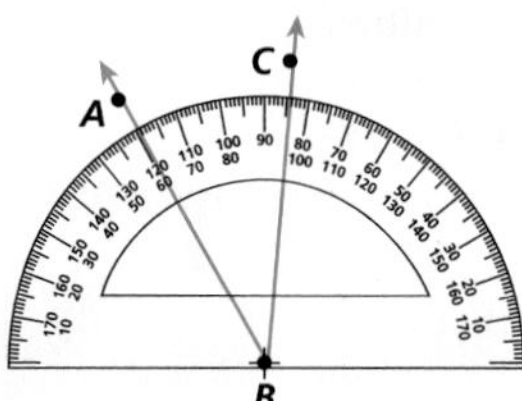

$\angle ABC = 95° - 60° = 35°$

Since $35° < 90°$, the angle is acute.

EXERCISES

34. Use a protractor to find the measure of ∠*ABC*. Then classify the angle.

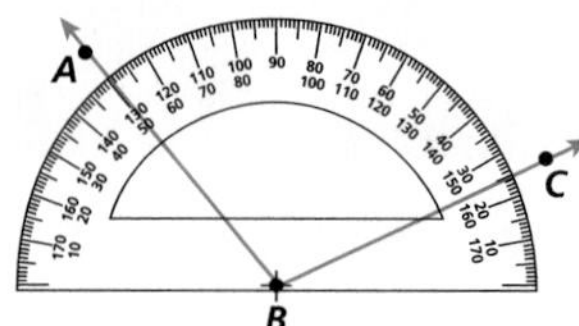

9-7 Perimeter (pp. 514–517)

GPS M6A3

EXAMPLE

■ **Find the perimeter of the figure.**

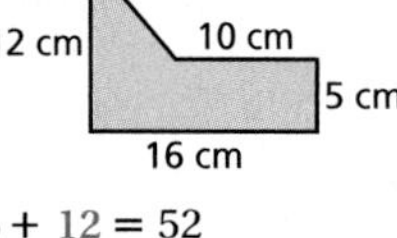

Add all the side lengths.

$P = 9 + 10 + 5 + 16 + 12 = 52$

The perimeter is 52 cm.

EXERCISES

35. Find the perimeter of the figure.

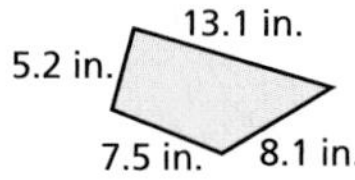

36. What is the length of *n* if the perimeter is 20 ft?

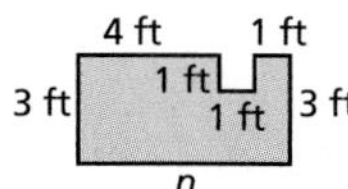

9-8 Circles and Circumference (pp. 520–523)

GPS M6A3

EXAMPLE

■ **Find the circumference of the circle. Use 3.14 for π.**

$C = \pi d$

$C \approx 3.14 \cdot 6$

$C \approx 18.84$ cm

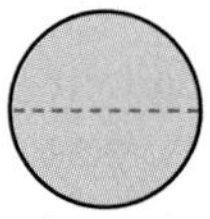

d = 6 cm

EXERCISES

Find each missing value to the nearest hundredth. Use 3.14 for π.

37. $d = 10$ ft; $C = \underline{?}$ **38.** $C = 28.26$ m; $d = \underline{?}$

39. $r = 8$ cm; $C = \underline{?}$ **40.** $C = 69.08$ ft; $r = \underline{?}$

What metric unit of measure provides the best estimate? Explain.

1. A flower pot can hold about 1 __?__ of water. L
2. A baby bird has a mass of about 15 __?__. g
3. The length of a cricket is about 3 __?__ long. cm

Use the table for Problems 4–6.

Baby Darian Cole	
Birth Date	May 1, 2005, 11:45 A.M.
Weight	7 lb
Length	1 ft 8 in.

4. If Darian was moved to the nursery at 2:25 P.M., how long was he in the hospital room? 2 hr 40 min
5. Convert Darian's weight to ounces. 112 oz
6. How long was Darian in inches? 20 in.

Estimate the temperature.

7. 48°C is about ■°F. 126°
8. 70°F is about ■°C. 20°

Use a protractor to find the measure of each angle. Then classify the angle.

9. 125°; obtuse

10. 40°; acute

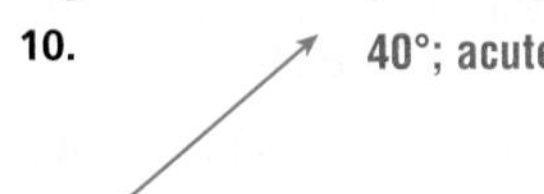

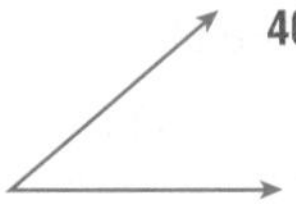

Find the perimeter of each figure.

11. 40 m

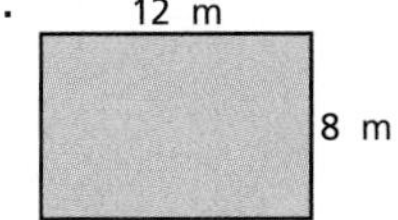

12. 36 cm

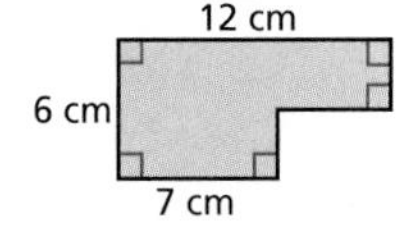

13. 52 ft

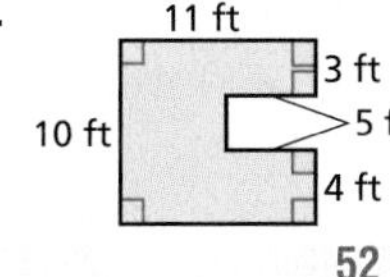

Name the circle and two radii, and then find the circumference for each circle. Use 3.14 for π and round to the nearest hundredth.

14.

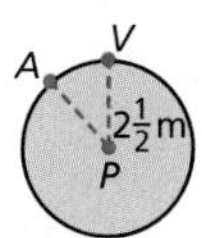

15.

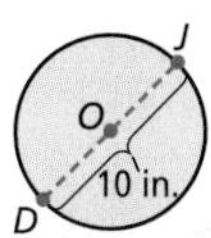

16.

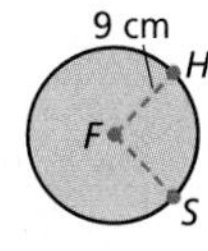

Find each missing value to the nearest hundredth. Use 3.14 for π.

17. $r = 4$ cm; $C =$ __?__ 25.12 cm
18. $d = 10$ ft; $C =$ __?__ 31.4 ft
19. $C = 37.68$ ft; $d =$ __?__ 12 ft
20. A gardener is digging a rose garden. Find the circumference of the rose garden by rounding π to 3. 63 m

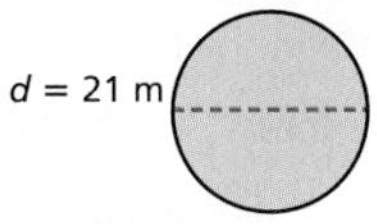

$d = 21$ m

Chapter Test

CHAPTER 9

Organizer

Objective: Assess students' mastery of concepts and skills in Chapter 9.

Online Edition

Resources

Assessment Resources

Chapter 9 Tests
- Free Response (Levels A, B, C)
- Multiple Choice (Levels A, B, C)
- Performance Assessment

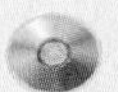

***IDEA Works!* CD-ROM**
Modified Chapter 9 Test

Answers

14. circle P; $\overline{PA}$ and $\overline{PV}$ are radii; $C = 15.7$ m
15. circle O; $\overline{OJ}$ and $\overline{OD}$ are radii; $C = 31.4$ in.
16. circle F; $\overline{FS}$ and $\overline{FH}$ are radii; $C = 56.52$ cm

Organizer

Objective: Provide opportunities to learn and practice common test-taking strategies.

 Online Edition

Resources

 *CRCT Prep* **Workbook**

 *CRCT Prep* **CD-ROM**

 *CRCT Practice* **Online**

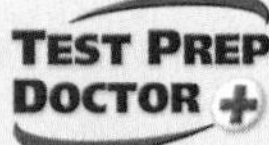

go.hrw.com
KEYWORD: MR7 TestPrep

TEST PREP DOCTOR This test tackler explains how diagrams provided with a test item can inadvertently mislead students. If students assume that information from a diagram is true based on "what they see," they will likely misinterpret the information. Advise students that diagrams are not always drawn to scale and they should not rely solely on the appearance of the drawing to answer the question. Students need to look at how the drawing is labeled and perhaps redraw the art to scale to better depict the scenario.

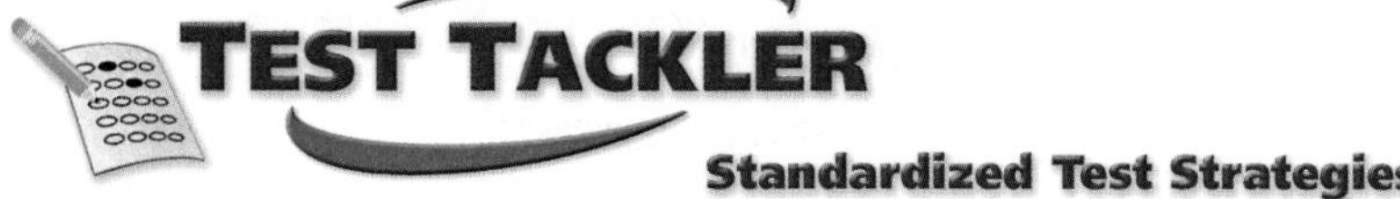

CHAPTER 9 TEST TACKLER

Standardized Test Strategies

Any Question Type: Use a Diagram

Diagrams are a helpful tool. If a diagram is included in a test item, study it closely as it may contain useful information. Sometimes it is helpful to draw your own diagram.

EXAMPLE 1

Multiple Choice A small circle is inside a large circle. The diameter of the small circle is 10 feet. If the circumference of the large circle is 4 times greater than the circumference of the small circle, what is the radius of the large circle? (Round *pi* to 3.)

 Ⓐ 20 ft  Ⓑ 30 ft 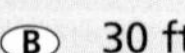 Ⓒ 40 ft Ⓓ 120 ft

Draw a diagram to help you visualize the problem.
Draw two circles and label them with all the information given in the problem.

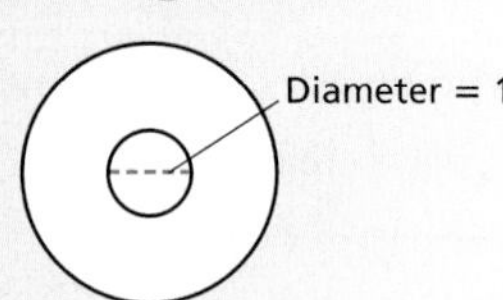

The circumference of the small circle is about 30 feet. The circumference of the large circle is about 120 feet. Divide by 2π. $120 \div (3 \cdot 2) = 20$, so the radius is about 20 feet.

Choice A is correct.

EXAMPLE 2

Short Response $\triangle ABC$ is similar to $\triangle FDE$. Find the missing length.

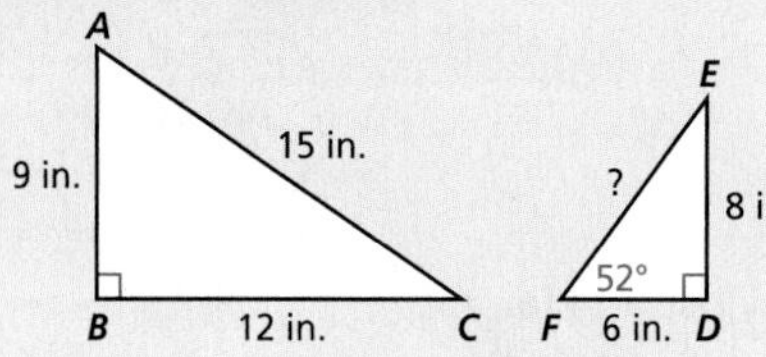

These triangles do not look similar and are not drawn to scale, but the information in the problem says that they are.

Set up a proportion to find the missing length and solve for x. $\frac{x}{6} = \frac{15}{9}$

The unknown side length is 10 in.

Test Tackler

If you have trouble understanding what a test item is asking, draw a diagram to help you visualize the question.

Read each test item and answer the questions that follow.

Item A
Multiple Choice The temperature at the ski lodge was 21°F at 9:00 P.M. At sunrise, the temperature was 34°F. How many degrees did the temperature rise overnight?

Ⓐ 54°F
Ⓒ 13°F
Ⓑ 25°F
Ⓓ 4°F

1. What information will help you solve the problem?
2. Sketch a diagram to help you solve this problem. Be sure to label the diagram with all of the information you know.

Item B
Short Answer Prove that the two rectangles below are similar. Explain your reasoning.

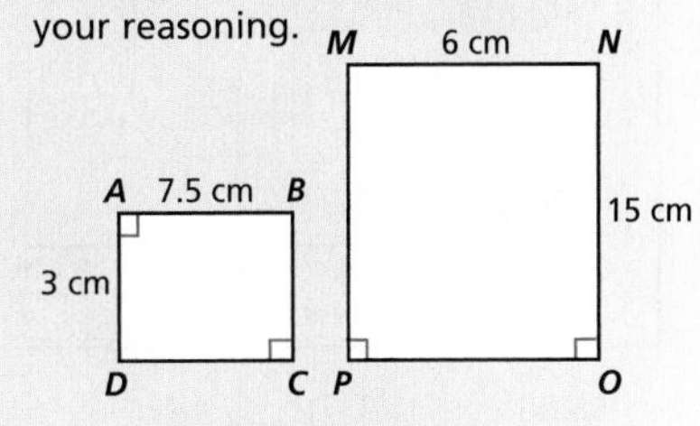

3. What information can you get from the diagram to help you prove that the figures are similar?
4. Do you think the drawings accurately illustrate the given information? If not, why?
5. What is the length of $\overline{DC}$?

Item C
Gridded Response The longest side of a triangle is 14.4 centimeters. Its shortest side is 5.9 centimeters shorter than the longest side. If the perimeter of the triangle is 35.2 centimeters, what is the length of the third side?

6. How do you determine the perimeter of a triangle?
7. Sketch a diagram of the triangle. Explain how sketching the diagram can help you answer the problem.
8. Tell how you would fill in your response to this test item on a grid.

Item D
Multiple Choice Which angle pairs are vertical angles?

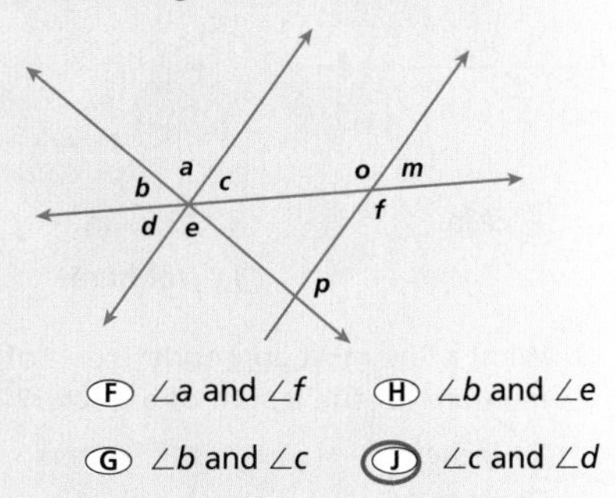

Ⓕ ∠a and ∠f
Ⓗ ∠b and ∠e
Ⓖ ∠b and ∠c
Ⓙ ∠c and ∠d

9. Which answer choice can you immediately eliminate? Why?
10. How can you use the diagram to help you eliminate the other choices?
11. Explain which answer choice is correct.

Test Tackler

Let students know that even though a test item may not include a diagram, it may be beneficial for them to make a quick sketch. Show students the importance of labeling their sketch with the information provided in the test item.

Answers

1. The information I need to solve the problem is the temperature in the evening and the temperature in the morning.
2. 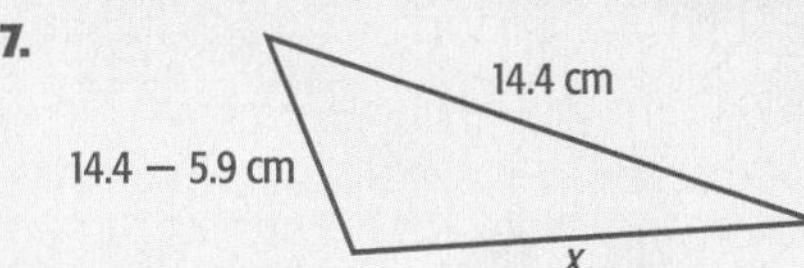

3. The information from the diagram that helps me prove that the figures are similar is that corresponding side lengths are proportional. $\frac{3}{7.5} = \frac{6}{15}$
4. Possible answer: The drawings of the rectangles do not represent the information accurately. $\overline{AB}$ should be $2\frac{1}{2}$ times as long as $\overline{AD}$ and $\overline{NO}$ should be $2\frac{1}{2}$ times as long as $\overline{MN}$.
5. 7.5 cm
6. The perimeter of a triangle is equal to the sum of the length of its sides.
7. 14.4 cm; 14.4 − 5.9 cm; x

   $14.4 + 8.5 + x = 35.2$ cm

   The diagram helps to visualize the relationships of the sides and suggests how to find the length of the third side.
8. 

9. Possible answer: I can immediately eliminate choice **F** because angles *a* and *f* are not opposite angles formed by two intersecting lines.
10. Possible answer: I can use the diagram to circle all of the vertical angles and use that information to eliminate the other choices.
11. Choice **J** is the correct choice because angles *c* and *d* are opposite angles that are formed by two intersecting lines.

Organizer

Objective: Provide review and practice for Chapters 1–9 and standardized tests.

Online Edition

Resources

Assessment Resources
Chapter 9 Cumulative Test

***CRCT Prep* Workbook**

***CRCT Prep* CD-ROM**

***CRCT Practice* Online**

go.hrw.com
KEYWORD: MR7 TestPrep

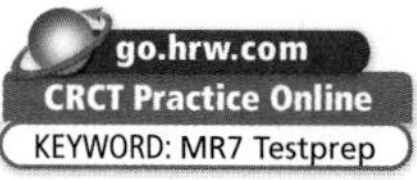

CRCT Prep

Cumulative Assessment, Chapters 1–9

Multiple Choice

1. The world's largest ball of twine is located in Cawker City, Kansas. It weighs 17,571 pounds. About how many tons does this ball of twine weigh?

   (A) 9 tons (C) 11 tons
   (B) 10 tons (D) 12 tons

2. The two triangles shown below are similar. What is the length of the unknown side n?

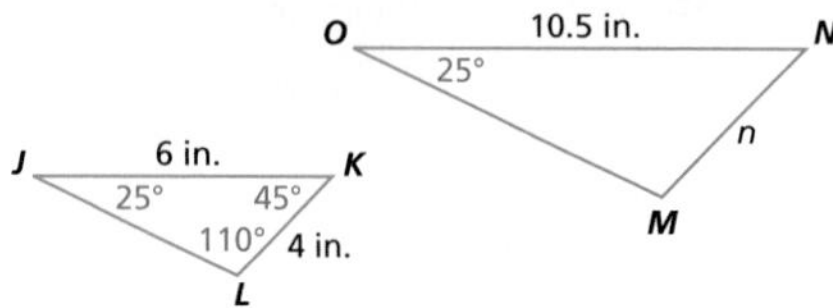

   (F) 7 in. (H) 15.75 in.
   (G) 8.5 in. (J) Not here

3. What is the most appropriate unit of measure for the length of a tractor?

   (A) Inches (C) Millimeters
   (B) Feet (D) Pounds

4. In 2002, the U.S. Census reported that 37.4 million Latinos were living in the United States. Approximately 3.2 million of these Latinos were from Puerto Rico. What percent of the Latino population in 2002 came from Puerto Rico?

   (F) 0.086% (H) 8.6%
   (G) 0.86% (J) 86%

5. Josh's violin lessons start at 8:55 A.M. and last 95 minutes. What time will Josh's lesson end?

   (A) 9:45 A.M. (C) 10:30 A.M.
   (B) 10:15 A.M. (D) 10:45 A.M.

6. An online survey by Kids' Money asked children to share how much money they receive for an allowance. The results from 6- to 12-year-olds are shown below. According to this survey, what is the average allowance for children between the ages of 8 and 12?

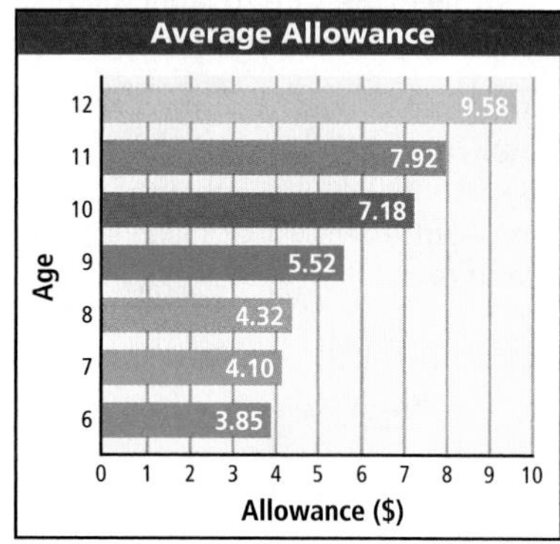

   (F) $6.06 (H) $7.18
   (G) $6.90 (J) $8.49

7. Shelly has a bookshelf that is $48\frac{3}{4}$ inches long. If Shelly's textbooks are each $3\frac{1}{2}$ inches wide, how many books can Shelly fit on a shelf?

   (A) 15 books (C) 13 books
   (B) 14 books (D) 12 books

TEST PREP DOCTOR

For item 14, students may think of dividing by 3 to find the answer. They should remember that dividing by a fraction means multiplying by its reciprocal, which is 3. When determining the fifth term, point out that the first term, 6, already exists and that the second term is 6 times 3.

Answers

14. Gene paid more for a gallon of gas than Janice. Gene paid $1.89 per gallon and Janice paid $1.87.

15a. The model's dimensions are 20 cm long by 10 cm wide.

15b. The lane width of the model is 1 cm.

16a. The perimeter of a regulation football field is $386\frac{2}{3}$ yd.

16b. The end zone of a regulation football field is 720 in. long.

17. See 4-Point Response work sample.

8. Which metric unit should be used to show how much liquid a jar can hold?

(F) Kilograms (H) Millimeters
(G) Milligrams (J) Milliliters

9. Which of the following statements about plane figures is NOT true?

(A) A square is always a rhombus.
(B) A rectangle is always a square.
(C) A trapezoid is always a quadrilateral.
(D) A rhombus is always a parallelogram.

When converting between metric units, multiply by a power of 10 when changing from larger units to smaller units. Divide by a power of 10 when changing from smaller units to larger units.

10. Jordan's locker number is greater than 225 but less than 250. It is divisible by 3 and 9, but not by 2, 4, or 5. What is Jordan's locker number?

(F) 231 (H) 243
(G) 237 (J) 249

11. In 1912, a reticulated python was found to be 10.7 meters long. How many centimeters long was this snake?

(A) 1.07 (C) 107
(B) 10.7 (D) 1,070

12. What is the 5th term in a sequence that begins on 6 and is divided each time by $\frac{1}{3}$?

(F) $\frac{2}{9}$ (H) 162
(G) $\frac{2}{27}$ (J) 486

13. Jessie is $1\frac{1}{2}$ times taller than her sister. If her sister is 4 feet tall, how many inches taller is Jessie than her sister?

(A) 6 (C) 48
(B) 24 (D) 72

STANDARDIZED TEST PREP

Short Response

14. Gene and Janice's gas tanks are empty. It cost Gene $48.52 to fill up his 25.7-gallon gas tank. At another gas station, Janice filled up her 13.8 gallon tank and paid $25.80. Who paid the most for a gallon of gas? Explain. **Gene**

15. Larry is making a model of an Olympic-size swimming pool. The scale is 2 cm = 5 m.

a. An Olympic-size pool is 50 m long by 25 m wide. What are the dimensions of the model? Show your work. **20 cm × 10 cm**

b. There are 8 lanes in the actual pool. Each lane is 2.5 m wide. How many centimeters wide are the lanes in the model? Show your work. **1 cm**

16. A regulation football field is 160 feet wide and 420 feet long. These dimensions include the end zones.

a. What is the perimeter of a regulation football field in yards? Show your work. **$386\frac{2}{3}$ yd**

b. A football field has two end zones at the end of each side of the playing field. If the playing field is 100 yards long, how many inches long is one end zone? Show your work. **720 in.**

Extended Response

17. Tara is planning to build a stone border around a large walnut tree. The stones are 6 inches long.

a. How many stones will Tara need if she creates a square border that is 8 feet long? Show your work.

b. How many stones will Tara need if she creates a circular border that has an 8-foot diameter? Use $\frac{22}{7}$ for π. Show your work.

c. If the stones cost $2.69 each, how much money will Tara save if she builds a circular border instead of a square border? Explain.

CRCT Prep

Short Response Rubric

Items 14–16

2 Points = The student's answer is an accurate and complete execution of the task or tasks.

1 Point = The student's answer contains attributes of an appropriate response but is flawed.

0 Points = The student's answer contains no attributes of an appropriate response.

Extended Response Rubric

Item 17

4 Points = The student demonstrates a thorough understanding of all concepts and shows all work correctly.

3 Points = The student demonstrates a basic understanding of all concepts, but the work shows some flaws reflecting inattentive execution of mathematical procedures or some misunderstanding of the underlying mathematics.

2 Points = The student demonstrates only a partial understanding of the concepts or procedures embodied in the tasks. The approach may be correct but the work shows a misunderstanding of one or more important concepts.

1 Point = The student demonstrates a very limited understanding of the concepts or procedures embodied in the tasks. The response may show some understanding but exhibits many flaws or is incomplete.

0 Points = The student provides no response at all, or a completely incorrect or uninterpretable response.

Student Work Samples for Item 17

4-Point Response

a. Teresa will need 64 stones for a square border that is 8 ft long.
8×4÷0.5 = 64 stones

b. $C = \pi d = \frac{22}{7} \times 8 = 25\frac{1}{7}$ ft
$25\frac{1}{7} \div \frac{1}{2} = 50\frac{2}{7}$ stones
She needs to round up to the next stone, so she will need 51 stones.

c. (64×$2.69)−(51×$2.69)=$34.97
She will save $34.97 if she builds the circular border.

The student showed all work in finding the correct number of stones. Questions were answered in complete sentences, with full explanations.

3-Point Response

a. Teresa will need 64 stones.

b. $C = \pi d = \left(\frac{22}{7} \times 8\right) = 25.14$ ft
25.14 ÷ 0.5 = 50.28 stones

c. She will save $36.91.

The work is not shown, but the answer to part **a** is correct. The work shown in part **b** is correct, but 51 stones are needed. Part **c** is incorrect.

2-Point Response

a. 8×4 = 32 ft

b. $C = \pi d = \left(\frac{22}{7} \times 8\right) = 25.14$ ft

c. (32×2.69)−(25.14×2.69) = $18.45

In parts **a** and **b**, the correct distances were found, but the number of stones needed was not determined. Part **c** is incorrect.

CHAPTER 10

Measurement: Area and Volume

Section 10A

Area

- **10-1 Estimating and Finding Area**
- **10-2 Area of Triangles and Trapezoids**
- **10-2 Technology Lab** Area Formulas
- **10-3 Area of Composite Figures**
- **10-4 Comparing Perimeter and Area**
- **10-5 Hands-On Lab** Explore Area of Circles
- **10-5 Area of Circles**

Section 10B

Volume and Surface Area

- **10-6 Hands-On Lab** Draw Views of Three-Dimensional Figures
- **10-6 Three-Dimensional Figures**
- **10-7 Hands-On Lab** Explore Volume of Prisms and Cylinders
- **10-7 Volume of Prisms**
- **10-8 Volume of Cylinders**
- **10-9 Hands-On Lab** Model Three-Dimensional Figures
- **10-9 Surface Area**

Pacing Guide for 45-Minute Classes

Chapter 10

Countdown to Testing Weeks 22, 23, 24

DAY 1	DAY 2	DAY 3	DAY 4	DAY 5
10-1 Lesson	10-2 Lesson	10-3 Technology Lab 10-3 Lesson	10-3 Lesson 10-4 Lesson	10-4 Lesson 10-5 Hands-On Lab
DAY 6	**DAY 7**	**DAY 8**	**DAY 9**	**DAY 10**
10-5 Hands-On Lab 10-5 Lesson	10-5 Lesson Ready to Go On? Focus on Problem Solving	10-6 Hands-On Lab	10-6 Lesson	10-7 Hands-On Lab
DAY 11	**DAY 12**	**DAY 13**	**DAY 14**	**DAY 15**
10-7 Lesson	10-8 Lesson	10-9 Hands-On Lab 10-9 Lesson	10-9 Lesson Ready to Go On? Multi-Step Test Prep	Chapter 10 Review
DAY 16				
Chapter 10 Test				

Pacing Guide for 90-Minute Classes

Chapter 10

DAY 1	DAY 2	DAY 3	DAY 4	DAY 5
10-1 Lesson 10-2 Lesson	10-3 Technology Lab 10-3 Lesson 10-4 Lesson	10-4 Lesson 10-5 Hands-On Lab 10-5 Lesson	10-5 Lesson Ready to Go On? Focus on Problem Solving 10-6 Hands-On Lab	10-6 Lesson 10-7 Hands-On Lab
DAY 6	**DAY 7**	**DAY 8**		
10-7 Lesson 10-8 Lesson	10-9 Hands-On Lab 10-9 Lesson Ready to Go On? Multi-Step Test Prep	Chapter 10 Review Chapter 10 Test		

ONGOING ASSESSMENT and INTERVENTION

Assess Prior Knowledge

Before Chapter 10

DIAGNOSE	PRESCRIBE
Diagnose readiness for the chapter.	Prescribe intervention.
Are You Ready? SE p. 539	***Are You Ready? Intervention*** Skills 34, 40, 42, 72, 76

Formative Assessment

Before Every Lesson

DIAGNOSE	PRESCRIBE
Diagnose readiness for the lesson.	Prescribe intervention.
Warm Up TE, every lesson	**Skills Bank** SE pp. 749–761
	Reteach CRB, Chapters 1–10

During Every Lesson

DIAGNOSE	PRESCRIBE
Diagnose understanding of lesson concepts.	Prescribe intervention.
Think and Discuss SE, every lesson	***Questioning Strategies*** Chapter 10
Write About It SE, lesson exercises	**Reading Strategies** CRB, every lesson
Journal TE, lesson exercises	***Success for ELL*** pp. 165–182

After Every Lesson

DIAGNOSE	PRESCRIBE
Diagnose mastery of lesson concepts.	Prescribe intervention.
Lesson Quiz TE, every lesson	**Reteach** CRB, every lesson
Test Prep SE, every lesson	**Problem Solving** CRB, every lesson
Test and Practice Generator	**Test Prep Doctor** TE, lesson exercises
	***Homework Help* Online**

Before Chapter 10 Testing

DIAGNOSE	PRESCRIBE
Diagnose mastery of concepts in the chapter.	Prescribe intervention.
Ready to Go On? SE pp. 562, 586	***Ready to Go On? Intervention*** Chapter 10
Focus on Problem Solving SE p. 563	**Scaffolding Questions** TE p. 587
Multi-Step Test Prep SE p. 587	
Section Quizzes AR pp. 187–188	
Test and Practice Generator	

Before High Stakes Testing

DIAGNOSE	PRESCRIBE
Diagnose mastery of benchmark concepts.	Prescribe intervention.
CRCT Prep SE pp. 594–595	***CRCT Prep Workbook***
***CRCT Prep* CD-ROM**	

Summative Assessment

After Chapter 10

DIAGNOSE	PRESCRIBE
Check mastery of chapter concepts.	Prescribe intervention.
Multiple-Choice Tests (Forms A, B, C)	**Reteach** CRB, every lesson
Free-Response Tests (Forms A, B, C)	***Lesson Tutorial Videos*** Chapter 10
Performance Assessment AR pp. 189–202	
Test and Practice Generator	
Check mastery of benchmark concepts.	Prescribe intervention.
CRCT	***CRCT Prep Workbook***

KEY: **SE** = *Student Edition* **TE** = *Teacher's Edition* **CRB** = *Chapter Resource Book* **AR** = *Assessment Resources* Available online Available on CD-ROM

CHAPTER 10

Supporting the Teacher

Chapter 10 Resource Book

Practice A, B, C
pp. 3–5, 12–14, 20–22, 28–30, 36–38, 45–47, 53–55, 61–63, 69–71

Reading Strategies ELL
pp. 10, 18, 26, 34, 43, 51, 59, 67, 75

Puzzles, Twisters, and Teasers
pp. 11, 19, 27, 35, 44, 52, 60, 68, 76

Reteach
pp. 6–7, 15, 23, 31, 39–40, 48, 56, 64, 72

Problem Solving
pp. 9, 17, 25, 33, 42, 50, 58, 66, 74

Challenge
pp. 8, 16, 24, 32, 41, 49, 57, 65, 73

Parent Letter pp. 1–2

Transparencies

Lesson Transparencies, Volume 2 .... Chapter 10
- Warm Ups
- Problem of the Day
- Teaching Transparencies
- Lesson Quizzes

Know-It Notebook .... Chapter 10
- Additional Examples
- Vocabulary
- Chapter Review
- Big Ideas

Alternate Openers: Explorations .... pp. 83–91

Countdown to CRCT .... pp. 43–48

Teacher Tools

Power Presentations®
Complete PowerPoint® presentations for Chapter 10 lessons

Lesson Tutorial Videos® SPANISH
Holt authors Ed Burger and Freddie Renfro present tutorials to support the Chapter 10 lessons.

One-Stop Planner® SPANISH
Easy access to all Chapter 10 resources and assessments, as well as software for lesson planning, test generation, and puzzle creation

IDEA Works!®
Key Chapter 10 resources and assessments modified to address special learning needs

Lesson Plans .... pp. 83–91

Questioning Strategies .... Chapter 10

Solutions Key .... Chapter 10

Interdisciplinary Posters and Worksheets .... Chapter 10

TechKeys

Lab Resources

Project Teacher Support

Parent Resources

Workbooks

Homework and Practice Workbook SPANISH
Teacher's Guide .... pp. 42–46

Know-It Notebook
Teacher's Guide .... Chapter 10

Problem Solving Workbook SPANISH
Teacher's Guide .... pp. 42–46

CRCT Prep
Teacher's Guide

Technology Highlights for the Teacher

Power Presentations

Dynamic presentations to engage students. Complete PowerPoint® presentations for every lesson in Chapter 10.

2-1 Solving One-Step Equations

Isolate a variable by using inverse operations which "undo" operations on the variable.

An equation is like a balanced scale. To keep the balance, perform the same operation on both sides.

Inverse Operations	
Operation	**Inverse Operation**
Addition	Subtraction
Subtraction	Addition

One-Stop Planner SPANISH

Easy access to Chapter 10 resources and assessments. Includes lesson-planning, test-generation, and puzzle-creation software.

Premier Online Edition SPANISH

Chapter 10 includes Tutorial Videos, Lesson Activities, Lesson Quizzes, Homework Help, and Chapter Project.

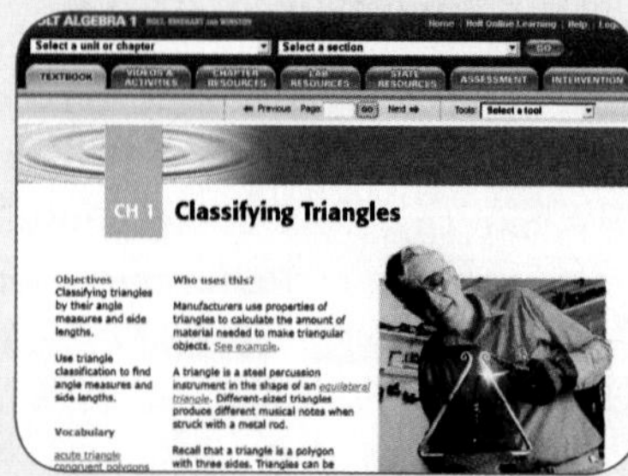

KEY: **SE** = *Student Edition* **TE** = *Teacher's Edition*  English Language Learners  Spanish version available  Available online  Available on CD-ROM

Reaching All Learners

Resources for All Learners

Hands-On Lab Activities	Chapter 10
Technology Lab Activities	Chapter 10
Homework and Practice Workbook SPANISH	pp. 83–91
Know-It Notebook SPANISH	Chapter 10
Problem Solving Workbook SPANISH	pp. 83–91

DEVELOPING LEARNERS

Practice A	CRB, every lesson
Reteach	CRB, every lesson
Inclusion	TE pp. 577, 583
Questioning Strategies	Chapter 10
Modified Chapter 10 Resources	*IDEA Works!*
Homework Help Online	

ON-LEVEL LEARNERS

Practice B	CRB, every lesson
Puzzles, Twisters, and Teasers	CRB, every lesson
Mulitple Representations	TE p. 559
Cooperative Learing	TE pp. 552, 573

ADVANCED LEARNERS

Practice C	CRB, every lesson
Challenge	CRB, every lesson
Extension	TE pp. 541, 587, 588, 589
Critical Thinking	TE p. 567

English Language Learners

ENGLISH LANGUAGE LEARNERS

Are You Ready? Vocabulary	SE p. 539
Vocabulary Connections	SE p. 540
Lesson Vocabulary	SE, every lesson
Vocabulary Review	SE p. 590
English Language Learners	TE pp. 541, 543, 567, 583, 597
Reading Strategies	CRB, every lesson
Success for English Language Learners	pp. 165–182
Multilingual Glossary	

Reaching All Learners Through...

Inclusion	TE pp. 577, 583
Visual Cues	TE p. 551
Kinesthetic Experience	TE p. 555
Concrete Manipulatives	TE p. 547
Multiple Representations	TE p. 559
Cooperative Learning	TE pp. 552, 573
Modeling	TE pp. 557, 583
Critical Thinking	TE p. 567
Test Prep Doctor	TE pp. 545, 549, 561, 569, 575, 579, 585, 594
Common Error Alert	TE pp. 547, 559, 583
Scaffolding Questions	TE p. 587

Technology Highlights for Reaching All Learners

Lesson Tutorial Videos SPANISH

Starring Holt authors Ed Burger and Freddie Renfro! Live tutorials to support every lesson in Chapter 10.

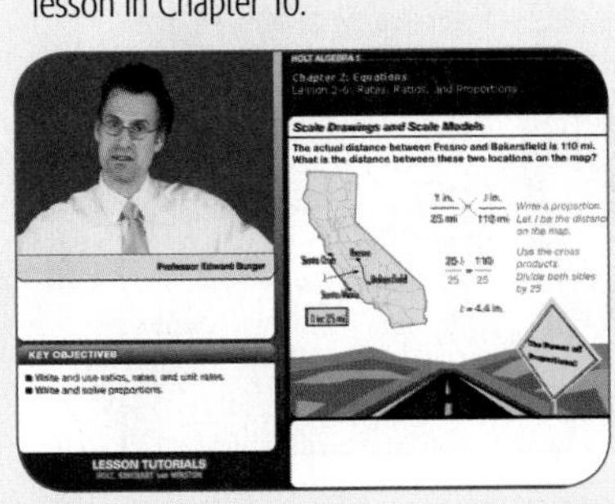

Multilingual Glossary

Searchable glossary includes definitions in English, Spanish, Vietnamese, Chinese, Hmong, Korean, and 4 other languages.

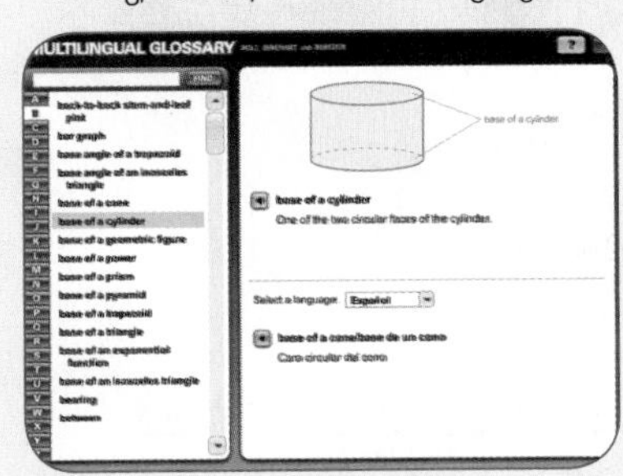

Online Interactivities

Interactive tutorials provide visually engaging alternative opportunities to learn concepts and master skills.

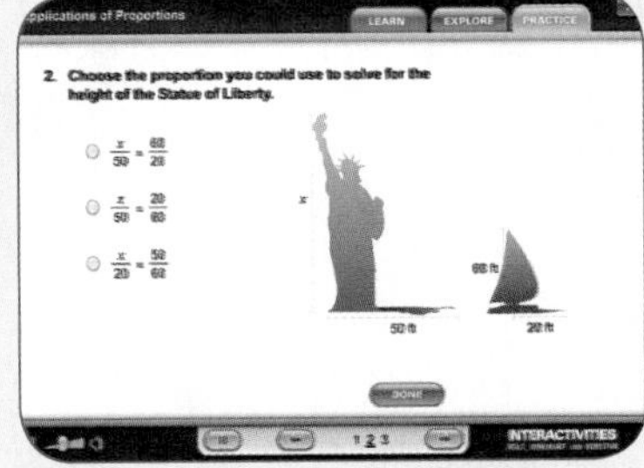

KEY: **SE** = *Student Edition* **TE** = *Teacher's Edition* **CRB** = *Chapter Resource Book* 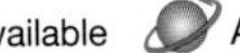 Spanish version available 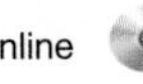 Available online Available on CD-ROM

Ongoing Assessment

Assessing Prior Knowledge

Determine whether students have the prerequisite concepts and skills for success in Chapter 10.

Are You Ready? SPANISH .... SE p. 539

Warm Up .... TE, every lesson

Test Preparation

Provide review and practice for Chapter 10 and standardized tests.

Multi-Step Test Prep .... SE p. 587

Study Guide: Review .... SE pp. 590–592

CRCT Prep .... SE pp. 594–595

Countdown to CRCT Transparencies .... pp. 43–48

CRCT Prep Workbook

***CRCT Prep* CD-ROM**

IDEA Works!

Alternative Assessment

Assess students' understanding of Chapter 10 concepts and combined problem-solving skills.

Chapter 10 Project .... SE p. 538

Performance Assessment SPANISH .... AR pp. 201–202

Portfolio Assessment SPANISH .... AR p. xxxiv

Daily Assessment

Provide formative assessment for each day of Chapter 10.

Questioning Strategies .... Chapter 10

Think and Discuss .... SE, every lesson

Write About It .... SE, lesson exercises

Journal .... TE, lesson exercises

Lesson Quiz .... TE, every lesson

Modified Lesson Quizzes .... *IDEA Works!*

Weekly Assessment

Provide formative assessment for each week of Chapter 10.

Focus on Problem Solving .... SE p. 563

Multi-Step Test Prep .... SE p. 587

Ready to Go On? SPANISH .... SE pp. 562, 586

Cumulative Assessment .... SE pp. 594–595

Test and Practice Generator SPANISH ... *One-Stop Planner*

Formal Assessment

Provide summative assessment of Chapter 10 mastery.

Section Quizzes SPANISH .... AR pp. 187–188

Chapter 10 Test .... SE p. 593

Chapter Test (Levels A, B, C) SPANISH .... AR pp. 189–200
- Multiple Choice
- Free Response

Cumulative Test SPANISH .... AR pp. 203–206

Test and Practice Generator SPANISH ... *One-Stop Planner*

Modified Chapter 10 Test .... *IDEA Works!*

Technology Highlights for Ongoing Assessment

Are You Ready? SPANISH

Automatically assess readiness and prescribe intervention for Chapter 10 prerequisite skills.

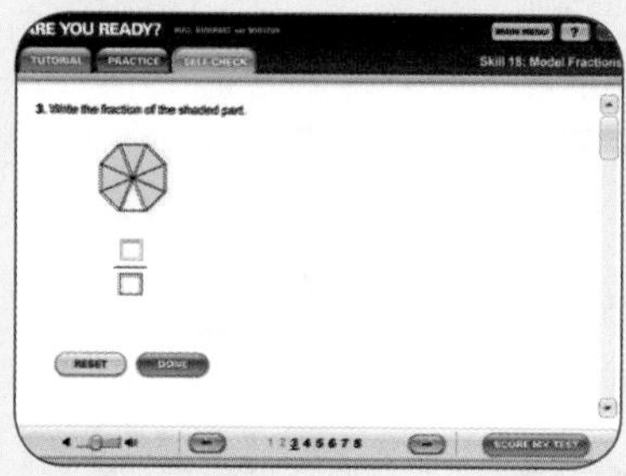

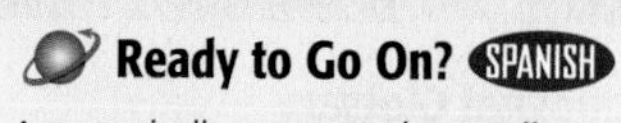

Ready to Go On? SPANISH

Automatically assess understanding of and prescribe intervention for Sections 10A and 10B.

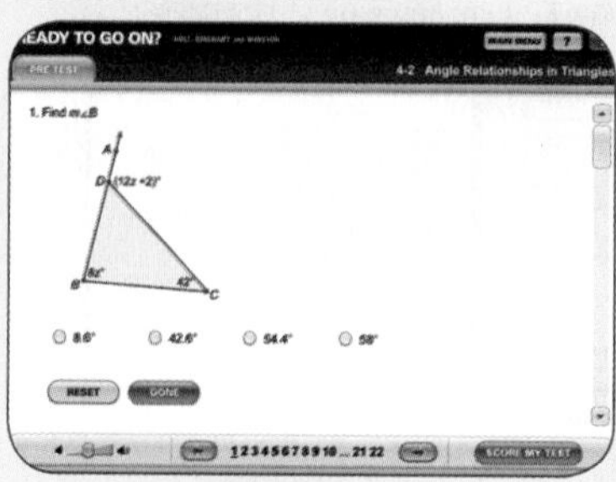

Test and Practice Generator SPANISH

Use Chapter 10 problem banks to create assessments and worksheets to print out or deliver online. Includes dynamic problems.

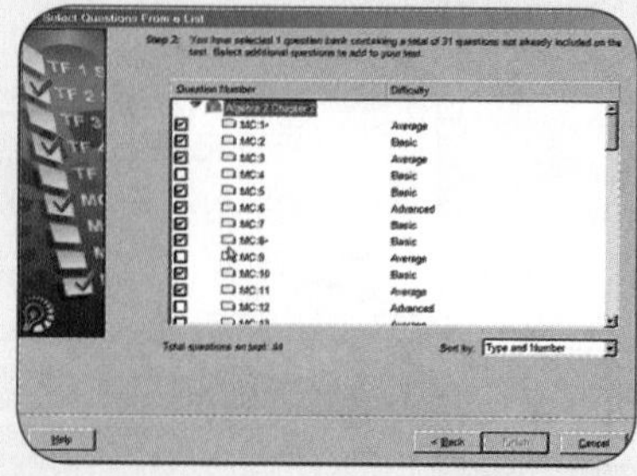

KEY: **SE** = *Student Edition* **TE** = *Teacher's Edition* **AR** = *Assessment Resources*  SPANISH Spanish version available 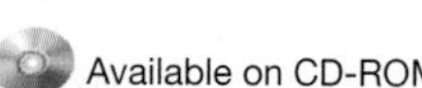 Available online Available on CD-ROM

Formal Assessment

Three levels (A, B, C) of multiple-choice and free-response chapter tests are available in the *Assessment Resources.*

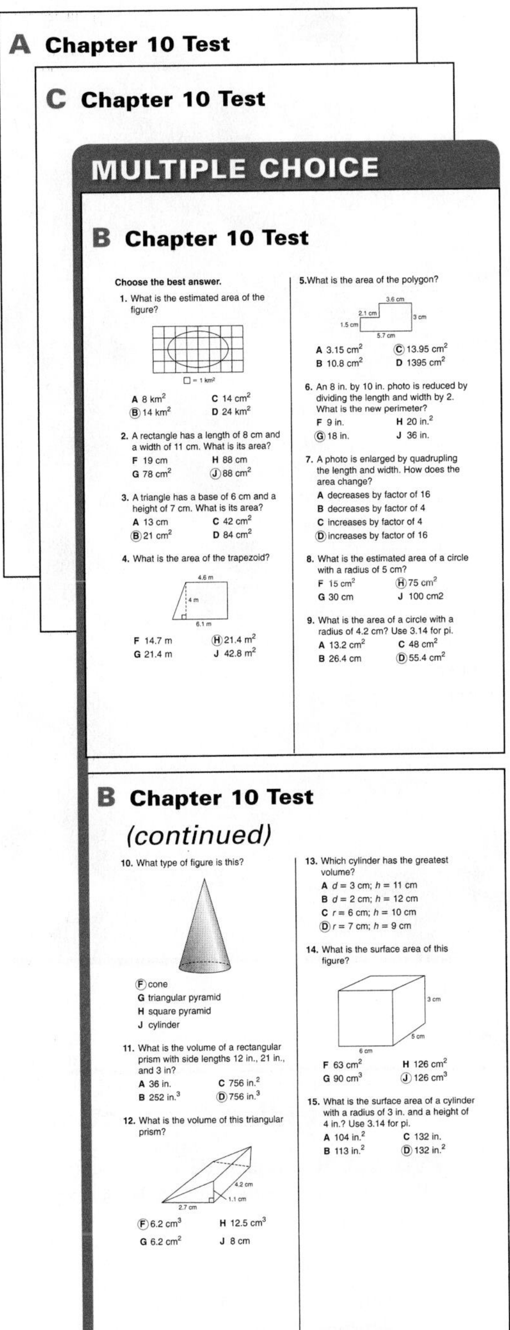

A Chapter 10 Test

C Chapter 10 Test

MULTIPLE CHOICE

B Chapter 10 Test

Choose the best answer.

1. What is the estimated area of the figure?
A 8 km² C 14 cm²
(B) 14 km² D 24 km²

2. A rectangle has a length of 8 cm and a width of 11 cm. What is its area?
F 19 cm H 88 cm
G 78 cm² (J) 88 cm²

3. A triangle has a base of 6 cm and a height of 7 cm. What is its area?
A 13 cm C 42 cm²
(B) 21 cm² D 84 cm²

4. What is the area of the trapezoid?
F 14.7 m (H) 21.4 m²
G 21.4 m J 42.8 m²

5. What is the area of the polygon?
A 3.15 cm² (C) 13.95 cm²
B 10.8 cm² D 1395 cm²

6. An 8 in. by 10 in. photo is reduced by dividing the length and width by 2. What is the new perimeter?
F 9 in. H 20 in.²
(G) 18 in. J 36 in.

7. A photo is enlarged by quadrupling the length and width. How does the area change?
A decreases by factor of 16
B decreases by factor of 4
C increases by factor of 4
(D) increases by factor of 16

8. What is the estimated area of a circle with a radius of 5 cm?
F 15 cm² (H) 75 cm²
G 30 cm J 100 cm2

9. What is the area of a circle with a radius of 4.2 cm? Use 3.14 for pi.
A 13.2 cm² C 48 cm²
B 26.4 cm (D) 55.4 cm²

B Chapter 10 Test (continued)

10. What type of figure is this?
(F) cone
G triangular pyramid
H square pyramid
J cylinder

11. What is the volume of a rectangular prism with side lengths 12 in., 21 in., and 3 in?
A 36 in. C 756 in.²
B 252 in.³ (D) 756 in.³

12. What is the volume of this triangular prism?
(F) 6.2 cm³ H 12.5 cm³
G 6.2 cm² J 8 cm

13. Which cylinder has the greatest volume?
A $d = 3$ cm; $h = 11$ cm
B $d = 2$ cm; $h = 12$ cm
C $r = 6$ cm; $h = 10$ cm
(D) $r = 7$ cm; $h = 9$ cm

14. What is the surface area of this figure?
F 63 cm² H 126 cm²
G 90 cm³ (J) 126 cm³

15. What is the surface area of a cylinder with a radius of 3 in. and a height of 4 in.? Use 3.14 for pi.
A 104 in.² C 132 in.
B 113 in.² (D) 132 in.²

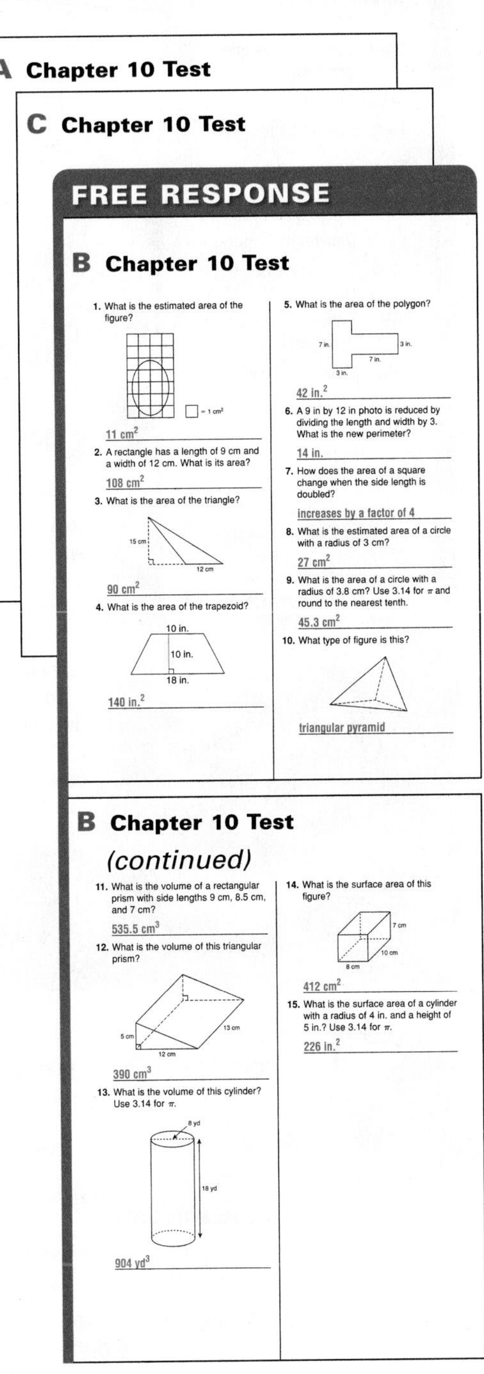

A Chapter 10 Test

C Chapter 10 Test

FREE RESPONSE

B Chapter 10 Test

1. What is the estimated area of the figure? 11 cm²

2. A rectangle has a length of 9 cm and a width of 12 cm. What is its area? 108 cm²

3. What is the area of the triangle? 90 cm²

4. What is the area of the trapezoid? 140 in.²

5. What is the area of the polygon? 42 in.²

6. A 9 in by 12 in photo is reduced by dividing the length and width by 3. What is the new perimeter? 14 in.

7. How does the area of a square change when the side length is doubled? increases by a factor of 4

8. What is the estimated area of a circle with a radius of 3 cm? 27 cm²

9. What is the area of a circle with a radius of 3.8 cm? Use 3.14 for π and round to the nearest tenth. 45.3 cm²

10. What type of figure is this? triangular pyramid

B Chapter 10 Test (continued)

11. What is the volume of a rectangular prism with side lengths 9 cm, 8.5 cm, and 7 cm? 535.5 cm³

12. What is the volume of this triangular prism? 390 cm³

13. What is the volume of this cylinder? Use 3.14 for π. 904 yd³

14. What is the surface area of this figure? 412 cm²

15. What is the surface area of a cylinder with a radius of 4 in. and a height of 5 in.? Use 3.14 for π. 226 in.²

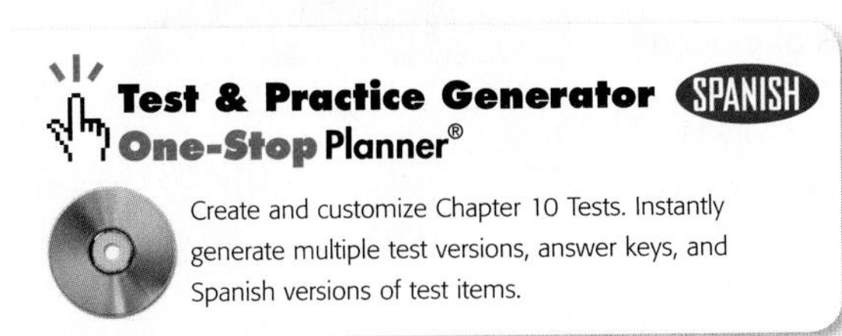
Test & Practice Generator SPANISH
One-Stop Planner®
Create and customize Chapter 10 Tests. Instantly generate multiple test versions, answer keys, and Spanish versions of test items.

CHAPTER 10

Why Learn This?

Tell students that area and volume are useful in many fields. For example, architects, set designers, carpenters, and engineers use these concepts every day as they plan and build two- and three-dimensional objects. Landscape architects calculate the areas of planted regions and then use volume to determine the amount of soil and mulch that will be needed.

Using Data

To begin the study of this chapter, have students:

- Describe any patterns that appear in the Coverage Chart. The product of the depth of the wood chips and the area covered is always 320.
- Determine the area that could be covered by one cubic yard of wood chips at a depth of 5 in. 64ft^2
- Calculate the cost of covering 400 ft^2 at a depth of 4 in., given that wood chips cost $14 for one cubic yard. $70

On page 594, students will find cumulative CRCT practice.

CHAPTER 10

Measurement: Area and Volume

go.hrw.com
Chapter Project Online
KEYWORD: MR7 Ch10

Coverage Chart (1 yd^3 of wood chips)

Depth of Chips (in.)	Area Covered (ft^2)
$\frac{1}{2}$	640
1	320
2	160
3	120
4	80

Career *Landscape Architect*

Almost every shopping center has walkways, lawns, and trees. A landscape architect designs these so that they are appealing and well suited to the environment. Landscape architects also plan the layouts of residential areas, office parks, and school campuses.

To calculate costs, landscape architects must estimate how much material is needed to cover planted areas. For example, the table shows the number of square feet that can be covered by 1 cubic yard of wood chips.

PROBLEM SOLVING

Problem Solving Project

Understand, Plan, Solve, and Look Back

Have students:

- Complete the Landscape Architect's Cost Estimate worksheet
- Design several new planted areas, exchange the dimensions with classmates, and calculate the total cost for covering these new areas with wood chips.
- Research different types of ground covers and the costs associated which each. How do the costs vary?
- Describe other situations in which areas and volumes may affect costs.

Social Studies Connection

Project Resources

All project resources for teachers and students are provided online.

Materials:

- Landscape Architect's Cost Estimate worksheet

Project Teacher Support
KEYWORD: MR7 PSProject10

ARE YOU READY?

Vocabulary

Choose the best term from the list to complete each sentence.

	centimeters
	cube
	feet
	hexagon
	inches
	liters
	meters
	parallelogram
	square
	trapezoid

1. A(n) __?__ is a quadrilateral with opposite sides that are parallel and congruent. parallelogram
2. Some customary units of length are __?__ and __?__. Some metric units of length are __?__ and __?__. inches; feet; centimeters; meters
3. A(n) __?__ is a quadrilateral with side lengths that are all congruent and four right angles. square
4. A(n) __?__ is a polygon with six sides. hexagon

Complete these exercises to review skills you will need for this chapter.

Add and Multiply Whole Numbers, Fractions, and Decimals

Find each sum or product.

5. $1.5 + 2.4 + 3.6 + 2.5$ 10
6. $2 \cdot 3.5 \cdot 4$ 28
7. $\frac{22}{7} \cdot 21$ 66
8. $\frac{1}{2} \cdot 5 \cdot 4$ 10
9. $3.2 \cdot 5.6$ 17.92
10. $\frac{1}{2} \cdot 10 \cdot 3$ 15
11. $(2 \cdot 5) + (6 \cdot 8)$ 58
12. $2(3.5) + 2(1.5)$ 10
13. $9(20 + 7)$ 243

Estimate Metric Lengths

Use a centimeter ruler to measure each line to the nearest centimeter.

14.  6 cm

15. 4 cm

Identify Polygons

Name each polygon. Determine whether it appears to be regular or not regular.

16. 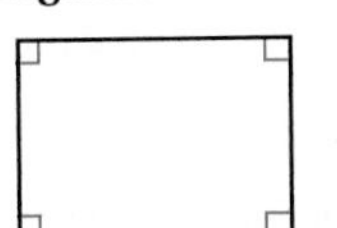

rectangle; not regular

17. 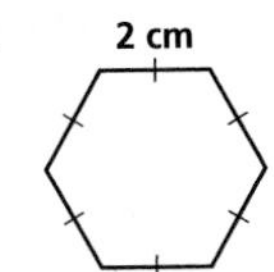

octagon; regular

18. 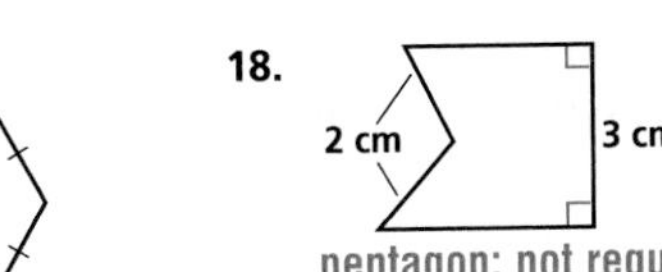

pentagon; not regular

CHAPTER 10

Organizer

Objective: Assess students' understanding of prerequisite skills.

Prerequisite Skills

Add and Multiply Whole Numbers, Fractions, and Decimals

Estimate Metric Lengths

Identify Polygons

Assessing Prior Knowledge

INTERVENTION 

Diagnose and Prescribe

Use this page to determine whether intervention is necessary or enrichment is appropriate.

Resources

 ***Are You Ready? Intervention and Enrichment* Worksheets**

 ***Are You Ready?* CD-ROM**

 ***Are You Ready?* Online**

my.hrw.com

ARE YOU READY?

Diagnose and Prescribe

Prerequisite Skill	*Are You Ready? Intervention*, Chapter 10 — Worksheets	CD-ROM	Online
Add and Multiply Whole Numbers, Fractions, and Decimals	Skills 34, 40, 42	Activities 34, 40, 42	Diagnose and Prescribe Online
Estimate Metric Lengths	Skill 72	Activity 72	
Identify Polygons	Skill 76	Activity 76	

***Are You Ready? Enrichment*, Chapter 10**

 Worksheets

CD-ROM

Online

CHAPTER 10 Study Guide: Preview

Organizer

Objective: Help students organize the new concepts they will learn in Chapter 10.

Online Edition
Multilingual Glossary

Resources

PuzzlePro®
One-Stop Planner®

***Multilingual Glossary* Online**

go.hrw.com
KEYWORD: MR7 Glossary

Answers to *Vocabulary Connections*

Possible answers:

1. A cylinder can roll. A cylinder has a circular base.
2. A polyhedron is made up of many bases, or faces.
3. A pyramid has sides that are triangles and a base that is a polygon.
4. You may find one vertex of a polyhedron at its highest point, opposite the base.

CHAPTER 10

Study Guide: Preview

Study Guide: Preview

Where You've Been

Previously, you

- selected appropriate units to measure perimeter, area, and volume.
- classified polygons.
- identified three-dimensional figures.

In This Chapter

You will study

- solving problems involving area.
- identifying, drawing, and building three-dimensional figures.
- finding the surface area of prisms, pyramids, and cylinders.
- finding the volume of prisms and cylinders.

Where You're Going

You can use the skills learned in this chapter

- to find the volume of pyramids, cones, and spheres.
- to find the surface area of spheres.

Key Vocabulary/Vocabulario

area	área
base	base (de un polígono o figura tridimensional)
cylinder	cilindro
edge	arista
face	cara
polyhedron	poliedro
pyramid	pirámide
surface area	área total
vertex	vértice
volume	volumen

Vocabulary Connections

To become familiar with some of the vocabulary terms in the chapter, consider the following. You may refer to the chapter, the glossary, or a dictionary if you like.

1. The word *cylinder* comes from the Greek *kylindein,* meaning "to roll." What do you think the three-dimensional shape of a **cylinder** can do? What shape base do you expect it to have?
2. The word *polyhedron* comes from the Greek *polys,* meaning "many" and *hedra,* meaning "base." What do you think **polyhedrons** are made up of?
3. The Egyptian pyramids are huge stone structures whose outside walls, in the form of four triangles, meet in a point at the top. What shapes do you think make up a **pyramid**?
4. The word *vertex* can mean "highest point." Where do you think you can find one **vertex** of a three-dimensional figure?

Grade 6 CRCT GPS

M6N1.

g. Solve problems involving fractions, decimals, and percents.

M6M2.

a. Measure length to the nearest half, fourth, eighth and sixteenth of an inch.

c. Compare and contrast units of measure for perimeter, area, and volume.

M6M3.

a. Determine the formula for finding the volume of fundamental solid figures.

b. Compute the volumes of fundamental solid figures, using appropriate units of measure.

c. Estimate the volumes of simple geometric solids.

d. Solve application problems involving the volume of fundamental solid figures.

M6M4.

a. Find the surface area of right rectangular prisms and cylinders using manipulatives and constructing nets.

b. Compute the surface area of right rectangular prisms and cylinders using formulae.

c. Estimate the surface areas of simple geometric solids.

d. Solve application problems involving surface area of right rectangular prisms and cylinders.

M6G2.

a. Compare and contrast right prisms and pyramids.

b. Compare and contrast cylinders and cones.

c. Interpret and sketch front, back, top, bottom and side views of solid figures.

d. Construct nets for prisms, cylinders, pyramids, and cones.

M6A3.

Students will evaluate algebraic expressions, including those with exponents, and solve simple one-step equations using each of the four basic operations.

Georgia Mathematics Performance Standards statements are written out completely on pp. GA28–GA35.

Reading Strategy: Learn Math Vocabulary

Many new math terms fill the pages of your textbook. By learning these new terms and their meanings when they are introduced, you will be able to apply this knowledge to different concepts throughout your math classes.

Some ways that may help you learn vocabulary include the following:

- Try to find the meaning of the new term by its context.
- Use the prefix or suffix to figure out the meaning of the term.
- Relate the new term to familiar everyday words or situations.

Vocabulary Word	Definition	Study Tip
Origin	The point (0, 0) where the *x*-axis and *y*-axis intersect on the coordinate plane	The word begins with an "O" which can remind you that the coordinates of the origin are (0, 0).
Quadrants	The *x*- and *y*- axis divide the coordinate plane into four regions. Each region is called a quadrant.	The prefix *quad* means "four." A *quadrilateral* is a four-sided figure, for example.
Coordinate	One of the numbers of an ordered pair that locate a point on a coordinate graph	*Think: x* coordinates with *y*.

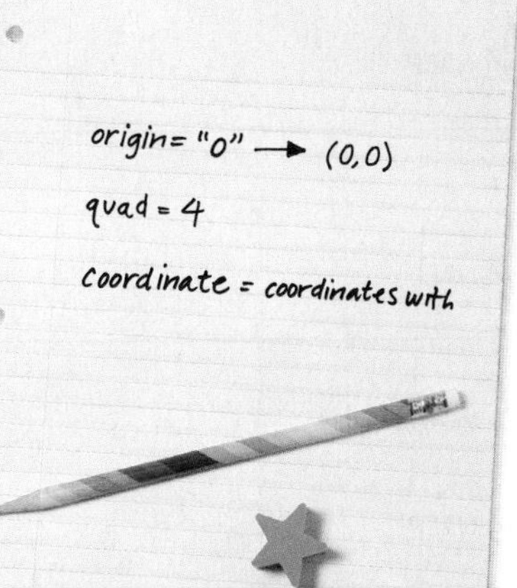

Try This

Complete the table as you work through the chapter to help you learn the vocabulary words.

	Vocabulary Word	Definition	Study Tip
1.	Area	▒	▒
2.	▒	▒	▒
3.	▒	▒	▒

Reading and Writing Math

Reading and Writing Math

Organizer

Objective: Help students apply strategies to understand and retain key concepts.

Online Edition

Resources

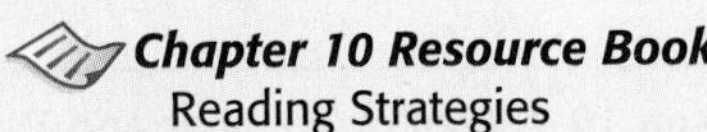

Chapter 10 Resource Book
Reading Strategies

ENGLISH LANGUAGE LEARNERS

Reading Strategy: Learn Math Vocabulary

Discuss As students list the definitions for the vocabulary terms, have them discuss different study tips that might help in retaining the meanings.

Extend Students can apply this technique to learning vocabulary in all subject areas as well as building their vocabulary in nonacademic areas.

Answers to *Try This*

Check students' work.

Grade 6 CRCT GPS

Standards	10-1	10-2	LAB 10-2	10-3	10-4	LAB 10-5	10-5	LAB 10-6	10-6	LAB 10-7	10-7	10-8	LAB 10-9	10-9
M6N1							★							
M6M2					★						★			
M6M3										★	★	★		
M6M4														★
M6G2								★	★				★	
M6A3	★	★		★	★	★	★			★	★	★		

******Georgia Mathematics Process Standards*** **are covered throughout the book.**
For a complete list, see pp. GA28–GA35.

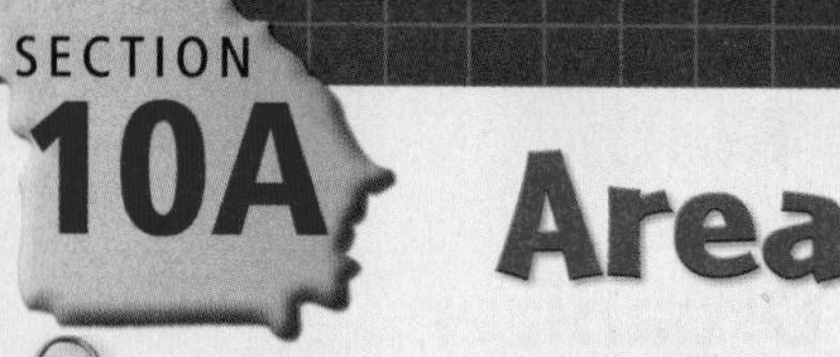

Area

One-Minute Section Planner

Lesson	Materials	MiC and Lab Resources
Lesson 10-1 Estimating and Finding Area • Estimate the area of irregular figures and find the area of rectangles and parallelograms. ☑ CRCT ☑ SAT-10 ☑ ITBS ☑ CTBS ☑ NAEP	Australian map, graph paper	**MiC:** ***Reallotment*** pp. 37–40 ***Hands-On Lab Activities*** 10-1
Lesson 10-2 Area of Triangles and Trapezoids • Find the area of triangles and trapezoids. **10-2 Technology Lab** Area Formulas • Use geometry sofware to explore area. ☑ CRCT ☑ SAT-10 ☑ ITBS ☑ CTBS ☑ NAEP	Geometry software	**MiC:** ***Reallotment*** pp. 7–11, 13–22 ***Technology Lab Activities*** 10-2
Lesson 10-3 Area of Composite Figures • Break a polygon into simpler parts to find its area. ☑ CRCT ☑ SAT-10 ☑ ITBS ☑ CTBS ☑ NAEP		**MiC:** ***Reallotment*** pp. 7–9, 18 ***Technology Lab Activities*** 10-3
Lesson 10-4 Comparing Perimeter and Area • Make a model to explore how area and perimeter are affected by changes in the dimensions of a figure. ☑ CRCT ☑ SAT-10 ☑ ITBS ☑ CTBS ☑ NAEP		**MiC:** ***Reallotment*** pp. 13–22, 37–40
10-5 Hands-On Lab Explore Area of Circles • Use a compass, scissors, and paper folding to explore the area of circles. **Lesson 10-5** Area of Circles • Find the area of a circle. ☑ CRCT ☐ SAT-10 ☐ ITBS ☐ CTBS ☑ NAEP	Compasses (MK), scissors, folding paper	**MiC:** ***Reallotment*** pp. 44–45 ***Hands-On Lab Activities*** 10-5

MK = *Manipulatives Kit*

Mathematics in Context

The unit ***Reallotment*** from the *Mathematics in Context* © 2006 series can be used with Section 10A. See Section Planner above for suggestions for integrating *MiC* with *Holt Mathematics*.

Section Overview

Professional Development

Estimating and Finding Area — *Lessons 10-1, 10-2, 10-3*

You would need to find the area of your backyard to know how much sod is needed to cover it.

The **area** of a figure is the amount of surface it covers.

Area Formulas	
Rectangle	$A = \ell w$
Parallelogram	$A = bh$
Triangle	$A = \frac{1}{2}bh$
Square	$A = s^2$

Comparing Perimeter and Area — *Lesson 10-4*

When the dimensions of a figure change, its perimeter and area are affected differently.

Original Figure

A rectangle is 2 in. by 3 in.

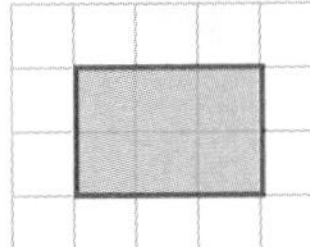

$P = 10$ in.
$A = 6$ in^2

Changed Figure

The dimensions change by a factor of 2, or are doubled.

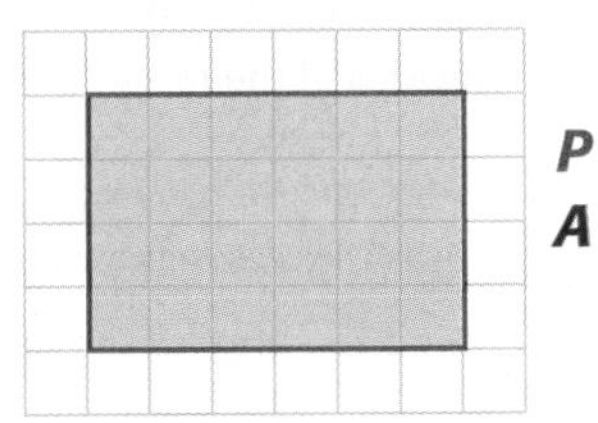

$P = 20$ in.
$A = 24$ in^2

Changed Perimeter and Area

Perimeter changes by a factor of 2.
$P = 10$ in. → $P = 20$ in.

Area changes by a factor 2^2 or 4.
$A = 6$ in^2 → $A = 24$ in^2

A triangle is 3 cm by 4 cm by 5 cm.

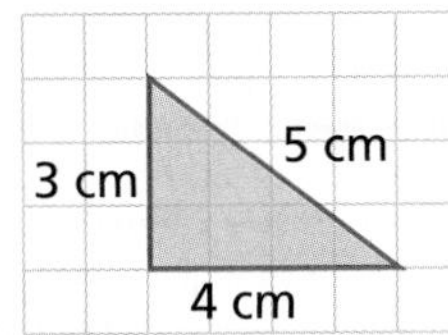

$P = 12$ cm
$A = 6$ cm^2

The dimensions change by a factor of $\frac{1}{2}$, or are halved.

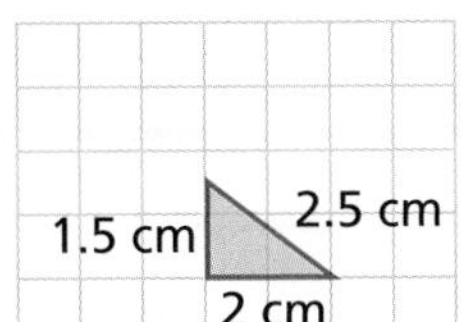

$P = 6$ cm
$A = 1.5$ cm^2

The perimeter changes by a factor of $\frac{1}{2}$.
$P = 12$ cm → $P = 6$ cm

The area changes by a factor of $\frac{1}{2}$, or $\frac{1}{4}$.
$A = 6$ in^2 → $A = 1.5$ cm^2

Area of Circles — *Lesson 10-5*

Finding the area of circles is important in many situations and is also necessary for finding the volume or the surface area of a cylinder.

Area of a Circle
the amount of surface it covers

$A = \pi r^2$

Find the area of a circle with radius 5 cm.

$A = \pi r^2$
$A = \pi 5^2$
$A = 25\pi$ cm^2

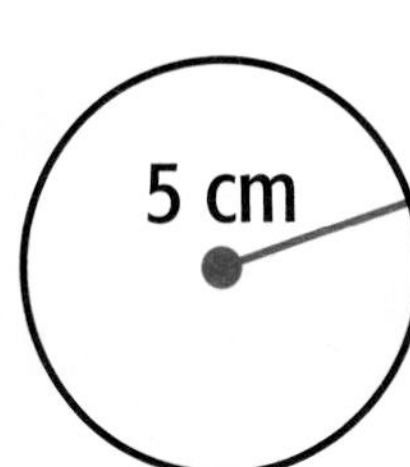

10-1 Organizer

Pacing: Traditional 1 day
Block $\frac{1}{2}$ day

Objective: Students estimate the area of irregular figures and find the area of rectangles and parallelograms.

GPS **M6A3**
Hands-On Lab
In *Hands-On Lab Activities*

Online Edition
Tutorial Videos

Countdown to CRCT Week 22

Power Presentations with PowerPoint®

Warm Up

1. What is the perimeter of a square with side lengths of 15 in.? **60 in.**
2. What is the perimeter of a rectangle with length 16 cm and width 11 cm? **54 cm**

Problem of the Day

Two wibbles equal four wabbles, and eight wabbles equal two bibbles. If a square has a perimeter of 16 wibbles, what is its area in square bibbles?
4 square bibbles

Also available on transparency

Math Fact !!

Ancient Egyptian surveyors found the area of a four-sided field by finding one-half the sum of each pair of opposite sides and then finding their product. If the field is not rectangular, the method leads to an overestimate.

Georgia Performance Standards

M6A3 Students will evaluate algebraic expressions, including those with exponents, and solve simple one-step equations using each of the four basic operations.

M6P1.b Solve problems that arise in mathematics and in other contexts.

10-1 Estimating and Finding Area

Learn to estimate the area of irregular figures and to find the area of rectangles and parallelograms.

Vocabulary
area

When colonists settled the land that would become the United States, ownership boundaries were sometimes natural landmarks such as rivers, trees, and hills. Landowners who wanted to know the size of their property needed to estimate the area of their land.

The **area** of a figure is the amount of surface it covers. We measure area in square units.

EXAMPLE 1 Estimating the Area of an Irregular Figure

Georgia Performance Standards
M6A3 Evaluate algebraic expressions and solve simple one-step equations using each of the four basic operations. Also, M6P1.b.

Estimate the area of the figure.

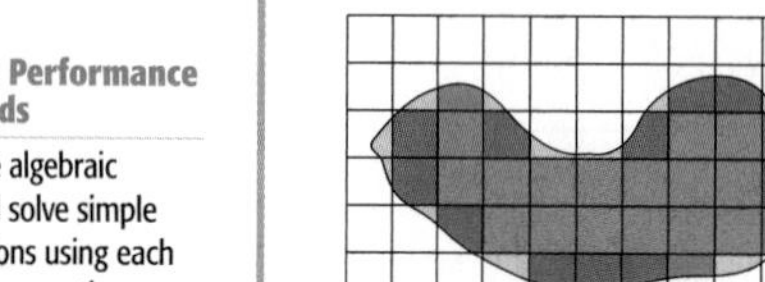

□ = 1 mi^2

Count full squares: 16 red squares.
Count almost-full squares: 11 blue squares.
Count squares that are about half-full: 4 green squares ≈ 2 full squares.
Do not count almost empty yellow squares.
Add. 16 + 11 + 2 = 29

The area of the figure is about 29 mi^2.

AREA OF A RECTANGLE

To find the area of a rectangle, multiply the length by the width.

$$A = \ell w$$
$$A = 4 \cdot 3 = 12$$

The area of the rectangle is 12 square units.

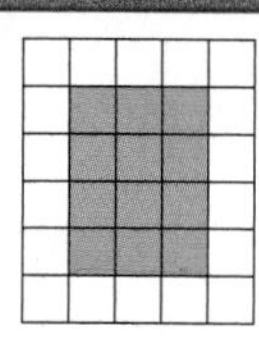

EXAMPLE 2 Finding the Area of a Rectangle

Find the area of the rectangle.

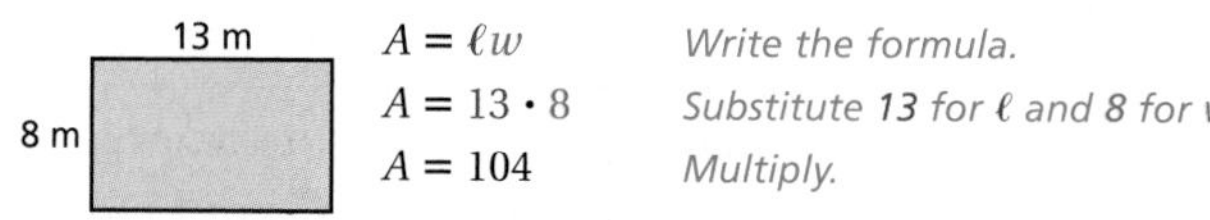

13 m
8 m

$A = \ell w$ *Write the formula.*
$A = 13 \cdot 8$ *Substitute 13 for ℓ and 8 for w.*
$A = 104$ *Multiply.*

The area is 104 m^2.

1 Introduce

Alternate Opener

EXPLORATION

10-1 Estimating and Finding Area

Mr. and Mrs. Domínguez want to have the bottom of their pool refinished. A sketch of the pool is shown below with the side length of each square representing 1 yard. Before they begin the refinishing project, they have to estimate the area in square yards of the bottom of the pool.

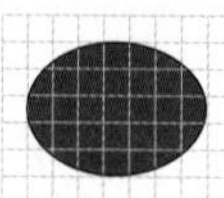

1. Estimate the area, in square yards, of the bottom of the pool.
2. Compare your estimate with the estimates of others in your class, and then average your estimates.
3. What are three other real-world situations in which you might want to estimate area?

Think and Discuss

4. **Discuss** the strategies you used for estimating the area of the bottom of the pool.
5. **Explain** how you could use squares to help you estimate the areas of irregular shapes.

Motivate

ENGLISH LANGUAGE LEARNERS

Have students draw several simple figures on graph paper (available in Teacher Tools) and have them find the perimeter of each figure. Then have them count the number of squares inside each figure. Explain that this is the *area* of the figure and that area is measured in square units.

Explorations and answers are provided in *Alternate Openers: Explorations Transparencies.*

You can use the formula for the area of a rectangle to write a formula for the area of a parallelogram. Imagine cutting off the triangle drawn in the parallelogram and sliding it to the right to form a rectangle.

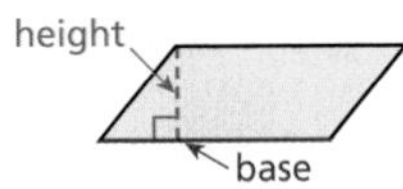

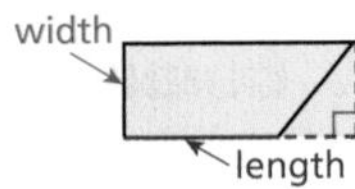

The area of a parallelogram = bh. The area of a rectangle = ℓw.

The **base** of the parallelogram is the **length** of the rectangle.
The **height** of the parallelogram is the **width** of the rectangle.

EXAMPLE 3 Finding the Area of a Parallelogram

Find the area of the parallelogram.

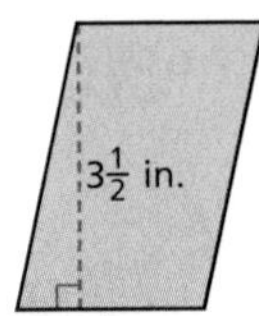

$A = bh$ *Write the formula.*

$A = 2\frac{1}{3} \cdot 3\frac{1}{2}$ *Substitute $2\frac{1}{3}$ for b and $3\frac{1}{2}$ for h.*

$A = \frac{7}{3} \cdot \frac{7}{2}$ *Multiply.*

$A = \frac{49}{6}$, or $8\frac{1}{6}$ The area is $8\frac{1}{6}$ in^2.

EXAMPLE 4 *Recreation Application*

A rectangular park is made up of a rectangular spring-fed pool and a limestone picnic ground that surrounds it. The rectangular park is 30 yd by 25 yd, and the pool is 10 yd by 4 yd. What is the area of the limestone picnic ground?

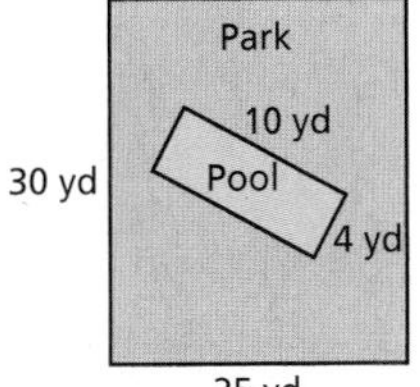

To find the area of the picnic ground, subtract the area of the pool from the area of the park.

park area	−	pool area	=	picnic ground area	
(30 · 25)	−	(10 · 4)	=	n	*Substitute for ℓ and w in $A = \ell w$.*
750	−	40	=	710	*Use the order of operations.*

The area of the limestone picnic ground is 710 yd^2.

Possible answers to *Think and Discuss*

1. The area of the rectangle is twice the area of the triangle.
2. $A = s^2$, where s is the length of each side.

Think and Discuss

GPS M6P2.c, M6P4.a

1. **Explain** how the area of a triangle and the area of a rectangle that have the same base and the same height are related.
2. **Give** a formula for the area of a square.

Power Presentations with PowerPoint®

Additional Examples

Example 1

Estimate the area of the figure. 30 mi^2

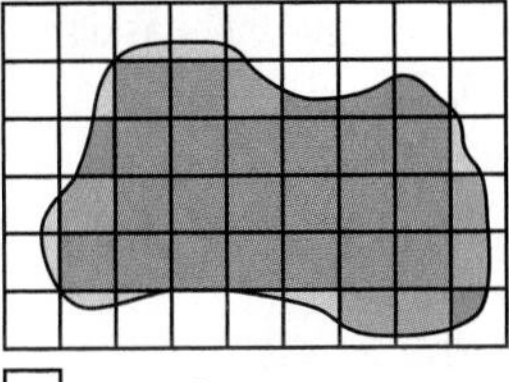

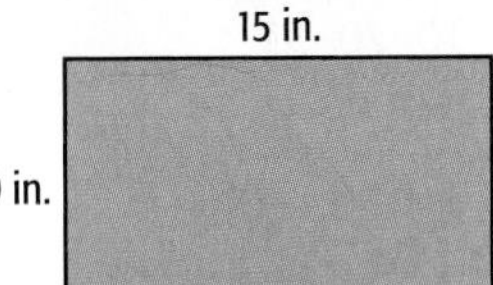

Example 2

Find the area of the rectangle. 135 in^2

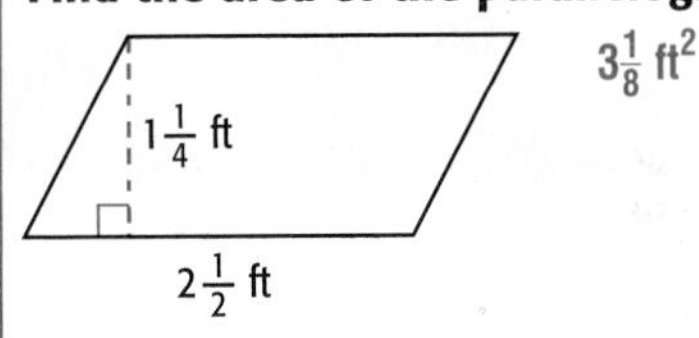

Example 3

Find the area of the parallelogram. $3\frac{1}{8}$ ft^2

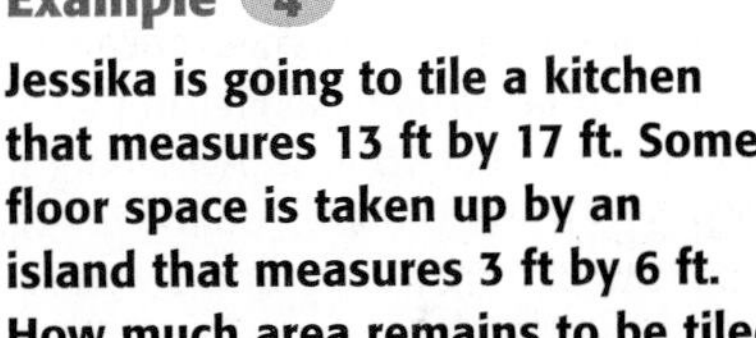

Example 4

Jessika is going to tile a kitchen that measures 13 ft by 17 ft. Some floor space is taken up by an island that measures 3 ft by 6 ft. How much area remains to be tiled in the kitchen? 203 ft^2

Also available on transparency

2 Teach

Guided Instruction

In this lesson, students learn to estimate the area of irregular figures and find the area of rectangles, triangles, and parallelograms. Review the vocabulary associated with these figures. Teach students to estimate the area of an irregular figure on a grid by counting full, almost-full, and half-full squares. Then teach students the formulas for finding the area of rectangles and parallelograms.

Reaching All Learners

Through Curriculum Integration

Social Studies Have students use graph paper (available in Teacher Tools) to trace outlines of states on a map of Australia. Then have them use the method shown in Example 1 to estimate the area of various states.

3 Close

Summarize

Review the formulas for area of a rectangle and parallelogram. Help students to recite them from memory.

10-1 Exercises

Assignment Guide

If you finished Example 1 assign:
Average 1–3, 25–31
Advanced 11–13, 25–31

If you finished Example 2 assign:
Average 1–6, 25–31
Advanced 11–16, 25–31

If you finished Example 3 assign:
Average 1–9, 25–31
Advanced 11–19, 25–31

If you finished Example 4 assign:
Average 1–10, 20–31
Advanced 11–31

Homework Quick Check

Quickly check key concepts.
Exercises: 12, 14, 16, 18

Math Background

A formula that does not require the use of height exists for triangles and for a special class of quadrilaterals.

Heron's formula is so named because the Greek mathematician Heron proved it around the year 75 B.C.E. According to Heron's formula, the area of any triangle with sides of length a, b, and c equals $\sqrt{s(s-a)(s-b)(s-c)}$. The semi-perimeter s equals one-half the perimeter of a figure.

Answers

20. 926 in^2

Georgia Performance Standards

M6P1.a Build new mathematical knowledge through problem solving.

M6P1.c Apply and adapt a variety of appropriate strategies to solve problems.

M6P3.a Organize and consolidate their mathematical thinking through communication.

10-1 Exercises

M6P1.a, M6P1.c, M6P3.a

go.hrw.com
Homework Help Online
KEYWORD: MR7 10-1
Parent Resources Online
KEYWORD: MR7 Parent

GUIDED PRACTICE

See Example 1 — Estimate the area of each figure.

1. 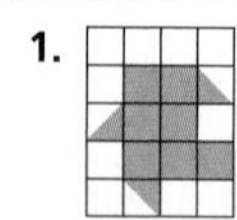 about 8.5 square units

2. 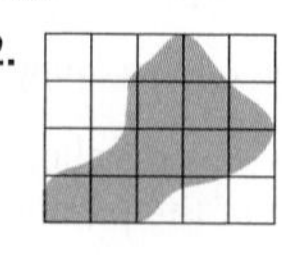 about 9 square units

3.  about 4 square units

See Example 2 — Find the area of each rectangle.

4. 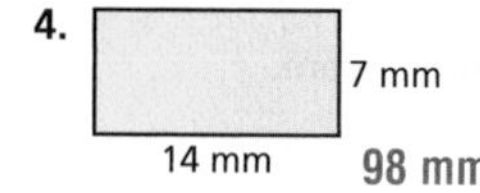

98 mm^2

5. 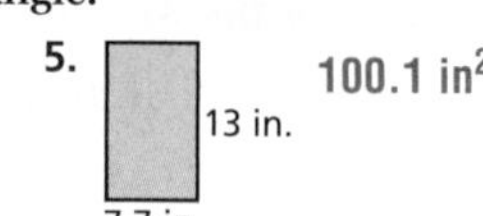

100.1 in^2

6. 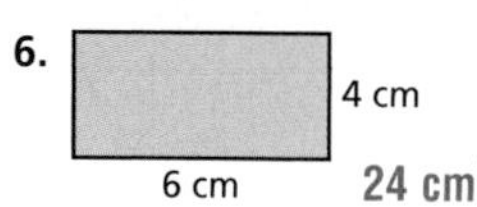

24 cm^2

See Example 3 — Find the area of each parallelogram.

7. 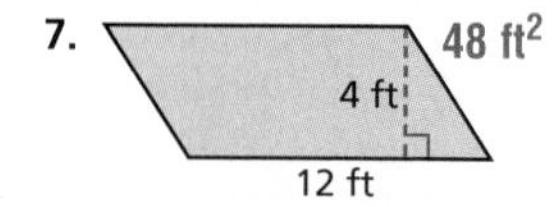

48 ft^2

8. 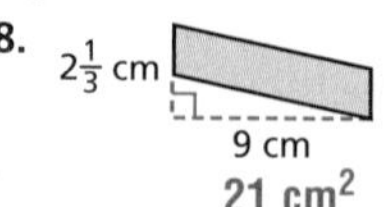

21 cm^2

9. 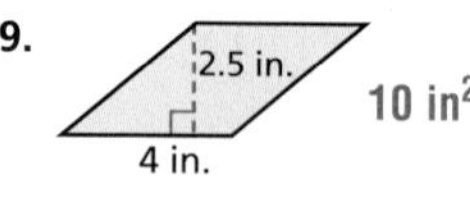

10 in^2

See Example 4

10. Mindy is designing a rectangular fountain in a courtyard. The rest of the courtyard will be covered with stone. The rectangular courtyard is 12 ft by 15 ft. What is the area of the courtyard that will be covered with stone? 168 ft^2

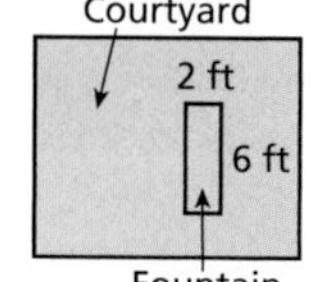

INDEPENDENT PRACTICE

See Example 1 — Estimate the area of each figure.

11. 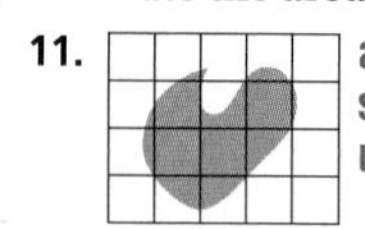 about 6 square units

12. 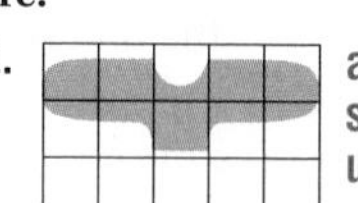 about 5 square units

13. 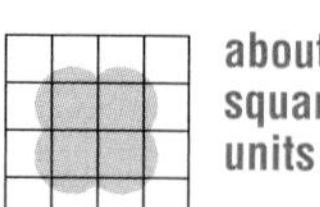 about 4 square units

See Example 2 — Find the area of each rectangle.

14. 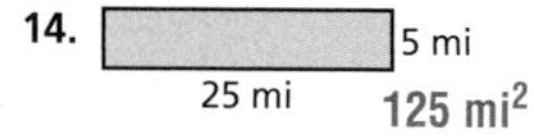

125 mi^2

15. 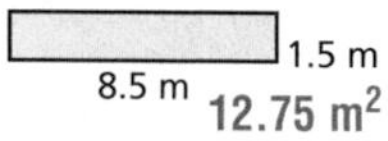 1.5 m, 8.5 m — 12.75 m^2

16. 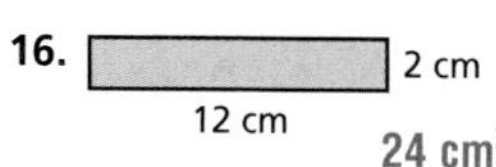

24 cm^2

See Example 3 — Find the area of each parallelogram.

17. 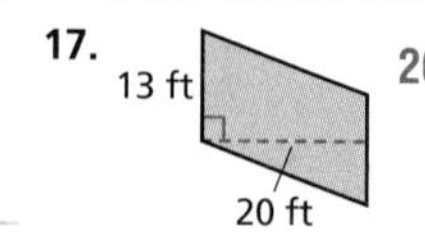

260 ft^2

18. 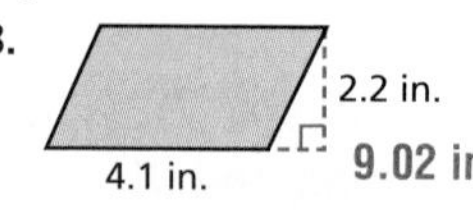

9.02 in^2

19. 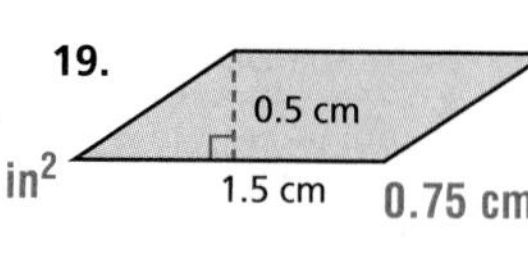

0.75 cm^2

See Example 4

20. Bob is planting in a rectangular container. In the center of the container, he places a smaller rectangular tub with mint. The tub is 8 in. by 3 in. He plants flowers around the tub. What is the area of the container planted with flowers?

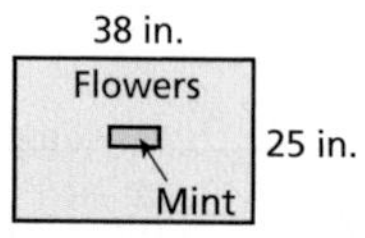

CRCT GPS
Extra Practice p. 733

RETEACH 10-1

LESSON 10-1 **Reteach**
Estimating and Finding Area

You can use grid paper to estimate and find area of figures. The area of a figure is the amount of surface it covers. Area is measured in square units.

To estimate the area of the figure below, first find the number of fully shaded squares. Next, find the number of nearly full squares. Then, find the number of half or nearly half-shaded squares.

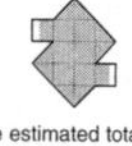

There are 6 fully shaded squares.
There are 2 nearly full squares.
There are 8 half-shaded squares.
$(8 \cdot \frac{1}{2} = 4)$

Find the estimated total number of squares shaded.
$6 + 2 + 4 = 12$. The area of the figure is about 12 square units.

Estimate the area of each figure. Possible answers:

1. 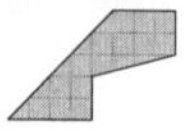 18 units
2.  27 units

To find the area of a rectangle, find the total number of square units.

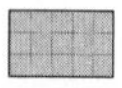

There are 3 rows of 5 squares.
$3 \cdot 5 = 15$
So, the area of the rectangle is 15 square units.

Find the area of each rectangle.

3.  12 square units
4. 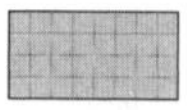 32 square units

PRACTICE 10-1

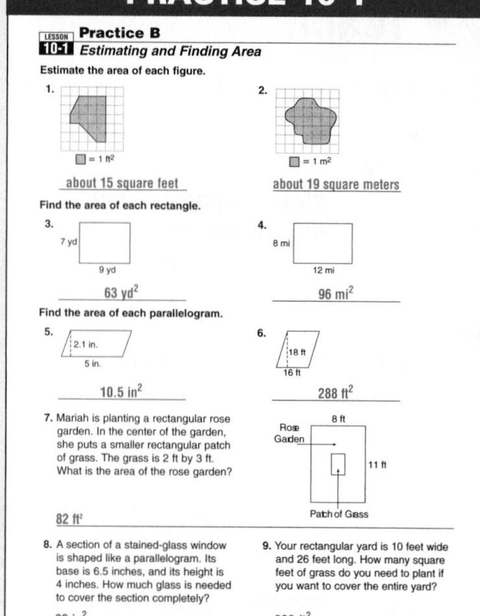
LESSON 10-1 **Practice B**
Estimating and Finding Area

Estimate the area of each figure.

1. $\square$ = 1 ft^2 — about 15 square feet
2. $\square$ = 1 m^2 — about 19 square meters

Find the area of each rectangle.

3. 7 yd, 9 yd — 63 yd^2
4. 8 mi, 12 mi — 96 mi^2

Find the area of each parallelogram.

5. 2.1 in., 5 in. — 10.5 in^2
6. 18 ft, 16 ft — 288 ft^2

7. Mariah is planting a rectangular rose garden. In the center of the garden, she puts a smaller rectangular patch of grass. The grass is 2 ft by 3 ft. What is the area of the rose garden? (Rose Garden, 8 ft, 11 ft, Patch of Grass) — 82 ft^2

8. A section of a stained-glass window is shaped like a parallelogram. Its base is 6.5 inches, and its height is 4 inches. How much glass is needed to cover the section completely? — 26 in^2

9. Your rectangular yard is 10 feet wide and 26 feet long. How many square feet of grass do you need to plant if you want to cover the entire yard? — 260 ft^2

Social Studies LINK

Iceland has many active volcanoes and frequent earthquakes. There are more hot springs in Iceland than in any other country in the world.

Sightseers watch the eruption of Geyser Namafjall in the Myvatn Region of North Iceland.

Use the map for Exercises 21 and 22.

21. Choose a Strategy One square on the map represents 1,700 km^2. Which is a reasonable estimate for the area of Iceland?

- (A) Less than 65,000 km^2
- (B) Between 90,000 and 105,000 km^2 (circled)
- (C) Between 120,000 and 135,000 km^2
- (D) Greater than 150,000 km^2

22. Estimation About 10% of the area of Iceland is covered with glaciers. Estimate the area covered by glaciers. Possible answer: Between 9,000 and 10,500 km^2

23. Write About It The House is Iceland's oldest building. When it was built in 1765, the builders measured length in *ells*. The base of the House is 14 ells wide and 20 ells long. Explain how to find the area in ells of the House. Multiply 14 by 20, which is 280 square ells

24. Challenge The length of one ell varied from country to country. In England, one ell was equal to $1\frac{1}{4}$ yd. Suppose the House were measured in English ells. Find the area in yards of the House. $437\frac{1}{2}$ yd^2

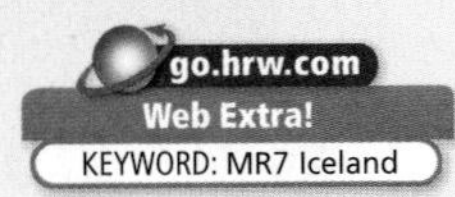

CRCT Prep • GPS Support • Spiral Review

25. Multiple Choice A small square is inside a larger square. The larger square is 14 feet long. The smaller square is 2 feet long. What is the area of the shaded region?

14 ft

2 ft

- (A) 52 ft^2
- (B) 192 ft^2 (circled)
- (C) 196 ft^2
- (D) 200 ft^2

26. Multiple Choice Find the area of a rectangle with length 3 in. and width 12 in.

- (F) 9 in^2
- (G) 18 in^2
- (H) 36 in^2 (circled)
- (J) 144 in^2

List all the factors of each number. (Lesson 4-2)

27. 20 1, 2, 4, 5, 10, 20 **28.** 85 1, 5, 17, 85 **29.** 59 1, 59 **30.** 40 1, 2, 4, 5, 8, 10, 20, 40

31. A tree casts a shadow that is 14 feet long. At the same time, a 5.5-foot-tall boy casts a shadow that is 11 feet long. How tall is the tree? (Lesson 7-5) 7 ft

CHALLENGE 10-1

LESSON 10-1 **Challenge**
Chewing Gum Archaeology

Archaeologists found the oldest piece of chewing gum in Sweden—it was 9,000 years old! The scientists studied the gum to learn about the people who may have made and chewed it. You can be a chewing gum archaeologist, too. How? When a standard-sized wad of chewed gum is stepped on, you can study the area of the flattened gum to find the weight of the person who squished it!

Estimate the area covered by each flattened piece of gum below. Then use the table to find the gum squisher's weight. Possible answers:

Bubble gum was invented in Pennsylvania in 1928.

Estimated Area of Squished Gum	Estimated Weight of Gum Squisher
about 25 cm^2	about 50 lb
about 50 cm^2	about 100 lb
about 75 cm^2	about 150 lb
about 100 cm^2	about 200 lb

1.

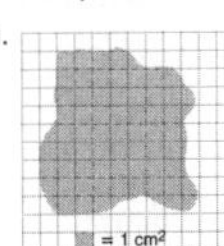

Estimated Area: about 65 cm^2
Estimated Weight: about 150 lb

2. = 1 cm^2

Estimated Area: about 27 cm^2
Estimated Weight: about 50 lb

3.

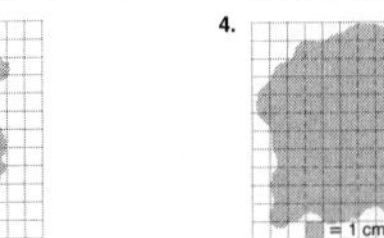

Estimated Area: about 59 cm^2
Estimated Weight: about 100 lb

4. = 1 cm^2

Estimated Area: about 105 cm^2
Estimated Weight: about 200 lb

PROBLEM SOLVING 10-1

LESSON 10-1 **Problem Solving**
Estimating and Finding Area

Use the table to answer each question.

State Information

State	Approx. Width (mi)	Approx. length (mi)	Water Area (mi^2)
Colorado	280	380	376
Kansas	210	400	462
New Mexico	343	370	234
North Dakota	211	340	1,724
Pennsylvania	160	283	1,239

1. New Mexico is the 5th largest state in the United States. What is its approximate total area?
   126,910 mi^2
2. Kansas is the 15th largest state in the United States. What is its approximate total area?
   84,000 mi^2
3. What is the difference between North Dakota's land area and water area?
   70,016 mi^2
4. What is Pennsylvania's approximate land area?
   45,280 mi^2

Circle the letter of the correct answer.

5. What is the difference between Colorado's land area and Pennsylvania's land area?
   - A 106,400 mi^2
   - B 61,120 mi^2 (circled)
   - C 60,120 mi^2
   - D 45,280 mi^2
6. About what percent of the total area of Pennsylvania is covered by land?
   - F about 3%
   - G about 30%
   - H about 67%
   - J about 97% (circled)
7. Rhode Island is the smallest state. Its total land area is approximately 1,200 mi^2. Rhode Island is approximately 40 miles long. About how wide is Rhode Island?
   - A about 20 mi
   - B about 40 mi
   - C about 50 mi
   - D about 30 mi (circled)
8. The entire United States covers 3,794,085 square miles of North America. About how much of that area is not made up of the 5 states in the chart?
   - F 2,537,470 mi^2
   - G 3,359,755 mi^2 (circled)
   - H 3,686,525 mi^2
   - J 3,1310,818 mi^2

Ongoing Assessment and Intervention

Diagnose ***Before*** **the Lesson**
10-1 Warm Up, TE p. 542

Monitor ***During*** **the Lesson**
10-1 Know-It Notebook
10-1 Questioning Strategies

Assess ***After*** **the Lesson**
10-1 Lesson Quiz, TE p. 545

Interdisciplinary LINK

Social Studies

Exercises 21–24 involve the estimation and calculation of area as related to Iceland. Students study Iceland in middle school social studies programs, such as Holt, Rinehart & Winston's *People, Places, and Change.*

Test Prep Doctor In Exercise 26, students who answered **F** or **J** may have squared the length or width. Students who answered **G** may have added two lengths to one width.

Journal

Have students think of and write about real-world situations in which areas of rectangles, triangles, and parallelograms must be found. Have them find the area in each situation, using the appropriate area formula.

Power Presentations with PowerPoint®

10-1 Lesson Quiz

Find the area of each figure.

1. 41.4 m^2

4.5 m

9.2 m

2.

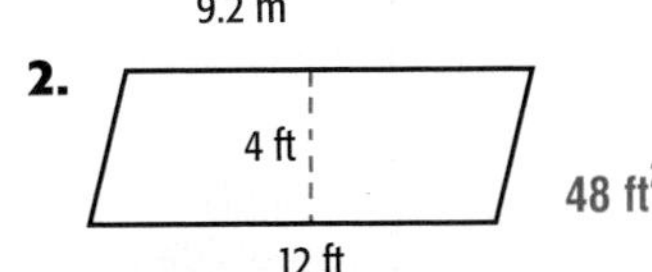

48 ft^2

3. What is the area of a parallelogram with base 16 in. and height 10 in.? 160 in^2

4. A square fish pond that is 6 ft long is surrounded by a square walk that is 18 ft long. What is the area covered by the walk? 288 ft^2

Also available on transparency

10-2 Organizer

Pacing: Traditional 1 day
Block $\frac{1}{2}$ day

Objective: Students find the area of triangles and trapezoids.

Online Edition
Tutorial Videos

Countdown to CRCT Week 22

Power Presentations with PowerPoint®

Warm Up

True or false.

1. If the height of a rectangle equals the base of a parallelogram and the base of the rectangle equals the height of the parallelogram, then the rectangle and the parallelogram have the same area. True
2. Find the area of a rectangle with a length of 53 in. and a width of 47 in. 2,491 in^2

Problem of the Day

Which is a better deal, 3 discs for \$5.00 or 4 discs for \$7.00? 3/\$5.00

Also available on transparency

Math Humor

"I can't be wrong," said the student. "She used a pencil and I used a calculator!"

Georgia Performance Standards

M6A3 Students will evaluate algebraic expressions, including those with exponents, and solve simple one-step equations using each of the four basic operations.

M6P4.c Recognize and apply mathematics in contexts outside of mathematics.

10-2 Area of Triangles and Trapezoids

Learn to find the area of triangles and trapezoids.

Georgia Performance Standards

M6A3 Evaluate algebraic expressions and solve simple one-step equations using each of the four basic operations. Also, M6P4.c.

The Flatiron Building in New York City was built in 1902. Many people consider it to be New York's first skyscraper. The foundation of the building is shaped like a triangle. You can find the area of the triangle to find how much land the building occupies.

You can divide any parallelogram into two congruent triangles. The area of each triangle is half the area of the parallelogram.

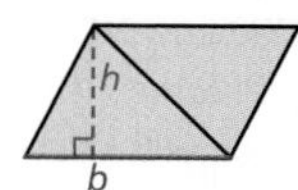

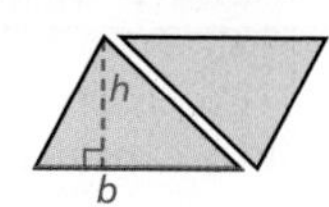

AREA OF A TRIANGLE

The area A of a triangle is half the product of its base b and its height h.

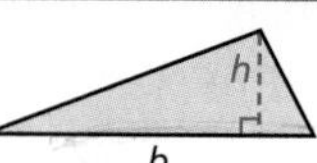

$A = \frac{1}{2}bh$

bh/2

EXAMPLE 1 **Finding the Area of a Triangle**

Find the area of each triangle.

A

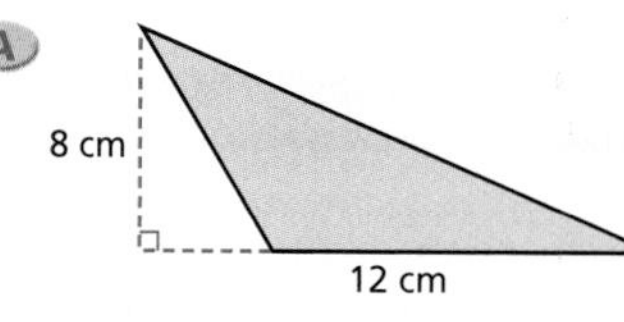

$A = \frac{1}{2}bh$ *Write the formula.*

$A = \frac{1}{2}(12 \cdot 8)$ *Substitute 12 for b. Substitute 8 for h.*

$A = \frac{1}{2}(96)$ *Multiply.*

$A = 48$

The area is 48 cm^2.

B

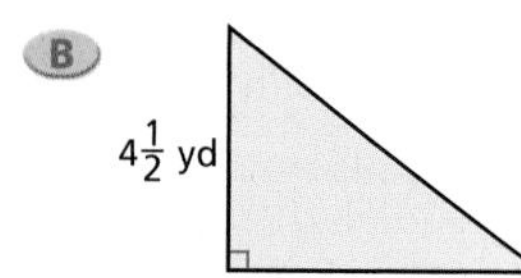

$A = \frac{1}{2}bh$ *Write the formula.*

$A = \frac{1}{2}\left(6 \cdot 4\frac{1}{2}\right)$ *Substitute 6 for b. Substitute $4\frac{1}{2}$ for h.*

$A = \frac{1}{2}(27)$ *Multiply.*

$A = 13\frac{1}{2}$

The area is $13\frac{1}{2}$ yd^2.

Caution!
The legs of a triangle must meet at a 90° angle in order to use their lengths as the base and height of the triangle.

1 Introduce

Alternate Opener

EXPLORATION

10-2 Area of Triangles and Trapezoids

You can use what you know about the area of a parallelogram to develop a formula for the area of a triangle.

1. Fold a sheet of paper in half. Use a ruler to draw a triangle on one side of the folded sheet. Label the base and height of the triangle as shown.
2. Cut out the triangle, cutting through both layers of the folded paper. This will create two congruent triangles.
3. Arrange the two triangles to form a parallelogram.
4. What is the height of the parallelogram? What is its base?
5. What is the area of the parallelogram?
6. How is the area of the triangle related to the area of the parallelogram?

Think and Discuss

7. **Show** how to write a formula for the area of a triangle with base b and height h.
8. **Explain** how to use your formula to find the area of this triangle.

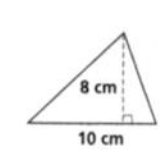

Motivate

Show students models of parallelograms, rectangles, and squares. Then show how triangles can be created by cutting the figures in half. Review the types of triangles students have learned. Students should be able to identify right, acute, and obtuse triangles and scalene, isosceles, and equilateral triangles.

Explorations and answers are provided in *Alternate Openers: Explorations Transparencies.*

EXAMPLE 2 Architecture Application

The diagram shows the outline of the foundation of the Flatiron Building. What is the area of the foundation?

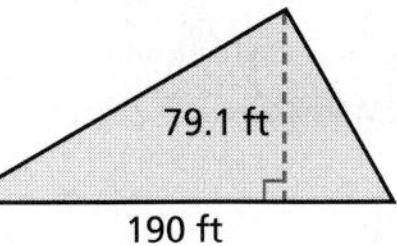

$A = \frac{1}{2}bh$ *Write the formula.*

$A = \frac{1}{2}(190 \cdot 79.1)$ *Substitute 190 for b. Substitute 79.1 for h.*

$A = \frac{1}{2}(15{,}029) = 7{,}514.5$ *Multiply.*

The area of the foundation is 7,514.5 ft^2.

A trapezoid can be divided into a rectangle and two triangles. The area of the trapezoid is the sum of the areas of the rectangle and the triangles.

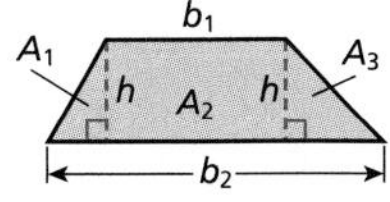

AREA OF A TRAPEZOID

The area A of a trapezoid is the product of half its height h and the sum of its bases b_1 and b_2.

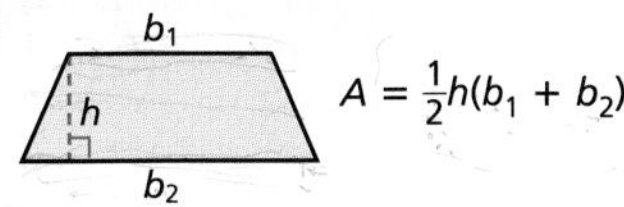

EXAMPLE 3 Finding the Area of a Trapezoid

Find the area of the trapezoid.

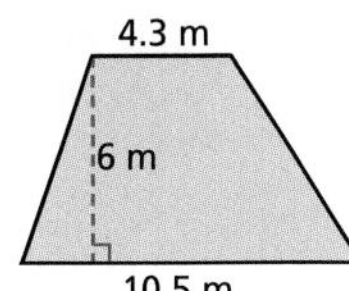

$A = \frac{1}{2}h(b_1 + b_2)$ *Write the formula.*

$A = \frac{1}{2}(6)(4.3 + 10.5)$ *Substitute 6 for h, 4.3 for b_1, and 10.5 for b_2.*

$A = \frac{1}{2}(6)(14.8) = 44.4$ *Multiply.*

The area is 44.4 m^2.

Possible answers to *Think and Discuss*

1. The area of the triangle is half the area of the parallelogram.
2. His work is correct. He used the distributive property of addition as his first step.

Think and Discuss

GPS M6P3.c, M6P4.a

1. **Explain** how the areas of a triangle and a parallelogram with the same base and height are related.
2. **Explain** whether Max's work is correct: To find the area of a trapezoid, Max multiplied the height by the top base and the height by the bottom base. He added the two numbers together and then divided the sum by 2.

COMMON ERROR ALERT

Students sometimes forget that the area of a triangle is *half* of the base times the height. Remind them that base times height gives the area of a parallelogram with those dimensions.

Power Presentations with PowerPoint®

Additional Examples

Example 1

Find the area of each triangle.

A. 120 ft^2

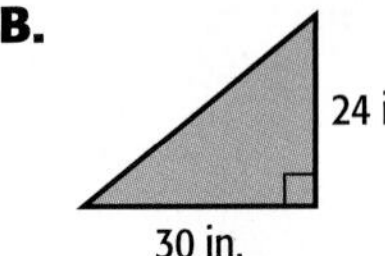

B. 360 in^2

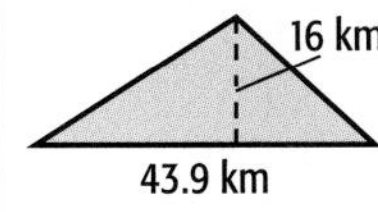

Example 2

The diagram shows the section of a forest being studied. What is the area of the section?

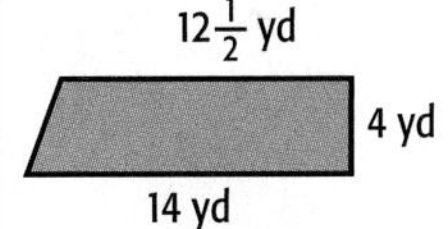

351.2 km^2

Example 3

Find the area of the trapezoid.

53 yd^2

$12\frac{1}{2}$ yd, 4 yd, 14 yd

Also available on transparency

2 Teach

Guided Instruction

In this lesson, students learn to find the area of triangles and trapezoids. Review using the formula $A = bh$ to find the area of a parallelogram. Describe the process for finding the area of a triangle, making sure that students understand that any side can serve as a base; the height is then the vertical distance to that base from the vertex of the angle opposite the base. Use models of parallelograms and triangles to illustrate the formulas presented in this lesson.

Reaching All Learners

Through Concrete Manipulatives

Have students work in pairs. Each pair draws a parallelogram and marks the base and the height. Students should then cut their parallelograms in half and demonstrate that the two triangles are congruent. Have students verbalize the formula for the area of a triangle. Next, have students draw a trapezoid, cut it into a rectangle and two triangles, and verbalize the formula for the area of a trapezoid.

3 Close

Summarize

Show models of triangles and trapezoids. Have students identify the bases and heights on each triangle. Ask students to explain why any side can be a base. because there is a height for each base Then have students describe the height for each base on the triangles. The height is the vertical distance from the base to the opposite vertex. Ask the same questions for a trapezoid. A trapezoid has only 2 bases—the parallel sides; the height is the vertical distance between them.

10-2 Exercises

Assignment Guide

If you finished Example 1 assign:
Average 1–3, 17, 28–34
Advanced 8–10, 18, 28–34

If you finished Example 2 assign:
Average 1–4, 17–18, 20, 28–34
Advanced 8–12, 17–18, 23, 28–34

If you finished Example 3 assign:
Average 1–4, 12–24, 28–34
Advanced 8–21, 25–34

Homework Quick Check

Quickly check key concepts.
Exercises: 12, 14, 16, 18

10-2 Exercises

M6P1.b, M6P3.a

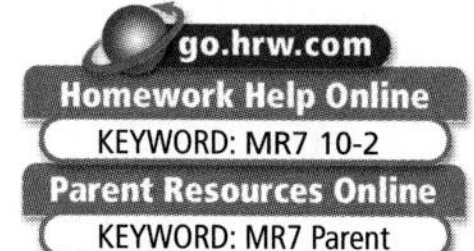

GUIDED PRACTICE

See Example 1

Find the area of each triangle.

1. 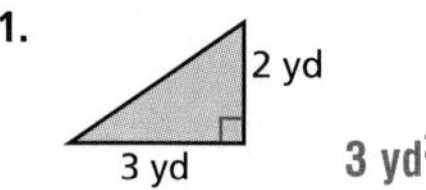

3 yd^2

2. 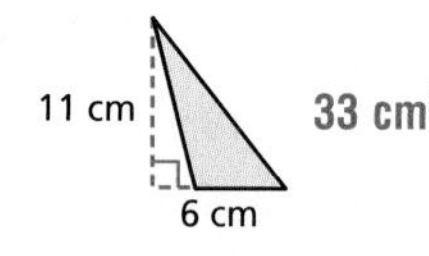

33 cm^2

3. 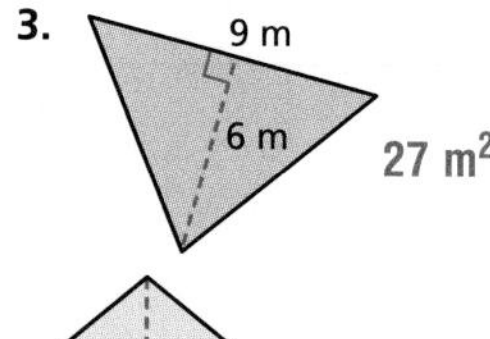

27 m^2

See Example 2

4. Harry plans to paint the triangular portion of the side of his house. How many square feet does he need to paint? 80 ft^2

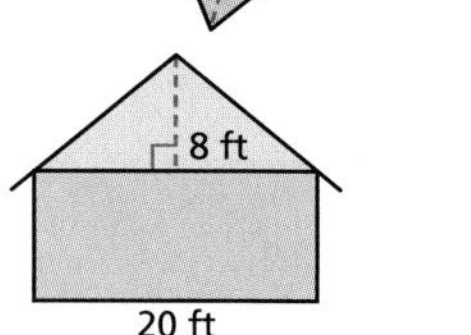

See Example 3

Find the area of each trapezoid.

5. 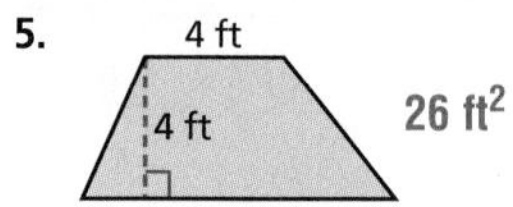

26 ft^2

6. 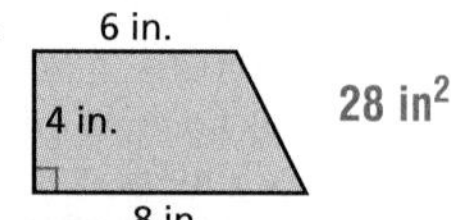

28 in^2

7. 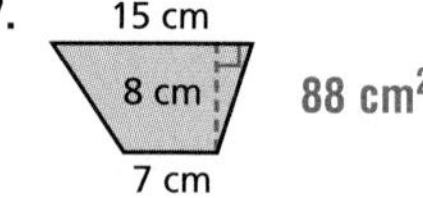

88 cm^2

INDEPENDENT PRACTICE

See Example 1

Find the area of each triangle.

8. 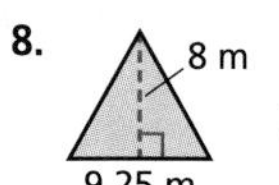

37 m^2

9. 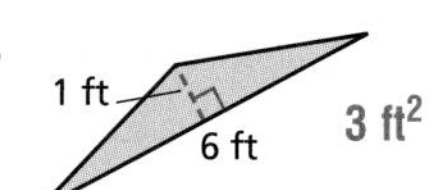

3 ft^2

10. 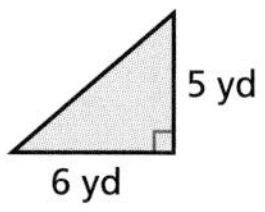 5 yd, 6 yd 15 yd^2

See Example 2

11. Sean is making pennants for the school football team. How many square inches of felt does he use for one pennant? 72 in^2

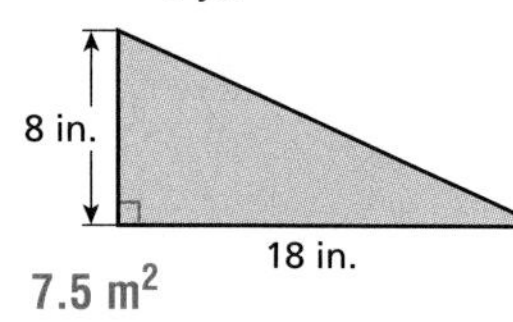

12. Erin has a triangular garden plot that is 5 meters long and 3 meters tall. What is the area of the plot? 7.5 m^2

See Example 3

Find the area of each trapezoid.

13. 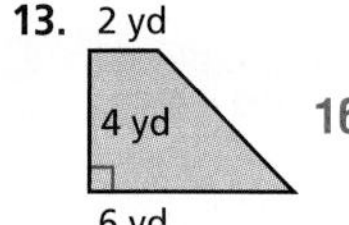

16 yd^2

14. 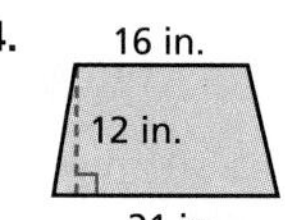

222 in^2

15. 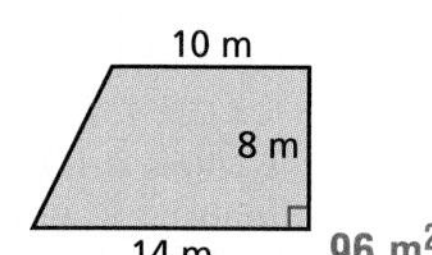

96 m^2

PRACTICE AND PROBLEM SOLVING

Extra Practice p. 733

16. The water in a drainage canal is 4 feet deep. What is the area of a cross section of the water in the ditch, which is shaped like a trapezoid? 52 ft^2

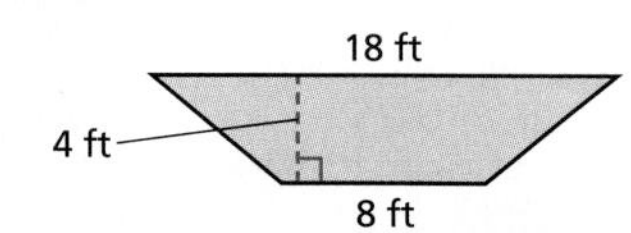

Georgia Performance Standards

M6P1.b Solve problems that arise in mathematics and in other contexts.

M6P3.a Organize and consolidate their mathematical thinking through communication.

RETEACH 10-2

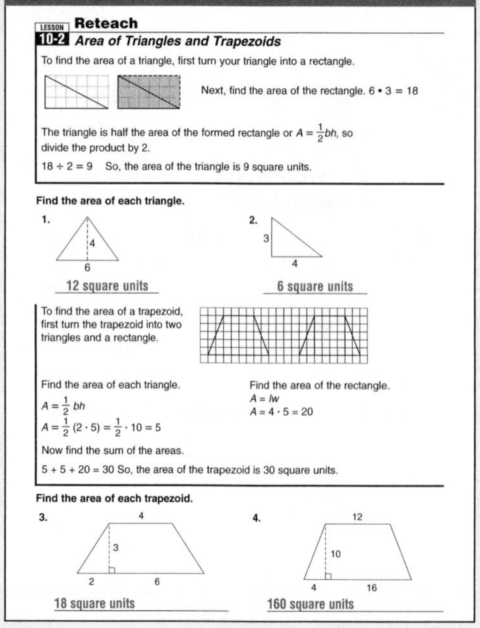

LESSON 10-2 **Reteach**
Area of Triangles and Trapezoids

To find the area of a triangle, first turn your triangle into a rectangle.

Next, find the area of the rectangle. 6 • 3 = 18

The triangle is half the area of the formed rectangle or $A = \frac{1}{2}bh$, so divide the product by 2.

18 ÷ 2 = 9 So, the area of the triangle is 9 square units.

Find the area of each triangle.

1. 4, 6 — 12 square units
2. 3, 4 — 6 square units

To find the area of a trapezoid, first turn the trapezoid into two triangles and a rectangle.

Find the area of each triangle.
$A = \frac{1}{2}bh$
$A = \frac{1}{2}(2 \cdot 5) = \frac{1}{2} \cdot 10 = 5$

Find the area of the rectangle.
$A = lw$
$A = 4 \cdot 5 = 20$

Now find the sum of the areas.
5 + 5 + 20 = 30 So, the area of the trapezoid is 30 square units.

Find the area of each trapezoid.

3. 4, 3, 2, 6 — 18 square units
4. 12, 10, 4, 16 — 160 square units

PRACTICE 10-2

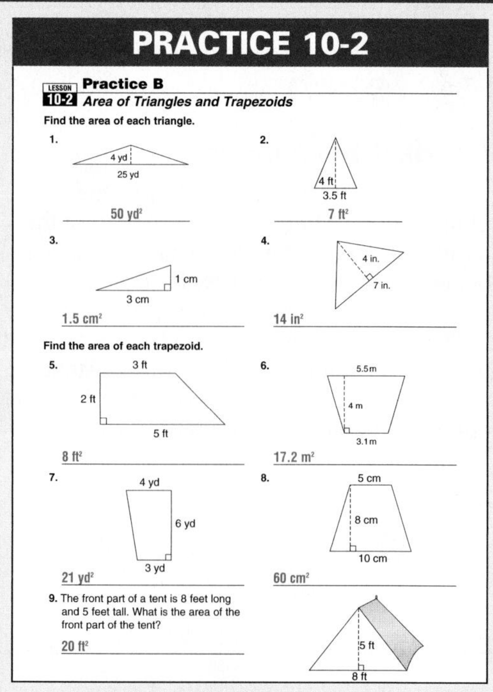
LESSON 10-2 **Practice B**
Area of Triangles and Trapezoids

Find the area of each triangle.

1. 4 yd, 25 yd — 50 yd²
2. 4 ft, 3.5 ft — 7 ft²
3. 1 cm, 3 cm — 1.5 cm²
4. 4 in., 7 in. — 14 in²

Find the area of each trapezoid.

5. 3 ft, 2 ft, 5 ft — 8 ft²
6. 5.5 m, 4 m, 3.1 m — 17.2 m²
7. 4 yd, 6 yd, 3 yd — 21 yd²
8. 5 cm, 8 cm, 10 cm — 60 cm²

9. The front part of a tent is 8 feet long and 5 feet tall. What is the area of the front part of the tent? 20 ft²

For Exercises 17–21, find the area of each figure.

17.
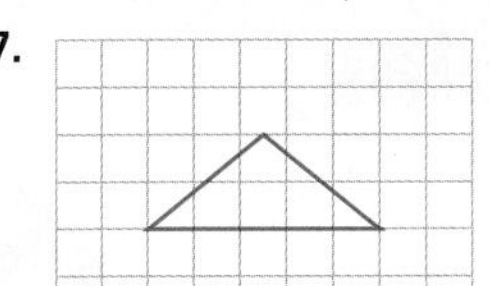
5 square units

18.
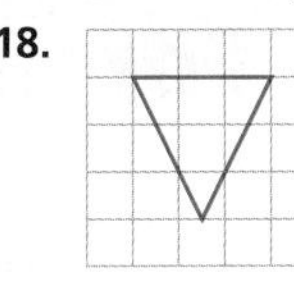
$4\frac{1}{2}$ square units

19.
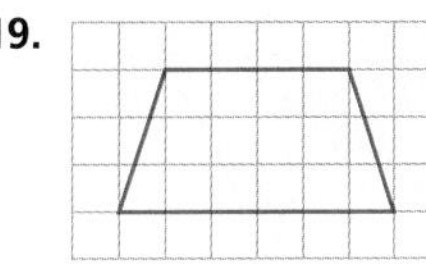
15 square units

20. triangle: $b = 2\frac{1}{2}$ in.; $h = 1\frac{3}{4}$ in. **21.** trapezoid: $b_1 = 18$ m; $b_2 = 27$ m; $h = 15.4$ m 346.5 m^2

LINK Social Studies

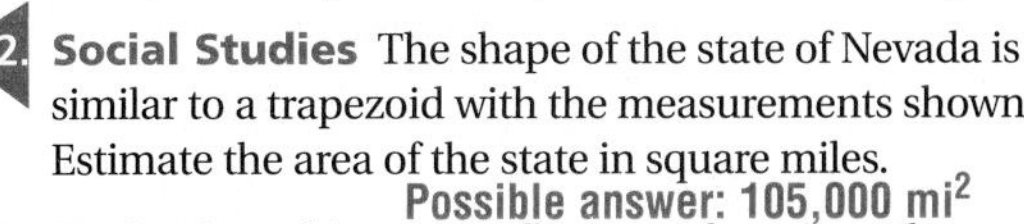

Nevada has many ghost towns scattered around the state. Many were once boom-towns built during the gold and silver mining rush.

22. **Social Studies** The shape of the state of Nevada is similar to a trapezoid with the measurements shown. Estimate the area of the state in square miles. Possible answer: 105,000 mi^2

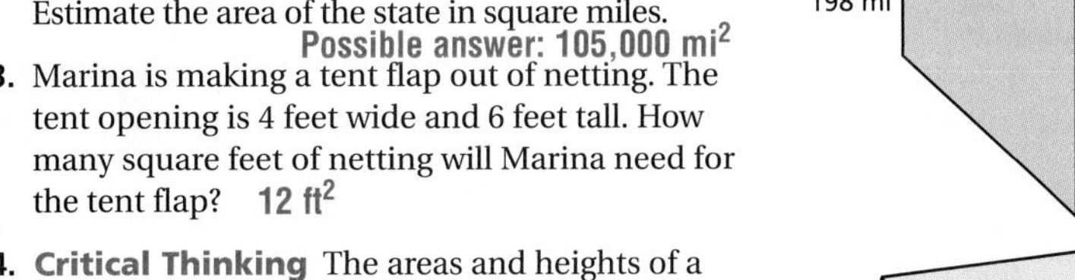

23. Marina is making a tent flap out of netting. The tent opening is 4 feet wide and 6 feet tall. How many square feet of netting will Marina need for the tent flap? 12 ft^2

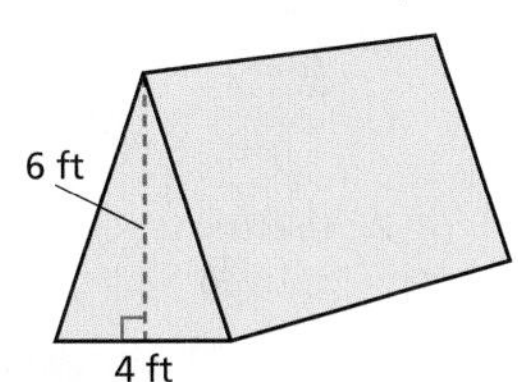

24. **Critical Thinking** The areas and heights of a triangle and a rectangle are the same. How do the lengths of their bases compare?

25. **Write a Problem** Write a problem about a trapezoid with bases 12 feet and 18 feet and height 10 feet. Check students' work.

26. **Write About It** Two triangles have the same base. The height of one triangle is half the height of the other. How do the areas of the triangles compare?

27. **Challenge** Find the area of the unshaded portion of the trapezoid. 270 m^2

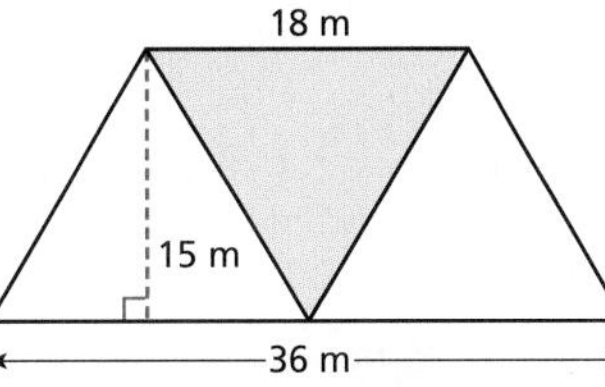

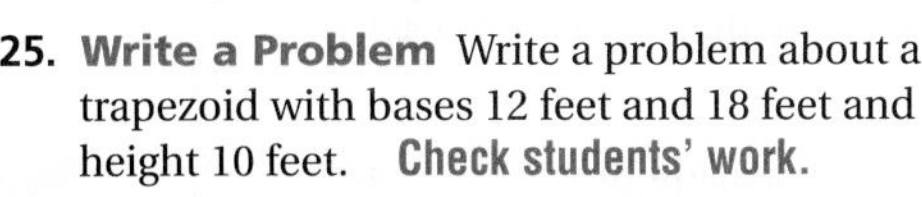

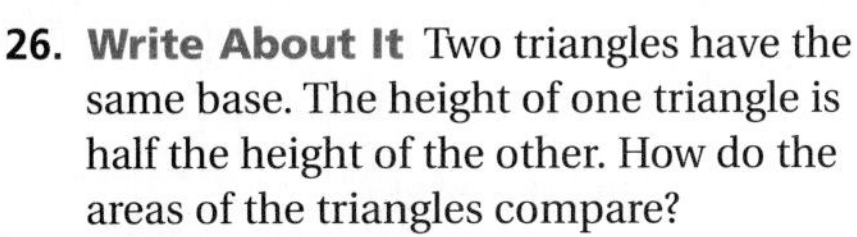

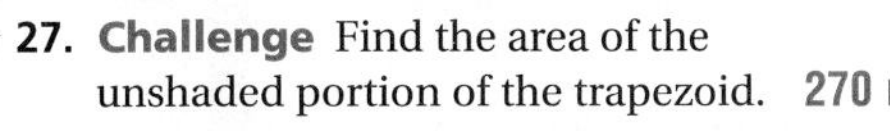

20. $2\frac{3}{16}$ in^2

24. Possible answer: The base of the triangle is twice as long as the base of the rectangle.

CRCT Prep • GPS Support • Spiral Review

28. **Multiple Choice** A building sign in the shape of a trapezoid has the measurements shown. Which expression can be used to find the area of the sign?

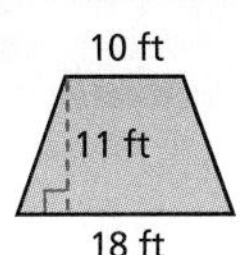

(A) $\frac{1}{2}(11)(10 + 18)$ (B) $\frac{1}{2}(18)(10)$ (C) $\frac{1}{2}(11)(10)(18)$ (D) $(11)(10 + 18)$

29. **Short Response** Find the area of a right triangle with legs measuring 14 cm and 25 cm. 175 cm^2

Multiply. Write each answer in simplest form. (Lesson 5-6)

30. $3 \cdot \frac{2}{7}$ $\frac{6}{7}$ **31.** $4 \cdot \frac{3}{5}$ $\frac{12}{5}$ **32.** $12 \cdot \frac{9}{10}$ $\frac{54}{5}$ **33.** $15 \cdot \frac{1}{2}$ $\frac{15}{2}$

34. Zeb earned $24,000 last year. This year, his salary increased by 5%. How much will he earn? (Lesson 7-9) $25,200

Ongoing Assessment and Intervention

Diagnose Before the Lesson
10-2 Warm Up, TE p. 546

Monitor During the Lesson
10-2 Know-It Notebook
10-2 Questioning Strategies

Assess After the Lesson
10-2 Lesson Quiz, TE p. 549

Answers

26. See p. A10.

Test Prep Doctor For Exercise 29, students need to remember two facts. First, the area of a triangle is *half* of the base times the height. Second, the legs of a right triangle can be used as the base and height of the triangle.

Journal

Have students explain the difference between a square foot and a square yard.

Power Presentations with PowerPoint®

10-2 Lesson Quiz

Find the area of each triangle.

1. 39.9 cm^2 (7.6 cm; 10.5 cm)

2. 84 mi^2 (7 mi; 24 mi)

Find the area of each trapezoid.

3. 22.5 mi^2 (6.5 m; 3 m; 8.5 m)

4. $113\frac{3}{4}$ in^2 ($6\frac{1}{2}$ in.; $9\frac{3}{4}$ in.; 14 in.)

Also available on transparency

CHALLENGE 10-2

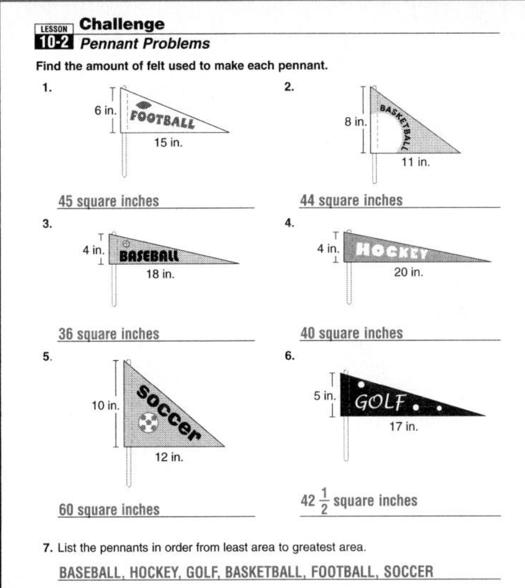

LESSON 10-2 **Challenge**
Pennant Problems

Find the amount of felt used to make each pennant.

1. (6 in., 15 in., FOOTBALL) 45 square inches
2. (8 in., 11 in., BASKETBALL) 44 square inches
3. (4 in., 18 in., BASEBALL) 36 square inches
4. (4 in., 20 in., HOCKEY) 40 square inches
5. (10 in., 12 in., SOCCER) 60 square inches
6. (5 in., 17 in., GOLF) $42\frac{1}{2}$ square inches
7. List the pennants in order from least area to greatest area.
BASEBALL, HOCKEY, GOLF, BASKETBALL, FOOTBALL, SOCCER

PROBLEM SOLVING 10-2

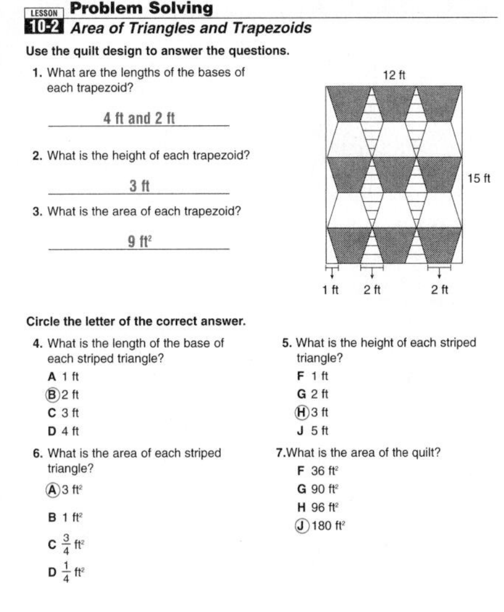

LESSON 10-2 **Problem Solving**
Area of Triangles and Trapezoids

Use the quilt design to answer the questions.

1. What are the lengths of the bases of each trapezoid?
4 ft and 2 ft
2. What is the height of each trapezoid?
3 ft
3. What is the area of each trapezoid?
9 ft²

Circle the letter of the correct answer.

4. What is the length of the base of each striped triangle?
A 1 ft
(B) 2 ft
C 3 ft
D 4 ft
5. What is the height of each striped triangle?
F 1 ft
G 2 ft
(H) 3 ft
J 5 ft
6. What is the area of each striped triangle?
(A) 3 ft²
B 1 ft²
C $\frac{3}{4}$ ft²
D $\frac{1}{4}$ ft²
7. What is the area of the quilt?
F 36 ft²
G 90 ft²
H 96 ft²
(J) 180 ft²

Organizer

Use with Lesson 10-2

Pacing:
Traditional $\frac{1}{2}$ day
Block $\frac{1}{4}$ day

Objective: Use geometry software to explore area and perimeter.

Materials: Computer, geometry software

Online Edition
TechKeys

Countdown to CRCT Week 22

Resources

Technology Lab Activities
Lab 10-2 Recording Sheet

Teach

Discuss

Have students discuss how to be sure that a quadrilateral constructed with the software is a rectangle. Help students use the software to practice constructing rectangles.

Close

Key Concept

Geometry software can be used to explore geometric formulas.

Assessment

Discuss how to use the software to create and explore figures.

1. Create triangle *ABC*, and use the software to find its area.
2. Create square *WXYZ* and use a calculator to find its area.

Georgia Performance Standards

M6P1.c Apply and adapt a variety of appropriate strategies to solve problems.

M6P2.a Recognize reasoning and proof as fundamental aspects of mathematics.

M6P2.b Make and investigate mathematical conjectures.

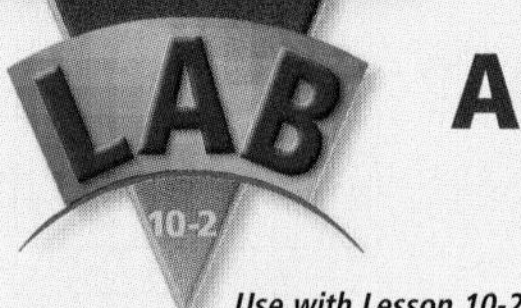

Area Formulas

Use with Lesson 10-2

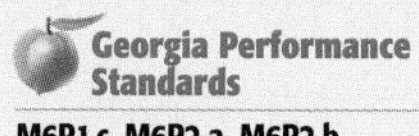

Georgia Performance Standards
M6P1.c, M6P2.a, M6P2.b

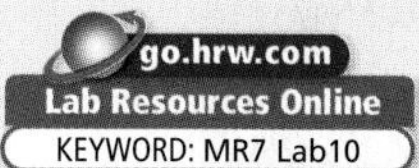

Geometry software can be used to explore geometric formulas.

Activity

1. Use your geometry software to explore the formula for the area of a rectangle, $A = \ell \cdot w$.

   a. Construct a rectangle *ABCD*. Choose four points and connect them with line segments, making sure the opposite sides are parallel.

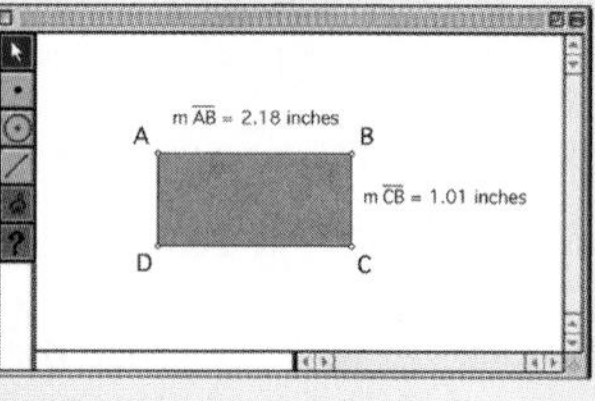

   b. Use the distance tool to measure the length of sides $\overline{AB}$ and $\overline{CB}$.

   Select the interior of the rectangle, and then use the area tool to measure the area.

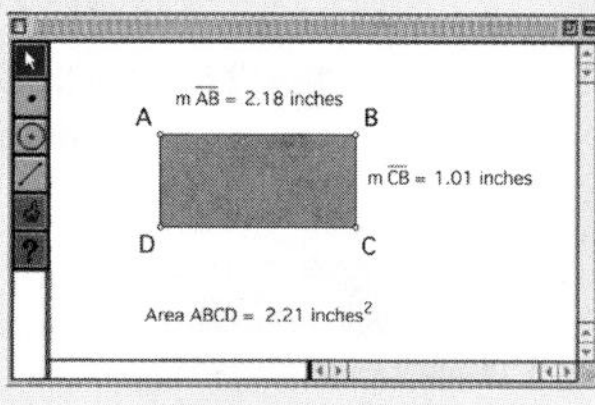

   c. Use a calculator or paper and pencil to find the product of the side lengths. Round to the hundredths place.
   $2.18 \cdot 1.01 \approx 2.20$

   Notice that the geometry software rounds the product to 2.21, which is close to 2.20.
   So $Area = AB \cdot CB = \ell \cdot w$.

Think and Discuss

1. Tell whether the perimeter *P* of rectangle *ABCD* is equal to $2 \cdot (AB + CB)$. **yes**
2. Determine whether the area of rectangle ABCD divided by 2 is equal to the perimeter. **No; half of the area of rectangle *ABCD* is not equal to its perimeter.**

Try This

1. Use geometry software to construct a triangle *ABC* where $m\angle B = 90°$.

   a. Measure the area of the triangle and the lengths of sides $\overline{AB}$ and $\overline{CB}$. Find $\frac{1}{2} \cdot AB \cdot CB$. **Check students' work.**

   b. Drag angle *A*, making sure $m\angle B = 90°$. Do this three more times to construct triangles with different areas and side lengths. For each triangle, find $\frac{1}{2} \cdot AB \cdot CB$. What do you conclude? **The area of each triangle is equal to $\frac{1}{2} \cdot AB \cdot CB$.**

Answers to *Assessment*

1. Students will choose three points and connect them with line segments and then click inside the triangle and use the area tool. Areas will vary. Check students' work.
2. Students will create four congruent segments that meet at right angles. They will use the distance tool to measure each side and then use the formula $A = s^2$ to find the square's area.

10-3 Area of Composite Figures

Learn to break a polygon into simpler parts to find its area.

You can find the areas of irregular polygons by breaking them apart into rectangles, parallelograms, and triangles.

EXAMPLE 1 Finding Areas of Composite Figures

Find the area of each polygon.

A

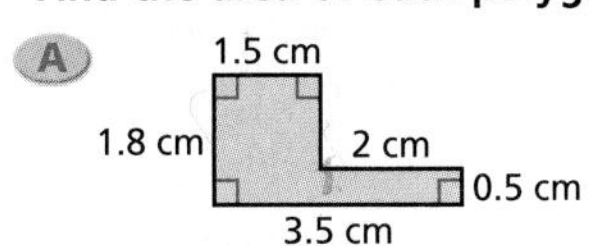

Think: Break the polygon apart into rectangles.

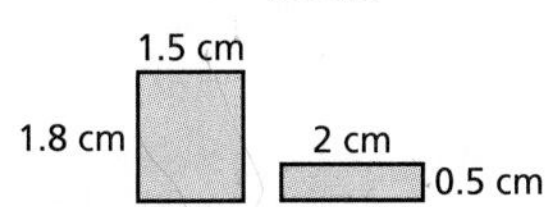

Find the area of each rectangle.

$A = \ell w$ $\quad A = \ell w$ *Write the formula for the area of a rectangle.*

$A = 1.8 \cdot 1.5$ $\quad A = 2 \cdot 0.5$

$A = 2.7$ $\quad A = 1$

$2.7 + 1 = 3.7$ *Add to find the total area.*

The area of the polygon is 3.7 cm^2.

B

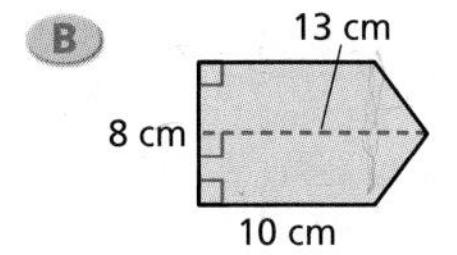

Think: Break the figure apart into a triangle and a rectangle.

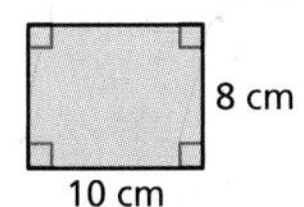

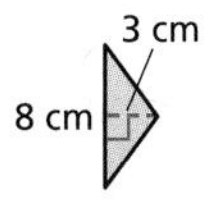

$A = \ell w$ $\quad A = \frac{1}{2}bh$ *Find the area of each polygon.*

$A = 8 \cdot 10$ $\quad A = \frac{1}{2} \cdot 8 \cdot 3$

$A = 80$ $\quad A = 12$

$80 + 12 = 92$ *Add to find the total area of the figure.*

The area of the figure is 92 cm^2.

Georgia Performance Standards

M6A3 Evaluate algebraic expressions and solve simple one-step equations using each of the four basic operations. Also, M6P1.b.

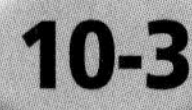

Organizer 10-3

Pacing: Traditional 1 day
Block $\frac{1}{2}$ day

Objective: Students break a polygon into simpler parts to find its area.

Hands-On Lab
In *Hands-On Lab Activities*

Online Edition
Tutorial Videos

Countdown to CRCT Week 22

Power Presentations with PowerPoint®

Warm Up

1. What is the area of a rectangle with length 10 cm and width 4 cm? **40 cm^2**
2. What is the area of a parallelogram with base 18 ft and height 12 ft? **216 ft^2**
3. What is the area of a triangle with base 16 cm and height 8 cm? **64 cm^2**

Problem of the Day

Four squares are stacked in a tower. The bottom square is 12 inches on a side. The perimeter of each of the other squares is half of the one below it. What is the perimeter of the combined figure? **69 in.**

Also available on transparency

1 Introduce

Alternate Opener

EXPLORATION

10-3 Area of Composite Figures

Phil and Louise are planning to sod their backyard. Sod is sold in square yards. They sketched their yard on a piece of graph paper, where the side length of each square represents 1 yard.

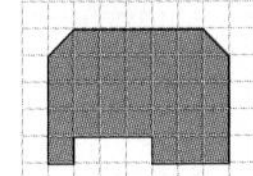

1. a. Divide the figure into several simpler figures.
   b. Name each figure from part **a**.
   c. Find the area in square yards of each figure.
   d. Add the areas in part **c**.

Think and Discuss

2. **Discuss** the strategies you used for finding area.
3. **Explain** how you could use squares to help you find the areas of irregular shapes.

2 Teach

Guided Instruction

In this lesson, students learn to break a polygon into simpler parts to find the area of the polygon. Teach students how to break a composite figure into rectangles, triangles, and parallelograms. Explain that the areas of the smaller figures can be added to find the area of the composite figure.

Teaching Tip

Visual Counting squares can be easier if students draw lines that begin and end at the intersection of the grid lines on the graph paper.

Explorations and answers are provided in *Alternate Openers: Explorations Transparencies.*

Georgia Performance Standards

M6A3 Students will evaluate algebraic expressions, including those with exponents, and solve simple one-step equations using each of the four basic operations.

M6P1.b Solve problems that arise in mathematics and in other contexts.

Power Presentations with PowerPoint®

Additional Examples

Example 1

Find the area of each polygon.

A.

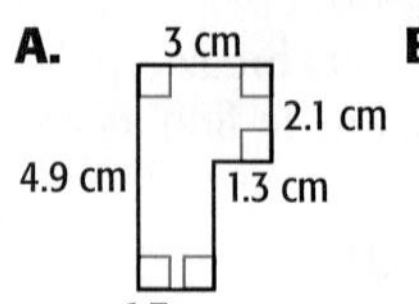

B.

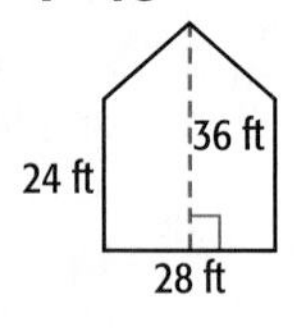

11.06 cm^2 840 ft^2

Example 2

Patrick made a design. Use the coordinate grid to find its area. 250 in^2

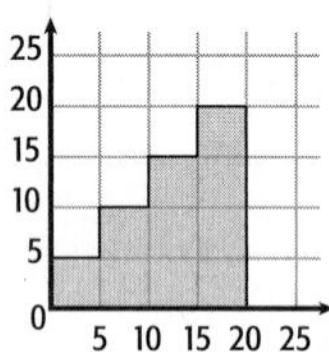

Also available on transparency

10-3 Exercises

Assignment Guide

If you finished Example 1 assign:
Average 1–2, 10–17
Advanced 4–5, 10–17

If you finished Example 2 assign:
Average 1–3, 7–8, 10–17
Advanced 4–6, 8–17

Homework Quick Check

Quickly check key concepts.
Exercises: 4, 6

Georgia Performance Standards

M6P3.a Organize and consolidate their mathematical thinking through communication.

M6P4.c Recognize and apply mathematics in contexts outside of mathematics.

EXAMPLE 2 ***Art Application***

Helpful Hint

You can also count the squares and multiply by the area of one square.
1 square = 4 square units
17 · 4 = 68 square units

Stan made a wall hanging. Use the coordinate grid to find its area.

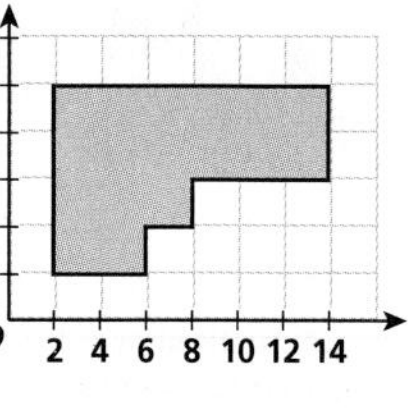

Think: Divide the wall hanging into rectangles.

Find the area of each rectangle.

Rectangle 1
$\ell = 8, w = 4; A = 8 \cdot 4 = 32$

Rectangle 2
$\ell = 6, w = 2; A = 6 \cdot 2 = 12$

Rectangle 3
$\ell = 4, w = 6; A = 4 \cdot 6 = 24$

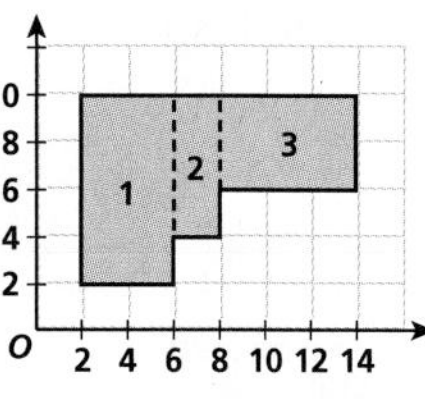

Add the areas of the three rectangles to find the total area of the wall hanging.

$32 + 12 + 24 = 68$ square units

The area of the wall hanging is 68 square units.

Possible answers to *Think and Discuss*

1. A regular octagon can be divided into 8 congruent triangles. If you already know the area of one, you can multiply that by 8 to find the area of the octagon.
2. The rectangles could have been drawn horizontally.

Think and Discuss GPS M6P1.c, M6P1.d

1. Explain how you can find the area of a regular octagon by breaking it apart into congruent triangles, if you know the area of one triangle.

2. Explain another way that you can divide the wall hanging in Example 2.

10-3 Exercises

Georgia Performance Standards
M6P3.a, M6P4.c

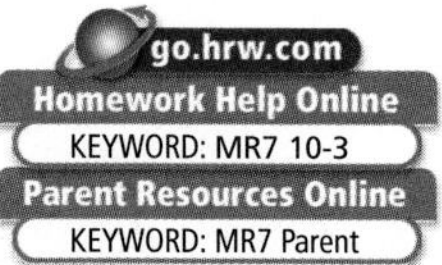

GUIDED PRACTICE

See Example 1 **Find the area of each polygon.**

1. (20 m, 50 m, 70 m, 90 m) $2{,}800\text{ m}^2$

2. (10.2 cm, 1 cm, 1.8 cm, 1 cm, 5.4 cm) 18.84 cm^2

See Example 2 3. Gina used tiles to create a design. Use the coordinate grid to find the area of Gina's design. 57 square units

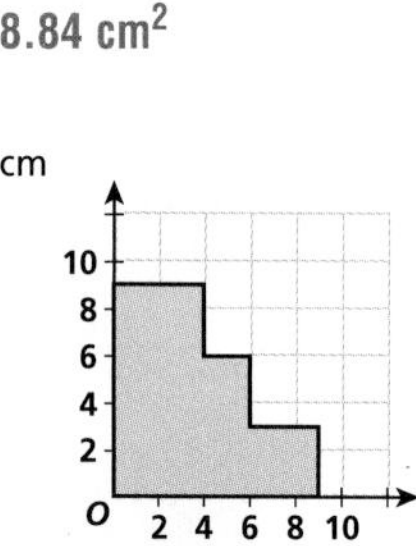

Reaching All Learners

Through Cooperative Learning

Have students work in pairs to find areas of composite figures. Each student draws a figure on a sheet of graph paper (available in Teacher Tools). Students trade figures with their partners; divide the figures into rectangles, triangles, and parallelograms; find the areas of the individual figures; and find the total area of each composite figure.

3 Close

Summarize

Have students explain how they would divide the figure below in order to find its area.

Possible answer: Divide the figure from left to right into a triangle, a rectangle, and a parallelogram. Then find the sum of the three areas.

INDEPENDENT PRACTICE

See Example 1

Find the area of each polygon.

4. 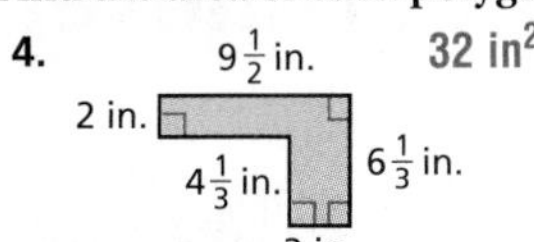

32 in^2

5. 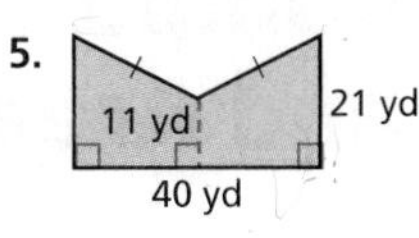

640 yd^2

See Example 2

6. Edgar plants daffodils around a rectangular pond. The yellow part of the diagram shows where the daffodils are planted. Use the coordinate grid to find the area of the yellow part of the diagram. 72 square units

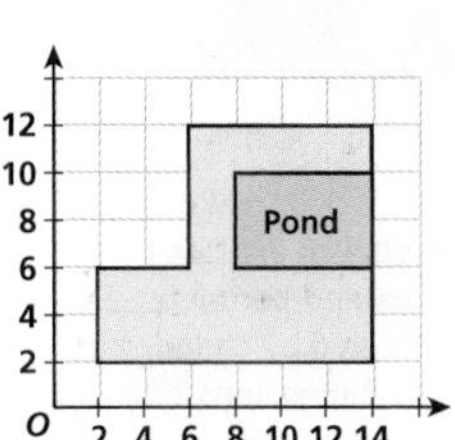

PRACTICE AND PROBLEM SOLVING

Extra Practice p. 733

7. **Social Studies** The map shows the approximate dimensions of the state of South Australia, outlined in red.

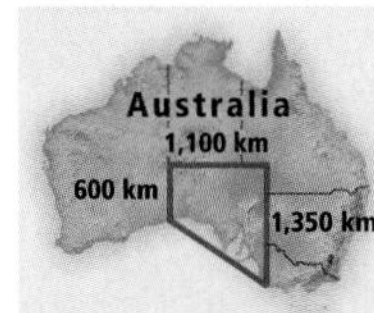
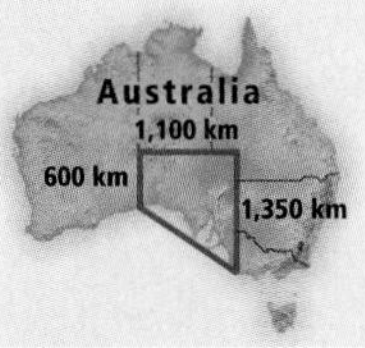

a. Estimate the area of the state of South Australia.

7a. Possible answer: $1{,}072{,}500 \text{ m}^2$

b. The total area of Australia is about 7.7 million km^2. About what fraction of the total area of Australia is the area of the state of South Australia? Possible answer: 14%

8. **Write About It** Draw a figure that can be broken up into two rectangles. Label the lengths of each side. Explain how you can find the area of the figure. Then find the area.

9. **Challenge** The perimeter of the figure is 42.5 cm. Find the area of this figure. 72.25 cm^2

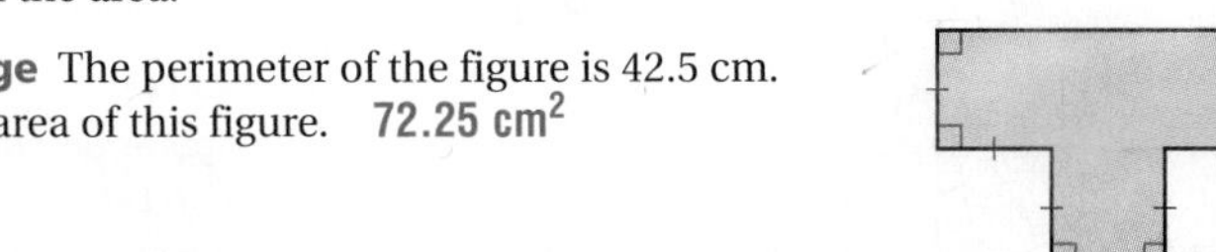

CRCT PREP • GPS SUPPORT • SPIRAL REVIEW

10. **Multiple Choice** What is the area of the polygon?

(F) 40 ft^2 (G) 65 ft^2 (H) 45 ft^2 (J) 90 ft^2

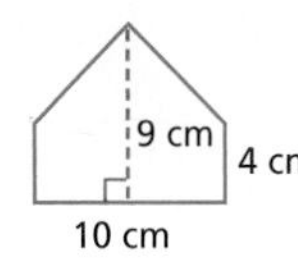

11. **Gridded Response** Use the coordinate grid to find the area, in square units, of the polygon. 40 square units

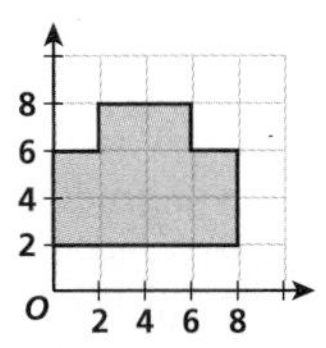

Find each sum or difference. Write the answer in simplest form. (Lesson 5-3)

12. $4\frac{1}{3} + 7\frac{5}{12}$ $11\frac{3}{4}$
13. $8\frac{1}{2} - 3\frac{1}{3}$ $5\frac{1}{6}$
14. $6\frac{2}{3} + 3\frac{1}{6}$ $9\frac{5}{6}$
15. $8\frac{7}{10} - 2\frac{2}{5}$ $6\frac{3}{10}$

Find the area of each polygon. (Lesson 10-1)

16. rectangle: $\ell = 14$ m; $w = 11$ m 154 m^2
17. parallelogram: $b = 18$ cm; $h = 8$ cm 144 cm^2

ONGOING ASSESSMENT and INTERVENTION

Diagnose **Before** the Lesson
10-3 Warm Up, TE p. 551

Monitor **During** the Lesson
10-3 Know-It Notebook
10-3 Questioning Strategies

Assess **After** the Lesson
10-3 Lesson Quiz, TE p. 553

Answers

8. See p. A11.

Power Presentations with PowerPoint®

10-3 Lesson Quiz

1. Find the area of the figure shown.

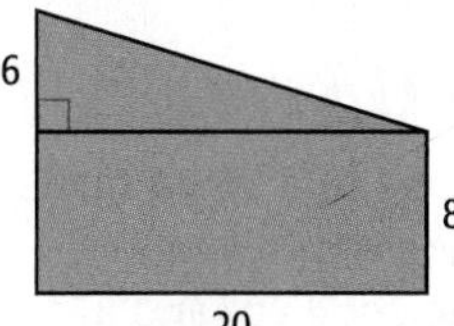

220 units^2

2. Phillip designed a countertop. Use the coordinate grid to find its area.

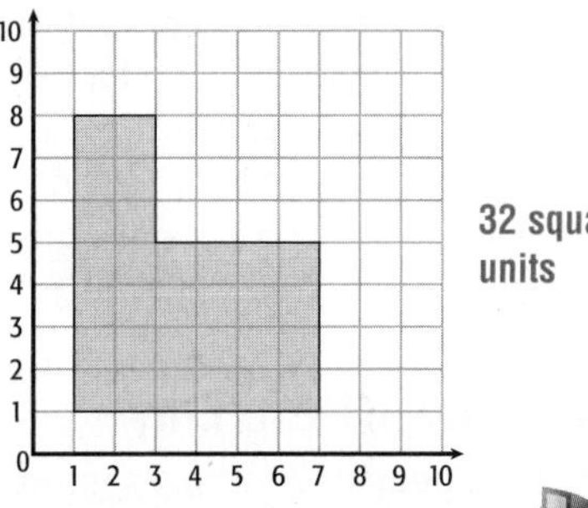

32 square units

Also available on transparency

RETEACH 10-3

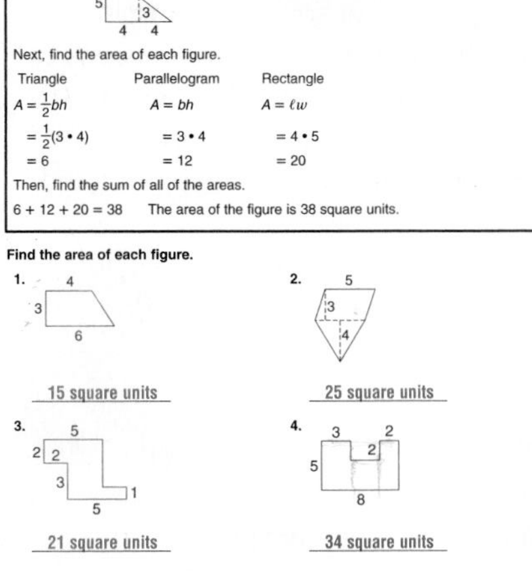

LESSON 10-3 Reteach

Area of Composite Figures

Sometimes you can use area formulas you know to help you find the area of other figures.

To find the area of the figure below, first divide the figure into figures you know.

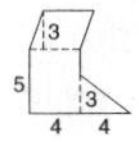

The figure is made up of a triangle, a parallelogram, and a rectangle.

Next, find the area of each figure.

Triangle	Parallelogram	Rectangle
$A = \frac{1}{2}bh$	$A = bh$	$A = \ell w$
$= \frac{1}{2}(3 \cdot 4)$	$= 3 \cdot 4$	$= 4 \cdot 5$
$= 6$	$= 12$	$= 20$

Then, find the sum of all of the areas.

$6 + 12 + 20 = 38$ The area of the figure is 38 square units.

Find the area of each figure.

1. 15 square units
2. 25 square units
3. 21 square units
4. 34 square units

PRACTICE 10-3

LESSON 10-3 Practice B

Area of Composite Figures

Find the area of each polygon.

1. 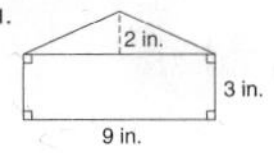 36 in^2
2. 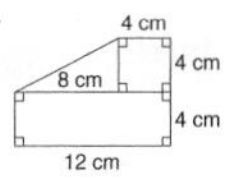 80 cm^2
3. 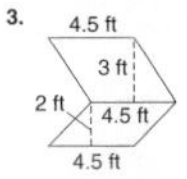 22.5 ft^2
4. 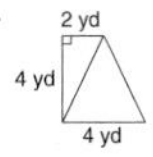 12 yd^2
5. 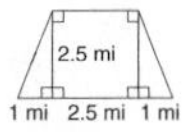 8.75 mi^2
6. 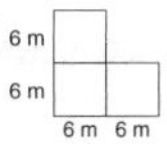 108 m^2

7. Three paintings are shaped like an 8-foot square, a 7-foot by 4-foot rectangle, and a triangle with a 6-foot base and a height of 7 feet. If those paintings are hung together on the outside of a building, how much of the building's wall will they cover altogether?

113 ft^2

8. Two diagonals divide a square carpet into 4 congruent triangles. The base of each triangle is 5 feet and the height is 2.5 feet. What is the area of the entire carpet?

25 ft^2

CHALLENGE 10-3
PROBLEM SOLVING 10-3

LESSON 10-3 Problem Solving

Area of Composite Figures

Write the correct answer.

1. The shape of Nevada can almost be divided into a perfect rectangle and a perfect triangle. About how many square miles does Nevada cover?

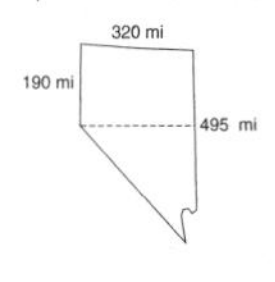

about $109{,}600 \text{ mi}^2$

2. The shape of Oklahoma can almost be divided into 2 perfect rectangles and 1 triangle. About how many square miles does Oklahoma cover?

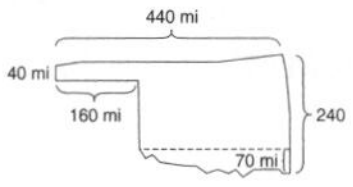

about $63{,}800 \text{ mi}^2$

3. The front side of an apartment building is a rectangle 60 feet tall and 25 feet wide. Bricks cover its surface, except for a door and 10 windows. The door is 7 feet tall and 3 feet wide. Each window is 4 feet tall and 2 feet wide. How many square feet of bricks cover the front side of the building?

$1{,}399 \text{ ft}^2$

4. Each side of a square garden is 12 meters long. A hedge wall 1 meter wide surrounds the garden. What is the area of the entire garden including the hedge wall? How many square meters of land does the hedge wall cover alone?

entire garden = 196 m^2; hedge wall = 52 m^2

Circle the letter of the correct answer.

5. A figure is formed by a square and a triangle. Its total area is 32.5 m^2. The area of the triangle is 7.5 m^2. What is the length of each side of the square?

(A) 5 meters C 15 meters
B 25 meters D 16.25 meters

6. A rectangle is formed by two congruent right triangles. The area of each triangle is 6 in^2. If each side of the rectangle is a whole number of inches, which of these could not be its perimeter?

F 26 inches (H) 24 inches
G 16 inches J 14 inches

10-4 Organizer

Pacing: Traditional 1 day
Block $\frac{1}{2}$ day

Objective: Students make a model to explore how area and perimeter are affected by changes in the dimensions of a figure.

Hands-On Lab
In *Hands-On Lab Activities*

Online Edition
Tutorial Videos, Interactivities

Countdown to CRCT Week 22

Power Presentations with PowerPoint®

Warm Up

1. What is the area of a figure made up of a rectangle with length 12 cm and height 4 cm and a parallelogram with length 12 cm and height 6 cm? 120 cm^2
2. What is the area of a figure consisting of a triangle sitting on top of a rectangle? The triangle has a base of 12 in. and height of 9 in., and the rectangle has a base of 12 in. and a height of 5 in. 114 in^2

Problem of the Day

If sixteen people sit, evenly spaced, in a circle for story time, who sits directly across from person 5? 13

Also available on transparency

10-4 Comparing Perimeter and Area

Learn to make a model to explore how area and perimeter are affected by changes in the dimensions of a figure.

Georgia Performance Standards

M6M2.a Use units of appropriate size and type to measure length and perimeter. Also, M6A3.

Ms. Cohn wants to enlarge a photo by doubling its length and width.

Recall that similar figures have exactly the same shape but not necessarily the same size. Doubling the dimensions of the photo will create a larger photo similar to the original.

You can draw a model on graph paper to see how the area and the perimeter of a figure change when its dimensions change.

EXAMPLE 1 Changing Dimensions

Find how the perimeter and the area of the figure change when its dimensions change.

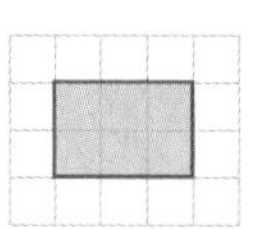

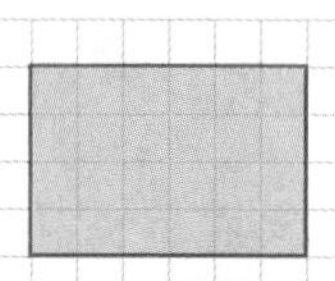

Draw a model of the two figures on graph paper. Label the dimensions.

$\square = 1 \text{ in}^2$

The original photo is a 3 in. × 2 in. rectangle.		The enlarged photo is a 6 in. × 4 in. rectangle.
$P = 2(\ell + w)$	*Use the formula for perimeter of a rectangle.*	$P = 2(\ell + w)$
$= 2(3 + 2)$	*Substitue for ℓ and w.*	$= 2(6 + 4)$
$= 2(5) = 10$	*Simplify.*	$= 2(10) = 20$
The perimeter is 10 in.		The perimeter is 20 in.
$A = \ell w$	*Use the formula for area of a rectangle.*	$A = \ell w$
$= 3 \times 2$	*Substitute for ℓ and w.*	$= 6 \times 4$
$= 6$	*Simplify.*	$= 24$
The area is 6 in^2.		The area is 24 in^2.

When the dimensions of the rectangle are doubled, the perimeter is also doubled, and the area becomes four times as great.

Georgia Performance Standards

M6M2.a Measure length to the nearest half, fourth, eighth and sixteenth of an inch.

M6A3 Students will evaluate algebraic expressions, including those with exponents, and solve simple one-step equations using each of the four basic operations.

1 Introduce

Alternate Opener

EXPLORATION

10-4 Comparing Perimeter and Area

Suzanne is enlarging a color copy of a 3 in. by 5 in. photograph to 6 in. by 10 in. A model is shown below.

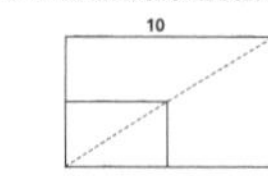

Find the perimeter of each color copy.

	Color Copy	Perimeter = 2 · Length + 2 · Width
1.	3 in. by 5 in.	
2.	6 in. by 10 in.	

3. How do the perimeters compare?

Find the area of each color copy.

	Color Copy	Area = Length · Width
4.	3 in. by 5 in.	
5.	6 in. by 10 in.	

6. How do the areas compare?

Think and Discuss

7. **Explain** how you compared the perimeters.
8. **Explain** how you compared the areas.

2 Teach

Guided Instruction

In this lesson, students learn to make a model to explore how area and perimeter are affected by changes in the dimensions of a figure. Teach students what happens to the perimeter and area of a figure when its dimensions are doubled, halved, and tripled.

Explorations and answers are provided in *Alternate Openers: Explorations Transparencies.*

EXAMPLE 2 *Measurement Application*

Use a centimeter ruler to measure the photo. Draw a rectangle whose sides are 3 times as long to enlarge the photo. How do the perimeter and the area change?

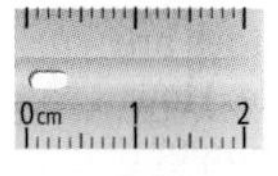

$P = 6$ cm
$A = 2$ cm^2

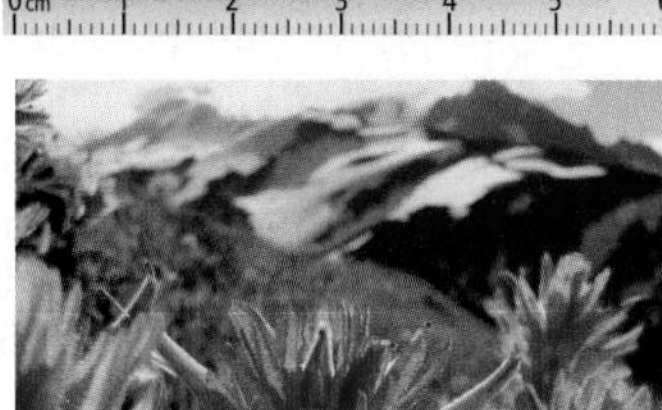

Multiply each dimension by 3. $P = 18$ cm
$A = 18$ cm^2

When the dimensions of the rectangle are multiplied by 3, the **perimeter** is multiplied by 3, and the **area** is multiplied by **9**, or 3^2.

Answers to *Think and Discuss*

1. The perimeter of the triangle doubles.
2. The area becomes one-fourth the area of the original figure.

Think and Discuss

GPS M6P2.c, M6P3.b

1. **Explain** how the perimeter of a triangle changes when all the side lengths are doubled.
2. **Tell** how the area of a rectangle changes when all the side lengths are divided in half.

10-4 Exercises

Georgia Performance Standards
M6P1.b, M6P3.a, M6P4.c

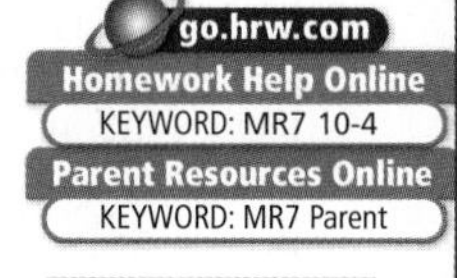

go.hrw.com
Homework Help Online
KEYWORD: MR7 10-4
Parent Resources Online
KEYWORD: MR7 Parent

GUIDED PRACTICE

See Example 1

1. Find how the perimeter and the area of the figure change when its dimensions change.

When the dimensions of the square are divided by 3, the perimeter is divided by 3, and the area is divided by 9 or 3^2.

See Example 2

2. Use a centimeter ruler to measure the rectangle. Draw a rectangle whose sides are 2 times as long to enlarge the rectangle. How do the perimeter and the area change?

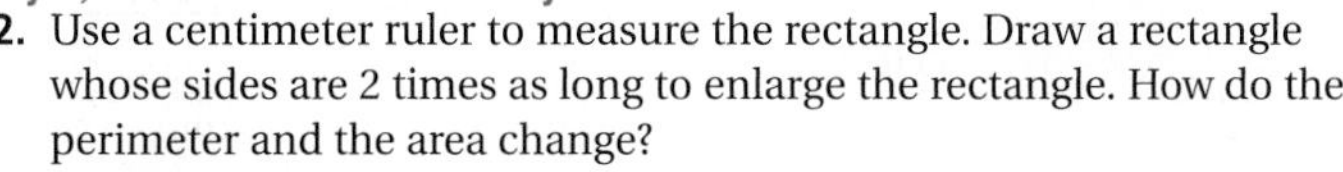

The perimeter is multiplied by 2 and the area is multiplied by 4, or 2^2.

Power Presentations with PowerPoint®

Additional Examples

Example 

Find how the perimeter and the area of the figure change when its dimensions change.

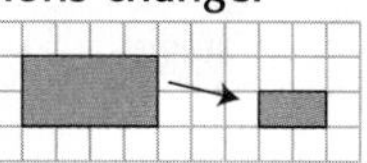

The perimeter is divided by 2, and the area is divided by 4.

Example 

Draw a rectangle whose dimensions are 4 times as large as the given rectangle. How do the perimeter and area change?

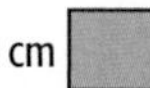

The perimeter is multiplied by 4, and the area is multiplied by 16.

Also available on transparency

10-4 Exercises

Assignment Guide

If you finished Example 1 assign:
Average 1, 9–17
Advanced 3, 9–17

If you finished Example 2 assign:
Average 1–6, 9–17
Advanced 3–17

Homework Quick Check

Quickly check key concepts.
Exercises: 4, 6

Reaching All Learners
Through Kinesthetic Experience

Have students find the perimeters and areas of figures in and around their classroom. Then have them figure out what the perimeters and areas of those items would be if the dimensions were halved and tripled. Students can record their findings and share them with the class.

3 Close

Summarize

Review how perimeter and area of a figure change when the scale changes. (Perimeter changes linearly with scale, and area changes with the square of the scale factor.)

Georgia Performance Standards

M6P1.b Solve problems that arise in mathematics and in other contexts.

M6P3.a Organize and consolidate their mathematical thinking through communication.

M6P4.c Recognize and apply mathematics in contexts outside of mathematics.

ONGOING ASSESSMENT and INTERVENTION

***Diagnose Before* the Lesson**
10-4 Warm Up, TE p. 554

***Monitor During* the Lesson**
10-4 Know-It Notebook
10-4 Questioning Strategies

***Assess After* the Lesson**
10-4 Lesson Quiz, TE p. 556

Answers

3–4. Complete answers on p. A10.

INDEPENDENT PRACTICE

See Example 1

3. Find how the perimeter and the area of the figure change when its dimensions change.

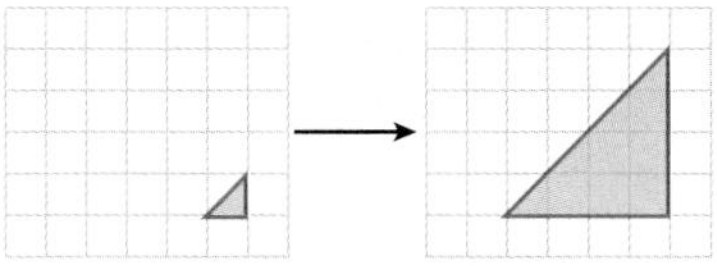

See Example 2

4. Use a centimeter ruler to measure the triangle. Draw a triangle whose sides are half as long to enlarge the triangle. How do the perimeter and the area change?

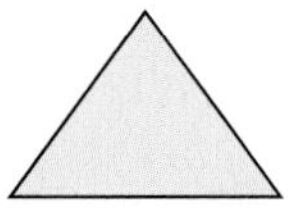

Student's methods and explanations may vary.

PRACTICE AND PROBLEM SOLVING

CRCT GPS Extra Practice p. 733

5. The schoolyard is a rectangle with a length of 120 ft and a width of 80 ft. The PE teacher plans to make a field in the schoolyard.
   a. What will the area of the field be if she divides only one of the dimensions of the schoolyard in half? **4,800 ft^2**
   b. What will the perimeter of the field be if she divides only the length in half? the width in half? **280 ft, 320 ft**
6. **Critical Thinking** If George enlarges a 3 in. × 4 in. photo so that it is 12 in. × 16 in., how will its area change? **The area will be 4^2 times greater.**
7. **Write About It** What happens to the area and the perimeter of a rectangle when the length and width are multiplied by 4?
8. **Challenge** A rectangle has a perimeter of 24 meters. If its length and width are whole numbers, what is its greatest possible area? **36 m^2**

7. When the dimensions are multiplied by 4 the area will be 4^2 times as great and the perimeter will be 4 times as great.

CRCT PREP • GPS SUPPORT • SPIRAL REVIEW

9. **Multiple Choice** A photo is 4 in. × 6 in. long. To enlarge the photo, Lee doubles both the length and width. Find the perimeter of the enlarged photo.
   Ⓐ 8 in. Ⓑ 12 in. Ⓒ 20 in. **Ⓓ 40 in.**
10. **Multiple Choice** If Jinny enlarges a 3 in. × 4 in. photo so that it is 12 in. × 16 in., how will its area change?
    Ⓕ The area will increase by 2 times.
    Ⓗ The area will increase by 3^2.
    Ⓖ The area will increase by 2^2 times.
    Ⓙ The area will increase by 4^2 times.

Write each fraction in simplest form. (Lesson 4-5)

11. $\frac{9}{12}$ **$\frac{3}{4}$**
12. $\frac{4}{16}$ **$\frac{1}{4}$**
13. $\frac{5}{10}$ **$\frac{1}{2}$**
14. $\frac{25}{100}$ **$\frac{1}{4}$**
15. $\frac{65}{100}$ **$\frac{13}{20}$**

Find the perimeter of each figure. (Lesson 9-7)

16.

310 ft

17.

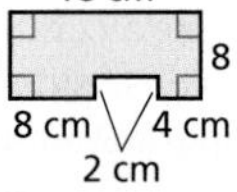

56 cm

Power Presentations with PowerPoint®

10-4 Lesson Quiz

Find how the perimeter and area of the triangle change when its dimensions change.

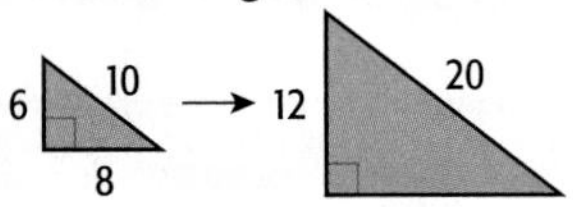

The perimeter is multiplied by 2, and the area is multiplied by 4; perimeter = 24, area = 24; perimeter = 48, area = 96.

Also available on transparency

CHALLENGE 10-4
PROBLEM SOLVING 10-4

LESSON 10-4 Problem Solving
Comparing Perimeter and Area

Write the correct answer.

1. Fiona's school photograph is 6 inches long and 5 inches wide. If she orders a triple enlargement how would this affect the area of the photo? How would the enlargement affect the frame she would need for the photo?
   The area of the enlarged photo will be 9 times larger than the original. She will need a frame 3 times larger than the frame for the original photo.
2. The Whitman's kitchen is 8 feet long and 6 feet wide. They are planning on renovating the kitchen to have more space. If they double just the width, how will it affect the area of the room? If they double just the length? If they double both measurements?
   If they double just 1 measurement, the area would double. If they double both measurements, the room's area would be 4 times larger.

Circle the letter of the correct answer.

3. Kent saw a table in a magazine that was 3 feet wide and 4 feet long. If he wants to make a similar version of the table with an area 4 times larger, what dimensions should he use? How will the perimeter of Kent's table differ from the table in the magazine?
   A 4 ft wide and 5 ft long
   Ⓑ 6 ft wide and 8 ft long
   C 9 ft wide and 12 ft long
   D 12 ft wide and 16 ft long
4. The triangular sail on Shakeera's boat is 8 meters wide and 10 meters tall. She wants to make a model of the boat that is $\frac{1}{20}$ of its actual size. How much canvas will Shakeera use for the model boat's sail? How does that amount compare to the canvas used for the real boat's sail?
   F 10 m^2 of canvas
   G 1 m^2 of canvas
   Ⓗ 0.1 m^2 of canvas
   J 0.01 m^2 of canvas
5. A triangle is 6.4 cm long and 8.2 cm tall. If you triple its dimensions, what would be the area of the enlarged triangle?
   A 78.72 cm^2 **Ⓒ 236.16 cm^2**
   B 157.44 cm^2 D 472.32 cm^2
6. The dimensions of a regular pentagon are doubled. The perimeter of the enlarged pentagon is 25 yards. What was the length of each side of the original pentagon?
   Ⓕ 2.4 yards H 5 yards
   G 12 yards J 16.25 yards

RETEACH 10-4

LESSON 10-4 Reteach
Comparing Perimeter and Area

When the dimensions of a figure change, the perimeter and area of the figure change.

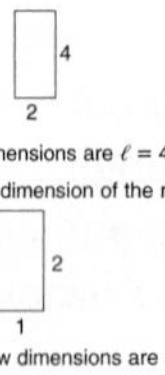

$P = 2\ell + 2w$
$= (2 \cdot 4) + (2 \cdot 2)$
$= 8 + 4$
$= 12$ units

$A = \ell w$
$= 4 \cdot 2$
$= 8$ square units

The dimensions are $\ell = 4$ and $w = 2$.

If each dimension of the rectangle is divided by 2, the perimeter and area change.

$P = 2\ell + 2w$
$= (2 \cdot 2) + (2 \cdot 1)$
$= 4 + 2$
$= 6$ units

$A = \ell w$
$= 2 \cdot 1$
$= 2$ square units

The new dimensions are $\ell = 2$ and $w = 1$.

When the dimensions of a rectangle are divided by 2, the perimeter is divided by 2 and the area is divided by 4.

Write how the perimeter and area change when the dimensions change.

1. 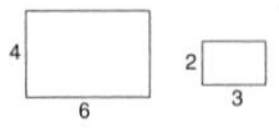
   When the dimensions of a rectangle are divided by 2, the perimeter is divided by 2 and the area is divided by 4.
2. 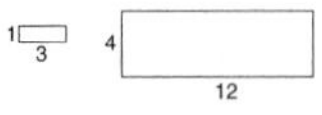
   When the dimensions of a rectangle are multiplied by 4, the perimeter is multiplied by 4 and the area is multiplied by 16.

PRACTICE 10-4

LESSON 10-4 Practice B
Comparing Perimeter and Area

Write how the perimeter and the area of the figure change when its dimensions change.

1. 
   $P =$ **26 in.** $P =$ **52 in.**
   $A =$ **40 in^2** $A =$ **160 in^2**
   When the dimensions of the rectangle are doubled, the perimeter is doubled, and the area is 4 times greater.
2. Use a centimeter ruler to measure the triangle. Then draw another triangle with dimensions that are half as great as the given triangle. How do the perimeter and the area change when the dimensions change?
   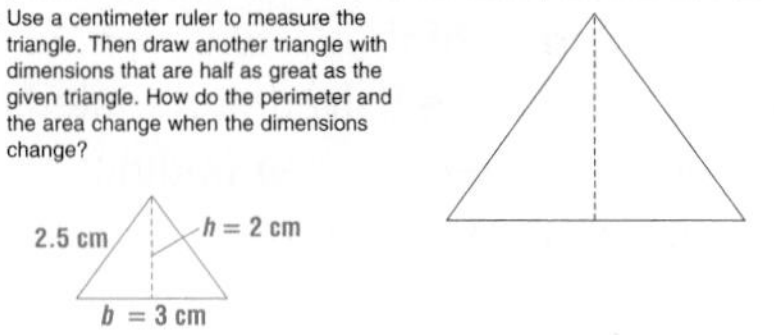

   When the dimensions of the triangle are half as great, the perimeter is divided by 2, and the area is divided by 4.
3. Nina wants to make a smaller version of a painting she saw in a museum. The museum painting was a square with each side measuring 6.4 feet. If Nina makes her copy half the size of the original painting, how much space will it cover on her wall?
   10.24 square feet
4. How many feet of wood will Nina need to make a frame for her painting from Exercise 3?
   12.8 feet of wood

Explore Area of Circles

Use with Lesson 10-5

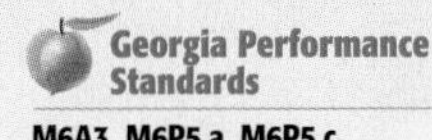

Georgia Performance Standards

M6A3, M6P5.a, M6P5.c

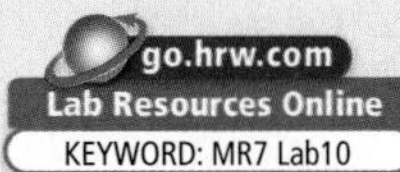

go.hrw.com
Lab Resources Online
KEYWORD: MR7 Lab10

You can use what you know about circles and *pi* to learn about the area of circles.

Activity

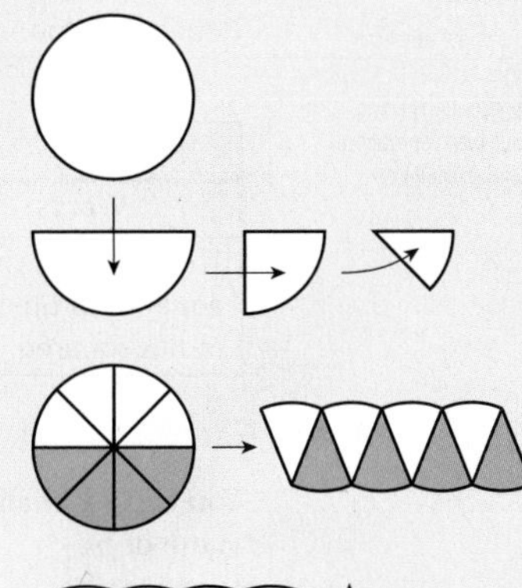

1. The *radius* of a circle is half of its diameter. Use a compass to draw a circle with a 2-inch radius. Cut your circle out and fold it three times as shown.
2. Unfold the circle, trace the folds, and shade one-half of the circle.
3. Cut along the folds, and fit the pieces together to make a figure that looks approximately like a parallelogram.

   Think of this figure as a parallelogram. The base and height of the parallelogram relate to the parts of the circle.

   base $b = \frac{1}{2}$ the circumference of the circle, or πr

   height h = the radius of the circle, or r

   To find the area of a parallelogram, use the equation $A = bh$.

   To find the area of a circle, use the equation $A = \pi r(r) = \pi r^2$.

Think and Discuss

1. Compare the lengths of all the diameters of a circle. **They have the same measure.**
2. Compare the lengths of all the radii of a circle. **They have the same measure.**

Try This

Find the area of each circle with the given measure. Use 3.14 for π. Round to the nearest tenth.

1. $r = 4$ yd **$A = 50.24$ yd^2**
2. 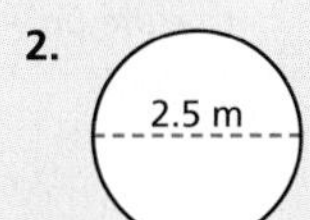

$A = 4.91$ m^2
3. $d = 10$ m **$A = 78.5$ m^2**
4. 7.5 ft **$A = 176.63$ ft^2**

Organizer

Use with Lesson 10-5

Pacing:
Traditional 1 day
Block $\frac{1}{2}$ day

Objective: Use what is known about circles and *pi* to learn about the area of circles.

Materials: Compass

Online Edition

Countdown to CRCT Week 23

Resources

Hands-On Lab Activities
Lab 10-5 Recording Sheet

Teach

Discuss

Have students recall which dimensions of a parallelogram are used to calculate its area and the formula for the area of a parallelogram.

Close

Key Concept

Finding the area of a circle can be related to finding the area of a parallelogram.

Assessment

Find the area of each circle with the given measurement. Use 3.14 for *pi*. Round to the nearest tenth.

1. $r = 25.3$ cm 2,009.9 cm^2
2. $d = 18.75$ mi 276.0 mi^2

Georgia Performance Standards

M6A3 Students will evaluate algebraic expressions, including those with exponents, and solve simple one-step equations using each of the four basic operations.

M6P5.a Create and use representations to organize, record, and communicate mathematical ideas.

M6P5.c Use representations to model and interpret physical, social, and mathematical phenomena.

10-5 Organizer

Pacing: Traditional 1 day
Block $\frac{1}{2}$ day

Objective: Find the area of a circle.

Online Edition
Tutorial Videos

Countdown to CRCT Week 23

Power Presentations with PowerPoint®

Warm Up

Evaluate

1. 6×4^2 96
2. 5.6×2^3 44.8

Simplify each expression.

3. $6 + n - 4$ $n + 2$
4. $5(n + 1)$ $5n + 5$

Problem of the Day

What is the area of a right triangle with legs measuring 31 in. and 21 in.? 325.5 in^2

Also available on transparency

Math Humor

If the area of a square space is represented in square units, why isn't the area of a circular space represented in circular units?

10-5 Area of Circles

Learn to find the area of a circle.

Georgia Performance Standards

M6A3 Evaluate algebraic expressions and solve simple one-step equations using each of the four basic operations. Also, M6N1.g, M6P4.c.

In medieval times, circular shields were usually made from wood that was covered with leather or steel. The amount of leather or steel needed to cover a shield depended upon the shield's area.

Area of a Circle	
Words	**Formula**
The area of a circle is equal to *pi* times the radius squared.	$A = \pi r^2$

You can estimate the area of a circle by using 3 to approximate the value of *pi*.

EXAMPLE 1 Estimating the Area of a Circle

3.14 or 22/7

Estimate the area of each circle. Use 3 to approximate *pi*.

A

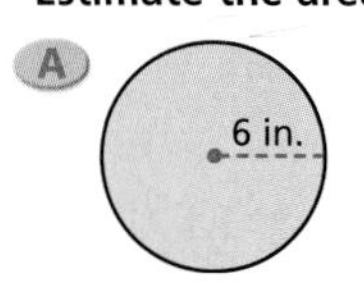

$A = \pi r^2$ — *Write the formula for the area.*
$A \approx 3 \cdot 6^2$ — *Replace π with 3 and r with 6.*
$A \approx 3 \cdot 36$ — *Use the order of operations.*
$A \approx 108 \text{ in}^2$ — *Multiply.*

B

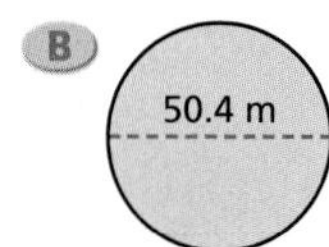

$A = \pi r^2$ — *Write the formula for the area.*
$r = d \div 2$ — *The length of the radius is half the length of the diameter.*
$r = 50.4 \div 2$
$r = 25.2$ — *Divide.*
$r \approx 25$ — *Round 25.2 to 25.*
$A \approx 3 \cdot 25^2$ — *Replace π with 3 and r with 25.*
$A \approx 3 \cdot 625$ — *Use the order of operations.*
$A \approx 1{,}875 \text{ m}^2$ — *Multiply.*

Georgia Performance Standards

M6N1.g Solve problems involving fractions, decimals, and percents.

M6A3 Students will evaluate algebraic expressions, including those with exponents, and solve simple one-step equations using each of the four basic operations.

M6P4.c Recognize and apply mathematics in contexts outside of mathematics.

1 Introduce

Alternate Opener

EXPLORATION

10-5 Area of Circles

You can use estimation to help you investigate the area of circles.

1. Estimate the area of the circle by counting whole and partial squares.
2. What is the radius *r* of the circle?
3. Calculate πr^2 using 3.14 for *pi*.
4. How does the value of πr^2 compare to your estimate of the circle's area?
5. Repeat the process for this circle. First estimate the area by counting whole and partial squares.
6. What is the radius of the circle?
7. Calculate πr^2 using 3.14 for *pi*.
8. How does the value of πr^2 compare to your estimate of the circle's area?

Think and Discuss

9. **Describe** any shortcuts you found for counting the squares.
10. **Explain** how you can use what you discovered to write a formula for the area of a circle with radius *r*.

Motivate

Show the class a standard paper plate and an $8\frac{1}{2}$-by-11 sheet of paper. Ask students whether they think it takes more paper to make the paper plate or the sheet of notebook paper. Tell students that the area formula in this lesson will help them answer this question.

Explorations and answers are provided in *Alternate Openers: Explorations Transparencies.*

EXAMPLE 2 Using the Formula for the Area of a Circle

Find the area of each circle. Use $\frac{22}{7}$ for *pi*.

A

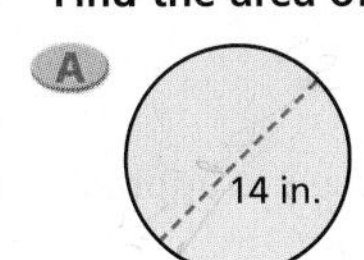

$A = \pi r^2$	*Write the formula for the area.*
$r = d \div 2$	*The length of the radius is half the length of the diameter.*
$r = 14 \div 2 = 7$	*Divide.*
$A \approx \frac{22}{7} \cdot 7^2$	*Replace π with $\frac{22}{7}$ and r with 7.*
$A \approx \frac{22}{\cancel{7}_1} \cdot \cancel{49}^7$	*Use the GCF to simplify.*
$A \approx 154 \text{ in}^2$	*Multiply.*

B

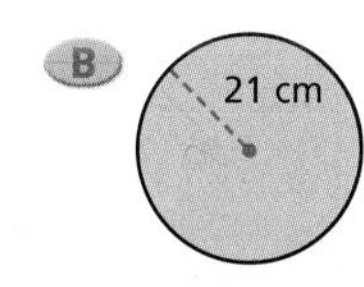

$A = \pi r^2$	*Write the formula for the area.*
$A \approx \frac{22}{7} \cdot 21^2$	*Replace π with $\frac{22}{7}$ and r with 21.*
$A \approx \frac{22}{7} \cdot 441$	*Use the order of operations.*
$A \approx \frac{9702}{7}$	*Multiply*
$A \approx 1386 \text{ cm}^2$	*Divide.*

EXAMPLE 3 *Art Application*

The mosaic has a diameter of 78 inches. Find the area of the terrazzo needed to cover the floor. Use 3.14 for *pi*.

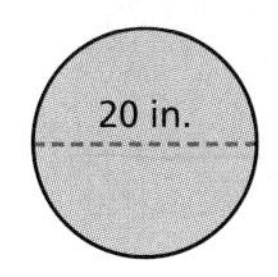

$A = \pi r^2$	*Write the formula for the area.*
$r = d \div 2$	*The length of the radius is half the length of the diameter.*
$r = 378 \div 2$	
$r = 189$	*Divide.*
$A \approx 3.14 \cdot 189^2$	*Replace π with 3.14 and r with 189.*
$A \approx 3.14 \cdot 35{,}721$	*Use the order of operations.*
$A \approx 112{,}163.94 \text{ in}^2$	*Multiply.*

Check Use 3 as an approximation for π. The area, πr^2, is approximately $3 \cdot 189^2 = 3 \cdot 35{,}721 = 107.163$, so the answer is reasonable.

Possible answers to *Think and Discuss*

1. An estimate is 3×1^2 or 3 cm.
2. 75 ft^2 represents an estimate of the area of a circle with a radius of 5 ft, $3 \times 5^2 = 75$. For the estimate, *pi* was rounded down to 3, therefore the actual area is greater than 75 ft^2.
3. Square the nearest whole number to the radius and multiply by 3.

Think and Discuss

GPS M6P1.c, M6P1.d, M6P2.c

1. **Describe** how you could estimate the area of a circle whose radius is 1 cm.
2. **Explain** why the area of a circle with a radius of 5 ft must be greater than 75 ft^2.
3. **Tell** how you can check that your answer is reasonable after you have calculated the area of a circle.

COMMON ERROR ALERT

When using the formula for area, some students may multiply the radius by 2 instead of squaring it. To prevent this, have them write the formula as $A = \pi \times r \times r$.

Power Presentations with PowerPoint®

Additional Examples

Example 

Estimate the area of each circle. Use 3 to approximate *pi*.

A.

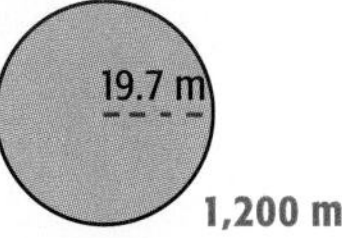

1,200 m^2

B.

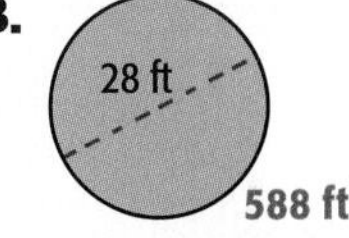

588 ft^2

Example 

Find the area of each circle. Use $\frac{22}{7}$ for *pi*.

A.

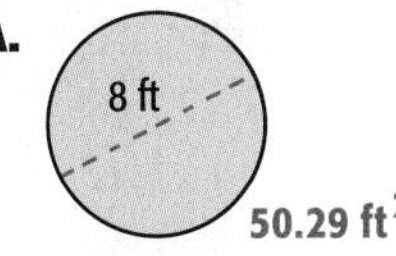

50.29 ft^2

B.

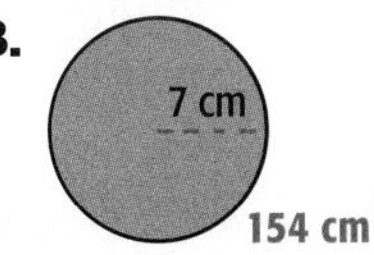

154 cm^2

Example 

A drum head has a radius of 18 in. Find the area of the material covering the drum head. Use 3.14 for *pi*. 1017.36 in^2

Also available on transparency

2 Teach

Guided Instruction

In this lesson, students learn to find the area of a circle. Begin by briefly reviewing *pi* and the two most common approximations for *pi* (3.14 and $\frac{22}{7}$). Then show students the formula for the area of a circle. Teach students how to estimate and calculate the area of a circle using the formula.

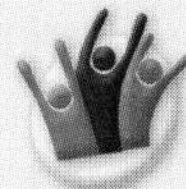

Reaching All Learners

Through Multiple Representations

Give students a sheet of a paper printed with a one-inch grid. Have students use a compass to draw a circle on the grid with a radius of 3 inches. Ask students to calculate the area of the circle using the area formula. Then have them estimate the area by counting the number of squares of the grid that are contained in the circle. Encourage students to improve their estimates by accounting for squares that are partially contained in the circle.

3 Close

Summarize

Revisit the question that was posed in Motivate. Give students the diameter of the paper plate (typically 9 in.) and have them calculate the plate's area. Then have students compare this to the area of the sheet of paper.

Possible answers:

Area of plate: $\approx 63.6 \text{ in}^2$

Area of sheet of paper: 93.5 in^2

10-5 Exercises

Assignment Guide

If you finished Example 1 assign:
Average 1–3, 25–34
Advanced 8–10, 25–34

If you finished Example 2 assign:
Average 1–6, 15–16, 25–34
Advanced 8–13, 16–17, 25–34

If you finished Example 3 assign:
Average 1–12, 18–21, 25–34
Advanced 8–34

Homework Quick Check

Quickly check key concepts.
Exercises: 8, 10, 12, 18

Georgia Performance Standards

M6P2.c Develop and evaluate mathematical arguments and proofs.

M6P3.a Organize and consolidate their mathematical thinking through communication.

M6P3.c Analyze and evaluate the mathematical thinking and strategies of others.

10-5 Exercises

M6P2.c, M6P3.a, M6P3.c

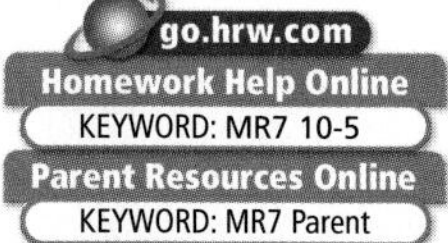

GUIDED PRACTICE

See Example 1 Estimate the area of each circle. Use 3 to approximate *pi*.

1. 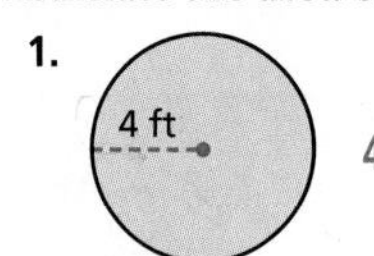

48 ft^2

2. 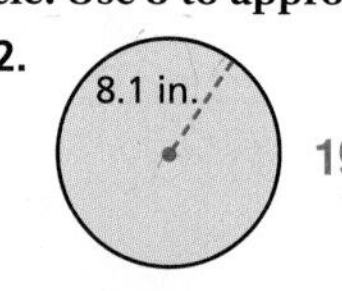

192 in^2

3. 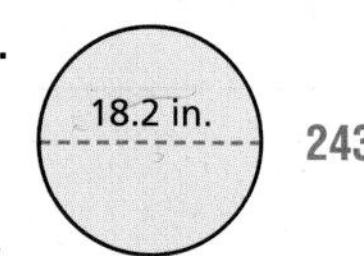

243 in^2

See Example 2 Find the area of each circle. Use $\frac{22}{7}$ for *pi*.

4. 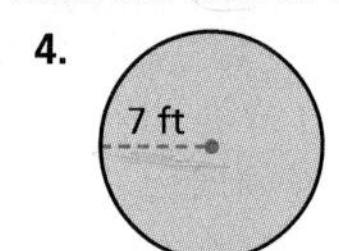

154 ft^2

5. 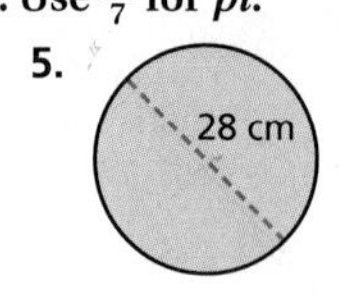

616 cm^2

6. 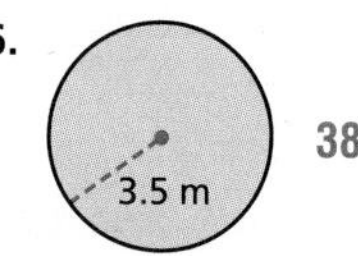

38.5 m^2

See Example 3

7. **Architecture** A circular window has a diameter of 4 ft. Find the area of the glass needed to fill the window. Use 3.14 for *pi*. 12.56 ft^2

INDEPENDENT PRACTICE

See Example 1 Estimate the area of each circle. Use 3 to approximate *pi*.

8. 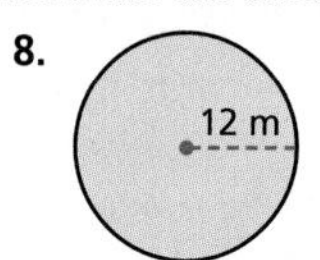

432 m^2

9. 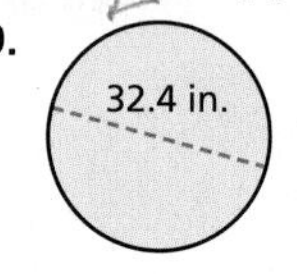

768 in^2

10. 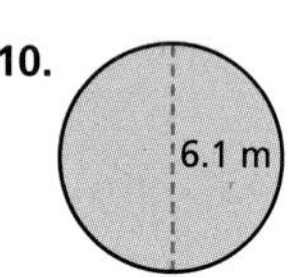

27 m^2

See Example 2 Find the area of each circle. Use $\frac{22}{7}$ for *pi*.

11. 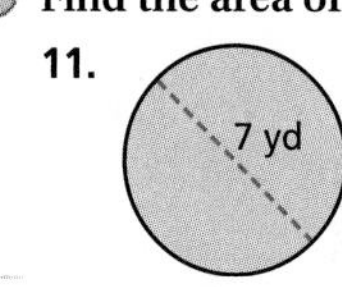

38.5 yd^2

12. 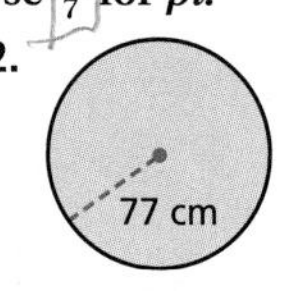

18,634 cm^2

13. 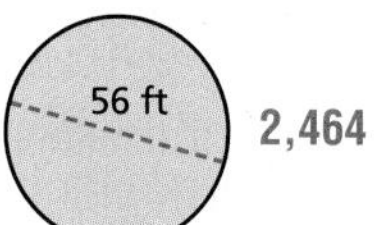

2,464 ft^2

See Example 3

14. A pizza recipe calls for the dough to be rolled out to form a circle with a diameter of 18 in. Find the area of the dough when it is rolled out. Use 3.14 for *pi*. 254.34 in^2

PRACTICE AND PROBLEM SOLVING

Extra Practice p. 733

Find the area and circumference of each circle. Use 3.14 for *pi* and round to the nearest hundredth.

15. 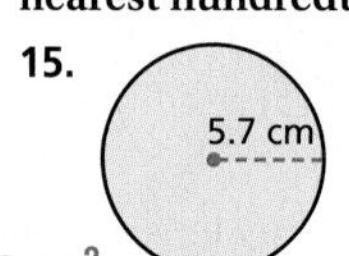

$A = 102.02$ cm^2
$C = 35.8$ cm

16. 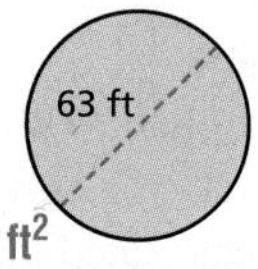 63 ft
$A = 3{,}115.67$ ft^2
$C = 197.82$ ft

17. 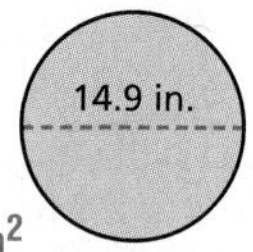 14.9 in.
$A = 174.28$ in^2
$C = 46.79$ in

RETEACH 10-5

LESSON 10-5 **Reteach**
Area of Circles

To estimate the area A of a circle, use the formula $A = \pi r^2$ and 3 for π.

$A = \pi r^2$
$\approx 3 \cdot 2^2$
$\approx 3 \cdot 4$
≈ 12 square units.

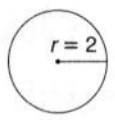

The area is about 12 square units.

r = 2

Estimate the area of each circle. Use 3 for π.

1. (radius 1) $A \approx$ 3 square units

2. 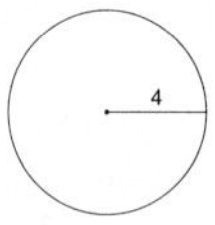 (radius 4) $A \approx$ 48 square units

3. 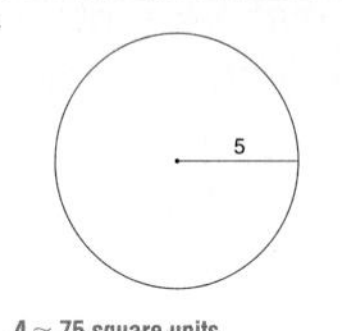

$A \approx$ 75 square units

4. 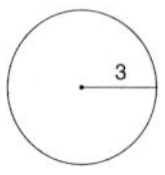 (radius 3) $A \approx$ 27 square units

PRACTICE 10-5

LESSON 10-5 **Practice B**
Area of Circles

Estimate the area of each circle.

1. 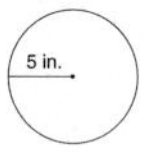 5 in. $A \approx$ 75 in^2
2. 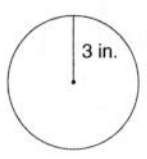 3 in. $A \approx$ 27 cm^2
3. 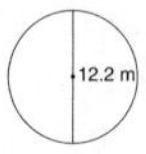 12.2 m $A \approx$ 108 m^2
4. 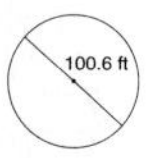 100.6 ft $A \approx$ 7,500 ft^2

Find the area of each circle. Use $\frac{22}{7}$ for *pi*.

5. 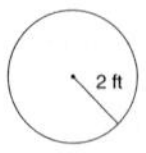 2 ft $A \approx$ 12.57 ft^2
6. 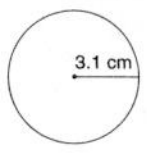 3.1 cm $A \approx$ 30.2 cm^2
7. 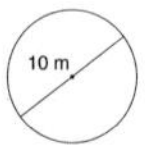 10 m $A \approx$ 78.57 m^2
8. 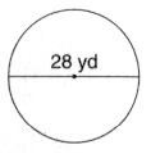 28 yd $A \approx$ 616 yd^2

9. Stonehenge, a circle of large carved stones in England, was built more than 1,000 years ago. The circle of stones has a diameter of 108 feet. About how many square feet of land does Stonehenge cover? Use $\frac{22}{7}$ for *pi*.
9,164.57 square feet

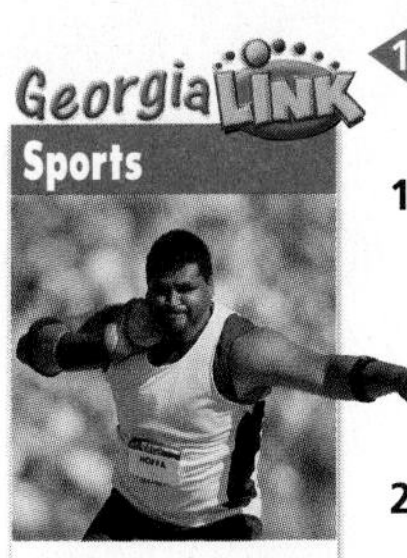

Georgia LINK
Sports

Former Olympian Reese Hoffa, of Athens, Georgia, set a personal record with a throw of 71 ft 1.25 in. in 2004.

18. **Sports** The diameter of the circle that a shot-putter stands in is 7 ft. What is the area of the circle? Use $\frac{22}{7}$ for *pi*. $38\frac{1}{2}$ ft^2

19. **Earth Science** Meteor Crater in central Arizona was formed when an asteroid struck Earth between 20,000 and 50,000 years ago. The circular crater has a diameter of 1.2 km. Find the area of the crater to the nearest hundredth. Use 3.14 for *pi*. 1.13 km^2

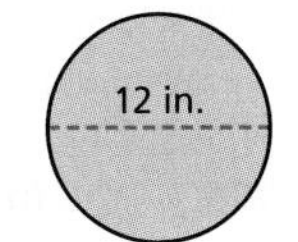

20. **Multi-Step** A restaurant makes pizzas with 6 in. diameters and 12 in. diameters.
    a. Estimate the difference between the areas of the two sizes of pizzas. (Use 3.14 for *pi*. Round to the nearest whole number.) Possible answer: 85 in^2
    b. Is the area of the 12 in. pizza about twice the area of the 6 in. pizza? Explain.

21. **Critical Thinking** The area of a circular garden plot is 30 ft^2. Explain why the diameter of the plot must be greater than 6 ft.

22. **What's the Error?** A student estimated the area of this circle as shown. Explain the student's error.

12 in.

$A = \pi r^2$
$A \approx 3 \cdot 12^2$
$A \approx 3 \cdot 144$
$A \approx 432$ in^2

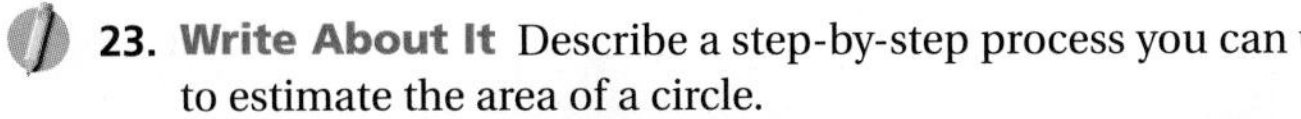

23. **Write About It** Describe a step-by-step process you can use to estimate the area of a circle.

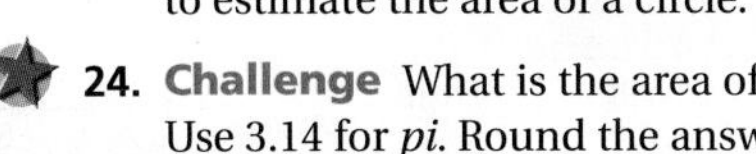

24. **Challenge** What is the area of the shaded part of the figure? Use 3.14 for *pi*. Round the answer to the nearest hundredth. 0.43 m^2

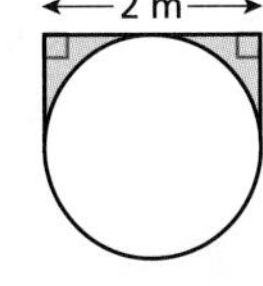

CRCT Prep • GPS Support • Spiral Review

25. **Multiple Choice** Jerome knows the radius of a baking pan. He needs to estimate the pan's area. Which method can Jerome use to estimate the area?
    Ⓐ Multiply the radius by 3.
    Ⓑ Divide the radius by 2 and square the result.
    Ⓒ Square the radius and multiply the result by 3. (circled)
    Ⓓ Multiply the radius by 3 and square the result.

26. **Gridded Response** Find the area, in square inches, of a circle with a diameter of 10 in. Use 3.14 for *pi*. 78.5

Multiply. Write each answer in simplest form. (Lesson 5-7)

27. $\frac{3}{8} \cdot \frac{4}{9}$ $\frac{1}{6}$
28. $\frac{7}{10} \cdot \frac{3}{14}$ $\frac{3}{20}$
29. $\frac{8}{9} \cdot \frac{5}{16}$ $\frac{5}{18}$
30. $\frac{6}{15} \cdot \frac{10}{21}$ $\frac{4}{21}$

Divide. Write each answer in simplest form. (Lesson 5-9)

31. $\frac{3}{5} \div 5$ $\frac{3}{25}$
32. $\frac{4}{9} \div 12$ $\frac{1}{27}$
33. $\frac{5}{6} \div \frac{2}{3}$ $\frac{5}{4}$ or $1\frac{1}{4}$
34. $2\frac{4}{5} \div 1\frac{1}{2}$ $\frac{28}{15}$ or $1\frac{13}{15}$

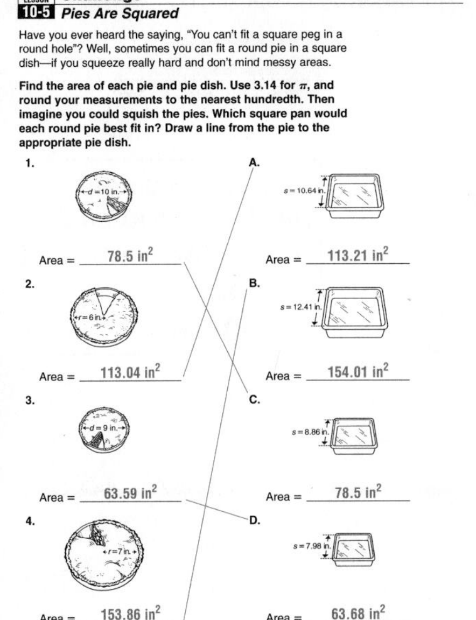

CHALLENGE 10-5

LESSON 10-5 **Challenge**
Pies Are Squared

Have you ever heard the saying, "You can't fit a square peg in a round hole"? Well, sometimes you can fit a round pie in a square dish—if you squeeze really hard and don't mind messy areas.

Find the area of each pie and pie dish. Use 3.14 for π, and round your measurements to the nearest hundredth. Then imagine you could squish the pies. Which square pan would each round pie best fit in? Draw a line from the pie to the appropriate pie dish.

1. d = 10 in. Area = 78.5 in^2
2. r = 6 in. Area = 113.04 in^2
3. d = 9 in. Area = 63.59 in^2
4. r = 7 in. Area = 153.86 in^2

A. s = 10.64 in. Area = 113.21 in^2
B. s = 12.41 in. Area = 154.01 in^2
C. s = 8.86 in. Area = 78.5 in^2
D. s = 7.98 in. Area = 63.68 in^2

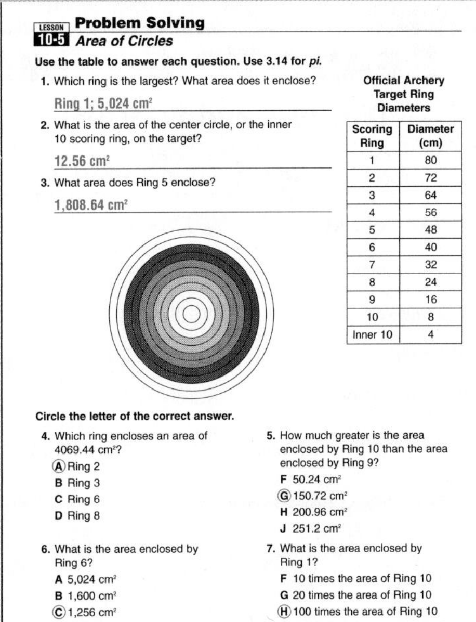

PROBLEM SOLVING 10-5

LESSON 10-5 **Problem Solving**
Area of Circles

Use the table to answer each question. Use 3.14 for *pi*.

1. Which ring is the largest? What area does it enclose?
   Ring 1; 5,024 cm^2
2. What is the area of the center circle, or the inner 10 scoring ring, on the target?
   12.56 cm^2
3. What area does Ring 5 enclose?
   1,808.64 cm^2

Official Archery Target Ring Diameters

Scoring Ring	Diameter (cm)
1	80
2	72
3	64
4	56
5	48
6	40
7	32
8	24
9	16
10	8
Inner 10	4

Circle the letter of the correct answer.

4. Which ring encloses an area of 4069.44 cm^2?
   Ⓐ Ring 2 (circled)
   B Ring 3
   C Ring 6
   D Ring 8
5. How much greater is the area enclosed by Ring 10 than the area enclosed by Ring 9?
   F 50.24 cm^2
   Ⓖ 150.72 cm^2 (circled)
   H 200.96 cm^2
   J 251.2 cm^2
6. What is the area enclosed by Ring 6?
   A 5,024 cm^2
   B 1,600 cm^2
   Ⓒ 1,256 cm^2 (circled)
   D 62.8 cm^2
7. What is the area enclosed by Ring 1?
   F 10 times the area of Ring 10
   G 20 times the area of Ring 10
   Ⓗ 100 times the area of Ring 10 (circled)
   J 1,000 times the area of Ring 10

Ongoing Assessment and Intervention

***Diagnose Before* the Lesson**
10-5 Warm Up, TE p. 558

***Monitor During* the Lesson**
10-5 Know-It Notebook
10-5 Questioning Strategies

***Assess After* the Lesson**
10-5 Lesson Quiz, TE p. 561

Answers

20b. No, the area of the 12-in. pizza is about 4 times as large as the 6-in. pizza.

21–23. See p. A11.

Test Prep Doctor For Exercise 26, remind students to use the radius, which is half the diameter. They must then square the radius and multiply by *pi*.

Journal

Have students explain why 3.14, rather than the actual value, is used for *pi* when doing pencil and paper calculations.

Power Presentations with PowerPoint®

10-5 Lesson Quiz

Estimate the area of each circle.

1. 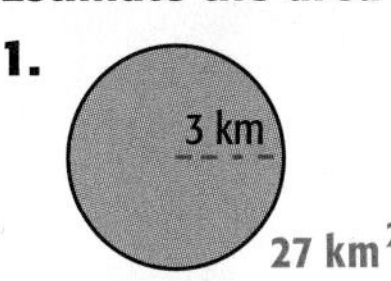

27 km^2

2. 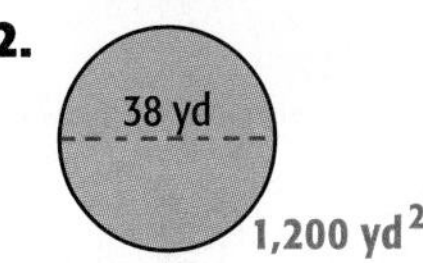

1,200 yd^2

Find the area of each circle. Use $\frac{22}{7}$ for *pi*.

3. 2.4 cm — 18.10 cm^2

4. 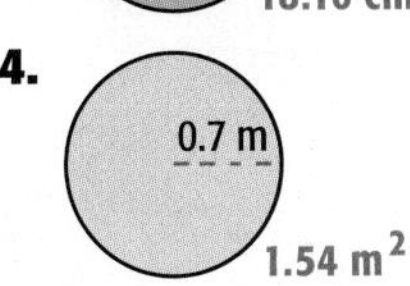

1.54 m^2

5. A coaster has a diameter of 6 inches. Find the area of the largest cup the coaster can hold. Use 3.14 for *pi*. 28.26 in^2

Also available on transparency

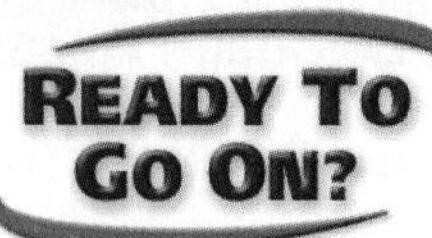

Organizer

Objective: Assess students' mastery of concepts and skills in Lessons 10-1 through 10-5.

Resources

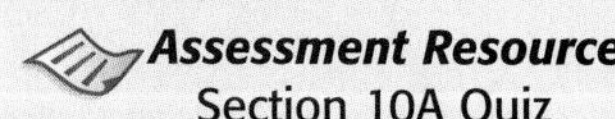

Assessment Resources Section 10A Quiz

Test & Practice Generator One-Stop Planner®

INTERVENTION

Resources

Ready to Go On? Intervention and Enrichment Worksheets

Ready to Go On? CD-ROM

Ready to Go On? Online

my.hrw.com

CHAPTER 10

SECTION 10A

READY TO GO ON?

Quiz for Lessons 10-1 Through 10-5

10-1 Estimating and Finding Area

Find the area of each figure.

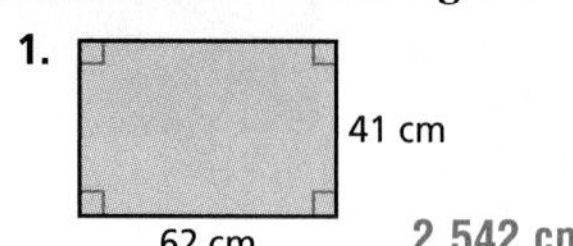

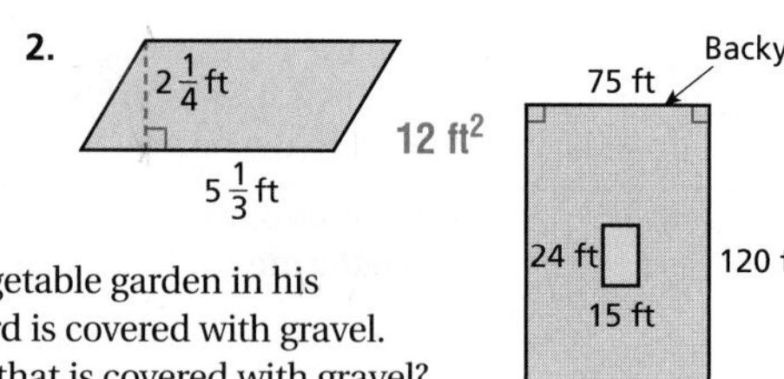

1. 41 cm; 62 cm — 2,542 cm^2
2. $2\frac{1}{4}$ ft; $5\frac{1}{3}$ ft — 12 ft^2
3. Mark is making a rectangular vegetable garden in his backyard. The rest of the backyard is covered with gravel. What is the area of the backyard that is covered with gravel? 8,640 ft^2

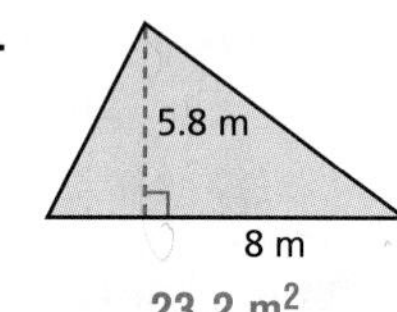

10-2 Area of Triangles and Trapezoids

Find the area of each figure.

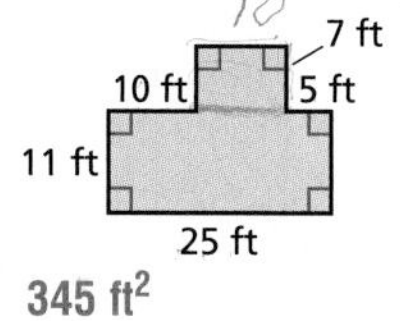

4. 2 cm; 3 cm — 3 cm^2
5. 4.5 ft; 3 ft; 7.5 ft — 18 ft^2
6. 5.8 m; 8 m — 23.2 m^2

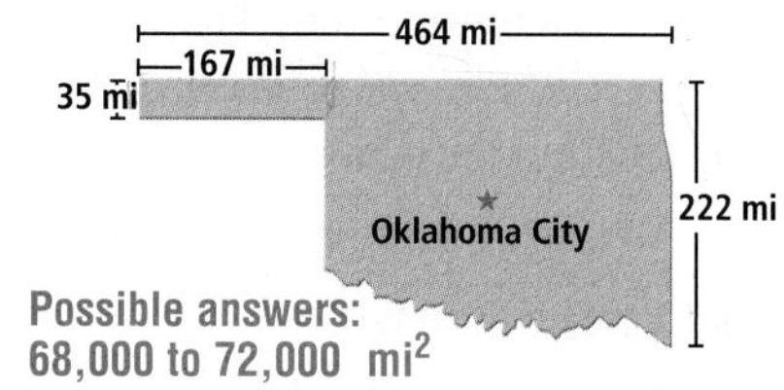

10-3 Area of Composite Figures

7. Find the area of the polygon.

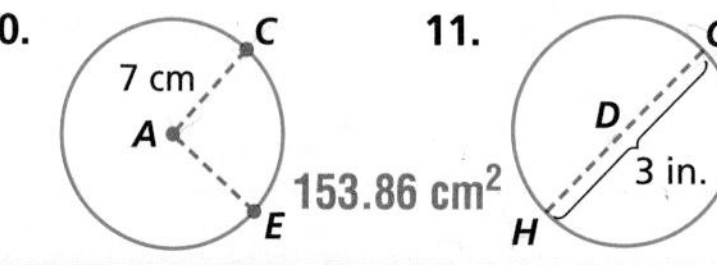

345 ft^2

8. Using the approximate dimensions, estimate the area of the state of Oklahoma.

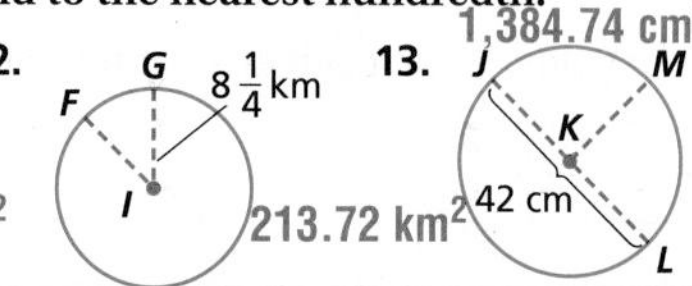

Possible answers: 68,000 to 72,000 mi^2

10-4 Comparing Perimeter and Area

9. The length and width of a rectangle are each multiplied by 4. Find how the perimeter and the area of the rectangle change.
The perimeter is multiplied by 4, and the area is multiplied by 4^2, or 16.

10-5 Area of Circles

Find the area of each circle. Use 3.14 for *pi*. Round to the nearest hundredth.

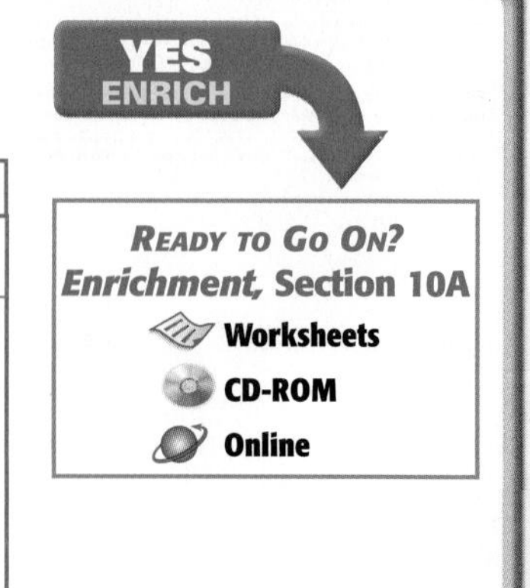

10. 7 cm; A, C, E — 153.86 cm^2
11. 3 in.; D, G, H — 7.07 in^2
12. $8\frac{1}{4}$ km; F, G, I — 213.72 km^2
13. 42 cm; J, K, L, M — 1,384.74 cm^2

Ready to Go On?

READY TO GO ON?

Diagnose and Prescribe

NO INTERVENE

YES ENRICH

Ready to Go On? Intervention	*Ready to Go On? Intervention, Section 10A* Worksheets	CD-ROM	Online
Lesson 10-1	10-1 Intervention	Activity 10-1	Diagnose and Prescribe Online
Lesson 10-2	10-2 Intervention	Activity 10-2	
Lesson 10-3	10-3 Intervention	Activity 10-3	
Lesson 10-4	10-4 Intervention	Activity 10-4	
Lesson 10-5	10-5 Intervention	Activity 10-5	

Ready to Go On? Enrichment, Section 10A
- Worksheets
- CD-ROM
- Online

Focus on Problem Solving

Solve

• Choose the operation

Read the whole problem before you try to solve it. Determine what action is taking place in the problem. Then decide whether you need to add, subtract, multiply, or divide in order to solve the problem.

Action	Operation
Combining or putting together	Add
Removing or taking away Comparing or finding the difference	Subtract
Combining equal groups	Multiply
Sharing equally or separating into equal groups	Divide

Read each problem and determine the action taking place. Choose an operation, and then solve the problem.

1. There are 3 lily ponds in the botanical gardens. They are identical in size and shape. The total area of the ponds is 165 ft^2. What is the area of each lily pond?

2. The greenhouse is made up of 6 rectangular rooms with an area of 4,800 ft^2 each. What is the total area of the greenhouse?

3. A shady area with 17 different varieties of magnolia trees, which bloom from March to June, surrounds the plaza in Magnolia Park. In the center of the plaza, there is a circular bed of shrubs as shown in the chart. If the total area of the park is 625 ft^2, what is the area of the plaza?

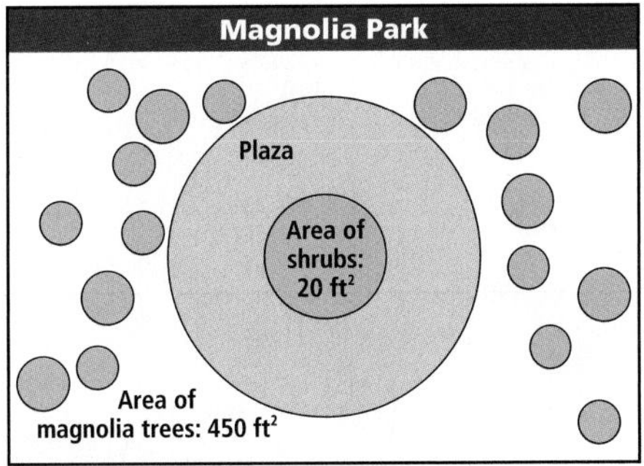

Answers

1. 55 ft^2
2. 28,800 ft^2
3. 155 ft^2

Focus on Problem Solving

Organizer

Objective: Focus on choosing an operation to solve a problem.

Online Edition

Resources

Chapter 10 Resource Book
Reading Strategies

Problem Solving Process

This page focuses on the third step of the problem-solving process:
Solve

Discuss

Have students discuss the words or phrases in each exercise that signaled which operation to choose.

Possible answers:

1. The *3 ponds* are *identical,* so *each* pond has the same area. Therefore, you want to separate the *total area* into 3 equal groups; divide.
2. *Each* of the *6* rooms are equal in area. To find the *total area,* combine 6 equal groups; multiply.
3. To find the *area of the plaza,* you must find the difference between the *total area* of the park and the area that *surrounds the plaza;* subtract.

SECTION 10B Volume and Surface Area

One-Minute Section Planner

Lesson	Materials	MiC and Lab Resources
10-6 Hands-On Lab Draw Views of Three-Dimensional Figures • Use drawings of solid figures to study different views. **Lesson 10-6** Three-Dimensional Figures • Name three-dimensional figures. ☐ CRCT ☐ SAT-10 ☑ ITBS ☐ CTBS ☑ NAEP	Grid paper, centimeter cubes (MK), three-dimensional figure models	**MiC:** ***Reallotment*** pp. 49–50 ***Hands-On Lab Activities*** 10-6
10-7 Hands-On Lab Explore Volume of Prisms and Cylinders • Use centimeter cubes explore the volume of prisms and cylinders. **Lesson 10-7** Volume of Prisms • Estimate and find the volumes of rectangular prisms and triangular prisms. ☑ CRCT ☑ SAT-10 ☐ ITBS ☑ CTBS ☑ NAEP	Centimeter cubes (MK), centimeter graph paper, index cards, prism and cylinder models (boxes, cans)	**MiC:** ***Reallotment*** pp. 49–53, 57–58 ***Hands-On Lab Activities*** 10-7
Lesson 10-8 Volume of Cylinders • Find volumes of cylinders. ☑ CRCT ☑ SAT-10 ☐ ITBS ☑ CTBS ☑ NAEP		**MiC:** ***Reallotment*** pp. 56–58 ***Hands-On Lab Activities*** 10-8 ***Technology Lab Activities*** 10-8
10-9 Hands-On Lab Model Three-Dimensional Figures • Use paper, scissors, and tape to make nets and form them into three-dimensional figures. **Lesson 10-9** Surface Area • Find the surface areas of prisms, pyramids, and cylinders. ☑ CRCT ☐ SAT-10 ☑ ITBS ☐ CTBS ☑ NAEP	Graph paper, scissors, tape	**MiC:** ***Reallotment*** pp. 49–53, 57–58 ***Hands-On Lab Activities*** 10-9

MK = *Manipulatives Kit*

Mathematics in Context

The unit ***Reallotment*** from the *Mathematics in Context* © 2006 series can be used with Section 10B. See Section Planner above for suggestions for integrating *MiC* with *Holt Mathematics*.

Section Overview

Three-Dimensional Figures — Lesson 10-6

Why? Buildings are examples of three-dimensional figures.

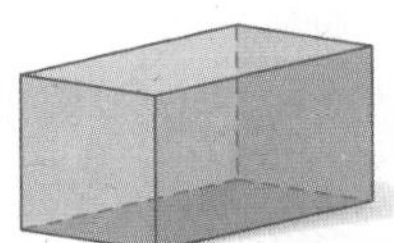
Rectangular prism

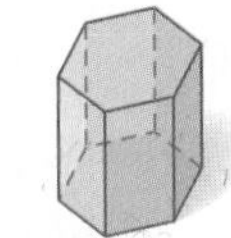
Hexagonal prism

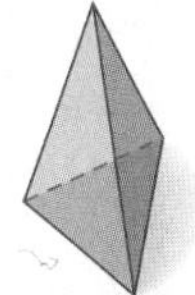
Triangular pyramid

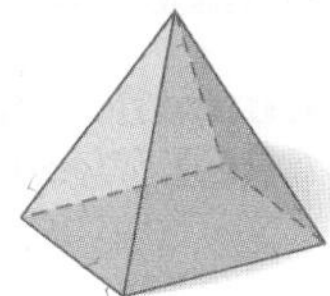
Square pyramid

A **prism** is a polyhedron with two congruent, parallel bases and other faces that are all parallelograms.

A **pyramid** has one polygon-shaped base, and the other faces are triangles that come to a point.

Cylinder

A **cylinder** has two congruent, parallel circular bases. A cylinder is not a polyhedron because not all of its surfaces are polygons.

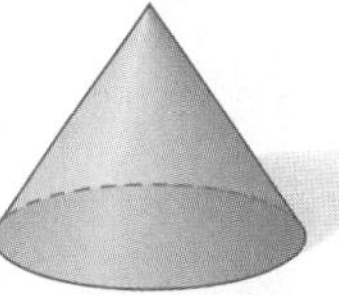
Cone

A **cone** has a circular base and a curved surface that comes to a point.

Volume — Lessons 10-7, 10-8

Volume is an important real-world concept.

Volume Formulas

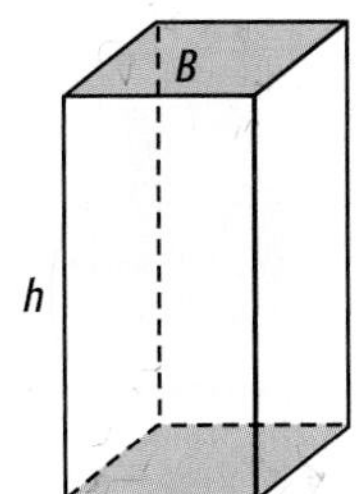

Prism $V = Bh$

B represents the area of the base of the prism, and ***h*** represents the height.

Cylinder $V = \pi r^2 h$

r represents the radius of the base, and ***h*** represents the height of the cylinder.

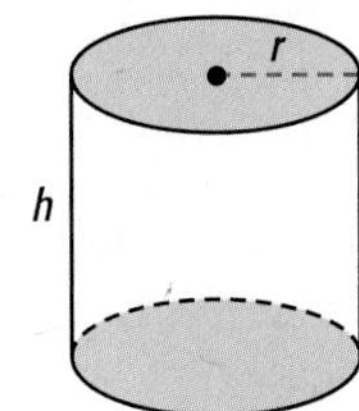

Surface Area — Lesson 10-9

You need to be able to determine surface area to solve real-world problems, such as finding the amount of paint needed to cover a three-dimensional surface.

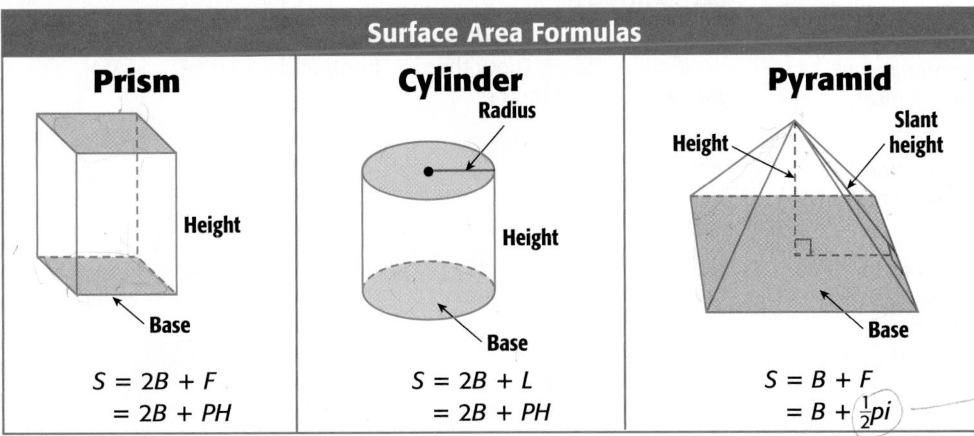

Prism	Cylinder	Pyramid
$S = 2B + F$ $= 2B + PH$	$S = 2B + L$ $= 2B + PH$	$S = B + F$ $= B + \frac{1}{2}pi$

Organizer

Use with Lesson 10-6

Pacing:
Traditional 1 day
Block $\frac{1}{2}$ day

Objective: Use drawings of three-dimensional figures to study different views.

Materials: Paper, pencil

Online Edition

Countdown to CRCT Week 23

Resources

Hands-On Lab Activities
Lab 10-6 Recording Sheet

Teach

Discuss

Discuss how to find different views of a three-dimensional figure. Take a book and lay it on the table. Stand so that your eyes are directly over the book and draw a sketch of the view on the board. Next, bend down so that your eyes are directly in front of the book and draw a sketch of the view. Finally, move right and bend down so that your eyes are directly to the side of the book and draw a sketch of the view.

Draw Views of Three-Dimensional Figures

Use with Lesson 10-6

Georgia Performance Standards
M6G2.c, M6P5.a, M6P5.b, M6P5.c

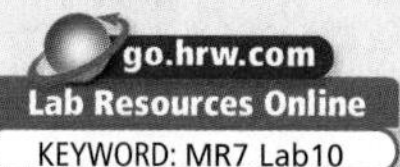

Activity 1

1 Draw a rectangular prism. Imagine that you are looking at the top of the prism, and draw what you would see. Draw the front and side views of the prism.

Top

Front

Side
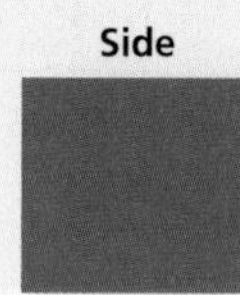

All the faces of a rectangular prism are rectangles.

2 Stack centimeter cubes to make the three-dimensional figure shown. Draw the top, front, and side views.

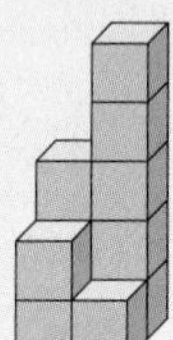

Top
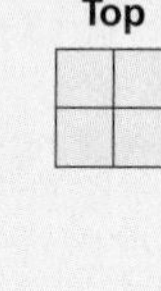

Front
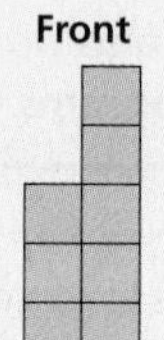

Side
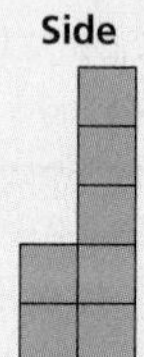

Each view shows a different configuration of squares representing the number of cubes you see.

Think and Discuss

1. Explain why a side view of a three-dimensional figure might change if you look at a different side. **Possible answer: Some blocks may be hidden from certain side views and visible from others.**

Try This

Draw the top, front, and side views of each three-dimensional figure.

1. 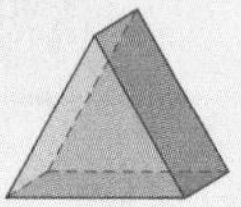
2. 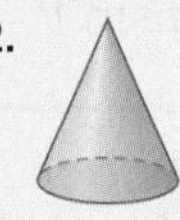
3. 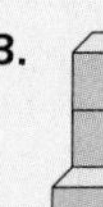 

Close

Key Concept

Drawing views of three-dimensional figures helps students develop their spatial reasoning skills.

Assessment

Build a three-dimensional figure using 5 centimeter cubes. Draw the top, front, and right side views of the figure.
Check students' work.

Activity 1

Answers to *Try This*

1. 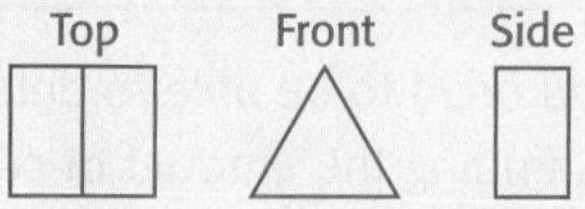 Top Front Side
2. 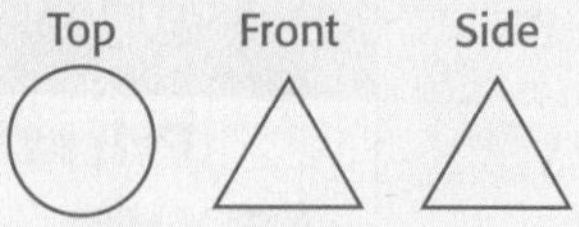 Top Front Side
3. 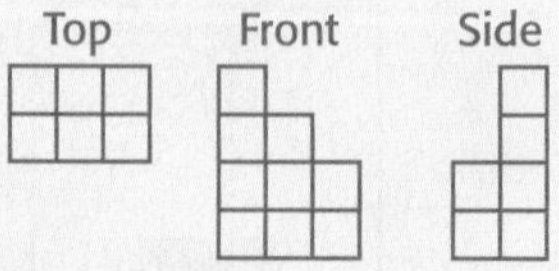 Top Front Side

Georgia Performance Standards

M6G2.c Interpret and sketch front, back, top, bottom and side views of solid figures.

M6P5.a Create and use representations to organize, record, and communicate mathematical ideas.

M6P5.b Select, apply, and translate among mathematical representations to solve problems.

M6P5.c Use representations to model and interpret physical, social, and mathematical phenomena.

Activity 2

You can use different views of a solid to construct the figure.

Using centimeter cubes, construct a three-dimensional figure that has the given views.

Top  Front 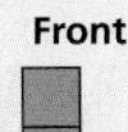 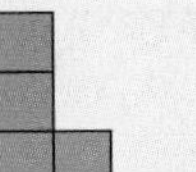 Side 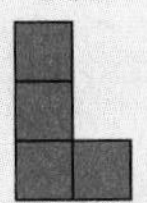

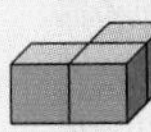

Step 1: Start with the top view of the solid and place the cubes.

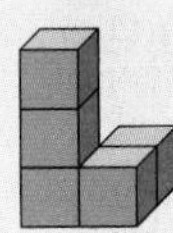

Step 2: Use the front view to stack two more cubes on the left side.

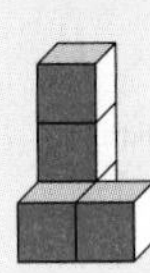

Step 3: Check that the side view is correct.
Since the side view is correct, there are no more cubes to add.

This is the three-dimensional figure that has the given views.

Think and Discuss

1. Explain why it is a good idea to start with the top view. **Possible answer: The top view helps you figure out how to position the cubes on the bottom layer.**

Try This

Using centimeter cubes, construct the three-dimensional figure that has the given views.

1. Top 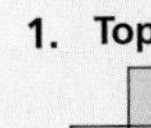 Front 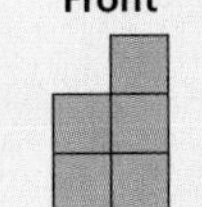 Side 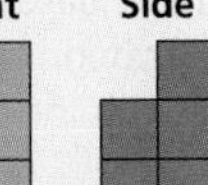

2. Top 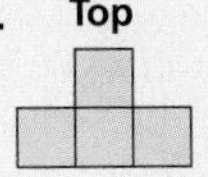 Front 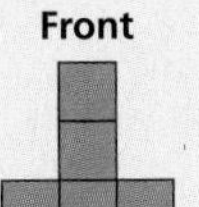 Side 

Activity 2

Answers to *Try This*

1. Possible answer:

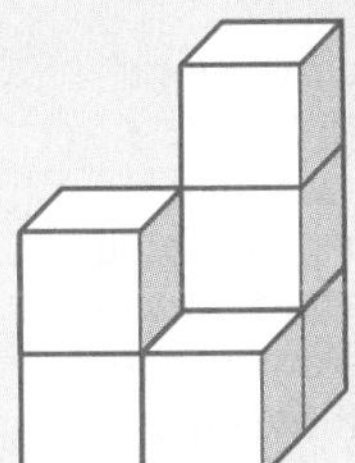

2.

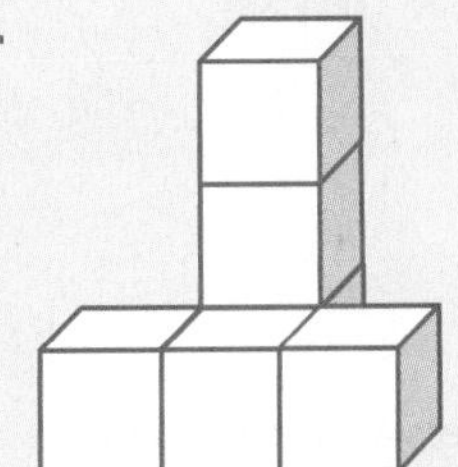

10-6 Organizer

Pacing: Traditional 1 day
Block $\frac{1}{2}$ day

Objective: Students name solid figures.

GPS M6M4.a, M6G2.a
Hands-On Lab
In *Hands-On Lab Activities*

Online Edition
Tutorial Videos, Interactivities

Countdown to CRCT Week 23

Power Presentations with PowerPoint®

Warm Up

Solve. Use 3.14 for π.

1. The diameter of a circle is 12 in. What is its circumference? 37.68 in.
2. The radius of a circle is 9 cm. What is its circumference? 56.52 cm
3. Find the area of a circle with a 12 ft radius. 452.16 ft^2

Problem of the Day

To measure the perimeter of her square patio, Becky used an old bicycle wheel with a 22 in. diameter. She rolled the wheel from one corner of the patio along the edge to the next corner. The wheel made 6.75 revolutions. What is the perimeter of the patio in feet? Use 3.14 for π. 155.43 ft

Also available on transparency

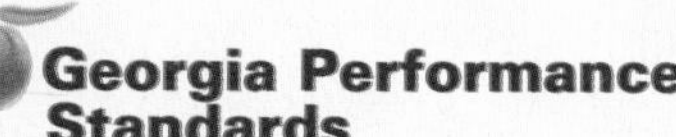

Georgia Performance Standards

M6P5.c Use representations to model and interpret physical, social, and mathematical phenomena.

10-6 Three-Dimensional Figures

Learn to name three-dimensional figures.

Vocabulary
polyhedron
face
edge
vertex
prism
base
pyramid
cylinder
cone

A **polyhedron** is a three-dimensional object with flat surfaces, called **faces**, that are polygons.

When two faces of a three-dimensional figure share a side, they form an **edge**. A point at which three or more edges meet is a **vertex** (plural: *vertices*).

A cube is formed by 6 square faces. It has 8 vertices and 12 edges. The sculpture in front of this building is based on a cube. The artist's work is not a polyhedron because of the hole cut through the middle.

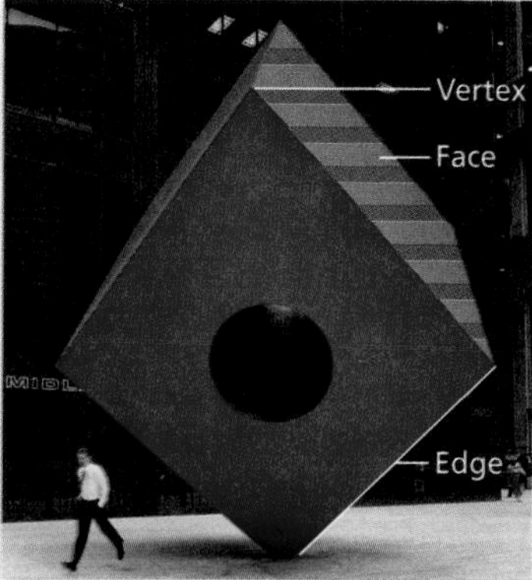

This sculpture, *Red Cube*, in front of the Marine Midland Bank in New York City was created by Isamu Noguchi.

EXAMPLE 1 Identifying Faces, Edges, and Vertices

Georgia Performance Standards

M6P5.c Use representations to model and interpret mathematical phenomena.

Identify the number of faces, edges, and vertices on each three-dimensional figure.

A

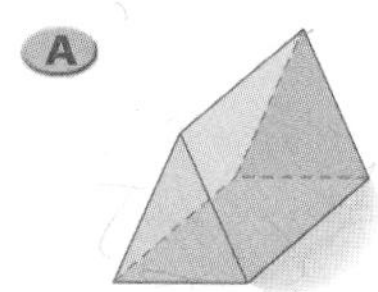

5 faces
9 edges
6 vertices

B

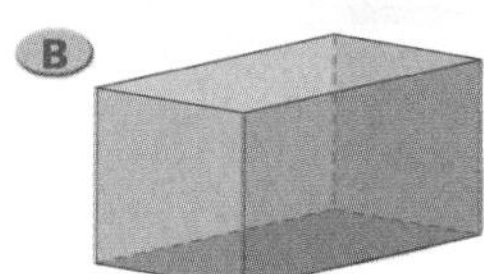

6 faces
12 edges
8 vertices

A **prism** is a polyhedron with two congruent, parallel **bases**, and other faces that are all parallelograms. A prism is named for the shape of its bases. A **cylinder** also has two congruent, parallel bases, but bases of a cylinder are circular. A cylinder is not a polyhedron because not every surface is a polygon.

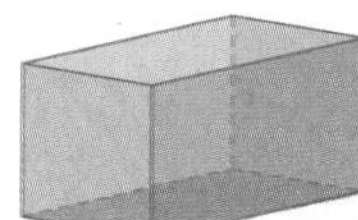

Rectangular prism

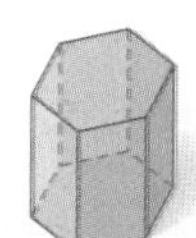

Hexagonal prism

Cylinder

1 Introduce

Alternate Opener

EXPLORATION

10-6 Three-Dimensional Figures

A cube is a solid figure with six faces, twelve edges, and eight vertices.

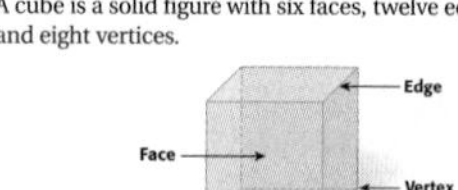

Determine how many faces, edges, and vertices each solid figure has.

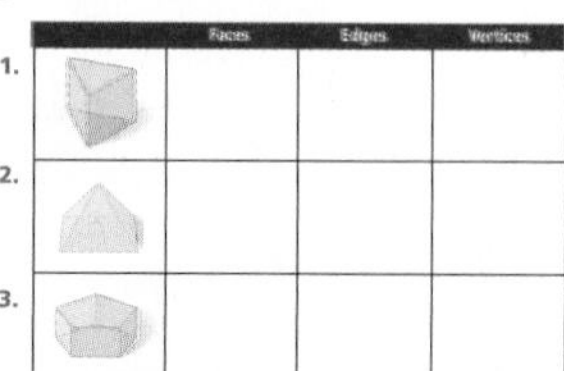

		Faces	Edges	Vertices
1.				
2.				
3.				

Think and Discuss

4. **Explain** how many edges it takes to form a vertex.
5. **Explain** how many faces it takes to form an edge.

Motivate

Display a collection of three-dimensional figures from everyday life. With the class, separate them into three-dimensional figures with no curved surfaces and three-dimensional figures with one or more curved surfaces. Have students name any of the three-dimensional figures that they are familiar with.

Explorations and answers are provided in *Alternate Openers: Explorations Transparencies*.

Helpful Hint

The point of a cone is called its *vertex.*

A **pyramid** has one polygon-shaped base and three or more triangular faces that share a vertex. A pyramid is named for the shape of its base. A **cone** has a circular base and a curved surface that comes to a point. A cone is not a polyhedron because not every face is a polygon.

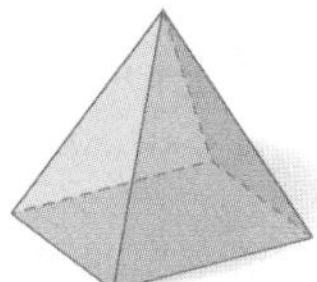
Square pyramid

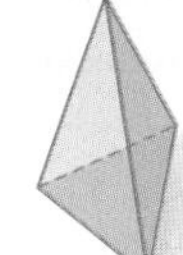
Triangular pyramid

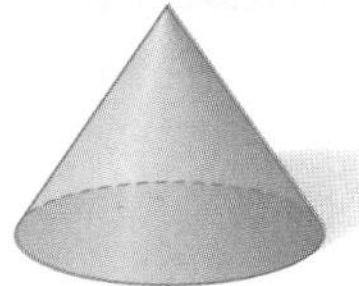
Cone

EXAMPLE 2 **Naming Three-Dimensional Figures**

Name each three-dimensional figure represented by each object.

A 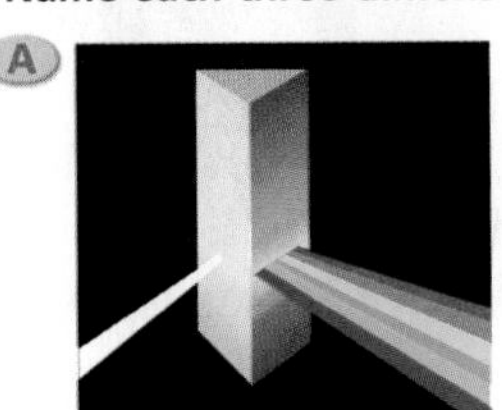

All the faces are flat and are polygons.
The figure is a polyhedron.
There are two congruent, parallel bases, so the figure is a prism.
The bases are triangles.
The figure is a triangular prism.

B  

There is a curved surface.
The figure is not a polyhedron.
There is a flat, circular base.
The lateral surface comes to a point.
The figure represents a cone.

C 

All the faces are flat and are polygons.
The figure is a polyhedron.
It has one base and the other faces are triangles that meet at a point, so the figure is a pyramid.
The base is a square.
The figure is a square pyramid.

Possible answers to *Think and Discuss*

1. Alike: They both have two parallel, flat bases. Different: A cylinder has circular bases, and a prism has polygon-shaped bases.
2. Alike: They both have one flat base and both come to a point. Different: A cone has a circular base, and a pyramid has a polygon-shaped base.

Think and Discuss 

1. **Explain** how a pyramid and a prism are alike and how they are different.
2. **Explain** how a cone and a pyramid are alike and how they are different.

Power Presentations with PowerPoint® 

Additional Examples

Example 1

Identify the number of faces, edges, and vertices on each three-dimensional figure.

A. 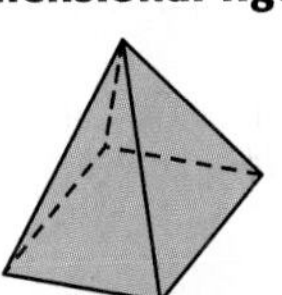
5 faces
8 edges
5 vertices

B. 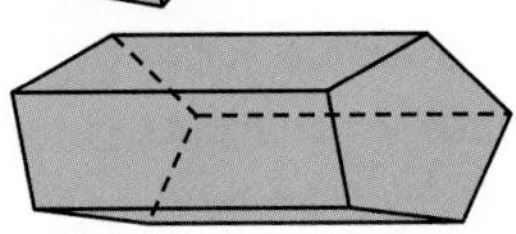

7 faces 15 edges 10 vertices

Example 2 

Name the three-dimensional figure represented by each object.

A. 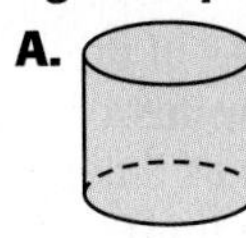

cylinder

B. 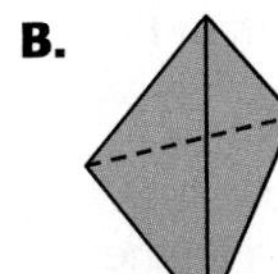

triangular pyramid

C. 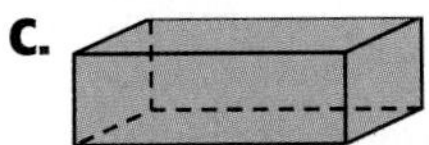

rectangular prism

Also available on transparency 

2 Teach

Guided Instruction

ENGLISH LANGUAGE LEARNERS

In this lesson, students learn to name three-dimensional figures. Teach the new vocabulary words in the lesson. Then teach students how to count faces, edges, and vertices on pictures of three-dimensional figures. Then explain how to decide whether or not a three-dimensional figure is a polyhedron.

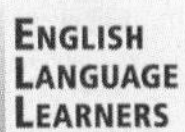 

Reaching All Learners

Through Critical Thinking

Have students research one famous architectural site, for example, the Great Wall of China, the Roman Colosseum, or the Great Pyramid. Tell them to find where it is located, when and why it was constructed, and what it was used for. Also have the students name the three-dimensional geometric figures used in the construction and why they think those shapes were used. Have each group share a picture of the structure and their research with the class.

3 Close

Summarize

You may display the collection of three-dimensional figures on the Teaching Transparency. Have students identify each figure and tell whether it is a *polyhedron*. For each polyhedron, have students tell the number of *faces*, *edges*, and *vertices*.

10-6 Exercises

Assignment Guide

If you finished Example 1 assign:
Average 1–3, 18, 29–37
Advanced 7–9, 19, 29–37

If you finished Example 2 assign:
Average 1–13, 20–26, 29–37
Advanced 7–37

Homework Quick Check

Quickly check key concepts.
Exercises: 8, 12, 20, 22, 24

Math Background

The vertices, edges, and faces of the polyhedrons discussed in this lesson satisfy a relationship known as Euler's formula. If V stands for the number of vertices, E for the number of edges, and F for the number of faces, then Euler's formula states that $V - E + F = 2$.

A regular polyhedron is a three-dimensional figure in which all the faces are identical regular polygons. The ancient Greeks suspected, but were unable to prove, that there are only five regular polyhedra. What the Greeks suspected was proven using Euler's formula.

Polyhedrons that satisfy Euler's formula are called *simply connected*.

Georgia Performance Standards

M6G2.b Compare and contrast cylinders and cones.

M6P1.b Solve problems that arise in mathematics and in other contexts.

M6P3.a Organize and consolidate their mathematical thinking through communication.

M6P3.c Analyze and evaluate the mathematical thinking and strategies of others.

10-6 Exercises

M6G2.b, M6P1.b, M6P3.a, M6P3.c

go.hrw.com
Homework Help Online
KEYWORD: MR7 10-6
Parent Resources Online
KEYWORD: MR7 Parent

GUIDED PRACTICE

See Example 1 Identify the number of faces, edges, and vertices on each three-dimensional figure.

1. 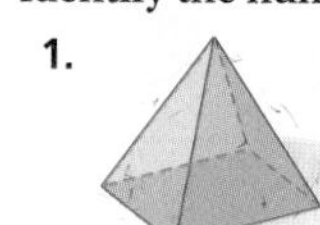
5 faces, 8 edges, 5 vertices

2. 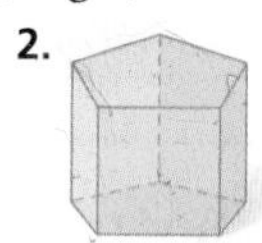
7 faces, 15 edges, 10 vertices

3. 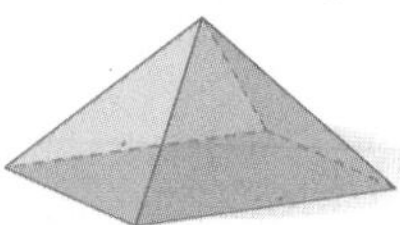
5 faces, 8 edges, 5 vertices

See Example 2 Name each three-dimensional figure represented by each object.

4. 
hexagonal prism

5. 
square pyramid

6. 
cube

INDEPENDENT PRACTICE

See Example 1 Identify the number of faces, edges, and vertices on each three-dimensional figure.

7. 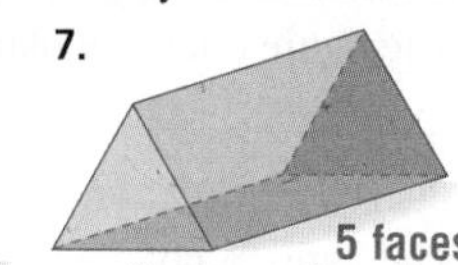
5 faces, 9 edges, 6 vertices

8. 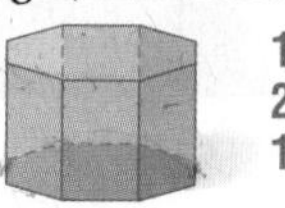
10 faces, 24 edges, 16 vertices

9. 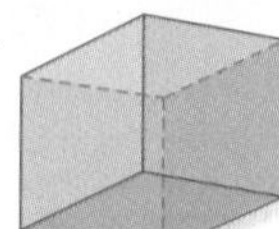
6 faces, 12 edges, 8 vertices

See Example 2 Name each three-dimensional figure represented by each object.

10. 
cylinder

11. rectangular prism

12. 
cone

PRACTICE AND PROBLEM SOLVING

Extra Practice p. 734

Name each figure and tell whether it is a polyhedron.

13. square pyramid, yes

14. cylinder, no

15. cone, no

Write the letter of all the figures that match each description.

16. prism A and D

17. has triangular faces B, C and D

18. has 6 faces A

19. has 5 vertices B

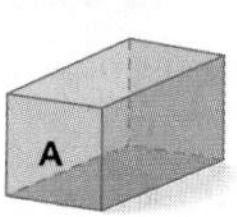

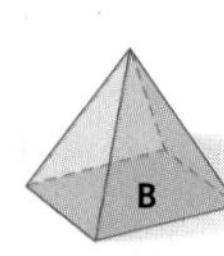

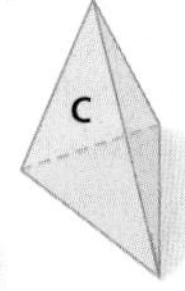

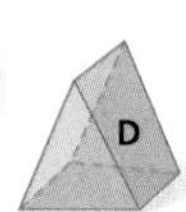

RETEACH 10-6

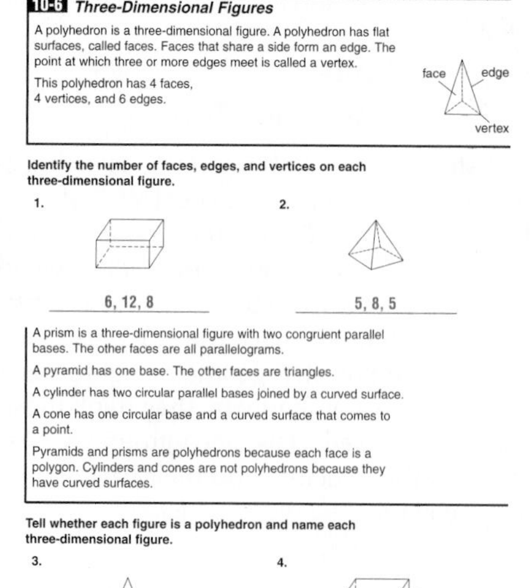

LESSON 10-6 **Reteach**
Three-Dimensional Figures

A polyhedron is a three-dimensional figure. A polyhedron has flat surfaces, called faces. Faces that share a side form an edge. The point at which three or more edges meet is called a vertex.

This polyhedron has 4 faces, 4 vertices, and 6 edges.

face edge vertex

Identify the number of faces, edges, and vertices on each three-dimensional figure.

1. 6, 12, 8

2. 5, 8, 5

A prism is a three-dimensional figure with two congruent parallel bases. The other faces are all parallelograms.

A pyramid has one base. The other faces are triangles.

A cylinder has two circular parallel bases joined by a curved surface.

A cone has one circular base and a curved surface that comes to a point.

Pyramids and prisms are polyhedrons because each face is a polygon. Cylinders and cones are not polyhedrons because they have curved surfaces.

Tell whether each figure is a polyhedron and name each three-dimensional figure.

3. no, cone

4. yes, rectangular prism

PRACTICE 10-6

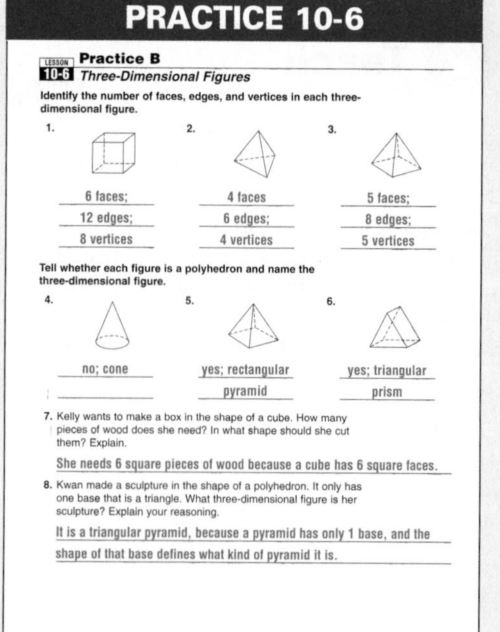

LESSON 10-6 **Practice B**
Three-Dimensional Figures

Identify the number of faces, edges, and vertices in each three-dimensional figure.

1. 6 faces; 12 edges; 8 vertices

2. 4 faces; 6 edges; 4 vertices

3. 5 faces; 8 edges; 5 vertices

Tell whether each figure is a polyhedron and name the three-dimensional figure.

4. no; cone

5. yes; rectangular pyramid

6. yes; triangular prism

7. Kelly wants to make a box in the shape of a cube. How many pieces of wood does she need? In what shape should she cut them? Explain.
She needs 6 square pieces of wood because a cube has 6 square faces.

8. Kwan made a sculpture in the shape of a polyhedron. It only has one base that is a triangle. What three-dimensional figure is her sculpture? Explain your reasoning.
It is a triangular pyramid, because a pyramid has only 1 base, and the shape of that base defines what kind of pyramid it is.

Write *true* or *false* for each statement.

20. A cone does not have a flat surface. false
21. The bases of a cylinder are congruent. true
22. All pyramids have five or more vertices. false
23. All of the edges of a cube are congruent. true
24. **Architecture** Name the three-dimensional figure represented by each building.

a. 
pyramid

b. 
rectangular prism

c. 
cylinder

25. **Critical Thinking** Li makes candles with her mother. She made a candle in the shape of a pyramid that had 9 faces. How many sides did the base of the candle have? Name the polyhedron formed by the candle. 8; octagonal pyramid
26. **What's the Error?** A student says that any polyhedron can be named if the number of faces it has is known. What is the student's error?
27. **Write About It** How are a cone and cylinder alike? How are they different?
28. **Challenge** A square pyramid is cut in half, and the cut is made parallel to the base of the pyramid. What are the shapes of the faces of the bottom half of the pyramid? squares and trapezoids

26. Possible answer: The number of faces does not tell what shape they have or what solid is formed.

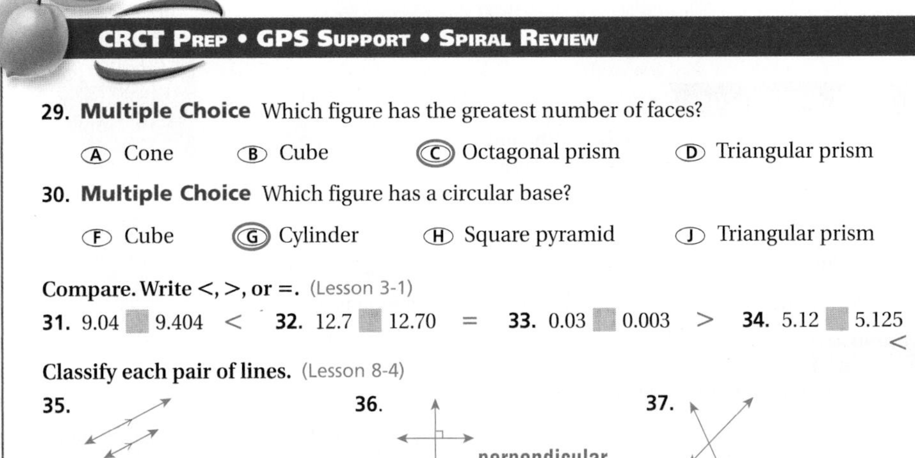

CRCT PREP • GPS SUPPORT • SPIRAL REVIEW

29. **Multiple Choice** Which figure has the greatest number of faces?

Ⓐ Cone Ⓑ Cube Ⓒ Octagonal prism Ⓓ Triangular prism

30. **Multiple Choice** Which figure has a circular base?

Ⓕ Cube Ⓖ Cylinder Ⓗ Square pyramid Ⓙ Triangular prism

Compare. Write <, >, or =. (Lesson 3-1)

31. 9.04 ▢ 9.404 < 32. 12.7 ▢ 12.70 = 33. 0.03 ▢ 0.003 > 34. 5.12 ▢ 5.125 <

Classify each pair of lines. (Lesson 8-4)

35. parallel 36. perpendicular 37. intersecting

CHALLENGE 10-6

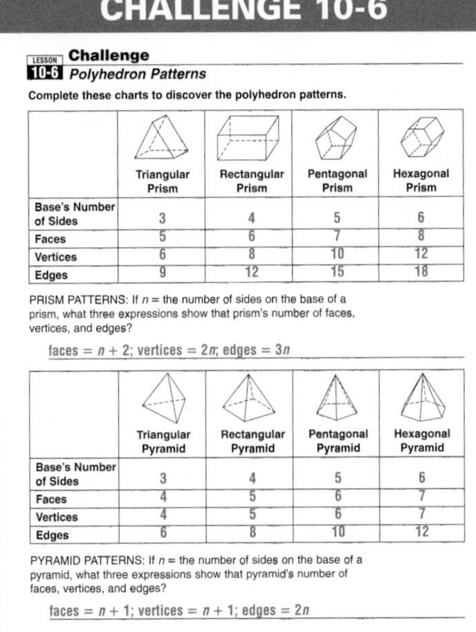

LESSON 10-6 **Challenge**
Polyhedron Patterns

Complete these charts to discover the polyhedron patterns.

	Triangular Prism	Rectangular Prism	Pentagonal Prism	Hexagonal Prism
Base's Number of Sides	3	4	5	6
Faces	5	6	7	8
Vertices	6	8	10	12
Edges	9	12	15	18

PRISM PATTERNS: If n = the number of sides on the base of a prism, what three expressions show that prism's number of faces, vertices, and edges?

faces = $n + 2$; vertices = $2n$; edges = $3n$

	Triangular Pyramid	Rectangular Pyramid	Pentagonal Pyramid	Hexagonal Pyramid
Base's Number of Sides	3	4	5	6
Faces	4	5	6	7
Vertices	4	5	6	7
Edges	6	8	10	12

PYRAMID PATTERNS: If n = the number of sides on the base of a pyramid, what three expressions show that pyramid's number of faces, vertices, and edges?

faces = $n + 1$; vertices = $n + 1$; edges = $2n$

PROBLEM SOLVING 10-6

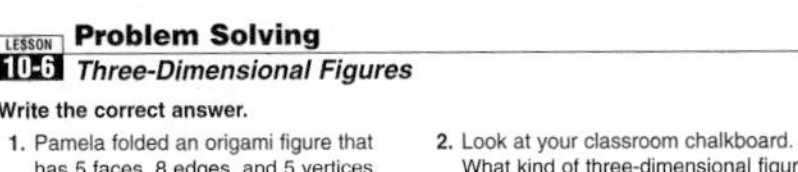

LESSON 10-6 **Problem Solving**
Three-Dimensional Figures

Write the correct answer.

1. Pamela folded an origami figure that has 5 faces, 8 edges, and 5 vertices. What kind of three-dimensional figure could Pamela have created?
a rectangular or square pyramid
2. Look at your classroom chalkboard. What kind of three-dimensional figure is the board eraser? What kind of three-dimensional figure is the chalk?
eraser: rectangular prism; chalk: cylinder
3. If you cut a cylinder in half between its two bases, what two three-dimensional figures are formed?
2 cylinders
4. You have two hexagons. How many rectangles do you need to create a hexagonal prism?
6 rectangles
5. All of the faces of a paperweight are triangles. Is this enough information to classify this three-dimensional figure? Explain.
Yes, it is a triangular pyramid.
6. Paulo says that if you know the number of faces a pyramid has, you also know how many vertices it has. Do you agree? Explain.
Yes; A pyramid always has the same number of faces and vertices.

Circle the letter of the correct answer.

7. How is a triangular prism different from a triangular pyramid?
Ⓐ The prism has 2 bases.
B The pyramid has 2 bases.
C All of the prism's faces are triangles.
D The pyramid has 5 faces.
8. Which of these statements is not true about a cylinder?
F It has 2 circular bases.
G It has a curved lateral surface.
H It is a solid figure.
Ⓙ It is a polyhedron.
9. A museum needs to ship a sculpture that has a curved lateral surface and one flat circular base. In what shape box should they mail the sculpture?
Ⓐ cone C cylinder
B cube D triangular prism
10. A glass prism reflects white light as a multicolored band of light called a spectrum. The prism has 5 glass faces with 9 edges and 6 vertices. What kind of prism it it?
F cube H triangular pyramid
G cone Ⓙ triangular prism

ONGOING ASSESSMENT and INTERVENTION

***Diagnose Before* the Lesson**
10-6 Warm Up, TE p. 566

***Monitor During* the Lesson**
10-6 Know-It Notebook
10-6 Questioning Strategies

***Assess After* the Lesson**
10-6 Lesson Quiz, TE p. 569

Answers

27. Possible answer: Cones and cylinders have curved sides. Cones have one circular base, and cylinders have two circular bases.

TEST PREP DOCTOR For Exercise 29, making a sketch of each three-dimensional figure's base will help identify the figure with the greatest number of faces.

Journal

Have students write brief definitions for the following new vocabulary: *polyhedron*, *face*, *edge*, and *vertex*. Have them draw a picture for each term.

Power Presentations with PowerPoint®

10-6 Lesson Quiz

1. Identify the number of faces, edges, and vertices in the figure shown. 8 faces, 18 edges, and 12 vertices

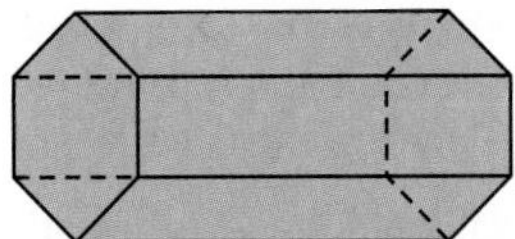

Identify the figure described.

2. two congruent circular faces connected by a curved surface cylinder
3. one flat circular face and a curved lateral surface that comes to a point cone

Also available on transparency

Organizer

Use with Lesson 10-7

Pacing:
Traditional 1 day
Block $\frac{1}{2}$ day

Objective: Use centimeter cubes to find the volume of a prism.

Materials: Centimeter graph paper, centimeter cubes, empty shoe box, index cards, empty soup can

Online Edition

Countdown to CRCT Week 23

Resources

Hands-On Lab Activities
Lab 10-7 Recording Sheet

Teach

Discuss

Discuss the relative ease of finding the volume of a rectangular object using centimeter cubes and the difficulties of doing the same for a cylindrical object.

Close

Key Concept

The formulas for volume can be demonstrated using centimeter cubes.

Assessment

Use the dimensions of each rectangular prism to find its volume.

1. $\ell = 3$; $w = 6$; $h = 9$ 162 cubic units

2. $\ell = 7$; $w = 11$; $h = 5$ 385 cubic units

Georgia Performance Standards

M6M3.a Determine the formula for finding the volume of fundamental solid figures.

M6M3.b Compute the volumes of fundamental solid figures, using appropriate units of measure.

M6M3.c Estimate the volumes of simple geometric solids.

M6A3 Students will evaluate algebraic expressions, including those with exponents, and solve simple one-step equations using each of the four basic operations.

Explore Volumes of Prisms and Cylinders

Use with Lesson 10-7

REMEMBER
- Volume is the number of cubic units needed to fill a space.

M6M3.a, M6M3.b, M6M3.c, M6A3

You can use centimeter cubes to help you find the volume of a *prism.*

Activity

Use the steps and diagrams below to fill in the table.

	Length (ℓ)	Width (w)	Height (h)	Total Number of Cubes (V)
Figure A	3	4	1	12
Figure B	3	4	2	24
Figure C	3	4	5	60

Figure A

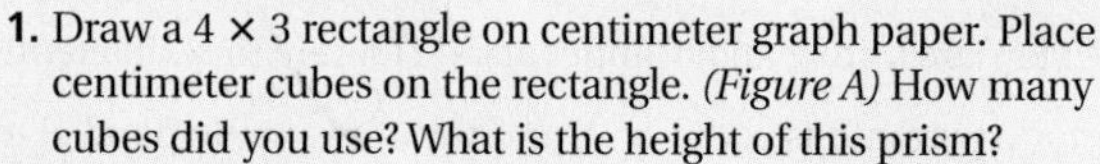

1. Draw a 4 × 3 rectangle on centimeter graph paper. Place centimeter cubes on the rectangle. *(Figure A)* How many cubes did you use? What is the height of this prism?

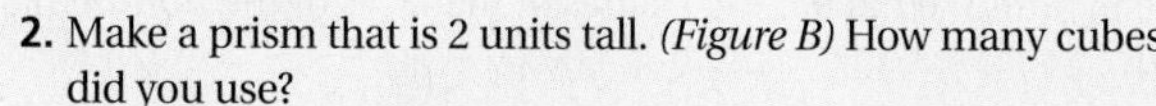

2. Make a prism that is 2 units tall. *(Figure B)* How many cubes did you use?
3. Make a prism that is 5 units tall. *(Figure C)* How many cubes did you use?

Figure B

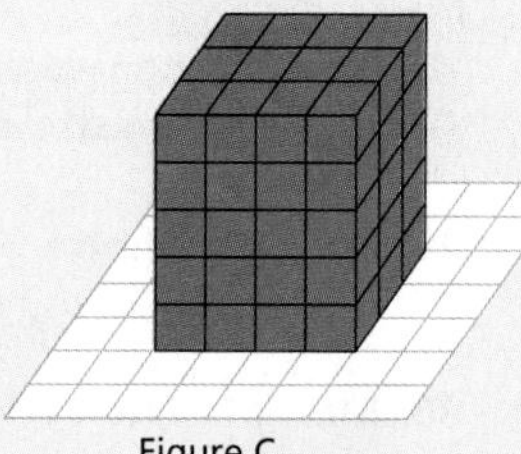

Figure C

Think and Discuss

1. How can you use the length, width, and height of a prism to find the total number of cubes without counting them? Multiply them together.

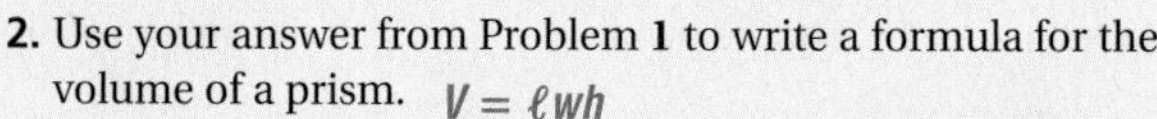

2. Use your answer from Problem **1** to write a formula for the volume of a prism. $V = \ell wh$
3. When the height of the prism is doubled, what happens to the volume? The volume is doubled.

Try This

Build each rectangular prism and find its volume.

1. $\ell = 4$; $w = 2$; $h = 3$ 24 cubic units
2. $\ell = 1$; $w = 4$; $h = 5$ 20 cubic units
3. $\ell = 3$; $w = 3$; $h = 3$ 27 cubic units
4. $\ell = 5$; $w = 10$; $h = 2$ 100 cubic units
5. Estimate the volume of a shoe box. Fill it with centimeter cubes. How close was your estimate? Check students' work.

You can use graph paper and centimeter cubes to estimate the volume of a *cylinder.*

Activity 2

Use the steps below to fill in the table to estimate the volume of a can.

	Estimated Area of Base (A)	Height (h)	Volume (V)
Can	■	■	■

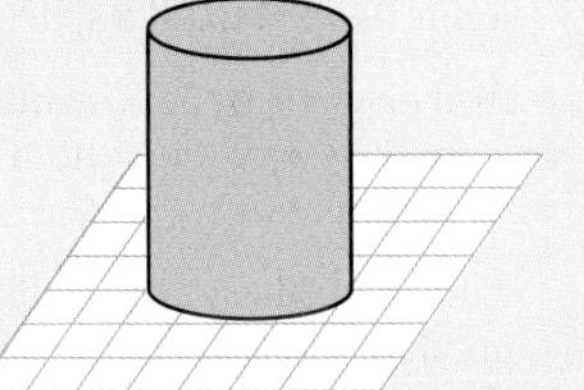

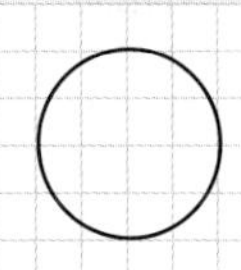

1. Trace around the bottom of a can on graph paper. Count the squares inside the circle to estimate the area A of the bottom of the can.

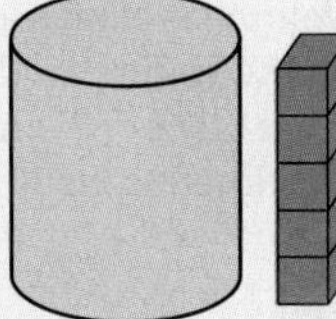

2. Use centimeter cubes to find the height of the can.

3. Use centimeter cubes to build a prism that covers the area of the circle and is the height of the can. Find the volume of the can by counting the cubes used to build the prism or by using $V = A \times h$.

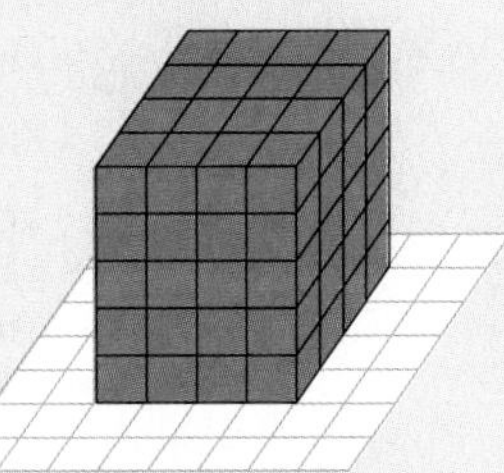

Think and Discuss

1. If you measure the radius of the base, what expression can you use to find the exact area of the circle? πr^2
2. Use the expression you found in Problem **1** to write a formula for the volume of a cylinder? $V = \pi r^2 h$
3. When the height of the cylinder is double, how does the volume change? **The volume is doubled.**

Try This

Estimate the volume of different-sized cans. **Check students' work.**

		Estimated Area of Base (A)	Height (h)	Volume (V)
1.	Tuna Can	■	■	■
2.		■	■	■
3.		■	■	■

10-7 Organizer

Pacing: Traditional 1 day
Block $\frac{1}{2}$ day

Objective: Students estimate and find the volumes of rectangular prisms and triangular prisms.

GPS M6M3.a., M6G2.b
Hands-On Lab
In *Hands-On Lab Activities*

Online Edition
Tutorial Videos, Interactivities

Countdown to CRCT Week 24

Power Presentations with PowerPoint®

Warm Up

Find the area of each figure. Use 3.14 for π.

1. rectangle with base length 8 in. and height 12 in. $96\ \text{in}^2$
2. circle with diameter 8 ft $50.24\ \text{ft}^2$

Problem of the Day

A rectangular park is bordered by a 3-foot-wide sidewalk. The park, including the sidewalk, measures 125 ft by 180 ft. What is the area of the park, not including the sidewalk?
$20{,}706\ \text{ft}^2$

Also available on transparency

Math Humor

Teacher: Use *volume* in a sentence.
Student: Turn down the volume.

Georgia Performance Standards

M6M3.d Solve application problems involving the volume of fundamental solid figures.

M6A3 Students will evaluate algebraic expressions, including those with exponents, and solve simple one-step equations using each of the four basic operations.

M6P1.c Apply and adapt a variety of appropriate strategies to solve problems.

M6P1.d Monitor and reflect on the process of mathematical problem solving.

10-7 Volume of Prisms

Learn to estimate and find the volumes of rectangular prisms and triangular prisms.

Vocabulary
volume

Georgia Performance Standards
M6M3.d Solve application problems involving the volume of fundamental solid figures. Also, M6A3, M6P1.c, M6P1.d.

Volume is the number of cubic units needed to fill a space.

You need 10, or $5 \cdot 2$, centimeter cubes to cover the bottom of this rectangular prism.

You need 3 layers of 10 cubes each to fill the prism. It takes 30, or $5 \cdot 2 \cdot 3$, cubes.

Volume is expressed in cubic units, so the volume of the prism is $5\ \text{cm} \cdot 2\ \text{cm} \cdot 3\ \text{cm} = 30$ cubic centimeters, or $30\ \text{cm}^3$.

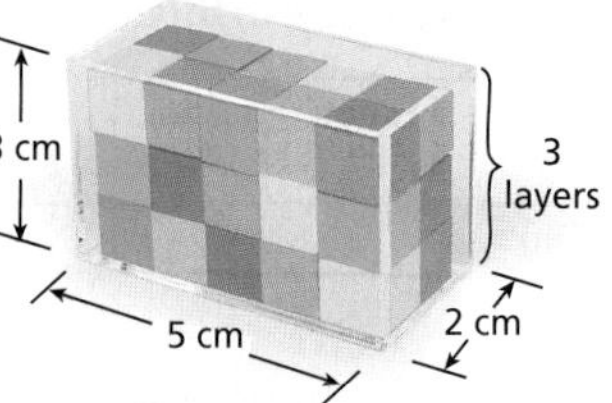

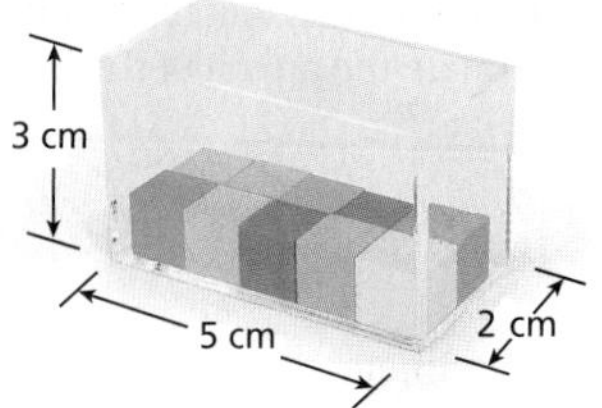

EXAMPLE 1 Finding the Volume of a Rectangular Prism

Find the volume of the rectangular prism.

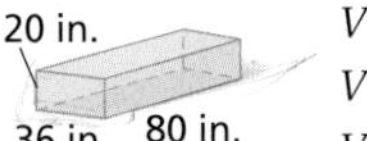

$V = \ell wh$ *Write the formula.*
$V = 80 \cdot 36 \cdot 20$ *$\ell = 80$; $w = 36$; $h = 20$*
$V = 57{,}600\ \text{in}^3$ *Multiply.*

To find the volume of any prism, you can use the formula $V = Bh$, where B is the area of the base, and h is the prism's height.

EXAMPLE 2 Finding the Volume of a Triangular Prism

Find the volume of each triangular prism.

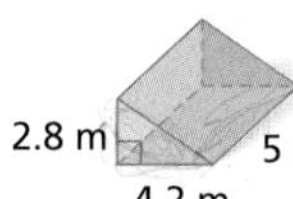

$V = Bh$ *Write the formula.*
$V = \left(\frac{1}{2} \cdot 2.8 \cdot 4.2\right) \cdot 5$ *$B = \frac{1}{2} \cdot 2.8 \cdot 4.2$; $h = 5$*
$V = 29.4\ \text{m}^3$ *Multiply.*

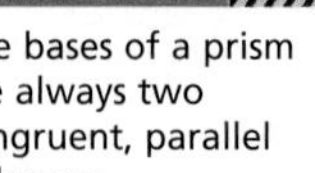

Caution!
The bases of a prism are always two congruent, parallel polygons.

B

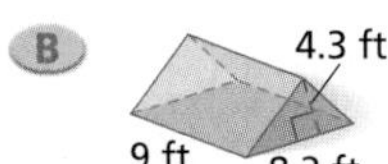

$V = Bh$ *Write the formula.*
$V = \left(\frac{1}{2} \cdot 8.2 \cdot 4.3\right) \cdot 9$ *$B = \frac{1}{2} \cdot 8.2 \cdot 4.3$; $h = 9$*
$V = 158.67\ \text{ft}^3$ *Multiply.*

1 Introduce

Alternate Opener

10-7 Volume of Prisms

Volume is the number of cubic units that fill a space. Notice how the volume of a rectangular prism increases as the height increases.

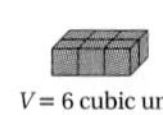
$V = 6$ cubic units

$V = 12$ cubic units

$V = 18$ cubic units

Find the volume of each rectangular prism

1. 2. 3. 4.

Think and Discuss

5. **Explain** how you found the volume of each rectangular prism.
6. **Discuss** why the formulas $V = \text{base} \cdot \text{height}$ and $V = \text{length} \cdot \text{width} \cdot \text{height}$ are equivalent.

Motivate

Review that prisms have two congruent bases connected by rectangular faces. Show students a rectangular prism. Ask students to name the prism and explain their answer. It is a rectangular prism because the bases are shaped like rectangles. Show them a triangular prism. Ask them to name the prism and explain their answer. It is a triangular prism because the bases are shaped like triangles.

Explorations and answers are provided in *Alternate Openers: Explorations Transparencies.*

EXAMPLE 3 **PROBLEM SOLVING APPLICATION**

A craft supplier ships 12 cubic trinket boxes in a case. What are the possible dimensions for a case of the trinket boxes?

1 Understand the Problem

The **answer** will be all possible dimensions for a case of 12 cubic boxes.

List the **important information:**

- There are 12 trinket boxes in a case.
- The boxes are cubic, or square prisms.

2 Make a Plan

You can make models using cubes to find the possible dimensions for a case of 12 trinket boxes.

3 Solve

Make different arrangements of 12 cubes.

$12 \times 1 \times 1$

$4 \times 3 \times 1$

$6 \times 2 \times 1$

$3 \times 2 \times 2$

The possible dimensions for a case of 12 cubic trinket boxes are the following: $12 \times 1 \times 1$, $4 \times 3 \times 1$, $6 \times 2 \times 1$, and $3 \times 2 \times 2$.

4 Look Back

Notice that each dimension is a factor of 12. Also, the product of the dimensions (length · width · height) is 12, showing that the volume of each case is 12 cubes.

Think and Discuss GPS M6M2.c, M6P3.b

1. **Explain** how to find the height of a rectangular prism if you know its length, width, and volume.
2. **Describe** the difference between the units used to measure perimeter, area, and volume.

Possible answers to *Think and Discuss*

1. Divide its volume by the product of its length and width.
2. Units are used for perimeter, square units for area, and cubic units for volume.

Power Presentations with PowerPoint®

Additional Examples

Example 1

Find the volume of the rectangular prism.

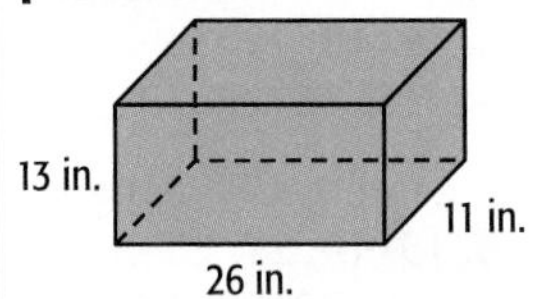

$3{,}718\text{ in}^3$

Example 2

Find the volume of each triangular prism.

A.

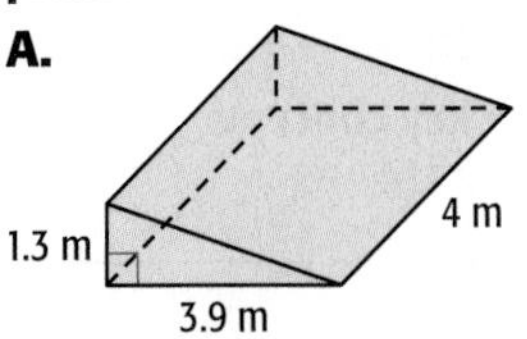

10.14 m^3

B.

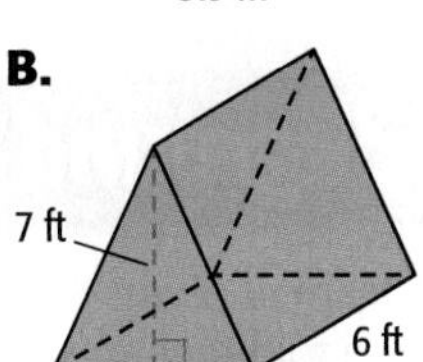

136.5 ft^3

Example 3

Suppose a facial tissue company ships 16 cubic boxes of tissue in each case. What are the possible dimensions for a case of tissue?

$16 \times 1 \times 1$, $8 \times 2 \times 1$, $4 \times 4 \times 1$, and $4 \times 2 \times 2$

Also available on transparency

2 Teach

Guided Instruction

In this lesson, students learn to estimate and find the volumes of rectangular prisms and triangular prisms. Explain and teach the formula for finding volume of a rectangular prism and the formula for finding volume of a triangular prism. Then teach students to make a model to find dimensions that would yield a given volume.

Reaching All Learners

Through Cooperative Learning

Have students construct rectangular and triangular prisms from nets (available in Teacher Tools). With a partner, students should measure and record the dimensions of their prisms. Then have students compute the volumes of both prisms independently and compare answers with each other. If the answers do not agree, partners should work together to find the correct answers.

3 Close

Summarize

Have students explain the new vocabulary term, *volume*. Review the formulas for finding the volume of a rectangular prism ($V = \ell wh$) and the volume of a triangular prism ($V = Bh$, where B is the area of the base).

Possible answer: Volume is the number of cubic units needed to fill a space.

10-7 Exercises

Assignment Guide

If you finished Example 1 assign:
Average 1–3, 15–16, 28–33
Advanced 8–10, 15–16, 28–33

If you finished Example 2 assign:
Average 1–6, 15–19, 21, 28–33
Advanced 8–13, 15–20, 28–33

If you finished Example 3 assign:
Average 1–16, 21–25, 28–33
Advanced 8–33

Homework Quick Check

Quickly check key concepts.
Exercises: 8, 12, 14, 16

Math Background

When students first learned about the exponent 2, they were told that an expression like 5^2 is read "five squared." That is related to the fact that a square with sides of length 5 units has an area of 5^2, or 25 square units.

A similar idea can be explained for this lesson. An expression like 6^3 can be related to a cube whose sides have a length of 6 units. By the formula for the volume of a rectangular prism, this cube has a volume of $6 \times 6 \times 6$, or 6^3 cubic units. Just as the model of a square illustrates why we refer to 5^2 as "five squared," the model of a cube illustrates why we refer to 6^3 as "six cubed."

Georgia Performance Standards

M6P1.a Build new mathematical knowledge through problem solving.

M6P2.c Develop and evaluate mathematical arguments and proofs.

M6P3.a Organize and consolidate their mathematical thinking through communication.

10-7 Exercises

M6P1.a, M6P2.c, M6P3.a

go.hrw.com
Homework Help Online
KEYWORD: MR7 10-7
Parent Resources Online
KEYWORD: MR7 Parent

GUIDED PRACTICE

See Example 1 Find the volume of each rectangular prism.

1. 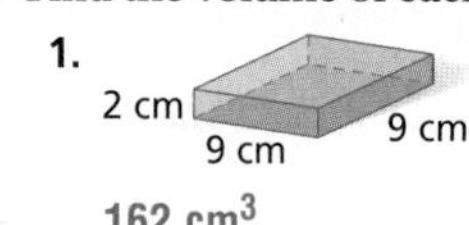

162 cm^3

2. 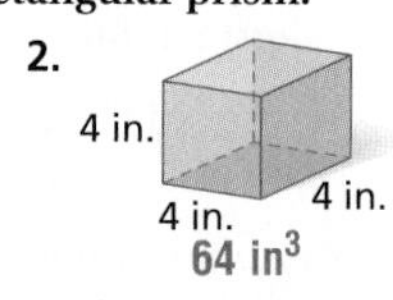

64 in^3

3. 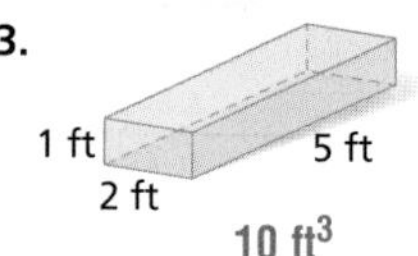

10 ft^3

See Example 2 Find the volume of each triangular prism.

4. 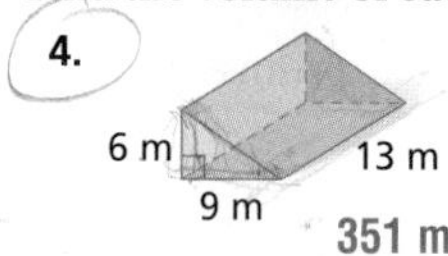

351 m^3

5. 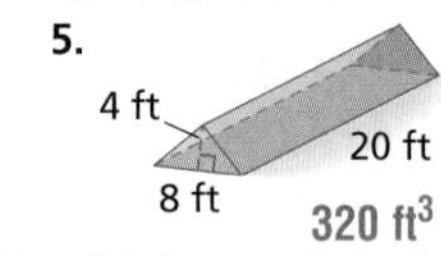

320 ft^3

6. 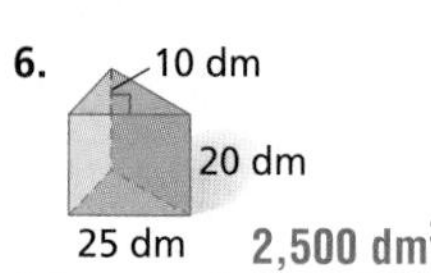

$2{,}500 \text{ dm}^3$

See Example 3
7. A toy company packs 10 cubic boxes of toys in a case. What are the possible dimensions for a case of toys? $1 \times 1 \times 10$ and $2 \times 5 \times 1$

INDEPENDENT PRACTICE

See Example 1 Find the volume of each rectangular prism.

8. 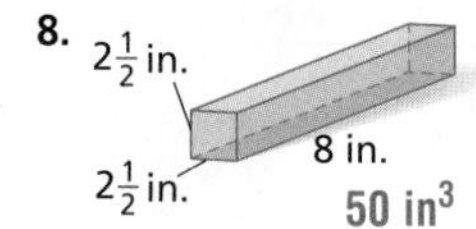

50 in^3

9. 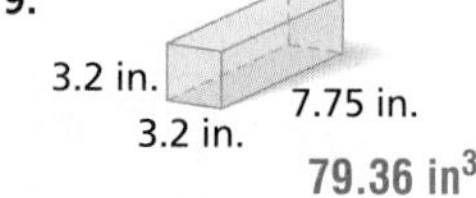

79.36 in^3

10. 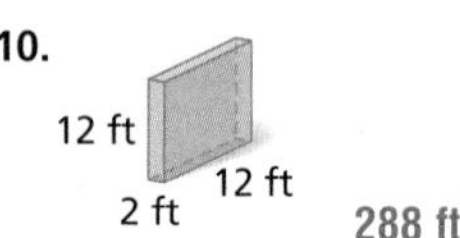

288 ft^3

See Example 2 Find the volume of each triangular prism.

11. 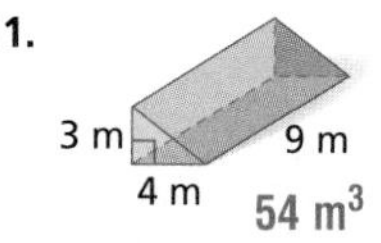

54 m^3

12. 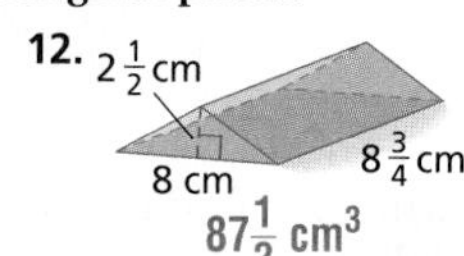

$87\frac{1}{2} \text{ cm}^3$

13. 71.72 ft^3 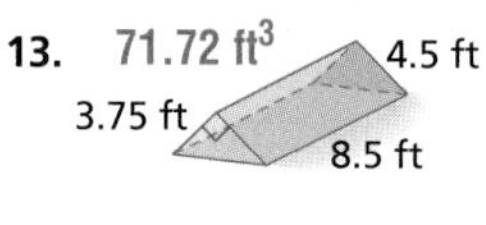

See Example 3
14. A printing company packs 18 cubic boxes of business cards in a larger shipping box. What are the possible dimensions for the shipping box?
$1 \times 1 \times 18$, $2 \times 1 \times 9$, $3 \times 1 \times 6$, $2 \times 3 \times 3$

PRACTICE AND PROBLEM SOLVING

CRCT GPS
Extra Practice p. 734

Find the volume of each figure.

15. 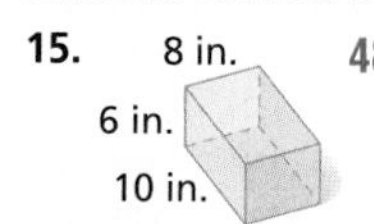

480 in^3

16. 3.5 cm, 3.5 cm, 7.25 cm
88.81 cm^3

17. 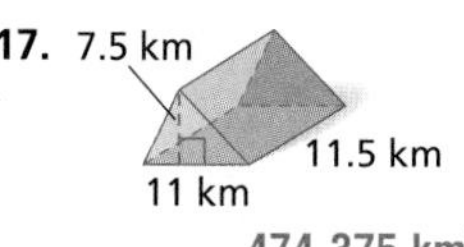

474.375 km^3

Find the missing measurement for each prism.

18. $\ell =$ ___?___; $w = 25$ m; $h = 4$ m; $V = 300 \text{ m}^3$ 3 m

19. $\ell = 9$ ft; $w =$ ___?___; $h = 5$ ft; $V = 900 \text{ ft}^3$ 20 ft

20. $B = 9.28$ in.; $h =$ ___?___; $V = 55.68 \text{ in}^3$ 6 in.

RETEACH 10-7

LESSON 10-7 **Reteach**
Volume of Prisms

Volume is the number of cubic units needed to fill a space. To find the volume of a rectangular prism, first find the area of the base.

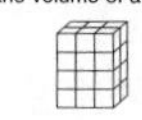

length = 3 units
width = 2 units
$A = \ell w = 3 \cdot 2 = 6$ square units.

The area of the base tells you how many cubic units are in the first layer of the prism.

Next, multiply the result by the number of layers in the prism. The prism has 4 layers, so multiply 6 by 4.

$6 \cdot 4 = 24$

So, the volume of the rectangular prism is 24 cubic units.

Find the volume of each rectangular prism.

1. 16 square units

2. 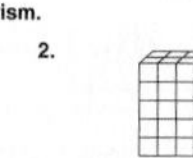
30 square units

To find the area of a triangular prism, first find the area of the base.

$A = \frac{1}{2}bh$
$= \frac{1}{2}(5 \cdot 4)$
$= 10$ square units

Then multiply the result by the height of the prism.

$10 \cdot 3 = 30$

The volume of the triangular prism is 30 cubic units.

Find the volume of each triangular prism.

3. 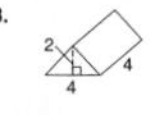

16 square units

4. 15 square units

PRACTICE 10-7

LESSON 10-7 **Practice B**
Volume of Prisms

Find the volume of each rectangular prism.

1. $s = 9.5$ in. — 857.375 in^3
2. 10 ft, 15 ft, 12 ft — $1{,}800 \text{ ft}^3$
3. 17 yd, 16 yd, 25 yd — $6{,}800 \text{ yd}^3$
4. 7.3 m, 6.1 m, 5.2 m — 231.556 m^3
5. 20 yd, 7 yd, 7 yd — 980 yd^3
6. $s = 15.2$ cm — $3{,}511.808 \text{ cm}^3$

Find the volume of each triangular prism.

7. 10 cm, 14 cm, 13 cm — 910 cm^3
8. 9.8 ft, 2.5 ft, 6 ft — 73.5 ft^3
9. 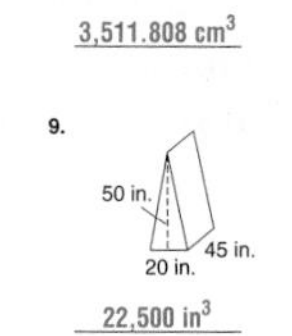

$22{,}500 \text{ in}^3$

10. Fawn built a sandbox that is 6 feet long, 5 feet wide, and $\frac{1}{2}$ foot tall. How many cubic feet of sand does she need to fill the box?
15 ft^3

11. Unfinished lumber is sold in units called board feet. A board foot is the volume of lumber contained in a board 1 inch thick, 1 foot wide, and 1 foot long. How many cubic inches of wood are in 1 board foot?
144 cubic inches of wood

Physical Science LINK

The density of a substance is a measure of its mass per unit of volume. The density of a particular substance is always the same. The formula for density D is the mass m of a substance divided by its volume V, or $D = \frac{m}{V}$.

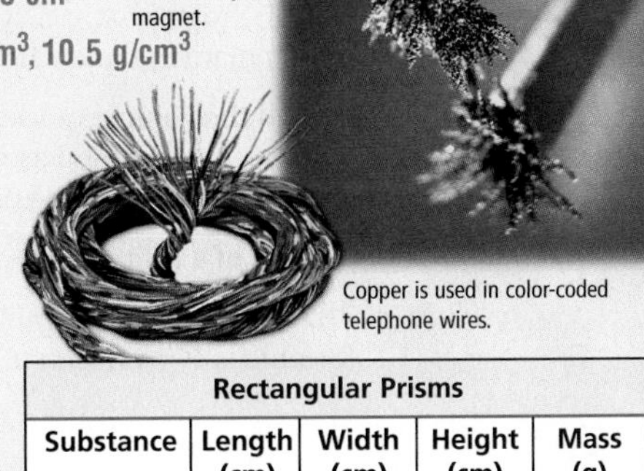

Iron filings are attracted by a magnet.

21. Find the volume of each substance in the table. **10 cm³, 1 cm³, 3.5 cm³, 300 cm³, 20 cm³**
22. Calculate the density of each substance. **8.96 g/cm³, 19.32 g/cm³, 5.02 g/cm³, 0.4 g/cm³, 10.5 g/cm³**
23. Water has a density of 1 g/cm³. A substance whose density is less than that of water will float. Which of the substances in the table will float in water? **pine**
24. A fresh egg has a density of approximately 1.2 g/cm³. A spoiled egg has a density of about 0.9 g/cm³. How can you tell whether an egg is fresh without cracking it open?
25. **Multi-Step** Alicia has a solid rectangular prism of a substance she believes is gold. The dimensions of the prism are 2 cm by 1 cm by 2 cm, and the mass is 20.08 g. Is the substance that Alicia has gold? Explain.
26. **Write About It** In a science lab, you are given a prism of copper. You determine that its dimensions are 4 cm, 2 cm, and 6 cm. Without weighing the prism, how can you determine its mass? Explain your answer.
27. **Challenge** A solid rectangular prism of silver has a mass of 84 g. What are some possible dimensions of the prism? **Possible answers: 2 cm × 4 cm × 1 cm, 1 cm × 1 cm × 8 cm, 2 cm × 2 cm × 2 cm**

Copper is used in color-coded telephone wires.

Rectangular Prisms				
Substance	Length (cm)	Width (cm)	Height (cm)	Mass (g)
Copper	2	1	5	89.6
Gold	$\frac{2}{3}$	$\frac{3}{4}$	2	19.32
Iron pyrite	0.25	2	7	17.57
Pine	10	10	3	120
Silver	2.5	4	2	210

Gold is used to make many pieces of jewelry.

CRCT Prep • GPS Support • Spiral Review

28. **Multiple Choice** A rectangular prism has a volume of 1,080 ft³. The height of the prism is 8 ft, and the width is 9 ft. What is the length of the prism?

    (A) 15 ft (circled) (B) 120 ft (C) 135 ft (D) 77,760 ft

29. **Gridded Response** The dimensions of a rectangular prism are 4.3 inches, 12 inches, and 1.5 inches. What is the volume, in cubic inches, of the prism? **77.4**

Find the GCF of each set of numbers. (Lesson 4-3)

30. 12, 18, 24 **6**
31. 15, 18, 30 **3**
32. 16, 24, 42 **2**
33. 18, 54, 63 **9**

CHALLENGE 10-7

LESSON 10-7 Challenge
Fish Tank Math

Did you know that most fish grow according to the size of their tank? In fact, a freshwater fish needs about 1 gallon of water for every inch of its body. The volume of 1 gallon of water is about 231 in³. So, a fish tank with a volume of a 700 in³ will hold 700 ÷ 231 ≈ 3 gallons of water. This size tank would be the healthiest home for a 3-inch-long fish.

Find the volume of each fish tank. Then match each fish to the best tank for it.

Angelfish ℓ = 6 in.

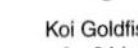

Koi Goldfish ℓ = 24 in.

Redtail Shark ℓ = 5 in.

Clown Loach ℓ = 12 in.

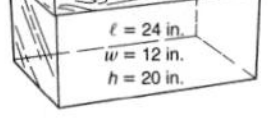

ℓ = 24 in., w = 12 in., h = 20 in.

Volume of Tank: **5,760 in³**
Gallons of Water: **about 25**
Fish: **koi goldfish**

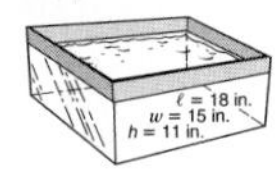

ℓ = 18 in., w = 15 in., h = 11 in.

Volume of Tank: **2,970 in³**
Gallons of Water: **about 13**
Fish: **clown loach**

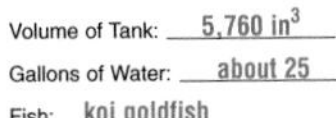

ℓ = 13 in., w = 10 in., h = 9 in.

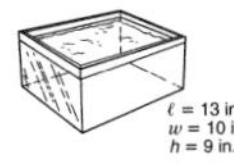

Volume of Tank: **1,170 in³**
Gallons of Water: **about 5**
Fish: **redtail shark**

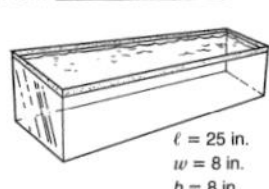

ℓ = 25 in., w = 8 in., h = 8 in.

Volume of Tank: **1,600 in³**
Gallons of Water: **about 7**
Fish: **angelfish**

PROBLEM SOLVING 10-7

LESSON 10-7 Problem Solving
Volume of Prisms

Write the correct answer.

1. At 726 feet tall, Hoover Dam is one of the world's largest concrete dams. In fact, it holds enough concrete to pave a two-lane highway from New York City to San Francisco! The dam is shaped like a rectangular prism with a base 1,224 feet long and 660 feet wide. About how much concrete forms Hoover Dam?
   about 586,491,840 ft³ of concrete
2. The Vietnam Veterans Memorial in Washington, D.C., is a 493.5-foot-long wall made of polished black granite engraved with the names of soldiers who died in the war. The wall is 0.25 feet thick and has an average height of 9 feet. About how many cubic feet of black granite was used in the Vietnam Veterans Memorial?
   about 1,110.375 ft³ of black granite
3. Benitoite, a triangular prism crystal, is the official state gem of California. One benitoite crystal found in California is 1.2 cm tall, with a base width of 2 cm and a base height of 1.3 cm. How many cubic centimeters of benitoite are in that crystal?
   1.56 cm³ of benitoite
4. The Flatiron Building in New York City is a triangular prism. A solid bronze souvenir model of the building is 5 inches tall, with a base height of 1.5 inches and a base width of 2.5 inches. How much bronze was used to make the model?
   9.375 in³ of bronze

Circle the letter of the correct answer.

5. Individual slices of pizza are sold in 2-inch-tall triangular prism boxes. The box base is 8 inches wide, with a 7-inch height. How many cubic inches of pizza will fit in each box?
   A 112 in³ C 60 in³
   B 102 in³ (D) 56 in³ (circled)
6. The world's largest chocolate bar is a huge rectangular prism weighing more than a ton! The bar is 9 feet long, 4 feet tall, and 1 foot wide. How many cubic feet of chocolate does it have?
   F 13 ft³ (H) 36 ft³ (circled)
   G 14 ft³ J 72 ft³
7. A box can hold 175 cubic inches of cereal. If the box is 7 inches long and 2.5 inches wide, how tall is it?
   A 25 in.
   (B) 10 in. (circled)
   C 17.5 in.
   D 9.5 in.
8. A triangular prism used to reflect light is made of 120 cm³ of glass. If the prism is 5 centimeters tall, what is the area of each of its triangular bases?
   F 24 cm
   G 12 cm
   H 12 cm²
   (J) 24 cm² (circled)

Ongoing Assessment and Intervention

Diagnose *Before* the Lesson
10-7 Warm Up, TE p. 572

Monitor *During* the Lesson
10-7 Know-It Notebook
10-7 Questioning Strategies

Assess *After* the Lesson
10-7 Lesson Quiz, TE p. 575

Answers

24. Check to see whether the egg floats in water; if it does, then the egg is spoiled.
25. Alicia does not have gold because the density of Alicia's substance is 5.02 g/cm³, and the density of gold is 19.32 g/cm³.
26. See p. A11.

Test Prep Doctor For Exercise 28, students using estimation in the volume formula can eliminate choices **B, C,** and **D.**

Journal

Have students write the formulas for volumes of rectangular and triangular prisms and explain what the variables in each formula stand for. Have them draw pictures to demonstrate their understanding.

Power Presentations with PowerPoint®

10-7 Lesson Quiz

Find the volume of each figure.

1. rectangular prism with length 20 cm, width 15 cm, and height 12 cm **3,600 cm³**
2. triangular prism with a height of 12 cm and a triangular base with base length 7.3 cm and height 3.5 cm **153.3 cm³**
3. Find the volume of the figure shown. **38.13 cm³**

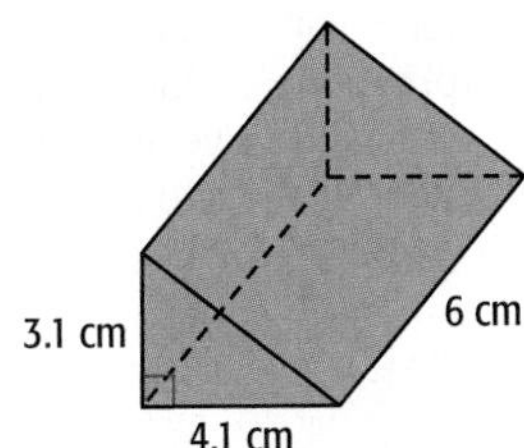

Also available on transparency

10-8 Organizer

Pacing: Traditional 1 day
Block $\frac{1}{2}$ day

Objective: Students find volumes of cylinders.

GPS M6M3.a
Hands-On Lab
In *Hands-On Lab Activities*

Technology Lab
In *Technology Lab Activities*

Online Edition
Tutorial Videos, Interactivities

Countdown to CRCT Week 24

Power Presentations with PowerPoint®

Warm Up

Find the volume of each figure described.

1. rectangular prism with length 12 cm, width 11 cm, and height 10 cm **1,320 cm^3**
2. triangular prism with height 11 cm and triangular base with base length 10.2 cm and height 6.4 cm **359.04 cm^3**

Problem of the Day

The height of a box is half its width. The length is 12 in. longer than its width. If the volume of the box is 28 in^3, what are the dimensions of the box? **1 in. × 2 in. × 14 in.**

Also available on transparency

Georgia Performance Standards

M6M3.b Compute the volumes of fundamental solid figures, using appropriate units of measure.

M6M3.d Solve application problems involving the volume of fundamental solid figures.

M6A3 Students will evaluate algebraic expressions, including those with exponents, and solve simple one-step equations using each of the four basic operations.

10-8 Volume of Cylinders

Learn to find volumes of cylinders.

Georgia Performance Standards

M6M3.b Compute the volumes of fundamental solid figures, using appropriate units of measure. Also, M6M3.d, M6A3.

Thomas Edison invented the first phonograph in 1877. The main part of this phonograph was a cylinder with a 4-inch diameter and a height of $3\frac{3}{8}$ inches.

To find the volume of a cylinder, you can use the same method as you did for prisms: Multiply the area of the base by the height.

volume of a cylinder = area of base × height

The area of the circular base is πr^2, so the formula is $V = Bh = \pi r^2 h$.

EXAMPLE 1 Finding the Volume of a Cylinder

Find the volume V of each cylinder to the nearest cubic unit.

A

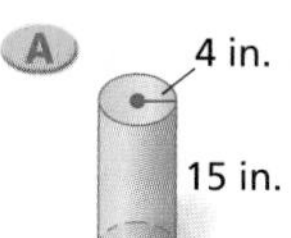

$V = \pi r^2 h$ *Write the formula.*

$V \approx 3.14 \times 4^2 \times 15$ *Replace π with 3.14, r with 4, and h with 15.*

$V \approx 753.6$ *Multiply.*

The volume is about 754 in^3.

B

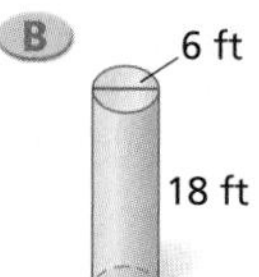

6 ft ÷ 2 = 3 ft *Find the radius.*

$V = \pi r^2 h$ *Write the formula.*

$V \approx 3.14 \times 3^2 \times 18$ *Replace π with 3.14, r with 3, and h with 18.*

$V \approx 508.68$ *Multiply.*

The volume is about 509 ft^3.

C

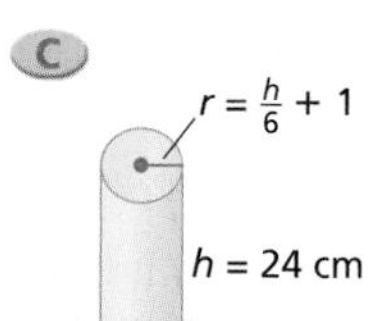

$r = \frac{h}{6} + 1$ *Find the radius.*

$r = \frac{24}{6} + 1 = 5$ *Substitute 24 for h.*

$V = \pi r^2 h$ *Write the formula.*

$V \approx 3.14 \times 5^2 \times 24$ *Replace π with 3.14, r with 5, and h with 24.*

$V \approx 1{,}884$ *Multiply.*

The volume is about 1,884 cm^3.

1 Introduce

Alternate Opener

EXPLORATION

10-8 Volume of Cylinders

The area of the base of a soup can is 4.9 in^2, and the height is 4 in. To find the volume of this can, multiply the area of the base times the height.

volume = area of base · height ($V = Bh$)

$V = 4.9 \cdot 4 = 19.6$ in^3

The soup can has a volume of 19.6 in^3.

h = 4 in.
B = 4.9 in^2

Find the volume of each cylinder.

	Area of Base	Height	Volume = Area of Base · Height
1.	12.6 in^2	8 in.	
2.	28.3 cm^2	10 cm	
3.	3.14 ft^2	2 ft	
4.	113.1 in^2	12 in.	
5.	176.7 cm^2	25 cm	

Think and Discuss

6. **Explain** how to find the volume of a cylinder.
7. **Discuss** why the formulas $V = B \cdot h$ and $V = \pi \cdot r^2 \cdot h$ are equivalent (r = radius).

Motivate

Tell students that the formula for volume of a cylinder involves multiplying the area of the base by the height. To exercise their mathematical reasoning, see whether students can come up with the formula on their own before looking in the text. $V = \pi r^2 h$

Explorations and answers are provided in *Alternate Openers: Explorations Transparencies.*

EXAMPLE 2 *Music Application*

The cylinder in Edison's first phonograph had a 4 in. diameter and a height of about 3 in. The standard phonograph manufactured 21 years later had a 2 in. diameter and a height of 4 in. Estimate the volume of each cylinder to the nearest cubic inch.

Remember!

The value of *pi* can be approximated as 3.14 or $\frac{22}{7}$.

A Edison's first phonograph

4 in. ÷ 2 = 2 in.	*Find the radius.*
$V = \pi r^2 h$	*Write the formula.*
$V \approx 3.14 \times 2^2 \times 3$	*Replace π with 3.14, r with 2, and h with 3.*
$V \approx 37.68$	*Multiply.*

The volume of Edison's first phonograph was about 38 in^3.

B Edison's standard phonograph

2 in. ÷ 2 = 1 in.	*Find the radius.*
$V = \pi r^2 h$	*Write the formula.*
$V \approx \frac{22}{7} \times 1^2 \times 4$	*Replace π with $\frac{22}{7}$, r with 1, and h with 4.*
$V \approx \frac{88}{7} = 12\frac{4}{7}$	*Multiply.*

The volume of the standard phonograph was about 13 in^3.

EXAMPLE 3 **Comparing Volumes of Cylinders**

Find which cylinder has the greater volume.

Cylinder 1: $V = \pi r^2 h$

$V \approx 3.14 \times 6^2 \times 12$

$V \approx 1{,}356.48\ cm^3$

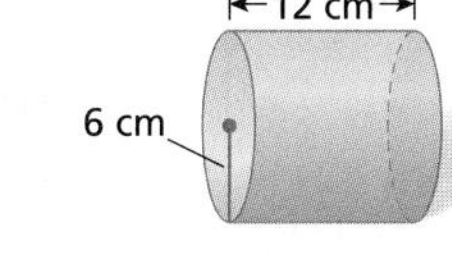

Cylinder 2: $V = \pi r^2 h$

$V \approx 3.14 \times 4^2 \times 16$

$V \approx 803.84\ cm^3$

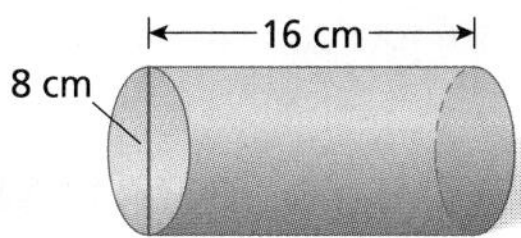

Cylinder 1 has the greater volume because $1{,}356.48\ cm^3 > 803.84\ cm^3$.

Possible answers to *Think and Discuss*

1. For both, you multiply the height by the area the base.
2. πr^2 represents the area of the base of the cylinder (a circle); h represents the height of the cylinder.

Think and Discuss GPS M3P3.a, M3P3.b

1. **Explain** how the formula for the volume of a cylinder is similar to the formula for the volume of a rectangular prism.
2. **Explain** which parts of a cylinder are represented by πr^2 and h in the formula $V = \pi r^2 h$.

Power Presentations with PowerPoint®

Additional Examples

Example 1

Find the volume V of each cylinder to the nearest cubic unit.

A. $r = 4$ ft, $h = 7$ ft about 352 ft^3

B. $d = 10$ cm, $h = 11$ cm about 864 cm^3

C. $r = \frac{h}{3} + 4$, $h = 9$ in. about 1,385 in^3

Example 2

Ali has a cylinder-shaped pencil holder with a 3-in. diameter and a height of 5 in. Scott has a cylinder-shaped pencil holder with a 4-in. diameter and a height of 6 in. Estimate the volume of each cylinder to the nearest cubic inch.

A. Ali's pencil holder about 35 in^3

B. Scott's pencil holder about 75 in^3

Example 3

Find which cylinder has the greater volume.

Cylinder 1:

$V \approx 84.78\ cm^3$

Cylinder 2:

$V \approx 169.56\ cm^3$

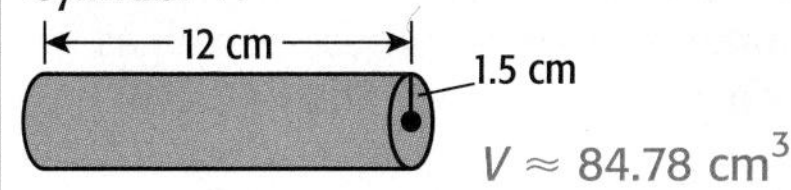

Cylinder 2 has the greater volume because $169.56\ cm^3 > 84.78\ cm^3$.

Also available on transparency

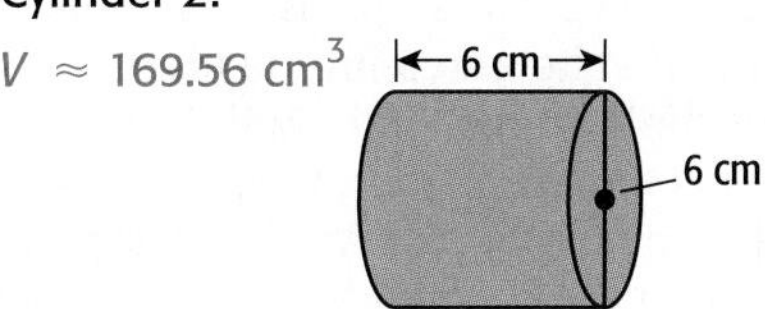

2 Teach

Guided Instruction

In this lesson, students learn to find volumes of cylinders. Teach students to use the formula for volume of a cylinder, and have students compare volumes of cylinders.

Teaching Tip

Inclusion Remind students that they can substitute 3.14 or $\frac{22}{7}$ as an estimated value for *pi.*

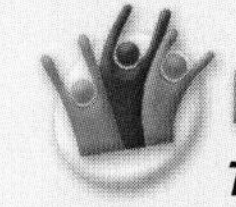

Reaching All Learners

Through Modeling

Discuss common household cylinders, for example, paper towel tubes, toilet paper tubes, oatmeal containers, shampoo bottles, etc. Have students measure and record the radius and height and compute the volume for some common household cylinders. Have students share their findings with the class.

3 Close

Summarize

Review the formula for volume of a cylinder and work through finding the volume of a cylinder that is 4 inches tall and has a radius of 2 inches.

$V = \pi r^2 h$

$V \approx 3.14 \cdot 2^2 \cdot 4$

$V \approx 50.24\ in^3$

10-8 Exercises

Assignment Guide

If you finished Example 1 assign:
Average 1–3, 14–16, 28–33
Advanced 6–8, 17–19, 28–33

If you finished Example 2 assign:
Average 1–4, 14–19, 28–33
Advanced 6–9, 14–19, 28–33

If you finished Example 3 assign:
Average 1–11, 17–33
Advanced 6–33

Homework Quick Check

Quickly check key concepts.
Exercises: 6, 8, 10, 18

Math Background

The ancient Greek mathematician Archimedes wrote a two-volume work entitled *On the Sphere and the Cylinder*. In it, he proved that a cylinder and sphere with equal heights and diameters have volumes, as well as surface areas, in the ratio of 3:2.

According to the historian Plutarch, Archimedes was so pleased with his proof that he asked his friends to inscribe it on his tomb. And Cicero claims to have found the inscription when he discovered Archimedes' grave more than 100 years later.

Georgia Performance Standards

M6P1.c Apply and adapt a variety of appropriate strategies to solve problems.

M6P3.a Organize and consolidate their mathematical thinking through communication.

M6P4.c Recognize and apply mathematics in contexts outside of mathematics.

10-8 Exercises

M6P1.c, M6P3.a, M6P4.c

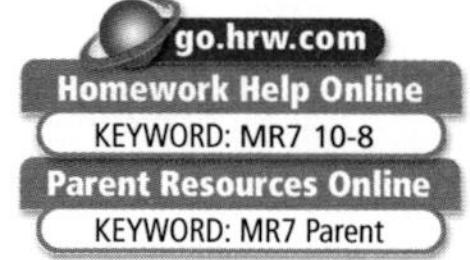

GUIDED PRACTICE

See Example 1 — **Find the volume V of each cylinder to the nearest cubic unit.**

1. 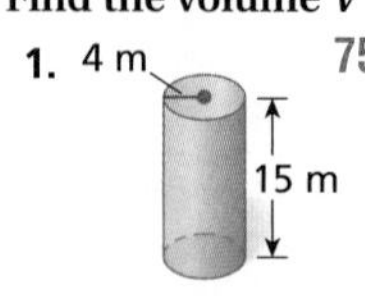

754 m³

2. 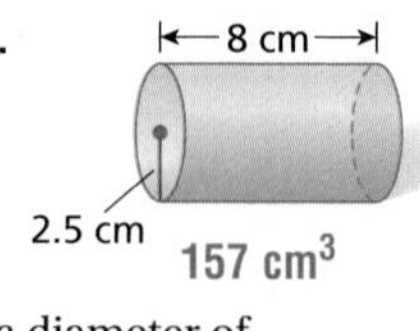

157 cm³

3. 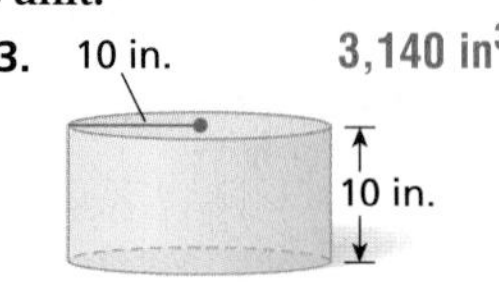

3,140 in³

See Example 2

4. A cylindrical bucket with a diameter of 4 inches is filled with rainwater to a height of 2.5 inches. Estimate the volume of the rainwater to the nearest cubic inch. **31 in³**

See Example 3

5. Find which cylinder, A or B, has the greater volume. **Cylinder B**

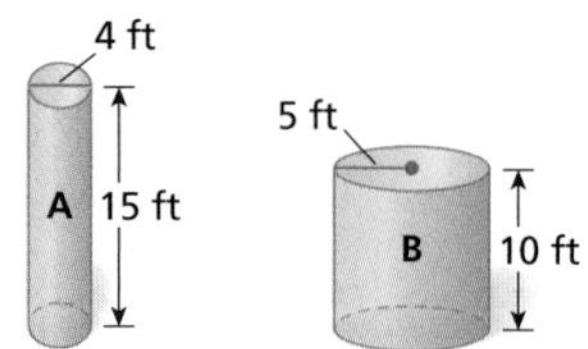

INDEPENDENT PRACTICE

See Example 1 — **Find the volume V of each cylinder to the nearest cubic unit.**

6. 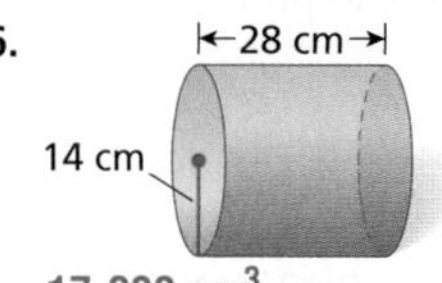

17,232 cm³

7. 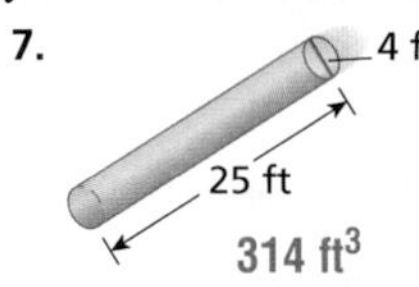

314 ft³

8. 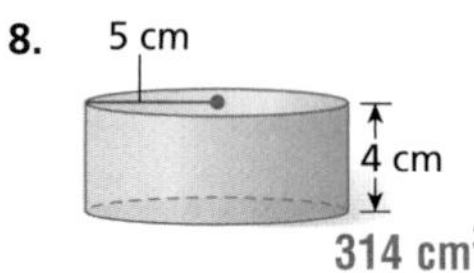

314 cm³

See Example 2

9. Wooden dowels are solid cylinders of wood. One dowel has a radius of 1 cm, and another dowel has a radius of 3 cm. Both dowels have a height of 10 cm. Estimate the volume of each dowel to the nearest cubic cm. **31 cm³ and 283 cm³**

See Example 3

10. Find which cylinder, X or Y, has the greater volume. **Cylinder X**

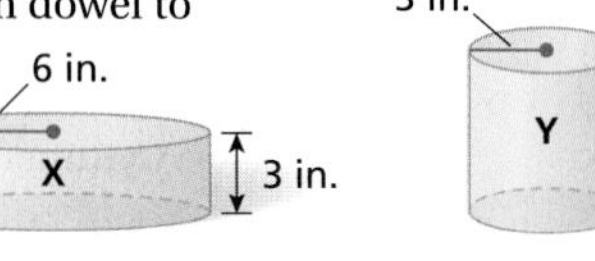

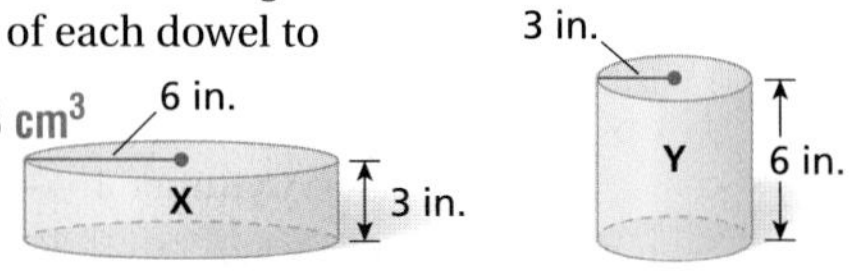

PRACTICE AND PROBLEM SOLVING

Extra Practice p. 734

Find the volume of each cylinder to the nearest cubic unit.

11. 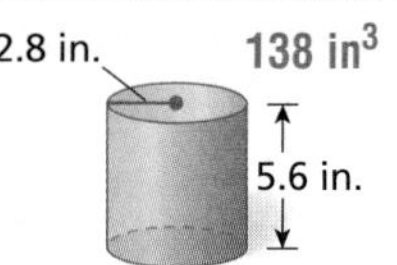

138 in³

12. 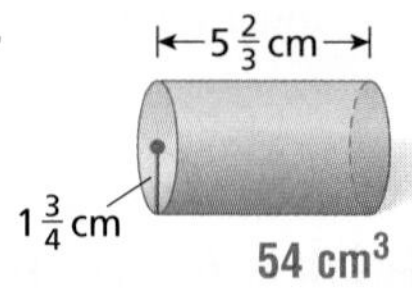

54 cm³

13. 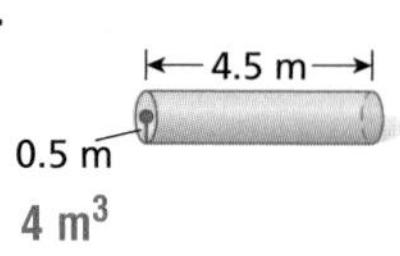

4 m³

Find the volume of each cylinder using the information given.

14. $r = 6$ cm; $h = 6$ cm **678.24 cm³**
15. $d = 4$ in.; $h = 8$ in. **100.48 in³**
16. $r = 2$ m; $h = 5$ m **62.8 m³**
17. $r = 7.5$ ft; $h = 11.25$ ft **1,987.03 ft³**
18. $d = 12\frac{1}{4}$ yd; $h = 5\frac{3}{5}$ yd **659.67 yd³**
19. $d = 20$ mm; $h = 40$ mm **12,560 mm²**

RETEACH 10-8

LESSON 10-8 **Reteach**
Volume of Cylinders

You can use what you know about area to help you find the volume of a cylinder.

(cylinder: radius 3, height 5)

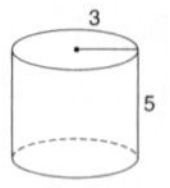

To find the volume of a cylinder, first find the area of the circular base.

$A = \pi r^2$ Use 3.14 for π.
$\approx 3.14 \cdot 3^2$
$\approx 3.14 \cdot 9$
≈ 28.26 square units

The area of the circular base is about 28.26 square units.

Next, multiply your answer by the height of the cylinder. The height of the cylinder is 5 units, so multiply 28.26 by 5.

$28.26 \cdot 5 = 141.3$

So, the volume of the cylinder is about 141.3 cubic units.

Find the volume of each cylinder.

1. 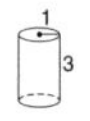 (radius 1, height 3) 9.42 cubic units
2. (radius 4, height 2) 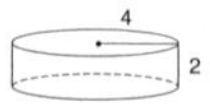 100.48 cubic units
3. 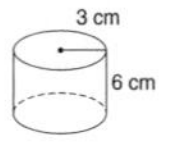 (radius 3 cm, height 6 cm) 169.56 cubic units
4. 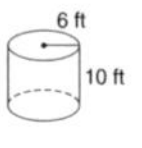 (radius 6 ft, height 10 ft) 1,130.4 cubic units

PRACTICE 10-8

LESSON 10-8 **Practice B**
Volume of Cylinders

Find the volume V of each cylinder to the nearest cubic unit.

1. 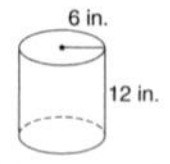 (6 in., 12 in.) $V \approx 1{,}356$ in³
2. 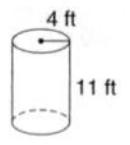 (4 ft, 11 ft) $V \approx 553$ ft³
3. 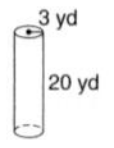 (3 yd, 20 yd) $V \approx 565$ yd³
4. 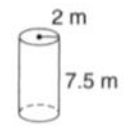 (2 m, 7.5 m) $V \approx 94$ m³
5. 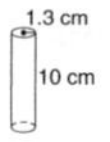 (1.3 cm, 10 cm) $V \approx 53$ cm³
6. 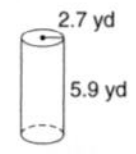 (2.7 yd, 5.9 yd) $V \approx 135$ yd³
7. 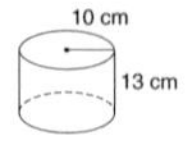 (10 cm, 13 cm) $V \approx 4{,}082$ cm³
8. 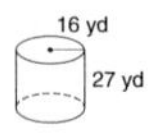 (16 yd, 27 yd) $V \approx 21{,}704$ yd³
9. 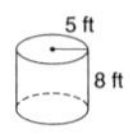 (5 ft, 8 ft) $V \approx 628$ ft³

10. A cylindrical package of oatmeal is 20 centimeters tall. The diameter of its base is 10 centimeters. About how much oatmeal does the package hold?
about 1,570 cubic centimeters of oatmeal

11. The volume of a can is about 50.24 in³. The radius of its base is 2 inches. How tall is the can?
4 inches

Multi-Step Find the volume of each shaded cylinder to the nearest cubic unit.

20. 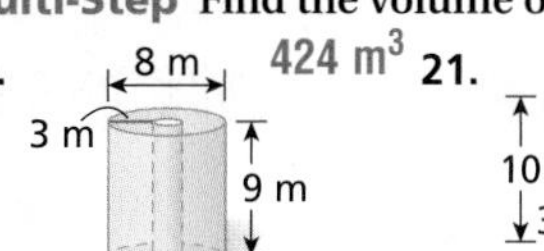

424 m^3

21. 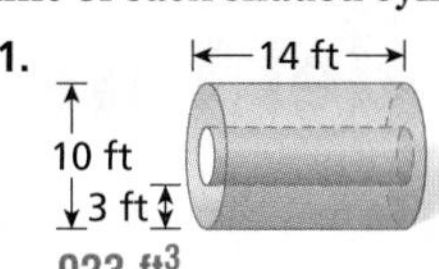

923 ft^3

22. 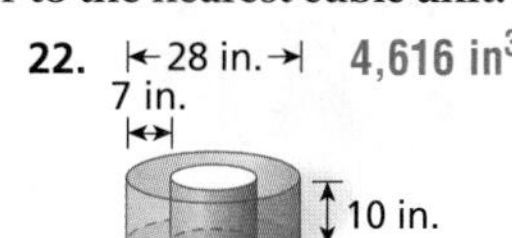

4,616 in^3

Georgia LINK
Science

Researchers at the Georgia Institute of Technology are studying how to use chemical-eating bacteria to clean up toxic waste sites and contaminated drinking water.

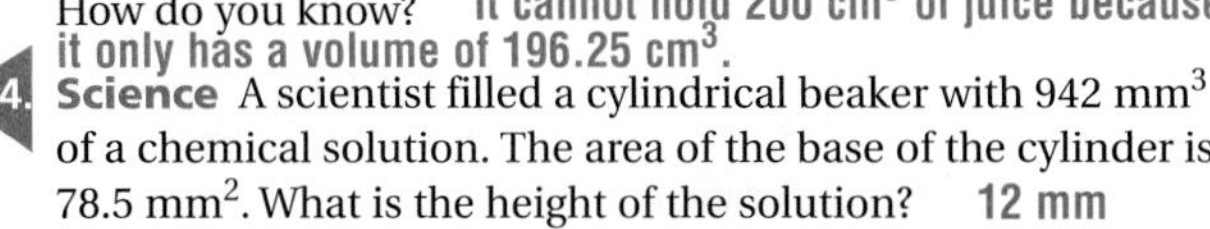

23. **Measurement** Could this blue can hold 200 cm^3 of juice? How do you know? It cannot hold 200 cm^3 of juice because it only has a volume of 196.25 cm^3.

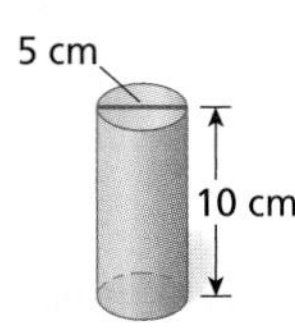

24. **Science** A scientist filled a cylindrical beaker with 942 mm^3 of a chemical solution. The area of the base of the cylinder is 78.5 mm^2. What is the height of the solution? 12 mm

25. **Choose a Strategy** Fran, Gene, Helen, and Ira have cylinders with different volumes. Gene's cylinder holds more than Fran's. Ira's cylinder holds more than Helen's, but less than Fran's. Whose cylinder has the largest volume? What color cylinder does each person have?

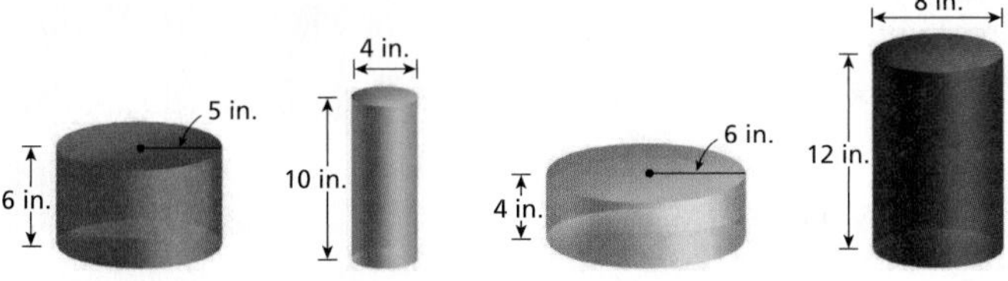

26. **Write About It** Explain why volume is expressed in cubic units of measurement.

27. **Challenge** Find the volume of the shaded area. 35.74 cm^3

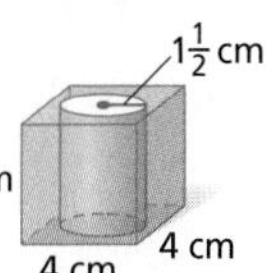

CRCT Prep • GPS Support • Spiral Review

28. **Multiple Choice** Find the volume of a cylinder with a height of $2\frac{1}{3}$ feet and a radius of $1\frac{1}{2}$ feet.

Ⓕ 19.75 ft^3 Ⓖ 16.5 ft^3 Ⓗ 11 ft^3 Ⓙ 5.5 ft^3

29. **Short Response** Chicken noodle soup is sold in a can that is 11 cm tall and has a radius of 2.5 cm. Tomato soup is sold in a can that is 7.5 cm tall and has a radius of 4 cm. Find the volume of both cans. Which can holds more soup? Chicken noodle: 215.875 cm^3; tomato: 376.8 cm^3; the tomato soup can holds more soup.

Identify a pattern in each sequence. Name the missing terms. (Lesson 1-7)

30. 10, 13, 16, 19, ▒, ▒, . . . 22, 25
31. 5, 8, 7, 10, ▒, ▒, . . . 9, 12
32. 4, 16, 64, 256, ▒, ▒, . . . 1,024 4,096

33. The diagram shows a school yard. What is the measure of $\angle W$? (Lesson 9-6) 115°

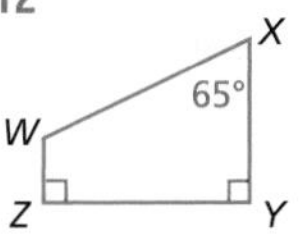

CHALLENGE 10-8

LESSON 10-8 Challenge
Champion Trees

Trees are among Earth's largest and oldest living things. The National Register of Big Trees measures trees throughout the United States to find the largest of each species—the champions. The four huge trees described below are the only champions that have been listed in the register since the program began in 1940.

Use the register's data to find the circumference and volume of each champion American tree trunk to the nearest foot and cubic foot.

"General Sherman"
Giant Sequoia, California
Circumference: 85 ft
Volume: 151,582 ft^3

h = 40 ft
r = 3.3 ft

"Jardine Juniper"
Rocky Mountain Juniper, Utah
Circumference: 21 ft
Volume: 1,368 ft^3

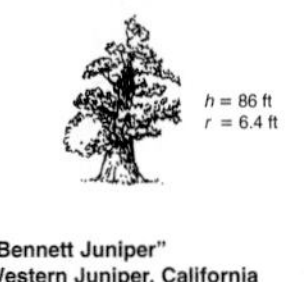

"Bennett Juniper"
Western Juniper, California
Circumference: 40 ft
Volume: 11,061 ft^3

"Wye Oak"
White Oak, Maryland
Circumference: 32 ft
Volume: 7,840 ft^3

PROBLEM SOLVING 10-8

LESSON 10-8 Problem Solving
Volume of Cylinders

Write the correct answer.

1. The Hubble Space Telescope was launched into space in 1990. Shaped like a cylinder, the telescope is 15.9 meters long, with a diameter of 4.2 meters. To the nearest whole cubic foot, what is the volume of the Hubble Space Telescope?
about 220 ft^3

2. The Living Color aquarium in Bermuda is the largest freestanding cylindrical aquarium in the Western Hemisphere. With a 10-foot diameter and an 18-foot height, the aquarium holds 10,400 gallons of water! What is the aquarium's volume in cubic feet?
1,413 ft^3

3. In 1902 an American music company built the world's largest music recording cylinder. Nicknamed "Brutus," the cylinder is 5 feet tall, with a 2-foot diameter. What is the volume of the "Brutus" cylinder?
15.7 ft^3

4. The world's largest glass of orange juice was filled in Florida in 1998. At 8 feet tall and with a 2-foot radius, the glass held about 700 gallons of orange juice. What was the volume of that huge glass of orange juice?
100.48 ft^3

Circle the letter of the correct answer.

5. A large can of soda is 7.5 inches tall and has a 3-inch diameter. A small can of soda is 5 inches tall with a 2.5-inch diameter. To the nearest cubic inch, how much more soda does the large can hold?
A 53 in^3 more soda
Ⓑ 28 in^3 more soda
C 25 in^3 more soda
D 20 in^3 more soda

6. A cylindrical candle is tightly packed in a rectangular box with a volume of 144 in^3. Which of these could be the dimensions of the candle?
F $h = 6$ in.; $r = 3$ in.
G $h = 2$ in.; $r = 5$ in.
Ⓗ $h = 4$ in.; $r = 3$ in.
J $h = 3$ in.; $r = 4$ in.

7. The maximum length for an official professional baseball bat is 36 inches. Its maximum diameter is 2.6 inches. To the nearest cubic inch, what is the maximum volume of a professional baseball bat?
A 21 in^3 Ⓒ 191 in^3
B 119 in^3 D 764 in^3

8. A can of tennis balls is 21 centimeters tall and has a diameter of 8 centimeters. What is the volume of the tennis ball can?
F 17,408.16 cm^3 H 527.52 cm^3
Ⓖ 1,055.04 cm^3 J 263.76 cm^3

Ongoing Assessment and Intervention

Diagnose ***Before*** **the Lesson**
10-8 Warm Up, TE p. 576

Monitor ***During*** **the Lesson**
10-8 Know-It Notebook
10-8 Questioning Strategies

Assess ***After*** **the Lesson**
10-8 Lesson Quiz, TE p. 579

Answers

25. Gene has the largest cylinder;
Gene—blue
Fran—red,
Ira—yellow,
Helen—green

26. Volume records how much three-dimensional space an object occupies.

Test Prep Doctor In Exercise 28, students can use $\frac{22}{7}$ for *pi*. The mixed numbers can be expressed as improper fractions with the following results: $\frac{22}{7} \times \left(\frac{3}{2}\right)^2 \times \frac{7}{3} = 16\frac{1}{2}$.

Journal

Have students write an explanation of how to find the volume of a cylinder.

Power Presentations with PowerPoint®

10-8 Lesson Quiz

Find the volume of each cylinder to the nearest cubic unit. Use 3.14 for π.

1. radius = 9 ft, height = 4 ft
1,017 ft^3

2. radius = 3.2 ft, height = 6 ft
193 ft^3

3. **Which cylinder has a greater volume?** cylinder b
a. radius 5.6 ft and height 12 ft
1,181.64 ft^3
b. radius 9.1 ft and height 6 ft
1,560.14 ft^3

4. **Jeff's drum kit has two small drums. The first drum has a radius of 3 in. and a height of 14 in. The other drum has a radius of 4 in. and a height of 12 in. Estimate the volume of each cylinder to the nearest cubic inch.**
a. First drum about 396 in^2
b. Second drum about 603 in^2

Also available on transparency

Organizer

Use with Lesson 10-9

Pacing:
Traditional $\frac{1}{2}$ day
Block $\frac{1}{4}$ day

Objective: Use a net to build a three-dimensional figure.

Materials: Heavy paper, scissors, tape

Online Edition

Countdown to CRCT Week 24

Resources

Hands-On Lab Activities
Lab 10-9 Recording Sheet

Teach

Discuss

Discuss the need for precision in cutting out the shapes for the three-dimensional figures. The cutouts must be precise for the three-dimensional figures to fit together correctly.

Close

Key Concept

Two-dimensional shapes can be assembled to form three-dimensional figures.

Assessment

1. When building a rectangular prism, why are the rectangles always cut out in matching pairs?
2. What shapes would you need to cut out to build a triangular prism out of paper?
3. What shapes would you need to cut out to build a cube?

Georgia Performance Standards

M6G2.c Interpret and sketch front, back, top, bottom and side view of solid figures.

M6G2.d Construct nets for prisms, cylinders, pyramids, and cones.

M6P5.a Create and use representations to organize, record, and communicate mathematical ideas.

M6P5.c Use representations to model and interpret physical, social, and mathematical phenomena.

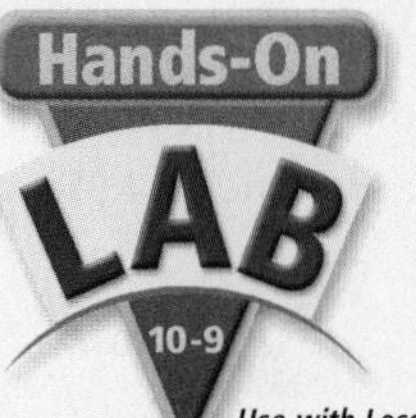

Model Three-Dimensional Figures

Use with Lesson 10-9

Georgia Performance Standards
M6G2.c, M6G2.d, M6P5.a, M6P5.c

You can build a solid figure by cutting its faces from paper, taping them together, and then folding them to form the solid. A pattern of shapes that can be folded to form a solid figure is called a *net*.

Activity

1. To make a pattern for a rectangular prism follow the steps below.

   a. Draw the following rectangles and cut them out:

   Two 2 in. × 3 in. rectangles

   Two 1 in. × 3 in. rectangles

   Two 1 in. × 2 in. rectangles

   b. Tape the pieces together to form the prism.

   c. Remove the tape from some of the edges so that the pattern lies flat.

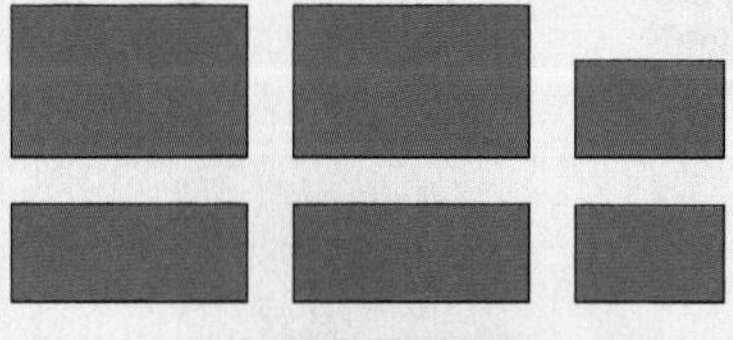

2. Create a net for a cylinder.

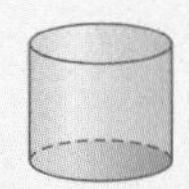

Think: What shapes can make a cylinder?

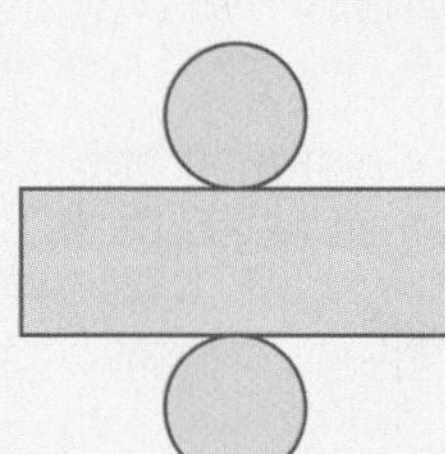

If a cylinder is "unfolded," the bases of the cylinder are circles, and the curved surface is a rectangle.

The net is made up of two circles and a rectangle.

Answers to *Assessment*

1. You need two of each rectangle because opposite sides of a rectangular prism are congruent rectangles.
2. 2 triangles, 3 rectangles
3. 6 identical squares

3. Create a net for a square pyramid.

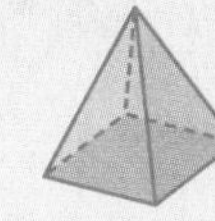

Think: What shapes can make a square pyramid?

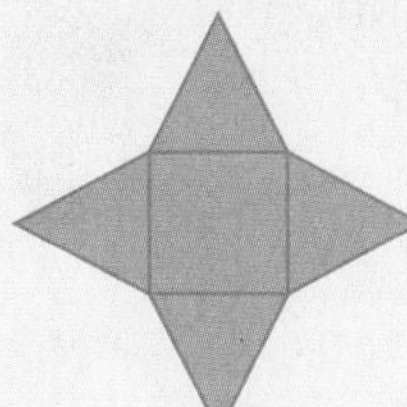

If the square pyramid is "unfolded," the base is a square, and the sides are triangles.

The net is made up of a square and four triangles.

Think and Discuss

1. Compare the nets for a rectangular prism and a cube.
2. Tell what shapes will always appear in a net for a triangular pyramid. **four triangles**
3. Tell what shapes will always appear in a net for a hexagonal prism. **six rectangles and two hexagons**

Try This

Tell whether each net can be folded to form a cube. If not, explain.

1. 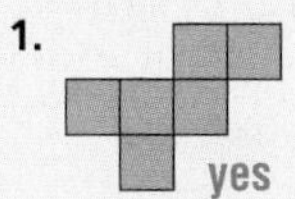 **yes**

2. 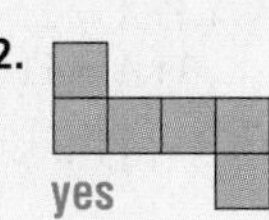 **yes**

3. 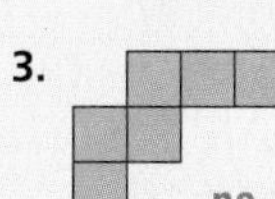 **no**

4. 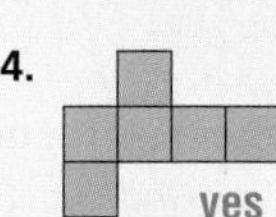 **yes**

Name the three-dimensional figure that can be formed from each net.

5. 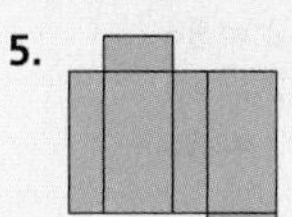 **rectangular prism**

6. 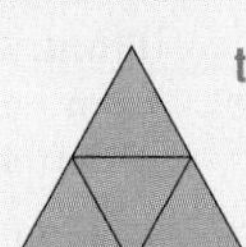 **triangular pyramid**

7. Create a net for a cone.

Answers to *Think and Discuss*

1. Both cubes and rectangular prisms have six faces, so the same number of polygons must be used to construct each. But a cube is made from 6 identical squares, while a rectangular prism can have up to 3 pairs of different-size rectangles for its sides.

Answers to *Try This*

3. Possible answer: two squares will overlap leaving one face of the cube missing.

7. 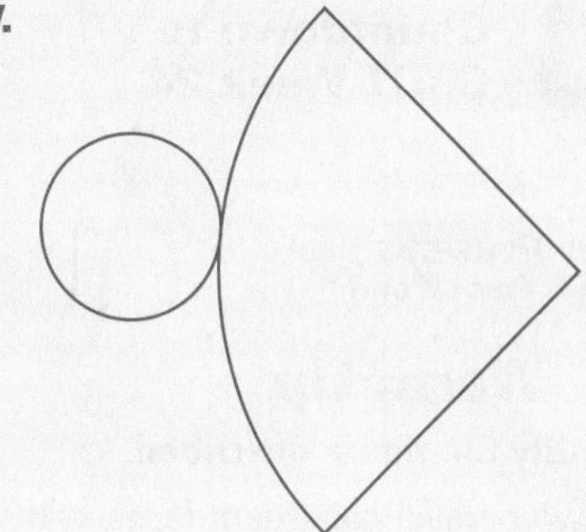

Sara Höfler
Orlando, Florida

Teacher to Teacher

Give each student a black-line net on colored paper. Then have each student use the net to work through each step of the problems listed under Try This. Have them use the scientific method to analyze the steps they take to solve the problems. As students go through this process, they can write a detailed account of their actions and thought processes. This activity is a great way to integrate science and language arts into the math curriculum.

10-9 Organizer

Pacing: Traditional 1 day
Block $\frac{1}{2}$ day

Objective: Students find the surface areas of prisms, pyramids, and cylinders.

GPS M6M2.c
Hands-On Lab
In *Hands-On Lab Activities*

Online Edition
Tutorial Videos, Interactivities

Countdown to CRCT Week 24

Power Presentations with PowerPoint®

Warm Up

Identify the figure described.

1. two parallel congruent faces, with the other faces being parallelograms prism
2. a polyhedron that has a vertex and a face at opposite ends, with the other faces being triangles pyramid

Problem of the Day

Which figure has the longer side and by how much: a square with an area of 81 ft^2 or a square with perimeter of 84 ft? a square with a perimeter of 84 ft; by 12 ft

Also available on transparency

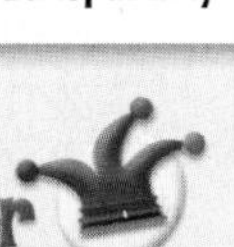

Math Humor

Teacher: A net can help you calculate the surface area of a polyhedron.
Student: Annette who?

Georgia Performance Standards

M6M4.a Find the surface area of right rectangular prisms and cylinders using manipulatives and constructing nets.

M6M4.b Compute the surface area of right rectangular prisms and cylinders using formulae.

M6M4.c Estimate the surface areas of simple geometric solids.

M6P5.a Create and use representations to organize, record, and communicate mathematical ideas.

M6P5.b Select, apply, and translate among mathematical representations to solve problems.

10-9 Surface Area

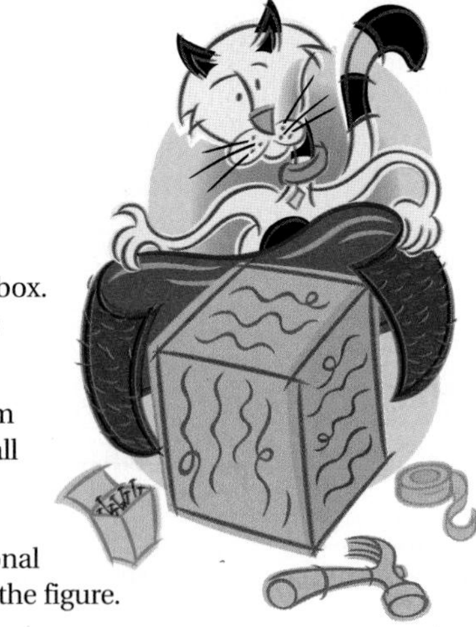

Learn to find the surface areas of prisms, pyramids, and cylinders.

Vocabulary
surface area
net

Katie made a toy for her cat to scratch by attaching carpet to the faces of a wooden box. The amount of carpet needed to cover the box is equal to the surface area of the box.

The **surface area** of a solid figure is the sum of the areas of its surfaces. To help you see all the surfaces of a three-dimensional figure, you can use a *net*. A **net** is the pattern made when the surface of a three-dimensional figure is layed out flat showing each face of the figure.

EXAMPLE 1 Finding the Surface Area of a Prism

Georgia Performance Standards

M6M4.a Find the surface area of right rectangular prisms and cylinders using manipulatives and constructing nets. Also, M6M4.b, M6M4.c, M6P5.a, M6P5.b.

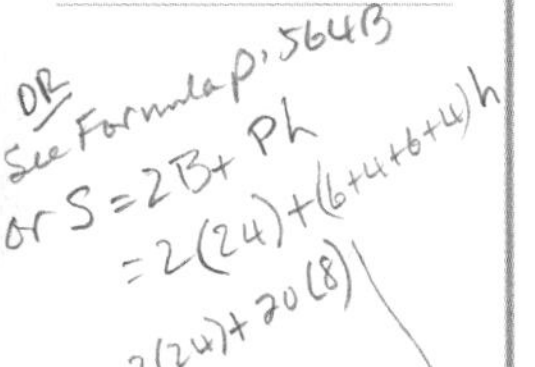

Find the surface area S of each prism.

A Method 1: Use a net.

5 in. 21 in. 11 in.

5 in. 5 in. 21 in. 11 in. 11 in. A B C D E F 5 in.

Draw a net to help you see each face of the prism.

Use the formula $A = \ell w$ to find the area of each face.

A: $A = 11 \times 5 = 55$
B: $A = 21 \times 11 = 231$
C: $A = 21 \times 5 = 105$
D: $A = 21 \times 11 = 231$
E: $A = 21 \times 5 = 105$
F: $A = 11 \times 5 = 55$

$S = 55 + 231 + 105 + 231 + 105 + 55 = 782$ *Add the areas of each face.*

The surface area is 782 in^2.

B Method 2: Use a three-dimensional drawing.

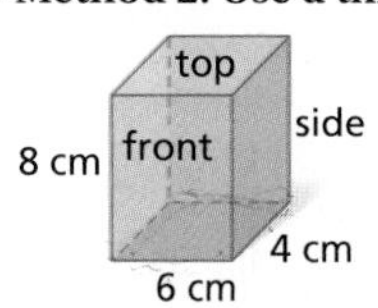

Find the area of the front, top, and side, and multiply each by 2 to include the opposite faces.

Front: $6 \times 8 = 48 \longrightarrow 48 \times 2 = 96$
Top: $6 \times 4 = 24 \longrightarrow 24 \times 2 = 48$
Side: $4 \times 8 = 32 \longrightarrow 32 \times 2 = 64$

$S = 96 + 48 + 64 = 208$ *Add the areas of the faces.*

The surface area is 208 cm^2.

1 Introduce

Alternate Opener

EXPLORATION

10-9 Surface Area

You can use grid paper to make nets that cover boxes, or rectangular solids. The area of the net is the *surface area of the solid.*

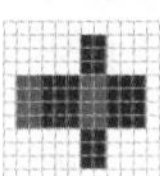

1. Find the combined area of the blue rectangles (the sides of the box).
2. Find the combined area of the green rectangles (the top and bottom of the box).
3. Add the areas you found in numbers 1 and 2. This is the surface area of the box.
4. On the grid below, draw a different net that can cover a box, and find its surface area.

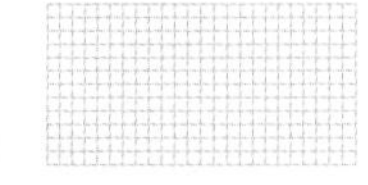

Think and Discuss

5. **Explain** how you can use a net to find surface area.

Motivate

Have students examine polyhedra and name the polygonal faces of each. For example, a square pyramid has one square face and four triangular faces. You may use the Teaching Transparency. Ask students to explain how to find the area of each individual face. Review formulas for area presented earlier in this chapter. Point out to students that finding the surface area of hexagonal prisms, cones, and other three-dimensional figures will be studied in a later course.

Explorations and answers are provided in *Alternate Openers: Explorations Transparencies.*

The surface area of a pyramid equals the sum of the area of the base and the areas of the triangular faces. To find the surface area of a pyramid, think of its net.

EXAMPLE 2 Finding the Surface Area of a Pyramid

Find the surface area S of the pyramid.

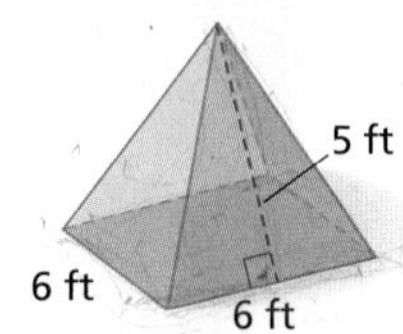

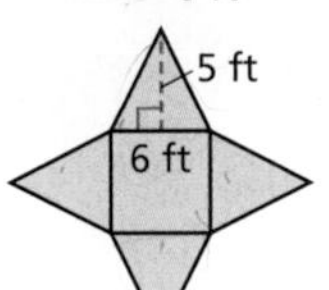

S = area of square + 4 × (area of triangular face)

$S = s^2 + 4 \times \left(\frac{1}{2}bh\right)$

$S = 6^2 + 4 \times \left(\frac{1}{2} \times 6 \times 5\right)$ *Substitute.*

$S = 36 + 4 \times 15$

$S = 36 + 60$

$S = 96$

The surface area is 96 ft^2.

The surface area of a cylinder equals the sum of the area of its bases and the area of its curved surface.

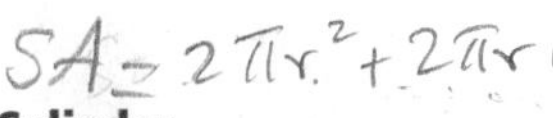

EXAMPLE 3 Finding the Surface Area of a Cylinder

Find the surface area S of the cylinder. Use 3.14 for π, and round to the nearest hundredth.

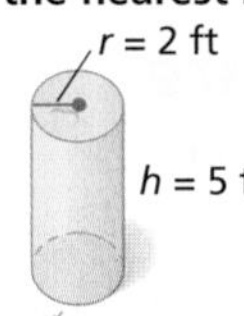

S = area of lateral surface + 2 × (area of each base)

$S = h \times (2\pi r) + 2 \times (\pi r^2)$

$S = 5 \times (2 \times \pi \times 2) + 2 \times (\pi \times 2^2)$ *Substitute.*

$S = 5 \times 4\pi + 2 \times 4\pi$

$S \approx 5 \times 4(3.14) + 2 \times 4(3.14)$ *Use 3.14 for π.*

$S \approx 5 \times 12.56 + 2 \times 12.56$

$S \approx 62.8 + 25.12$

$S \approx 87.92$

The surface area is about 87.92 ft^2.

Helpful Hint

To find the area of the curved surface of a cylinder, multiply its height by the circumference of the base.

Possible answers to *Think and Discuss*

1. Find the sum of the areas of its two pentagonal bases and its five rectangular faces.
2. Multiply the area of the face by 6.

Think and Discuss

1. Describe how to find the surface area of a pentagonal prism.

2. Tell how to find the surface area of a cube if you know the area of one face.

COMMON ERROR ALERT

Students may omit faces when finding the surface areas of solid figures. To remedy this, have them begin by listing the faces and checking them off as they find the area of each.

Power Presentations with PowerPoint®

Additional Examples

Example 

Find the surface area S of each prism.

A. 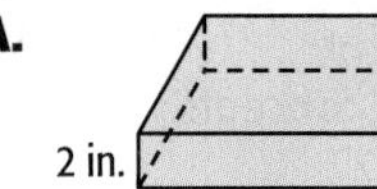

188 in^2

 **B.**

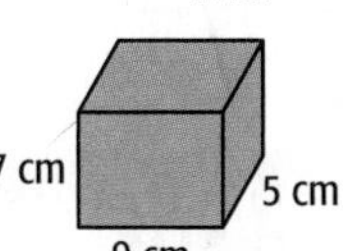

286 cm^2

Example 

Find the surface area S of the pyramid.

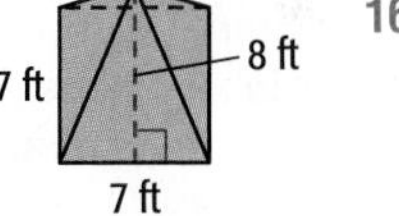

161 ft^2

Example 

Find the surface area S of the cylinder. Use 3.14 for π, and round to the nearest hundredth.

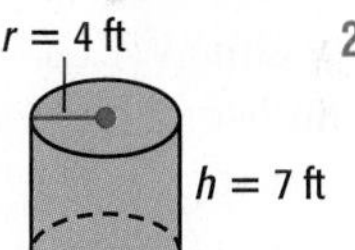

276.32 ft^2

Also available on transparency

2 Teach

Guided Instruction

In this lesson, students learn to find the surface area of prisms, pyramids, and cylinders. Teach students to use nets and three-dimensional drawings to identify all of the faces of the figures.

Inclusion Discuss why the curved surface of a cylinder is a rectangle. Point out that the dimensions of the rectangle are the circumference of the cylinder and the height of the cylinder.

Reaching All Learners

Through Modeling

Give students the nets for three-dimensional figures (available in Teacher Tools). Have them cut out the nets and assemble them to make models of the figures. Students can then use the graph paper squares to estimate surface area before computing the actual surface area. Comparing their actual answers with the estimates will help them determine whether their answers are reasonable.

3 Close

ENGLISH LANGUAGE LEARNERS

Summarize

Review the new vocabulary terms *surface area* and *net*. Ask students how a net can help when finding the surface area of a three-dimensional figure.

Possible answer: A net can help you see each face of the three-dimensional figure, and you need to add the areas of the faces to find the surface area.

10-9 Exercises

Assignment Guide

If you finished Example 1 assign:
Average 1–3, 23, 28–36
Advanced 10–12, 23, 28–36

If you finished Example 2 assign:
Average 1–6, 23, 28–36
Advanced 10–15, 23, 28–36

If you finished Example 3 assign:
Average 1–12, 22–36
Advanced 10–36

Homework Quick Check

Quickly check key concepts.
Exercises: 10, 12, 22

Math Background

Just as formulas for the perimeter and area of polygons were developed in Lessons 9-7, 10-1, and 10-2, nets and hands-on materials can be used here to develop formulas for the surface area of various three-dimensional figures.

Among the formulas you and your class can develop are the following:

- a cube with sides s: $S = 6s^2$
- a rectangular prism: $2\ell h + 2wh$, or $2(\ell w + \ell h + wh)$
- a square pyramid with a base of length s and lateral faces of height ℓ: $S = s^2 + 2s\ell$, or $s(s + 2\ell)$
- a cylinder with radius r and height h: $S = 2\pi r^2 + 2\pi rh$, or $2\pi r(r + h)$

Georgia Performance Standards

M6M4.d Solve application problems involving surface area of right rectangular prisms and cylinders.

M6P1.b Solve problems that arise in mathematics and in other contexts.

M6P3.a Organize and consolidate their mathematical thinking through communication.

M6P5.b Select, apply, and translate among mathematical representations to solve problems.

10-9 Exercises

Georgia Performance Standards
M6M4.d, M6P1.b, M6P3.a, M6P5.b

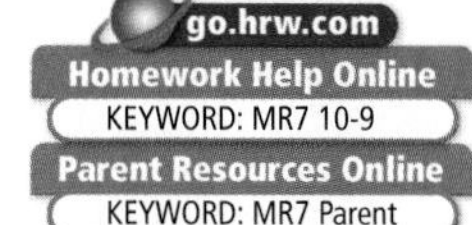

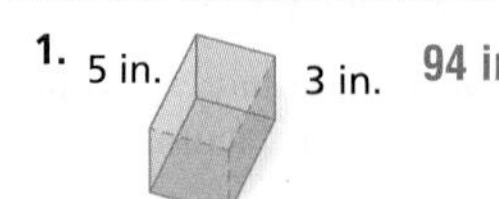

GUIDED PRACTICE

See Example 1 Find the surface area S of each prism.

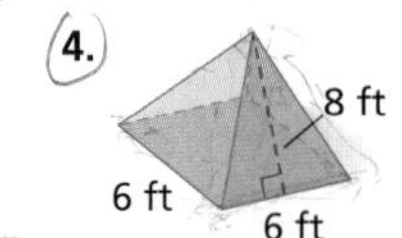

1. 5 in., 3 in., 4 in. **94 in²**
2. 4 m, 8 m, 2 m **112 m²**
3. 2 cm, 6 cm, 2 cm **56 cm²**

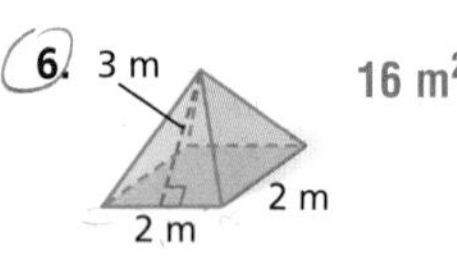

See Example 2 Find the surface area S of each pyramid.

4. 8 ft, 6 ft, 6 ft **132 ft²**
5. 29 cm, 30 cm, 30 cm **2,640 cm²**
6. 3 m, 2 m, 2 m **16 m²**

See Example 3 Find the surface area S of each cylinder. Use 3.14 for π, and round to the nearest hundredth.

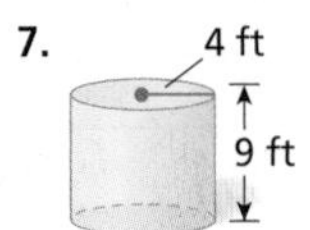

7. 4 ft, 9 ft **326.56 ft²**
8. 7 in., 10 in. **747.32 in²**
9. 6 m, 4 m **376.8 in²**

INDEPENDENT PRACTICE

See Example 1 Find the surface area S of each prism.

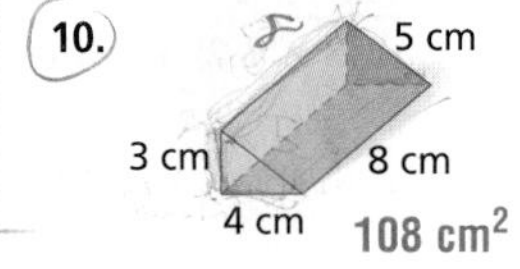

10. 5 cm, 3 cm, 8 cm, 4 cm **108 cm²**

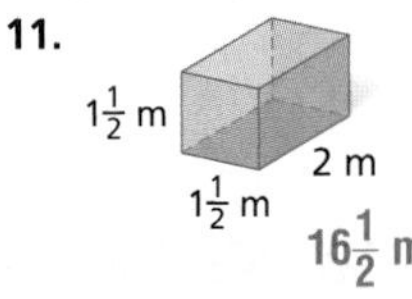

11. $1\frac{1}{2}$ m, $1\frac{1}{2}$ m, 2 m **$16\frac{1}{2}$ m²**

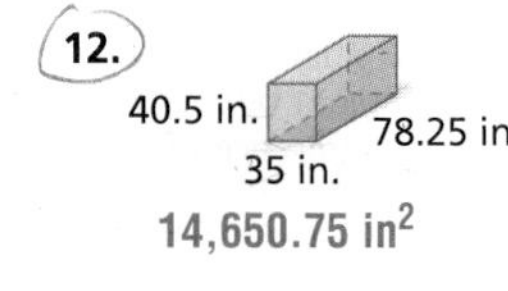

12. 40.5 in., 78.25 in., 35 in. **14,650.75 in²**

See Example 2 Find the surface area S of each pyramid.

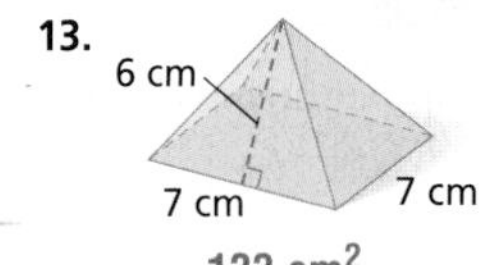

13. 6 cm, 7 cm, 7 cm **133 cm²**
14. 13.6 ft, 10.2 ft, 10.2 ft **381.48 ft²**

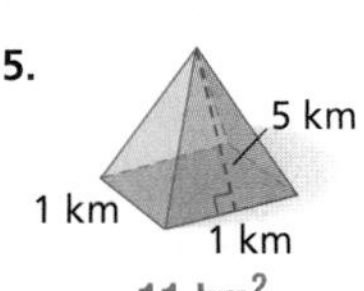

15. 5 km, 1 km, 1 km **11 km²**

See Example 3 Find the surface area S of each cylinder. Use 3.14 for π, and round to the nearest hundredth.

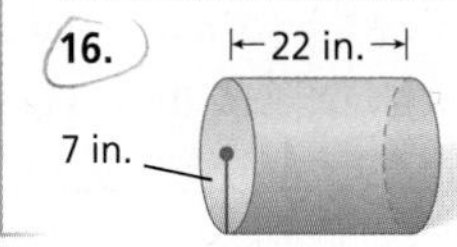

16. 22 in., 7 in. **1,274.84 in²**
17. 7.8 m, 6.75 m **712.72 m²**

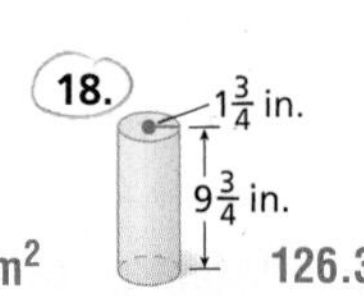

18. $1\frac{3}{4}$ in., $9\frac{3}{4}$ in. **126.39 in²**

RETEACH 10-9

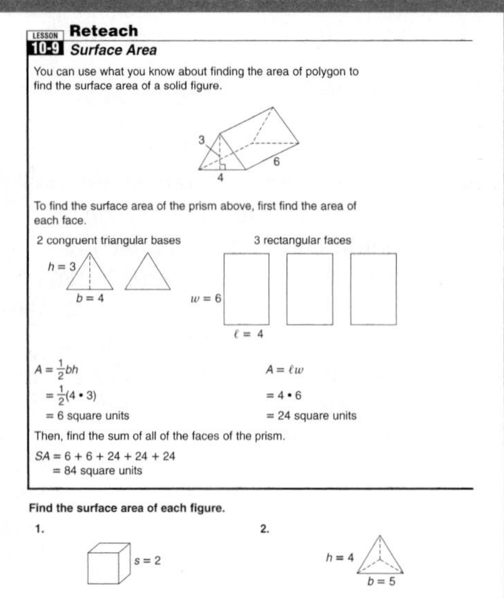

LESSON 10-9 Reteach
Surface Area

You can use what you know about finding the area of polygon to find the surface area of a solid figure.

To find the surface area of the prism above, first find the area of each face.

2 congruent triangular bases: $h = 3$, $b = 4$ — 3 rectangular faces: $w = 6$, $\ell = 4$

$A = \frac{1}{2}bh$ $= \frac{1}{2}(4 \cdot 3)$ = 6 square units

$A = \ell w$ $= 4 \cdot 6$ = 24 square units

Then, find the sum of all of the faces of the prism.

$SA = 6 + 6 + 24 + 24 + 24$ = 84 square units

Find the surface area of each figure.

1. $s = 2$ — 24 square units
2. $h = 4$, $b = 5$ — 40 square units

PRACTICE 10-9

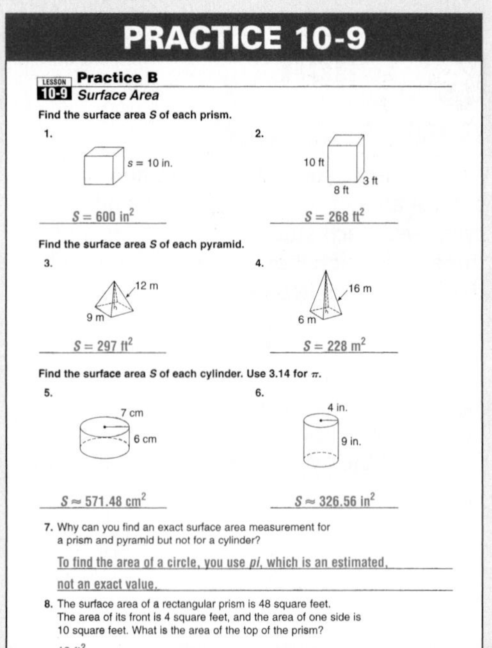

LESSON 10-9 Practice B
Surface Area

Find the surface area S of each prism.

1. s = 10 in. — S = 600 in²
2. 10 ft, 8 ft, 3 ft — S = 268 ft²

Find the surface area S of each pyramid.

3. 12 m, 9 m — S = 297 ft²
4. 16 m, 6 m — S = 228 m²

Find the surface area S of each cylinder. Use 3.14 for π.

5. 7 cm, 6 cm — $S \approx$ 571.48 cm²
6. 4 in., 9 in. — $S \approx$ 326.56 in²

7. Why can you find an exact surface area measurement for a prism and pyramid but not for a cylinder?
To find the area of a circle, you use pi, which is an estimated, not an exact value.

8. The surface area of a rectangular prism is 48 square feet. The area of its front is 4 square feet, and the area of one side is 10 square feet. What is the area of the top of the prism?
10 ft²

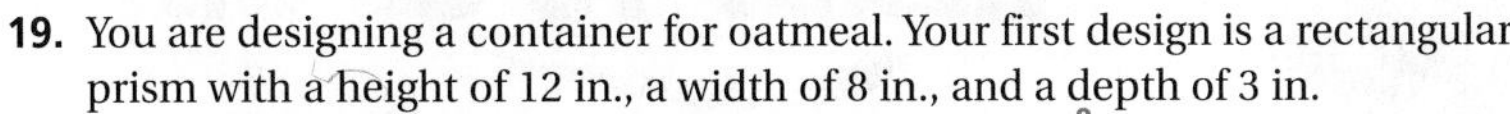

PRACTICE AND PROBLEM SOLVING

CRCT GPS Extra Practice p. 734

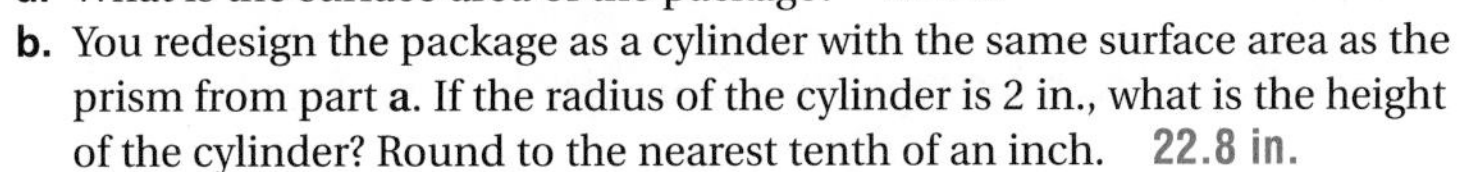

19. You are designing a container for oatmeal. Your first design is a rectangular prism with a height of 12 in., a width of 8 in., and a depth of 3 in.

a. What is the surface area of the package? **312 in^2**

b. You redesign the package as a cylinder with the same surface area as the prism from part **a.** If the radius of the cylinder is 2 in., what is the height of the cylinder? Round to the nearest tenth of an inch. **22.8 in.**

LINK Architecture

I. M. Pei is the architect of the pyramid-shaped addition to the Louvre in Paris, France.

go.hrw.com Web Extra! KEYWORD: MR7 Pei

20. **Architecture** The entrance to the Louvre Museum is a glass-paned square pyramid. The width of the base is 34.2 m, and the height of the triangular sides is 27 m. What is the surface area of the glass? **1,846.8 m^2**

Estimation Estimate the surface area of each figure. **Possible answers:**

21.

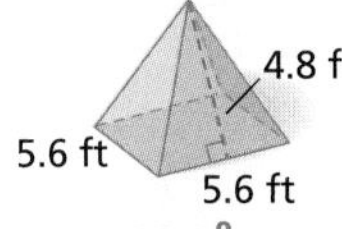

about 96 ft^2

22.

about 180 m^2

23.

about 190 cm^2

24. **Critical Thinking** If each of the dimensions of a rectangular prism is halved, how does this affect the surface area?

24. Possible answer: If the dimensions are halved, the surface area of the new prism will be $\frac{1}{4}$ the surface area of the original prism.

25. **What's the Question?** The surface area of a cube is 150 cm^2. The answer is 5 cm. What is the question? **Possible answer: What is the length of each side?**

26. **Write About It** How is finding the surface area of a rectangular pyramid different from finding the surface area of a triangular prism?

27. **Challenge** This cube is made of 27 smaller cubes whose sides measure 1 in.

a. What is the surface area of the large cube? **54 in^2**

b. Remove one small cube from each of the eight corners of the larger cube. What is the surface area of the solid formed? **54 in^2**

CRCT PREP • GPS SUPPORT • SPIRAL REVIEW

28. **Multiple Choice** Find the surface area of a cube with a side length of 9.4 yd.

Ⓐ 56.4 yd^2 Ⓑ 88.36 yd^2 Ⓒ 338.4 yd^2 **Ⓓ 530.16 yd^2**

29. **Gridded Response** Find the surface area, in meters, of a cylinder with a radius of 7 m and a height of 6 m. Use 3.14 for π and round to the nearest hundredth. **571.48**

Solve each equation. (Lesson 2-5)

30. $12 + y = 23$ **$y = 11$** **31.** $38 + y = 80$ **$y = 42$** **32.** $y + 76 = 230$ **$y = 154$**

Find each sum or difference. Write the answer in simplest form. (Lesson 5-3)

33. $5\frac{2}{3} - 1\frac{1}{9}$ **$4\frac{5}{9}$** **34.** $1\frac{1}{4} + 2\frac{3}{8}$ **$3\frac{5}{8}$** **35.** $2\frac{5}{6} - 2\frac{3}{4}$ **$\frac{1}{12}$** **36.** $4\frac{2}{5} + 3\frac{3}{10}$ **$7\frac{7}{10}$**

CHALLENGE 10-9

LESSON 10-9 **Challenge**

A Monumental Paint Job

Completed in 1927, the Lincoln Memorial in Washington, D.C., honors President Abraham Lincoln. The monument was built in the style of Greek temples, with 36 columns surrounding the outside of the monument and 8 columns surrounding the statue of Lincoln inside.

It's your job to paint the columns of the Lincoln Memorial. You will paint its exterior columns blue, and its interior columns red. Use the diagram to figure out how much paint you should buy and how much the paint will cost.

each outside column:
$h = 44$ ft
$r = 3.7$ ft

each inside column:
$h = 50$ ft
$r = 3.75$ ft

Surface Areas to Paint	Gallons of Paint Needed	Cost of Paint
Remember to consider the parts of each column that will **not** be painted.	One gallon of paint will cover 350 square feet. Round **up** to the nearest whole gallon.	Each gallon of paint costs $16.99.
Exterior Columns: **36,805.824 ft^2**	Exterior Columns: **106 gallons**	Blue Paint: **$1,800.94**
Interior Columns: **9,420 ft^2**	Interior Columns: **27 gallons**	Red Paint: **$458.73**

PROBLEM SOLVING 10-9

LESSON 10-9 **Problem Solving**

Surface Area

Write the correct answer.

1. The world's largest cookie was baked in Wisconsin in 1992. Its diameter was 34 feet and contained about 4 million chocolate chips! If the cookie was a cylinder 1 foot tall, and you wanted to cover it with icing, how many square inches would you have to ice? Use 3.14 for π.

276,721.92 in^2

2. The top of the Washington Monument is a square pyramid covered with white marble. Each triangular face is 58 feet tall and 34 feet wide. About how many square feet of marble covers the top of the monument? (The base is hollow.)

about 3,944 ft^2 of marble

3. The Parthenon, a famous temple in Greece, is surrounded by large stone columns. Each column is 10.4 meters tall and has a diameter of 1.9 meters. To the nearest whole square meter, what is the surface area of each column (not including the top and bottom)?

62 m^2

4. The tablet that the Statue of Liberty holds is 7.2 meters long, 4.1 meters wide, and 0.6 meters thick. The tablet is covered with thin copper sheeting. If the tablet was freestanding, how many square meters of copper covers the statue's tablet?

72.6 m^2 of copper

Circle the letter of the correct answer.

5. The largest Egyptian pyramid is called the Great Pyramid of Khufu. It has a 756-foot square base and a slant height of 481 feet. What is the total surface area of the faces of the Pyramid of Khufu?

Ⓐ 727,272 ft^2 C 727,727 ft^2
B 727,722 ft^2 D 772,272 ft^2

6. A glass triangular prism for a telescope is 5.5 inches tall. Each side of the triangular base is 4 inches long, with a 3-inch height. How much glass covers the surface of the prism?

F 6 in^2 H 39 in^2
G 12 in^2 **Ⓙ 78 in^2**

7. A can of frozen orange juice is 7.5 inches tall, and its base diameter is 3.5 inches. What size strip of paper is used for its label?

Ⓐ 84.43 in^2 C 576.98 in^2
B 26.25 in^2 D 101.66 in^2

8. Tara made fuzzy cubes to hang in her car. Each side of the 2 cubes is 4 inches long. How much fuzzy material did Tara use to make both cubes?

F 96 in^2 H 16 in^2
Ⓖ 192 in^2 J 128 in^2

ONGOING ASSESSMENT and INTERVENTION

***Diagnose* Before the Lesson**
10-9 Warm Up, TE p. 582

***Monitor* During the Lesson**
10-9 Know-It Notebook
10-9 Questioning Strategies

***Assess* After the Lesson**
10-9 Lesson Quiz, TE p. 585

Answers

26. The difference is the number of rectangular and triangular faces. A rectangular pyramid has 5 faces (1 rectangle and 4 triangles) and a triangular prism has 5 faces (2 triangles and 3 rectangles).

TEST PREP DOCTOR For Exercise 28, students using estimation ($10 \times 10 \times 6 = 600$) can eliminate choices **A, B,** and **C.**

Journal

Assign each student a prism, pyramid, or cylinder. Have the student draw a picture of the figure, draw its net, label its dimensions, and find its surface area.

Power Presentations with PowerPoint®

10-9 Lesson Quiz

Find the surface area of each figure. Use 3.14 for π.

1. rectangular prism with base length 6 ft, width 5 ft, and height 7 ft **214 ft^2**

2. cylinder with radius 3 ft and height 7 ft **188.4 ft^2**

3. Find the surface area of the figure shown. **208 ft^2**

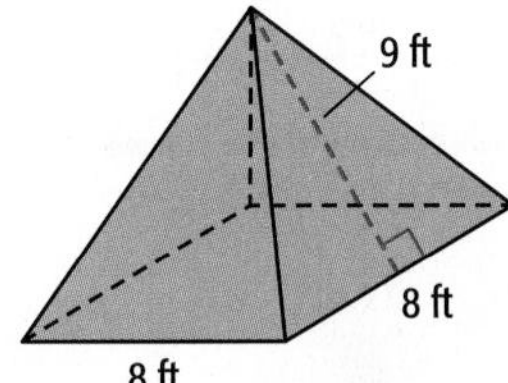

Also available on transparency

Organizer

Objective: Assess students' mastery of concepts and skills in Lessons 10-6 through 10-9.

Resources

Assessment Resources
Section 10B Quiz

INTERVENTION

Resources

***Ready to Go On? Intervention and Enrichment* Worksheets**

***Ready to Go On?* CD-ROM**

***Ready to Go On?* Online**

my.hrw.com

SECTION 10B

Ready to Go On?

Quiz for Lessons 10-6 Through 10-9

10-6 Three-Dimensional Figures

Identify the number of faces, edges, and vertices on each figure. Then name the figure and tell whether it is a polyhedron.

1. 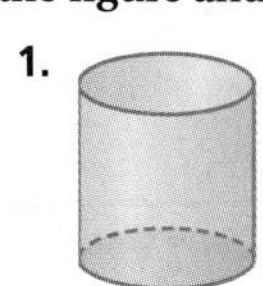 A cylinder is not a polygon.
2. 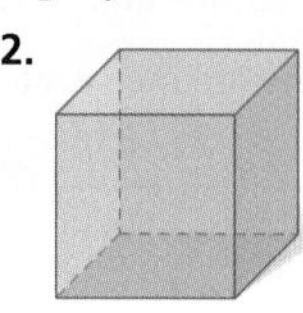 6 faces, 12 edges, 8 vertices; cube
3. 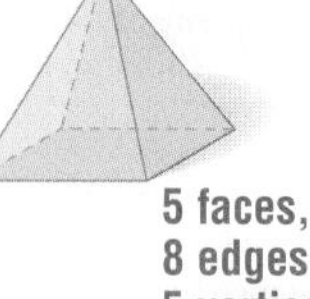 5 faces, 8 edges, 5 vertices; square pyramid

10-7 Volume of Prisms

Find the volume of each prism.

4. 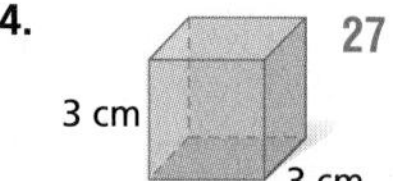

27 cm^3

5. 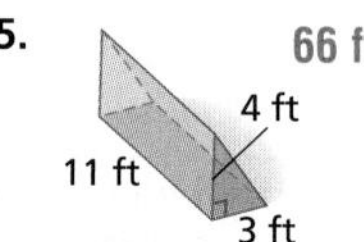

66 ft^3

6. 6 mm, 4.5 mm, 4.5 mm — 121.5 mm^3

7. There are 16 cubic boxes of erasers in a case. What are all the possible dimensions for a case of erasers? $2 \times 8 \times 1$, $2 \times 2 \times 4$, $4 \times 4 \times 1$

10-8 Volume of Cylinders

Find the volume *v* of each cylinder to the nearest cubic unit. Use 3.14 for *pi*.

8. 3 cm, 12 cm — 339.12 cm^3
9. 4 in., 8.5 in. — 106.76 in^3
10. 5.5 ft, 12.5 ft — $1{,}187.31\text{ ft}^3$

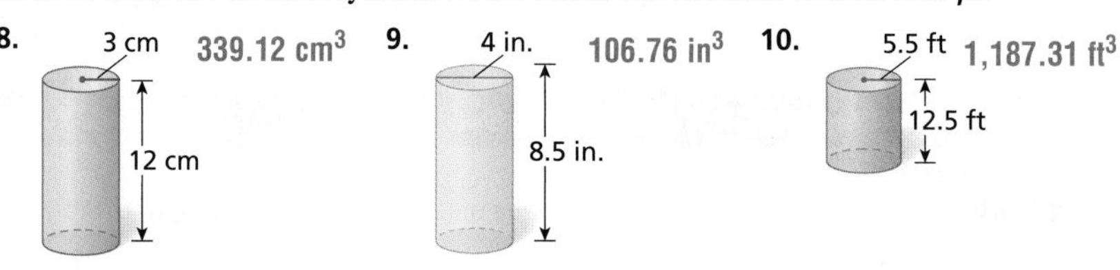

11. Which cylinder has the greater volume? The purple cylinder

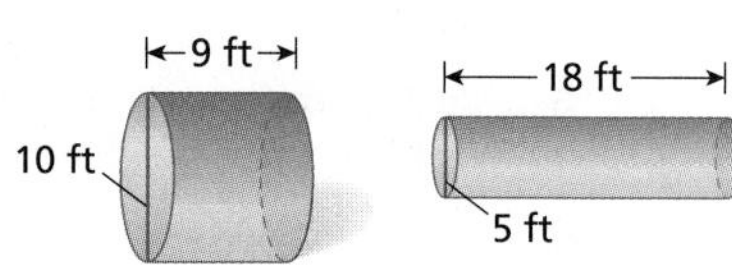

10-9 Surface Area

Find the surface area *s* of each figure. Use 3.14 for *pi*, and round to the nearest hundredth.

12. 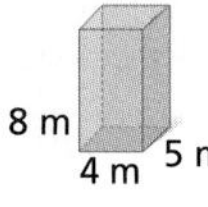

184 m^2

13. 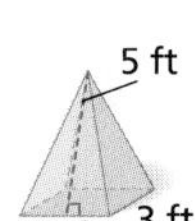

39 ft^2

14. 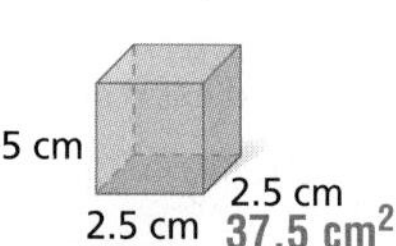

37.5 cm^2

READY TO GO ON? Diagnose and Prescribe

NO INTERVENE

Ready to Go On? Intervention	*Ready to Go On? Intervention,* Section 10B: Worksheets	CD-ROM	Online
Lesson 10-6	10-6 Intervention	Activity 10-6	Diagnose and Prescribe Online
Lesson 10-7	10-7 Intervention	Activity 10-7	
Lesson 10-8	10-8 Intervention	Activity 10-8	
Lesson 10-9	10-9 Intervention	Activity 10-9	

YES ENRICH

Ready to Go On? Enrichment, Section 10B
Worksheets
CD-ROM
Online

MULTI-STEP TEST PREP

CHAPTER 10

At Home in Space The International Space Station is a state-of-the-art laboratory in space. It is where we can learn to live and work "off planet." The space station is large enough to accommodate more than 30 experiments and provide living space for 6 astronauts. It is in the shape of a rectangular prism.

1. The table below shows the volumes of rectangular prisms that each have an 18-square-foot area for their bases but have different heights. Describe any patterns or proportional relationships in the table.
2. Write a rule to show how the heights in the table are related to the volumes. $V = 18h$
3. According to NASA, the average floor space in U.S. houses is about 1,800 ft^2. Ceilings are 8 ft high on average. How many cubic feet are in a house with these average measurements? 14,400 ft^3
4. The space station has 43,000 ft^3 of pressurized volume. About how many houses with the measurements from Problem 3 would fit in the space station? Explain.

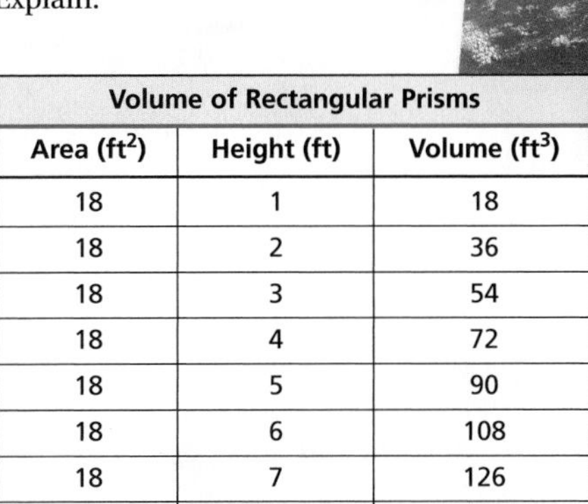

Volume of Rectangular Prisms		
Area (ft^2)	Height (ft)	Volume (ft^3)
18	1	18
18	2	36
18	3	54
18	4	72
18	5	90
18	6	108
18	7	126
18	8	144

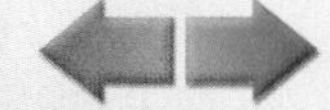

MULTI-STEP TEST PREP

CHAPTER 10

Organizer

Objective: Assess students' ability to apply concepts and skills in Chapter 10 in a real-world format.

PREMIER **Online Edition**

Resources

Middle School Assessments
www.mathtekstoolkit.org

Problem	Text reference
1	Lesson 10-7
2	Lesson 10-7
3	Lesson 10-7
4	Lesson 10-7

Multi-Step Test Prep

Answers

1. Possible answer: A pattern in the table is the height times 18.
4. About 3: Possible answer: The average volume of an American house is about 14,000 ft^3. Three times 14,000 is 42,000 which is close to the volume of the space station.

INTERVENTION

Scaffolding Questions

1. How are units of measurement used to express area? volume? Square units are used to express area; cubic units are used to express volume. How does area relate to volume in the table? The volume is the area multiplied by the height.
2. Which items in the table should be represented by variables? What variables can you use? height (h) and volume (V)
3. How can you find the volume of an average American house? Multiply the area of the floor space by the height of the ceiling.
4. What operation will you use to solve this problem? division How can you estimate the solution? 43,000 ÷ 14,400 is close to 42 ÷ 14, which is equal to 3, so the solution should be close to 3.

Extension

1. According to NASA, the average American house has a 100-amp service from the electric company. 100 amp × 110 volts = 11,000 watts or 11 kilowatts. The International Space Station uses approximately 110 kilowatts. About how many houses could it power? 10

GAME TIME

Organizer

Objective: Participate in games to practice and apply skills learned in Chapter 10.

Online Edition

Resources

Chapter 10 Resource Book
Puzzles, Twisters & Teasers

Polygon Hide-and-Seek

Purpose: To apply the skill of identifying polygons to a puzzle

Discuss As students identify each figure, have them justify each choice. Possible answer: For an obtuse scalene triangle, I choose $\triangle ABF$. It is an obtuse triangle because one of its angles, $\angle A$, measures greater than 90°. It is a scalene triangle because none of its three sides are congruent.

Extend Challenge students to create their own figures like the one in this lesson. Have them make a list of polygons for a classmate to find. Remind students to be sure that each polygon exists in their drawings. Check students' work.

Poly-Cross Puzzle

Purpose: To practice identifying solid figures in a crossword puzzle

Discuss Because spelling is important in this exercise, have students refer to the lessons in Chapter 10 to check spelling, if necessary.

Extend Have students create a matching card game, making one card for a figure's name and another for a sketch of the figure. They place all cards face down and take turns pulling pairs of cards. They return the cards if they are not a match. If they are, they keep the cards and take another turn.

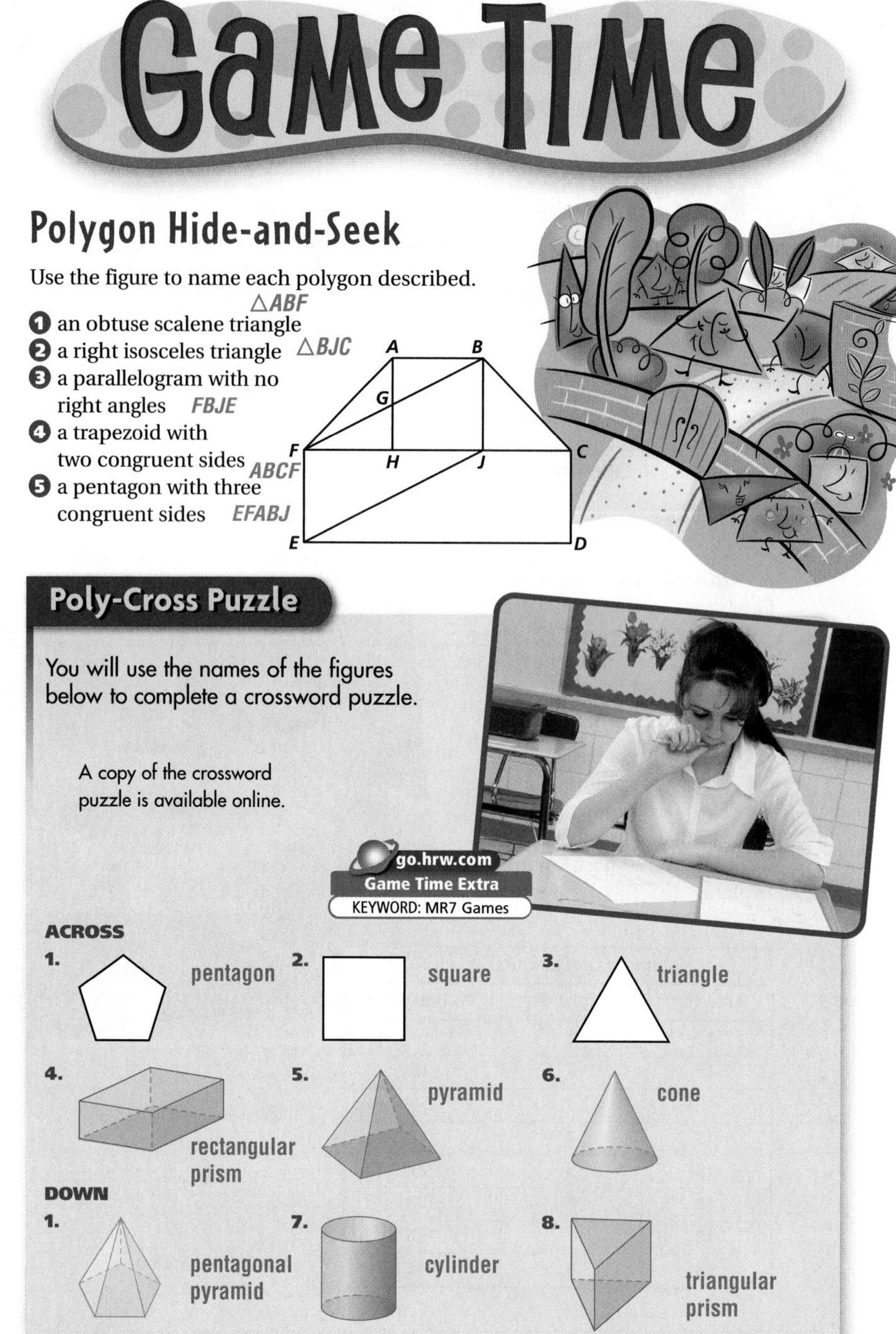

GAME TIME
Polygon Hide-and-Seek
Use the figure to name each polygon described.
1 an obtuse scalene triangle △ABF
2 a right isosceles triangle △BJC
3 a parallelogram with no right angles FBJE
4 a trapezoid with two congruent sides ABCF
5 a pentagon with three congruent sides EFABJ
A
B
G
F
H
J
C
E
D
Poly-Cross Puzzle
You will use the names of the figures below to complete a crossword puzzle.
A copy of the crossword puzzle is available online.
go.hrw.com
Game Time Extra
KEYWORD: MR7 Games
ACROSS
1. pentagon
2. square
3. triangle
4. rectangular prism
5. pyramid
6. cone
DOWN
1. pentagonal pyramid
7. cylinder
8. triangular prism

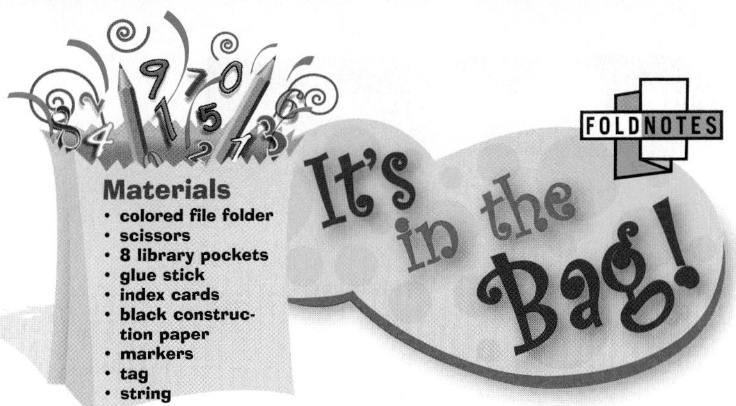

PROJECT **Area and Volume Suitcase**

Carry your notes with you as you travel through Chapter 10.

Directions

1. Cut the tabs off a colored file folder to form a rectangular folder with straight sides. **Figure A**

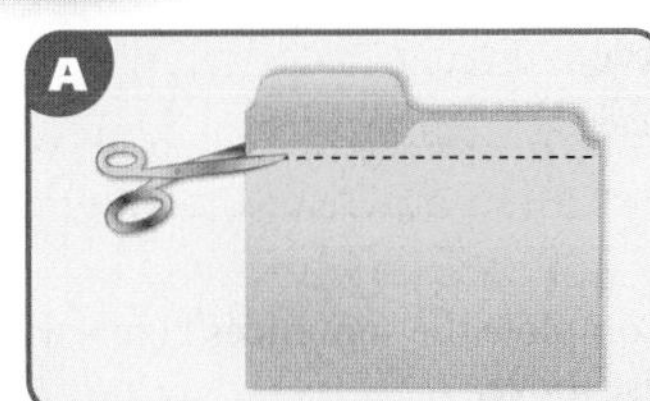

2. Open the folder. Glue library pockets inside the folder so that there are four on each side. Place an index card in each pocket. **Figure B**

3. Cut out "handles" from the construction paper. Glue these to the folder as shown. **Figure C**

4. Use a piece of string to attach a tag to one of the handles. Write your name and the name of your class on the tag. Write the name and number of the chapter on the front of the folder.

Taking Note of the Math

Write the names of the chapter's lessons on the library pockets. Then take notes on each lesson on the appropriate index card.

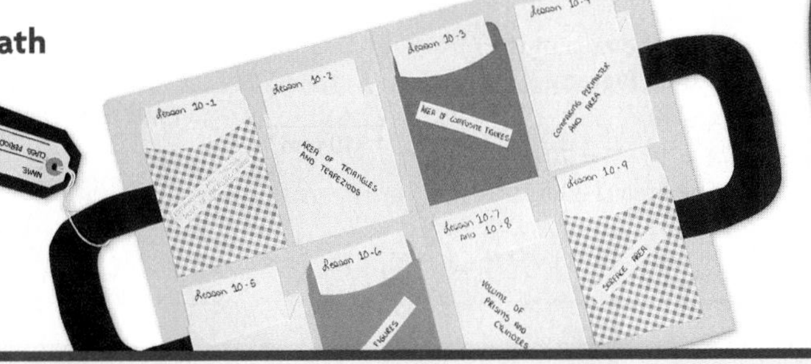

Organizer

Objective: Make a "suitcase" to store notes on area and volume.

Materials: colored file folder, scissors, 8 library pockets, glue stick, index cards, black construction paper, markers, tag, string

Online Edition

Using the Page

Preparing the Materials
If library pockets are not available, students can make pockets out of envelopes. To do so, seal a business-size envelope and cut it in half. Then trim the cut edge to form the pocket. Each envelope produces two pockets.

Making the Project
Remind students to glue the handles *inside* the folder. This makes for a neater appearance when the suitcase is closed.

Extending the Project
Have students glue a second file folder to the back of the first. Students can add pockets to this folder and use the pockets to store vocabulary flash cards, sample problems, or anything else that will help them review the material in the chapter.

Library pockets are the pockets you often find glued to the inside cover of a library book. Nowadays most library books have bar codes, which means that library pockets are not used as often. This can be good news for teachers because your local library may be able to donate unused pockets to your school.

Instead of using folders, students can use wallpaper samples or flattened cereal boxes for the project. Students can also use scraps of decorative paper to personalize the outside of their suitcases.

CHAPTER 10 Study Guide: Review

Organizer

Objective: Help students organize and review key concepts and skills presented in Chapter 10.

Online Edition
Multilingual Glossary

Countdown to CRCT Week 24

Resources

PuzzlePro®
One-Stop Planner®

***Multilingual Glossary* Online**

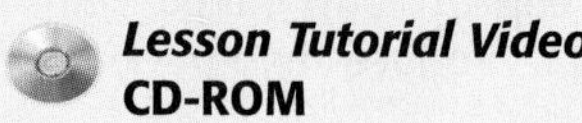

***Lesson Tutorial Videos* CD-ROM**

Answers

1. polyhedron
2. volume
3. vertex
4. 12 in^2
5. 18 ft^2
6. 12 in^2
7. 12 in^2

CHAPTER 10 Study Guide: Review

Vocabulary

Complete the sentences below with vocabulary words from the list above.

1. A __?__ is a three-dimensional object with flat faces that are polygons.
2. The number of cubic units needed to fill a space is called __?__.
3. The point at which three or more edges meet on a three-dimensional figure is called a __?__.

10-1 Estimating and Finding Area (pp. 542–545)

EXAMPLE

■ **Find the area of the rectangle.**

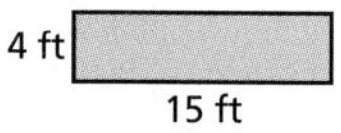

$A = \ell w$
$A = 15 \cdot 4 = 60$
The area is 60 ft^2.

■ **Find the area of the parallelogram.**

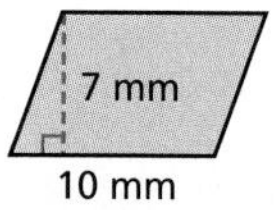

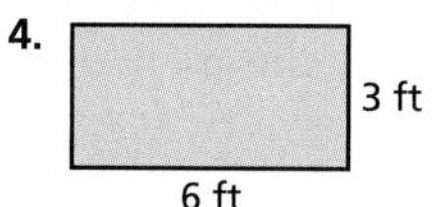

$A = bh$
$A = 10 \cdot 7 = 70$
The area is 70 mm^2.

EXERCISES

Find the area of each rectangle.

4. 3 ft, 6 ft

5. 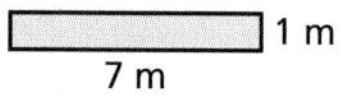 1 m, 7 m

Find the area of each parallelogram.

6.
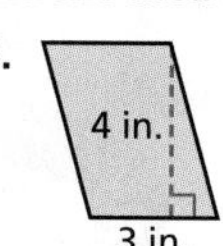

7.
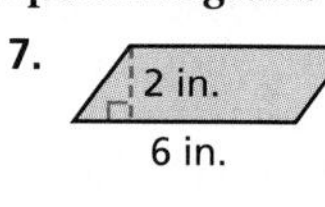

Study Guide: Review

10-2 Area of Triangles and Trapezoids (pp. 546–549)

GPS M6A3

EXAMPLE

- **Find the area of the trapezoid.**

4 m, 2 m, 10 m

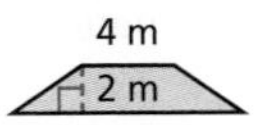

Use $A = \frac{1}{2}h(b_1 + b_2)$.
Substitute 10 for b_1, 4 for b_2, and 2 for h.

$A = \frac{1}{2}(2)(10 + 4)$
$= \frac{1}{2}(2)(14)$
$= \frac{1}{2}(28)$
$= 14\ m^2$

EXERCISES

Find the area of the triangle.

8. 11 in., 28 in.

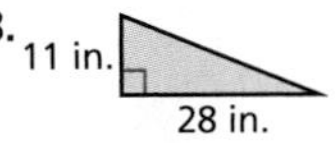

Find the area of the trapezoid.

9.

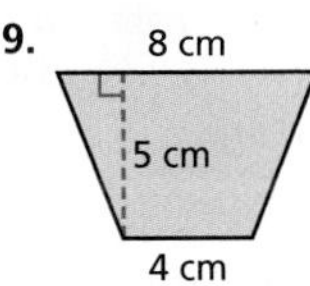

10-3 Area of Composite Figures (pp. 551–553)

GPS M6A3

EXAMPLE

- **Find the area of the polygon.**

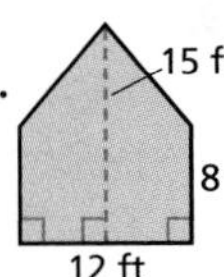

$A = 8 \cdot 12 = 96$
$A = \frac{1}{2} \cdot 12 \cdot 7 = 42$
The area of the figure is $42\ ft^2 + 96\ ft^2 = 138\ ft^2$.

EXERCISES

Find the area of each polygon.

10.

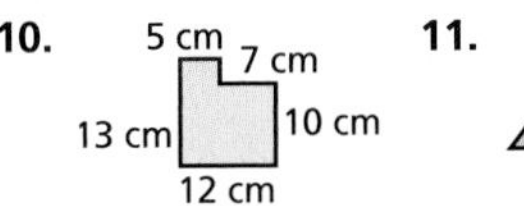

11.

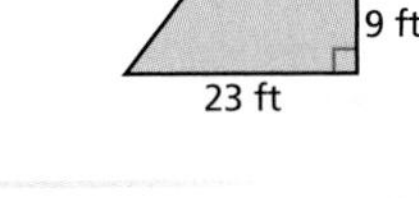

10-4 Comparing Perimeter and Area (pp. 554–556)

GPS M6M2.a, M6A3

EXAMPLE

- **Find how the perimeter and area of a rectangle change when its dimensions change.**
When the dimensions of the rectangle are multiplied by x, the perimeter is multiplied by x, and the area is multiplied by x^2.

EXERCISES

Find how the perimeter and area change when its dimensions change.

12.

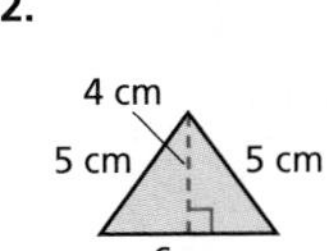

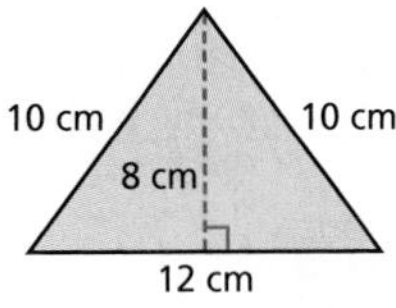

10-5 Area of Circles (pp. 558–561)

GPS M6N1.g, M6A3

EXAMPLE

- **Find the area of the circle. Use 3.14 for *pi*.**

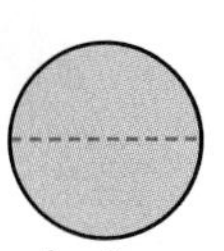

$d = 6$ cm

$A = \pi r^2$
$A \approx 3.14 \cdot 3^2$
$A \approx 3.14 \cdot 9 \approx 28.26\ cm^2$

EXERCISES

Find the area of each circle. Use $\frac{22}{7}$ for *pi*.

13. $d = 10$ ft 14. $r = 8$ cm 15. $d = 4$m

16. A circular window has a diameter of 14 ft. Find the area of the glass needed to fill the window. Use 3.14 for *pi*.

Study Guide: Review

Answers

8. 154 in^2
9. 30 cm^2
10. 135 cm^2
11. 175.5 ft^2
12. The perimeter is multiplied by 2, and the area is multiplied by 4, or 22.
13. $78\frac{4}{7}\ ft^2$
14. $201\frac{1}{7}\ cm^2$
15. $12\frac{4}{7}\ m^2$
16. 153.86 ft^2

Answers

17. 5 faces, 8 edges, 5 vertices; square pyramid
18. 6 faces, 12 edges, 8 vertices; rectangular prism
19. 384 cm3
20. 6,300 in3
21. 353 m3
22. 2,308 ft3
23. 125 m2
24. 102 cm2

Study Guide: Review

10-6 Three-Dimensional Figures (pp. 566–569)

GPS M6P5.c

EXAMPLE

- **Identify the number of faces, edges, and vertices on the solid figure. Then name the solid.**

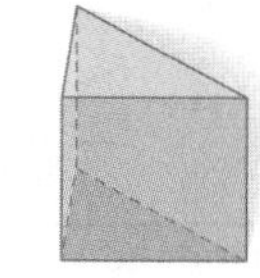

5 faces; 9 edges; 6 vertices

There are two congruent parallel bases, so the figure is a prism. The bases are triangles.

The solid is a triangular prism.

EXERCISES

Identify the number of faces, edges, and vertices on each solid figure. Then name the solid.

17.

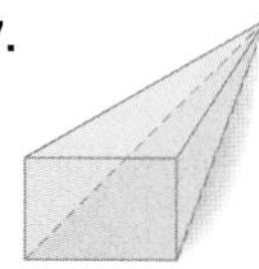

18.

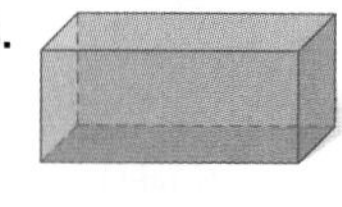

10-7 Volume of Prisms (pp. 572–575)

GPS M6M3.d, M6A3

EXAMPLE

- **Find the volume of the rectangular prism.**

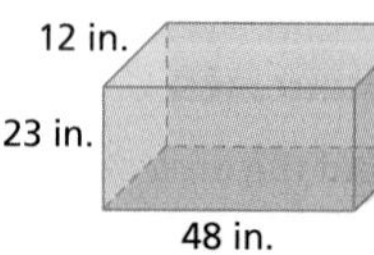

$V = \ell wh$

$V = 48 \cdot 12 \cdot 23$

$V = 13{,}248 \text{ in}^3$

EXERCISES

Find the volume of each prism.

19.

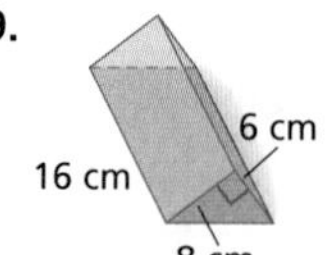

20.

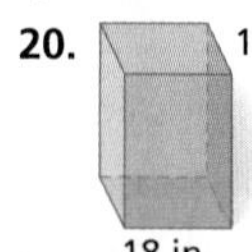

10-8 Volume of Cylinders (pp. 576–579)

GPS M6M3.b, M6M3.d, M6A3

EXAMPLE

- **Find the volume V of the cylinder to the nearest cubic unit.**

r = 4 cm

h = 16 cm

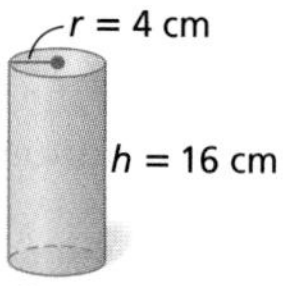

$V \approx 3.14 \cdot 4^2 \cdot 16$

$V \approx 803.84 \text{ cm}^3$

The volume is about 804 cm^3.

EXERCISES

Find the volume V of each cylinder to the nearest cubic unit.

21.

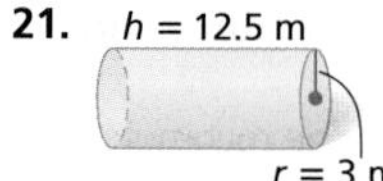

22.

10-9 Surface Area (pp. 582–585)

GPS M6M4.a, M6M4.b, M6M4.c

EXAMPLE

- **Find the surface area S of the cylinder.**

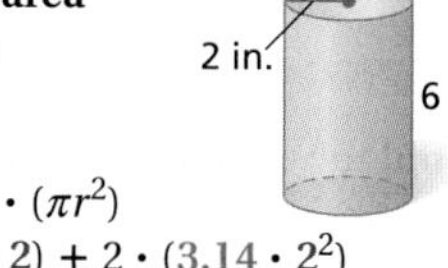

$S = h \cdot (2\pi r) + 2 \cdot (\pi r^2)$

$S \approx 6 \cdot (2 \cdot 3.14 \cdot 2) + 2 \cdot (3.14 \cdot 2^2)$

$S \approx 100.48 \text{ in}^2$

EXERCISES

Find the surface area S of each solid.

23.

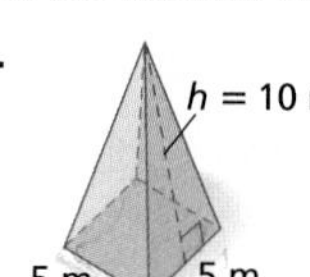

24.

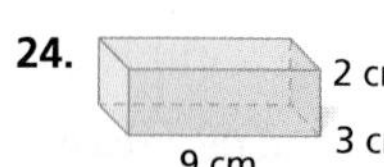

Find the area of each figure.

1. 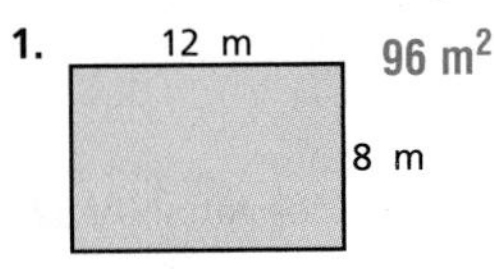

96 m²

2. 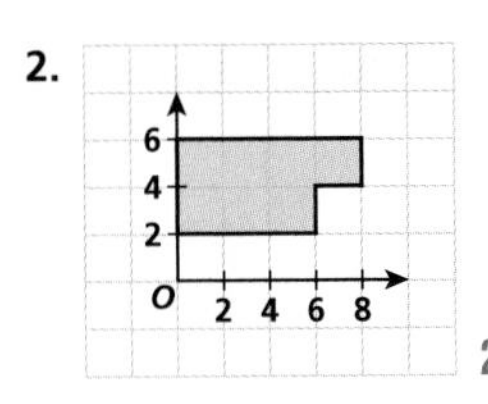

28 units

3. 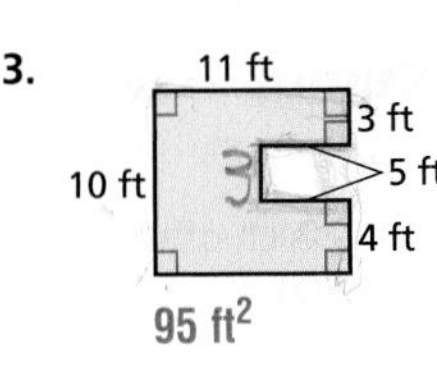

95 ft²

4. Find how the perimeter and the area of a rectangle change when the length and width are doubled.

5. A patio is in the shape of a trapezoid. What is the area of the patio? 168 cm²

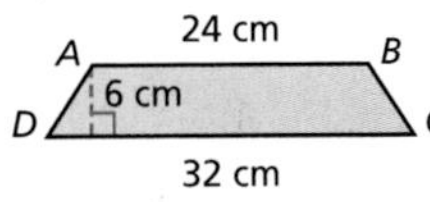

Find the area of each circle. Use 3.14 for *pi.* Round to the nearest hundredth.

6. 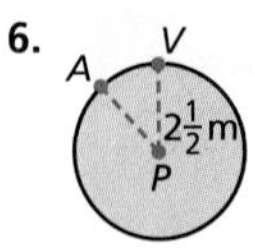

19.63 m²

7. 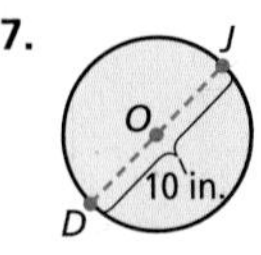

78.50 in²

8. 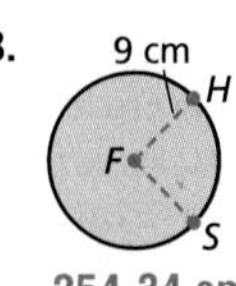

254.34 cm²

Identify the number of faces, edges, and vertices on each three-dimensional figure. Then name the figure and tell whether it is a polyhedron.

9. 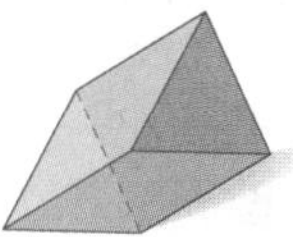

10. 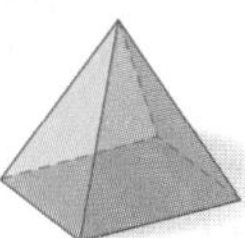

11. 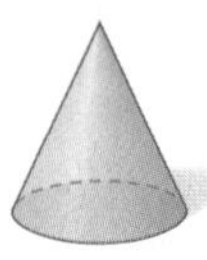

Find the volume of each three-dimensional figure.

12. 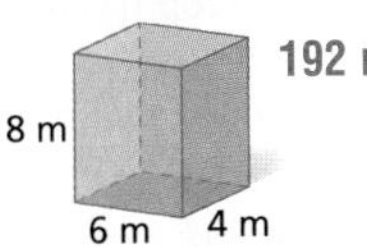

192 m³

13. 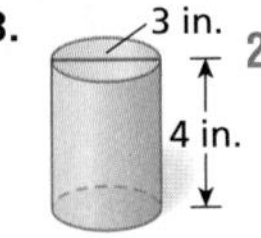

28.26 in³

14. 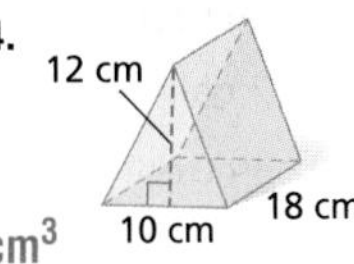

1,080 cm³

15. Patricia has two cylinder-shaped jars. Jar A has a radius of 6 cm and a height of 9 cm. Jar B has a diameter of 8 cm and a height of 17 cm. Which jar has the greater volume? How much greater? Jar A; 163.28 cm³

Find the surface area *S* of each three-dimensional figure.

16. 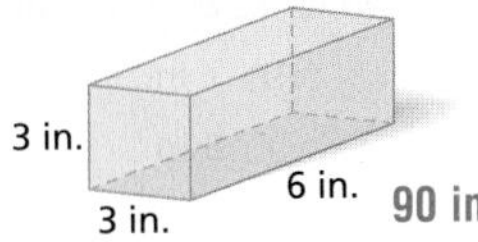

90 in²

17. 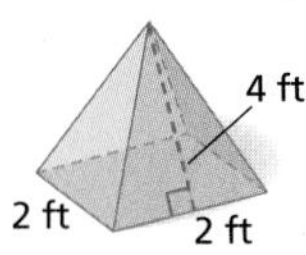

20 ft²

18. 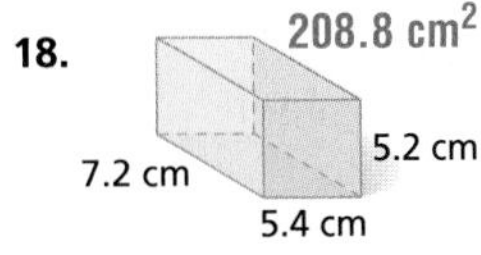

208.8 cm²

Chapter Test

Organizer

Objective: Assess students' mastery of concepts and skills in Chapter 10.

Online Edition

Resources

Assessment Resources

Chapter 10 Tests
- Free Response (Levels A, B, C)
- Multiple Choice (Levels A, B, C)
- Performance Assessment

***IDEA Works!* CD-ROM**
Modified Chapter 10 Test

Test & Practice Generator
One-Stop Planner®

Answers

4. The perimeter is multiplied by 2, and the area is multiplied by 4, or 2^2.
9. 5 faces; 9 edges; 6 vertices; yes; triangular prism
10. 5 faces; 8 edges; 5 vertices; yes; square pyramid
11. 2 faces; 1 edge, 1 vertex; no; cone

Organizer

Objective: Provide review and practice for Chapters 1–10 and standardized tests.

 **Online Edition**

Resources

 ***Assessment Resources***
Chapter 10 Cumulative Test

 ***CRCT Prep* Workbook**

 ***CRCT Prep* CD-ROM**

 ***CRCT Practice* Online**

go.hrw.com
KEYWORD: MR7 TestPrep

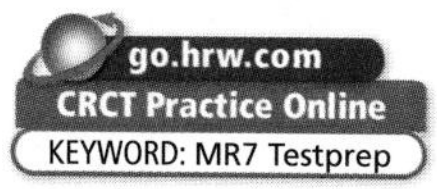

CRCT Prep

Cumulative Assessment, Chapters 1–10

Multiple Choice

1. Which of the following solid figures is NOT a polyhedron?

Ⓐ 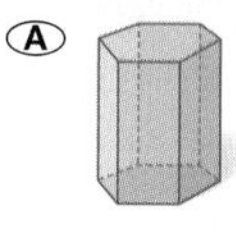 Ⓒ 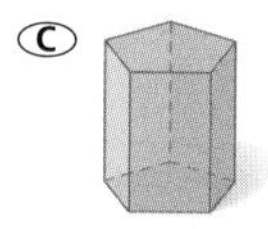

Ⓑ 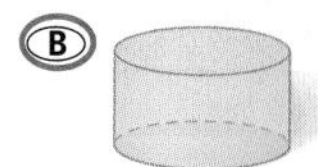 Ⓓ 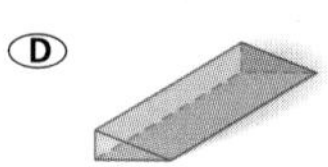

2. On May 1, 2005, in Galveston, Texas, the sun rose at 6:37 A.M. The sun set at 7:56 P.M. How much time elapsed from sunrise to sunset?

Ⓕ 1 hour and 39 minutes
Ⓖ 12 hours and 29 minutes
Ⓗ 13 hours and 9 minutes
Ⓙ 13 hours and 19 minutes

3. A gallon of paint will cover 250 square feet. About how many gallons of paint are needed to paint a rectangular billboard that is 120 feet long and 85 feet tall?

Ⓐ 2 gallons Ⓒ 22 gallons
Ⓑ 10 gallons Ⓓ 41 gallons

4. Justin has 3 cups of sugar in a canister. He uses $\frac{1}{3}$ cup of sugar in a cookie recipe. He uses $\frac{3}{4}$ of what is remaining in the canister to make a pitcher of lemonade. How much sugar is left?

Ⓕ $\frac{2}{3}$ cup Ⓗ $1\frac{11}{12}$ cups
Ⓖ 1 cup Ⓙ 2 cups

5. What is the prime factorization of 324?

Ⓐ $2^2 \times 3^4$ Ⓒ $2^2 \times 3^2 \times 27$
Ⓑ $2^2 \times 9^2$ Ⓓ $2^2 \times 81$

6. Maysville Middle School is hosting a craft fair. The circle graph shows how many different types of booths will be at the craft fair. To the nearest whole number, what percent of the booths will be selling jewelry?

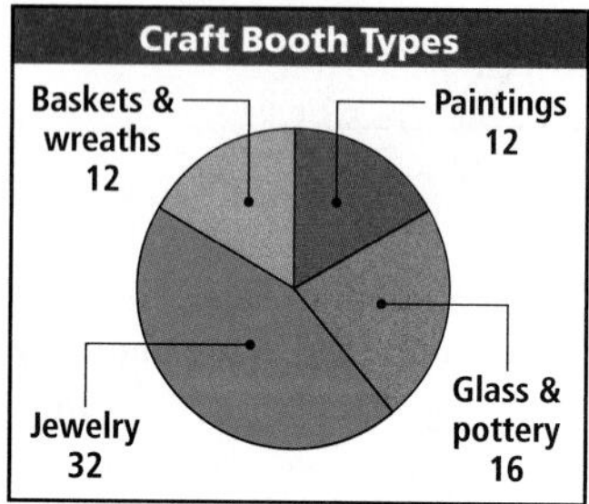

Ⓕ 80% Ⓗ 44%
Ⓖ 55% Ⓙ 33%

7. An antique round tabletop has a diameter of 3 feet. What is the area of the tabletop? Use 3.14 for *pi*. Round to the nearest tenth.

Ⓐ 7.1 ft^2 Ⓒ 18.8 ft^2
Ⓑ 9.4 ft^2 Ⓓ 28.3 ft^2

8. The scale on a map is 1 in:50 mi. If Cincinnati, Ohio, is about 300 miles from Chicago, Illinois, about how far apart are the two cities on the map?

Ⓕ 5 in. Ⓗ 7 in.
Ⓖ 6 in. Ⓙ 8 in.

TEST PREP DOCTOR

For item 5, students may start by evaluating each expression. Remind them to first check to see whether all factors in the expressions are prime. Choices **B, C,** and **D** contain factors that are not prime.

Answers

14a.

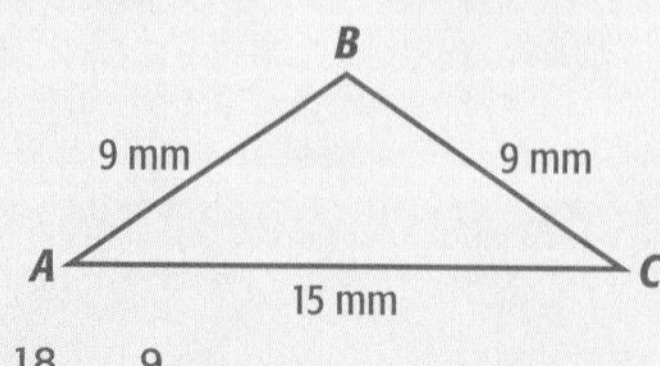

b. $\frac{18}{30} = \frac{9}{15}$
$270 = 270$

15. The new parking lot will be 4 times larger than the original parking lot.
The area of the original lot is $60 \times 35 = 2100$ m^2.
The area of the new lot is $120 \times 70 = 8400$ m^2.
$\frac{8400}{2100} = 4$

16. There are 72 inches in 2 yards.
$2.4s = 72$; $s = 30$ Carole can get thirty 2.4-inch strips from the fabric.

17. See 4-Point Response work sample.

9. In March of 2005, Steve Fossett became the first man to complete the first solo, nonstop flight around the world. He did not even stop to refuel. The 36,818-kilometer voyage took 67 hours and 2 minutes. How many kilometers did he travel per minute? Round to the nearest kilometer.

Ⓐ 5 km/min
Ⓑ 9 km/min
Ⓒ 23 km/min
Ⓓ 26 km/min

When finding the area of an irregular shape, divide the shape into smaller parts and add the smaller areas to find the overall area of the figure.

Use the table for item 10.

Superbowl Attendance					
Year	1967	1968	1969	1970	1971
Number of People	61,946	75,546	75,389	80,562	79,204

10. What was the mean attendance? Round to the nearest thousandth.

Ⓕ 74,000
Ⓖ 74,529
Ⓗ 74,600
Ⓙ 75,000

11. The area of a triangle is 57.12 cm^2. If the height of the triangle is 8.4 cm, how many centimeters long is the base?

Ⓐ 6.8
Ⓑ 13.6
Ⓒ 16.8
Ⓓ 239.9

12. Solve the equation for $\frac{2}{7}k = \frac{1}{6}$ for k.

Ⓕ $\frac{1}{21}$
Ⓖ $\frac{2}{42}$
Ⓗ $\frac{7}{12}$
Ⓙ $\frac{12}{7}$

13. Marcia is weighing her produce. A watermelon weighs 2.89 kg. How many grams are in 2.89 kg?

Ⓐ 2,890
Ⓑ 289
Ⓒ 28.9
Ⓓ 2.89

STANDARDIZED TEST PREP

Short Response

14. Triangle *WXY* is isosceles. The two short sides have a length of 18 mm. The other side has as length of 30 mm.
    a. Draw a triangle that is similar to triangle *WXY*.
    b. Write a proportion to prove that the two triangles are similar.

15. A company's rectangular parking lot is 35 m long and 60 m wide. The company is planning on expanding the area. If the dimensions are doubled, how many times greater will the area of the new parking lot be compared to the area of the original parking lot? Explain how you found your answer.

16. Carole has a piece of fabric that is 2 yards long. She wants to cut the fabric into 2.4-inch strips. Let *s* equal one of the fabric strips. Write and solve an equation to find how many 2.4-inch strips Carole can cut from the piece of fabric.

Extended Response

17. There are 3 pools in Marcie's neighborhood where she can go swimming. The dimensions are listed below. Pool 2 is a circular pool. The width is its radius.

Pool	Length (ft)	Depth (ft)	Width (ft)
1	25	5	8
2	–	6	9
3	15	4	9

a. Find the volume of each pool. Which pool has the greatest volume? Show your work. Use 3.14 for *pi*.
b. What is the circumference of pool 2?
c. Samantha's pool has the same volume as pool 1. However, her pool is in the shape of a cube. What are the dimensions of Samantha's pool?

CRCT Prep

Short Response Rubric

Items 14–16

2 Points = The student's answer is an accurate and complete execution of the task or tasks.

1 Point = The student's answer contains attributes of an appropriate response but is flawed.

0 Points = The student's answer contains no attributes of an appropriate response.

Extended Response Rubric

Item 17

4 Points = The student demonstrates a thorough understanding of all concepts and shows all work correctly.

3 Points = The student demonstrates a basic understanding of all concepts, but the work shows some flaws reflecting inattentive execution of mathematical procedures or some misunderstanding of the underlying mathematics.

2 Points = The student demonstrates only a partial understanding of the concepts or procedures embodied in the tasks. The approach may be correct, but the work shows a misunderstanding of one or more important concepts.

1 Point = The student demonstrates a very limited understanding of the concepts or procedures embodied in the tasks. The response may show some understanding but exhibits many flaws or is incomplete.

0 Points = The student provides no response at all or a completely incorrect or uninterpretable response.

Student Work Samples for Item 17

4-Point Response

a. $V = l \cdot w \cdot h = 25 \cdot 8 \cdot 5 = 1000$
Pool 1 has a volume of 1,000 ft^3.
$V = \pi r^2 h = 3.14 \cdot 81 \cdot 6 = 1{,}526.04$
Pool 2 has a volume of 1,526.04 ft^3.
$V = l \cdot w \cdot h = 15 \cdot 4 \cdot 9 = 540$
Pool 3 has a volume of 540 ft^3.
Pool 2 has the greatest volume.
b. The circumference of Pool 2 is
$2\pi r = 2\pi(9) = 56.52$ ft.
c. $V = s^3 = 1000$
$s = 10$
Samantha's pool is 10 feet by 10 feet by 10 feet.

The answers are correct and all work is clearly shown.

3-Point Response

ⓐ
Pool 1 – $V = 25 \times 8 \times 5 = 1{,}000$ ft^3
Pool 2 – $V = 3.14 \times (4.5)^2 \times 6 = 381.51$ ft^3
Pool 3 – $V = 15 \times 4 \times 9 = 540$ ft^3
Pool 1 has the greatest volume
ⓑ
Pool 1 – $P = 2(25) + 2(8) = 66$ ft
Pool 2 – $P = 2 \times 3.14 \times (4.5) = 28.26$ ft
Pool 3 – $P = 2(15) + 2(9) = 48$ ft
ⓒ
$V = s^3 = 1{,}000$; $s = 10$ ft

The wrong value was used for the radius in parts **a** and **b,** causing part **a** to be incorrect. All of the other work has been done correctly.

2-Point Response

ⓐ $V = 1{,}000$ ft^2
$V = 1{,}526$ ft^2
$V = 540$ ft^2

ⓑ $P = 66$ ft
$P = 56$ ft
$P = 48$ ft

ⓒ $V = 3s = 1{,}000$ ft $= 333.3$ ft

For the most part, answers appear to be correct but are not adequately identified. The formula used in part **c** is incorrect.

Problem Solving on Location

Organizer

Objective: To solve real-world problems involving measurement, geometry, area, and volume.

Online Edition

Martin Luther King Birth Home

Reading Strategies

Have students read problem 3. Then ask them what information they will need in order to solve the problem. The perimeter and area of each room Ask students whether this information is given in the problem. No Ask students how they can find this information. Perimeters and areas can be calculated using the data in the table.

Using Data Have students make a new table based on the one provided. Students' tables should include the name of each room and its length and width as well as the room's perimeter and area.

Problem Solving on Location

GEORGIA

M6P1.c, M6P4.c, M6P5.a

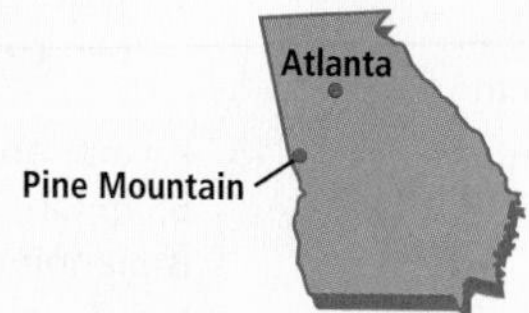

Martin Luther King Birth Home

Dr. Martin Luther King Jr. was born in Atlanta on January 15, 1929. The home in which the great civil rights leader was born still stands at 501 Auburn Avenue. Daily tours of the home give visitors a glimpse of Dr. King's early life.

Choose one or more strategies to solve each problem.

1. During the summer months, tours of the home begin at 9:30 A.M., with additional tours at 10:00 A.M., 10:30 A.M., and so on. The last tour of the day begins at 5:30 P.M. How many tours are offered each day? 17

2. The second story of the home has a rectangular hallway. The hallway's length is 17 feet greater than its width. The sum of the hallway's length and width is 27 feet. What is the length of the hallway? 22 feet

For 3, use the table.

3. In 1936, a group of African American teachers met in one of the rooms of the home to organize their fight for equal pay. The room that they used had a perimeter greater than 55 feet. It had an area less than 200 ft^2. Which room was used as the group's meeting place? living room

Martin Luther King Birth Home

Room	Length (ft)	Width (ft)
Dining room	15.5	14
Front bedroom	14	13.5
Birth room	15.25	14
Spare room	15.5	9
Living room	14	14

Problem Solving Focus

Problem 3 offers an ideal opportunity to focus on the strategy Use Logical Reasoning. For example, ask students what logical conclusions they can make based on the fact that the meeting room had a perimeter greater than 55 ft. The meeting room must have been the dining room, the birth room, or the living room.

Georgia Performance Standards

M6P1.c Apply and adapt a variety of appropriate strategies to solve problems.

M6P4.c Recognize and apply mathematics in contexts outside of mathematics.

M6P5.a Create and use representations to organize, record, and communicate mathematical ideas.

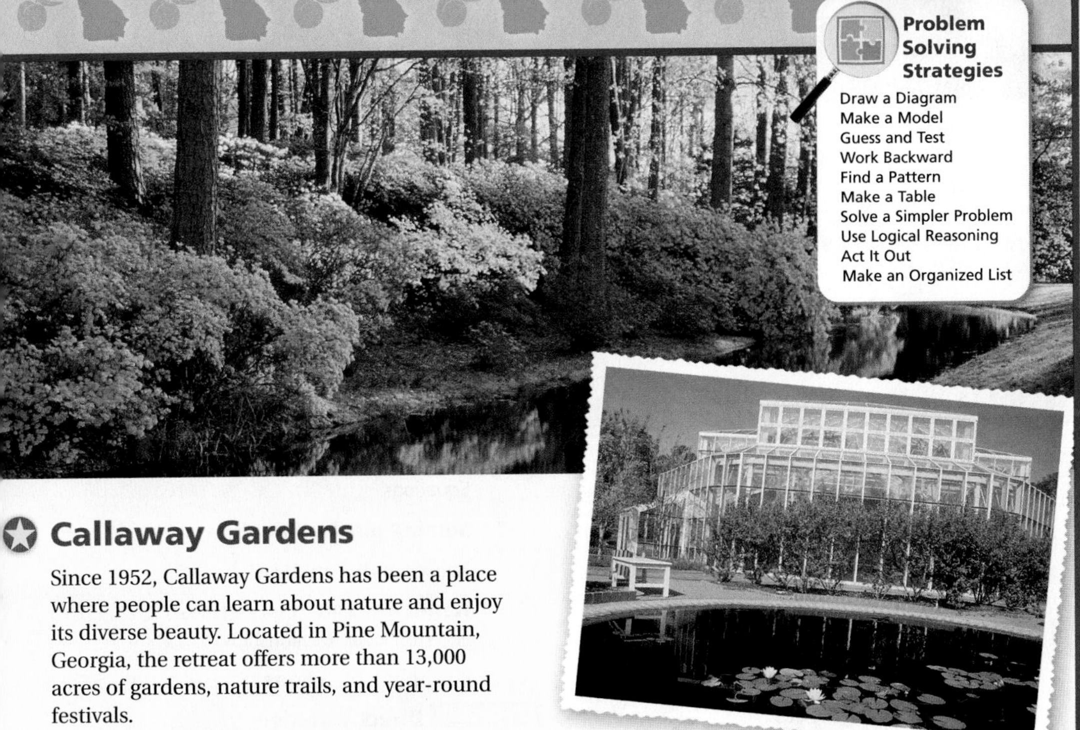

Problem Solving Strategies

- Draw a Diagram
- Make a Model
- Guess and Test
- Work Backward
- Find a Pattern
- Make a Table
- Solve a Simpler Problem
- Use Logical Reasoning
- Act It Out
- Make an Organized List

Callaway Gardens

Since 1952, Callaway Gardens has been a place where people can learn about nature and enjoy its diverse beauty. Located in Pine Mountain, Georgia, the retreat offers more than 13,000 acres of gardens, nature trails, and year-round festivals.

Choose one or more strategies to solve each problem.

1. Callaway Gardens has a butterfly conservatory. A pool in the conservatory is a rectangular prism with a volume of 550 ft^3. The length, width, and depth of the pool are whole numbers. The depth is no greater than 2 feet, and the length and width are both at least 10 feet. What are all the possible dimensions of the pool?

For 2 and 3, use the map.

2. Signs along the Laurel Springs Trail offer visitors a self-guided tour. Assume that the first sign is located 75 feet from the beginning of the trail and that the last sign is located 75 feet from the end of the trail. What is the distance between the first and last sign? (Note: 1 mile = 5,280 feet) 2,490 ft
3. A family hiked along three of the nature trails at Callaway Gardens and hiked a total of 3.9 miles. Which three trails did they choose? Overlook Azalea, Mountain Creek Lake, Holly

Callaway Gardens Hiking Trails

Day Butterfly Center
Holly Trail Length: 0.8 miles
Rhododendron Trail Length: 0.6 miles
Mountain Creek Lake Trail Length: 1.5 miles
Boathouse
Overlook Azalea Trail Length: 1.6 miles
Laurel Springs Trail Length: 0.5 miles
N E S W

1.

Length (ft)	Width (ft)	Depth (ft)
550	1	1
275	2	1
110	5	1
55	10	1
275	1	2
55	5	2

Callaway Gardens

ENGLISH LANGUAGE LEARNERS

Reading Strategies

Reading in small groups is an excellent strategy for ELL students. After dividing the class into small groups, have students read the problems and discuss any unfamiliar words or math concepts with their classmates. If everyone in a group has the same question, invite a spokesperson for the group to share their question with the entire class.

Using Data Before students begin solving problem 3, spend a moment discussing the data in the map. Ask students which trail is the longest. Overlook Azalea Ask them which trail is the shortest. Laurel Springs Also ask students to find the difference in the lengths of these two trails. 1.1 miles

Problem Solving Focus

For problem 2, focus on the second step in the Problem Solving Process: Make a Plan. Ask students to share their ideas on how they can solve this problem. Ask them which strategy or strategies might be most useful. Possible answer: Draw a Diagram Ask students what else they will need to do in order to solve the problem. Convert the length of the trail to feet.

Discuss different strategies that could be used to solve problem 2. If students choose to draw a diagram, ask volunteers to share their diagrams with the class and explain how they used the diagram to solve the problem. Discuss with the class whether it is possible to draw the diagram in more than one way.

CHAPTER 11

Integers, Graphs, and Functions

Section 11A

Understanding Integers

11-1 **Integers In Real-World Situations**
11-2 **Comparing and Ordering Integers**
11-3 **The Coordinate Plane**

Section 11B

Integer Operations

11-4 **Hands-On Lab** Model Integer Addition
11-4 **Adding Integers**
11-5 **Hands-On Lab** Model Integer Subtraction
11-5 **Subtracting Integers**
11-6 **Multiplying Integers**
11-7 **Dividing Integers**

Section 11C

Equations and Functions

11-8 **Hands-On Lab** Model Integer Equations
11-8 **Solving Integer Equations**
11-9 **Tables and Functions**
11-10 **Hands-On Lab** Explore Linear and Nonlinear Relationships
11-10 **Graphing Functions**
EXTENSION **Direct Variation**

Pacing Guide for 45-Minute Classes

Chapter 11

DAY 1	DAY 2	DAY 3	DAY 4	DAY 5
11-1 Lesson	11-2 Lesson	11-3 Lesson	Ready to Go On? Focus on Problem Solving **11-4 Hands-On Lab**	11-4 Lesson
DAY 6	**DAY 7**	**DAY 8**	**DAY 9**	**DAY 10**
11-5 Hands-On Lab 11-5 Lesson	11-5 Lesson	11-6 Lesson	11-7 Lesson	Ready to Go On? Focus on Problem Solving **11-8 Hands-On Lab**
DAY 11	**DAY 12**	**DAY 13**	**DAY 14**	**DAY 15**
11-8 Lesson	11-9 Lesson	**11-10 Hands-On Lab** 11-10 Lesson	11-10 Lesson Ready to Go On? Multi-Step Test Prep	EXTENSION
DAY 16	**DAY 17**			
Chapter 11 Review	Chapter 11 Review			

Pacing Guide for 90-Minute Classes

Chapter 11

DAY 1	DAY 2	DAY 3	DAY 4	DAY 5
11-1 Lesson 11-2 Lesson	11-3 Lesson Ready to Go On? Focus on Problem Solving **11-4 Hands-On Lab**	11-4 Lesson **11-5 Hands-On Lab** 11-5 Lesson	11-5 Lesson 11-6 Lesson	11-7 Lesson Ready to Go On? Focus on Problem Solving **11-8 Hands-On Lab**
DAY 6	**DAY 7**	**DAY 8**	**DAY 9**	
11-8 Lesson 11-9 Lesson	**11-10 Hands-On Lab** 11-10 Lesson Ready to Go On? Multi-Step Test Prep	EXTENSION Chapter 11 Review	Chapter 11 Test	

ONGOING ASSESSMENT and INTERVENTION

	DIAGNOSE	PRESCRIBE
Assess Prior Knowledge	**Before Chapter 11** Diagnose readiness for the chapter. 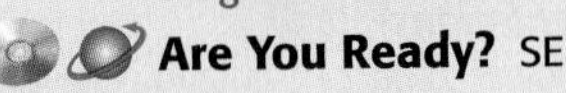 **Are You Ready?** SE p. 599	Prescribe intervention.  ***Are You Ready? Intervention*** Skills 4, 34, 58, 69
Formative Assessment	**Before Every Lesson** Diagnose readiness for the lesson. **Warm Up** TE, every lesson	Prescribe intervention. **Skills Bank** SE pp. 749–761 **Reteach** CRB, Chapters 1–11
	During Every Lesson Diagnose understanding of lesson concepts. **Think and Discuss** SE, every lesson **Write About It** SE, lesson exercises **Journal** TE, lesson exercises	Prescribe intervention. ***Questioning Strategies*** Chapter 11 **Reading Strategies** CRB, every lesson ***Success for ELL*** pp. 183–202
	After Every Lesson Diagnose mastery of lesson concepts. **Lesson Quiz** TE, every lesson **Test Prep** SE, every lesson ***Test and Practice Generator***	Prescribe intervention. **Reteach** CRB, every lesson **Problem Solving** CRB, every lesson **Test Prep Doctor** TE, lesson exercises ***Homework Help* Online**
	Before Chapter 11 Testing Diagnose mastery of concepts in the chapter. **Ready to Go On?** SE pp. 614, 632, 650 **Focus on Problem Solving** SE pp. 615, 633 **Multi-Step Test Prep** SE p. 651 **Section Quizzes** AR pp. 00–00 ***Test and Practice Generator***	Prescribe intervention. ***Ready to Go On? Intervention*** Chapter 11 **Scaffolding Questions** TE p. 651
	Before High Stakes Testing Diagnose mastery of benchmark concepts. **Test Tackler** SE pp. 660-661 **CRCT Prep** SE pp. 662–663 ***CRCT Prep* CD-ROM**	Prescribe intervention. ***CRCT Prep Workbook***
Summative Assessment	**After Chapter 11** Check mastery of chapter concepts. **Multiple-Choice Tests (Forms A, B, C)** **Free-Response Tests (Forms A, B, C)** **Performance Assessment** AR pp. 209–222 ***Test and Practice Generator*** Check mastery of benchmark concepts. **CRCT**	Prescribe intervention. **Reteach** CRB, every lesson ***Lesson Tutorial Videos*** Chapter 11  Prescribe intervention. ***CRCT Prep Workbook***

KEY: **SE** = *Student Edition* **TE** = *Teacher's Edition* **CRB** = *Chapter Resource Book* **AR** = *Assessment Resources* Available on CD-ROM  Available online

CHAPTER 11

Supporting the Teacher

Chapter 11 Resource Book

Practice A, B, C
pp. 3–5, 11–13, 19–21, 27–29, 35–37, 43–45, 51–53, 59–61, 67–69, 75–77

Reading Strategies ELL
pp. 9, 17, 25, 33, 41, 49, 57, 65, 73, 82

Puzzles, Twisters, and Teasers
pp. 10, 18, 26, 34, 42, 50, 58, 66, 74, 83

Reteach
pp. 6, 14, 22, 30, 38, 46, 54, 62, 70, 78–79

Problem Solving
pp. 8, 16, 24, 32, 40, 48, 56, 64, 72, 81

Challenge
pp. 7, 15, 23, 31, 39, 47, 55, 63, 71, 80

Parent Letter pp. 1–2

Transparencies

Lesson Transparencies, Volume 2 .... Chapter 11
- Warm Ups
- Problem of the Day
- Teaching Transparencies
- Lesson Quizzes

Know-It Notebook .... Chapter 11
- Additional Examples
- Vocabulary
- Chapter Review
- Big Ideas

Alternate Openers: Explorations .... pp. 92–101

Teacher Tools

Power Presentations®
Complete PowerPoint® presentations for Chapter 11 lessons

Lesson Tutorial Videos® SPANISH
Holt authors Ed Burger and Freddie Renfro present tutorials to support the Chapter 11 lessons.

One-Stop Planner® SPANISH
Easy access to all Chapter 11 resources and assessments, as well as software for lesson planning, test generation, and puzzle creation

IDEA Works!®
Key Chapter 11 resources and assessments modified to address special learning needs

Lesson Plans .... pp. 92–101

Questioning Strategies .... Chapter 11

Solutions Key .... Chapter 11

Interdisciplinary Posters and Worksheets .... Chapter 11

TechKeys

Lab Resources

Project Teacher Support

Workbooks

Homework and Practice Workbook SPANISH
Teacher's Guide .... pp. 46–51

Know-It Notebook
Teacher's Guide .... Chapter 11

Problem Solving Workbook SPANISH
Teacher's Guide .... pp. 46–51

CRCT Prep Workbook
Teacher's Guide

Technology Highlights for the Teacher

 **Power Presentations**

Dynamic presentations to engage students. Complete PowerPoint® presentations for every lesson in Chapter 11.

2-1 Solving One-Step Equations

Isolate a variable by using inverse operations which "undo" operations on the variable.

An equation is like a balanced scale. To keep the balance, perform the same operation on both sides.

Inverse Operations	
Operation	**Inverse Operation**
Addition	Subtraction
Subtraction	Addition

 **One-Stop Planner** SPANISH

Easy access to Chapter 11 resources and assessments. Includes lesson-planning, test-generation, and puzzle-creation software.

 **Premier Online Edition** SPANISH

Chapter 11 includes Tutorial Videos, Lesson Activities, Lesson Quizzes, Homework Help, and Chapter Project.

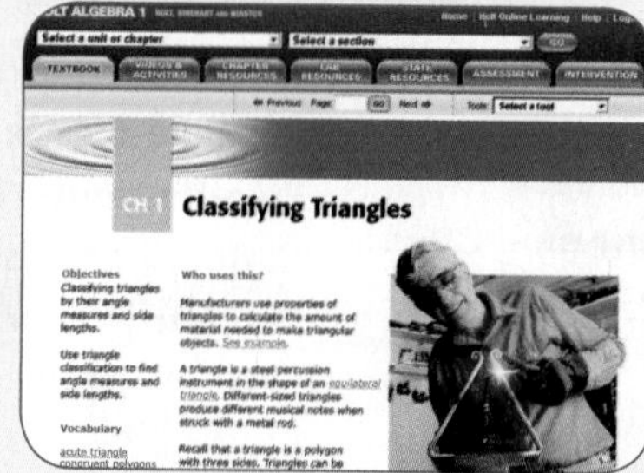

KEY: **SE** = *Student Edition* **TE** = *Teacher's Edition*  English Language Learners  Spanish version available  Available on CD-ROM  Available online

Reaching All Learners

Resources for All Learners

Hands-On Lab Activities .... Chapter 11
Technology Lab Activities .... Chapter 11
Homework and Practice Workbook SPANISH .... pp. 92–101
Know-It Notebook SPANISH .... Chapter 11
Problem Solving Workbook SPANISH .... pp. 92–101

DEVELOPING LEARNERS

Practice A .... CRB, every lesson
Reteach .... CRB, every lesson
Inclusion .... TE pp. 611, 637
Questioning Strategies .... Chapter 11
Modified Chapter 11 Resources .... *IDEA Works!*
Homework Help Online

ON-LEVEL LEARNERS

Practice B .... CRB, every lesson
Puzzles, Twisters, and Teasers .... CRB, every lesson
Multiple Representations .... TE pp. 611, 629, 641
Cognitive Strategies .... TE p. 637

ADVANCED LEARNERS

Practice C .... CRB, every lesson
Challenge .... CRB, every lesson
Extension .... TE pp. 601, 651, 654, 655
Critical Thinking .... TE p. 629

English Language Learners

ENGLISH LANGUAGE LEARNERS

Are You Ready? Vocabulary .... SE p. 599
Vocabulary Connections .... SE p. 600
Lesson Vocabulary .... SE, every lesson
Vocabulary Review .... SE p. 656
English Language Learners .... TE pp. 603, 641
Reading Strategies .... CRB, every lesson
Success for English Language Learners .... pp. 183–202
Multilingual Glossary

Reaching All Learners Through...

Inclusion .... TE pp. 611, 637
Visual Cues .... TE p. 607
Kinesthetic Experience .... TE p. 607
Concrete Manipulatives .... TE p. 618
Multiple Representations .... TE pp. 611, 629, 641
Cognitive Strategies .... TE p. 637
Cooperative Learning .... TE pp. 626, 647
Modeling .... TE p. 647
Critical Thinking .... TE p. 629
Test Prep Doctor .... TE pp. 605, 609, 613, 620, 631, 639, 643, 649, 660, 661, 662
Common Error Alert .... TE pp.607, 609, 611, 629, 637, 641, 653
Scaffolding Questions .... TE p. 651

Technology Highlights for Reaching All Learners

Lesson Tutorial Videos SPANISH

Starring Holt authors Ed Burger and Freddie Renfro! Live tutorials to support every lesson in Chapter 11.

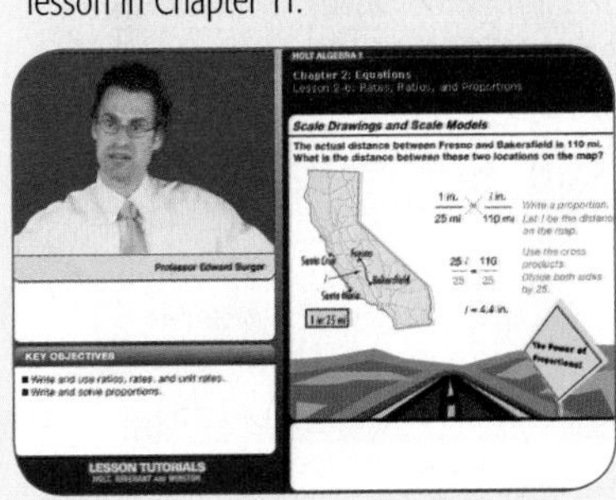

Multilingual Glossary

Searchable glossary includes definitions in English, Spanish, Vietnamese, Chinese, Hmong, Korean, and 4 other languages.

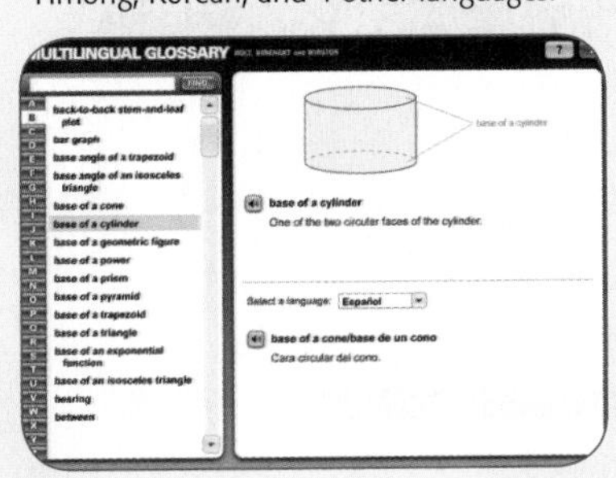

Online Interactivities

Interactive tutorials provide visually engaging alternative opportunities to learn concepts and master skills.

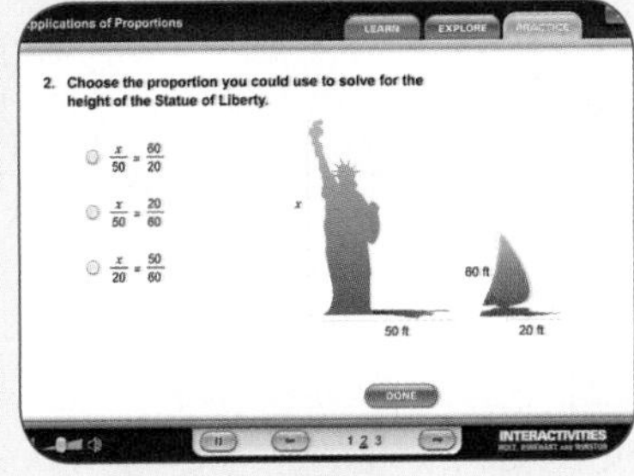

KEY: **SE** = *Student Edition* **TE** = *Teacher's Edition* **CRB** = *Chapter Resource Book* SPANISH Spanish version available 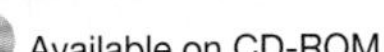 Available on CD-ROM Available online

Ongoing Assessment

Assessing Prior Knowledge

Determine whether students have the prerequisite concepts and skills for success in Chapter 11.

Are You Ready? SPANISH .... SE p. 599
Warm Up .... TE, every lesson

Test Preparation

Provide review and practice for Chapter 11 and standardized tests.

Multi-Step Test Prep .... SE p. 651
Study Guide: Review .... SE pp. 656–658
Test Tackler .... SE pp. 660–661
CRCT Prep .... SE pp. 662-663
CRCT Prep Workbook
***CRCT Prep* CD-ROM**
IDEA Works!

Alternative Assessment

Assess students' understanding of Chapter 11 concepts and combined problem-solving skills.

Chapter 11 Project .... SE p. 598
Performance Assessment SPANISH .... AR pp. 221–222
Portfolio Assessment SPANISH .... AR p. xxxiv

Daily Assessment

Provide formative assessment for each day of Chapter 11.

Questioning Strategies .... Chapter 11
Think and Discuss .... SE, every lesson
Write About It .... SE, lesson exercises
Journal .... TE, lesson exercises
Lesson Quiz .... TE, every lesson
Modified Lesson Quizzes .... *IDEA Works!*

Weekly Assessment

Provide formative assessment for each week of Chapter 11.

Focus on Problem Solving .... SE pp. 615, 633
Multi-Step Test Prep .... SE p. 651
Ready to Go On? SPANISH .... SE pp. 614, 632, 650
Cumulative Assessment .... SE pp. 662–663
Test and Practice Generator SPANISH .... *One-Stop Planner*

Formal Assessment

Provide summative assessment of Chapter 11 mastery.

Section Quizzes SPANISH .... AR pp. 207–208
Chapter 11 Test .... SE p. 659
Chapter Test (Levels A, B, C) SPANISH .... AR pp. 209–220
- Multiple Choice
- Free Response

Cumulative Test SPANISH .... AR pp. 223–226
Test and Practice Generator SPANISH .... *One-Stop Planner*
Modified Chapter 11 Test .... *IDEA Works!*

Technology Highlights for Ongoing Assessment

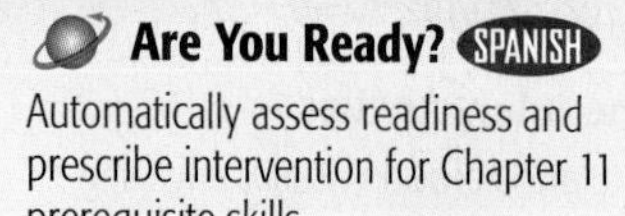

Are You Ready? SPANISH

Automatically assess readiness and prescribe intervention for Chapter 11 prerequisite skills.

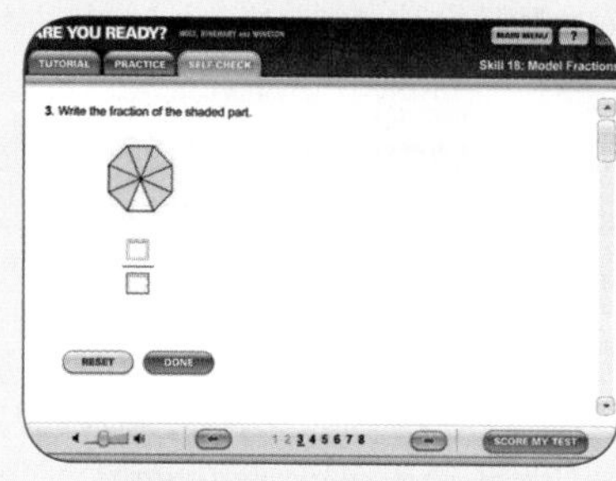

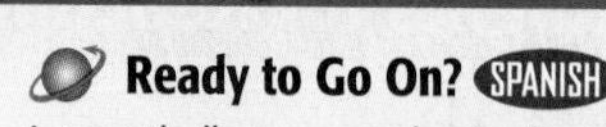

Ready to Go On? SPANISH

Automatically assess understanding of and prescribe intervention for Sections 11A, 11B, and 11C.

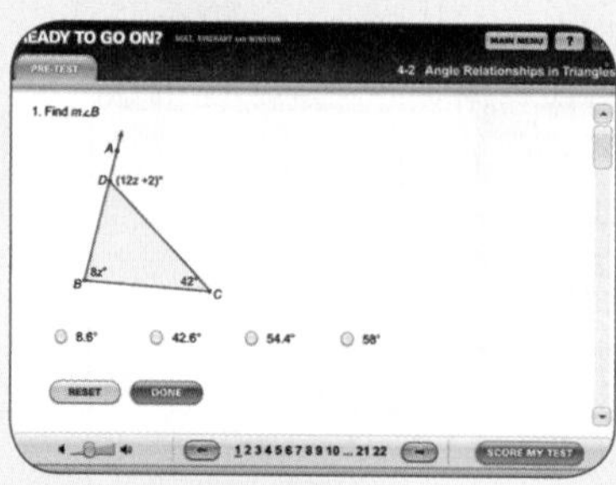

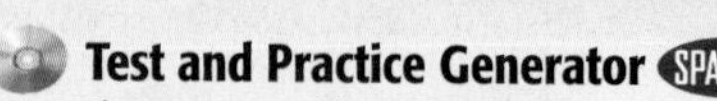

Test and Practice Generator SPANISH

Use Chapter 11 problem banks to create assessments and worksheets to print out or deliver online. Includes dynamic problems.

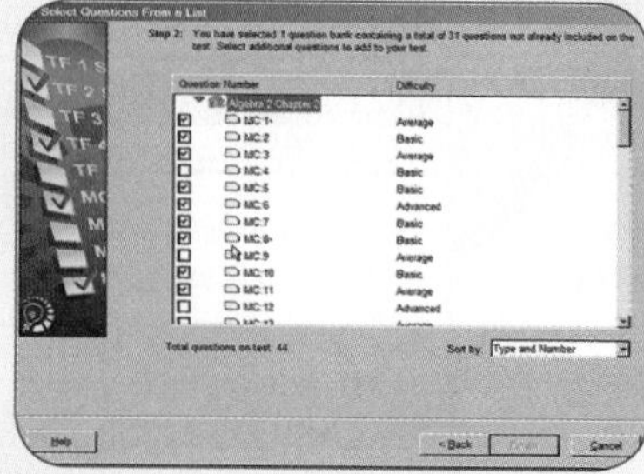

KEY: **SE** = *Student Edition* **TE** = *Teacher's Edition* **AR** = *Assessment Resources* SPANISH Spanish version available  Available on CD-ROM 

Three levels (A, B, C) of multiple-choice and free-response chapter tests are available in the *Assessment Resources.*

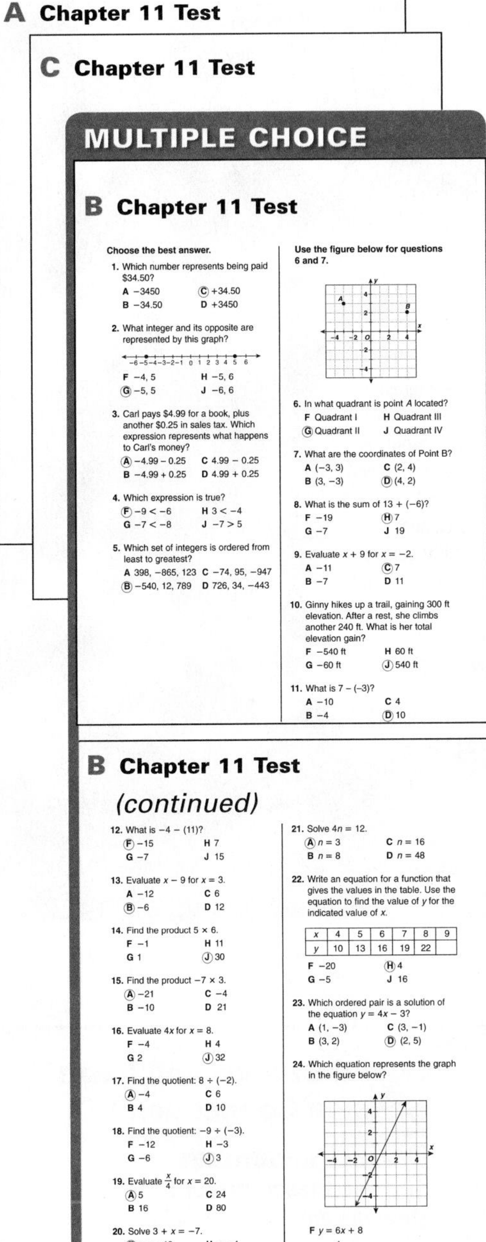

A Chapter 11 Test

C Chapter 11 Test

MULTIPLE CHOICE

B Chapter 11 Test

Choose the best answer.

1. Which number represents being paid $34.50?
   A −3450 (C) +34.50
   B −34.50 D +3450
2. What integer and its opposite are represented by this graph?
   F −4, 5 H −5, 6
   (G) −5, 5 J −6, 6
3. Carl pays $4.99 for a book, plus another $0.25 in sales tax. Which expression represents what happens to Carl's money?
   (A) −4.99 − 0.25 C 4.99 − 0.25
   B −4.99 + 0.25 D 4.99 + 0.25
4. Which expression is true?
   (F) −9 < −6 H 3 < −4
   G −7 < −8 J −7 > 5
5. Which set of integers is ordered from least to greatest?
   A 398, −865, 123 C −74, 95, −947
   (B) −540, 12, 789 D 726, 34, −443

Use the figure below for questions 6 and 7.

6. In what quadrant is point A located?
   F Quadrant I H Quadrant III
   (G) Quadrant II J Quadrant IV
7. What are the coordinates of Point B?
   A (−3, 3) C (2, 4)
   B (3, −3) (D) (4, 2)
8. What is the sum of 13 + (−6)?
   F −19 (H) 7
   G −7 J 19
9. Evaluate x + 9 for x = −2.
   A −11 (C) 7
   B −7 D 11
10. Ginny hikes up a trail, gaining 300 ft elevation. After a rest, she climbs another 240 ft. What is her total elevation gain?
    F −540 ft H 60 ft
    G −60 ft (J) 540 ft
11. What is 7 − (−3)?
    A −10 C 4
    B −4 (D) 10

B Chapter 11 Test (continued)

12. What is −4 − (11)?
    (F) −15 H 7
    G −7 J 15
13. Evaluate x − 9 for x = 3.
    A −12 C 6
    (B) −6 D 12
14. Find the product 5 × 6.
    F −1 H 11
    G 1 (J) 30
15. Find the product −7 × 3.
    (A) −21 C −4
    B −10 D 21
16. Evaluate 4x for x = 8.
    F −4 H 4
    G 2 (J) 32
17. Find the quotient: 8 ÷ (−2).
    (A) −4 C 6
    B 4 D 10
18. Find the quotient: −9 ÷ (−3).
    F −12 H −3
    G −6 (J) 3
19. Evaluate $\frac{x}{4}$ for x = 20.
    (A) 5 C 24
    B 16 D 80
20. Solve 3 + x = −7.
    (F) x = −10 H x = 4
    G x = −4 J x = 10
21. Solve 4n = 12.
    (A) n = 3 C n = 16
    B n = 8 D n = 48
22. Write an equation for a function that gives the values in the table. Use the equation to find the value of y for the indicated value of x.

x	4	5	6	7	8	9
y	10	13	16	19	22	

    F −20 (H) 4
    G −5 J 16
23. Which ordered pair is a solution of the equation y = 4x − 3?
    A (1, −3) C (3, −1)
    B (3, 2) (D) (2, 5)
24. Which equation represents the graph in the figure below?
    F y = 6x + 8
    G $y = \frac{1}{2}x - 3$
    H $y = \frac{5}{4}x + 4$
    (J) y = 2x − 1

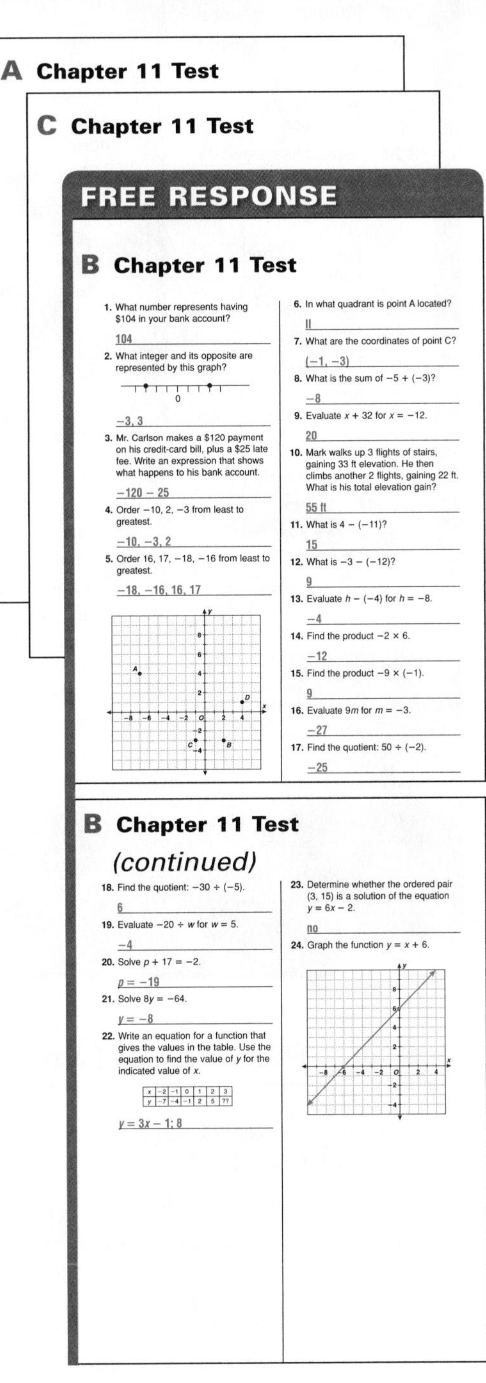

A Chapter 11 Test

C Chapter 11 Test

FREE RESPONSE

B Chapter 11 Test

1. What number represents having $104 in your bank account? 104
2. What integer and its opposite are represented by this graph? −3, 3
3. Mr. Carlson makes a $120 payment on his credit-card bill, plus a $25 late fee. Write an expression that shows what happens to his bank account. −120 − 25
4. Order −10, 2, −3 from least to greatest. −10, −3, 2
5. Order 16, 17, −18, −16 from least to greatest. −18, −16, 16, 17
6. In what quadrant is point A located? II
7. What are the coordinates of point C? (−1, −3)
8. What is the sum of −5 + (−3)? −8
9. Evaluate x + 32 for x = −12. 20
10. Mark walks up 3 flights of stairs, gaining 33 ft elevation. He then climbs another 2 flights, gaining 22 ft. What is his total elevation gain? 55 ft
11. What is 4 − (−11)? 15
12. What is −3 − (−12)? 9
13. Evaluate h − (−4) for h = −8. −4
14. Find the product −2 × 6. −12
15. Find the product −9 × (−1). 9
16. Evaluate 9m for m = −3. −27
17. Find the quotient: 50 ÷ (−2). −25

B Chapter 11 Test (continued)

18. Find the quotient: −30 ÷ (−5). 6
19. Evaluate −20 ÷ w for w = 5. −4
20. Solve p + 17 = −2. p = −19
21. Solve 8y = −64. y = −8
22. Write an equation for a function that gives the values in the table. Use the equation to find the value of y for the indicated value of x.

x	−2	−1	0	1	2	3
y	−7	−4	−1	2	5	??

    y = 3x − 1; 8
23. Determine whether the ordered pair (3, 15) is a solution of the equation y = 6x − 2. no
24. Graph the function y = x + 6.

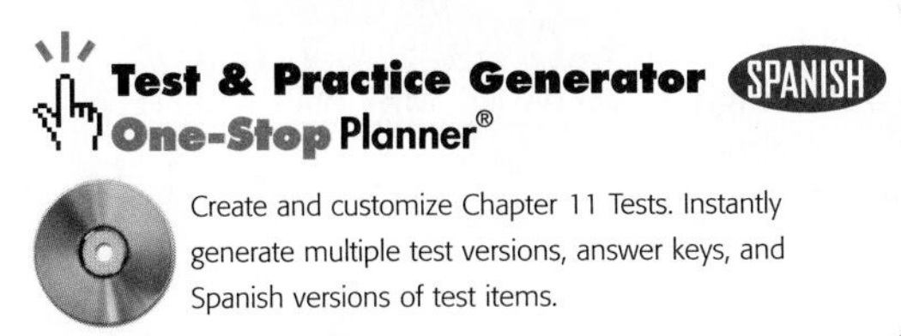

Create and customize Chapter 11 Tests. Instantly generate multiple test versions, answer keys, and Spanish versions of test items.

CHAPTER 11

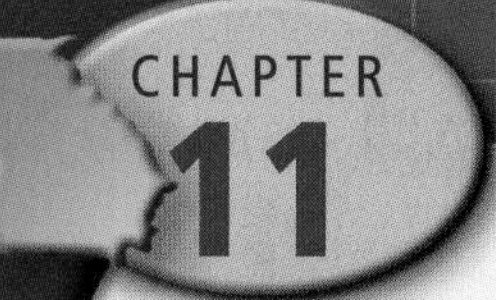

Why Learn This?

Tell students that many everyday situations make positive and negative numbers necessary. For example, elevation above and below sea level can be described by positive and negative integers, as shown in the table. Integers are used in many other fields besides geography. For instance, in finance, positive and negative integers are used to describe monetary changes.

Using Data

To begin the study of this chapter, have students:

- Interpret the meaning of −411, the lowest point in Asia. 411 meters below sea level
- Identify the continents with the lowest and the highest points. Antarctica; Asia
- Identify the elevation of the lowest point in North America. 86 meters below sea level

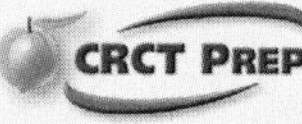

CRCT PREP On page 662, students will find cumulative CRCT practice.

CHAPTER 11

Integers, Graphs, and Functions

CRCT PREP

go.hrw.com
Chapter Project Online
KEYWORD: MR7 Ch11

Continent	Highest Point (m)	Lowest Point (m)
Africa	Mt. Kilimanjaro: 5,895	Lake Assal: −156
Antarctica	Vinson Massif: 4,897	Bentley Subglacial Trench: −2,538
Asia	Mt. Everest: 8,850	Dead Sea: −411
Australia	Mt. Kosciusko: 2,228	Lake Eyre: −12
Europe	Mt. Elbrus: 5,642	Caspian Sea: −28
North America	Mt. McKinley: 6,194	Death Valley: −86
South America	Mt. Aconcagua: 6,960	Valdes Peninsula: −40

Career *Geographer*

Geographers are interested in characteristics of our natural world, such as landforms, natural resources, and climate. Some geographers spend time in the field collecting information. Others create maps, charts, and graphs. Geographers use integers to express information such as high and low temperatures and elevations above and below sea level. The table lists the highest and lowest points on each continent.

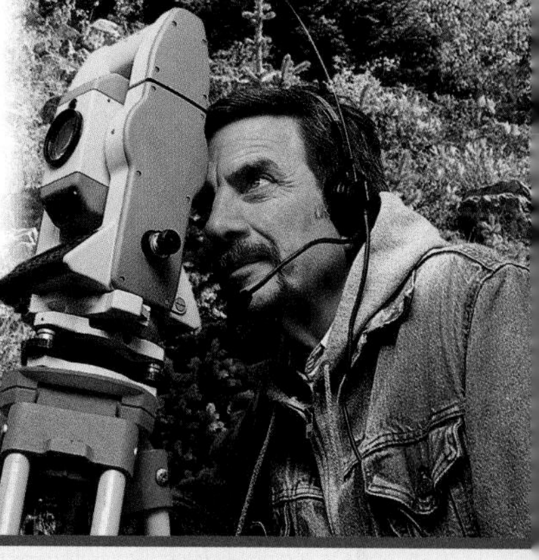

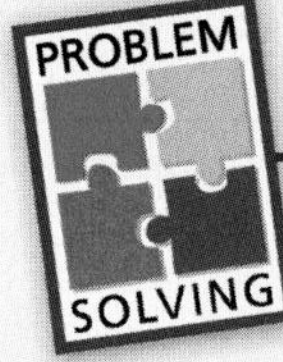

PROBLEM SOLVING

Problem Solving Project

Understand, Plan, Solve, and Look Back

Have students:

- Complete the Continental Ups and Downs worksheet to discover how integers can help them understand the topography of the earth.
- Create a scale model of a continent showing the high and low points. Compare their continent with the models of others, including those who chose different continents.
- Research the locations of the high and low points in each continent. Ask them if they can identify any patterns.

Social Studies and Earth Science Connection

Project Resources

All project resources for teachers and students are provided online.

Materials:

- Continental Ups and Downs worksheet, modeling materials

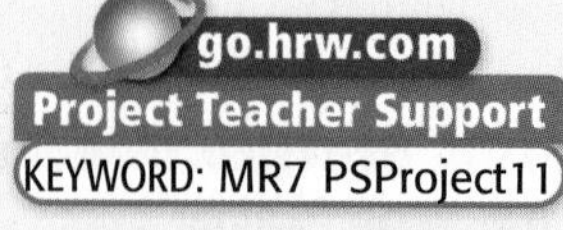

go.hrw.com
Project Teacher Support
KEYWORD: MR7 PSProject11

ARE YOU READY?

Vocabulary

Choose the best term from the list to complete each sentence.

1. When you ___?___ a numerical expression, you find its value. evaluate
2. ___?___ are the set of numbers 0, 1, 2, 3, 4, ... whole numbers
3. A(n) ___?___ is an exact location in space. point
4. A(n) ___?___ is a mathematical statement that two quantities are equal. equation

equation
evaluate
exponents
less than
point
whole numbers

Complete these exercises to review skills you will need for this chapter.

Compare Whole Numbers

Write <, >, or = to compare the numbers.

5. 9 ▪ 2 >
6. 4 ▪ 5 <
7. 8 ▪ 1 >
8. 3 ▪ 3 =
9. 412 ▪ 214 >
10. 1,076 ▪ 1,074 >
11. 502 ▪ 520 <
12. 9,123 ▪ 9,001 >

Whole Number Operations

Add, subtract, multiply, or divide.

13. $7 + 6$ 13
14. $15 - 8$ 7
15. $6 \cdot 7$ 42
16. $25 \div 5$ 5
17. $129 + 30$ 159
18. $32 - 25$ 7
19. $119 \cdot 5$ 595
20. $156 \div 6$ 26

Solve One-Step Equations

Solve each equation.

21. $4t = 32$ $t = 8$
22. $b - 4 = 12$ $b = 16$
23. $24 = 6r$ $r = 4$
24. $3x = 72$ $x = 24$
25. $8 = 4a$ $a = 2$
26. $m + 3 = 63$ $m = 60$

Graph Ordered Pairs

Graph each ordered pair.

27. (1, 3)
28. (0, 5)
29. (3, 2)
30. (4, 0)
31. (6, 4)
32. (2, 5)
33. (0, 1)
34. (1, 0)

ARE YOU READY? CHAPTER 11

Organizer

Objective: Assess students' understanding of prerequisite skills.

Prerequisite Skills

Compare Whole Numbers
Whole-Number Operations
Solve One-Step Equations
Graph Ordered Pairs

Assessing Prior Knowledge

INTERVENTION 

Diagnose and Prescribe

Use this page to determine whether intervention is necessary or enrichment is appropriate.

Resources

Are You Ready? Intervention and Enrichment Worksheets

 *Are You Ready?* CD-ROM

Are You Ready? Online

Answers

27–34. See p. A11.

ARE YOU READY?

Diagnose and Prescribe

NO INTERVENE

Prerequisite Skill	*Are You Ready? Intervention*, Chapter 11 — Worksheets	CD-ROM	Online
Compare Whole Numbers	Skill 4	Activity 4	Diagnose and Prescribe Online
Whole-Number Operations	Skill 34	Activity 34	
Solve One-Step Equations	Skill 58	Activity 58	
Graph Ordered Pairs	Skill 69	Activity 69	

YES ENRICH

Are You Ready? Enrichment, Chapter 11

Worksheets
CD-ROM
Online

CHAPTER 11 Study Guide: Preview

Organizer

Objective: Help students organize the new concepts they will learn in Chapter 11.

Online Edition
Multilingual Glossary

Resources

PuzzlePro®
One-Stop Planner®

Multilingual Glossary **Online**

go.hrw.com
KEYWORD: MR7 Glossary

Answers to *Vocabulary Connections*

Possible answers:

1. The input will be a quantity that generates a unique output.
2. The graph of a linear equation is a straight line.
3. Opposites are on different sides of, and equidistance from, the origin.
4. In two-dimensional space, the origin is at (0, 0).
5. A coordinate plane has four quadrants.

CHAPTER 11

Study Guide: Preview

Where You've Been

Previously, you

- graphed and located ordered pairs of whole numbers on a coordinate grid.
- graphed a given set of data.
- used equations to represent real-life situations.

In This Chapter

You will study

- using integers to represent real-life situations.
- using tables and symbols to represent sequences.
- using data tables to generate formulas representing relationships like perimeter.
- graphing and locating ordered pairs on four quadrants of a coordinate plane.

Where You're Going

You can use the skills learned in this chapter

- to interpret graphs of functions that represent real-world situations.
- to solve multi-step equations with integers and positive and negative fractions and decimals.

Key Vocabulary/Vocabulario

coordinates	coordenado
function	función
input	valor de entrada
integer	enteros
linear equation	ecuación lineal
output	valor de salida
opposites	opuestos
origin	origen
quadrants	cuadrante

Vocabulary Connections

To become familiar with some of the vocabulary terms in the chapter, consider the following. You may refer to the chapter, the glossary, or a dictionary if you like.

1. The word *input* can mean "an amount put in." What type of **input** do you think you will use to find the output of a function?
2. The word *linear* means "relating to a straight line." What do you think the graph of a **linear equation** will look like?
3. The word *opposite* can mean "across from." Where do you think **opposites** will lie on a number line?
4. The word *origin* can mean "the point at which something begins." At what coordinates do you think the **origin** is?
5. The word *quadrant* comes from the Latin *quattuor,* meaning "four." How many **quadrants** do you think a coordinate plane has?

Study Guide: Preview

Grade 6 CRCT GPS

M6A2.
Students will consider relationships between varying quantities.

a. Analyze and describe patterns arising from mathematical rules, tables, and graphs.
d. Describe proportional relationships mathematically using $y = kx$, where k is the constant of proportionality.
e. Graph proportional relationship in the form $y = kx$ and describe characteristics of the graphs.
f. In a proportional relationship expressed as $y = kx$, solve for one quantity given values of the other two. Given quantities may be whole numbers, decimals, or fractions. Solve problems using the relationship $y = kx$.
g. Use proportional reasoning ($a/b = c/d$ and $y = kx$) to solve problems.

M6A3.
Students will evaluate algebraic expressions, including those with exponents, and solve simple one-step equations using each of the four basic operations.

M6P1.
Students will solve problems (using appropriate technology).

M6P2.
Students will reason and evaluate mathematical arguments.

M6P4.
Students will make connections among mathematical ideas and to other disciplines.

M6P5.
Students will represent mathematics in multiple ways.

******Georgia Mathematics Performance Standards* **statements are written out completely on pp. GA28–GA35.**

Writing Strategy: Write a Convincing Argument

Being able to write a convincing argument about a math concept proves that you have a solid understanding of the concept.

A good argument should include

- an answer.
- support to prove the statement (including examples if necessary).
- a summary statement.

From Lesson 10-4

6. Critical Thinking If George enlarges a 3 in. × 4 in. photo so that it is 12 in. × 16 in., how will its area change?

Step 1 **Answer statement:**
The area of the new photo will be 16 times as great as that of the original photo.

Step 2 **Support:**
The dimensions of the 3 in. × 4 in. photo are multiplied by 4 to be enlarged to 12 in. × 16 in.

The area of the new photo is 16 times as great as that of the original photo.

area of original = $3 \times 4 = 12$ in^2

area of enlarged = $12 \times 16 = 192$ in^2

area of original: area of enlarged

12:192

1:16

16 in.
4 in.
Original photo
3 in.
12 in.
Enlarged photo

Step 3 **Summary Statement:**
Therefore, to find the area of the enlarged photo, multiply the original area by 4^2, or 16.

Try This

Write a convincing argument to show whether or not a rectangle with whole-number dimensions can have an area of 15 m^2 and a perimeter of 15 m.

Reading and Writing Math

Grade 6 CRCT GPS

Standards	11-1	11-2	11-3	LAB 11-4	11-4	LAB 11-5	11-5	11-6	11-7	LAB 11-8	11-8	11-9	LAB 11-10	11-10	Ext.
M6A2.a												★	★	★	
M6A2.d															★
M6A2.e															★
M6A2.f															★
M6A2.g															★
M6A3					★		★	★	★	★	★	★		★	
M6P1		★						★			★	★			★
M6P2				★		★									★
M6P4			★						★			★	★		
M6P5	★	★	★	★	★	★	★			★	★		★	★	

Reading and Writing Math

Organizer

Objective: Help students apply strategies to understand and retain key concepts.

Online Edition

Resources

Chapter 11 Resource Book
Reading Strategies

Writing Strategy: Write a Convincing Argument

Discuss Students will have practiced persuasive writing in their language arts class. Discuss what a good persuasive paper needs.

In math, convincing arguments need to be supported with facts and examples to convince a reader that the answer or conclusion is correct.

Extend Let students know that they will learn special techniques for making convincing arguments when they study geometry.

Possible Answers to *Try This*

Answer Statement: A rectangle with whole-number dimensions cannot have an area of 15 m^2 and a perimeter of 15 m.

Support: To find the area of a rectangle, I must multiply the width by the length. The whole-number dimensions of the rectangle with an area of 15 m^2 are 1 m × 15 m and 3 m × 5 m. The perimeter of a rectangle is found by adding the lengths and widths of the rectangle. In a rectangle with dimensions of 1 m × 15 m, the perimeter is 32 m.

In a rectangle with dimensions of 3 m × 5 m, the perimeter is 16 m.

Summary Statement: Using whole-number dimensions, a rectangle with an area of 15 m^2 cannot have a perimeter of 15 m.

Understanding Integers

One-Minute Section Planner

Lesson	Materials	MiC and Lab Resources
Lesson 11-1 Integers in Real-World Situations • Identify and graph integers, find opposites, and find the absolute value of an integer. ☐ CRCT ☐ SAT-10 ☐ ITBS ☐ CTBS ☐ NAEP	Two-colored counters (MK)	
Lesson 11-2 Comparing and Ordering Integers • Compare and order integers. ☐ CRCT ☑ SAT-10 ☐ ITBS ☑ CTBS ☑ NAEP	Large sticky notes	***Hands-On Lab Activities*** 11-2
Lesson 11-3 The Coordinate Plane • Locate and graph points on the coordinate plane. ☐ CRCT ☑ SAT-10 ☑ ITBS ☐ CTBS ☑ NAEP	Graph paper, state maps	**MiC: *Figuring All the Angles*** pp. 8–11 ***Technology Lab Activities*** 11-3

MK = *Manipulatives Kit*

Mathematics in Context

The unit ***Figuring All the Angles*** from the *Mathematics in Context* © 2006 series can be used with Section 11A. See Section Planner above for suggestions for integrating *MiC* with *Holt Mathematics*.

Section Overview

Understanding, Comparing, and Ordering Integers — *Lessons 11-1, 11-2*

By including integers, we can solve equations such as $x + 4 = 2$ and evaluate subtraction expressions such as $4 - 9$.

The **integers** are the set of whole numbers and their opposites.

Opposites are the same distance from 0, but on opposite sides of 0. The opposite of 0 is itself, 0.

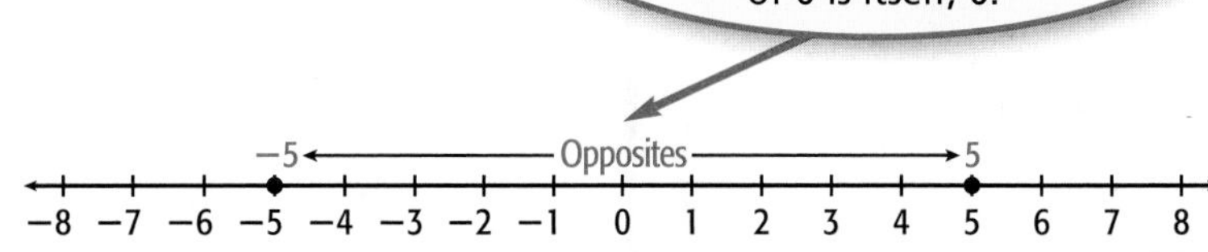

Integers are **ordered from least to greatest** as you move left to right along the number line.

To order the integers −12, 14, −28, 77, 0, 51, and −79 from least to greatest, consider their relative positions on a number line.

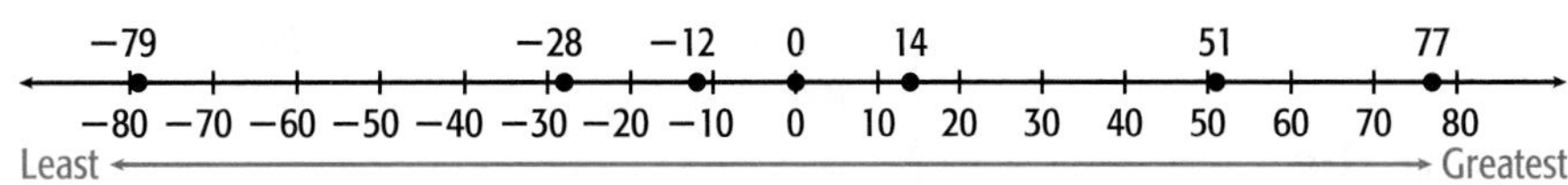

The numbers written from least to greatest are −79, −28, −12, 0, 14, 51, and 77.

Graphing on a Coordinate Plane — *Lesson 11-3*

When a coordinate plane includes integers, the horizontal and vertical axes divide the plane into four quadrants.

Each point on the coordinate plane is identified by an **ordered pair** of numbers: an *x*-coordinate and a *y*-coordinate.

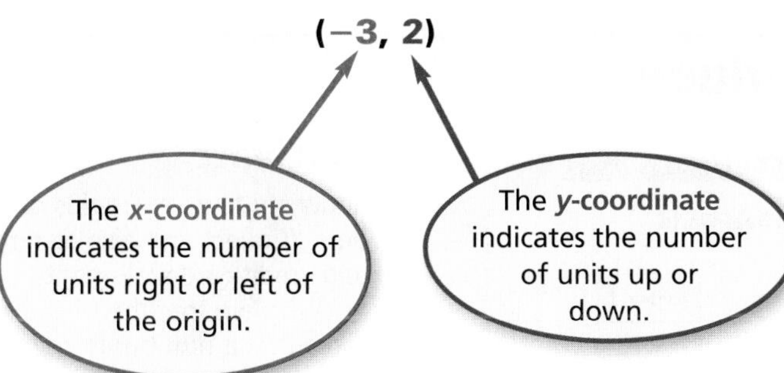

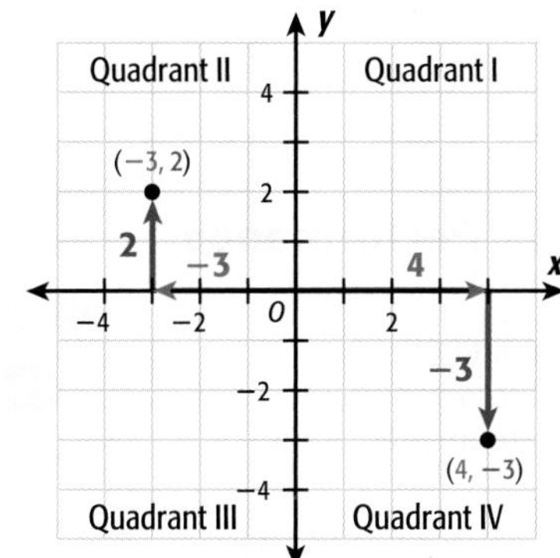

11-1 Organizer

Pacing: Traditional 1 day
Block $\frac{1}{2}$ day

Objective: Students identify and graph integers and find opposites of an integer.

Online Edition
Tutorial Videos

Power Presentations with PowerPoint®

Warm Up

Add or subtract.

1. 16 + 25   41
2. 84 − 12   72
3. Graph the even numbers from 1 to 10 on a number line.

0 1 2 3 4 5 6 7 8 9 10

Problem of the Day

Carlo uses a double-pan balance and three different weights to weigh bird seed. If his weights are 1 lb, 2 lb, and 5 lb, what whole-pound amounts is he able to weigh?
1, 2, 3, 5, 6, 7, and 8 lb

Also available on transparency

Math Fact !

Business people traditionally use black ink to represent profits and red ink to represent losses. That is why you are *in the red* when you are losing money.

Georgia Performance Standards

M6P5.a Create and use representations to organize, record, and communicate mathematical ideas.

M6P5.b Select, apply, and translate among mathematical representations to solve problems.

M6P5.c Use representations to model and interpret physical, social, and mathematical phenomena.

11-1 Integers in Real-World Situations

Learn to identify and graph integers, and find opposites.

Vocabulary
- positive number
- negative number
- opposites
- integer

The highest temperature recorded in the United States is 134°F, in Death Valley, California. The lowest recorded temperature is 80° below 0°F, in Prospect Creek, Alaska.

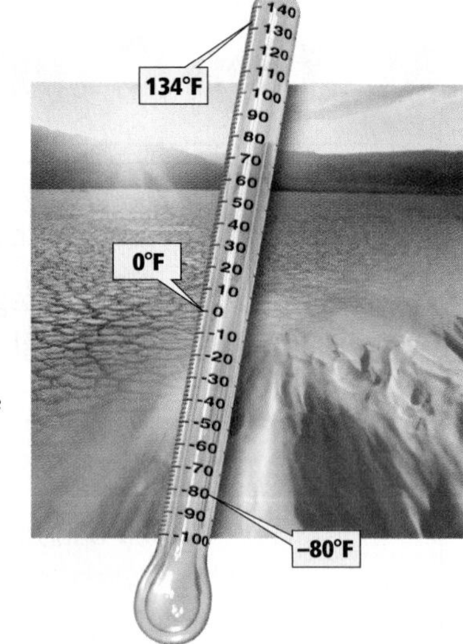

Positive numbers are greater than 0. They may be written with a positive sign (+), but they are usually written without it. So, the highest temperature can be written as +134°F or 134°F.

Negative numbers are less than 0. They are always written with a negative sign (−). So, the lowest temperature is written as −80°F.

EXAMPLE 1 Identifying Positive and Negative Numbers in the Real World

Georgia Performance Standards
M6P5.a Create and use representations to organize, record, and communicate mathematical ideas. Also, M6P5.b, M6P5.c.

Name a positive or negative number to represent each situation.

A **a gain of 20 yards in football**
Positive numbers can represent *gains* or *increases.*
+20

B **spending $75**
Negative numbers can represent *losses* or *decreases.*
−75

C **10 feet below sea level**
Negative numbers can represent values *below* or *less than* a certain value.
−10

You can graph positive and negative numbers on a number line.

Remember!
The set of whole numbers includes zero and the counting numbers. {0, 1, 2, 3, 4, ...}

On a number line, **opposites** are the same distance from 0 but on different sides of 0. Zero is its own opposite.

Integers are the set of all whole numbers and their opposites.

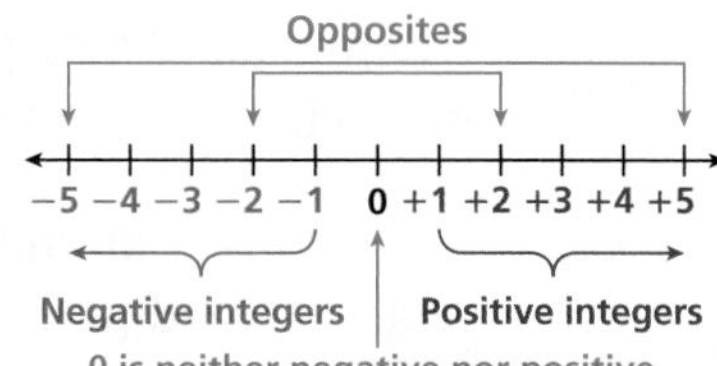

1 Introduce

Alternate Opener

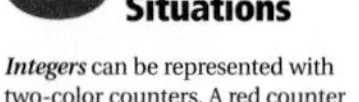

11-1 Integers in Real-World Situations

Integers can be represented with two-color counters. A red counter represents −1, and a yellow counter represents 1. Each red and yellow pair is called a zero pair.

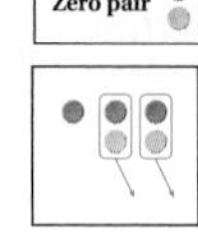

A zero pair has a value of zero. To find the value on an integer mat, remove zero pairs.

The value on this mat is −1.

Find the value on each mat.

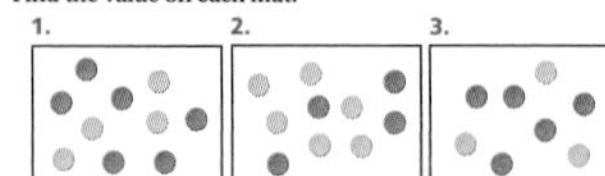

4. Create four different mats that show a value of −1.

Think and Discuss

5. **Discuss** how you can tell whether the value on a mat will be positive or negative.
6. **Describe** the strategies you used to create different mats that show a value of −1.

Motivate

Show students examples of negative numbers. (Collect and display temperatures, bank and credit card statements, stock reports, etc.) Explain that the negative sign (−) indicates that a number is negative, or less than zero. You may want to mention that negative amounts of money often indicate debt, or money owed. (You may use the two-color counters in the Manipulatives Kit.)

Explorations and answers are provided in *Alternate Openers: Explorations Transparencies.*

EXAMPLE 2 Graphing Integers

Graph each integer and its opposite on a number line.

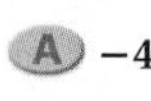 −4

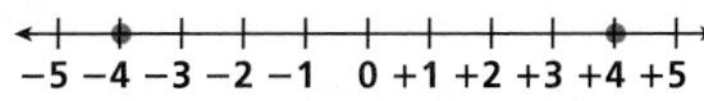

+4 is the same distance from 0 as −4.

 3

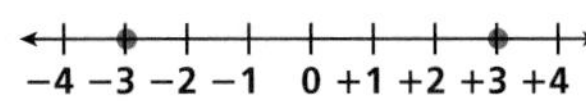

−3 is the same distance from 0 as 3.

 0

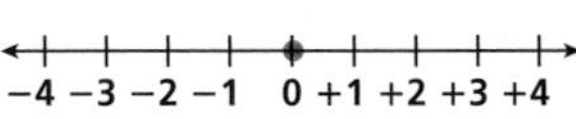

Zero is its own opposite.

EXAMPLE 3 Writing Integer Expressions to Represent Situations

Steffe works on the ground floor of a museum restoring ancient vases. Using the elevator, she goes down 2 floors to get a broken vase, then goes up 6 floors to talk to an ancient civilization expert, and then goes down 3 floors to meet a museum guide. Use integers to model this situation.

You can use a number line to model Steffe's movements on the elevator.

0	*Steffe starts on the ground floor, 0.*
−2	*Steffe goes down two floors.*
+6	*Steffe goes up six floors.*
−3	*Steffe goes back down three floors.*

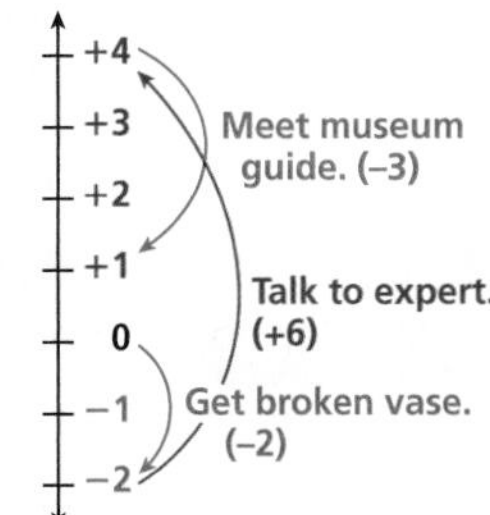

Answers to *Think and Discuss*

1. No; only whole numbers and their opposites are integers.
2. −14; 11
3. The integers could be written in the order Steffe moves to different floors to represent the situation; −2 + 6 − 3

Think and Discuss

GPS M6P2.c, M6P3.b

1. **Tell** whether −3.2 is an integer? Why or why not?
2. **Give** the opposite of 14. What is the opposite of −11?
3. **Explain** how you could use the integers in Example 3 to write an expression to represent the situation. Write the expression.

COMMON ERROR ALERT

Caution students not to think that all opposites are negative. An opposite can be positive or negative.

Power Presentations with PowerPoint®

Additional Examples

Example 1

Name a positive or negative number to represent each situation.

A. a jet climbing to an altitude of 20,000 feet **+20,000**

B. taking $15 out of the bank **−15**

C. 7 degrees below zero **−7**

Example 2

Graph each integer and its opposite on a number line.

A. +2

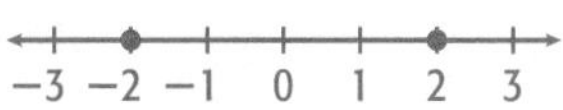

B. −5

C. +1

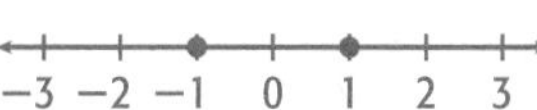

Example 3

Mark enters his office building on the ground floor. Using the elevator, he goes up 6 floors to place a call, then down 4 floors for lunch, and then up 8 floors for a meeting. Write an expression to represent this situation.
+6 − 4 + 8

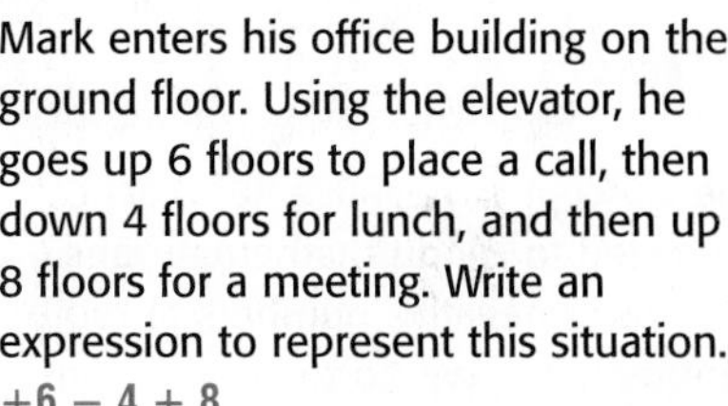

Also available on transparency

2 Teach

Guided Instruction

In this lesson, students learn to identify and graph positive and negative integers and find opposites. First, introduce integer number lines and teach students how to graph positive and negative integers. Then discuss and demonstrate opposites.

Teaching Tip **Reading Math** Explain to students that the number −2 can be read "negative two" or "the opposite of 2," so −(−2) is "the opposite of −2," or 2.

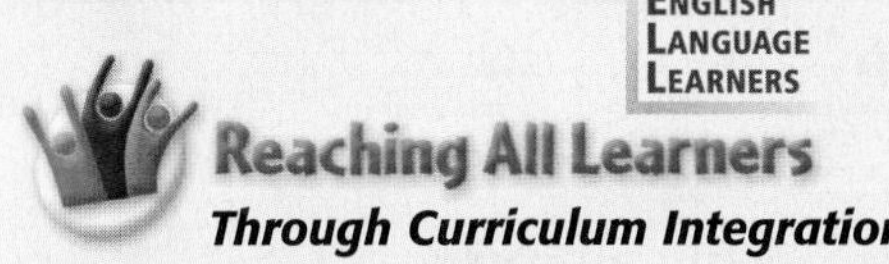

ENGLISH LANGUAGE LEARNERS

Reaching All Learners

Through Curriculum Integration

Language Arts To help students understand the concept of opposite integers, discuss what *opposite* means in contexts other than math. Have students generate a list of opposite terms (e.g., black and white, up and down, tall and short). Then have students name some pairs of opposite integers (e.g., 1 and −1, −13 and 13).

3 Close

ENGLISH LANGUAGE LEARNERS

Summarize

You may wish to have the students state for the class brief definitions of the new vocabulary in the lesson: *positive, negative, opposites,* and *integer*. Discuss how the terms relate to each other.

Possible answers: A positive number is greater than 0. A negative number is less than 0. Opposites are positive and negative numbers that are the same distance from 0 on a number line (except for 0, which is its own opposite). Integers are the set of all whole numbers and their opposites.

11-1 Exercises

Assignment Guide

If you finished Example 1 assign:
Average 1–2, 29, 35, 43–48
Advanced 8–11, 29, 43–48

If you finished Example 2 assign:
Average 1–6, 18–22, 29, 35–36, 43–48
Advanced 8–16, 21–22, 29, 37–38, 43–48

If you finished Example 3 assign:
Average 1–29, 35–48
Advanced 8–48

Homework Quick Check

Quickly check key concepts.
Exercises: 10, 14, 20, 24, 26

Answers

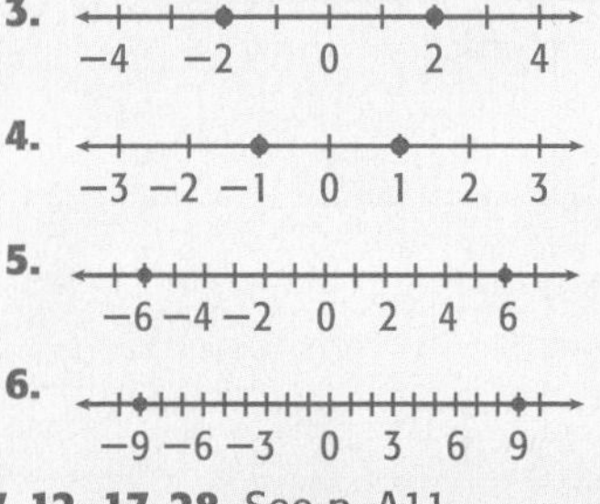

3. number line from −4 to 4 with points at −2 and 2
4. number line from −3 to 3 with points at −1 and 1
5. number line with points at −6 and 6
6. number line with points at −9 and 9

7, 12–17, 28. See p. A11.

Math Background

The concept of negative numbers can be traced to Hindu mathematicians. They used negative numbers to represent debts, as we do today, and formulated rules for the arithmetic of integers. Their ideas were acquired by Arab mathematicians, who passed the ideas on to European scientists over time.

Georgia Performance Standards

M6P3.a Organize and consolidate their mathematical thinking through communication.

M6P4.c Recognize and apply mathematics in contexts outside of mathematics.

M6P5.a Create and use representations to organize, record, and communicate mathematical ideas.

11-1 Exercises

M6P3.a, M6P4.c, M6P5.a

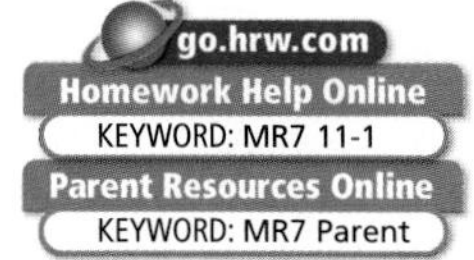

GUIDED PRACTICE

See Example 1 Name a positive or negative number to represent each situation.

1. an increase of 5 points **+5**
2. a loss of 15 yards **−15**

See Example 2 Graph each integer and its opposite on a number line.

3. −2
4. 1
5. −6
6. 9

See Example 3

7. Arnold has $8 in his piggy bank. He takes out $4 to buy a magazine. Later his mother gives him $5, which he puts in his piggy bank. Use integers to model this situation.

INDEPENDENT PRACTICE

See Example 1 Name a positive or negative number to represent each situation.

8. earning $50 **+50**
9. 20° below zero **−20**
10. 7 feet above sea level **+7**
11. a decrease of 39 points **−39**

See Example 2 Graph each integer and its opposite on a number line.

12. −5
13. 6
14. 2
15. −3
16. 9

See Example 3

17. Carla volunteers at the Help for Seniors program. She starts at the volunteers' center on Elm Street and rides her bike to senior citizens' homes. She rides due south 3 blocks to the first senior's home, then she rides 4 blocks due north to the next home, then 2 more blocks due north to the third home, and finally 3 blocks due south back to the center. Use integers to model this situation.

PRACTICE AND PROBLEM SOLVING

CRCT GPS
Extra Practice p. 735

Write a situation that each integer could represent. **Possible answers:**

18. +49 **a gain of 49 yards**
19. −83 **spending $83**
20. −7 **7 degrees below zero**
21. +15 **earning $15**
22. −2 **digging 2 ft below ground**

Write the opposite of each integer.

23. −92 **+92**
24. +75 **−75**
25. −25 **+25**
26. +1,001 **−1,001**
27. 0 **0**

28. **Astronomy** Use the table to graph the average surface temperatures of the given planets on a number line.

Planet	Earth	Mars	Jupiter
Average Surface Temperature (°C)	15	−65	−110

29. A certain stock dropped 3 points in the stock market. Another stock gained 5 points. Write an integer to represent each stock's gain or loss. **−3; +5**

Decimals and fractions can also be positive or negative. Write the opposite of each decimal or fraction.

30. $+\frac{1}{2}$ **$-\frac{1}{2}$**
31. −2.7 **+2.7**
32. $-\frac{3}{8}$ **$+\frac{3}{8}$**
33. +6.2 **−6.2**
34. +0.1 **−0.1**

RETEACH 11-1

LESSON 11-1 **Reteach**
Integers in Real-World Situations

Positive numbers are greater than 0. Use a positive number to represent a gain or increase. Include the positive sign (+).

an increase of 10 points +10
a flower growth of 2 inches +2
a gain of 15 yards in football +15

Negative numbers are less than 0. Use a negative number to represent a loss or decrease. Also use a negative number to represent a value below or less than a certain value. Include the negative sign (−).

a bank withdrawal of $30 −30
a decrease of 9 points −9
2° below zero −2

−5 −4 −3 −2 −1 0 1 2 3 4 5
negative numbers positive numbers

Opposites are the same distance from zero on a number line, but in different directions. −3 and 3 are opposites because each number is 3 units from zero on a number line.

Integers are the set of all whole numbers and their opposites.

Name a positive or negative number to represent each situation.

1. an increase of 3 points **+3**
2. spending $10 **−10**
3. earning $25 **+25**
4. a loss of 5 yards **−5**

Graph each integer and its opposite on a number line.

−10 −9 −8 −7 −6 −5 −4 −3 −2 −1 0 1 2 3 4 5 6 7 8 9 10

5. −1 **−1, 1**
6. 9 **−9, 9**
7. 6 **−6, 6**
8. −5 **−5, 5**

PRACTICE 11-1

LESSON 11-1 **Practice B**
Integers in Real-World Situations

Name a positive or negative number to represent each situation.

1. depositing $85 in a bank account **+85 or 85**
2. riding an elevator down 3 floors **−3**
3. the foundation of a house sinking 5 inches **−5**
4. a temperature of 98° above zero **+98 or 98**

Graph each integer and its opposite on the number line. **Check student's graphs.**

−6 −5 −4 −3 −2 −1 0 1 2 3 4 5 6

5. −2 **−2 and +2**
6. +3 **−3 and +3**
7. −5 **−5 and +5**
8. +1 **−1 and +1**

9. Felix is a superintendent for an apartment building. Using the elevator, he goes from the ground floor down 1 floor to the basement to get his tools, then goes up 5 floors to fix the heater in one of the apartments, and then down 2 floors to fix the stove in another of the apartments. Write an expression to represent this situation. **− 1 + 5 − 2**

10. The highest point in the state of Louisiana is Driskall Mountain. It rises 535 feet above sea level. Write the elevation of Driskall Mountain as an integer. **+535**

11. The lowest point in the state of Louisiana is New Orleans. This city's elevation is 8 feet below sea level. Write the elevation of New Orleans as an integer. **−8**

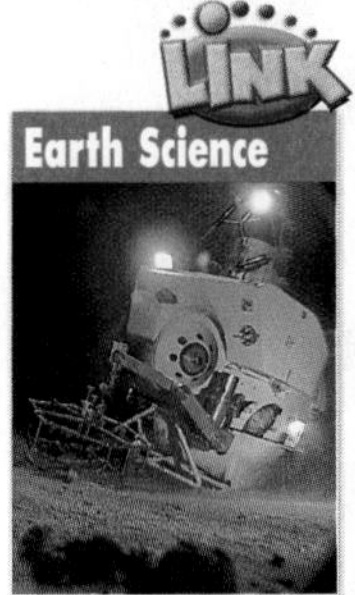

Underwater vehicles called submersibles are used to explore the deepest parts of the ocean. The Alvin, pictured above, was used to photograph and explore the Titanic in 1987.

35. **Sports** When the Mountain Lions football team returned the kickoff, they gained 45 yards. Write an integer to represent this situation. +45

36. **Earth Science** The Mariana Trench is the deepest part of the Pacific Ocean, reaching a depth of 10,924 meters. Write the depth in meters of the Mariana Trench as an integer. −10,924

37. **Earth Science** From June 21 to December 21, most of the United States loses 1 to 2 minutes of daylight each day. But on December 21, most of the country begins to gain 1 to 2 minutes of daylight each day. What integer could you write for a gain of 2 minutes? a loss of 2 minutes? +2; −2

38. Match each temperature with the correct point on the thermometer.

a. −10°F G	b. 5°F C	c. 10°F A
d. −2°F E	e. −9°F F	f. 7°F B

39. Which situation is least likely to be represented by −8?
   - Ⓐ a temperature drop of 8°F
   - Ⓑ a depth of 8 meters
   - Ⓒ a growth of 8 centimeters (circled)
   - Ⓓ a time 8 years ago

40. **Write A Problem** Write a problem about the temperature rising and dropping. Start with the temperature labeled G on the thermometer. Then write an expression to represent the situation.

41. **Write About It** Is −0.5 an integer? Explain.

42. **Challenge** What is the opposite of the integer 3 units away from −8? Explain. 5 and 11

CRCT Prep • GPS Support • Spiral Review

43. **Multiple Choice** Which situation could the integer −50 represent?
   - Ⓐ An increase of $50 in a bank account
   - Ⓑ The temperature on a warm spring day
   - Ⓒ The distance driven on the way to the beach
   - Ⓓ A decrease of 50 employees (circled)

44. **Multiple Choice** Which integer can represent *200 years ago*?

Ⓕ −200 (circled) Ⓖ 200*x* Ⓗ 200 Ⓙ *x* − 200

Estimate by rounding to the indicated place value. (Lesson 3-2)

45. 1.892 − 0.243; tenths 1.7
46. 13.4132 + 0.513; tenths 13.9
47. 11.4307 − 5.2164; thousandths 6.214

48. Hugo is filling a tub with water. The height of the water is increasing $\frac{1}{5}$ foot each minute. Use pictures to model how much the height of the water will change in 4 minutes, and then write your answer in simplest form. (Lesson 4-8) $\frac{4}{5}$ ft

Ongoing Assessment and Intervention

Diagnose ***Before*** **the Lesson**
11-1 Warm Up, TE p. 602

Monitor ***During*** **the Lesson**
11-1 Know-It Notebook
11-1 Questioning Strategies

Assess ***After*** **the Lesson**
11-1 Lesson Quiz, TE p. 605

Answers

40. Possible answer: The temperature was −10 degrees at 8:00 A.M. It rose 20 degrees during the day but dropped 35 degrees by midnight. −10 + 20 − 35

41. No; −0.5 is not a whole number.

42. 5 and 11; possible answer: there are two integers 3 units away from −8, −5 and −11. Their opposites are 5 and 11.

48. See p. A11.

Common Error Alert

Listen for students using the term *plus* when they mean "positive" and *minus* when they mean "negative." Have the class use the terms *positive* and *negative* correctly.

For Exercise 43, students who remember that increases and distances are represented by positive numbers can eliminate choices **A** and **C.** Choice **B** can be eliminated because a warm spring day's temperature will not be negative.

Journal

Have students write about a situation in which they might use negative numbers.

11-1 Lesson Quiz

Name a positive or negative number to represent each situation.

1. saving $15 +15
2. 12 feet below sea level −12
3. What is the opposite of −6? 6
4. When the Swanton Bulldogs football team passed the football, they gained 25 yards. Write an integer to represent this situation. +25

Also available on transparency

CHALLENGE 11-1

LESSON 11-1 **Challenge**
Boiling Up and Freezing Down

Draw a line on the thermometer to show each given temperature record. Then label each state's name at its correct line on the thermometer.

1. The lowest temperature in California was recorded on January 20, 1937. It was −45°F.
2. The highest temperature in North Carolina was recorded on August 21, 1983. It was 110°F.
3. The lowest temperature in Georgia was recorded on January 27, 1940. It was −17°F.
4. The highest temperature in Maine was recorded on July 10, 1911. It was 105°F.
5. The lowest temperature in Missouri was recorded on February 13, 1905. It was −40°F.
6. The lowest temperature in Texas was recorded on February 8, 1933. It was −23°F.
7. The highest temperature in Maryland was recorded on July 10, 1936. It was 109°F.
8. The lowest temperature in Massachusetts was recorded on January 12, 1981. It was −35°F.
9. The highest temperature in Oklahoma was recorded on June 27, 1994. It was 120°F.
10. The highest temperature in Mississippi was recorded on July 29, 1930. It was 115°F.

Thermometer (F): 220, 210 Water boils, 200, 190, 180, 170, 160, 150, 140, 130, 120, 110, 100, 90, 80, 70, 60, 50, 40, 30 Water freezes, 20, 10, 0, −10, −20, −30, −40, −50

Oklahoma, Mississippi, North Carolina, Maryland, Maine
Georgia, Texas
Massachusetts, Missouri, California

PROBLEM SOLVING 11-1

LESSON 11-1 **Problem Solving**
Integers in Real-World Situations

Write the correct answer.

1. The element mercury is used in thermometers because it expands as it is heated. Mercury melts at 38°F below zero. Write this temperature as an integer.
   −38°F
2. Denver, Colorado, earned the nickname "Mile High City" because of its elevation of 5,280 feet above sea level. Write Denver's elevation as an integer in feet and miles.
   +5,280 feet or +1 mile
3. The lowest temperature recorded in San Francisco was 20°F. Buffalo's lowest recorded temperature was the opposite of San Francisco's. What was Buffalo's record temperature?
   −20°F
4. Greenland holds the record for the lowest temperature recorded on Earth. That temperature in degrees Fahrenheit is 65 degrees below zero. What is Earth's lowest recorded temperature written as an integer?
   −65°F
5. In 1960, explorers on the submarine *Trieste 2* set the world record for the deepest dive. The ship reached 35,814 feet below sea level. Write this depth as an integer.
   −35,814 feet
6. In 1960, Joseph W. Kittinger, Jr., set the record for the highest parachute jump. He jumped from an air balloon at 102,800 feet above sea level. Write this altitude as an integer.
   +102,800 feet

Circle the letter of the correct answer.

7. Which situation cannot be represented by the integer −10?
   - A an elevation of 10 feet below sea level
   - Ⓑ a temperature increase of 10°F
   - C a golf score of 10 under par
   - D a bank withdrawal of $10
8. Paper was invented in China one thousand, nine hundred years ago. Which integer represents this date?
   - F 1,900
   - G 900
   - Ⓗ −1,900
   - J −1,000
9. The elevation of the Dead Sea is about 1,310 feet below sea level. Which integer represents this elevation?
   - Ⓐ −1,310
   - B −131
   - C 131
   - D 1,310
10. The quarterback had a 10-yard loss and then a 25-yard gain. Which integer represents a 25-yard gain?
   - F −25
   - G −10
   - Ⓗ 25
   - J 10

11-2 Organizer

Pacing: Traditional 1 day
Block $\frac{1}{2}$ day

Objective: Students compare and order integers.

GPS M6P1.c., M6P1.d.
Hands-On Lab
In *Hands-On Lab Activities*

Online Edition
Tutorial Videos

Power Presentations with PowerPoint®

Warm Up

Compare. Write <, >, or =.

1. 8,426 ■ 8,246 >
2. 9,625 ■ 6,852 >
3. 2,071 ■ 2,171 <
4. 2,250 ■ 2,250 =

Problem of the Day

Four friends are waiting in line at the amusement park. Jenna is in front of Kyle. Kyle is behind Gary and in front of Maggie. Gary is first. In what order are they waiting?
Gary, Jenna, Kyle, Maggie

Also available on transparency

Math Humor

Why was 6 afraid of 7?
Because seven eight nine!

11-2 Comparing and Ordering Integers

Learn to compare and order integers.

Georgia Performance Standards

M6P1.c Apply and adapt a variety of appropriate strategies to solve problems. Also, M6P1.d, M6P5.a, M6P5.b.

The table shows three golfers' scores from a golf tournament.

Player	Score
David Berganio	+6
Sergio Garcia	−16
Tiger Woods	−4

In golf, the player with the lowest score wins the game. You can compare integers to find the winner of the tournament.

Sergio Garcia

EXAMPLE 1 Comparing Integers

Use the number line to compare each pair of integers. Write < or >.

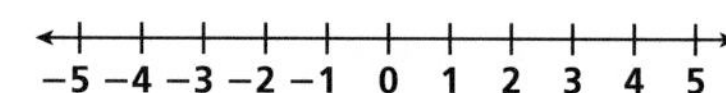

Remember!
Numbers on a number line increase in value as you move from left to right.

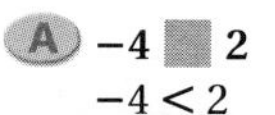

A) −4 ■ 2
−4 < 2 — *−4 is to the left of 2 on the number line.*

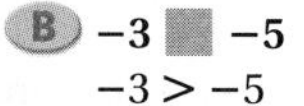

B) −3 ■ −5
−3 > −5 — *−3 is to the right of −5 on the number line.*

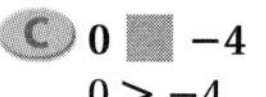

C) 0 ■ −4
0 > −4 — *0 is to the right of −4 on the number line.*

EXAMPLE 2 Ordering Integers

Order the integers in each set from least to greatest.

A) 4, −2, 1

Graph the integers on the same number line.

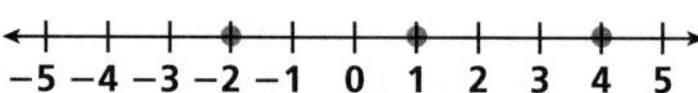

Then read the numbers from left to right: −2, 1, 4.

Georgia Performance Standards

M6P1.c Apply and adapt a variety of approprriate strategies to solve problems.

M6P1.d Monitor and reflect on the process of mathematical problem solving.

M6P5.a Create and use representations to organize, record, and communicate mathematical ideas.

M6P5.b Select, apply, and translate among mathematical representations to solve problems.

1 Introduce

Alternate Opener

EXPLORATION

11-2 Comparing and Ordering Integers

1. The completed table shows the average January temperatures in degrees Fahrenheit and degrees Celsius for some U.S. cities. Complete the other table by ordering the cities from warmest to coolest.

	°F	°C
Juneau, AK	24	−4
Phoenix, AZ	54	12
Atlanta, GA	41	5
Des Moines, IA	19	−7
Bismarck, ND	9	−13
Houston, TX	50	10
Boston, MA	29	−2
Kansas City, MO	26	−3

Source: Statistical Abstract of the United States

Warmest

	°F	°C

Coolest

Boston is colder than Houston because 29 < 50 in degrees Fahrenheit and −2 < 10 in degrees Celsius.

Houston is warmer than Boston because 50 > 29 in degrees Fahrenheit and 10 > −2 in degrees Celsius.

2. Use inequality symbols to compare the Kansas City temperature in degrees Celsius with each of the other temperatures in degrees Celsius.

Think and Discuss

3. **Describe** your method for ordering the cities from warmest to coolest.

Motivate

Draw and label a number line from 10 to 50, with intervals of 5. Have students graph 20, 25, 45, 35, 30, 10, and 40 on the number line. Teach students to compare pairs of numbers using the terms *greater than* and *less than* and their symbols (e.g., 10 is less than 40; 25 > 20). Discuss how a number line helps to identify which number is greater.

Explorations and answers are provided in *Alternate Openers: Explorations Transparencies.*

Order the integers in each set from least to greatest.

B −2, 0, 2, −5

Graph the integers on the same number line.

Then read the numbers from left to right: −5, −2, 0, 2.

EXAMPLE 3 *Problem Solving Application*

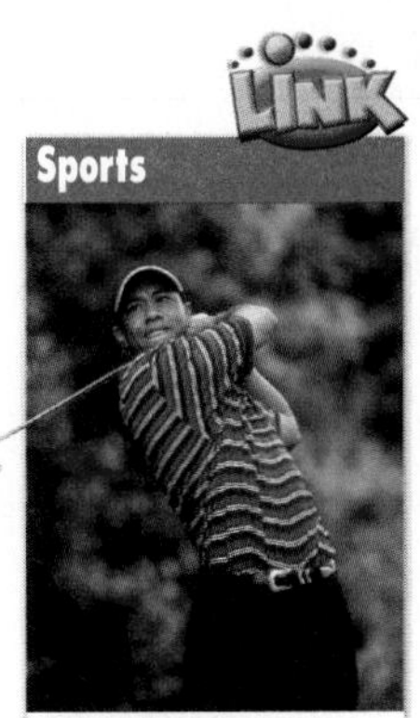

At a golf tournament, David Berganio scored +6, Sergio Garcia scored −16, and Tiger Woods scored −4. One of these three players was the winner of the tournament. Who won the tournament?

1 Understand the Problem

The **answer** will be the player with the *lowest* score.
List the **important information:**

- David Berganio scored +6.
- Sergio Garcia scored −16.
- Tiger Woods scored −4.

2 Make a Plan

You can draw a diagram to order the scores from least to greatest.

3 Solve

Draw a number line and graph each player's score on it.

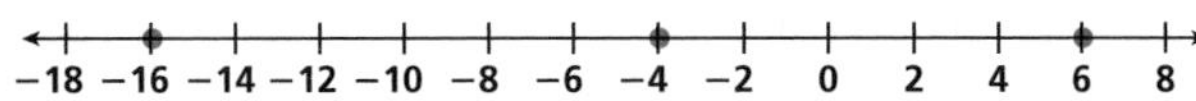

Sergio Garcia's score, –16, is farthest to the left, so it is the lowest score. Sergio Garcia won this tournament.

4 Look Back

Negative integers are always less than positive integers, so David Berganio cannot be the winner. Since Sergio Garcia's score of −16 is less than Tiger Woods's score of −4, Sergio Garcia won.

Sports LINK

In golf, *par* is the standard number of strokes needed to hit the ball into the hole. A score of −12 means "12 strokes under par." A score of +2 means "2 strokes over par."

go.hrw.com
Web Extra!
KEYWORD: MR7 Golf

Think and Discuss

GPS M6P2.c, M6P3.b

1. **Tell** which is greater, a negative or a positive integer. Explain.
2. **Tell** which is greater, 0 or a negative integer. Explain.
3. **Explain** how to tell which of two negative integers is greater.

Power Presentations with PowerPoint®

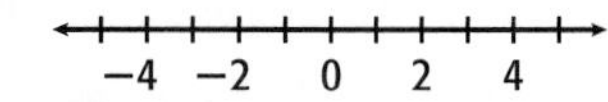

Additional Examples

Example 1

Use the number line to compare each pair of integers. Write < or >.

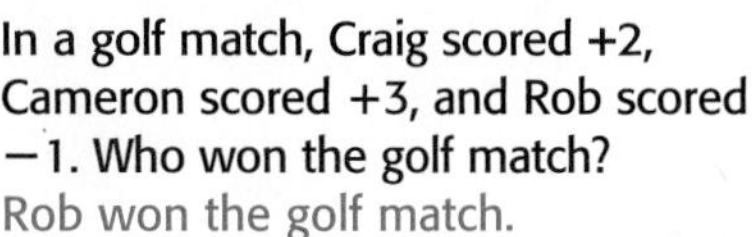

A. −2 ▢ 2 <
B. 3 ▢ −5 >
C. −1 ▢ −4 >

Example 2

Order the integers in each set from least to greatest.

A. −2, 3, −1 −2, −1, 3
B. 4, −3, −5, 2 −5, −3, 2, 4

Example 3

In a golf match, Craig scored +2, Cameron scored +3, and Rob scored −1. Who won the golf match?
Rob won the golf match.

Also available on transparency

Answers to *Think and Discuss*

1. Possible answer: a positive integer; positive integers are located to the right of negative integers on a number line.
2. 0; it is to the right of all negative integers on a number line.
3. Possible answer: The integer that is farther to the right on a number line is the greater of two integers.

2 Teach

Guided Instruction

In this lesson, students learn to compare and order integers. First, teach students to compare integers by graphing the integers on a number line. Then teach how sets of 3, 4, or more integers can be ordered by graphing the set on a number line. Emphasize that the greater integer is always to the right of the lesser integer.

Teaching Tip

Visual Remind students that in a comparison the inequality sign always "points to" the lesser of two numbers.

Reaching All Learners

Through Kinesthetic Experience

For a kinesthetic approach, have students write the integers being compared on sticky notes and arrange them on a large number line on the board. Have them explain why they placed the numbers in the position they did, and encourage them to rearrange the notes if placed incorrectly. Chips may also be used.

3 Close

Summarize

Have students list two integers that are greater than −10 and two integers that are less than −10. Then have students list the integers, including −10, in order from least to greatest, and discuss how a number line shows the integers' relationships to −10.

Possible answers: Greater than −10: −5, 2; less than −10: −11, −20; least to greatest: −20, −11, −10, −5, 2; A number line shows that −20 and −11 are less than −10 because they are to the left of −10 on the number line and that −5 and 2 are greater than −10 because they are to the right of −10 on the number line.

11-2 Exercises

Assignment Guide

If you finished Example 1 assign:
Average 1–3, 19–26, 34, 39–49
Advanced 8–11, 19–26, 36, 39–49

If you finished Example 2 assign:
Average 1–6, 19–35, 39–49
Advanced 8–17, 19–33, 39–49

If you finished Example 3 assign:
Average 1–22, 29–49
Advanced 8–49

Homework Quick Check

Quickly check key concepts.
Exercises: 14, 18, 22, 32, 34

11-2 Exercises

Georgia Performance Standards
M6P1.b, M6P3.a, M6P3.c, M6P5.b

Homework Help Online
KEYWORD: MR7 11-2
Parent Resources Online
KEYWORD: MR7 Parent

GUIDED PRACTICE

See Example 1 Use the number line to compare each pair of integers. Write $<$ or $>$.

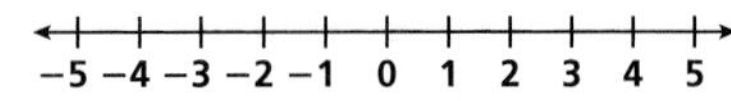

1. -4 ▒ -5 $>$ **2.** -2 ▒ 0 $<$ **3.** -1 ▒ 3 $<$

See Example 2 Order the integers in each set from least to greatest.

4. 9, 0, –2 **–2, 0, 9** **5.** 7, –4, 3, –5 **–5, –4, 3, 7** **6.** 8, –6, –1, 10 **–6, –1, 8, 10**

See Example 3 **7.** Use the table.

a. At what time was the temperature the lowest? **3:30 A.M.**

b. What was the highest temperature? **1°F**

Time	Temperature (°F)
10:00 P.M.	1
Midnight	–4
3:30 A.M.	–6
6:00 A.M.	1

INDEPENDENT PRACTICE

See Example 1 Use the number line to compare each pair of integers. Write $<$ or $>$.

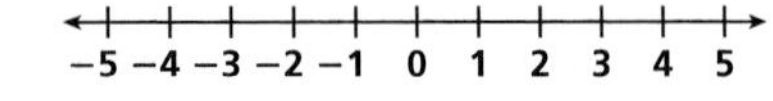

8. 0 ▒ 2 $<$ **9.** 4 ▒ -4 $>$ **10.** -3 ▒ -1 $<$ **11.** -5 ▒ 2 $<$

See Example 2 Order the integers in each set from least to greatest.

12. 11, –6, –3 **–6, –3, 11** **13.** 15, –8, 7 **–8, 7, 15** **14.** 5, –12, 0, 1 **–12, 0, 1, 5**

15. –9, 13, –1, –16 **–16, –9, –1, 13** **16.** 24, –6, 7, –10, 4 **–10, –6, 4, 7, 24** **17.** 22, 0, –19, 8, –3 **–19, –3, 0, 8, 22**

See Example 3 **18. Earth Science** Use the table, which shows the depths of the world's three largest oceans.

a. Which ocean is the deepest? **Pacific**

b. Which oceans are less than 35,000 feet deep? **Atlantic and Indian**

Ocean	Depth (ft)
Pacific	–36,200
Atlantic	–30,246
Indian	–24,442

PRACTICE AND PROBLEM SOLVING

Extra Practice p. 735

Compare. Write $<$ or $>$.

19. -30 ▒ 25 $<$ **20.** 0 ▒ -49 $>$ **21.** -16 ▒ -51 $>$ **22.** -17 ▒ 17 $<$

23. -64 ▒ -15 $<$ **24.** 77 ▒ 300 $<$ **25.** -28 ▒ 1 $<$ **26.** 25 ▒ -30 $>$

Order the integers in each set from least to greatest.

27. –39, 14, 21 **–39, 14, 21** **28.** –18, –9, –31 **–31, –18, –9** **29.** 0, –26, 43, –12 **–26, –12, 0, 43**

30. 15, –25, –4, 31 **–25, –4, 15, 31** **31.** –67, 82, –73, –10, 20 **–73, –67, –10, 20, 82** **32.** 42, –27, 69, –50, 38 **–50, –27, 38, 42, 69**

Georgia Performance Standards

M6P1.b Solve problems that arise in mathematics and in other contexts.

M6P3.a Organize and consolidate their mathematical thinking through communication.

M6P3.c Analyze and evaluate the mathematical thinking and strategies of others.

M6P5.b Select, apply, and translate among mathematical representations to solve problems.

RETEACH 11-2

Reteach
LESSON 11-2 *Comparing and Ordering Integers*

You can use a number line to compare and order integers.

As you move right on a number line, the values of the integers increase. As you move left on a number line, the values of the integers decrease.

Compare –4 and 2.

–5 –4 –3 –2 –1 0 1 2 3 4 5

–4 is to the left of 2, so $-4 < 2$.

Compare the integers. Write $<$ or $>$.

1. –5 –4 –3 –2 –1 0 1 2 3 4 5
1 [>] –4

2. –5 –4 –3 –2 –1 0 1 2 3 4 5
–5 [<] –2

3. –3 [<] 2 4. –1 [>] –4 5. 5 [>] 0 6. –2 [<] 3

Order –3, 4 and –1 from least to greatest.

–5 –4 –3 –2 –1 0 1 2 3 4 5

List the numbers as they appear from left to right.

The integers in order from least to greatest are –3, –1, 4.

Order the integers from least to greatest.

7. –2, –5, –1 8. 0, –5, 5 9. –4, 2, –3 10. 3, –1, –4

–5, –2, –1 –5, 0, 5 –4, –3, 2 –4, –1, 3

PRACTICE 11-2

Practice B
LESSON 11-2 *Comparing and Ordering Integers*

Use the number line to compare each pair of integers. Write $<$ or $>$.

–10 –9 –8 –7 –6 –5 –4 –3 –2 –1 0 1 2 3 4 5 6 7 8 9 10

1. 10 [>] –2 2. 0 [<] 3 3. –5 [<] 0

4. –7 [<] 6 5. –6 [>] –9 6. –8 [>] –10

Order the integers in each set from least to greatest.

7. 5, –2, 6 8. 0, 9, –3 9. –1, 6, 1

–2, 5, 6 –3, 0, 9 –1, 1, 6

10. –8, –9, 9 11. 15, 1, –5 12. –4, –7, –2

–9, –8, 9 –5, 1, 15 –7, –4, –2

Order the integers in each set from greatest to least.

13. 8, –6, 4 14. –2, 1, 2 15. 0, 7, –8

8, 4, –6 2, 1, –2 7, 0, –8

16. –1, 1, 0 17. –12, 2, 1 18. –10, –12, –11

1, 0, –1 2, 1, –12 –10, –11, –12

19. The lowest point in the Potomac River is 1 foot above sea level. The lowest point in the Colorado River is 70 feet above sea level. The lowest point in the Delaware River is sea level. Write the names of these three rivers in order from the lowest to the highest elevation.

Delaware River, Potomac River, Colorado River

20. The lowest recorded temperature in Alabama was 27°F below zero. In Florida, the lowest recorded temperature was 2°F below zero. The lowest temperature ever recorded in Hawaii was 12°F above zero. Write the names of these three states in order from the highest to the lowest recorded temperatures.

Hawaii, Florida, Alabama

33. Which set of integers is written in order from greatest to least?

Ⓐ 0, −4, −3, −1 Ⓒ 9, −9, −10, −15

Ⓑ 2, −4, 8, −16 Ⓓ −8, −7, −6, −5

34. Earth Science The normal high temperature in January for Barrow, Alaska, is −7°F. The normal high temperature in January for Los Angeles is 68°F. Compare the two temperatures using < or >. 68 > −7 or −7 < 68

35. Geography The table shows elevations for several natural features. Write the features in order from the least elevation to the greatest elevation.

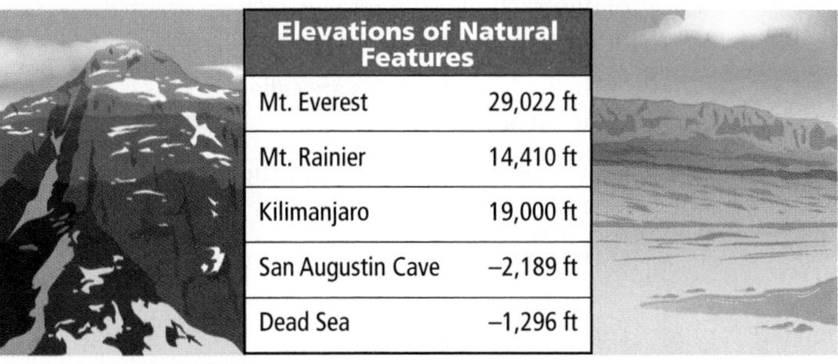

Elevations of Natural Features	
Mt. Everest	29,022 ft
Mt. Rainier	14,410 ft
Kilimanjaro	19,000 ft
San Augustin Cave	−2,189 ft
Dead Sea	−1,296 ft

35. San Augustin Cave, Dead Sea, Mt. Rainier, Kilimanjaro, Mt. Everest

36. What's the Error? Your classmate says that 0 < −91. Explain why this is incorrect. all negative numbers are less than 0

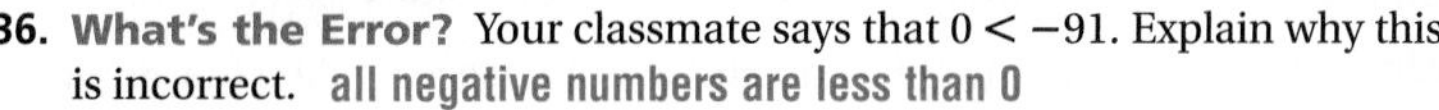

37. Write About It Explain how you would order from least to greatest three numbers that include a positive number, a negative number, and zero.

38. Challenge There is a missing integer from the list below. The missing integer is both the median and the mode. What is the integer? (*Hint:* There could be more than one correct answer.) 2, −10, 7, −7, 5, −5 −5 or 2

CRCT Prep • GPS Support • Spiral Review

39. Multiple Choice Which set of integers is written in order from greatest to least?

Ⓐ −3, −9, −6 Ⓑ −3, 2, 5 Ⓒ 2, −1, −3 Ⓓ 4, 10, 12

40. Short Response The table shows the elevations relative to sea level of several cities. Order the cities from the least elevation to the greatest elevation.
Death Valley, Boston, Cincinnati, San Antonio, Salt Lake City

City	Boston	Cincinnati	Death Valley	Salt Lake City	San Antonio
Elevation (ft)	16	483	−282	4,226	807

If the angles can form a triangle, classify it as acute, obtuse, or right. (Lesson 8-5)

41. 45°, 76°, 59° acute **42.** 12°, 90°, 78° right **43.** 88°, 22°, 90° cannot form a triangle **44.** 10°, 5°, 165° obtuse

Graph each integer and its opposite on a number line. (Lesson 11-1)

45. −9 **46.** 7 **47.** −2 **48.** 8 **49.** −5

Ongoing Assessment and Intervention

***Diagnose Before* the Lesson**
11-2 Warm Up, TE p. 606

***Monitor During* the Lesson**
11-2 Know-It Notebook
11-2 Questioning Strategies

***Assess After* the Lesson**
11-2 Lesson Quiz, TE p. 609

Common Error Alert

Point out to students that in Exercise 33 they are asked to find the set of integers ordered from greatest to least.

Answers

37. See p. A11.

45. [number line from −10 to 10 with points at −9 and 9]

46. [number line from −10 to 10 with points at −7 and 7]

47. [number line from −10 to 10 with points at −2 and 2]

48–49. See p. A11.

Test Prep Doctor For Exercise 39, students choosing **B** or **D** may have misread the directions. Students choosing **A** might benefit from graphing the integers on a number line.

Journal

Have students think of and write about real-world situations in which sets of positive and negative integers are used.

Challenge 11-2

Lesson 11-2 Challenge
Integer Maze

During winter, bears and many other animals hibernate, or go into a sleeplike state. When they do so, their body temperatures greatly decrease. How much can their temperatures change during hibernation?

Write the following integers along the maze so they are increasing from start to finish. The shaded box in the maze will have the answer to the question.

5, −14, −39, −3, 61, −60, −23, −72, −48, −11, 100, −45, 10, −57, −1, −29, −64, −37, 0, −65, 74, 98, −28, −7, −63, −49, −21, −54, 27, 53, −9, −32, −16, 35, −30, −18, −52, 86, −46, 42, −56, −41, −22, −43, 19

Problem Solving 11-2

Lesson 11-2 Problem Solving
Comparing and Ordering Integers

Use the table below to answer each question.

Continental Elevation Facts

Continent	Highest Point	Elevation (ft) above sea level	Lowest Point	Elevation (ft) below sea level
Africa	Mount Kilimanjaro	19,340	Lake Assal	−512
Antarctica	Vinson Massif	16,066	Bentley Subglacial Trench	−8,327
Asia	Mount Everest	29,035	Dead Sea	−1,349
Australia	Mount Kosciusko	7,310	Lake Eyre	−52
Europe	Mount Elbrus	18,510	Caspian Sea	−92
North America	Mount McKinley	20,320	Death Valley	−282
South America	Mount Aconcagua	22,834	Valdes Peninsula	−131

1. What is the highest point on Earth? What is its elevation?
Mount Everest; 29,035 feet above sea level

2. What is the lowest point on Earth? What is its elevation?
Bentley Subglacial Trench; 8,327 feet below sea level

3. Which point on Earth is higher, Mount Elbrus or Mount Kilimanjaro?
Mount Kilimanjaro

4. Which point on Earth is lower, the Caspian Sea or Lake Eyre?
Caspian Sea

Circle the letter of the correct answer.

5. Which continent has a higher elevation than North America?
A Antarctica
Ⓑ South America
C Europe
D Australia

6. Which continent has a lower elevation than Africa?
F Australia
G Europe
Ⓗ Asia
J South America

7. Write the continents in order by their highest points, from highest elevation to lowest elevation.
Asia, South America, North America, Africa, Europe, Antarctica, Australia

Power Presentations with PowerPoint®

11-2 Lesson Quiz

Order the integers in each set from least to greatest.

1. −3, 7, 4 −3, 4, 7

2. −11, 2, 5, −15 −15, −11, 2, 5

Compare. Write <, >, or =.

3. −3 ■ −4 >

4. −12 ■ −10 <

5. A location in Carlsbad Caverns is 752 ft below sea level, and another location is 910 ft below sea level. Which location is closer to sea level? the location at −752 feet

Also available on transparency

11-3 Organizer

Pacing: Traditional 1 day
Block $\frac{1}{2}$ day

Objective: Students locate and graph points on a coordinate plane.

Technology Lab
In *Technology Lab Activities*

Online Edition
Tutorial Videos

Power Presentations with PowerPoint®

Warm Up

Use the number line to compare each pair of integers. Write < or >.

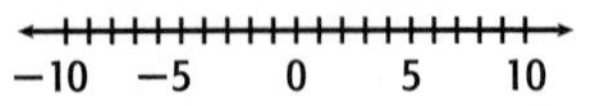

1. 7 ▇ −7 > **2.** −8 ▇ −3 <

3. 0 ▇ −4 > **4.** −2 ▇ −5 >

Problem of the Day

While delivering pizza, Christian drove 4 miles south, 6 miles west, 2 miles north, 8 miles east, and then 2 miles north. How far is Christian from where he started? 2 miles

Also available on transparency

Math Fact

The numbers assigned to each point on a coordinate plane are called *Cartesian coordinates*. This name is in honor of French mathematician René Descartes.

11-3 The Coordinate Plane

Learn to locate and graph points on the coordinate plane.

Vocabulary
coordinate plane
axes
x-axis
y-axis
quadrants
origin
coordinates
x-coordinate
y-coordinate

A **coordinate plane** is formed by two number lines in a plane that intersect at right angles. The point of intersection is the zero on each number line.

- The two number lines are called the **axes**.
- The horizontal axis is called the ***x*-axis**.
- The vertical axis is called the ***y*-axis**.
- The two axes divide the coordinate plane into four **quadrants**.
- The point where the axes intersect is called the **origin**.

Quadrant II
Quadrant I
y-axis
x-axis
Origin
Quadrant III
Quadrant IV

EXAMPLE 1 Identifying Quadrants

Georgia Performance Standards

M6P5.a Create and use representations to organize, record, and communicate mathematical ideas. Also, M6P4.a, M6P4.b.

Helpful Hint
Points on the axes are not in any quadrant.

Name the quadrant where each point is located.

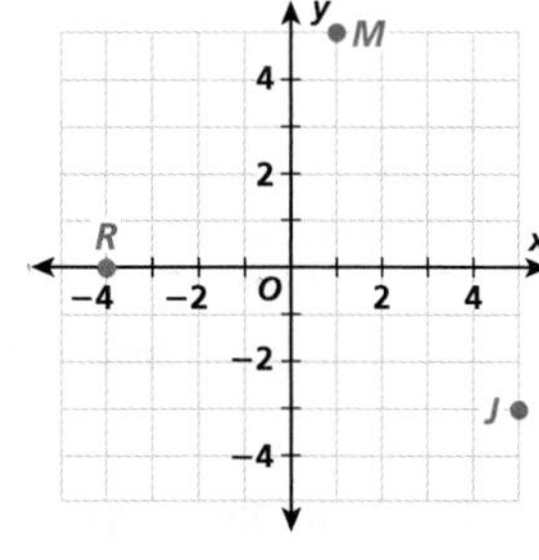

A *M*
Quadrant I

B *J*
Quadrant IV

C *R*
x-axis
no quadrant

An ordered pair gives the location of a point on a coordinate plane. The first number tells how far to move right (positive) or left (negative) from the origin. The second number tells how far to move up (positive) or down (negative).

The numbers in an ordered pair are called **coordinates**. The first number is called the ***x*-coordinate**. The second number is called the ***y*-coordinate**.

The ordered pair for the origin is (0, 0).

Georgia Performance Standards

M6P4.a Recognize and use connections among mathematical ideas.

M6P4.b Understand how mathematical ideas interconnect and build on one another to produce a coherent whole.

M6P5.a Create and use representations to organize, record, and communicate mathematical ideas.

1 Introduce

Alternate Opener

EXPLORATION

11-3 The Coordinate Plane

On the *coordinate plane* below, the color of the first number in each ordered pair matches the color of the *x-axis*, and the color of the second number in each ordered pair matches the color of the *y-axis*.

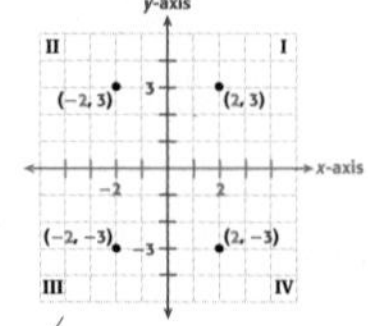

1. The four points graphed are labeled with their ordered pairs. How are these four ordered pairs alike? How are they different?
2. Plot the points (3, 4), (−3, 4), (−3, −4), and (3, −4) on the same coordinate plane.

Think and Discuss

3. **Describe** what each number in an ordered pair tells you.

Motivate

To introduce students to the four-quadrant coordinate plane, give the following two examples: (1) In order to reach a second-floor window, you move the ladder directly below the window and then climb up. (2) To dig for treasure, you walk to the spot and then dig down to the treasure. Both examples involve a horizontal move followed by a vertical move.

Explorations and answers are provided in *Alternate Openers: Explorations Transparencies.*

EXAMPLE 2 Locating Points on a Coordinate Plane

Give the coordinates of each point.

A K

From the origin, K is 1 unit right and 4 units up.

(1, 4)

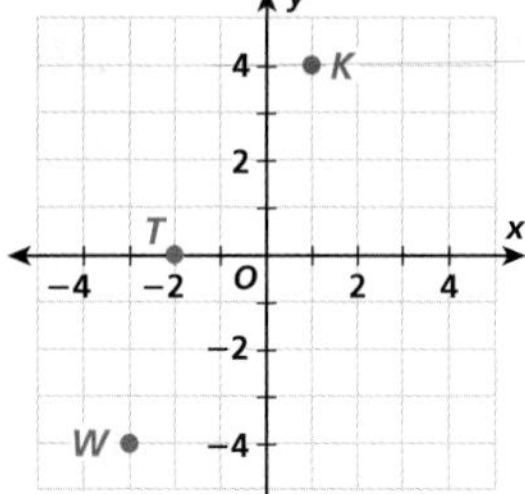

B T

From the origin, T is 2 units left on the x-axis.

(−2, 0)

C W

From the origin, W is 3 units left and 4 units down.

(−3, −4)

EXAMPLE 3 Graphing Points on a Coordinate Plane

Graph each point on a coordinate plane.

A $P(-3, -2)$

From the origin, move 3 units left and 2 units down.

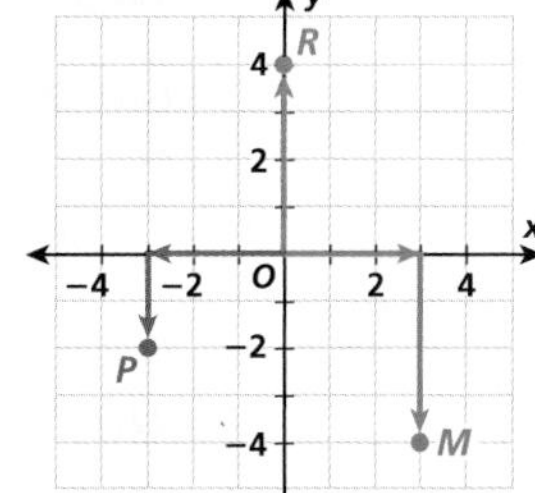

B $R(0, 4)$

From the origin, move 4 units up.

C $M(3, -4)$

From the origin, move 3 units right and 4 units down.

Answers to *Think and Discuss*

1. the first number; the second number
2. Possible answer: Move 5 units to the right on the *x*-axis for both points. But you move up 4 units for (5, 4) and down 4 units for (5, −4).
3. Possible answer: because coordinates describe a location in relation to the origin

Think and Discuss

GPS M6P1.d, M6P3.b, M6P3.d

1. **Tell** which number in an ordered pair indicates how far to move left or right from the origin and which number indicates how far to move up or down.
2. **Describe** how graphing the point (5, 4) is similar to graphing the point (5, −4). How is it different?
3. **Tell** why it is important to start at the origin when you are graphing points.

COMMON ERROR ALERT

Some students may forget what the first and second numbers in an ordered pair mean. To help them, remind students of the two examples used to motivate them in the introduction.

Power Presentations with PowerPoint®

Additional Examples

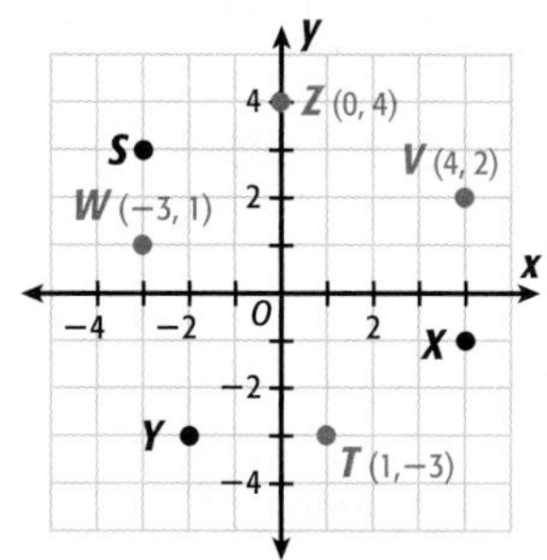

Example 1

Name the quadrant where each point is located.

A. X Quadrant IV

B. Y Quadrant III

C. S Quadrant II

Example 2

Give the coordinates of each point.

A. X (4, −1) **B.** Y (−2, −3) **C.** S (−3, 3)

Example 3

Graph each point on a coordinate plane. (See answers above.)

A. $V(4, 2)$ **B.** $W(-3, 1)$

C. $Z(0, 4)$ **D.** $T(1, -3)$

Also available on transparency

2 Teach

Guided Instruction

In this lesson, students learn to locate and graph points on a coordinate plane. First, identify the four quadrants of the plane (Teaching Transparency) and teach students that the first number in an ordered pair tells where to move horizontally from the origin and that the second number tells where to move vertically. Then teach students to give the coordinates of points in different quadrants. Finally, teach them to graph points, given the coordinates.

Inclusion Remind students to always begin at the origin (0, 0) when finding coordinates or graphing points on a coordinate plane.

Reaching All Learners

Through Multiple Representations

Geography Have students work in groups to draw coordinate grid lines on maps of your state. Instruct students to draw the *x*- and *y*-axes through the state capital and the other lines at $\frac{1}{2}$-inch increments above, below, to the left, and to the right of the axes. Have the students label the grid lines, beginning with the axes, with the appropriate numbers and give coordinates for various cities and towns on the map.

3 Close

Summarize

To review new vocabulary, have the students draw coordinate planes and label the *x*-axis, *y*-axis, quadrants I–IV, and the origin. Then have students graph a point in each quadrant and identify each point's *x*-coordinate and *y*-coordinate.

11-3 Exercises

Assignment Guide

If you finished Example 1 assign:
Average 1–3, 10–15, 55–65
Advanced 1–3, 10–15, 55–65

If you finished Example 2 assign:
Average 1–6, 10–21, 28–35, 50, 55–65
Advanced 1–6, 10–21, 28–35, 50, 55–65

If you finished Example 3 assign:
Average 1–51, 55–65
Advanced 1–48, 52–65

Homework Quick Check

Quickly check key concepts.
Exercises: 14, 16, 20, 28, 48

Answers

7–9.

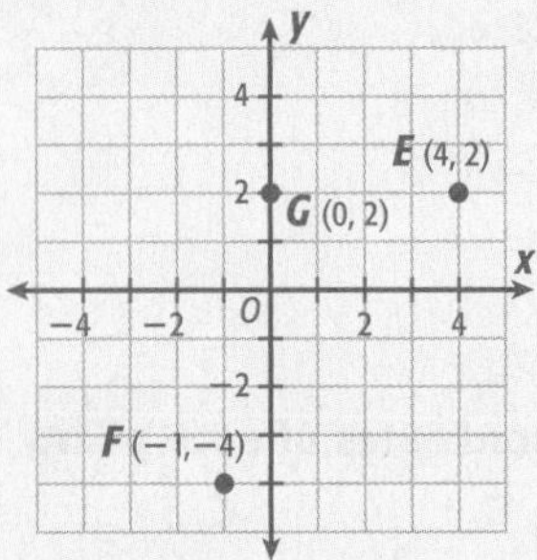

22–27, 36–48. See p. A11.

11-3 Exercises

Georgia Performance Standards

M6P1.a, M6P1.b, M6P3.a, M6P5.a

go.hrw.com
Homework Help Online
KEYWORD: MR7 11-3
Parent Resources Online
KEYWORD: MR7 Parent

GUIDED PRACTICE

Use the coordinate plane for Exercises 1–6.

See Example 1 — Name the quadrant where each point is located.

1. T **III** 2. U **no quadrant** 3. B **I**

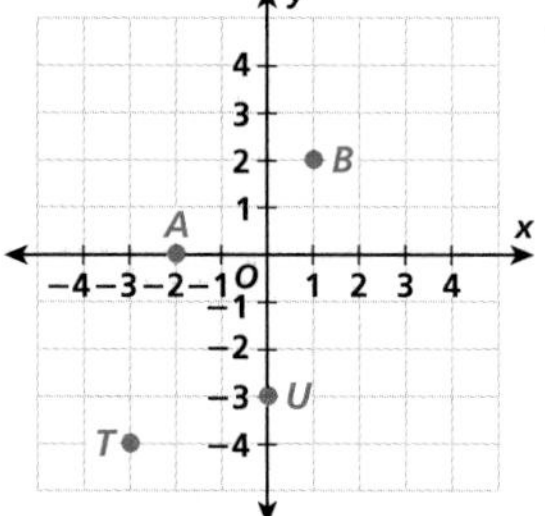

See Example 2 — Give the coordinates of each point.

4. A **(−2, 0)** 5. B **(1, 2)** 6. U **(0, −3)**

See Example 3 — Graph each point on a coordinate plane.

7. $E(4, 2)$ 8. $F(-1, -4)$ 9. $G(0, 2)$

INDEPENDENT PRACTICE

Use the coordinate plane for Exercises 10–21.

See Example 1 — Name the quadrant where each point is located.

10. Q **no quadrant** 11. X **II** 12. H **III**
13. Y **I** 14. Z **II** 15. P **IV**

See Example 2 — Give the coordinates of each point.

16. P **(3, −4)** 17. R **(−2, 4)** 18. Y **(2, 2)**
19. T **(4, 4)** 20. H **(−2, −3)** 21. Q **(−3, 0)**

See Example 3 — Graph each point on a coordinate plane.

22. $L(0, 3)$ 23. $M(3, -3)$ 24. $S(2, 0)$
25. $V(-4, 3)$ 26. $N(-2, -1)$ 27. $B(4, 3)$

PRACTICE AND PROBLEM SOLVING

Extra Practice p. 735

Name the quadrant where each ordered pair is located.

28. $(3, -1)$ **IV** 29. $(2, 1)$ **I** 30. $(-2, 3)$ **II** 31. $(-4, -3)$ **III**
32. $\left(4\frac{1}{2}, -3\right)$ **IV** 33. $\left(10, -7\frac{1}{2}\right)$ **IV** 34. $\left(-6, 2\frac{1}{3}\right)$ **II** 35. $\left(-8\frac{1}{3}, -\frac{1}{2}\right)$ **III**

Graph each ordered pair.

36. $(0, -5)$ 37. $(-4, -4)$ 38. $(5, 0)$ 39. $(3, 2)$
40. $(-2, 2)$ 41. $(0, -3)$ 42. $(1, -4)$ 43. $(0, 0)$
44. $\left(-2\frac{1}{2}, 3\right)$ 45. $\left(5, 3\frac{1}{2}\right)$ 46. $\left(-4\frac{1}{3}, 0\right)$ 47. $\left(0, -\frac{1}{2}\right)$

48. Graph points $A(-1, -1)$, $B(2, 1)$, $C(2, -2)$, and $D(-1, -2)$. Connect the points. What type of quadrilateral do the points form? **trapezoid**

RETEACH 11-3

LESSON 11-3 **Reteach**
The Coordinate Plane

The coordinate plane is divided into four quadrants. They are numbered I, II, III, and IV.

An ordered pair tells the location of a point. The x-coordinate tells you how far to move right or left. The y-coordinate tells you how far to move up or down.

The coordinates of point A are (5, −4) because it is 5 units to the right of the origin and 4 units down. It is located in quadrant IV.

Name the quadrant on axis where each point is located. Then give the coordinates of each point.

1. D **II; (−4, 1)** 2. Q **III; (−3, −6)**
3. F **x-axis; (6, 0)** 4. T **I; (5, 5)**
5. P **IV; (4, −5)** 6. W **y-axis; (0, −4)**

Graph each point on the coordinate plane.

7. B (−1, 6)
8. R (8, −5)
9. V (−3, −4)
10. Z (0, −6)

PRACTICE 11-3

LESSON 11-3 **Practice B**
The Coordinate Plane

Use the coordinate plane for Exercises 1–12.

Name the quadrant where each point is located.

1. D **II** 2. P **II**
3. Y **III** 4. B **IV**
5. C **I** 6. X **I**

Give the coordinates of each point.

7. X **(2, 1)** 8. A **(3, −2)**
9. P **(−1, 3)** 10. Q **(−4, 1)**
11. Y **(−2, −2)** 12. D **(−2, 2)**

Graph each point on the coordinate plane at right. **Check students' graphs.**

13. X (3, 1) 14. T (−2, −2)
15. C (1, −2) 16. U (0, −3)
17. P (2, 0) 18. A (−4, −1)

19. Does every point lie in a quadrant? Explain.
No, if a point is on either axis it does not lie in a quadrant.

20. When a point lies on the x-axis, what do you know about its y-coordinate? When a point lies on the y-axis, what do you know about its x-coordinate?
Its y-coordinate is 0; its x-coordinate is 0.

Georgia Performance Standards

M6P1.a Build new mathematical knowledge through problem solving.

M6P1.b Solve problems that arise in mathematics and in other contexts.

M6P3.a Organize and consolidate their mathematical thinking through communication.

M6P5.a Create and use representations to organize, record, and communicate mathematical ideas.

Social Studies LINK

We use a coordinate system on Earth to find exact locations. The *equator* is like the *x*-axis, and the *prime meridian* is like the *y*-axis.

The lines that run east-west are *lines of latitude.* They are measured in degrees north and south of the equator.

The lines that run north-south are *lines of longitude.* They are measured in degrees east and west of the prime meridian.

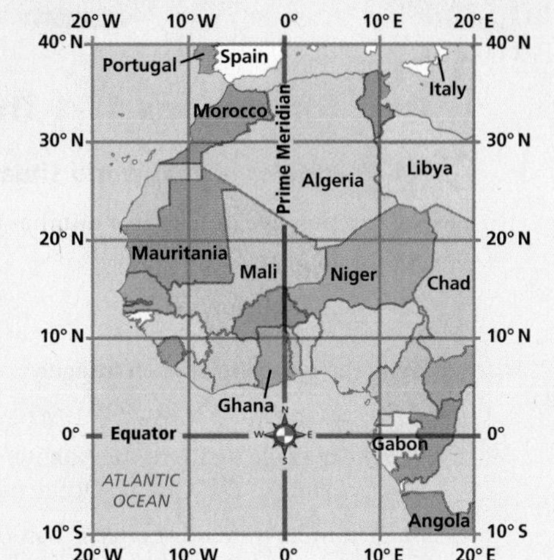

49. In what country is the location 0° latitude, 10° E longitude? Gabon
50. Give the coordinates of a location in Algeria. Possible answer: 30° N latitude, 0° longitude
51. Name two countries that lie along the 30° N line of latitude. Possible answers: Morocco, Libya, Algeria
52. Where would you be if you were located at 10° S latitude, 10° W longitude? Atlantic Ocean
53. **Write About It** How is the coordinate system we use to locate places on Earth different from the coordinate plane? How is it similar?

54. **Challenge** Begin at 10° S latitude, 20° E longitude. Travel 40° north and 20° west. What country would you be in now? Algeria

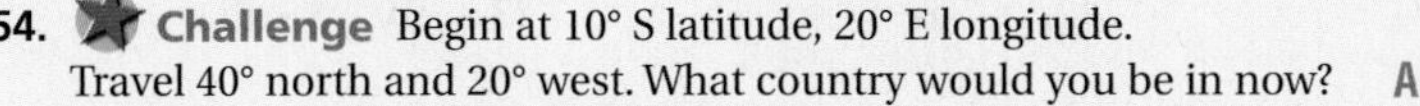

CRCT Prep • GPS Support • Spiral Review

55. **Multiple Choice** In which quadrant is the point $(-1, 2)$ located?

Ⓐ Quadrant I Ⓑ Quadrant II Ⓒ Quadrant III Ⓓ Quadrant IV

56. **Multiple Choice** Which of the following coordinates is the farthest to the right of the origin on a coordinate plane?

Ⓕ $(-19, 7)$ Ⓖ $(0, 12)$ Ⓗ $(4, 15)$ Ⓙ $(7, 0)$

Write each fraction or mixed number as a decimal. (Lesson 4-4)

57. $4\frac{2}{5}$ 4.4 58. $\frac{9}{10}$ 0.9 59. $5\frac{3}{4}$ 5.75 60. $\frac{9}{20}$ 0.45 61. $\frac{1}{5}$ 0.2

Compare. Write < or >. (Lesson 11-2)

62. 0 ▢ −4 > 63. −345 ▢ 78 < 64. −12 ▢ −6 < 65. 14 ▢ 18 <

Ongoing Assessment and Intervention

Diagnose Before the Lesson
11-3 Warm Up, TE p. 610

Monitor During the Lesson
11-3 Know-It Notebook
11-3 Questioning Strategies

Assess After the Lesson
11-3 Lesson Quiz, TE p. 613

Interdisciplinary LINK

Social Studies

Exercises 49–54 involve using the coordinate system of Earth's latitude and longitude for naming locations on a map. These mapping skills are used in middle school social studies programs, such as Holt, Rinehart & Winston's *People, Places, and Change.*

Answer

53. See p. A11.

Test Prep Doctor For Exercise 55, students may find it helpful to draw a coordinate plane and label the quadrants.

Journal

Have students write about how giving someone directions is like writing an ordered pair.

CHALLENGE 11-3

LESSON 11-3 Challenge
Plot and See

Graph each point below in the order given. Connect the points as you graph them to see a creature that lives most of its life 50 feet below sea level, or −50 feet.

START: (0, 20), (1, 19), (3, 18), (5, 15), (6, 15), (6, 12), (10, 8), (12, 8), (11, 6), (9, 6), (9, 7), (3, 11), (0, 11), (−2, 12), (3, 4), (2, 1), (3, −4), (−1, −13), (0, −17), (4, −18), (7, −17), (7, −16), (5, −16), (6, −14), (8, −15),(9, −18), (6, −20), (3, −20), (−3, −18), (−4, −13), (−2, −4), (−3, −1), (−4, −2), (−6, 2), (−5, 5), (−10, 12), (−6, 18), (0, 20) STOP!

Check students' graphs. The picture should be a seahorse.

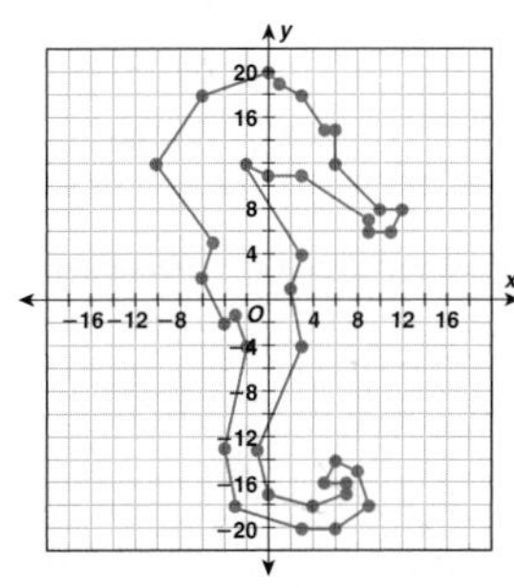

PROBLEM SOLVING 11-3

LESSON 11-3 Problem Solving
The Coordinate Plane

Use the coordinate plane on the map of Texas below to answer each question.

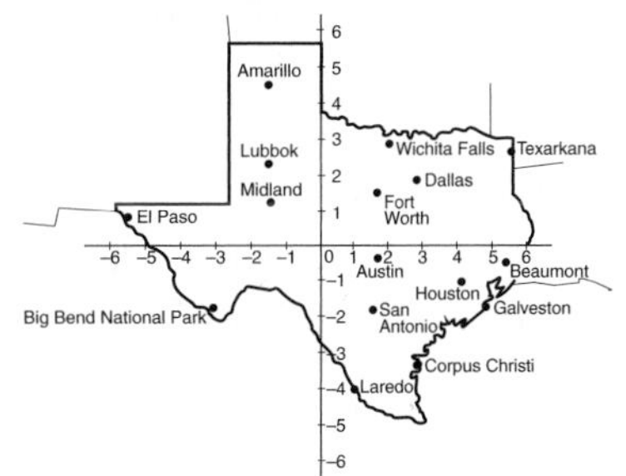

1. Which location in Texas is closest to the ordered pair (5, −2)? Galveston
2. What ordered pair best describes the location of Dallas, Texas? (3, 2)
3. Which location in Texas is closest to the ordered pair (−6, 1)? El Paso
4. Which location in Texas is located in Quadrant III of this coordinate plane? Big Bend National Park
5. Which three locations in Texas all have positive *y*-coordinates and nearly the same *x*-coordinate? Midland, Lubbock, and Amarillo
6. Which cities on this map of Texas have locations with *y*-coordinates less than −3? Laredo and Corpus Christi

Power Presentations with PowerPoint®

11-3 Lesson Quiz

Name the quadrant where each ordered pair is located.

1. $(3, -5)$ IV
2. $(-4, -2)$ III
3. $(6, 2)$ I
4. $(-7, 9)$ II

Give the coordinates of each point.

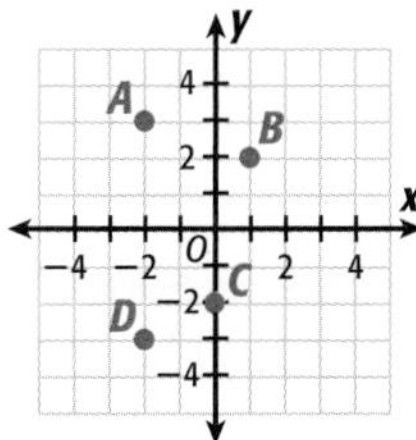

5. *A* $(-2, 3)$
6. *B* $(1, 2)$
7. *C* $(0, -2)$
8. *D* $(-2, -3)$

Also available on transparency

Organizer

Objective: Assess students' mastery of concepts and skills in Lessons 11-1 through 11-3.

Resources

 ***Assessment Resources***
Section 11A Quiz

INTERVENTION 

Resources

 ***Ready to Go On? Intervention and Enrichment*** **Worksheets**

 ***Ready to Go On?*** **CD-ROM**

 ***Ready to Go On?*** **Online**

my.hrw.com

Answers

10, 26–33. See p. A11.

SECTION 11A

Quiz for Lessons 11-1 Through 11-3

11-1 Integers in Real-World Situations

Name a positive or negative number to represent each situation.

1. a gain of 10 yards **+10**
2. 45 feet below sea level **−45**
3. 5 degrees below zero **−5**
4. earning $50 **+50 or 50**

Write the opposite of each integer.

5. 9 **−9**
6. −17 **+17**
7. 1 **−1**
8. −20 **+20**
9. The average depth of the Atlantic Ocean is 3,926 meters. Write the depth in meters of the Atlantic Ocean as an integer. **−3,926**
10. A company's food service is based on the ground floor of the building. Using the elevator, the chef delivers a fruit tray to the 8th floor. He then goes down 3 floors to deliver drinks. His last stop is up 5 more floors to deliver sandwiches. Use integers to model this situation.

11-2 Comparing and Ordering Integers

Compare. Write < or >.

11. 9 ■ −22 **>**
12. −7 ■ 4 **<**
13. −10 ■ −19 **>**

Order the integers in each set from least to greatest.

14. 2, −7, 14 **−7, 2, 14**
15. 25, −9, 4, −21 **−21, −9, 4, 25**
16. 10, 0, −23, −17, 8 **−23, −17, 0, 8, 10**
17. During an archaeological dig, the farther down an object is found, the older it is. If pieces of jewelry are found at −7 ft, −17 ft, −4 ft, and −9 ft, which piece is oldest? **the one found at −17 ft.**

11-3 The Coordinate Plane

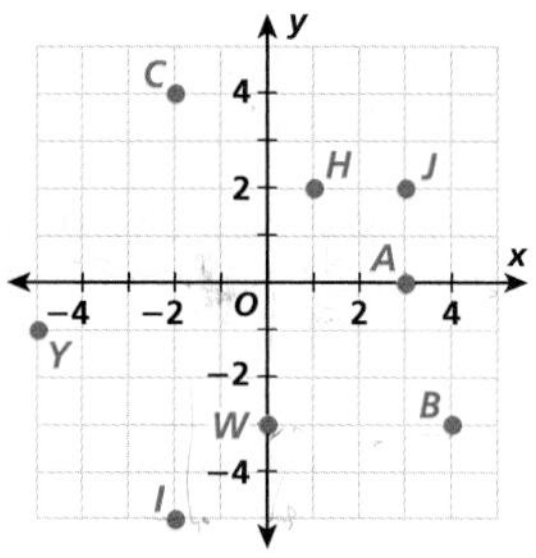

Use the coordinate plane for problems 18–25.

Name the quadrant where each point is located.

18. *A* **no quadrant**
19. *Y* **III**
20. *J* **I**
21. *C* **II**

Give the coordinates of each point.

22. *H* **(1, 2)**
23. *I* **(−2, −5)**
24. *W* **(0, −3)**
25. *B* **(4, −3)**

Graph each point on a coordinate plane.

26. $N(-5, -2)$
27. $S(0, 4)$
28. $R(-2, 6)$
29. $M(2, 2)$
30. $Q(4, -1)$
31. $P(-3, 0)$
32. $T\left(1\frac{1}{2}, 5\right)$
33. $H\left(-3, 1\frac{1}{2}\right)$

Ready to Go On?

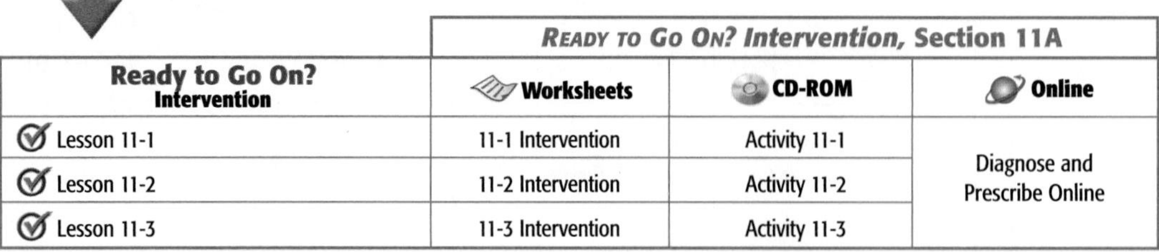

Ready to Go On? Intervention	*Ready to Go On? Intervention,* Section 11A: Worksheets	CD-ROM	Online
Lesson 11-1	11-1 Intervention	Activity 11-1	Diagnose and Prescribe Online
Lesson 11-2	11-2 Intervention	Activity 11-2	
Lesson 11-3	11-3 Intervention	Activity 11-3	

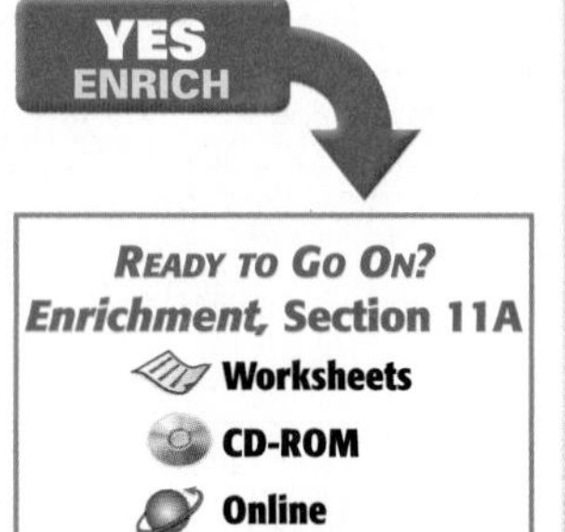

***Ready to Go On? Enrichment,* Section 11A**
Worksheets
CD-ROM
Online

Focus on Problem Solving

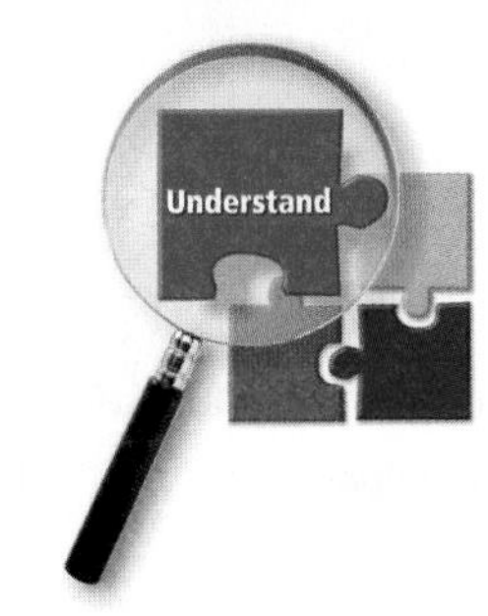

Understand the Problem

• **Restate the question**

After reading a real-world problem (perhaps several times), look at the question in the problem. Rewrite the question as a statement in your own words. For example, if the question is "How much money did the museum earn?" you could write, "Find the amount of money the museum earned."

Now you have a simple sentence telling you what you must do. This can help you understand and remember what the problem is about. This can also help you find the necessary information in the problem.

Read the problems below. Rewrite each question as a statement in your own words.

1. Israel is one of the hottest countries in Asia. A temperature of 129°F was once recorded there. This is the opposite of the coldest recorded temperature in Antarctica. How cold has it been in Antarctica?

2. The average recorded temperature in Fairbanks, Alaska, in January is about −10°F. In February, the average temperature is about −4°F. Is the average temperature lower in January or in February?

3. The south pole on Mars is made of frozen carbon dioxide, which has a temperature of −193°F. The coldest day recorded on Earth was −129°F, in Antarctica. Which temperature is lower?

4. The pirate Blackbeard's ship, the *Queen Anne's Revenge,* sank at Beauford Inlet, North Carolina, in 1718. In 1996, divers discovered a shipwreck believed to be the *Queen Anne's Revenge.* The ship's cannons were found 21 feet below the water's surface, and the ship's bell was found 20 feet below the surface. Were the cannons or the bell closer to the surface?

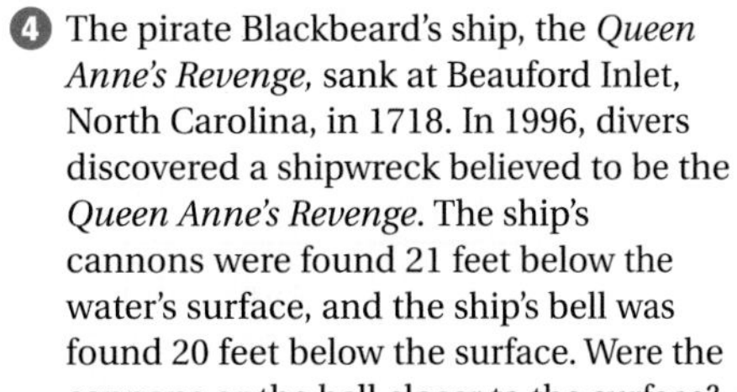

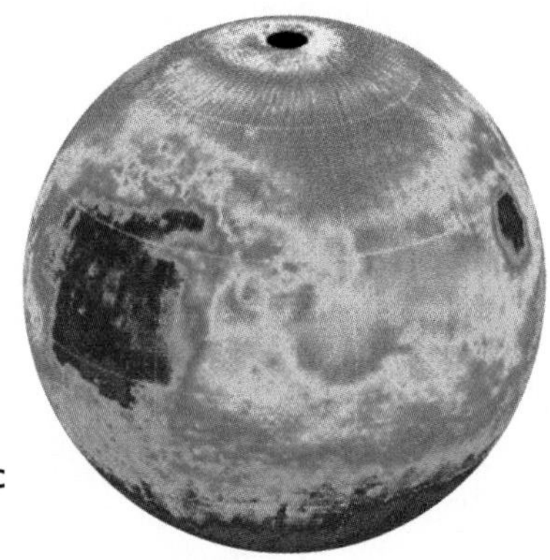

In this photo of Mars, different colors represent different temperature ranges. When the photo was taken, it was summer in the northern hemisphere and winter in the southern hemisphere.

-65°C  **-120°C**

Answers

1. −129°F

2. January

3. −193°F

4. The bell was closer to the surface.

Focus on Problem Solving

Organizer

Objective: Focus on understanding the problem.

Online Edition

Resources

Chapter 11 Resource Book
Reading Strategies

Problem Solving Process

This page focuses on the first step of the problem-solving process: **Understand the Problem**

Discuss

Have students identify the quantities being compared in the problems and then simplify the problems using their own words.

1. the hottest temperature in Israel and the coldest temperature in Antarctica; Find the opposite of 129°F.

2. −10°F and −4°F; tell which is lower, −10 or −4.

3. −193°F and −129°F; tell which is lower, −193 or −129.

4. 20 feet below the water's surface and 21 feet below the water's surface; tell which is closer to 0, −21 or −20.

SECTION 11B

Integer Operations

One-Minute Section Planner

Lesson	Materials	MiC and Lab Resources
11-4 Hands-On Lab Model Integer Addition • Use two-color counters to model addition of integers. **Lesson 11-4** Adding Integers • Add integers. ☑ CRCT ☑ SAT-10 ☐ ITBS ☐ CTBS ☐ NAEP	Two-color counters (MK), number lines	***Hands-On Lab Activities*** 11-4
11-5 Hands-On Lab Model Integer Subtraction • Use two-color counters to model subtraction of integers. **Lesson 11-5** Subtracting Integers • Subtract integers. ☑ CRCT ☑ SAT-10 ☐ ITBS ☐ CTBS ☐ NAEP	Two-color counters (MK), number lines	***Hands-On Lab Activities*** 11-5
Lesson 11-6 Multiplying Integers • Multiply integers. ☑ CRCT ☑ SAT-10 ☐ ITBS ☑ CTBS ☑ NAEP	Two-colored counters (MK), number cubes (MK)	***Technology Lab Activities*** 11-6
Lesson 11-7 Dividing Integers • Divide integers. ☑ CRCT ☑ SAT-10 ☐ ITBS ☑ CTBS ☑ NAEP		***Technology Lab Activities*** 11-7

MK = *Manipulatives Kit*

Mathematics in Context

There are no units from the *Mathematics in Context* © 2006 series suggested to be used with Section 11B.

Section Overview

Integer Operations

Lessons 11-4 through 11-7

When you know how to operate with integers, you can solve equations and problems involving integers.

Addition	Rule	Examples
Add integers with like signs.	Find the sum of their absolute values. Then use the sign of the integers.	5 + 4 = 9 (−6) + (−2) = −8
Add integers with unlike signs.	Find the difference of their absolute values. Then use the sign of the integer with the greater absolute value.	9 + (−3) = 6 −8 + 7 = −1

8 − 7 = −1

Subtraction	Rule	Examples
Subtract integers.	To subtract an integer, add its opposite.	2 − (−3) = 2 + 3 = 5 −7 − 1 = −7 + (−1) = −8

Multiplication and Division	Rule	Examples
Multiply or divide integers with like signs.	Find the product or quotient of their absolute values. The answer will be positive.	4 · 5 = 20 −24 ÷ −6 = 4
Multiply or divide integers with unlike signs.	Find the product or quotient of their absolute values. The answer will be negative.	−8 · 3 = −24 36 ÷ −4 = −9

Organizer

Use with Lesson 11-4

Pacing:
Traditional $\frac{1}{2}$ day
Block $\frac{1}{4}$ day

Objective: Use two-color counters to model addition of integers.

Materials: Two-color counters

Online Edition
Integer Chips

Resources

Hands-On Lab Activities
Lab 11-4 Recording Sheet

Teach

Discuss

Have students review what each red and yellow counter represents.

Close

Key Concept

Two-color counters can be used to model addition of integers.

Assessment

Represent each expression with two-color counters.

1. −4

2. 3

3. 3 + (−1)

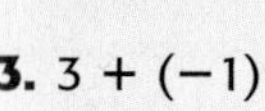

4. −2 + (−2)

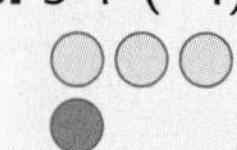

Answers to *Try This*

1–4. See p. A11.

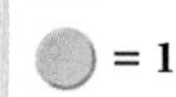

Model Integer Addition

Use with Lesson 11-4

KEY

(yellow) = 1 (red) = −1

REMEMBER

Subtracting zero from a number does not change the number's value.

Georgia Performance Standards

M6P2.c, M6P5.a, M6P5.b, M6P5.c

Two-color counters can be used to represent integers. Yellow counters represent positive numbers and red counters represent negative numbers.

Activity

Model with two-color counters.

1 3 + 4

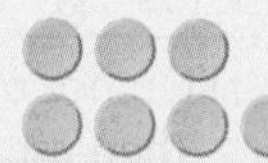

3 + 4 = 7

2 −5 + (−3)

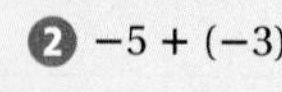

−5 + (−3) = −8

One red and one yellow counter together equal zero, and are called a zero pair. Whenever you have a zero pair, you can remove it without changing the value of the model.

3 3 + (−4)

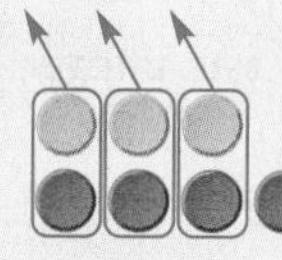

3 + (−4) = −1

Think and Discuss

1. When adding integers, would changing the order in which you add them affect the answer? Explain. **Changing the order of the integers in an addition problem does not affect the answer. For example, −6 + 4 = 2 and 4 + (−6) = 2.**
2. When can you remove counters from an addition model? **You may remove counters from an addition problem when you have zero pairs.**

Try This

Model with two-color counters.

1. −8 + (−4) **−12** **2.** −8 + 4 **−4** **3.** 8 + (−4) **+4** **4.** 8 + 4 **+12**

Georgia Performance Standards

M6P2.c Develop and evaluate mathematical arguments and proofs.

M6P5.a Create and use representations to organize, record, and communicate mathematical ideas.

M6P5.b Select, apply, and translate among mathematical representations to solve problems.

M6P5.c Use representations to model and interpret physical, social, and mathematical phenomena.

Karen Smith
Duxbury, Massachusetts

Teacher to Teacher

Game for Combining Integers

Divide the class into pairs. I use two-sided discs; the red side is negative, and the yellow side is positive. Each pair of students should have ten discs and a pencil and paper to mark off each round. Tell the students that one red and one yellow disc will cancel each other out because of the Inverse Property of Addition. Students take turns tossing all ten discs onto a desk and then use the cancellation rule to determine their score (e.g., 6 red and 4 yellow = −2 points). The students add scores from one round to the next. At the end of ten rounds, the student whose score is the closest to zero wins.

11-4 Adding Integers

Learn to add integers.

M6A3 Evaluate algebraic expressions. Also, M6P5.a, M6P5.b, M6P5.c.

One of the world's most active volcanoes is Kilauea, in Hawaii. Kilauea's base is 9 km below sea level. The top of Kilauea is 10 km above the base of the mountain.

You can add the integers −9 and 10 to find the height of Kilauea above sea level.

Adding Integers on a Number Line
Move **right** on a number line to add a **positive** integer.
Move **left** on a number line to add a **negative** integer.

EXAMPLE 1 Writing Integer Addition

Write the addition modeled on each number line.

A

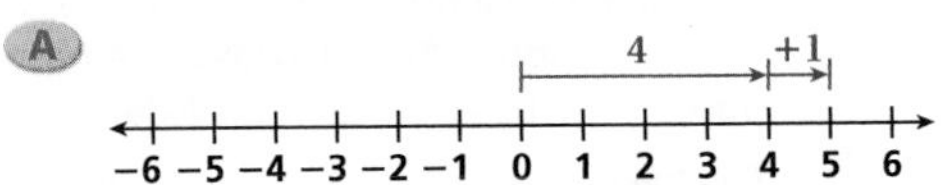

The addition modeled is $4 + 1 = 5$.

B

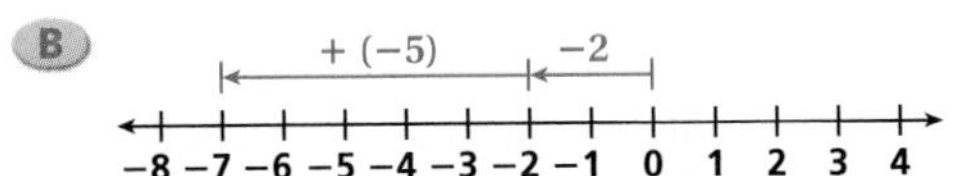

The addition modeled is $-2 + (-5) = -7$.

C

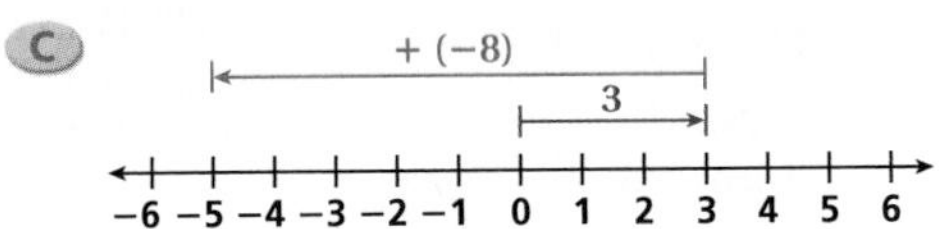

The addition modeled is $3 + (-8) = -5$.

Writing Math

Parentheses are used to separate addition, subtraction, multiplication, and division signs from negative integers.

$-2 + (-5) = -7$

Organizer 11-4

Pacing: Traditional 1 day
Block $\frac{1}{2}$ day

Objective: Students add integers.

GPS M6A3.
Hands-On Lab
In *Hands-On Lab Activities*

Online Edition
Tutorial Videos, Interactivities

Power Presentations with PowerPoint®

Warm Up

Add.

1. $2 + 3$ 5 **2.** $7 + 4$ 11

3. $8 + 5$ 13 **4.** $17 + 12$ 29

Name the integer that corresponds to each point.

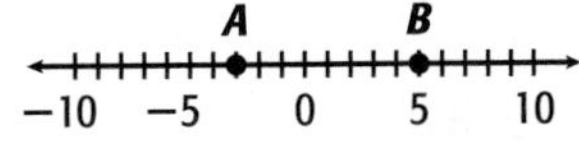

5. *A* −3 **6.** *B* 5

Problem of the Day

Karen earned 40 points on part I of a test, 26 points on part II, and 25 points on part III. What number of points did Karen earn on parts I and III combined? 65

Also available on transparency

Math Fact

It is not possible to reach a temperature lower than absolute zero. To convert absolute zero to the Fahrenheit scale, you must add negative 459° (−459°).

1 Introduce

Alternate Opener

EXPLORATION

11-4 Adding Integers

You can use a thermometer to model addition of integers.

1. Suppose the temperature starts at −10°F and increases 30° during the day. Complete the addition statement to show the new temperature.
   $-10° + 30° =$ ____
2. Suppose the temperature starts at 20°F and drops 40° overnight. Complete the addition statement to show the new temperature.
   $20° + (-40°) =$ ____
3. Draw a thermometer and show $20° + (-10°)$. Find the sum.

Think and Discuss

4. **Describe** how to add a positive integer using a thermometer.
5. **Describe** how to add a negative integer using a thermometer.

Motivate

Ask students to help write rules for a game called *Pegs & Holes*, in which *P* stands for pegs and *H* stands for holes. (Adding pegs and holes follows the same rules as adding integers.) Give examples, such as $4P + 5P = 9P$ and $2H + 3H = 5H$. Adding *P*'s to *H*'s is different. For example, $5P + 3H = 2P$, $4P + 4H = 0$, and $1P + 6H = 5H$. Create more examples. See if the students can state a rule for each case.

Explorations and answers are provided in *Alternate Openers: Explorations Transparencies.*

Georgia Performance Standards

M6A3 Students will evaluate algebraic expressions, including those with exponents, and solve simple one-step equations using each of the four basic operations.

M6P5.a Create and use representations to organize, record, and communicate mathematical ideas.

M6P5.b Select, apply, and translate among mathematical representations to solve problems.

M6P5.c Use representations to model and interpret physical, social, and mathematical phenomena.

Power Presentations with PowerPoint®

Additional Examples

Example 1

Write the addition modeled on each number line.

A.

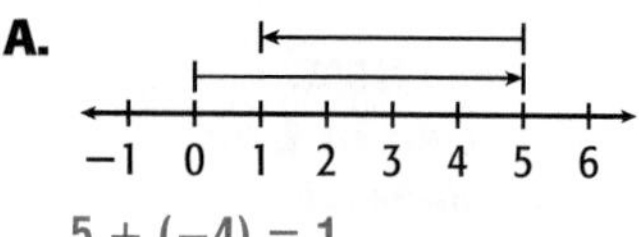

$5 + (-4) = 1$

B.

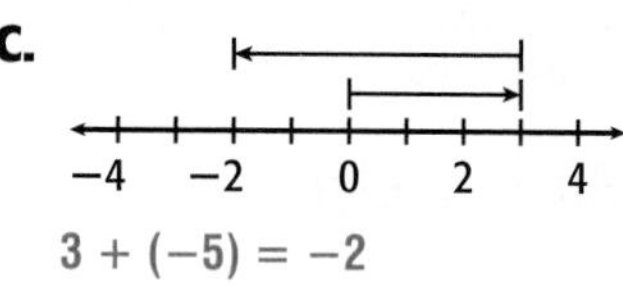

$-4 + 7 = 3$

C.

$3 + (-5) = -2$

Example 2

Find each sum.

A. $-3 + (-2)$ -5

B. $6 + (-8)$ -2

Example 3

Evaluate $y + (-2)$ for $y = 7$. 5

Example 4

A sunken ship is 12 m below sea level. A search plane flies 35 m above the sunken ship. How far above the sea is the plane?

23 m above the sea

Also available on transparency

EXAMPLE 2 Adding Integers

Find each sum.

A $6 + (-5)$

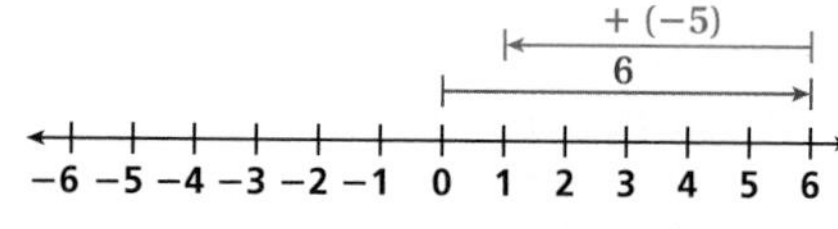

Think:

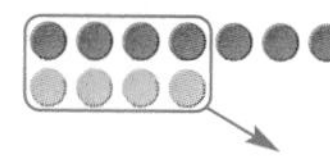

$6 + (-5) = 1$

B $-7 + 4$

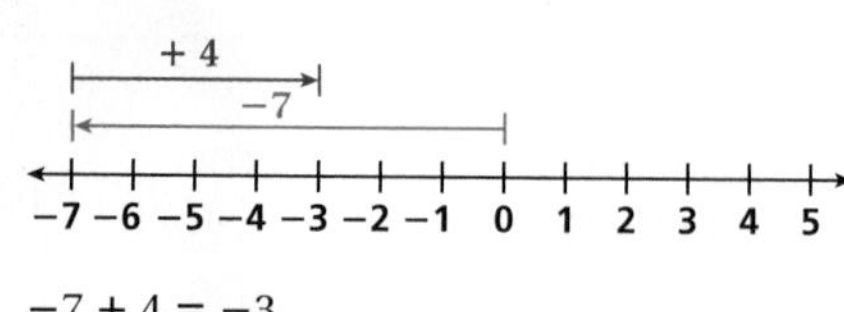

Think:

$-7 + 4 = -3$

EXAMPLE 3 Evaluating Integer Expressions

Evaluate $x + 3$ for $x = -9$.

$x + 3$	*Write the expression.*
$-9 + 3$	*Substitute −9 for x.*
-6	*Add.*

Think:

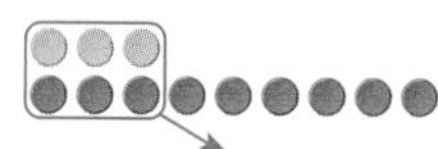

EXAMPLE 4 *Earth Science Application*

The base of Kilauea is 9 km below sea level. The top is 10 km above the base. How high above sea level is Kilauea?

The base is 9 km below sea level and the top is 10 km above the base.

$-9 + 10$

1

Kilauea is 1 km above sea level.

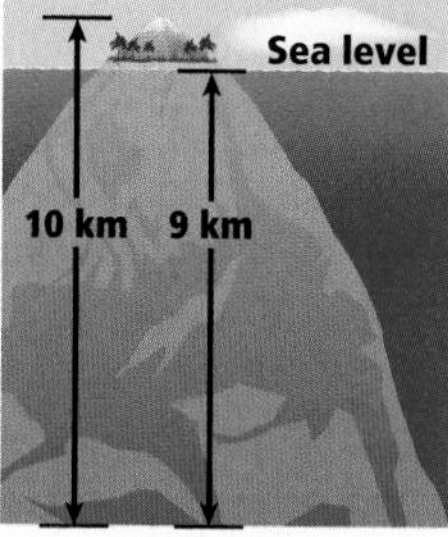

Possible answers to *Think and Discuss*

1. Greater than; When you add a positive integer to any integer, you move to the right on the number line.
2. zero

Think and Discuss GPS M6P1.d, M6P3.b

1. Tell if the sum of a positive integer and −8 is greater than −8 or less than −8. Explain.

2. Give the sum of a number and its opposite.

2 Teach

Guided Instruction

In this lesson, students learn to add integers. First, teach the rules for adding integers on a number line (Teaching Transparency) and the rules for adding integers using two-color counters (Manipulatives Kit). Then teach addition using a number line and counters. Next, have students model addition of integers on a number line as well as model addition using counters.

Reaching All Learners

Through Concrete Manipulatives

Some students may not be ready to make the transition from concrete models (counters) to pictorial models (number lines) when adding positive and negative integers. Allow these students to use color counters provided in the Manipulatives Kit when working through the examples.

3 Close

Summarize

Review the procedures for adding integers. Discuss how to use counters and how to use a number line when adding integers with opposite signs. Ask students to tell how to use each method to find the sum of $-7 + 3$.

Possible answers:

a. Counters: Use 7 red counters and 3 yellow counters. Make pairs of red and yellow counters (there will be 3 pairs), and then remove them. There are 4 red counters left, so $-7 + 3 = -4$.

b. Number line: Count 7 units to the left of 0, to −7. Then count 3 units right from −7, to −4. $-7 + 3 = -4$.

11-4 Exercises

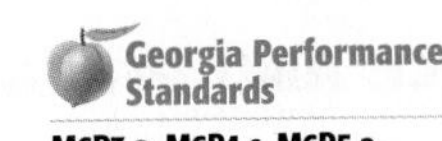

M6P3.a, M6P4.c, M6P5.a, M6P5.b

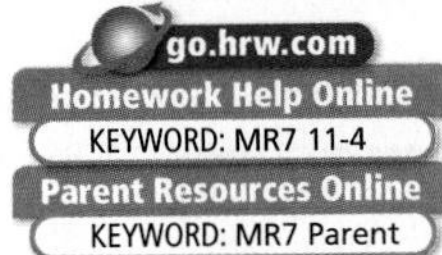

GUIDED PRACTICE

See Example 1 Write the addition modeled on the number line.

1.

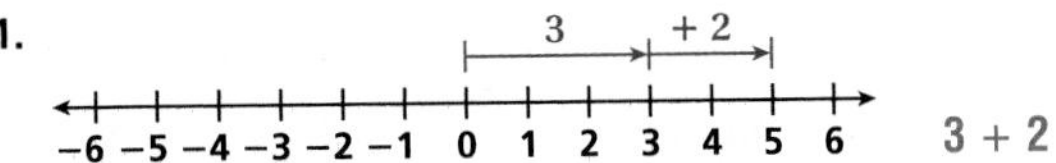

3 + 2 = 5

See Example 2 Find each sum.

2. −5 + 9 4
3. −3 + (−2) −5
4. 8 + (−7) 1
5. 10 + (−3) 7
6. −4 + (−8) −12
7. −1 + 5 4

See Example 3 Evaluate $n + (-2)$ for each value of n.

8. $n = -10$ −12
9. $n = 2$ 0
10. $n = -2$ −4
11. $n = -15$ −17
12. $n = 12$ 10
13. $n = -20$ −22

See Example 4

14. A submarine at the water's surface dropped down 100 ft. After thirty minutes at that depth, it dove an additional 500 ft. What was its depth after the second dive? −600 ft

INDEPENDENT PRACTICE

See Example 1 Write the addition modeled on each number line.

15.

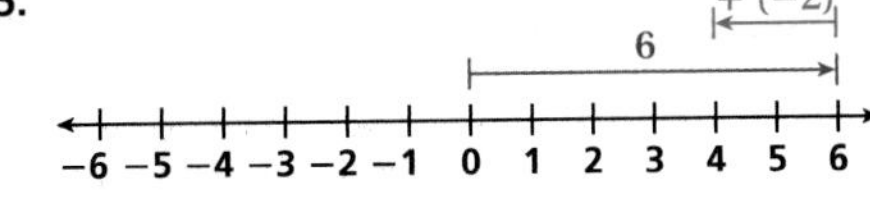

6 + (−2) = 4

16. + (−2) −4

−6 −5 −4 −3 −2 −1 0 1 2 3 4 5 6

−4 + (−2) = −6

See Example 2 Find each sum.

17. 4 + 7 11
18. 2 + (−12) −10
19. 9 + (−9) 0
20. 10 + (−21) −11
21. −8 + 2 −6
22. −2 + 8 6
23. −1 + (−6) −7
24. −25 + (14) −11

See Example 3 Evaluate $-6 + a$ for each value of a.

25. $a = -10$ −16
26. $a = 7$ 1
27. $a = -2$ −8
28. $a = -6$ −12
29. $a = 4$ −2
30. $a = -9$ −15
31. $a = 8$ 2
32. $a = -20$ −26

See Example 4

33. Jon works on a cruise ship and sleeps in a cabin that is 6 feet below sea level. The main deck is 35 feet above Jon's cabin. How far above sea level is the main deck? 29 feet

34. **Recreation** Preston dives to a depth of 15 feet. He stops briefly and then dives an additional 17 feet. What is Preston's depth after his second dive? −32 feet

11-4 Exercises

Assignment Guide

If you finished Example 1 assign:
Average 1, 35–41, 63–75
Advanced 15–16, 35–42, 63–75

If you finished Example 2 assign:
Average 1–7, 35–50, 63–75
Advanced 15–24, 35–50, 63–75

If you finished Example 3 assign:
Average 1–13, 35–56, 63–75
Advanced 15–32, 40–56, 63–75

If you finished Example 4 assign:
Average 1–42, 51–59, 63–75
Advanced 15–75

Homework Quick Check

Quickly check key concepts.
Exercises: 16, 20, 24, 28, 34

Math Background

Color counters and number lines are useful tools for understanding addition of integers with opposite signs. Mastering these tools prepares students to better understand the more formal method:

- Find the absolute value of each addend.
- Subtract the smaller absolute value from the larger absolute value.
- Attach the sign of the addend that has the greater absolute value to the difference from the last step.

RETEACH 11-4

LESSON 11-4 **Reteach**
Adding Integers

Two-color counters can help you understand integers.

(+1) (−1)

One positive counter and one negative counter is called a zero pair because together they have a value of zero.

zero pair

1 + (−1) = 0

You can use two-color counters to find the sum of integers.

To use counters to find the sum of −3 and 5, model the addition expression first.

Then remove all the zero pairs.

The remaining counters represent the sum.
−3 + 5 = 2

Use counters to find each sum.

1. −4 + 7 3
2. 4 + (−8) −4
3. −3 + −6 −9
4. −3 + 1 −2
5. −2 + 7 5
6. 5 + (−6) −1
7. −8 + (−3) −11
8. 10 + 2 12
9. 9 + −12 −3
10. 4 + (−10) −6
11. −8 + −5 −13
12. 6 + −5 1

PRACTICE 11-4

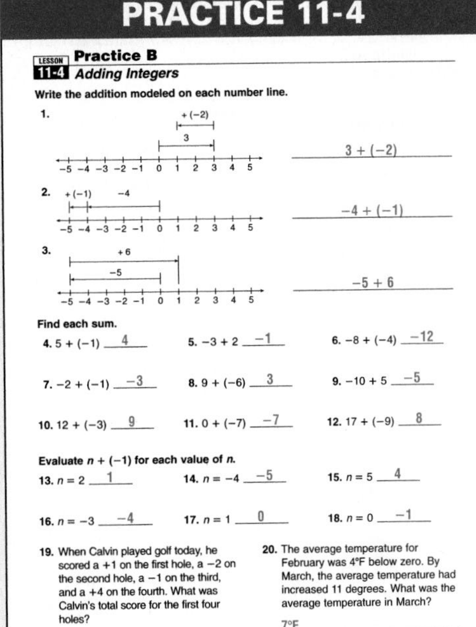

LESSON 11-4 **Practice B**
Adding Integers

Write the addition modeled on each number line.

1. 3 + (−2)
2. −4 + (−1)
3. −5 + 6

Find each sum.

4. 5 + (−1) 4
5. −3 + 2 −1
6. −8 + (−4) −12
7. −2 + (−1) −3
8. 9 + (−6) 3
9. −10 + 5 −5
10. 12 + (−3) 9
11. 0 + (−7) −7
12. 17 + (−9) 8

Evaluate $n + (-1)$ for each value of n.

13. $n = 2$ 1
14. $n = -4$ −5
15. $n = 5$ 4
16. $n = -3$ −4
17. $n = 1$ 0
18. $n = 0$ −1

19. When Calvin played golf today, he scored a +1 on the first hole, a −2 on the second hole, a −1 on the third, and a +4 on the fourth. What was Calvin's total score for the first four holes? +2 or 2

20. The average temperature for February was 4°F below zero. By March, the average temperature had increased 11 degrees. What was the average temperature in March? 7°F

M6P3.a Organize and consolidate their mathematical thinking through communication.

M6P4.c Recognize and apply mathematics in contexts outside of mathematics.

M6P5.a Create and use representations to organize, record, and communicate mathematical ideas.

M6P5.b Select, apply, and translate among mathematical representations to solve problems.

ONGOING ASSESSMENT

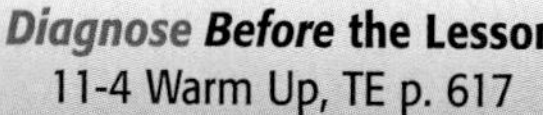

and INTERVENTION

Diagnose **Before** the Lesson
11-4 Warm Up, TE p. 617

Monitor **During** the Lesson
11-4 Know-It Notebook
11-4 Questioning Strategies

Assess **After** the Lesson
11-4 Lesson Quiz, TE p. 620

Answers

35–42. See p. A11.

60. Yes; possible answer: For each expression you will have 7 zero pairs for an answer of 3.

71–75. See p. A12.

TEST PREP DOCTOR For Exercise 64, students who remember that the sum of two negative integers is negative will eliminate choice **F.** Students can eliminate **G** and **J** if they remember that the sign of the sum of two integers with different signs is the sign of the integer with the greater absolute value.

Journal

Have students write about why the rules are different for the addition of positive integers and the addition of negative integers.

Power Presentations with PowerPoint®

11-4 Lesson Quiz

Find each sum.

1. $7 + (-3)$ 4

2. $-5 + 2$ -3

3. $-8 + (-4)$ -12

4. Evaluate $x + 5$ for $x = -4$. 1

5. At midnight on a winter night, the temperature was -12°F. By 10 A.M. the temperature had risen 42°F. What was the new temperature? 30°F

Also available on transparency

PRACTICE AND PROBLEM SOLVING

CRCT GPS
Extra Practice p. 735

Model each addition problem on a number line.

35. $3 + (-1)$ **36.** $-2 + (-4)$ **37.** $-6 + 5$ **38.** $1 + (-2)$

39. $-1 + 6$ **40.** $5 + (-3)$ **41.** $-3 + (-1)$ **42.** $0 + (-5)$

Find each sum.

43. $-18 + 25$ 7 **44.** $8 + (-2)$ 6 **45.** $-5 + (-6)$ -11 **46.** $-12 + (-7)$ -19

47. $-6 + (-3)$ -9 **48.** $4 + (-1)$ 3 **49.** $20 + (-3)$ 17 **50.** $30 + (-25)$ 5

Evaluate each expression for the given value of the variable.

51. $x + (-3)$; $x = 7$ 4 **52.** $-9 + n$; $n = 7$ -2 **53.** $a + 5$; $a = -6$ -1

54. $m + (-2)$; $m = -4$ -6 **55.** $-10 + x$; $x = -7$ -17 **56.** $n + 19$; $n = -5$ 14

57. Earth Science The temperature at midnight was -2°F. During the next 4 hours, a decrease of 4°F was recorded. What was the temperature at 4 A.M.? -6°F

58. Sports In the 2001 U.S. Women's Open, Cristie Kerr had the following scores for the four rounds of golf: -1, $+3$, $+1$, and 0. What was her total score? $+3$

Georgia LINK Sports

Cristie Kerr shot -12 to finish third at the 2005 Chick-fil-A Charity Championship in Stockbridge, Georgia.

59. Choose a Strategy The first Roman emperor, Augustus, was born in 63 B.C.E. and died in 14 C.E. How many years did he live? (*Hint*: Years B.C.E. are like negative numbers. Years C.E. are like positive numbers. There was no year 0.) 76 yrs

60. Critical Thinking Will the expression $-7 + 10$ have the same sum as $10 + (-7)$? Explain your answer.

61. Write About It When adding two integers, what will the sign of the answer be when one integer is positive and the other is negative? Explain. sometimes positive, sometimes negative; the answer will have the sign of the larger number

62. Challenge Evaluate $-3 + (-2) + (-1) + 0 + 1 + 2 + 3 + 4$. Then use this pattern to find the sum of the integers from -10 to 11 and from -100 to 101. 4; 11; 101

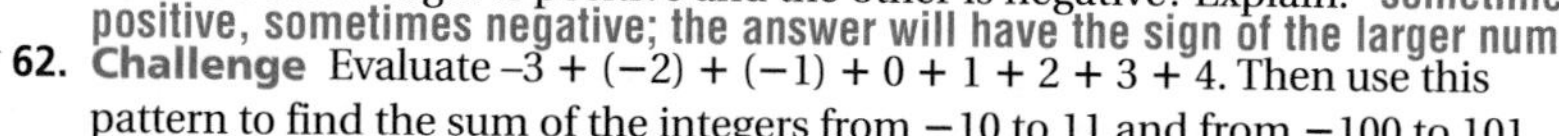

CRCT PREP • GPS SUPPORT • SPIRAL REVIEW

63. Multiple Choice Julie earned $1,350 at her part-time job. Her paycheck showed deductions of $148.50. What was the total amount of her paycheck?

Ⓐ $1,165.50 Ⓑ $1,201.50 Ⓒ $1,498.50 Ⓓ $1,534.50

64. Multiple Choice Which sum is NOT negative?

Ⓕ $-38 + (-24)$ Ⓖ $-61 + 43$ Ⓗ $-54 + 68$ Ⓙ $-29 + 11$

65. Short Response Evaluate $b + 7$ for $b = -2$, -4, and -8. 5, 3, -1

Find each value. (Lesson 1-3)

66. 5^3 125 **67.** 4^1 4 **68.** 9^2 81 **69.** 12^3 1,728 **70.** 7^4 2,401

Graph each point on a coordinate plane. (Lesson 11-3)

71. $J(5, 7)$ **72.** $M(-2, 4)$ **73.** $L(4, -3)$ **74.** $A(-1, -6)$ **75.** $W(0, 5)$

CHALLENGE 11-4

LESSON 11-4 **Challenge**
Time Adds Up

Solve the addition problems below to find the date each toy or game was invented. Then use those dates to label the time line at the bottom of the page.

	Invention	Addition	Date
1.	Frisbee	50 + (−2)	1948
2.	Pogo Stick	−11 + 32	1921
3.	Crossword Puzzle	−1 + 17 + (−3)	1913
4.	Skateboard	−43 + 101	1958
5.	Yo-Yo	38 + (−9)	1929
6.	Rollerblades	−25 + 105	1980
7.	Teddy Bear	−2 + 8 + (−3)	1903
8.	Slinky	50 + (−4)	1946

Check students' time lines.

Time Line of Toys and Games

1900 1910 1920 1930 1940 1950 1960 1970 1980 1990 2000

PROBLEM SOLVING 11-4

LESSON 11-4 **Problem Solving**
Adding Integers

In 1997, Tiger Woods became the youngest golfer ever to win the Masters Tournament. There are four rounds of 18 holes in the Masters Tournament. Use Woods's scorecard to answer questions 1–6.

Tiger Woods																		
Hole	1	2	3	4	5	6	7	8	9	10	11	12	13	14	15	16	17	18
Rd. 1	1	0	0	1	0	0	0	1	1	−1	0	−1	−1	0	−2	0	−1	0
Rd. 2	0	−1	1	0	−1	0	0	−1	0	0	0	0	−2	−1	−1	0	0	0
Rd. 3	0	−1	0	0	−1	0	−1	−1	0	0	−1	0	0	0	−1	0	0	−1
Rd. 4	0	−1	0	0	1	0	1	−1	0	0	−1	0	−1	−1	0	0	0	0

1. What was Woods's total score for round 1 of the tournament?
   -2

2. What was his total score for the second round of the tournament?
   -6

3. What was his total score for the third round of the tournament?
   -7

4. What was his total score for the fourth round of the tournament?
   -3

Circle the letter of the correct answer.

5. Woods's final score in 1997 was the lowest in the history of the Masters Tournament. What was Woods's record-breaking final score?
   A −16
   B −17
   Ⓒ −18
   C −20

6. Tom Kite placed second in the 1997 Masters Tournament. His final score was 12 strokes higher than Tiger Woods's final score. What was Kite's final score?
   F −30
   G −12
   Ⓗ − 6
   J 0

7. Which of the following is the sum of Woods's scores on the 8th hole?
   A 2
   B 1
   C −1
   Ⓓ −2

8. Which of the following is the sum of Woods's scores on the 15th hole?
   F 4
   Ⓖ −4
   H 0
   J 1

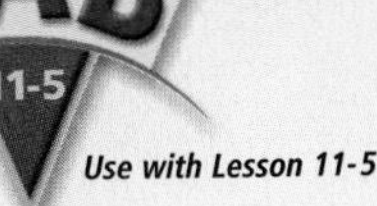

Model Integer Subtraction

Use with Lesson 11-5

Georgia Performance Standards

M6P2.c, M6P5.a, M6P5.b, M6P5.c

KEY

 = 1  = −1

REMEMBER

Adding zero to a number does not change the number's value.

 + = 0

Activity

Model with two-color counters.

1. 3 − 2

3 − 2 = 1

2. −3 − (−2)

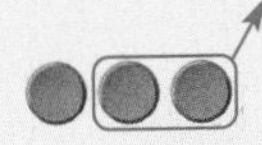

−3 − (−2) = −1 −3 + 2 = −1

3. 3 − (−2)

You do not have any red counters, so you cannot subtract −2. Add zero pairs until you have enough red counters to subtract.

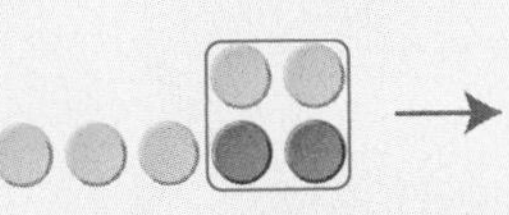

Add 2 zero pairs.

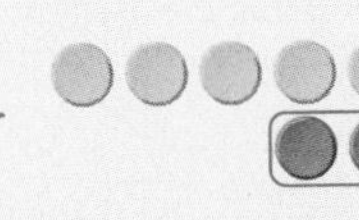

Now you can subtract −2.

3 − (−2) = 5

Think and Discuss

Possible answers:

1. How do you show subtraction with counters? **by removing counters**
2. Why can you add zero pairs to a subtraction model? **Adding zero pairs is like adding 0, which doesn't change the value of the number.**

Try This

Model with two-color counters.

1. 5 − 4 **1**
2. 4 − (−5) **9**
3. −4 − 5 **−9**
4. −4 − (−5) **1**
5. 8 − 5 **3**
6. 5 − (−8) **13**
7. −5 − 8 **−13**
8. −8 − (−8) **0**

Answers to *Try This*

1.

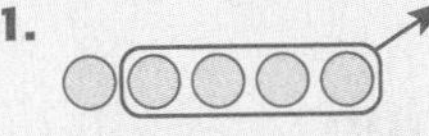

2.

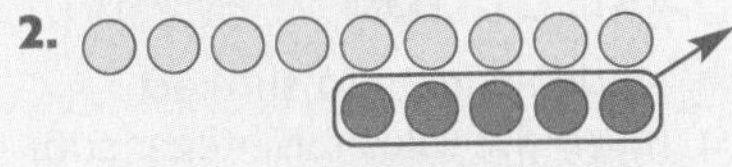

3.

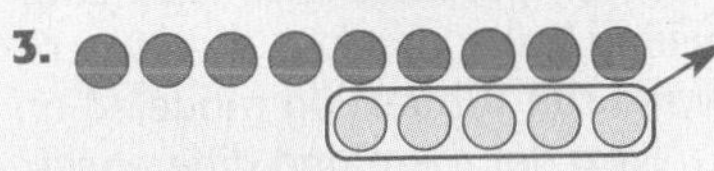

4.

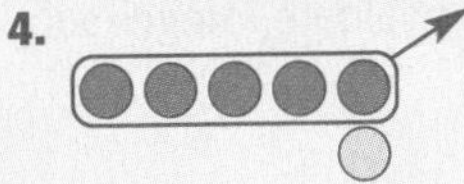

5.

6.

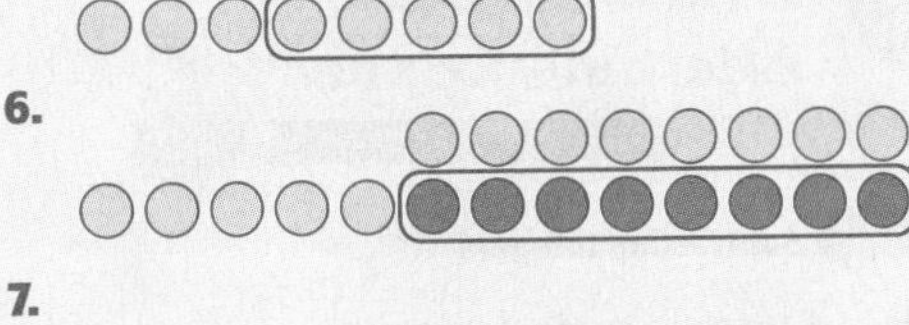

7.

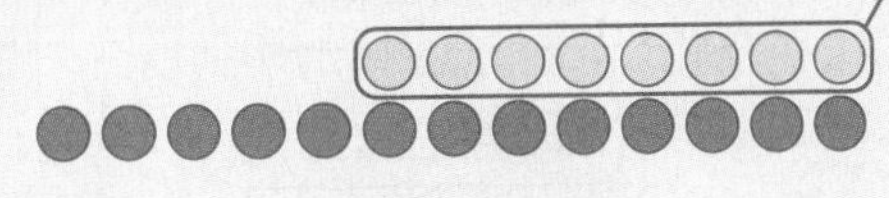

8.

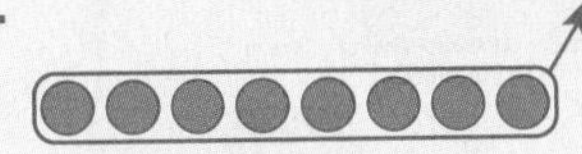

Organizer

Use with Lesson 11-5

Pacing:

Traditional $\frac{1}{2}$ day
Block $\frac{1}{4}$ day

Objective: Use two-color counters to model subtraction of integers.

Materials: Two-color counters

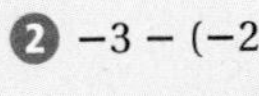

Online Edition
Integer Chips

Resources

Hands-On Lab Activities
Lab 11-5 Recording Sheet

Teach

Discuss

Have students review what each side of the two-color counter represents. Discuss what is represented by a pair of counters in which one is red and one is yellow.

Close

Key Concept

Two-color counters can be used to model integer subtraction.

Assessment

Represent each expression with two-color counters.

1. −2
2. 4

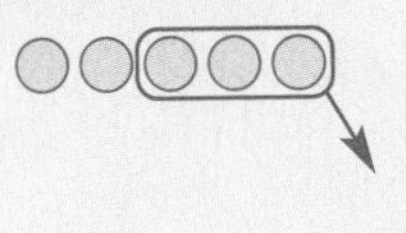

3. 5 − 3
4. −2 − (4)

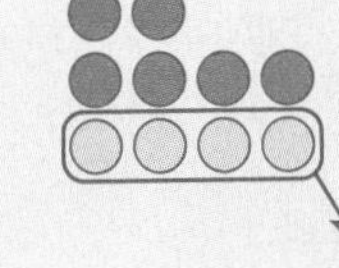

Georgia Performance Standards

M6P2.c Develop and evaluate mathematical arguments and proofs.

M6P5.a Create and use representations to organize, record, and communicate mathematical ideas.

M6P5.b Select, apply, and translate among mathematical representations to solve problems.

M6P5.c Use representations to model and interpret physical, social, and mathematical phenomena.

11-5 Organizer

Pacing: Traditional $1\frac{1}{2}$ day
Block $\frac{3}{4}$ day

Objective: Students subtract integers.

Hands-On Lab
In *Hands-On Lab Activities*

Online Edition
Tutorial Videos, Interactivities

Power Presentations with PowerPoint®

Warm Up

Find each sum.

1. $-4 + 6$ 2 **2.** $5 + 12$ 17

3. $-3 + 3$ 0 **4.** $-8 + 9$ 1

Give the opposite of each number.

5. 7 −7 **6.** −8 8

7. −3 3 **8.** 1 −1

Problem of the Day

Jamal knows his average score on 3 science tests. If he adds the average and the amount that each score differs from the average, what will his sum be? the average

Also available on transparency

11-5 Subtracting Integers

Learn to subtract integers.

Georgia Performance Standards

M6A3 Evaluate algebraic expressions. Also, M6P5.a, M6P5.b, M6P5.c.

On a number line, integer subtraction is the opposite of integer addition. Integer subtraction "undoes" integer addition.

Subtracting Integers on a Number Line
Move left on a number line to subtract a positive integer.
Move right on a number line to subtract a negative integer.

EXAMPLE 1 Writing Integer Subtraction

Write the subtraction modeled on each number line.

A

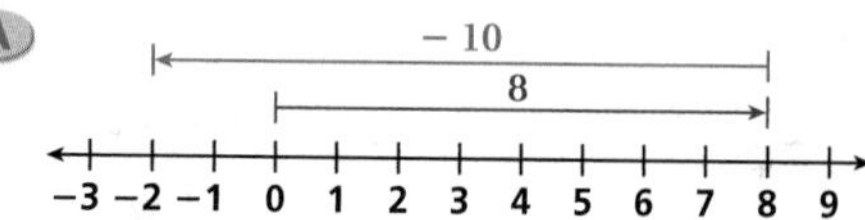

The subtraction modeled is $8 - 10 = -2$.

B

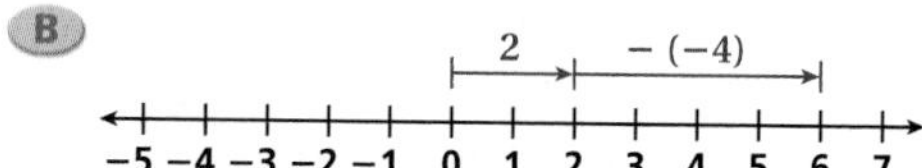

The subtraction modeled is $2 - (-4) = 6$.

EXAMPLE 2 Subtracting Integers

Find each difference.

A $7 - 4$

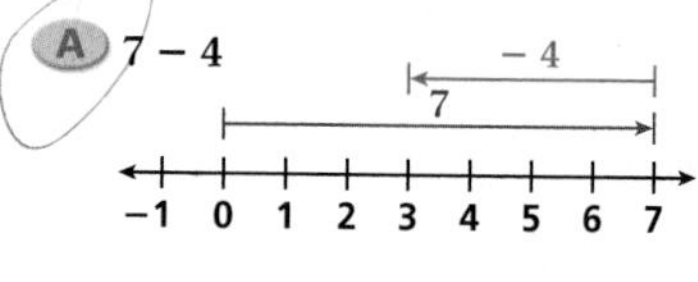

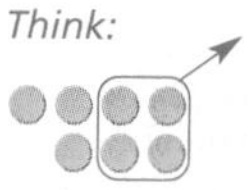

$7 - 4 = 3$

B $-8 - (-2)$

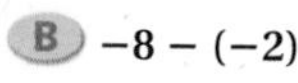

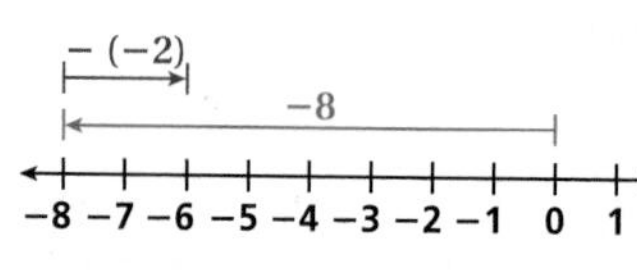

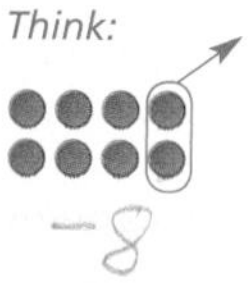

$-8 - (-2) = -6$

Georgia Performance Standards

M6A3 Students will evaluate algebraic expressions, including those with exponents, and solve simple one-step equations using each of the four basic operations.

M6P5.a Create and use representations to organize, record, and communicate mathematical ideas.

M6P5.b Select, apply, and translate among mathematical representations to solve problems.

M6P5.c Use representations to model and interpret physical, social, and mathematical phenomena.

1 Introduce

Alternate Opener

EXPLORATION

11-5 Subtracting Integers

You can use a number line to model subtracting integers.

To subtract 20 from 50, begin at the number being subtracted, 20, and count the number of units to the number 50.

The direction is **right**, so the difference is **positive**.

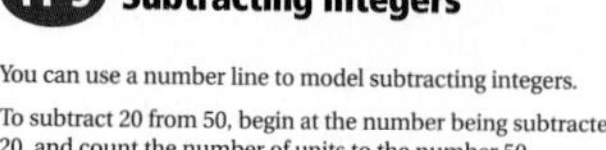

$50 - 20 = 30$

To subtract −20 from −60, begin at the number being subtracted, −20, and count the number of units to the number −60.

The direction is left, so the difference is negative.

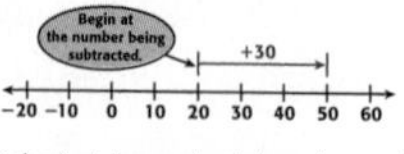

$-60 - (-20) = -40$

Use a number line to find each difference.

1. $12 - 10 =$ ___
2. $15 - 20 =$ ___
3. $-8 - 5 =$ ___
4. $-6 - (-4) =$ ___
5. $2 - (-4) =$ ___
6. $7 - (-2) =$ ___

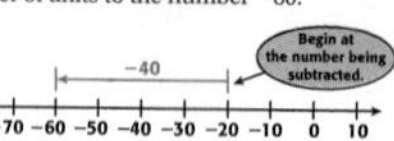

Think and Discuss

7. **Describe** how to use a number line to model subtraction.

2 Teach

Guided Instruction

In this lesson, students learn to subtract integers. First, teach the rules for integer subtraction (Teaching Transparency). Then teach students to write the subtraction modeled on number lines. Next, let them find differences using number lines and evaluate integer subtraction expressions.

Explorations and answers are provided in *Alternate Openers: Explorations Transparencies.*

EXAMPLE 3 **Evaluating Integer Expressions**

Evaluate $x - (-4)$ for $x = -5$.

$x - (-4)$	*Write the expression.*	
$-5 - (-4)$	*Substitute −5 for x.*	*Think:* 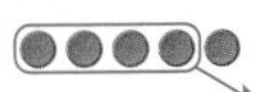
-1	*Subtract.*	

Possible answers to *Think and Discuss*

1. right; left
2. To add a positive integer, you move in the direction opposite of when you subtract a positive integer.

Think and Discuss  GPS M6P1.d, M6P3.b

1. **Describe** the direction you would move to add a positive integer. to subtract a positive integer.
2. **Explain** how the answers to Example 1 help show that addition and subtraction are inverses.

11-5 Exercises

Georgia Performance Standards

M6P1.b, M6P3.c, M6P5.a, M6P5.b

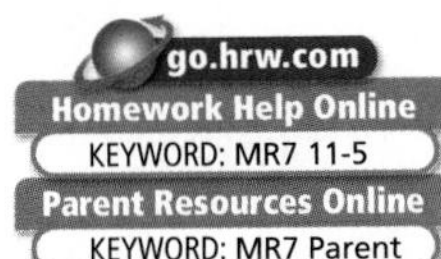

go.hrw.com
Homework Help Online
KEYWORD: MR7 11-5
Parent Resources Online
KEYWORD: MR7 Parent

GUIDED PRACTICE

See Example 1

1. Write the subtraction modeled on the number line. $6 - 5 = 1$

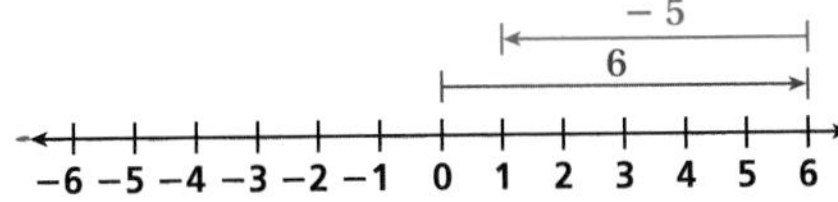

See Example 2 Find each difference.

2. $6 - 3$ 3
3. $3 - 6$ −3
4. $10 - (-4)$ 14
5. $-12 - (-4)$ −8

See Example 3 Evaluate $n - (-6)$ for each value of n.

6. $n = -4$ 2
7. $n = 2$ 8
8. $n = -15$ −9
9. $n = 7$ 13

INDEPENDENT PRACTICE

See Example 1

10. Write the subtraction modeled on the number line. $-2 - (-3) = 1$

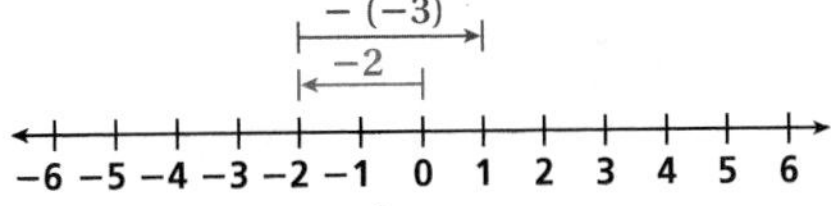

See Example 2 Find each difference.

11. $3 - 7$ −4
12. $-4 - 9$ −13
13. $2 - (-9)$ 11
14. $-22 - (-2)$ −20

See Example 3 Evaluate $m - (-3)$ for each value of m.

15. $m = -1$ 2
16. $m = 7$ 10
17. $m = -8$ −5
18. $m = -5$ −2
19. $m = 4$ 7
20. $m = -9$ −6
21. $m = -15$ −12
22. $m = 13$ 16

Power Presentations with PowerPoint® 

Additional Examples

Example 1

Write the subtraction modeled on each number line.

A. 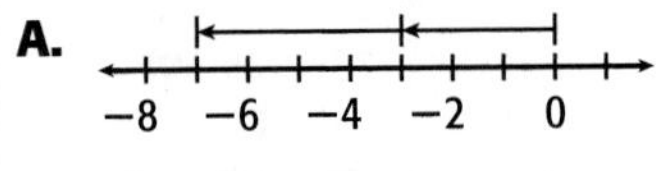

$-3 - 4 = -7$

B. 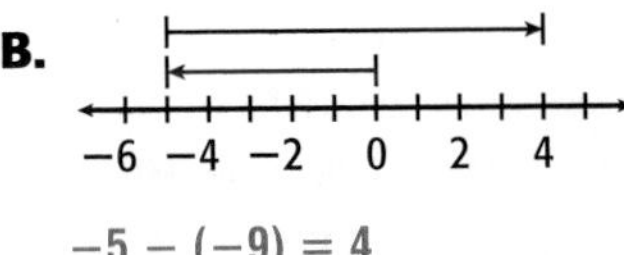

$-5 - (-9) = 4$

Example 2

Find each difference.

A. $4 - 6$ −2 **B.** $3 - (-3)$ 6

Example 3

Evaluate $a - 4$ for $a = 2$. −2

Also available on transparency 

11-5 Exercises

Assignment Guide

If you finished Example 1 assign:
Average 1, 43–54
Advanced 10, 43–54

If you finished Example 2 assign:
Average 1–5, 23–30, 43–54
Advanced 10–14, 23–30, 43–54

If you finished Example 3 assign:
Average 1–39, 43–54
Advanced 10–54

Homework Quick Check

Quickly check key concepts.
Exercises: 14, 18, 20, 26, 30

Reaching All Learners

Through Curriculum Integration

Social Studies Have students find and list the record high and low temperatures for various countries. Then have students subtract to find the difference between the high and low temperatures for a given country.

3 Close

Summarize

Emphasize to students that subtraction of an integer on a number line looks the same as addition of that integer's opposite.

Georgia Performance Standards

M6P1.b Solve problems that arise in mathematics and in other contexts.

M6P3.c Analyze and evaluate the mathematical thinking and strategies of others.

M6P5.a Create and use representations to organize, record, and communicate mathematical ideas.

M6P5.b Select, apply, and translate among mathematical representations to solve problems.

ONGOING ASSESSMENT and INTERVENTION

Diagnose ***Before*** **the Lesson**
11-5 Warm Up, TE p. 622

Monitor ***During*** **the Lesson**
11-5 Know-It Notebook
11-5 Questioning Strategies

Assess ***After*** **the Lesson**
11-5 Lesson Quiz, TE p. 624

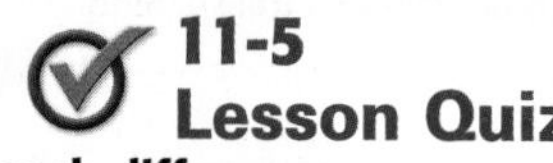

Power Presentations with PowerPoint®

11-5 Lesson Quiz

Find each difference.

1. $8 - 5$ 3 **2.** $-9 - (-3)$ -6

Evaluate $x - (-7)$ for each value of x.

3. $x = -2$ 5 **4.** $x = 5$ 12

5. The peak of Mt. Everest is approximately 26,544 ft above sea level. The shore of the Dead Sea is about 1,200 ft below sea level. How much higher is the peak of Mt. Everest than the shore of the Dead Sea? 27,744 ft

Also available on transparency

PRACTICE AND PROBLEM SOLVING

CRCT GPS
Extra Practice p. 735

40–41. See p. A12.

Find each difference.

23. $-12 - (-6)$ -6 **24.** $7 - (-3)$ 10 **25.** $-4 - (-3)$ -1 **26.** $8 - (-2)$ 10

27. $19 - (-2)$ 21 **28.** $-5 - 10$ -15 **29.** $50 - 20$ 30 **30.** $-2 - 7$ -9

Evaluate each expression for the given value of the variable.

31. $n - (-10), n = 2$ 12 **32.** $-6 - m, m = -9$ 3 **33.** $x - 2, x = 6$ 4

34. $4 - y, y = 9$ -5 **35.** $j - 21, j = -17$ -38 **36.** $101 - h, h = -75$ 176

37. Earth Science The surface of an underground water supply was 10 m below sea level. After one year, the depth of the water supply has decreased by 9 m. How far below sea level is the water's surface now? -19 m

38. Construction A 200-foot column holds an oil rig platform above the ocean's surface. The column rests on the ocean floor 175 feet below sea level. How high is the platform above sea level? 25 ft

39. Earth Science During summer 1997, NASA landed the *Pathfinder* on Mars. On July 9, *Pathfinder* reported a temperature of -1°F on the planet's surface. On July 10, it reported a temperature of 8°F. Find the difference between the temperature on July 10 and the temperature on July 9. 9°F

40. What's the Error? Ty says that $0 - (-4) = -4$. Explain why this is incorrect.

41. Write About It Will the difference between two negative numbers ever be positive? Use examples to support your answer.

42. Challenge This pyramid was built by subtracting integers. Two integers are subtracted from left to right, and their difference is centered above them. Find the missing numbers.

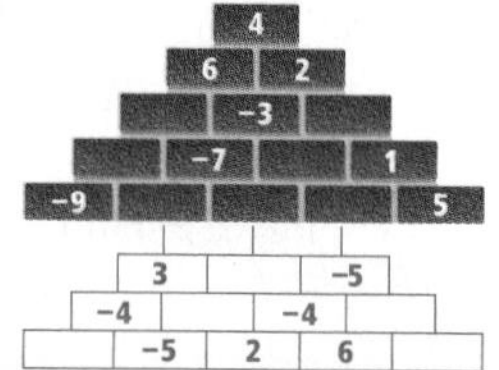

CRCT PREP • GPS SUPPORT • SPIRAL REVIEW

43. Multiple Choice Evaluate $h - (-8)$ for $h = 3$.

Ⓐ -11 Ⓑ -5 Ⓒ 5 Ⓓ 11

44. Multiple Choice Trina's score on a game show was -250 points. Gwen's score was -320 points. By how many points was Trina ahead of Gwen?

Ⓕ 570 points Ⓖ 70 points Ⓗ -70 points Ⓙ -570 points

Write each decimal as a percent. (Lesson 7-8)

45. 0.02 2% **46.** 0.53 53% **47.** 0.26 26% **48.** 0.44 44% **49.** 3.1 310%

Name the quadrant where each ordered pair is located. (Lesson 11-3)

50. $(4, -6)$ IV **51.** $(-1, 5)$ II **52.** $(2, 3)$ I **53.** $(-2, -4)$ III **54.** $(-10, 5)$ II

CHALLENGE 11-5
PROBLEM SOLVING 11-5

LESSON 11-5 **Problem Solving**
Subtracting Integers

Write the correct answer.

1. The average surface temperature on Earth is 59°F. The average surface temperature on Mars is 126°F lower than on Earth. What is the average surface temperature on Mars?
-67°F

2. The average surface temperature on Saturn is 46°F colder than on Jupiter. Jupiter's average surface temperature is 162°F below zero. What is the average surface temperature on Saturn?
-208°F

3. Venus has the hottest average surface temperature at 854°F. Mercury, the planet closest to the Sun, has an average surface temperature that is 522°F colder than Venus's. What is Mercury's average surface temperature?
332°F

4. Pluto, the planet farthest from the Sun, has an average surface temperature of 355°F below zero. Neptune, its closest neighbor, has the coldest average surface temperature. It is 10°F colder on Neptune than on Pluto. What is the average surface temperature on Neptune?
-365°F

Circle the letter of the correct answer.

5. Which of the following is the difference between 247°F below zero and 221°F above zero?
A -26°F
B 129°F
Ⓒ -468°F
D 468°F

6. Which of the following is the difference between 806°C above zero and 328°C below zero?
Ⓕ 1,134°C
G 478°C
H -478°C
J $-1{,}134$°C

7. Which of the following is the difference between -40°C and -30°C?
Ⓐ -10°C
B 708C
C -120°C
D -1°C

8. Which of the following is the difference between 8,700°F and -344°F?
F 8,356°F
G 900°F
H -9°F
Ⓙ 9,044°F

RETEACH 11-5

LESSON 11-5 **Reteach**
Subtracting Integers

Two-color counters can help you understand integers.

One positive counter and one negative counter is called a zero pair because together they have a value of zero.

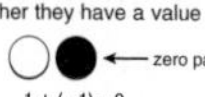

$1 + (-1) = 0$

You can use two-color counters to find the difference between integers. $5 - 7$
The first integer tells you how many counters to start off with.

If there are not enough counters to subtract, add zero pairs.

Then take away the number of counters given by the second integer.

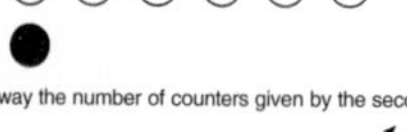

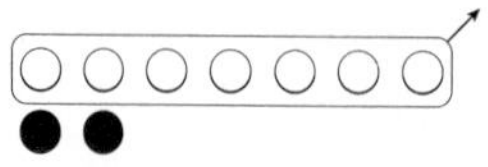

The remaining counters represent the difference. $5 - 7 = -2$

Use counters to find each difference.

1. $-3 - (5)$ -8 **2.** $5 - 8$ -3 **3.** $-9 - (-7)$ -2 **4.** $1 - 6$ -5

5. $-4 - (-3)$ -1 **6.** $2 - (-5)$ 7 **7.** $-6 - 4$ -10 **8.** $5 - (-4)$ 9

9. $2 - (-3)$ 5 **10.** $-7 - (-3)$ -4 **11.** $10 - 8$ 2 **12.** $-4 - (-5)$ 1

PRACTICE 11-5

LESSON 11-5 **Practice B**
Subtracting Integers

Write the subtraction modeled on each number line.

1. (number line: -3, -1; -5 to 5) $-1 - 3$

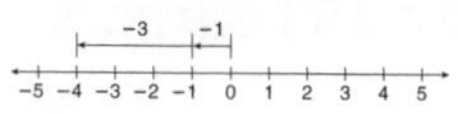

2. (number line: $+4$, $-(-2)$; -2 to 8) $4 - (-2)$

3. (number line: $-(-1)$, -5; -5 to 5) $-5 - (-1)$

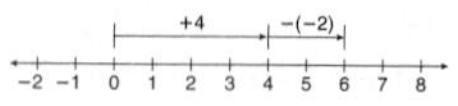

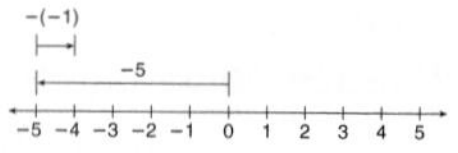

Find each difference.

4. $8 - (-1)$ 9 **5.** $-5 - 2$ -7 **6.** $-10 - (-3)$ -7

7. $-2 - (-1)$ -1 **8.** $4 - (-6)$ 10 **9.** $-9 - (-5)$ -4

10. $15 - (-8)$ 23 **11.** $0 - (-6)$ 6 **12.** $-20 - (-9)$ -11

Evaluate $n - (-2)$ for each value of n.

13. $n = 2$ 4 **14.** $n = -4$ -2 **15.** $n = 5$ 7

16. $n = -3$ -1 **17.** $n = 1$ 3 **18.** $n = 0$ 2

19. In a golf tournament, Sarah scored a +2 on the first round and a -4 on the second round. What was the difference between her scores on the first two rounds?
6

20. Washington, D.C., has an elevation of 1 foot above sea level. The elevation of New Orleans is 8 feet below sea level. What is the difference in the two cities' elevations?
9 feet

11-6 Multiplying Integers

Learn to multiply integers.

Georgia Performance Standards

M6A3 Evaluate algebraic expressions. Also, M6P1.b.

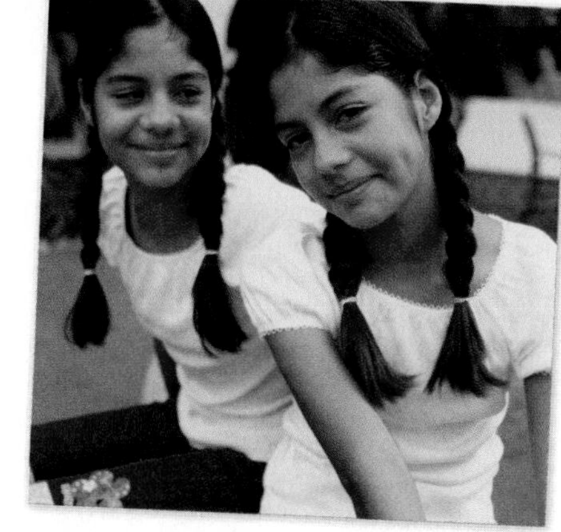

You have seen that you can multiply whole numbers to count items in equally sized groups.

There are three sets of twins in the sixth grade. How many sixth graders are twins?

A set of twins is 2 people.

$3 \cdot 2 = 6$ *3 sets of 2 is 6.*

So 6 students in the sixth grade are twins.

Multiplying with integers is similar.

Numbers	$3 \cdot 2$	$-3 \cdot 2$	$3 \cdot (-2)$	$-3 \cdot (-2)$
Words	3 groups of 2	the opposite of 3 groups of 2	3 groups of −2	the opposite of 3 groups of −2
Addition	$2 + 2 + 2$	$-(2 + 2 + 2)$	$(-2) + (-2) + (-2)$	$-[(-2) + (-2) + (-2)]$
Product	6	−6	−6	6

EXAMPLE  **Multiplying Integers**

Find each product.

A $4 \cdot 3$

$4 \cdot 3 = 12$ *Think: 4 groups of 3*

B $2 \cdot (-4)$

$2 \cdot (-4) = -8$ *Think: 2 groups of −4*

C $-5 \cdot 2$

$-5 \cdot 2 = -10$ *Think: **the opposite of** 5 groups of 2*

D $-3 \cdot (-4)$

$-3 \cdot (-4) = 12$ *Think: **the opposite of** 3 groups of −4*

Remember!

To find the opposite of a number, change the sign. The opposite of 6 is −6. The opposite of −4 is 4.

Organizer 11-6

Pacing: Traditional 1 day
Block $\frac{1}{2}$ day

Objective: Students multiply integers.

Technology Lab
In *Technology Lab Activities*

Online Edition
Tutorial Videos

Power Presentations with PowerPoint®

Warm Up

Find each product.

1. $8 \cdot 4$ 32 **2.** $7 \cdot 12$ 84
3. $3 \cdot 9$ 27 **4.** $6 \cdot 5$ 30
5. $80 \cdot 6$ 480 **6.** $50 \cdot 6$ 300
7. $40 \cdot 90$ 3,600 **8.** $20 \cdot 700$ 14,000

Problem of the Day

Catherine has $14.00 and earns $12.00 for each lawn she mows. If she mows 4 lawns and buys 5 DVDs that cost $11.95 each, including tax, how much money does she have left? $2.25

Also available on transparency

Math Fact !

Because the product of two numbers with the same sign can never be negative, no negative number has a real square root.

1 Introduce

Alternate Opener

EXPLORATION

11-6 Multiplying Integers

Complete each table.

1.

$2 \cdot 3 = 6$	$-2 \cdot (3) = -6$	$2 \cdot (-3) = -6$	$-2 \cdot (-3) = 6$
$2 \cdot 2 =$	$-2 \cdot (2) =$	$2 \cdot (-2) =$	$-2 \cdot (-2) =$
$2 \cdot 1 =$	$-2 \cdot (1) =$	$2 \cdot (-1) =$	$-2 \cdot (-1) =$

2.

$3 \cdot 3 =$	$-3 \cdot (3) =$	$3 \cdot (-3) =$	$-3 \cdot (-3) =$
$3 \cdot 2 =$	$-3 \cdot (2) =$	$3 \cdot (-2) =$	$-3 \cdot (-2) =$
$3 \cdot 1 =$	$-3 \cdot (1) =$	$3 \cdot (-1) =$	$-3 \cdot (-1) =$

3.

$4 \cdot 3 =$	$-4 \cdot (3) =$	$4 \cdot (-3) =$	$-4 \cdot (-3) =$
$4 \cdot 2 =$	$-4 \cdot (2) =$	$4 \cdot (-2) =$	$-4 \cdot (-2) =$
$4 \cdot 1 =$	$-4 \cdot (1) =$	$4 \cdot (-1) =$	$-4 \cdot (-1) =$

Think and Discuss

4. Describe the patterns you notice in each of the tables.

2 Teach

Guided Instruction

In this lesson, students learn to multiply integers (Teaching Transparency). First, review the four possible situations for integer multiplication, (+) · (+), (+) · (−), (−) · (−), and (−) · (+). Then teach the rules for multiplying integers. Give special attention to the rule (−) · (−) = (+). Next, teach students to evaluate expressions that involve the multiplication of integers.

Explorations and answers are provided in *Alternate Openers: Explorations Transparencies.*

Georgia Performance Standards

M6A3 Students will evaluate algebraic expressions, including those with exponents, and solve simple one-step equations using each of the four basic operations.

M6P1.b Solve problems that arise in mathematics and in other contexts.

MULTIPLYING INTEGERS

If the signs are the same, the product is positive.

$4 \cdot 3 = 12$ $-6 \cdot (-3) = 18$

If the signs are different, the product is negative.

$-2 \cdot 5 = -10$ $7 \cdot (-8) = -56$

The product of any number and 0 is 0.

$0 \cdot 9 = 0$ $(-12) \cdot 0 = 0$

Power Presentations with PowerPoint®

Additional Examples

Example 1

Find each product.

A. $5 \cdot 2$ 10

B. $4 \cdot (-5)$ −20

C. $-3 \cdot 2$ −6

D. $-2 \cdot (-4)$ 8

Example 2

Evaluate $-7x$ for each value of x.

A. $x = -3$ 21

B. $x = 5$ −35

Also available on transparency

EXAMPLE 2 Evaluating Integer Expressions

Remember!

$5x$ means $5 \cdot x$.

Evaluate $5x$ for each value of x.

A $x = -4$

$5x$ *Write the expression.*

$5 \cdot (-4)$ *Substitute −4 for x.*

-20 *The signs are different, so the answer is negative.*

B $x = 0$

$5x$ *Write the expression.*

$5 \cdot 0$ *Substitute 0 for x.*

0 *Any number times 0 is 0.*

Possible answers to *Think and Discuss*

1. Similar: Both can be shown as repeated addition. Different: You have to decide whether the product is positive or negative when multiplying integers.

Think and Discuss

GPS M6P1.d

1. Explain how multiplying integers is similar to multiplying whole numbers. How is it different?

11-6 Exercises

Assignment Guide

If you finished Example 1 assign:
Average 1–8, 44–51
Advanced 17–24, 44–51

If you finished Example 2 assign:
Average 1–24, 44–51
Advanced 17–38, 41–51

Homework Quick Check

Quickly check key concepts.
Exercises: 18, 20, 22, 24

11-6 Exercises

Georgia Performance Standards
M6P3.a, M6P3.c, M6P4.c

go.hrw.com
Homework Help Online
KEYWORD: MR7 11-6
Parent Resources Online
KEYWORD: MR7 Parent

GUIDED PRACTICE

See Example 1 Find each product.

1. $6 \cdot 4$ 24
2. $5 \cdot (-2)$ −10
3. $-3 \cdot 7$ −21
4. $-2 \cdot 3$ −6
5. $-9 \cdot (-1)$ 9
6. $13 \cdot 0$ 0
7. $-8 \cdot (-2)$ 16
8. $-6 \cdot (-6)$ 36

See Example 2 Evaluate $3n$ for each value of n.

9. $n = 3$ 9
10. $n = -2$ −6
11. $n = 11$ 33
12. $n = -5$ −15
13. $n = -8$ −24
14. $n = -12$ −36
15. $n = 6$ 18
16. $n = 10$ 30

Georgia Performance Standards

M6P3.a Organize and consolidate their mathematical thinking through communication.

M6P3.c Analyze and evaluate the mathematical thinking and strategies of others.

M6P4.c Recognize and apply mathematics in contexts outside of mathematics.

Reaching All Learners

Through Cooperative Learning

Have students work in groups to generate positive and negative numbers by simultaneously rolling a number cube and flipping a two-color counter (provided in the Manipulatives Kit). Let red indicate negative and yellow indicate positive. The students record pairs of numbers and find their products. After five different products have been found, have them order the products from least to greatest. It would be helpful to model how to play this game before assigning it to students.

3 Close

Summarize

Give the students four multiplication situations (positive times positive, positive times negative, negative times positive, and negative times negative), and have a volunteer give an expression as an example of each situation. Have another student evaluate the expression and state the rule for multiplying that pair of integers.

Possible answer:
Rules: Positive times negative or negative times positive gives a negative product; negative times negative or positive times positive gives a positive product.

INDEPENDENT PRACTICE

See Example 1 — Find each product.

17. 5 • 9 **45**
18. −7 • 6 **−42**
19. 8 • (−4) **−32**
20. −6 • (−9) **54**
21. −13 • (−3) **39**
22. 4 • 12 **48**
23. 6 • (−12) **−72**
24. −7 • (−11) **77**

See Example 2 — Evaluate $-4a$ for each value of a.

25. $a = 6$ **−24**
26. $a = 12$ **−48**
27. $a = 3$ **−12**
28. $a = -7$ **28**
29. $a = -10$ **40**
30. $a = 7$ **−28**
31. $a = -15$ **60**
32. $a = -22$ **88**

PRACTICE AND PROBLEM SOLVING

Extra Practice p. 736

Evaluate each expression for the given value of the variable.

33. $n \cdot (-7)$; $n = -2$ **14**
34. $-6 \cdot m$; $m = 4$ **−24**
35. $9x$; $x = 6$ **54**
36. $-5m$; $m = 5$ **−25**
37. $x \cdot 10$; $x = -9$ **−90**
38. $-8 \cdot n$; $n = -1$ **8**

Georgia LINK — Earth Science

The normal tidal range of the Savannah River near Savannah, GA, is about 8 feet.

39. **Earth Science** When the moon, the sun, and Earth are in a straight line, spring tides occur on Earth. Spring tides may cause high and low tides to be two times as great as normal. If high tides at a certain location are usually 2 ft and low tides are usually −2 ft, what might the spring tides be? **4 ft to −4 ft**

40. **Critical Thinking** What number property is true for integer multiplication? **Commutative Property**

41. **What's the Error?** Ava says the value of $-6b$ when $b = -6$ is −36. What is her error? What is the correct answer? **A negative multiplied by a negative is positive; 36.**

42. **Write About It** What is the sign of the product when you multiply three negative integers? four negative integers? Use examples to explain. **negative; positive. possible examples: −2 • −2 • −2 = −8; −2 • −2 • −2 • −2 = 16**

43. **Challenge** Name 2 integers whose product is −36 and whose sum is 0. **6 and −6**

CRCT PREP • GPS SUPPORT • SPIRAL REVIEW

44. **Multiple Choice** During a game, Frieda scored −10 points for each question she missed. She missed 5 questions. What was the total number of points she scored on missed questions?

Ⓐ −50 (circled)   Ⓑ −2   Ⓒ 2   Ⓓ 50

45. **Extended Response** What is the sign of the product when 4 negative integers are multiplied? when 5 negative integers are multiplied? Describe a rule that can be used to determine the sign of the product when the number of negative integers is even and when the number of negative integers is odd.

46. Kim cut $6\frac{1}{3}$ yards of ribbon into $\frac{1}{3}$-yard pieces. How many pieces of ribbon did Kim cut? (Lesson 5-9) **19**

Find each sum. (Lesson 11-4)

47. 3 + 6 **9**
48. −5 + 1 **−4**
49. −4 + (−9) **−13**
50. 7 + (−7) **0**
51. 2 + (−5) **−3**

ONGOING ASSESSMENT and INTERVENTION

Diagnose Before the Lesson
11-6 Warm Up, TE p. 625

Monitor During the Lesson
11-6 Know-It Notebook
11-6 Questioning Strategies

Assess After the Lesson
11-6 Lesson Quiz, TE p. 627

Answers

45. Positive; negative; possible answer: when an even number of negative integers are multiplied, the product is positive. When an odd number of negative integers are multiplied, the product is negative.

Power Presentations with PowerPoint®

11-6 Lesson Quiz

Find each product.

1. 6 • (4) **24**
2. 3 • (−2) **−6**
3. −9 • (−2) **18**
4. −6 • 5 **−30**
5. Evaluate $3y$ for $y = -7$. **−21**
6. During a football game, Raymond's team lost 6 yards on each of 3 plays and gained 8 yards on each of 2 plays. What integer represents the total change in the team's position? **−2**

Also available on transparency

RETEACH 11-6

LESSON 11-6 Reteach
Multiplying Integers

You can use two-color counters to multiply integers.

(+1) (−1)

Multiply −4 by 2.

First, think about the numerical expression in words.

−4 • 2 means "the opposite of 4 groups of 2."

Then use counters to represent the expression.

4 groups of 2

4 groups of 2 are 8.

The opposite of 8 is −8.

−4 • 2 = −8.

Use counters to find each product.

1. 3 • (−3) **−9**
2. −5 • (−1) **5**
3. 2 • 3 **6**
4. −3 • 4 **−12**
5. −4 • (4) **−16**
6. 0 • (−3) **0**
7. −11 • (1) **−11**
8. −6 • −2 **12**
9. −2 • (−4) **8**
10. 7 • (−2) **−14**
11. 5 • 3 **15**
12. −8 • (−2) **16**

PRACTICE 11-6

LESSON 11-6 Practice B
Multiplying Integers

Write the sign of each product.

1. 7 • 8 **positive**
2. 5 • (−9) **negative**
3. −4 • 12 **negative**
4. −6 • (−11) **positive**
5. −3 • 8 **negative**
6. −12 • (−18) **positive**

Find each product.

7. 5 • (−7) **−35**
8. −4 • 3 **−12**
9. −8 • (−2) **16**
10. −9 • (−1) **9**
11. 5 • (−6) **−30**
12. −10 • (−4) **40**
13. 6 • (−8) **−48**
14. 0 • (−3) **0**
15. 7 • (−9) **−63**

Evaluate $4n$ for each value of n.

16. $n = 2$ **8**
17. $n = -4$ **−16**
18. $n = -7$ **−28**
19. $n = -3$ **−12**
20. $n = 11$ **44**
21. $n = 0$ **0**

Evaluate $-3n$ for each value of n.

22. $n = -5$ **15**
23. $n = 0$ **0**
24. $n = 6$ **−18**
25. $n = -8$ **24**
26. $n = 7$ **−21**
27. $n = -1$ **3**

28. Last month, Tyler made five withdrawals of $25 each from his bank account and no deposits. What multiplication expression models Tyler's bank transactions last month? **5 • (−25)**

29. The Atlantic Ocean is sinking 4 inches every 100 years. Write a multiplication expression that models how much the Atlantic Ocean will sink in 300 years. How many inches will it sink in that time? **3 • (−4); 12 inches**

CHALLENGE 11-6
PROBLEM SOLVING 11-6

LESSON 11-6 Problem Solving
Multiplying Integers

Write the correct answer.

1. The coldest temperature ever recorded in Rhode Island was 25°F below zero. Though Nevada lies much farther south, its coldest temperature was twice as cold as Rhode Island's. What was Nevada's record cold temperature? **−50°F**

2. Tom and Kim made up a game in which black tiles equal +5 points each, and red tiles equal −3 points each. The person with the most points wins. At the end of the game Tom had 6 red tiles and 4 black tiles, and Kim had 4 red tiles and 3 black tiles. Who won? **Kim**

3. During a month-long drought, the amount of water in the family's well changed −4 gallons a day. How much did the amount of water in the well change after one week? **−28 gallons**

4. Sperm whales dive deeper than any other mammals. They regularly dive to 3,937 feet below sea level. But they sometimes dive to twice this depth! To what elevation can sperm whales dive? **−7,874 feet**

Circle the letter of the correct answer.

5. On Monday morning, the value of LCM stock was $15 a share. Then the value of the stock changed by −3 dollars a day for 4 days in a row. What was the value of one share of LCM stock after the fourth day?
   - A $1
   - Ⓑ $3 (circled)
   - C $6
   - D $12

6. Lake Manitoba and Lake Winnipeg are two of the largest lakes in Canada. The greatest depth of Lake Manitoba is 12 feet. Lake Winnipeg is 5 times deeper than Lake Manitoba. What is the greatest depth of Lake Winnipeg?
   - F 5 feet
   - G 17 feet
   - H 50 feet
   - Ⓙ 60 feet (circled)

7. Which addition expression could be used to check the product of 5 • (−3)?
   - A 5 + 5 + 5
   - B −3 + (−3) + (−3)
   - C 5 + 5 + 5 + 5 + 5
   - Ⓓ −3 + (−3) + (−3) + (−3) + (−3) (circled)

8. Which property allows you to rewrite −2 • (−4) as −4 • (−2)?
   - Ⓕ Commutative Property (circled)
   - G Distributive Property
   - H Integer Property
   - J Associative Property

11-7 Organizer

Pacing: Traditional 1 day
Block $\frac{1}{2}$ day

Objective: Students divide integers.

Technology Lab
In *Technology Lab Activities*

Online Edition
Tutorial Videos

Power Presentations with PowerPoint®

Warm Up

Find each quotient.

1. 18 ÷ 2 9 **2.** 42 ÷ 7 6
3. 56 ÷ 8 7 **4.** 24 ÷ 6 4
5. 3,600 ÷ 4 900 **6.** 540 ÷ 60 9

Problem of the Day

Hank wanted to record the number of marbles he lost to his friend Marcus each day for 5 days. He forgot to record one day, but for the other days he wrote 8, 2, 3, and 4. The average number he lost was 4. What number did he forget to write? 3

Also available on transparency

Math Humor

Student: I love doing gazintas. They're my favorite!

Math teacher: I don't understand. What do you mean by *gazintas*?

Student: You know. Like, three gazinta 12 four times; two gazinta 18 nine times…

Georgia Performance Standards

M6A3 Students will evaluate algebraic expressions, including those with exponents, and solve simple one-step equations using each of the four basic operations.

M6P4.c Recognize and apply mathematics in contexts outside of mathematics.

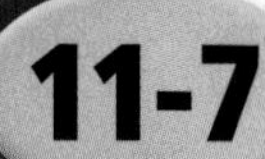

11-7 Dividing Integers

Learn to divide integers.

Georgia Performance Standards

M6A3 Evaluate algebraic expressions. Also, M6P4.c.

Mona is a biologist studying an endangered species of wombat. Each year she records the change in the wombat population.

Year	Change in Population
1	−2
2	−5
3	−1
4	−4

Baby Australian wombat

Remember!

To find the mean of a list of numbers:
1. Add all the numbers together.
2. Divide by how many numbers are in the list.

One way to describe the change in the wombat population over time is to find the mean of the data in the table.

$$\frac{-2 + (-5) + (-1) + (-4)}{4} = \frac{-12}{4} = -12 \div 4 = \blacksquare$$

Multiplication and division are inverse operations. To solve a division problem, think of the related multiplication.

To solve −12 ÷ 4, think: What number times 4 equals −12?

$$-3 \cdot 4 = -12, \text{ so } -12 \div 4 = -3$$

The mean change in the wombat population is −3. So on average, the population **decreased by 3 wombats** per year.

EXAMPLE 1 Dividing Integers

Find each quotient.

A $12 \div (-3)$

Think: What number times −3 equals 12?

$-4 \cdot (-3) = 12$, so $12 \div (-3) = -4$.

B $-15 \div (-3)$

Think: What number times −3 equals −15?

$5 \cdot (-3) = -15$, so $-15 \div (-3) = 5$.

1 Introduce

Alternate Opener

EXPLORATION

11-7 Dividing Integers

For each multiplication statement, you can write two related division statements.

Multiplication statement	Division statements
2 · 3 = 6	6 ÷ 3 = 2 and 6 ÷ 2 = 3

Complete each table.

1.

Multiply	4 · (−3) =	−4 · (−3) =	−4 · 3 =
Divide	−12 ÷ 4 =	12 ÷ (−4) =	−12 ÷ (−4) =
	−12 ÷ (−3) =	12 ÷ (−3) =	−12 ÷ 3 =

2.

Multiply	2 · (−5) =	−2 · (−5) =	−2 · 5 =
Divide	−10 ÷ 2 =	10 ÷ (−2) =	−10 ÷ (−2) =
	−10 ÷ (−5) =	10 ÷ (−5) =	−10 ÷ 5 =

3.

Multiply	8 · (−3) =	−8 · (−3) =	−8 · 3 =
Divide	−24 ÷ 8 =	24 ÷ (−8) =	−24 ÷ (−8) =
	−24 ÷ (−3) =	24 ÷ (−3) =	−24 ÷ 3 =

Think and Discuss

4. Describe what you think the sign rules are for dividing a positive integer by a negative integer, a negative integer by a positive integer, and a negative integer by a negative integer.

Motivate

Remind students that division is the inverse of multiplication by writing 5 · 2 = 10; therefore, 10 ÷ 5 = 2 and 10 ÷ 2 = 5. Tell them that with this information they can discover the rules for dividing integers. Give examples, such as −3 · −4 = 12 and 2 · −3 = −6. See if anyone discovers the rules for dividing integers.

Explorations and answers are provided in *Alternate Openers: Explorations Transparencies.*

Because division is the inverse of multiplication, the rules for dividing integers are the same as the rules for multiplying integers.

DIVIDING INTEGERS

If the signs are the same, the quotient is positive.

$24 \div 3 = 8$ $\quad -6 \div (-3) = 2$

If the signs are different, the quotient is negative.

$-20 \div 5 = -4$ $\quad 72 \div (-8) = -9$

Zero divided by any integer equals 0.

$\frac{0}{14} = 0$ $\quad \frac{0}{-11} = 0$

You cannot divide any integer by 0.

EXAMPLE 2 Evaluating Integer Expressions

Remember!

$\frac{x}{3}$ means $x \div 3$.

Evaluate $\frac{x}{3}$ for each value of *x*.

A $x = 6$

$\frac{x}{3}$	*Write the expression.*
$\frac{6}{3} = 6 \div 3$	*Substitute 6 for x.*
$= 2$	*The signs are the same, so the answer is positive.*

B $x = -18$

$\frac{x}{3}$	*Write the expression.*
$\frac{-18}{3} = -18 \div 3$	*Substitute −18 for x.*
$= -6$	*The signs are different, so the answer is negative.*

C $x = -12$

$\frac{x}{3}$	*Write the expression.*
$\frac{-12}{3} = -12 \div 3$	*Substitute −12 for x.*
$= -4$	*The signs are different, so the answer is negative.*

Think and Discuss GPS M6P3.a

1. **Describe** the sign of the quotient of two integers with like signs.
2. **Describe** the sign of the quotient of two integers with unlike signs.

COMMON ERROR ALERT

Some students may think the quotient of two negative numbers is negative. Remind students that the rules for adding integers are different from the rules for multiplying and dividing integers.

Power Presentations with PowerPoint®

Additional Examples

Example 1

Find each quotient.

A. $-30 \div 6$ $\quad -5$

B. $-42 \div (-7)$ $\quad 6$

Example 2

Evaluate $\frac{d}{4}$ for each value of *d*.

A. $d = 16$ $\quad 4$

B. $d = -24$ $\quad -6$

C. $d = -12$ $\quad -3$

Also available on transparency

Teaching Tip **Multiple Representations** You may wish to have students evaluate some expressions with the variable in the denominator. For example:

Evaluate $\frac{27}{x}$ for $x = -3$.

$\frac{27}{x} = \frac{27}{-3} = -9$

Answers to *Think and Discuss*

1. positive
2. negative

2 Teach

Guided Instruction

In this lesson, students learn to divide integers (Teaching Transparency). First, review multiplication of integers and state the rules. Then write related division statements. For example, $-2 \cdot 3 = -6$, so $-6 \div -2 = 3$ and $-6 \div 3 = -2$. Point out that the sign rules for dividing integers are the same as the sign rules for multiplying integers.

Reaching All Learners

Through Critical Thinking

Have students place the correct signs in front of the dividend and the divisor to make the sentence true. Have them list all possible answers.

1. ▢ 8 ÷ ▢ 8 = −1 +,− or −,+
2. ▢ 36 ÷ ▢ 4 = 9 +,+ or −,−
3. ▢ 10 ÷ ▢ 2 = −5 +,− or −,+
4. ▢ 63 ÷ ▢ 7 = 9 +,+ or −,−
5. ▢ 12 ÷ ▢ 4 = −3 +,− or −,+

3 Close

Summarize

Summarize the rules for adding, subtracting, multiplying, and dividing integers. Also give expressions as examples to illustrate each rule.

11-7 Exercises

Assignment Guide

If you finished Example 1 assign:
Average 1–4, 9–12, 25–28, 48–56
Advanced 9–16, 29–32, 48–56

If you finished Example 2 assign:
Average 1–20, 25–28, 33–44, 48–56
Advanced 9–41, 45–56

Homework Quick Check

Quickly check key concepts.
Exercises: 14, 16, 18, 36

Math Background

Another direct connection can be made between the rules of multiplication and division. Because division can be written as multiplication by the reciprocal, the rules for multiplication can be applied directly to any division problem. Examples:

$$-6 \div 2 = -6 \times \frac{1}{2}$$
$$6 \div -2 = 6 \times -\frac{1}{2}$$
$$-6 \div -2 = -6 \times -\frac{1}{2}$$

11-7 Exercises

Georgia Performance Standards
M6P1.a, M6P3.a, M6P4.c

go.hrw.com
Homework Help Online
KEYWORD: MR7 11-7
Parent Resources Online
KEYWORD: MR7 Parent

GUIDED PRACTICE

See Example 1 Find each quotient.

1. $64 \div 8$ 8 2. $10 \div (-2)$ −5 3. $-21 \div (-7)$ 3 4. $-64 \div 2$ −32

See Example 2 Evaluate $\frac{m}{2}$ for each value of m.

5. $m = -4$ −2 6. $m = 20$ 10 7. $m = -30$ −15 8. $m = 50$ 25

INDEPENDENT PRACTICE

See Example 1 Find each quotient.

9. $45 \div 9$ 5 10. $-42 \div 6$ −7 11. $32 \div (-4)$ −8 12. $54 \div (-6)$ −9
13. $-60 \div (-10)$ 6 14. $-75 \div 15$ −5 15. $22 \div 11$ 2 16. $-48 \div (-4)$ 12

See Example 2 Evaluate $\frac{n}{4}$ for each value of n.

17. $n = 4$ 1 18. $n = -32$ −8 19. $n = 12$ 3 20. $n = -24$ −6
21. $n = 64$ 16 22. $n = -92$ −23 23. $n = 56$ 14 24. $n = -28$ −7

PRACTICE AND PROBLEM SOLVING

Extra Practice p. 736

Divide.

25. $-12 \div 2$ −6 26. $\frac{16}{-4}$ −4 27. $-6 \div (-6)$ 1 28. $-56 \div (-7)$ 8
29. $\frac{-30}{-3}$ 10 30. $-45 \div 9$ −5 31. $\frac{-35}{5}$ −7 32. $\frac{-63}{9}$ −7

Evaluate each expression for the given value of the variable.

33. $n \div (-7); n = -21$ 3 34. $\frac{m}{3}; m = -15$ −5 35. $\frac{x}{4}; x = 32$ 8
36. $y \div (-3); y = -6$ 2 37. $\frac{a}{3}; a = -9$ −3 38. $w \div (-2); w = -18$ 9
39. $-48 \div n; n = -8$ 6 40. $\frac{p}{-2}; p = -20$ 10 41. $j \div 9; j = -99$ −11

42. The graph shows the low temperatures for 5 days in Fairbanks, Alaska.
   a. Find the mean low temperature for Monday, Tuesday, and Wednesday. −3°F
   b. Find the mean low temperature for all 5 days. −2°F
   c. **Critical Thinking** Which mean low temperature was higher? Explain. the mean low temperature for all 5 days; −2 > −3
   d. Find the range of the data. 11°F

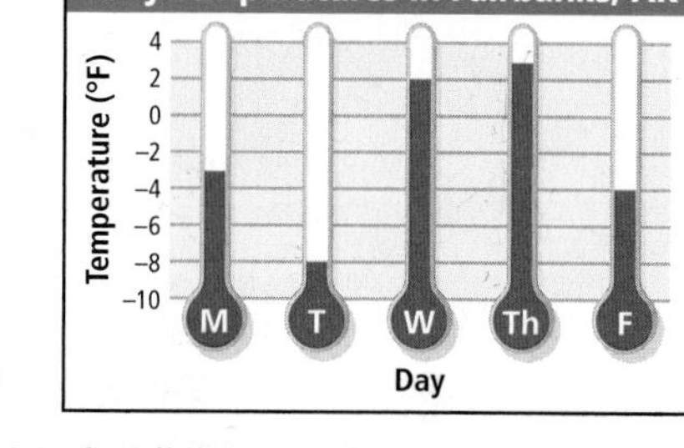

RETEACH 11-7

LESSON 11-7 **Reteach**
Dividing Integers

You can use two-color counters to divide integers.

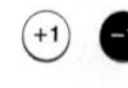

Divide −8 by 2.

First, think about the numerical expression in words.

−8 ÷ 2 means "−8 divided into 2 equal groups."

Then use counters to represent the expression.

There are 4 negative counters in each group.

−8 ÷ 2 = −4

Use counters to find each quotient.

1. −15 ÷ 3 −5 2. −12 ÷ 2 −6 3. 9 ÷ 3 3 4. 16 ÷ 4 4
5. −11 ÷ 1 −11 6. −6 ÷ 3 −2 7. −20 ÷ 4 −5 8. 21 ÷ 3 7
9. −14 ÷ 7 −2 10. −7 ÷ 7 −1 11. −18 ÷ 3 −6 12. 12 ÷ 4 3
13. 4 ÷ 2 2 14. −18 ÷ 9 −2 15. −5 ÷ 5 −1 16. −20 ÷ 5 −4

PRACTICE 11-7

LESSON 11-7 **Practice B**
Dividing Integers

Write the sign of each quotient.

1. 56 ÷ 8 positive 2. −45 ÷ (−9) positive 3. 36 ÷ (−12) negative
4. 54 ÷ (−6) negative 5. −84 ÷ 7 negative 6. −225 ÷ (−15) positive

Find each quotient.

7. −45 ÷ 9 −5 8. 15 ÷ (−3) −5 9. −56 ÷ 8 −7
10. −10 ÷ (−5) 2 11. 28 ÷ (−7) −4 12. −36 ÷ (−6) 6
13. 81 ÷ 9 9 14. −72 ÷ 9 −8 15. −121 ÷ (−11) 11

Evaluate $\frac{n}{-3}$ for each value of n.

16. $n = 6$ −2 17. $n = -18$ 6 18. $n = -24$ 8
19. $n = -36$ 12 20. $n = 30$ −10 21. $n = -21$ 7

Evaluate $n \div 2$ for each value of n.

22. $n = -14$ −7 23. $n = 20$ 10 24. $n = -24$ −12
25. $n = 8$ 4 26. $n = -18$ −9 27. $n = -22$ −11

28. What two division equations can you use to check the answer to the problem 6 • (−4) = −24?
−24 ÷ 6 = −4 or
−24 ÷ (−4) = 6

29. Why are the rules for dividing integers similar to the rules for multiplying integers?
because division is the inverse of multiplication

30. What two multiplication equations can you use to check the answer to the problem −32 ÷ 8 = −4?
8 • (−4) = −32 or
(−4) • 8 = −32

31. Name two integers whose product is −18 and whose quotient is −2.
6 and −3 or −6 and 3

Georgia Performance Standards

M6P1.a Build new mathematical knowledge through problem solving.

M6P3.a Organize and consolidate their mathematical thinking through communication.

M6P4.c Recognize and apply mathematics in contexts outside of mathematics.

Life Science LINK

The Mediterranean monk seal is one of the world's rarest mammals. Monk seals have become endangered largely because divers hunt them for their skin and disturb their habitat.

Annette found this table in a science article about monk seals.

Changes in Population of Monk Seals

Years	1971–1975	1976–1980	1981–1985	1986–1990	1991–1995	1996–2000	2001–2005
Change	550	−300	−150	−50	100	200	−100

43. **a.** According to the table, what was the change in the monk seal population from 1976 to 1980? **−300**

b. What does this number mean? **a decrease of 300 seals from 1976 to 1980**

44. Find the mean change per year from 1971 to 1975. (*Hint:* This is a range of 5 years, so divide by 5.) What does your answer mean? **110; an increase of 110 seals each year from 1971 to 1975**

45. Find the mean change per year from 1981 to 1990. What does your answer mean? **−20; a decrease of 20 seals per year from 1981 to 1990**

46. **Write About It** Why is it important to use both positive and negative numbers when tracking the changes in a population?

47. **Challenge** Suppose that there were 250 monk seals in 1971. How many were there in 2005? **500**

CRCT Prep • GPS Support • Spiral Review

48. **Multiple Choice** Which quotient is greatest?

Ⓐ $-8 \div (-2)$ B $-10 \div 5$ C $-10 \div (-5)$ D $15 \div (-5)$

49. **Multiple Choice** The change in population for a species is recorded in the table. What is the mean of the data?

Year	1	2	3	4
Change in Population	−2	+5	−7	−4

F −4   Ⓖ −2   H 1   J 3

Find the missing measurement for each prism. (Lesson 10-7)

50. $\ell = 9$ cm; $w = 24$ cm; $h = \underline{?}$; $V = 1{,}296$ cm^3 **6 cm**

51. $\ell = 8$ m; $w = \underline{?}$; $h = 13$ m; $V = 728$ cm^3 **7 m**

Evaluate $k - (-4)$ for each value of k. (Lesson 11-5)

52. $k = -5$ **−1**   **53.** $k = 7$ **11**   **54.** $k = -13$ **−9**   **55.** $k = -4$ **0**   **56.** $k = 16$ **20**

CHALLENGE 11-7

LESSON 11-7 Challenge
Divide and Answer

Long ago, people in India began using negative numbers. They were the first known people to do so. When did the people of India start using negative numbers?

Solve each division problem below. Then in the box at the bottom of the page, write each problem's letter in the blank above its quotient. When you have solved all the problems, you will have found the answer to the question.

A $18 \div (-3)$ **−6**
D $-27 \div (-9)$ **3**
E $-81 \div 9$ **−9**
F $24 \div (-3)$ **−8**
G $-35 \div (-5)$ **7**
H $24 \div (-2)$ **−12**
N $-40 \div (-8)$ **5**
O $32 \div (-8)$ **−4**
R $-17 \div 17$ **−1**
S $-48 \div (-8)$ **6**
T $22 \div (-2)$ **−11**
U $-100 \div (-10)$ **10**
Y $16 \div (-8)$ **−2**

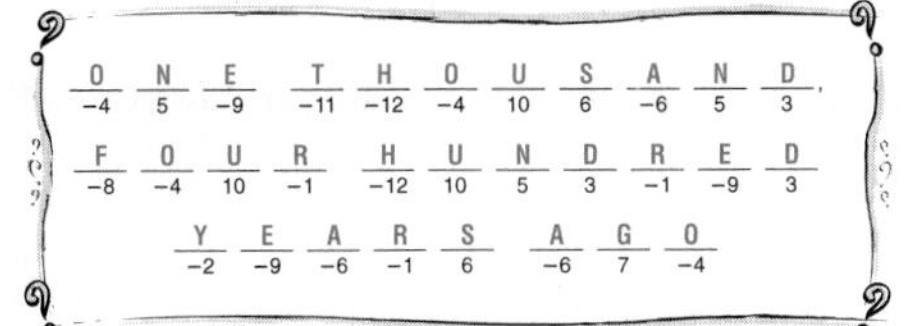

O N E T H O U S A N D,
−4 5 −9 −11 −12 −4 10 6 −6 5 3
F O U R H U N D R E D
−8 −4 10 −1 −12 10 5 3 −1 −9 3
Y E A R S A G O
−2 −9 −6 −1 6 −6 7 −4

PROBLEM SOLVING 11-7

LESSON 11-7 Problem Solving
Dividing Integers

Use the table below to answer questions 1–6.

Temperatures for Barrow, Alaska

	JAN	FEB	MAR	APRIL	MAY	JUNE	JULY	AUG	SEPT	OCT	NOV	DEC
Temp (°F)	−13	−18	−15	−2	19	34	39	38	31	14	−2	−11

1. What is the average temperature in Barrow for December and January? **−12°F**
2. What is the average temperature in Barrow for March and July? **12°F**
3. Which month's average temperature is half as warm as August's? **May**
4. What is the average temperature in Barrow for October and November? **6°F**
5. What is the average temperature in Barrow for January through April? **−12°F**
6. What is the city's average temperature for September through December? **8°F**

Circle the letter of the correct answer.

7. A submarine dove to a depth of 168 feet in 7 minutes. What was the average rate of change in its location?
A 24 feet
B 168 feet
Ⓒ −24 feet
D −168 feet

8. In its first 4 months of business, Skyscraper Records reported its losses as −$1,520. What was the company's average monthly loss?
F −$1,520
Ⓖ −$380
H −$38
J $380

9. Which of these expressions checks the solution to the division problem $-8 \div (-2) = 4$?
A $-8 \cdot (-2)$
B $4 \cdot 4$
C $-2 \cdot (2)$
Ⓓ $4 \cdot (-2)$

10. A glacier is melting 3 in^3 a year. At that rate, how long will it take for the glacier to change by −24 in^3?
F 72 years
G 6 years
Ⓗ 8 years
J 24 years

Ongoing Assessment and Intervention

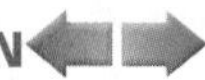

Diagnose ***Before*** **the Lesson**
11-7 Warm Up, TE p. 628

Monitor ***During*** **the Lesson**
11-7 Know-It Notebook
11-7 Questioning Strategies

Assess ***After*** **the Lesson**
11-7 Lesson Quiz, TE p. 631

Interdisciplinary LINK

Life Science

Exercises 43–47 involve changes in the population of an endangered species. Protection of endangered species is studied in middle school life science programs such as *Holt Science & Technology*.

Answers

46. so you know whether the population is growing or shrinking

Test Prep Doctor For Exercise 48, students who apply the rules for division can see that two quotients will be negative, **B** and **D,** and two quotients will be positive, **A** and **C.** Because positive numbers are greater than negative numbers, the correct choice will be the greater positive quotient.

Journal

Have students describe in writing how integer division can be used in the real world.

Power Presentations with PowerPoint®

11-7 Lesson Quiz

Find each quotient.

1. $18 \div (-3)$ **−6**   **2.** $-36 \div (-6)$ **6**

3. $-64 \div (-8)$ **8**   **4.** $-45 \div 3$ **−15**

Evaluate $\frac{x}{4}$ for each value of x.

5. $x = -12$ **−3**   **6.** $x = 20$ **5**

7. Carmen's mom has $3,200 in her bank account. If she uses the money to make monthly rent payments of $375, how many whole payments can she make? **8**

Also available on transparency

SECTION 11B

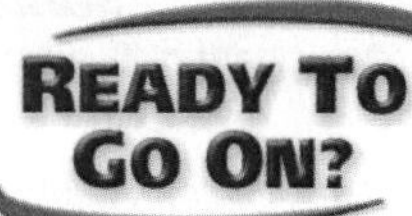

Organizer

Objective: Assess students' mastery of concepts and skills in Lessons 11-4 through 11-7.

Resources

 ***Assessment Resources***
Section 11B Quiz

Test & Practice Generator
One-Stop Planner®

INTERVENTION 

Resources

 ***Ready to Go On? Intervention and Enrichment* Worksheets**

 ***Ready to Go On?* CD-ROM**

 ***Ready to Go On?* Online**

my.hrw.com

CHAPTER 11

SECTION 11B

Quiz for Lessons 11-4 Through 11-7

11-4 Adding Integers

Write the addition modeled on each number line.

1. $-4 + 7 = 3$
2. $5 + (-6) = -1$

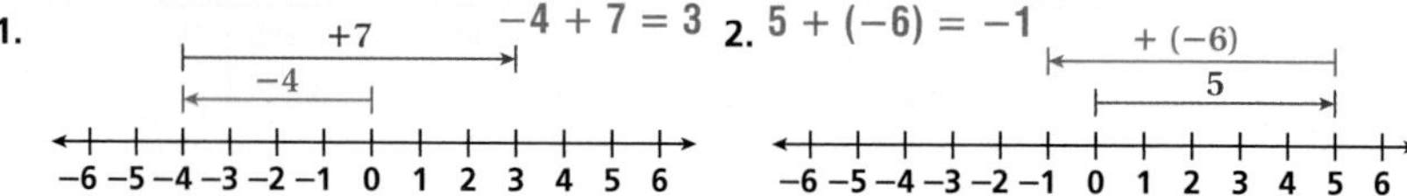

Find each sum.

3. $7 + (-3)$ **4**
4. $-10 + 6$ **−4**
5. $-7 + (-3)$ **−10**

Evaluate $-5 + x$ for each value of x.

6. $x = 7$ **2**
7. $x = -4$ **−9**
8. $x = 2$ **−3**
9. An archaeological team digs 6 feet below the surface on the first day. The team digs an additional 3 feet on the second day. At what depth is the archaeological team at the end of the second day? **−9 ft**

11-5 Subtracting Integers

Write the subtraction modeled on each number line.

10. $4 - 8 = -4$

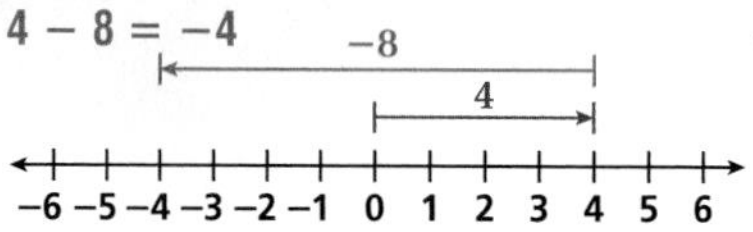

−8
4
−6 −5 −4 −3 −2 −1 0 1 2 3 4 5 6

11. $-2 - (-4) = 2$

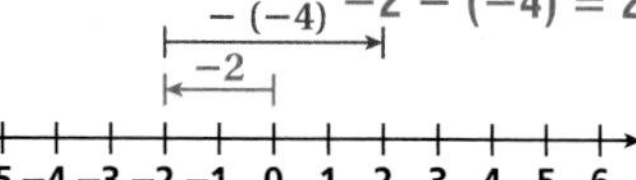

12. Evaluate $x - (-7)$ for $x = -2$. **5**
13. The temperature on January 5 was −7°F. On January 6, it was 2°F. Find the difference between the temperature on January 5 and January 6. **9°F**

11-6 Multiplying Integers

Evaluate $6x$ for each value of x.

14. $x = -2$ **−12**
15. $x = 1$ **6**
16. $x = -7$ **−42**

Find each product.

17. $3 \cdot (-7)$ **−21**
18. $-10 \cdot 8$ **−80**
19. $-12 \cdot (-5)$ **60**

11-7 Dividing Integers

Evaluate $\frac{x}{4}$ for each value of x.

20. $x = -24$ **−6**
21. $x = 44$ **11**
22. $x = -124$ **−31**

Find each quotient.

23. $72 \div (-9)$ **−8**
24. $-15 \div (-3)$ **5**
25. $-40 \div 10$ **−4**

Ready to Go On?

READY TO GO ON?

Diagnose and Prescribe

NO INTERVENE

Ready to Go On? Intervention	*Ready to Go On?* Intervention, Section 11B: Worksheets	CD-ROM	Online
Lesson 11-4	11-4 Intervention	Activity 11-4	Diagnose and Prescribe Online
Lesson 11-5	11-5 Intervention	Activity 11-5	
Lesson 11-6	11-6 Intervention	Activity 11-6	
Lesson 11-7	11-7 Intervention	Activity 11-7	

***Ready to Go On? Enrichment,* Section 11B**

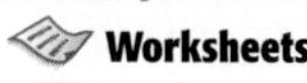 Worksheets

 CD-ROM

 Online

Focus on Problem Solving

Make a Plan

- **Choose a problem-solving strategy**

The following strategies can help you solve problems.

- Act It Out
- Draw a Diagram
- Make a Model
- Guess and Test
- Work Backward
- Find a Pattern
- Make a Table
- Solve a Simpler Problem
- Use Logical Reasoning
- Make an Organized List

Tell which strategy from the list above you would use to solve each problem. Explain your choice. Then solve the problem.

1. The temperature on a winter day is −6°F at 8:00 A.M., −4°F at 9:00 A.M., and −2°F at 10:00 A.M. The temperature continues to change by the same amount each hour. What is the temperature at 2:00 P.M.?

2. Caleb lives in one of the states listed in the table. His home is at an elevation of 600 feet. There is a park in his state at an elevation of 150 feet. Which state does Caleb live in?

State	Lowest Elevation (ft)	Highest Elevation (ft)
California	−282	14,494
Louisiana	−8	535
West Virginia	240	4,861

3. On a map of Nadia's town, the library is located at (2, 3), the museum is located at (1, −2), city hall is located at (−2, −3), and the aquarium is located at (−4, 2). She wants to organize a field trip to the two buildings that are closest to each other. Which two buildings should she choose?

4. In the past month, Ethan's savings account had withdrawals and deposits in the amounts of −\$25, +\$45, +\$15, −\$40, and +\$60. He wants to check the receipts for one of the withdrawals and one of the deposits. How many different combinations of one withdrawal and one deposit are there?

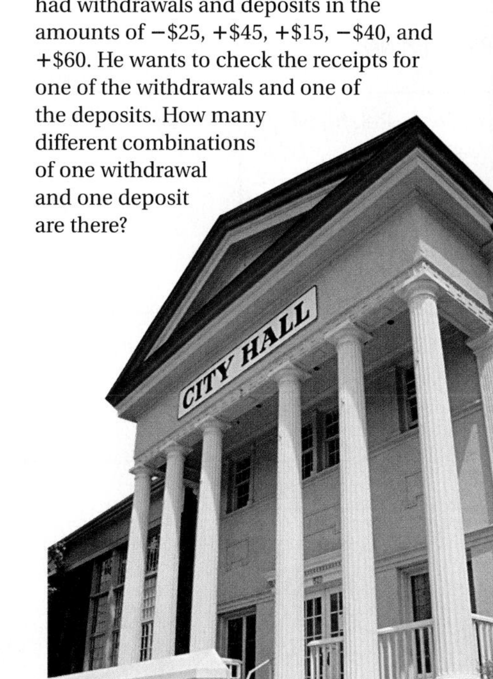

Focus on Problem Solving

Organizer

Objective: Focus on choosing a problem-solving strategy.

Online Edition

Resources

Chapter 11 Resource Book
Reading Strategies

Problem Solving Process

This page focuses on the second step of the problem-solving process:
Make a Plan

Discuss

Have students describe the strategy or strategies they used to solve each problem.

1. Possible answer: Look for a pattern and/or draw a diagram. The temperature moves 2 units to the right on the number line every hour.
2. Possible answer: Use logical reasoning. Caleb's home is at an elevation of 600 ft, so he cannot live in Louisiana. There is a park in his state at an elevation of 150 ft, so he cannot live in West Virginia. Therefore, he lives in California.
3. Possible answer: Draw a diagram. Graph the points on a coordinate plane and look for the two points that are closest together.

Answers

1. 6°F
2. California
3. the museum and city hall
4. 6

4. Possible answer: Make an organized list. List all the possible combinations of withdrawals and deposits:
−\$25/+\$45, −\$25/+\$15, −\$25/+\$60, −\$40/+\$45, −\$40/+\$15, and −\$40/+\$60.

SECTION 11C

Equations and Functions

One-Minute Section Planner

Lesson	Materials	MiC and Lab Resources
11-8 Hands-On Lab Model Integer Equations • Use algebra tiles to model and solve integer equations. **Lesson 11-8** Solving Integer Equations • Solve equations containing integers. ☑ CRCT ☑ SAT-10 ☑ ITBS ☑ CTBS ☑ NAEP	Algebra tiles (MK)	***Hands-On Lab Activities*** 11-8
Lesson 11-9 Tables and Functions • Use data in a table to write an equation for a function, and use the equation to find a missing value. ☑ CRCT ☑ SAT-10 ☑ ITBS ☐ CTBS ☑ NAEP		**MiC: *Expressions and Formulas*** pp. 18–21 ***Technology Lab Activities*** 11-9
11-10 Hands-On Lab Explore Linear and Nonlinear Relationships • Use graph-paper drawings to explore linear nonlinear relationships. **Lesson 11-10** Graphing Functions • Represent linear functions using ordered pairs and graphs. ☑ CRCT ☑ SAT-10 ☑ ITBS ☑ CTBS ☑ NAEP	Square tiles (MK), graph paper	**MiC: *Expressions and Formulas*** pp. 18–21 ***Hands-On Lab Activities*** 11-10 ***Technology Lab Activities*** 11-10
Extension Integer Exponents • Recognize negative exponents by examining patterns. ☑ CRCT ☐ SAT-10 ☐ ITBS ☐ CTBS ☐ NAEP		

MK = *Manipulatives Kit*

Mathematics in Context

The unit ***Expressions and Formulas*** from the *Mathematics in Context* © 2006 series can be used with Section 11C. See Section Planner above for suggestions for integrating *MiC* with *Holt Mathematics*.

Section Overview

Integer Equations

Lesson 11-8

Solving equations is necessary in many problem-solving situations.

When solving equations with integers, the goal is the same as with whole numbers—use the inverse of the operation on the variable to isolate the variable on one side of the equation.

$$\begin{aligned} x + 10 &= -54 \\ -10 \quad & \quad -10 \\ x &= -64 \end{aligned}$$

$$-175x = -14{,}000$$

$$\frac{-175x}{-175} = \frac{-14{,}000}{-175}$$

$$x = 80$$

Tables and Functions

Lesson 11-9

You can use a function to convert between customary units and metric units.

A **function** is a rule that relates two variables such that each **input** value of one variable corresponds to exactly one **output** value of the other variable.

A function table shows some of the values for a function.

Input x	3	4	5	6	10
Output y	7	9	11	13	

You can write an equation for the function that gives these values and use the equation to find the missing output value.

Each **output** is 1 more than 2 times the **input.**

y = 2 times x plus 1

$y = 2x + 1$

$y = 2(10) + 1$

$y = 20 + 1$

$y = 21$

When x is 10, y is 21.

Graphing Functions

Lesson 11-10

Why? You can use the graph of the linear relationship between degrees Celsius and kelvins to convert temperatures.

Graph the function described by the equation $y = 2x + 1$.

Make a function table.

x	$2x + 1$	y
−3	2(−3) + 1	−5
0	2(0) + 1	1
1	2(1) + 1	3

Write the ordered pairs.

(x, y)

(−3, −5)

(0, 1)

(1, 3)

Graph the ordered pairs on a coordinate plane.

Draw a line through the points.

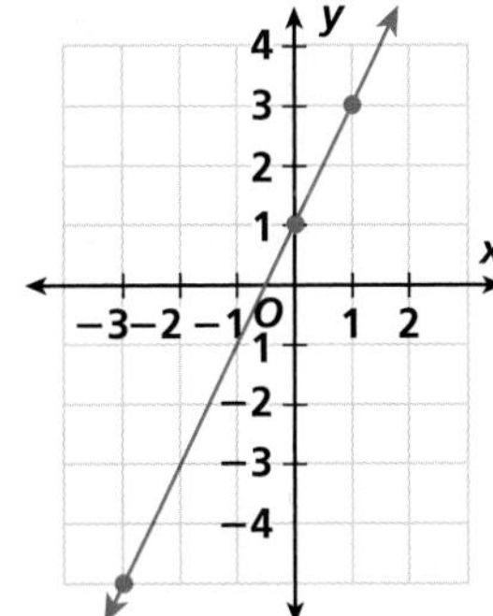

Every point on the line represents a solution to the equation.

When you graph the ordered pairs of a function, the points may form a straight line. An equation for such a function is called a **linear equation.**

Organizer

Use with Lesson 11-8

Pacing:
Traditional $\frac{1}{2}$ day
Block $\frac{1}{4}$ day

Objective: Use algebra tiles to model and solve integer equations.

Materials: Algebra tiles, equation mat

Online Edition
Algebra Tiles

Resources

Hands-On Lab Activities
Lab 11-8 Recording Sheet

Teach

Discuss

Discuss with students what each algebra tile represents. Also discuss what the two sides of the equation mat represent.

Close

Key Concept

Algebra tiles and an equation mat can be used to model and solve integer equations.

Assessment

1. How can you represent the equation $x - 5 = -2$ with algebra tiles?
2. How do you solve the equation using the algebra tiles? What must you do first?

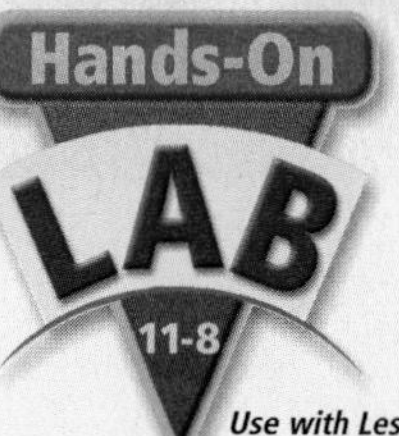

Model Integer Equations

Use with Lesson 11-8

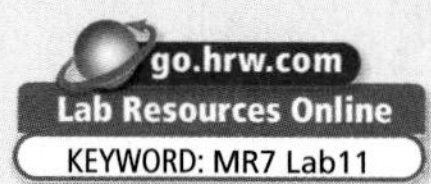

Georgia Performance Standards
M6A3, M6P5.a, M6P5.b, P6P5.c

KEY	REMEMBER
▫ = 1 ▪ = −1 ▭ = x	You can add or subtract the same number on both sides of an equation. Adding or subtracting zero does not change a number's value.

You can use algebra tiles to model equations. An equation mat represents the two sides of an equation. To find the value of the variable, get the x-tile by itself on one side of the mat. You may remove the same number of yellow tiles or the same number of red tiles from both sides.

Activity

Use algebra tiles to model and solve each equation.

1. $x + 2 = 6$

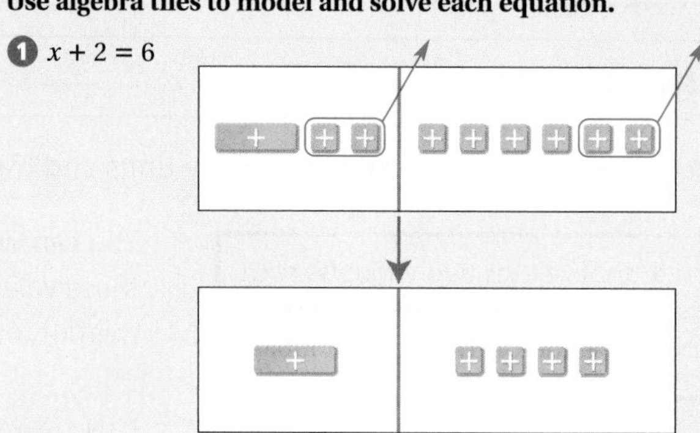

Remove 2 yellow tiles from both sides of the mat.

$x = 4$

2. $x - 3 = -5$

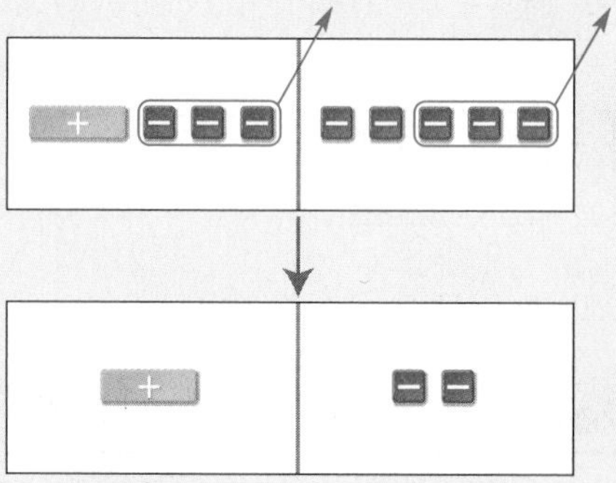

Use red tiles to model subtraction. Remove 3 red tiles from both sides of the mat.

$x = -2$

Answers to *Assessment*

1.

2. Add 3 zero pairs to the right side of the equation.

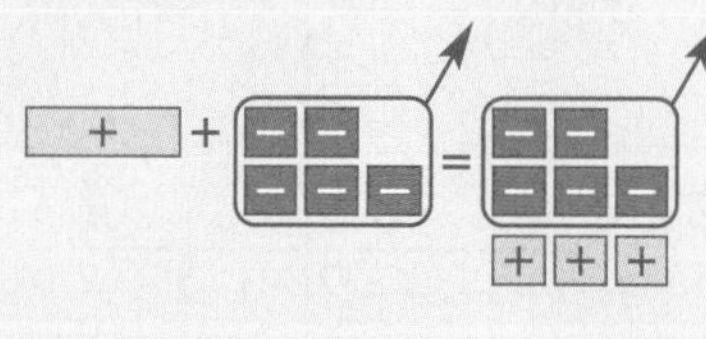

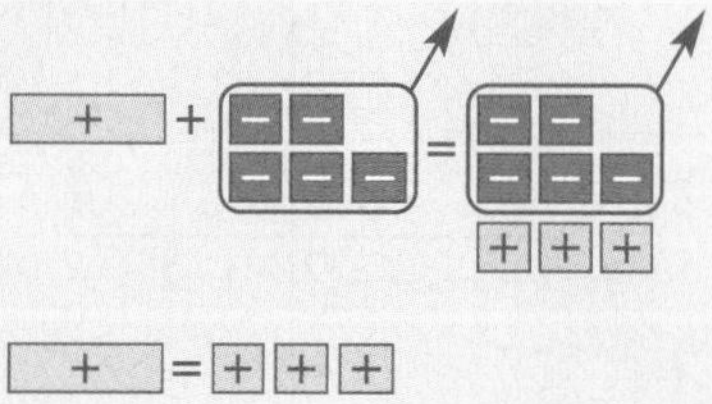

Georgia Performance Standards

M6A3 Students will evaluate algebraic expressions, including those with exponents, and solve simple one-step equations using each of the four basic operations.

M6P5.a Create and use representations to organize, record, and communicate mathematical ideas.

M6P5.b Select, apply, and translate among mathematical representations to solve problems.

M6P5.c Use representations to model and interpret physical, social, and mathematical phenomena.

3 $x + 6 = 2$

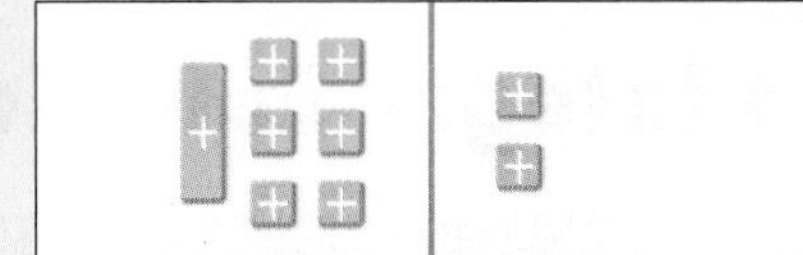

Adding red tiles to both sides will allow you to remove zero pairs. If you add 6 red tiles to the left side, you must add 6 red tiles to the right side to keep the equation balanced.

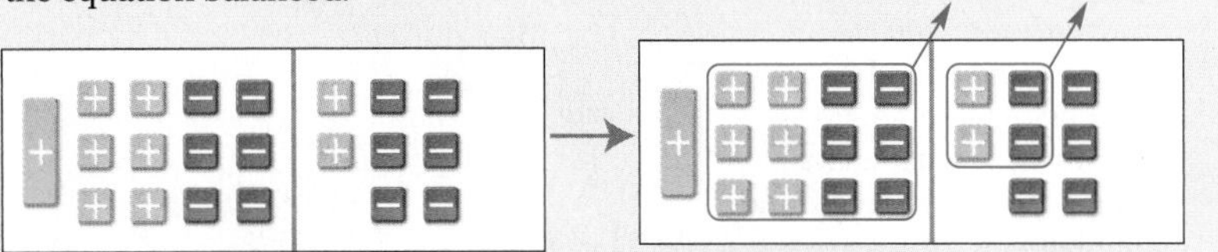

Add 6 red tiles to both sides.

Now you can remove zero pairs from both sides of the mat.

$x = -4$

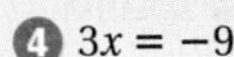

4 $3x = -9$

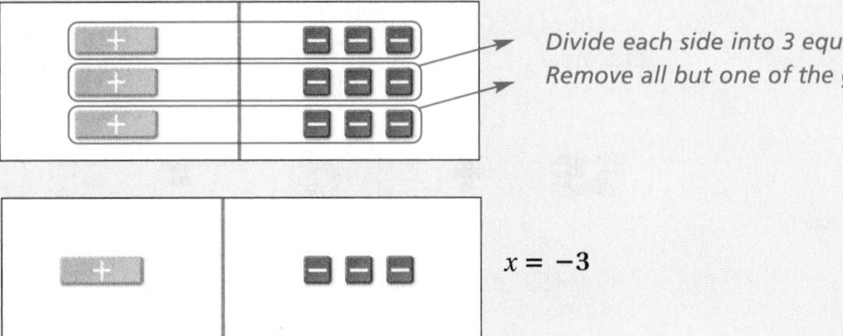

Divide each side into 3 equal groups. Remove all but one of the groups.

$x = -3$

Think and Discuss

1. In 4, why did you divide both sides into 3 groups? **You divided both sides into groups in order to isolate the bar representing *x*.**
2. Why can you add zero pairs to an equation mat? Why is it not necessary to add them to both sides? **Because zero pairs represent 0, it doesn't change the value of the equation.**
3. When you add zero to an equation, how do you know the number of red and yellow tiles to add? **You add as many as you need in order to have enough tiles to subtract an equal number from both sides.**
4. How can you use algebra tiles to check your answers? **You can work the problem backward using algebra tiles to check your work.**

Try This

Use algebra tiles to model and solve each equation.

1. $x + 6 = 3$ **−3**
2. $x - 1 = -8$ **−7**
3. $2x = 14$ **7**
4. $4x = -8$ **−2**

Answers to *Try This*

1. $x + 6 = 3$

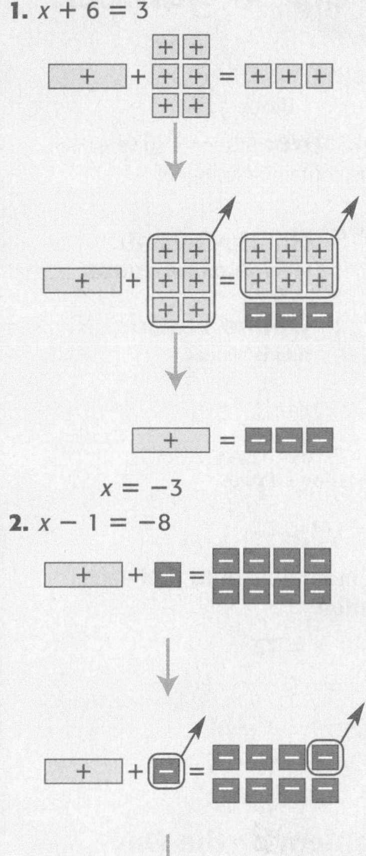

$x = -3$

2. $x - 1 = -8$

$x = -7$

3. $2x = 14$

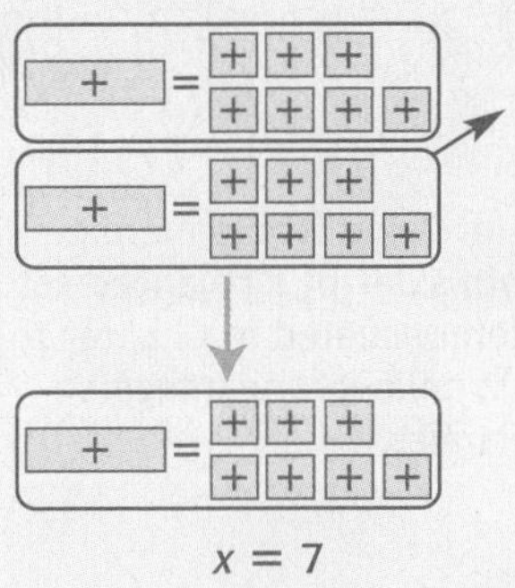

$x = 7$

4. $4x = -8$

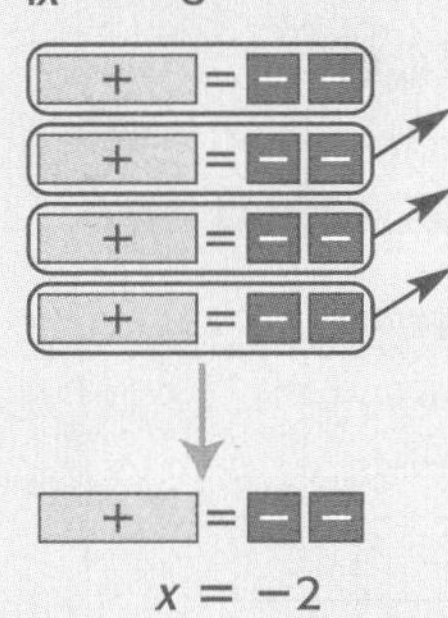

$x = -2$

11-8 Organizer

Pacing: Traditional 1 day
Block $\frac{1}{2}$ day

Objective: Students solve equations containing integers.

Hands-On Lab
In *Hands-On Lab Activities*

Online Edition
Tutorial Videos

Power Presentations with PowerPoint®

Warm Up

Use mental math to find each solution.

1. $6 + x = 12$ $\quad x = 6$
2. $3x = 15$ $\quad x = 5$
3. $\frac{x}{5} = 4$ $\quad x = 20$
4. $x - 8 = 12$ $\quad x = 20$

Problem of the Day

Marie spent \$15 at the fruit stand, buying peaches that cost \$2 per container and strawberries that cost \$3 per container. She bought the same number of containers of each fruit. How many containers each of peaches and strawberries did she buy? 3

Also available on transparency

French philosopher and mathematician René Descartes was the first to use *a*, *b*, and *c* to represent known quantities and *x*, *y*, and *z* to represent unknown quantities.

Georgia Performance Standards

M6A3 Students will evaluate algebraic expressions, including those with exponents, and solve simple one-step equations using each of the four basic operations.

M6P1.d Monitor and reflect on the process of mathematical problem solving.

M6P5.c Use representations to model and interpret physical, social, and mathematical phenomena.

11-8 Solving Integer Equations

Learn to solve equations containing integers.

Georgia Performance Standards

M6A3 Solve simple one-step equations using each of the four asic operations. Also, M6P1.d, M6P5.c.

The entrance to the Great Pyramid of Khufu is 55 ft above ground. The underground chamber is 102 ft below ground. From the entrance, what is the distance to the underground chamber?

To solve this problem, you can use an equation containing integers.

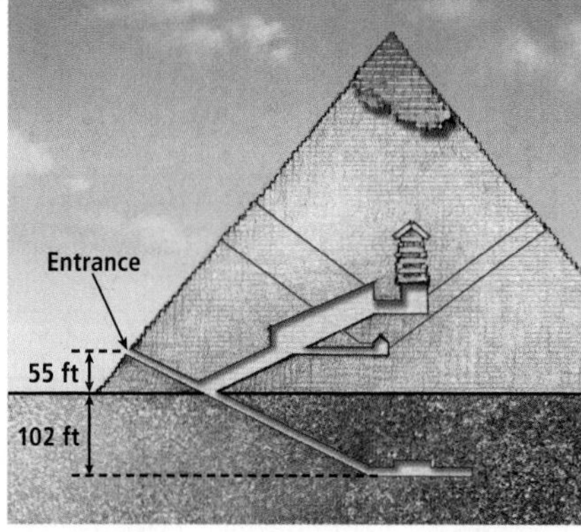

height of entrance + distance to underground chamber = height of underground chamber

$$55 + d = -102$$

$$\begin{aligned} 55 + d &= -102 \quad \text{Write the equation.} \\ -55 \quad & \quad -55 \quad \text{Subtract 55 from both sides.} \\ d &= -157 \end{aligned}$$

It is −157 ft from the entrance to the underground chamber. The sign is negative, which means you go down 157 ft.

EXAMPLE 1 Adding and Subtracting to Solve Equations

Helpful Hint

Subtracting a number is the same as adding its opposite. To solve this equation using algebra tiles, you can add four red tiles to both sides and then remove zero pairs.

A Solve $4 + x = -2$. Check your answer.

$$\begin{aligned} 4 + x &= -2 \quad \text{4 is added to x.} \\ -4 \quad & \quad -4 \quad \text{Subtract 4 from both sides to undo the addition.} \\ x &= -6 \end{aligned}$$

Check

$4 + x = -2$ — *Write the equation.*

$4 + (-6) \stackrel{?}{=} -2$ — *Substitute −6 for x.*

$-2 \stackrel{?}{=} -2$ ✔ — *−6 is a solution.*

1 Introduce

Alternate Opener

EXPLORATION

11-8 Solving Integer Equations

You can use algebra tiles to model solving integer equations.

represents −1. represents 1. represents an unknown amount *x*.

The equation $x - 3 = 5$ is modeled.

$x - 3 = 5$

To get *x* alone on one side, add three positive tiles to each side of the mat. This allows you to remove three zero pairs from the left side.

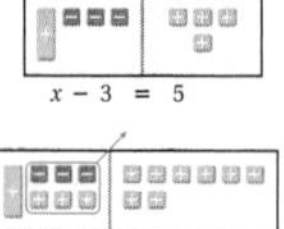

$x - 3 = 5$
$+3 \quad +3$

The solution is 8.

$x = 8$

Use algebra tiles to solve each equation.

1. $x + 5 = 9$
2. $x - 6 = 2$
3. $x + 4 = -1$
4. $6 = x - 7$
5. $8 = x + 2$
6. $3 = x - 9$

Think and Discuss

7. **Explain** how you know whether to add positive tiles or negative tiles to each side of the mat.

Motivate

Solve an equation involving whole numbers by operating on both sides of a balanced set of scales, as was demonstrated in Chapter 2. Then solve an equation involving integers and show the similarities.

Explorations and answers are provided in *Alternate Openers: Explorations Transparencies.*

B Solve $y - 6 = -5$. Check your answer.

$y - 6 = -5$ — *6 is subtracted from y.*

$\underline{\;+6 \quad +6\;}$ — *Add 6 to both sides to undo the subtraction.*

$y \quad = \quad 1$

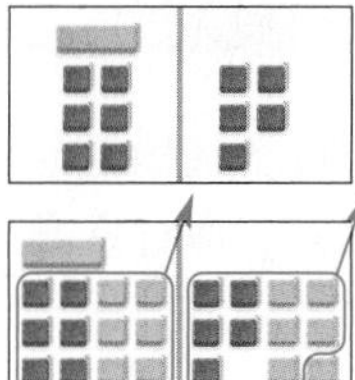

Check

$y - 6 = -5$ — *Write the equation.*

$1 - 6 \stackrel{?}{=} -5$ — *Substitute 1 for y.*

$-5 \stackrel{?}{=} -5$ ✓ — *1 is a solution.*

EXAMPLE 2 Multiplying and Dividing to Solve Equations

Solve each equation. Check your answers.

A $-3a = 15$

$\frac{-3a}{-3} = \frac{15}{-3}$ — *a is multiplied by −3. Divide both sides by −3 to undo the multiplication.*

$a = -5$

Check

$-3a = 15$ — *Write the equation.*

$-3(-5) \stackrel{?}{=} 15$ — *Substitute −5 for a.*

$15 \stackrel{?}{=} 15$ ✓ — *−5 is a solution.*

B $\frac{b}{-4} = -2$

$-4 \cdot \frac{b}{-4} = -4 \cdot (-2)$ — *b is divided by −4. Multiply both sides by −4 to undo the division.*

$b = 8$

Check

$\frac{b}{-4} = -2$ — *Write the equation.*

$8 \div (-4) \stackrel{?}{=} -2$ — *Substitute 8 for b.*

$-2 \stackrel{?}{=} -2$ ✓ — *8 is a solution.*

Think and Discuss

GPS M6P1.d, M6P3.b

1. Tell what operation you would use to solve $x + 12 = -32$.

2. Tell whether the solution to $-9t = -27$ will be positive or negative without actually solving the equation.

3. Explain how to check your answer to an integer equation.

COMMON ERROR ALERT

Some students may have difficulty affixing signs to integers when writing equations to solve word problems. Have students search for key words that would indicate the use of negative integers. For example, in the lesson opener, "The underground chamber is 102 feet **below** ground."

Power Presentations with PowerPoint®

Additional Examples

Example 1

Solve each equation.

A. $-8 + y = -13$ $\quad y = -5$

B. $n - 2 = -8$ $\quad n = -6$

Example 2

Solve each equation.

A. $4m = -20$ $\quad m = -5$

B. $\frac{x}{3} = -7$ $\quad x = -21$

Also available on transparency

Answers to *Think and Discuss*

1. subtraction
2. positive, because a negative integer multiplied by a positive integer has a negative product
3. Possible answer: In the original equation, substitute the solution for the variable and follow the order of operations. The solution is correct if the left side of the equation equals the right side.

2 Teach

Guided Instruction

In this lesson, students learn to solve equations containing integers. First, teach students to solve and check solutions to addition and subtraction equations containing integers. Then teach them to solve and check solutions to multiplication and division equations. Remind students that to solve an equation, they must "undo" the operation being performed on the variable.

Inclusion Remind students to think of the rules for adding, subtracting, multiplying, and dividing integers when they are solving for a variable. Have them check the solution each time to catch any mistakes.

Reaching All Learners

Through Cognitive Strategies

While students are solving examples or exercises, have them circle the operation and the integer that is operating on the variable. Then, directly below the circled operation and integer, have students write the inverse operation and the same integer that was circled. Remind students to keep the equation balanced by writing the inverse operation and the same integer that was circled on the other side of the equation.

3 Close

Summarize

Discuss the steps for finding and checking the solution to addition, subtraction, multiplication, and division equations with integers. Be sure to include and spend time on equations involving subtracting negatives and equations involving multiplying and dividing by negatives.

11-8 Exercises

Assignment Guide

If you finished Example 1 assign:
Average 1–8, 33–34, 43–45, 71–79
Advanced 17–24, 33–34, 49–50, 71–79

If you finished Example 2 assign:
Average 1–50, 61–65, 71–79
Advanced 17–79

Homework Quick Check
Quickly check key concepts.
Exercises: 18, 24, 30, 62

Math Background

Before students studied this chapter, they may not have been able to solve or understand the solution to an equation such as $x + 1 = 0$. Through the study of integers, students can now solve equations of the form $x + a = b$, $x - a = b$, $ax = b$, and $\frac{x}{a} = b$, where a and b are integers. The one exception is that equations in this lesson of the form $ax = b$ are restricted to cases in which $\frac{b}{a}$ is an integer.

Georgia Performance Standards

M6P1.b Solve problems that arise in mathematics and in other contexts.

M6P3.a Organize and consolidate their mathematical thinking through communication.

M6P4.c Recognize and apply mathematics in contexts outside of mathematics.

11-8 Exercises

Georgia Performance Standards
M6P1.b, M6P3.a, M6P4.c

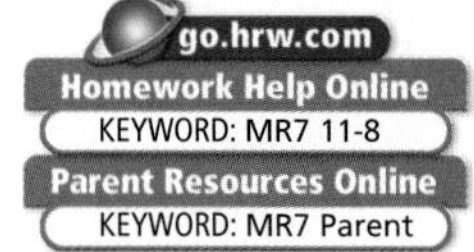

Homework Help Online
KEYWORD: MR7 11-8
Parent Resources Online
KEYWORD: MR7 Parent

GUIDED PRACTICE

See Example 1 — Solve each equation. Check your answers.

1. $m - 3 = 9$ $m = 12$
2. $a - 8 = -13$ $a = -5$
3. $z - 12 = -3$ $z = 9$
4. $j - 2 = 7$ $j = 9$
5. $p + 2 = -7$ $p = -9$
6. $k - 9 = 21$ $k = 30$
7. $g - 10 = -2$ $g = 8$
8. $h + 15 = 25$ $h = 10$

See Example 2

9. $-4b = 32$ $b = -8$
10. $\frac{w}{3} = 18$ $w = 54$
11. $5c = -35$ $c = -7$
12. $\frac{p}{-5} = 10$ $p = -50$
13. $6f = -36$ $f = -6$
14. $-2c = 72$ $c = -36$
15. $\frac{r}{10} = -90$ $r = -900$
16. $\frac{d}{-12} = 144$ $d = -1{,}728$

INDEPENDENT PRACTICE

See Example 1 — Solve each equation. Check your answers.

17. $g - 9 = -5$ $g = 4$
18. $v - 7 = 19$ $v = 26$
19. $t - 13 = -27$ $t = -14$
20. $s - 4 = -21$ $s = -17$
21. $x + 2 = -12$ $x = -14$
22. $y + 9 = -10$ $y = -19$
23. $20 + w = 10$ $w = -10$
24. $z + 15 = 50$ $z = 35$

See Example 2

25. $6j = 48$ $j = 8$
26. $7s = -49$ $s = -7$
27. $\frac{a}{-2} = 26$ $a = -52$
28. $-2r = 10$ $r = -5$
29. $\frac{m}{-12} = 4$ $m = -48$
30. $\frac{k}{5} = -4$ $k = -20$
31. $u \div 6 = -10$ $u = -60$
32. $6t = -36$ $t = -6$

PRACTICE AND PROBLEM SOLVING

CRCT GPS
Extra Practice p. 736

Solve each equation. Check your answers.

33. $x - 12 = 5$ $x = 17$
34. $w - 3 = -2$ $w = 1$
35. $-7k = 28$ $k = -4$
36. $g \div 7 = -2$ $g = -14$
37. $\frac{m}{-3} = 5$ $m = -15$
38. $a - 10 = 9$ $a = 19$
39. $n - 19 = -22$ $n = -3$
40. $2h = 42$ $h = 21$
41. $13g = -39$ $g = -3$
42. $s \div 6 = -3$ $s = -18$
43. $24 + f = 16$ $f = -8$
44. $q - 15 = -4$ $q = 11$
45. $d - 26 = 7$ $d = 33$
46. $-6c = 54$ $c = -9$
47. $h \div (-4) = 21$ $h = -84$
48. $7k = 70$ $k = 10$
49. $b - 17 = 15$ $b = 32$
50. $u - 82 = -7$ $u = 75$
51. $-8a = -64$ $a = 8$
52. $v + 1 = -9$ $v = -10$
53. $\frac{t}{11} = -5$ $t = -55$
54. $31 + j = -14$ $j = -45$
55. $c + 23 = 10$ $c = -13$
56. $\frac{r}{-2} = -8$ $r = 16$
57. $15n = -60$ $n = -4$
58. $z \div (-5) = -9$ $z = 45$
59. $j - 20 = -23$ $j = -3$
60. $f + 20 = -60$ $f = -80$

61. A submarine captain sets the following diving course: dive 200 ft, stop, and then dive another 200 ft. If this pattern is continued, how many dives will be necessary to reach a location 14,000 ft below sea level? **70 dives**

62. While exploring a cave, Lin noticed that the temperature dropped 4°F for every 30 ft that she descended. What is Lin's depth if the temperature is 8° lower than the temperature at the surface? **−60 ft**

63. **Sports** After two rounds in the 2001 LPGA Champions Classic, Wendy Doolan had a score of –12. Her score in the second round was –8. What was her score in the first round? **−4**

64. **Critical Thinking** If the product of a variable and a number is positive and the number is negative, what is the sign of the value of the variable? **negative**

RETEACH 11-8

LESSON 11-8 **Reteach**
Solving Integer Equations

You can write related equations between addition and subtraction equations.
$7 + 6 = 13$ $13 - 6 = 7$

You can write related equations between multiplication and division equations.
$3 \cdot -4 = -12$ $-12 \div -4 = 3$

Use related equations to solve each of the following.

A. $x + 4 = -2$ **Think:** $-2 - 4 = x$ $x = -6$	**Check:** $x + 4 = -2$ $-6 + 4 \stackrel{?}{=} -2$ $-2 = -2$	Substitute.
B. $-3a = 15$ **Think:** $15 \div -3 = a$ $a = -5$	**Check:** $-3a = 15$ $-3 \cdot (-5) \stackrel{?}{=} 15$ $15 = 15$	Substitute.
C. $m - 6 = 1$ **Think:** $1 + 6 = m$ $m = 7$	**Check:** $m - 6 = 1$ $7 - 6 \stackrel{?}{=} 1$ $1 = 1$	Substitute.
D. $b \div 4 = 6$ **Think:** $6 \cdot 4 = b$ $b = 24$	**Check:** $b \div 4 = 6$ $24 \div 4 \stackrel{?}{=} 6$ $6 = 6$	Substitute.

Use related facts to solve each equation. Then check each answer.

1. $x + 8 = 12$ $x = 4$
2. $x \div 9 = 4$ $x = 36$
3. $x - 12 = 7$ $x = 19$
4. $5x = 40$ $x = 8$
5. $x \div 3 = 6$ $x = 18$
6. $x + (-12) = 16$ $x = 28$
7. $7x = -42$ $x = -6$
8. $x - (-8) = 23$ $x = 15$
9. $x - 3 = -9$ $x = -6$
10. $-4x = 28$ $x = -7$
11. $x + (-9) = -13$ $x = -4$
12. $x \div (-5) = -4$ $x = 20$

PRACTICE 11-8

LESSON 11-8 **Practice B**
Solving Integer Equations

Write what you should do to solve each equation.

1. $x - 4 = -10$ Add 4 to both sides.
2. $-2x = 8$ Divide both sides by −2.
3. $-3 + x = 12$ Subtract −3 from both sides.
4. $x \div 6 = -9$ Multiply both sides by 6.
5. $-7 + x = -15$ Subtract −7 from both sides.
6. $35 = -5x$ Divide both sides by −5.

Solve each equation. Check your answers.

7. $-45 \div x = -5$ $x = 9$
8. $x - 9 = -1$ $x = 8$
9. $36 \div x = -6$ $x = -6$
10. $x - 10 = -12$ $x = -2$
11. $-8x = 56$ $x = -7$
12. $x \div 7 = -9$ $x = -63$
13. $3x = -36$ $x = -12$
14. $15 + x = 21$ $x = 6$
15. $-4x = 64$ $x = -16$
16. $x \div (-3) = -5$ $x = 15$
17. $x \div -12 = -5$ $x = 60$
18. $x - 13 = -9$ $x = 4$
19. $-7 + x = 4$ $x = 11$
20. $-9x = 54$ $x = -6$
21. $49 \div x = -7$ $x = -7$
22. If you multiply a value x by −2 and the product is −14, what sign is the value of x? Explain.
positive; because the product of a negative and a positive value is negative
23. You separate an amount into 3 equal groups of −6. Write and solve an division equation to model this situation.
$x \div 3 = -6$; $x = -18$

Use the graph for Exercises 65 and 66.

Georgia LINK History

There are many wrecks dating back to the Civil War and earlier lying off the coast of Georgia.

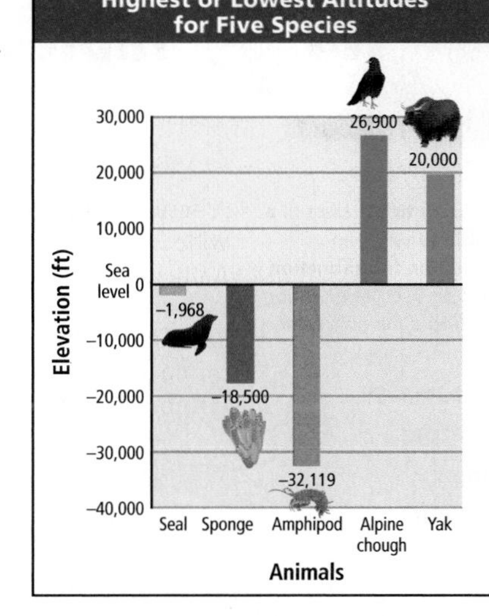

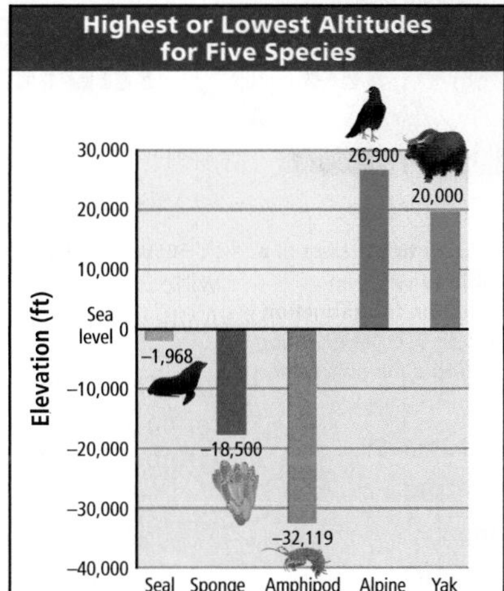

65. **Life Science** Scientists have found live bacteria at elevations of 135,000 ft. This is 153,500 ft above one of the animals in the graph. Which one? (*Hint:* Solve $x + 153{,}500 = 135{,}000$.) $x = -18{,}500$; sponge

66. **Social Studies** The world's highest capital city is La Paz, Bolivia, with an elevation of 11,808 ft. The highest altitude that a yak has been found at is how much higher than La Paz? (*Hint:* Solve $11{,}808 + x = 20{,}000$.) 8,192 ft

67. Carla is a diver. On Friday, she dove 5 times as deep as she dove on Monday. If she dove to −120 ft on Friday, how deep did she dive on Monday? −24 ft

68. **Write A Problem** Write a word problem that could be solved using the equation $x - 3 = -15$.

69. **Write About It** Is the solution to $3n = -12$ positive or negative? How could you tell without solving the equation?

70. **Challenge** Find each answer.

a. $12 \div (-3 \cdot 2) \div 2$ −1 **b.** $12 \div (-3 \cdot 2 \div 2)$ −4

Why are the answers different even though the numbers are the same? order of operations

CRCT Prep • GPS Support • Spiral Review

71. **Multiple Choice** Kathie and her three friends each owe $24 for dinner. Solve the equation $\frac{t}{4} = 24$ to determine the total amount t of the dinner.

(A) $96 (B) $28 (C) $20 (D) $6

72. **Short Response** David is 12 years younger than his sister Candace. David is 9 years old. Write an equation for the situation. Let c be Candace's age. Then solve the equation to find her age. $c - 12 = 9$; Candace is 21 years old.

Determine if the given statements are *sometimes, always,* or *never* true. (Lesson 8-6)

73. A square is a rhombus always

74. A parallelogram is a square. sometimes

Find each product. (Lesson 11-6)

75. $5 \cdot (-7)$ −35

76. $-9 \cdot 9$ −81

77. $2 \cdot 6$ 12

78. $10 \cdot 0$ 0

79. $-8 \cdot (-4)$ 32

CHALLENGE 11-8

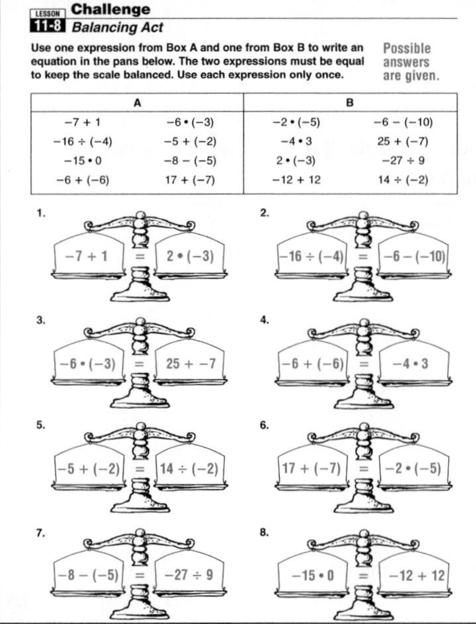

LESSON 11-8 **Challenge**
Balancing Act

Use one expression from Box A and one from Box B to write an equation in the pans below. The two expressions must be equal to keep the scale balanced. Use each expression only once. Possible answers are given.

A		B	
−7 + 1	−6 • (−3)	−2 • (−5)	−6 − (−10)
−16 ÷ (−4)	−5 + (−2)	−4 • 3	25 + (−7)
−15 • 0	−8 − (−5)	2 • (−3)	−27 ÷ 9
−6 + (−6)	17 + (−7)	−12 + 12	14 ÷ (−2)

1. −7 + 1 = 2 • (−3)
2. −16 ÷ (−4) = −6 − (−10)
3. −6 • (−3) = 25 + −7
4. −6 + (−6) = −4 • 3
5. −5 + (−2) = 14 ÷ (−2)
6. 17 + (−7) = −2 • (−5)
7. −8 − (−5) = −27 ÷ 9
8. −15 • 0 = −12 + 12

PROBLEM SOLVING 11-8

LESSON 11-8 **Problem Solving**
Solving Integer Equations

For questions 1–8, the temperatures found are in °F.

1. The highest recorded temperature in Africa is the solution to $x \div (-4) = -34$. What is Africa's highest recorded temperature? 136°F

2. The lowest recorded temperature in Australia is the solution to $7x = -56$. What is Australia's lowest recorded temperature? −8°F

3. To find Africa's lowest recorded temperature, solve the following equation: $80 - x = 91$. −11°F

4. To find Europe's highest recorded temperature, solve the following equation: $x \div -2 = -61$. 122°F

5. The solution to $-2x = -116$ is the highest recorded temperature in Antartica. What is Antartica's highest recorded temperature? 58°F

6. The solution to $x + (-23) = -90$ is the lowest recorded temperature in Europe. What is Europe's lowest recorded temperature? −67°F

Circle the letter of the correct answer.

7. Which of the following is a solution to $x + (-11) = -140$?
A 12
(B) −129
C −151
D −1,540

8. Which of the following is a solution to $-110 + x = 19$?
F 91
(G) 129
H −5
J −2,090

9. Which of the following is a solution to $5x = -75$?
A −375
B −80
C −70
(D) −15

10. Which of the following is a solution to $-270 \div x = -30$?
F 8,100
G −300
(H) 9
J −240

Ongoing Assessment and Intervention

***Diagnose Before* the Lesson**
11-8 Warm Up, TE p. 636

***Monitor During* the Lesson**
11-8 Know-It Notebook
11-8 Questioning Strategies

***Assess After* the Lesson**
11-8 Lesson Quiz, TE p. 639

Answers

68. Possible answer: Three less than a number is −15. What is that number?

69. Negative; a negative number divided by a positive number gives a negative quotient.

Test Prep Doctor For Exercise 71, students should first identify the operation needed to solve the equation. Students choosing **B** or **C** mistakenly used addition or subtraction to solve the equation. Students choosing **D** did not use the inverse operation.

Journal

Have students write about why there is a need for integers in our number system.

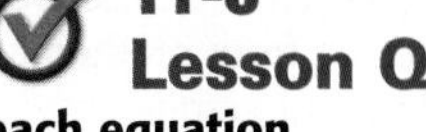

Power Presentations with PowerPoint®

11-8 Lesson Quiz

Solve each equation.

1. $5 + x = -6$ $x = -11$
2. $y - 9 = -7$ $y = 2$
3. $-6a = 24$ $a = -4$
4. $\frac{x}{5} = -9$ $x = -45$
5. A submarine captain sets the following diving course: dive 300 ft, stop, and then dive another 300 ft. If this pattern is continued, how many dives will be necessary to reach a location 3,000 ft below sea level? 10

Also available on transparency

11-9 Organizer

Pacing: Traditional 1 day
Block $\frac{1}{2}$ day

Objective: Students use data in a table to write an equation for a function and to use the equation to find a missing value.

Technology Lab
In *Technology Lab Activities*

Online Edition
Tutorial Videos

Power Presentations with PowerPoint®

Warm Up

Evaluate each expression for the given value of the variable.

1. $4x - 1$ for $x = 2$ 7
2. $7y + 3$ for $y = 5$ 38
3. $\frac{1}{2}x + 2$ for $x = -6$ −1
4. $8y - 3$ for $y = -2$ −19

Problem of the Day

Maria rented an electric car at a rate of $40 per day and $0.15 per mile. She returned the car the same day, gave the rental clerk a $100 bill, and got $21.75 back in change. How far did Maria drive the car? 255 miles

Also available on transparency

When *x* was equal to zero, no one listened to its opinion. They all agreed its input had no value.

Georgia Performance Standards

M6A2.a Analyze and describe patterns arising from mathematical rules, tables, and graphs.

M6A3 Students will evaluate algebraic expressions, including those with exponents, and solve simple one-step equations using each of the four basic operations.

M6P1.c Apply and adapt a variety of appropriate strategies to solve problems.

M6P1.d Monitor and reflect on the process of mathematical problem solving.

M6P4.c Recognize and apply mathematics in contexts outside of mathematics.

11-9 Tables and Functions

Learn to use data in a table to write an equation for a function and to use the equation to find a missing value.

Vocabulary
function
input
output

Georgia Performance Standards

M6A2.a Analyze and describe patterns arising from mathematical rules, tables, and graphs. Also, M6A3, M6P1.c, M6P1.d, M6P4.c.

A baseball pitch thrown too high, low, or wide is considered outside the strike zone. A pitcher threw a ball 4 inches too low. How far in centimeters was the ball outside the strike zone? Make a table to show how the number of centimeters increases as the number of inches increases.

Andrew Toos/Cartoon Resource.com

"Come on, ump, that pitch was at least four centimeters outside!"

Inches	Centimeters
1	2.54
2	5.08
3	7.62
4	10.16

(Inches: +1, +1, +1; Centimeters: +2.54, +2.54, +2.54)

The number of centimeters is 2.54 times the number of inches. Let x represent the number of inches and y represent the number of centimeters. Then the equation $y = 2.54x$ relates centimeters to inches.

A **function** is a rule that relates two quantities so that each **input** value corresponds exactly to one **output** value.

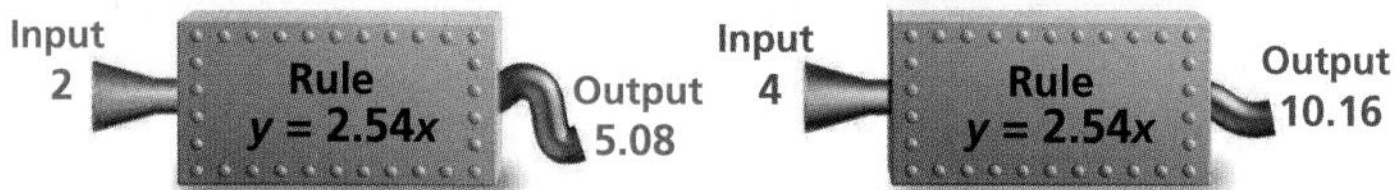

When the input is 4 in., the output is 10.16 cm. So the ball was 10.16 centimeters outside the strike zone.

You can use a function table to show some of the values for a function.

EXAMPLE 1 Writing Equations from Function Tables

Write an equation for a function that gives the values in the table. Use the equation to find the value of *y* for the indicated value of *x*.

x	3	4	5	6	7	10
y	7	9	11	13	15	■

y is 2 times $x + 1$. *Compare x and y to find a pattern.*
$y = 2x + 1$ *Use the pattern to write an equation.*
$y = 2(10) + 1$ *Substitute 10 for x.*
$y = 20 + 1 = 21$ *Use your function rule to find y when x = 10.*

Helpful Hint

When all the *y*-values are greater than the corresponding *x*-values, use addition and/or multiplication in your equation.

1 Introduce

Alternate Opener

EXPLORATION

11-9 Tables and Functions

A school has scheduled a trip for 210 students to a theme park. The school can rent up to six buses for $200 each. Each bus seats a maximum of 60 students. Tickets to the theme park cost $25 per student.

1. Use the first example as a guide to complete the table.

Group Number	Number of Students	Cost of Bus Rental and Tickets	Total Cost
1	10	$200 + 25 \cdot 10 = 200 + 250$	$450.00
2	20		
3	30		
4	40		
5	50		
6	60		

2. What numbers in the table remain constant?
3. What numbers in the table vary?
4. Use the cost of the bus ($200), the cost of each ticket ($25), and the number of students (x) to write an equation for the total cost (c). (*Hint:* Look at the middle column of the table to write the equation.)

Think and Discuss

5. **Explain** what makes the total cost of a group vary.
6. **Discuss** possible ways of reducing the total cost of taking 210 students to the theme park.

Motivate

To introduce students to functions, have them complete a table with familiar data, such as the following:

Tables	1	2	3	4
Legs	4	8	12	16

Ask students to discuss any patterns they notice in the table.

Possible answer: The number of tables keeps increasing by 1. The number of legs keeps increasing by 4. The number of legs is 4 times the number of tables.

Explorations and answers are provided in *Alternate Openers: Explorations Transparencies.*

You can write equations for functions that are described in words.

EXAMPLE  **Translating Words into Math**

Write an equation for the function. Tell what each variable you use represents.

The length of a rectangle is 5 times its width.

ℓ = length of rectangle — *Choose variables for the equation.*

w = width of rectangle

$\ell = 5w$ — *Write an equation.*

EXAMPLE  **PROBLEM SOLVING APPLICATION**

Car washers tracked the number of cars they washed and the total amount of money they earned. They charged the same price for each car they washed. They earned \$60 for 20 cars, \$66 for 22 cars, and \$81 for 27 cars. Write an equation for the function.

 **Understand the Problem**

The **answer** will be an equation that describes the relationship between the number of cars washed and the money earned.

 **Make a Plan**

You can make a table to display the data.

 **Solve**

Let c be the number of cars. Let m be the amount of money earned.

c	20	22	27
m	60	66	81

m is equal to 3 times c. — *Compare c and m.*

$m = 3c$ — *Write an equation.*

 **Look Back**

Substitute the c and m values in the table to check that they are solutions of the equation $m = 3c$.

$m = 3c$ (20, 60)
$60 \stackrel{?}{=} 3 \cdot 20$
$60 \stackrel{?}{=} 60$ ✓

$m = 3c$ (22, 66)
$66 \stackrel{?}{=} 3 \cdot 22$
$66 \stackrel{?}{=} 66$ ✓

$m = 3c$ (27, 81)
$81 \stackrel{?}{=} 3 \cdot 27$
$81 \stackrel{?}{=} 81$ ✓

Answers to *Think and Discuss*

1. Substitute 20 for x, and then multiply. When x is 20, y is 100.

Think and Discuss GPS M6P3.b

1. Explain how you find the y-value when the x-value is 20 for the function $y = 5x$.

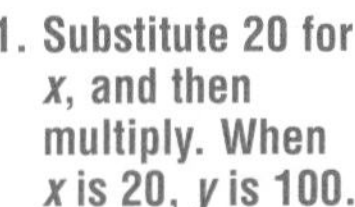

COMMON ERROR ALERT

Some students may write an equation for a relationship using only x-values or only y-values instead of the relationship between x- *and* y-values. To prevent this error, have students color code their tables, using one color for all x-values and one color for all y-values.

Power Presentations with PowerPoint®

Additional Examples

Example 

Write an equation for a function that gives the values in the table. Use the equation to find the value of y for the indicated value of x.

x	3	4	5	6	7	10
y	13	16	19	22	25	■

$y = 3x + 4$; when $x = 10$, $y = 34$.

Example 

Write an equation for the function. Tell what each variable you use represents.

The height of a painting is 7 times its width.

$h = 7w$; h = height, w = width

Example 

The school choir tracked the number of tickets sold and the total amount of money received. The choir members received \$80 for 20 tickets, \$88 for 22 tickets, and \$108 for 27 tickets. If each ticket costs the same, write an equation for the function.

$m = 4t$

Also available on transparency

2 Teach

Guided Instruction

In this lesson, students learn to use data in a table to write an equation for a function and to use the equation to find a missing value. Define *function*, *input*, and *output*. First teach students to write equations for functions shown in tables and described with words. Then work through the steps for solving a real-world problem involving functions.

Reaching All Learners

Through Multiple Representations

Have students make tables of values that can be expressed as functions. For example, students might make a table showing the relationship of plates to silverware at the dinner table:

Plates	1	2	3	4
Silverware	3	6	9	12

Have students write equations for the functions that represent the values in their tables.

For the example above, the equation might be $y = 3x$.

3 Close

Summarize

ENGLISH LANGUAGE LEARNERS

Review the new vocabulary in the lesson: *function*, *input*, and *output*. Ask students to explain how the terms relate to each other.

Possible answer: A *function* is a rule that relates two quantities such that each *input* value corresponds exactly to one *output* value

11-9 Exercises

Assignment Guide

If you finished Example 1 assign:
Average 1–2, 10–11, 22–30
Advanced 5–6, 12–13, 22–30

If you finished Example 2 assign:
Average 1–3, 10–13, 22–30
Advanced 5–8, 11–13, 22–30

If you finished Example 3 assign:
Average 1–11, 14–17, 22–30
Advanced 5–14, 18–30

Homework Quick Check

Quickly check key concepts.
Exercises: 6, 8, 10, 14

Math Background

The function concept is used today throughout mathematics. The definition given in the present lesson corresponds to the definition devised by the mathematician Lejeune Dirichlet in the nineteenth century.

When y is a function of x, x is called the *independent variable*, and y is called the *dependent variable*. Whenever a value is assigned to x, a value is automatically assigned to y by some rule or correspondence. The set of all possible values of x is called the *domain* of a function. The set of all possible values of y is called the *range* of a function.

Georgia Performance Standards

M6P3.a Organize and consolidate their mathematical thinking through communication.

M6P3.c Analyze and evaluate the mathematical thinking and strategies of others.

M6P5.b Select, apply, and translate among mathematical representations to solve problems.

11-9 Exercises

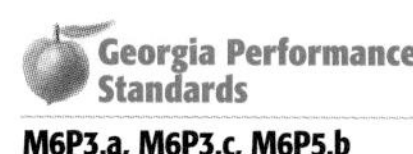

Georgia Performance Standards
M6P3.a, M6P3.c, M6P5.b

go.hrw.com
Homework Help Online
KEYWORD: MR7 11-9
Parent Resources Online
KEYWORD: MR7 Parent

GUIDED PRACTICE

See Example 1 Write an equation for a function that gives the values in each table. Use the equation to find the value of y for the indicated value of x.

1.

x	1	2	3	6	9
y	7	8	9	12	

$y = x + 6$; 15

2.

x	3	4	5	6	10
y	16	21	26	31	

$y = 5x + 1$; 51

See Example 2 Write an equation for the function. Tell what each variable you use represents. Possible answers:

3. Jen is 6 years younger than her brother.
j = Jen's age, b = brother's age, $j = b - 6$

See Example 3

4. Brenda sells balloon bouquets. She charges the same price for each balloon in a bouquet. The cost of a bouquet with 6 balloons is \$3, with 9 balloons is \$4.50, and with 12 balloons is \$6. Write an equation for the function.
c = cost of bouquet, b = number of balloons, $c = \$0.50b$

INDEPENDENT PRACTICE

See Example 1 Write an equation for a function that gives the values in each table. Use the equation to find the value of y for the indicated value of x.

5.

x	0	1	2	5	7
y	0	4	8	20	

$y = 4x$; 28

6.

x	4	5	6	7	12
y	0	2	4	6	

$y = 2x - 8$; 16 Possible answers:

See Example 2 Write an equation for the function. Tell what each variable you use represents.

7. The cost of a case of bottled juices is \$2 less than the cost of twelve individual bottles. c = cost of a case, s = cost of 1 bottle, $c = 12s - 2$

8. The population of New York is twice as large as the population of Michigan.
n = population of New York, m = population of Michigan, $n = 2m$

See Example 3

9. Oliver is playing a video game. He earns the same number of points for each prize he captures. He earned 1,050 points for 7 prizes, 1,500 points for 10 prizes, and 2,850 points for 19 prizes. Write an equation for the function.
p = number of points, m = number of prizes, $p = 150m$

PRACTICE AND PROBLEM SOLVING

Extra Practice p. 736

Write an equation for a function that gives the values in each table, and then find the missing terms.

10.

x	−1	0	1	2	5	7
y		3.4	4.4	5.4		10.4

$y = x + 3.4$; 2.4; 8.4

11.

x	2	3	5	9	11	14
y	−6	−10	−18	−34	−42	

$y = -4x + 2$; −54

12.

x	20	24	28	32	36	40
y	−5	−6	−7		−9	−10

$y = \frac{x}{-4}$; −8

13.

x	−5	−3	−1	0	1	3
y	−11	−7		−1	1	

$y = 2x - 1$; −3; 5

14. **Multi-Step** The height of a triangle is 5 centimeters more than twice the length of its base. Write an equation relating the height of the triangle to the length of its base. Find the height when the base is 20 centimeters long.
b = base of triangle, h = height of triangle, $h = 2b + 5$; $h = 45$

RETEACH 11-9

LESSON 11-9 **Reteach**
Tables and Functions

A function is a rule that relates two quantities so that each input value corresponds to exactly one output value. In the table below, the x-values are the input and the y-values are the output.

x	0	1	2	3	4	5	6	7
y	4	5	6	7	8	9	10	?

To write an equation for a table of values, first compare the x- and y-values to find a pattern.

Each y-value is 4 more than its corresponding x-value.

Then use the pattern to write a rule for the table.

$y = x + 4$

You can use the rule to find a missing value in a table. To find the value of y in table above when $x = 7$, substitute 7 for x in the equation.

$y = x + 4$
$y = 7 + 4$
$y = 11$
So y is 11 when x is 7.

Write an equation for a function that gives the values in each table. Use the equation to find the value of y for the indicated value of x.

1.

x	1	2	3	4	5	6
y	3	6	9	12	15	?

$y = 3x$, $y = 18$

2.

x	18	17	16	15	14	13
y	15	14	13	?	11	10

$y = x - 3$, $y = 12$

You can also write equations for functions that are described in words.

The length of the pool is 6 times the width of the pool.

ℓ = length of pool
w = width of pool — Choose variables for the equation.

$\ell = 6w$ — Write an equation.

Write an equation for the function. Tell what each variable you use represents.

3. Todd is 6 inches taller than Scott.
t = Todd's height
s = Scott's height
$t = s + 6$

4. Alana is 4 times as old as Tracey.
a = Alana's age
t = Tracey's age
$a = 4t$

PRACTICE 11-9

LESSON 11-9 **Practice B**
Tables and Functions

Write an equation for a function that gives the values in each table. Use the equation to find the value of y for the indicated value of x.

1.

x	1	2	3	4	5
y	7	14	21	28	♦

$y = 7x$
$y = 35$

2.

x	2	3	4	5	6
y	−3	−2	−1	0	♦

$y = x - 5$
$y = 1$

3.

x	20	16	12	8	4
y	10	8	6	4	♦

$y = x \div 2$
$y = 2$

4.

x	7	8	9	10	11
y	11	12	13	14	♦

$y = x + 4$
$y = 15$

Write an equation for the function. Tell what each variable you use represents.

5. Amanda is 7 years younger than her cousin.
Possible answer: $y = x - 7$; y = Amanda's age; x = her cousin's age

6. The population of North Carolina is twice as large as the population of South Carolina.
Possible answer: $n = 2s$; n = population of North Carolina; s = population of South Carolina

7. An Internet book company charges \$7 for each paperback book, plus \$2.75 for shipping and handling per order.
Possible answer: $y = 7x + 2.75$; y = total price of order; x = number of books purchased

8. Henry records how many days he rides his bike and how far he rides each week. He rides the same distance each time. He rode 18 miles in 3 days, 24 miles in 4 days, and 42 miles in 7 days. Write an equation for the function.
$m = 6d$; m = miles, and d = days

Write an equation for each function. Define the variables that you use.

15. The Denominators

$125.00
plus $55 per hour

16. 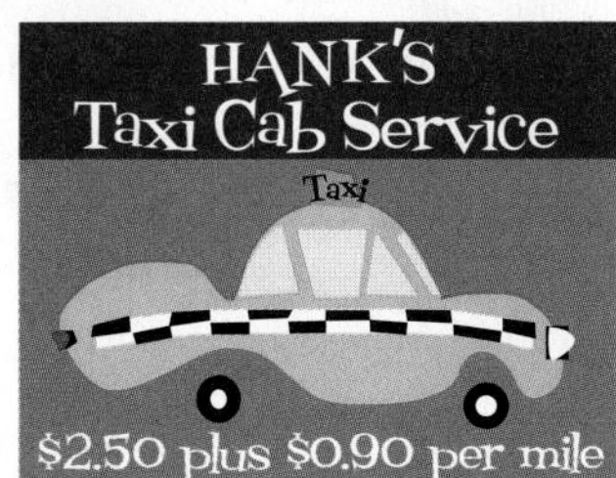

17. **Multi-Step** Georgia earns \$6.50 per hour at a part-time job. She wants to buy a sweater that costs \$58.50. Write an equation relating the number of hours she works to the amount of money she earns. Find how many hours Georgia needs to work to buy the sweater.
h = number of hours worked, $58.50 = 6.5h$; 9 hours

Use the table for Exercises 18–20.

Width (pixels)	Length (pixels)
30	95
40	125
50	155
60	185

18. **Graphic Design** Margo is designing a Web page displaying similar rectangles. Use the table to write an equation relating the width of a rectangle to the length of a rectangle. Find the length of a rectangle that has a width of 250 pixels. $l = 3w + 5$; 755 pixels

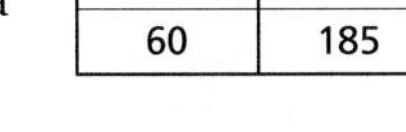

19. **What's the Error?** Margo predicted that the length of a rectangle with a width of 100 pixels would be 310 pixels. Explain the error she made. Then find the correct length.

20. **Write About It** Explain how to write an equation for the data in the table.

21. **Challenge** Write an equation that would give the same y-values as $y = 2x + 1$ for $x = 0, 1, 2, 3$. Possible answer: $2y = 4x + 2$

CRCT Prep • GPS Support • Spiral Review

22. **Multiple Choice** Sunny Lawn Care charges \$25 per visit plus \$2 per cubic foot. Which equation models this situation?

(A) $y = x + 2$ (B) $y = x + 25$ (C) $y = 25x + 2$ **(D)** $y = 2x + 25$

23. **Multiple Choice** Which is an equation for the function that gives the values in the table?

x	3	4	5	6	7
y	8	11	14	17	20

(F) $y = 2x + 2$ (H) $y = 2x + 6$
(G) $y = 3x - 1$ (J) $y = 3x + 1$

Solve each equation. Check your answers. (Lesson 3-9)

24. $4.2 + n = 6.7$ $n = 2.5$
25. $x - 2.3 = 1.6$ $x = 3.9$
26. $1.5w = 3.6$ $w = 2.4$
27. $\frac{p}{4} = 1.3$ $p = 5.2$

Find the volume of each cylinder using the information given. (Lesson 10-8)

28. $r = 6$ cm; $h = 6.4$ cm 723.456 cm^3
29. $r = 5$ ft; $h = 9$ ft 706.5 ft^3
30. $d = 7$ m; $h = 11$ m 423.115 m^3

Ongoing Assessment and Intervention

***Diagnose Before* the Lesson**
11-9 Warm Up, TE p. 640

***Monitor During* the Lesson**
11-9 Know-It Notebook
11-9 Questioning Strategies

***Assess After* the Lesson**
11-9 Lesson Quiz, TE p. 643

Answers

15. Let c be the total cost and h be the number of hours.
$c = \$125 + \$55h$

16. Let f be the total cab fare and m be the number of miles.
$f = \$2.50 + \$0.90m$

19–20. See p. A12.

Test Prep Doctor For students having difficulty with Exercise 23, suggest that they check to see whether each equation is true for the first term in the table. Choices **H** and **J** can be eliminated by checking the first term. Checking the second term will eliminate choice **F.**

Journal

Have students think of and write about real-world situations in which a function is used to find the relationship between two quantities. Have them write the equation for the function and find the y-values for any three x-values.

CHALLENGE 11-9

LESSON 11-9 Challenge
Multifunctional Measurements

Any function can be written as two different equations—one for each variable. Write two different equations for the function that gives the values in each table. Then choose either equation to answer the question that follows.

A **stone** is a British unit of weight.

stones (s)	1	2	3	4	5
pounds (p)	14	28	42	56	70

1. $p =$ $14 \times s$
2. $s =$ $p \div 14$

3. In a competition called Stones of Strength, athletes must lift five huge rocks onto platforms. The first rock weighs 245 pounds. How many stone does it weigh?
$17\frac{1}{2}$ stone

A **fathom** is a unit sailors use to measure the depth of water.

fathoms (m)	4	6	8	10	12
feet (f)	24	36	48	60	72

4. $f =$ $6 \times m$
5. $m =$ $f \div 6$

6. Years ago, sailors on riverboats shouted "mark twain" when the river's depth was 2 fathoms—barely deep enough for a boat to navigate safely. How many feet deep was the water at mark twain?
12 feet

An **acre** is a unit for measuring areas of land.

acre (a)	1,280	1,920	2,560	3,200	3,840
square miles (s)	2	3	4	5	6

7. $a =$ $640 \times s$
8. $s =$ $a \div 640$

9. King Ranch in Texas covers about 1,300 square miles—larger than the entire state of Rhode Island! How many acres of land does King Ranch cover?
832,000 acres

PROBLEM SOLVING 11-9

LESSON 11-9 Problem Solving
Tables and Functions

Use the tables to answer each question.

Table 1

miles	kilometers
2	3.22
3	4.83
4	6.44
5	8.05

Table 2

ounces	grams
1	28.35
2	56.7
3	85.05
4	113.4

Table 3

gallons	liters
5	18.95
10	37.9
15	56.85
20	75.8

1. Write an equation for a function that gives the values in table 1. Define the variables you use. Use your equation to find the missing term in the table.
Possible answer:
$k = 1.61m$; k = kilometers;
m = miles

2. Write an equation for a function that gives the values in table 2. Define the variables you use. Use your equation to find the missing term in the table.
Possible answer:
$g = 28.35z$; g = grams;
z = ounces

3. Write an equation for a function that gives the values in table 3. Define the variables you use. Use your equation to find the missing term in the table.
Possible answer:
$l = 3.79g$; l = liters;
g = gallons

4. There are 4 quarts in a gallon. Write an equation for a function relating quarts to liters. Then use your equation to find how many liters of oil a 50-quart barrel can hold.
Possible answer:
$l = 0.9475q$; l = liters;
q = quarts; 47.375 liters of oil

Circle the letter of the correct answer.

5. The Rocky Mountains stretch 3,750 miles across North America. What is this length in kilometers?
A 2,329.2 kilometers
B 1,164.6 kilometers
(C) 6,037.5 kilometers
D 12,075 kilometers

6. A hummingbird egg only weighs 0.25 grams! How many ounces does the egg weigh?
F about 7.0875 ounces
(G) about 0.009 ounces
H about 28 ounces
J about 9 ounces

Power Presentations with PowerPoint®

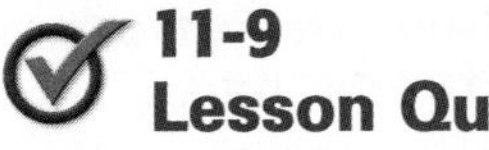

11-9 Lesson Quiz

1. Write an equation for a function that gives the values in the table below. Use the equation to find the value for y for the indicated value of x. $y = 3x$; 21

x	0	1	3	5	7
y	0	3	9	15	

2. Write an equation for the function. Tell what each variable you use represents. The height of a round can is 2 times its radius. $h = 2r$, where h is the height and r is the radius

Also available on transparency

Organizer

Use with Lesson 11-10

Pacing:
Traditional $\frac{1}{2}$ day
Block $\frac{1}{4}$ day

Objective: Use graph-paper drawings to explore linear and nonlinear relationships.

Materials: Graph paper

 Online Edition

Resources

Hands-On Lab Activities
Lab 11-10 Recording Sheet

Teach

Discuss

Have students describe some numerical patterns. Ask a student to use a pattern to create a sequence on graph paper.

Close

Key Concept

Graph-paper drawings can be used to model linear and nonlinear relationships.

Assessment

1. Explain how to form the next figure in each pattern.
2. Explain how you can use the graph to show that the function $y = \sqrt{x}$ is nonlinear.
3. Explain how you can use the table to show that the function $y = \sqrt{x}$ is nonlinear.

Explore Linear and Nonlinear Relationships

Use with Lesson 11-10

M6A2.a, M6P4.a, M6P4.b, M6P5.b

You can learn about linear and nonlinear relationships by looking at patterns.

Activity

1. This model shows stage 1 to stage 3 of a pattern.

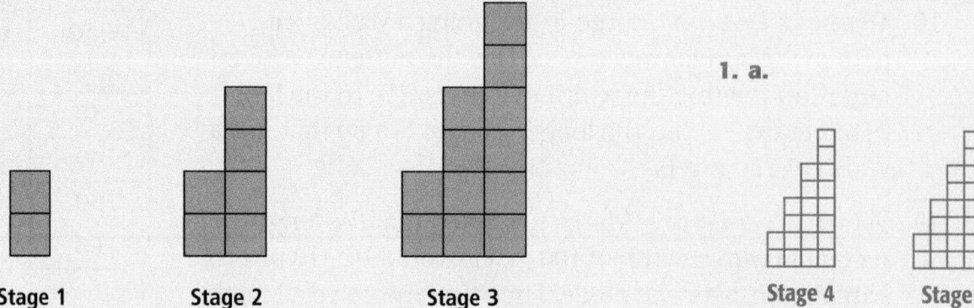

a. Use square tiles or graph paper to model stages 4, 5, and 6.

b. Record each stage and the perimeter of each figure in a table.

c. Graph the ordered pairs (x, y) from the table on a coordinate plane.

Stage (x)	Perimeter (y)
1	6
2	12
3	18
4	24
5	30
6	36

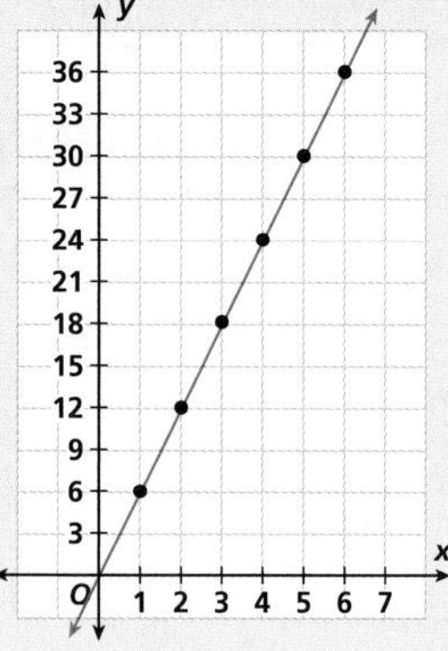

If you connected the points you graphed, you would draw a straight line. This shows that the relationship between the stage and the perimeter of the figure is linear. The equation for this line is $y = 6x$.

Answers to *Assessment*

1. First example: At each stage, make a new column of squares on the right side, 2 units higher than the previous column. Second example: At each stage, make a square using the specified number of blocks.
2. Possible answer: The points on the graph do not lie on a straight line.
3. Possible answer: The ratio of the change in y to the change in x is not constant.

Georgia Performance Standards

M6A2.a Analyze and describe patterns arising from mathematical rules, tables, and graphs.

M6P4.a Recognize and use connections among mathematical ideas.

M6P4.b Understand how mathematical ideas interconnect and build on one another to produce a coherent whole.

M6P5.b Select, apply, and translate among mathematical representations to solve problems.

2 This table shows the ordered pairs for stages 1, 4, and 9 of a pattern.

Stage (x)	Square Root (y)
1	1
4	2
9	3
16	4
25	5
36	6

$1 = 1 \cdot 1$ or $1 = 1^2$

$4 = 2 \cdot 2$ or $4 = 2^2$

$9 = 3 \cdot 3$ or $9 = 3^2$

The square root of 4 is 2, which is written like this: $\sqrt{4} = 2$.

a. You can model this by arranging squares in 1-by-1, 2-by-2, and 3-by-3 blocks.

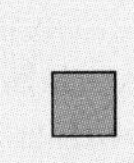
Stage 1

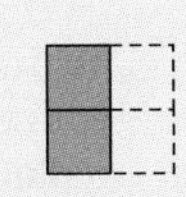
Stage 4

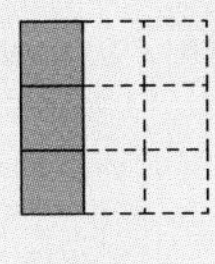
Stage 9

b. Record each stage number and the number's square root in a table. Graph the ordered pairs (x, y) from the table on a coordinate plane.

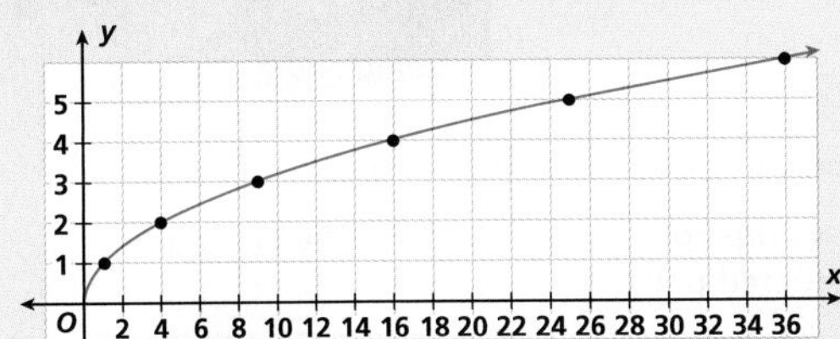

If you connect the graphed points, you draw a curved line. This shows that the relationship between the stage number and that number's square root is nonlinear. The equation for this curve is $y = \sqrt{x}$.

Think and Discuss

1. Explain what pattern you see in the y-values of the ordered pairs from the graph above.
The y-values are changing at a constant rate of 1.

Try This

Use the x-values 1, 2, 3, and 4 to find ordered pairs for each equation. Then graph the equation. Tell whether the relationship between x and y is linear or nonlinear.

1. $y = 2 + x$ linear
2. $y = 4x$ linear
3. $y = x^3$ nonlinear
4. $y = x + 4$ linear
5. $y = x(2 + x)$ nonlinear
6. $y = x + x$ linear
7. $y = 2x$ linear
8. $y = x^2$ nonlinear
9. $y = 3 + 2x$ linear

6.

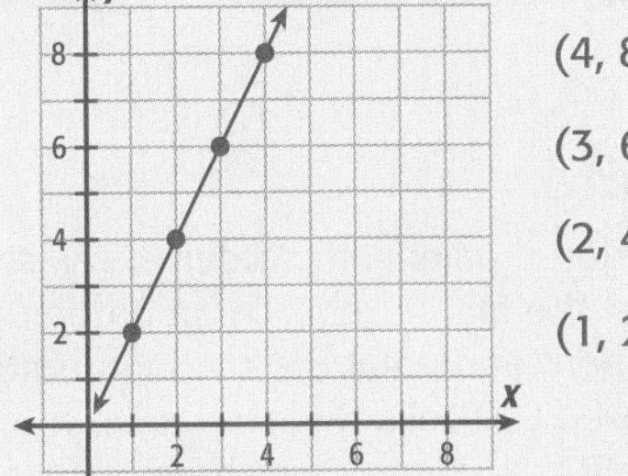

(4, 8)
(3, 6)
(2, 4)
(1, 2)

7.

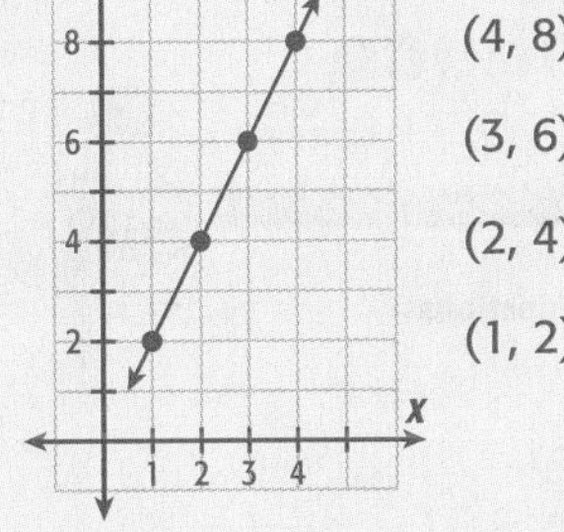

(4, 8)
(3, 6)
(2, 4)
(1, 2)

8.

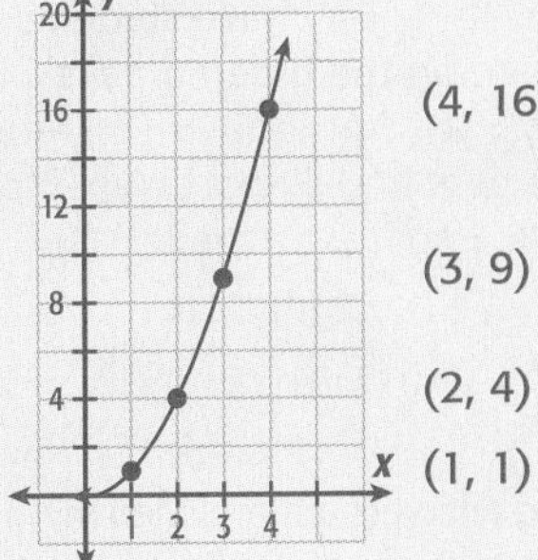

(4, 16)
(3, 9)
(2, 4)
(1, 1)

9.

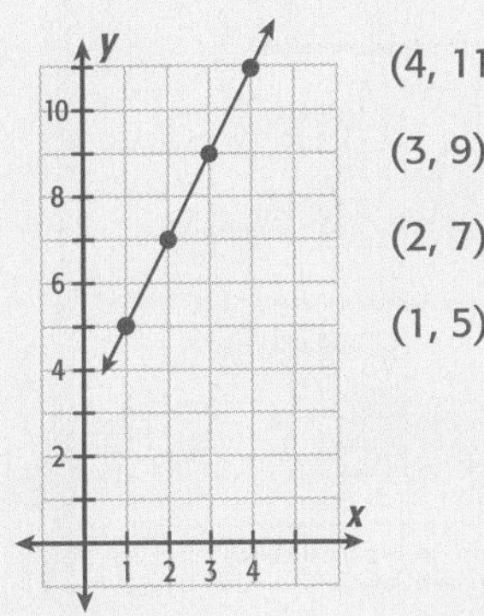

(4, 11)
(3, 9)
(2, 7)
(1, 5)

Answers to *Try This*

1. (1, 3), (2, 4), (3, 5), (4, 6)

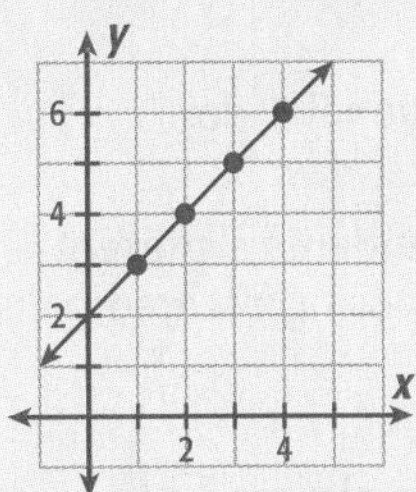

2. (1, 4), (2, 8), (3, 12), (4, 16)

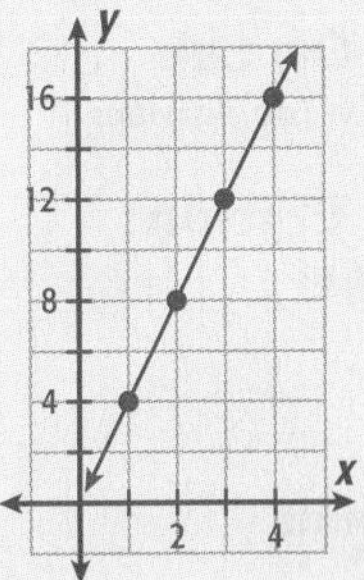

3. (1, 1), (2, 8), (3, 27), (4, 64)

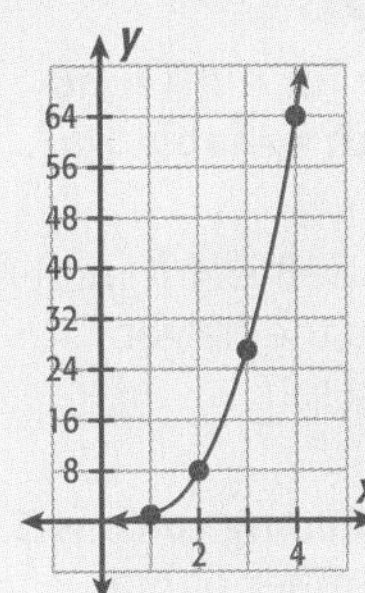

4. (1, 5), (2, 6), (3, 7), (4, 8)

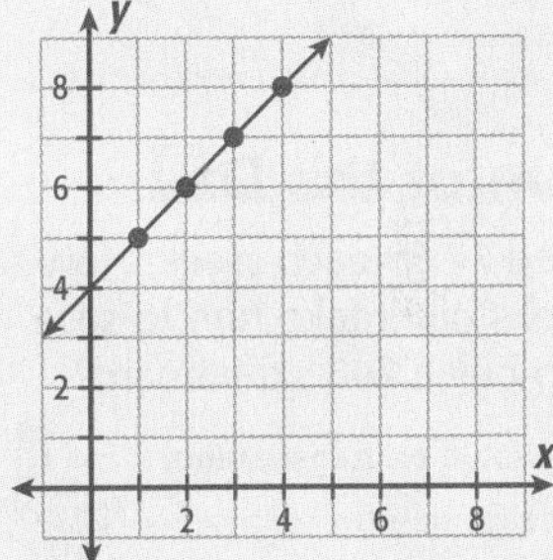

5. (1, 3), (2, 8), (3, 15), (4, 24)

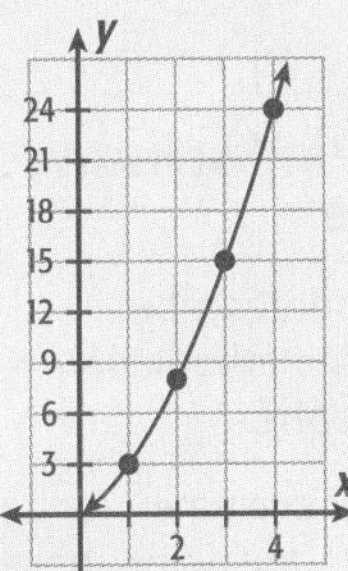

11-10 Organizer

Pacing: Traditional 1 day
Block $\frac{1}{2}$ day

Objective: Students represent linear functions using ordered pairs and graphs.

Technology Lab
In *Technology Lab Activities*

Hands-On Lab
In *Hands-On Lab Activities*

Online Edition
Tutorial Videos

Power Presentations with PowerPoint®

Warm Up

Write an equation for each function. Tell what each variable you use represents.

1. The length of a wall is 4 ft more than three times the height. $\ell = 3h + 4$, where ℓ is length and h is height
2. The number of trading cards is 3 less than the number of buttons. $c = b - 3$, where c is the number of cards and b is the number of buttons

Problem of the Day

Steve saved \$1.50 each week. How many weeks did it take him to save enough to buy a \$45 skateboard? 30

Also available on transparency

11-10 Graphing Functions

Learn to represent linear functions using ordered pairs and graphs.

Vocabulary
linear equation

Christa is ordering CDs online. Each CD costs \$16, and the shipping and handling charge is \$6 for the whole order.

The total cost y depends on the number of CDs x. This function is described by the equation $y = 16x + 6$.

To find solutions of an equation with two variables, first choose a replacement value for one variable and then find the value of the other variable.

Georgia Performance Standards
M6A2.a Analyze and describe patterns arising from mathematical rules, tables, and graphs. Also, M6A3, M6P5.a, M6P5.b.

EXAMPLE 1 Finding Solutions of Equations with Two Variables

Use the given x-values to write solutions of the equation $y = 16x + 6$ as ordered pairs.

Make a function table by using the given values for x to find values for y.

x	$16x + 6$	y
1	16(1) + 6	22
2	16(2) + 6	38
3	16(3) + 6	54
4	16(4) + 6	70

Write these solutions as ordered pairs.

(x, y)
(1, 22)
(2, 38)
(3, 54)
(4, 70)

Check if an ordered pair is a solution of an equation by putting the x and y values into the equation to see if they make it a true statement.

EXAMPLE 2 Checking Solutions of Equations with Two Variables

Determine whether the ordered pair is a solution to the given equation.

(8, 16); $y = 2x$

$y = 2x$ *Write the equation.*

$16 \stackrel{?}{=} 2(8)$ *Substitute 8 for x and 16 for y.*

$16 \stackrel{?}{=} 16$ ✔

So (8, 16) is a solution of $y = 2x$.

Georgia Performance Standards

M6A2.a Analyze and describe patterns arising from mathematical rules, tables, and graphs.

M6A3 Students will evaluate algebraic expressions, including those with exponents, and solve simple one-step equations using each of the four basic operations.

M6P5.a Create and use representations to organize, record, and communicate mathematical ideas.

M6P5.b Select, apply, and translate among mathematical representations to solve problems.

1 Introduce

Alternate Opener

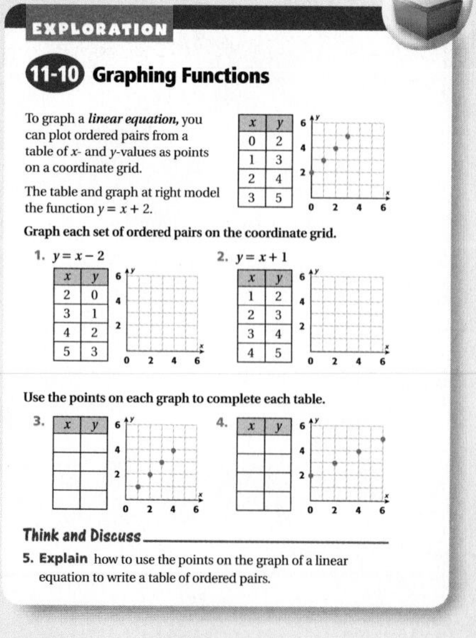

EXPLORATION

11-10 Graphing Functions

To graph a *linear equation,* you can plot ordered pairs from a table of x- and y-values as points on a coordinate grid.

The table and graph at right model the function $y = x + 2$.

x	y
0	2
1	3
2	4
3	5

Graph each set of ordered pairs on the coordinate grid.

1. $y = x - 2$

x	y
2	0
3	1
4	2
5	3

2. $y = x + 1$

x	y
1	2
2	3
3	4
4	5

Use the points on each graph to complete each table.

3.

x	y

4.

x	y

Think and Discuss

5. **Explain** how to use the points on the graph of a linear equation to write a table of ordered pairs.

Motivate

Review ordered pairs with students. Ask students what the first number in an ordered pair tells them and what the second number in an ordered pair tells them. how far and what direction to move from the origin along the x-axis; how far and what direction to move parallel to the y-axis Have students explain how to graph the ordered pairs (2, 3) and (−4, −2). From the origin, move 2 spaces to the right and 3 spaces up. From the origin, move 4 spaces to the left and 2 spaces down.

Explorations and answers are provided in *Alternate Openers: Explorations Transparencies.*

You can also graph the solutions of an equation on a coordinate plane. When you graph the ordered pairs of some functions, they form a straight line. The equations that express these functions are called **linear equations**.

EXAMPLE 3 Reading Solutions on Graphs

Use the graph of the linear function to find the value of y for the given value of x.

$x = 1$

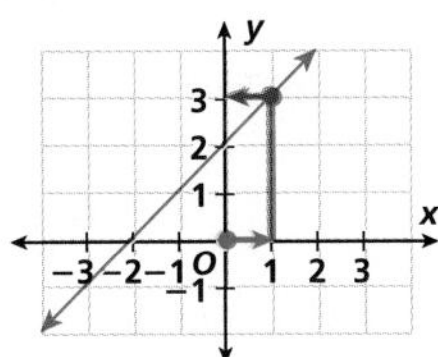

Start at the origin and move 1 unit right. Move up until you reach the graph. Move left to find the y-value on the y-axis.

When $x = 1$, $y = 3$. The ordered pair is (1, 3).

EXAMPLE 4 Graphing Linear Functions

Graph the function described by the equation.

$y = 2x + 1$

Make a function table. Substitute different values for x.

x	$2x + 1$	y
−1	2(−1) + 1	−1
0	2(0) + 1	1
1	2(1) + 1	3

Write the solutions as ordered pairs.

(x, y)

(−1, −1)

(0, 1)

(1, 3)

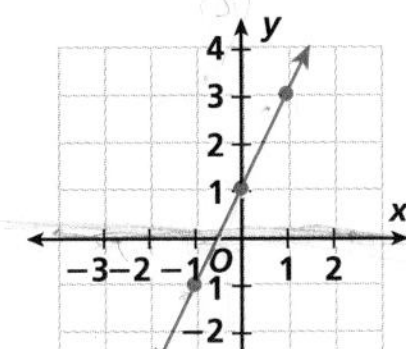

Graph the ordered pairs on a coordinate plane. Draw a line through the points to represent all the values of x you could have chosen and the corresponding values of y.

Possible answers to *Think and Discuss*

1. By extending the table, an infinite number of values of x and y can be found; (2, 5) and (−2, −3).
2. Yes; when you graph the solutions to this equation the ordered pairs form a straight line.

Think and Discuss

GPS M6P1.d, M6P2.c

1. **Explain** why the points in Example 4 are not the only points on the graph. Name two points that you did not plot.
2. **Tell** whether the equation $y = 10x - 5$ describes a linear function.

Power Presentations with PowerPoint®

Additional Examples

Example 1

Use the given x-values to write solutions of the equation as ordered pairs.

$y = 4x + 2$; $x = 1, 2, 3, 4$ (1, 6), (2, 10), (3, 14), (4, 18)

Example 2

Determine whether the ordered pair is a solution to the given equation.

(3, 21); $y = 7x$ (3, 21) is a solution.

Example 3

Use the graph of the linear function to find the value of y for the given value of x.

$x = 4$ When $x = 4$, $y = 2$.

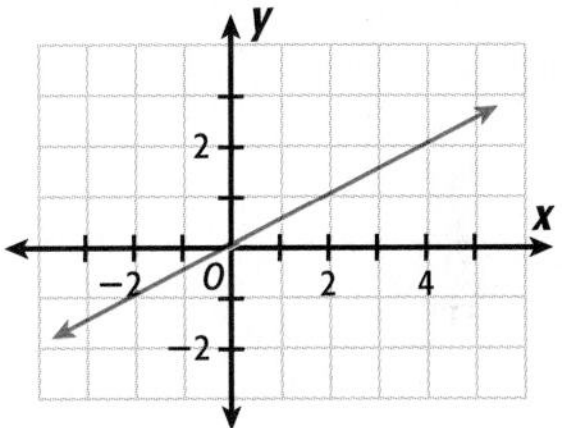

Example 4

Graph the function described by the equation.

$y = -x - 2$

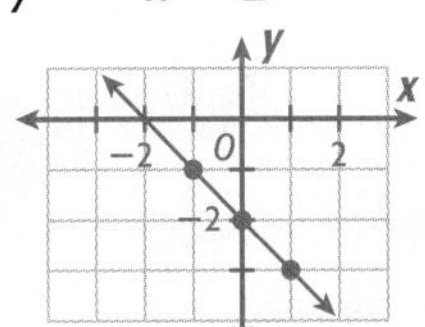

Also available on transparency

2 Teach

Guided Instruction

In this lesson, students learn to represent linear functions using ordered pairs and graphs. Teach students to find and check solutions for equations with two variables. Demonstrate how to read a graph to find an approximate y-value, given the x-value. Finally, teach students to graph a function described by a particular equation.

Teaching Tip

Modeling After working through all of the examples, have students graph the functions described by the equations in Examples 1 and 2.

Reaching All Learners

Through Cooperative Learning

Have students work in pairs to write an equation with two variables. Equations should be similar in form to the ones in Examples 1, 2, and 4. Collect students' equations, and randomly redistribute them so that each pair of students has a different pair's equation. Have the students make a function table for the equations and write solutions of the equations as ordered pairs. Then have the students graph the functions described by the equations.

3 Close

Summarize

Review how to represent an equation using ordered pairs and how to graph a function described by an equation. Remind students that when the ordered pairs of a function form a straight line, the equation representing the function is called a *linear equation*

11-10 Exercises

Assignment Guide

If you finished Example 1 assign:
Average 1–2, 38–46
Advanced 11–12, 38–46

If you finished Example 2 assign:
Average 1–4, 29, 38–46
Advanced 11–14, 29, 38–46

If you finished Example 3 assign:
Average 1–7, 29, 38–46
Advanced 11–20, 29, 38–46

If you finished Example 4 assign:
Average 1–18, 24–33, 38–46
Advanced 11–46

Homework Quick Check

Quickly check key concepts.
Exercises: 12, 14, 24, 26

Answers

8.

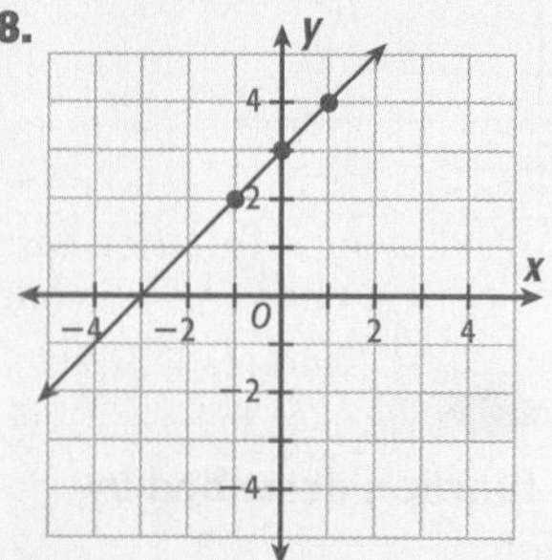

9–10, 21–28. See p. A12.

Math Background

Exact values cannot be read from an actual graph because the line has thickness and there are measurement errors. A graph can only abstractly determine *x*- and *y*-values.

Georgia Performance Standards

M6P1.a Build new mathematical knowledge through problem solving.

M6P4.c Recognize and apply mathematics in contexts outside of mathematics.

M6P5.a Create and use representations to organize, record, and communicate mathematical ideas.

M6P5.b Select, apply, and translate among mathematical representations to solve problems.

11-10 Exercises

Georgia Performance Standards
M6P1.a, M6P4.c, M6P5.a, M6P5.b

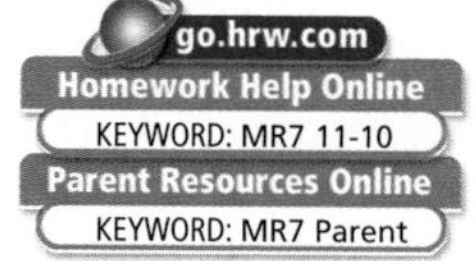

go.hrw.com
Homework Help Online
KEYWORD: MR7 11-10
Parent Resources Online
KEYWORD: MR7 Parent

GUIDED PRACTICE

See Example 1 Use the given *x*-values to write solutions of each equation as ordered pairs.

1. $y = 6x + 2$ for $x = 1, 2, 3, 4$ (1, 8); (2, 14); (3, 20); (4, 26)
2. $y = -2x$ for $x = 1, 2, 3, 4$ (1, −2); (2, −4); (3, −6); (4, −8)

See Example 2 Determine whether each ordered pair is a solution to the given equation.

3. (2, 12); $y = 4x$ no
4. (5, 9); $y = 2x - 1$ yes

See Example 3 Use the graph of the linear function to find the value of *y* for each given value of *x*.

5. $x = 1$ 2
6. $x = 0$ 1
7. $x = -1$ 0

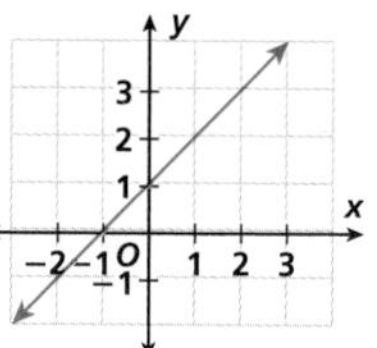

See Example 4 Graph the function described by each equation.

8. $y = x + 3$
9. $y = 3x - 1$
10. $y = -2x + 3$

INDEPENDENT PRACTICE

See Example 1 Use the given *x*-values to write solutions of each equation as ordered pairs.

11. $y = -4x + 1$ for $x = 1, 2, 3, 4$ (1, −3); (2, −7); (3, −11); (4, −15)
12. $y = 5x - 5$ for $x = 1, 2, 3, 4$ (1, 0); (2, 5); (3, 10); (4, 15)

See Example 2 Determine whether each ordered pair is a solution to the given equation.

13. (3, −10); $y = -6x + 8$ yes
14. (−8, 1); $y = 7x - 15$ no

See Example 3 Use the graph of the linear function to find the value of *y* for each given value of *x*.

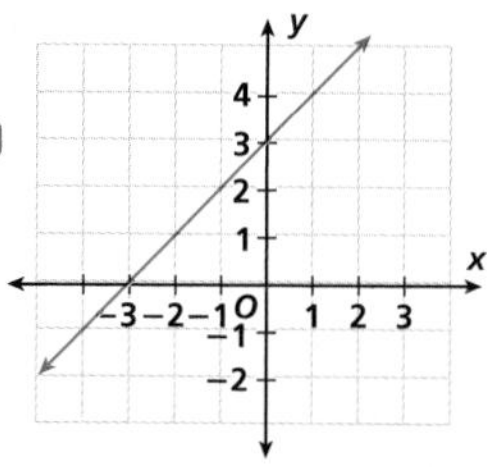

15. $x = -2$ 1
16. $x = 1$ 4
17. $x = -3$ 0
18. $x = 0$ 3
19. $x = -1$ 2
20. $x = 2$ 5

See Example 4 Graph the function described by each equation.

21. $y = 4x + 1$
22. $y = -x - 2$
23. $y = x - 2$
24. $y = -2x - 4$
25. $y = 3x - 2$
26. $y = -x$

PRACTICE AND PROBLEM SOLVING

CRCT GPS
Extra Practice p. 736

Complete each table, and then use the table to graph the function.

27. $y = x - 2$ −3; −2; −1; 0

x	−1	0	1	2
y	■	■	■	■

28. $y = 2x - 4$ −6; −4; −2; 0

x	−1	0	1	2
y	■	■	■	■

29. Which of the ordered pairs below is not a solution of $y = 4x + 9$?
(1, 14), (0, 9), (−1, 5), (−2, 1), (2, 17) (1, 14)

RETEACH 11-10

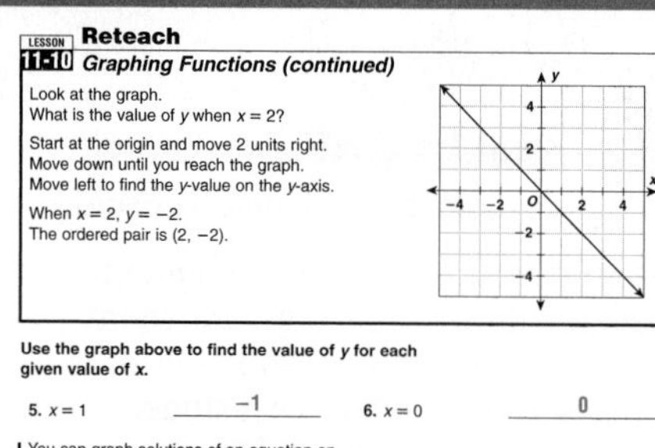

LESSON 11-10 Reteach
Graphing Functions (continued)

Look at the graph.
What is the value of *y* when *x* = 2?
Start at the origin and move 2 units right.
Move down until you reach the graph.
Move left to find the *y*-value on the *y*-axis.
When *x* = 2, *y* = −2.
The ordered pair is (2, −2).

Use the graph above to find the value of *y* for each given value of *x*.

5. *x* = 1 −1
6. *x* = 0 0

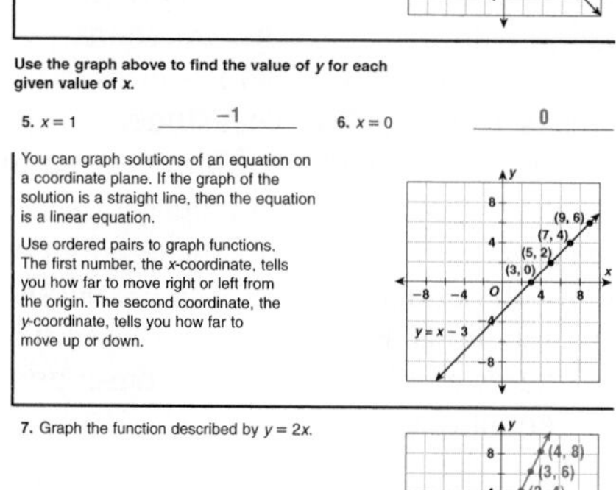

You can graph solutions of an equation on a coordinate plane. If the graph of the solution is a straight line, then the equation is a linear equation.

Use ordered pairs to graph functions. The first number, the *x*-coordinate, tells you how far to move right or left from the origin. The second coordinate, the *y*-coordinate, tells you how far to move up or down.

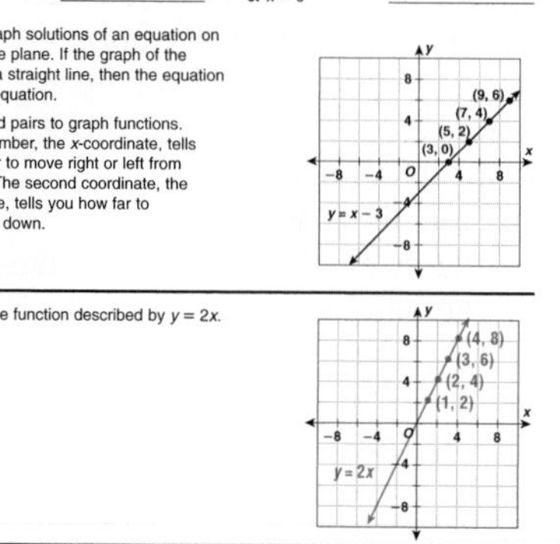

7. Graph the function described by *y* = 2*x*.

PRACTICE 11-10

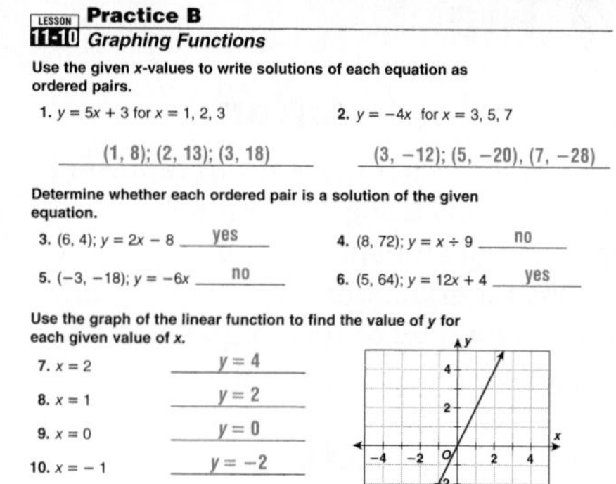

LESSON 11-10 Practice B
Graphing Functions

Use the given *x*-values to write solutions of each equation as ordered pairs.

1. *y* = 5*x* + 3 for *x* = 1, 2, 3 (1, 8); (2, 13); (3, 18)
2. *y* = −4*x* for *x* = 3, 5, 7 (3, −12); (5, −20), (7, −28)

Determine whether each ordered pair is a solution of the given equation.

3. (6, 4); *y* = 2*x* − 8 yes
4. (8, 72); *y* = *x* ÷ 9 no
5. (−3, −18); *y* = −6*x* no
6. (5, 64); *y* = 12*x* + 4 yes

Use the graph of the linear function to find the value of *y* for each given value of *x*.

7. *x* = 2 *y* = 4
8. *x* = 1 *y* = 2
9. *x* = 0 *y* = 0
10. *x* = −1 *y* = −2
11. *x* = −2 *y* = −4

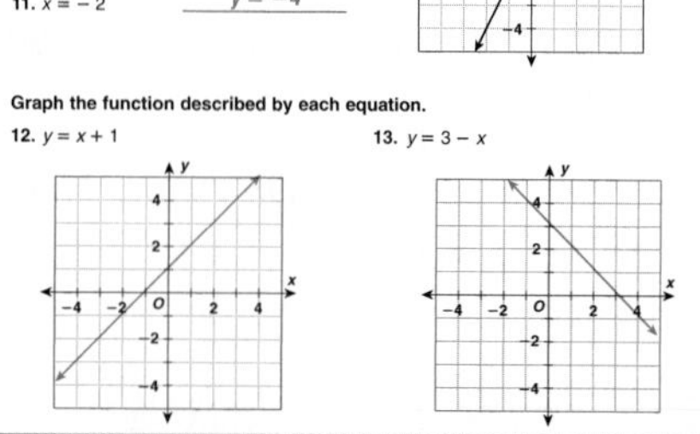

Graph the function described by each equation.

12. *y* = *x* + 1
13. *y* = 3 − *x*

Physical Science LINK

Temperature can be expressed according to different scales. The Kelvin scale is divided into units called kelvins, and the Celsius scale is divided into degrees Celsius.

The table shows several temperatures recorded in degrees Celsius and their equivalent measures in kelvins.

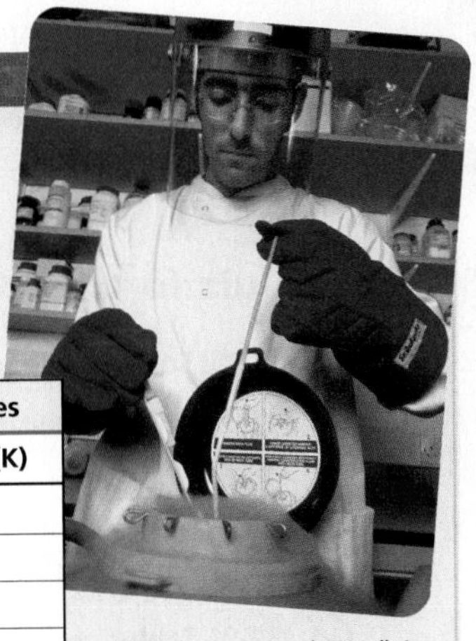

Equivalent Temperatures

Celsius (°C)	Kelvin (K)
−100	173
−50	223
0	273
50	323
100	373

A technician preserves brain cells in this tank of liquid nitrogen, which is at −196°C, for later research.

30. Write an equation for a function that gives the values in the table. Define the variables that you use. $K = C + 273$, K= kelvins, C = degrees Celsius

31. Graph the function described by your equation.

32. Use your graph to find the value of y when x is 0. $y = 273$

33. Use your equation to find the equivalent Kelvin temperature for –54°C. 219 kelvins

34. Use your equation to find the equivalent Celsius temperature for 77 kelvins. −196°C

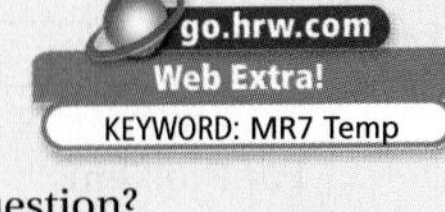

35. **What's the Question?** The answer is −273°C. What is the question? What temperature on the Celsius scale is equivalent to 0 kelvins?

36. **Write About It** Explain how to use your equation to determine whether 75°C is equivalent to 345 kelvins. Then determine whether the temperatures are equivalent.

37. **Challenge** How many ordered-pair solutions exist for the equation you wrote in Exercise 30? an infinite number of ordered pairs

CRCT Prep • GPS Support • Spiral Review

38. Multiple Choice Which of the ordered pairs is NOT a solution of $y = -5x + 10$?

Ⓐ (−20, 6) Ⓑ (5, −15) Ⓒ (4, −10) Ⓓ (2, 0)

39. Multiple Choice The equation $y = 12x$ shows the number of inches y in x feet. Which ordered pair is on the graph of the equation?

Ⓕ (−2, 24) Ⓖ (1, 13) Ⓗ (4, 48) Ⓙ (12, 1)

Find the mean of each data set. (Lesson 6-2)

40. 0, 5, 2, 3, 7, 1 3

41. 6, 6, 6, 6, 6, 6, 6, 6, 6 6

42. 2, 3, 4, 5, 6, 7, 8, 1, 9 5

Solve each equation. Check your answers. (Lesson 11-8)

43. $\left(\frac{y}{-10}\right) = 12$ $y = -120$

44. $p + 25 = -4$ $p = -29$

45. $j - 3 = -15$ $j = -12$

46. $5m = -20$ $m = -4$

ONGOING ASSESSMENT and INTERVENTION

***Diagnose Before* the Lesson**
11-10 Warm Up, TE p. 646

***Monitor During* the Lesson**
11-10 Know-It Notebook
11-10 Questioning Strategies

***Assess After* the Lesson**
11-10 Lesson Quiz, TE p. 649

Answers

31. See p. A12.

36. When C = 75 and K = 345, check to see whether the equation is balanced. It is not, so the temperatures are not the same. 75 degrees Celsius is equivalent to 348 kelvins.

TEST PREP DOCTOR For Exercise 39, remind students that a point on the graph of an equation has coordinates that are a solution to the equation. Substitute the coordinates from each answer choice into the equation to determine which point is on the graph.

Journal

Have students graph the functions represented by the equations they wrote about for the Lesson 11-9 Journal activity.

CHALLENGE 11-10

LESSON 11-10 **Challenge**
Cricket Thermometers

How can you tell the temperature outside when you don't have a thermometer? Just ask a cricket!

As temperatures increase, crickets chirp faster. When the first frost occurs, the chirping stops because the crickets are too cold to move.

To use a cricket thermometer, count how many times you hear a cricket chirp in 15 seconds (c).

Then use this equation to estimate the temperature outside in degrees Fahrenheit (t).

$t = \frac{1}{4}c + 40$

Only male crickets chirp. Scientists once thought the chirp was a mating call, but it's not. Female crickets are deaf!

Use the cricket temperature equation to complete the function table. Then use the table to graph the cricket temperature function.

Function table		Ordered Pairs
c	t	(c, t)
0	40	(0, 40)
20	45	(20, 45)
40	50	(40, 50)
60	55	(60, 55)
80	60	(80, 60)
100	65	(100, 65)

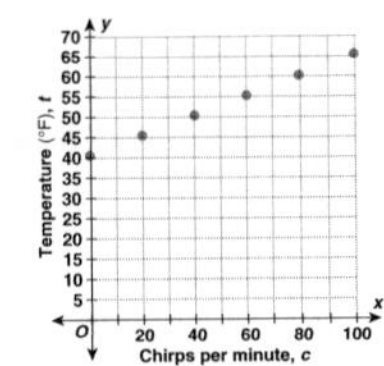

PROBLEM SOLVING 11-10

LESSON 11-10 **Problem Solving**
Graphing Functions

Use the table to answer each question.

Equivalent Temperatures

Celsius (°C)	Fahrenheit (°F)
−20	−4
−10	14
0	32
10	50
20	68

1. $F = \frac{9}{5}C + 32$ is an equation for the function that gives the values in the table. What does each variable represent in the equation? Use the equation to complete the table.
   F = degrees Fahrenheit;
   C = degrees Celsius

2. Write a different equation for a function that gives the values in the table.
   $C = \frac{5}{9}(F - 32)$

3. Is the ordered pair (30, 86) a solution for either equation? Why or why not? What does each value in the ordered pair represent?
   Yes, the ordered pair is (C, F); $86 = \frac{9}{5}(30) + 32$

4. Graph the function described by either equation on the graph at right.
   Check students' graphs.

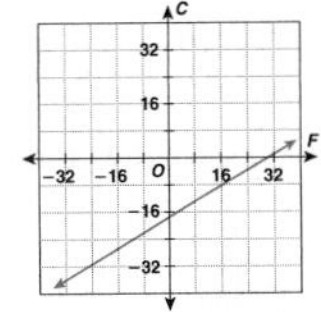

Circle the letter of the correct answer.

5. Use your graph to find the equivalent Fahrenheit temperature for −8°C.
   Ⓐ 18°F
   B 28°F
   C 42°F
   D 46°F

6. What Celsius temperature is equivalent to −58°F?
   Ⓕ −50°C H 50°C
   G 14.4°C J −40°C

7. Which is not a solution for the equation in Exercise 1?
   A (100, 212) Ⓒ (−40, 104)
   B (0, 32) D (60, 140)

Power Presentations with PowerPoint®

11-10 Lesson Quiz

1. Use the given x-values to write solutions as ordered pairs to the equation $y = -3x + 1$ for x = 0, 1, 2, and 3. (0, 1), (1, −2), (2, −5), (3, −8)

2. Determine whether (4, −2) is a solution to the equation $y = -5x + 3$.
no, $-2 \neq -5(4) + 3$

3. Graph the function described by the equation $y = -x + 3$.

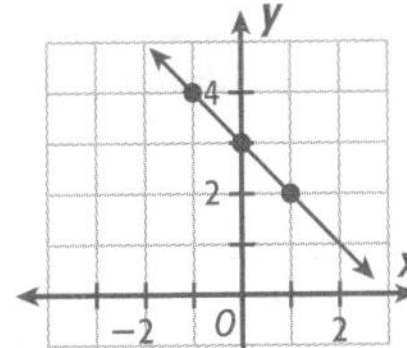

Also available on transparency

SECTION 11C

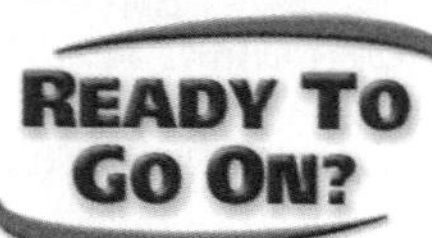

Organizer

Objective: Assess students' mastery of concepts and skills in Lessons 11-8 through 11-10.

Resources

 ***Assessment Resources***
Section 11C Quiz

INTERVENTION 

Resources

 ***Ready to Go On? Intervention and Enrichment* Worksheets**

 ***Ready to Go On?* CD-ROM**

 ***Ready to Go On?* Online**

my.hrw.com

Answers

18–20. See p. A12.

CHAPTER 11

SECTION 11C

Ready to Go On?

Quiz for Lessons 11-8 Through 11-10

11-8 Solving Integer Equations

Solve each equation. Check your answers.

1. $5 + x = -20$ $x = -25$ **2.** $3a = -27$ $a = -9$ **3.** $p \div 2 = -16$ $p = -32$ **4.** $c - 2 = -7$ $c = -5$

5. The temperature was twice as cold on Monday as it was on Sunday. If it was −4°F on Monday, how cold was it on Sunday? −2°F

11-9 Tables and Functions

Write an equation for a function that gives the values in each table. Use the equation to find the value of *y* for each indicated value of *x*.

6.

x	2	3	4	5	8
y	7	9	11	13	■

$y = 2x + 3$; 19

7.

x	1	4	5	6	8
y	■	18	23	28	38

$y = 5x - 2$; 3

For Problems 8–10, write an equation for the function. Tell what each variable you use represents.

8. The number of plates is 5 less than 3 times the number of cups. $p = 3c - 5$; p = plates, c = cups

9. The time Rodney spends running is 10 minutes more than twice the time he spends stretching. $r = 2s + 10$; r = time spent running, s = time spent stretching

10. The height of a triangle is twice the length of its base. $h = 2b$; h = height, b = base

11. A store manager tracked T-shirt sales. The store charges the same price for each T-shirt. On Monday, 5 shirts were sold for a total of \$60. On Tuesday, 8 shirts were sold for a total of \$96. On Wednesday, 11 shirts were sold for a total of \$132. Write an equation for the function. $t = 12s$; t = total, s = number of shirts

11-10 Graphing Functions

Use the given *x*-values to write solutions of each equation as ordered pairs.

12. $y = 4x + 6$ for $x = 1, 2, 3, 4$ (1, 10), (2, 14), (3, 18), (4, 22)

13. $y = 10x - 7$ for $x = 2, 3, 4, 5$ (2, 13), (3, 23), (4, 33), (5, 43)

Use the graph of the linear function at right to find the value of *y* for each given value of *x*.

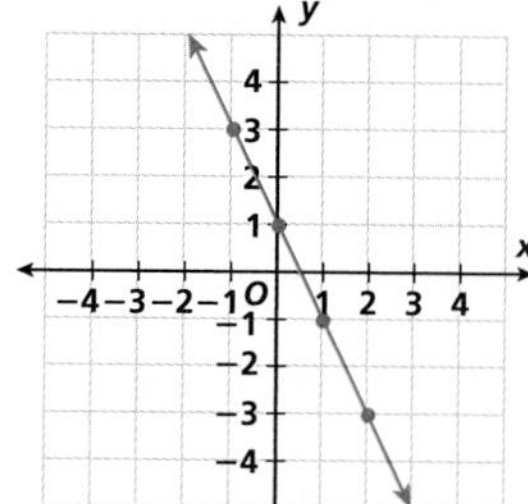

14. $x = 3$ −5 **15.** $x = 0$ 1

16. $x = -1$ 3 **17.** $x = -2$ 5

Graph the function described by each equation.

18. $y = x + 5$ **19.** $y = 3x + 2$ **20.** $y = -2x$

READY TO GO ON?
Diagnose and Prescribe

NO INTERVENE

YES ENRICH

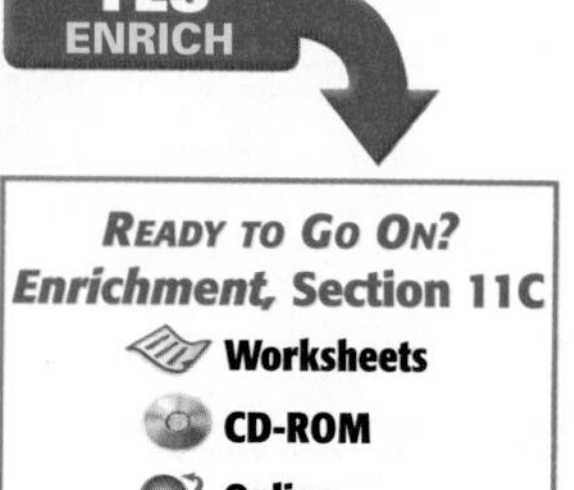

Ready to Go On? Intervention	*Ready to Go On? Intervention*, Section 11C: Worksheets	CD-ROM	Online
Lesson 11-8	11-8 Intervention	Activity 11-8	Diagnose and Prescribe Online
Lesson 11-9	11-9 Intervention	Activity 11-9	
Lesson 11-10	11-10 Intervention	Activity 11-10	

***Ready to Go On? Enrichment*, Section 11C**
Worksheets
CD-ROM
Online

MULTI-STEP TEST PREP

CHAPTER 11

It's All Mine Underground mines make it possible to reach coal deposits deep beneath the earth. The headframe is the only part of the mine that is visible above the ground. It contains the machinery that lowers miners into the shaft and carries the coal back to the surface. The diagram shows a typical mining operation.

1. What is the total distance the coal travels as it goes from level C to the top of the headframe? **946 ft**
2. How far do miners travel in the elevator as they descend from level A to level B? from level B to level C? **380 ft; 236 ft**
3. What is the mean depth of the three levels? **−572 ft**
4. A new level is added to the mine. It is three times as deep as level A. What is the depth of the new level? Where is it located in relation to the other levels? **−720 ft; between levels B and C**
5. In 3 hours, each miner produces 18 tons of coal. In 5 hours, each miner produces 30 tons of coal. In 8 hours, each miner produces 48 tons of coal. Make a table and write an equation for the function. $c = 6h$
6. Use your equation to find the number of tons of coal that each miner produces in a 40-hour work week. **240 tons**

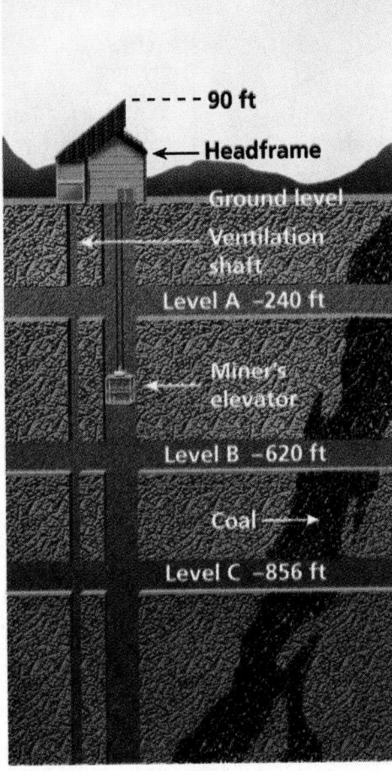

Multi-Step Test Prep

MULTI-STEP TEST PREP

CHAPTER 11

Organizer

Objective: Assess students' ability to apply concepts and skills in Chapter 11 in a real-world format.

 Online Edition

Resources

 ***Middle School Assessments***
www.mathtekstoolkit.org

Problem	Text reference
1	Lesson 11-5
2	Lesson 11-5
3	Lesson 11-7
4	Lesson 11-6
5	Lesson 11-9
6	Lesson 11-10

Answers

5.

Hours	3	5	8
Tons of Coal	18	30	48

INTERVENTION 

Scaffolding Questions

1. What operation can you use to solve this problem? How? Subtraction; find the difference; 90 − (−856).
2. How can you find the distance from Level A to Level B? Use subtraction; −240 − (−620).
3. How do you find the mean of a set of items? Add the items, and then divide by the number of items in the set. Will the mean be positive or negative? Why? Negative; the sum of the three items is negative; when this is divided by 3, the result is still negative.
4. What product do you need to find? 3 · (−240) Will the product be positive or negative? Why? Negative; the product of a positive integer and a negative integer is negative.
5. How is the number of tons of coal related to the number of hours? The number of tons of coal is 3 times the number of hours. What variables can you use to write the equation? c = tons of coal, h = no. of hours
6. What value should you substitute into your equation? $h = 40$

Extensions

1. Suppose the owners of the mine want to construct a new level that is exactly halfway between Level A and Level B. What should the depth of the new level be? −430 ft
2. How much coal do 5 miners produce in 3.5 hours? 105 tons

Extension

Pacing: Traditional 1 day
Block $\frac{1}{2}$ day

Objective: Students recognize direct variation and identify the constant of proportionality.

Online Edition

Using the Pages

In Lesson 11-9, students translated between data tables and equations. In Lesson 11-10, students graphed functions. In this extension, students apply these skills to linear equations of the form $y = kx$.

EXTENSION Direct Variation

Learn to recognize direct variation and identify the constant of proportionality.

Vocabulary

direct variation

constant of proportionality

M6A2.d Describe proportional relationships mathematically using $y = kx$, where k is the constant of proportionality. Also, M6A2.e, M6A2.f, M6A2.g.

At a frog-jumping contest, Evan's frog jumped 60 inches. Isabella's frog jumped 72 inches. Jacob's frog jumped 78 inches. How many feet did each frog jump?

You know that there are 12 inches in 1 foot, 24 inches in 2 feet, and 36 inches in 3 feet. As the number of inches increases, the number of feet increases.

Inches	12	24	36
Feet	1	2	3
$\frac{\text{Inches}}{\text{Feet}}$	$\frac{12}{1}$	$\frac{24}{2} = \frac{12}{1}$	$\frac{36}{3} = \frac{12}{1}$

Each ratio of inches to feet is equivalent to 12:1. The relationship between feet and inches is said to *vary directly*. A **direct variation** relationship can be represented by a linear equation in the form $y = kx$, where k is a positive number called the **constant of proportionality**.

EXAMPLE 1 Finding Values Using a Direct Variation Equation

At a jumping contest, Evan's frog jumped 60 inches. Isabella's frog jumped 72 inches. Jacob's frog jumped 78 inches. Use the equation $y = 12x$, where y is the number of inches and x is the number of feet, to find the missing values in the table.

	Evan's frog	Isabella's frog	Jacob's frog
Inches (y)	60	72	■
Feet (x)	■	6	6.5

$y = 12x$

$60 = 12x$ *Substitute.*

$\frac{60}{12} = \frac{12x}{12}$ *Solve.*

$5 = x$ *Simplify.*

$y = 12x$

$y = 12(6.5)$

$y = 78$

Evan's frog jumped 5 feet. Jacob's frog jumped 78 inches.

Georgia Performance Standards

M6A2.d Describe proportional relationships mathematically using $y = kx$, where k is the constant of proportionally.

M6A2.e Graph proportional relationships in the form $y = kx$ and describe characteristics of the graphs.

M6A2.f In a proportional relationship expressed as $y = kx$, solve for one quantity given values of the other two. Given quantities may be whole numbers, decimals, or fractions. Solve problems using the relationship $y = kx$.

M6A2.g Use proportional reasoning ($a/b = c/d$ and $y = kx$) to solve problems.

1 Introduce

Motivate

Tell the class that all spiders have 8 legs. Therefore, 2 spiders have a total of 16 legs, 3 spiders have a total of 24 legs, 4 spiders have a total of 32 legs, and so on. The total number of legs is 8 times the number of spiders. Explain that this type of relationship is called a direct variation. Tell students that they will be learning about tables, equations, and graphs of direct variations.

2 Teach

Guided Instruction

In this extension, students learn to recognize direct variation and identify the constant of proportionality. Discuss the relationship between feet and inches that is presented at the beginning of the extension. Then review Example 1 with the class. Emphasize that in a direct variation, two quantities are related by multiplication. The number by which one quantity is multiplied to get the other quantity is the constant of proportionality. Be sure students understand that in Example 1 the constant of proportionality is 12. Then show students how to graph a direction-variation equation by presenting Example 2.

The graph of a direct variation is a straight line that passes through the origin.

EXAMPLE 2 **Graphing a Direct Variation Equation**

Graph the direct variation equation $y = 12x$, where y is the number of inches and x is the number of feet.

Use the data from Example 1 to graph the coordinate pairs (5, 60), (6, 72), (6.5, 78). Draw a line connecting the points.

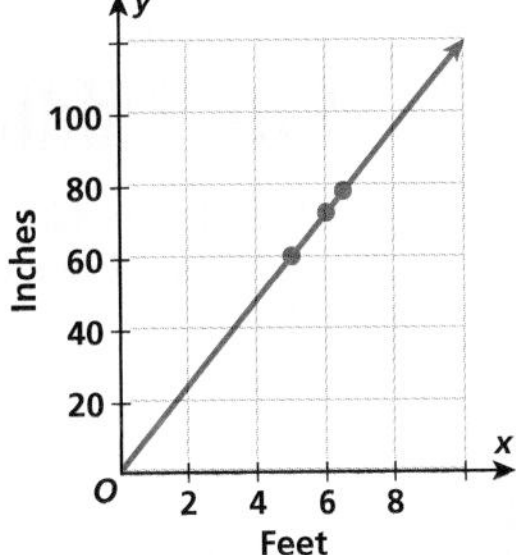

COMMON ERROR ALERT

Some students may find that their points do not lie on a straight line because they incorrectly marked values along the x- or y-axis when setting up the graph. Have students check that each unit along the x-axis represents the same quantity and that each unit along the y-axis represents the same quantity.

EXTENSION Exercises

6.

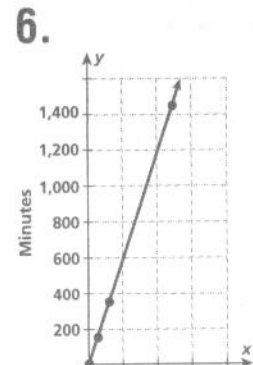

7.

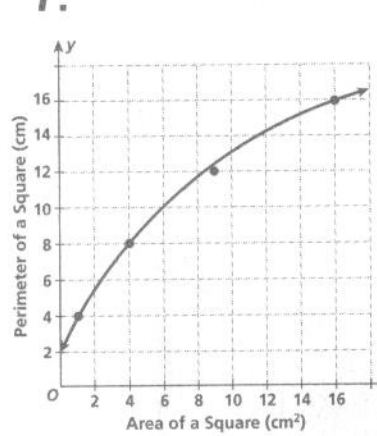

8.

Identify the constant of proportionality for each direct variation equation.

1. $y = 13x$ 13
2. $t = 0.39z$ 0.39
3. $d = \frac{1}{3}v$ $\frac{1}{3}$
4. $y = x$ 1

5. There are 60 minutes in an hour. Find the missing values in the table using the direct variation equation $y = 60x$, where x is the number of hours and y is the number of minutes.

Hours (x)	Minutes (y)
▒ 0	0
3	▒ 180
▒ 6	360
24	▒ 1440

6. Graph the direct variation from Exercise 5.

Graph the ordered pairs to determine whether the data set shows direct variation.

7. No.

Area of a Square (cm²)	1	4	9	16
Perimeter of a Square (cm)	4	8	12	16

8. No.

Sales Tax ($)	.01	.20	.40	.50
Sale Price ($)	1	4	8	10

9. **Critical Thinking** Does every linear equation represent a direct variation relationship? Explain. No, a linear equation only represents a direct variation when the y-intercept is zero.

Additional Examples

Example 1

Tyler rides his bike at a constant speed of 9 mi/h. Complete the table using the equation $y = 9x$, where x is the number of hours he rides and y is the number of miles he travels.

Hours (x)	1	1.5	3	
Miles (y)	9	13.5		45

When $x = 3$, $y = 27$. When $y = 45$, $x = 5$.

Example 2

Graph the equation $y = 9x$, where x is the number of hours Tyler rides his bike and y is the number of miles he travels.

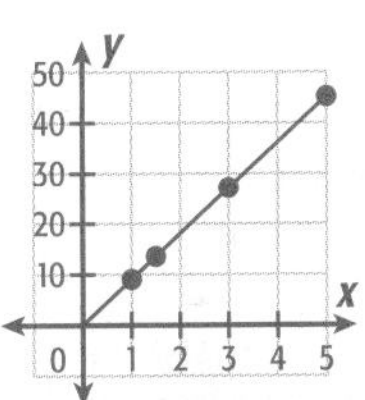

Also available on transparency

Teaching Tip

Remind students that the graph of a direct variation is always a straight line that passes through the point (0,0). If students graph a direct variation and do not end up with a straight line passing through the origin, they should check their work for errors.

3 Close

Summarize

Go over the three different ways of representing a direct variation relationship (table, equation, and graph). Then have students use the equation $y = 3x$ to complete the table and graph the relationship.

x	2	▒	9
y	6	24	▒

When $y = 24$, $x = 8$. When $x = 9$, $x = 27$.

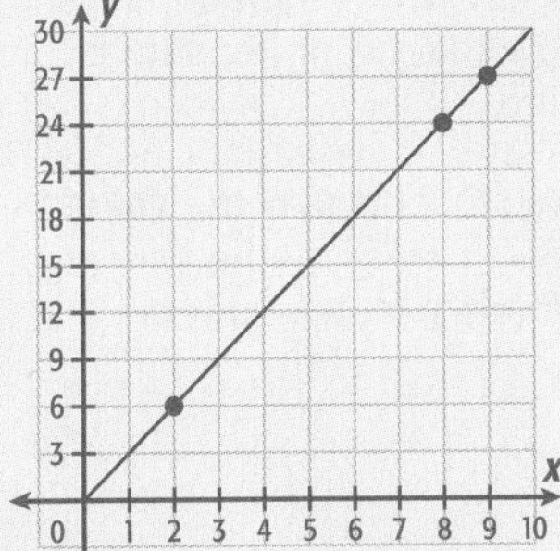

Game Time

Organizer

Objective: Participate in games to practice and apply skills learned in Chapter 11.

Online Edition

Resources

Chapter 11 Resource Book
Puzzles, Twisters & Teasers

A Math Riddle

Purpose: To apply the skill of graphing points to solve a riddle

Discuss Ask students to identify common mistakes they may encounter when doing this activity. Ask students what they can do to avoid those mistakes.

Possible answer: Confusing *x*- and *y*-coordinates: be sure to plot points in the correct order; leaving out a pair of points: cross off pairs of points as you plot them; not connecting in the right order: connect points as you plot each pair.

Extend Have students write their names on graph paper, making the letters using straight lines. Have students identify the ordered pairs and create a puzzle like the one in this activity. Then have them randomly trade papers and complete the puzzle to determine whose paper they have.

Zero Sum

Purpose: To practice adding integers in a game format

Discuss When a student wins a round, have him or her write a number sentence to show that his or her sum is closest to zero.

Extend Have students play the game with a different objective—the winning player is the one with the sum farthest from 0.

Game Time

A Math Riddle

What coin doubles in value when half is subtracted?
a half dollar

To find the answer, graph each set of points. Connect each pair of points with a straight line.

1. (−8, 3) (−6, 3)	2. (−9, 1) (−7, 5)	3. (−7, 5) (−5, 1)	4. (−3, 1) (−3, 5)
5. (−1, 1) (−1, 5)	6. (−3, 3) (−1, 3)	7. (1, 1) (3, 5)	8. (3, 5) (5, 1)
9. (2, 3) (4, 3)	10. (6, 1) (6, 5)	11. (6, 1) (8, 1)	12. (9, 1) (9, 5)
13. (9, 5) (11, 5)	14. (9, 3) (11, 3)	15. (−9, −5) (−9, −1)	16. (−9, −1) (−7, −3)
17. (−7, −3) (−9, −5)	18. (−6, −1) (−6, −5)	19. (−6, −5) (−4, −5)	20. (−4, −5) (−4, −1)
21. (−4, −1) (−6, −1)	22. (−3, −1) (−3, −5)	23. (−3, −5) (−1, −5)	24. (1, −1) (1, −5)
25. (1, −5) (3, −5)	26. (4, −5) (6, −1)	27. (6, −1) (8, −5)	28. (5, −3) (7, −3)
29. (9, −5) (9, −1)	30. (9, −1) (11, −3)	31. (11, −3) (9, −3)	32. (9, −3) (11, −5)

Zero Sum

Each card contains either a positive number, a negative number, or 0. The dealer deals three cards to each player. On your turn, you may exchange one or two of your cards for new ones, or you may keep your three original cards. After everyone has had a turn, the player whose sum is closest to 0 wins the round and receives everyone's cards. The dealer deals a new round and the game continues until the dealer runs out of cards. The winner is the player with the most cards at the end of the game.

go.hrw.com
Game Time Extra
KEYWORD: MR7 Games

A complete copy of the rules and game pieces are available online.

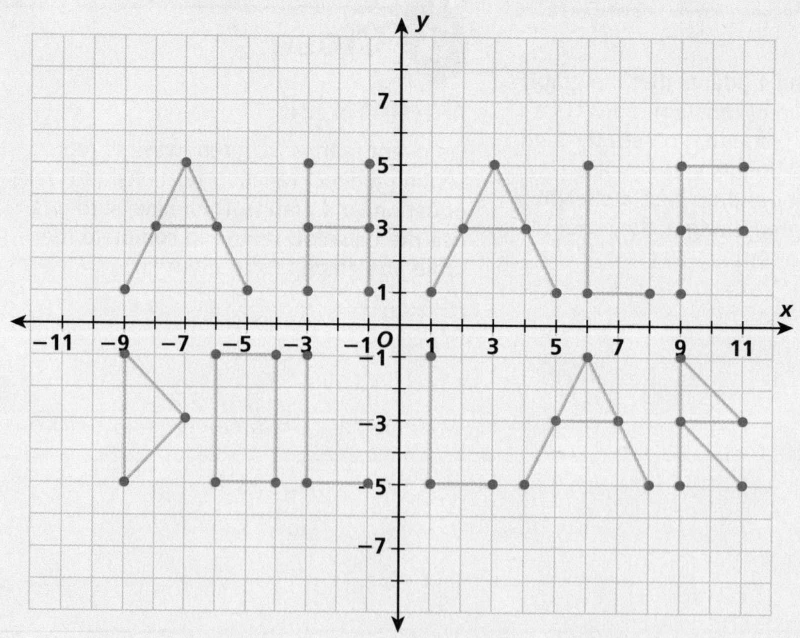

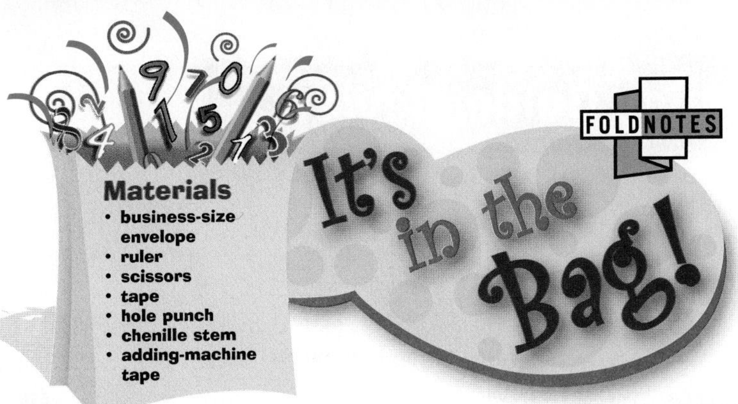

PROJECT Positive-Negative Pull-Out

Pull questions and answers out of the bag to check your knowledge of integers and functions.

Directions

1. Seal the envelope. Then cut it in half.
2. Hold the envelope with the opening at the top. Lightly draw lines $\frac{3}{4}$ inch from the bottom and from each side. Fold the envelope back and forth along these lines until the envelope is flexible and easy to work with. **Figure A**
3. Put your hand into the envelope and push out the sides and bottom to form a bag. There will be two triangular points at the bottom of the bag. Tape these to the bottom so that the bag sits flat. **Figure B**
4. Make a 2-inch slit on the front of the bag about an inch from the bottom. Punch two holes at the top of each side of the bag and insert half of a chenile stem to make handles. **Figure C**

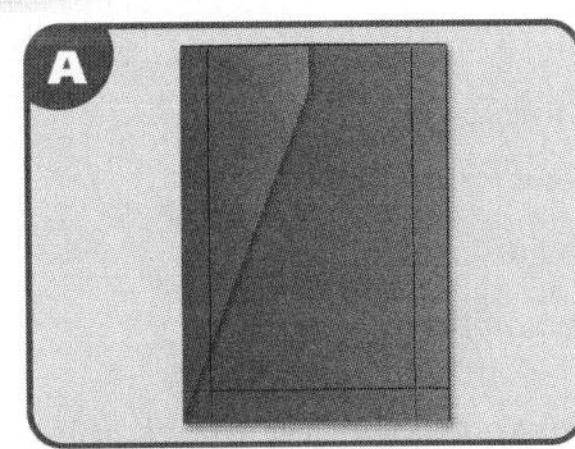

Taking Note of the Math

Starting at the end of the adding-machine tape, write a question about integers and functions, and then write the answer. After you have written several questions and answers, roll up the tape, place it in the bag, and pull the end through the slit.

Organizer

Objective: Make a question-and-answer pull-out bag that will help students review integers and functions.

Materials: business-size envelope, ruler, scissors, tape, hole punch, chenille stem, adding-machine tape

Online Edition

Using the Page

Preparing the Materials
Use adding-machine tape that is $1\frac{3}{4}$ inches wide. Each student will need about 18 inches of the tape.

Making the Project
Have students fold the end of their adding-machine tape into a triangular point. This will make it easier to thread the tape through the slit in the bag.

Extending the Project
Students can add additional questions and answers to the back of the adding-machine tape.

Each business-size envelope makes two bags, so this is an ideal project to have students do in pairs. Once students have written their questions and answers and placed the adding-machine tape in the bag, they can trade bags with their partner and try to answer each other's questions.

Students can use the bag to store integer chips or other manipulatives related to the chapter.

CHAPTER 11

Study Guide: Review

Organizer

Objective: Help students organize and review key concepts and skills presented in Chapter 11.

Online Edition
Multilingual Glossary

Resources

PuzzlePro®
One-Stop Planner®

***Multilingual Glossary* Online**
go.hrw.com
KEYWORD: MR7 Glossary

Lesson Tutorial Videos
CD-ROM

Test & Practice Generator
One-Stop Planner®

Answers

1. output, input
2. coordinate plane, quadrants
3. +10
4. −50
5. 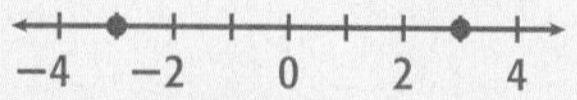 (number line from −4 to 4 with points at −3 and 3)
6.  (number line from −3 to 3 with points at −1 and 1)
7.  (number line from −10 to 10 with points at −9 and 9)
8.  (number line from −3 to 3 with point at 0)
9. <
10. <
11. <
12. −1, 2, 4
13. −3, 0, 4
14. −8, −6, 0

CHAPTER 11

Study Guide: Review

Vocabulary

axes	610	origin	610
coordinate plane	610	output	640
coordinates	610	positive number	602
function	640	quadrants	610
input	640	*x*-axis	610
integer	602	*x*-coordinate	610
linear equation	646	*y*-axis	610
negative number	602	*y*-coordinate	610
opposites	602		

Complete the sentences below with vocabulary words from the list above.

1. For the equation $y = 3x$, the __?__ is 12 when the __?__ is 4.
2. The axes separate the __?__ into four __?__.

11-1 Integers in Real-World Situations (pp. 602–605)

GPS M6P5.a

EXAMPLE

- **Name a positive or negative number to represent each situation.**

  15 feet below sea level −15
  a bank deposit of $10 +10

- **Graph +4 on a number line.**

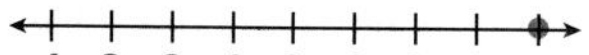

  (number line from −4 to 4 with point at 4)

EXERCISES

Name a positive or negative number to represent each situation.

3. a raise of $10
4. a loss of $50

Graph each integer and its opposite on a number line.

5. −3
6. 1
7. −9
8. 0

11-2 Comparing and Ordering Integers (pp. 606–609)

GPS M6P1.c

EXAMPLE

- **Compare −2 and 3. Write < or >.**

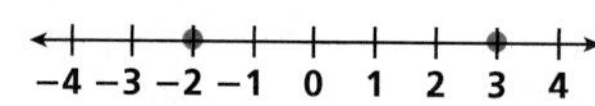

$-2 < 3$ *−2 is left of 3 on the number line.*

EXERCISES

Compare. Write < or >.

9. 3 ▢ 4
10. −2 ▢ 5
11. 0 ▢ 6

Order the integers in each set from least to greatest.

12. 2, −1, 4
13. −3, 0, 4
14. −6, −8, 0

Study Guide: Review

11-3 The Coordinate Plane (pp. 610–613)

GPS M6P5.a

EXAMPLE

■ **Give the coordinates of *A* and name the quadrant where it is located.**

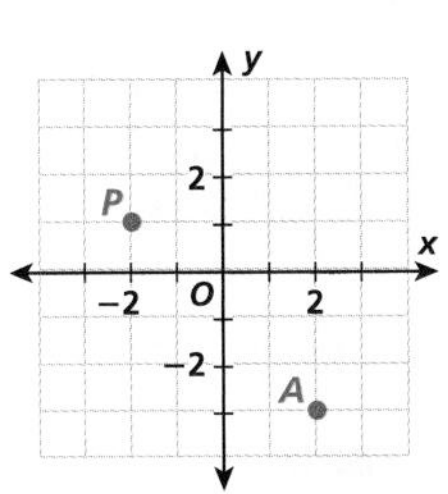

A is in the fourth quadrant. Its coordinates are (2, –3).

EXERCISES

Give the coordinates of each point.

15. *A* **16.** *C*

Name the quadrant where each point is located.

17. *A* **18.** *B*

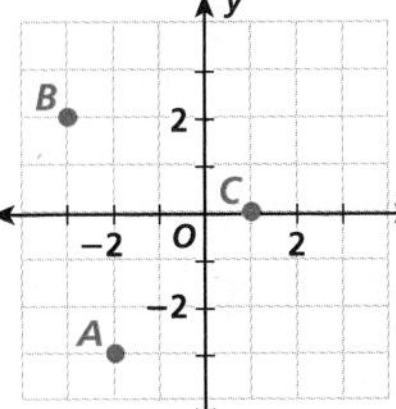

11-4 Adding Integers (pp. 617–620)

GPS M6A3

EXAMPLE

■ **Find the sum: 3 + (−2).**

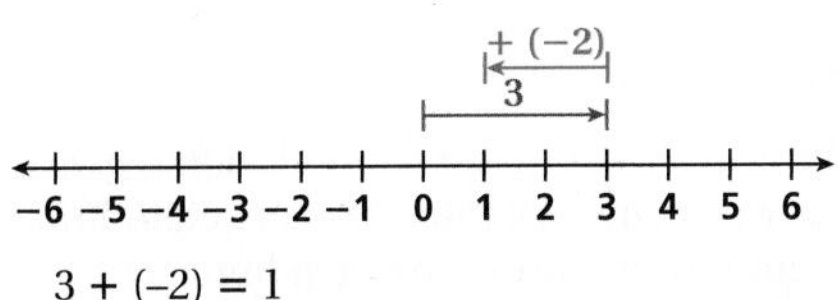

3 + (–2) = 1

EXERCISES

Find each sum.

19. −4 + 2 **20.** 4 + (−4)

21. 3 + (−2) **22.** −3 + (−2)

Evaluate *x* + 3 for each value of *x*.

23. $x = -20$ **24.** $x = 5$

11-5 Subtracting Integers (pp. 622–624)

GPS M6A3

EXAMPLE

■ **Evaluate *n* − 4 for *n* = −1.**

(−1) − 4 = −5

EXERCISES

Find each difference.

25. −6 − 2 **26.** 5 − (−4)

Evaluate *x* − (−1) for each value of *x*.

27. $x = 12$ **28.** $x = -7$

11-6 Multiplying Integers (pp. 625–627)

GPS M6A3

EXAMPLE

■ **Find the product: 3 · (−2).**

Think: 3 groups of −2

3 · (−2) = −6

■ **Evaluate −2*x* for *x* = −4.**

−2(−4) = 8

EXERCISES

Find each product.

29. 5 · (−2) **30.** 3 · 2

31. −3 · (−2) **32.** −4 · 2

Evaluate −9*y* for each value of *y*.

33. $y = 2$ **34.** $y = -5$

Study Guide: Review

Answers

15. (−2, −3)
16. (1, 0)
17. III
18. II
19. −2
20. 0
21. 1
22. −5
23. −17
24. 8
25. −8
26. 9
27. 13
28. −6
29. −10
30. 6
31. 6
32. −8
33. −18
34. 45

Answers

35. −3
36. 27
37. 2
38. −2
39. $w = 4$
40. $a = -12$
41. $q = -7$
42. $x = -5$
43. $y = 2x + 2$; $y = 18$
44. $\ell = 4w$; ℓ = length, w = width
45. (1, −3), (2, −1), (3, 1), (4, 3)
46. (1, 8), (2, 9), (3, 10), (4, 11)
47. yes
48. no

Study Guide: Review

11-7 Dividing Integers (pp. 628–631)

GPS M6A3

EXAMPLE

■ **−24 ÷ 4**

Think: −6 · 4 = −24

−24 ÷ 4 = −6

EXERCISES

Find each quotient.

35. 6 ÷ (−2) **36.** 9 ÷ 3

37. −14 ÷ (−7) **38.** −4 ÷ 2

11-8 Solving Integer Equations (pp. 636–639)

GPS M6A3

EXAMPLE

■ **Solve $x + 4 = 18$.**

$$\begin{aligned} x + 4 &= 18 \\ \underline{-4} \quad &\underline{-4} \\ x \quad &= 14 \end{aligned}$$

Subtract 4 from both sides.

EXERCISES

Solve each equation. Check your answers.

39. $w - 5 = -1$ **40.** $\frac{a}{-4} = 3$

41. $2q = -14$ **42.** $x + 3 = -2$

11-9 Tables and Functions (pp. 640–643)

GPS M6A2.a, M6A3

EXAMPLE

■ **Write an equation for a function that gives the values in the table. Use the equation to find the value of y for the indicated value of x.**

x	2	3	4	5	6	12
y	5	8	11	14	17	■

y is 3 times x minus 1. *Find a pattern.*

$y = 3x - 1$ *Write an equation.*

$y = 3(12) - 1$ *Substitute 12 for x.*

$y = 36 - 1 = 35$

EXERCISES

Write an equation for a function that gives the values in each table. Use the equation to find the value of y for each indicated value of x.

43.

x	2	3	4	5	6	8
y	6	8	10	12	14	■

Write an equation to describe the function. Tell what each variable you use represents.

44. The length of a rectangle is 4 times its width.

11-10 Graphing Functions (pp. 646–649)

GPS M6A2.a, M6A3

EXAMPLE

■ **Graph the function described by the equation $y = 3x + 4$.**

Make a table. *Write as ordered pairs.*

x	$3x + 4$	y	(x, y)
−2	3(−2) + 4	−2	(−2, −2)
−1	3(−1) + 4	1	(−1, 1)
0	3(0) + 4	4	(0, 4)

Graph the ordered pairs on a coordinate plane.

EXERCISES

Use the given x-values to write solutions of each equation as ordered pairs.

45. $y = 2x - 5$ for x = 1, 2, 3, 4

46. $y = x + 7$ for x = 1, 2, 3, 4

Determine whether each ordered pair is a solution to the given equation.

47. (3, 12); $y = 5x - 3$ **48.** (6, 14); $y = x + 7$

CHAPTER TEST

Name a positive or negative number to represent each situation.

1. 30° below zero −30
2. a bank deposit of $75 +75
3. a loss of 5 yards −5
4. On the first down of a football game, the quarterback threw for a 6-yard gain. On the second down, he was sacked for a 4-yard loss. On the third down, he ran for a 2-yard gain. Use integers to model this situation.

Compare. Write < or >.

5. −4 ■ 4 <
6. 2 ■ −9 >
7. −10 ■ 8 <
8. −2 ■ −12 >

Order each set of integers from least to greatest.

9. 21, −19, 34 −19, 21, 34
10. −16, −2, 13, 46 −16, −2, 13, 46
11. −10, 0, 25, −7, 18 −10, −7, 0, 18, 25

Graph each point on a coordinate plane.

12. $A(2, 3)$
13. $B(3, -2)$
14. $C(-1, 3)$
15. $D\left(-1, 2\frac{1}{2}\right)$
16. $E(0, 1)$

Add, subtract, multiply, or divide.

17. −4 + 4 0
18. −2 − 9 −11
19. −3 · 8 −24
20. 12 ÷ (−3) −4
21. −48 ÷ (−4) 12
22. 13 + (−9) 4
23. 8 − (−11) 19
24. −7 · (−6) 42

Evaluate each expression for the given value of the variable.

25. $n + 3, n = -10$ −7
26. $9 - x, x = -9$ 18
27. $4m, m = -6$ −24
28. $\frac{15}{a}, a = -3$ −5
29. $(-11) + z, z = 28$ 17
30. $w - (-8), w = 13$ 21

Solve each equation.

31. $\frac{b}{7} = -3$ $b = -21$
32. $-9 \cdot f = -81$ $f = 9$
33. $r - 14 = -32$ $r = -18$
34. $y + 17 = 22$ $y = 5$

Write an equation for a function that gives the values in each table. Use the equation to find the value of *y* for each indicated value of *x*.

35.

x	2	3	4	5	6	7
y	■	8	11	14	17	20

$y = 3x - 1$; 5

36.

x	1	2	3	4	5	9
y	8	10	12	14	16	■

$y = 2x + 6$; 24

Write an equation for the function. Tell what each variable you use represents.

37. The number of buttons on the jacket is 4 more than the number of zippers. $b = z + 4$; b = buttons, z = zippers
38. The length of a parallelogram is 2 in. more than twice the height. $l = 2h + 2$; l = length, h = height

39. (1, 2), (2, 7), (3, 12), (4, 17) 40. (0, −3), (1, −1), (2, 1), (3, 3)

Use the given *x*-values to write solutions of each equation as ordered pairs. Then graph the function described by each equation.

39. $y = 5x - 3$ for $x = 1, 2, 3, 4$
40. $y = 2x - 3$ for $x = 0, 1, 2, 3$

Chapter Test

12–16.

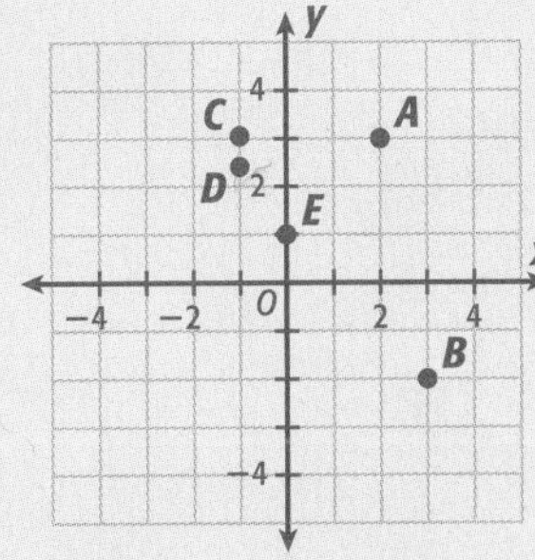

40. (0, −3), (1, −1), (2, 1), (3, 3)

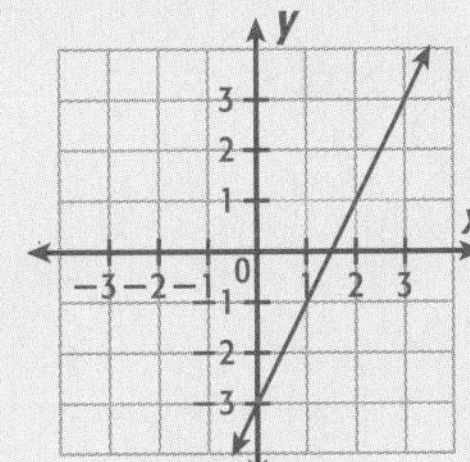

39. (1, 2), (2, 7), (3, 12), (4, 17)

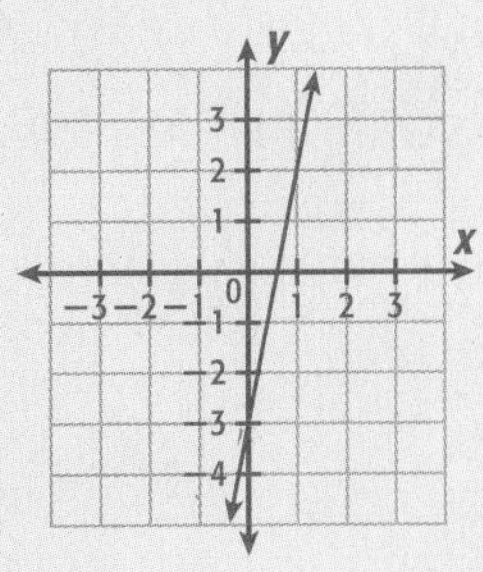

CHAPTER TEST

Organizer

Objective: Assess students' mastery of concepts and skills in Chapter 11.

Online Edition

Resources

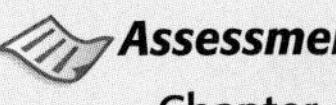

Assessment Resources

Chapter 11 Tests
- Free Response (Levels A, B, C)
- Multiple Choice (Levels A, B, C)
- Performance Assessment

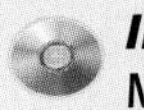

***IDEA Works!* CD-ROM**
Modified Chapter 11 Test

Answers

4.

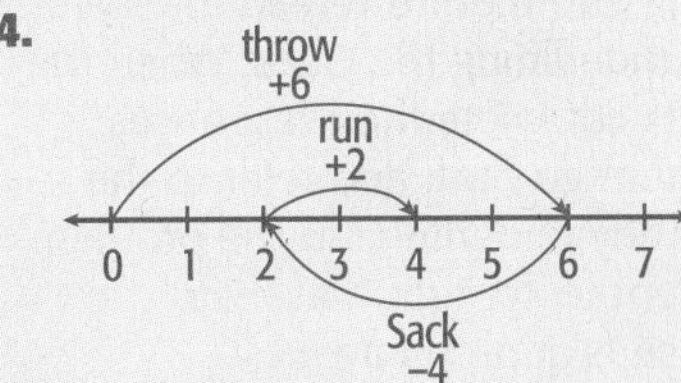

Organizer

Objective: Provide opportunities to learn and practice common test-taking strategies.

Online Edition

Resources

***CRCT Prep* Workbook**

***CRCT Prep* CD-ROM**

***CRCT Practice* Online**

go.hrw.com
KEYWORD: MR7 TestPrep

This test tackler describes how to identify context clues in a test item and how to use them to answer a test item correctly. Encourage students to read a problem statement once for understanding and then to reread the statement, underlining the clues. When the students complete their responses, have them go back and refer to the words they underlined in the problem statement to confirm that their response is appropriate.

Standardized Test Strategies

Multiple Choice: Identifying Keywords and Context Clues

When reading a test item, pay attention to key words and context clues given in the problem statement. These clues will guide you in providing a correct response.

EXAMPLE 1

Which angle is obtuse?

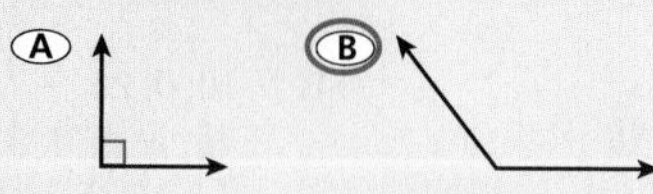
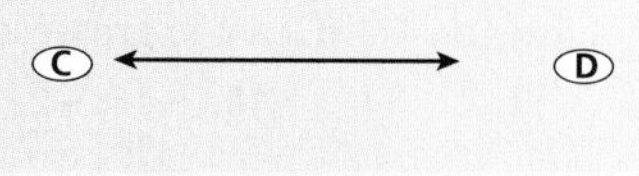

- Look for context clues. Identify what they mean.
- In this test item, **obtuse** is the context clue. It means an angle whose measure is **greater than** 90°.

Find the choice that shows an **obtuse** angle.
A: This angle's measure is 90° because it has a right angle symbol.
B: This angle's measure is greater than 90°. It is an obtuse angle.
C: This angle's measure is 180° because it is a straight angle.
D: This angle's measure is less than 90°. It is an acute angle.

The correct answer is B.

EXAMPLE 2

Kenneth makes flower deliveries along Oak Street. He starts at the flower shop on Oak Street. His first delivery is 8 blocks directly west of the shop. His second delivery takes him 4 blocks directly east of his first delivery. His third delivery takes him 5 blocks east of his second delivery. Write an expression using integers to model this situation.

(F) $-4 - 5 + 8$ (G) $8 + 4 - 5$ (H) $-8 - 4 - 5$ (J) $-8 + 4 + 5$

- Look for key words.
- In this test item, the key words are **expression** and **integers.**

Find the choice that shows the correct **integer expression** to model the situation.
F: The first delivery is 8 blocks west. This expression does not begin with –8.
G: The first delivery is 8 blocks west. This expression does not begin with –8.
H: The expression begins with −8, but 4 blocks west would be + 4.
J: This expression's integers correctly correspond to the deliveries.

The correct answer is J.

Test Tackler

If you have trouble understanding what a test item is asking, draw a diagram to help you visualize the question.

Read each test item and answer the questions that follow.

Item A
Multiple Choice Jenny is trimming the edges of a card with ribbon. The rectangular card measures 8 inches by 12 inches. How much ribbon does Jenny need to trim the card?

Ⓐ 36 inches
Ⓑ 40 inches
Ⓒ 64 inches
Ⓓ 72 inches

1. What are the dimensions of the card?
2. Which words in the problem statement are clues that you need to find the perimeter of the card?
3. When you calculate the perimeter, why are the units not given in square units?

Item B
Multiple Choice Sam has two cylinders. One cylinder has a height of 25 cm and a diameter of 8 cm. The other cylinder has a height of 15 cm and a diameter of 20 cm. What is the difference between the volumes of the two cylinders?

Ⓕ $400\pi\text{ cm}^3$
Ⓖ $1{,}100\pi\text{ cm}^3$
Ⓗ $1{,}500\pi\text{ cm}^3$
Ⓙ $4{,}400\pi\text{ cm}^3$

4. Make a list of the key words given in the problem statement and link each word to its mathematical meaning.
5. Which choice, if any, can be eliminated? Why?

Item C
Multiple Choice Madeline has 28 daisies and 42 violets. Find the GCF to find the greatest number of wrist corsages that can be made if each corsage has the same number of daisies and the same number of violets.

Ⓐ 4
Ⓑ 7
Ⓒ 14
Ⓓ 21

6. What is the math term that describes what is being tested?
7. Identify the keywords in this problem statement.

Item D
Multiple Choice An office supply store states that 4 out of 5 customers would recommend the store to another person. Given this information, what percent of customers would NOT recommend the office supply store to someone else?

Ⓕ 10%
Ⓖ 20%
Ⓗ 40%
Ⓙ 80%

8. What information is needed to solve this problem?
9. Which choice can be eliminated immediately? Why?
10. Write a proportion to find the percent of customers who would recommend the office store to someone else.
11. Describe two different ways to solve this problem.

Test Tackler

Read each problem aloud, emphasizing context clues. Review with students the unit of measurement that correspond to answers for perimeter, circumference, area, volume, and surface area.

Answers

1. The dimensions of the card are 8 inches by 12 inches.
2. The word *trim* means to go around the edges.
3. When you find perimeter, you are adding the dimensions along all edges, so the units will not be squared.
4. Key words:
   Cylinder: A three-dimensional figure with two parallel, congruent circular bases connected by a curved lateral surface
   Diameter: A line segment that passes through the center of a circle and has endpoints on the circle
   Difference: The result when one number is subtracted from another number
   Radius: A line segment with one endpoint at the center of a circle and the other endpoint on the circle
   Volume: The number of cubic units needed to fill a given space
   Volume formula for a cylinder: $V = \pi r^2 h$ where h = height and r = radius
5. Choice **J**, because it is too large
6. Greatest Common Factor
7. The key terms to help me solve this problem are "greatest" and "same number."
8. 4 out of 5 represents 80%. Subtract 80 from 100 to find the percentage of people who would not recommend the store.
9. Choice **J** can be eliminated because it represents the percent of people who will recommend the store to someone else.
10. $\frac{4}{5} = \frac{x}{100}$
11. This problem can be solved by subtracting the percentage of people who will recommend the store from 100%. The problem can also be solved by using the ratio of people who will not recommend the store in a proportion.

Organizer

Objective: Provide review and practice for Chapters 1–11 and standardized tests.

Online Edition

Resources

Assessment Resources
Chapter 11 Cumulative Test

***CRCT Prep* Workbook**

***CRCT Prep* CD-ROM**

***CRCT Practice* Online**

go.hrw.com
KEYWORD: MR7 TestPrep

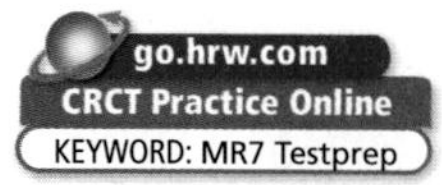

CRCT Prep

Cumulative Assessment, Chapters 1–11

Multiple Choice

1. Marla bought a shirt on sale for \$22, which was $\frac{1}{8}$ off the original price. What decimal represents the discount received?

(A) 0.125 (C) 0.725
(B) 0.225 (D) 0.825

2. William is bringing small bottles of fruit juice for the company picnic. There are 154 people coming to the company picnic. If the drinks come in packages of 6, how many packages will William need to buy so that each guest can have 3 drinks?

(F) 20 boxes (H) 75 boxes
(G) 26 boxes (J) 77 boxes

3. Ashlee has 36 basketballs, 48 bean bags, and 60 flying disks. She is making playground sets for the teachers. She wants to put the same number of basketballs, bean bags, and flying disks in each set. What is the greatest number of sets she can make if she uses all of the items?

(A) 3 (C) 12
(B) 6 (D) 18

4. At 5:30 P.M., 75% of the people at company A had gone home. What fraction of people had NOT yet gone home?

(F) $\frac{3}{4}$ (H) $\frac{1}{4}$
(G) $\frac{1}{2}$ (J) $\frac{1}{25}$

5. What is the ratio of the number of students who play the drums to the number of students who play the trumpet? Give the ratio in simplest form.

School Band	
Instrument	**Number of Students**
Drums	10
Trombone	14
Trumpet	8
Tuba	3

(A) 10 to 3 (C) 5 to 7
(B) 5 to 4 (D) 10 to 27

6. If $\angle KHG$ and $\angle JHM$ are congruent, what is the measure of $\angle GHJ$?

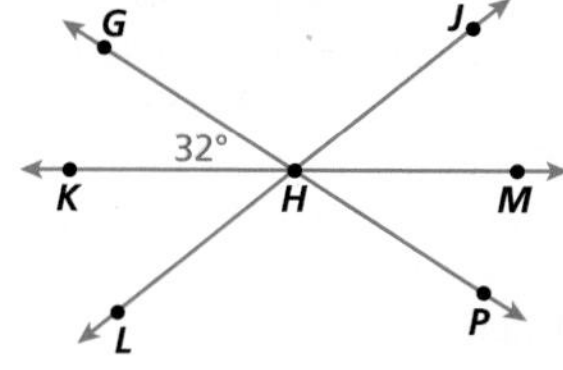

(F) 148° (H) 108°
(G) 116° (J) 96°

7. What is the reciprocal of $1\frac{3}{5}$?

(A) $-1\frac{3}{5}$ (C) $\frac{8}{5}$
(B) $\frac{5}{8}$ (D) 8

8. Find the prime factorization of 80.

(F) $2 \cdot 5^2$ (H) $2^3 \cdot 10$
(G) $2^2 \cdot 5$ (J) $2^4 \cdot 5$

TEST PREP DOCTOR

For item 5, students should remember that the key to setting up a ratio is the word *to*. Also, they may overlook simplifying the ratio.

Answers

14a. \$32 − 3(\$18) = −\$22

b. Possible answer:
$-22 + d = 15$
$d = 15 + 22$
$d = 37$
Graham deposited \$37 on Wednesday.

15. The coordinates of the yellow square are (1, 1), (1, 3), (3, 3), (3, 1). To find the coordinates of the new square after the translation, I added (−5) to the *y*-coordinates and (−3) to the *x*-coordinates of the original square.

16. See 4-Point Response work sample.

9. Louie buys a baseball bat for \$125, a catcher's mitt for \$55, and a baseball for \$3. The tax rate is 5%. If Louie gives the cashier \$200, how much change will he get back?

Ⓐ \$6.15 Ⓒ \$9.25

Ⓑ \$7.85 Ⓓ \$10.75

10. There are 4 shows a day at the local performing arts theater. The first show starts at 10:15 A.M. Each show lasts 30 minutes, and there is a 1 hour and 30 minute break between shows. What time does the third show end?

Ⓕ 12:15 P.M. Ⓗ 2:45 P.M.

Ⓖ 12:45 P.M. Ⓙ 3:15 P.M.

When adding integers, move right on a number line to add a positive number and move left on a number line to add a negative number.

11. Wyatt has received the following scores on his chapter spelling tests: 92, 98, 90, 97, and 92. What is the mean score of Wyatt's spelling tests?

Ⓐ 92 Ⓒ 94.5

Ⓑ 93.8 Ⓓ 97

12. Joshua runs 35% of the way from his house to the gym. If the gym is 5 miles from Joshua's house, how many miles does Joshua run on his way to the gym?

Ⓕ 1.75 Ⓗ 3.5

Ⓖ 2.25 Ⓙ 4

13. What is 65 cm expressed in meters?

Ⓐ 0.065 Ⓒ 6.5

Ⓑ 0.65 Ⓓ 650

STANDARDIZED TEST PREP

Short Response

14. On Monday, the balance in Graham's checking account was \$32. On Tuesday, he wrote three \$18 checks. After a deposit on Wednesday, his balance was \$15.

 a. Find Graham's balance on Tuesday.

 b. Write and solve an equation that can be used to find the amount of Graham's deposit. Let d = the amount of Graham's deposit. Show your work.

15. Find the coordinates of the vertices of the yellow square. Then explain how to find the new coordinates of the square after it is translated 5 units down and 3 units left.

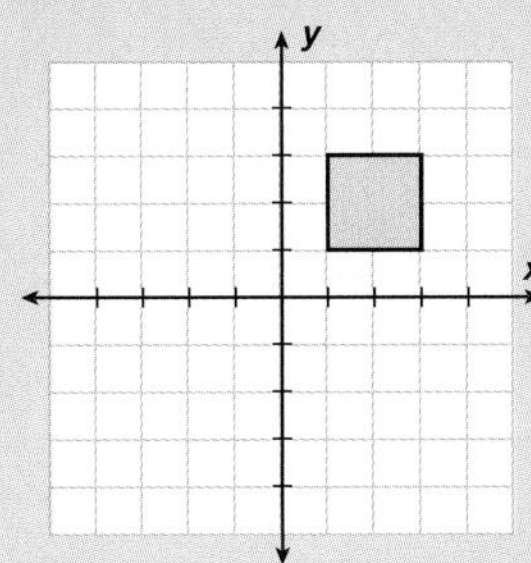

Extended Response

16. A store sold 44 art masks in September for \$528. In October, the store sold 41 art masks for \$492. In November, the store sold 38 art masks for \$456. All the masks cost the same.

 a. Make a table to display the data, and then graph the data. Is the function linear? Explain your answer.

 b. Write an equation to represent the function. Tell what each variable represents.

 c. In December, the store sold 67 masks. What were the total mask sales in December?

CRCT Prep

Short Response Rubric

Items 14–15

2 Points = The student's answer is an accurate and complete execution of the task or tasks.

1 Point = The student's answer contains attributes of an appropriate response but is flawed.

0 Points = The student's answer contains no attributes of an appropriate response.

Extended Response Rubric

Item 16

4 Points = The student demonstrates a thorough understanding of all concepts and shows all work correctly.

3 Points = The student demonstrates a basic understanding of all concepts, but the work shows some flaws reflecting inattentive execution of mathematical procedures or some misunderstanding of the underlying mathematics.

2 Points = The student demonstrates only a partial understanding of the concepts or procedures embodied in the tasks. The approach may be correct, but the work shows a misunderstanding of one or more important concepts.

1 Point = The student demonstrates a very limited understanding of the concepts or procedures embodied in the tasks. The response may show some understanding but exhibits many flaws or is incomplete.

0 Points = The student provides no response at all or a completely incorrect or uninterpretable response.

Student Work Samples for Item 16

4-Point Response

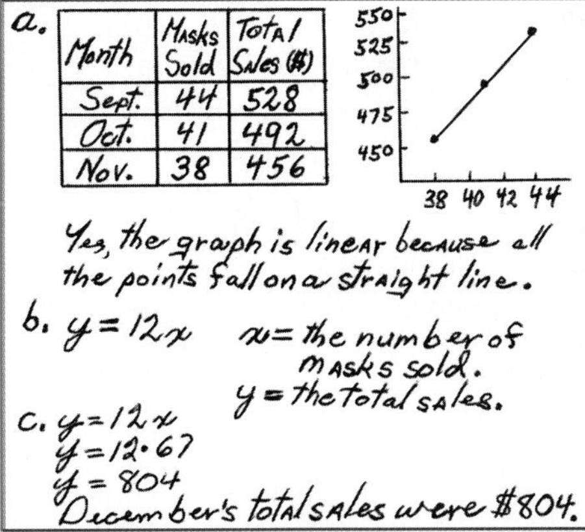

Responses demonstrate a complete understanding of all concepts and questions are answered with complete sentences.

3-Point Response

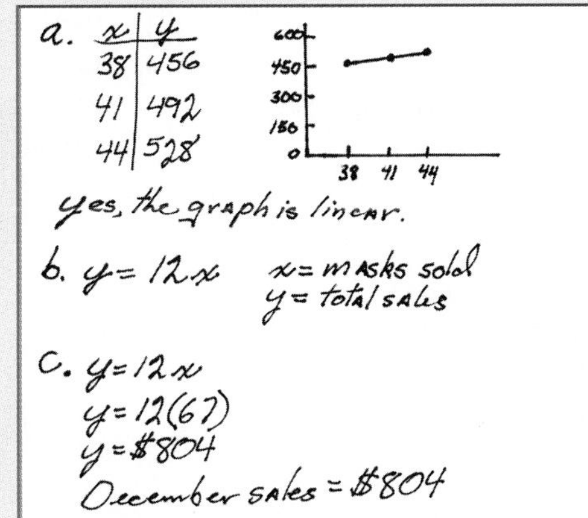

The table and graph in part **a** lack detail and accuracy. Work in parts **b** and **c** is correct.

2-Point Response

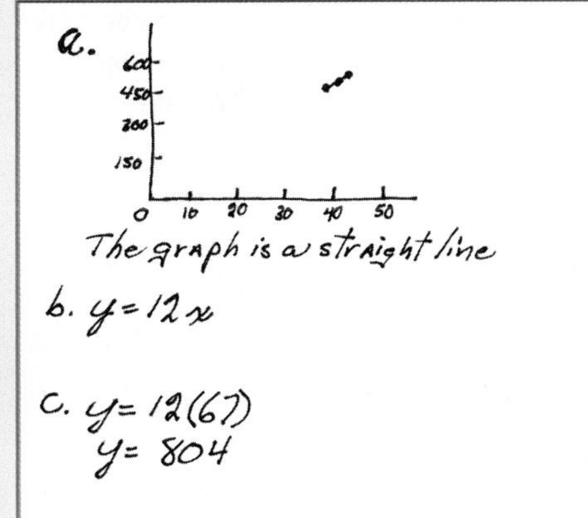

The table is missing in part **a** and the increments on the graph are too small to allow for a definite conclusion. Responses are incomplete.

CHAPTER 12

Probability

Section 12A	Section 12B
Understanding Probability	**Using Probability**
12-1 Introduction to Probability	**12-5 Compound Events**
12-2 Experimental Probability	**12-5 Hands-On Lab** Explore Permutations and Combinations
12-2 Hands-On Lab Simulations	**12-6 Making Predictions**
12-3 Counting Methods and Sample Spaces	**EXTENSION Independent and Dependent Events**
12-4 Theoretical Probability	

Pacing Guide for 45-Minute Classes

Chapter 12

DAY 1	DAY 2	DAY 3	DAY 4	DAY 5
12-1 Lesson	12-2 Lesson	12-2 Hands-On Lab 12-3 Lesson	12-3 Lesson 12-4 Lesson	12-4 Lesson Ready to Go On? Focus on Problem Solving
DAY 6	**DAY 7**	**DAY 8**	**DAY 9**	**DAY 10**
12-5 Lesson	12-5 Hands-On Lab 12-6 Lesson	12-6 Lesson Ready to Go On? Multi-Step Test Prep	Extension	Chapter 12 Review
DAY 11				
Chapter 12 Test				

Pacing Guide for 90-Minute Classes

Chapter 12

DAY 1	DAY 2	DAY 3	DAY 4	DAY 5
12-1 Lesson 12-2 Lesson	12-2 Hands-On Lab 12-3 Lesson 12-4 Lesson	12-4 Lesson Ready to Go On? Focus on Problem Solving 12-5 Lesson	12-5 Hands-On Lab 12-6 Lesson Ready to Go On? Multi-Step Test Prep	Extension Chapter 12 Review
DAY 6				
Chapter 12 Test				

ONGOING ASSESSMENT and INTERVENTION

	DIAGNOSE	PRESCRIBE
Assess Prior Knowledge	**Before Chapter 12**	
	Diagnose readiness for the chapter.	Prescribe intervention.
	Are You Ready? SE p. 665	***Are You Ready? Intervention*** Skills 18, 26, 27, 32
Formative Assessment	**Before Every Lesson**	
	Diagnose readiness for the lesson.	Prescribe intervention.
	Warm Up TE, every lesson	**Skills Bank** SE pp. 749–761
		Reteach CRB, Chapters 1–12
	During Every Lesson	
	Diagnose understanding of lesson concepts.	Prescribe intervention.
	Think and Discuss SE, every lesson	***Questioning Strategies*** Chapter 12
	Write About It SE, lesson exercises	**Reading Strategies** CRB, every lesson
	Journal TE, lesson exercises	***Success for ELL*** pp. 203–214
	After Every Lesson	
	Diagnose mastery of lesson concepts.	Prescribe intervention.
	Lesson Quiz TE, every lesson	**Reteach** CRB, every lesson
	Test Prep SE, every lesson	**Problem Solving** CRB, every lesson
	Test and Practice Generator	**Test Prep Doctor** TE, exercises lesson
		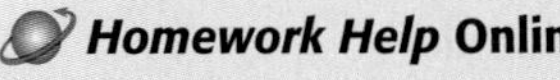 ***Homework Help*** **Online**
	Before Chapter 12 Testing	
	Diagnose mastery of concepts in the chapter.	Prescribe intervention.
	Ready to Go On? SE pp. 686, 698	***Ready to Go On? Intervention*** Chapter 12
	Focus on Problem Solving SE p. 687	**Scaffolding Questions** TE p. 699
	Multi-Step Test Prep SE p. 699	
	Section Quizzes AR pp. 227–228	
	Test and Practice Generator	
	Before High Stakes Testing	
	Diagnose mastery of benchmark concepts.	Prescribe intervention.
	CRCT Prep SE pp. 708–709	***CRCT Prep Workbook***
	CRCT Prep **CD-ROM**	
Summative Assessment	**After Chapter 12**	
	Check mastery of chapter concepts.	Prescribe intervention.
	Multiple-Choice Tests (Forms A, B, C)	**Reteach** CRB, every lesson
	Free-Response Tests (Forms A, B, C)	***Lesson Tutorial Videos*** Chapter 12
	Performance Assessment AR pp. 229–242	
	Test and Practice Generator	
	Check mastery of benchmark concepts.	Prescribe intervention.
	CRCT	***CRCT Prep Workbook***

KEY: **SE** = *Student Edition* **TE** = *Teacher's Edition* **CRB** = *Chapter Resource Book* **AR** = *Assessment Resources* Available online Available on CD-ROM

CHAPTER 12

Supporting the Teacher

Chapter 12 Resource Book

Practice A, B, C
pp. 3–5, 12–14, 20–22, 28–30, 36–38, 44–46

Reading Strategies ELL
pp. 10, 18, 26, 34, 42, 50

Puzzles, Twisters, and Teasers
pp. 11, 19, 27, 35, 43, 51

Reteach
pp. 6–7, 15, 23, 31, 39, 47

Problem Solving
pp. 9, 17, 25, 33, 41, 49

Challenge
pp. 8, 16, 24, 32, 40, 48

Parent Letter pp. 1–2

Transparencies

Lesson Transparencies, Volume 2 .... Chapter 12
- Warm Ups
- Problem of the Day
- Teaching Transparencies
- Lesson Quizzes

Know-It Notebook .... Chapter 12
- Additional Examples
- Vocabulary
- Chapter Review
- Big Ideas

Alternate Openers: Explorations .... pp. 102–107

Teacher Tools

Power Presentations®
Complete PowerPoint® presentations for Chapter 12 lessons

Lesson Tutorial Videos® SPANISH
Holt authors Ed Burger and Freddie Renfro present tutorials to support the Chapter 12 lessons.

One-Stop Planner® SPANISH
Easy access to all Chapter 12 resources and assessments, as well as software for lesson planning, test generation, and puzzle creation

IDEA Works!®
Key Chapter 12 resources and assessments modified to address special learning needs

Lesson Plans .... pp. 102–107

Questioning Strategies .... Chapter 12

Solutions Key .... Chapter 12

Interdisciplinary Posters and Worksheets .... Chapter 12

TechKeys

Lab Resources

Project Teacher Support

Parent Resources 

Workbooks

Homework and Practice Workbook SPANISH
Teacher's Guide .... pp. 51–54

Know-It Notebook
Teacher's Guide .... Chapter 12

Problem Solving Workbook SPANISH
Teacher's Guide .... pp. 51–54

CRCT Prep
Teacher's Guide

Technology Highlights for the Teacher

Power Presentations

Dynamic presentations to engage students. Complete PowerPoint® presentations for every lesson in Chapter 12.

2-1 Solving One-Step Equations

Isolate a variable by using inverse operations which "undo" operations on the variable.

An equation is like a balanced scale. To keep the balance, perform the same operation on both sides.

Inverse Operations	
Operation	**Inverse Operation**
Addition	Subtraction
Subtraction	Addition

One-Stop Planner SPANISH

Easy access to Chapter 12 resources and assessments. Includes lesson-planning, test-generation, and puzzle-creation software.

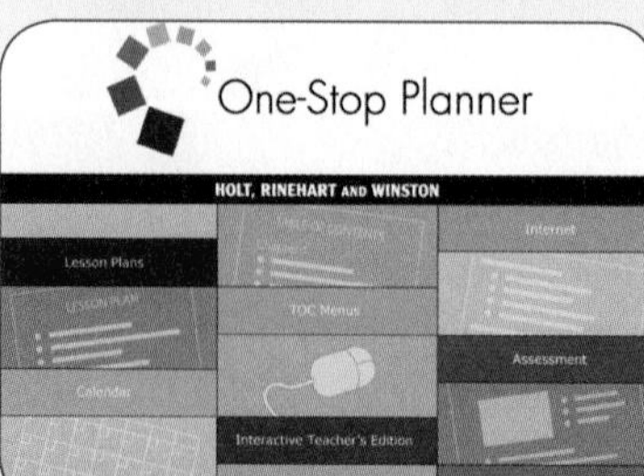

Premier Online Edition SPANISH

Chapter 12 includes Tutorial Videos, Lesson Activities, Lesson Quizzes, Homework Help, and Chapter Project.

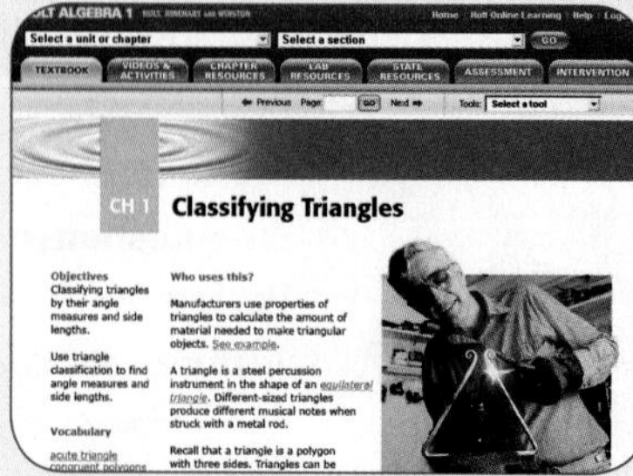

KEY: **SE** = *Student Edition* **TE** = *Teacher's Edition*  English Language Learners  Spanish version available  Available online  Available on CD-ROM

Reaching All Learners

Resources for All Learners

Hands-On Lab Activities	Chapter 12
Technology Lab Activities	Chapter 12
Homework and Practice Workbook SPANISH	pp. 102–107
Know-It Notebook SPANISH	Chapter 12
Problem Solving Workbook SPANISH	pp. 102–107

DEVELOPING LEARNERS

Practice A	CRB, every lesson
Reteach	CRB, every lesson
Inclusion	TE p. 669
Questioning Strategies	Chapter 12
Modified Chapter 12 Resources	*IDEA Works!*
Homework Help Online	

ON-LEVEL LEARNERS

Practice B	CRB, every lesson
Puzzles, Twisters, and Teasers	CRB, every lesson
Cooperative Learning	TE p. 689
Modeling	TE pp. 669, 695

ADVANCED LEARNERS

Practice C	CRB, every lesson
Challenge	CRB, every lesson
Extension	TE pp. 667, 699, 702, 703
Critical Thinking	TE p. 679

English Language Learners

ENGLISH LANGUAGE LEARNERS

Are You Ready? Vocabulary	SE p. 665
Vocabulary Connections	SE p. 666
Lesson Vocabulary	SE, every lesson
Vocabulary Review	SE p. 704
English Language Learners	TE pp. 669, 672, 673, 683, 688, 689, 711
Reading Strategies	CRB, every lesson
Success for English Language Learners	pp. 203–214
Multilingual Glossary	

Reaching All Learners Through...

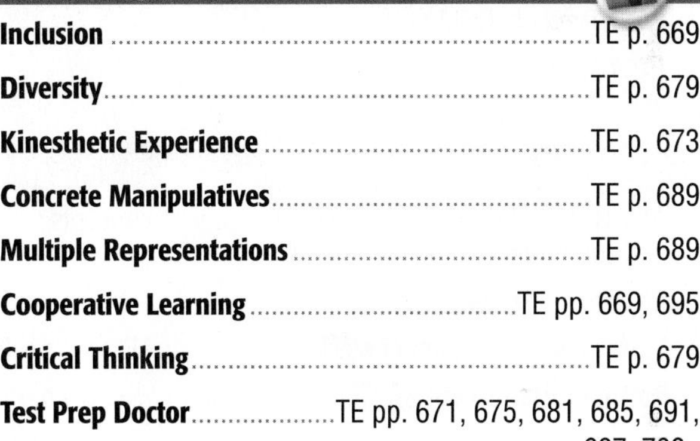

Inclusion	TE p. 669
Diversity	TE p. 679
Kinesthetic Experience	TE p. 673
Concrete Manipulatives	TE p. 689
Multiple Representations	TE p. 689
Cooperative Learning	TE pp. 669, 695
Critical Thinking	TE p. 679
Test Prep Doctor	TE pp. 671, 675, 681, 685, 691, 697, 708
Common Error Alert	TE pp. 679, 683, 689, 695, 701
Scaffolding Questions	TE p. 669

Technology Highlights for Reaching All Learners

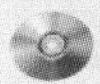

Lesson Tutorial Videos SPANISH

Starring Holt authors Ed Burger and Freddie Renfro! Live tutorials to support every lesson in Chapter 12.

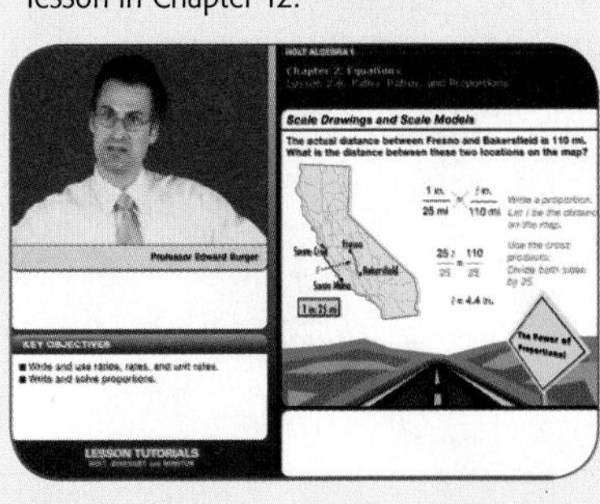

Multilingual Glossary

Searchable glossary includes definitions in English, Spanish, Vietnamese, Chinese, Hmong, Korean, and 4 other languages.

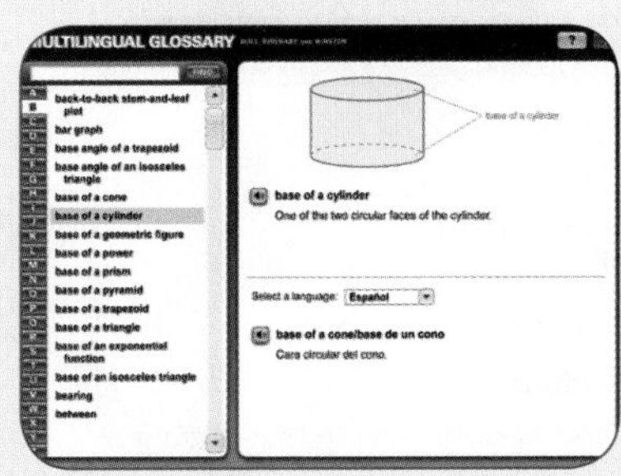

Online Interactivities

Interactive tutorials provide visually engaging alternative opportunities to learn concepts and master skills.

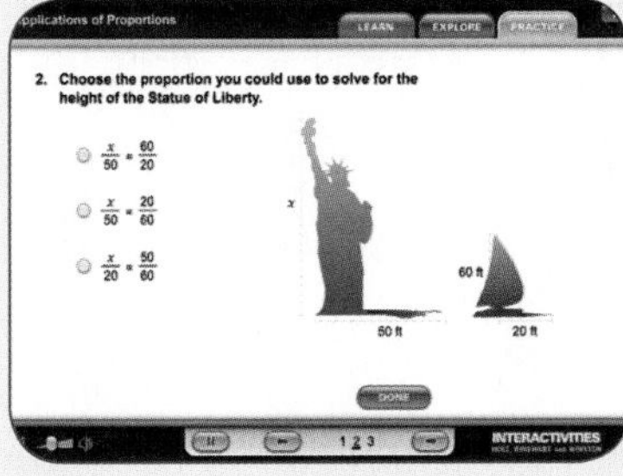

KEY: **SE** = *Student Edition* **TE** = *Teacher's Edition* **CRB** = *Chapter Resource Book*  SPANISH Spanish version available  Available online  Available on CD-ROM

Ongoing Assessment

Assessing Prior Knowledge

Determine whether students have the prerequisite concepts and skills for success in Chapter 12.

Are You Ready? SPANISH .... SE p. 665

Warm Up .... TE, every lesson

Test Preparation

Provide review and practice for Chapter 12 and standardized tests.

Multi-Step Test Prep .... SE p. 669

Study Guide: Review .... SE pp. 704–706

CRCT Prep .... SE pp. 708–709

CRCT Prep Workbook

***CRCT Prep* CD-ROM**

IDEA Works!

Alternative Assessment

Assess students' understanding of Chapter 12 concepts and combined problem-solving skills.

Chapter 12 Project .... SE p. 598

Performance Assessment SPANISH .... AR pp. 241–242

Portfolio Assessment SPANISH .... AR p. xxxiv

Daily Assessment

Provide formative assessment for each day of Chapter 12.

Questioning Strategies .... Chapter 12

Think and Discuss .... SE, every lesson

Write About It .... SE, lesson exercises

Journal .... TE, lesson exercises

Lesson Quiz .... TE, every lesson

Modified Lesson Quizzes .... *IDEA Works!*

Weekly Assessment

Provide formative assessment for each week of Chapter 12.

Focus on Problem Solving .... SE p. 687

Multi-Step Test Prep .... SE p. 699

Ready to Go On? SPANISH .... SE pp. 686, 698

Cumulative Assessment .... SE pp. 708–709

Test and Practice Generator SPANISH .... *One-Stop Planner*

Formal Assessment

Provide summative assessment of Chapter 12 mastery.

Section Quizzes SPANISH .... AR pp. 227–228

Chapter 12 Test .... SE p. 707

Chapter Test (Levels A, B, C) SPANISH .... AR pp. 229–240

- Multiple Choice
- Free Response

Cumulative Test SPANISH .... AR pp. 243–246

Test and Practice Generator SPANISH .... *One-Stop Planner*

Modified Chapter 12 Test .... *IDEA Works!*

Technology Highlights for Ongoing Assessment

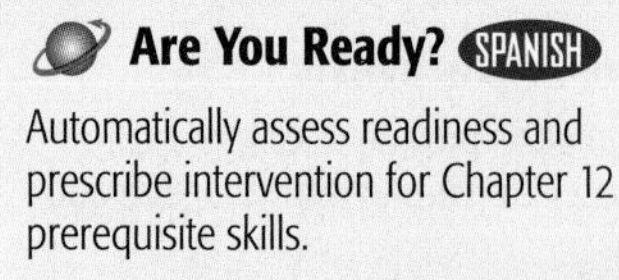

Are You Ready? SPANISH

Automatically assess readiness and prescribe intervention for Chapter 12 prerequisite skills.

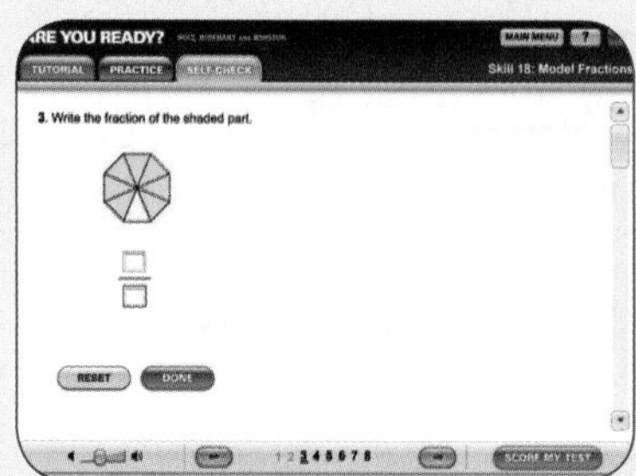

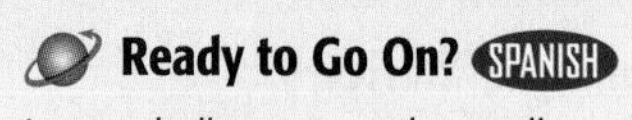

Ready to Go On? SPANISH

Automatically assess understanding of and prescribe intervention for Sections 12A and 12B.

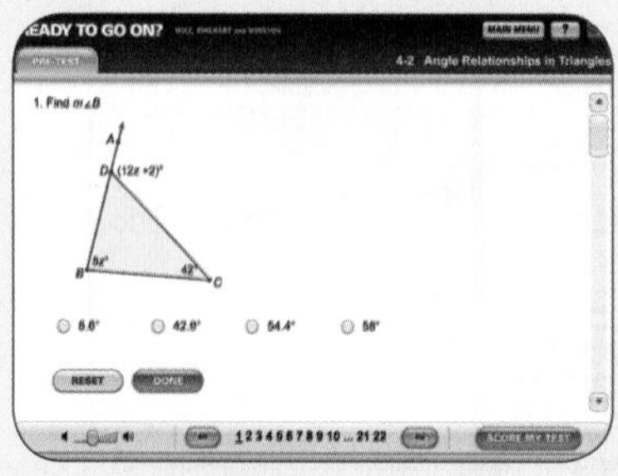

Test and Practice Generator SPANISH

Use Chapter 12 problem banks to create assessments and worksheets to print out or deliver online. Includes dynamic problems.

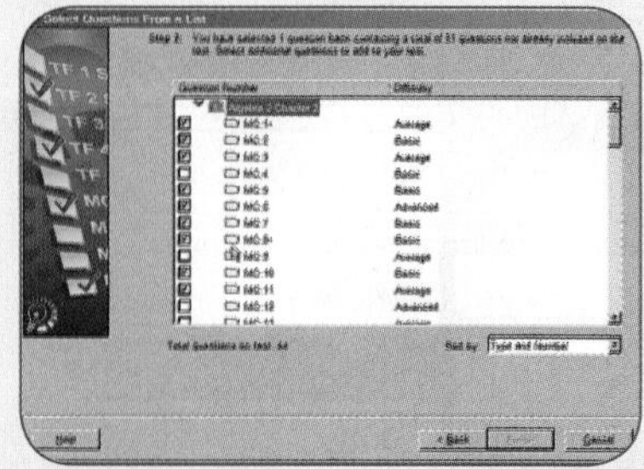

KEY: **SE** = *Student Edition* **TE** = *Teacher's Edition* **AR** = *Assessment Resources* SPANISH Spanish version available  Available online  Available on CD-ROM

Formal Assessment

Three levels (A, B, C) of multiple-choice and free-response chapter tests are available in the *Assessment Resources.*

A Chapter 12 Test

C Chapter 12 Test

MULTIPLE CHOICE

B Chapter 12 Test

Choose the best answer.

1. What is the likelihood of a dropped slice of toast landing butter-side down?
   A impossible (C) as likely as not
   B unlikely D certain

2. There is a 25% chance of snow tomorrow. What is this as a decimal?
   F 0.025 H 2.5
   (G) 0.25 J 25.0

3. There is a $\frac{2}{7}$ chance that any particular date will fall on a weekend. Write this rounded to the nearest percent.
   A 0.29 C 28.57%
   B 28% (D) 29%

4. So far this season, Ernesto's times at bat have produced 24 strikes, 18 balls, and 8 hits. What is the probability that the next pitch he faces will result in a hit?
   F 25% H 8%
   (G) 16% J 4%

5. So far today, 7 robins and 9 bluebirds have visited your bird feeder. What is the experimental probability that the next bird to visit will be a bluebird?
   A $\frac{1}{8}$ (C) $\frac{9}{16}$
   B $\frac{7}{16}$ D $\frac{7}{9}$

6. A cooking class baked 3 undercooked cakes, 5 burned cakes, 4 that fell, and 2 successful cakes. Which outcome is most likely for the next cake?
   F undercooked H fallen
   (G) burned J successful

7. Jamal has 3 pairs of pants and 4 shirts. How many different possible outfits could he wear?
   A 3 C 7
   B 4 (D) 12

8. Mai is shopping for either a mountain bike or a road bike. Both are available in blue, yellow, or green. How many choices are there?
   F 2 H 5
   G 3 (J) 6

9. A restaurant menu has 4 appetizers, 6 main courses, and 3 desserts. How many combinations of an appetizer, a main course, and a dessert are possible?
   A 13 C 24
   B 18 (D) 72

10. You spin a spinner divided into equal red, blue, and green sections. What is the probability of the spinner stopping in the green section?
    F 0 H $\frac{2}{3}$
    (J) $\frac{1}{3}$ J 1

B Chapter 12 Test *(continued)*

11. What is the probability of rolling an even number on a number cube?
    A $\frac{1}{6}$ C $\frac{2}{3}$
    (B) $\frac{1}{2}$ D $\frac{5}{6}$

12. There is a 5% chance of hail today. What is the probability of no hail?
    F 5% (H) 95%
    G 50% J 100%

13. A spinner is divided into unequal red, blue, and yellow sections. The respective probabilities of the spinner stopping in the red and blue sections are 20% and 50%. What is the probability it will stop in the yellow section?
    (A) 30% C 70%
    B 50% D 100%

14. Suppose you flip a coin and then roll a number cube. What is the probability of getting heads and a 4?
    (F) $\frac{1}{12}$ H $\frac{1}{2}$
    G $\frac{1}{6}$ J $\frac{5}{12}$

15. If you roll a number cube twice, what is the probability of getting two 5s?
    (A) $\frac{1}{36}$ C $\frac{1}{6}$
    B $\frac{1}{12}$ D $\frac{1}{3}$

16. Ken has a brown shirt, 2 blue shirts, brown pants, tan pants, black shoes, and brown shoes. If he picks at random, what is the probability that he will pick a blue shirt, tan pants, and black shoes?
    F $\frac{1}{12}$ H $\frac{1}{2}$
    (G) $\frac{1}{6}$ J $\frac{2}{3}$

17. If the probability of rain on any given day is 20%, in a 30-day month, how many days would you predict will have rain?
    A 2 C 20
    (B) 6 D 30

18. A survey shows that 60% of students take the bus to school. If there are 450 students in the school, how many would you predict will take the bus?
    F 27 (H) 270
    G 60 J 450

19. If you flip a coin 24 times, how many heads do you expect to get?
    F $\frac{1}{2}$ H 24
    (G) 12 J 50%

A Chapter 12 Test

C Chapter 12 Test

FREE RESPONSE

B Chapter 12 Test

1. Write impossible, unlikely, as likely as not, likely, or certain to describe the likelihood of your winning the lottery.
   unlikely

2. There is a 5% chance of Colleen winning a new DVD player. What is this as a decimal?
   0.05

3. There is a $\frac{5}{7}$ chance that any particular date will fall on a weekday. Write this rounded to the nearest percent.
   71%

4. On the last spelling test, 4 students got an A, 6 got a B, 7 got a C, 5 got a D, and 3 got an F. What is the probability that a student who takes the next spelling test will get a B?
   24%

5. A survey of your friends finds that 11 own a dog, 12 own a cat, and 7 have no pet. Find the experimental probability that the next person you ask will be a cat-owner.
   $\frac{12}{30} = \frac{2}{5}$

6. Kim has been playing a video game. She scored as a Beginner in 3 games, as a Champ in 6 games, as a Super Champ in 5 games, and as a World Hero in 2 games. What is the most likely outcome the next time she plays?
   Champ

7. Danica can choose an outfit from the following clothes: two pairs of slacks (navy or black), four blouses (red, blue, white, and striped), and three pairs of shoes (blue, black, and sandals). How many different choices of outfits does she have?
   24 choices

8. José is shopping for either a skateboard or a scooter. Both are available in black, blue, or silver. How many choices are there?
   6 choices

9. You go to the local restaurant for lunch. You have 3 choices of a main dish (chicken, fish, or beef), 2 choices for a vegetable (peas or beans), and 2 choices for soup (tomato or vegetable). How many different choices are there for a lunch of a main dish, vegetable, and soup?
   12 choices

10. What is the probability of this spinner landing on D?

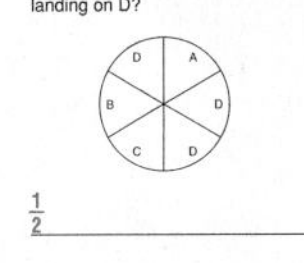

   $\frac{1}{2}$

B Chapter 12 Test *(continued)*

11. What is the probability of rolling a number less than 5 on a number cube?
    $\frac{2}{3}$

12. Rebecca has a 10% chance of not completing the marathon. What is the probability that she will complete the marathon?
    90%

13. A spinner is divided into unequal red, blue, and yellow sections. The respective probabilities of the spinner stopping in the red and blue sections are 30% and 60%. What is the probability it will stop in the yellow section?
    10%

14. If you roll a number cube and then draw a card from a normal deck of playing cards, what is the probability of rolling a 5 and drawing a red card?
    $\frac{1}{12}$

15. If you roll a number cube twice, what is the probability of rolling a 3 followed by a 1?
    $\frac{1}{36}$

16. The drama teacher casts the parts of Romeo and Juliet by putting slips with the names of the 10 boys in the class in a bag and the names of the 12 girls in another bag and drawing a slip from each. What is the chance that Leon will be cast as Romeo and Tashonda as Juliet?
    $\frac{1}{120}$

17. If the probability of snow on any given day is 10%, in a 30-day month, how many days would you predict will have snow?
    3 days

18. About 4% of the items produced by a company are defective. Out of 8000 items, how many would you predict will be defective?
    320 items

19. If you roll a 12-sided die 300 times, how many times can you expect to roll an odd number?
    150 times

Create and customize Chapter 12 Tests. Instantly generate multiple test versions, answer keys, and Spanish versions of test items.

CHAPTER 12

Why Learn This?

Tell students that probability is used to determine the likelihood that an event will happen. One way to find the probability that an event will happen is to study past trials and use information about the past to predict the future. For example, if a coin is tossed 10 times and lands heads up 4 times, you could predict that if you toss the same coin 100 times, it will land heads up 40 times. A financial advisor uses an investment fund's past performance to predict its future performance.

Using Data

To begin the study of this chapter, have students:

- Find the compound interest earned on a \$100 investment over 5 years at 8%. \$47
- Estimate the interest rate on a \$100 investment that returned \$18 after 2 years. about 8.5%
- Estimate the amount of time it will take a \$100 investment to earn \$100 in interest at 9%. about 8 years

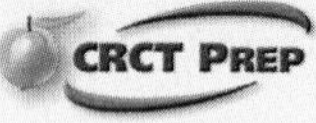

CRCT PREP On page 708, students will find cumulative CRCT practice.

CHAPTER 12

Probability

CRCT PREP

go.hrw.com
Chapter Project Online
KEYWORD: MR7 Ch12

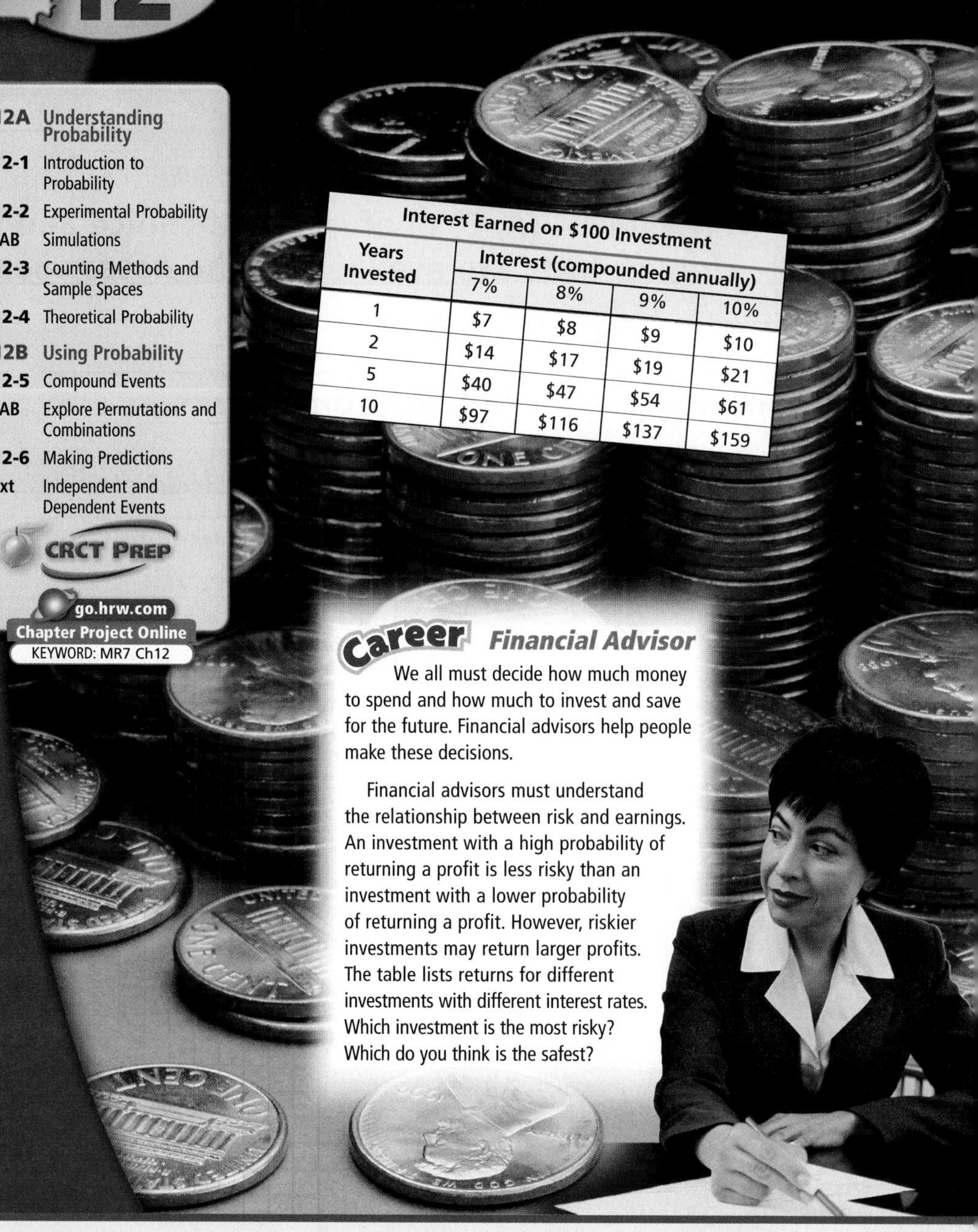

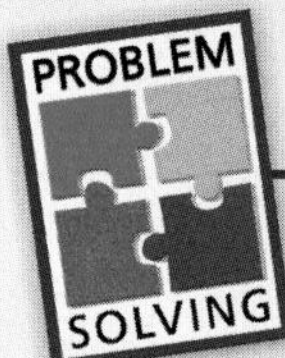

Interest Earned on \$100 Investment

Years Invested	Interest (compounded annually)			
	7%	8%	9%	10%
1	\$7	\$8	\$9	\$10
2	\$14	\$17	\$19	\$21
5	\$40	\$47	\$54	\$61
10	\$97	\$116	\$137	\$159

Career *Financial Advisor*

We all must decide how much money to spend and how much to invest and save for the future. Financial advisors help people make these decisions.

Financial advisors must understand the relationship between risk and earnings. An investment with a high probability of returning a profit is less risky than an investment with a lower probability of returning a profit. However, riskier investments may return larger profits. The table lists returns for different investments with different interest rates. Which investment is the most risky? Which do you think is the safest?

PROBLEM SOLVING

Problem Solving Project

Understand, Plan, Solve, and Look Back

Have students:

- Examine the chart and explain what interest rate they would prefer. Which investment do they consider the safest?
- Complete the Financial Planning worksheet to learn more about probability.
- Find the earnings at each interest rate over a 20-year period.
- Research an investment fund's earnings 10 years ago and 5 years ago, and what it is earning today. Predict the fund's earnings 5 years from now.

Social Studies and Economics Connection

Project Resources

All project resources for teachers and students are provided online.

Materials:

- Financial Planning worksheet

go.hrw.com
Project Teacher Support
KEYWORD: MR7 PSProject12

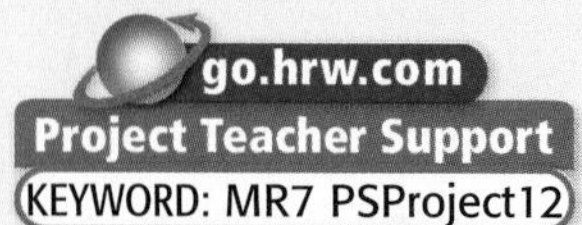

ARE YOU READY?

Vocabulary

Choose the best term from the list to complete each sentence.

equivalent
frequency
part
percent
ratio
simplest form
table
whole

1. The denominator of a fraction represents the __?__, and the numerator represents the __?__. whole; part
2. Fractions that represent the same value are __?__ fractions. equivalent
3. A __?__ is a comparison of two quantities by division. ratio
4. Tally marks in a table show the __?__, or total, for each result. frequency
5. A ratio of a number to 100 is called a __?__. percent

Complete these exercises to review skills you will need for this chapter.

Model Fractions

Write the fraction in simplest form that represents the shaded portion.

6. 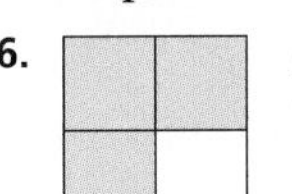 $\frac{3}{4}$

7. 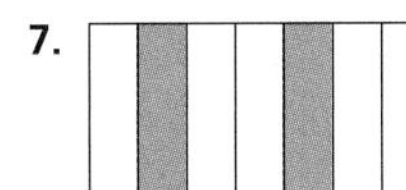 $\frac{2}{7}$

8. 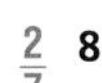 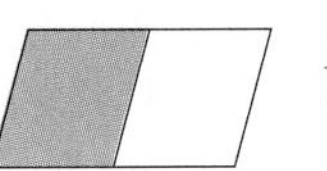 $\frac{1}{2}$

Write Fractions as Decimals

Write each fraction as a decimal.

9. $\frac{9}{10}$ 0.9
10. $\frac{1}{2}$ 0.5
11. $\frac{12}{25}$ 0.48
12. $\frac{11}{20}$ 0.55

Compare Fractions, Decimals, and Percents

Compare. Write <, >, or =.

13. 0.35 ■ 0.4 <
14. 0.25 ■ 25% =
15. $\frac{3}{5}$ ■ 0.7 <
16. 0.5 ■ $\frac{23}{50}$ >

Write Ratios

Write each ratio.

17. blue circles to total circles

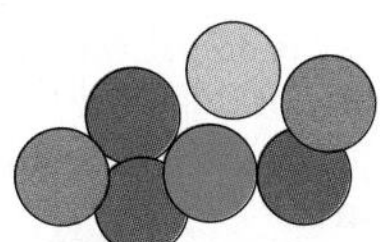

3:7

18. squares to triangles

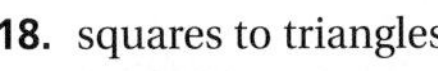

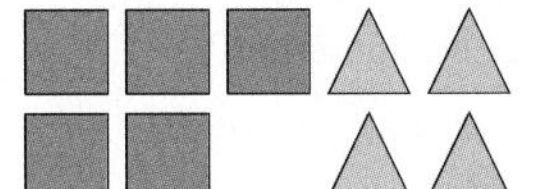

5:4

ARE YOU READY? CHAPTER 12

Organizer

Objective: Assess students' understanding of prerequisite skills.

Prerequisite Skills

Model Fractions

Write Fractions as Decimals

Compare Fractions, Decimals, and Percents

Write Ratios

Assessing Prior Knowledge

INTERVENTION 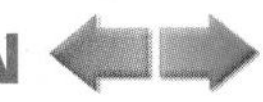

Diagnose and Prescribe

Use this page to determine whether intervention is necessary or enrichment is appropriate.

Resources

 ***Are You Ready? Intervention and Enrichment* Worksheets**

 ***Are You Ready?* CD-ROM**

 ***Are You Ready?* Online**

my.hrw.com

ARE YOU READY?

Diagnose and Prescribe

NO INTERVENE

Prerequisite Skill	*Are You Ready? Intervention,* Chapter 12: Worksheets	CD-ROM	Online
Model Fractions	Skill 18	Activity 18	Diagnose and Prescribe Online
Write Fractions as Decimals	Skill 26	Activity 26	
Compare Fractions, Decimals, and Percents	Skill 32	Activity 32	
Write Ratios	Skill 27	Activity 27	

YES ENRICH

Are You Ready? Enrichment, Chapter 12

Worksheets
CD-ROM
Online

CHAPTER 12 **Study Guide: Preview**

Organizer

Objective: Help students organize the new concepts they will learn in Chapter 12.

 **Online Edition**
Multilingual Glossary

Resources

 ***Multilingual Glossary* Online**

go.hrw.com
KEYWORD: MR7 Glossary

Answers to *Vocabulary Connections*

Possible answers:

1. Experimental probability is based on the number of favorable outcomes in a series of trials.
2. Yes; a compound event is made up of two or more simple events.
3. A prediction is a guess about something that will happen in the future.
4. The chances of two equally likely events are equal.

CHAPTER 12

Study Guide: Preview

Where You've Been

Previously, you

- listed all possible outcomes of a probability experiment.
- used fractions to describe the results of an experiment.
- generated equivalent forms of rational numbers.

In This Chapter

You will study

- finding sample spaces using lists and tree diagrams.
- finding the probabilities of simple events and their complements.
- expressing probabilities as fractions, decimals, and percents.
- finding probabilities of compound events.

Where You're Going

You can use the skills learned in this chapter

- to find probabilities involving permutations and combinations.
- to find odds for and against specified outcomes.

Study Guide: Preview

Key Vocabulary/Vocabulario

complement	complemento
compound event	suceso compuesto
equally likely	resultados igualmente probables
experiment	experimento (probabilidad)
experimental probability	probabilidad experimental
outcome	resultado (probabilidad)
prediction	predicción
probability	probabilidad
theoretical probability	probabilidad teórica

Vocabulary Connections

To become familiar with some of the vocabulary terms in the chapter, consider the following. You may refer to the chapter, the glossary, or a dictionary if you like.

1. The word *experiment* can mean "the process of testing." What do you think **experimental probability** is based on?
2. The word *compound* can mean "composed of separate elements." Do you think a **compound event** is made up of one event? Why or why not?
3. To *predict* something means to "foretell on the basis of observation, experience, or scientific reason." What do you think a **prediction** is?
4. When things are *equal,* they are of the same measure or quantity. How do you think the chances of two **equally likely** events compare?

Grade 6 CRCT GPS

M6N1.
Students will understand the meaning of the four arithmetic operations as related to positive rational numbers and will use these concepts to solve problems.
f. Use fractions, decimals, and percents interchangeably.

M6A2.
Students will consider relationships between varying quantities.
g. Use proportional reasoning ($a/b = c/d$ and $y = kx$) to solve problems.

M6D2.
Students will use experimental and simple theoretical probability and understand the nature of sampling. They will also make predictions from investigations.
a. Predict the probability of a given event through trials/simulations (experimental probability), and represent the probability as a ratio.
b. Determine, and use a ratio to represent, the theoretical probability of a given event.
c. Discover that experimental probability approaches theoretical probability when the number of trials is large.

***Georgia Mathematics Performance Standards* statements are written out completely on pp. GA28–GA35.**

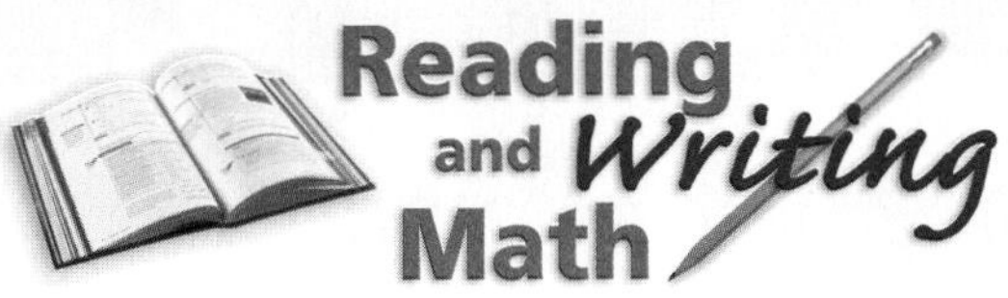

Reading and Writing Math

Study Strategy: Prepare for Your Final Exam

In your math class, you use skills that you have learned throughout the year, so most final exams cover material from the beginning of the course.

A timeline and checklist like the one shown can help you study for the final exam in an organized way.

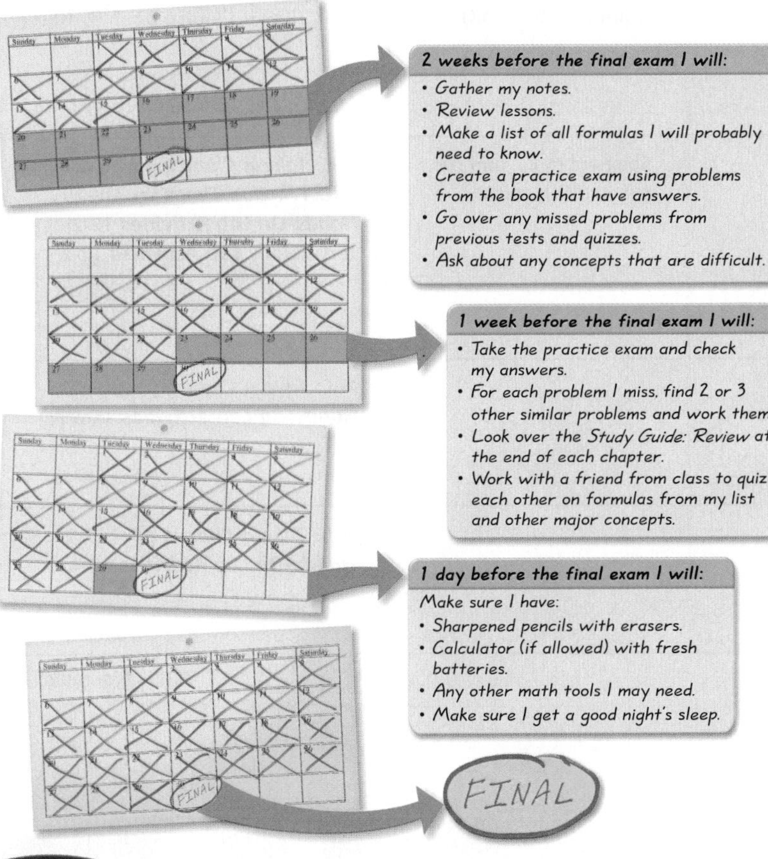

2 weeks before the final exam I will:
• Gather my notes.
• Review lessons.
• Make a list of all formulas I will probably need to know.
• Create a practice exam using problems from the book that have answers.
• Go over any missed problems from previous tests and quizzes.
• Ask about any concepts that are difficult.
1 week before the final exam I will:
• Take the practice exam and check my answers.
• For each problem I miss, find 2 or 3 other similar problems and work them.
• Look over the Study Guide: Review at the end of each chapter.
• Work with a friend from class to quiz each other on formulas from my list and other major concepts.
1 day before the final exam I will:
Make sure I have:
• Sharpened pencils with erasers.
• Calculator (if allowed) with fresh batteries.
• Any other math tools I may need.
• Make sure I get a good night's sleep.
FINAL

Try This

1. Create a timeline and checklist of your own to help you prepare for your final exam.

Grade 6 CRCT GPS

Standards	12-1	12-2	LAB 12-2	12-3	12-4	12-5	LAB 12-5	12-6	Ext.
M6N1.f	★								
M6A2.g								★	
M6D2.a		★	★						
M6D2.b	★				★	★		★	★
M6D2.c		★							
M6P1		★		★	★	★		★	★
M6P2			★						
M6P4	★	★							★
M6P5	★			★	★	★	★		

Reading and Writing Math — Chapter 12

Organizer

Objective: Help students apply strategies to understand and retain key concepts.

 **Online Edition**

Resources

 ***Chapter 12 Resource Book***
Reading Strategies

Study Strategy: Prepare for Your Final Exam

Discuss Have students discuss the results of not being organized and not planning.

Extend Make students aware of the connection between having an organized plan for finals and having an organized plan for major events in their lives, such as getting a job, selecting a college, or buying a car.

Answers to *Try This*

1. Check students' work.

SECTION 12A

Understanding Probability

One-Minute Section Planner

Lesson	Materials	MiC and Lab Resources
Lesson 12-1 Introduction to Probability • Estimate the likelihood of an event, and write and compare probabilities. ☑ CRCT ☑ SAT-10 ☑ ITBS ☑ CTBS ☑ NAEP	Number cubes (MK)	**MiC:** ***Take a Chance*** pp. 1–7, 10–17
Lesson 12-2 Experimental Probability • Find the experimental probability of an event. **12-2 Hands-On Lab** Simulations • Use a number cube and coin to simulate probability experiments. ☑ CRCT ☑ SAT-10 ☑ ITBS ☑ CTBS ☑ NAEP	Spinners (MK), number cubes (MK), coins	**MiC:** ***Take a Chance*** pp. 20–23 **MiC:** ***Fraction Times*** pp. 14–20 ***Hands-On Lab Activities*** 12-2 ***Technology Lab Activities*** 12-2
Lesson 12-3 Counting Methods and Sample Spaces • Make an organized list to find all possible outcomes. ☐ CRCT ☑ SAT-10 ☐ ITBS ☐ CTBS ☑ NAEP		**MiC:** ***Take a Chance*** pp. 20–23 ***Hands-On Lab Activities*** 12-3
Lesson 12-4 Theoretical Probability • Find the theoretical probability and complement of an event. ☑ CRCT ☑ SAT-10 ☑ ITBS ☑ CTBS ☑ NAEP		**MiC:** ***Take a Chance*** pp. 1–7, 26–31 ***Hands-On Lab Activities*** 12-4

MK = *Manipulatives Kit*

Mathematics in Context

The units ***Take a Chance*** and ***Fraction Times*** from the *Mathematics in Context* © 2006 series can be used with Section 12A. See Section Planner above for suggestions for integrating *MiC* with *Holt Mathematics.*

Section Overview

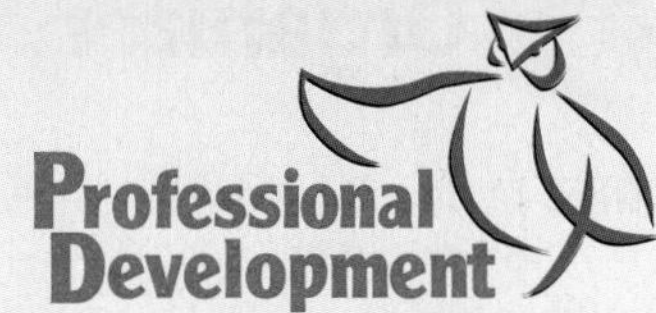

Introduction to Probability

Lesson 12-1

Probability is used in making predictions, such as predictions about the weather.

Probabilities are written as fractions or decimals from 0 to 1 or percents from 0% to 100%. The higher an event's probability, the more likely that event is to happen.

Probability is the measure of how likely an event is to occur.

Probability	Likelihood
0%	Never happen
50%	Same chance of happening as of not happening
100%	Always happen

Experimental Probability

Lesson 12-2

Performing an experiment is one way to estimate the probability of an event.

Vocabulary	Definition	Example
Experiment	An activity involving chance that can have different results	Two coins are tossed.
Outcome	A result of an experiment	HT (H = heads, T = tails)
Sample space	The set of all possible outcomes	HH, HT, TH, TT
Experimental probability	$\frac{\text{Number of times event occurs}}{\text{Total number of trials}}$	If you toss two coins 100 times, and they both come up heads on 24 of those trials, then the experimental probability of both coming up heads, based on this experiment, is as follows: probability = $\frac{24}{100} = \frac{6}{25} = 0.24 = 24\%$.

Counting Methods and Theoretical Probability

Lessons 12-3, 12-4

Why? Counting methods are ways to find the sample space, or all the possible outcomes of an experiment.

A tree diagram is one way to organize information.

Charles is having soup and salad for lunch. He can choose from onion, tomato, and potato soup. He can have a chef, garden, or spinach salad. How many different lunches could Charles have?

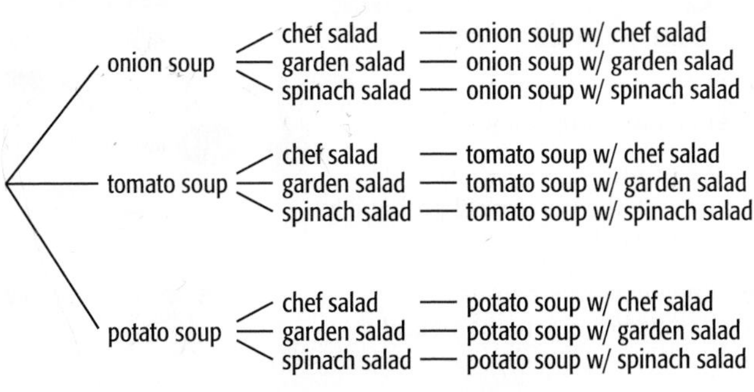

There are 9 different lunches that Charles could have.

One situation in which you can use theoretical probability is when all outcomes have the same chance of occurring, such as tossing fair coins or number cubes. In other words, the outcomes are equally likely.

Theoretical Probability

$$\frac{\text{number of ways event can occur}}{\text{total number of possible outcomes}}$$

12-1 Organizer

Pacing: Traditional 1 day
Block $\frac{1}{2}$ day

Objective: Students estimate the likelihood of an event and write and compare probabilities.

PREMIER **Online Edition**
Tutorial Videos, Interactivities

Power Presentations with PowerPoint®

Warm Up

Write each fraction as a decimal and as a percent.

1. $\frac{3}{4}$ 0.75; 75%

2. $\frac{1}{2}$ 0.50, 50%

3. $\frac{2}{9}$ $0.\overline{2}$; 22.2%

4. $\frac{3}{8}$ 0.375; 37.5%

Problem of the Day

What fraction of the numbers from 0 to 99 are divisible by 3? $\frac{34}{100}$, or $\frac{17}{50}$

Also available on transparency

Math Humor

Did you hear the joke about the statistician? probably

12-1 Introduction to Probability

Learn to estimate the likelihood of an event and to write and compare probabilities.

Vocabulary
probability

Georgia Performance Standards

M6D2.b Determine, and use a ratio to represent, the theoretical probability of a given event. Also, M6N1.f, M6P4.a, M6P4.b, M6P5.c.

The weather report gives a 5% chance of rain today. Will you wear your raincoat? What if the report gives a 95% chance of rain?

In this situation, you are using probability to help make a decision. **Probability** is the measure of how likely an event is to occur. In this case, both 5% and 95% are probabilities of rain.

Probabilities are written as fractions or decimals from 0 to 1 or as percents from 0% to 100%. The higher an event's probability, the more likely that event is to happen.

- Events with a probability of 0, or 0%, never happen.
- Events with a probability of 1, or 100%, always happen.
- Events with a probability of 0.5, or 50%, have the same chance of happening as of not happening.

Impossible	Unlikely	As likely as not	Likely	Certain
0 0%		0.5 $\frac{1}{2}$ 50%		1 100%

A 95% chance of rain means rain is highly likely. A 5% chance of rain means rain is highly unlikely.

EXAMPLE 1 Estimating the Likelihood of an Event

Helpful Hint
A standard number cube is numbered from 1 to 6.

Write *impossible, unlikely, as likely as not, likely,* or *certain* to describe each event.

A **The month of June has 30 days.**
certain

B **A coin toss comes up heads.**
as likely as not

C **You roll a 9 on a standard number cube.**
impossible

D **This spinner lands on red.**
likely

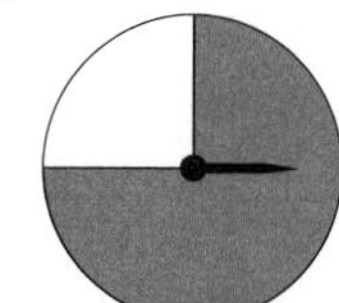

Georgia Performance Standards

M6N1.f Use fractions, decimals, and percents interchangeably.

M6D2.b Determine, and use a ratio to represent, the theoretical probability of a given event.

M6P4.a Recognize and use connections among mathematical ideas.

M6P4.b Understand how mathematical ideas interconnect and build on one another to produce a coherent whole.

M6P5.c Use representations to model and interpret physical, social, and mathematical phenomena.

1 Introduce

Alternate Opener

EXPLORATION

12-1 Introduction to Probability

Probability describes how likely it is that an event will occur. For example, it is likely that a dog will eat a treat, and it is unlikely that a human being will live 200 years.

Tell whether each event is likely or unlikely to happen.

	Event	Probability
1.	Having a blackout during a thunderstorm	
2.	Losing your money in an old vending machine	
3.	Winning the lottery	
4.	Finding a $100 bill on the street	
5.	Passing a test for which you studied very hard	
6.	Being in a traffic jam at 5:00 P.M. on Monday	
7.	Hearing your favorite song when you first turn on the radio	

Think and Discuss

8. Describe an event that is impossible.
9. Describe an event that is certain to happen.

Motivate

To introduce students to probability, ask students to roll a number cube 6 times and record each of the 6 outcomes. Discuss and compare the outcomes to introduce the concept of probability. If the activity is done in small groups, collect outcome data from each group for comparison.

Explorations and answers are provided in *Alternate Openers: Explorations Transparencies.*

EXAMPLE 2 Writing Probabilities

A **The weather report gives a 35% chance of rain for tomorrow. Write this probability as a decimal and as a fraction.**

$35\% = 0.35$ *Write as a decimal.*

$35\% = \frac{35}{100} = \frac{7}{20}$ *Write as a fraction in simplest form.*

B **The chance that Ethan is chosen to represent his class in the student council is 0.6. Write this probability as a fraction and as a percent.**

$0.6 = \frac{6}{10} = \frac{3}{5}$ *Write as a fraction in simplest form.*

$0.6 = 60\%$ *Write as a percent.*

C **There is a $\frac{9}{25}$ chance of getting a green gumball out of a certain machine. Write this probability as a decimal and as a percent.**

$\frac{9}{25} = 9 \div 25 = 0.36$ *Write as a decimal.*

$\frac{9}{25} = \frac{9 \cdot 4}{25 \cdot 4} = \frac{36}{100} = 36\%$ *Write as a percent.*

Helpful Hint

In Example 2C, after you find the decimal form of $\frac{9}{25}$, you can use it to find the percent.

$0.36 = 36\%$

EXAMPLE 3 Comparing Probabilities

A **On a flowering plant called the four o'clock, there is a 50% chance the flowers will be pink, a 25% chance the flowers will be white, and a 25% chance the flowers will be red. Is it more likely that the flowers will be pink or white?**

Compare: $50\% > 25\%$

The flowers are more likely to be pink than white.

B **When you spin this spinner, there is a 25% chance that it will land on red, a 50% chance that it will land on yellow, and a 25% chance that it will land on blue. Is it more likely to land on red or on blue?**

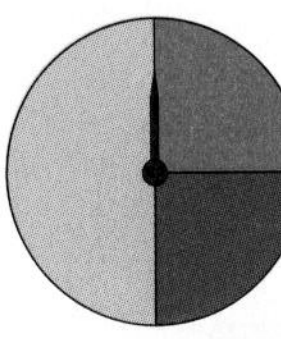

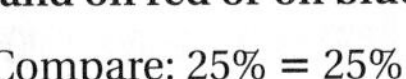

Compare: $25\% = 25\%$

It is as likely to land on red as on blue.

Possible answers to *Think and Discuss:*

1. playing a board game
2. impossible: a cat will fly; likely: I will get an A on my report card; as likely as not: I flip a coin and it lands heads up; unlikely: it will snow in Florida; certain: the sun will rise tomorrow.

Think and Discuss

GPS M6P3.a, M6P3.b

1. **Give an example** of a situation that involves probability.
2. **Name** events that can be described by each of the following terms: *impossible, likely, as likely as not, unlikely,* and *certain.*

Power Presentations with PowerPoint®

Additional Examples

Example 1

Write *impossible, unlikely, as likely as not, likely,* or *certain* to describe each event.

A. You roll an even number on a standard number cube. as likely as not

B. February has 28 days. certain

C. A spinner is equally divided into green, blue, yellow, and red. The spinner lands on blue. unlikely

D. A spinner with sectors labeled 2, 4, 6, 8, and 10 lands on an odd number. impossible

Example 2

A. Write the probability 75% as a decimal and as a fraction. $0.75, \frac{3}{4}$

B. Write the probability 0.8 as a fraction and as a percent. $\frac{4}{5}$, 80%

C. Write the probability $\frac{7}{50}$ as a decimal and as a percent. 0.14, 14%

Example 3

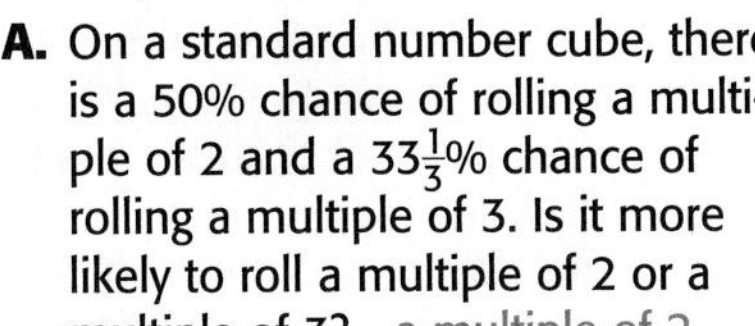

A. On a standard number cube, there is a 50% chance of rolling a multiple of 2 and a $33\frac{1}{3}\%$ chance of rolling a multiple of 3. Is it more likely to roll a multiple of 2 or a multiple of 3? a multiple of 2

B. When you spin a certain spinner, it has a 15% chance of landing on yellow, a 15% chance of landing on green, and a 70% chance of landing on purple. Is it more likely to land on purple or green? land on purple

Also available on transparency

2 Teach

Guided Instruction

ENGLISH LANGUAGE LEARNERS

In this lesson, students learn to estimate the likelihood of an event and to write and compare probabilities. Define the term *probability,* and explain the terms *impossible, unlikely, as likely as not, likely,* and *certain.* Have students express given probabilities as decimals, fractions, and percents. Then teach students how to compare given probabilities to determine which is more likely.

Teaching Tip

Inclusion Review with students how to express numbers as decimals, fractions, and percents.

Reaching All Learners

Through Cooperative Learning

Have students in groups discuss probabilities of events in other school subjects. Examples: "It is certain that we will have a spelling test on Friday." "It is likely that we will run laps in physical education." "It is impossible for humans to live without H_2O."

3 Close

Summarize

Review probability concepts presented in the lesson and the likelihood of different events.

12-1 Exercises

Assignment Guide

If you finished Example 1 assign:
Average 1–2, 12–18, 23–32
Advanced 5–8, 14–18, 23–32

If you finished Example 2 assign:
Average 1–3, 12–18, 23–32
Advanced 5–9, 15–18, 23–32

If you finished Example 3 assign:
Average 1–11, 16–32
Advanced 5–32

Homework Quick Check

Quickly check key concepts.
Exercises: 6, 8, 10, 16

Math Background

The study of probability has its origins in problems that arise in games of chance. Most famous among these is known as the "problem of the points."

The problem of the points involves the question of how to divide the stakes in an interrupted game of chance between two equally skilled players, knowing the scores of the players and the number of points needed to win. In 1654, Blaise Pascal and Pierre de Fermat established a correspondence in which they discussed the problem and solved it correctly, but differently. This correspondence is considered the foundation of the mathematical study of probability.

Georgia Performance Standards

M6P1.a Build new mathematical knowledge through problem solving.

M6P3.a Organize and consolidate their mathematical thinking through communication.

M6P4.c Recognize and apply mathematics in contexts outside of mathematics.

12-1 Exercises

M6P1.a, M6P3.a, M6P4.c

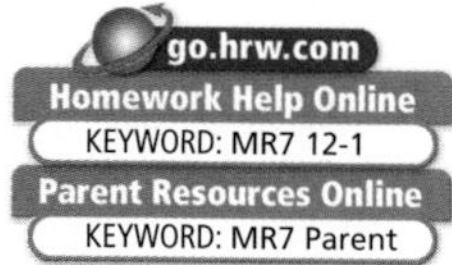

GUIDED PRACTICE

See Example 1

Write *impossible, unlikely, as likely as not, likely,* or *certain* to describe each event.

1. This year has 12 months. certain
2. You win the lottery. unlikely

See Example 2

3. Suppose that the chance of reaching into a bag of coins and selecting a quarter is 40%. Write this probability as a decimal and as a fraction. 0.4, $\frac{2}{5}$

See Example 3

4. If there are two children in a family, there is a 25% chance that both children are boys, a 25% chance that both children are girls, and a 50% chance that one child is a boy and the other is a girl. Which is more likely, that both children are boys or that one child is a boy and the other is a girl? boy and girl

INDEPENDENT PRACTICE

See Example 1

Write *impossible, unlikely, as likely as not, likely,* or *certain* to describe each event.

5. The spinner at right lands on green. likely
6. The spinner at right lands on blue. impossible
7. You guess one winning number between 1 and 500. unlikely
8. You correctly guess one of eight winning numbers between 1 and 10. likely

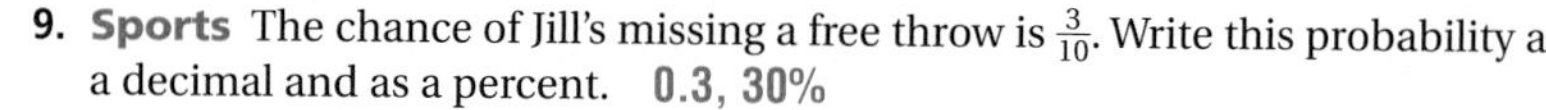

See Example 2

9. **Sports** The chance of Jill's missing a free throw is $\frac{3}{10}$. Write this probability as a decimal and as a percent. 0.3, 30%

See Example 3

10. The probability of Daniel randomly selecting a long-sleeved shirt from his closet is 0.20. Write this probability as a fraction and a percent. $\frac{1}{5}$, 20%
11. If you choose from a bag of mixed nuts, there is a 45% chance of choosing a peanut, a 20% chance of choosing a pecan, a 15% chance of choosing a cashew, and a 20% chance of choosing a walnut. Is it less likely that you will choose a pecan or a cashew from the bag? cashew

PRACTICE AND PROBLEM SOLVING

Extra Practice p. 737

Describe the events as *impossible, unlikely, as likely as not, likely,* or *certain.*

12. The probability of winning a game is $\frac{2}{3}$. likely
13. The probability of being chosen for a team is 0.09. unlikely
14. There is a 50% chance of snow today. as likely as not
15. Your chances of being struck by lightning are $\frac{1}{2,000,000}$. unlikely
16. **Critical Thinking** Why is the event *It will be Saturday in one of the next 7 days* certain? There is always a Saturday in a 7 day week.

RETEACH 12-1

LESSON 12-1 **Reteach**
Introduction to Probability

Probability is the measure of how likely it is that an event will occur.

You can write the probability of an event as a fraction or decimal from 0 to 1, or as a percent from 0% to 100%, inclusive.

The probability of tossing a penny and it landing on heads is $\frac{1}{2}$.

To write the probability as a decimal, divide the numerator by the denominator.

$1 \div 2 = 0.5$ The probability of landing on heads is 0.5.

To write the probability as a percent, first write the fraction as a decimal. Then move the decimal point two places to the right.

$1 \div 2 = 0.5 = 50\%$ The probability of landing on heads is 50%.

Write the probability.

1. The probability of Joy winning the race is 0.4. Write this probability as a fraction and as a percent.
   $\frac{2}{5}$, 40%

The higher the probability, the more likely the event is to occur.

Events with a probability of 0 or 0% never happen.
Events with a probability of 1 or 100% always happen.

Events with a probability of $\frac{1}{2}$, 0.5, or 50%, have the same chance of happening as of not happening.

If you have a bag of red marbles and blue marbles, the probability of pulling out a green marble is 0. The event is impossible because there are no green marbles in the bag.

Write *impossible, unlikely, as likely as not, likely,* or *certain* to describe each event.

2. A week has seven days. certain
3. Rolling a 7 on a standard number cube. impossible

PRACTICE 12-1

LESSON 12-1 **Practice B**
Introduction to Probability

Write *impossible, unlikely, as likely as not, likely,* or *certain* to describe each event.

1. landing on blue likely
2. landing on green impossible
3. landing on red unlikely
4. landing on blue or red certain
5. You will spin the spinner clockwise.
   as likely as not

blue red blue blue blue

Write each probability as a decimal and as a fraction.

6. There is a 10% chance of rain tomorrow. 0.1, $\frac{1}{10}$
7. There is a 75% chance of snow tomorrow. 0.75, $\frac{3}{4}$
8. There is a 25% chance of hail tomorrow. 0.25, $\frac{1}{4}$

Compare probabilities.

Prize Winning Probabilities	
Color TV	17%
DVD player	22%
Watch	13%
Stereo	21%
Diamond ring	27%

9. Are you more likely to win a color TV or a watch?
   a color TV
10. Are you more likely to win a DVD player or a stereo?
   a DVD player
11. Are you more likely to win a diamond ring, a DVD player, or a stereo?
   a diamond ring
12. A bag has 4 red marbles, 3 blue marbles, 4 green marbles, and 1 black marble. Which term best describes the probability of picking a black marble from the bag: impossible, likely, as likely as not, unlikely, or impossible?
   unlikely

Life Science LINK

Each year, millions of people donate blood.

There are eight different human blood types, which are shown in the chart, along with the percent of people who have each type. It is very important that people receive the right type of blood. If they do not, their bodies will not recognize the foreign blood cells and will attack the cells.

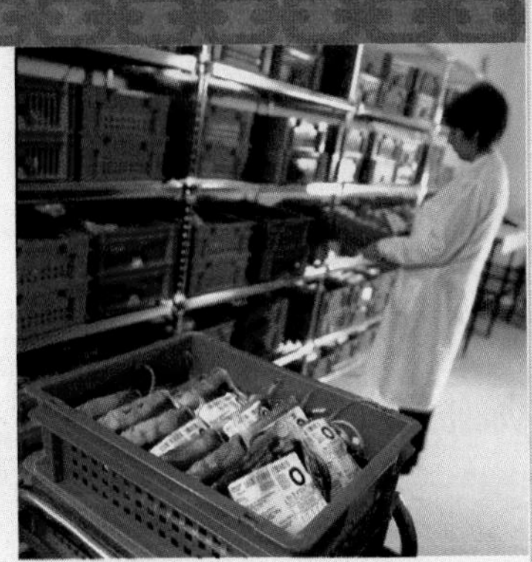

The donated blood in these bags is Type O.

17. How would you describe the probability of a person having AB positive blood: impossible, unlikely, as likely as not, likely, or certain? Explain. **unlikely; 3 people out of 100 could have AB positive blood.**

18. If a person is randomly chosen, which blood type is he or she most likely to have? **O positive**

19. If a person is randomly chosen, which blood type is he or she least likely to have? **AB negative**

20. Write the probability that a randomly chosen person will have A negative blood as a decimal and as a fraction in simplest form. **0.06; $\frac{3}{50}$**

21. **Write About It** Blood banks especially encourage people with certain types of blood to donate. Which blood types do you think these are? Explain.

22. **Challenge** A person with AB positive blood can safely receive O, A, B, or AB blood. What is the probability that a randomly chosen person could donate blood to a person with AB positive blood? **probability of 1**

Blood Types in the United States

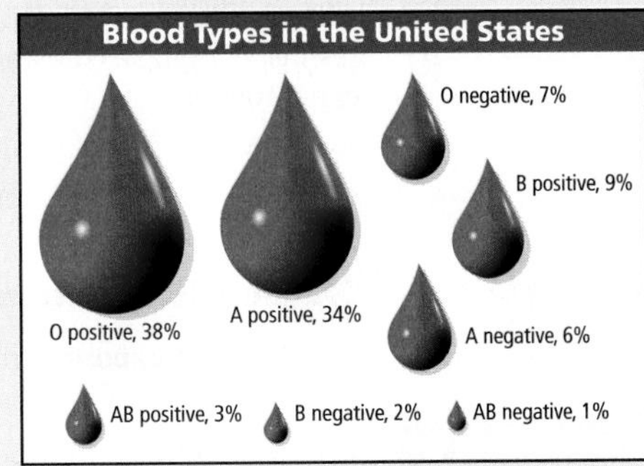

CRCT Prep • GPS Support • Spiral Review

23. **Multiple Choice** Eddie has a $\frac{9}{20}$ chance of winning the election. What is the probability of Eddie winning the election written as a percent?

Ⓐ 0.45 Ⓑ 0.55 **Ⓒ 45%** Ⓓ 55%

24. **Gridded Response** There is a $\frac{7}{10}$ chance of rain today. What is this probability written as a decimal? **0.7**

Write the prime factorization of each number. (Lesson 4-2)

25. 76 **$2^2 \times 19$** **26.** 12 **$2^2 \times 3$** **27.** 16 **2^4** **28.** 18 **2×3^2** **29.** 128 **2^7**

Find each missing value to the nearest hundredth. Use 3.14 for π. (Lesson 9-8)

30. $d = 2$ in.; $C = ?$ **6.28 in.** **31.** $r = 5$ cm; $C = ?$ **31.4 cm** **32.** $C = 28.26\ m$; $d = ?$ **9 m**

CHALLENGE 12-1

LESSON 12-1 **Challenge**
Shark!

If you are like most people, you think sharks are scary. People have feared these ancient creatures for thousands of years.

But we actually have little to fear—statistically speaking, that is. Sharks rarely attack people. In fact, you have a greater chance of being killed by a bee than by a shark! Still, knowing the probability of where most sharks attack might make your next trip to the beach a little more relaxing. Or will it?

The Great White shark is one of the 25 species of sharks known to attack people. It has about 3,000 razor-sharp teeth!

Complete the tables below to describe the probabilities of where shark attacks are most likely to occur.

Where Sharks Attack People

Location of Attack (feet from shore)	Probability Fraction	Probability Percent
0–50	$\frac{31}{100}$	31%
51–100	$\frac{11}{100}$	11%
101–150	$\frac{3}{50}$	6%
151–200	$\frac{3}{100}$	3%
201–5,200	$\frac{27}{100}$	27%
Farther than 5,201	$\frac{11}{50}$	22%

1. How many feet from shore do most sharks attack people?
   0–50 feet
2. Why do you think this is the most likely location for attacks?
   Possible answer: because most people swim close to shore

PROBLEM SOLVING 12-1

LESSON 12-1 **Problem Solving**
Introduction to Probability

Floods are categorized by their probability of occurrence. For example, a flood categorized as a 20-year flood means it has a 1 in 20 chance of occurring in any given year. Complete the flood probability chart below. Then use it to answer the questions. Write answers in simplest form.

Flood Probabilities of Occurrence

	Category	Probability Fraction	Probability Decimal	Probability Percent
1.	2-year flood	$\frac{1}{2}$	0.5	50%
2.	5-year flood	$\frac{1}{5}$	0.2	20%
3.	10-year flood	$\frac{1}{10}$	0.1	10%
4.	50-year flood	$\frac{1}{50}$	0.02	2%
5.	100-year flood	$\frac{1}{100}$	0.01	1%

6. Which flood category in the table is the most likely to occur in a given year? The least likely?
   most: 2-year flood;
   least: 100-year flood
7. Following the naming system in the table, what category name would you use for a flood that is certain to occur in any given year?
   A a 1-week flood
   B a 1-month flood
   Ⓒ a 1-year flood
   D a 3-year flood
8. The Yukon River in Alaska had a 100-year flood in 1992. Does this mean that another 100-year flood could not occur on the Yukon River until 2092? Explain.
   No; The probability of occurrence is always 1%.
9. The Mississippi River system had a rare 500-year flood in 1993. What is the percent of probability that another 500-year flood will occur on the Mississippi River system next year?
   F 2%
   Ⓖ 0.2%
   H 0.02%
   J 0.002%

Ongoing Assessment and Intervention

Diagnose **Before** the Lesson
12-1 Warm Up, TE p. 668

Monitor **During** the Lesson
12-1 Know-It Notebook
12-1 Questioning Strategies

Assess **After** the Lesson
12-1 Lesson Quiz, TE p. 671

Interdisciplinary LINK

Life Science

Exercises 17–22 involve questions about the distribution of human blood types. Students learn about blood types in middle school science programs such as *Holt Science and Technology*.

Answer

21. See p. A12.

Test Prep Doctor In Exercise 23, choices **A** and **B** can be eliminated because they are not written as percents. Choice **D** can be eliminated because $\frac{9}{20}$ is less than $\frac{1}{2}$ and 55% is greater than $\frac{1}{2}$.

Journal

Have students write a description of a spinner that, when spun, has an outcome that is always certain.

Power Presentations with PowerPoint®

12-1 Lesson Quiz

Write *impossible, unlikely, equally likely, likely,* or *certain* to describe each event.

1. The sun will rise tomorrow. certain
2. You will roll 13 when rolling two dice. impossible
3. There is a 0.125 chance of picking the winning ticket. Write this probability as a fraction and as a percent. $\frac{1}{8}$, 12.5%
4. At Hamburger Hut, there is a 20% chance of getting a plastic dinosaur cup and a 35% chance of getting a plastic rabbit cup. Is it less likely that you will receive a rabbit cup or dinosaur cup? dinosaur cup

Also available on transparency

12-2 Organizer

Pacing: Traditional 1 day
Block $\frac{1}{2}$ day

Objective: Students find the experimental probability of an event.

GPS **M6D2.a**
Technology Lab
In *Technology Lab Activities*

Online Edition
Tutorial Videos, Interactivities

Power Presentations with PowerPoint®

Warm Up

Write *impossible, unlikely, equally likely, likely,* or *certain* to describe each event.

1. A particular person's birthday falls on the first of a month. unlikely
2. You roll an odd number on a fair number cube. equally likely
3. There is a 0.14 probability of picking the winning ticket. Write this as a fraction and as a percent. $\frac{7}{50}$, 14%

Problem of the Day

Max picks a letter out of this problem at random. What is the probability that the letter is in the first half of the alphabet? $\frac{57}{101}$

Also available on transparency

Math Fact

Ars Conjectandi was the first book devoted entirely to probability. It was written by Jacques Bernoulli in 1713.

Georgia Performance Standards

M6D2.a Predict the probability of a given event through trials/simulations (experimental probability), and represent the probability as a ratio.

M6P1.b Solve problems that arise in mathematics and in other contexts.

M6P4.c Recognize and apply mathematics in contexts outside of mathematics.

12-2 Experimental Probability

Learn to find the experimental probability of an event.

Vocabulary
experiment
outcome
experimental probability

Four Possibilities

An **experiment** is an activity involving chance that can have different results. Flipping a coin and spinning a spinner are examples of experiments.

The different results that can occur are called **outcomes** of the experiment. If you are flipping a coin, heads is one possible outcome.

EXAMPLE 1 Identifying Outcomes

Georgia Performance Standards
M6D2.a Predict the probability of a given event through trials/simulations. Also, M6P1.b, M6P4.c.

For each experiment, identify the outcome shown.

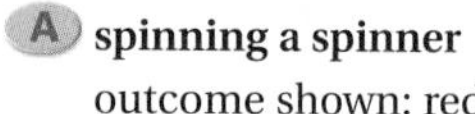

A spinning a spinner
outcome shown: red

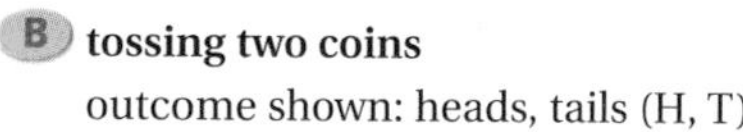

B tossing two coins
outcome shown: heads, tails (H, T)

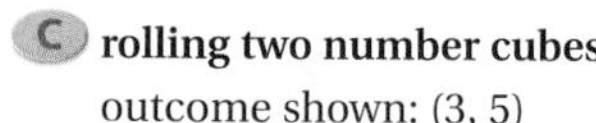

C rolling two number cubes
outcome shown: (3, 5)

Performing an experiment is one way to estimate the probability of an event. If an experiment is repeated many times, the **experimental probability** of an event is the ratio of the number of times the event occurs to the total number of times the experiment is performed.

EXPERIMENTAL PROBABILITY

$$\text{probability} \approx \frac{\text{number of times the event occurs}}{\text{total number of trials}}$$

1 Introduce

Alternate Opener

EXPLORATION

12-2 Experimental Probability

You can find the ***experimental probability*** of an event by dividing the number of times an event occurs by the total number of times the experiment is performed.

$$\text{probability} = \frac{\text{number of times an event occurs}}{\text{total number of trials}}$$

1. The data in the table show the number of free throws five players made in a season. Find the $\frac{\text{made}}{\text{attempts}}$ ratio for each player.

	Bo	Jack	Ali	Kim	José
Free Throws Made	30	32	15	36	24
Attempts	48	64	25	48	49
$\frac{\text{Made}}{\text{Attempts}}$					

2. Which player has the best chance of making a free throw?
3. Which player has the worst chance of making a free throw?

Think and Discuss

4. **Discuss** how you determined the answers for numbers 2 and 3.
5. **Explain** how to write each $\frac{\text{made}}{\text{attempts}}$ ratio as a percent.

Motivate

ENGLISH LANGUAGE LEARNERS

Review the term *probability* and the different likelihoods of events (e.g., unlikely, certain, etc.). Remind students that probability can be expressed as a fraction, decimal, or percent. Have them express $\frac{1}{4}$ as a percent and as a decimal. 25%; 0.25

Explorations and answers are provided in *Alternate Openers: Explorations Transparencies.*

EXAMPLE 2 Finding Experimental Probability

For one month, Tosha recorded the time at which her school bus arrived. She organized her results in a frequency table.

Time	7:00–7:04	7:05–7:09	7:10–7:15
Frequency	8	9	3

Writing Math

The probability of an event can be written as *P*(event). *P*(blue) means "the probability that blue will be the outcome."

A **Find the experimental probability that the bus will arrive between 7:00 and 7:04.**

$$P(\text{between 7:00 and 7:04}) \approx \frac{\text{number of times the event occurs}}{\text{total number of trials}}$$

$$= \frac{8}{20} = \frac{2}{5}$$

B **Find the experimental probability that the bus will arrive before 7:10.**

$$P(\text{before 7:10}) \approx \frac{\text{number of times the event occurs}}{\text{total number of trials}}$$

$$= \frac{8+9}{20}$$ *Before 7:10 includes 7:00–7:04 and 7:05–7:09.*

$$= \frac{17}{20}$$

EXAMPLE 3 Comparing Experimental Probabilities

Ian tossed a cone 30 times and recorded whether it landed on its base or on its side. Based on Ian's experiment, which way is the cone more likely to land?

On its side

On its base

Outcome	On its base	On its side
Frequency	𝍸 ll	𝍸 𝍸 𝍸 𝍸 lll

$$P(\text{base}) \approx \frac{\text{number of times the event occurs}}{\text{total number of trials}} = \frac{7}{30}$$

$$P(\text{side}) \approx \frac{\text{number of times the event occurs}}{\text{total number of trials}} = \frac{23}{30}$$

Find the experimental probability of each outcome.

$$\frac{7}{30} < \frac{23}{30}$$ *Compare the probabilities.*

It is more likely that the cone will land on its side.

Possible answers to *Think and Discuss:*

1. Not necessarily: even though the outcomes have the same chances of happening, they may not occur the same number of times.
2. Each time you repeat the experiment you will probably get slightly different results. The more times you repeat the experiment, the closer your experiments probablility will get to the actual probability.

Think and Discuss

GPS M6P2.b, M6P3.b

1. **Explain** whether you and a friend will get the same experimental probability for an event if you perform the same experiment.
2. **Tell** why it is important to repeat an experiment many times.

Power Presentations with PowerPoint®

Additional Examples

Example 1

For each experiment, identify the outcome shown.

A. tossing two coins

tails, heads (T, H)

B. rolling two number cubes

(2, 6)

Example 2

For one month, Mr. Crowe recorded the time at which his train arrived. He organized his results in a frequency table.

Time	6:50–6:52	6:53–6:56	6:57–7:00
Freq.	7	8	5

A. Find the experimental probability of the train arriving between 6:57 and 7:00. $\frac{1}{4}$

B. Find the experimental probability of the train arriving before 6:57. $\frac{3}{4}$

Example 3

Erika tossed a cylinder 30 times and recorded whether it landed on one of its bases or on its side. According to Erika's experiment, which way is the cylinder more likely to land?

Outcome	On a base	On its side
Freq.	𝍸 llll	𝍸 𝍸 𝍸 𝍸 l

more likely to land on its side

Also available on transparency

2 Teach

Guided Instruction

In this lesson, students learn to find the experimental probability of an event. Introduce the new vocabulary for the lesson: *experiment, outcome,* and *experimental probability*. Emphasize that finding experimental probability requires you to do an experiment and collect data or use existing data. Teach students to express experimental probability as a fraction and to compare experimental probabilities.

Reaching All Learners

Through Kinesthetic Experience

Give students spinners divided into 5 equal sections labeled 1–5 (provided in the Manipulatives Kit). Have each student conduct 20 trials with the spinner, recording the outcomes in a tally table. Then have them write the experimental probability for each outcome and then compare the probabilities to determine which, if any, outcome is more likely.

3 Close

Summarize

ENGLISH LANGUAGE LEARNERS

Review the new vocabulary: *experiment, outcome,* and *experimental probability.* Give the students examples of a given experiment, and review how to find *experimental probability*.

12-2 Exercises

Assignment Guide

If you finished Example 1 assign:
Average 1, 9–10, 15–22
Advanced 4–5, 10, 15–22

If you finished Example 2 assign:
Average 1–2, 9–11, 15–22
Advanced 4–7, 11, 15–22

If you finished Example 3 assign:
Average 1–8, 12–22
Advanced 4–22

Homework Quick Check

Quickly check key concepts.
Exercises: 4, 6, 8, 12

Math Background

When you are calculating experimental probability, it is crucial that you repeat the experiment many times. When an experiment is repeated under essentially unchanged conditions, *statistical regularity* occurs. Under statistical regularity, the experimental probability of an event varies less and less as the number of trials in an experiment increases.

An example can help make this clear. If a coin were tossed 10 times, it would not be unusual for it to land heads up 7 times. However, if the same coin were tossed 1,000 times and it landed heads up 700 times, you would probably conclude that the coin was unfair.

Georgia Performance Standards

M6D2.c Discover that experimental probability approaches theoretical probability when the number of trials is large.

M6P3.a Organize and consolidate their mathematical thinking through communication.

12-2 Exercises

M6D2.c, M6P3.a

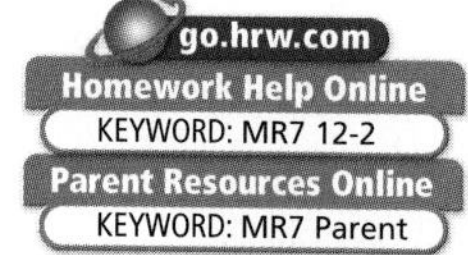

go.hrw.com
Homework Help Online
KEYWORD: MR7 12-2
Parent Resources Online
KEYWORD: MR7 Parent

GUIDED PRACTICE

See Example 1 **1.** Identify the outcome shown on the spinner. 6

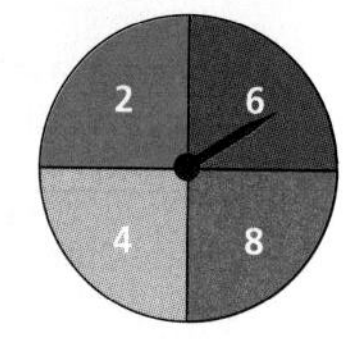

Sports Josh recorded the number of hits his favorite baseball player made in each of 15 games. He organized his results in a frequency table.

Number of Hits	0	1	2	3
Frequency	4	8	2	1

See Example 2 **2.** Find the experimental probability that this player will get one hit in a game. $\frac{8}{15}$

See Example 3 **3.** Based on Josh's results, is this player more likely to get two hits in a game or no hits in a game? How many hits will this player most likely get in a game? no hits; 1 hit

INDEPENDENT PRACTICE

See Example 1 For each experiment, identify the outcome shown.

4.

4

5.

HTH

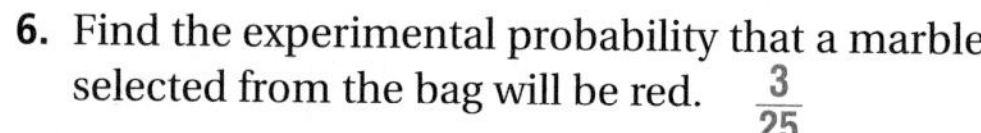

Jennifer has a bag of marbles. She removed one marble, recorded the color, and placed it back in the bag. She repeated this process several times and recorded her results in the table.

Color	Frequency
White	𝍸
Red	|||
Yellow	𝍸
Black	𝍸 𝍸 ||

See Example 2 **6.** Find the experimental probability that a marble selected from the bag will be red. $\frac{3}{25}$

7. Find the experimental probability that a marble selected from the bag will not be black. $\frac{13}{25}$

See Example 3 **8.** Based on Jennifer's experiment, which color marble is she most likely to select from the bag? black

PRACTICE AND PROBLEM SOLVING

Extra Practice p. 737

Identify the outcome for each situation.

9. yellow

10. 4

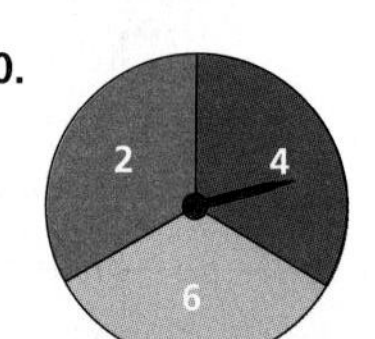

RETEACH 12-2

LESSON 12-2 **Reteach**
Experimental Probability

An experiment is an activity involving chance that can have different results. Rolling a standard number cube is an experiment.

The different results that are possible are called the outcomes of an experiment. If you are rolling a standard number cube, 5 is one possible outcome.

Identify the outcome shown.

1. spinning a spinner — 3

2. tossing a coin — heads

If you perform an experiment many times, you can estimate the probability of an event.

To find the experimental probability of an event, use a formula.

probability $\approx \frac{\text{number of times the event occurs}}{\text{total number of trials}}$

Suppose you rolled a standard number cube 20 times and it landed on 5 six times. The probability of rolling a 5 is

$P(\text{rolling } 5) \approx \frac{6}{20} = \frac{3}{10}$

Find the experimental probability of each event.

Pulling Marbles Out of a Bag

Red	Blue	Green
𝍸 ||||	𝍸		𝍸

3. The experimental probability of pulling out a red marble. $\frac{9}{20}$

4. The experimental probability of pulling out a green marble. $\frac{1}{4}$

PRACTICE 12-2

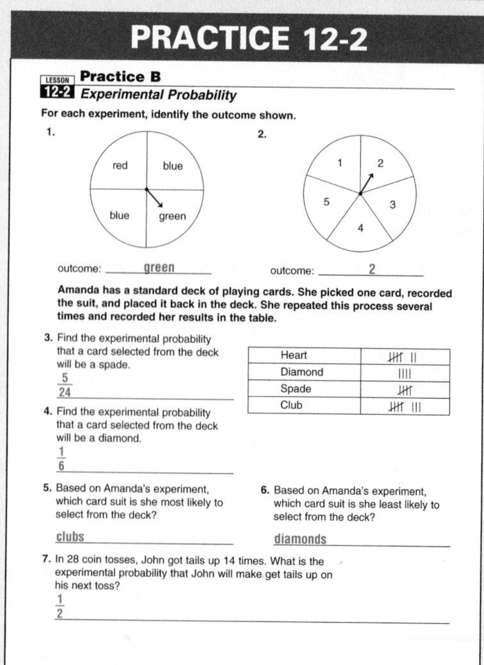

LESSON 12-2 **Practice B**
Experimental Probability

For each experiment, identify the outcome shown.

1. outcome: green

2. outcome: 2

Amanda has a standard deck of playing cards. She picked one card, recorded the suit, and placed it back in the deck. She repeated this process several times and recorded her results in the table.

Heart	𝍸 ||
Diamond	||||
Spade	𝍸
Club	𝍸 |||

3. Find the experimental probability that a card selected from the deck will be a spade. $\frac{5}{24}$

4. Find the experimental probability that a card selected from the deck will be a diamond. $\frac{1}{6}$

5. Based on Amanda's experiment, which card suit is she most likely to select from the deck? clubs

6. Based on Amanda's experiment, which card suit is she least likely to select from the deck? diamonds

7. In 28 coin tosses, John got tails up 14 times. What is the experimental probability that John will make get tails up on his next toss? $\frac{1}{2}$

11. **Weather** Janet recorded the high temperature every day in January. She recorded her results in a frequency table.

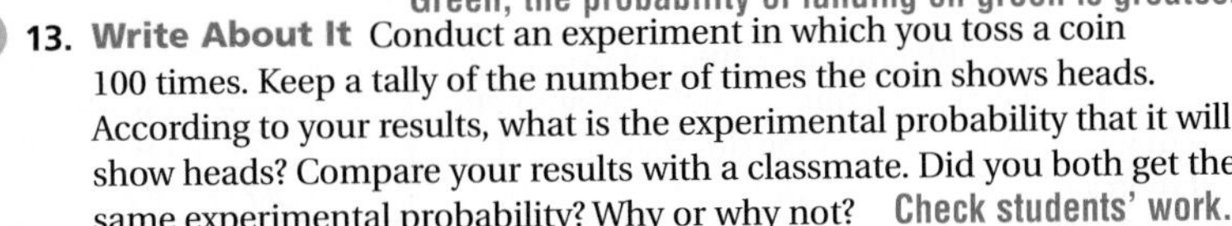

Temperature (°F)	26–35	36–45	46–55	56–65
Number of Days	10	9	11	1

According to Janet's results, what is the probability that a day in January will be warmer than 55°F? Describe this probability as certain, likely, as likely as not, unlikely, or impossible. $\frac{1}{31}$; unlikely

12. Mariana recorded the results of spinning a spinner with 3 sections.

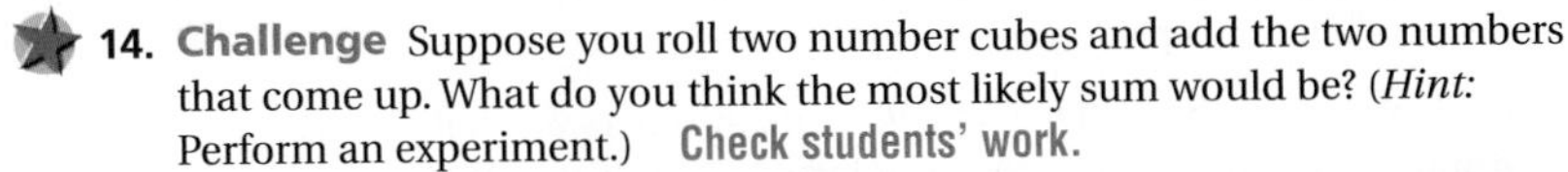

Outcome	Red	Blue	Green
Spins	25	19	56

a. Use the results in the table to find the experimental probability of the spinner landing on each color. 25%, 19%, 56%

b. Which section of the spinner do you think might be the greatest? Explain. Green; the probability of landing on green is greatest.

13. **Write About It** Conduct an experiment in which you toss a coin 100 times. Keep a tally of the number of times the coin shows heads. According to your results, what is the experimental probability that it will show heads? Compare your results with a classmate. Did you both get the same experimental probability? Why or why not? Check students' work.

14. **Challenge** Suppose you roll two number cubes and add the two numbers that come up. What do you think the most likely sum would be? (*Hint:* Perform an experiment.) Check students' work.

CRCT Prep • GPS Support • Spiral Review

15. **Multiple Choice** Identify the outcome shown on the spinner.

Ⓐ blue
Ⓒ red
Ⓑ green
Ⓓ yellow

16. **Multiple Choice** Sam plays baseball. Five of his games started at 5:00 P.M. Four started at 5:15 P.M. One started at 5:45 P.M. What is the experimental probability that his next game will start at 5:00 P.M.?

Ⓕ $\frac{1}{10}$ Ⓖ $\frac{2}{5}$ Ⓗ $\frac{1}{2}$ Ⓙ $\frac{9}{10}$

Evaluate each expression for $x = 5$. (Lesson 2-1)

17. $x + 7$ 12
18. $4x$ 20
19. $3x + 6$ 21
20. $x + 5$ 10
21. $2x - 7$ 3

22. Arthur has a 91% chance of making a free throw. His brother Lance has a 93% chance of making a free throw. Is it more likely that Arthur or Lance will make the free throw? (Lesson 12-1) Lance

Ongoing Assessment and Intervention

Diagnose Before the Lesson
12-2 Warm Up, TE p. 672

Monitor During the Lesson
12-2 Know-It Notebook
12-2 Questioning Strategies

Assess After the Lesson
12-2 Lesson Quiz, TE p. 675

Test Prep Doctor Students who chose **F** for Exercise 16 may have mistakenly identified the probability of Sam's next game starting at 5:45 P.M. Those who chose **G** may have mistakenly identified the probability of his next game starting at 5:15 P.M. Those who chose **J** may have mistakenly identified the probability of his next game not starting at 5:45 P.M.

Journal

Have students write a real-world problem similar to the one in Example 3.

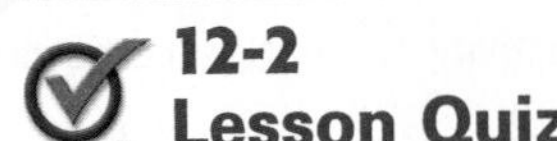

12-2 Lesson Quiz

1. The spinner below was spun. Identify the outcome shown. outcome: green

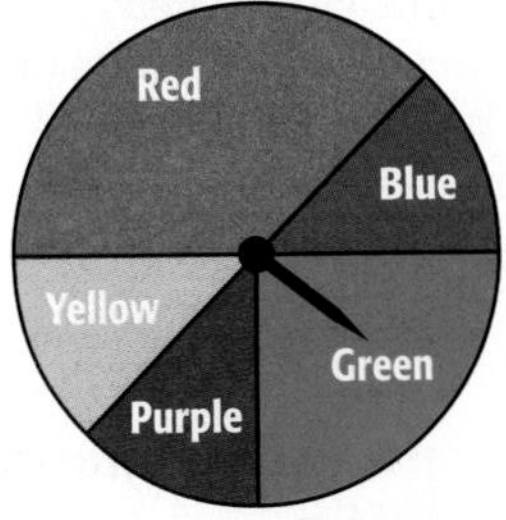

Sandra spun the spinner above several times and recorded the results in the table.

Color	Red	Blue	Green	Purple	Yellow
Freq.	4	2	1	2	0

2. Find the experimental probability that the spinner will land on blue. $\frac{2}{9}$

3. Find the experimental probability that the spinner will land on red. $\frac{4}{9}$

4. Based on the experiment, what is the probability that the spinner will land on red or blue? $\frac{2}{3}$

Also available on transparency

CHALLENGE 12-2

LESSON 12-2 **Challenge**
Batter Up!

A batting average is the probability of a player getting a hit. A hit is a favorable outcome.

How do you find this probability? Say Janet gets 30 hits at 100 at bats. Then her hitting probability is $\frac{30}{100}$, or 30%. This means that each time Janet steps up to the plate, she has a 30% chance of hitting the ball. For baseball, you multiply the percentages by 10 to get a batting average. So, Janet's hitting probability of 30% means her batting average is 300. Because very few professional baseball players hit above 300, you can see how hard it is to get a hit in the major leagues!

Complete the table below to find which major league player had the all-time highest career batting average. Round the decimals to the nearest thousandth.

Players with the Highest Career Batting Averages

Player	At Bats	Hits	Average
Babe Ruth	8,399	2,873	342
Ty Cobb	11,434	4,189	366
Harry Heilmann	7,787	2,660	341
Ed Delahanty	7,505	2,597	346
Ted Williams	7,706	2,654	344
Rogers Hornsby	8,173	2,930	358
Billy Hamilton	6,268	2,158	344
Joe Jackson	4,981	1,772	355
Dan Brouthers	6,711	2,296	342
Tris Speaker	10,195	3,514	344

PROBLEM SOLVING 12-2

LESSON 12-2 **Problem Solving**
Experimental Probability

Write the correct answer. Write answers in simplest form.

1. Brandy tossed a fair coin several times. She recorded the result of each toss in this table. What is the experimental probability that Brandy's next toss will land heads up?

Heads Up	卌 卌 卌 I
Tails Up	卌 卌 IIII

$\frac{8}{15}$

2. In this table, Charles recorded the gender of each person who shopped at his store this morning. What is the experimental probability that his next customer will be a woman?

Male	卌 卌 卌 卌 II
Female	卌 卌 卌 III

$\frac{9}{20}$

3. Nita packed 4 pairs of shorts for her beach vacation—a blue pair, a white pair, a denim pair, and a black pair. Without looking, she pulls out the blue pair from her suitcase. What is the outcome?

blue shorts

4. Mick rolled two number cubes at the same time. Each cube is numbered 1 through 6. The cubes showed a sum of 7. What is the outcome for this experiment?

7

Abdul recorded the number of free throws his favorite basketball player made in each of 24 games. He organized his results in this frequency table. Circle the letter of the correct answer.

Free Throws Made	0	1	2	3	4
Frequency	1	4	7	9	3

5. What is the experimental probability that this player will make 1 free throw in the next game?

A $\frac{1}{24}$
Ⓑ $\frac{1}{6}$
C $\frac{7}{24}$
D $\frac{1}{8}$

6. Based on Abdul's experiment, how many free throws will this player most likely make in any given game?

Ⓕ 3
G 4
H 0
J 2

Organizer

Use with Lesson 12-2

Pacing:

Traditional $\frac{1}{2}$ day
Block $\frac{1}{4}$ day

Objective: Use a number cube and coin to simulate probability experiments.

Materials: Number cube, coin

 **Online Edition**

Resources

 ***Hands-On Lab Activities***
Lab 12-2 Recording Sheet

Teach

Discuss

Discuss what each roll of the number cube represents and how students should record their results in the table. Then discuss what each coin toss represents and how students should record their results.

Close

Key Concept

Some difficult experiments can be simulated with a model.

Assessment

1. In activity 1, what outcome does rolling a 3 represent?
2. A student conducted the simulation in activity 1. The first 10 rolls were 4, 2, 5, 3, 4, 2, 4, 5, 2, and 1. What does her simulation tell about the actual contest? Does the simulation model a winning combination?

Georgia Performance Standards

M6D2.a Predict the probability of a given event through trials/simulations (experimental probability), and represent the probability as a ratio.

M6P2.b Make and investigate mathematical conjectures.

M6P2.c Develop and evaluate mathematical arguments and proofs.

Simulations

Use with Lesson 12-2

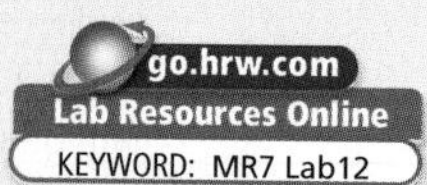

Georgia Performance Standards
M6D2.a, M6P2.b, M6P2.c

A **simulation** is a model of an experiment that would be difficult or inconvenient to actually perform. In this lab, you will conduct simulations.

Activity

A cereal company is having a contest. To win a prize, you must collect six different cards that spell *YOU WIN*. One of the six letters is put into each cereal box. The letters are divided equally among the boxes. How many boxes do you think you will have to buy to collect all six cards?

1	2	3	4	5	6
Y	O	U	W	I	N
/	~~////~~ /	////	//	//	/

1. Since there are six different cards that are evenly distributed, you can use a number cube to simulate collecting the letters. Each of the numbers from 1 to 6 will represent a letter. A roll of the number cube will simulate buying one box of cereal, and the number rolled will represent the letter inside that box.
2. Roll the number cube, and keep track of the numbers you roll. Continue to roll the number cube until you have rolled every number at least once.

Think and Discuss

1. Look at the results in the table above. What was the last number rolled? How do you know?
2. How many rolls did it take to get all six numbers in your simulation? **Possible answer: 15**
3. How many boxes of cereal do you think you would have to buy to get all six letters? If you bought this many boxes, would you be sure to win? Explain.

Try This

1. Repeat the simulation three more times. Record your results. **Check students' work.**
2. Combine your data with the data of 5 of your classmates. Find the mean number of rolls from all 6 sets of data. **Possible answer:** $\frac{9 + 12 + 15 + 6 + 13 + 17}{6} = 12$
3. How many boxes of cereal do you think you would have to buy to get all six letters? Is this number different from what you thought after the first simulation? Explain.

Answers to *Assessment*

1. buying a box of cereal containing the letter *U*
2. It is going to take more than 10 boxes to win a prize. This player has the letters *Y, O, U, W,* and *I*, but does not have an *N*, because no 6 was rolled.

Activity 1

Answers to *Think and Discuss*

1. 1 or 6; since 1 and 6 were each rolled only once, and the simulation is complete once all numbers have been rolled, then either 1 or 6 was the last number rolled.
3. Possible answer: 15; every simulation will have a different result, so even if you use results from your experiment to estimate the number of boxes you should buy, you can never be sure that you will win.

Answers to *Try This*

3. Possible answer: 12; yes, the results of my first two simulations were 15 and 9.

Activity 2

Amy is a basketball player who usually makes $\frac{1}{2}$ of the baskets that she attempts. Suppose she makes 20 shots in each game. If she plays ten games, in how many games do you think she will make at least four baskets in a row?

Trial	Results
1	THTHHTTHTTHTHTTHHHTT
2	HHTTTHTHTHHHHHTTHTHT
3	HTTTHTTTHTHTTTHTTHTT
4	HTHTHTHTHTTHTHTTTTTT
5	THTTTTHHTHTHHTHTTHTT
6	HTTHTHHHHHTHHHHHHHHH
7	TTHHTTHHHTHTHHTTHTTT
8	HTTHTTHTTTHHTTHTTHTT
9	HHHTTTTTHHHHHTHHTHHT
10	HTTHHTTHHHTHHTHTHHHH

1. There are two possible outcomes every time Amy shoots the ball—either she will make the basket or she will miss. Since Amy makes $\frac{1}{2}$ of her shots, you can toss a coin to simulate one shot. Let heads represent making the basket, and let tails represent missing.
2. Toss the coin 20 times to simulate one game. Keep track of your results.
3. Repeat 2 nine more times to simulate ten games.

Think and Discuss

1. Why does tossing a coin 20 times represent only one trial? **Each trial represents one game and Amy makes 20 shots in a game.**
2. Do any of your sequences contain four or more heads in a row? How many? **Possible answer: yes; 4**
3. In how many games do you think Amy will make at least four baskets in a row? Out of *every* ten games, will Amy always make at least four baskets in a row this number of times?
4. You can use your simulation to find the experimental probability that Amy will make at least four or more baskets in a row. Divide the number of trials in which the coin came up heads at least four times in a row by the total number of trials. What is the experimental probability that Amy will make at least four baskets in a row? **Possible answer: $\frac{4}{10} = 0.4$**
5. Suppose Amy made only $\frac{1}{3}$ of her shots. Would you still be able to use a coin as a simulation? Why or why not? **No, because the probability of a coin landing on a particular side is $\frac{1}{2}$; there is no way to simulate $\frac{1}{3}$ with a coin.**

Try This

1. In a group of ten families that each have four children, how many families do you think will have two girls and two boys? Make a prediction, and then design and carry out a simulation to answer this question. (Assume that having a boy and having a girl are equally likely events.) Was your prediction close? **Check students' work.**
2. Use your results from the previous problem to give the experimental probability that a family with four children will have two girls and two boys. **Check students' work.**
3. Think of an experiment, and design your own simulation to model it. **Check students' work.**

Activity 2

Answers to *Think and Discuss*

3. Possible answer: 4; every simulation will have different results, and the actual game results are dependent on outside factors that the experiment does not account for. So even if you use results from your experiment to estimate the number of baskets in a row that she will make, there is no guarantee that this will occur in every game.

12-3 Organizer

Pacing: Traditional 1 day
Block $\frac{1}{2}$ day

Objective: Students make an organized list to find all possible outcomes.

GPS M6D1.a, M6D1.b
Hands-On Lab
In *Hands-On Lab Activities*

Online Edition
Tutorial Videos, Interactivities

Power Presentations with PowerPoint®

Warm Up

Tim took one marble from a bag, recorded the color, and returned it to the bag. He repeated this several times and recorded the results.

Green	Red	Yellow	Purple
~~IIII~~ ~~IIII~~ II	III	IIII	I

1. Find the experimental probability that a marble selected from the bag will be green. $\frac{3}{5}$
2. Find the experimental probability that a marble selected from the bag will not be yellow. $\frac{4}{5}$

Problem of the Day

What is the probability that the sum of four consecutive whole numbers is divisible by 4? 0

Also available on transparency

12-3 Counting Methods and Sample Spaces

Learn to make an organized list to find all possible outcomes.

Vocabulary
sample space

Sample spaces are used in finding probability. The **sample space** for an experiment is all the possible outcomes. You can use { } to show sample spaces.

When you need to find many possible outcomes, you can make a tree diagram. A tree diagram is one way to organize information.

EXAMPLE 1 **PROBLEM SOLVING APPLICATION**

PROBLEM SOLVING

Georgia Performance Standards

M6P1.c Apply and adapt a variety of appropriate strategies to solve problems. Also, M6P1.b, M6P1.d, M6P5.b.

At a circus, the clowns have two choices of clown suits—polka dots or stripes. They have three choices of wigs—pigtails, rainbow hair, or blue hair. What are the different costumes the clowns can wear?

1 Understand the Problem

List the **important information:**

- There are two types of clown suits.
- There are three types of wigs.

2 Make a Plan

You can draw a tree diagram to find all the possible costumes.

3 Solve

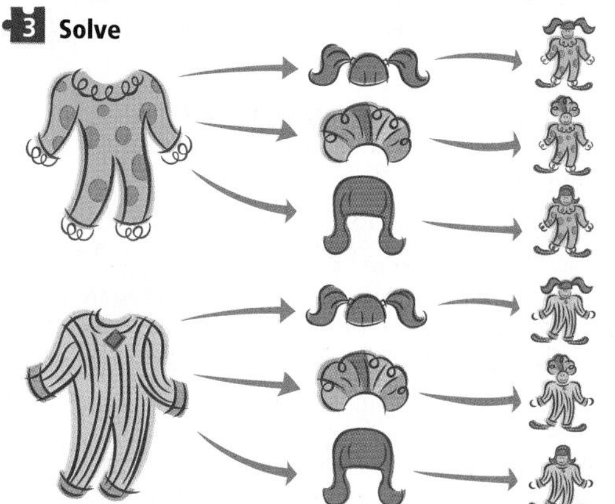

Pair the first pair of pants with each shirt.

Pair the second pair of pants with each shirt.

Follow each branch on the tree diagram to find all of the possible outcomes: {polka dots and pigtails, polka dots and rainbow hair, polka dots and blue hair, stripes and pigtails, stripes and rainbow hair, stripes and blue hair}.

4 Look Back

There are 6 branches at the end of the tree diagram. There are 6 possible costumes listed.

Georgia Performance Standards

M6P1.b Solve problems that arise in mathematics and in other contexts.

M6P1.c Apply and adapt a variety of appropriate strategies to solve problems.

M6P1.d Monitor and reflect on the process of mathematical problem solving.

M6P5.b Select, apply, and translate among mathematical representations to solve problems.

1 Introduce

Alternate Opener

EXPLORATION

12-3 Counting Methods and Sample Spaces

A teacher made a quiz with three true or false questions. You can make an organized list to determine all of the answer possibilities for the three questions.

1. Complete the tree diagram to list all possible answer outcomes.

Question 1 Question 2 Question 3 Outcome

T T T TTT; F; T; F

2. How many outcomes are possible?

Think and Discuss

3. **Discuss** your method for organizing the list of outcomes.
4. **Explain** how you could determine the number of outcomes possible with four questions.

Motivate

Display 4 different boxes and 2 different items (such as a pencil and a stapler) that could fit in any of the boxes. Ask students to name all of the possible ways one item could be put inside of one box. stapler in box 1, pencil in box 1, stapler in box 2, pencil in box 2, stapler in box 3, pencil in box 3, stapler in box 4, pencil in box 4

Explorations and answers are provided in *Alternate Openers: Explorations Transparencies.*

Another way to keep track of possible outcomes is to make an organized list.

EXAMPLE 2 Making an Organized List

Marissa is shopping for a portable MP3 player. The player comes in black, silver, and red. She can choose between models that store 120 songs or 240 songs. What are all the possible MP3 players Marissa can choose from?

black, 120 songs — *List all the players that are black.*
black, 240 songs

silver, 120 songs — *List all the players that are silver.*
silver, 240 songs

red, 120 songs — *List all the players that are red.*
red, 240 songs

The Fundamental Counting Principle is a way to find the number of outcomes in a sample space without making a list. To use the Fundamental Counting Principle, multiply the number of choices in each category.

In the example above, there are 3 colors and 2 models of MP3 players. The total number of MP3 players to choose from is $3 \cdot 2 = 6$.

EXAMPLE 3 Using the Fundamental Counting Principle

Students at Jefferson Middle School must take one fine arts class and one athletics class. The fine arts class choices are band, orchestra, choir, and art. The athletics class choices are P.E., soccer, basketball, volleyball, football, and tennis. How many possible combinations are there?

There are 4 choices for fine arts classes and 6 choices for athletics classes.

$4 \cdot 6 = 24$ — *Multiply the number of choices in each category.*

There are 24 possible combinations.

Possible answers to *Think and Discuss:*

1. When you make an organized list, you are less likely to forget information or leave anything out.
2. Organize the list in a different way, listing the information in a different order. Compare the lists to see whetner they have the same items.

Think and Discuss GPS M6P1.d, M6P3.b

1. Explain the advantages of an organized list over a random list.

2. Describe how you can check whether your list is accurate.

COMMON ERROR ALERT

Some students may leave out entire groups of entries when completing their tree diagrams. Explain that each of the second choices must be listed beside each of the first choices.

Power Presentations with PowerPoint®

Additional Examples

Example 1 

Matt wants to take a 3-day weekend trip to visit his grandparents. He can take either Friday or Monday off from work, and he can either fly, drive, take a train, or take a bus. How many options are available to Matt? 8

Example 2 

One girl and one boy will be chosen to go to the state science fair. The girl finalists are Alia, Brenda, Cathy, Deb, and Erika. The boy finalists are Frank, Greg, and Hal. How many different pairs of one girl and one boy can be formed? 15

Example 3 

Rick wants to buy a mammal and a reptile for pets. The pet shop has dogs, cats, rabbits, hamsters, and ferrets, which are all mammals. It also has lizards, monitors, and boa constrictors, which are all reptiles. How many combinations of one mammal and one reptile are possible? 15

Also available on transparency

2 Teach

Guided Instruction

In this lesson, students make an organized list to find all possible outcomes. First define *sample space,* then teach students to make a tree diagram to show all possible outcomes. Then teach them to make an organized list without the help of a tree diagram.

Teaching Tip **Critical Thinking** Have students choose their preferred method for finding all possible outcomes and explain their choices.

Reaching All Learners

Through Diversity

Have students work in pairs to make tree diagrams to organize the possible outcomes of choices they make at home. Possible ideas include sandwiches (choices of breads and meats), outfits for school (choices of pants/skirts and tops), and ways to make the bed (choices of sheets and blankets).

3 Close

Summarize

Have students name a situation in which a tree diagram could be used to find possible combinations. Work through the process of finding the number of outcomes in a sample space with and without making a tree diagram.

12-3 Exercises

Assignment Guide

If you finished Example 1 assign:
Average 1, 7–9, 13–19
Advanced 4, 7–9, 13–19

If you finished Example 2 assign:
Average 1–2, 7–9, 13–19
Advanced 4–5, 7–9, 13–19

If you finished Example 3 assign:
Average 1–7, 10–19
Advanced 4–19

Homework Quick Check

Quickly check key concepts.
Exercises: 4, 6, 10

Math Background

When three number cubes are rolled, the sums of 9 and 10 can each be produced using six different combinations of addends. But, in practice, 10 appears as a sum more often than 9 when three number cubes are rolled. By analyzing the problem using the methods of this lesson, it can be shown that there are 216 different ways in which three number cubes can be rolled, with 27 ways leading to a sum of 10, and 25 ways leading to a sum of 9.

Answers

1–2, 4. See p. A12.

Georgia Performance Standards

M6P1.c Apply and adapt a variety of appropriate strategies to solve problems.

M6P3.a Organize and consolidate their mathematical thinking through communication.

M6P4.c Recognize and apply mathematics in contexts outside of mathematics.

12-3 Exercises

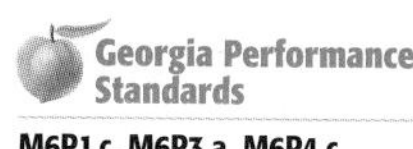

Georgia Performance Standards
M6P1.c, M6P3.a, M6P4.c

go.hrw.com
Homework Help Online
KEYWORD: MR7 12-3
Parent Resources Online
KEYWORD: MR7 Parent

GUIDED PRACTICE

See Example 1

1. Use the ZCool Foods menu. If Carl chooses a main dish and a side dish, what are all the possible outcomes?

See Example 2

2. **School** Patrice, Jason, and Kenya are auditioning for the school play. The director has two roles available, a doctor and a teacher. Each can be played by either a boy or a girl. What are all the possible ways the two roles can be assigned?

See Example 3

3. **School** Mr. Li is offering a make-up science test. He can give the test on Monday, Tuesday, or Thursday, before school, during lunch, or after school. How many different times can Mr. Li give his make-up test? **9**

INDEPENDENT PRACTICE

See Example 1

4. **Recreation** Use the Outdoor Club flyer. The Outdoor Club is planning its annual Spring Festival. The members must vote to choose the day of the event and the main activity. What are all the possible outcomes?

See Example 2

5. Greta's apartment building is protected by a security system that requires a pass code to let in residents. The code is made up of numbers from 1 to 3. The code is three digits long, and a digit cannot repeat. What are all the possible pass codes? **123, 132, 213, 231, 312, 321**

See Example 3

6. **Sports** A middle school is purchasing new basketball jerseys. Each jersey will have a letter and a number on it. The possible letters are A–Z, and the possible numbers are 0–9. How many possible combinations are there? **260**

PRACTICE AND PROBLEM SOLVING

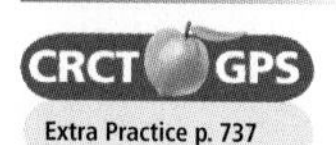

Extra Practice p. 737

7. Keisha will choose a shirt and a skirt or a pair of pants from her closet to wear to school. Find the number of different outfits she can make if she has
   a. 3 shirts, 3 pants, and 3 skirts. **27**
   b. 7 shirts, 5 pants, and 3 skirts. **105**

RETEACH 12-3

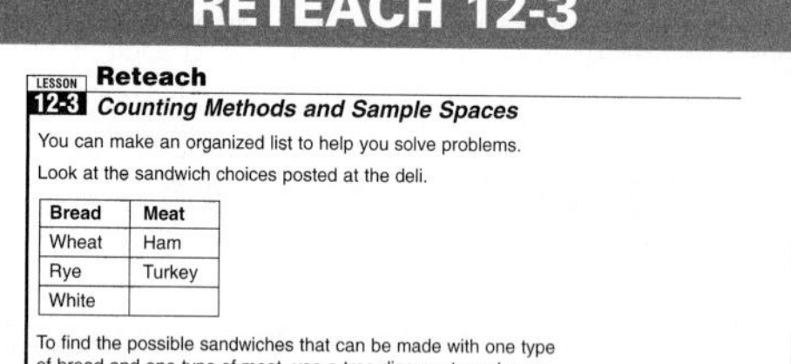

LESSON 12-3 **Reteach**
Counting Methods and Sample Spaces

You can make an organized list to help you solve problems.

Look at the sandwich choices posted at the deli.

Bread	Meat
Wheat	Ham
Rye	Turkey
White	

To find the possible sandwiches that can be made with one type of bread and one type of meat, use a tree diagram to make an organized list of the sandwiches.

Bread	Meat	Combination
wheat	ham	ham on wheat
	turkey	turkey on wheat
rye	ham	ham on rye
	turkey	turkey on rye
white	ham	ham on white
	turkey	turkey on white

Then follow the branches to find the total number of outcomes.

There are 6 possible sandwiches.

Solve.

1. Erin can choose a waffle cone, sugar cone, or chocolate-dipped cone at the carnival. Her choices for ice cream are chocolate, vanilla, strawberry, or cookies and cream. How many different ice cream cones combinations are available to her?

   12 different cones

2. Mrs. Baylus is a parent involved in a neighborhood car pool. She can drive on Monday, Wednesday, or Friday, before school or after school. How many different times can Mrs. Baylus drive for the car pool?

   6 different times

PRACTICE 12-3

LESSON 12-3 **Practice B**
Counting Methods and Sample Spaces

Answer each question.

1. Brian wants to buy a new bicycle. He can choose a 10-speed or 3-speed bike. The bikes come in red, blue, black, and purple. How many different bikes can Brian choose from?

Speed	Color	Combination
10-speed	red	red 10-speed bike
	blue	blue 10-speed bike
	black	black 10-speed bike
	purple	purple 10-speed bike
3-speed	red	red 3-speed bike
	blue	blue 3-speed bike
	black	black 3-speed bike
	purple	purple 3-speed bike

8 different bikes

2. Mr. Simon can leave for Miami on Monday, Tuesday, or Wednesday. He can fly, drive, or take a train. How many different travelling options does Mr. Simon have?

Day	Method	Combination
Monday	fly	fly on Monday
	drive	drive on Monday
	train	take train on Monday
Tuesday	fly	fly on Tuesday
	drive	drive on Tuesday
	train	take train on Tuesday
Wednesday	fly	fly on Wednesday
	drive	drive on Wednesday
	train	take train on Wednesday

9 different options

3. The marching band is choosing new uniforms. They can select black or white pants. They can choose a blue, red, green, or black shirt. From how many different uniforms can the band choose?

Pants	Shirt	Combination
black	blue	black pants, blue shirt
	red	black pants, red shirt
	green	black pants, green shirt
	black	black pants, black shirt
white	blue	white pants, blue shirt
	red	white pants, red shirt
	green	white pants, green shirt
	black	white pants, black shirt

8 different uniforms

4. Sara, Jimmy, and Chantall are sitting beside one another on a bench. In how many different orders could they possibly be sitting from left to right?

1st	2nd	3rd
Sara	Jimmy	Chantall
	Chantall	Jimmy
Jimmy	Sara	Chantall
	Chantall	Sara
Chantall	Sara	Jimmy
	Jimmy	Sara

6 different orders

8. Omar is redecorating his bedroom. He can choose one paint color, one border, and one type of brush.
   a. How many different combinations of paint, border, and brush are possible? **12**
   b. If Omar found another brush that he could use, how many different combinations would be possible? **18**

9. **Social Studies** Japanese children play a game called *Jan-Ken-Pon*. You may know it as Rock, Paper, Scissors. Two players shout at the same time, "*jan-ken-pon!*" On "*pon!*" each player shows one of three hand positions—closed fist (*gu*), open hand palm down (*pa*), or index and middle finger extended to form a V (*choki*). How many different outcomes are possible in this game? **9**

10. **Choose a Strategy** At a meeting, each person shook hands with every other person exactly one time. There were a total of 28 handshakes. How many people were at the meeting? **8**

11. **Write About It** Suppose you are going to choose one boy and one girl from your class for a group project. How can you find the number of possible combinations? Explain.

12. **Challenge** A sailor has five flags: blue, green, red, orange, and yellow. Suppose she wants to fly three flags, but their order is not important; red, orange, yellow is the same as yellow, orange, red. List the different combinations of flags that are possible. How many combinations are there? **10**

CRCT Prep • GPS Support • Spiral Review

13. **Multiple Choice** A cafeteria sells 3 types of cereal and 2 types of juice for breakfast. Bo can choose 1 cereal and 1 juice. How large is the sample space?

   Ⓐ 2   Ⓑ 3    Ⓒ 6   Ⓓ 18

14. **Gridded Response** Bikes R Us sells customized bicycles. There are 5 different color frames, 2 types of tires, and 4 types of seats. How many different combinations are available for 1 frame, 1 type of tire, and 1 type of seat? **40**

Add or subtract. Write each answer in simplest form. (Lesson 5-2)

15. $\frac{1}{3} + \frac{3}{4}$ **$1\frac{1}{12}$**   16. $\frac{3}{8} + \frac{2}{5}$ **$\frac{31}{40}$**   17. $\frac{7}{8} - \frac{1}{4}$ **$\frac{5}{8}$**   18. $\frac{5}{6} - \frac{1}{2}$ **$\frac{1}{3}$**

19. Use the data in the table to make a stem-and-leaf plot. (Lesson 6-9)

Height of Sunflowers (in.)	18	22	15	17	18	21	16	20

Ongoing Assessment and Intervention

***Diagnose Before* the Lesson**
12-3 Warm Up, TE p. 678

***Monitor During* the Lesson**
12-3 Know-It Notebook
12-3 Questioning Strategies

***Assess After* the Lesson**
12-3 Lesson Quiz, TE p. 681

Answers

11. You can make a tree diagram. Start with all the boys' names and match them with each of the girls' names.

19. **Height of Sunflowers (in.)**

Stems	Leaves
1	5 6 7 8 8
2	0 1 2

Key: 2|0 means 20

Test Prep Doctor For Exercises 13 and 14, remind students that using the Fundamental Counting Principle or creating a diagram or list of outcomes can produce the number of combinations.

Journal

Have students explain a situation in which a tree diagram or organized list can be used to find all the possible outcomes.

CHALLENGE 12-3

LESSON 12-3 Challenge
Pascal's Triangle

A mathematician named Blaise Pascal is often called the father of probability theory. In 1654, Pascal investigated the chances of getting different values when rolling dice. Pascal's triangle, shown below, was one result of Pacal's probability work.

Each number in Pascal's triangle is the sum of the two numbers just above it. The triangle has an infinite number or rows—it can go on forever. The first row, Row 0, is always 1. The first entry in each row (Entry 0) is always 1, too.

You can use Pascal's triangle to find combinations. For example, say you want to choose 2 different pizza topping from the 5 toppings available. How many different choices do you have? To answer this question, all you have to do is look at Row 5 (number in group), Entry 2 (number in combination) in Pascal's triangle—10.

```
Row 0                                 1
Row 1                              1     1
Row 2    Entry 2, Row 5         1     2     1
Row 3                        1     3     3     1
Row 4                     1     4     6     4     1
Row 5                  1     5    10    10     5     1
Row 6               1     6    15    20    15     6     1
Row 7            1     7    21    35    35    21     7     1
Row 8         1     8    28    56    70    56    28     8     1
```

So, you could choose 10 different 2-topping combinations for your pizza.

Use Pascal's triangle to answer each question. To find some combinations, you may have to add rows to the triangle.

1. The ice cream parlor offers 8 different sundae toppings. You want to choose 6 different toppings. How many different 6-topping combinations can you choose?
   28 combinations

2. There are 7 musical notes in the major scale—A, B, C, D, E, F, and G. Combinations of 3 notes played together are called chords. How many different chords can you play without repeating notes?
   35 chords

3. There are 6 people going scuba diving. For safety, they are grouped in pairs. How many different scuba-diving pairs can be formed?
   15 pairs

4. You must choose 3 different digits for your computer password. How many different passwords can you choose from the digits 0 through 9?
   120 passwords

PROBLEM SOLVING 12-3

LESSON 12-3 Problem Solving
Counting Methods and Sample Spaces

Write the correct answer.

1. Computer spreadsheet programs use letter-number combinations to name cells. How many different cells can a spreadsheet have where its name has 1 English letter followed by 1 digit?
   260 different cells

2. An airline has five different flights to San Francisco today. Each flight offers first-class or coach seats. From how many different tickets to San Francisco can you choose today?
   10 different tickets

3. On Friday, the school cafeteria is serving pizza, hamburgers, chicken, milk, chocolate milk, and juice. From how many different meal-drink combinations can you choose?
   9 combinations

4. Tanya packed 4 T-shirts, 6 pairs of shorts, and 2 pairs of shoes for her vacation. How many different short-shirt-shoes outfit combinations can she wear?
   48 different outfits

Circle the letter of the correct answer.

5. There are 4 people at a meeting. Every person shakes hands with each other person once. How many handshakes are done in all?
   A 16 handshakes
   B 12 handshakes
   C 8 handshakes
   Ⓓ 6 handshakes

6. There are 3,628,800 different ways to arrange the digits 0 through 9! How many different ways can you arrange the digits 1, 2, and 3?
   F 4 different ways
   Ⓖ 6 different ways
   H 7 different ways
   J 9 different ways

7. A spinner has 6 equal sections labeled *A*, *B*, *C*, *D*, *E*, and *F*. A second spinner has 5 equal sections colored red, blue, green, yellow, and black. If you spin both spinners at the same time, how many different possible outcomes are there?
   A 5   C 11
   B 6   Ⓓ 30

8. How many different ways can you get from point *A* to point *G*?

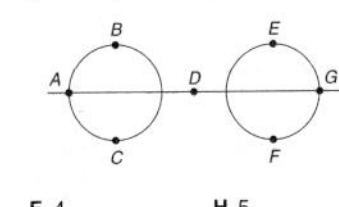

   F 4   H 5
   Ⓖ 9   J 12

Power Presentations with PowerPoint®

12-3 Lesson Quiz

1. A baseball coach has 4 pitchers, 3 catchers, and 2 shortstops on his team. How many different combinations of players can he use for the positions? **24**

2. You are taking a 5-question true/false test. How many possible combinations of answers are there? **10**

3. You are planning a small game booth at the local street fair. You have a choice of 3 games and 4 different prizes. How many combinations of games and prizes are there? **12**

Also available on transparency

12-4 Organizer

Pacing: Traditional 1 day
Block $\frac{1}{2}$ day

Objective: Students find the theoretical probability of an event.

GPS M6D2.c
Hands-On Lab
In *Hands-On Lab Activities*

Online Edition
Tutorial Videos

Power Presentations with PowerPoint®

Warm Up

A cafe offers a soup-and-sandwich combination lunch. You can choose tomato soup, chicken noodle soup, or clam chowder. You can choose a turkey, ham, veggie, or tuna sandwich. How many lunch combinations are there? 12

Problem of the Day

Rory dropped a quarter, a nickel, a dime, and a penny. What is the probability that all four landed tails up? $\frac{1}{16}$

Also available on transparency

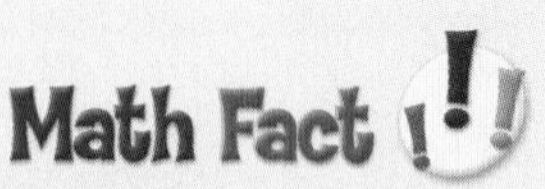

Dice have been found in Egyptian tombs dating from 2000 B.C.E.

12-4 Theoretical Probability

Learn to find the theoretical probability and complement of an event.

Vocabulary
theoretical probability
equally likely
fair
complement

M6D2.b Determine, and use a ratio to represent, the theoretical probability of a given event. Also, M6P1.b, M6P5.c.

Another way to describe the probability of an event is to use **theoretical probability**. One situation in which you can use theoretical probability is when all outcomes have the same chance of occurring. In other words, the outcomes are **equally likely**.

Equally likely outcomes

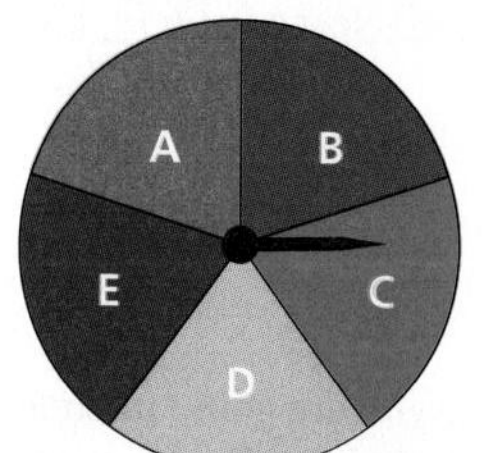

There is the same chance that the spinner will land on any of these letters.

Not equally likely outcomes

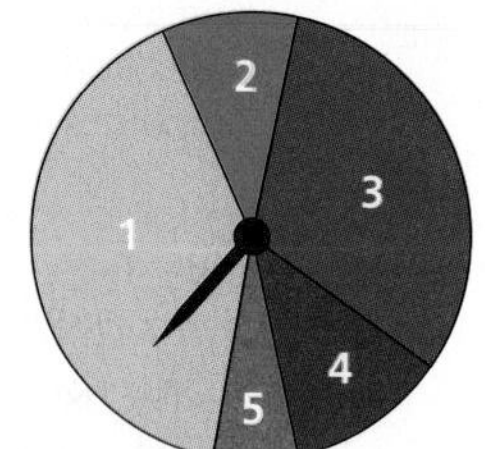

There is a greater chance that the spinner will land on 1 than on any other number.

An experiment with equally likely outcomes is said to be **fair**. You can usually assume that experiments involving items such as coins and number cubes are fair.

THEORETICAL PROBABILITY

$$\text{probability} = \frac{\text{number of ways the event can occur}}{\text{total number of equally likely outcomes}}$$

EXAMPLE 1 Finding Theoretical Probability

Remember!
The sample space is heads, tails (H, T).

A **What is the probability that a fair coin will land heads up?**

There are two possible outcomes when flipping a coin, heads or tails. Both are equally likely because the coin is fair.

$P(\text{heads}) = \frac{\quad}{\text{2 possible outcomes}}$ 

There is only one way for the coin to land heads up.

$P(\text{heads}) = \frac{\text{1 way event can occur}}{\text{2 possible outcomes}}$

$P(\text{heads}) = \frac{\text{1 way event can occur}}{\text{2 possible outcomes}} = \frac{1}{2}$

Georgia Performance Standards

M6D2.b Determine, and use a ratio to represent, the theoretical probability of a given event.

M6P1.b Solve problems that arise in mathematics and in other contexts.

M6P5.c Use representations to model and interpret physical, social, and mathematical phenomena.

1 Introduce

Alternate Opener

EXPLORATION

12-4 Theoretical Probability

When you flip a fair coin, the *theoretical probability* of getting tails is 50% and the theoretical probability of getting heads is 50%. These two outcomes are equally likely to occur.

Determine whether the outcomes in each experiment are all equally likely to occur.

		Equally Likely	Not Equally Likely
1.	(number cube)		
2.	(spinner 1, 2, 3, 4)		
3.	(spinner 1, 2, 3, 4)		

Think and Discuss

4. Explain how you determined whether the outcomes in numbers 1–3 were equally likely or not.

Motivate

Ask students to explain experimental probability and how to write experimental probability as a fraction. Tell them that although experimental probability can only be found if an experiment has been conducted, theoretical probability can be found without conducting an experiment.

Explorations and answers are provided in *Alternate Openers: Explorations Transparencies.*

B **What is the probability of rolling a number less than 5 on a fair number cube?**

There are six possible outcomes when a fair number cube is rolled: 1, 2, 3, 4, 5, or 6.

$P(\text{less than } 5) = \frac{\blacksquare}{6 \text{ possible outcomes}}$

There are 4 ways to roll a number less than 5: 1, 2, 3, or 4.

$P(\text{less than } 5) = \frac{4 \text{ ways event can occur}}{6 \text{ possible outcomes}}$

$P(\text{less than } 5) = \frac{4 \text{ ways event can occur}}{6 \text{ possible outcomes}} = \frac{4}{6} = \frac{2}{3}$

When you toss a coin, there are two possible outcomes: heads or tails. What is $P(\text{heads}) + P(\text{tails})$?

$P(\text{heads}) + P(\text{tails}) = \frac{1}{2} + \frac{1}{2} = \frac{2}{2} = 1$

The probabilities of all the outcomes in the sample space add up to 1 (or 100%, if the probabilities are given as percents).

When you combine all the ways that an event can NOT happen, you have the **complement** of the event.

Event	Complement of the Event
A coin landing heads up on a toss	A coin landing tails up on a toss
Rolling 5 on a number cube	Rolling 1, 2, 3, 4, or 6 on a number cube

EXAMPLE 2 **Finding the Complement of an Event**

Suppose there is a 10% chance of rain today. What is the probability that it will NOT rain?

In this situation, there are two possible outcomes, either it will rain or it will not rain.

$P(\text{rain}) + P(\text{not rain}) = 100\%$

$P(\text{not rain}) = 100\% - 10\%$ *Subtract.*

$P(\text{not rain}) = 90\%$

Think and Discuss GPS M6P3.b

1. **Give an example** of a fair experiment. Give an example of an unfair experiment.
2. **Describe** the complement of the following situation. There is a 60% chance of snow.

Possible answers to *Think and Discuss:*

1. Check students' work.
2. 40%

COMMON ERROR ALERT

When calculating probability and finding more than one favorable outcome, some students may incorrectly find the probability of only one of two or more favorable outcomes occurring. Have these students find each probability separately and then add them together.

Power Presentations with PowerPoint®

Additional Examples

Example 1

A. What is the probability of this fair spinner landing on 3? $\frac{1}{3}$

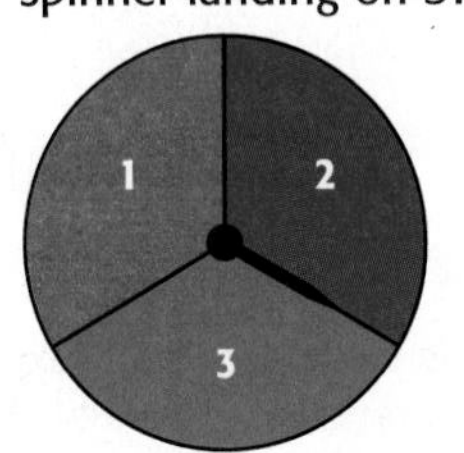

B. What is the probability of rolling a number greater than 4 on a fair number cube? $\frac{1}{3}$

Example 2

Suppose there is a 45% chance of snow tomorrow. What is the probability that it will not snow? 55%

Also available on transparency

Answers to *Think and Discuss*

1. Possible answers: You pull a tile from a bag with 5 red, 5 blue, 5 green, and 5 white tiles. You spin a spinner that is $\frac{3}{5}$ yellow and $\frac{2}{5}$ pink.
2. $P(\text{snow}) + P(\text{no snow}) = 100\%$
   $60\% + P(\text{no snow}) = 100\%$
   $P(\text{no snow}) = 100\% - 60\% = 40\%$

2 Teach

Guided Instruction

In this lesson, students learn to find the theoretical probability of an event. Define the new vocabulary for the lesson: *theoretical probability, equally likely, fair,* and *complement.* Teach students to write the theoretical probabilities of events happening and not happening. Point out that the sum of the probability of an event happening and the probability of that event not happening is 1, or 100%.

Reaching All Learners
Through Curriculum Integration

Life Science Gregor Mendel crossbred plants that had round-pea genes with plants that had wrinkled-pea genes. The first-generation offspring all had round peas. When these plants were bred with each other, 25% of the second generation had wrinkled peas, and the rest had round peas. Have students use probability to write a hypothesis about getting round peas in the second generation.

Possible answer: The probability of getting round peas in the second generation is $\frac{3}{4}$, so round peas are likely in the second generation.

3 Close

ENGLISH LANGUAGE LEARNERS

Summarize

Review the new vocabulary in the lesson: *theoretical probability, equally likely, fair,* and *complement.* Discuss how *equally likely* and *fair* relate to each other.

Possible answer: Outcomes with the same chance of happening are said to be *equally likely*. An experiment or game with equally likely outcomes is *fair*.

12-4 Exercises

Assignment Guide

If you finished Example 1 assign:
Average 1–2, 10–17, 37–43
Advanced 5–7, 10–17, 37–43

If you finished Example 2 assign:
Average 1–13, 18–43
Advanced 5–43

Homework Quick Check

Quickly check key concepts.
Exercises: 6, 8, 10, 12

Math Background

The symbol ≈ is used with both experimental and theoretical probability. Any calculation of probability is always an estimate. The symbol = is used in the theoretical probability after the assumption of a fair experiment.

Georgia Performance Standards

M6P3.a Organize and consolidate their mathematical thinking through communication.

M6P3.c Analyze and evaluate the mathematical thinking and strategies of others.

M6P4.c Recognize and apply mathematics in contexts outside of mathematics.

12-4 Exercises

M6P3.a, M6P3.c, M6P4.c

GUIDED PRACTICE

See Example 1

1. What is the probability that a fair coin will land tails up? $\frac{1}{2}$
2. What is the probability of randomly choosing a vowel from the letters *A, B, C, D,* and *E*? $\frac{2}{5}$

See Example 2

3. The probability that a spinner will land on blue is 26%. What is the probability that it will NOT land on blue? 74%
4. Suppose you have an unfair number cube and the probability of rolling a 2 is 0.7. What is the probability that you will NOT roll a 2? 0.3

INDEPENDENT PRACTICE

See Example 1

5. What is the probability of rolling the number 3 on a fair number cube? $\frac{1}{6}$
6. What is the probability of rolling a number that is a multiple of 3 on a fair number cube? $\frac{1}{3}$
7. Find the probability that a yellow marble will be chosen from a bag that contains 3 green marbles, 2 red marbles, and 4 yellow marbles. $\frac{4}{9}$

See Example 2

8. **Weather** Suppose there is an 81% chance of snow today. What is the probability that it will NOT snow? 19%
9. On a game show, the chance that the spinner will land on the winning color is 0.04. Find the probability that it will NOT land on the winning color. 0.96

PRACTICE AND PROBLEM SOLVING

Extra Practice p. 738

A fair number cube is rolled. Find each probability.

10. $P(4)$ $\frac{1}{6}$
11. $P(\text{not } 3)$ $\frac{5}{6}$
12. $P(1, 2, \text{or } 3)$ $\frac{1}{2}$
13. $P(\text{number greater than } 0)$ 1
14. $P(\text{odd number})$ $\frac{1}{2}$
15. $P(\text{number divisible by } 5)$ $\frac{1}{6}$
16. $P(\text{prime number})$ $\frac{1}{2}$
17. $P(\text{negative number})$ 0

18. **Critical Thinking** This net can be folded to make a solid figure. The solid figure can then be rolled like a number cube. Give the probability of rolling each number with the solid figure. $\frac{1}{8}$

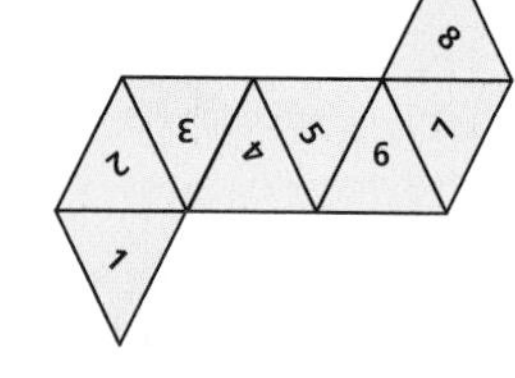

19. A board game has a die (singular of dice) with 12 faces. Give the probability of rolling a number that is a factor of 12. 50%
20. **Social Studies** In a recent presidential election, the probability that an eligible person voted was about 45%. Is it more likely that an eligible person voted or did not vote? It is more likely that an eligible person did not vote.

RETEACH 12-4

LESSON 12-4 **Reteach**
Theoretical Probability

You can use theoretical probability to estimate the probability of an event.

To find the theoretical probability of an event, first find the number of ways the event can occur. Then divide that number by the total number of possible outcomes.

Think about a standard number cube. To find the theoretical probability of rolling a number greater than 2, find the number of possible outcomes that are greater than 2.

3, 4, 5, and 6 are greater than 2. So there are 4 outcomes that are greater than 2.

There are 6 possible outcomes, so divide 4 by 6.

$$\text{Probability} = \frac{\text{number of ways event can occur}}{\text{total number of possible outcomes}}$$

$$P(\text{rolling a number greater than 2}) = \frac{4}{6} = \frac{2}{3}$$

Find the theoretical probability of each event.

(Spinner with sections 1, 2, 3, 4, 5, 6, 7, 8)

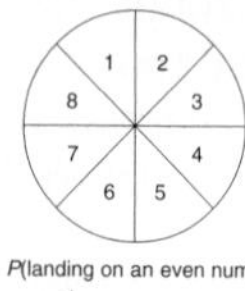

1. $P(\text{landing on an even number})$ $\frac{1}{2}$
2. $P(\text{landing on a prime number})$ $\frac{1}{2}$
3. $P(\text{landing on a number divisible by 3})$ $\frac{1}{4}$
4. $P(\text{landing on a number with 3 factors})$ $\frac{1}{8}$
5. $P(\text{landing on a number greater than 8})$ 0
6. $P(\text{landing on a number less than 9})$ 1

PRACTICE 12-4

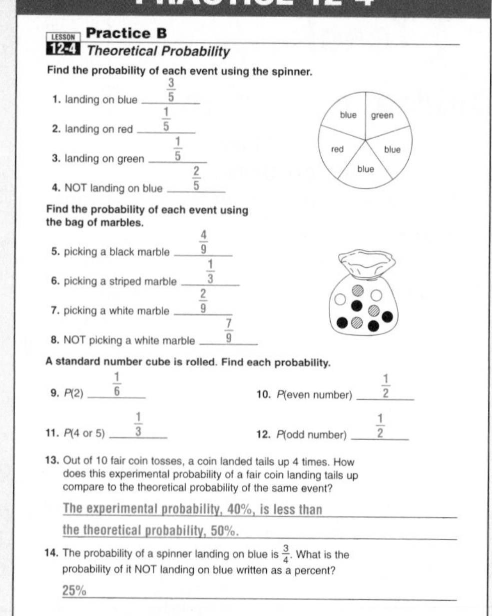

LESSON 12-4 **Practice B**
Theoretical Probability

Find the probability of each event using the spinner.

1. landing on blue $\frac{3}{5}$
2. landing on red $\frac{1}{5}$
3. landing on green $\frac{1}{5}$
4. NOT landing on blue $\frac{2}{5}$

Find the probability of each event using the bag of marbles.

5. picking a black marble $\frac{4}{9}$
6. picking a striped marble $\frac{1}{3}$
7. picking a white marble $\frac{2}{9}$
8. NOT picking a white marble $\frac{7}{9}$

A standard number cube is rolled. Find each probability.

9. $P(2)$ $\frac{1}{6}$
10. $P(\text{even number})$ $\frac{1}{2}$
11. $P(4 \text{ or } 5)$ $\frac{1}{3}$
12. $P(\text{odd number})$ $\frac{1}{2}$
13. Out of 10 fair coin tosses, a coin landed tails up 4 times. How does this experimental probability of a fair coin landing tails up compare to the theoretical probability of the same event?
The experimental probability, 40%, is less than the theoretical probability, 50%.
14. The probability of a spinner landing on blue is $\frac{3}{4}$. What is the probability of it NOT landing on blue written as a percent?
25%

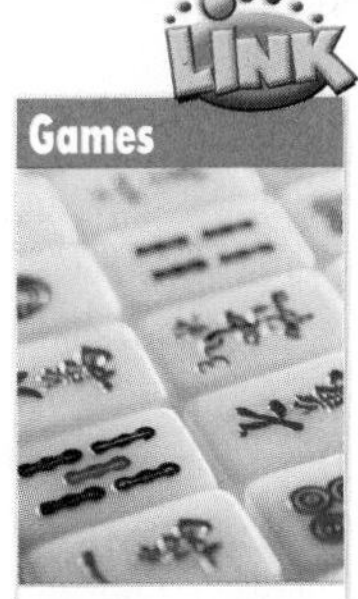

Games

Mah Jong was developed in China. Although the game's exact history is unknown, Mah Jong may be over 2,000 years old.

go.hrw.com
Web Extra!
KEYWORD: MR7 Game

For Exercises 21–26, *A* represents an event. The probability that *A* will happen is given. Find the probability that *A* will NOT happen.

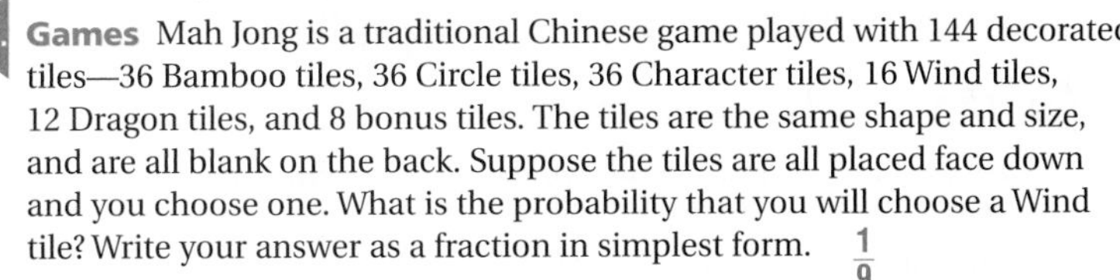

21. $P(A) = 47\%$ 53%
22. $P(A) = 0.9$ 0.1
23. $P(A) = \frac{7}{12}$ $\frac{5}{12}$
24. $P(A) = \frac{5}{8}$ $\frac{3}{8}$
25. $P(A) = 0.23$ 0.77
26. $P(A) = 100\%$ 0%

27. Games Mah Jong is a traditional Chinese game played with 144 decorated tiles—36 Bamboo tiles, 36 Circle tiles, 36 Character tiles, 16 Wind tiles, 12 Dragon tiles, and 8 bonus tiles. The tiles are the same shape and size, and are all blank on the back. Suppose the tiles are all placed face down and you choose one. What is the probability that you will choose a Wind tile? Write your answer as a fraction in simplest form. $\frac{1}{9}$

Nine pieces of paper with the numbers 1, 2, 2, 3, 4, 4, 5, 6, and 6 printed on them are placed in a bag. A student chooses one without looking. Compare the probabilities. Write <, >, or =.

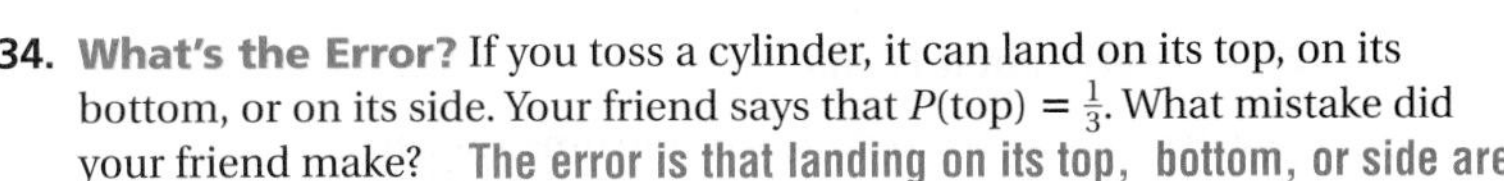

28. $P(1)$ ▒ $P(5)$ =
29. $P(3)$ ▒ $P(2)$ >
30. $P(4)$ ▒ $P(6)$ =
31. $P(4)$ ▒ $P(5) + P(6)$ <
32. $P(3) + P(5)$ ▒ $P(6)$ =
33. $P(\text{less than } 3)$ ▒ $P(6)$ >

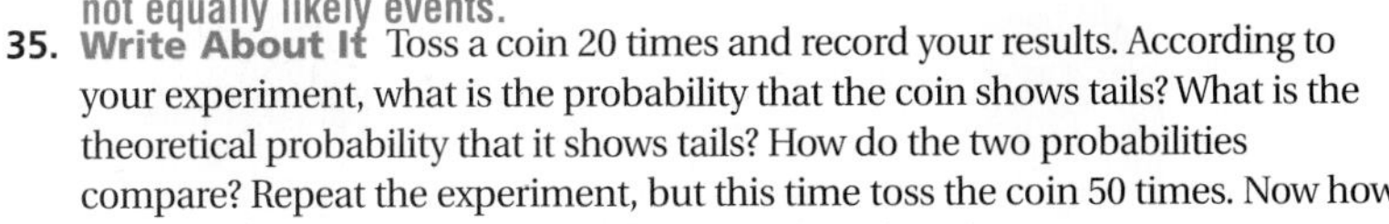

34. What's the Error? If you toss a cylinder, it can land on its top, on its bottom, or on its side. Your friend says that $P(\text{top}) = \frac{1}{3}$. What mistake did your friend make? The error is that landing on its top, bottom, or side are not equally likely events.

35. Write About It Toss a coin 20 times and record your results. According to your experiment, what is the probability that the coin shows tails? What is the theoretical probability that it shows tails? How do the two probabilities compare? Repeat the experiment, but this time toss the coin 50 times. Now how do the probabilities compare? Check students' work.

36. Challenge Suppose you perform an experiment in which you toss a fair coin and roll a fair number cube. Find the theoretical probability that heads *and* 3 will be the outcomes. $\frac{1}{12}$

CRCT Prep • GPS Support • Spiral Review

37. Multiple Choice There is a 25% chance of snow on Friday. What is the probability that it will NOT snow on Friday?

Ⓐ 0% Ⓑ 25% Ⓒ 75% Ⓓ 100%

38. Extended Response A drawer contains 6 blue socks, 4 brown socks, and 10 white socks. Arnold chooses one sock without looking. What is the probability of choosing each color sock? Compare the possibilities. Write <, >, or =.
$P(\text{blue}) = \frac{3}{10}$; $P(\text{brown}) = \frac{1}{5}$; $P(\text{white}) = \frac{1}{2}$; $P(\text{brown}) < P(\text{blue}) < P(\text{white})$

Find each quotient. (Lesson 11-7)

39. $84 \div 4$ 21
40. $-25 \div 5$ −5
41. $-60 \div (-20)$ 3
42. $-55 \div 5$ −11

43. Paulina will use 15 feet of ribbon to decorate baskets for her friends. If each basket requires 1.2 feet of ribbon, how many baskets can she decorate? (Lesson 3-8) 12

Ongoing Assessment and Intervention

Diagnose Before the Lesson
12-4 Warm Up, TE p. 682

Monitor During the Lesson
12-4 Know-It Notebook
12-4 Questioning Strategies

Assess After the Lesson
12-4 Lesson Quiz, TE p. 685

Test Prep Doctor For Exercise 37, students who remember that the sum of the probability of an event and the probability of its complement is 1, or 100%, should be able to eliminate choices **A, B,** and **D.**

Journal

Have students write an explanation for how theoretical probability is different from experimental probability. Have them give examples of each type of probability.

CHALLENGE 12-4

LESSON 12-4 **Challenge**
Plant Probabilities

Botanists often develop new plants by crossing two "parent" plants. Each parent plant gives one gene to each seedling, or "child" plant. Imagine the first parent has two red genes (RR), which produce red flowers. The second parent has two white genes (WW), which produce white flowers. Complete this chart to organize the probabilities of producing a new plant with pink flowers (RW).

		Red-flowering Plant	
		R	R
White-flowering Plant	W	RW	RW
	W	RW	RW

Now imagine crossing two of the new pink-flowering plants. Complete this chart to see the results. Then use both charts to answer the questions that follow.

		Pink-flowering Plant	
		R	W
Pink-flowering Plant	R	RR	RW
	W	RW	WW

1. What is the probability that a plant in the first crossing will be pink? 1
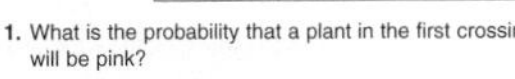
2. What is the probability that a plant in the second crossing will be pink? $\frac{1}{2}$

3. What is the probability that a plant in the second crossing will be red? $\frac{1}{4}$
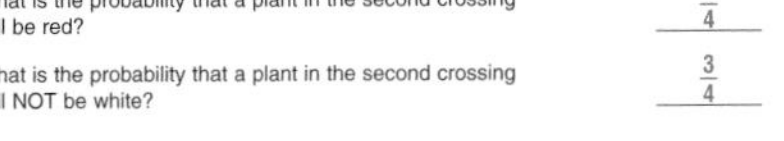
4. What is the probability that a plant in the second crossing will NOT be white? $\frac{3}{4}$

PROBLEM SOLVING 12-4

LESSON 12-4 **Problem Solving**
Theoretical Probability

Each time a letter is drawn, it is returned to the bag. Write the correct answer. Write answers in simplest form.

Numbers of Tiles for Each Letter

Letter	Tiles	Letter	Tiles
A	9	O	8
B	2	P	2
C	2	Q	1
D	4	R	6
E	12	S	4
F	2	T	6
G	3	U	4
H	2	V	2
I	9	W	2
J	1	X	1
K	1	Y	2
L	4	Z	1
M	2	BLANK	2
N	6		

1. At the beginning of a game, each player picks letter tiles from a bag without looking. What is the probability that a player will pick a blank tile? $\frac{1}{50}$
2. Which letter are you most likely to pick from the bag? Write this probability as a fraction, decimal, and percent. E; $\frac{3}{25}$, 0.12, 12%
3. Which letters are you least likely to pick from the bag? What is the probability that you will pick any one of those letters? Write this probability as a fraction, decimal, and percent. J, K, Q, X, and Z; $\frac{1}{100}$; 0.01; 1%

Circle the letter of the correct answer.

4. The probability of randomly picking a letter is $\frac{3}{50}$. What could that letter possibly be?
   A E
   B G
   Ⓒ N, R, or T
   D V, W, or Y
5. The probability of randomly picking a letter is $\frac{1}{25}$. What could that letter possibly be?
   F A
   G B
   H C, F, H, or M
   Ⓙ D, L, S, or U
6. What is the probability that you will select a vowel tile from the bag?
   A $\frac{9}{100}$
   Ⓒ $\frac{11}{25}$
   B $\frac{26}{49}$
   D $\frac{21}{50}$
7. Most words with a *Q* must also have a *U*. What is the probability that you will select a *U*?
   F $\frac{1}{100}$
   H $\frac{1}{20}$
   Ⓖ $\frac{1}{25}$
   D $\frac{1}{300}$

Power Presentations with PowerPoint®

12-4 Lesson Quiz

Use the spinner shown for problems 1–3.

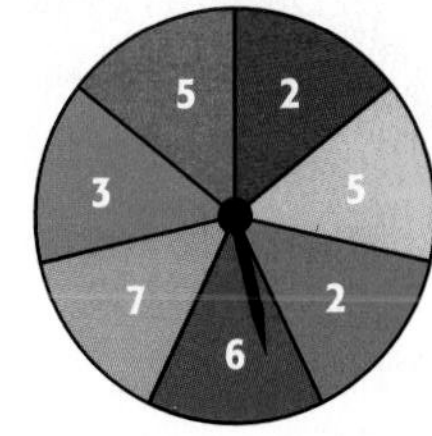

1. $P(2)$ $\frac{2}{7}$
2. $P(\text{odd number})$ $\frac{4}{7}$
3. $P(\text{factor of } 6)$ $\frac{4}{7}$
4. Suppose there is a 2% chance of spinning the winning number at a carnival game. What is the probability of not winning? 98%

Also available on transparency

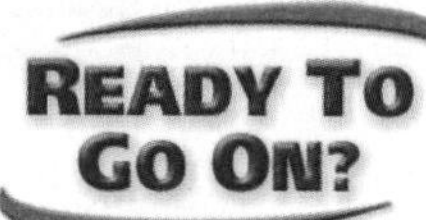

Organizer

Objective: Assess students' mastery of concepts and skills in Lessons 12-1 through 12-4.

Resources

Assessment Resources
Section 12A Quiz

Test & Practice Generator
One-Stop Planner®

INTERVENTION

Resources

Ready to Go On? Intervention and Enrichment Worksheets

***Ready to Go On?* CD-ROM**

***Ready to Go On?* Online**

my.hrw.com

Answers

8. spaghetti: tomato
spaghetti: pesto
fettuccine: tomato
fettuccine: pesto
bow tie: tomato
bow tie: pesto

CHAPTER 12

READY TO GO ON?

SECTION 12A

Ready to Go On?

Quiz for Lessons 12-1 Through 12-4

12-1 Introduction to Probability

For Problems 1 and 2, write *impossible, unlikely, as likely as not, likely,* or *certain* to describe the event.

1. This spinner lands on blue. impossible
2. You roll an even number on a standard number cube. as likely as not
3. The chance that Mitch will win concert tickets is 0.15. Write this probability as a fraction and as a percent. $\frac{3}{20}$; 15%
4. The chance of rain is 33% on Tuesday, 45% on Wednesday, and 35% on Thursday. On which day is it most likely to rain? Wednesday

12-2 Experimental Probability

For each experiment, identify the outcome shown.

5.  1

6. 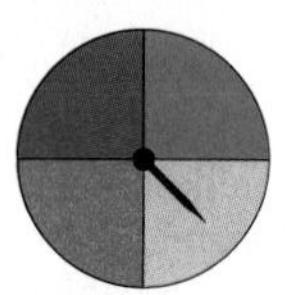 yellow

7. Jeremy recorded the number of times a spinner landed on each number. Based on Jeremy's experiment, on which number is the spinner most likely to land? 2

Outcome	1	2	3
Frequency	𝍸 II	𝍸 𝍸 II	𝍸 I

12-3 Counting Methods and Sample Spaces

8. Mindy's Deli serves 3 kinds of pasta with 2 kinds of sauce. The different pastas are spaghetti, fettuccine, and bow tie. The different sauces are tomato and pesto. What are all the possible outcomes that include 1 pasta and 1 sauce?
9. Cynthia is choosing an outfit for the first day of class. Her choices are black or blue pants and a white, yellow, or pink shirt. How many possible combinations can she choose from? 6

12-4 Theoretical Probability

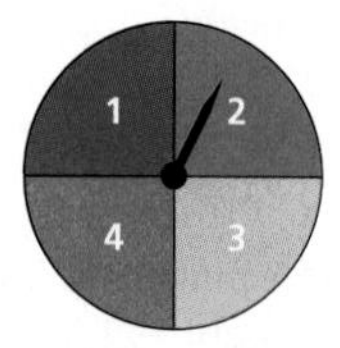

10. What is the probability that this spinner will land on 2? $\frac{1}{4}$
11. What is the probability of rolling a number less than 3 on a number cube? $\frac{1}{3}$
12. Kirk has a 33% chance of scoring in the basketball game. What is the probability that Kirk will NOT score in the game? 67%

READY TO GO ON?

Diagnose and Prescribe

Ready to Go On? Intervention	*Ready to Go On? Intervention, Section 12A* Worksheets	CD-ROM	Online
Lesson 12-1	12-1 Intervention	Activity 12-1	Diagnose and Prescribe Online
Lesson 12-2	12-2 Intervention	Activity 12-2	
Lesson 12-3	12-3 Intervention	Activity 12-3	
Lesson 12-4	12-4 Intervention	Activity 12-4	

Focus on Problem Solving

Look Back

- Estimate to check that your answer is reasonable

When you have finished solving a problem, take a minute to reread the problem. See if your answer makes sense. Make sure that your answer is reasonable given the situation in the problem.

One way to do this is to estimate the answer before you begin solving the problem. Then when you get your final answer, compare it with your original estimate. If your answer is not close to your estimate, check your work again.

Each problem below has an answer given, but it is not right. How do you know that the answer is not reasonable? Give your own estimate of the correct answer.

1. A rental car agency has 55 blue cars, 32 red cars, and 70 white cars. A customer is given a car at random. How many color outcomes are possible?

   Answer: 2,100

2. A box has 120 marbles. If the probability of drawing a blue marble is $\frac{3}{8}$ and the probability of drawing a red marble is $\frac{5}{8}$, how many of each color are in the box?

   Answer: 100 blue marbles and 20 red marbles

3. A store manager decides to survey one out of every ten shoppers. How many would be surveyed out of 350 shoppers?

   Answer: 3 shoppers

4. Sue has just started to collect old dimes. She has six dimes from 1941, five dimes from 1932, and one dime from 1930. If she chooses one dime at random, what is the probability that it is from before 1932?

   Answer: 50%

Answers

1. 3
2. 45 blue marbles and 75 red marbles
3. 35 shoppers
4. $\frac{1}{12}$

Focus on Problem Solving

Organizer

Objective: Focus on checking for a reasonable answer.

Online Edition

Resources

Chapter 12 Resource Book
Reading Strategies

Problem Solving Process

This page focuses on the last step of the problem-solving process: **Look Back**

Discuss

Have students explain how they knew each answer was unreasonable.

1. For each customer, there are only three possible colors they could get. So 2,100 is too large to be the correct answer.
2. The numbers 100 and 20 are not divisible by 3, and the probability of drawing a blue marble is 3 out of 8, which means that the number of blue marbles must be divisible by 3.
3. 350 divided by 10 is much larger than 3 since $3 \times 10 = 30$.
4. There is only 1 dime that is older than 1932, and a 50% probability would suggest that half of the time, or 6 out of 12 times, you would draw the same dime.

SECTION **12B**

Using Probability

One-Minute Section Planner

Lesson	Materials	MiC and Lab Resources
Lesson 12-5 Compound Events • List all the outcomes and find the theoretical probability of a compound event. **12-5 Hands-On Lab** Explore Permutations and Combinations • Use index cards to model permutations and combinations. ☑ CRCT ☑ SAT-10 ☑ ITBS ☑ CTBS ☑ NAEP	Boxes with small items inside, index cards	**MiC:** ***Take a Chance*** pp. 26–31 ***Hands-On Lab Activities*** 12-5 ***Technology Lab Activities*** 12-5
Lesson 12-6 Making Predictions • Use probability to predict events. ☑ CRCT ☑ SAT-10 ☐ ITBS ☐ CTBS ☑ NAEP		
Extension Independent and Dependent Events • Find the probability of independent and dependent events. ☑ CRCT ☐ SAT-10 ☐ ITBS ☐ CTBS ☑ NAEP		

MK = *Manipulatives Kit*

Mathematics in Context

The unit ***Take a Chance*** from the *Mathematics in Context* © 2006 series can be used with Section 12B. See Section Planner above for suggestions for integrating *MiC* with *Holt Mathematics.*

Section Overview

Compound Events
Lesson 12-5

 There are counting methods to help determine the probabilities of multiple events.

Assume that the births of boys and girls are equally likely. If a family is going to have 4 children, what is the probability that exactly 2 will be girls? (B = boy, G = girl)

> A **compond event** consists of two or more single events.

There are **16** possible ways for the gender birth order to occur.

BBBB BBBG BBGB BBGG
BGBB BGBG BGGB BGGG
GBBB GBBG GBGB GBGG
GGBB GGBG GGGB GGGG

There are **6** possible ways that there could be exactly 2 girls.

BBGG BGBG BGGB
GGBB GBGB GBBG

The probability of exactly 2 girls out of 4 births is as follows:

$$P(\text{exactly two girls}) = \frac{\text{6 ways event can occur}}{\text{16 possible outcomes}} = \frac{3}{8} = 37.5\%$$

Making Predictions
Lesson 12-6

 Insurance companies use probabilities to make predictions about life expectancy.

If you roll a number cube 24 times, how many times can you expect to roll a 5?

$P(\text{rolling a } 5) = \frac{1}{6}$ Use the probability to set up a proportion.

$$\frac{1}{6} = \frac{x}{24}$$
$$6 \cdot x = 1 \cdot 24$$
$$6x = 24$$
$$x = 4$$

Independent and Dependent Events
Extension

 Understanding how one event affects another will help you plan.

Independent Events

The occurrence of one event ***does not*** affect the probability of the other.

Example:

Roll a number cube and toss a coin. find the probability of rolling a number less than 3 and getting heads.

$P(3, \text{heads}) = \frac{2}{6} \cdot \frac{1}{2} = \frac{1}{6} = 16\frac{2}{3}\%$

Dependent Events

The occurrence of one event ***does*** affect the probability of the other.

Example:

Pick two marbles from a bag containing 4 red marbles and 1 blue marble without replacing the first. Find the probability of picking two red marbles.

$P(\text{red, red}) = \frac{4}{5} \cdot \frac{3}{4} = \frac{3}{5} = 60\%$

12-5 Organizer

Pacing: Traditional 1 day
Block $\frac{1}{2}$ day

Objective: Students list all the outcomes and find the theoretical probability of a compound event.

GPS M6D2.b
Technology Lab
In *Technology Lab Activities*

Online Edition
Tutorial Videos

Power Presentations with PowerPoint®

Warm Up

A game die with eight sides numbered 1 through 8 is rolled. Find each probability.

1. $P(1, 2, \text{or } 3)$ $\frac{3}{8}$
2. $P(\text{even number})$ $\frac{1}{2}$
3. $P(\text{number greater than } 9)$ 0

Problem of the Day

Sam and Pam can have an apple, an orange, or a pear. What is the probability that they will pick the same snack? $\frac{1}{3}$

Also available on transparency

Math Fact

When two events cannot occur at the same time, they are called *disjoint* or *mutually exclusive*. So the probability of two mutually exclusive events occurring is 0.

Georgia Performance Standards

M6D2.b Determine, and use a ratio to represent, the theoretical probability of a given event.

M6P1.b Solve problems that arise in mathematics and in other contexts.

M6P5.a Create and use representations to organize, record, and communicate mathematical ideas.

M6P5.b Select, apply, and translate among mathematical representations to solve problems.

12-5 Compound Events

Learn to list all the outcomes and find the theoretical probability of a compound event.

Vocabulary
compound event

If a family is going to have four children, there are 16 possibilities for the birth order of the children based on gender (boy, B, or girl, G).

BBBB, BBBG, BBGB, BBGG,
BGBB, BGBG, BGGB, BGGG,
GBBB, GBBG, GBGB, GBGG,
GGBB, GGBG, GGGB, GGGG

A **compound event** consists of two or more single events. For example, the birth of one child is a single event. The births of four children make up a compound event.

EXAMPLE 1 Finding Probabilities of Compound Events

Georgia Performance Standards

M6D2.b Determine, and use a ratio to represent, the theoretical probability of a given event. Also, M6P1.b, M6P5.a, M6P5.b.

Theresa rolls a fair number cube and then flips a fair coin.

A **Find the probability that the number cube will show an odd number and that the coin will show tails.**

First find all of the possible outcomes.

Number Cube

Coin		1	2	3	4	5	6
	H	1, H	2, H	3, H	4, H	5, H	6, H
	T	1, T	2, T	3, T	4, T	5, T	6, T

There are 12 possible outcomes, and all are equally likely.
Three of the outcomes have an odd number and tails:
1, T; 3, T; and 5, T.

$$P(\text{odd, tails}) = \frac{\text{3 ways event can occur}}{\text{12 possible outcomes}} = \frac{3}{12} = \frac{1}{4}$$

Write your answer in simplest form.

B **Find the probability that the number cube will show a 2 and that the coin will show heads.**

Only one outcome is 2, H.

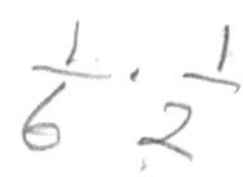

$$P(2, H) = \frac{\text{1 way event can occur}}{\text{12 possible outcomes}} = \frac{1}{12}$$

1 Introduce

Alternate Opener

EXPLORATION

12-5 Compound Events

A *compound event* consists of two or more single events.

A bat had two babies. The birth of each baby bat is a single event. The birth of both bats is a compound event.

First bat born

Second bat born	Female	Male
Female	FF	MF
Male	FM	MM

1. List all possible outcomes for two offspring.
2. Divide 1 (FF) by the total number of outcomes to find the probability that both bats are female.
3. Divide 1 (MM) by the total number of outcomes to find the probability that both bats are male.
4. Divide 2 (MF and FM) by the total number of outcomes to find the probability that one bat is female and the other is male.

Think and Discuss

5. **Explain** how to find the probability that three males would be born among four births.

Motivate

ENGLISH LANGUAGE LEARNERS

Have students give you examples of the use of the term *compound*, outside of math.

Possible answer: A compound word is a single word, such as *airplane*, made up of two or more single words. Explain that compound events consist of two or more single events.

Explorations and answers are provided in *Alternate Openers: Explorations Transparencies.*

C **The following experiment is going to be performed.**

Step 1: Toss a fair coin. **Step 2:** Spin the spinner. **Step 3:** Choose a marble.

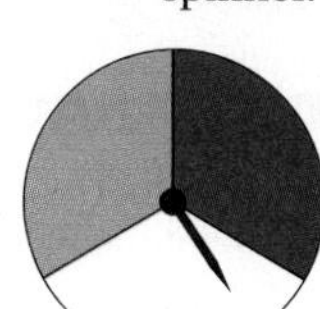

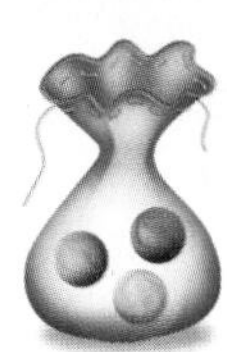

What is the probability that the coin will show heads, the spinner will land on orange, and a red marble will be chosen?

Coin	Spinner	Marble	Outcome
Heads	purple	red	→ heads, purple, red
		yellow	→ heads, purple, yellow
		green	→ heads, purple, green
	orange	red	→ heads, orange, red
		yellow	→ heads, orange, yellow
		green	→ heads, orange, green
	white	red	→ heads, white, red
		yellow	→ heads, white, yellow
		green	→ heads, white, green
Tails	purple	red	→ tails, purple, red
		yellow	→ tails, purple, yellow
		green	→ tails, purple, green
	orange	red	→ tails, orange, red
		yellow	→ tails, orange, yellow
		green	→ tails, orange, green
	white	red	→ tails, white, red
		yellow	→ tails, white, yellow
		green	→ tails, white, green

There are 18 equally likely outcomes.

$$P(\text{heads, orange, red}) = \frac{1 \text{ way event can occur}}{18 \text{ possible outcomes}} = \frac{1}{18}$$

Remember!

You could also use the Fundamental Counting Principle to find the total possble outcomes.

coin · spinner · marble
2 · 3 · 3
= 18 total outcomes

Possible answers to *Think and Discuss:*

1. rolling a number cube and pulling a marble out of a bag
2. Multiply the number of possible outcomes for each independent event to find the number of possible outcomes for the compound event.

Think and Discuss GPS M6P1.a, M6P3.b

1. **Give an example** of a compound event.
2. **Explain** any pattern you noticed while finding the number of possible outcomes in a compound event.

COMMON ERROR ALERT

When finding the number of possible outcomes for a compound event, students may add the number of outcomes for each independent event. However, the correct operation to use is multiplication.

Power Presentations with PowerPoint®

Additional Examples

Example 1

Jerome spins the spinner and rolls a fair number cube.

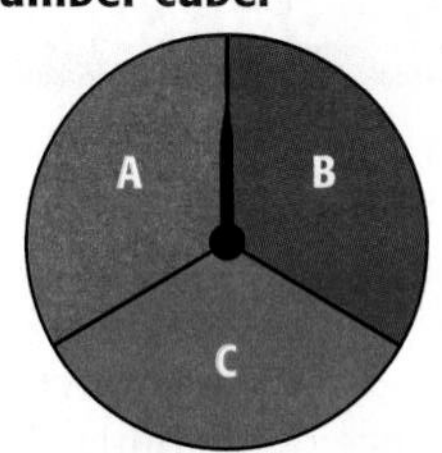

A. Find the probability of the number cube showing an even number and the spinner showing B. $\frac{1}{6}$

B. Find the probability of the number cube showing 4 and the spinner showing A. $\frac{1}{18}$

C. In the experiment proposed in the student book, what is the probability of the coin showing tails, the spinner showing purple, and a green marble being chosen? $\frac{1}{18}$

Also available on transparency

2 Teach

Guided Instruction

In this lesson, students learn to list all the outcomes and find the theoretical probability of a compound event. Define the term *compound event.* Teach students to use tables and tree diagrams to list the possible outcomes of compound events.

Teaching Tip **Multiple Representations** Have students make a tree diagram to display the possible outcomes in Example 1A and a table to display the possible outcomes in Example 1C.

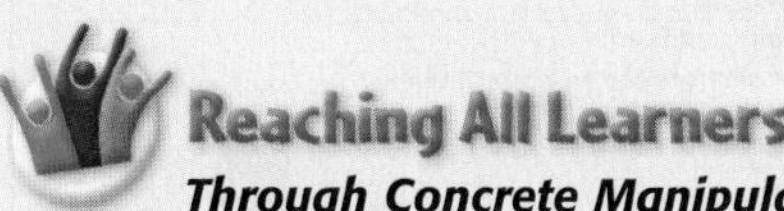

Reaching All Learners

Through Concrete Manipulatives

Give each group a coin, a number cube, and a spinner (number cubes and spinners are provided in the Manipulatives Kit). Have the groups design and conduct experiments involving compound events. Each group should first compute the theoretical probability of a given outcome and then conduct the experiment and find the experimental probability of that outcome. Have group members discuss the relationship between their theoretical and experimental probabilities.

3 Close

ENGLISH LANGUAGE LEARNERS

Summarize

Review the term *compound event* and discuss ways to find the possible outcomes of a compound event. Also review how to write a theoretical probability as a fraction.

12-5 Exercises

Assignment Guide

If you finished Example 1 assign:
Average 1–11, 14–29
Advanced 3–29

Homework Quick Check

Quickly check key concepts.
Exercises: 4, 6, 8, 10, 14

Math Background

If events A and B are independent, then the probability of both A and B occurring equals $P(A) \cdot P(B)$. Here, independence of two events means that the occurrence of one had no relation to the occurrence of the other. With this formula, Example 1A yields the result $P(\text{odd, tails}) = P(\text{odd}) \cdot P(\text{tails}) = \frac{3}{6} \cdot \frac{1}{2} = \frac{1}{4}$. Example 1B yields the result $P(2, \text{head}) = P(2) \cdot P(\text{head}) = \frac{1}{6} \cdot \frac{1}{2} = \frac{1}{12}$. Example 1C yields the result $P(\text{heads, orange, red}) = P(\text{heads}) \cdot P(\text{orange}) \cdot P(\text{red}) = \frac{1}{2} \cdot \frac{1}{3} \cdot \frac{1}{3} = \frac{1}{18}$.

Georgia Performance Standards

M6P3.a Organize and consolidate their mathematical thinking through communication.

M6P3.c Analyze and evaluate the mathematical thinking and strategies of others.

M6P4.c Recognize and apply mathematics in contexts outside of mathematics.

12-5 Exercises

M6P3.a, M6P3.c, M6P4.c

go.hrw.com
Homework Help Online
KEYWORD: MR7 12-5
Parent Resources Online
KEYWORD: MR7 Parent

GUIDED PRACTICE

See Example 1

1. Patrick rolled a fair number cube twice. Find the probability that the number cube will show an even number both times. $\frac{1}{4}$
2. A boy and a girl each flip a coin. What is the probability that the boy's coin will show heads and the girl's coin will show tails? $\frac{1}{4}$

INDEPENDENT PRACTICE

See Example 1

3. If you spin the spinner twice, what is the probability that it will land on green on the first spin and on purple on the second spin? $\frac{1}{9}$
4. What is the probability that the spinner will land on either green or purple on the first spin and yellow on the second spin? $\frac{2}{9}$
5. What is the probability that the spinner will land on the same color twice in a row? $\frac{1}{3}$

PRACTICE AND PROBLEM SOLVING

Extra Practice p. 738

An experiment involves spinning each spinner once. Find each probability.

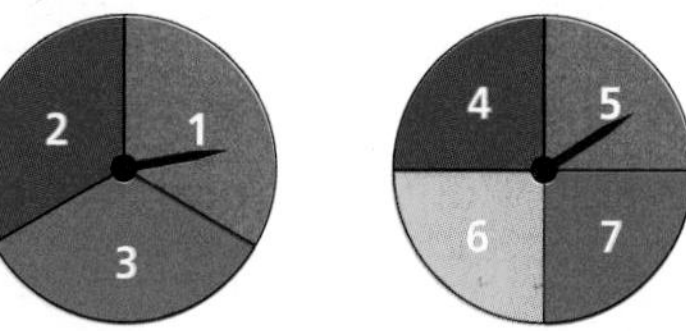

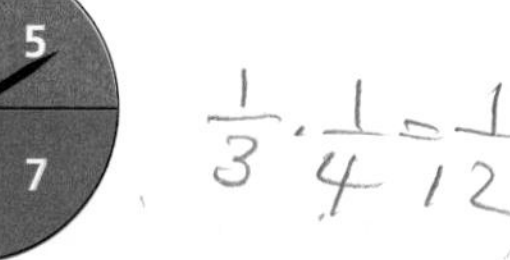

6. P(2 on spinner 1 and 5 on spinner 2) $\frac{1}{12}$
7. P(not 1 on spinner 1 and not 7 on spinner 2) $\frac{1}{2}$
8. P(even number on both spinners) $\frac{1}{6}$
9. P(odd number on spinner 1 and even number on spinner 2) $\frac{1}{3}$
10. P(number on spinner 2 is greater than number on spinner 1) 1
11. P(same number on both spinners) 0
12. P(a multiple of 3 on both spinners) $\frac{1}{12}$
13. P(different number on each spinner) 1
14. A jar contains tiles that are numbered 1, 2, 3, 4, and 5. Danny removes a tile from the jar, replaces the tile, and draws a second tile. What is the probability that Danny will draw the same number both times? $\frac{1}{5}$

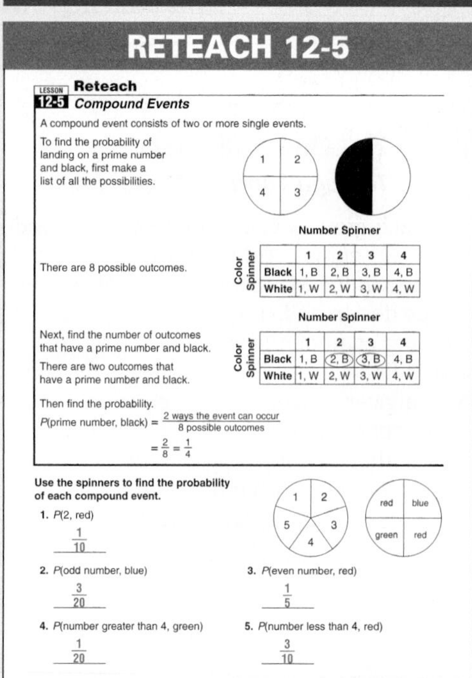

RETEACH 12-5

LESSON 12-5 **Reteach**
Compound Events

A compound event consists of two or more single events.

To find the probability of landing on a prime number and black, first make a list of all the possibilities.

There are 8 possible outcomes.

Number Spinner (columns) / Color Spinner (rows)

	1	2	3	4
Black	1, B	2, B	3, B	4, B
White	1, W	2, W	3, W	4, W

Next, find the number of outcomes that have a prime number and black.

There are two outcomes that have a prime number and black.

Number Spinner (columns) / Color Spinner (rows)

	1	2	3	4
Black	1, B	(2, B)	(3, B)	4, B
White	1, W	2, W	3, W	4, W

Then find the probability.

$P(\text{prime number, black}) = \frac{2 \text{ ways the event can occur}}{8 \text{ possible outcomes}} = \frac{2}{8} = \frac{1}{4}$

Use the spinners to find the probability of each compound event.

1. P(2, red) $\frac{1}{10}$
2. P(odd number, blue) $\frac{3}{20}$
3. P(even number, red) $\frac{1}{5}$
4. P(number greater than 4, green) $\frac{1}{20}$
5. P(number less than 4, red) $\frac{3}{10}$

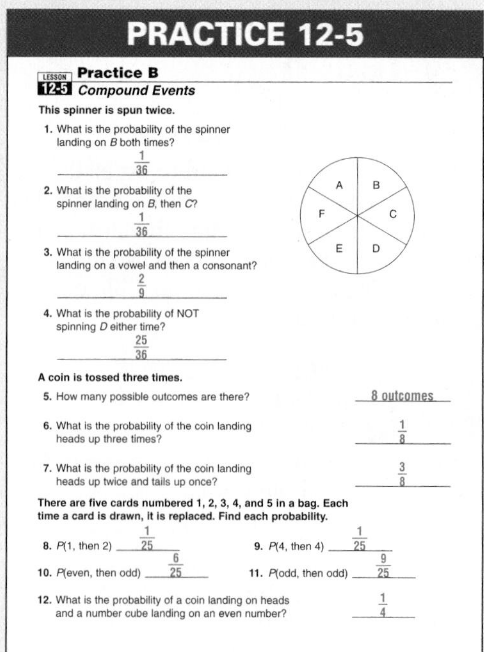

PRACTICE 12-5

LESSON 12-5 **Practice B**
Compound Events

This spinner is spun twice.

1. What is the probability of the spinner landing on B both times? $\frac{1}{36}$
2. What is the probability of the spinner landing on B, then C? $\frac{1}{36}$
3. What is the probability of the spinner landing on a vowel and then a consonant? $\frac{2}{9}$
4. What is the probability of NOT spinning D either time? $\frac{25}{36}$

A coin is tossed three times.

5. How many possible outcomes are there? 8 outcomes
6. What is the probability of the coin landing heads up three times? $\frac{1}{8}$
7. What is the probability of the coin landing heads up twice and tails up once? $\frac{3}{8}$

There are five cards numbered 1, 2, 3, 4, and 5 in a bag. Each time a card is drawn, it is replaced. Find each probability.

8. P(1, then 2) $\frac{1}{25}$
9. P(4, then 4) $\frac{1}{25}$
10. P(even, then odd) $\frac{6}{25}$
11. P(odd, then odd) $\frac{9}{25}$
12. What is the probability of a coin landing on heads and a number cube landing on an even number? $\frac{1}{4}$

A fair number cube is rolled, and a fair coin is tossed. Compare the probabilities. Write <, >, or =.

15. P(3 and tails) ▒ P(5 and heads) =

16. P(even number and tails) ▒ P(odd number and heads) =

17. P(number less than 3 and tails) ▒ P(odd number and tails) <

18. P(number greater than 5 and heads) ▒ P(prime number and tails) <

Georgia LINK — Life Science

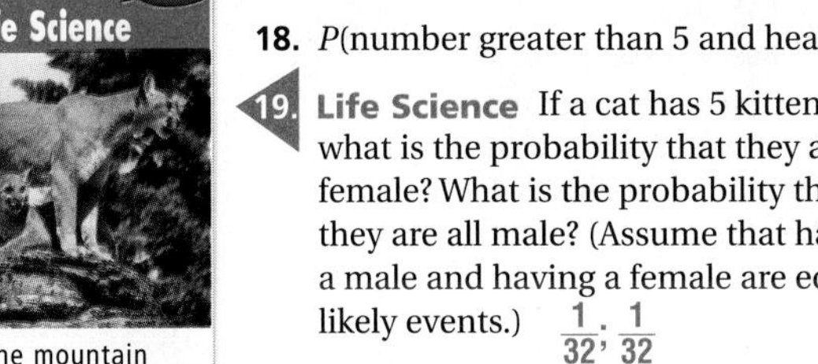

The mountain lion is the largest cat native to Georgia.

19. **Life Science** If a cat has 5 kittens, what is the probability that they are all female? What is the probability that they are all male? (Assume that having a male and having a female are equally likely events.) $\frac{1}{32}$, $\frac{1}{32}$

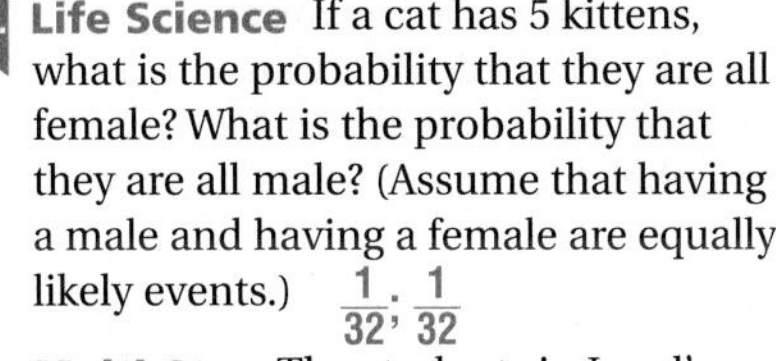

20. **Multi-Step** The students in Jared's class have ID numbers made up of two digits from 1 through 6. The same digit can be used twice. In fact, the same digit is used twice in Jared's ID number. If Jared rolls 2 number cubes, what is the probability that he does NOT roll his ID number? $\frac{35}{36}$

21. **What's the Error?** One of your classmates said, "If you flip a coin and roll a number cube, the probability of getting heads and a 3 is $\frac{1}{2} + \frac{1}{6} = \frac{2}{3}$." What mistake did your classmate make? Explain how to find the correct answer. The classmate added; should have multiplied.

22. **Write About It** Describe a situation that involves a compound event. Possible answer: rolling a fair number cube and flipping a coin

23. **Challenge** You roll a number cube six times. What is the probability of rolling the numbers 1 through 6 in order? $\frac{1}{46,656}$

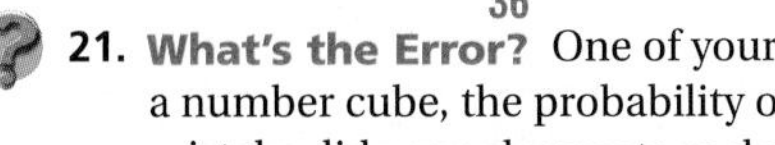

CRCT Prep • GPS Support • Spiral Review

24. **Multiple Choice** A fair number cube is rolled twice. What is the probability that the first roll will be even and the second roll will be odd?

Ⓐ $\frac{1}{6}$ (B) $\frac{1}{4}$ (circled) Ⓒ $\frac{1}{2}$ Ⓓ $\frac{5}{6}$

25. **Multiple Choice** A fair number cube is rolled once, and a coin is flipped once. What is the probability of a 5 on the number cube and heads on the coin toss?

Ⓕ $\frac{1}{2}$ Ⓖ $\frac{1}{4}$ Ⓗ $\frac{1}{6}$ (J) $\frac{1}{12}$ (circled)

Order each set of numbers from least to greatest. (Lesson 3-1)

26. 1.2, 0.445, 1.06, 0.9 0.445, 0.9, 1.06, 1.2

27. 2.45, 2.678, 2.007, 2.02 2.007, 2.02, 2.45, 2.678

28. 7.99, 7.999, 7.9, 7.09 7.09, 7.9, 7.99, 7.999

29. Suppose there is a 15% chance that Cy will finish all his work before he leaves class. What is the probability that he will NOT finish? (Lesson 12-3) 85%

Ongoing Assessment and Intervention

Diagnose ***Before*** **the Lesson**
12-5 Warm Up, TE p. 688

Monitor ***During*** **the Lesson**
12-5 Know-It Notebook
12-5 Questioning Strategies

Assess ***After*** **the Lesson**
12-5 Lesson Quiz, TE p. 691

Test Prep Doctor Exercise 25 represents a compound event. Students using a sample space or a tree diagram should be able to eliminate choices **F, G,** and **H.**

Journal

Have students describe an experiment involving compound events. Have them find the theoretical probabilities of a few different outcomes of the experiment.

Power Presentations with PowerPoint®

12-5 Lesson Quiz

An experiment involves one spin of the spinner and one flip of the coin. Find each probability.

1. What is the probability of the spinner landing on red and the coin landing tails up? $\frac{1}{6}$

2. What is the probability of the spinner landing on an odd number and the coin landing heads up? $\frac{1}{3}$

3. What is the probability of the spinner landing on an even number and the coin landing tails up? $\frac{1}{6}$

Also available on transparency

CHALLENGE 12-5

LESSON 12-5 Challenge
Give Probability a Hand

Have you ever made a decision by playing Rock, Paper, Scissors? Did you know that people all over the world have played this game for hundreds of years? In it, a player makes his or her hand into the shape of three possible throws at the same time—Rock, Paper, or Scissors. Rock beats Scissors, Scissors beats Paper, and Paper beats Rock.

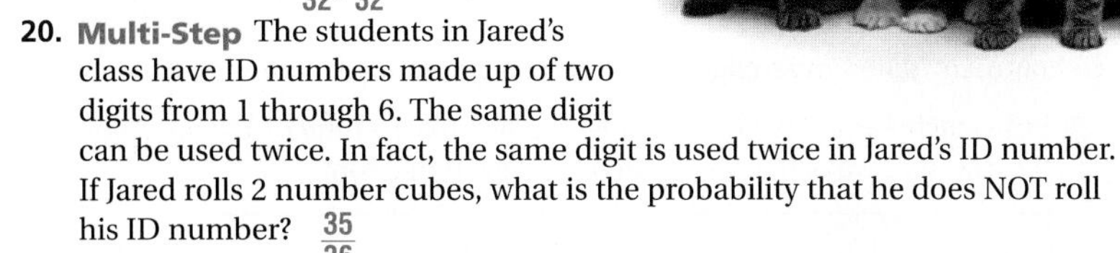

Imagine you are playing Rock, Paper, Scissors with a friend. You are Player 1, and your friend is Player 2. Find each probability.

1. P(1 rock, 2 paper) = $\frac{1}{9}$
2. P(both scissors) = $\frac{1}{9}$
3. P(1 not rock, 2 scissors) = $\frac{2}{9}$
4. P(1 not scissors, 2 not paper) = $\frac{4}{9}$
5. Which throw has the highest chance of winning each round of the game? Explain.

Possible answer: None; all of the throws have an equal probability of winning because each throw beats one other throw.

Imagine you are playing Rock, Paper, Scissors with two friends. You are Player 1, and your friends are Player 2 and Player 3. Find each probability.

6. P(1 rock, 2 paper, 3 scissors) = $\frac{1}{27}$
7. P(all paper) = $\frac{1}{27}$
8. P(1 not scissors, 2 scissors, 3 not paper) = $\frac{4}{27}$

PROBLEM SOLVING 12-5

LESSON 12-5 Problem Solving
Compound Events

You have two decks of playing cards. You draw one card from each deck at the same time. Write the correct answer.

Standard Deck of Playing Cards

Suit	Color	Number
Spades	Black	13
Hearts	Red	13
Clubs	Black	13
Diamonds	Red	13

1. What is the probability that you will draw a black card from Deck 1 and a red card from Deck 2? $\frac{1}{4}$

2. What is the probability that you will draw a club card from both decks? $\frac{1}{16}$

3. What is the probability that you will draw a heart from Deck 1 and a black card from Deck 2? $\frac{1}{8}$

You roll two standard number cubes at the same time. Circle the letter of the correct answer.

4. What is the probability that you roll doubles, or the same two numbers?
   A $\frac{1}{2}$
   B $\frac{1}{3}$
   (C) $\frac{1}{6}$ (circled)
   D $\frac{1}{12}$

5. What is the probability of rolling a sum less than 6?
   (F) $\frac{5}{18}$ (circled)
   G $\frac{1}{6}$
   H $\frac{1}{9}$
   J $\frac{1}{18}$

6. Which sums are you least likely to get? What is the probability of rolling either of those sums?
   A 2 or 3; $\frac{1}{12}$
   B 2 or 4; $\frac{1}{9}$
   B 2 or 6; $\frac{1}{6}$
   (D) 2 or 12; $\frac{1}{18}$ (circled)

7. Which sum are you most likely to get? What is the probability of rolling that sum?
   (F) 7; $\frac{1}{6}$ (circled)
   G 8; $\frac{1}{9}$
   H 9; $\frac{1}{9}$
   J 10; $\frac{1}{12}$

Organizer

Use with Lesson 12-5

Pacing:
Traditional $\frac{1}{2}$ day
Block $\frac{1}{4}$ day

Objective: Use index cards to model permutations and combinations.

Materials: Index cards

Resources

Hands-On Lab Activities
Lab 12-5 Recording Sheet

Teach

Discuss

Discuss what each arrangement of index cards represents.

Close

Key Concept

A compound event is called a permutation when the order of the outcomes matters. If the order of the outcomes does not matter, then a compound event is called a combination.

Assessment

Identify the following as a permutation or combination.

1. your locker combination permutation
2. your selection of a shirt, shorts, and shoes for Saturday combination

M6P5.a Create and use representations to organize, record, and communicate mathematical ideas.

M6P5.b Select, apply, and translate among mathematical representations to solve problems.

M6P5.c Use representations to model and interpret physical, social, and mathematical phenomena.

Explore Permutations and Combinations

Use with Lesson 12-5

Georgia Performance Standards
M6P5.a, M6P5.b, M6P5.c

Lab Resources Online
KEYWORD: MR7 Lab12

For a compound event, you often must count the arrangements of individual outcomes. To do this, you must know whether the order of the outcomes in these arrangements matters. With three outcomes *A, B,* and *C,* when is *A-B-C* different from *C-B-A,* and when is it considered to be the same?

Activity 1

In how many different arrangements can Ellen, Susan, and Jeffrey sit in a row?

1. Write each name on 6 index cards. You will have a total of 18 cards. Show all the different ways the cards can be arranged in a row.

Arrangement	1	2	3	4	5	6
First Seat	Ellen	Ellen	Susan	Susan	Jeffrey	Jeffrey
Second Seat	Susan	Jeffrey	Jeffrey	Ellen	Susan	Ellen
Third Seat	Jeffrey	Susan	Ellen	Jeffrey	Ellen	Susan

There are 6 different ways that these three people can sit in a row.

Notice that the order of the students in the different arrangements is important. "Ellen, Susan, Jeffrey" is different from "Ellen, Jeffrey, Susan." An arrangement in which order is important is called a **permutation.**

Think and Discuss

1. Think of another situation in which the order in an arrangement is important. Can you think of a situation in which the order would NOT be important? Explain. Check students' work.

Try This

1. Cindy, Laurie, Marty, and Joel are running for president of their class. The person who gets the second greatest amount of votes will be the vice president. How many different ways can the election turn out? 24

Activity 2

1. Abe, Babe, Cora, and Dora are going to work on a project in groups of 2. How many different ways can they pair off?

   Write each name on 3 index cards. You will have a total of 12 cards. Show all pairings.

Abe	Babe		Babe	Cora		Cora	Dora
Abe	Cora		Babe	Dora			
Abe	Dora						

   There are 6 different possible pairs.

Notice that in this situation, the order in the pairs is not important. "Abe, Cora" is the same as "Cora, Abe." When order is not important, the arrangements are called **combinations.**

Think and Discuss

Tell whether each of the following is a permutation or a combination. Explain.

1. There are 20 horses in a race. Ribbons are given for first, second, and third place. How many possible ways can the ribbons be awarded? **Permutation; order is important.**
2. There are 20 violin players trying out for the school band and 6 players will be chosen. How many different ways could students be selected for the band? **Combination; order is not important.**
3. Connie has 10 different barrettes. She wears 2 each day. How many ways can she choose 2 barrettes each morning? **Combination; order is not important.**
4. Yoko belongs to a book club, and she has just received 25 new books. How many possible ways are there for them to be placed on the shelf? **Permutation; order is important.**

Try This

1. The video club is sponsoring a double feature. How many ways can club members choose 2 movies from a list of 6 possibilities? **15**
2. Ms. Baker must pick a team of 3 students to send to the state mathematics competition. She has decided to choose 3 students from the 5 with the highest grades in her class. Ms. Baker can either send 3 equal representatives, or she can send a captain, an assistant captain, and a secretary. Which choice results in more possible teams? Explain. Find the number of teams possible for each choice.

Activity 1

Answers to *Think and Discuss*

1. Possible answer: The order is important when conducting a systematic sample in which every third person will be surveyed. Even if the first three people through the door are the same in each case, the order in which they enter affects the survey results. The order is not important in a situation in which the first three people into a store win a prize. All three people will win, regardless of who was first, second, or third to enter.

Activity 2

Answers to *Try This*

2. Choosing three equal team members is a combination problem and results in 10 possible teams; choosing a captain, an assistant captain, and a secretary is a permutation problem and results in 60 possible teams. The permutation problem has more possible teams because the order in which team members are chosen is important.

12-6 Organizer

Pacing: Traditional 1 day
Block $\frac{1}{2}$ day

Objective: Students use probability to predict future events.

Online Edition
Tutorial Videos

Power Presentations with PowerPoint®

Warm Up

1. Zachary rolled a fair number cube twice. Find the probability of the number cube showing an odd number both times. $\frac{1}{4}$
2. Larissa rolled a fair number cube twice. Find the probability of the number cube showing the same number both times. $\frac{1}{36}$

Problem of the Day

The average of three numbers is 45. If the average of the first two numbers is 47, what is the third number? 41

Also available on transparency

Math Humor

Teacher: Does anyone know the weather prediction for tomorrow?
Student: It will rain nickels and dimes.
Teacher: Now why would you say that?
Student: I heard on the radio that there would be change in the weather.

12-6 Making Predictions

Learn to use probability to predict events.

Vocabulary
prediction
population
sample

A **prediction** is a guess about something in the future. One way to make a prediction is to collect information by conducting a survey. The **population** is the whole group being surveyed. To save time and money, researchers often make predictions based on a **sample**, which is part of the group being surveyed. Another way to make a prediction is to use probability.

The Old Farmer's Almanac predicts weather, sunrise and sunset times, and tides.

Georgia Performance Standards
M6D2.b Determine, and use a ratio to represent, the theoretical probability of a given event. Also, M6A2.g, M6P1.c, M6P1.d.

EXAMPLE 1 Using Sample Surveys to Make Predictions

Based on a sample survey, an airline claims that its flights have a 92% probability of being on time. Out of 1,000 flights, how many would you predict will be on time?

You can write a proportion. Remember that *percent* means "per hundred."

$\frac{92}{100} = \frac{x}{1{,}000}$ *Think: 92 out of 100 is how many out of 1,000?*

$100 \cdot x = 92 \cdot 1{,}000$ *The cross products are equal.*

$100x = 92{,}000$ *x is multiplied by 100.*

$\frac{100x}{100} = \frac{92{,}000}{100}$ *Divide both sides by 100 to undo the multiplication.*

$x = 920$

You can predict that about 920 of 1,000 flights will be on time.

EXAMPLE 2 Using Theoretical Probability to Make Predictions

If you roll a number cube 24 times, how many times do you expect to roll a 5?

$P(\text{rolling a 5}) = \frac{1}{6}$

$\frac{1}{6} = \frac{x}{24}$ *Think: 1 out of 6 is how many out of 24?*

$6 \cdot x = 1 \cdot 24$ *The cross products are equal.*

$6x = 24$ *x is multiplied by 6.*

$\frac{6x}{6} = \frac{24}{6}$ *Divide both sides by 6 to undo the multiplication.*

$x = 4$

You can expect to roll a 5 about 4 times.

Georgia Performance Standards

M6A2.g Use proportional reasoning ($a/b = c/d$ and $y = kx$) to solve problems.

M6D2.b Determine, and use a ratio to represent, the theoretical probability of a given event.

M6P1.c Apply and adapt a variety of appropriate strategies to solve problems.

M6P1.d Monitor and reflect on the process of mathematical problem solving.

1 Introduce

Alternate Opener

EXPLORATION

12-6 Making Predictions

You can use probabilities to make ***predictions***. For example, the probability of rolling a 1 on a number cube is $\frac{1}{6}$. If you roll the cube 12 times, how many times do you predict you will roll a 1?

Each time you roll the cube, the probability of rolling a 1 is $\frac{1}{6}$.

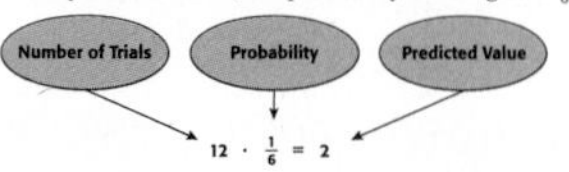

So you expect to roll a 1 twice when you roll a cube 12 times.

Use the model as a guide to make each prediction.

	Event	Probability	Number of Trials	Predicted Value
1.	Getting heads when flipping a coin	$\frac{1}{2}$	Flip the coin 20 times.	
2.	Spinning a 2 on a spinner divided into 4 equal sections	$\frac{1}{4}$	Spin the spinner 24 times.	

Think and Discuss

3. **Explain** how to find a predicted value.
4. **Discuss** whether it is certain that you will roll a 1 twice when you roll a number cube 12 times.

Motivate

To get students ready for the lesson, review how to solve proportions. Work together to solve the proportion $\frac{2}{3} = \frac{x}{6}$.

1. The cross products are equal.
$3x = 12$
2. x is multiplied by 3, so divide both sides by 3 to undo the multiplication.
$\frac{3x}{3} = \frac{12}{3}$
3. Solve.
$x = 4$

Explorations and answers are provided in *Alternate Openers: Explorations Transparencies*.

EXAMPLE 3 **PROBLEM SOLVING APPLICATION**

A stadium sells yearly parking passes. If you have a parking pass, you can park at the stadium for any event during that year.

Based on a sample group of fans, the managers of the stadium estimate that the probability that a person with a pass will attend any one event is 80%. The parking lot has 300 spaces. If the managers want the lot to be full at every event, how many passes should they sell?

1 Understand the Problem

The **answer** will be the number of parking passes they should sell.

List the **important information:**

- P(person with pass attends event) = 80%
- There are 300 parking spaces.

2 Make a Plan

The managers want to fill all 300 spaces. But, on average, only 80% of parking pass holders will attend. So 80% of pass holders must equal 300. You can write an equation to find this number.

3 Solve

$\frac{80}{100} = \frac{300}{x}$	*Think: 80 out of 100 is 300 out of how many?*
$100 \cdot 300 = 80 \cdot x$	*The cross products are equal.*
$30{,}000 = 80x$	*x is multiplied by 80.*
$\frac{30{,}000}{80} = \frac{80x}{80}$	*Divide both sides by 80 to undo the multiplication.*
$375 = x$	

The managers should sell 375 parking passes.

4 Look Back

If the managers sold only 300 passes, the parking lot would not usually be full because only about 80% of the people with passes will attend any one event. The managers should sell more than 300 passes, so 375 is a reasonable answer.

Think and Discuss GPS M6P2.c, M6P3.b

1. Tell whether you expect to be exactly right if you make a prediction based on a sample. Explain your answer.

Answer to *Think and Discuss:*

1. No; a prediction, by definition, is just a guess and a sample is also a prediction as to the makeup of a population. So you can not expect a guess based on a prediction to be exact.

COMMON ERROR ALERT

Students may set up their proportions incorrectly. If x represents the number of times a favorable outcome occurs, it should be in the numerator. If it represents the number of possible outcomes, then it belongs in the denominator.

Power Presentations with PowerPoint®

Additional Examples

Example 

A store claims that 78% of shoppers end up buying something. Out of 1,000 shoppers, how many would you predict will buy something?

about 780

Example 

If you roll a number cube 30 times, how many times do you expect to roll a number greater than 2?

about 20 times

Example 

Suppose the managers of a second stadium, like the one in the student book, also sell yearly parking passes. The managers of the second stadium estimate that the probability of a person with a pass attending any one event is 50%. The parking lot has 400 spaces. If the managers want the lot to be full at every event, how many passes should they sell?

800

Also available on transparency

2 Teach

Guided Instruction

In this lesson, students learn to use probability to predict future events. Define the terms *prediction, population,* and *sample*. Teach students to set up proportions to make predictions involving probability. Have students verify each answer by substituting the value for x in each proportion.

Reaching All Learners

Through Cooperative Learning

Have students working in groups research airlines' Web sites and find the percent of flights that are on time. (This information is usually updated monthly.) You may wish to assign a different airline to each group. Have them predict the number of on-time flights out of 1,000 flights (or out of 750 flights to make it a little more challenging).

3 Close

Summarize

Review that a *prediction* is a guess about something in the future. Remind students that probability and proportions can be used to make predictions.

12-6 Exercises

Assignment Guide

If you finished Example 1 assign:
Average 1, 8, 15–24
Advanced 4, 8, 15–24

If you finished Example 2 assign:
Average 1–2, 8, 15–24
Advanced 4–6, 8, 15–24

If you finished Example 3 assign:
Average 1–7, 10–24
Advanced 4–24

Homework Quick Check

Quickly check key concepts.
Exercises: 4, 6, 10

Math Background

The idea of using data and probability to analyze and make predictions about real-world events can be traced to seventeenth century England.

John Graunt and his friend Sir William Petty collected and analyzed data concerning birth rates and death rates in the mid-seventeenth century.

Today data collection and analysis are central to the operation of governments and insurance companies, and statistical methods play an important role in both sciences and social sciences.

Georgia Performance Standards

M6P1.a Build new mathematical knowledge through problem solving.

M6P3.a Organize and consolidate their mathematical thinking through communication.

M6P3.c Analyze and evaluate the mathematical thinking and strategies of others.

M6P4.c Recognize and apply mathematics in contexts outside of mathematics.

12-6 Exercises

Georgia Performance Standards
M6P1.a, M6P3.a, M6P3.c, M6P4.c

go.hrw.com
Homework Help Online
KEYWORD: MR7 12-6
Parent Resources Online
KEYWORD: MR7 Parent

GUIDED PRACTICE

See Example 1
1. Based on a sample survey, a local newspaper states that 12% of the city's residents have volunteered at an animal shelter. Out of 5,000 residents, how many would you predict have volunteered at the animal shelter? 600

See Example 2
2. If you roll a fair number cube 30 times, how many times would you expect to roll a number that is a multiple of 3? 10

See Example 3
3. **Recreation** Airlines routinely overbook flights, which means that they sell more tickets than there are seats on the planes. Suppose an airline estimates that 93% of customers will show up for a particular flight. If the plane seats 186 people, how many tickets should the airline sell? 200 tickets

INDEPENDENT PRACTICE

See Example 1
4. Based on a sample survey, a local newspaper claims that 64% of the town's households receive their paper. Out of 15,000 households, how many would you predict receive the paper? 9,600

See Example 2
5. If you flip a coin 64 times, how many times do you expect the coin to show tails? 32

6. A bag contains 2 black chips, 5 red chips, and 4 white chips. You pick a chip from the bag, record its color, and put the chip back in the bag. If you repeat this process 99 times, how many times do you expect to remove a red chip from the bag? 45

See Example 3
7. **Life Science** The director of a blood bank is eager to increase his supply of O negative blood, because O negative blood can be given to people with any blood type. The probability that a person has O negative blood is 7%. The director would like to have 9 O negative donors each day. How many total donors does the director need to find each day to reach his goal of O negative donors? 129 donors

PRACTICE AND PROBLEM SOLVING

Extra Practice p. 738

8. A sample survey of 50 people in Harrisburg indicates that 10 of them know the name of the mayor of their neighboring city.

a. Out of 5,500 Harrisburg residents, how many would you expect to know the name of the mayor of the neighboring city? 1,100

b. **Multi-Step** Out of 600 Harrisburg residents, how many would you predict do not know the name of the mayor of the neighboring city? 480

9. **Critical Thinking** A survey is being conducted as people exit a frozen yogurt store. They are being asked if they prefer frozen yogurt or ice cream. Should predictions be made about the population of the town based on the survey? Explain. No; they are only surveying people who like frozen yogurt.

RETEACH 12-6

LESSON 12-6 **Reteach**
Making Predictions

A prediction is a guess about something in the future. You can use theoretical probability to make predictions.

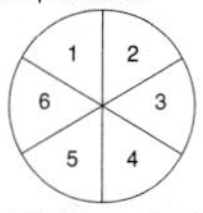

(Spinner with sections 1, 2, 3, 4, 5, 6)

Look at the spinner above. To find the number of times you expect to land on a composite number in 27 spins, first find the theoretical probability of the event.

$P(\text{composite number}) \approx \frac{2}{6} = \frac{1}{3}$

This means that the spinner will land on a composite number about $\frac{1}{3}$ of the time.

Then multiply the theoretical probability by the number of times that you carry out the experiment.

Find $\frac{1}{3}$ of 27 times.

$\frac{1}{3} \cdot 27$
$= \frac{27}{3}$
$= 9$

You can predict that the spinner will land on a composite number about 9 times in 27 spins.

Look at the spinner above. Use theoretical probability to make a prediction.

1. Landing on an odd number in 42 spins.
21 times

2. Landing on a number that is neither prime nor composite in 30 spins.
5 times

3. Landing on a number that is less than 5 in 18 spins.
12 times

PRACTICE 12-6

LESSON 12-6 **Practice B**
Making Predictions

Use the sample survey to make predictions.

Favorite Sports

Sport	Number of Students
Football	28
Basketball	35
Soccer	20
Baseball	45
Hockey	15
Other	7

1. If you randomly selected a person, what is the probability that his or her favorite sport is basketball?
$\frac{7}{30}$

2. In a group of 200 people, how many do you predict would choose baseball as their favorite sport?
60 people

3. In a class of 45 students, how many students do you predict would choose soccer as their favorite sport?
6 students

4. In a group of 100 people, how many do you predict would choose hockey as their favorite sport?
10 people

5. Based on a sample survey, a local newspaper states that 75% of all the city's voters turned out for the city council elections. If you randomly selected 200 people in that city, how many do you predict would have voted in the election?
150 people

6. If you roll a fair number cube 30 times, how many times would you expect to roll an odd number?
15 times

7. Based on a sample survey, a company claims that 8% of its customers were unhappy with the DVD players they bought. If the company sold DVD players to 2,000 people last year, how many of those customers do you predict were unhappy with their DVDs?
160 customers

8. If you toss a fair coin 48 times, how many times do you predict it will land tails up?
24 times

Social Studies LINK

The Native Canadians lived in Canada before the Europeans arrived. The French were the first Europeans to settle successfully in Canada.

The graph shows the results of a survey of 400 Canadian citizens.

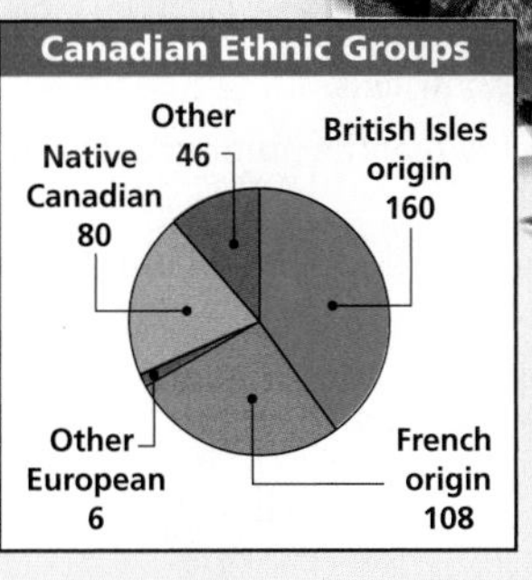

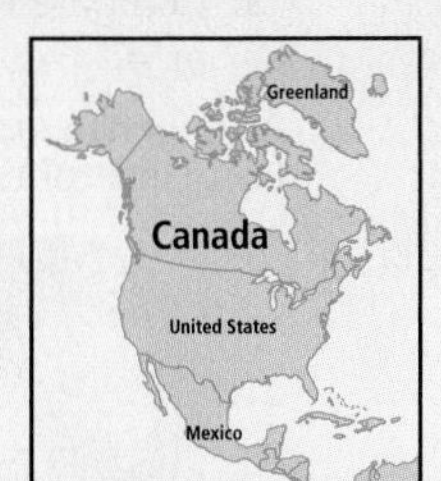

10. Out of 75 Canadians, how many would you predict are of French origin? about 20

11. A random group of Canadians includes 18 Native Canadians. How many total Canadians would you predict are in the group? about 90

12. **What's the Error?** A student said that in any group of Canadians, 20 of them will be Native Canadians. What mistake did this student make?

13. **Write About It** How could you predict the number of people of French *or* Native Canadian origin in a group of 150 Canadians?

14. **Challenge** In a group of Canadians, 15 are in the Other European origin category. Predict how many Canadians in the same group are NOT in that category. 985

CRCT Prep • GPS Support • Spiral Review

15. **Multiple Choice** Jay played a game and won 24 out of 100 times. Which is the best estimate of the experimental probability of Jay winning his next game?

Ⓐ 5% Ⓑ 25% Ⓒ 50% Ⓓ 75%

16. **Multiple Choice** You roll a fair number cube 36 times. How many times do you expect to roll a 4?

Ⓕ 36 Ⓖ 9 Ⓗ 6 Ⓙ $\frac{1}{6}$

Solve each question. Check your answers. (Lesson 11-8)

17. $x + 10 = -2$ $x = -12$

18. $x - 20 = -5$ $x = 15$

19. $-9x = 45$ $x = -5$

20. $x \div (-2) = -5$ $x = 10$

A fair number cube is rolled. Find each probability. (Lesson 12-4)

21. $P(5)$ $\frac{1}{6}$

22. $P(\text{not } 2)$ $\frac{5}{6}$

23. $P(3) + P(4)$ $\frac{1}{3}$

24. $P(\text{number divisible by } 3)$ $\frac{1}{3}$

CHALLENGE 12-6

LESSON 12-6 **Challenge**
Predictions in a Flash

Lightning strikes somewhere on Earth almost 9 million times a day! However, very few people are struck by lightning. In fact, your chance of being struck by lightning each year in the United States is only 1 in 600,000. But wait! This is not a simple probability. Where you live, the time of day, and even your hobbies affect your chances of being hit. To be on the safe side, stay indoors during a storm, and avoid open spaces, trees, poles and other tall objects that can attract lightning.

The people who live in the states listed below have the highest probabilities of being struck by lightning. Use their given probabilities and populations to predict how many people in each state will likely be struck by lightning next year.

1. 
Florida; 16 million; 0.0003%
48 people

2. 
North Carolina; 8 million; 0.0002%
16 people

3.  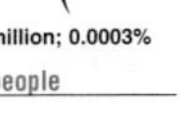
Texas; 21 million; 0.00007%
about 15 people

4. 
New York; 19 million; 0.00009%
about 17 people

PROBLEM SOLVING 12-6

LESSON 12-6 **Problem Solving**
Making Predictions

Write the correct answer.

U.S. Public High School Graduation Rates, Top 5 States

State	Number of Students	Percent that Graduate
Iowa	497,301	83.2%
Minnesota	854,034	84.7%
Nebraska	288,261	87.9%
North Dakota	112,751	84.5%
Utah	480,255	83.7%

1. In which state are students most likely to graduate from public high school? About how many of the students who are enrolled in that state now do you predict will graduate?
Nebraska; about 253,381 students

2. About how many students enrolled in North Dakota public high schools now do you predict will graduate?
about 95,275 students

Circle the letter of the correct answer.

3. About how many students enrolled in Minnesota public high schools now do you predict will graduate?
A about 717,389 students
Ⓑ about 723,367 students
C about 743,010 students
D about 7,233,667 students

4. About how many more students in public high schools do you predict will graduate in Iowa than in Utah?
F about 413,754 more students
G about 401,973 more students
Ⓗ about 11,781 more students
J about 1,781 more students

5. The total U.S. high school graduation rate is 68.1%. There are 48,857,321 students enrolled in public schools. About how many of those students do you predict will graduate?
A about 332 million students
B about 20 million students
Ⓒ about 33 million students
D about 16 million students

6. About 11% of all students in the U.S. are enrolled in private schools. There are more than 48 million students in the U.S. About how many do you predict will go to private schools?
Ⓕ about 5,280,000 students
G about 6 million students
H about 52,800 students
J about 528,000 students

Ongoing Assessment and Intervention

***Diagnose Before* the Lesson**
12-6 Warm Up, TE p. 694

***Monitor During* the Lesson**
12-6 Know-It Notebook
12-6 Questioning Strategies

***Assess After* the Lesson**
12-6 Lesson Quiz, TE p. 697

Interdisciplinary LINK

Social Studies

Exercises 10–14 focus on the history and culture of Canada.

Answers

12–13. See p. A12.

Test Prep Doctor For Exercise 16, students should remember to use theoretical probability and a proportion to make the prediction.

Journal

Have students explain in their own words how proportions and probability can be used to make predictions. Have students give examples.

Power Presentations with PowerPoint®

12-6 Lesson Quiz

1. The owner of a local pizzeria estimates that 72% of his customers order pepperoni on their pizza. Out of 250 orders taken in one day, how many would you predict to have pepperoni? 180

2. A bag contains 9 red chips, 4 blue chips, and 7 yellow chips. You pick a chip from the bag, record its color, and put the chip back in the bag. If you do this 100 times, how many times do you expect to remove a yellow chip from the bag? 35

3. A quality-control inspector has determined that 3% of the items he checks are defective. If the company he works for produces 3,000 items per day, how many does the inspector predict will be defective? 90

Also available on transparency

Organizer

Objective: Assess students' mastery of concepts and skills in Lessons 12-5 through 12-6.

Resources

Assessment Resources
Section 12B Quiz

Test & Practice Generator
One-Stop Planner®

INTERVENTION

Resources

Ready to Go On? Intervention and Enrichment **Worksheets**

Ready to Go On? **CD-ROM**

Ready to Go On? **Online**

my.hrw.com

CHAPTER 12

SECTION 12B

Quiz for Lessons 12-5 Through 12-6

12-5 Compound Events

Billie rolls a fair number cube and then flips a fair coin.

1. Find the probability that the number cube will show an even number and the coin will show tails. $\frac{1}{4}$
2. Find the probability that the number cube will show a 6 and the coin will show tails. $\frac{1}{12}$
3. Compare P(4 and heads) and P(odd number and heads). Write $<$, $>$, or $=$. $<$

An experiment involves spinning a spinner and choosing a marble from a bag. For Problems 4–6, use the diagrams.

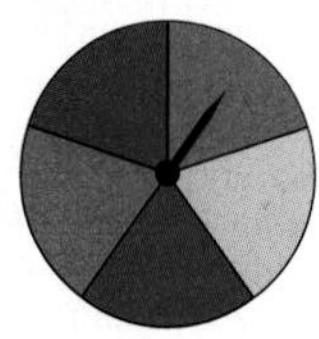
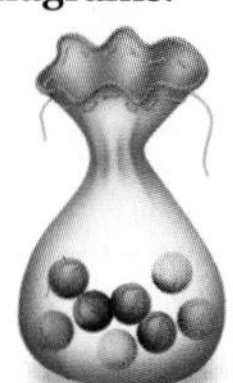

4. What is the probability of spinning red on the spinner and choosing a red marble from the bag? $\frac{1}{5}$
5. What is the probability of spinning yellow and choosing a marble that is NOT yellow? $\frac{3}{20}$
6. What is the probability of spinning a color that is NOT blue and choosing a marble that is NOT blue? $\frac{9}{20}$

12-6 Making Predictions

7. Based on a sample survey, 26% of the local people have a pet dog. Out of 600 people, how many people do you predict will have a pet dog? **156**
8. If you roll a number cube 54 times, how many times do you expect to roll a number less than 3? **18**
9. Based on previous attendance, the managers for a summer concert series estimate the probability that a person will attend any one event to be 90%. The chairs set up around the stage seat 450 people. If the mangers want to be at full capacity every concert, how many tickets should they sell? **500**
10. Based on a sample survey, a newspaper states that only 45% of the local population gets the recommended amount of sleep each night. If there are 45,000 people in town, how many people are not getting enough sleep? **24,750**

Ready to Go On?

READY TO GO ON?
Diagnose and Prescribe

NO INTERVENE

Ready to Go On? Intervention	*Ready to Go On? Intervention,* Section 12B: Worksheets	CD-ROM	Online
Lesson 12-5	12-5 Intervention	Activity 12-5	Diagnose and Prescribe Online
Lesson 12-6	12-6 Intervention	Activity 12-6	

YES ENRICH

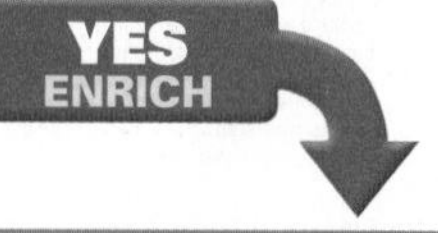

Ready to Go On? Enrichment, **Section 12B**
- Worksheets
- CD-ROM
- Online

MULTI-STEP TEST PREP

Spin to Win Jasper Middle School is having a spring carnival for students and their families. Every guest may spin either the Big Wheel or the Lucky Circle. Guests win a door prize if the Big Wheel's spinner lands on *A* or if the Lucky Circle's spinner lands on an even number.

1. Is a guest more likely to win a door prize by spinning the Big Wheel or by spinning the Lucky Circle? Explain.
2. Miguel chooses to spin the Big Wheel. His sister, Anna, chooses to spin the Lucky Circle. How many different outcomes of their spins are possible? 20
3. What is the probability that Miguel and Anna both win a door prize? $\frac{1}{10}$
4. Find the probability that two guests in a row win a prize spinning the Big Wheel. $\frac{1}{16}$
5. During the carnival, 160 guests spin the Big Wheel and 125 guests spin the Lucky Circle. Which spinner do you predict will have the greater number of winners? Explain.

Multi-Step Test Prep

MULTI-STEP TEST PREP

Organizer

Objective: Assess students' ability to apply concepts and skills in Chapter 12 in a real-world format.

Online Edition

Resources

Middle School Assessments
www.mathtekstoolkit.org

Problem	Text reference
1	Lesson 12-4
2	Lesson 12-3
3	Lesson 12-5
4	Lesson 12-5
5	Lesson 12-6

Answers

1. The Lucky Circle; the probability of winning a prize with the Lucky Circle is $\frac{2}{5}$, the probability of winning a prize with the Big Wheel is $\frac{1}{4}$; $\frac{2}{5} > \frac{1}{4}$.
5. The Lucky Circle; the expected number of winners for the Big Wheel is 40 and the expected number of winners for the Lucky Circle is 50.

INTERVENTION

Scaffolding Questions

1. What is the probability of winning a prize with the Big Wheel? $\frac{1}{4}$ How many possible outcomes are there when you spin the Lucky Circle? 5 How many of those outcomes result in winning a prize? 2 How can you find the probability of winning a prize with the Lucky Circle? Divide; the probability is $\frac{2}{5}$.
2. What are all the possible outcomes? {A1, A2, A3, A4, A5, B1, B2, B3, B4, B5, C1, C2, C3, C4, C5, D1, D2, D3, D4, D5} How many outcomes are in your list? 20
3. Of the outcomes in your list, which ones represent a win for both Miguel and Anna? A2 and A4 How can you use this information to find the probability that both Miguel and Anna win a prize? Divide; $\frac{2}{20} = \frac{1}{10}$.
4. What are all the possible outcomes when two guests in a row spin the Big Wheel? AA, AB, AC, AD, BA, BB, BC, BD, CA, CB, CC, CD, DA, DB, DC, DD Which of those outcomes represents both guests winning? AA
5. How can you predict the number of guests who will win with the Big Wheel? the Lucky Circle? Solve $\frac{1}{4} = \frac{x}{160}$. Solve $\frac{2}{5} = \frac{x}{125}$.

Extension

1. What is the probability that neither Miguel nor Anna will win a prize? $\frac{9}{20}$
2. What is the probability that two guests in a row will win a prize spinning the Lucky Circle? $\frac{4}{25}$

Extension

Pacing: Traditional 1 day
Block $\frac{1}{2}$ day

Objective: Students find the probability of independent and dependent events.

Online Edition

Using the Extension

In Lesson 12-5, students learned to find the probability of compound events. In this lesson, students learn the difference between independent and dependent compound events and how to find the probability of each kind.

EXTENSION

Independent and Dependent Events

Learn to find the probability of independent and dependent events.

Vocabulary

independent events

dependent events

For **independent events**, the occurrence of one event has no effect on the probability that the second event will occur.

To find the probability that two independent events will occur, multiply the probabilities of the two events as follows:

Probability of Two Independent Events

$$P(A \text{ and } B) = P(A) \cdot P(B)$$

Probability of both events — Probability of first event — Probability of second event

EXAMPLE 1 Finding the Probability of Independent Events

Find the probability of rolling a 3 on a number cube and the spinner shown landing on A.

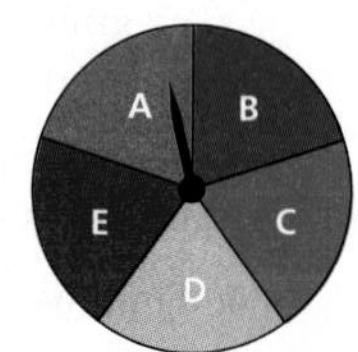

The outcome of rolling the number cube does not affect the outcome of spinning the spinner, so the events are independent.

$P(3 \text{ and } A) = P(3) \cdot P(A)$ — *Use the formula.*

$= \frac{1}{6} \cdot \frac{1}{5}$ — *The probability of rolling a 3 is $\frac{1}{6}$. The probability of the spinner landing on A is $\frac{1}{5}$.*

$= \frac{1}{30}$ — *Multiply.*

The probability of rolling a 3 and the spinner landing on A is $\frac{1}{30}$.

Georgia Performance Standards

M6D2.b Determine, and use a ratio to represent, the theoretical probability of a given event. Also, M6P1.b, M6P4.c.

Suppose you have a bag containing 3 red marbles and 2 blue marbles. You draw two marbles, one after the other. The first marble you draw affects the marbles that remain in the bag, so the two draws are *dependent events*. For **dependent events**, the occurrence of one event has an effect on the probability that the second event will occur.

To find the probability that two dependent events will occur, multiply the probabilities of the two events as follows:

Probability of Two Dependent Events

$$P(A \text{ and } B) = P(A) \cdot P(B \text{ after } A)$$

Probability of both events — Probability of first event — Probability of second event *after* the first event has occurred

Georgia Performance Standards

M6D2.b Determine, and use a ratio to represent, the theoretical probability of a given event.

M6P1.b Solve problems that arise in mathematics and in other contexts.

M6P4.c Recognize and apply mathematics in contexts outside of mathematics.

1 Introduce

Motivate

When you studied compound events, you flipped a coin and rolled a number cube. The outcome of flipping the coin did not affect the outcome of rolling the number cube.

In this extension, you will study situations in which the outcome of the second event is affected by the outcome of the first event.

2 Teach

Guided Instruction

In this extension, students learn to find the probability of independent and dependent events. First explain independent events and teach the students how to use the formula to find the probability of two independent events. Then explain dependent events and teach them how to use the formula to find the probability of two dependent events.

EXAMPLE 2 Finding the Probability of Dependent Events

A bag contains 3 red marbles and 2 blue marbles. Find the probability of drawing a red marble and then a blue marble.

$P(\text{red and blue}) = P(\text{red}) \cdot P(\text{blue after red})$

$P(\text{red}) = \frac{3}{5}$ *There are 3 red marbles out of the 5 marbles.*

$P(\text{blue after red}) = \frac{2}{4} = \frac{1}{2}$ *There are 4 marbles left, and 2 are blue.*

$P(\text{red after blue}) = P(\text{red}) \cdot P(\text{blue after red})$

$= \frac{3}{5} \cdot \frac{1}{2} = \frac{3}{10}$ *Multiply.*

The probability of drawing a red marble and then a blue marble is $\frac{3}{10}$.

Students sometimes forget to reduce the number of possible outcomes by one when calculating the probability of the second event of a dependent compound event.

Additional Examples

Example 

Find the probability of rolling an even number on a number cube and the spinner shown landing on C. $\frac{1}{10}$

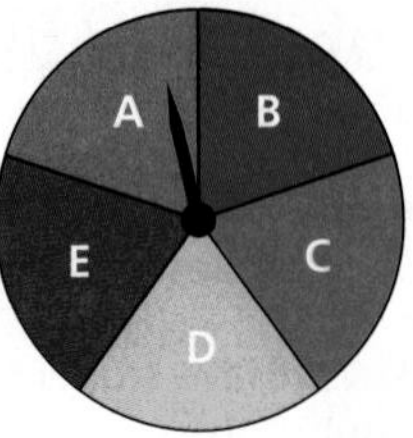

Example 

A bag contains 5 red marbles and 4 blue marbles. Find the probability of drawing a red marble and then a blue marble. $\frac{5}{18}$

Also available on transparency

EXTENSION Exercises

Determine whether the events are independent or dependent.

1. Adrian chooses a baseball card from a stack. Then Jemma chooses a card from those remaining in the stack. **dependent**
2. Mike draws a 7 from ten cards numbered 1 through 10. He replaces the card. Then Alison draws a 5. **independent**

Find the probability of each event for the spinners shown.

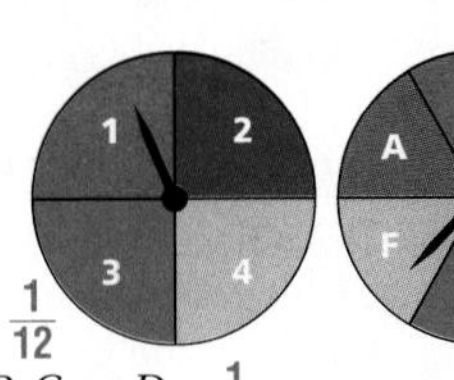

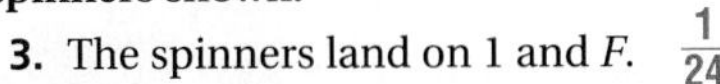

3. The spinners land on 1 and *F*. $\frac{1}{24}$

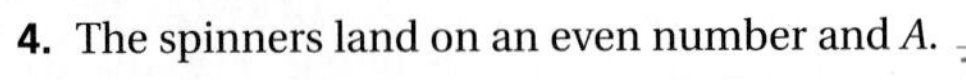

4. The spinners land on an even number and *A*. $\frac{1}{12}$

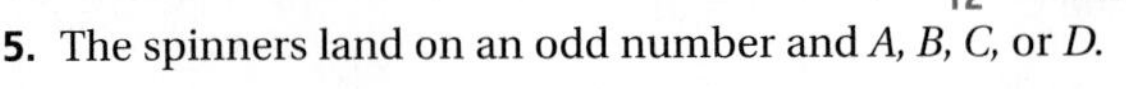

5. The spinners land on an odd number and *A, B, C,* or *D*. $\frac{1}{3}$

A bag contains 4 green marbles and 6 yellow marbles. You draw a marble and put it aside. Then you draw a second marble. Find the probability of each event.

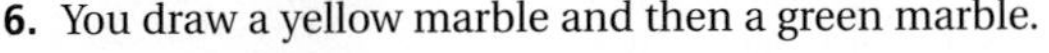

6. You draw a yellow marble and then a green marble. $\frac{4}{15}$

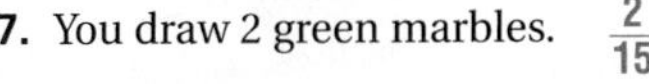

7. You draw 2 green marbles. $\frac{2}{15}$

8. **Write About It** Explain the difference between independent and dependent events.

9. **Challenge** Nicole has 10 coins in her purse: 3 pennies, 3 nickels, 2 dimes, and 2 quarters. She removes a coin from the purse and then chooses a second coin without replacing the first. What is the probability that the two coins will add up to exactly 50 cents? $\frac{1}{45}$

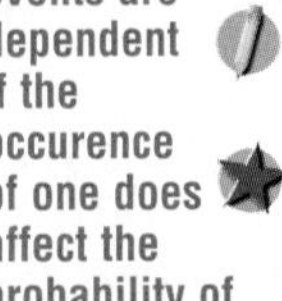

8. Two events are independent if the occurence of one does not affect the probability of the other. Two events are dependent if the occurence of one does affect the probability of the other.

3 Close

Summarize

Ask students to explain the difference between independent and dependent events. Have a student describe two independent events and then describe how the events could become dependent.

Game Time

Organizer

Objective: Participate in games to practice and apply skills learned in Chapter 12.

 **Online Edition**

Resources

Chapter 12 Resource Book
Puzzles, Twisters & Teasers

Probability Brain Teasers

Purpose: To apply probability ideas to solving riddles

Discuss Have students use models to act out problems 2 and 3. For problem 2, have them use 2-color counters to represent black and white socks. For problem 3, have them use index cards labeled with the names Dale, Melvin, Carter, and Ken and the phrases "Dale's food," "Melvin's food," etc.

Extend Give students the following brain teaser: Four students are playing a game in which they draw a card that shows a number and then roll a pair of number cubes and find the sum. If the sum matches the number on a player's card, the player scores. The four cards are shown:

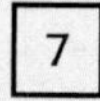 7 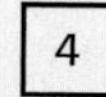 4  11  10

Amy has the greatest probability of scoring. Ben and Kurt have half the probability of scoring that Amy does. The number on Kurt's card is 3 more than the number on Amy's card. Match the player with his or her card. Amy: 7; Ben: 4; Sam: 11; Kurt: 10

Round and Round and Round

Purpose: To practice probability in a game format

Discuss Review the rules of play with students. Have students discuss reasons why one spinner could win more often than the others.

Possible answers: if one spinner has higher numbers overall than the others, or if one spinner has more of the higher numbers and just a few low numbers, while the other spinners have more low numbers and just a few high numbers

Game Time

Probability Brain Teasers

Can you solve these riddles that involve probability? Watch out—some of them are tricky!

1. In Wade City, 5% of the residents have unlisted phone numbers. If you selected 100 people at random from the town's phone directory, how many of them would you predict have unlisted numbers?
2. Amanda has a drawer that contains 24 black socks and 18 white socks. If she reaches into the drawer without looking, how many socks does she have to pull out in order to be *certain* that she will have two socks of the same color?
3. Dale, Melvin, Carter, and Ken went out to eat. Each person ordered something different. When the food came, the waiter could not remember who had ordered what, so he set the plates down at random in front of the four friends. What is the probability that exactly three of the boys got what they ordered?

Round and Round and Round

This is a game for two players.

The object of this game is to determine which of the three spinners is the winning spinner (lands on the greater number most often).

Both players choose a spinner and spin at the same time. Record which spinner lands on the greater number. Repeat this 19 times, keeping track of which spinner wins each time. Repeat this process until you have played spinner A against spinner B, spinner B against spinner C, and spinner A against spinner C. Spin each pair of spinners 20 times and record the results.

Which spinner wins more often, A or B?
Which spinner wins more often, B or C?
Which spinner wins more often, A or C?
Is there anything surprising about your results?

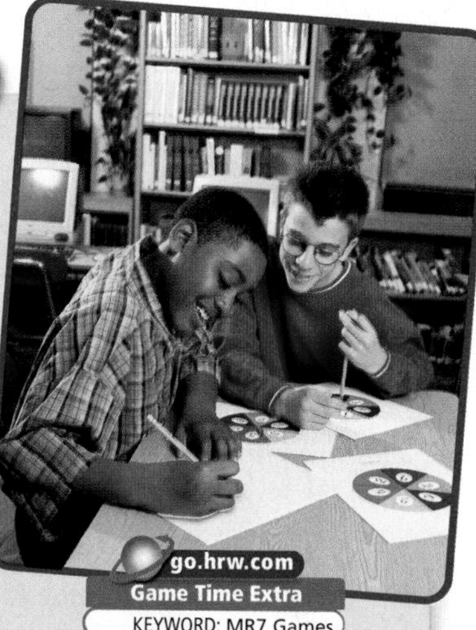

go.hrw.com
Game Time Extra
KEYWORD: MR7 Games

A complete copy of the rules and game pieces are available online.

Extend Have students create new spinners for the game. Challenge them to create a set of spinners in which no spinner is certain to beat another spinner. Check students' work.

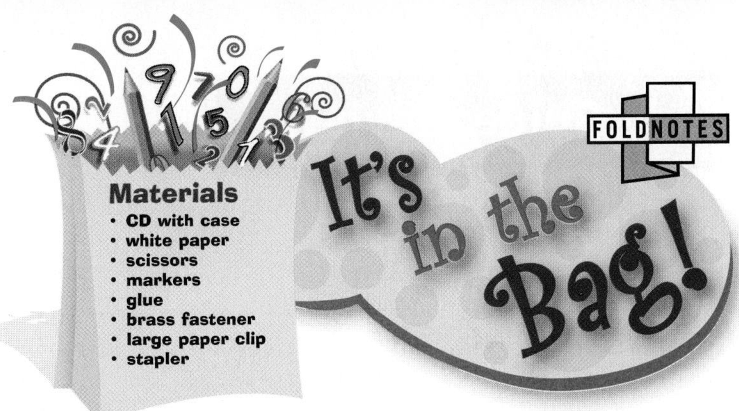

PROJECT CD Spinner

Use a CD to make a spinner. Then take notes on probability in a booklet that you store in the CD case.

Directions

1. Trace around the CD to make a circle on white paper. Divide the circle into thirds, color each third a different color, and cut out the circle. Glue the circle onto the CD. **Figure A**

2. Carefully remove the plastic CD holder from the back of the CD case. Place the CD in the holder and insert a brass fastener into the center of the CD. Bend the ends of the fastener so it stays in place, and put the holder back into the CD case. **Figure B**

3. Attach a large paper clip to the brass fastener to make a spinner. **Figure C**

4. Cut several sheets of white paper so they are $4\frac{3}{4}$ inches by $4\frac{3}{4}$ inches. Staple them together to form a booklet that fits in the cover of the CD case.

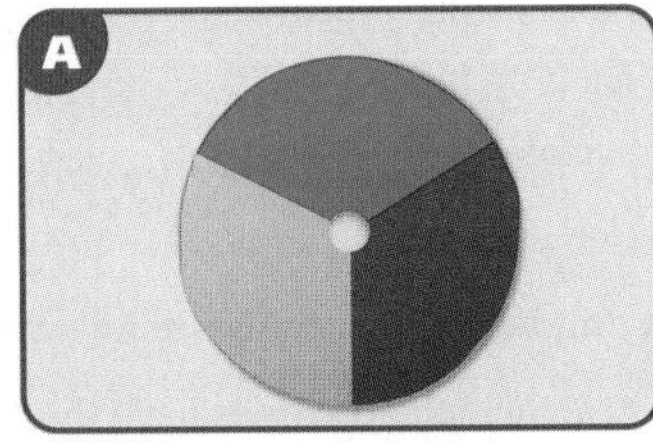

Taking Note of the Math

Use the booklet to record notes on probability. Be sure to include probabilities related to the spinner that you made.

Organizer

Objective: Make a spinner and a notebook in which to record notes about probability.

Materials: CD with case, white paper, scissors, markers, glue, brass fastener, large paper clip, stapler

Using the Page

Preparing the Materials
Several days before doing the project, ask students to bring in any CDs or CD-ROMs that they are no longer using. Remind students to bring in the cases as well.

Making the Project
In Step 2, tell students that it will be easier to remove the CD holder from the back of the CD case if they first take the cover off the case.

When students insert the brass fastener into the CD, tell them to leave a bit of space between the top of the fastener and the surface of the CD. This will allow the paper clip to spin freely.

Extending the Project
Challenge students to design a spinner with three sections such that the probability associated with each section is $\frac{1}{4}$, $\frac{1}{8}$, and $\frac{5}{8}$.

Tips from the Bag Ladies!

Office-supply stores sell sheets of self-stick labels for CDs. These are perfect for this project!

There are many ways to extend and enhance the project. For example, you might have students design a game of chance to go along with their spinner. The game and its rules can be part of the booklet that goes in the CD case. Students can also make a variety of spinners and investigate both the experimental and theoretical probabilities for each one.

CHAPTER 12 Study Guide: Review

Organizer

Objective: Help students organize and review key concepts and skills presented in Chapter 12.

Online Edition
Multilingual Glossary

Resources

Multilingual Glossary Online

go.hrw.com
KEYWORD: MR7 Glossary

Lesson Tutorial Videos CD-ROM

Answers

1. equally likely
2. experiment; outcome
3. probability
4. theoretical probability
5. sample space
6. certain
7. 0.75, $\frac{3}{4}$
8. white

CHAPTER 12

Study Guide: Review

Vocabulary

Complete the sentences below with vocabulary words from the list above.

1. When all outcomes have the same probability of occurring, the outcomes are __?__.
2. A(n) __?__ is an activity involving chance that can have different results. Each possible result is called a(n) __?__.
3. The measure of how likely an event is to occur is the event's __?__.
4. __?__ is the ratio of the number of ways an event can occur to the total number of possible outcomes.
5. The set of all possible outcomes for an experiment is the __?__.

12-1 Introduction to Probability (pp. 668–671)

GPS M6D2.b, M6N1.f

EXAMPLE

- **Is it *impossible, unlikely, as likely as not, likely,* or *certain* that the spinner will land on yellow?**

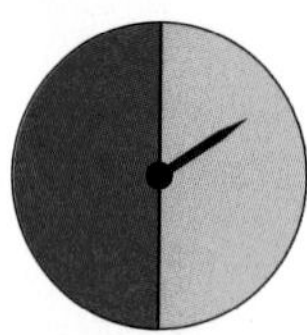

Half of the spinner is yellow, so it is as likely to land on yellow as not.

EXERCISES

6. Is it *impossible, unlikely, as likely as not, likely,* or *certain* that next week will have 7 days?
7. There is a 75% chance that George will win a race. Write this probability as a decimal and as a fraction.
8. Barry has a 30% chance of picking a black sock and a 50% chance of picking a white sock from his drawer. Which color sock is he more likely to pick?

12-2 Experimental Probability (pp. 672–675)

GPS M6D2.a

EXAMPLE

- **Margie recorded the number of times a spinner landed on each color. Based on Margie's experiment, on which color is the spinner most likely to land?**

Outcomes	Red	Blue	Green
Frequency	~~IIII~~ ~~IIII~~ IIII	IIII	~~IIII~~ II

$P(\text{red}) \approx \frac{14}{25}$ $P(\text{blue}) \approx \frac{4}{25}$ $P(\text{green}) \approx \frac{7}{25}$

The spinner will most likely land on red.

EXERCISES

9. One day, the cafeteria supervisor recorded the number of students who chose each type of beverage. She organized her results in a table. Find the experimental probability that a student will choose juice.

Beverage	Juice	Milk	Water
Frequency	20	37	18

12-3 Counting Methods and Sample Spaces (pp. 678–681)

GPS M6P1.c

EXAMPLE

- **Liz is wrapping a gift. She can use gold or silver paper and either a red or white ribbon. From how many different combinations can Liz choose?**

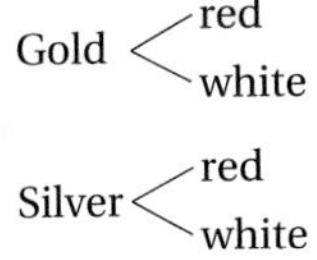

Follow each branch to find all outcomes.

There are 4 different combinations.

EXERCISES

10. The local restaurant has a lunch special in which you can pick an appetizer, a sandwich, and a drink. How many different lunch-special combinations are there if you have the following choices?

appetizers: soup or salad

sandwiches: turkey, roast beef, or ham

drinks: juice, milk, or iced tea

12-4 Theoretical Probability (pp. 682–685)

GPS M6D2.b

EXAMPLE

- **What is the probability of rolling a 4 on a fair number cube?**

There are six possible outcomes when a number cube is rolled: 1, 2, 3, 4, 5, or 6. All are equally likely because the number cube is fair.

$$P = \frac{\text{number of ways event can occur}}{\text{total number of possible outcomes}}$$

$$P(4) = \frac{1 \text{ way event can occur}}{6 \text{ possible outcomes}} = \frac{1}{6}$$

EXERCISES

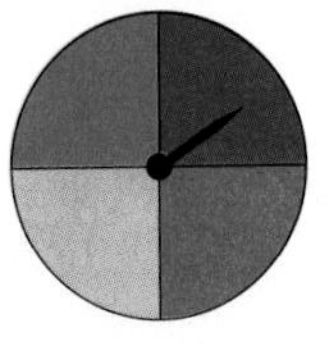

11. What is the probability that the spinner will land on yellow?

12. What is the probability of rolling a number greater than 3 on a fair number cube?

13. There is a 25% chance of choosing a purple marble from a bag. Find the probability of choosing a marble that is NOT purple.

Study Guide: Review

Answers

9. $\frac{20}{75} = \frac{4}{15}$
10. 18 combinations
11. $\frac{1}{4}$
12. $\frac{1}{2}$
13. 75%

Answers

14. $\frac{1}{6}$

15. $\frac{1}{8}$

16. 100 items

17. 25 times

18. 1,575 teenagers

19. 100 students

Study Guide: Review

12-5 Compound Events (pp. 688–691)

GPS M6D2.b

EXAMPLE

■ **What is the probability of spinning red or blue and having the coin land heads up?**

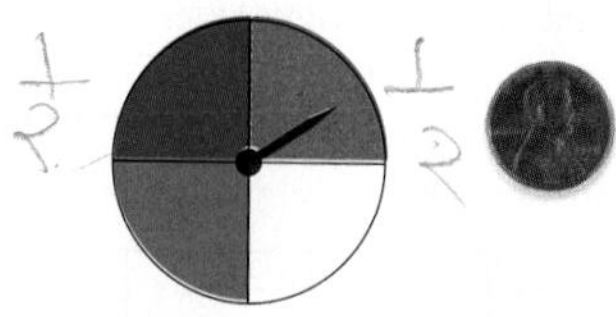

	Red	Blue	Green	White
Heads	red, H	blue, H	green, H	white, H
Tails	red, T	blue, T	green, T	white, T

There are 8 possible outcomes, and all are equally likely.

$$P(\text{red or blue, H}) = \frac{\text{2 ways event can occur}}{\text{8 possible outcomes}}$$
$$= \frac{2}{8} = \frac{1}{4}$$

EXERCISES

14. Find the probability that a blue marble will be chosen, the first coin will show heads, and the second coin will show tails.

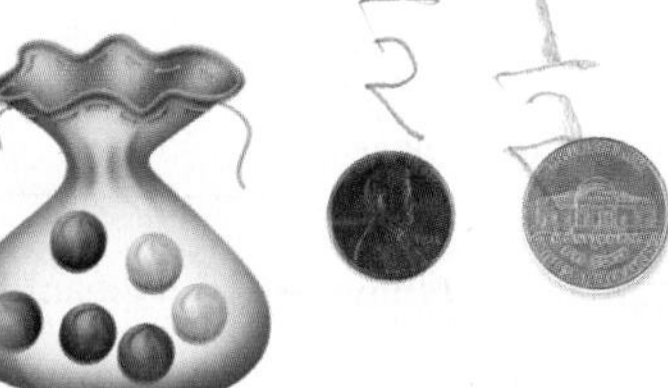

15. Jacob rolled a fair number cube, flipped a fair penny, and then flipped a fair quarter. Find the probability that the number cube will show an even number and both coins will show heads.

12-6 Making Predictions (pp. 694–697)

GPS M6A2.g, M6D2.b

EXAMPLE

■ **If you spin the spinner 30 times, how many times do you expect it to land on red?**

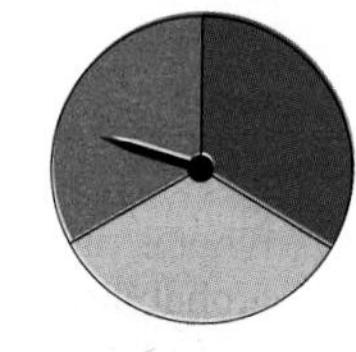

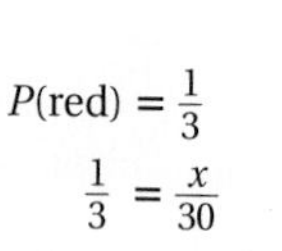

$P(\text{red}) = \frac{1}{3}$

$\frac{1}{3} = \frac{x}{30}$

$3 \cdot x = 1 \cdot 30$ — *The cross products are equal.*

$3x = 30$ — *x is multiplied by 3.*

$\frac{3x}{3} = \frac{30}{3}$ — *Divide both sides by 3 to undo the multiplication.*

$x = 10$

You can expect it to land on red about 10 times.

EXERCISES

16. Based on a sample survey, about 2% of the items produced by a company are defective. Out of 5,000 items, how many can you predict will be defective?

17. If you roll a fair number cube 50 times, how many times can you expect to roll an even number?

18. In a sample survey, 500 teenagers indicated that 175 of them use their computers regularly. Out of 4,500 teenagers, predict how many use their computers regularly.

19. In a sample survey, 100 sixth-grade students indicated that 20 of them take music lessons. Out of 500 sixth-grade students, predict how many take music lessons.

CHAPTER TEST

CHAPTER 12

For Items 1 and 2, write *impossible, unlikely, as likely as not, likely,* or *certain* to describe each event.

1. You roll a 3 on a standard number cube. unlikely
2. You pick a blue marble from a bag of 5 white marbles and 20 blue marbles. likely
3. There is a 12% chance of rain tomorrow. Write this probability as a decimal and as a fraction. 0.12; $\frac{3}{25}$
4. The probability that Mark will be selected for a scholarship is 0.8. Write this probability as a percent and as a fraction. 80%; $\frac{4}{5}$
5. Iris asked 60 students what time they go to bed. Her results are in the table. Find the experimental probability that a student chosen at random goes to bed at 8:30 P.M. $\frac{2}{5}$

Time (P.M.)	8:00	8:30	9:00	9:30
Frequency	12	24	18	6

6. Find the experimental probability that a student chosen at random goes to bed before 8:30 P.M. $\frac{1}{5}$
7. Josh threw darts at a dartboard 10 times. Assume that he threw the darts randomly and did not aim. Based on his results, what is the probability that a dart will land in the center circle? $\frac{1}{10}$

8. What is the probability of rolling an even number greater than 2 on a fair number cube? $\frac{1}{3}$
9. The baseball game has a 64% chance of being rained out. What is the probability that it will NOT be rained out? 36%
10. Peter has four photos to arrange in a frame. How many different ways can he arrange the photos? 24 ways
11. Marsha can wear jeans or black pants with a red, blue, or white shirt. How many different outfits can she choose from? 6
12. If you roll a number cube 36 times, how many times do you expect to roll an even number? 18
13. Find the probability that you will pick a blue marble from both bags and that the spinner will land on blue. $\frac{1}{24}$

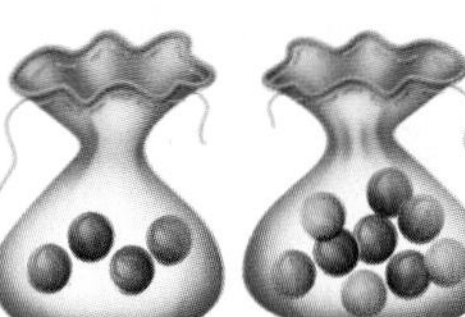
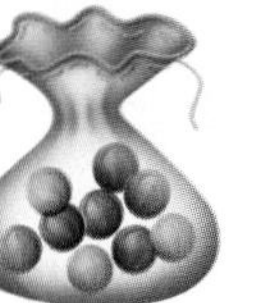
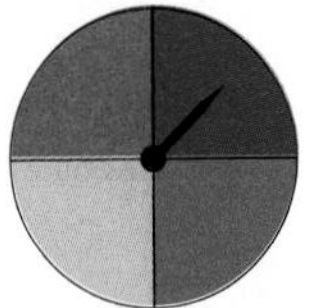

Chapter Test

CHAPTER TEST

CHAPTER 12

Organizer

Objective: Assess students' mastery of concepts and skills in Chapter 12.

Online Edition

Resources

Assessment Resources

Chapter 12 Tests
- Free Response (Levels A, B, C)
- Multiple Choice (Levels A, B, C)
- Performance Assessment

***IDEA Works!* CD-ROM**
Modified Chapter 12 Test

Test & Practice Generator
One-Stop Planner®

Organizer

Objective: Provide review and practice for Chapters 1–12 and standardized tests.

Online Edition

Resources

Assessment Resources
Chapter 12 Cumulative Test

***CRCT Prep* Workbook**

***CRCT Prep* CD-ROM**

***CRCT Practice* Online**

go.hrw.com
KEYWORD: MR7 TestPrep

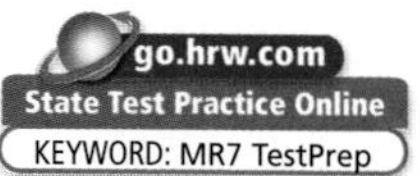

CRCT Prep

Cumulative Assessment, Chapters 1–12

Multiple Choice

1. A humpback whale swimming on the water's surface dives 500 feet. It then dives another 175 feet. Which expression represents this situation?

Ⓐ −175 + 500　　Ⓒ −500 − 175
Ⓑ 675 − 175　　Ⓓ 500 + 175

2. The weather report states that there is a 60% chance of a thunderstorm. What is this probability written as a fraction in simplest form?

Ⓕ $\frac{3}{5}$　　Ⓗ $\frac{30}{60}$
Ⓖ $\frac{6}{10}$　　Ⓙ $\frac{60}{100}$

3. There were 18 teachers and 45 students registered to participate in a 5K walk-a-thon. Which ratio accurately compares the number of students to the number of teachers?

Ⓐ 1:5　　Ⓒ 3:15
Ⓑ 5:2　　Ⓓ 18:45

4. Which three-dimensional figure is a square pyramid?

Ⓕ 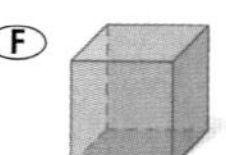

Ⓖ 

Ⓗ 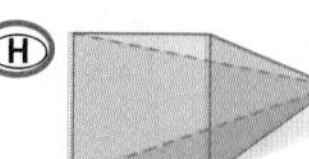

Ⓙ 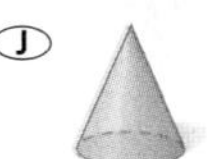

5. Jason delivers newspapers. He earns \$0.22 for every newspaper he delivers. He wants to buy a new printer for his computer that costs \$264. If n equals the number of newspapers he delivers, which equation can be used to find the number of newspapers Jason needs to deliver in order to have enough money to buy the printer?

Ⓐ $n - 0.22 = 264$　　Ⓒ $\frac{n}{0.22} = 264$
Ⓑ $0.22 + n = 264$　　Ⓓ $0.22n = 264$

6. The two figures are similar. Which proportion can be used to find the missing side length?

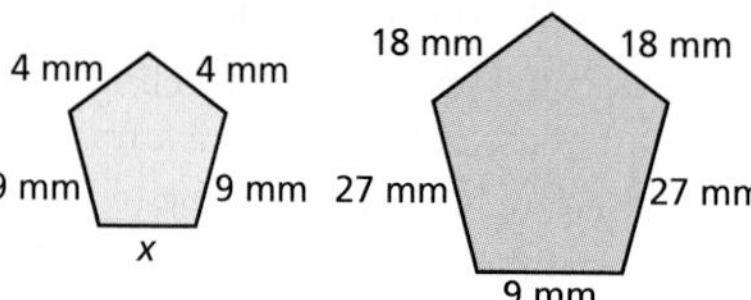

Ⓕ $\frac{4}{x} = \frac{18}{27}$　　Ⓗ $\frac{9}{x} = \frac{9}{18}$
Ⓖ $\frac{9}{x} = \frac{27}{4}$　　Ⓙ $\frac{4}{x} = \frac{18}{9}$

7. Victor owns 638 model trains. He can put 24 trains in a protective case. If each case costs \$5.65, how much money will Victor have to spend to put all of his model trains in cases?

Ⓐ \$135.60　　Ⓒ \$152.55
Ⓑ \$146.90　　Ⓓ \$158.25

8. What is 70% of 30?

Ⓕ 0.21　　Ⓗ 21
Ⓖ 2.1　　Ⓙ 210

TEST PREP DOCTOR

Students who chose **G** or **J** for item 2 may have forgotten to write the fraction in simplest form. Students who chose **H** may need to review writing percents as fractions.

Answers

14a. The probability that the 13-year-old will state that she watches 4 hours of television a day during the summer is 35%, or 0.35.

b. John can predict that 50 teenagers out of 500 will state that they watch less than 2 hours a day during the summer; $\frac{2}{20} = 0.1$; $0.1 \times 500 = 50$.

15. RB, B, SO; RB, B, SA; RB, CA, SO; RB, CA, SA; RB, CO, SO; RB, CO, SA; CH, B, SO; CH, B, SA; CH, CA, SO; CH, CA, SA; CH, CO, SO; CH, CO, SA; F, B, SO; F, B, SA; F, CA, SO; F, CA, SA; F, CO, SO; F, CO, SA; there are 18 combinations.

16. See 4-Point Response work sample.

9. The weights of four puppies are listed below. Which puppy is the heaviest?

Puppy	Weight (lb)
Toby	$5\frac{1}{4}$
Rusty	$5\frac{2}{5}$
Alex	$5\frac{5}{8}$
Jax	$5\frac{2}{3}$

(A) Toby (C) Alex
(B) Rusty (D) Jax

10. A fair number cube is rolled. What is the probability that the cube will NOT land on 4?

(F) $\frac{1}{6}$ (H) $\frac{2}{3}$
(G) $\frac{1}{3}$ (J) $\frac{5}{6}$

A probability can be written as a decimal, fraction, or percent. Probabilities are always between 0 and 1 (or 0% and 100%). The greater the probability, the more likely the event is to occur.

11. The movie *Gone with the Wind* is 3 hours and 42 minutes long. How many minutes long is the movie?

(A) 180 (C) 222
(B) 202 (D) 284

12. Nancy is stenciling 5-inch-wide stars, end-to-end, around her rectangular bedroom. Her bedroom is $12\frac{3}{4}$ feet wide and $15\frac{1}{4}$ feet long. How many whole stars will Nancy stencil?

(F) 62 (H) 96
(G) 64 (J) 134

13. Carl drives at an average rate of 60 miles per hour. How many hours will it take him to drive 240 miles?

(A) 4 (C) 24
(B) 12 (D) 48

STANDARDIZED TEST PREP

Short Response

14. John asked a group of teenagers how many hours of television they watch per day during the summer. He put his results in a frequency table.

Hours	0–2	3–5	6–8	10–12
Teenagers	//	𝍸 //	𝍸 /	𝍸

a. Based on this survey, what is the probability that a teenager will spend 4 hours a day watching television in the summer?

b. John plans to ask 500 teenagers the same survey question. How many of those teenagers can he predict watch less than 2 hours of television per day during the summer? Explain. **50**

15. A restaurant offers a choice of roast beef, chicken, or fish; broccoli, carrots, or corn; and soup or salad. If you can choose one main dish, one vegetable, and one side, what are all the possible outcomes?

Extended Response

16. There are 5 blue tiles, 7 red tiles, and 8 yellow tiles in a jar.

a. If you pick a tile without looking, what is the probability of picking a blue tile? Express this probability as a percent, a fraction, and a decimal.

b. If you pick a tile without looking, what is the probability of NOT picking a yellow tile? Write your answer in simplest form.

c. You conduct an experiment in which you pick a tile out of the jar 50 different times. Each time you record the color of tile and then replace the tile before you pick another. How many times would you expect to pick a blue tile? Explain.

CRCT Prep

Short Response Rubric

Items 14–15

2 Points = The student's answer is an accurate and complete execution of the task or tasks.

1 Point = The student's answer contains attributes of an appropriate response but is flawed.

0 Points = The student's answer contains no attributes of an appropriate response.

Extended Response Rubric

Item 16

4 Points = The student demonstrates a thorough understanding of all concepts and shows all work correctly.

3 Points = The student demonstrates a basic understanding of all concepts, but the work shows some flaws reflecting inattentive execution of mathematical procedures or some misunderstanding of the underlying mathematics.

2 Points = The student demonstrates only a partial understanding of the concepts or procedures embodied in the tasks. The approach may be correct, but the work shows a misunderstanding of one or more important concepts.

1 Point = The student demonstrates a very limited understanding of the concepts or procedures embodied in the tasks. The response may show some understanding but exhibits many flaws or is incomplete.

0 Points = The student provides no response at all or a completely incorrect or uninterpretable response.

Student Work Samples for Item 16

4-Point Response

17 a. The probability of picking a blue tile is 25%, 0.25, or $\frac{1}{4}$ because there are 20 tiles in all and 5 of the tiles are blue.

b. $\frac{3}{5}$

c. Since there is a 25% theoretical probability of picking a blue tile, if I pick a tile 50 times, I would expect to pick a blue tile 25% of the time. So I would pick a blue tile between 12 and 13 times because 25% of 50 is 12.5.

The student demonstrated an understanding of the concepts and answered all questions completely.

3-Point Response

a. A blue Tile is 25%, $\frac{1}{4}$ & 0.25.

b. $\frac{12}{20} = \frac{3}{5}$

c. I would expect to pick a blue Tile 25% of The Time or $.25 \times 50 = 12.5$

The student answered all parts correctly but did not explain the result obtained in part **c.**

2-Point Response

a. 25%

b. $\frac{12}{20}$

c. $50 \times 25\% = 1{,}250\%$

The student did not simplify the answer to part **b.** In part **c,** the student did not write the percent as a fraction or a decimal before multiplying.

Problem Solving on Location

Organizer

Objective: To solve real-world problems involving integers, the coordinate plane, and other concepts.

Online Edition

The Georgia Gold Rush

ENGLISH LANGUAGE LEARNERS

Reading Strategies

Have students read problem 1 at least two times. The first time students read the problem, they should get an overall sense of what the problem is asking. For the second reading, encourage students to focus on the details and take note of the information they will need to solve the problem.

Georgia Performance Standards

M6P1.c Apply and adapt a variety of appropriate strategies to solve problems.

M6P4.c Recognize and apply mathematics in contexts outside of mathematics.

M6P5.a Create and use representations to organize, record, and communicate mathematical ideas.

Problem Solving on Location

GEORGIA

Georgia Performance Standards

M6P1.c, M6P4.c, M6P5.a

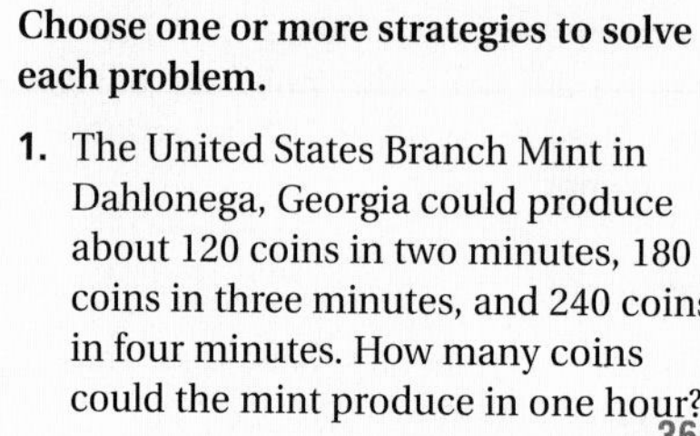

The Georgia Gold Rush

In 1828, Benjamin Parks discovered gold near the present-day town of Dahlonega. His discovery soon attracted fortune-seekers from every part of the country. By 1838, a U.S. mint had been built in Dahlonega to turn the gold into coins.

Choose one or more strategies to solve each problem.

1. The United States Branch Mint in Dahlonega, Georgia could produce about 120 coins in two minutes, 180 coins in three minutes, and 240 coins in four minutes. How many coins could the mint produce in one hour? **3600**
2. About how long would it have taken the mint to produce 3,000 coins? **50 min**

In a bag, there are two $1 coins, three $2 coins, and five $5 coins. You draw a coin from the bag at random.

3. What is the probability that a $3 coin will be drawn? $\frac{3}{10}$
4. What is the probability that a $1 coin will be drawn? $\frac{1}{5}$
5. A $5 coin is drawn and put aside. What is the probability that a $3 coin is then drawn from the bag? $\frac{1}{3}$

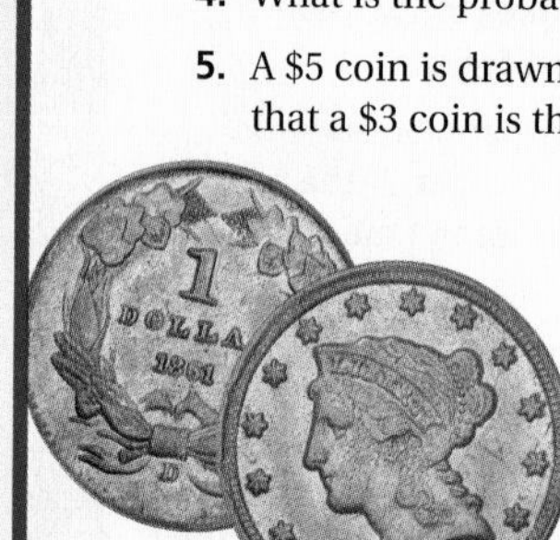

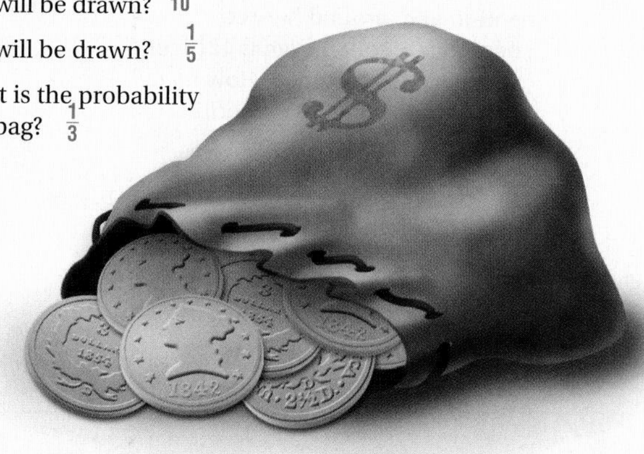

Problem Solving Focus

For problem 2, focus on the second step in the Problem Solving Process: Make a Plan. Have students work with a partner to discuss strategies that may be useful in solving the problem. Then have students share their suggested strategies with the entire class.

Discuss combinations of strategies that might be useful in solving problem 2. For example, students may want to use Make a Table to convert the data in problem 1 to a table. Then they might use Look for a Pattern to extend the table.

Extension Ask students how many coins the mint could produce in one day, assuming it operated around the clock. 86,400

Lake Fishing

Georgia is known for having some of the best lakes for fishing in the United States. Throughout the year, its lakes are brimming with striped bass, catfish, and trout. In fact, every part of the state offers a perfect spot to put your line in the water.

Choose one or more strategies to solve the problem.

1. Four of Georgia's lakes are known for largemouth bass: Jackson Lake, Lake Russell, Lake Walter F. George, and Lake Sinclair. How many different ways can you choose two of these lakes for a fishing trip? 6

For Problems 2 and 3, use the graph.

2. A fisherman is trying to catch flathead catfish. He lowers his hook to a depth of -5 ft and waits 6 minutes. Then he lowers his hook to -10 ft and waits another 6 minutes. Continuing this pattern, how long does it take until his hook reaches the recommended maximum depth for this type of fish? 42 min
3. When bream are at their maximum depth, they are 21 feet closer to the surface than whiting. When whiting are at their maximum depth, they are 10 feet deeper than largemouth bass. What is the maximum depth of bream? -4 ft

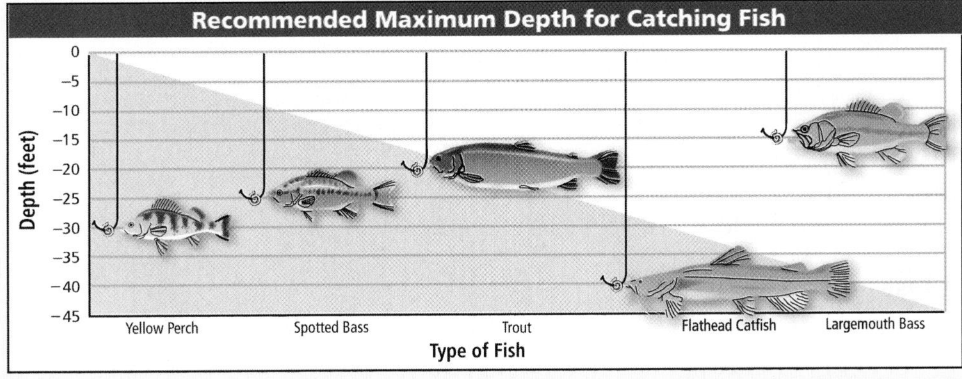

Lake Fishing

Ask students to rewrite the question in problem 1 as a statement that tells them what they must find. Find the number of different ways you can choose two of the four lakes.

Using Data Focus students' attention on the graph. Have students identify the fish that can be found at the greatest depths. Flathead catfish Also ask students to find the difference in the maximum depth of largemouth bass and the maximum depth of yellow perch. 15 ft

Problem Solving Focus

Ask students how they can use the strategy Act It Out to help them solve problem 1. For example, students may wish to write the names of the lakes on index cards or on sticky notes. Then they can act out the process of choosing two lakes. Encourage students to keep an organized list of the combinations that they find.

Student Handbook

Exponent
Base

CRCT GPS Practice

CRCT GPS Practice

CRCT GPS Practice ▪ Chapter 1

LESSON 1-1

1. The area of Canada is 3,851,788 square miles. The area of the United States is 3,717,792 square miles. Which country has the greater area? Canada

2. In 2001, it was estimated that 14,902,000 students attended high school and 14,889,000 attended college. Were more students in high school or in college? high school

Order the numbers from least to greatest.

3. 783; 772; 1,702 772; 783; 1,702
4. 10,318; 1,308; 10,301 1,308; 10,301; 10,318
5. 34,903; 32,788; 32,679 32,679; 32,788; 34,903
6. 24,615; 24,829; 24,560 24,560; 24,615; 24,829
7. 1,345; 1,780; 1,356 1,345; 1,356; 1,780
8. 29,992; 22,929; 22,922 22,922; 22,929; 29,992

LESSON 1-2

Estimate each sum or difference by rounding to the place value indicated.

9. 7,685 + 8,230; thousands 16,000
10. 23,218 + 37,518; ten thousands 60,000
11. 52,087 − 35,210; ten thousands 10,000
12. 292,801 − 156,127; hundred thousands 100,000
13. 14,325 + 25,629; hundreds 39,900
14. 9,210 − 396; hundreds 8,800

15. Mr. Peterson needs topsoil for his garden. His rectangular garden is 78 in. long and 48 in. wide. A bag of topsoil covers an area of 500 square inches. How many bags should Mr. Peterson buy? 8 bags of topsoil

16. Natalie's family is having a picnic at an amusement park. The park is 153 miles from Natalie's house. If the family drives 55 mi/h, about how long will it take them to get to the park? about 3 hours

LESSON 1-3

Write each expression in exponential form.

17. $5 \times 5 \times 5 \times 5 \times 5 \times 5$ 5^6
18. $3 \times 3 \times 3 \times 3$ 3^4
19. $10 \times 10 \times 10 \times 10 \times 10$ 10^5
20. $2 \times 2 \times 2 \times 2$ 2^4
21. $7 \times 7 \times 7$ 7^3
22. 9×9 9^2

Find each value.

23. 5^2 25
24. 5^5 3,125
25. 6^3 216
26. 10^5 100,000
27. 9^1 9
28. 3^6 729
29. 4^3 64
30. 2^5 32

31. Patricia e-mailed a joke to 4 of her friends. Each of those friends e-mailed the joke to 4 other friends. If this pattern continues, how many people will receive the e-mail on the fifth round of e-mails? 4^5, or 1,024 people

CRCT GPS Practice ▪ Chapter 1

LESSON 1-4

Evaluate each expression.

32. $15 + 7 \times 3$ 36
33. $3 \times 3^2 + 13 - 5$ 35
34. $10 \div (3 + 2) \times 2^3 - 8$ 8
35. $4^2 - 12 \div 3 + (7 - 5)$ 14
36. $10 \times (25 - 11) \div 7 + 6$ 26
37. $(3 + 6) \times 18 \div 2 + 7$ 88

38. The sixth-grade band students sell cases of fruit for a fund-raiser. Emily sold 18 cases of oranges for $12 each, 11 cases of apples for $10 each, and 5 cases of grapefruit for $14 each. Evaluate $18 \times 12 + 11 \times 10 + 5 \times 14$ to find how much money she should collect in all. $396

LESSON 1-5

Evaluate.

39. 15 + 7 + 23 + 5 50
40. $4 \times 13 \times 5$ 260
41. 34 + 16 + 22 + 18 90

Use the Distributive Property to find each product.

42. 5×54 270
43. 3×32 96
44. 7×26 182
45. 9×73 657

LESSON 1-6

For Exercises 46–48, choose a solution method and solve. Explain your choice.

Month	Days of Rain	Month	Days of Rain
January	6	July	15
February	5	August	9
March	7	September	17
April	14	October	14
May	12	November	8
June	10	December	5

46. The table shows the number of days it rained each month. How many days total did it rain in the year? paper and pencil; 122 days

47. The coldest temperature in a city was 11°F. The warmest temperature that same year was 89°F. What is the difference between the highest and lowest temperatures? mental math; 78°F

48. Heather is a member of a dance company. She practices 14 hours a week. How many hours does she practice each year? (*Hint:* There are 52 weeks in a year.) calculator; 728 hours

LESSON 1-7 49–54. See p. A12.

Identify a pattern in each arithmetic sequence and then find the missing terms.

49. 8, 16, 24, ■, ■, ■
50. 6, 11, 16, ■, ■, ■
51. 100, 85, 70, ■, ■, ■

52.

Position	1	2	3	4	5	6	7	8
Value of Term	1	12	23	34	45	■	■	■

Identify a pattern in each sequence. Name the missing terms.

53. 496, 248, 260, ■, 142, 71, ■
54. 1, 8, 4, 32, 16, ■, 64, 512, ■

CRCT GPS Practice ▪ Chapter 2

LESSON 2-1

Evaluate each expression to find the missing values in the tables.

1.

y	$23 + y$
17	40
27	■ 50
37	■ 60

2.

w	$w \times 3 + 10$
4	22
5	■ 25
6	■ 28

3.

x	$x \div 8$
40	5
48	■ 6
56	■ 7

LESSON 2-2

4. Earth has a diameter of 7,926 miles. Let d represent the diameter of the Moon, which is smaller than the diameter of Earth. Write an expression to show how much larger the diameter of Earth is than the diameter of the Moon. $7{,}926 - d$

Write each phrase as a numerical or algebraic expression.

5. the sum of 322 and 18 $322 + 18$
6. the product of 7 and 12 7×12
7. the quotient of n and 8 $\frac{n}{8}$
8. 14 more than x $x + 14$

Write two phrases for each expression. 9–13. See p. A12.

9. (23)(6)
10. $52 - p$
11. $y \div 4$
12. $8 + 4$
13. $13 \cdot m$

LESSON 2-3

Write an expression for the missing value in each table.

14.

Albert's Age	Ashley's Age
10	1
14	5
18	9
n	■ $n - 9$

15.

Hooves	Horses
16	4
12	3
8	2
n	■ $n \div 4$

16. A parallelogram has a base of 4 inches. The table shows the area of the parallelogram for different heights. Write an expression that can be used to find the area of the parallelogram when its height is h inches.

Base (in.)	Height (in.)	Area (in^2)
4	4	16
4	5	20
4	6	24
4	h	■ $4h$

CRCT GPS Practice ▪ Chapter 2

LESSON 2-4

Determine whether the given value of each variable is a solution.

17. $a + 15 = 34$, when $a = 17$ no
18. $t - 9 = 14$, when $t = 23$ yes

19. Rachel says she is 5 feet tall. Her friend measured her height as 60 inches. Determine if these two measurements are equal. 5 feet is equal to 60 inches.

LESSON 2-5

Solve each equation. Check your answers.

20. $r + 13 = 36$ $r = 23$
21. $52 = 24 + n$ $n = 28$
22. $6 + s = 10$ $s = 4$

23. Towns A, B, and C are located along Main Road, as shown on the map. Town A is 34 miles from town C. Town B is 12 miles from town C. Find the distance d between town A and town B. 22 miles

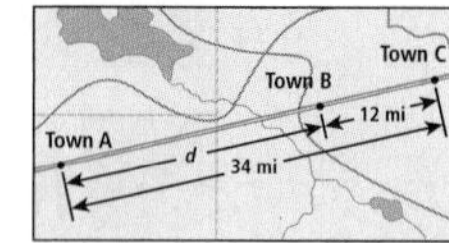

LESSON 2-6

Solve each equation. Check your answers.

24. $z - 9 = 5$ $z = 14$
25. $v - 17 = 14$ $v = 31$
26. $24 = w - 6$ $w = 30$

27. Reggie withdrew $175 from his bank account to go shopping. After his withdrawal, there was $234 left in Reggie's account. How much money did Reggie have in his account before his withdrawal? $409

LESSON 2-7

Solve each equation. Check your answers.

28. $4y = 20$ $y = 5$
29. $21 = 3t$ $t = 7$
30. $72 = 9g$ $g = 8$

31. The area of a rectangle is 54 in^2. Its width is 6 in. What is its length? 9 inches

32. A squirrel can run 36 miles in 3 hours. Solve the equation $3m = 36$ to find the number of miles a squirrel can run in 1 hour. $m = 12$; a squirrel can run 12 miles an hour.

LESSON 2-8

Solve each equation. Check your answers.

33. $\frac{n}{4} = 6$ $n = 24$
34. $7 = \frac{t}{5}$ $t = 35$
35. $\frac{a}{8} = 12$ $a = 96$

36. Sydney likes to run and ride a bike for exercise. Each day, she runs for one-third the time that she rides her bike. Yesterday, Sydney ran for 15 minutes. How many minutes did she ride her bike? 45 minutes

CRCT GPS Practice ■ Chapter 3

LESSON 3-1

Write each decimal in standard form, expanded form, and words.

1. 1.32 1 + 0.3 + 0.02, one and thirty-two hundredths
2. 0.6 + 0.003 + 0.0008 0.6038, six thousand thirty-eight ten-thousandths
3. five and three thousandths 5.003, 5 + 0.003

4. Joshua ran 1.45 miles, and Jasmine ran 1.5 miles. Who ran farther? Jasmine ran farther.

Order the decimals from least to greatest.

5. 3.89, 3.08, 3.8 3.08, 3.8, 3.89
6. 20.65, 20.09, 20.7 20.09, 20.65, 20.7
7. 0.053, 0.43, 0.340 0.053, 0.340, 0.43

LESSON 3-2

8. The femur is the upper leg bone, and the tibia is one of the lower leg bones. The average length of the femur is 50.5 cm, and the average length of the tibia is 43.03 cm. Estimate the total length of the leg if the bones were placed end to end. about 94 cm

Estimate by rounding to the indicated place value.

9. 5.856 − 1.3497; hundredths about 4.51
10. 4.7609 + 7.2471; tenths about 12.0

Estimate each product or quotient.

11. 20.84 ÷ 3.201 about 7
12. 31.02 × 4.91 about 150
13. 39.76 ÷ 7.94 about 5

Estimate a range for the sum.

14. 8.38 + 24.92 + 4.8 from 36 to 38.5
15. 38.27 + 2.99 + 15.32 from 55 to 56.5

LESSON 3-3

Find each sum or difference.

16. 1.65 + 4.53 + 3.2 9.38
17. 2.2 + 6.8 9.0
18. 7 − 0.6 6.4

Evaluate 6.35 − *s* for each value of *s*.

19. $s = 3.2$ 3.15
20. $s = 2.108$ 4.242
21. $s = 5.0421$ 1.3079

22. Brianna is shopping for school clothes and wants to purchase the following items: a shirt for $19.50, shoes for $35.00, a skirt for $12.39, socks for $6.99, and a pair of jeans for $19.95. Not including tax, how much money will Brianna need to purchase these items? $93.83

LESSON 3-4

Write each number in scientific notation.

23. 60,000 6×10^4
24. 423,800 4.238×10^5
25. 8,500,000 8.5×10^6

Write each number in standard form.

26. 5.632×10^5 563,200
27. 2.1×10^8 210,000,000
28. 1.425×10^4 14,250

CRCT GPS Practice ■ Chapter 3

LESSON 3-5

Find each product.

29. 0.5 × 0.7 0.35
30. 0.3 × 0.06 0.018
31. 6.12 × 5.9 36.108

Evaluate 4*x* for each value of *x*.

32. $x = 2.071$ 8.284
33. $x = 5.42$ 21.68
34. $x = 7.85$ 31.4

35. Each car tire costs $69.99. How much will 4 tires cost? $279.96

LESSON 3-6

Find each quotient.

36. 0.84 ÷ 6 0.14
37. 11.07 ÷ 9 1.23
38. 27.6 ÷ 12 2.3

Evaluate 0.564 ÷ *x* for each given value of *x*.

39. $x = 4$ 0.141
40. $x = 12$ 0.047
41. $x = 2$ 0.282

42. Marci pays $8.97 at the grocery store for 3 pounds of cherries. How much does each pound cost? $2.99

LESSON 3-7

Find each quotient.

43. 4.5 ÷ 0.9 5
44. 59.7 ÷ 0.4 149.25
45. 8.32 ÷ 8 1.04

46. Lisa paid $13.41 for 4.5 pounds of ground chicken. How much did each pound cost? $2.98

LESSON 3-8

47. Jocelyn has 3.5 yards of ribbon. She needs 0.6 yards of ribbon to make one bow. How many bows can Jocelyn make? 5 bows

48. Louie has a piece of wood that is 46.8 cm long. If he cuts the piece into 4 equal sections, how long will each section be? 11.7 cm

LESSON 3-9

Solve each equation. Check your answer.

49. $b - 5.2 = 2.6$ $b = 7.8$
50. $5t = 24.5$ $t = 4.9$
51. $\frac{p}{3} = 1.8$ $p = 5.4$

52. The area of a rectangle is 41 cm². Its length is 8.2 cm. What is its width? 5 cm

53. The area of Henry's kitchen is 168 ft². The cost of tile is $4.62 per square foot. What is the total cost to tile the kitchen? $776.16

CRCT GPS Practice ■ Chapter 4

LESSON 4-1

Tell whether each number is divisible by 2, 3, 4, 5, 6, 9, and 10.

1. 12,680 2, 4, 5, 10
2. 174 2, 3, 6
3. 1,638 2, 3, 6, 9
4. 735 3, 5

Tell whether each number is prime or composite.

5. 97 prime
6. 9 composite
7. 111 composite
8. 256 composite

LESSON 4-2

List all of the factors of each number.

9. 28 1, 2, 4, 7, 14, 28
10. 51 1, 3, 17, 51
11. 70 1, 2, 5, 7, 10, 14, 35, 70
12. 24 1, 2, 3, 4, 6, 8, 12, 24

Write the prime factorization of each number.

13. 48 $2^4 \cdot 3$
14. 72 $2^3 \cdot 3^2$
15. 81 3^4
16. 150 $2 \cdot 3 \cdot 5^2$

LESSON 4-3

Find the GCF of each set of numbers.

17. 15 and 35 5
18. 16 and 40 8
19. 22 and 68 2
20. 6, 36, and 60 6
21. 27, 36, and 54 9
22. 14, 28, and 63 7

23. Alice has 42 red beads and 24 white beads. What is the greatest number of bracelets Alice can make if each bracelet has the same number of red beads and the same number of white beads and if every bead is used? 6 bracelets

LESSON 4-4

Write each decimal as a fraction or mixed number.

24. 0.31 $\frac{31}{100}$
25. 1.9 $1\frac{9}{10}$
26. 2.53 $2\frac{53}{100}$
27. 0.07 $\frac{7}{100}$

Write each fraction or mixed number as a decimal.

28. $1\frac{7}{8}$ 1.875
29. $\frac{5}{9}$ $0.\overline{5}$
30. $6\frac{3}{5}$ 6.6
31. $\frac{5}{6}$ $0.8\overline{3}$

Order the fractions and decimals from least to greatest.

32. 0.3, $\frac{3}{5}$, 0.53 0.3, 0.53, $\frac{3}{5}$
33. 0.8, 0.67, $\frac{7}{8}$ 0.67, 0.8, $\frac{7}{8}$
34. 0.68, $\frac{2}{3}$, $\frac{3}{4}$ $\frac{2}{3}$, 0.68, $\frac{3}{4}$

LESSON 4-5

Find the missing numbers that make the fractions equivalent.

35. $\frac{4}{5} = \frac{■}{20}$ 16
36. $\frac{8}{12} = \frac{2}{■}$ 3
37. $\frac{6}{7} = \frac{■}{28}$ 24
38. $\frac{24}{3} = \frac{■}{1}$ 8

Write each fraction in simplest form.

39. $\frac{6}{10}$ $\frac{3}{5}$
40. $\frac{7}{9}$ $\frac{7}{9}$
41. $\frac{4}{16}$ $\frac{1}{4}$
42. $\frac{2}{6}$ $\frac{1}{3}$

CRCT GPS Practice ■ Chapter 4

LESSON 4-6

Write each mixed number as an improper fraction.

43. $3\frac{1}{4}$ $\frac{13}{4}$
44. $6\frac{5}{7}$ $\frac{47}{7}$
45. $1\frac{2}{9}$ $\frac{11}{9}$
46. $2\frac{7}{10}$ $\frac{27}{10}$

47. Brett's favorite soup recipe calls for $\frac{14}{4}$ cups of chicken broth. Write $\frac{14}{4}$ as a mixed number. $3\frac{1}{2}$

LESSON 4-7

Compare. Write <, >, or =.

48. $\frac{2}{5}$ ■ $\frac{4}{5}$ <
49. $\frac{5}{6}$ ■ $\frac{7}{8}$ <
50. $\frac{1}{3}$ ■ $\frac{9}{27}$ =
51. $\frac{9}{15}$ ■ $\frac{2}{5}$ >

52. Natalie lives $\frac{1}{6}$ mile from school. Peter lives $\frac{3}{10}$ mile from school. Who lives closer to the school? Natalie

Order the fractions from least to greatest.

53. $\frac{3}{5}, \frac{5}{9}, \frac{4}{5}$ $\frac{5}{9}, \frac{3}{5}, \frac{4}{5}$
54. $\frac{1}{6}, \frac{3}{7}, \frac{1}{3}$ $\frac{1}{6}, \frac{1}{3}, \frac{3}{7}$
55. $\frac{1}{2}, \frac{5}{8}, \frac{7}{12}$ $\frac{1}{2}, \frac{7}{12}, \frac{5}{8}$

LESSON 4-8

56. Rose is filling a tub with water. The height of the water is increasing $\frac{1}{8}$ foot each minute. Use pictures to model how much the height of the water will change in 5 minutes, and then write your answer in simplest form. $\frac{5}{8}$ feet

Subtract. Write each answer in simplest form.

57. $1 - \frac{7}{9}$ $\frac{2}{9}$
58. $2\frac{5}{6} - 1\frac{1}{6}$ $1\frac{2}{3}$
59. $5\frac{7}{10} - 3\frac{3}{10}$ $2\frac{2}{5}$
60. $2 - \frac{3}{4}$ $1\frac{1}{4}$

Evaluate each expression for $x = \frac{7}{12}$. Write each answer in simplest form.

61. $\frac{11}{12} - x$ $\frac{1}{3}$
62. $x + 1\frac{1}{12}$ $1\frac{2}{3}$
63. $x - \frac{5}{12}$ $\frac{1}{6}$

LESSON 4-9

Estimate each sum or difference by rounding to 0, $\frac{1}{2}$, or 1.

64. $\frac{7}{8} + \frac{7}{15}$ about $1\frac{1}{2}$
65. $\frac{5}{6} + \frac{1}{11}$ about 1
66. $\frac{7}{12} - \frac{4}{9}$ about 0

Use the table for Exercises 67 and 68.

67. The table shows the number of hours each day that Michael worked. About how many hours did Michael work on Monday and Tuesday? about 10 hours

68. About how many more hours did he work on Thursday than on Friday? about $1\frac{1}{2}$ hours

Michael's Work Schedule

Day	Hours Worked
Monday	$4\frac{5}{6}$
Tuesday	$5\frac{1}{4}$
Thursday	$6\frac{1}{10}$
Friday	$4\frac{5}{12}$

CRCT GPS Practice ■ Chapter 5

LESSON 5-1

1. There are 18 girls on the dance team. Barrettes are sold in packs of 6. Ponytail holders are sold in packs of 2. What is the least number of packs they could buy so that each girl has a barrette and a ponytail holder and none are left over? 3 packs of barrettes and 9 packs of ponytail holders

Find the least common multiple (LCM).

2. 9 and 15 45
3. 12 and 16 48
4. 10 and 12 60
5. 3, 4, and 5 60

LESSON 5-2

Add or subtract. Write each answer in simplest form.

6. $\frac{3}{5}+\frac{2}{3}$ $1\frac{4}{15}$
7. $\frac{7}{8}-\frac{1}{6}$ $\frac{17}{24}$
8. $\frac{1}{3}+\frac{1}{2}$ $\frac{5}{6}$
9. About $\frac{1}{3}$ of the animals at the zoo are birds. The mammals make up $\frac{2}{5}$ of the zoo's population. What fraction of the zoo's animals are mammals or birds? $\frac{11}{15}$

LESSON 5-3

Find each sum or difference. Write the answer in simplest form.

10. $18\frac{1}{3}+16\frac{1}{6}$ $34\frac{1}{2}$
11. $5\frac{3}{4}+3\frac{5}{12}$ $9\frac{1}{6}$
12. $12\frac{1}{2}-8\frac{2}{5}$ $4\frac{1}{10}$
13. Joan has a rottweiler and a Chihuahua. The rottweiler weighs $99\frac{1}{2}$ lb, and the Chihuahua weighs $3\frac{1}{4}$ lb. How much more does Joan's rottweiler weigh than her Chihuahua? $96\frac{1}{4}$ lb

LESSON 5-4

Subtract. Write each answer in simplest form.

14. $4\frac{2}{5}-2\frac{9}{10}$ $1\frac{1}{2}$
15. $9\frac{1}{6}-5\frac{5}{6}$ $3\frac{1}{3}$
16. $6-1\frac{7}{12}$ $4\frac{5}{12}$
17. Adam purchased a 10 lb bag of dog food. His dog ate $7\frac{1}{3}$ lb. of dog food in one week. How many pounds of dog food were left after one week? $2\frac{2}{3}$ lb

LESSON 5-5

Solve each equation. Write the solution in simplest form.

18. $a+5\frac{3}{10}=9$ $a=3\frac{7}{10}$
19. $1\frac{3}{8}=x-2\frac{1}{4}$ $x=3\frac{5}{8}$
20. $6\frac{5}{6}=t+1\frac{2}{3}$ $t=5\frac{1}{6}$
21. Taylor needs to change a lightbulb that is $12\frac{1}{2}$ feet above the floor. Without a ladder, Taylor can reach $6\frac{2}{3}$ feet. How tall must her ladder be in order for her to reach the lightbulb? $5\frac{5}{6}$ feet

LESSON 5-6

Multiply. Write each answer in simplest form.

22. $2\cdot\frac{1}{5}$ $\frac{2}{5}$
23. $3\cdot\frac{1}{6}$ $\frac{1}{2}$
24. $2\cdot\frac{2}{11}$ $\frac{4}{11}$

CRCT GPS Practice ■ Chapter 5

25. There are 16 players on the baseball team. Of these players, $\frac{1}{4}$ are girls. How many girls play on the baseball team? 4 girls

LESSON 5-7

Multiply. Write each answer in simplest form.

26. $\frac{1}{10}\cdot\frac{5}{6}$ $\frac{1}{12}$
27. $\frac{8}{9}\cdot\frac{3}{4}$ $\frac{2}{3}$
28. $\frac{5}{7}\cdot\frac{3}{10}$ $\frac{3}{14}$

Evaluate the expression $a\cdot\frac{1}{10}$ for each value of a. Write the answer in simplest form.

29. $a=\frac{4}{5}$ $\frac{2}{25}$
30. $a=\frac{2}{3}$ $\frac{1}{15}$
31. $a=\frac{5}{9}$ $\frac{1}{18}$
32. Camille spent $\frac{2}{5}$ of her weekly allowance on meals in restaurants. She spent $\frac{1}{2}$ of that money on pizza. What fraction of her weekly allowance did Camille spend on pizza? $\frac{1}{5}$

LESSON 5-8

Multiply. Write each answer in simplest form.

33. $\frac{1}{4}\cdot 1\frac{2}{3}$ $\frac{5}{12}$
34. $2\frac{3}{5}\cdot\frac{1}{3}$ $\frac{13}{15}$
35. $\frac{7}{8}\cdot 1\frac{1}{3}$ $1\frac{1}{6}$

Find each product. Write the answer in simplest form.

36. $1\frac{1}{3}\cdot 1\frac{3}{5}$ $2\frac{2}{15}$
37. $4\cdot 2\frac{6}{7}$ $11\frac{3}{7}$
38. $\frac{2}{5}$ of $4\frac{1}{2}$ $1\frac{4}{5}$
39. An art class has 18 students, and $\frac{1}{3}$ of the students are painting. How many of the students in the class are painting? 6 students

LESSON 5-9

Find the reciprocal.

40. $\frac{7}{9}$ $\frac{9}{7}$
41. $\frac{2}{13}$ $\frac{13}{2}$
42. $\frac{1}{12}$ $\frac{12}{1}$ or 12
43. $\frac{8}{5}$ $\frac{5}{8}$

Divide. Write each answer in simplest form.

44. $\frac{1}{6}\div 3$ $\frac{1}{18}$
45. $\frac{4}{7}\div 2$ $\frac{2}{7}$
46. $2\frac{1}{2}\div 1\frac{3}{4}$ $1\frac{3}{7}$
47. Debbie bought $8\frac{1}{2}$ lb of ground turkey. She packed the turkey in $\frac{1}{2}$ lb containers and put them in the freezer. How many containers of ground turkey did she pack? 17 containers

LESSON 5-10

Solve each equation. Write the answer in simplest form.

48. $\frac{3}{5}a=12$ $a=20$
49. $6b=\frac{3}{7}$ $b=\frac{1}{14}$
50. $\frac{3}{8}x=5$ $x=13\frac{1}{3}$
51. $3s=\frac{7}{9}$ $s=\frac{7}{27}$
52. $\frac{5}{12}m=3$ $m=7\frac{1}{5}$
53. $\frac{9}{10}t=6$ $t=6\frac{2}{3}$
54. Joanie used $\frac{2}{3}$ of a box of invitations to invite friends to her birthday party. If she sent out 12 invitations, how many total invitations were in the box? 18 invitations

CRCT GPS Practice ■ Chapter 6

LESSON 6-1 1–2. Complete answers on p. A12.

1. Each year a community holds a 5 km race. In 1998, 1,345 people participated in the race. In 1999, 1,415 people participated. In 2000, 1,532 people participated. In 2001, 1,607 people participated, and in 2002, 1,781 people participated. Use the data to make a table. Then use your table to describe how participation changed over time. The participation increased from 1998 to 2002.
2. Make a table using the basketball data below. Then use your table to tell which player had the most points, rebounds, and assists.

   In 1,560 games, Kareem Abdul-Jabbar scored 38,387 points, grabbed 17,440 rebounds, and made 5,660 assists. In 897 games, Larry Bird scored 21,791 points, grabbed 8,974 rebounds, and made 5,695 assists. In 963 games, Bill Russell scored 14,522 points, grabbed 21,620 rebounds, and made 4,100 assists. points: Kareem Abdul-Jabbar, rebounds: Bill Russell, assists: Larry Bird

LESSON 6-2

Find the mean, median, mode, and range of each data set.

3.

Points Scored				
16	18	23	13	15

mean: 17, median: 16, no mode, range: 10

4.

Hours Worked							
37	42	43	38	39	40	45	40

mean: 40.5, median: 40, mode: 40, range: 8

LESSON 6-3

5. a. The table shows a student's test scores. Find the mean, median, and mode of the test scores. mean: 85.5, median: 84.5, no mode

Test Scores			
78	82	87	95

   b. On the next test the student scored a 92. Find the mean, median, and mode with the new test score. mean: 86.8, median: 87, no mode
6. The daily temperatures for the first eight days of April were 52°F, 63°F, 61°F, 54°F, 52°F, 55°F, 68°F, and 75°. What are the mean, median, and mode of this data set? Which one best describes the data set? mean: 60, median: 58, mode: 52, median

LESSON 6-4

Use the bar graph to answer each question.

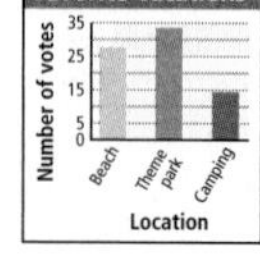

7. Which type of vacation received the most votes? theme park
8. Which types of vacations received more than 20 votes? beach, theme park
9. Use the data given below to make a bar graph. See p. A12.

Number of Days with Temperatures over 100°F			
June	3	August	14
July	5	September	7

CRCT GPS Practice ■ Chapter 6

LESSON 6-5

10. Use the data of students' heights to make a frequency table with intervals. Then use your frequency table to make a histogram.

Heights of Students (in.)							
63	58	48	60	60	65	56	57
56	62	61	58	59	55	64	50

11. Make a line plot of the data. 10–11. See p. A12–13.

Number of Miles Biked																								
14	45	33	34	32	37	44	19	35	36	17	33	35	40	41	38	47	31	44	23	27	20	33	45	27

LESSON 6-6

Name the ordered pair for each location on the grid.

12. L (0, 2)
13. M (2, 3)
14. R (4, 0)

Graph and label each point on a coordinate grid. 15–17. See p. A13.

15. $A(0, 3)$
16. $B(5\frac{1}{2}, 3)$
17. $C(2, 1\frac{1}{2})$

LESSON 6-7 18. Complete answer on p. A13.

18. Use the data in the table to make a double-line graph. Did toy sales increase or decrease for store A? increase

Toy Sales	January	March	May	July
Store A	\$460	\$580	\$950	\$1200
Store B	\$520	\$450	\$880	\$1250

LESSON 6-8 19. See p. A13.

19. Explain why this bar graph is misleading.
20. What might people believe from the misleading graph? People might believe that Viking received twice as many votes as Ram.

LESSON 6-9

21. Use the data in the table to make a stem-and-leaf plot. Then use your stem-and-leaf plot to find the mean, median, and mode of the data. mean: 35, median: 35, mode: 35; complete answer on p. A13.

Time Spent Doing Homework (min)				
15	35	60	65	15
10	35	60	20	35

LESSON 6-10

22. The table shows the shoe sizes of the female students in Mrs. Woodward's gym class. Which graph would be the more appropriate to show the data—a stem-and-leaf plot or a line plot? Draw the more appropriate graph. See p. A13.

Shoe Sizes of Female Students																	
7	8	$7\frac{1}{2}$	8	9	5	$9\frac{1}{2}$	7	$7\frac{1}{2}$	$7\frac{1}{2}$	$8\frac{1}{2}$	8	7	$6\frac{1}{2}$	7	8	10	9

CRCT GPS Practice ■ Chapter 7

LESSON 7-1

Use the table to write each ratio.

1. cooking books to poetry books 4:5
2. biography books to total books 3:37
3. A pack of 12 pens costs $5.52. A pack of 8 pens costs $3.92. Which is the better deal? the pack of 12 pens

Types of Books in Doug's Collection			
Reference	10	Comic	7
Mystery	8	Poetry	5
Biography	3	Cooking	4

LESSON 7-2

Use a table to find three equivalent ratios.

4. $\frac{2}{5}$ 4:10, 6:15, 8:20 5. 5 to 12 10:24, 15:36, 20:48 6. 1:2 2:4, 3:6, 4:8 7. $\frac{6}{7}$ 12:14, 18:21, 24:28

8. The table shows how many pizzas Travis Middle School orders for certain numbers of students. Predict the number of pizzas the school orders for 175 students. 35 pizzas

Students	50	100	150	200	250
Pizzas	10	20	30	40	50

LESSON 7-3

Find the missing value in each proportion.

9. $\frac{5}{4} = \frac{n}{12}$ $n = 15$ 10. $\frac{2}{9} = \frac{4}{n}$ $n = 18$ 11. $\frac{6}{10} = \frac{n}{5}$ $n = 3$ 12. $\frac{7}{8} = \frac{21}{n}$ $n = 24$

13. To make 2 quarts of punch, Jenny adds 16 grams of juice mix to 2 quarts of water. How much mix does Jenny need to make 3 quarts of punch? 24 grams

LESSON 7-4

14. The two triangles are similar. Find the missing length y and the measure of $\angle B$. $y = 4$ in.; $m\angle B = 27°$

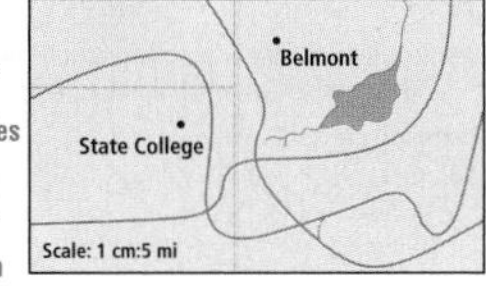

LESSON 7-5

15. A telephone pole casts a shadow that is 32 yd long. At the same time, a yardstick casts a shadow that is 4 yd long. How tall is the telephone pole? 8 yards

LESSON 7-6

Use the map to answer each question.

16. On the map, the distance from State College to Belmont is 2 cm. What is the actual distance between the two locations? 10 miles
17. Henderson City is 83 miles from State College. How many centimeters apart should the two locations be placed on the map? 16.6 cm

Belmont
State College
Scale: 1 cm:5 mi

CRCT GPS Practice ■ Chapter 7

LESSON 7-7

Write each percent as a fraction in simplest form.

18. 50% $\frac{1}{2}$ 19. 34% $\frac{17}{50}$ 20. 8% $\frac{2}{25}$ 21. 12% $\frac{3}{25}$

22. Michael's baseball team won 85% of its games. Write 85% as a fraction in simplest form. $\frac{17}{20}$

Write each percent as a decimal.

23. 13% 0.13 24. 76% 0.76 25. 5% 0.05 26. 70% 0.7

27. At the toy store, sales increased by 26%. Write 26% as a decimal. 0.26

LESSON 7-8

Write each decimal as a percent.

28. 0.56 56% 29. 0.092 9.2% 30. 0.4 40% 31. 0.735 73.5%

Write each fraction as a percent.

32. $\frac{4}{5}$ 80% 33. $\frac{4}{25}$ 16% 34. $\frac{7}{16}$ 43.75% 35. $\frac{5}{8}$ 62.5%

36. In Mrs. Piper's class, $\frac{17}{20}$ of the students have a pet. What percent of the students in the class have pets? 85%

LESSON 7-9

37. A theater sold a total of 570 tickets for a new movie. Of those tickets, 30% were children's tickets. How many children's tickets were sold? 171 tickets
38. Kathy has listened to 80% of the music on a CD. If 26 minutes have passed, how many more minutes of music are left on the CD? 6.5 minutes
39. Find 30% of 98. 29.4 40. Find 15% of 220. 33 41. Find 5% of 72. 3.6

LESSON 7-10

42. Ashley wants to buy a sweater regularly priced at $19.95. It is on sale for 25% off the regular price. About how much will she pay for the sweater after the discount? $15.00
43. Margo and her three friends went to dinner. The bill was $34.62. They left a tip that was 15% of the bill. About how much was the tip? $5.25
44. Patricia is buying new roller skates that cost $59.99. The sales tax rate is 7%. About how much will the total cost of the roller skates be? $64.20

CRCT GPS Practice ■ Chapter 8

LESSON 8-1

Use the diagram to name each geometric figure.

1. three points Possible answers: X, Y, B
2. two lines $\overleftrightarrow{XY}$; $\overleftrightarrow{AY}$
3. a point shared by two lines Y
4. a plane BCD

Use the diagram to give a possible name to each figure.

5. three line segments $\overline{XY}$; $\overline{XZ}$; $\overline{YZ}$
6. three ways to name the line $\overleftrightarrow{XY}$; $\overleftrightarrow{XZ}$; $\overleftrightarrow{YZ}$
7. six rays $\overrightarrow{XY}$; $\overrightarrow{XZ}$; $\overrightarrow{YX}$; $\overrightarrow{YZ}$; $\overrightarrow{ZY}$; $\overrightarrow{ZX}$
8. another name for ray XY ray XZ

LESSON 8-2

Use a protractor to measure each angle. Classify each angle as acute, right, obtuse, or straight.

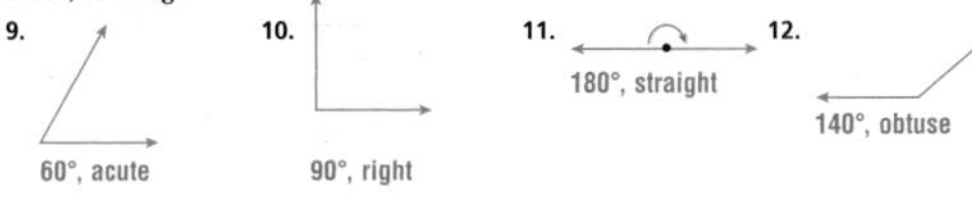

9. 60°, acute 10. 90°, right 11. 180°, straight 12. 140°, obtuse

LESSON 8-3

Find each unknown angle measure.

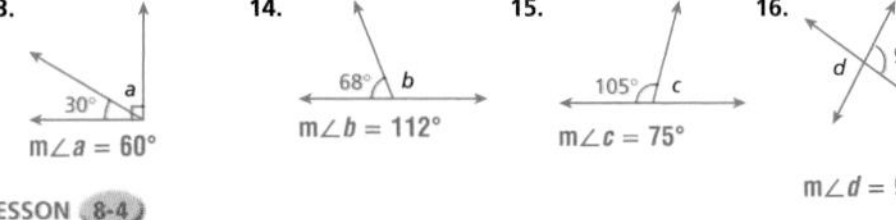

13. $m\angle a = 60°$ 14. $m\angle b = 112°$ 15. $m\angle c = 75°$ 16. $m\angle d = 98°$

LESSON 8-4

Classify each pair of lines.

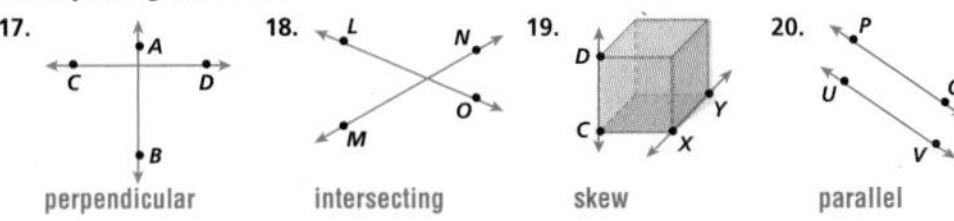

17. perpendicular 18. intersecting 19. skew 20. parallel

CRCT GPS Practice ■ Chapter 8

LESSON 8-5

Use the diagram to find the measure of each indicated angle.

21. $\angle FJH$ 110°
22. $\angle FJG$ 70°

Classify each triangle using the given information.

23. The perimeter of the triangle is 14 in. 24. The perimeter of the triangle is 45 ft. 25. The perimeter of the triangle is 20 ft.

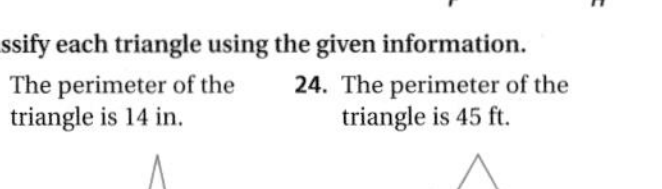

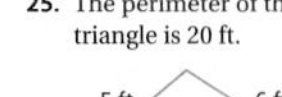

isosceles equilateral scalene

LESSON 8-6

Give the most descriptive name for each figure.

26. trapezoid 27. rectangle 28. parallelogram 29. rhombus

Complete each statement.

30. A parallelogram with four right angles can be a ___?___ or a ___?___. rectangle, square
31. A quadrilateral with two parallel sides is a ___?___. trapezoid

LESSON 8-7

Tell whether each shape is a polygon. If so, give it's name and tell whether it appears to be regular or not regular.

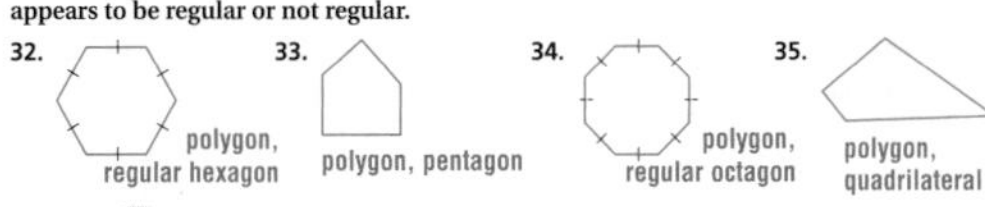

32. polygon, regular hexagon 33. polygon, pentagon 34. polygon, regular octagon 35. polygon, quadrilateral

LESSON 8-8

Identify a possible pattern. Use the pattern to draw the missing figure.

36.  ?

37. 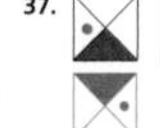 ?

CRCT GPS Practice

CRCT GPS Practice ■ Chapter 8

LESSON 8-9

Decide whether the figures in each pair are congruent. If not, explain.

38. The figures are congruent.

39. The figures are not congruent. Both are rectangles, but they have different sizes.

LESSON 8-10

Tell whether each is a translation, rotation, or reflection.

40. reflection

41. translation

42. rotation

Draw each transformation.

43. Draw a translation 2 cm to the right.

44. Draw a 90° clockwise rotation about the point.

45. Draw a vertical reflection across the line.

LESSON 8-11

Determine whether each dashed line appears to be a line of symmetry.

46. yes, yes

47. yes

48. no

49. no

Find all of the lines of symmetry in each design.

50.

51.

52.

CRCT GPS Practice ■ Chapter 9

LESSON 9-1

What unit of measure provides the best estimate? Explain.

1. A book is about 12 ___?___ long. inches; about 12 widths of your thumb
2. A newborn baby weights about 8 ___?___. pounds; about 8 loaves of bread
3. A small aquarium holds about 10 ___?___ of water. gallons; about 10 large containers of milk

LESSON 9-2

What unit of measure provides the best estimate? Explain.

4. An earthworm is about 10 ___?___ long. centimeters; about 10 widths of your finger
5. A leaf has a mass of about 250 ___?___. milligrams; about 250 very small insects
6. The mass of a fork is about 40 ___?___. grams; about 40 large paper clips

LESSON 9-3

Convert.

7. 156 in = ■ ft 13
8. 6 T = ■ lb 12,000
9. 24 qt = ■ gal 6
10. 13,200 ft = ■ mi 2.5
11. 8 pt = ■ qt 4
12. 33 yd = ■ ft 11
13. A marathon is about 26.2 miles. How many feet long is a marathon? 138,336

LESSON 9-4

14. The height of a telephone pole is 15 meters. How many centimeters is this? 1,500 cm

Convert.

15. A hat has a mass of about 86 g. 86 g = ■ kg 0.086
16. A rain gauge holds about 0.5 L of water. 0.5 L = ■ mL 500
17. 550 g = ■ kg 0.55
18. 88 cm = ■ mm 880
19. 1,585 m = ■ km 1.585
20. 5,500 mg = ■ g 5.5
21. 200 mL = ■ L 0.2
22. 2.2 mL = ■ L 0.0022

LESSON 9-5

23. 1,095 days = ■ yr 3
24. 4 min 23 s = ■ s 263
25. 3 weeks = ■ hr 504
26. 96 h = ■ days 4
27. 78 weeks = ■ yr 1.5
28. 1h 35 min = ■ min 95
29. Rochelle's birthday party starts at 7:30 P.M. and lasts for 3 hours 45 minutes. What time does her party end? 11:15 P.M.

Estimate the temperature.

30. 18° C is about ■° F 66
31. 35° F is about ■° C 2.5
32. 44° C is about ■° F 118

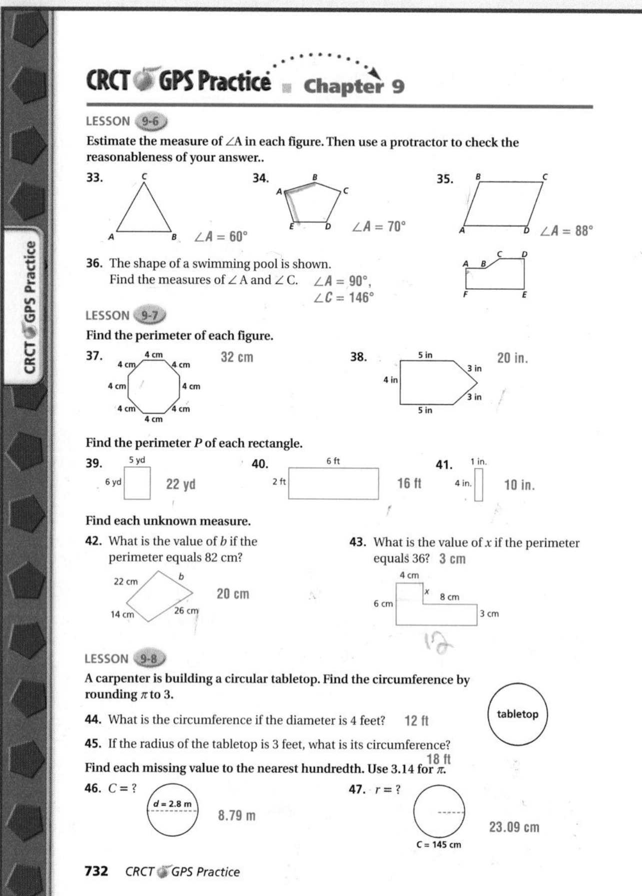

CRCT GPS Practice ■ Chapter 9

LESSON 9-6

Estimate the measure of ∠A in each figure. Then use a protractor to check the reasonableness of your answer..

33. ∠A = 60°
34. ∠A = 70°
35. ∠A = 88°
36. The shape of a swimming pool is shown. Find the measures of ∠A and ∠C. ∠A = 90°, ∠C = 146°

LESSON 9-7

Find the perimeter of each figure.

37. 32 cm
38. 20 in.

Find the perimeter *P* of each rectangle.

39. 22 yd
40. 16 ft
41. 10 in.

Find each unknown measure.

42. What is the value of *b* if the perimeter equals 82 cm? 20 cm
43. What is the value of *x* if the perimeter equals 36? 3 cm

LESSON 9-8

A carpenter is building a circular tabletop. Find the circumference by rounding π to 3.

44. What is the circumference if the diameter is 4 feet? 12 ft
45. If the radius of the tabletop is 3 feet, what is its circumference? 18 ft

Find each missing value to the nearest hundredth. Use 3.14 for π.

46. *C* = ? 8.79 m
47. *r* = ? 23.09 cm

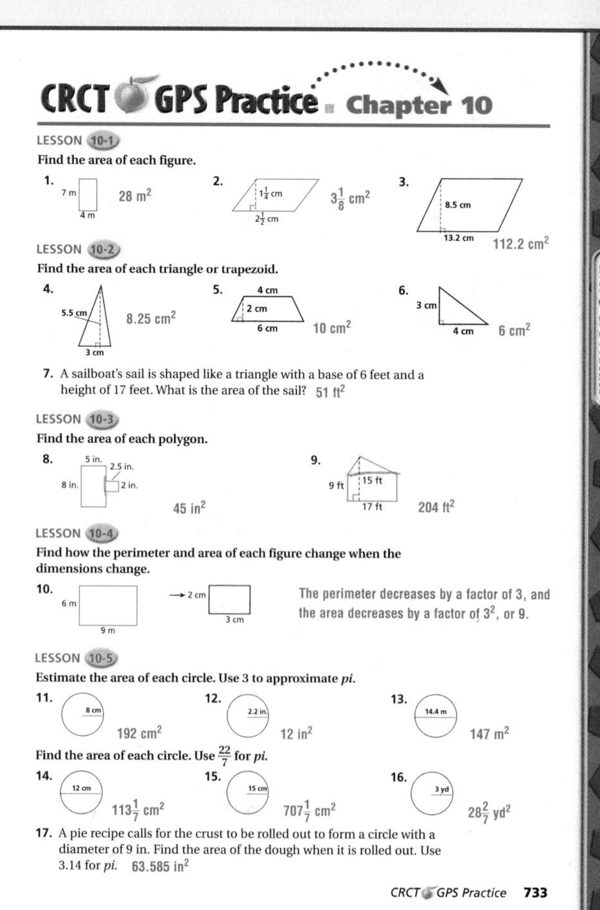

CRCT GPS Practice ■ Chapter 10

LESSON 10-1

Find the area of each figure.

1. 28 m²
2. $3\frac{1}{8}$ cm²
3. 112.2 cm²

LESSON 10-2

Find the area of each triangle or trapezoid.

4. 8.25 cm²
5. 10 cm²
6. 6 cm²
7. A sailboat's sail is shaped like a triangle with a base of 6 feet and a height of 17 feet. What is the area of the sail? 51 ft²

LESSON 10-3

Find the area of each polygon.

8. 45 in²
9. 204 ft²

LESSON 10-4

Find how the perimeter and area of each figure change when the dimensions change.

10. The perimeter decreases by a factor of 3, and the area decreases by a factor of 3², or 9.

LESSON 10-5

Estimate the area of each circle. Use 3 to approximate *pi*.

11. 192 cm²
12. 12 in²
13. 147 m²

Find the area of each circle. Use $\frac{22}{7}$ for *pi*.

14. $113\frac{1}{7}$ cm²
15. $707\frac{1}{7}$ cm²
16. $28\frac{2}{7}$ yd²
17. A pie recipe calls for the crust to be rolled out to form a circle with a diameter of 9 in. Find the area of the dough when it is rolled out. Use 3.14 for *pi*. 63.585 in²

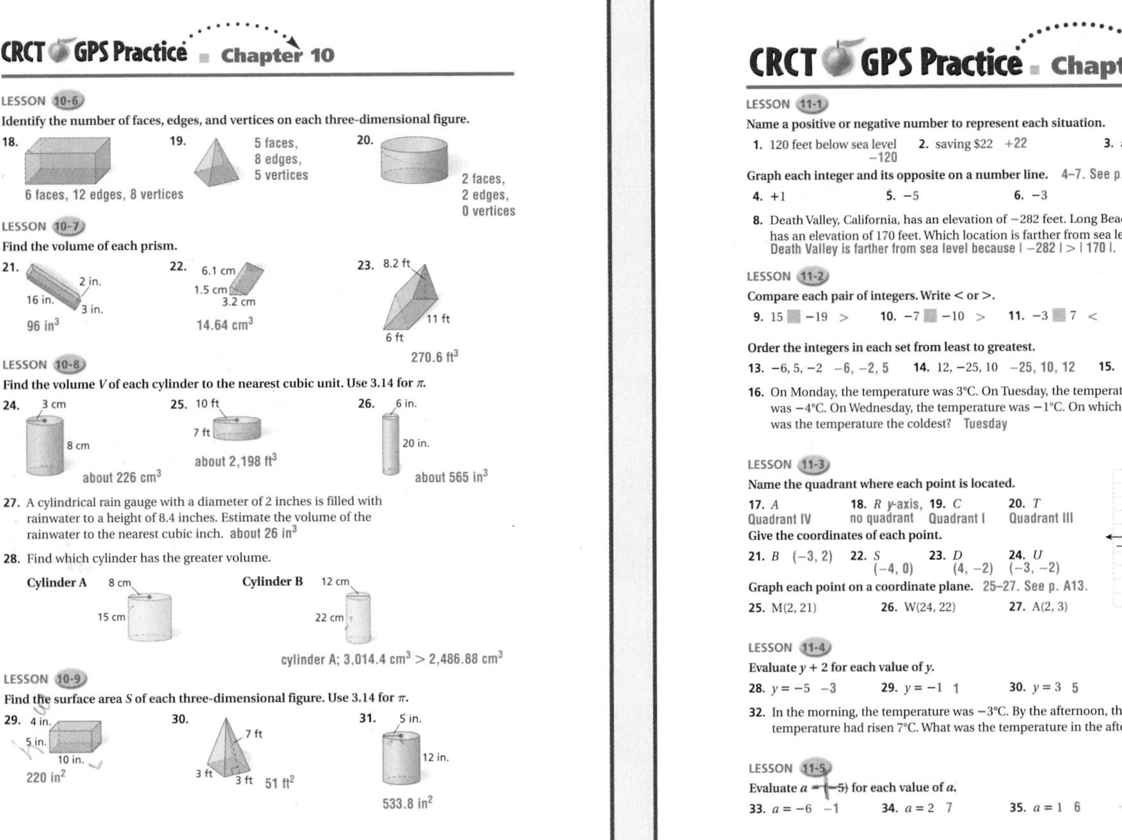

CRCT GPS Practice ■ Chapter 10

LESSON 10-6

Identify the number of faces, edges, and vertices on each three-dimensional figure.

18. 6 faces, 12 edges, 8 vertices
19. 5 faces, 8 edges, 5 vertices
20. 2 faces, 2 edges, 0 vertices

LESSON 10-7

Find the volume of each prism.

21. 16 in., 2 in., 3 in. — 96 in^3
22. 6.1 cm, 1.5 cm, 3.2 cm — 14.64 cm^3
23. 8.2 ft, 11 ft, 6 ft — 270.6 ft^3

LESSON 10-8

Find the volume V of each cylinder to the nearest cubic unit. Use 3.14 for π.

24. 3 cm, 8 cm — about 226 cm^3
25. 10 ft, 7 ft — about 2,198 ft^3
26. 6 in., 20 in. — about 565 in^3
27. A cylindrical rain gauge with a diameter of 2 inches is filled with rainwater to a height of 8.4 inches. Estimate the volume of the rainwater to the nearest cubic inch. about 26 in^3
28. Find which cylinder has the greater volume.

Cylinder A 8 cm, 15 cm Cylinder B 12 cm, 22 cm

cylinder A; 3,014.4 cm^3 > 2,486.88 cm^3

LESSON 10-9

Find the surface area S of each three-dimensional figure. Use 3.14 for π.

29. 4 in., 5 in., 10 in. — 220 in^2
30. 7 ft, 3 ft, 3 ft — 51 ft^2
31. 5 in., 12 in. — 533.8 in^2

734 CRCT GPS Practice

CRCT GPS Practice ■ Chapter 11

LESSON 11-1

Name a positive or negative number to represent each situation.

1. 120 feet below sea level −120
2. saving $22 +22
3. a decrease of 5° −5

Graph each integer and its opposite on a number line. 4–7. See p. A13.

4. +1
5. −5
6. −3
7. +2
8. Death Valley, California, has an elevation of −282 feet. Long Beach, California, has an elevation of 170 feet. Which location is farther from sea level? Death Valley is farther from sea level because | −282 | > | 170 |.

LESSON 11-2

Compare each pair of integers. Write < or >.

9. 15 ▒ −19 >
10. −7 ▒ −10 >
11. −3 ▒ 7 <
12. −8 ▒ 2 <

Order the integers in each set from least to greatest.

13. −6, 5, −2 −6, −2, 5
14. 12, −25, 10 −25, 10, 12
15. −1, −3, 4, 0 −3, −1, 0, 4
16. On Monday, the temperature was 3°C. On Tuesday, the temperature was −4°C. On Wednesday, the temperature was −1°C. On which day was the temperature the coldest? Tuesday

LESSON 11-3

Name the quadrant where each point is located.

17. A Quadrant IV
18. R y-axis, no quadrant
19. C Quadrant I
20. T Quadrant III

Give the coordinates of each point.

21. B (−3, 2)
22. S (−4, 0)
23. D (4, −2)
24. U (−3, −2)

Graph each point on a coordinate plane. 25–27. See p. A13.

25. M(2, 21)
26. W(24, 22)
27. A(2, 3)

LESSON 11-4

Evaluate $y + 2$ for each value of y.

28. $y = -5$ −3
29. $y = -1$ 1
30. $y = 3$ 5
31. $y = -8$ −6
32. In the morning, the temperature was −3°C. By the afternoon, the temperature had risen 7°C. What was the temperature in the afternoon? 4°C

LESSON 11-5

Evaluate $a - (-5)$ for each value of a.

33. $a = -6$ −1
34. $a = 2$ 7
35. $a = 1$ 6
36. $a = -5$ 0

CRCT GPS Practice 735

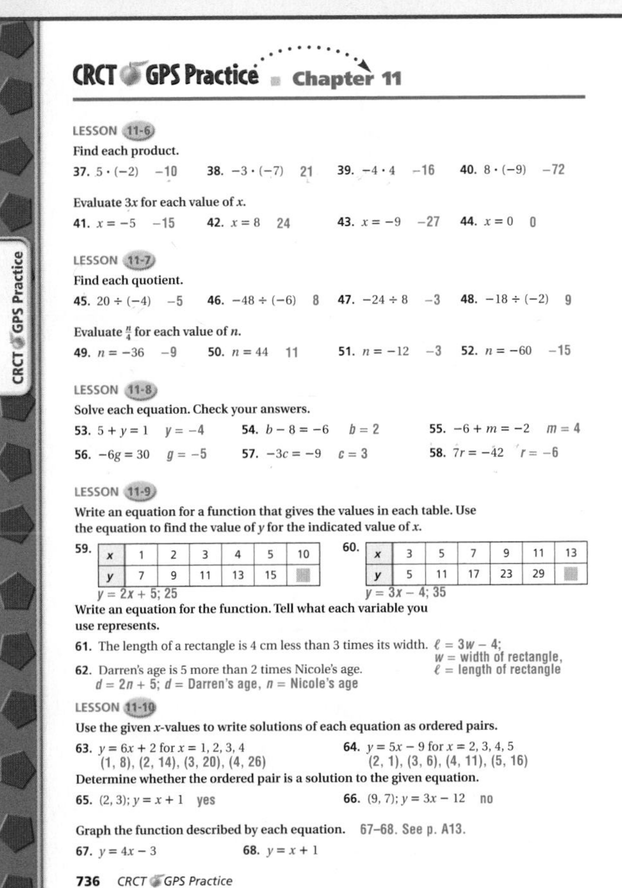

CRCT GPS Practice ■ Chapter 11

LESSON 11-6

Find each product.

37. $5 \cdot (-2)$ −10
38. $-3 \cdot (-7)$ 21
39. $-4 \cdot 4$ −16
40. $8 \cdot (-9)$ −72

Evaluate $3x$ for each value of x.

41. $x = -5$ −15
42. $x = 8$ 24
43. $x = -9$ −27
44. $x = 0$ 0

LESSON 11-7

Find each quotient.

45. $20 \div (-4)$ −5
46. $-48 \div (-6)$ 8
47. $-24 \div 8$ −3
48. $-18 \div (-2)$ 9

Evaluate $\frac{n}{4}$ for each value of n.

49. $n = -36$ −9
50. $n = 44$ 11
51. $n = -12$ −3
52. $n = -60$ −15

LESSON 11-8

Solve each equation. Check your answers.

53. $5 + y = 1$ $y = -4$
54. $b - 8 = -6$ $b = 2$
55. $-6 + m = -2$ $m = 4$
56. $-6g = 30$ $g = -5$
57. $-3c = -9$ $c = 3$
58. $7r = -42$ $r = -6$

LESSON 11-9

Write an equation for a function that gives the values in each table. Use the equation to find the value of y for the indicated value of x.

59.

x	1	2	3	4	5	10
y	7	9	11	13	15	▒

$y = 2x + 5$; 25

60.

x	3	5	7	9	11	13
y	5	11	17	23	29	▒

$y = 3x - 4$; 35

Write an equation for the function. Tell what each variable you use represents.

61. The length of a rectangle is 4 cm less than 3 times its width. $\ell = 3w - 4$; w = width of rectangle, ℓ = length of rectangle
62. Darren's age is 5 more than 2 times Nicole's age. $d = 2n + 5$; d = Darren's age, n = Nicole's age

LESSON 11-10

Use the given x-values to write solutions of each equation as ordered pairs.

63. $y = 6x + 2$ for $x = 1, 2, 3, 4$ (1, 8), (2, 14), (3, 20), (4, 26)
64. $y = 5x - 9$ for $x = 2, 3, 4, 5$ (2, 1), (3, 6), (4, 11), (5, 16)

Determine whether the ordered pair is a solution to the given equation.

65. (2, 3); $y = x + 1$ yes
66. (9, 7); $y = 3x - 12$ no

Graph the function described by each equation. 67–68. See p. A13.

67. $y = 4x - 3$
68. $y = x + 1$

736 CRCT GPS Practice

CRCT GPS Practice ■ Chapter 12

LESSON 12-1

Write *impossible, unlikely, as likely as not, likely,* or *certain* to describe each event.

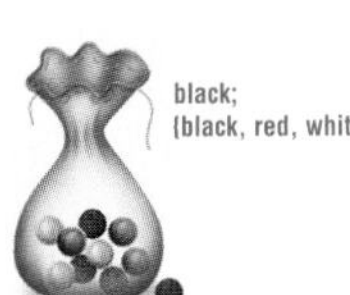

1. picking a green marble from this bag of marbles impossible
2. picking a red marble from this bag of marbles as likely as not
3. The chance of winning a sweepstakes is 3%. Write this probability as a decimal and as a fraction. 0.03, $\frac{3}{100}$
4. A particular brand of cereal is offering a prize in each box. There is a 34% chance the toy will be a rubber ball, a 50% chance it will be a small figurine, and a 16% chance it will be a game. Is it more likely that the prize will be a rubber ball or a game? a rubber ball

LESSON 12-2

For each experiment, identify the outcome shown.

5. 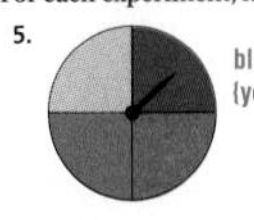 blue; {yellow, red, blue, green}
6. black; {black, red, white}

For one month, Maggie recorded the weather. She organized her results in a frequency table.

Weather	Sunny	Cloudy	Rainy
Frequency	17	6	7

7. Find the experimental probability of cloudy weather. $\frac{1}{5}$
8. Based on Maggie's findings, is it more likely that the weather will be cloudy or rainy? rainy

LESSON 12-3

9. Miguel is buying a new car. He has three choices for the exterior color: black, silver, or blue. He has two choices for the interior color: black or brown. What are the different color combinations Miguel can choose from? black exterior, black interior; black exterior, brown interior; silver exterior, black interior; silver exterior, brown interior; blue exterior, black interior; blue exterior, brown interior
10. For breakfast, Brianna can have oatmeal, cold cereal, or eggs and then a banana, an apple, or an orange. How many different breakfast combinations can Brianna choose from? 9
11. At summer camp, the campers can participate in 3 different activities each morning: hiking, swimming, and arts and crafts and 2 different activities each afternoon: tennis and biking. How many possible combinations of activities are there? 12

CRCT GPS Practice ■ Chapter 12

LESSON 12-4

12. What is the probability of rolling an even number on a fair number cube? $\frac{1}{2}$
13. What is the probability of randomly choosing the letter *T* from the letters *M, A, T, H, E, M, A, T, I, C, S*? $\frac{2}{11}$
14. The weather report stated that there is a 42% chance of snow today. What is the probability that it will NOT snow? 58%
15. During its grand opening, a store is giving away prizes. The chance of winning a prize is 0.16. Find the probability of NOT winning a prize. 0.84

LESSON 12-5

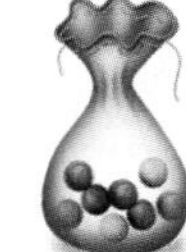

16. Find the probability of spinning red on the spinner and choosing a red marble from the bag. $\frac{1}{5}$
17. Find the probability of spinning yellow and choosing a marble that is NOT yellow. $\frac{3}{20}$
18. Find the probability of spinning a color that is NOT blue and choosing a marble that is NOT blue. $\frac{9}{20}$

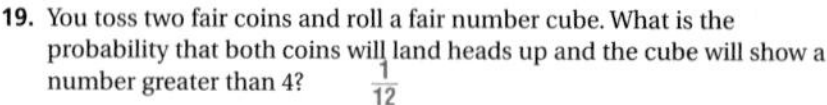

19. You toss two fair coins and roll a fair number cube. What is the probability that both coins will land heads up and the cube will show a number greater than 4? $\frac{1}{12}$

LESSON 12-6

20. Based on a sample survey, a local newspaper stated that 26% of the population has a pet dog. Out of 600 people, how many people can you predict will have a pet dog? 156 people
21. If you roll a number cube 54 times, how many times do you expect to roll a number less than 3? 18 times
22. A promotion team is selling tickets for unreserved seats to a concert. The promotion team estimates that 75% of the people who purchase a ticket will attend the concert. If the stadium seats 15,000 people and the promotion team wants to have all of the seats full at the concert, how many concert tickets should they sell? 20,000 tickets

738 CRCT GPS Practice

Problem Solving Handbook

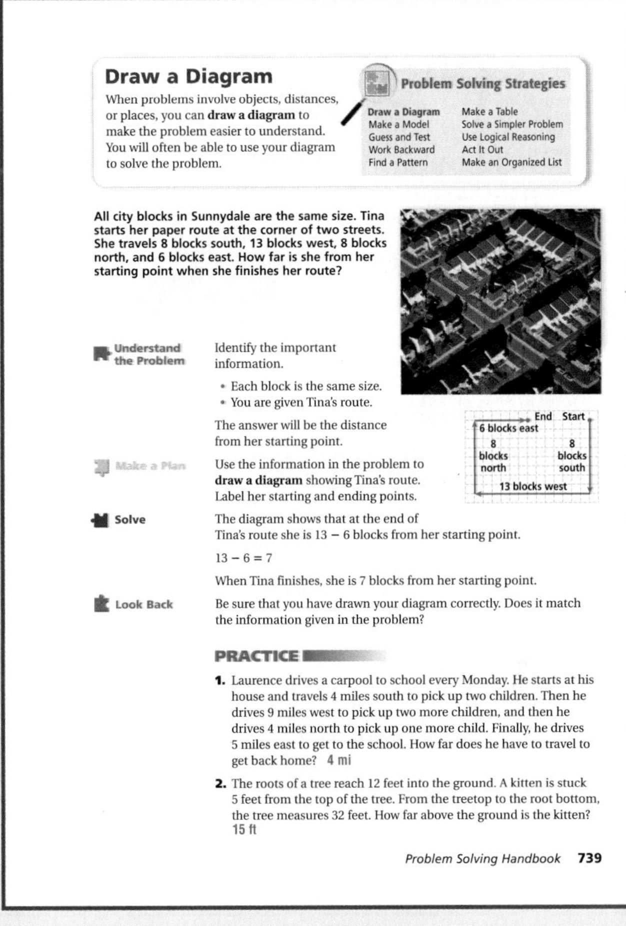

Draw a Diagram

When problems involve objects, distances, or places, you can **draw a diagram** to make the problem easier to understand. You will often be able to use your diagram to solve the problem.

Problem Solving Strategies

Draw a Diagram	Make a Table
Make a Model	Solve a Simpler Problem
Guess and Test	Use Logical Reasoning
Work Backward	Act It Out
Find a Pattern	Make an Organized List

All city blocks in Sunnydale are the same size. Tina starts her paper route at the corner of two streets. She travels 8 blocks south, 13 blocks west, 8 blocks north, and 6 blocks east. How far is she from her starting point when she finishes her route?

Understand the Problem Identify the important information.

- Each block is the same size.
- You are given Tina's route.

The answer will be the distance from her starting point.

Make a Plan Use the information in the problem to **draw a diagram** showing Tina's route. Label her starting and ending points.

Solve The diagram shows that at the end of Tina's route she is 13 − 6 blocks from her starting point.

$13 - 6 = 7$

When Tina finishes, she is 7 blocks from her starting point.

Look Back Be sure that you have drawn your diagram correctly. Does it match the information given in the problem?

PRACTICE

1. Laurence drives a carpool to school every Monday. He starts at his house and travels 4 miles south to pick up two children. Then he drives 9 miles west to pick up two more children, and then he drives 4 miles north to pick up one more child. Finally, he drives 5 miles east to get to the school. How far does he have to travel to get back home? 4 mi
2. The roots of a tree reach 12 feet into the ground. A kitten is stuck 5 feet from the top of the tree. From the treetop to the root bottom, the tree measures 32 feet. How far above the ground is the kitten? 15 ft

Problem Solving Handbook **739**

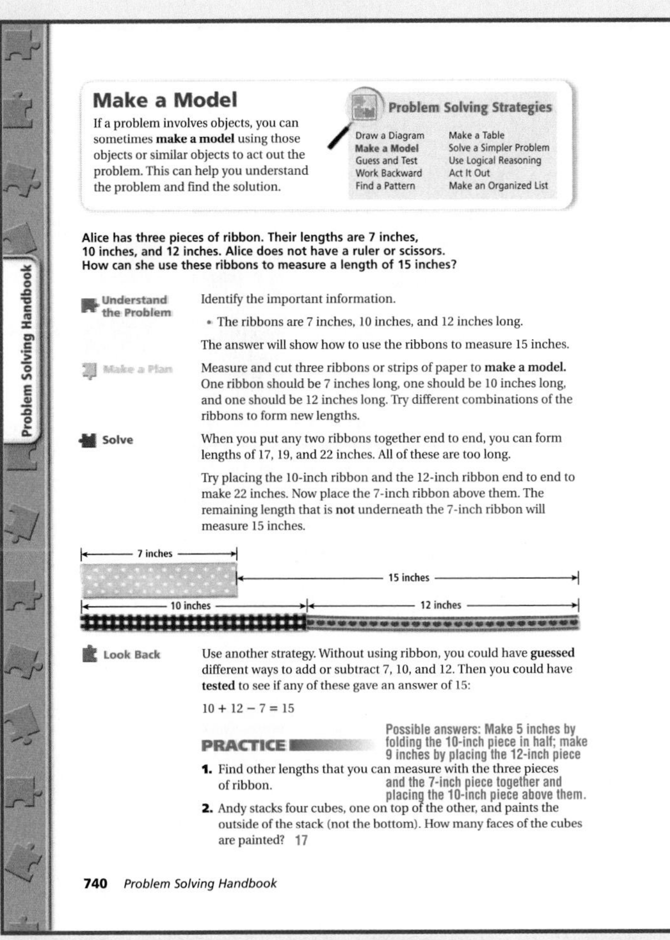

Make a Model

If a problem involves objects, you can sometimes **make a model** using those objects or similar objects to act out the problem. This can help you understand the problem and find the solution.

Problem Solving Strategies

Draw a Diagram	Make a Table
Make a Model	Solve a Simpler Problem
Guess and Test	Use Logical Reasoning
Work Backward	Act It Out
Find a Pattern	Make an Organized List

Alice has three pieces of ribbon. Their lengths are 7 inches, 10 inches, and 12 inches. Alice does not have a ruler or scissors. How can she use these ribbons to measure a length of 15 inches?

Understand the Problem Identify the important information.

- The ribbons are 7 inches, 10 inches, and 12 inches long.

The answer will show how to use the ribbons to measure 15 inches.

Make a Plan Measure and cut three ribbons or strips of paper to **make a model.** One ribbon should be 7 inches long, one should be 10 inches long, and one should be 12 inches long. Try different combinations of the ribbons to form new lengths.

Solve When you put any two ribbons together end to end, you can form lengths of 17, 19, and 22 inches. All of these are too long.

Try placing the 10-inch ribbon and the 12-inch ribbon end to end to make 22 inches. Now place the 7-inch ribbon above them. The remaining length that is **not** underneath the 7-inch ribbon will measure 15 inches.

Look Back Use another strategy. Without using ribbon, you could have **guessed** different ways to add or subtract 7, 10, and 12. Then you could have **tested** to see if any of these gave an answer of 15:

$10 + 12 - 7 = 15$

PRACTICE

1. Find other lengths that you can measure with the three pieces of ribbon. Possible answers: Make 5 inches by folding the 10-inch piece in half; make 9 inches by placing the 12-inch piece and the 7-inch piece together and placing the 10-inch piece above them.
2. Andy stacks four cubes, one on top of the other, and paints the outside of the stack (not the bottom). How many faces of the cubes are painted? 17

740 *Problem Solving Handbook*

Guess and Test

If you do not know how to solve a problem, you can always make a **guess**. Then **test** your guess using the information in the problem. Use the result to make a better guess. Repeat until you find the correct answer.

Problem Solving Strategies

Draw a Diagram	Make a Table
Make a Model	Solve a Simpler Problem
Guess and Test	Use Logical Reasoning
Work Backward	Act It Out
Find a Pattern	Make an Organized List

There were 25 problems on a test. For each correct answer, 4 points were given. For each incorrect answer, 1 point was subtracted. Tania answered all 25 problems. Her score was 85. How many correct and incorrect answers did she have?

Understand the Problem Identify the important information.

- There were 25 problems on the test.
- A correct answer received 4 points, and an incorrect answer lost 1 point.
- Tania answered all of the problems and her score was 85.

The answer will be the number of problems that Tania got correct and incorrect.

Make a Plan Start with a **guess** for the number of correct answers. Then **test** to see whether the total score is 85.

Solve Make a first guess of 20 correct answers.

Correct	Incorrect	Score	Result
20	5	$(20 \times 4) - (5 \times 1) = 80 - 5 = 75$	Too low—guess higher
23	2	$(23 \times 4) - (2 \times 1) = 92 - 2 = 90$	Too high—guess lower
22	3	$(22 \times 4) - (3 \times 1) = 88 - 3 = 85$	Correct ✓

Tania had 22 correct answers and 3 incorrect answers.

Look Back Notice that the guesses made while solving this problem were not just "wild" guesses. Guessing and testing in an organized way will often lead you to the correct answer.

PRACTICE

1. The sum of Joe's age and his younger brother's age is 38. The difference between their ages is 8. How old are Joe and his brother? Joe is 23; his brother is 15.
2. Amy bought some used books for $4.95. She paid $0.50 each for some books and $0.35 each for the others. She bought fewer than 8 books at each price. How many books did Amy buy? How many cost $0.50? 12 books; 5 cost $0.50.

Problem Solving Handbook **741**

Problem Solving Handbook

Work Backward

Some problems give you a sequence of information and ask you to find something that happened at the beginning. To solve a problem like this, you may want to start at the end of the problem and **work backward.**

Problem Solving Strategies

Draw a Diagram	Make a Table
Make a Model	Solve a Simpler Problem
Guess and Test	Use Logical Reasoning
Work Backward	Act It Out
Find a Pattern	Make an Organized List

Jaclyn and her twin sister, Bailey, received money for their birthday. They used half of their money to buy a video game. Then they spent half of the money they had left on a pizza. Finally, they spent half of the remaining money to rent a movie. At the end of the day, they had $4.50. How much money did they have to start out with?

Understand the Problem Identify the important information.

- The girls ended with $4.50.
- They spent half of their money at each of three stops.

The answer will be the amount of money they started with.

Make a Plan Start with the amount you know the girls have left, $4.50, and **work backward** through the information given in the problem.

Solve Jaclyn and Bailey had $4.50 at the end of the day.

They had twice that amount before renting a movie. 2 × $4.50 = $9

They had twice that amount before buying a pizza. 2 × $9 = $18

They had twice that amount before buying a video game. 2 × $18 = $36

The girls started with $36.

Look Back Using the starting amount of $36, work from the beginning of the problem. Find the amount they spent at each location and see whether they are left with $4.50.

Start: $36
Video game: $36 ÷ 2 = $18
Pizza: $18 ÷ 2 = $9
Movie rental: $9 ÷ 2 = $4.50 ✓

PRACTICE

1. The Lauber family has 4 children. Chris is 5 years younger than his brother Mark. Justin is half as old as his brother Chris. Mary, who is 10, is 3 years younger than Justin. How old is Mark? 31
2. If you divide a mystery number by 4, add 8, and multiply by 3, you get 42. What is the mystery number? 24

Find a Pattern

In some problems, there is a relationship between different pieces of information. Examine this relationship and try to **find a pattern.** You can then use this pattern to find more information and the solution to the problem.

Problem Solving Strategies

Draw a Diagram	Make a Table
Make a Model	Solve a Simpler Problem
Guess and Test	Use Logical Reasoning
Work Backward	Act It Out
Find a Pattern	Make an Organized List

Students are using the pattern at right to build stairways for a model house. How many blocks are needed to build a stairway with seven steps?

Understand the Problem The answer will be the total number of blocks in a stairway with seven steps.

Make a Plan Try to **find a pattern** between the number of steps and the number of blocks needed.

Notice that the first step is made of one block. The second step is made of two blocks, the third step is made of three blocks, and the fourth step is made of four blocks.

Step	Number of Blocks in Step	Total Number of Blocks in Stairway
2	2	1 + 2 = 3
3	3	1 + 2 + 3 = 6
4	4	1 + 2 + 3 + 4 = 10

To find the total number of blocks, add the number of blocks in the first step, the second step, the third step, and so on.

Solve The seventh step will be made of seven blocks. The total number of blocks will be 1 + 2 + 3 + 4 + 5 + 6 + 7 = 28.

Look Back Use another strategy. You can **draw a diagram** of a stairway with 7 steps. Count the number of blocks in your diagram. There are 28 blocks.

PRACTICE

1. A cereal company adds baseball cards to the 3rd box, the 6th box, the 11th box, the 18th box, and so on of each case of cereal. In a case of 40 boxes, how many boxes will have baseball cards? 6 boxes
2. Describe the pattern and find the missing numbers.
   1; 4; 16; 64; 256; ▒; ▒; 16,384 1,024; 4,096

Make a Table

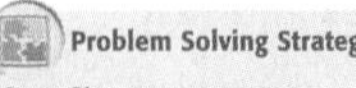

When you are given a lot of information in a problem, it may be helpful to organize that information. One way to organize information is to **make a table.**

Problem Solving Strategies

Draw a Diagram	**Make a Table**
Make a Model	Solve a Simpler Problem
Guess and Test	Use Logical Reasoning
Work Backward	Act It Out
Find a Pattern	Make an Organized List

Mrs. Melo's students scored the following on their math test: 90, 80, 77, 78, 91, 92, 73, 62, 83, 79, 72, 85, 93, 84, 75, 68, 82, 94, 98, and 82. An A is given for 90 to 100 points, a B for 80 to 89 points, a C for 70 to 79 points, a D for 60 to 69 points, and an F for less than 60 points. Find the number of students who scored each letter grade.

Understand the Problem Identify the important information.

- You have been given the list of scores and the letter grades that go with each score.

The answer will be the number of each letter grade.

Make a Plan **Make a table** to organize the scores. Use the information in the problem to set up your table. Make one row for each letter grade.

Letter Grade	Number
A (90–100)	卌 I
B (80–89)	卌 I
C (70–79)	卌 I
D (60–69)	II
F (below 60)	

Solve Read through the list of scores. As you read each score, make a tally in the appropriate place in your table. There are 20 test scores, so be sure you have 20 tallies in all.

Mrs. Melo gave out six A's, six B's, six C's, two D's, and no F's.

Look Back Use another strategy. Another way you could solve this problem is to **make an organized list.** Order the scores from least to greatest, and count how many scores are in each range.

62, 68, 72, 73, 75, 77, 78, 79, 80, 82, 82, 83, 84, 85, 90, 91, 92, 93, 94, 98
D C B A

PRACTICE

1. The debate club has 6 members. Each member will debate each of the other members exactly once. How many total debates will there be? 15
2. At the library, there are three story-telling sessions. Each one lasts 45 minutes, with 30 minutes between sessions. If the first session begins at 10:00 A.M., what time does the last session end? 1:15 P.M.

Solve a Simpler Problem

Sometimes a problem contains large numbers or requires many steps. Try to **solve a simpler problem** that is similar. Solve the simpler problem first, and then try the same steps to solve the original problem.

Problem Solving Strategies

Draw a Diagram	Make a Table
Make a Model	**Solve a Simpler Problem**
Guess and Test	Use Logical Reasoning
Work Backward	Act It Out
Find a Pattern	Make an Organized List

At the end of a soccer game, each player shakes hands with every player on the opposing team. How many handshakes are there at the end of a game between two teams that each have 20 players?

Understand the Problem Identify the important information.

- There are 20 players on each team.
- Each player will shake hands with every player on the opposing team.

The answer will be the total number of handshakes exchanged.

Make a Plan **Solve a simpler problem.** For example, suppose each team had just one player. Then there would only be one handshake between the two players. Expand the number of players to two and then three.

Solve When there is 1 player, there is 1 × 1 = 1 handshake. For 2 players, there are 2 × 2 = 4 handshakes. And for 3 players, there are 3 × 3 = 9 handshakes.

Players Per Team	Diagram	Handshakes
1		1
2		4
3		9

If each team has 20 players, there will be 20 × 20 = 400 handshakes.

Look Back If the pattern is correct, for 4 players there will be 16 handshakes and for 5 players there will be 25 handshakes. Complete the next two rows of the table to check these answers.

PRACTICE

1. Martha has 5 pairs of pants and 4 blouses that she can wear to school. How many different outfits can she make? 20
2. What is the smallest 5-digit number that can be divided by 50 with a remainder of 17? 10,017

Use Logical Reasoning

Sometimes a problem may provide clues and facts that you must use to answer a question. You can **use logical reasoning** to solve this kind of problem.

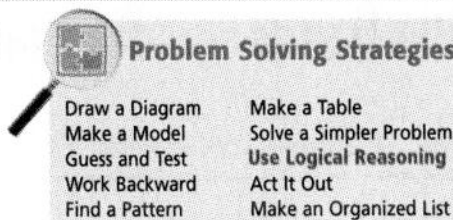

Kevin, Ellie, and Jillian play three different sports. One person plays soccer, one likes to run track, and the other swims. Ellie is the sister of the swimmer. Kevin once went shopping with the swimmer and the track runner. Match each student with his or her sport.

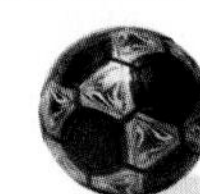

Understand the Problem Identify the important information.

- There are three people, and each person plays a different sport.
- Ellie is the sister of the swimmer.
- Kevin once went shopping with the swimmer and the track runner.

The answer will tell which student plays each sport.

Make a Plan Start with clues given in the problem, and **use logical reasoning** to find the answer.

Solve Make a table with a column for each sport and a row for each person. Work with the clues one at a time. Write "yes" in a box if the clue applies to that person. Write "no" if the clue does not apply.

	Soccer	Track	Swim
Kevin		no	no
Ellie			no
Jillian			

- Ellie is the sister of the swimmer, so she is not the swimmer.
- Kevin went shopping with the swimmer and the track runner. He is not the swimmer or the track runner.

So Kevin must be the soccer player, and Jillian must be the swimmer. This leaves Ellie as the track runner.

Look Back Compare your answer to the clues in the problem. Make sure none of your conclusions conflict with the clues.

PRACTICE

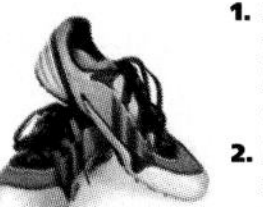

1. Karin, Brent, and Lola each ordered a different slice of pizza: pepperoni, plain cheese, and ham-pineapple. Karin is allergic to pepperoni. Lola likes more than one topping. Which kind of pizza did each person order? Karin–plain cheese, Brent–pepperoni, Lola–ham-pineapple
2. Leo, Jamal, and Kara are in fourth, fifth, and sixth grades. Kara is not in fourth grade. The sixth-grader is in chorus with Kara and has the same lunch time as Leo. Match the students with their grades. Leo–4th, Kara–5th, Jamal–6th

Act It Out

Some problems involve actions or processes. To solve these problems, you can **act it out.** Actively modeling the problem can help you find the solution.

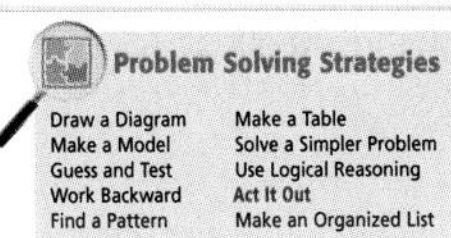

Wei rolls a number cube and flips a coin at the same time. What fraction of all the possible results involve the number cube showing an even number and the coin landing heads up?

Understand the Problem List the important information.

- Wei is rolling a number cube and flipping a coin at the same time.

The answer will be the fraction of all the possible results in which the number cube shows an even number and the coin lands heads up.

Make a Plan **Act it out** to find out how many different results are possible. Then find the fraction of the results that involve an even number and heads.

Solve Use a number cube and a coin. Turn them over one at a time to list all the possible results. Then circle the results in which the number cube shows an even number and the coin lands heads up.

Count the total number of possible results. There are 12 possible results. Count the number of circled results. There are 3 circled results. The fraction of the results with the number cube showing an even number and the coin landing heads up is $\frac{3}{12}$ or $\frac{1}{4}$.

Look Back Check the list of all the possible results to make sure you haven't missed any. Also check that you have circled all the results in which the number cube shows an even number and the coin lands heads up.

PRACTICE

1. Jeremy flips a quarter and a nickel at the same time. What fraction of all the possible results involve both coins landing heads up? $\frac{1}{4}$
2. Alyson rolls a red number cube and a blue number cube at the same time. What fraction of all the possible results involve both number cubes showing a 6? $\frac{1}{36}$

Make an Organized List

In some problems, you will need to find how many different ways something can happen. It is often helpful to **make an organized list.** This will help you count the outcomes and be sure that you have included all of them.

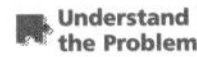

In a game at an amusement park, players throw 3 darts at a target to score points and win prizes. If each dart lands within the target area, how many different total scores are possible?

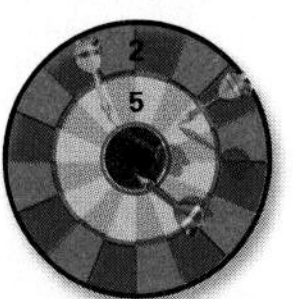

Understand the Problem Identify the important information.

- A player throws three darts at the target.

The answer will be the number of different scores a player could earn.

Make a Plan **Make an organized list** to determine all possible outcomes and score totals. List the value of each dart and the point total for all three darts.

Solve You can organize your list by the number of darts that land in the center. All three darts could hit the center circle. Or, two darts could hit the center circle and the third could hit a different circle. One dart could hit the center circle, or no darts could hit the center circle.

3 Darts Hit Center	2 Darts Hit Center	1 Dart Hits Center	0 Darts Hit Center
10 + 10 + 10 = 30	10 + 10 + 5 = 25	10 + 5 + 5 = 20	5 + 5 + 5 = 15
	10 + 10 + 2 = 22	10 + 5 + 2 = 17	5 + 5 + 2 = 12
		10 + 2 + 2 = 14	5 + 2 + 2 = 9
			2 + 2 + 2 = 6

Count the different outcomes. There are 10 possible scores.

Look Back You could have listed outcomes in random order, but because your list is organized, you can be sure that you have not missed any possibilities. Check to be sure that every score is different.

PRACTICE

1. A restaurant has three different kinds of pancakes: cinnamon, blueberry, and apple. If you order one of each kind, how many different ways can the three pancakes be stacked? 6
2. How many ways can you make change for a quarter using dimes, nickels, and pennies? 12

Skills Banks

Skills Bank — Review Skills

Place Value—Trillions Through Thousandths

You can use a place-value chart to read and write numbers.

EXAMPLE

What is the place value of the digit 3 in 8,126,300,567.1?

The digit 3 is in the hundred-thousands place.

PRACTICE

Write the place value of the underlined digit.

1. 14,536,992.1 millions
2. 34.071 ones
3. 6,190.05 hundreds
4. 5,027,549,757,20.2 trillions
5. 103.526 tens
6. 3.721 hundredths
7. 65,331,040,421 ten-billions
8. 75,983.009 thousandths

Compare and Order Whole Numbers

As you read a number line from left to right, the numbers are ordered from least to greatest.

407 412 415 418

400 402 404 406 408 410 412 414 416 418 420

You can use a number line and place value to compare whole numbers. Use the symbols > (is greater than) and < (is less than).

EXAMPLE

Compare. Write <, >, or =.

A 412 ■ 418
418 is to the right of 412 on a number line.
412 < 418

B 415 ■ 407
1 ten is greater than 0 tens.
415 > 407

PRACTICE

Compare. Write <, >, or =.

1. 419 ■ 410 >
2. 9,161 ■ 8,957 >
3. 5,036 ■ 5,402 <
4. 617 ■ 681 <
5. 700 ■ 698 >
6. 1,611 ■ 1,489 >

Round Whole Numbers

You can use a number line or rounding rules to round whole numbers to the nearest 10, 100, 1,000, or 10,000.

EXAMPLE 1

Round 547 to the nearest 10.

Look at the number line.

540 541 542 543 544 545 546 547 548 549 550

547 is closer to 550 than to 540. So 547 rounded to the nearest 10 is 550.

ROUNDING RULES

If the digit to the right is 5 or greater, increase the digit in the rounding place by 1.

If the digit to the right is less than 5, keep the digit in the rounding place the same.

EXAMPLE 2

Round 12,573 to the nearest 1,000.

12,573 *Find the digit in the thousands place.*

↑ *Digit is 5 or greater. Add 1.* *Look at the digit to its right.*

12,573 rounded to the nearest 1,000 is 13,000.

PRACTICE

Round each number to the given place value.

1. 15,638; nearest 100 15,600
2. 37,519; nearest 1,000 38,000
3. 9,298; nearest 10 9,300
4. 69,504; nearest 10,000 70,000
5. 852; nearest 1,000 1,000
6. 33,449; nearest 100 33,400

Round Decimals

You can use rounding rules to round decimals to the nearest whole number, tenth, hundredth, thousandth, or ten-thousandth.

EXAMPLE

Round each decimal to the given place value.

A **5.16; whole number**
1 < 5 So 5.16 rounds to 5.

B **13.45605; ten-thousandth**
5 ≥ 5 So 13.45605 rounds to 13.4561.

PRACTICE

Round each decimal to the given place value.

1. 3.982; tenth 4.0
2. 6.3174; hundredth 6.32
3. 1.471; whole number 1
4. 48.1526; hundredth 48.15
5. 5.03654; ten-thousandth 5.0365
6. 0.083; tenth 0.1

Place Value Patterns

You can use basic facts and place value to solve math problems mentally.

EXAMPLE

Solve mentally.

A **300 + 200**
Basic fact: 3 + 2 = 5 *Think: 3 hundreds + 2 hundreds*
300 + 200 = 500

B **200 × 600**
Basic fact: 2 × 6 = 12 *Think: There are four zeros in the factors, so place four zeros in the product.*
200 × 600 = 120,000

PRACTICE

Solve mentally.

1. 500 + 400 900
2. 80 − 50 30
3. 700 × 30 21,000
4. 2,500 ÷ 50 50
5. 1,200 + 600 1,800
6. 20 × 9,000 180,000
7. 650 − 300 350
8. 320 ÷ 8 40

Roman Numerals

Instead of using place value, as with the decimal system, combinations of letters are used to represent numbers in the Roman numeral system.

I = 1	V = 5	X = 10
L = 50	C = 100	D = 500
M = 1,000		

No letter can be written more than three times in a row. If a letter is written before a letter that represents a larger value, then subtract the first letter's value from the second letter's value.

EXAMPLE

Write each decimal number as a Roman numeral and each Roman numeral as a decimal number.

A 3
3 = I + I + I = III

B 9
9 = X − I = IX

C CLV
CLV = 100 + 50 + 5 = 155

D XC
XC = 100 − 10 = 90

PRACTICE

Write each decimal number as a Roman numeral and each Roman numeral as a decimal number.

1. 12 XII
2. 25 XXV
3. 209 CCIX
4. 54 LIV
5. VIII 8
6. LXXII 72
7. XIX 19
8. MMIV 2004

Addition

Addition is used to find the total of two or more quantities. The answer to an addition problem is called the *sum*.

EXAMPLE

4,617 + 5,682

Step 1: Add the ones.	Step 2: Add the tens.	Step 3: Add the hundreds. Regroup.	Step 4: Add the thousands.
4,617 + 5,682 9	4,617 + 5,682 99	1 4,617 + 5,682 299	1 4,617 + 5,682 10,299

The sum is 10,299.

PRACTICE

Find the sum.

1. 711 + 591 1,302
2. 2,580 + 2,345 4,925
3. 21,470 + 13,329 34,799
4. $165 + $304 $469
5. 6,905 + 872 7,777
6. 47,231 + 3,254 50,485

Subtraction

Subtraction is used to take away one quantity from another quantity or to compare two quantities. The answer to a subtraction problem is called the *difference*. The difference tells how much greater or smaller one number is than the other.

EXAMPLE

780 − 468

Step 1: Subtract the ones. Regroup.	Step 2: Subtract the tens.	Step 3: Subtract the hundreds.
7 10 7 8 0 − 4 6 8 2	7 10 7 8 0 − 4 6 8 1 2	7 10 7 8 0 − 4 6 8 3 1 2

The difference is 312.

PRACTICE

Find the difference.

1. 6,785 − 2,426 4,359
2. 3,000 − 1,930 1,070
3. 932 − 868 64
4. 41,003 − 22,500 18,503
5. $1,075 − $918 $157
6. 12,035 − 640 11,395

Multiply Whole Numbers

Multiplication is used to combine groups of equal amounts. The answer to a multiplication problem is called the *product*.

EXAMPLE

105 × 214

Step 1: Think of 214 as 2 hundreds, 1 ten, and 4 ones. Multiply by 4 ones.	Step 2: Multiply by 1 ten, or 10.	Step 3: Multiply by 2 hundreds, or 200.	Step 4: Add the partial products.
2 105 × 214 420 ← 4 × 105	105 × 214 420 1050 ← 10 × 105	1 105 × 214 420 1050 21000 ← 200 × 105	105 × 214 420 1050 +21000 22,470

The product is 22,470.

PRACTICE

Find the product.

1. 350 × 112 39,200
2. 3,218 × 231 743,358
3. 187 × 136 25,432
4. 5,028 × 225 1,131,300
5. 642 × 428 274,776
6. 2,039 × 570 1,162,230

Multiply by Powers of Ten

You can use mental math to multiply by powers of ten.

EXAMPLE

4,000 × 100

Step 1: Look for a basic fact using the nonzero part of the factors.	Step 2: Add the number of zeros in the factors. Place that number of zeros in the product.
4 × 1 = 4	4,000 × 100 = 400,000

The product is 400,000.

PRACTICE

Multiply.

1. 600 × 100 60,000
2. 90 × 1,000 90,000
3. 2,000 × 10 20,000
4. 400 × 10 4,000
5. 10,000 × 1,000 10,000,000
6. 7,100 × 1,000 7,100,000

Divide Whole Numbers

Division is used to separate a quantity into equal groups. The answer to a division problem is known as the *quotient*.

EXAMPLE

672 ÷ 16

Step 1: Write the first number inside the long division symbol and the second number to the left. Place the first digit of the quotient.	Step 2: Multiply 4 by 16, and place the product under 67.	Step 3: Bring down the next digit of the dividend.
16)672 *16 cannot go into 6, so try 67.*	4 16)672 *Subtract 64* − 64 *from 67.* 3	42 16)672 *Divide 32* − 64↓ *by 16.* 32 −32 0

The quotient is 42.

PRACTICE

Find the quotient.

1. 578 ÷ 34 17
2. 736 ÷ 8 92
3. 826 ÷ 118 7
4. 945 ÷ 45 21
5. 6,312 ÷ 263 24
6. 5,989 ÷ 53 113

Divide with Zeros in the Quotient

Sometimes when dividing, you need to use zeros in the quotient as placeholders.

EXAMPLE

3,648 ÷ 12

Step 1: Divide 36 by 12 because 12 > 3.	Step 2: Place a zero in the quotient because 12 > 4.	Step 3: Bring down the 8.
3 12)3,648	30 12)3,648 −36↓ 04	304 12)3,648 −36 ↓ 048 −48 0

The quotient is 304.

PRACTICE

Find the quotient.

1. 424 ÷ 4 106
2. 5,796 ÷ 28 207
3. 540 ÷ 18 30
4. 7,380 ÷ 123 60
5. 12,045 ÷ 3 4,015
6. 10,626 ÷ 21 506

Compatible Numbers

Compatible numbers are numbers that are easy to compute mentally. They are often based on groups of 10 or on basic facts.

EXAMPLE 1

A. 7 + 6 + 3 + 4

(7 + 3) + (6 + 4) *Make groups of 10.*

10 + 10

20

B. 2 × 32 × 5

(2 × 5) × 32 *Make a group of 10.*

10 × 32

320

EXAMPLE 2

Estimate 358 ÷ 9.

Basic fact: 36 ÷ 9 = 4 *360 is compatible with 9. 360 ÷ 9 = 40*

358 ÷ 9 ≈ 40

PRACTICE

Use compatible numbers to solve.

1. 15 + 42 + 38 + 25 120
2. 4 × 3 × 25 300
3. 17 + 51 + 23 + 19 110
4. 6 × 15 × 4 360
5. 11 + 123 + 57 + 9 200
6. 2 × 7 × 20 × 5 1,400

Estimate by rounding to find compatible numbers.

7. 473 ÷ 80 6
8. 118 ÷ 4 30
9. 57 ÷ 11 5

Mental Math

You can use the Distributive Property to find products mentally.

EXAMPLE

6 × 32

Step 1: Write 32 as the sum of a multiple of 10 and a one-digit number.	Step 2: Use the Distributive Property.	Step 3: Use mental math to multiply and then to add.
6 × 32 6 × (30 + 2)	6 × (30 + 2) (6 × 30) + (6 × 2)	(6 × 30) + (6 × 2) 180 + 12 = 192

PRACTICE

Use the Distributive Property to find each product.

1. 5 × 66 330
2. 3 × 42 126
3. 8 × 21 168
4. 7 × 84 588
5. 5 × 93 465
6. 4 × 75 300

Multiples

GPS M6N1.a

Multiples of a number can be found by multiplying the number by 1, 2, 3, and so on.

EXAMPLE

Find the first five multiples of 3.

$3 \cdot 1 = 3$	*Multiply 3 times 1.*	$3 \cdot 4 = 12$	*Multiply 3 times 4.*
$3 \cdot 2 = 6$	*Multiply 3 times 2.*	$3 \cdot 5 = 15$	*Multiply 3 times 5.*
$3 \cdot 3 = 9$	*Multiply 3 times 3.*		

The first five multiples of 3 are 3, 6, 9, 12, and 15.

PRACTICE

Find the first five multiples of each number.

1. 9 2. 10 3. 20 4. 15 5. 7 6. 18

1. 9, 18, 27, 36, 45 3. 20, 40, 60, 80, 100 5. 7, 14, 21, 28, 35
2. 10, 20, 30, 40, 50 4. 15, 30, 45, 60, 75 6. 18, 36, 54, 72, 90

Evaluate Formulas

GPS M6A3

When you **evaluate a formula**, you substitute numerical values for the variables in the formula and then simplify.

EXAMPLE

The formula $d = rt$ is used to find distance. Evaluate the formula for $r = 50$ mi/h and $t = 6$ h.

$d = rt$

$d = 50 \cdot 6$ *Substitute 50 for r and 6 for t.*

$d = 300$ *Multiply.*

The distance d is 300 miles.

PRACTICE

1. Evaluate the formula $d = rt$ for $r = 25$ ft/s and $t = 10$ s. 250 ft
2. The formula $C = 2\pi r$ is used to find the circumference of a circle. Evaluate the formula for $r = 14$ in. Use $\frac{22}{7}$ for π. 88 in.
3. The formula $A = \frac{1}{2}bh$ is used to find the area of a triangle. Evaluate the formula for $b = 10$ cm and $h = 8$ cm. 40 cm^2
4. The formula $V = \ell wh$ is used to find volume of a rectangular prism. Evaluate the formula for $\ell = 4$ ft, $w = 6$ ft, and $h = 2$ ft. 48 ft^3
5. The formula $C = \frac{5}{9}(F - 32)$ is used to convert Fahrenheit temperatures to Celsius temperatures. Evaluate the formula for $F = 41°$. 5°
6. The formula $I = Prt$ is used to find simple interest. Evaluate the formula for $P = \$100$, $r = 0.05$, and $t = 2$. \$10

Properties

Addition and multiplication follow some properties, or laws. Knowing the addition and multiplication properties can help you evaluate expressions.

Addition Properties		
Commutative	You can add numbers in any order.	$5 + 1 = 1 + 5$
Associative	When you are only adding, you can group any of the numbers together.	$(9 + 3) + 2 = 9 + (3 + 2)$
Identity Property of Zero	The sum of any number and zero is equal to the number.	$9 + 0 = 9$
Inverse Property	The sum of any number and its opposite is 0.	$4 + (-4) = 0$

Multiplication Properties		
Commutative	You can multiply numbers in any order.	$5 \times 8 = 8 \times 5$
Associative	When you are only multiplying, you can group any of the numbers together.	$(4 \times 9) \times 7 = 4 \times (9 \times 7)$
Identity Property of One	The product of any number and one is equal to the number.	$6 \times 1 = 6$
Inverse Property	For any number except 0, the product of the number and its reciprocal is 1.	$3 \times \frac{1}{3} = 1$
Property of Zero	The product of any number and zero is zero.	$5 \times 0 = 0$
Distributive	When you multiply a number times a sum, you can find the sum first and then multiply, or multiply each number in the sum and then add.	$6 \times (4 + 5) =$ $6 \times 4 + 6 \times 5$

EXAMPLE

Tell which property is shown in the equation $(3 + 4) + 7 = 3 + (4 + 7)$.

The Associative Property of Addition is shown.

PRACTICE

Tell which property is shown. 1–9. See p. A13.

1. $6 \times (3 \times 2) = (6 \times 3) \times 2$
2. $12 \times 9 = 9 \times 12$
3. $0 + d = d$
4. $k \times 1 = k$
5. $8 + 5 = 5 + 8$
6. $2 \times (3 + 10) = (2 \times 3) + (2 \times 10)$
7. $9 + (-9) = 0$
8. $99 \times 0 = 0$
9. $y(3 + 10) = 3y + 10y$

Fractional Part of a Region

GPS M6N1.g

You can use fractions to name parts of a whole. The denominator tells how many equal parts are in the whole. The numerator tells how many of those parts are being considered.

EXAMPLE

Tell what fraction of each region is shaded.

A 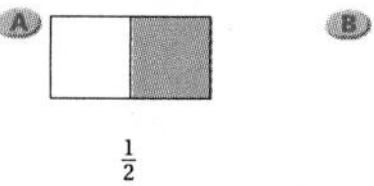 $\frac{1}{2}$

B 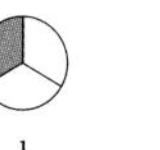 $\frac{1}{3}$

C 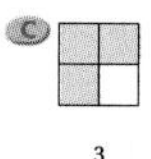 $\frac{3}{4}$

PRACTICE

Tell what fraction of each region is shaded.

1. 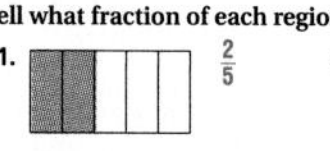 $\frac{2}{5}$
2. 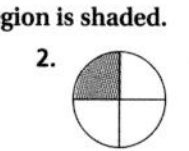 $\frac{1}{4}$
3. 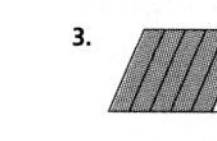 $\frac{5}{6}$
4. 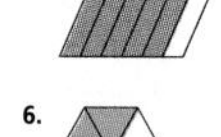 $\frac{3}{8}$
5. $\frac{4}{6}$ or $\frac{2}{3}$
6. $\frac{2}{6}$ or $\frac{1}{3}$

Fractional Part of a Set

GPS M6N1.g

You can use fractions to name part of a set. The denominator tells how many items are in the set. The numerator tells how many of those items are being used.

EXAMPLE

Tell what fraction of each set are stars.

A ■☆■☆●☆●■■■

3 out of 10 shapes are stars.

$\frac{3}{10}$ of the shapes are stars.

B ☆●☆☆●☆☆

5 out of 7 shapes are stars.

$\frac{5}{7}$ of the shapes are stars.

PRACTICE

Tell what fraction of each set is shaded.

1. ☆☆☆☆☆☆ $\frac{3}{6}$, or $\frac{1}{2}$
2. ■■■■□ $\frac{4}{5}$
3. ●☆○○☆○ $\frac{2}{6}$, or $\frac{1}{3}$
4. ■■■□□ $\frac{3}{5}$
5. ●○□□ $\frac{1}{4}$
6. ☆●■○▯△♡ $\frac{3}{7}$

Pictographs

Pictographs are graphs that use pictures to display data. Pictographs include a key to tell what each picture represents.

EXAMPLE

How many students chose red as their favorite color?

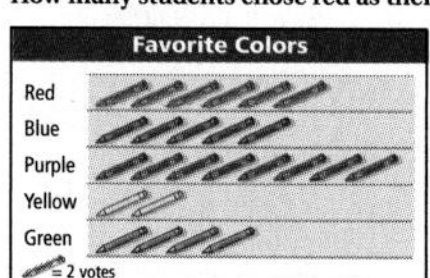

Each ✏ stands for 2 students.

There are 6 ✏ in the row for red.

$6 \times 2 = 12$

So 12 students chose red as their favorite color.

PRACTICE

Use the pictograph for Exercises 1–4.

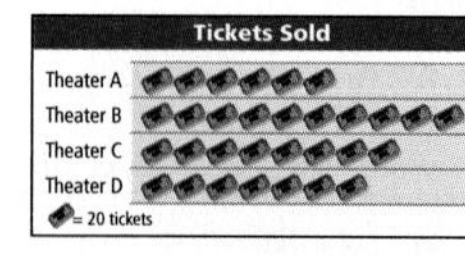

1. How many tickets did theater A sell? 120 tickets
2. Which theater sold the most tickets? theater B
3. How many more tickets did theater C sell than theater D? 20 more tickets
4. Theater E sold 180 tickets. How would this be shown on the pictograph? 9 ticket symbols

Use the pictograph for Exercises 5–7.

Mr. Carr took a survey of sixth-graders in his school. He asked them which type of pet they have. He recorded the data in a table.

Types of Pets

Dog

Cat

Bird

Fish

Other

= 2 students

5. How many students have pet birds? 8
6. How many more students have pet cats than pet fish? 6
7. How many students were surveyed? 78
8. Elizabeth took a survey of her neighbors. She recorded the number of children in each family in a table. Use the data to make a pictograph. See p. A13.

Children	Families
0	1
1	6
2	4
3 or more	2

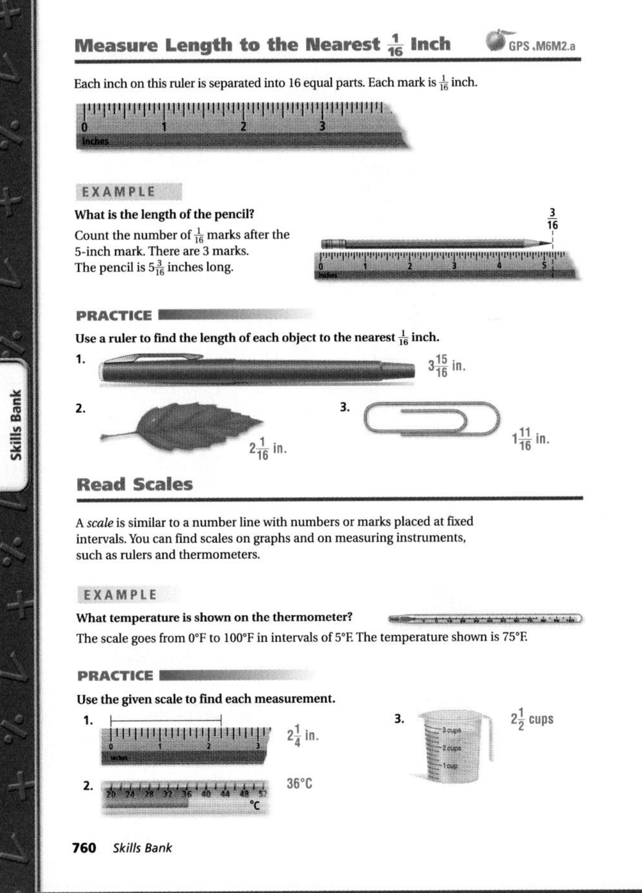

Measure Length to the Nearest $\frac{1}{16}$ Inch

GPS M6M2.a

Each inch on this ruler is separated into 16 equal parts. Each mark is $\frac{1}{16}$ inch.

EXAMPLE

What is the length of the pencil?

Count the number of $\frac{1}{16}$ marks after the 5-inch mark. There are 3 marks. The pencil is $5\frac{3}{16}$ inches long.

PRACTICE

Use a ruler to find the length of each object to the nearest $\frac{1}{16}$ inch.

1. $3\frac{15}{16}$ in.
2. $2\frac{1}{16}$ in.
3. $1\frac{11}{16}$ in.

Read Scales

A *scale* is similar to a number line with numbers or marks placed at fixed intervals. You can find scales on graphs and on measuring instruments, such as rulers and thermometers.

EXAMPLE

What temperature is shown on the thermometer?

The scale goes from 0°F to 100°F in intervals of 5°F. The temperature shown is 75°F.

PRACTICE

Use the given scale to find each measurement.

1. $2\frac{1}{4}$ in.
2. 36°C
3. $2\frac{1}{2}$ cups

Time

Seconds, minutes, hours, days, weeks, months, and years are units you can use to measure time.

EXAMPLE

Which instrument would you use to measure how long it takes to read a page in a book?

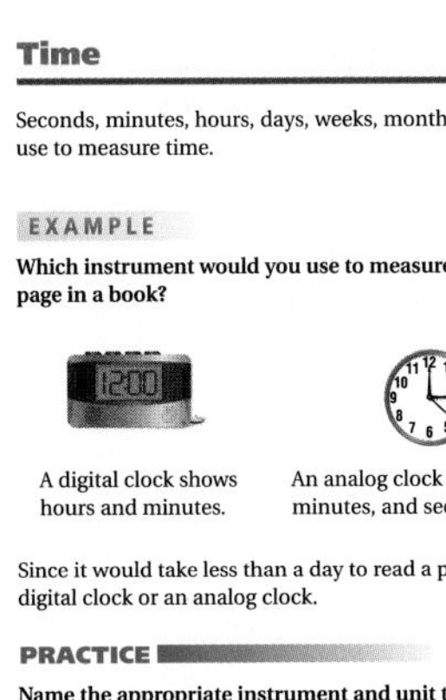

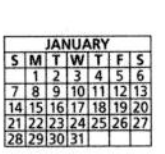

A digital clock shows hours and minutes. An analog clock shows hours, minutes, and seconds. A calendar shows days, weeks, months, and years.

Since it would take less than a day to read a page in a book, you could use a digital clock or an analog clock.

PRACTICE

Name the appropriate instrument and unit to measure time for each event.

1. completing 6th grade calendar; months
2. running a mile analog clock; minutes or seconds
3. eating lunch analog clock, digital clock; minutes
4. Earth revolving around the Sun calendar; year

Right Triangle Trigonometry

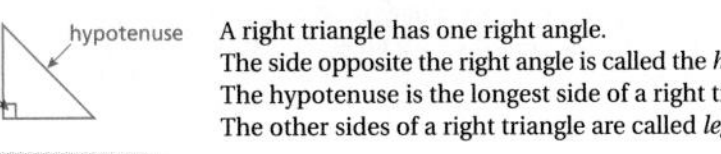

A right triangle has one right angle. The side opposite the right angle is called the *hypotenuse*. The hypotenuse is the longest side of a right triangle. The other sides of a right triangle are called *legs*.

EXAMPLE

Determine if the triangle is a right triangle. If so, identify the hypotenuse.

$\triangle ABC$ has a 90° angle.
$\triangle ABC$ is a right triangle.
Line segment CA is the hypotenuse.

PRACTICE

Determine if each triangle is a right triangle. If so, identify the hypotenuse.

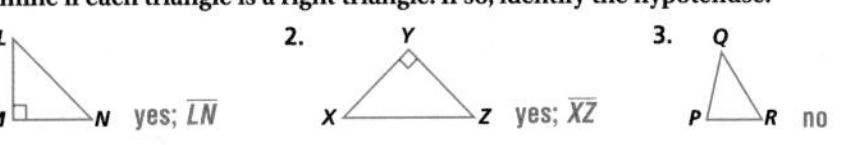

1. yes; $\overline{LN}$
2. yes; $\overline{XZ}$
3. no

Skills Bank Preview Skills

Absolute Value

The **absolute value** of a number is its distance from zero on the number line. The symbol for absolute value is | |. Absolute value can never be negative.

EXAMPLE

Find the absolute value of each number.

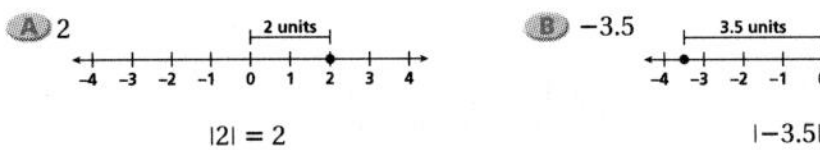

A 2 — $|2| = 2$

B −3.5 — $|-3.5| = 3.5$

PRACTICE

Find the absolute value of each number.

1. −7 7 2. 12 12 3. $\frac{1}{2}$ $\frac{1}{2}$ 4. $-2\frac{1}{2}$ $2\frac{1}{2}$ 5. −4.8 4.8 6. 0 0

Solve Two-Step Equations

GPS M6A3

You can use inverse operations to solve two-step equations.

EXAMPLE

5 times a number minus 7 is 8. Write and solve an equation to find the number.

Step 1: Let x represent the number.

Step 2: Translate the verbal equation into an algebraic equation.

5 times a number	minus	7	is	8
$5x$	−	7	=	8

Step 3: Solve $5x - 7 = 8$ using inverse operations.

$5x - 7 = 8$
$\underline{+7 \quad +7}$ *Add 7 to both sides to undo subtraction.*
$5x = 15$
$\frac{5x}{5} = \frac{15}{5}$ *Divide both sides by 5 to undo multiplication.*
$x = 3$

PRACTICE

Write and solve an equation to find each number.

1. The sum of 4 and 3 times a number is 28. $4 + 3x = 28$; $x = 8$
2. 7 plus twice a number is 17. $7 + 2x = 17$; $x = 5$
3. 4 times a number minus 5 is 11. $4x - 5 = 11$; $x = 4$

Rational Numbers

GPS M6N1.g

A **rational number** is any number that can be written as a fraction $\frac{a}{b}$, where a and b are integers and $b \neq 0$. Integers, such as 5 and −7, are rational numbers because they can be written as $\frac{5}{1}$ and $\frac{-7}{1}$. Terminating decimals are also rational numbers. For example, 0.57 may be written as $\frac{57}{100}$.

When a rational number is written in the form $\frac{a}{b}$, it can mean:

- a parts, each of size $\frac{1}{b}$.
- a divided by b.
- the ratio of a to b.

Use a number line to help you order and compare rational numbers.

EXAMPLE 1

Locate each pair of rational numbers on a number line. Then compare the numbers using < or >.

A $-\frac{3}{4}$ and $-\frac{1}{2}$

B $\frac{3}{2}$ and 0.75

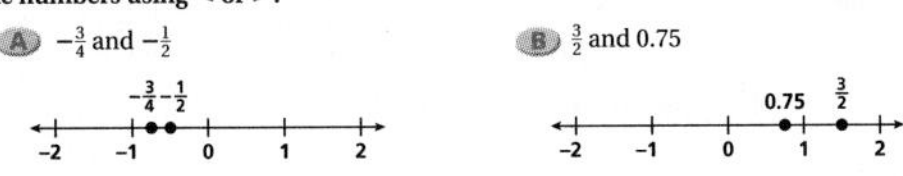

Graph both numbers on a number line. $-\frac{3}{4}$ is to the left of $-\frac{1}{2}$, so $-\frac{3}{4} < -\frac{1}{2}$.

Graph both numbers on a number line. $\frac{3}{2}$ is to the right of 0.75, so $\frac{3}{2} > 0.75$.

Use the order of operations to help you simplify expressions with rational numbers.

EXAMPLE 2

Simplify $1 + (2 \div \frac{1}{3})$.

$1 + (2 \div \frac{1}{3})$ *Simplify using the order of operations.*
$1 + (2 \times \frac{3}{1})$ *Rewrite as multiplication using the reciprocal of $\frac{1}{3}$, $\frac{3}{1}$.*
$1 + (2 \times 3)$ *Remember: $\frac{3}{1} = 3$*
$1 + 6$ *Multiply.*
1 *Add.*

Notice in Example 2 that $2 \div \frac{1}{3} = 6$. In this case, the quotient is greater than the dividend because the divisor is less than 1.

PRACTICE

Locate each pair of rational numbers on a number line. Then compare the numbers using < or >. 1–4. For number lines, see page A13.

1. $\frac{1}{3}$ and $-\frac{1}{3}$ $\frac{1}{3} > -\frac{1}{3}$ 2. $-\frac{1}{2}$ and $-\frac{3}{2}$ $-\frac{1}{2} > -\frac{3}{2}$ 3. 0.5 and $\frac{3}{4}$ $0.5 < \frac{3}{4}$ 4. $-1\frac{1}{2}$ and −2 $-1\frac{1}{2} > -2$

Simplify each expression.

5. $(4 \div \frac{1}{4}) + 2$ 18 6. $12 - (2 \div \frac{1}{4})$ 4 7. $(1 \div \frac{1}{2}) - 0.5$ 1.5 8. $(\frac{2}{3} \times 6) + 3.5$ 7.5

Sectors of Circles

Two radii form a central angle of a circle. A **sector** of a circle is the part of the circle enclosed by two radii and an arc connecting them. Given a circle of radius r and a central angle that measures $m°$, the area of the sector is $\frac{m}{360}\pi r^2$.

EXAMPLE

Find the area of the sector. Use 3.14 for *pi*.

$A = \frac{m}{360}\pi r^2$

$= \frac{90}{360} \cdot 3.14 \cdot 6^2$ *Substitute 90 for m and 6 for r.*

$= \frac{1}{4} \cdot 3.14 \cdot 36 = 28.26$ *Simplify.*

The area of the sector is 28.26 in^2

PRACTICE

Find the area of each sector. Use 3.14 for *pi*.

1. 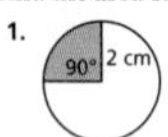 3.14 cm^2
2. 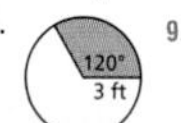 9.42 ft^2
3. 75.36 m^2

Properties of Ellipses and Spheres

An **ellipse** looks like a stretched out circle. The sum of the distances from two different points on the ellipse to two other points is the same.

$a + b = c + d$

A **sphere** is a three-dimensional figure whose surface is made up of all the points that are the same distance from a given point called the center.

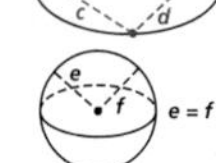
$e = f$

EXAMPLE

Find the value of x.

A 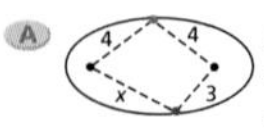

$x + 3 = 4 + 4$
$x + 3 = 8$ *Add.*
$x = 5$ *Subtract 3.*

B 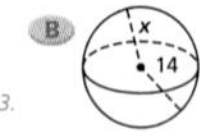

$x = 14$
All points on the surface of the sphere are the same distance from the center.

PRACTICE

Find the value of x.

1. 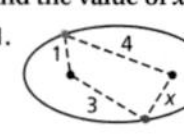 2
2. 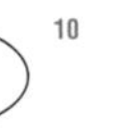 10
3. 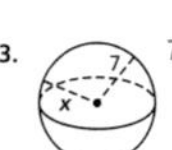 7

Graph Cumulative Frequency

 GPS M6D1.b

You have seen how to make a cumulative frequency table for a data set. You can also graph the cumulative frequencies for a data set.

EXAMPLE

The midterm test scores for Mr. Andrews's math class are given in the table at right. Make a cumulative frequency table. Then make a histogram of the cumulative frequencies.

Midterm Test Scores					
70	86	70	74	77	95
82	62	69	79	7	80
87	68	72	72	91	87
98	73	64	81	77	73
99	76	68	95	85	80

Divide the data into equally sized intervals.

Midterm Score	Frequency	Cumulative Frequency
60–64	2	2
65–69	3	5
70–74	8	13
75–79	4	17
80–84	4	21
85–89	4	25
90–94	1	26
95–99	4	30

The cumulative frequency column shows a running total of all frequencies.

The frequency tells the number of times an event, category, or group occurs.

To make a histogram of the cumulative frequencies, draw a bar for the cumulative frequency for each interval.

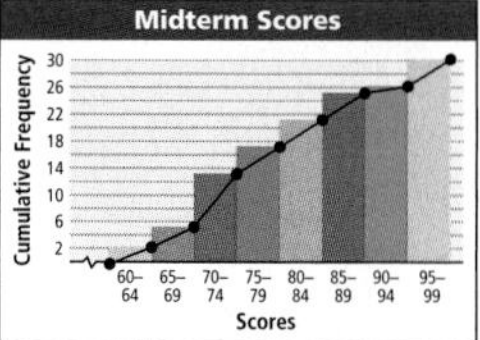

To make a line graph of the cumulative frequencies, place points in the lower left corner of the first bar and upper right corner of every bar. Then connect those points with line segments, as shown.

PRACTICE

1. Make a cumulative frequency histogram and line graph for the data set. See p. A13.

Students' Heights (cm)					
160	130	142	153	164	160
161	162	132	155	140	130
150	145	140	138	166	155
154	155	160	160	155	158

Relative Frequency and Relative Frequency Distributions

 GPS M6D1.b

In a data set, the relative frequency of a data value is that value's frequency divided by the total number of data values.

$$\text{relative frequency} = \frac{\text{frequency}}{\text{total number of data values}}$$

Relative frequencies can be shown in tables or displayed in histograms.

EXAMPLE

The average class size in 20 schools is given in the table. Make a relative frequency table and a relative frequency histogram of the data.

Average Class Size				
22	25	20	28	31
37	24	19	29	32
38	35	19	32	34
38	25	38	26	33

Divide the data into equally sized intervals.

Class Size	Frequency	Relative Frequency
19–23	4	$\frac{4}{20} = \frac{1}{5}$
24–28	5	$\frac{5}{20} = \frac{1}{4}$
29–33	5	$\frac{5}{20} = \frac{1}{4}$
34–38	6	$\frac{6}{20} = \frac{3}{10}$

There are 20 data points. Divide each frequency by 20 to find the relative frequency.

To make a histogram, draw a bar for each relative frequency.

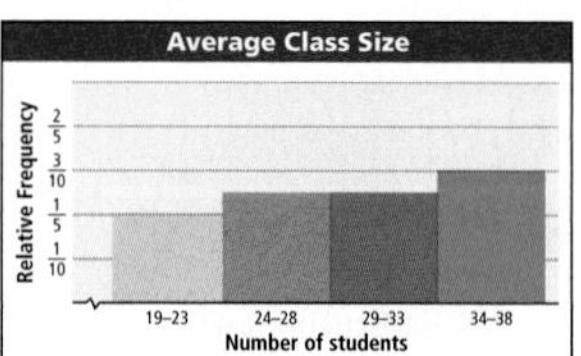

PRACTICE

1. Survey the students in your class and record the number of books read by each student in the past year. Make a relative frequency histogram to display the data. Check students' answers.

Rotational Symmetry

GPS M6G1.b

A figure has rotational symmetry if, when rotated less than 360° around a central point, it coincides with itself. The central point is called the center of rotation. A figure that coincides with itself after a rotation of 180° is said to have point symmetry.

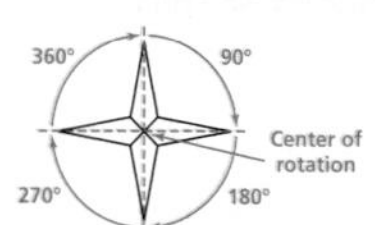

rotational symmetry and point symmetry

EXAMPLE

List the number of degrees between 0 and 360 that each figure must turn to show rotational symmetry. Then tell if each figure has point symmetry.

A 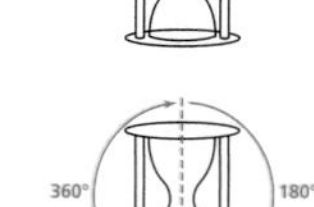

B 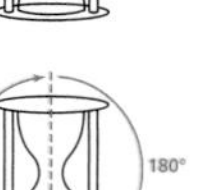

C 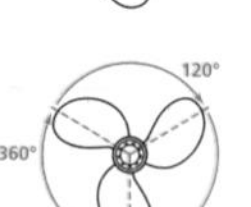

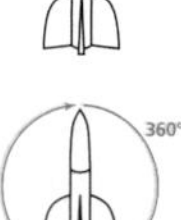

The figure will show rotational symmetry only after a rotation of 180°. The figure has point symmetry.

The figure will show rotational symmetry after rotations of 120° and 240°. The figure does not have point symmetry.

The figure will not show rotational symmetry in a rotation less than 360° The figure does not have point symmetry.

PRACTICE

List the number of degrees between 0 and 360 that each figure must turn to show rotational symmetry. Then tell if each figure has point symmetry.

1. 
2. 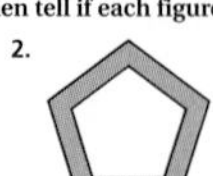
3. 
4. 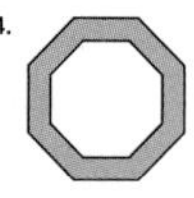

1. 90°, 180°, 270°; the figure has point symmetry.
2. 72°, 144°, 216°, 288°; the figure does not have point symmetry.
3. 180°; the figure has point symmetry.
4. 45°, 90°, 135°, 180°, 225°, 270°, 315°; the figure has point symmetry.

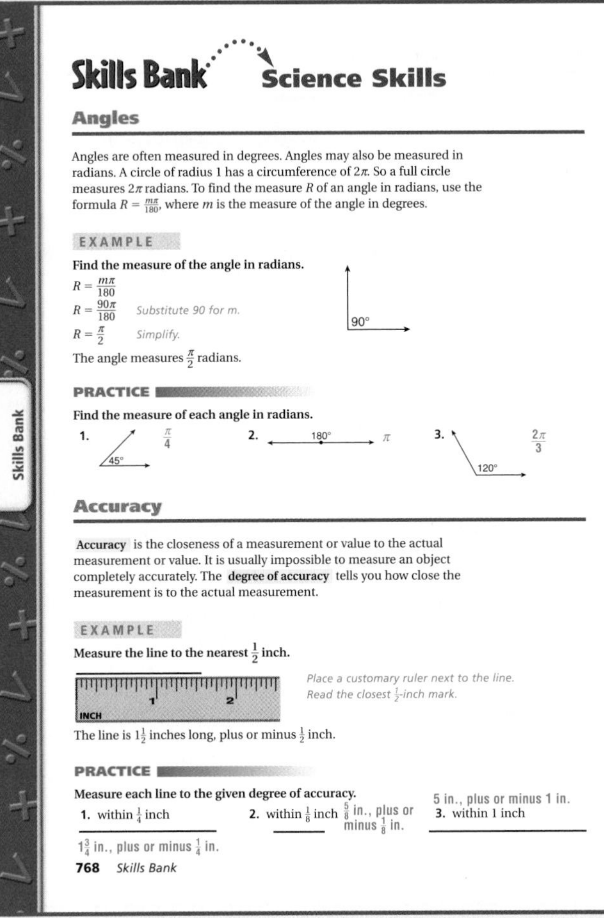

Skills Bank — Science Skills

Angles

Angles are often measured in degrees. Angles may also be measured in radians. A circle of radius 1 has a circumference of 2π. So a full circle measures 2π radians. To find the measure R of an angle in radians, use the formula $R = \frac{m\pi}{180°}$, where m is the measure of the angle in degrees.

EXAMPLE

Find the measure of the angle in radians.

$R = \frac{m\pi}{180}$

$R = \frac{90\pi}{180}$ *Substitute 90 for m.*

$R = \frac{\pi}{2}$ *Simplify.*

The angle measures $\frac{\pi}{2}$ radians.

PRACTICE

Find the measure of each angle in radians.

1. 45° $\frac{\pi}{4}$
2. 180° π
3. 120° $\frac{2\pi}{3}$

Accuracy

Accuracy is the closeness of a measurement or value to the actual measurement or value. It is usually impossible to measure an object completely accurately. The **degree of accuracy** tells you how close the measurement is to the actual measurement.

EXAMPLE

Measure the line to the nearest $\frac{1}{2}$ inch.

Place a customary ruler next to the line. Read the closest $\frac{1}{2}$-inch mark.

The line is $1\frac{1}{2}$ inches long, plus or minus $\frac{1}{2}$ inch.

PRACTICE

Measure each line to the given degree of accuracy.

1. within $\frac{1}{4}$ inch
2. within $\frac{1}{8}$ inch $\frac{5}{8}$ in., plus or minus $\frac{1}{8}$ in.
3. within 1 inch 5 in., plus or minus 1 in.

$1\frac{3}{4}$ in., plus or minus $\frac{1}{4}$ in.

Compute Measurements of Combined Units

Sometimes a measurement is given in a combination of units. For example, a piece of wood may measure 3 feet 4 inches. You can add or subtract measurements that are a combination of units.

EXAMPLE 1

4 ft 8 in. + 5 ft 6 in.

Step 1: Line up the units.	Step 2: Add the inches.	Step 3: Add the feet.	Step 4: Rewrite the answer in simplest form.
4 ft 8 in. + 5 ft 6 in.	4 ft 8 in. + 5 ft 6 in. 14 in.	4 ft 8 in. + 5 ft 6 in. 9 ft 14 in.	*Think: 12 in. = 1 ft* 9 ft 14 in. = 10 ft 2 in.

The sum is 10 ft 2 in.

EXAMPLE 2

3 hr 20 min − 1 hr 50 min

Step 1: Line up the units.	Step 2: Regroup if needed.	Step 3: Subtract the minutes.	Step 4: Subtract the hours.
3 hr 20 min − 1 hr 50 min	2 hr 80 min − 1 hr 50 min	2 hr 80 min − 1 hr 50 min 30 min	2 hr 80 min − 1 hr 50 min 1 hr 30 min

The difference is 1 hr 30 min.

PRACTICE

Add.

1. 7 ft 2 in. + 6 ft 8 in. 13 ft 10 in.
2. 8 lb 6 oz + 4 lb 12 oz 13 lb 2 oz
3. 2 gal 1 qt + 4 gal 1 qt 6 gal 2 qt
4. 12 ft 11 in. + 3 ft 4 in. 16 ft 3 in.
5. 4 hr 12 min + 3 hr 42 min 7 hr 54 min
6. 152 yd 2 ft + 75 yd 6 in. 227 yd 2 ft 6 in.
7. 5 yd 2 ft 3 in. + 8 yd 1 ft 8 in. 14 yd 11 in.
8. 2 hr 36 min 45 s + 5 hr 42 min 20 s 8 hr 19 min 5 s

Subtract.

9. 20 ft 8 in. − 7 ft 6 in. 13 ft 2 in.
10. 10 yd 1 ft − 5 yd 2 ft 4 yd 2 ft
11. 6 lb 5 oz − 2 lb 8 oz 3 lb 13 oz
12. 12 h 13 min − 6 h 25 min 5 hr 48 min
13. 5 min 15 s − 4 min 55 s 20 s
14. 3 mi 550 yd − 1 mi 760 yd 1 mi 1,550 yd
15. 4 gal 1 c − 3 qt 1 pt 3 gal 1 pt 1 c
16. 1 day − 8 hr 36 min 15 hr 24 min

Compare Units

GPS M6M2.c

When converting area from one unit to another, you must remember that area is measured in square units.

1 square foot = 1 foot × 1 foot
= 12 inches × 12 inches
= 144 square inches

Customary Units for Area	
1 square foot (ft^2) = 144 square inches (in^2)	1 acre (a) = 4,850 square yards (yd^2)
1 square yard (yd^2) = 9 square feet (ft^2)	1 acre (a) = 43,560 square feet (ft^2)
1 square yard (yd^2) = 1,296 square inches (in^2)	1 square mile (mi^2) = 640 acres (a)

Multiply to convert from larger units to smaller units.

Divide to convert from smaller units to larger units.

EXAMPLE 1

Find the area of the rectangle in square feet and in square inches.

$3 \text{ ft} \times 5 \text{ ft} = 15 \text{ ft}^2$ *Think: $1 \text{ ft}^2 = 144 \text{ in}^2$*

$15 \text{ ft}^2 = 15 \times 144 \text{ in}^2 = 2{,}160 \text{ in}^2$

EXAMPLE 2

Which is the greater area, 3 yd^2 or 25 ft^2?

$3 \text{ yd}^2 = 3 \times 9 \text{ ft}^2 = 27 \text{ ft}^2$ *Think: $1 \text{ yd}^2 = 9 \text{ ft}^2$*

$27 \text{ ft}^2 > 25 \text{ ft}^2$

$3 \text{ yd}^2 > 25 \text{ ft}^2$

PRACTICE

1. Find the area of the rectangle in square yards and square feet. 60 yd^2; 540 ft^2
2. A plot of land is 1.5 miles long and 1 mile wide. What is the area of the land in square miles and in acres? 1.5 mi^2; 960 acres

Compare. Write <, >, or =.

3. $12{,}500 \text{ yd}^2$ ▮ 3 acres <
4. 6 yd^2 ▮ 42 ft^2 >
5. 4 ft^2 ▮ 576 in^2 =
6. 5 yd^2 ▮ $6{,}500 \text{ in}^2$ <
7. 2.3 mi^2 ▮ 1,430 acres >
8. 0.5 acre ▮ $21{,}700 \text{ ft}^2$ >

Surface Area to Volume Ratio

GPS M6M3.b

Surface area is the sum of the areas of all the faces or surfaces of a solid figure. *Volume* is the amount of space within the solid figure. Area is a measurement of two dimensions, length and width. Volume is a measure of three dimensions, length, width, and height. A surface area to volume ratio compares the surface area and volume of a solid.

EXAMPLE 1

Find the surface area and volume of the rectangular prism.

$S = 2wh + 2\ell w + 2\ell h$
$= (2 \times 4 \times 3) + (2 \times 6 \times 4) + (2 \times 6 \times 3)$
$= 24 + 48 + 36$
$= 108 \text{ ft}^2$

$V = \ell \times w \times h$
$= 6 \times 4 \times 3$
$= 72 \text{ ft}^3$

EXAMPLE 2

What is the surface area to volume ratio for the cube?

$S = 6s^2$
$= 6 \times 5 \times 5$
$= 150 \text{ m}^2$

$V = \ell \times w \times h$
$= 5 \times 5 \times 5$
$= 125 \text{ m}^3$

The ratio of surface area to volume for the cube is $150 \text{ m}^2:125 \text{ m}^3$ or $6 \text{ m}^2:5 \text{ m}^3$.

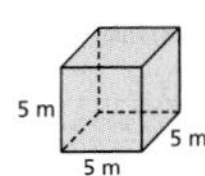

PRACTICE

Find the surface area and volume of each rectangular prism.

1. 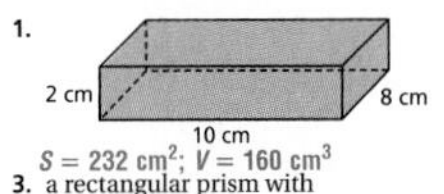

$S = 232 \text{ cm}^2$; $V = 160 \text{ cm}^3$

2. 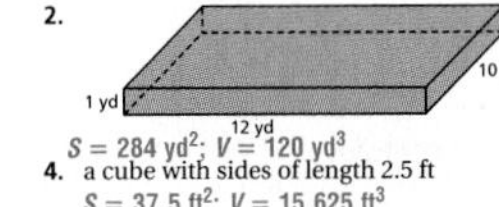

$S = 284 \text{ yd}^2$; $V = 120 \text{ yd}^3$

3. a rectangular prism with $\ell = 13$ km, $w = 10$ km, and $h = 3$ km $S = 398 \text{ km}^2$; $V = 390 \text{ km}^3$
4. a cube with sides of length 2.5 ft $S = 37.5 \text{ ft}^2$; $V = 15.625 \text{ ft}^3$

Write the surface area to volume ratio for each solid.

5. 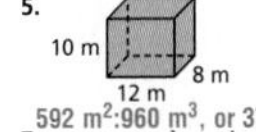

$592 \text{ m}^2:960 \text{ m}^3$, or $37 \text{ m}^2:60 \text{ m}^3$

6. 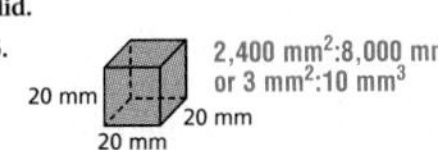

$2{,}400 \text{ mm}^2:8{,}000 \text{ mm}^3$, or $3 \text{ mm}^2:10 \text{ mm}^3$

7. a rectangular prism with $\ell = 5$ ft, $w = 4$ ft, and $h = 11$ ft $238 \text{ ft}^2:220 \text{ ft}^3$, or $119 \text{ ft}^2:110 \text{ ft}^3$
8. a rectangular prism with $\ell = 8$ dm, $w = 8$ dm, and $h = 4$ dm $256 \text{ dm}^2:256 \text{ dm}^3$, or $1 \text{ dm}^2:1 \text{ dm}^3$

Solve Literal Formulas

GPS M6A3

Formulas are equations that show a relationship between two or more quantities. Formulas can be used to find missing information or to calculate a quantity. For example, the formula $A = \ell w$ is used to find the area of a rectangle. We can solve the formula $A = \ell w$ for w using the same rules used to solve equations.

EXAMPLE

A **Solve $A = \ell w$ for w.**

$A = \ell w$

$\frac{A}{\ell} = \frac{\ell w}{\ell}$ *Divide both sides by ℓ.*

$\frac{A}{\ell} = w$

B **The formula $V = \ell wh$ is used to find the volume of a rectangular prism. Solve $V = \ell wh$ for h.**

$V = \ell wh$

$\frac{V}{\ell} = \frac{\ell wh}{\ell}$ *Divide both sides by ℓ.*

$\frac{V}{\ell} = wh$

$\frac{V}{\ell w} = \frac{wh}{w}$ *Divide both sides by w.*

$\frac{V}{\ell w} = h$

PRACTICE

Solve.

1. The formula $d = rt$ is used to find distance.
   Solve $d = rt$ for r. $r = \frac{d}{t}$
2. The formula $P = 2\ell + 2w$ is used to find the perimeter of a rectangle.
   Solve $P = 2\ell + 2w$ for ℓ. $\ell = \frac{P - 2w}{2}$
3. The formula $V = \pi r^2 h$ is used to find the volume of a cylinder.
   Solve $V = \pi r^2 h$ for h. $h = \frac{V}{\pi r^2}$
4. The formula $C = \frac{5}{9}(F - 32)$ is used to convert from degrees Fahrenheit to degrees Celsius.
   Solve $C = \frac{5}{9}(F - 32)$ for F. $F = \left(\frac{9}{5} \times C\right) + 32$
5. The formula $A = \frac{1}{2}bh$ is used to find the area of a triangle.
   Solve $A = \frac{1}{2}bh$ for b. $b = \frac{2A}{h}$
6. The formula $I = Prt$ is used to find simple interest.
   Solve $I = Prt$ for P. $P = \frac{I}{rt}$

Exponential Function Behavior

Data that changes exponentially increases or decreases by a common factor.

The Richter scale is used to express the magnitude of earthquakes. Each counting number represents a magnitude that is 10 times stronger than the one before it.

Magnitude	Relative Strength
0	1
1	10^1
2	10^2
3	10^3
4	10^4
5	10^5
6	10^6
7	10^7
8	10^8

EXAMPLE

How much stronger is an earthquake of magnitude 4 than one of magnitude 2?

An earthquake of magnitude 4 has a relative strength of 10^4. An earthquake of magnitude 2 has a relative strength of 10^2.

An earthquake of magnitude 4 is 10^2, or 100, times stronger than an earthquake of magnitude 2.

PRACTICE

1. In 1976, an earthquake in China registered 8 on the Richter scale. In 1999, an earthquake in Colombia registered 6 on the Richter scale. Which earthquake was weaker and by what factor?
   the earthquake in Colombia; 100 times weaker
2. Earthquake A registered 3 on the Richter scale. Earthquake B was 10,000 times stronger than earthquake A. What was the magnitude of earthquake B? 7

You can see exponential population growth by observing bacteria in an environment with unlimited resources. Use the graph of bacteria growth for Exercises 3–5.

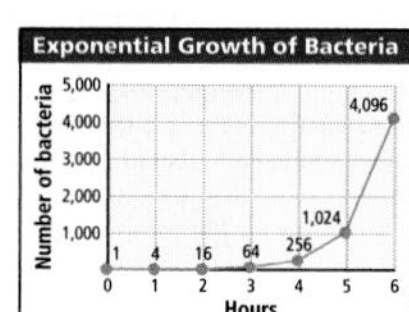

3. By what factor does the graph show the bacteria population increasing each hour? 4
4. If the bacteria continue to grow at this rate, how many bacteria will there be in 8 hours? Write the answer in both exponential and standard form.
   4^8; 65,536 bacteria
5. How many more bacteria will there be in 10 hours than in 8 hours? 4^2, or 16, times more bacteria

Half-life

Half-life is the time that it takes for half of a certain amount of radioactive material to decay. You can use information about the half-life of an element to determine how much of a sample will remain after a given time or to find the age of a sample.

EXAMPLE 1

The half-life of sodium-24 is 15 hours. If you have a 6 g sample of sodium-24, how much will remain after 45 hours?

Every 15 hours, one-half of the sample decays.

Time	0 hours	15 hours	30 hours	45 hours
Amount of Sample	6 g	3 g	1.5 g	0.75 g

After 45 hours, 0.75 g of sodium-24 will remain.

EXAMPLE 2

The half-life of bismuth-212 is 60.5 minutes. If you have a 4 g sample of bismuth-212 from a sample that was originally 16 g, how old is the sample?

Every 60.5 minutes, one-half of the sample decays.

Time	0 min	60.5 min	121 min
Amount of Sample	16 g	8 g	4 g

The sample is 121 minutes old.

PRACTICE

Solve.

1. Radium-226 has a half-life of 1,600 years. How many years will it take for an 8 g sample to decay to 0.5 g? 6,400 years
2. Cobalt-60 has a half-life of 5.26 years. A 10 g sample of cobalt-60 has decayed to 1.25 g. How old is the sample? 15.78 years
3. Iodine-131 has a half-life of 8.07 days. How much of a 4.4 g sample will there be after 40.35 days? 0.1375 g
4. A sample of phosphorus-24 decayed from 12 g to 1.5 g in 42.9 days. What is the half-life of phosphorus-24? 14.3 days
5. You have a 0.6 g sample of sodium-24. The half-life of sodium-24 is 15 hours. The original sample size was 9.6 g. How old is the sample? 60 hours

Selected Answers

Selected Answers

Chapter 1

1-1 Exercises

1. Mount Aconcagua is taller. 3. 349; 642; 726 5. 497; 809; 1,264 7. 982; 3,255; 5,001 9. the theme park with 17,459,000 in attendance 11. New York City 13. 126; 480; 619 15. 423; 805; 1,046 17. 666; 1,359; 1,764 19. 978; 1,502; 4,228 21. < 23. = 25. < 27. > 29. < 31. 823; 601; 533; 149 33. 3,461; 2,649; 1,947 35. 7,498; 7,467; 7,239 37. Montana, California, Texas 43. J 45. twenty-four thousand, four hundred ninety-eight 47. four million, six hundred five thousand, nine hundred twenty-six 49. 300,000 51. 6,000

1-2 Exercises

1. 7,000 3. 1,500 bottles of water 5. about 2 gallons 7. 40,000 9. 20,000 11. 40 golf balls 13. 500 15. 0 17. 11,000 19. 40,000 21. 70,000 23. 400,000 25. 10 square miles 27. 40,000 square miles 33. 400; 36 rounds to 40, and 8 rounds to 10 35. 2,615 37. 2,496 39. 1,000 + 300 + 50 + 4 41. 400,000 + 10,000 + 6,000 + 700 + 3

1-3 Exercises

1. 8^3 3. 6^5 5. 5^5 7. 16 9. 625 11. 343 13. 2^6 15. 8^2 17. 6^5 19. 7^7 21. 4^2 23. 243 25. 81 27. 512 29. 256 31. 144 33. 16 × 16 × 16 35. 31 × 31 × 31 × 31 × 31 × 31 37. 50 × 50 × 50 39. 1 × 1 × 1 × 1 × 1 × 1 × 1 × 1 × 1 × 1 41. 8 × 8 × 8 × 8 × 8 43. 1,000,000 45. 6,651 47. 100,000 49. 512 51. 125 53. > 55. < 57. > 59. 1,024

cells 61. 8; 2^8, or 256 65. D 67. 8,245; 8,452; 8,732 69. 11,901; 12,681; 12,751 71. 50,000

1-4 Exercises

1. 33 3. 50 5. 4 7. $138 9. 10 11. 32 13. 14 15. 25 17. 40 19. 24 21. 1,250 pages 23. 18 25. 57 27. 1 29. 22 31. 64 33. 22 35. $(7 + 2) \times 6 - (4 - 3) = 53$ 37. $5^2 - 10 + (5 + 4^2) = 36$ 39. $9^2 - 2 \times (15 + 16) - 8 = 11$ 41. $4^2 \times (3 - 2) \div 4 = 4$ 43. 30 m^2 45. 300 m^3 49. J 51. 3,273 53. 70,007 55. 125 57. 256

1-5 Exercises

1. 40 3. 50 5. 320 7. 120 9. 156 11. 99 13. 108 15. 40 17. 50 19. 640 21. 108 23. 426 25. 138 27. 372 29. 328 31. 40 33. 60 35. 198 37. 111 39. 70 41. 70°F 43. 153 45. 198 47. 56 49. 275 51. 340 53. 192 55. 108 eggs 57. $208 63. 2,718 mi 65. 1,367,000 67. 62 69. 56

1-6 Exercises

1. paper and pencil; 364 3. calculator; 64,890 5. mental math; middle row 7. 111 9. 515,844 11. 210 13. 350 19. 936; 13 · 3 = 39; 39 · 24 = 936 21. 30 23. 12 25. Distributive Property 26. Commutative Property

1-7 Exercises

1. add 12; 60; 72; 84 3. add 11; 51; 62 5. add 7 and subtract 2; 12; 19 7. multiply by 6 and divide by 2; 9; 162 9. subtract 14; 28; 14; 0 11. add 3; 20; 23 13. add 21 and subtract 4; 41; 62; 58 15. divide by 4 and multiply by 2; 100; 25 17. 5, 14, 23, 32, 41 19a. 2018 b. 1994 c. yes; 2006 + 2(12) = 2030 21. subtract 4 and add 5 27. A 29. 60 31. 120

Chapter 1 Study Guide: Review

1. sequence, term 2. base, exponent 3. order of operations 4. evaluate 5. 8,731; 8,735; 8,737; 8,740 6. 53,337; 53,341; 53,452; 53,456 7. 8,791; 81,790; 87,091; 87,901 8. 2,651; 22,561; 25,615; 26,551 9. 91,363; 93,613; 96,361; 96,631 10. 10,101; 10,110; 11,010; 11,110 11. 1,000 12. 6,000 13. 20,000 14. 800 15. 5^3 16. 3^4 17. 7^5 18. 8^2 19. 4^4 20. 1^3 21. 256 22. 16 23. 216 24. 27 25. 1 26. 2,401 27. 125 28. 100 29. 81 30. 59 31. 11 32. 26 33. 17 34. 5 35. 45 36. 9 37. 3 38. 30 39. 520 40. 80 41. 1,080 42. 40 43. 320 44. 100 45. 130 46. 168 47. 135 48. 204 49. 152 50. 216 51. 165 52. 62° 53. Add 5; 24, 29. 54. Subtract 2; 13, 11. 55. Add 4 and subtract 2; 20, 22. 56. Multiply by 3; 81, 243, 729. 57. Add 5 and subtract 2; 71, 74.

Chapter 2

2-1 Exercises

1. 56; 65 3. 24; 38; 32; 36 5. 23; 25 7a. 2 hr: 100 − 120 miles; 3 hr: 150 − 180 miles; 4 hr: 200 − 240 miles; 5 hr: 250 − 300 miles b. between 350 and 420 miles 9. 32°F; 50°F; 77°F 11. 32 13. 13 15. 8 17. 56 19. 10 21. 110 23. 24 zlotys 29. 38 31. 5^6 33. $919

2-2 Exercises

1. 4,028 − m 3. $15x$ 5. $\frac{p}{5}$

7. (149)(2) 9. the product of 345 and 196; 345 times 196 11. the difference of d and 5; 5 less than d 13. $5x$ 15. 325 ÷ 5 17. 137 + 675 19. $j - 14$ 21. take away 19 from 243; 243 minus 19 23. 75 multiplied by 342; the product of 342 and 75 25. the product of 45 and 23; 45 times 23 27. the difference of 228 and b; b less than 228 29. $15 \div d$ 31. $67m$ 33. 678 − 319 37. $d \div 4$ 41. C 43. 360 45. 360 47. 8 49. 16

2-3 Exercises

1. $4n$ 3. $5w$ 5. $7n$ 7. s^2 9. $n + 5$ 11. $88n$ 13. $n + 7$; $3n + 1$ 17. G 19. 29 21. 21 23. 245 25. 126

2-4 Exercises

1. no 3. yes 5. yes 7. 53 feet is equal to 636 inches. 9. no 11. yes 13. no 15. yes 17. no 19. yes 21. 300 m is equal to 30,000 cm. 23. yes 25. no 27. no 29. yes 31. no 33. yes 35. 17 ≠ 350 ÷ 20; no, they do not have the same amount of money. 37. 6 39. 2 41. 3 47. H 49. 9^4 51. 8^2

2-5 Exercises

1. $x = 36$ 3. $n = 19$ 5. $p = 18$ 7. 6 blocks 9. $r = 7$ 11. $b = 25$ 13. $z = 9$ 15. $g = 16$ 17. 6 meters 19. $n = 7$ 21. $y = 19$ 23. $h = 78$ 25. $b = 69$ 27. $t = 26$ 29. $m = 22$ 31. $p + 20 = 36$ 33. 880 m 37. B 39. 648; 798; 923 41. 1,036; 1,498; 2,163 43. 9, 7, 5

2-6 Exercises

1. $p = 17$ 3. $a = 31$ 5. $n = 33$ 7. $y = 25$ 9. $a = 38$ 11. $a = 97$ 13. $p = 33$ 15. $s = 31$ 17. $x = 36$ 19. $a = 21$ 21. $f = 14$ 23. $r = 154$ 25. $g = 143$ 27. $m = 18$ 29. 13 million 33. D 35. 71 37. 22 39. $y = 38$ 41. $b = 56$

2-7 Exercises

1. $x = 3$ 3. $a = 9$ 5. $c = 11$ 7. 45 feet 9. $a = 4$ 11. $x = 4$ 13. $t = 7$ 15. $m = 11$ 17. 6 feet 19. $y = 9$ 21. $y = 8$ 23. $y = 20$ 25. $z = 40$ 27. $y = 23$ 29. $y = 18$ 31. $y = 8$ 33. $a = 14$ 35. $x = 3$ 37. $t = 6$ 39. 15 to 177 segments 41. 4,000 light-sensitive cells 45. C 47. 7,000 49. $b = 42$ 51. $n = 212$

2-8 Exercises

1. $y = 12$ 3. $r = 63$ 5. $j = 36$ 7. $f = 60$ 9. 90 min 11. $c = 26$ 13. $g = 98$ 15. $x = 144$ 17. $r = 81$ 19. $c = 96$ 21. $c = 165$ 23. $c = 70$ 25. $c = 60$ 27. $\frac{w}{381} = 76$; $w =$ 28,956 m 33. J 35. Add 5; 25, 30, 35 37. $r = 13$ 39. $p = 9$

Chapter 2 Extension

1. −2 0 2 4 6 8 10
3. −2 0 2 4 6 8 10
5. −2 0 2 4 6 8 10
7. −2 0 2 4 6 8 10
9. −2 0 2 4 6 8 10
11. −2 0 2 4 6 8 10 12

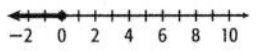

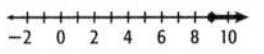

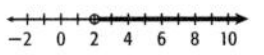

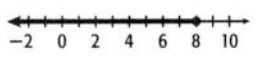

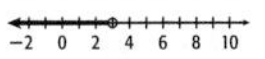

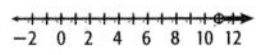

13. $t \le 9$ 15. $x < 4$ 17. $c > 1$ 19. $d \ge 6$ 21. $p > 6$ 23. $r \le 3$ 25. $f > 27$ 27. $q \ge 3$ 29. $p > 11$ 31. $s + 2 \ge 5$ 33. $a < 20{,}320$

Chapter 2 Study Guide: Review

1. algebraic expression 2. equation 3. variable 4. constant 5. 7, 6 6. 6, 10 7. 9, 18, 27, 36 8. 30, 33, 36, 39 9. 75, 80, 85, 90 10. $15 + b$ 11. 6 × 5 12. $9t$ 13. $g \div 9$ 14. the product of 4 and z; 4 times z 15. 15 plus x; the sum of 15 and x 16. 54 divided by 6; the quotient of 54 and 6 17. m divided by 20; the quotient of m and 20 18. 3 minus y; the difference of y and 3 19. the sum of 5,100 and 64; 64 added to 5,100 20. y minus 3; the difference of y and 3 21. g minus 20; the difference of g and 20 22. $3n + 1$ 23. $n - 1$ 24. yes 25. no 26. yes 27. yes 28. $x = 6$ 29. $n = 14$ 30. $c = 29$ 31. $y = 6$ 32. $p = 27$ 33. $w = 9$ 34. $b = 11$ 35. $n = 44$ 36. $p = 16$ 37. $d = 57$ 38. $k = 45$ 39. $d = 9$ 40. $p = 63$ 41. $n = 67$ 42. $r = 14$ 43. $w = 144$ 44. $h = 60$ 45. $p = 167$ 46. $v = 8$ 47. $y = 9$ 48. $c = 7$ 49. $n = 2$ 50. $s = 8$ 51. $t = 10$ 52. $a = 8$ 53. $y = 8$ 54. $r = 42$ 55. $t = 15$ 56. $y = 18$ 57. $n = 72$ 58. $z = 52$ 59. $b = 100$ 60. $n = 77$ 61. $p = 90$

Chapter 3

3-1 Exercises

1. 1 + 0.9 + 0.08; one and ninety-eight hundredths 3. 0.0765; seven hundred sixty-five ten-thousandths 5. Osmium 7. 4.09, 4.1, 4.18 9. 7 + 0.08 + 0.009 + 0.0003; seven and eight hundred ninety-three ten-thousandths 11. 7.15; 7 + 0.1 + 0.05 13. the Chupaderos meteorite 15. 1.5, 1.56, 1.62 17. nine and seven thousandths 19. ten and twenty-two thousandths 21. one hundred forty-two and six thousand five hundred forty-one ten-thousandths 23. ninety-two thousand, seven hundred fifty-five hundred thousandths 25. < 27. < 29. < 31. three hundredths 33. one tenth 35. 4.034, 1.43, 1.424, 1.043, 0.34 37. 652.12, 65.213, 65.135, 61.53 39. Ross 154 41. Alpha Centauri, Proxima Centauri 45. C 47. 9,000 49. $n = 123$ 51. $c = 52$

3-2 Exercises

1. about 12 miles 3. 12 5. 5.4988 7. 120 9. from 44 to 46.5 11. about 450 miles 13. 3.4 15. 5.157 17. 20 19. 6 21. from 14 to 17 23. 48 25. 17 27. $0.22, $0.10, $0.08, $0.04 29. (12 × 8) − (18 × 4) = 24, or about 24 cents 37. 6 inches in April, 10 inches in May, 2 inches in June 39. $x = 69$ 41. 8.009, 8.05, 8.304 43. 30.211, 30.709, 30.75

3-3 Exercises

1. 20.2 miles 3. 12.65 miles 5. 5.6 7. 4.9 9. 3.55 11. 4.948 13. $567.38 15. 1.5 17. 18 19. 4.3 21. 2.3 23. 5.87 25. 9.035 27. 8.669 29. 0.143 31. 3.778 33. 3.8179 35. 1 37. 52.836 39. 29.376 41. 84.966 43. $72.42 45. 0.196 49. C 51. $s = 70$ 53. $t = 1{,}464$ 55. 60

3-4 Exercises

1. 593,700 3. 609,120 5. 5.0×10^5 7. 6,793,000 9. 382,000 11. 278,000 13. 3,818,000 15. 412,900 17. 9.0×10^4 19. 1.607×10^6 21. 6.0×10^6 23. 321,100 25. 7,700 27. 4,030,000 29. $$6.2 \times 10^6$ 31. 123,400 33. 208,000 35. 54.3 37. 1.5×10^5 39. 6.52×10^2 41. 6.5342×10^4 43. 2.8001×10^4 45. Range: 38,000 to 120,000; possible answer: 100,000 47. $150{,}000 = 1.5 \times 10^5$ 49. 24,600,000; 2.16×10^7 53. D 55. Commutative Property 57. Associative Property 59. 1.9 61. 1.2

3-5 Exercises

1. $1.68 3. 0.24 5. 0.21 7. 16.52 9. 35.63 11. 2.59 km 13. 0.027 15. 0.217 17. 0.00042 19. 0.012 21. 13.321 23. 26.04 25. 1.148 27. 2.5914 29. 0.009 31. 0.0612 33. 26.46 35. 1.6632 37. 0.2444 39. 4.1184 41. 14.06 43. 37.38 45. 62.1 47. 5.8 49. 4.65 pounds 51. 7.38 lb 55. B 57. $x = 32$ 59. $t = 51$ 61. 1 + 0.2 + 0.03 63. 20 + 6 + 0.07 65. 80 + 0.002

3-6 Exercises

1. 0.23 3. 0.35 5. 0.078 7. 0.104 9. $8.82 11. 0.22 13. 0.27 15. 0.171 17. 0.076 19. 0.107 21. 1.345 23. 0.236 29. when the divisor is greater than the portion of the dividend being divided into 31. C 33. Subtract 5; 60. 35. Alternate adding 7 and subtracting 4; 21. 37. 20.8 39. 710,000

3-7 Exercises

1. 5 3. 17 5. 6 7. 54.6 mi/h 9. 6 11. 8 13. 217.5 15. 11 17. 5 19. 11.6 gallons of gas 21. 6.3 23. 191.1 25. 184.74 27. 12.2 29. 12.2 31. 1,270 33. 1,125 35. 920 37. 21.5×10^7 39. about 232 gills; about $4,640 45. C 47. > 49. > 51. 16.06 53. 3.12

3-8 Exercises

1. 10 belts 3. 2.25 meters 5. 8 bunches 7. 3 packs 13. C 15. $y = 63$ 17. $y = 17$ 19. 9.1 21. 14

3-9 Exercises

1. $a = 7.1$ 3. $c = 12.8$ 5. $d = 3.488$ 7. 60.375 m^2 9. $b = 9.3$ 11. $r =$ 20.8 13. $a = 10.7$ 15. $f = 6.56$ 17. $z = 4$ 19a. 1.6 meters b. $14.40 21. $q = 24.7$ 23. $b = 4.2$ 25. $a = 13.9$ 27. $z = 13$ 29a. 19.5 units, 21 units b. 50.5 units 31. 1.9×10^6 33. 9 capsules 39. H 41. $7z$ 43. 5.1 45. 16.08

Chapter 3 Study Guide: Review

1. front-end estimation 2. scientific notation 3. clustering 4. 5 + 0.6 + 0.08; five and sixty-eight hundredths 5. 1 + 0.007 + 0.0006; one and seventy-six ten-thousandths 6. 1 + 0.2 + 0.003; one and two hundred three thousandths 7. 20 + 3 + 0.005; twenty-three and five thousandths 8. 70 + 1 + 0.03 + 0.008; seventy-one and thirty-eight thousandths 9. 90 + 9 + 0.9 + 0.09 + 0.009; ninety-nine and nine thousand, nine hundred ninety-nine ten thousandths 10. 1.12, 1.2, 1.3 11. 11.07, 11.17, 11.7 12. 0.033, 0.3, 0.303 13. 5.009, 5.5, 5.950 14. 101.025, 101.25, 101.52 15. 11.32 16. 2.3 17. 14 18. 80 19. 9 20. 5 21. 24.85 22. 5.3 23. 33.02 24. 4.9225 25. 32.33 26. 14.624 27. 2.58 28. 2.8718 29. 1.47 30. 6.423 31. 2 32. 4.83 33. 126,000 34. 54,600 35. 6,700,000 36. 180,600 37. 4,200 38. 7,890 39. 5.5×10^5 40. 7.23×10^3 41. 1.3×10^6 42. 1.48×10^1 43. 9.042×10^2 44. 8.91402×10^8 45. 30,200 46. 429,300 47. 1,700,000 48. 5,390 49. 685 50. 14,500,000 51. 9.44 52. 0.865 53. 0.0072 54. 24.416 55. 0.54 56. 10.5148 57. 9.72 58. 39.528 59. 1.03 60. 0.72 61. 3.85 62. 2.59 63. $3.64 64. 8.1 65. $6.1\overline{6}$ 66. $3.87\overline{6}$ 67. 52.275 68. 0.75 meter 69. 14 containers 70. 9 cars 71. $a = 13.38$ 72. $y = 2.62$ 73. $n = 2.29$ 74. $p = 6.02$ 75. $5.00

Chapter 4

4-1 Exercises

1. 2, 4 3. none 5. composite 7. composite 9. composite 11. composite 13. 3 15. 3, 5, 9 17. 2, 4 19. 2 21. composite 23. prime 25. composite 27. prime 29. composite

31. prime **33.** no, no, no, no **35.** yes, no, yes, no, no, no, no **37.** True **39.** True **41.** 1, 4, or 7 **43.** 1, 4, or 7 **45.** 0, 3, 6, or 9 **47.** Prime numbers from 50 to 100 are 53, 59, 61, 71, 73, 79, 83, 89, and 97. **49.** Mackinac Straits **55.** D **57.** 7, 11, 15, 19, 23 **59.** 6, 30, 150, 750, 3,750 **61.** 30

4-2 Exercises

1. 1, 2, 3, 4, 6, 12 **3.** 1, 2, 4, 13, 26, 52 **5.** $2^4 \cdot 3$ **7.** $2 \cdot 3 \cdot 11$ **9.** 1, 2, 3, 4, 6, 8, 12, 24 **11.** 1, 2, 3, 6, 7, 14, 21, 42 **13.** 1, 67 **15.** 1, 5, 17, 85 **17.** 7^2 **19.** $2^2 \cdot 19$ **21.** 3^4 **23.** $2^2 \cdot 5 \cdot 7$ **33a.** 15 boys per team **b.** 5 teams of 9 players **35.** $3^2 \cdot 11$ **37.** $2^2 \cdot 71$ **39.** $2^2 \cdot 3 \cdot 5 \cdot 7$ **41.** $2^2 \cdot 5 \cdot 37$ **43.** $2^2 \cdot 5^2$ **45.** 7^3 **47.** Insects; Clams **53.** 60 **55.** 3, 5 **57.** 2, 3, 4, 5, 6, 9, 10 **59.** 2, 4, 5, 10 **61.** 2, 3, 4, 5, 6, 9, 10

4-3 Exercises

1. 9 **3.** 7 **5.** 6 **7.** 4 arrangements **9.** 14 **11.** 2 **13.** 4 **15.** 12 **17.** 3 teams **19.** 12 **21.** 5 **23.** 2 **25.** 75 **27.** 4 **29.** 6 baskets **31.** 2 **33.** 9 **35.** 6 **37.** 6 rows **39.** 4 groups **43.** A **45.** $y = 27$ **47.** $z = 8$ **49.** $2 \times 3 \times 7$ **51.** 3×17 **53.** $5^2 \times 2^3$

4-4 Exercises

1. $\frac{3}{20}$ **3.** $\frac{43}{10}$ **5.** 0.4 **7.** 0.125 **9.** 0.21, $\frac{2}{3}$, 0.78 **11.** $\frac{1}{9}$, 0.3, 0.52 **13.** $5\frac{71}{100}$ **15.** $3\frac{23}{100}$ **17.** $2\frac{7}{10}$ **19.** $6\frac{3}{10}$ **21.** 1.6 **23.** 3.275 **25.** 0.375 **27.** 0.625 **29.** $\frac{1}{9}$, 0.29, $\frac{3}{8}$ **31.** $\frac{1}{10}$, 0.11, 0.13 **33.** 0.31, $\frac{3}{7}$, 0.76 **35.** $90 + 2 + \frac{3}{10}$ **37.** $100 + 7 + \frac{1}{10} + \frac{7}{100}$ **39.** $0.1\overline{6}$; repeats **41.** $0.41\overline{6}$; repeats **43.** 0.8; terminates **45.** $0.8\overline{3}$; repeats **47.** $0.91\overline{6}$; repeats **49.** > **51.** < **53.** < **55.** < **57.** $4\frac{1}{2}$, 4.48, 3.92 **59.** 125.25, 125.205, $125\frac{1}{5}$ **61.** Jill **63.** $\frac{1}{20}$

67. D **69.** 21.47 **71.** 23.45 **73.** 14 **75.** 16

4-5 Exercises

1. $\frac{2}{3}, \frac{8}{12}$ **3.** $\frac{1}{2}, \frac{5}{10}$ **5.** 25 **7.** 21 **9.** $\frac{1}{5}$ **11.** $\frac{1}{4}$ **21.** 15 **23.** 70 **25.** 6 **27.** 140 **29.** $\frac{1}{4}$ **31.** $\frac{1}{5}$ **33.** $\frac{3}{4}$ **35.** $\frac{1}{2}$ **37.** $\frac{3}{6} = \frac{1}{2}$ **39.** $\frac{2}{3} = \frac{8}{12}$ **41.** $\frac{1}{4}$ **43.** $\frac{2}{5}$ **47.** Baskets and wreaths are $\frac{12}{72} = \frac{1}{6}$; jewelry is $\frac{32}{72} = \frac{4}{9}$; glass and pottery are $\frac{16}{72} = \frac{2}{9}$; paintings are $\frac{12}{72} = \frac{1}{6}$. **51.** B **53.** $x = 45$ **55.** $w = 18$ **57.** $0.\overline{6}$ **59.** 3.2

4-6 Exercises

1. $2\frac{2}{5}$ **3.** $\frac{8}{3}$ **5.** $\frac{12}{5}$ **7.** $8\frac{3}{5}$ **9.** $\frac{20}{9}$ **11.** $\frac{13}{3}$ **13.** $\frac{25}{6}$ **15.** $\frac{19}{5}$ **17.** 4; whole number **19.** $8\frac{3}{5}$; mixed number **21.** $8\frac{7}{10}$; mixed number **23.** 15; whole number **25.** $\frac{53}{11}$ **27.** $\frac{93}{5}$ **29.** 3; 5 **31.** 13; 9 **33.** 2; 10 **35.** $28\frac{4}{9}$ yards **37.** = **39.** < **41.** $40\frac{1}{2}$; $50\frac{1}{2}$ **43.** $\frac{9}{5}$ **47.** A **49.** 1,038; 1,497; 2,560 **51.** 1,765; 4,706; 11,765 **53.** 21 to 22 **55.** 1, 3, 19, 57 **57.** 1, 2, 3, 6, 9, 18, 27, 54

4-7 Exercises

1. > **3.** = **5.** yes **7.** $\frac{1}{4}, \frac{1}{3}, \frac{2}{5}$ **9.** $\frac{1}{6}, \frac{1}{2}, \frac{2}{3}$ **11.** < **13.** > **15.** = **17.** > **19.** $\frac{3}{7}, \frac{1}{2}, \frac{3}{5}$ **21.** $\frac{1}{3}, \frac{3}{8}, \frac{4}{9}$ **23.** $\frac{2}{3}, \frac{7}{10}, \frac{3}{4}$ **25.** $\frac{1}{4}, \frac{3}{8}, \frac{2}{3}$ **27.** < **29.** > **31.** > **33.** > **35.** $\frac{3}{10}, \frac{2}{5}, \frac{1}{2}$ **37.** $\frac{1}{5}, \frac{7}{15}, \frac{2}{3}$ **39.** $\frac{2}{5}, \frac{4}{9}, \frac{11}{15}$ **41.** $\frac{5}{12}, \frac{5}{8}, \frac{3}{4}$ **43.** Laura; $\frac{3}{5} > \frac{4}{7}$ **45.** $1\frac{1}{8}, 1\frac{2}{5}, 3, 3\frac{2}{5}, 3\frac{4}{5}$ **47.** $\frac{1}{2}, \frac{3}{4}, 3\frac{1}{15}, 3\frac{1}{10}, 3\frac{1}{5}$ **49.** yes **53.** C **55.** 4.5×10^1 **57.** 1.6×10^6 **59.** $\frac{1}{12}$ **61.** $\frac{3}{10}$ **63.** $\frac{1}{11}$

4-8 Exercises

1. $\frac{1}{2}$ foot **3.** $7\frac{1}{7}$ **5.** $5\frac{1}{6}$ **7.** $\frac{2}{5}$ **9.** $\frac{1}{5}$ **11.** $\frac{2}{7}$ **13.** $1\frac{3}{5}$ **15.** $\frac{6}{5}$ or $1\frac{1}{5}$ **17.** $\frac{1}{10}$ **19.** $\frac{5}{8}$ **21.** $\frac{14}{33}$ **23.** $\frac{2}{3}$ **25.** $13\frac{1}{3}$ **27.** $\frac{17}{24}$ **29.** $\frac{4}{9}$ **31.** $\frac{5}{7}$ **33.** $8\frac{2}{3}$

35. $\frac{3}{4}$ hour **37.** $1\frac{3}{4}$ hr **39.** 1 foot **51.** $\frac{2}{6}, \frac{3}{7}, \frac{5}{4}$ **53.** $\frac{3}{10}, \frac{1}{3}, \frac{3}{8}$

4-9 Exercises

1. about 1 **3.** about $\frac{1}{2}$ **5.** 16 miles **7.** about $\frac{1}{2}$ **9.** about 0 **11.** about $1\frac{1}{2}$ **13.** about 2 **15.** 4 tons **17.** $3\frac{1}{2}$ tons **19.** > **21.** < **23.** > **25.** about 2 **27.** about 3 **29.** about $13\frac{1}{2}$ **31.** $\frac{1}{2}$ in. **33.** about $9\frac{1}{2}$ in. **37.** B **39.** 3 **41.** 10 **43.** $n + 5$

Chapter 4 Extension

1. intersection: empty; union: all whole numbers **3.** intersection: 1, 2, 3, 4, 6, 9, 12, 18, 36; union: 1, 2, 3, 4, 6, 8, 9, 12, 18, 24, 36, 72 **5.** yes **7.** no

Chapter 4 Study Guide: Review

1. improper fraction; mixed number **2.** repeating decimal; terminating decimal **3.** prime number; composite number **4.** 2 **5.** 2, 3, 5, 6, 9, 10 **6.** 2, 3, 6, 9 **7.** 2, 4 **8.** 2, 5, 10 **9.** 2 **10.** composite **11.** composite **12.** prime **13.** composite **14.** prime **15.** composite **16.** composite **17.** prime **18.** composite **19.** prime **20.** 1, 2, 3, 4, 5, 6, 10, 12, 15, 20, 30, 60 **21.** 1, 2, 3, 4, 6, 8, 9, 12, 18, 24, 36, 72 **22.** 1, 29 **23.** 1, 2, 4, 7, 8, 14, 28, 56 **24.** 1, 2, 17, 85 **25.** 1, 71 **26.** $5 \cdot 13$ **27.** $2 \cdot 47$ **28.** $2 \cdot 5 \cdot 11$ **29.** 3^4 **30.** $3^2 \cdot 11$ **31.** $2^2 \cdot 19$ **32.** 97 **33.** $5 \cdot 11$ **34.** $2 \cdot 23$ **35.** 12 **36.** 25 **37.** 9 **38.** $\frac{37}{100}$ **39.** $1\frac{4}{5}$ **40.** $\frac{2}{5}$ **41.** 0.875 **42.** 0.4 **43.** $0.\overline{7}$ **44.** Possible answer: $\frac{2}{3}; \frac{8}{12}$ **45.** Possible answer: $\frac{8}{10}; \frac{16}{20}$ **46.** Possible answer: $\frac{1}{4}; \frac{2}{8}$ **47.** $\frac{7}{8}$ **48.** $\frac{3}{10}$ **49.** $\frac{7}{10}$ **50.** $\frac{34}{9}$ **51.** $\frac{29}{12}$ **52.** $\frac{37}{7}$ **53.** $3\frac{5}{6}$ **54.** $3\frac{2}{5}$ **55.** $5\frac{1}{8}$ **56.** > **57.** > **58.** $\frac{3}{8}, \frac{2}{3}, \frac{7}{8}$

59. $\frac{3}{12}, \frac{1}{3}, \frac{4}{6}$ **60.** 1 **61.** $\frac{3}{4}$ **62.** $\frac{3}{5}$ **63.** $6\frac{5}{7}$ **64.** 1 **65.** $\frac{1}{2}$ **66.** 11 **67.** $2\frac{1}{2}$

Chapter 5

5-1 Exercises

1. 3 packs of pencils and 4 packs of erasers **3.** 36 **5.** 20 **7.** 48 **9.** 40 **11.** 63 **13.** 150 **15.** 8 **17.** 20 **19.** 18 **21.** 12 **23.** 24 **25.** 66 **27.** 60 **29.** 140 **31.** 12 **33c.** 12 **d.** 120, 144, 168, and 192 **35.** 12 and 16 **37a.** 120 **37b.** 120 **37c.** 4 **41.** B **43.** 0.03 **45.** 0.24 **47.** > **49.** > **51.** $4\frac{5}{7}$

5-2 Exercises

1. $\frac{5}{12}$ ton **3.** $\frac{3}{10}$ **5.** $\frac{13}{14}$ **7.** $\frac{1}{6}$ cup **9.** $\frac{7}{12}$ **11.** $\frac{9}{20}$ **13.** $1\frac{2}{15}$ **15.** $1\frac{1}{8}$ **17.** $\frac{7}{15}$ **19.** $\frac{7}{18}$ **21.** $\frac{1}{3}$ **23.** $\frac{28}{33}$ **25.** $\frac{7}{18}$ **27.** $\frac{1}{5}$ **29.** $\frac{2}{2}$ or 1 **31.** $1\frac{1}{8}$ **33.** $\frac{1}{2}$ **35.** $\frac{4}{7}$ **37.** $\frac{3}{4}$ **39.** $\frac{7}{8}$ **41.** $\frac{1}{6}$ gallon **43.** $\frac{9}{40}$ lb **49.** $\frac{11}{12}$ mi **51.** 1.1 **53.** 0.125 **55.** > **57.** >

5-3 Exercises

1. $10\frac{5}{12}$ **3.** $6\frac{1}{12}$ **5.** $4\frac{1}{4}$ **7.** $6\frac{7}{12}$ **9.** $6\frac{1}{4}$ **11.** $8\frac{7}{12}$ **13.** $29\frac{3}{5}$ **15.** $34\frac{1}{2}$ **17.** $3\frac{51}{90}$ **19.** $20\frac{13}{36}$ **21.** $12\frac{5}{24}$ **23a.** $26\frac{3}{5}$ lb **b.** $2\frac{1}{10}$ lb **c.** $11\frac{1}{10}$ lb **25.** $1\frac{7}{10}$ **27.** $23\frac{3}{4}$ **29.** $13\frac{1}{4}$ **31.** $18\frac{2}{5}$ **33.** $\frac{1}{2}$ mi **35.** 5 **37.** $1\frac{1}{12}$ **39.** $8\frac{1}{9}$ **41.** 0 **43.** $9\frac{3}{8}$ km **45.** $16\frac{1}{2}$ yards **51.** J **53.** $1\frac{1}{2}$ **55.** $1\frac{2}{5}$ **57.** $\frac{49}{60}$ **59.** $1\frac{1}{15}$

5-4 Exercises

1. $\frac{3}{4}$ **3.** $1\frac{2}{3}$ **5.** $2\frac{3}{5}$ **7.** $3\frac{4}{5}$ **9.** $7\frac{7}{8}$ **11.** $4\frac{13}{18}$ **13.** $2\frac{1}{5}$ **15.** $6\frac{2}{3}$ **17.** $1\frac{4}{9}$ **19.** $8\frac{9}{11}$ **21.** $11\frac{2}{9}$ **23.** $12\frac{13}{18}$ **25.** $7\frac{1}{4}$ in. **27.** $7\frac{1}{3}$ **29.** $3\frac{8}{11}$ **31.** $11\frac{4}{7}$ **33.** $4\frac{11}{12}$ **35.** $1\frac{5}{6}$ **37.** $\frac{1}{12}$ **39.** $13\frac{5}{12}$ **41.** $1\frac{1}{12}$ yards^2 **43.** $1\frac{11}{12}$ yards^2 **47.** C **49.** $a = 16$ **51.** $z = 9$ **53.** 17 **55.** 23

5-5 Exercises

1. $4\frac{1}{2}$ **3.** $5\frac{5}{8}$ **5.** $4\frac{1}{10}$ **7.** $57\frac{3}{4}$ in. **9.** $3\frac{5}{8}$ **11.** $4\frac{5}{6}$ **13.** $8\frac{7}{9}$ **15.** $6\frac{1}{4}$ feet **17.** $5\frac{1}{10}$ **19.** $7\frac{9}{10}$ **21.** $\frac{1}{3}$ **23.** 16 ounces **25.** $\frac{3}{8}$ in. **27.** $7\frac{7}{18}$ **29.** $5\frac{5}{12}$ **31.** $4\frac{1}{4}$ **37.** B **39.** 12 **41.** 72 **43.** $\frac{7}{20}$ **45.** $7\frac{17}{30}$

5-6 Exercises

1. $\frac{8}{9}$ **3.** 3 **5.** $\frac{3}{7}$ **7.** 6 **9.** 8 **11.** 9 **13.** 27 boys **15.** $\frac{3}{4}$ **17.** $\frac{4}{5}$ **19.** $\frac{6}{11}$ **21.** 10 **23.** 6 **25.** 2 **27.** $5\frac{5}{7}$ **29.** $3\frac{5}{9}$ **31.** 7 **33.** 15 **35.** 5 **37.** $\frac{48}{5}$ or $9\frac{3}{5}$ **39.** 45 **41.** > **43.** = **45.** < **47.** > **49.** \$33 **51.** 165 feet tall **55.** C **57.** $75 - w$ **59.** $p \div 7$ **61.** $8\frac{5}{7}$ **63.** $6\frac{3}{8}$

5-7 Exercises

1. $\frac{1}{6}$ **3.** $\frac{3}{7}$ **5.** $\frac{2}{15}$ **7.** $\frac{1}{20}$ **9.** $\frac{2}{21}$ **11.** $\frac{5}{9}$ **13.** $\frac{1}{4}$ **15.** $\frac{5}{11}$ **17.** $\frac{2}{15}$ **19.** $\frac{1}{8}$ **21.** $\frac{4}{27}$ **23.** $\frac{5}{48}$ **25.** $\frac{4}{15}$ **27.** $\frac{1}{14}$ **29.** $\frac{27}{35}$ **31.** $\frac{9}{55}$ **33.** $\frac{1}{4}$ cup **35.** < **37.** > **39.** < **41a.** Multiply by $\frac{1}{4}$. **b.** $\frac{1}{12}$ **43.** $\frac{3}{8}$ lb **45.** $\frac{3}{8}$ **49.** D **51.** $n = 3$ **53.** $a = 13$ **55.** $\frac{4}{9}$ **57.** $\frac{12}{21}$

5-8 Exercises

1. $\frac{5}{6}$ **3.** $\frac{11}{14}$ **5.** $\frac{13}{15}$ **7.** $2\frac{1}{16}$ **9.** $21\frac{5}{7}$ **11.** $12\frac{7}{20}$ **13.** $\frac{15}{16}$ **15.** $\frac{7}{15}$ **17.** $1\frac{1}{18}$ **19.** $\frac{13}{14}$ **21.** $2\frac{2}{7}$ **23.** $15\frac{1}{2}$ **25.** $23\frac{1}{2}$ **27.** $3\frac{3}{5}$ **29.** $\frac{10}{27}$ **31.** $1\frac{1}{4}$ **33.** $\frac{1}{6}$ **35.** $13\frac{3}{4}$ **37.** $2\frac{2}{3}$ **39.** $17\frac{1}{2}$ **41.** $\frac{7}{25}$ of a bag **43.** yes **45.** $1\frac{3}{7}$ **47.** 28 **49.** $1\frac{7}{8}$ **51.** $21\frac{3}{4}$ **53.** 240 **55a.** $1\frac{1}{2} \cdot 7 = 10\frac{1}{2}$ h **b.** less than 12 h **59.** C **61.** 5.4×10^2 **63.** 5.4×10^4 **65.** $\frac{1}{2}$ **67.** 4

5-9 Exercises

1. $\frac{7}{2}$ **3.** 9 **5.** $\frac{5}{13}$ **7.** $1\frac{5}{7}$ **9.** $2\frac{1}{6}$ **11.** $\frac{9}{50}$ **13.** $4\frac{4}{7}$ **15.** 10 **17.** $\frac{12}{11}$ **19.** $\frac{11}{8}$ **21.** $\frac{7}{6}$ **23.** $\frac{4}{21}$ **25.** $1\frac{5}{14}$ **27.** 12 **29.** $\frac{3}{10}$ **31.** $2\frac{22}{45}$ **33.** $\frac{2}{3}$ **35.** $\frac{1}{40}$ **37.** $1\frac{17}{25}$ **39.** $4\frac{2}{3}$ **41.** $\frac{3}{28}$

43. 16 bags **45.** yes **47.** yes **49.** $\frac{5}{2}, \frac{25}{4}$ **51.** $\frac{1}{5}, \frac{1}{5}$ **53.** The reciprocal of a fraction has the fraction's numerator as its denominator and has the fraction's denominator as its numerator. The product of a fraction and its reciprocal is 1. **55.** $\frac{11}{12}$ **57.** $1\frac{1}{14}$ **59.** $41\frac{19}{75}$ **61.** $24\frac{2}{9}$ in. **67.** H **68.** 2; 4.32 **69.** 1; 9.5 **70.** 3; 16.192 **71.** 2; 0.04 **73.** $\frac{7}{8}$ **75.** $5\frac{13}{15}$

5-10 Exercises

1. $z = 16$ **3.** $x = 7\frac{1}{2}$ **5.** 24 **7.** $x = 9$ **9.** $t = \frac{1}{10}$ **11.** $y = 20$ **13.** $j = 12\frac{6}{7}$ **15.** \$10 **17.** $y = 10$ **19.** $t = 16$ **21.** $b = 14$ **23.** $x = 9\frac{1}{3}$ **25.** $n = 12$ **27.** $y = \frac{2}{3}$ **29.** $n = 2$ **31.** 4 minutes **33.** 11 dresses **35.** 20 more pages **41.** B **43.** 35 **45.** 2 **47.** 3 **49.** $1\frac{1}{5}$ **51.** $\frac{15}{28}$

Chapter 5 Study Guide: Review

1. reciprocals **2.** least common denominator **3.** 30 **4.** 48 **5.** 27 **6.** 60 **7.** 225 **8.** 660 **9.** $\frac{33}{40}$ **10.** $\frac{3}{4}$ **11.** $\frac{1}{15}$ **12.** $\frac{5}{24}$ **13.** $4\frac{7}{10}$ **14.** $3\frac{1}{18}$ **15.** $\frac{7}{15}$ **16.** $3\frac{2}{3}$ **17.** $1\frac{1}{2}$ **18.** $5\frac{2}{3}$ **19.** $2\frac{5}{8}$ **20.** $6\frac{13}{14}$ **21.** $1\frac{1}{8}$ **22.** $4\frac{3}{4}$ feet **23.** $30\frac{3}{20}$ **24.** $14\frac{11}{12}$ **25.** $5\frac{5}{12}$ **26.** $3\frac{4}{9}$ **27.** $5\frac{7}{15}$ **28.** $3\frac{3}{10}$ **29.** 7 oz **30.** $\frac{5}{7}$ **31.** $\frac{3}{4}$ **32.** $2\frac{4}{7}$ **33.** $2\frac{1}{2}$ **34.** 3 **35.** $1\frac{1}{5}$ **36.** 21 members **37.** $\frac{1}{3}$ **38.** $\frac{15}{28}$ **39.** $\frac{1}{10}$ **40.** $\frac{7}{25}$ **41.** $\frac{5}{81}$ **42.** $\frac{3}{14}$ **43.** $\frac{8}{15}$ **44.** $\frac{9}{10}$ **45.** $1\frac{1}{4}$ **46.** 2 **47.** $\frac{4}{21}$ **48.** $\frac{3}{20}$ **49.** $\frac{5}{9}$ **50.** 8 times **51.** $a = \frac{1}{8}$ **52.** $b = 2$ **53.** $m = 17\frac{1}{2}$ **54.** $g = \frac{2}{15}$ **55.** $r = 10\frac{4}{5}$ **56.** $s = 50$ **57.** $p = \frac{1}{9}$ **58.** $j = 1\frac{53}{64}$

Chapter 6

6-1 Exercises

1.

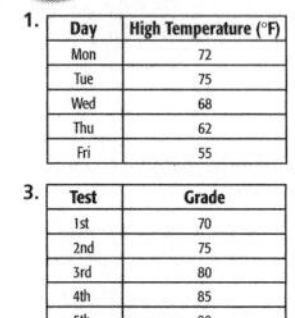

Day	High Temperature (°F)
Mon	72
Tue	75
Wed	68
Thu	62
Fri	55

3.

Test	Grade
1st	70
2nd	75
3rd	80
4th	85
5th	90

5.

Date	Thickness (in.)
December 3	1
December 18	2
January 3	5
January 18	11
February 3	17

7. Jeffery is in sixth grade. Victoria is in seventh, and Arthur is in eighth. **11.** 81 **13.** 216 **15.** 2 times 12; 2 multiplied by 12 **17.** m divided by 3, the quotient of m and 3

6-2 Exercises

1. mean = 22 **3.** mean = 6.5 **5.** mean = 57.2, median = 55, no mode, range = 23 **7.** range = 19, mean = 508.2, median = 508.5, mode = 500 **9.** 11 **11.** 12 **13.** 4 **15.** 6, 7, 12, 15, 15 **19.** C **21.** 25 **23.** 2 **25.** 5

6-3 Exercises

1a. mean = 4.75, median = 5, no mode **b.** mean = 10, median = 7, no mode **3.** mean = 225, median = 187.5, mode = 240; median **5.** with: mean = 710.4, median = 788, no mode without: mean = 877.75, median = 868, no mode **7.** mean ≈ 118.29, median = 128, no mode **13.** 70 **15.** $n = \frac{9}{10}$ **17.** median: 35; no mode; range = 45

6-4 Exercises

1. green

3. Number of Students in Mr. Jones's Classes

5. orange

7. Days with Rainfall

9. 14 million mi^2 **11.** ≈ 8.14 million mi^2

13a. Scores of Practice Games

b. Blue: mean = 47.3, range = 26; Green: mean = 47.3, range = 16 **c.** Possible answer: The green squad; their performance is more consistent, and their scores have steadily increased over time. **17.** J **19.** $\frac{1}{5}$ **21.** $2\frac{1}{3}$

6-5 Exercises

1.

Type of Instrument	
Trumpet	卌
Drums	II
Tuba	I
Trombone	III
French horn	IIII

3.

Number of Years of Each Presidential Term			
Number (Intervals)	0–4	5–8	9–12
Frequency	26	15	1

5.

Pets	
Dog	卌I
Cat	卌
Bird	III
Fish	III
Hamster	II

7.

Final Medal Standing at the Summer Olympic Games for the Top 25 Countries					
Number (Intervals)	0–20	21–40	41–60	61–80	81–100
Frequency	14	8	3	0	2

9. histogram

11.

Census	Frequency
0–999,999	3
1,000,000–1,999,999	2
2,000,000–2,999,999	0
3,000,000–3,999,999	1
4,000,000–4,999,999	1
5,000,000–5,999,999	0
6,000,000–6,999,999	1

Populations of Australia's States and Territories

13. no **17.** B **19.** 1 + 0.2 + 0.03; one and twenty-three hundredths **21.** 20 + 6 + 0.07; twenty-six and seven-hundredths **23.** 19 **25.** 9

6-6 Exercises

1. (2, 3) **3.** (7, 6) **5.** (4, 5) **7–9.**

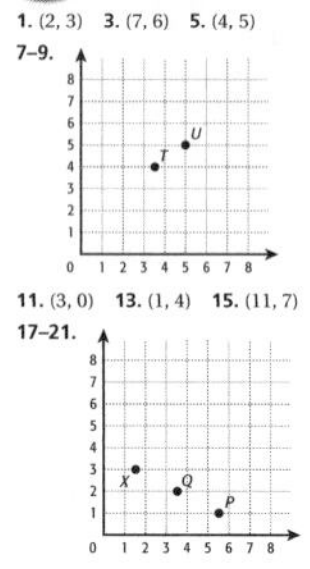

11. (3, 0) **13.** (1, 4) **15.** (11, 7) **17–21.**

23. A **25.** C **27.** P **29.** (9, 8) **31.** (1, 5) **33.** (9, 0) **35.** $(5\frac{1}{2}, 0)$

39. D **41.** $3^3 \times 5^2$ **43.** $2^2 \times 3^2 \times 5$ **45.** $\frac{3}{28}$ **47.** $\frac{3}{14}$

6-7 Exercises

1. School Enrollment

3. 125

5. Comparison of Stock Prices

7. 70 million

9. Soccer Team Fund-Raising Efforts

11. Max **15.** C **17.** $s = 18$ **19.** $m = 15$

6-8 Exercises

5. The vertical axis begins at 430 rather than zero. **7.** the yearly increments changed

9.

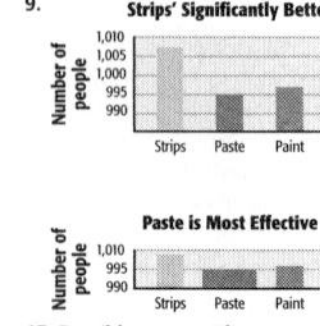

17. Possible answer: The temperature was twice as high at 11:00 A.M. **19.** 124

21–23.

6-9 Exercises

1. Daily High Temperatures (°F)

Stems	Leaves
3	7 9
4	0 5 8
5	1 6

Key: 3|7 means 37

3. 44 **5.** 32 **7.** 34 **9.** 41 **11.** 52 **13.** 42 **15.** A

17. Number of Cars with One Passenger

Stems	Leaves
8	0 1 2 3 7 8 9
9	2 4 4 5 9
10	0 1 3 9
11	
12	4 5

Key: 8|0 means 80

21. 2,500 **23.** 225,971; 2,004,801; 298,500,004 **25.** $\frac{7}{4}$ **27.** 5

6-10 Exercises

1. line graph **3a.** Possible answer: Line graph; it shows change over time.

b.

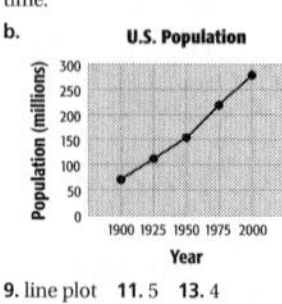

9. line plot **11.** 5 **13.** 4

Chapter 6 Study Guide: Review

1. histogram **2.** ordered pair **3.** mode

4.

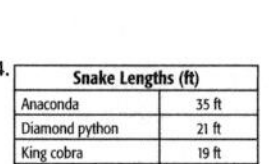

Snake Lengths (ft)	
Anaconda	35 ft
Diamond python	21 ft
King cobra	19 ft
Boa constrictor	16 ft

5. mean: 37; median: 38; mode: 39; range: 7 **6.** with outlier: mean ≈ 14.29; median = 11; mode = 12; without outlier: mean ≈ 10.33; median = 10.5; mode = 12 **7.** with outlier: mean = 31; median = 32; mode = 32; without outlier: mean = 35.75; median = 33; mode = 32 **8.** with outlier: mean ≈ 19.67; median = 14; mode = none; without outlier: mean = 13.2; median = 13; mode = none **9.** 8th grade

10.

11.

Points Scored			
Points (Intervals)	1–4	5–8	9–12
Frequency	2	3	1

12.

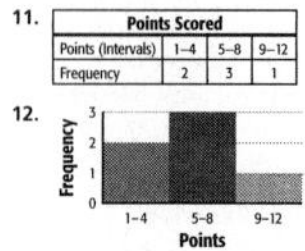

13. (4, 1) **14.** (3, 2)

15.

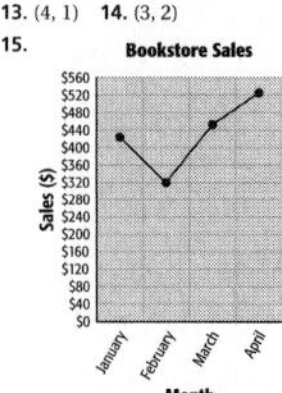

16. April **17.** Sales decreased from January to February and then increased from February to April. **18.** The scale starts out in

increments of one mile and then it changes to 5 miles.

19. **Basketball Scores**

Stems	Leaves
2	0 2 6 8
3	4
4	0 4 6

Key: 2|0 means 20

20. smallest value: 20, largest value: 46, mean: 32.5, median: 31, no mode, range: 26 **21.** bar graph

Chapter 7

7-1 Exercises

1. 3:10 **3.** 41:16 **5.** the 8-ounce bag **7.** 19:3 **11.** the 15 lb bag **13.** 24 to 11, 24:11, twenty-four to eleven **15.** 7 to 10, 7:10, seven to ten **17.** 5 to 9, 5:9, five to nine **19.** $\frac{100}{101}$, 100:101, 100 to 101 **21.** 8:5 **23.** 5:8 **25.** 8:16 **27.** Wednesday **33.** The 24-ounce box is the better deal. **35.** 3 **37.** 1 **39.** $m = \frac{11}{18}$ **41.** $h = \frac{2}{3}$

7-2 Exercises

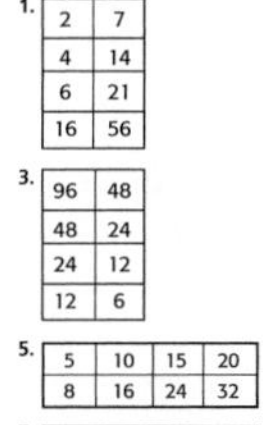

1.

2	7
4	14
6	21
16	56

3.

96	48
48	24
24	12
12	6

5.

5	10	15	20
8	16	24	32

7.

24	12	6	3
16	8	4	2

9. 35 min

11.

5	8
10	16
15	24
20	24

13.

6	12	18	48	96
7	14	21	56	112

15.

11	22	33	44
25	50	75	100

17.

51	102	153	204
75	150	225	300

19. $\frac{8}{9}$ **21.** 24; 15 **27.** about 70,000,000 **31.** B **33.** 94; 448.5; 447; 452

7-3 Exercises

3. 7 **5.** 35 **9.** 15 **11.** 55 **13.** 2 **15.** 3 **17.** 7 **19.** 3 **21.** $\frac{21}{6}$ **23.** 113 euros, 160 Canadian dollars, 828 renminbi, 440 shekels, and 910 Mexican pesos. **27.** C **29.** < **31.** = **33.** 4 to 9, $\frac{4}{9}$ **35.** 6:13, 6 to 13

7-4 Exercises

1. The length of the missing side is 4 cm. $m\angle G = 37°$ **3.** The length of the missing side, n, is 3 inches. $m\angle M = 110°$ **5.** sides; $\overline{AC}$ and $\overline{XY}$; $\overline{XW}$ and $\overline{AB}$; $\overline{BC}$ and $\overline{WY}$; angles: X and A; W and B; Y and C **7.** Less than **9.** $m\angle H = 80°$, $m\angle J = 80°$, $m\angle Z = 100°$; the length of $\overline{WX}$ is 5.5 yd, the length of $\overline{ZY}$ is 5.5 yd, and the length of $\overline{WZ}$ is 4 yd. **11.** No; the corresponding sides are not in proportion. **17.** G **19.** Distributive Property **21.** 5 **23.** 0.7

7-5 Exercises

1. 15 ft **3.** 18 ft **5.** 104 in. **7.** 120 m **11.** 14.2 **13.** 4.9 **15.** $8\frac{1}{4}$ **17.** $8\frac{4}{5}$

7-6 Exercises

1. 300 ft **3.** No **5.** 2.5 inches **7.** north wall: 2 in.; west wall: 3 in.; south wall: 5 in.; east wall: 4.25 in. **9.** 357 km **17.** 64 in. **19.** 38.4 **21.** 3.87 **23.** $x = 3$ **25.** $k = 42$ **27.** $p = 1$

7-7 Exercises

1. **3.**

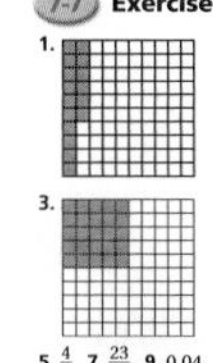

5. $\frac{4}{5}$ **7.** $\frac{23}{25}$ **9.** 0.04 **11.** 0.64

13. **15.**

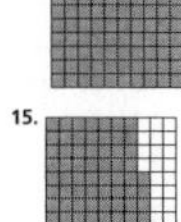

17. $\frac{3}{4}$ **19.** $\frac{18}{25}$ **21.** $\frac{16}{25}$ **23.** $\frac{17}{20}$ **25.** 0.44 **27.** 0.29 **29.** 0.6 **31.** 0.07 **33.** 0.02 **35.** 0.01 **37.** 0.7 **39.** 0.37 **41.** 0.08 **43.** 0.75 **45.** 1 **47.** 0.52 **49.** 0.12 **51.** 11% = 0.11 **53.** No **59.** H **61.** 17 **63.** 10

7-8 Exercises

1. 39% **3.** 80% **5.** 44% **7.** 70% **9.** 70% **11.** 60% **13.** 34% **15.** 62% **17.** 30% **19.** 45% **21.** 12.5% **23.** 74% **25.** 40% **27.** 4%, $\frac{1}{25}$ **29.** 45%, $\frac{9}{20}$ **31.** 1%, $\frac{1}{100}$ **33.** 60%, $\frac{3}{5}$ **35.** 14%, $\frac{7}{50}$ **37.** 80%, 0.8 **39.** 83.33%, 0.83 **41.** 34%, 0.34 **43.** 4%, 0.04 **45.** 26.67%, 0.27 **47.** < **49.** = **51.** > **53.** < **55.** about 48%; about 52% **57.** 0.098, $\frac{7}{8}$, 90% **59.** 0.21, $\frac{7}{25}$, 38% **61.** 17%, $\frac{5}{9}$, 0.605 **63.** 97% **67.** D **69.** $1\frac{1}{4}$ **71.** $\frac{9}{10}$ **73.** 3 ft **75.** 2.25 ft

7-9 Exercises

1. 44 T-shirts **3.** 6.72 **5.** 0.4

7. 37.8 **9.** 6 dolls **11.** 30 minutes **13.** 28.6 **15.** 18.2 **17.** 94.5 **19.** 2.28 **21.** 5.2 **23.** 12.32 **25.** 40.56 **27.** 31 **29.** 12 **31a.** 9 feet **b.** 108 square feet **33.** 12 atoms of hydrogen, 6 atoms of carbon, and 6 atoms of oxygen **39.** \$57.60 **41.** $\frac{39}{50}$ **43.** $\frac{99}{100}$ **45.** 87.5%

7-10 Exercises

1. about \$7.65 **3.** about \$151.20 **5.** about \$18.75 **7.** about \$11.10 **9.** about \$55.65 **11.** Yes **13.** \$339.20 **19.** Music Palace CDs sell for \$11.97. Awesome Sound CDs sell for \$11.69. Awesome Sound has the better deal. **21.** yes **23.** 3 **25.** 13 **27.** 600

Chapter 7 Extension

1. \$148.75 **3.** \$32 **5.** \$250 **7.** 3% **9.** \$367.20 **11.** \$37,500

Chapter 7 Study Guide: Review

1. discount **2.** percent **3.** corresponding angles **4.** Possible answers: 2:4; 3:6; 6:12 **5.** 12 oz for \$2.64 **6.** Possible answers:

3	6	9	12
10	20	30	40

7. Possible answers:

5	10	15	20
21	42	63	84

8. Possible answers:

15	30	45	60
7	14	21	28

9. \$47.25 **10.** $n = 9$ **11.** $n = 3$ **12.** $n = 14$ **13.** $n = 2$ **14.** $n =$ 11 inches; $m\angle A = 90°$ **15.** 94 ft **16.** 43.75 miles **17.** 3 inches **18.** $\frac{3}{4}$ **19.** $\frac{3}{50}$ **20.** $\frac{3}{10}$ **21.** 0.08 **22.** 0.65 **23.** 0.2 **24.** 89.6% **25.** 70% **26.** 5.7% **27.** 12% **28.** 70% **29.** 25% **30.** 87.5% **31.** 80% **32.** 6.25% **33.** 12 **34.** 5.94 **35.** 117 tickets **36.** about \$19.00 **37.** about \$4.35 **38.** about \$1.08

Chapter 8

8-1 Exercises

3. K **7.** $\overline{AB}$ **15.** C

21. **23.**

25a. points **b.** line **c.** line segment **d.** ray **27.** $\overline{XY}$, $\overline{XY}$, $\overline{XY}$ **31.** A **33.** $k = 21$ **35.** $k = 100$ **37.** $3\frac{1}{4}$ **39.** $13\frac{2}{3}$ **41.** $11\frac{4}{7}$

8-2 Exercises

1. 90° **3.** 60°

5. **7.**

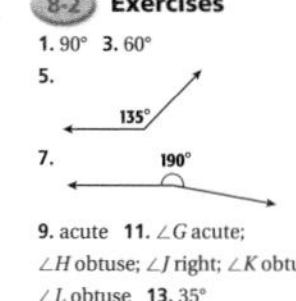

9. acute **11.** ∠G acute; ∠H obtuse; ∠J right; ∠K obtuse; ∠L obtuse **13.** 35°

15. **17.** **19.**

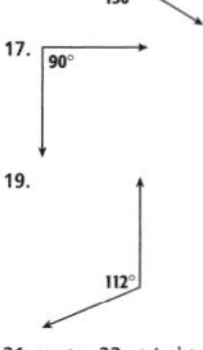

21. acute **23.** ∠A obtuse; ∠B obtuse; ∠C acute; ∠D obtuse; ∠E obtuse; ∠F acute

25.

27. straight **29.** acute **35.** G **37.** 40%; $\frac{2}{5}$ **39.** 90%; $\frac{9}{10}$ **41.** 3.6 **43.** 17.5

8-3 Exercises

1. adjacent **3.** $m\angle a = 9°$ **5.** adjacent **7.** $m\angle c = 78°$ **9.** angles 1, 5, 6, 7 and 8 **11.** 108°, 108°, 72° **13.** 35° **15.** 75° **17.** 28° **19.** 59° **21.** 78° **23.** 99° **25.** angles C and D are congruent angles **29.** D **31.** $n = 2$ **33.** $p = 0.25$ **35.** straight **37.** acute

8-4 Exercises

1. intersecting **3.** perpendicular **5.** skew **7.** skew **9.** parallel **13.** $\overline{BF}$, $\overline{GH}$, $\overline{EF}$, $\overline{CG}$ **15.** $\overline{AB}$, $\overline{EF}$, $\overline{FG}$, $\overline{BC}$ **17.** sometimes **19.** never **25.** H

27–31.

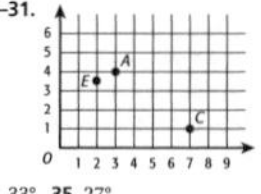

33. 33° **35.** 27°

8-5 Exercises

1. obtuse triangle **3.** 82° **5.** isosceles **7.** 60° **9.** scalene **11.** yes, right **13.** no **15.** yes, obtuse **19.** $1\frac{1}{6}$ ft, equilateral

21. **23.**

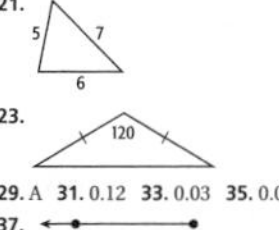

29. A **31.** 0.12 **33.** 0.03 **35.** 0.076

37. **39.**

8-6 Exercises

1. rectangle **3.** square **5.** squares **7.** quadrilateral **9.** parallelogram **11.** trapezoid **13.** quadrilateral, parallelogram, rectangle, rhombus, square **15.** quadrilateral, parallelogram, rhombus **17.** never **19.** always **21.** sometimes **23.** sometimes

25. not possible **27.** not possible **29a.** If the frame is 10 in. by 13 in., the total length of the sides is 46 in., not 38 in. **c.** 8 in. by 11 in. **35.** Quadrilateral, parallelogram, rhombus; *rhombus* is the most descriptive **37.** 2, 6, 18, 54, 162 **39.** never

8-7 Exercises

1. polygon, hexagon, regular **3.** polygon, triangle, regular **5.** not a polygon **7.** not a polygon **9.** not formed by line segments **11.** not formed by line segments **13.** hexagon **15.** 1,440°, 144° **17.** never **19.** sometimes **25.** 108 **27.** $d = 4.04$ **29.** $x = 8.4$

8-8 Exercises

1. **3.**

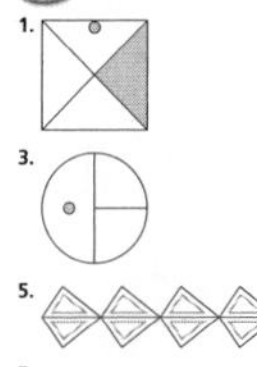

5. **7.** **9.**

The lines should be green.

13. C **15.** 81 **17.** 27 **19.** 1,024 **21.** $2 \cdot 5^2$ **23.** $2 \cdot 107$

8-9 Exercises

1. not congruent; different sizes **3.** Figure A **5.** The figures are irregular hexagons that are not congruent.

7.

11. A **13.** $y = 9$ **15.** $n = 8$ **17.** $\frac{8}{21}$ **19.** $\frac{3}{8}$

8-10 Exercises

1. reflection **3.** translation

5.

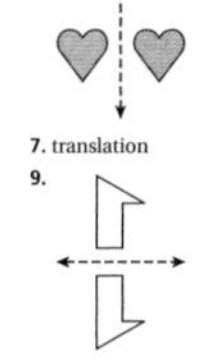

7. translation

9.

13.

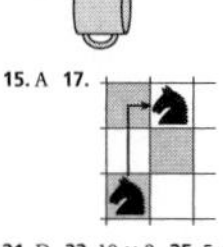

15. A **17.**

21. D **23.** 19 × 3 **25.** 5 + 9 **27.** $6\frac{71}{100}$ **29.** $2\frac{22}{55}$

8-11 Exercises

1. The line is a line of symmetry. **3.** The line is a line of symmetry. **5.** 3 lines of symmetry **7.** 4 lines of symmetry **9.** The line is not a line of symmetry. **11.** The line is not a line of symmetry. **13.** 8 lines of symmetry **15.** 1 line of symmetry **17.** 3; 1; none **21.** B **23.** > **25.** 24.68 **27.** 74.35

Chapter 8 Study Guide: Review

1. trapezoid **2.** polygon **3.** Possible answer: $\overrightarrow{ED}$, $\overrightarrow{AD}$ **4.** acute **5.** obtuse **6.** acute **7.** straight **8.** $b = 27°$ **9.** $d = 98°$ **10.** perpendicular **11.** skew **12.** obtuse scalene **13.** parallelogram **14.** triangle; not regular **15.** rectangle; not regular **16.** Add 1 shaded and 1 white triangle each time. **17.** not congruent; different sizes **18.** congruent **19.** translation

20.

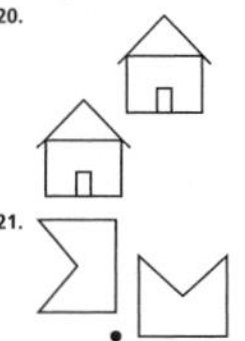

21.

22. The line is a line of symmetry.

Chapter 9

9-1 Exercises

1. in. **3.** gal **5.** mi **7.** qt **9.** ft **11.** gal **13.** oz **17.** about 1 qt **21.** $8\frac{1}{4}$ lb **27.** Possible answers: *rod*: a unit of length equal to $5\frac{1}{2}$ yards; *peck*: a dry measure of capacity equal to 8 quarts; *dram*: a very small unit of weight equal to 0.0625 ounce **29.** F **31.** 1, 3, 5, 9, 15, 45 **33.** 1, 2, 4, 5, 8, 10, 16, 20, 40, 80 **35.** acute

9-2 Exercises

1. m **3.** L **5.** about 7 cm **7.** g **9.** L **11.** the width of his fist **13.** km **15.** kg **17.** mL **19.** Yes; possible answer: The balloon weighs 0.8 g more with the air. **23.** C **25.** 8 **27.** 16 **29.** 36 **31.** 60

9-3 Exercises

1. 108 **3.** 7 **5.** 3 **7.** 8 **9.** 3 **11.** 22 **13.** about 24 cups **15.** 48 **17.** 2 **19.** 2 **21.** 6,000 **23.** 3 **25.** 5 **27.** < **29.** = **31.** < **33.** = **35.** >

37. about 434 yards **39a.** 9 yd **b.** 324 in. **41.** 3,520; 2 **43.** 1,750 T **47.** 4 pints **49.** Possible answer: First, convert either the inches to feet or the feet to inches so that both lengths have the same unit. Then compare. **51.** A **53.** $x = 9$ **55.** $d = 17$

9-4 Exercises

1. 0.115 km **3.** 0.852 **5.** 3,500 **7.** 4,400 **9.** 0.5 **11.** 600 **13.** 0.110 **15.** 22,500 **17.** 2.460 **19.** 9.68 **21.** 0.782 **23.** 21.6 L; 21,600 mL **25.** $x = 0.23850$ **27.** 7,000 **29.** = **31.** < **33.** = **35.** St. Louis Gateway Arch; 18 m **39.** 55 cups; 124 mL **41.** 0.452 kg; 452,000 mg; 0.136 kg **43.** obtuse **45.** sometimes **47.** never

9-5 Exercises

1. 1,200 **3.** $2\frac{1}{2}$ **5.** 480 **7.** 2:15 P.M. **9.** 54 **11.** 60 **13.** 4 **15.** 2 **17.** 26 **19.** 12:00 P.M. **21.** 198 **23.** > **25.** < **27.** 480; 470 **29.** about 28°C **35.** C **37.** > **39.** < **41.** 5.55 **43.** 9.447

9-6 Exercises

1. 52°; acute **3.** 90°; right **5.** 45° **7.** $\angle A = 150°$; $\angle B = 90°$ **9.** 180°; straight **11.** 40° **13.** 108° **17.** 5.5° **23.** 65°; acute; 65 < 90 **25.** 2 **27.** 2

9-7 Exercises

1. 2 in. **3.** 40 m **5.** 7 yd **7.** 96 in. **9.** 7 cm **11.** 42 m **13.** 6 in. **15.** 42 in. **17.** 2 km **19a.** 44 ft × 20 ft **b.** 128 ft **25.** 24.68 **27.** 74.35 **29.** $x = 3$ **31.** $k = 42$

9-8 Exercises

1. circle G, diameter $\overline{EF}$, and radii $\overline{GF}$, $\overline{GE}$, and $\overline{GD}$ **3.** 12 ft **5.** 12.56 in. **7.** 15 yd **9.** 4.71 m **11.** 0.5 in. **13.** 5.75 ft, 36.11 ft **15.** 5 **17.** 9.42 ft **21.** 61 cm **23.** 880 revolutions **25.** $\frac{10}{2}, \frac{3}{4}, \frac{1}{2}$ **27.** $\frac{3}{4}, \frac{5}{8}, \frac{7}{16}$ **29.** 5% **31.** 100%

Chapter 9 Study Guide: Review

1. perimeter; circumference **2.** diameter **3.** customary system **4.** in.; about seven widths of your thumbs **5.** mi; about 800 times 18 football fields **6.** lb; about 2 loaves of bread **7.** fl oz; about a spoonful **8.** $\frac{1}{8}$ in. **9.** mm; about 32 times the thickness of a dime **10.** mg; about 5 times the mass of a very small insect **11.** kg; about two textbooks **12.** L; about two blender containers **13.** 2 cm **14.** 15, 840 ft **15.** 54 yd **16.** 12 c **17.** 3 gal **18.** 8 lb **19.** 4 T **20.** 4 lb **21.** 144 in. **22.** 4 qt **23.** 99 ft **24.** 250 yd **25.** 3,200 mL **26.** 0.007 L **27.** 0.3425 km **28.** 0.042 kg **29.** 0.051 m **30.** 71,000 m **31.** 1 hr **32.** 59,400 s **33.** 105 days **34.** 105° **35.** 33.9 in. **36.** 6 ft **37.** 31.4 ft **38.** 9 m **39.** 50.24 cm **40.** 11 ft

Chapter 10

10-1 Exercises

1. about 8.5 square units **3.** about 4 square units **5.** 100.1 in^2 **7.** 48 ft^2 **9.** 10 in^2 **11.** about 6 square units **13.** about 4 square units **15.** 12.75 m^2 **17.** 260 ft^2 **19.** 0.75 cm^2 **25.** B **27.** 1, 2, 4, 5, 10, 20 **29.** 1, 59 **31.** 7 ft

10-2 Exercises

1. 3 yd^2 **3.** 27 m^2 **5.** 32.5 ft^2 **7.** 88 cm^2 **9.** 3 ft^2 **11.** 72 in^2 **13.** 16 yd^2 **15.** 96 m^2 **17.** 5 square units **19.** 15 square units **21.** 346.5 m^2 **23.** 12 ft^2 **29.** 175 cm^2 **31.** $\frac{12}{5}$ **33.** $\frac{15}{2}$

10-3 Exercises

1. 2,800 m^2 **3.** 54 cm^2 **5.** 640 yd^2 **11.** 40 square units **13.** $5\frac{1}{6}$ **15.** $6\frac{3}{10}$ **17.** 144 cm^2

10-4 Exercises

1. When the dimensions of the square are divided by 3, the perimeter is divided by 3, and the area is divided by 9 or 3^2.
3. When the dimensions of the triangle are multiplied by 4, the perimeter is multiplied by 4, and the area is multiplied by 16 or 4^2.
5a. 4,800 ft **5b.** 280 ft, 320 ft **9.** J **11.** $\frac{1}{4}$ **13.** $\frac{1}{4}$ **15.** 310 ft

10-5 Exercises

1. 48 ft^2 **3.** 243 in^2 **5.** 616 cm^2 **7.** 12.56 ft^2 **9.** 768 in^2 **11.** 38.5 yd^2 **13.** 2,464 ft^2 **15.** A = 102.02 cm^2, C = 35.8 cm **17.** A = 174.28 in^2, C = 46.79 in. **19.** $38\frac{1}{2}$ ft^2 **25.** C **27.** $\frac{1}{6}$ **29.** $\frac{5}{18}$ **31.** $\frac{3}{25}$ **33.** $1\frac{1}{4}$

10-6 Exercises

1. 5 faces, 8 edges, 5 vertices **3.** 5 faces, 8 edges, 5 vertices **5.** square pyramid **7.** 5 faces, 9 edges, 6 vertices **9.** 6 faces, 12 edges, 8 vertices **11.** rectangular prism **13.** square pyramid, yes **15.** cone, no **17.** B, C and D **19.** B **21.** true **23.** true **25.** 8; octagonal pyramid **29.** C **31.** < **33.** > **35.** parallel **37.** intersecting

10-7 Exercises

1. 162 cm^3 **3.** 10 ft^3 **5.** 320 ft^3 **7.** 1 × 1 × 10 and 2 × 5 × 1 **9.** 79.36 in^3 **11.** 54 m^3 **13.** 71.72 ft^3 **15.** 480 in^3 **17.** 474.375 km^3 **19.** 20 ft **21.** 10 cm^3, 1 cm^3, 3.5 cm^3, 300 cm^3, 20 cm^3 **23.** pine **25.** Alicia does not have gold. **29.** 77.4 **31.** 3 **33.** 9

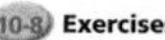

10-8 Exercises

1. 754 m³ **3.** 3,140 in³ **5.** Cylinder B **7.** 314 ft³ **9.** 31 cm³ and 283 cm³ **11.** 138 in³ **13.** 4 m³ **15.** 100.48 in³ **17.** 1,987.03 ft³ **19.** 12,560,000 mm³ **21.** 923 ft³ **23.** It cannot hold 200 cm³ of juice because it only has a volume of 196.25 cm³. **29.** the tomato soup can holds more soup **31.** 9, 12 **33.** 115°

10-9 Exercises

1. 94 in² **3.** 56 cm² **5.** 2,640 cm² **7.** 326.56 ft² **9.** 376.8 m² **11.** $16\frac{1}{2}$ m² **13.** 133 cm² **15.** 11 km² **17.** 712.717 m² **19.** about 96 ft² **21.** about 190 cm² **23a.** 312 in² **b.** 8.3 in. **29.** 571.48 **31.** $y = 42$ **33.** $4\frac{5}{9}$ **35.** $\frac{1}{12}$

Chapter 10 Study Guide: Review

1. polyhedron **2.** volume **3.** vertex **4.** 12 in² **5.** 18 ft² **6.** 12 in² **7.** 7 in² **8.** 154 in² **9.** 30 cm² **10.** 135 cm² **11.** 175.5 ft² **12.** The perimeter is multiplied by 2, and the area is multiplied by 4 or 2^2. **13.** 78.5 ft² **14.** 200.96 cm² **15.** 12.57 m² **16.** 113.04 in² **17.** 5 faces, 8 edges, 5 vertices; square pyramid **18.** 6 faces, 12 edges, 8 vertices; rectangular prism **19.** 384 cm³ **20.** 6,300 in³ **21.** 353 m³ **22.** 2,308 ft³ **23.** 125 m² **24.** 105 cm²

Chapter 11

11-1 Exercises

1. +5

3. −4 −2 0 2 4

5. −7 −5 −3 −1 1 3 5 7

7. +8 −4 +5 **9.** −20 **11.** −39

13. −6 −4 −2 0 2 4 6

15. −4 −2 0 2 4

17. −3 −4 +2 −3 **19.** spending $83 **21.** earning $15 **23.** +92 **25.** +25 **27.** 0 **29.** −3; +5 +2.7 −6.2 **30.** +45 **32.** +2; −2 **34.** C **38.** D **40.** 1.7 **42.** 6.215

11-2 Exercises

1. > **3.** < **5.** −5, −4, 3, 7 **7a.** 3:30 A.M. **b.** 1°F **9.** > **11.** < **13.** −8, 7, 15 **15.** −16, −9, −1, 13 **17.** −19, −3, 0, 8, 22 **19.** < **21.** > **23.** < **25.** < **27.** −39, 14, 21 **29.** −26, −12, 0, 43 **31.** −73, −67, −10, 20, 82 **33.** C **35.** San Augustin Cave, Dead Sea, Mr. Rainier, Kilimanjaro, Mt. Everest **39.** C **41.** acute **43.** cannot form a triangle

45. −10 −8 −6 −4 −2 0 2 4 6 8 10

47. −10 −8 −6 −4 −2 0 2 4 6 8 10

49. −10 −8 −6 −4 −2 0 2 4 6 8 10

11-3 Exercises

1. III **3.** I **5.** (1, 2)

7–9.

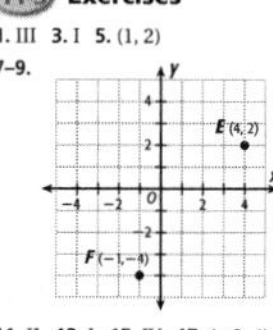

11. II **13.** I **15.** IV **17.** (−2, 4) **19.** (4, 4) **21.** (−3, 0)

23.

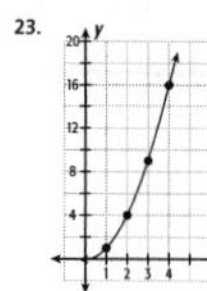

25.

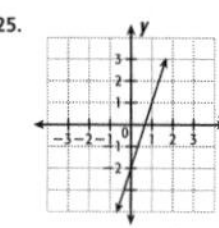

27.

29. I **31.** III **33.** IV **35.** III

37–47.

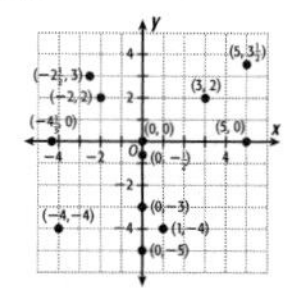

49. Gabon **55.** B **57.** 4.4 **59.** 5.75 **61.** 0.2 **63.** < **65.** <

11-4 Exercises

1. 3 + 2 = 5 **3.** −5 **5.** 7 **7.** 4 **9.** 0 **11.** −17 **13.** −22 **15.** 6 + (−2) = 4 **17.** 11 **19.** 0 **21.** −6 **23.** −7 **25.** −16 **27.** −8 **29.** −2 **31.** 2 **33.** 29 feet

35.

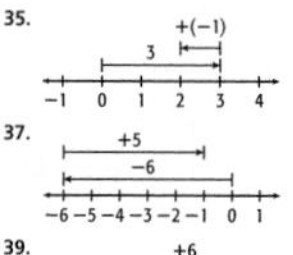

37. +5, −6; −6 −5 −4 −3 −2 −1 0 1

39. +6, −1; −3 −2 −1 0 1 2 3 4 5 6

41. +(−1), −3; −5 −4 −3 −2 −1 0

43. 7 **45.** −11 **47.** −9 **49.** 17 **51.** 4 **53.** −1 **55.** −17 **57.** −6°F **63.** H **65.** 125 **67.** 81 **69.** 2,401

71–73.

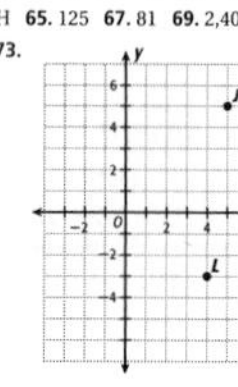

11-5 Exercises

1. 6 − 5 = 1 **3.** −3 **5.** −8 **7.** 8 **9.** 13 **11.** −4 **13.** 11 **15.** 2 **17.** −5 **19.** 7 **21.** −12 **23.** −6 **25.** −1 **27.** 21 **29.** 30 **31.** 12 **33.** 4 **35.** −38 **37.** −19 m **39.** 9°F **43.** D **45.** 2% **47.** 26% **49.** 310% **51.** II **53.** III

11-6 Exercises

1. 24 **3.** −21 **5.** 9 **7.** 16 **9.** 9 **11.** 33 **13.** −24 **15.** 18 **17.** 45 **19.** −32 **21.** 39 **23.** −72 **25.** −24 **27.** −12 **29.** 40 **31.** 60 **33.** 14 **35.** 54 **37.** −90 **39.** 4 ft to −4 ft **45.** positive; negative **47.** 9 **49.** −13 **51.** −3

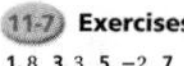

11-7 Exercises

1. 8 **3.** 3 **5.** −2 **7.** −15 **9.** 5 **11.** −8 **13.** 6 **15.** 2 **17.** 1 **19.** 3 **21.** 16 **23.** 14 **25.** −6 **27.** 1 **29.** 10 **31.** −7 **33.** 3 **35.** 8 **37.** −3 **39.** 6 **41.** −11 **43a.** −300 **43b.** a decrease of 300 seals from 1976 to 1980 **45.** −20 **47.** 500 **48.** A **49.** G **50.** 6 cm **51.** 7 m **52.** −1 **53.** 11 **54.** −9 **55.** 0 **56.** 20

11-8 Exercises

1. $m = 12$ **3.** $z = 9$ **5.** $p = -9$ **7.** $g = 8$ **9.** $b = -8$ **11.** $c = -7$ **13.** $f = -6$ **15.** $r = -9$ **17.** $g = 4$ **19.** $t = -14$ **21.** $x = -14$ **23.** $w = -10$ **25.** $j = 8$ **27.** $a = -52$ **29.** $m = -48$ **31.** $u = -60$ **33.** $x = 17$ **35.** $k = -4$ **37.** $m = -15$ **39.** $n = -3$ **41.** $g = -3$ **43.** $f = -8$ **45.** $d = 33$ **47.** $h = -84$ **49.** $b = 32$ **51.** $a = 8$ **53.** $t = -55$ **55.** $c = -13$ **57.** $n = -4$ **59.** $j = -3$ **61.** 70 dives **63.** −4 **65.** $x = -18{,}5000$, sponge **67.** −24 ft **71.** D **73.** always **75.** −35 **77.** 12 **79.** 32

11-9 Exercises

1. 15 **3.** $j = b - 6$ **7.** $c = 12s - 2$ **9.** $p = 150m$ **11.** −54 **13.** −3; 1 **15.** Let c be the total cost and h be the number of hours. $c = \$125 + \$55h$ **17.** 9 hours **23.** G **25.** $x = 3.9$ **27.** $p = 52$ **29.** 706.5 ft³

11-10 Exercises

1. (1, 8); (2, 14); (3, 20); (4, 26) **3.** no **5.** 2 **7.** 0

9.

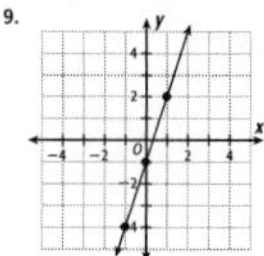

11. (1, −3); (2, −7); (3, −11); (4, −15) **13.** yes **15.** 1 **17.** 0 **19.** 2

21.

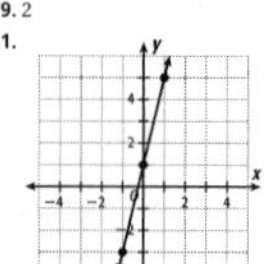

23.

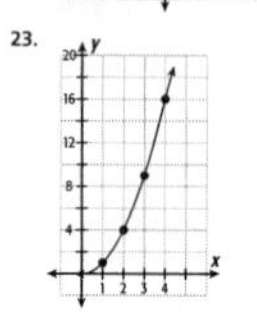

25.

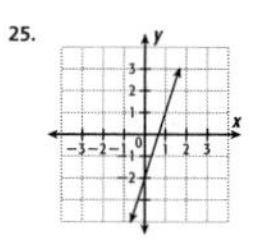

27. −3; −2; −1; 0 **29.** (1, 14)

31.

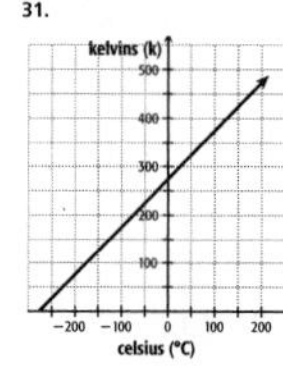

Additional Answers

Chapter 1

1-2 Exercises

29. How does the size of Lake Superior compare with the size of Lake Erie?

30. Possible answer: Round each area to the nearest thousand and then subtract.

38. 200 + 60 + 9

39. 1,000 + 300 + 50 + 4

40. 30,000 + 2,000 + 400 + 90 + 8

41. 400,000 + 10,000 + 6,000 + 700 + 3

1-3 Exercises

38. 4

39. $1 \times 1 \times 1 \times 1 \times 1 \times 1 \times 1 \times 1 \times 1$

40. $17 \times 17 \times 17 \times 17 \times 17 \times 17$

41. $8 \times 8 \times 8 \times 8 \times 8$

42. $12 \times 12 \times 12 \times 12$

1-5 Exercises

58. Possible answer:
17 + (9 + 3)
17 + (3 + 9) Commutative
(17 + 3) + 9 Associative
20 + 9 Simplify.
29 Add.

60. Possible answer: 5(50 + 3) is multiplying a number by a sum. The 5 can be multiplied by each of the numbers in the parentheses or by the sum, 53. 5(50) + 3 does not multiply a number by a sum. You must follow the order of operations and multiply 5(50) before adding 3.

1-6 Exercises

For Exercises 7–13, the calculation method depends on the individual's skill level. Possible methods are given.

7. 111; pencil and paper

8. 55; pencil and paper

9. 515,844; calculator

10. 575; pencil and paper

11. 210; mental math

12. 298; mental math

13. 350; mental math

16. Possible answer: Use paper and pencil if the numbers are small but not easy to work with. Use mental math if the numbers are small and easy to work with. Use a calculator if there are several large numbers.

Chapter 2

2-2 Exercises

8. the sum of *r* and 87; *r* plus 87

9. the product of 345 and 196; 345 times 196

10. the quotient of 476 and 28; 476 divided by 28

11. the difference of *d* and 5; 5 less than *d*

20. 65 added to *h*; 65 more than *h*

21. take away 19 from 243; 243 minus 19

22. the quotient of 125 and *n*; 125 divided by n

23. 75 multiplied by 342; the product of 342 and 75

24. the quotient of *d* and 27; *d* divided by 27

25. the product of 45 and 23; 45 times 23

26. the sum of 629 and *c*; *c* more than 629

27. the difference of 228 and *b*; *b* less than 228

34. Manda; Possible answer: *s* represents the number of pairs of shoes, 2*s* represents the number of shoes.

35. Possible answer: James is 5 years older than his sister Kate. Let *x* represent Kate's age. The expression *x* + 5 represents James' age.

38. Possible answer: What is the difference between the total number of missions *t* and the number of missing missions from 1966 to 1970?

39. Possible answer: Subtraction; the total missions minus the manned missions yields the number of unmanned missions.

42. $x - 280$; Possible answer: The number of miles from Ames to Canton is represented by *x*; Tim has *x* miles, minus 280, left to travel; the difference between *x* and 280; 280 less than *x*.

2-3 Exercises

8. $2n$

Position	1	2	3	4	*n*
Value of Term	2	4	6	8	

9. $n + 5$

Position	1	2	3	4	*n*
Value of Term	6	7	8	9	

10. $10n$

Position	1	2	3	4	*n*
Value of Term	10	20	30	40	

14. Substitute the values 1, 2, 3, 4, and so on, for *n* in the expression. Make a table showing each number and the corresponding value of the expression.

15. Yes; for example, expressions n^2 and $3n - 2$ both describe the data in this table:

Position (*n*)	Value of Term
1	1
2	4

2-4 Exercises

42. Substitute 8 for *x* and find the distance around the base. 8 + 8 + (8 + 3) + (8 + 3) = 38. The base is 36, so the width can not be 8 ft.

2-6 Exercises

30. The value of *n* is greater than or equal to 15. Any number less than 15 will result in a negative number.

31. The student subtracted 17 from 51 instead of doing the inverse operation, addition.

Chapter 3

3-1 Exercises

42. Possible answer: Writing *hundred* after *four* was the error. The 4 is in the ones position. Correct answer: four and twenty-two hundredths.

3-3 Hands-On Lab

Activity 2

Try This

1. 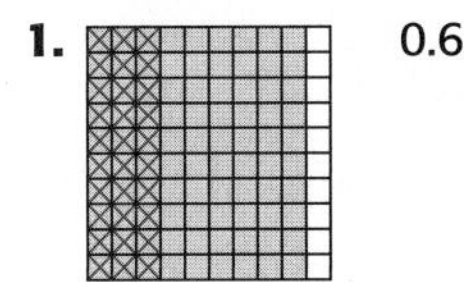 0.6

2. 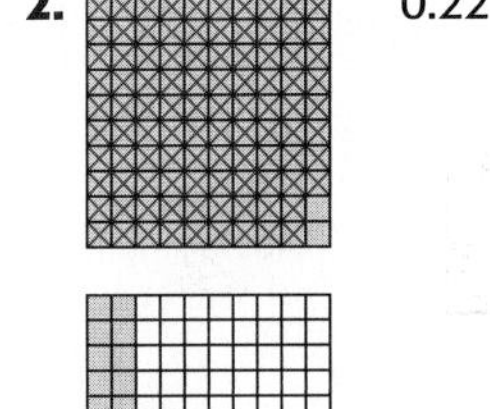 0.22

3. 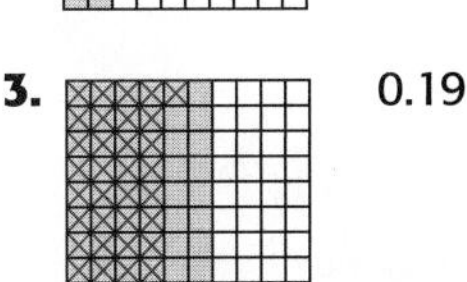 0.19

4. 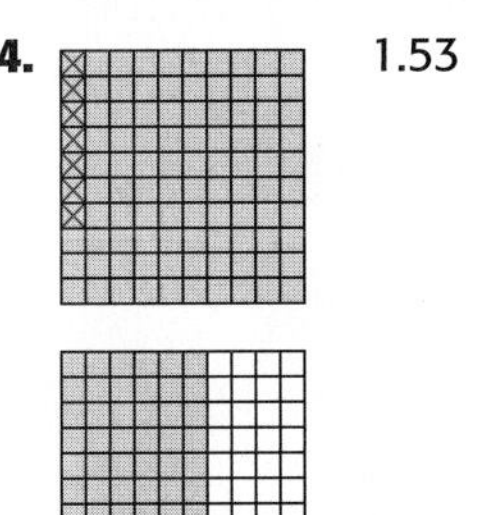 1.53

5. 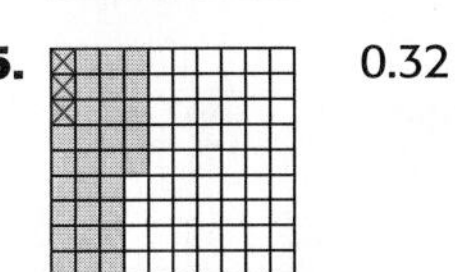 0.32

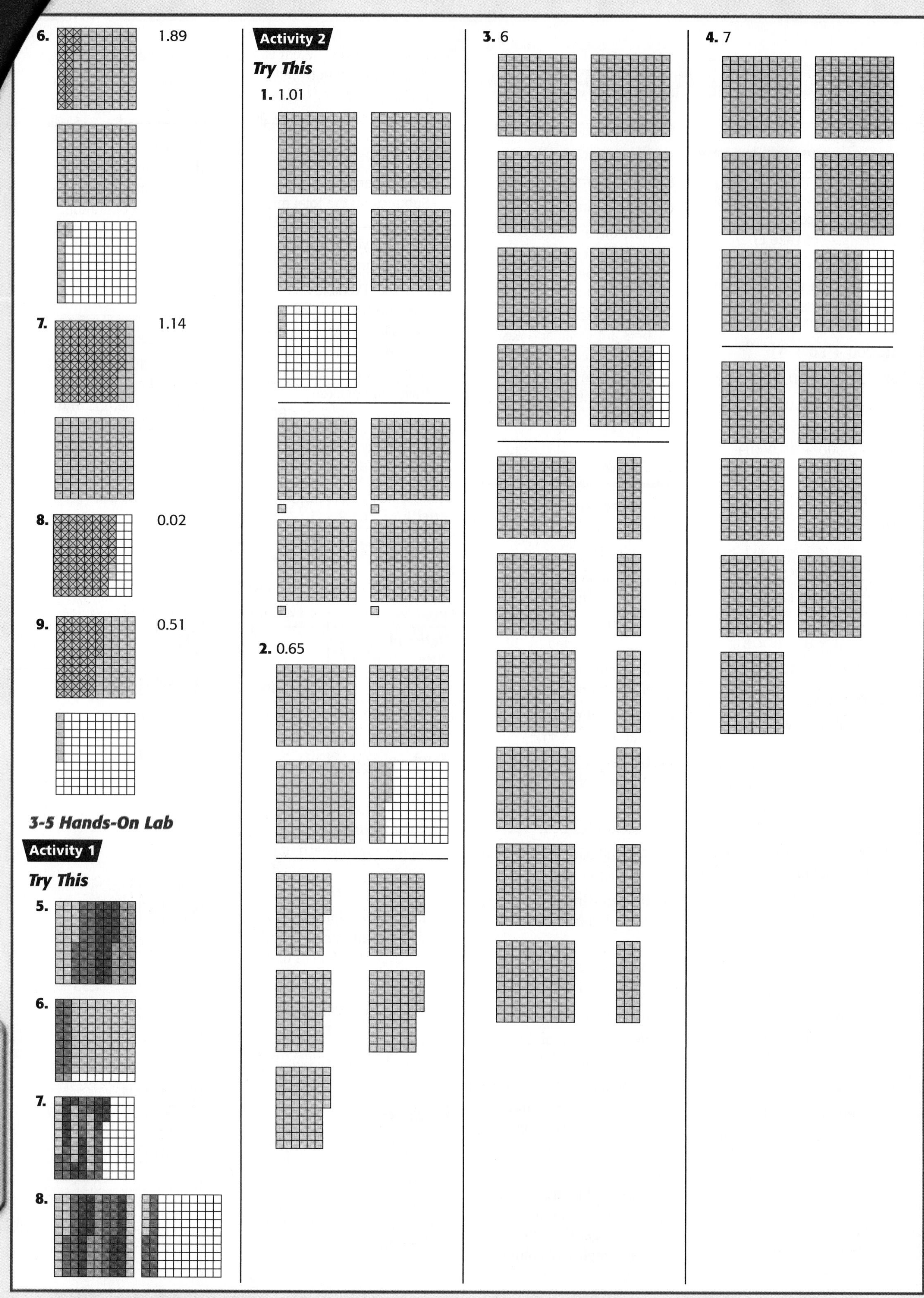
6.
1.89
7.
1.14
8.
0.02
9.
0.51
3-5 Hands-On Lab
Activity 1
Try This
5.
6.
7.
8.
Activity 2
Try This
1. 1.01
2. 0.65
3. 6
4. 7
Additional Answers

5.

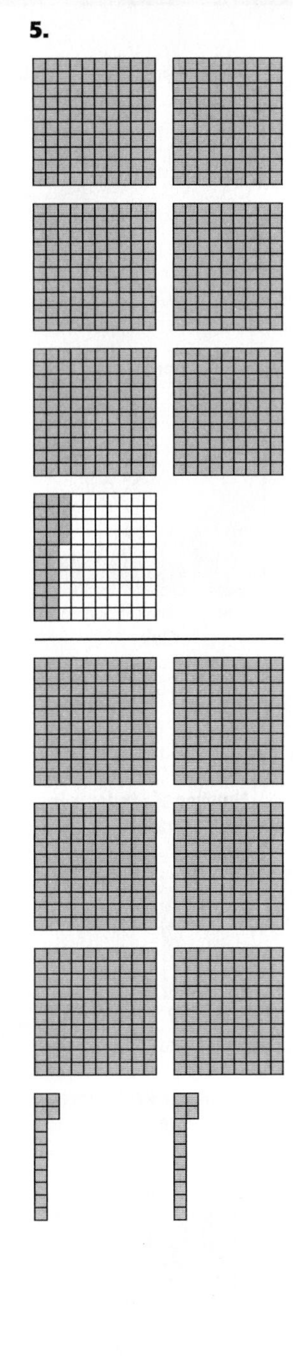

6.

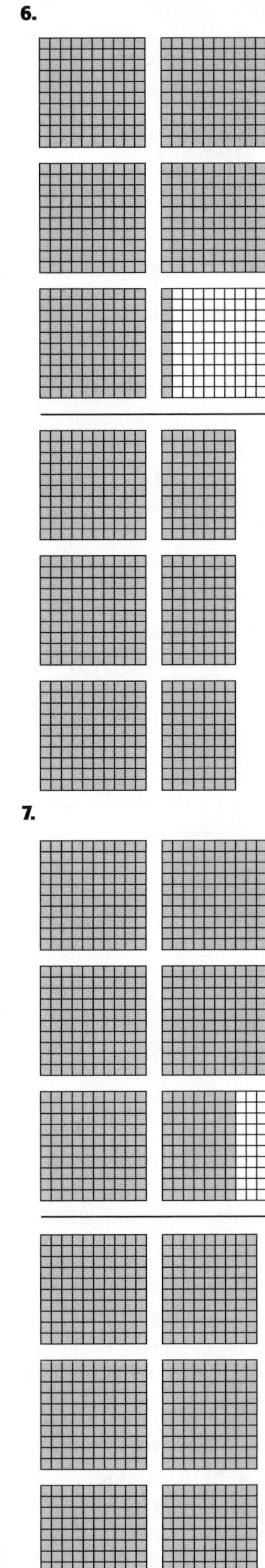

7.

8.

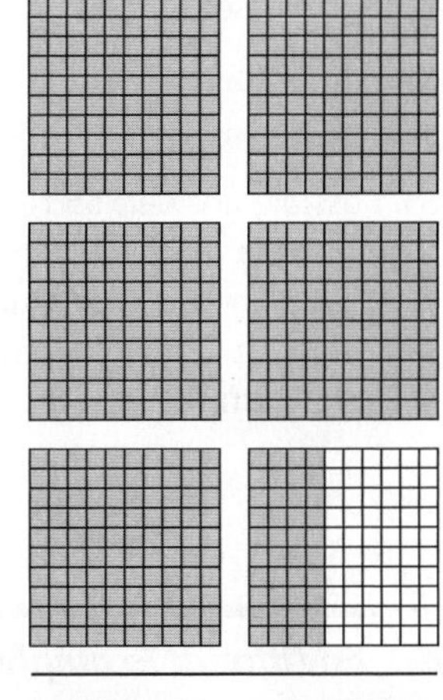

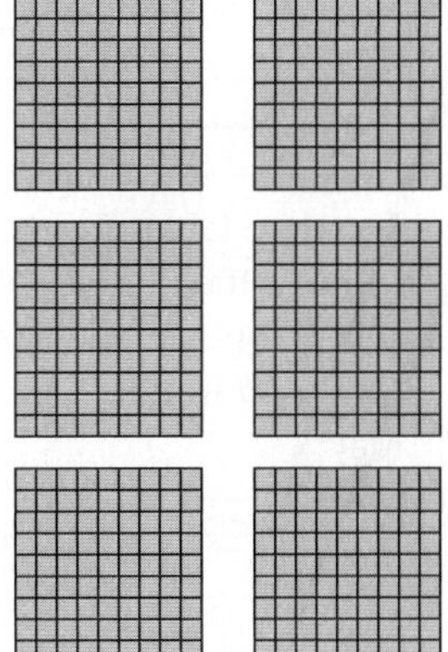

Chapter 4

4-3 Exercises

40. 2^2 and 3 are factors of 12 and 24. $2^2 \cdot 3 = 12$, so 12 is the GCF of 12 and 24.

4-4 Exercises

56. Peter; $1\frac{3}{5} = 1\frac{6}{10} > 1\frac{5}{10} = 1.5$

4-5 Exercises

47. Baskets and wreaths are $\frac{12}{72} = \frac{1}{6}$; jewelry is $\frac{32}{72} = \frac{4}{9}$; glass and pottery are $\frac{16}{72} = \frac{2}{9}$; paintings are $\frac{12}{72} = \frac{1}{6}$.

48. Use two of the $\frac{1}{4}$ tsp measuring spoons; four of the $\frac{1}{8}$ tsp measuring spoons.

49. There are an unlimited number of fractions equivalent to $\frac{1}{4}$. You can continue to multiply the numerator and denominator by the same number to find some equivalent fractions.

4-7 Exercises

54. No and yes. $\frac{1}{2} > \frac{2}{5}$ because $\frac{5}{10} > \frac{4}{10}$. Kevin needs $\frac{5}{10}$ gallon of milk, but he only has $\frac{4}{10}$ gallon. $3.5 < \frac{21}{5}$ because $3\frac{1}{2} < 4\frac{1}{5}$. He needs $3\frac{1}{2}$ lb of potatoes, and he has $4\frac{1}{5}$ lb.

4-9 Exercises

35. Possible answer: Estimate the fraction part of each mixed number. Add the fractions, and then add the whole numbers.

$5\frac{1}{3} + 8\frac{7}{8}$. Round $5\frac{1}{3}$ to $5\frac{1}{2}$, because $\frac{1}{3}$ is closer to $\frac{1}{2}$ than to 0. Round $8\frac{7}{8}$ to 9, because $\frac{7}{8}$ is closer to 1 than to $\frac{1}{2}$. The estimated sum is $14\frac{1}{2}$.

Extension

1. A: 0, 2, 4, 6, …

B: 1, 3, 5, 7, …

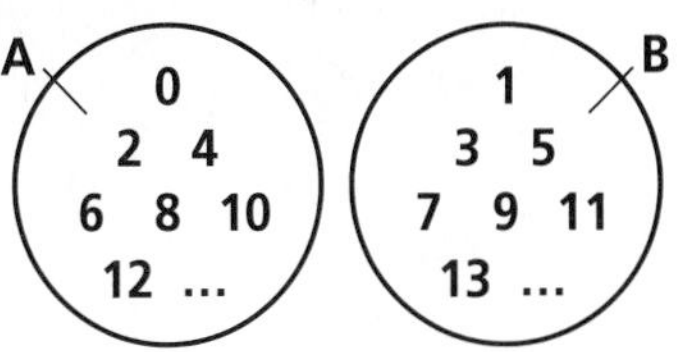

intersection: empty

union: all whole numbers

2. A: 1, 2, 3, 6, 9, 18

B: 1, 2, 4, 5, 8, 10, 20, 40

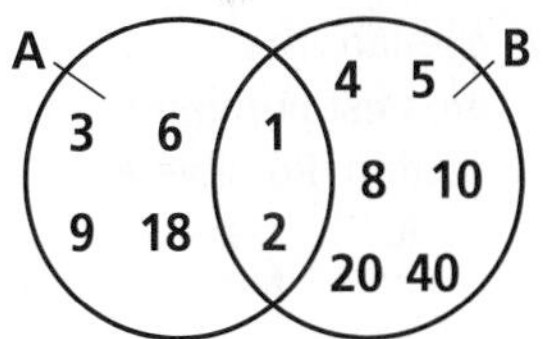

intersection: 1, 2

union: 1, 2, 3, 4, 5, 6, 8, 9, 10, 18, 20, 40

3. A: 1, 2, 3, 4, 6, 8, 9, 12, 18, 24, 36, 72

B: 1, 2, 3, 4, 6, 9, 12, 18, 36

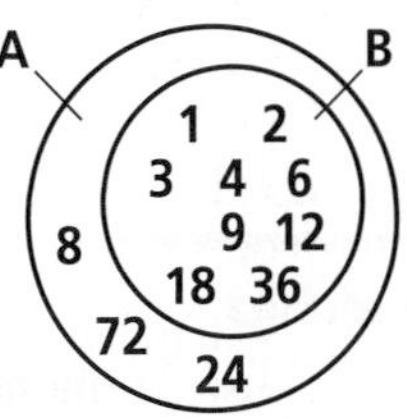

intersection: 1, 2, 3, 4, 6, 9, 12, 18, 36

union: 1, 2, 3, 4, 6, 8, 9, 12, 18, 24, 36, 72

4. A: 2, 4, 6, 8, 10, 12, …

B: 4, 6, 8, 9, 10, 12, 14, 15, …

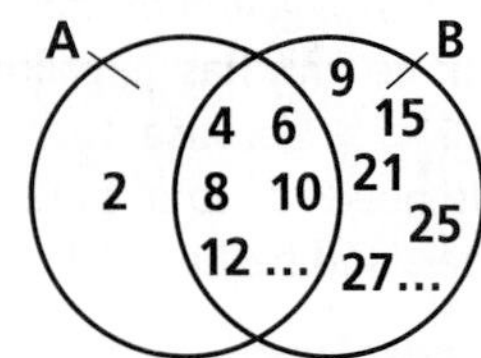

intersection: even numbers except 2

union: 2 and all composite numbers

9. Possible answer: Draw a Venn diagram with set A as the factors of one number and set B as the factors of the other number. The greatest number in the intersection is the GCF. Possible example:

A: factors of 16 B: factors of 24

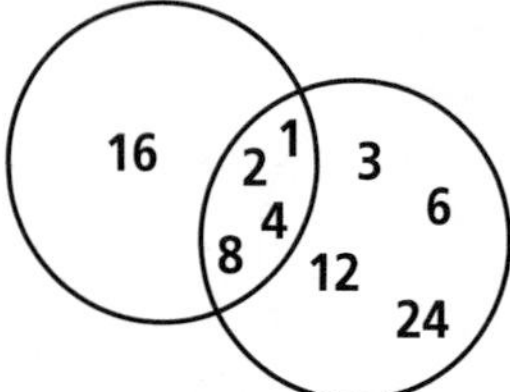

10. Possible answer: Draw 3 circles, one for the factors of each number. Common factors will appear in the area where all three circles overlap. The GCF is the greatest number in this section. Possible example:

A: factors of 36 B: factors of 24 C: factors of 20

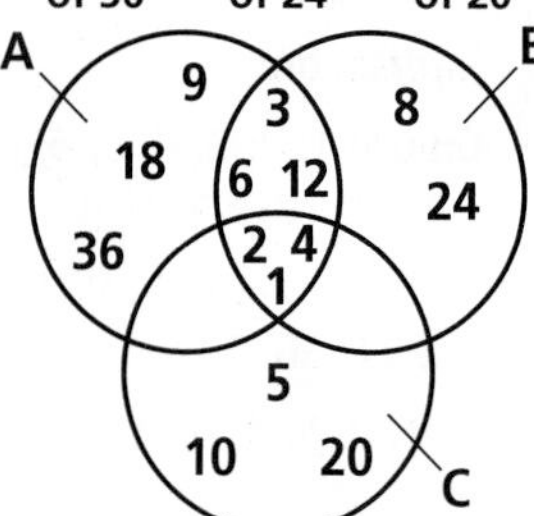

Chapter 5

5-2 Exercises

45. Possible answer: The student subtracted the numerators and denominators in $\frac{7}{8} - \frac{3}{4}$ and got a difference of $\frac{4}{4} = 1$. The correct difference is $\frac{1}{8}$ lb.

46. Possible answer: Subtract $\frac{3}{4} - \frac{3}{5}$. Use the LCD of 20, so $\frac{15}{20} - \frac{12}{20} = \frac{3}{20}$ lb.

5-6 Exercises

53. Possible answer: 55 ft; 55 ft; the answers are the same. One-fifth of a number is the same as dividing a number by 5.

Chapter 6

6-1 Additional Examples

1.

Date	People in Audience
May 1	275
May 2	302
May 3	322

From the table, you can see that the number of people in the audience increased from May 1 to May 3.

2.

Time	Temperature (°F)
3 A.M.	53
5 A.M.	52
7 A.M.	50
9 A.M.	53
11 A.M.	57

The temperature dropped until 7 A.M., then it rose. One conclusion is that on this day the low temperature was 50°F.

6-1 Exercises

1.

Day	High Temperature (°F)
Mon	72
Tue	75
Wed	68
Thu	62
Fri	55

3.

Test	Grade
1st	70
2nd	75
3rd	80
4th	85
5th	90

4. Possible answer: Joe's grades improved steadily over the five exams. Joe will do well on his sixth exam.

5.

Date	Thickness (in.)
December 3	1
December 18	2
January 3	5
January 18	11
February 3	17

Possible answer: It became safe to ice-skate around January 10.

9.

Week	Cars Built
1	2
2	5
3	8
4	11

Possible answer: The number of model cars built increased by 3 each week. At this rate, Ty should build 14 model cars in the 5th week.

6-1 Lesson Quiz

1.

Age	Heart Rate
new born	135
2	110
6	95
10	87
20	71
40	72
60	74

6-3 Exercises

1. a. mean = 4.75, median = 5, no mode

b. mean = 10, median = 7, no mode

2. with: mean = 45.4, median = 42, no mode; without: mean = 40.2, median = 40, no mode

5. with: mean = 710.4, median = 788, no mode; without: mean = 877.75, median = 868, no mode

6-A Ready to Go On

7. with Alaska—mean: 2,395, median: 1,095, no mode; withput Alaska—mean: 980, median: 840, no mode

6-4 Additional Examples

1. a. The coniferous forest has the least average summer temperature.

b. The grasslands and the rain forest have average summer temperatures of 30° or greater.

2.

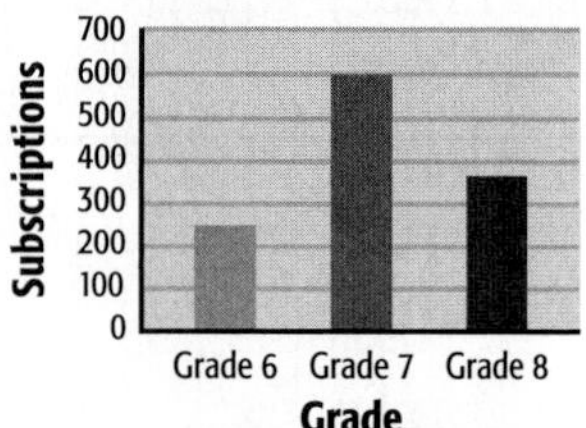

3.

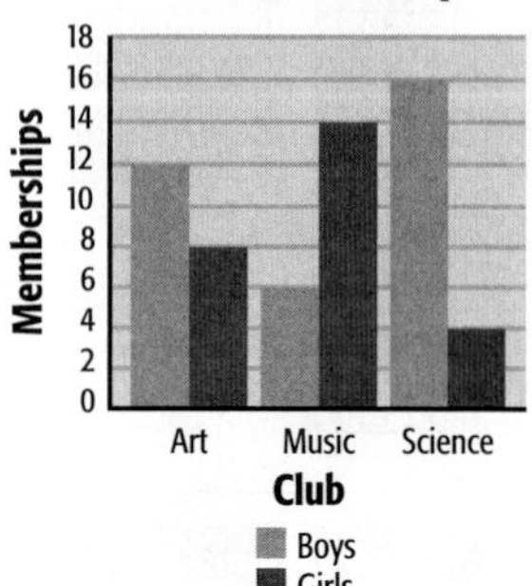

6-4 Exercises

3.

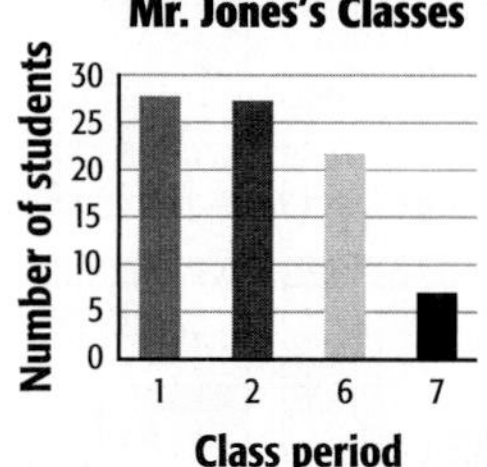

4.

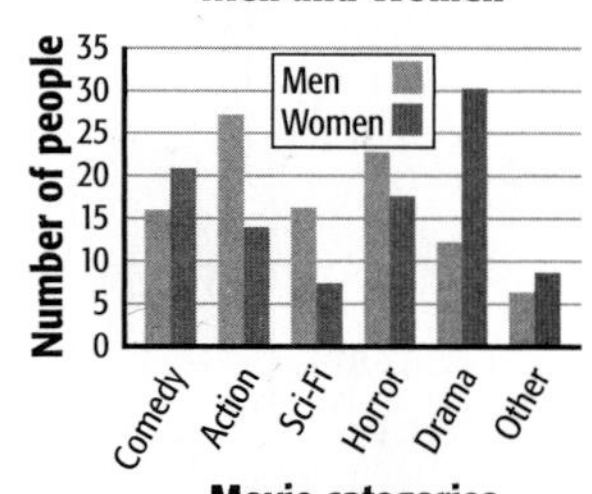

7.

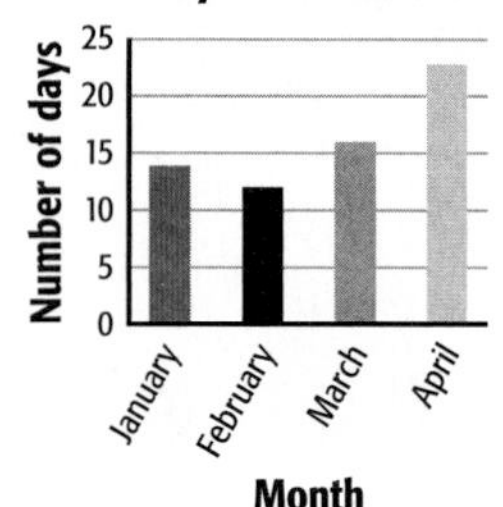

8. Heart Rates (Beats per Minute) Before and After Exercise

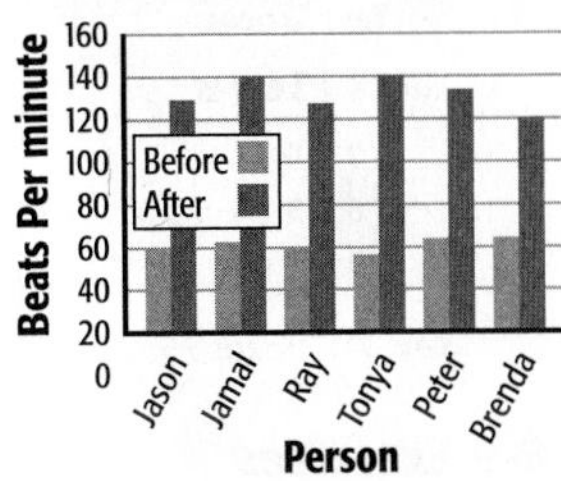

13a. Scores of Practice Games

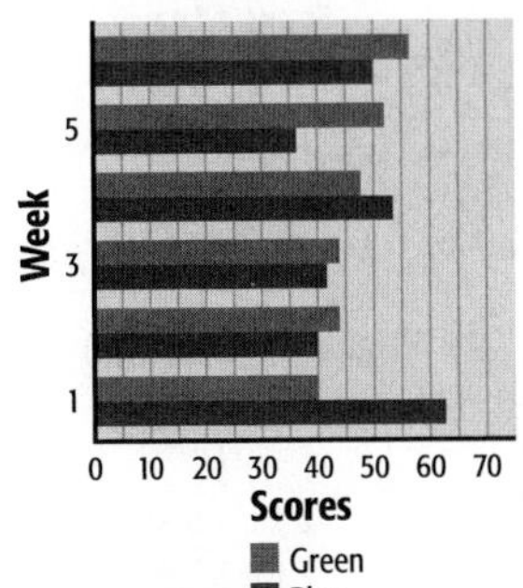

14. Possible answer: Find the five most populated cities in an up-to-date reference book. Draw the axes. Label the vertical axis "Population." Choose an appropriate scale. Mark off equal intervals from 0 to your maximum. Label the horizontal axis "Cities," and list the cities. For each city, draw a bar. Give the graph a title.

15. Ms. Walker's Grades

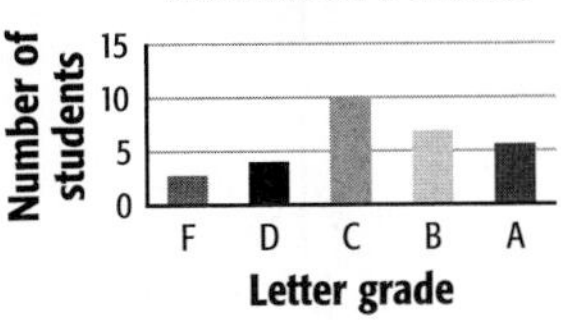

6-4 Lesson Quiz

3. Number of Daily Servings

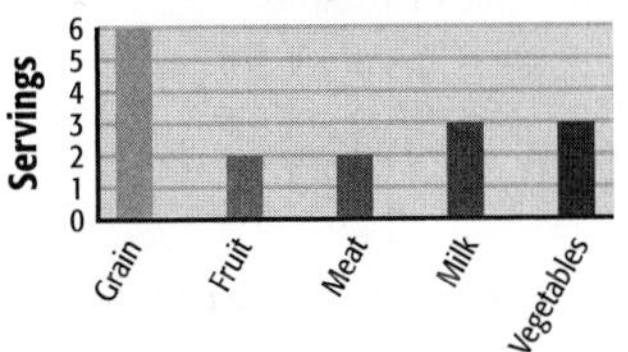

6-5 Additional Examples

2.

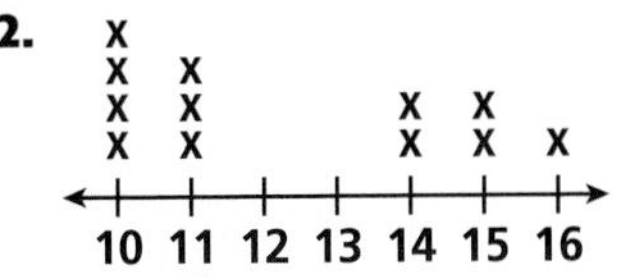

3.

Pages Read Last Week					
Pages	0–9	10–19	20–29	30–39	40–49
Frequency	2	4	1	2	1

4.

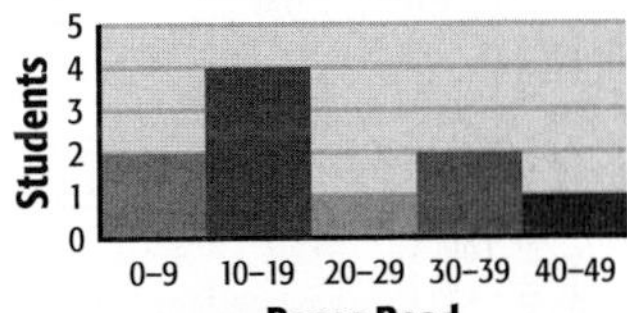

6-5 Exercises

1.

Type of Instrument	
Trumpet	卌
Drums	II
Tuba	I
Trombone	III
French horn	IIII

Tuba

2.

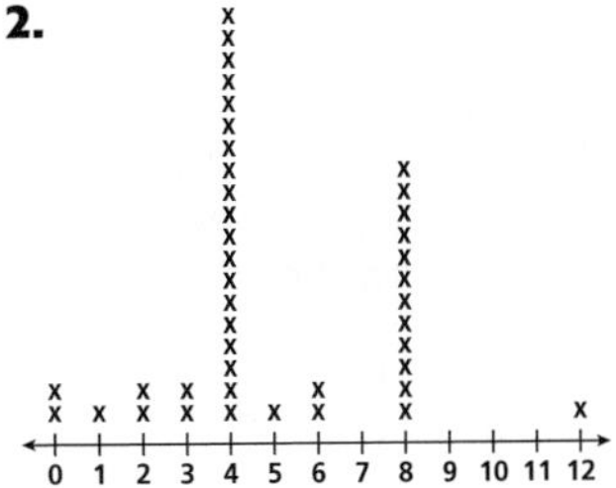

3.

Number of Years of Each Presidential Term				
Number (Intervals)	0–3	4–7	8–11	12–15
Frequency	7	22	12	1

4. Number of Years of Each Presidential Term

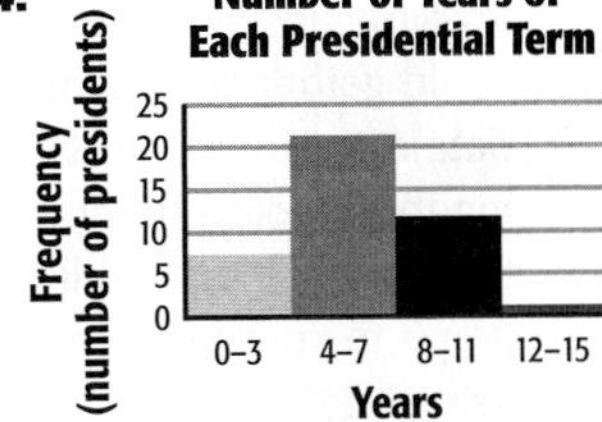

5.

Pets	
Dog	卌 I
Cat	卌
Bird	IIII
Fish	III
Hamster	II

Dog

6.

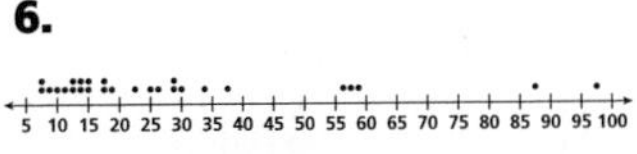

7.

Final Medal Standing at the Summer Olympic Games for the Top 25 Countries					
Number (intervals)	1–20	21–40	41–60	61–80	81–100
Frequency	14	8	3	0	2

8. Number of Olympic Medals Won

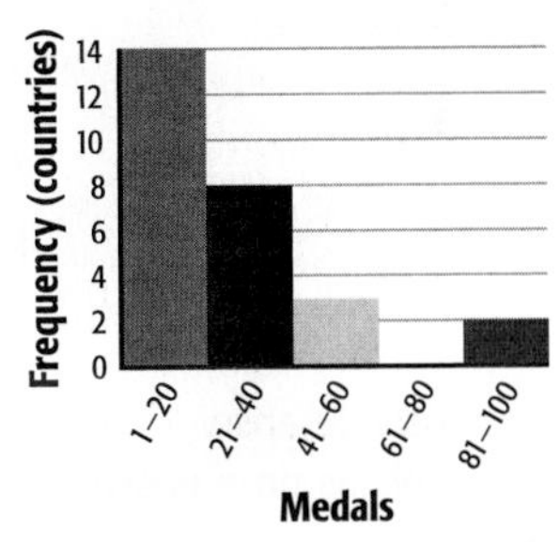

11.

Populations of Australia's States and Territories	
Census	Frequency
0–999,999	3
1,000,000–1,999,999	2
2,000,000–2,999,999	0
3,000,000–3,999,999	1
4,000,000–4,999,999	1
5,000,000–5,999,999	0
6,000,000–6,999,999	1

12. Populations of Australia's States and Territories

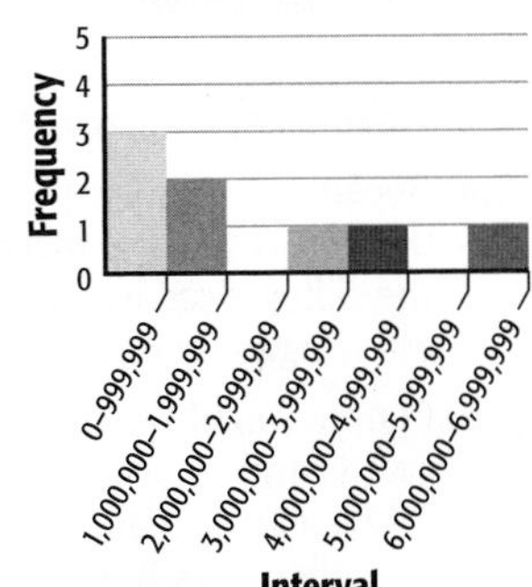

18.

Number of Goals Scored Each Game				
Goals	0–2	3–5	6–8	9–11
Frequency	4	9	3	1

6-5 Lesson Quiz

1.

Number of Days Spent on Vacation				
Days	0–4	5–9	10–14	15–19
Frequency	卌	III	卌 I	IIII

2.

Number of Days Spent on Vacation				
Days	0–4	5–9	10–14	15–19
Frequency	5	3	6	4

6-6 Exercises

7–10.

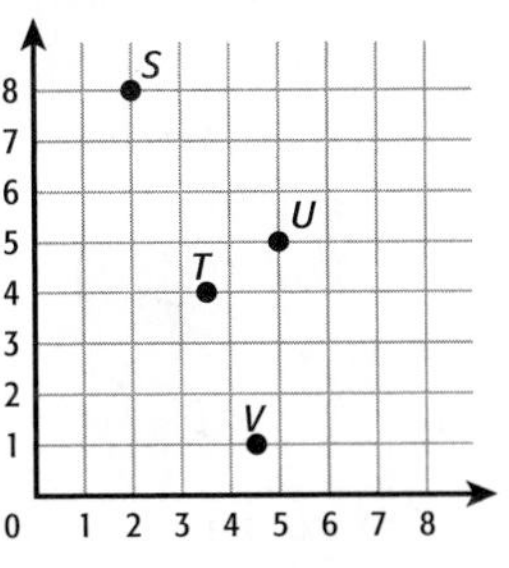

17–22.

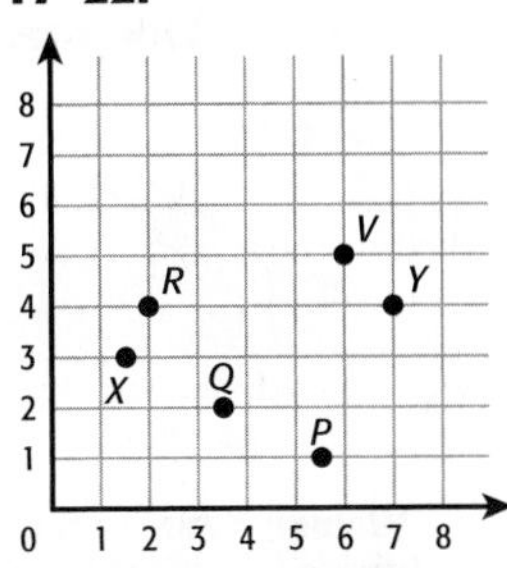

35. $(5\frac{1}{2}, 0)$; The fourth corner would have the x-coordinate of *B* and a y-coordinate of *M*.

36. The point located at (3, 2) will be one unit farther to the right of (2, 3) and one unit lower.

6-6 Lesson Quiz

5–6.

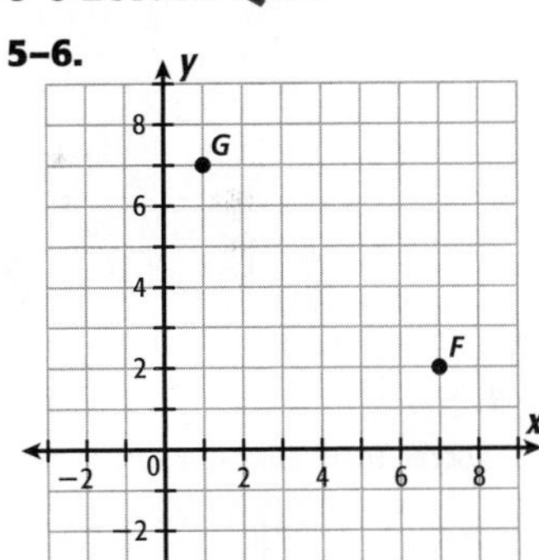

6-7 Additional Examples

1. Population of New Hampshire

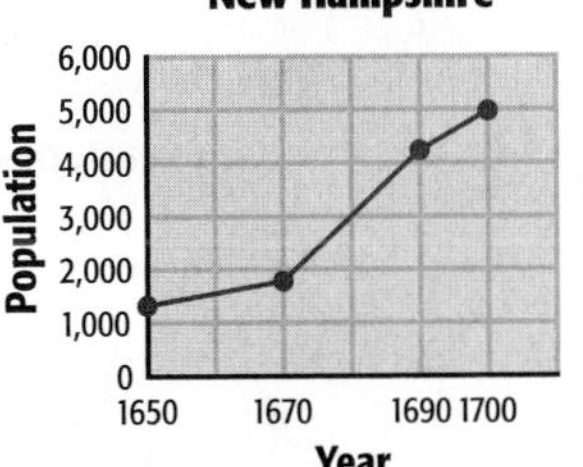

2. Stock Prices

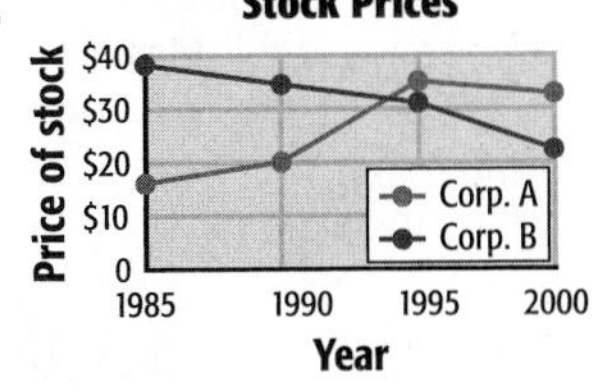

Additional Answers

6-7 Exercises

1. School Enrollment

4,000
3,000
2,000
1,000
0
Students
2000 2001 2002 2003
Year

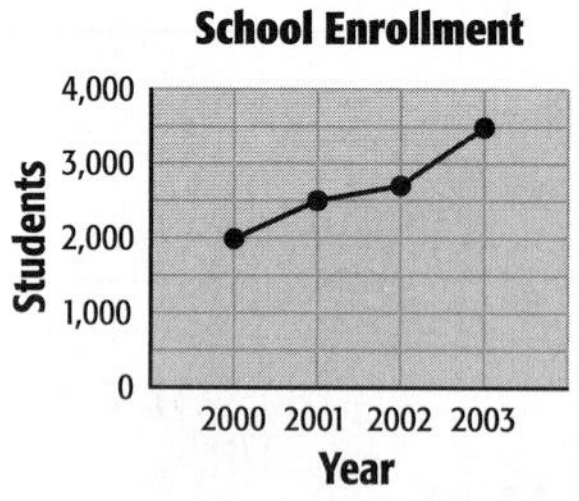

5. Comparison of Stock Prices

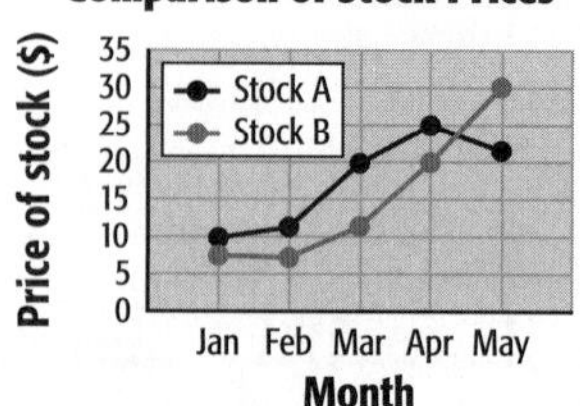

6. Winning Times in the Iditarod Dog Sled Race

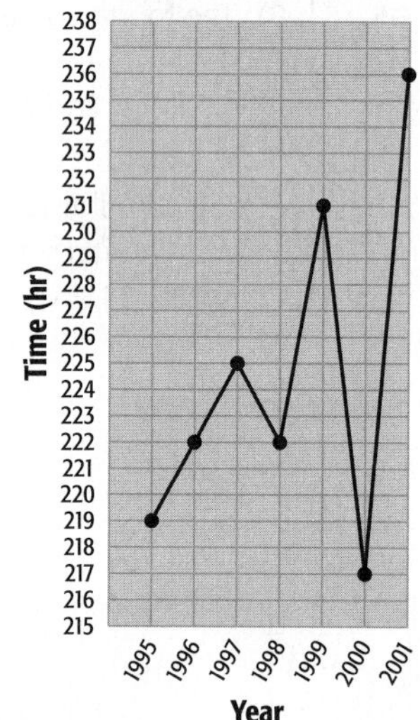

9. Soccer Team Fund-Raising Efforts

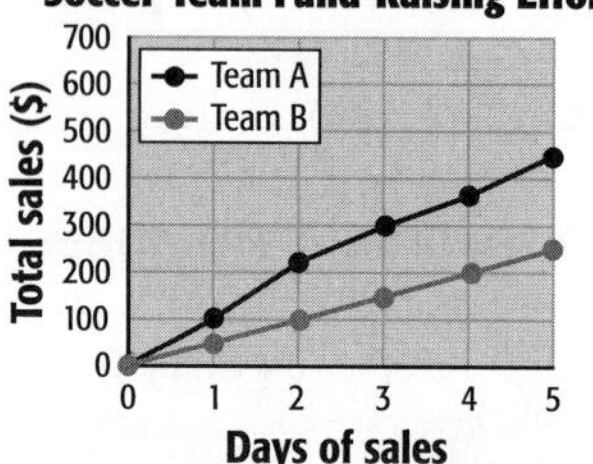

12. Sara Beth's Dogs

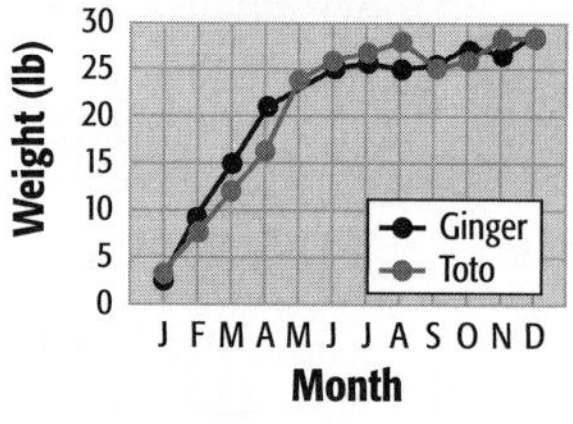

13. Soup's Temperature During Lunch

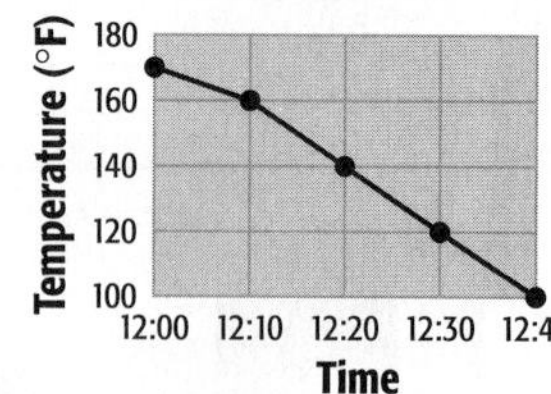

Possible answer: The soup cools as time passes.

21. Tickets

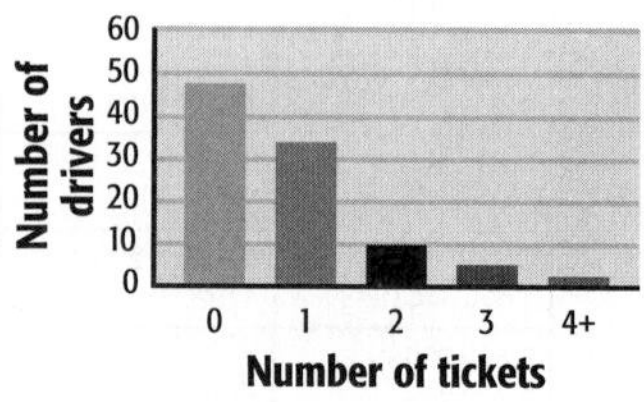

6-7 Lesson Quiz

1. Aluminum Cans Collected

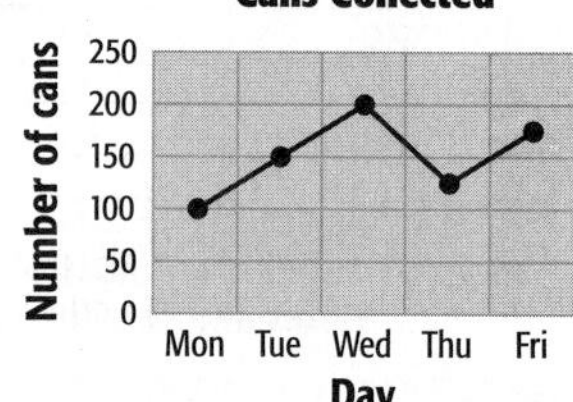

6-8 Additional Examples

1.a. Because the lower part of the vertical axis is missing, the differences in prices are exaggerated.

b. People might believe that cars B and C cost $1\frac{1}{2}$ to $2\frac{1}{2}$ times as much as Car A. In reality, Cars B abd C are only a few thousand dolllars more than Car A.

2.a. If you look at the scale for each graph, you will notice that the April graph goes form 54° to 66° and the May graph goes from 68° to 80°.

b. People might believe that the temperatures in May were about the same as the temperatures in April. In reality, the temperatures in April were about 15 degrees lower.

c. The scale goes from $0 to $80, and then increases by $5.

6-8 Exercises

9. Strips' Significantly Better

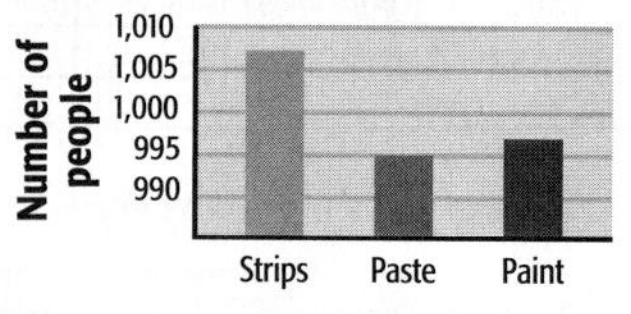

Paste is Most Effective

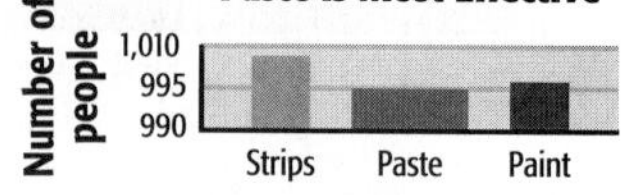

11. Possible answer:

Mean Cholesterol Level of Patients Taking New Drug

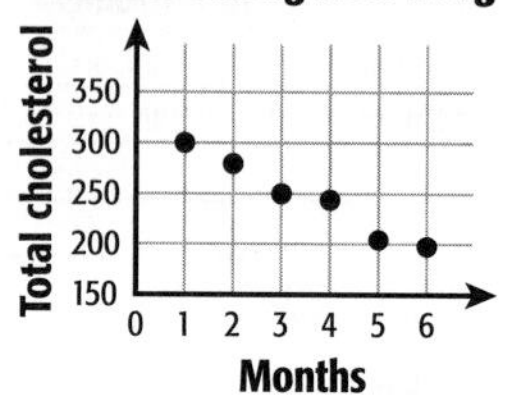

The vertical scale begins at 150.

12. Possible answer:

Effects of Medication on Cholesterol Levels

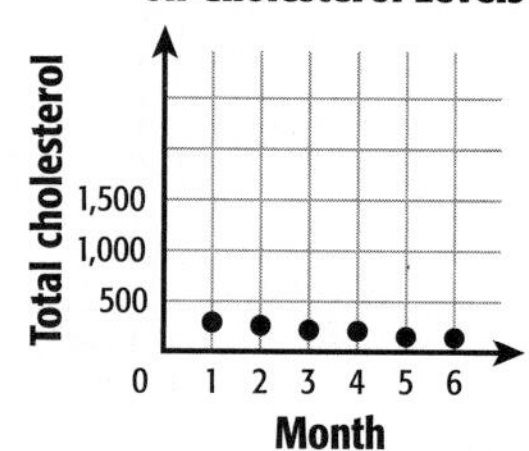

The vertical scale is far too large.

15. Possible answer: They could gather cholesterol data on patients not taking the medication and then make a double-line graph to compare the two sets of data.

17. Possible answers: The temperature was twice as high at 11:00 A.M. as at 10:00 A.M. Start at zero and make each interval in the vertical scale equal.

20-24.

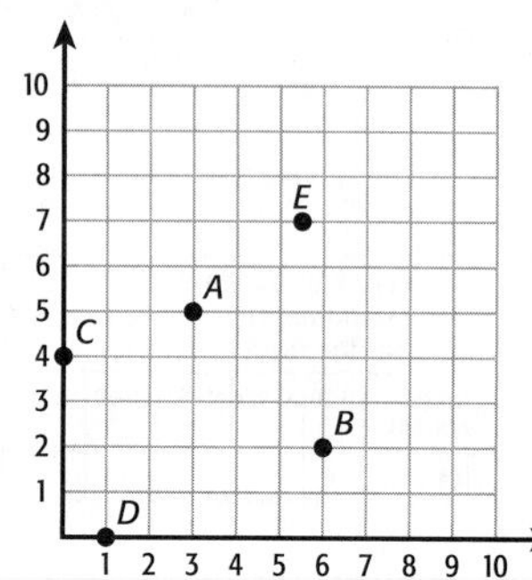

6-9 Additional Examples

1. Test Scores

Stems	Leaves
7	5 9
8	3 4 6 6 8
9	1 4 9

Key: 7|5 means 75

6-9 Exercises

1. Daily High Temperatures (°F)

Stems	Leaves
3	7 9
4	0 5 8
5	1 6

Key: 3|7 means 37

8. Heights of Plants (cm)

Stems	Leaves
1	2 5
2	0 7 8 8
3	0 7
4	0 7

Key: 1|2 means 12

17. Number of Cars with One Passenger

Stems	Leaves
8	0 1 2 3 7 8 9
9	2 4 4 5 9
10	0 1 3 9
11	
12	4 5

Key: 8|0 means 80

19. Ages in Josh's Family

Stems	Leaves
1	3 5 7 9
2	
3	
4	5
5	
6	9

Key: 1|3 means 13

6-9 Lesson Quiz

1.

Stems	Leaves
2	1 2 7 8 9
3	0 1 4 4 5 6
4	0 2 6 9
5	2

Key: 2|1 means 21

Additional Answers

6-10 Additional Examples

1.a.

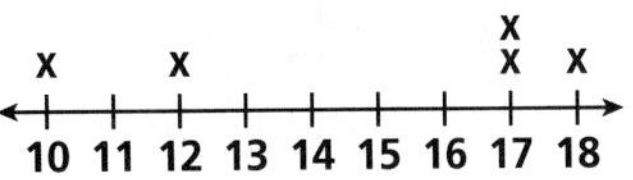

b. **Height of Plants**

Stems	Leaves
1	1 1 4
2	6 7
3	5

2|6 means 26

6-10 Exercises

1.

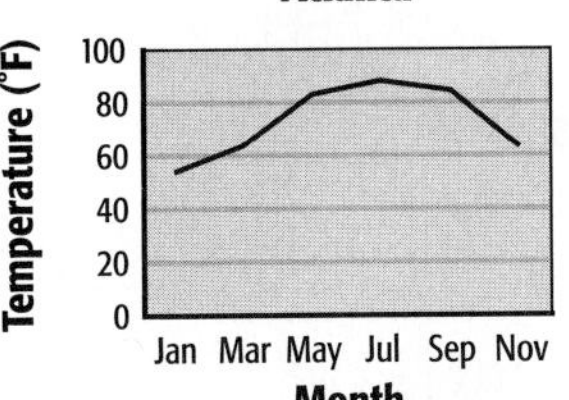

2.

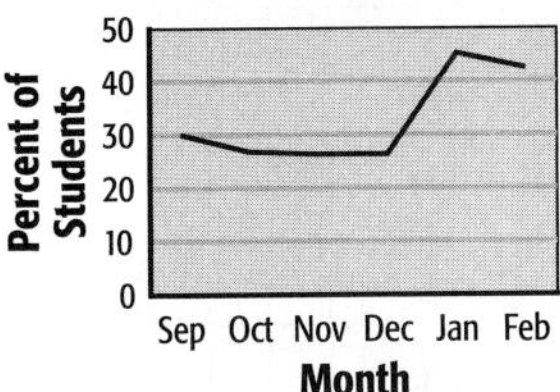

3a. Possible answer: Line graph; it shows change over time.

b.

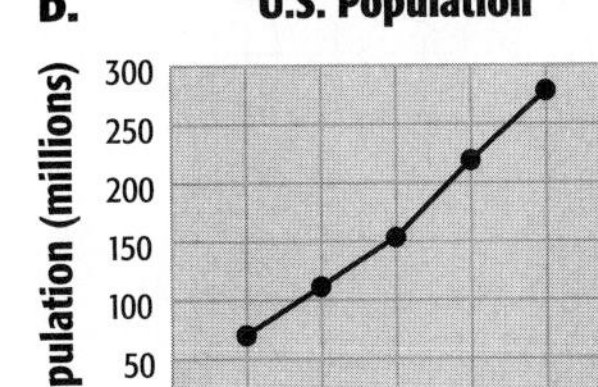

4. a line plot;

20 25 30 35 40 45 50

Possible answer: Out of the 15 bits of data graphed on the line plot, the eighth one, from either direction, is the median. The mode is the location on the number line with the most marks.

5. Possible answer: The zoo's educational center wants to make a poster about animal life spans. How could it best display the information in the table? bar graph

6. Possible answer: Similarities: both graphs organize data; differences: bar graphs show amounts in categories, and line graphs show change over time.

7.

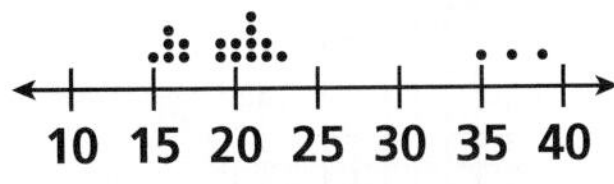

The line plot shows the outliers more clearly.

9. A line plot is best because the frequency of the data will be easily seen.

median = 35

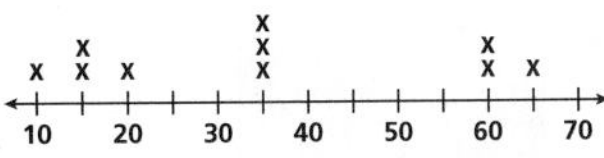

6-B Ready to Go On

5–6.

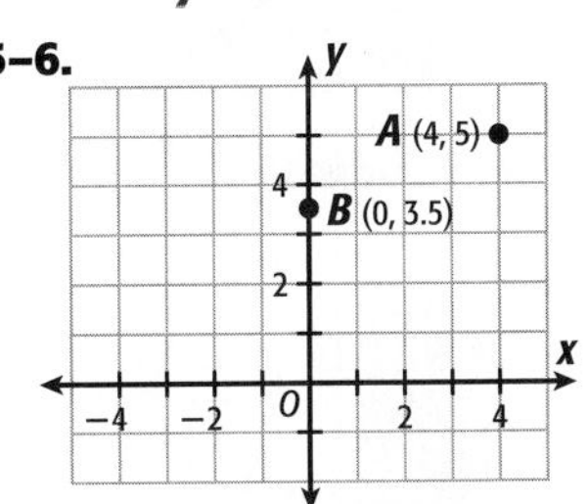

7.

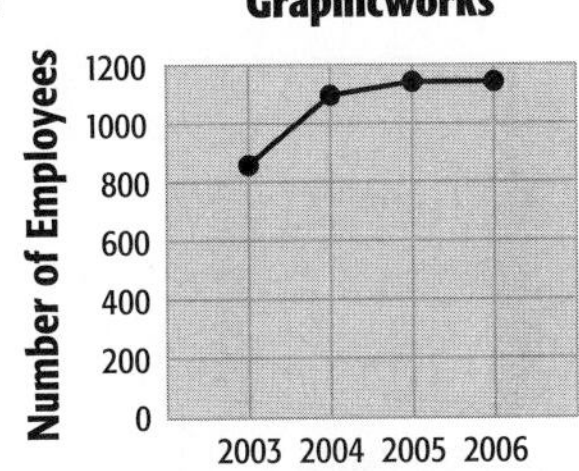

9.

Stems	Leaves
1	5 6 6 6 8 9
2	0 0 0 0 1 1 2 2 2

Key: 1|5 means 15

10. No. A line graph should show changes in data over time. The data in the bar graph shows the number of students who liked each kind of flavored juice.

Multi-Step Test Prep

1.

Treat Yourself to Trail Mix

Ounces	Cost (dollars)
4	1
8	2
12	3
16	4
20	5
24	6

Deet's Treats Trail Mix

Ounces	Cost (dollars)
8	2
16	4
24	6
32	8
40	10
48	12

Trail Mix for Sale

Ounces	Cost (dollars)
4	.50
8	1
12	1.50
16	2
20	2.50
24	3
28	3.50
32	4
36	4.50
40	5

2. Treat Yourself to Trail Mix: This graph is not misleading.

Deet's Treats Trail Mix: it does not take into account that trail mix is available in 4-ounce packages.

Trail Mix for Sale: it does not show correct prices.

Overall, Treat Yourself to Trail Mix is probably the best choice.

3. Since 1 pound equals 16 ounces, 4 pounds equals 64 ounces. Therefore, the price guide should show prices for 4 ounces, 8 ounces, 12 ounces, and so on, up to 64 ounces. To find the cost of any number of ounces, divide the number of ounces by 4.

Price Guide

Ounces	Cost (dollars)
0	0
4	1
8	2
12	3
16	4
20	5
24	6
28	7
32	8
36	9
40	10
44	11
48	12
52	13
56	14

4. There are 9 different ways to purchase 4 pounds of trail mix. The combinations are shown in the table.

Number of 4-ounce Packages	Number of 8-ounce Packages	Total Ounces
0	8	64
2	7	64
4	6	64
6	5	64
8	4	64
10	3	64
12	2	64
14	1	64
16	0	64

Chapter 7

7-1 Exercises

12. 10 to 7, 10:7, $\frac{10}{7}$

13. 24 to 11, 24:11, twenty-four to eleven

14. four to thirty, 4:30, $\frac{4}{30}$

15. 7 to 10, 7:10, seven to ten

16. sixteen to twenty, 16:20, $\frac{16}{20}$

17. 5 to 9, 5:9, five to nine

18. fifty to seventy-nine, 50:79, $\frac{50}{79}$

19. $\frac{100}{101}$, 100:101, 100 to 101

7-2 Exercises

4.

3	5
6	10
9	15
12	20

5.

5	10	15	20
8	16	24	32

6.

9	18	27	36
4	8	12	16

7.

24	12	6	3
16	8	4	2

8.

25	50	75	100
26	52	78	104

10.

6	5
12	10
18	15
24	20

11.

5	8
10	16
15	24
20	24

12.

12	4
24	8
36	12
48	16

13.

6	12	18	48	96
7	14	21	56	112

14.

13	26	39	42
20	40	60	80

15.

11	22	33	44
25	50	75	100

16.

5	10	15	20
18	36	54	72

17.

51	102	153	204
75	150	225	300

7-3 Exercises

23. 113 euros, 160 Canadian dollars, 828 renminbi, 440 shekels, and 910 Mexican pesos.

24. Possible answer: They inverted the x and the 30. The proportion should be $\frac{1}{8.28} = \frac{30}{x}$, and $30 U.S. is equivalent to 248.4 of China's renminbi.

25. Possible answer: U.S. dollars; they are worth more than Canadian dollars.

7-4 Exercises

9. $m\angle H = 80°$, $m\angle J = 80°$, $m\angle Z = 100°$; the length of $\overline{WX}$ is 5.5 yd, the length of $\overline{ZY}$ is 5.5 yd, and the length of $\overline{WZ}$ is 4 yd.

10. Yes; the corresponding angles are equal and the corresponding sides are in proportion.

11. No; the corresponding sides are not in proportion.

15.

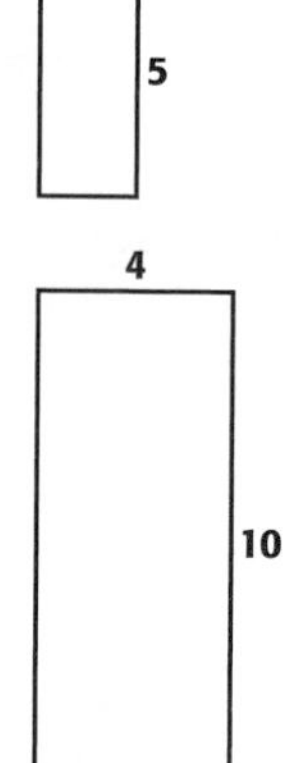

7-6 Exercises

7b–7c.

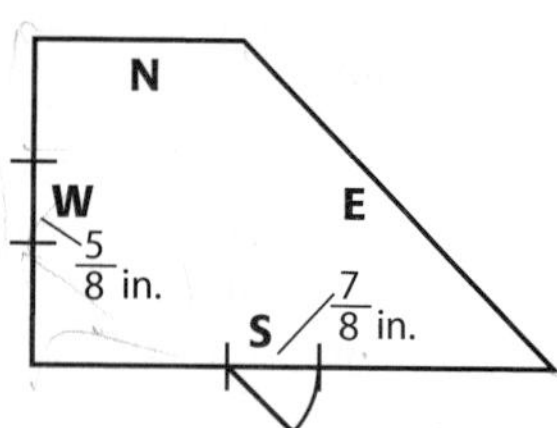

7-7 Hands-On Lab Think and Discuss

1.

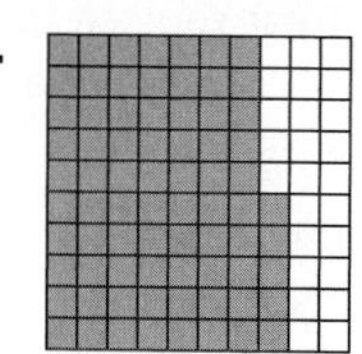

2. Possible answer: Use the proportion $\frac{3}{4} = \frac{x}{100}$ to find the number of squares that should be shaded.

Try This

1.

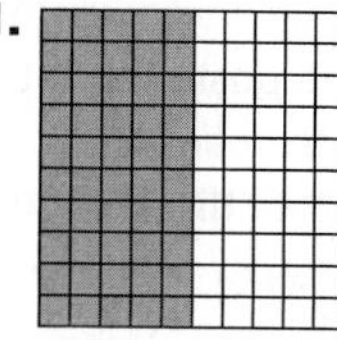

2.

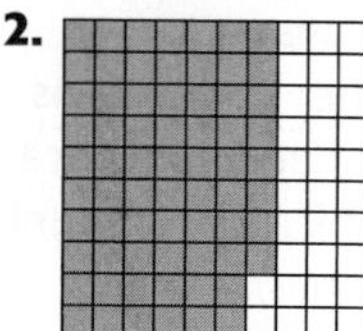

3.

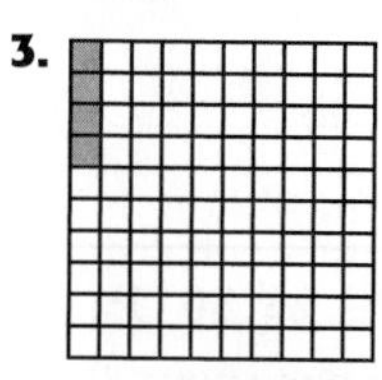

4.

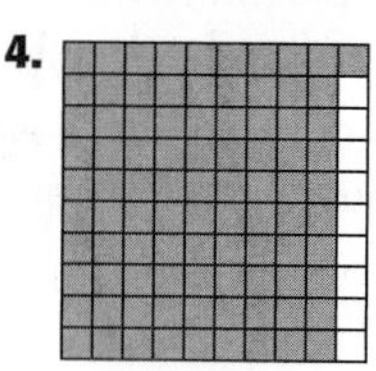

5.

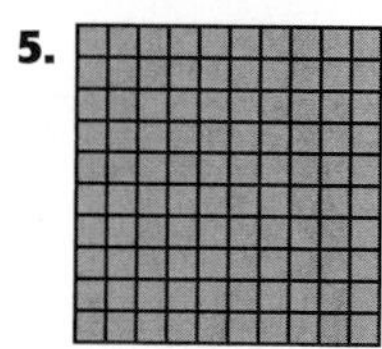

7-7 Exercises

1.

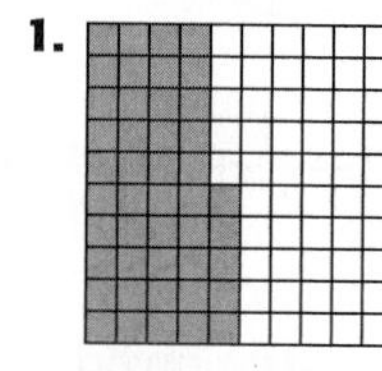

2.

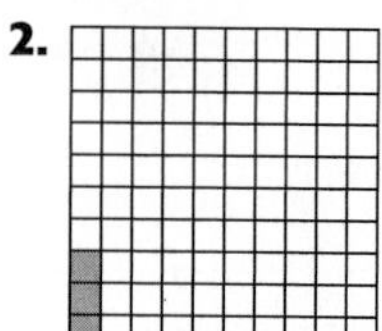

3.

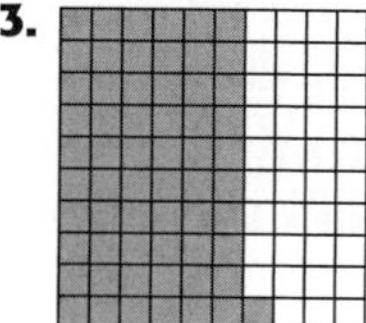

12.

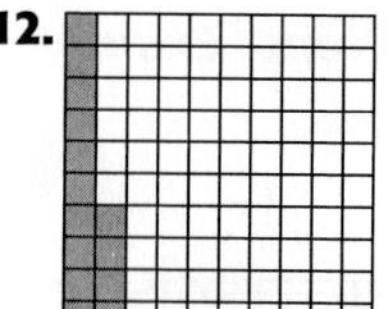

13.

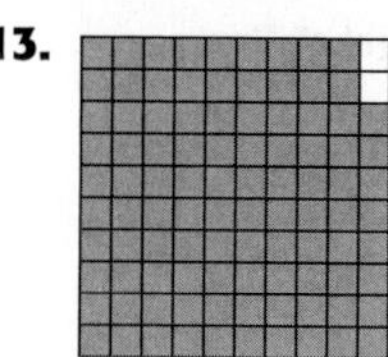

14.

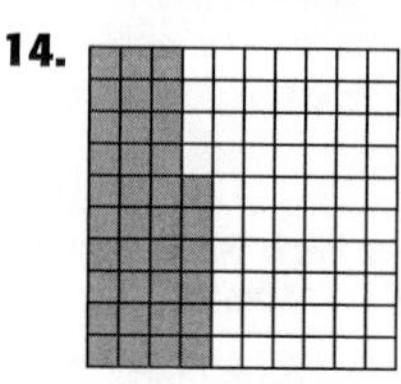

15.

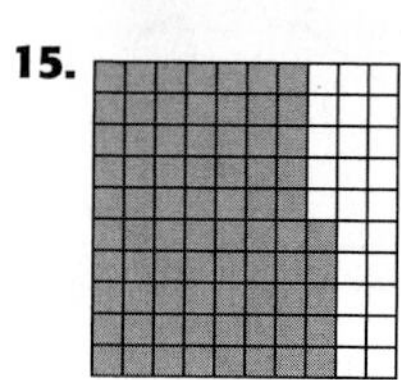

44. $\frac{47}{50}$, 0.94

49.

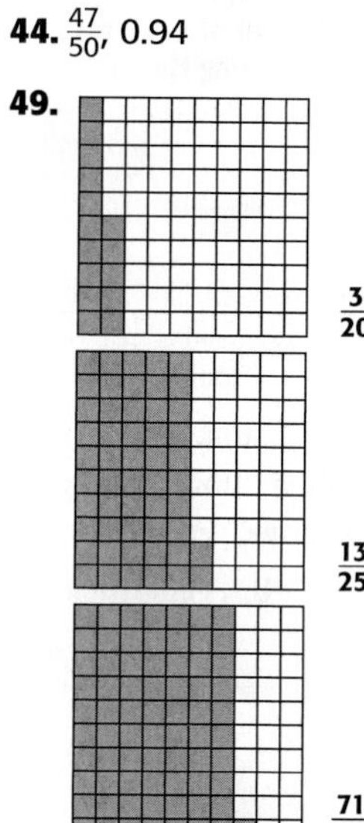

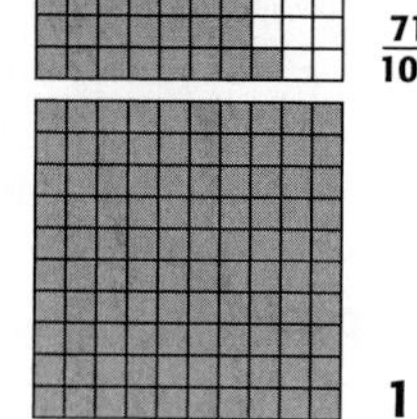

51.

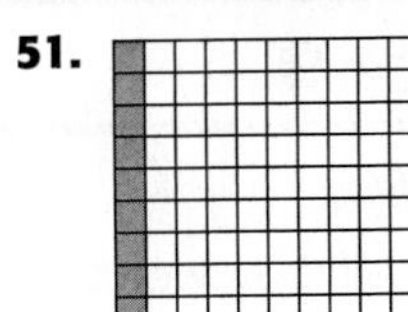

11% = 0.11

7-8 Technology Lab Assessment

1. 3 [÷] 26 [ENTER]

2. 0.082 [MATH] 1 [ENTER]

3. 32.4 [÷] 100 [MATH] 1 [ENTER]

7-10 Exercises

15. $19.46 is 40% of the initial price. This amount should be subtracted from the initial price to find the sale price of $29.19.

16. A discount amount is subtracted from the original cost. The sales tax and tip amount are added to the total cost. A discount could be used at a store where something is 25% off. Sales tax is added to the price of almost every item you buy, such as a television. Tip is the amount you add to the bill for the waiter when you are in a restaurant.

17. No; the price is more if you take off 50% and then 20% than if you take off 70%. $10.00 × 50% = $5.00; $5.00 × 20% = $1.00 and $5.00 − $1.00 = $4.00; $10.00 × 70% = $7.00 and $10.00 − $7.00 = $3.00

19. Music Palace CDs sell for $11.97. Awesome Sound CDs sell for $11.69. Awesome Sound has the better deal.

Chapter 8

8-1 Exercises

20. 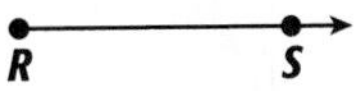 R S

21.  L M

22.  A B

23. 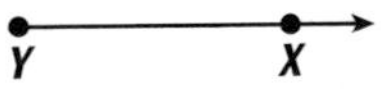 Y X

24.  K J H

29. The first letter in the name of a ray should be the name of the endpoint. *V* is the endpoint of the ray.

8-2 Exercises

4. **5.** **6.**

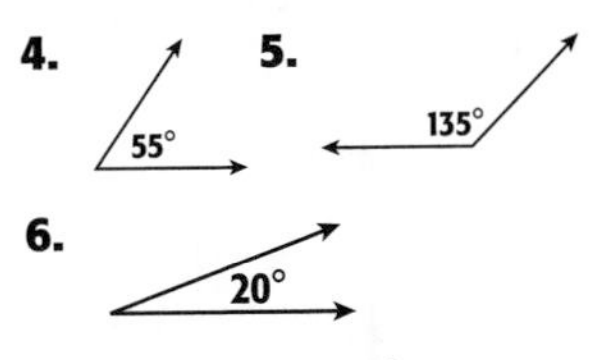

7. **15.**

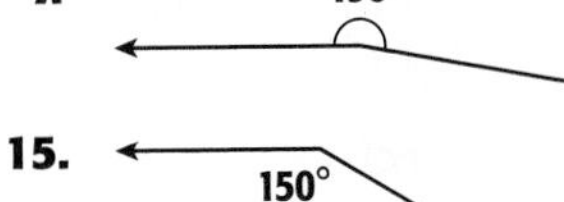

16. **17.**

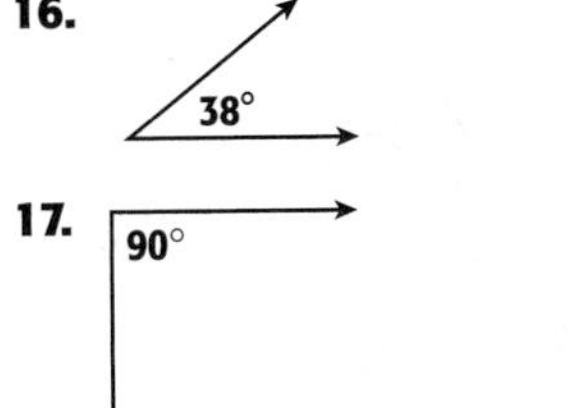

18.

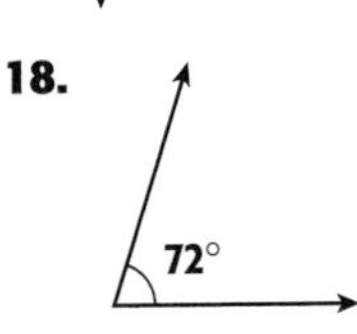

19.

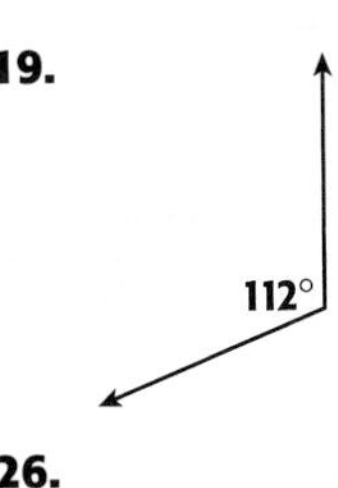

26.

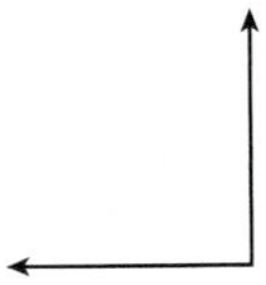

30. yes;

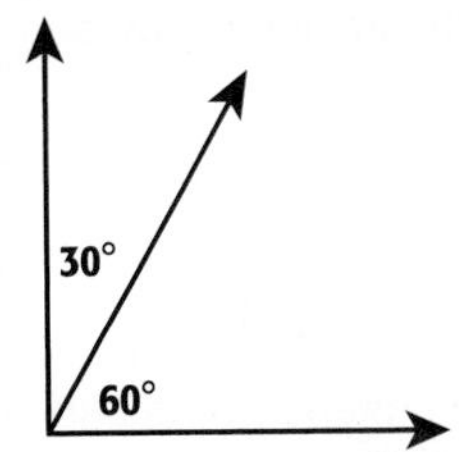

31. The student read the wrong scale on the protractor. The student should estimate the measure of the angle before measuring it.

32. The measure of an acute angle is less than 90°, while the measure of an obtuse angle is greater than 90° and less than 180°.

8-3 Exercises

20. **21.**

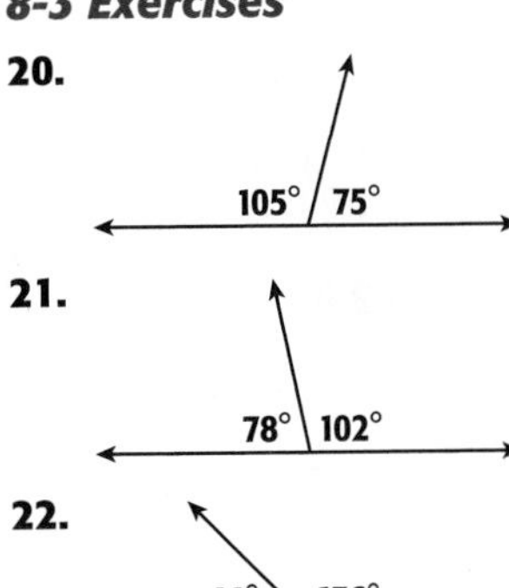

22. **23.**

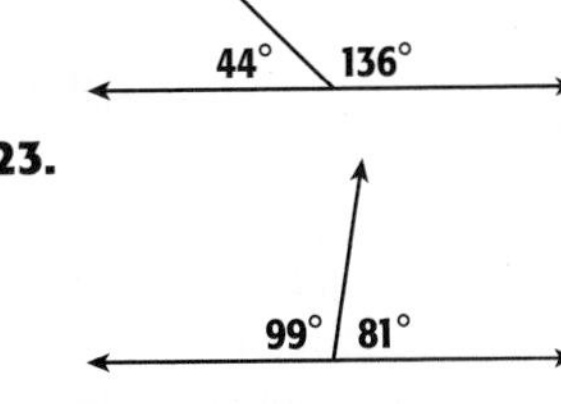

26. Possible answer:

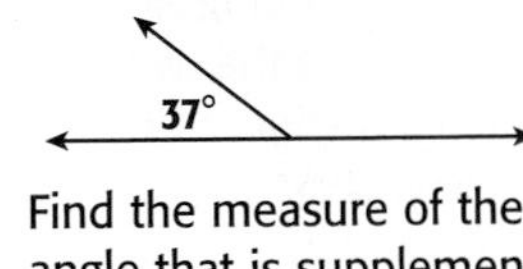

Find the measure of the angle that is supplementary to an angle of 37°.

8-4 Exercises

11. a. Possible answer:

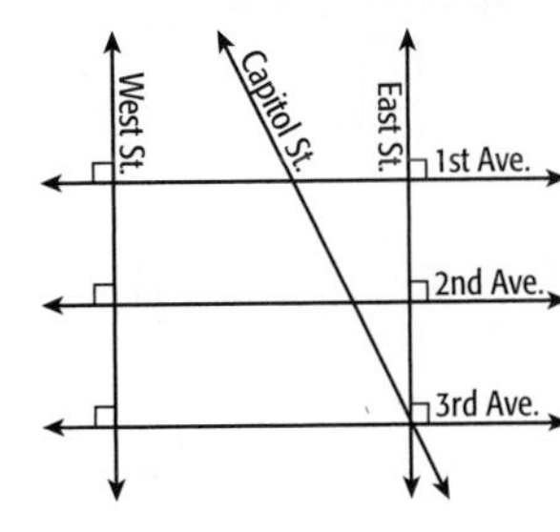

b. Possible answer:

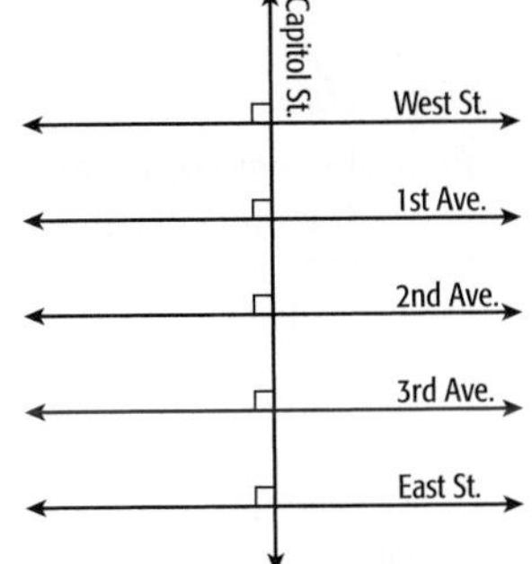

22. Both perpendicular and intersecting lines cross at exactly one point. Perpendicular lines must form right angles, but intersecting lines may not.

27–31.

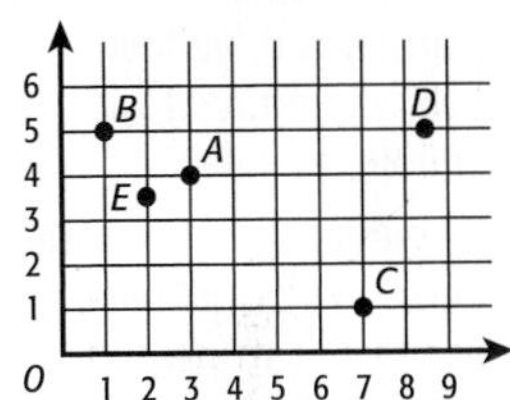

8-5 Exercises

27. Possible answer: Because the sum of the angle in a triangle is 180°. A triangle can not have an angle of 0°.

36.

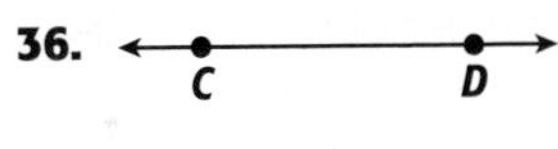

37.

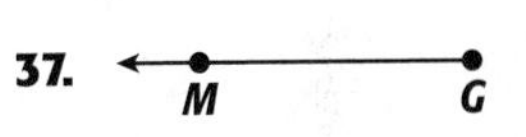

38.  X Y

39. • A

8-6 Exercises

13. quadrilateral, parallelogram, rectangle, rhombus, (square)

14. quadrilateral, parallelogram, (rectangle)

15. quadrilateral, parallelogram, (rhombus)

24. **26.**

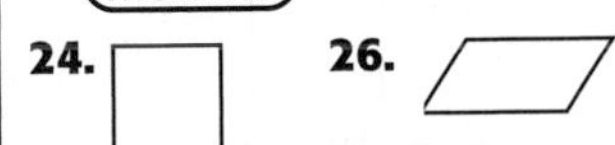

31. A rectangle is a parallelogram and must have two pairs of parallel sides. The figure could be a trapezoid.

32. A square is a rectangle because it contains four right angles; it is a rhombus because all four of its sides are congruent.

8-8 Exercises

1. Possible answer: Rotate figure 90° clockwise.

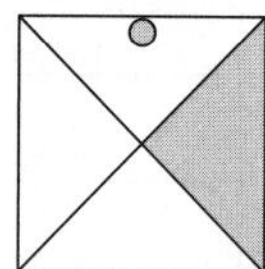

2. Possible answer: Move dot and triangle one position counterclockwise.

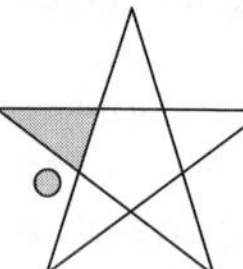

3. Possible answer: purple, purple, red, yellow, green, yellow; red, yellow, green, yellow, purple
4. Possible answer: Rotate figure 90° clockwise, and move dot to next clockwise section.

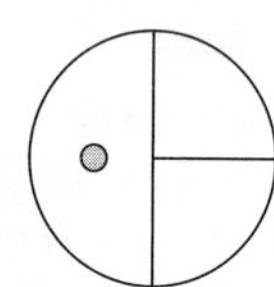

5. Possible answer: The number of objects doubles each time.

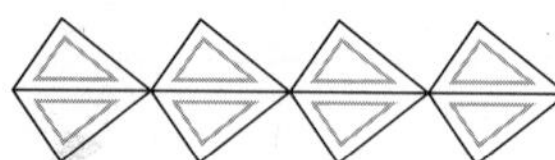

7. □△○⊟△⊖

8.

9.

The lines should be green.

8B Ready to Go On

17. The shaded part of the triangle is moving clockwise around each section.

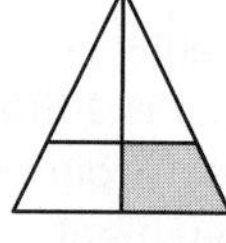

18. Divide each square into four smaller squares.

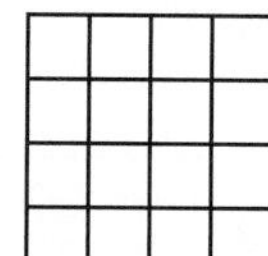

19. The rotation of the square is alternating between 45° clockwise and 45° counterclockwise

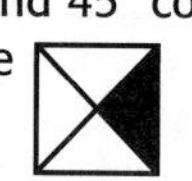

20. The circle is divided into equal, even-numbered parts, beginning with 2 parts.

8-9 Exercises

7.

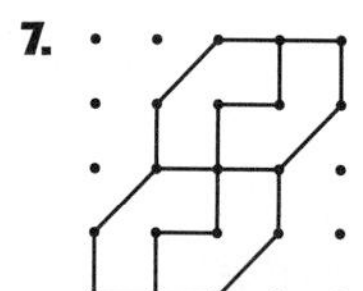

8.

3 in.
4 in. 4 in.
3 in.

3 in.
4 in. 4 in.
3 in.

Check students' answers. Side lengths measure between 2 in. and 6 in. Corresponding side lengths of the two rectangles should be congruent.

8-10 Exercises

9.

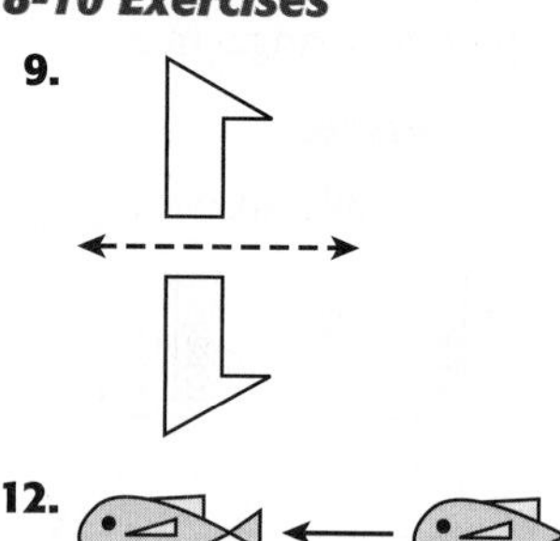

12.

13.

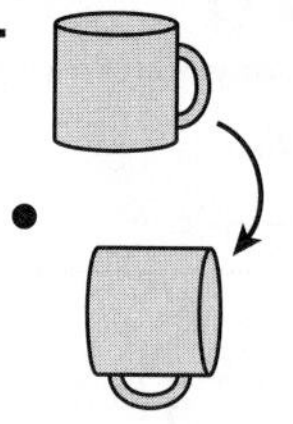

14.

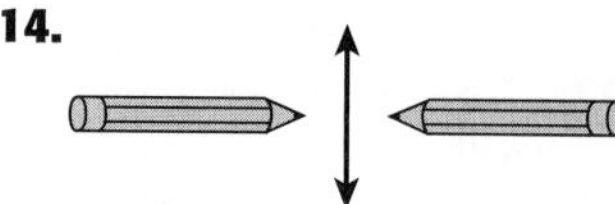

19. Possible answer: To translate the piece, move it along a straight line; to rotate the piece, move it in a circular path; to reflect the piece, flip it over a line to create a mirror image.

20.

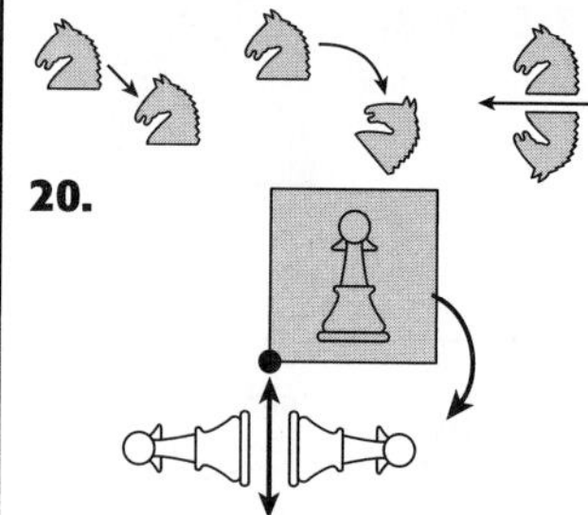

8-11 Exercises

17.

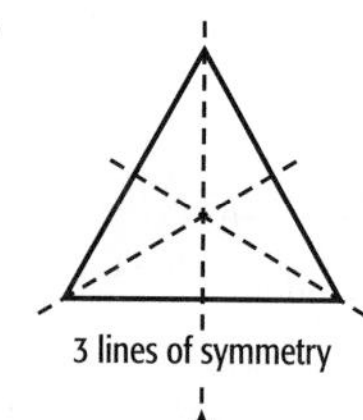

3 lines of symmetry

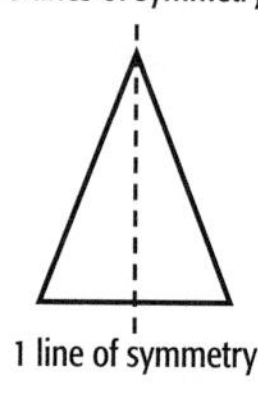

1 line of symmetry

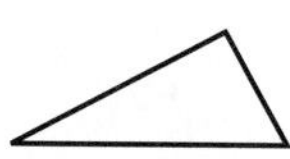

no lines of symmetry

Multi-Step Test Prep

4. 135°; The octagon can be divided into 6 triangles, so the sum of the interior angle measures is $6 \times 180° = 1{,}080°$ and each angle measure is $1{,}080° \div 8 = 135°$.

5.

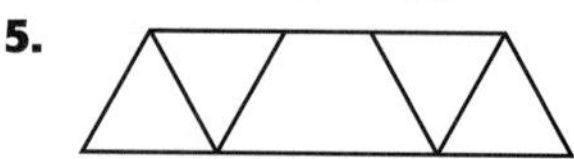

6. 20 of Tile A and 10 of Tile B

Chapter 9

9-1 Exercises

9. Foot; possible answer: the height of a flagpole is more than the distance from my shoulder to my elbow but less than the distance of 18 football fields.
10. Inch; possible answer: the width of a compact-disc case is more than the width of my thumb but less than the distance from my shoulder to my elbow.
11. Gallon; possible answer: the gas tank on a car can hold more than a large container of milk.
12. Cup; possible answer: a baby bottle can hold as much as a glass of juice holds but less than what a small container of paint holds.
13. Ounce; possible answer: an egg weighs more than a slice of bread but less than a loaf of bread.
14. Pound; possible answer: a chair weighs more than a loaf of bread but less than a small car.
22. Yard; possible answer: the circumference of a person's waist is about the same as the distance from the waist to the floor, which is about a yard.
25. Possible answer: Which benchmark should be used to measure the height of a desk, a pen or a paper clip?

Chapter 10

10-2 Exercises

26. Possible answer: The triangle with half the height of the other has half the area of the other.

10-3 Exercises

8. Possible answer:

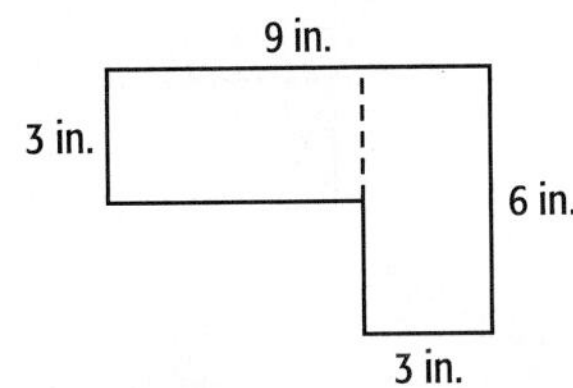

Draw a line dividing the figure into two parts. Find the area of each part and add the areas.
$A = (3 \times 6) + (3 \times 6) = 36 \text{ in}^2$

10-4 Exercises

3. When the dimensions of the triangle are multiplied by 4, the perimeter is multiplied by 4, and the area is multiplied by 16, or 4^2.

4. Check students' drawings for triangle with side lengths 1.25 cm, 1.25 cm, and 1.5 cm. The perimeter is divided by 2 and the area is divided by 4, or 2^2.

10-5 Exercises

21. If the diameter were 6 ft, the area would be approximately $3.14 \cdot 3^2 = 28.26 \text{ ft}^2$, which is less than 30 ft^2, so the diameter must be greater than 6 ft.

22. The student used the diameter rather than the radius in the formula for the area.

23. First find the radius and round it to the nearest whole number. Round π to 3. Then use these values in the area formula, $A = \pi r^2$.

10-7 Exercises

26. Find the density of copper in the table. Because the density of a substance remains the same, multiply the volume of your prism by the density of copper to find your prism's mass.

Chapter 11

Are You Ready

27–34.

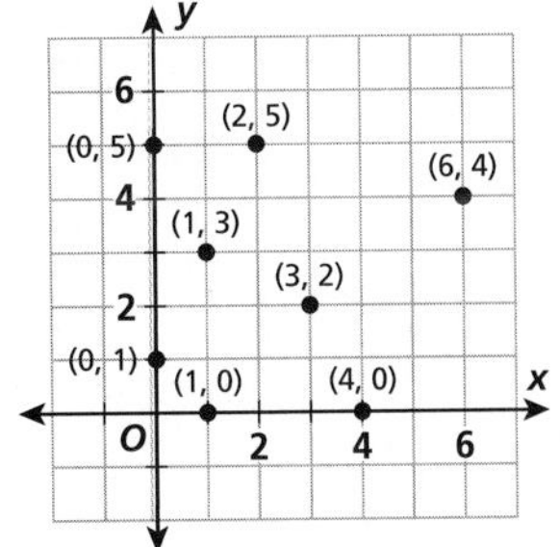

11-1 Exercises

7.

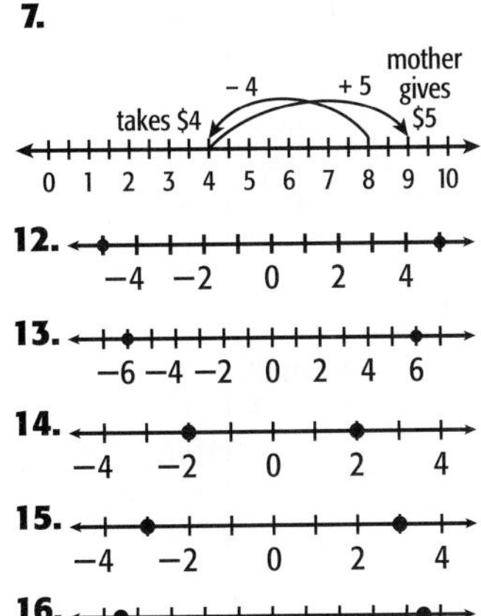

12. **13.** **14.** **15.** **16.**

17.

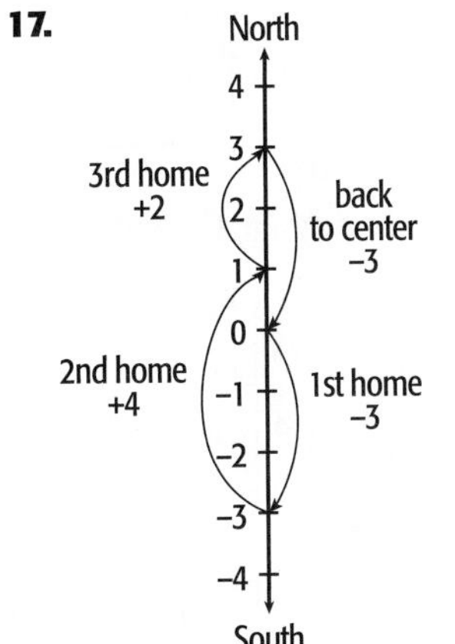

28.

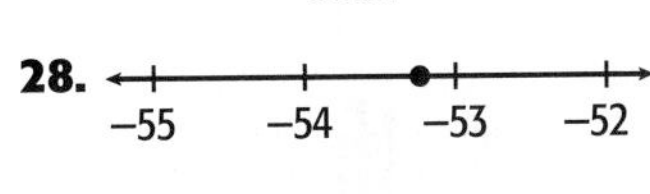

48.

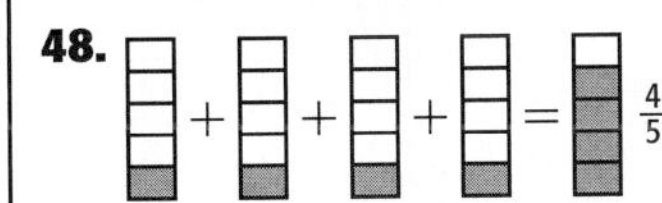

11-2 Exercises

37. Negative numbers are less than 0. Positive numbers are greater than 0. So, the order would be negative, 0, positive.

48.

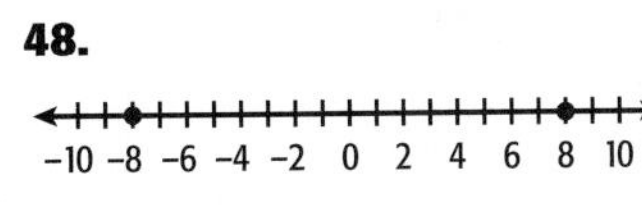

49.

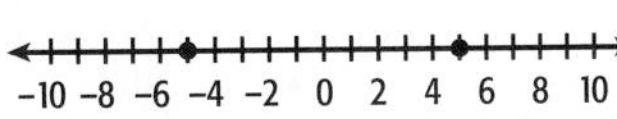

11-3 Exercises

22–27.

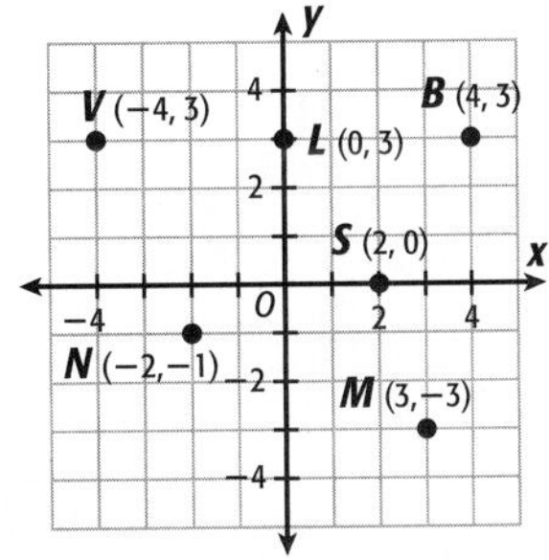

36–47.

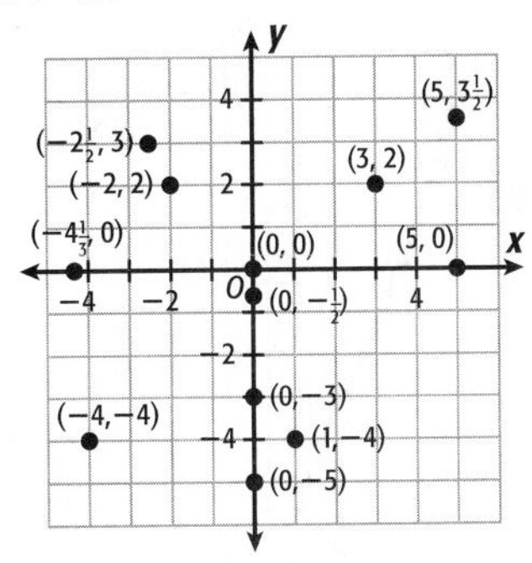

48.

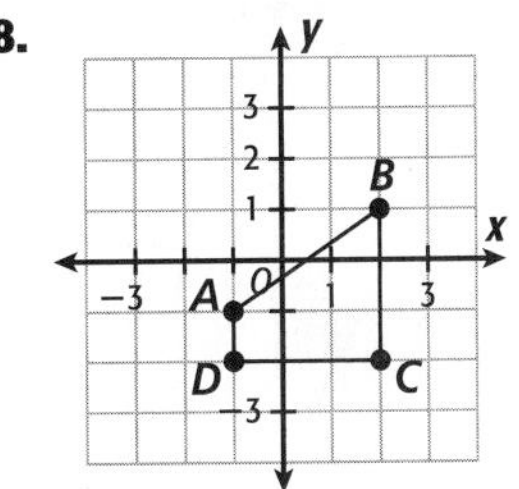

53. Possible answer: The coordinate plane has x- and y-coordinates, and the Earth's coordinate system has longitude and latitude. They are similar in that both have a grid system.

11A Ready to Go On

10.

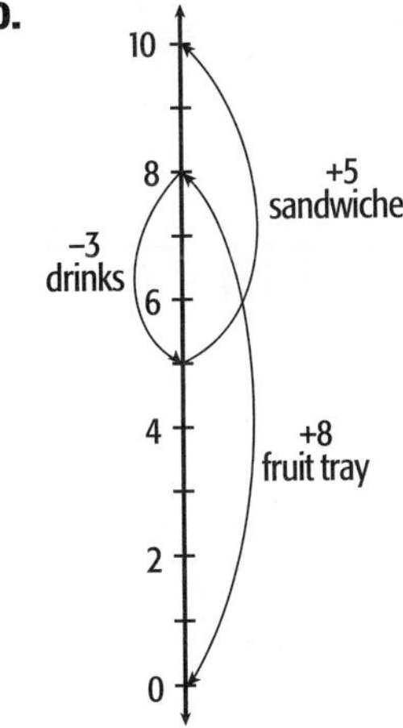

26–33.

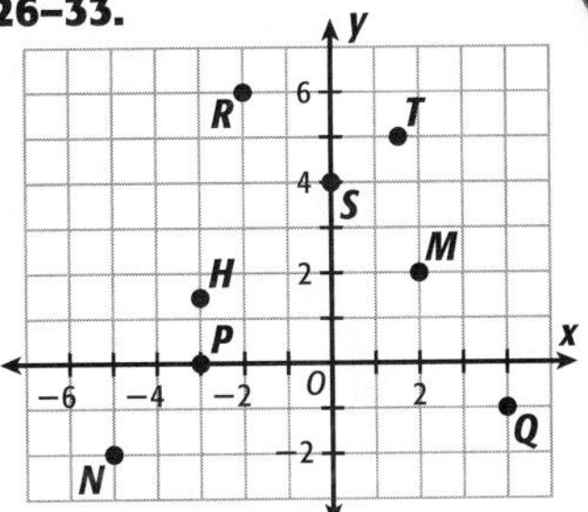

11-4 Hands-On Lab
Try This

1.

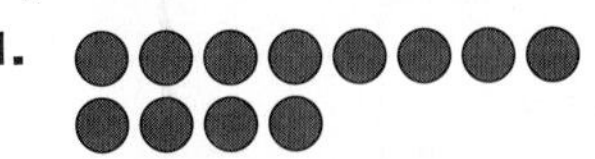

2.

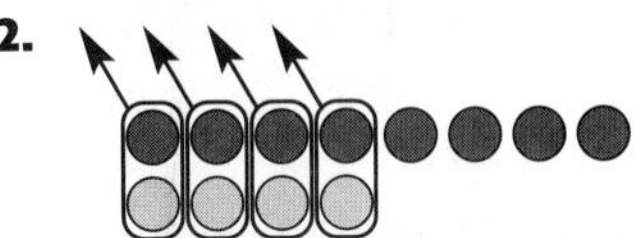

3.

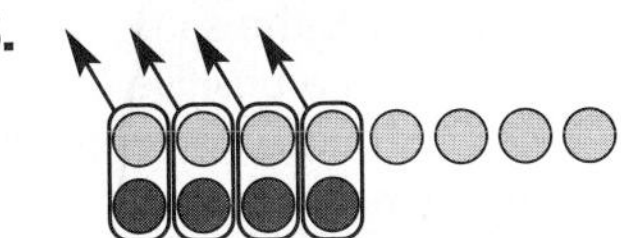

4.

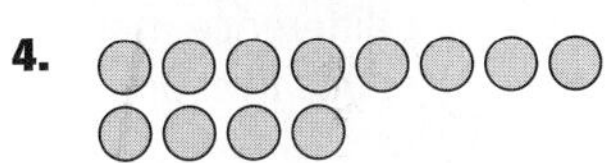

11-4 Exercises

35.

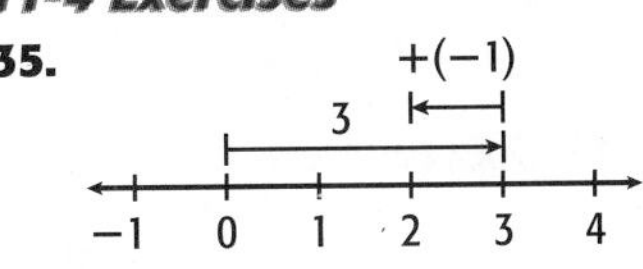

36.

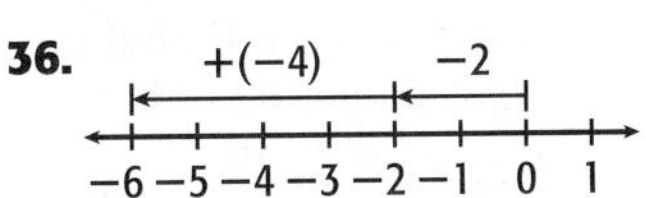

37.

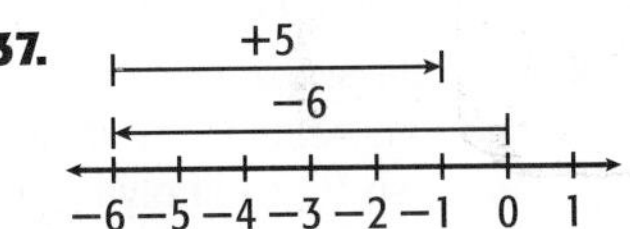

38.

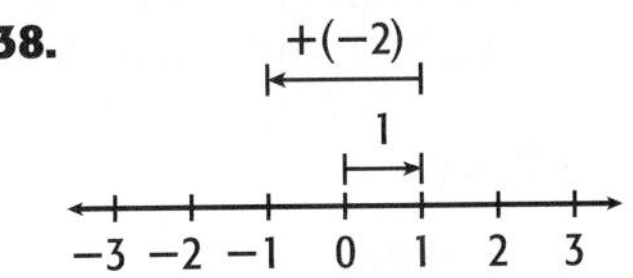

39.

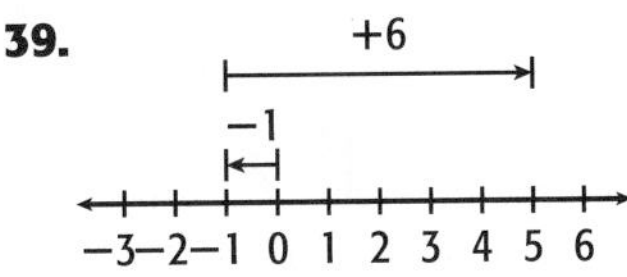

40.

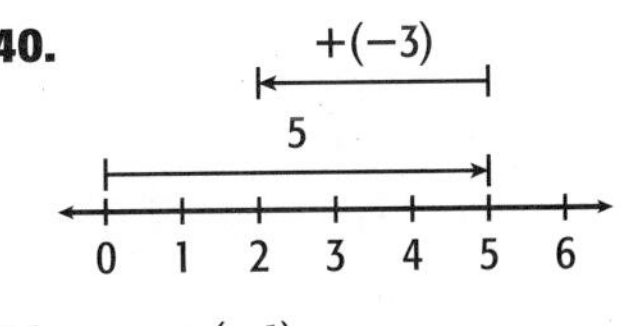

41.

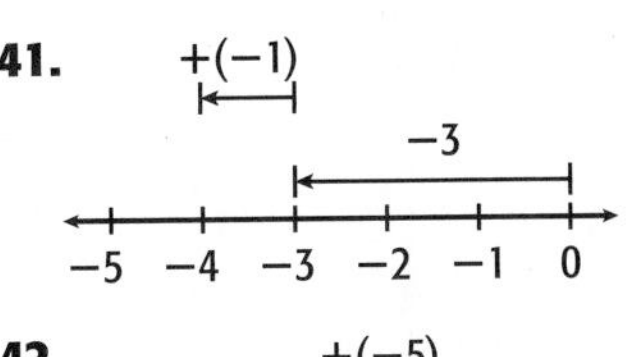

42.

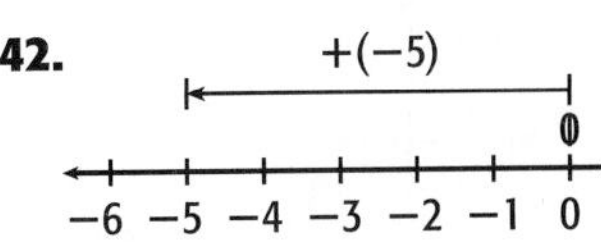

71–75.

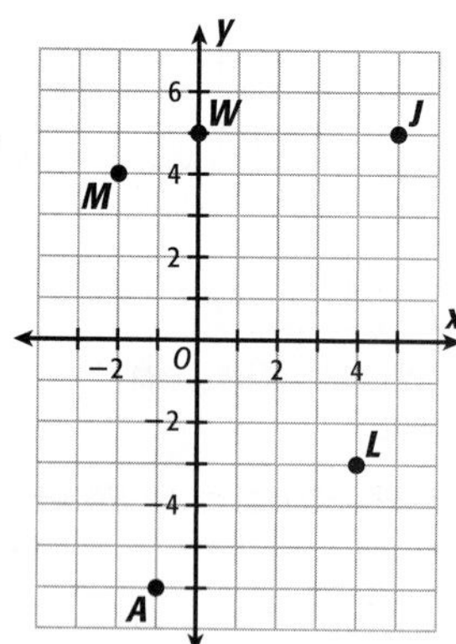

11-5 Exercises

40. Zero minus a negative number is the same as zero plus a positive number and that sum will alway be positive.

41. Yes, the difference may be negative, positive, or zero. Examples:
$-2 - (-4) = 2,$
$-6 - (-6) = 0,$
$-8 - (-2) = -6$

11-9 Exercises

19. Possible answer: The student may have tripled the width and added 10 instead of 5. The correct answer is 305 pixels.

20. Possible answer: Each ℓ, value is greater than its w value, so try multiplying or adding. When w is multiplied by 3 and 5 is added, the result is ℓ, $\ell = 3w + 5$. This works for all the pairs.

11-10 Exercises

9.

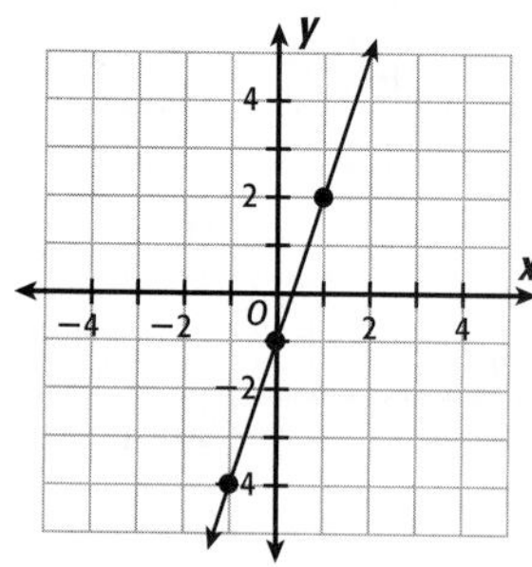

10.

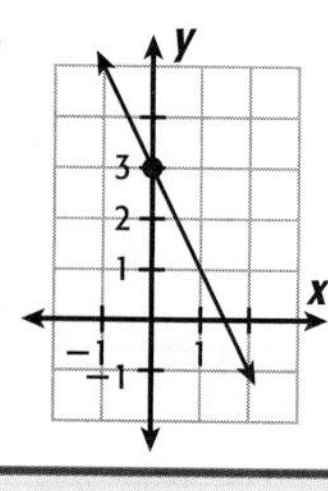

21.

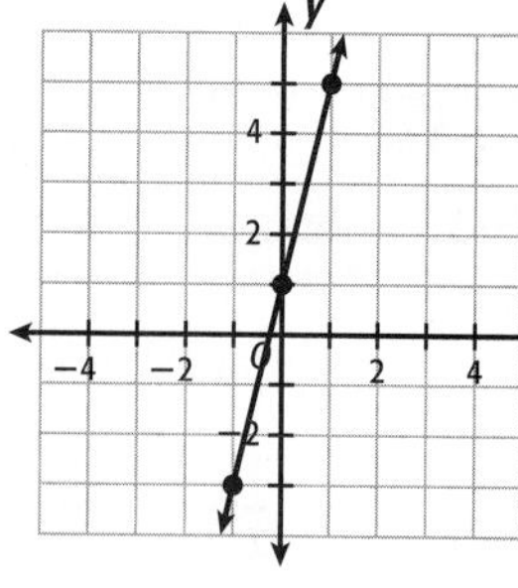

22.

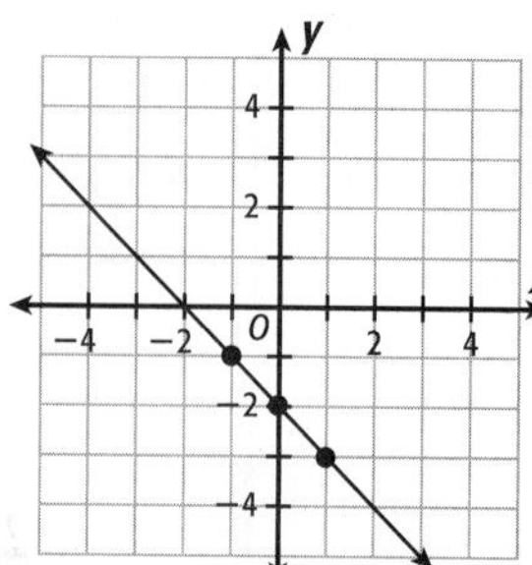

23.

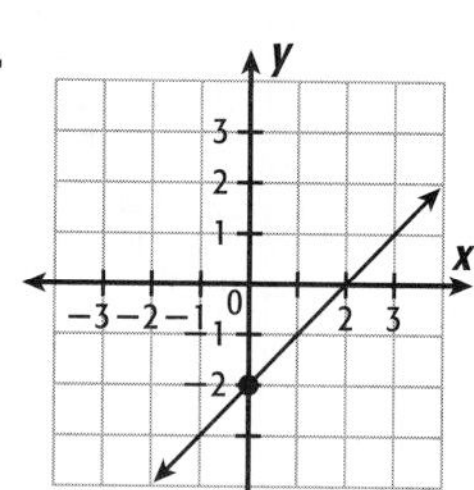

24.

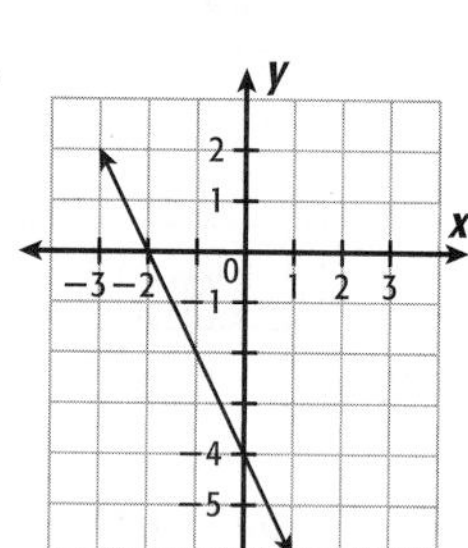

25.

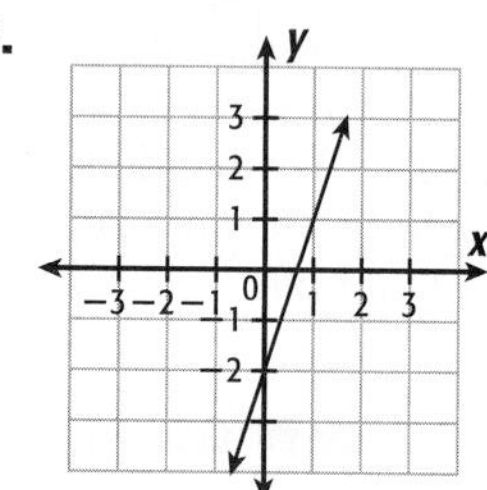

26.

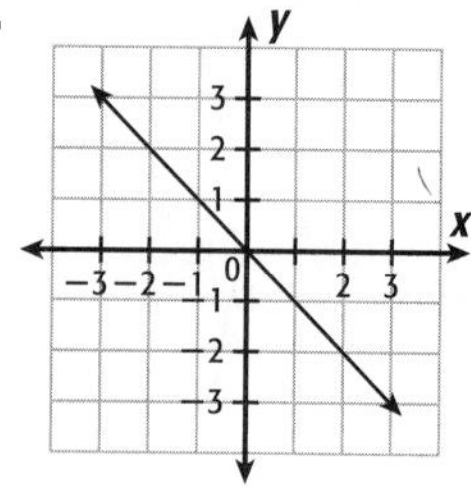

27. −3, −2, −1, 0

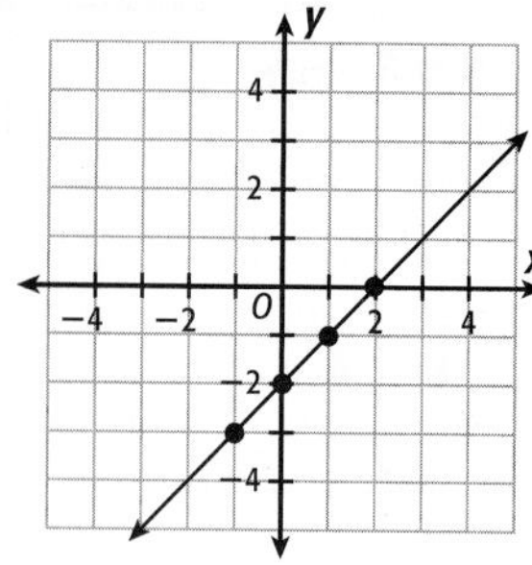

28. −6, −4, −2, 0

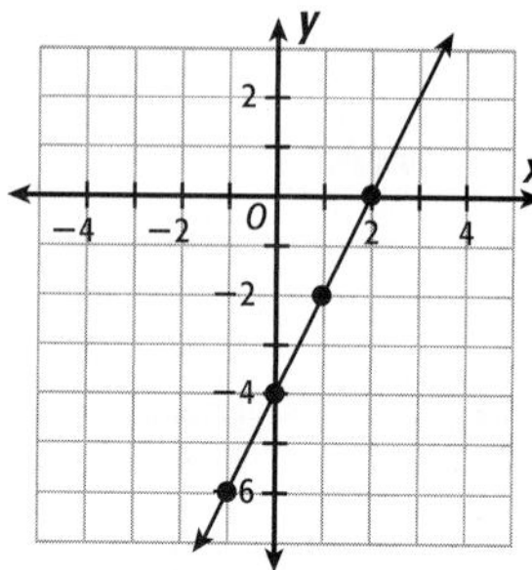

31.

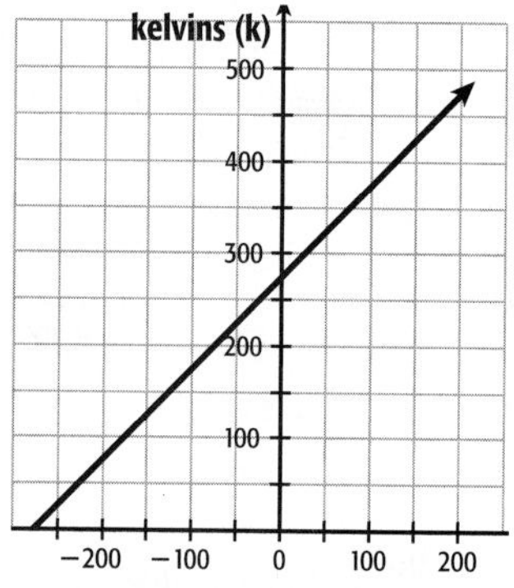

11C Ready to Go On

18.

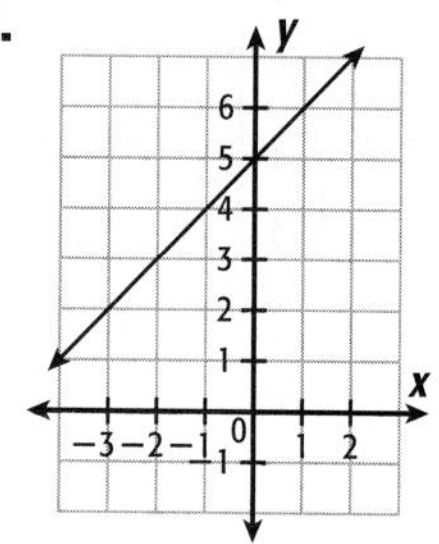

19.

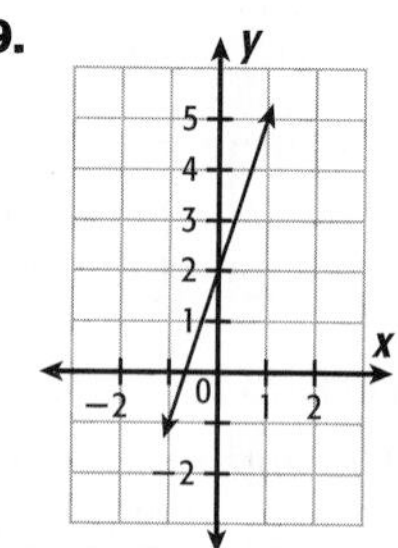

20.

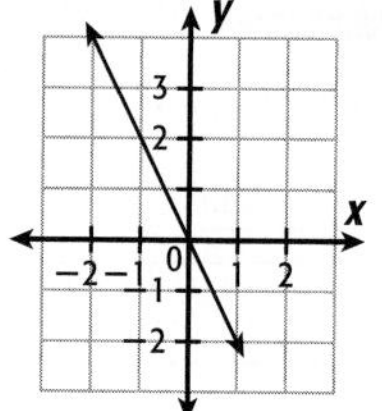

Chapter 12

12-1 Exercises

21. Possible answer: all types that are not O positive or A positive, because when needed, these would be the hardest to locate

12-3 Exercises

1. turkey and fruit, turkey and salad, taco and fruit, taco and salad, pasta and fruit, pasta and salad

2. doctor: Patrice, teacher: Jason; doctor: Patrice, teacher: Kenya; doctor: Jason, teacher: Patrice; doctor: Jason, teacher: Kenya; doctor: Kenya, teacher: Patrice; doctor: Kenya, teacher: Jason

4. Sat: foot race; Sat: hike; Sat: bicycle race; Sat: swimming race; Sat: scavenger hunt; Sun: foot race; Sun: hike; Sun: bicycle race; Sun: swimming race; Sun: scavenger hunt

12-6 Exercises

12. The student should have said 20%, not 20, of the group will be native Canadians.

13. First find what percent of the Canadians in the sample group are of French origin. Then find what percent of the Canadians in the sample group are of native Canadian origin. Multiply both percents by 150 and add the products.

Extra Practice

Chapter 1

49. add 8; 32, 40, 48

50. add 5; 21, 26, 31

51. subtract 15; 55, 40, 25

52. add 11; 56, 67, 78

53. divide by 2, and add 12; 130, 83

54. multiply by 8, and divide by 2; 128, 256

Chapter 2

9. the product of 23 and 6; 23 times 6

10. the difference of 52 and *p*; 52 minus 6

11. the quotient of *y* and 6; *y* divided by 6

12. the sum of 8 and 4; 8 plus 4

13. the product of 13 and *m*; 13 multiplied by *m*

Chapter 6

1. The participation increased from 1998 to 2002.

5K Race	
Year	**Number of Participants**
1998	1,345
1999	1,415
2000	1,532
2001	1,607
2002	1,781

2. points: Kareem Abdul-Jabbar, rebounds: Bill Russell, assists: Larry Bird

Basketball Data			
Player	**Points**	**Rebounds**	**Assists**
Jabbar	38,387	17,440	5,660
Bird	21,791	8,974	5,695
Russell	14,522	21,620	4,100

9.

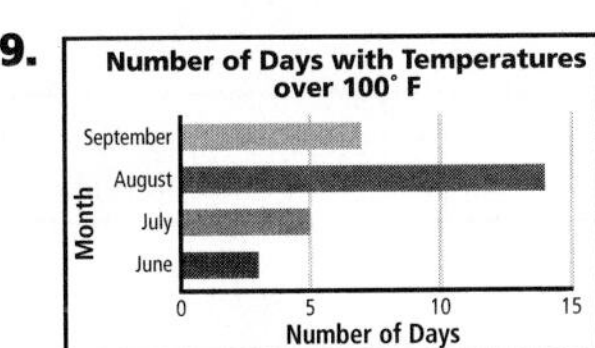

10.

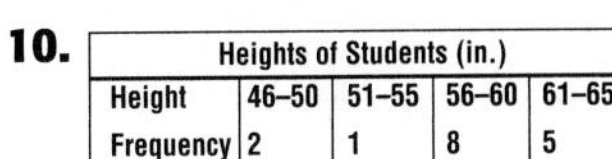

Heights of Students (in.)				
Height	46–50	51–55	56–60	61–65
Frequency	2	1	8	5

11.

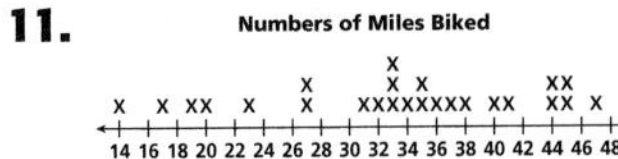

15–17.

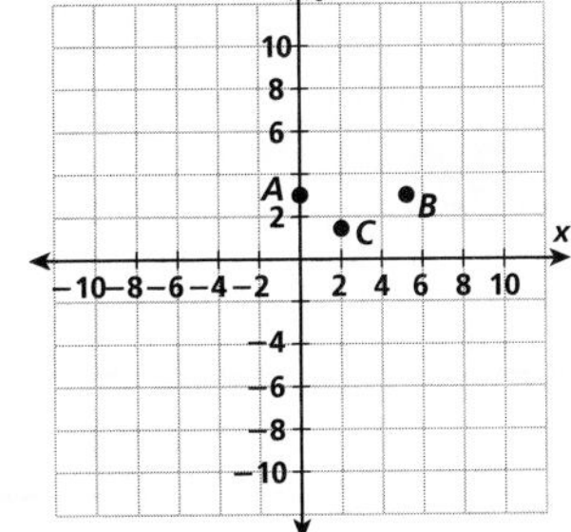

18. increase

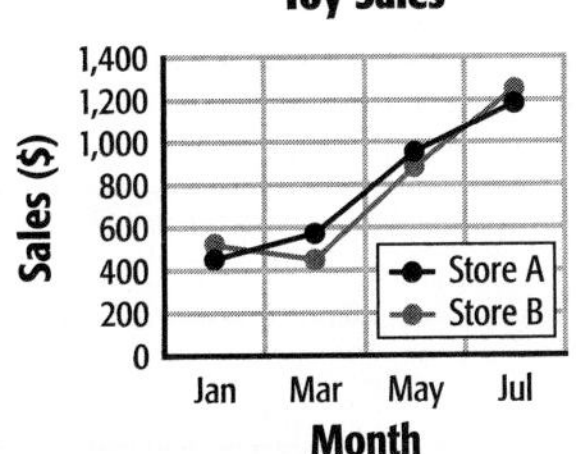

19. The scale starts at 30. It looks as if twice as many people voted for Viking, but in reality Viking r eceived only about 20 more votes than Ram.

21. mean: 35, median: 35, mode: 35

Time Spent Doing Homework (min)

Stems	Leaves
1	0 5 5
2	0
3	5 5 5
4	
5	
6	0 0 5

Key: 1|0 means 10

22.

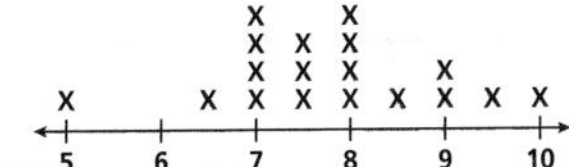

Chapter 11

4. **5.** **6.** **7.**

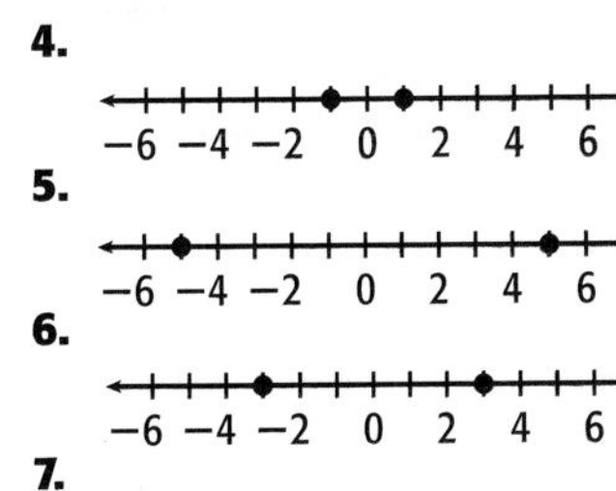

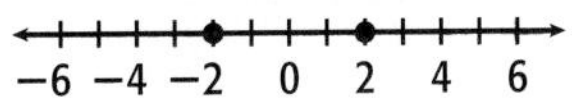

25–27.

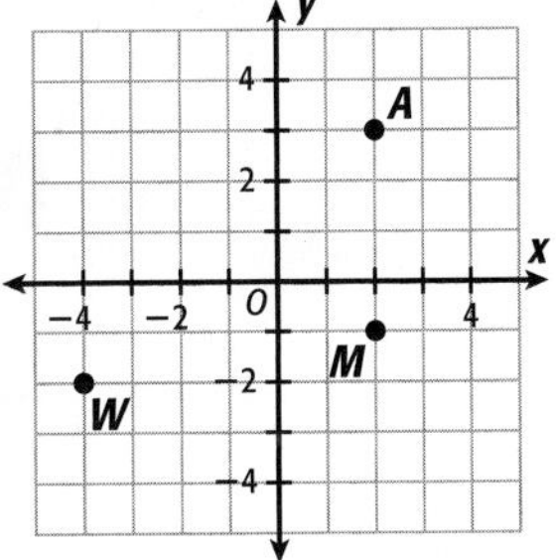

Chapter 12

67.

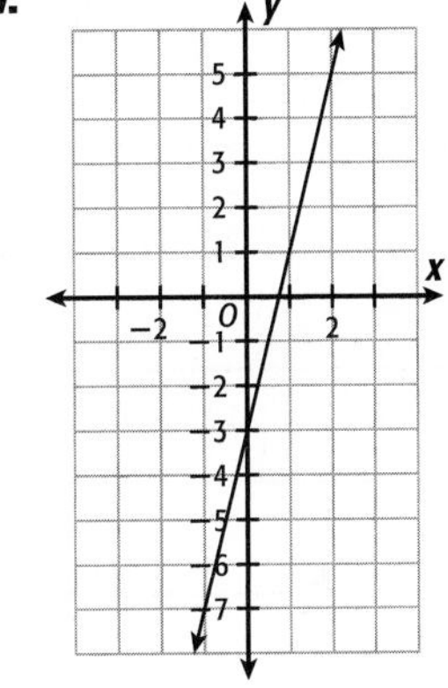

68.

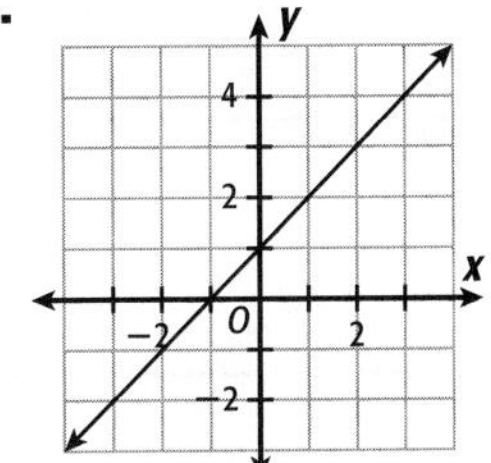

Skills Bank

Properties

1. Associative Property of Multiplication

2. Commutative Property of Multiplication

3. Identity Property of Zero

4. Identity Property of One

5. Commutative Property of Addition

6. Distributive Property

7. Associative Property of Addition

8. Multiplicative Property of Zero

9. Distributive Property

Pictographs

8.

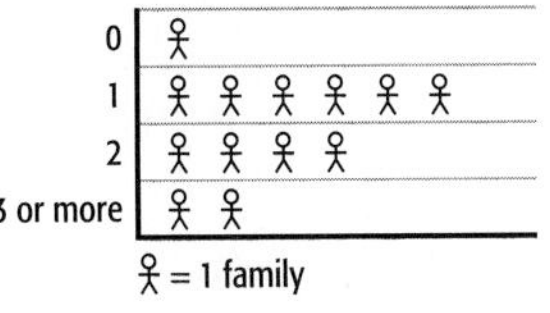

Rational Numbers

1.

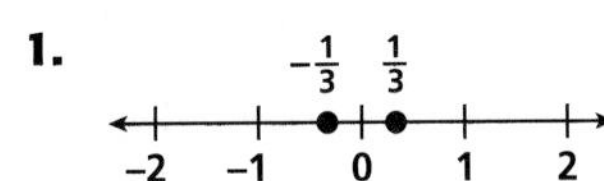

2.

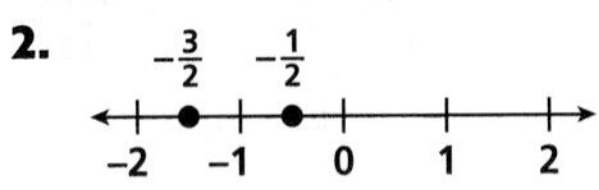

3.

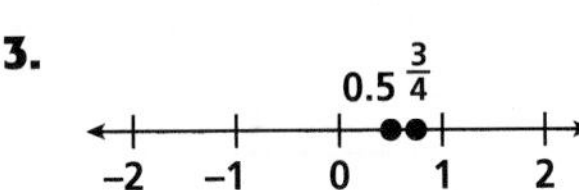

4.

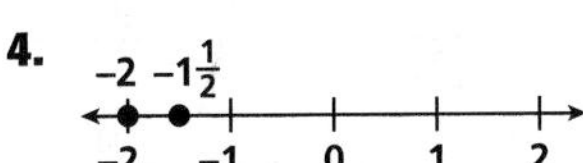

Graph Cumulative Frequency

1. Possible answer:

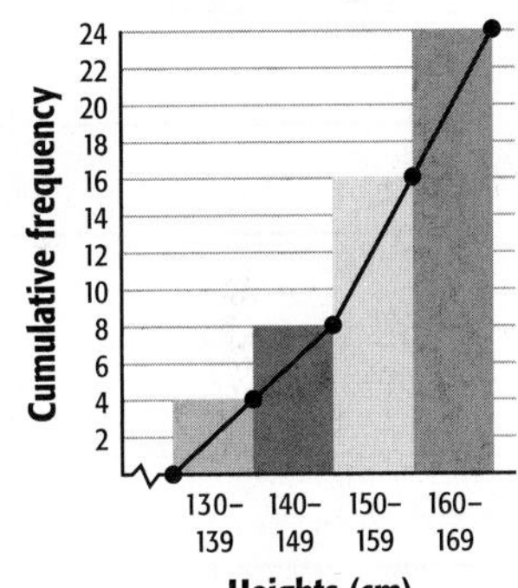

Additional Answers

Notes

Glossary/Glosario

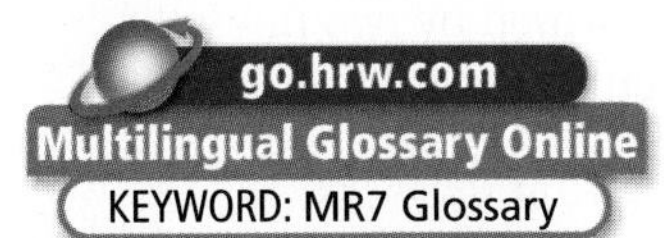

ENGLISH	SPANISH	EXAMPLES
absolute value The distance of a number from zero on a number line; shown by | |. (p. 762)	**valor absoluto** Distancia a la que está un número de 0 en una recta numérica. El símbolo del valor absoluto es | |.	$\|-5\| = 5$
acute angle An angle that measures less than 90°. (p. 421)	**ángulo agudo** Ángulo que mide menos de 90°.	
acute triangle A triangle with all angles measuring less than 90°. (p. 437)	**triángulo acutángulo** Triángulo en el que todos los ángulos miden menos de 90°.	
addend A number added to one or more other numbers to form a sum.	**sumando** Número que se suma a uno o más números para formar una suma.	In the expression 4 + 6 + 7, the numbers 4, 6, and 7 are addends.
Addition Property of Opposites The property that states that the sum of a number and its opposite equals zero.	**Propiedad de suma de los opuestos** Propiedad que establece que la suma de un número y su opuesto es cero.	$12 + (-12) = 0$
adjacent angles Angles in the same plane that have a common vertex and a common side. (p. 424)	**ángulos adyacentes** Ángulos en el mismo plano que comparten un vértice y un lado.	$\angle 1$ and $\angle 2$ are adjacent angles.
algebraic expression An expression that contains at least one variable. (p. 54)	**expresión algebraica** Expresión que contiene una o más variables.	$x + 8$ $4(m - b)$
algebraic inequality An inequality that contains at least one variable. (p. 90)	**desigualdad algebraica** Desigualdad que contiene una o más variables.	$x + 3 > 10$ $5a > b + 3$
alternate exterior angles A pair of angles formed by two lines intersected by a third line. (p. 433)	**ángulos alternos externos** Par de ángulos formados por dos líneas intersecadas por una tercera.	$\angle 4$ and $\angle 5$ are alternate exterior angles.

ENGLISH	SPANISH	EXAMPLES
alternate interior angles A pair of angles formed by two lines intersected by a third line. (p. 433)	**ángulos alternos internos** Par de ángulos formados por dos líneas intersecadas por una tercera.	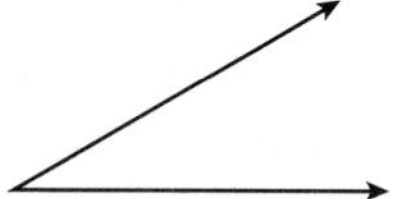 ∠3 and ∠6 are alternate interior angles.
angle A figure formed by two rays with a common endpoint called the vertex. (p. 420)	**ángulo** Figura formada por dos rayos con un extremo común llamado vértice.	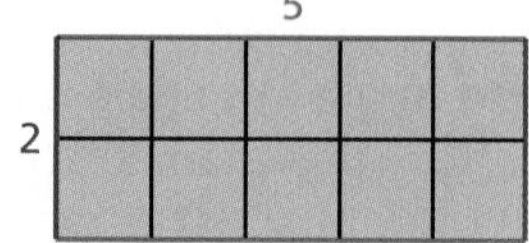
area The number of square units needed to cover a given surface. (p. 542)	**área** El número de unidades cuadradas que se necesitan para cubrir una superficie.	5 / 2 The area is 10 square units.
arithmetic sequence A sequence in which the terms change by the same amount each time. (p. 33)	**término (de una sucesión)** Elemento o número de una sucesión.	The sequence 2, 5, 8, 11, 14. . . is an arthmetic sequence.
Associative Property of Addition The property that states that for three or more numbers, their sum is always the same, regardless of their grouping. (p. 26)	**Propiedad asociativa de la suma** Establece que agrupar tres o más números en cualquier orden siempre da como resultado la misma suma.	$2 + 3 + 8 = (2 + 3) + 8 = 2 + (3 + 8)$
Associative Property of Multiplication The property that states that for three or more numbers, their product is always the same, regardless of their grouping. (p. 26)	**Propiedad asociativa de la multiplicación** Establece que agrupar tres o más números en cualquier orden siempre da como resultado el mismo producto.	$2 \cdot 3 \cdot 8 = (2 \cdot 3) \cdot 8 = 2 \cdot (3 \cdot 8)$
asymmetrical Not identical on either side of a central line; not symmetrical.	**asimétrico** Que no es idéntico a ambos lados de una línea central; no simétrico.	
average The sum of the items in a set of data divided by the number of items in the set; also called *mean*.	**promedio** La suma de los elementos de un conjunto de datos, dividida entre el número de elementos del conjunto. También se le llama *media*.	Data set: 4, 6, 7, 8, 10 Average: $\frac{4+6+7+8+10}{5} = \frac{35}{5} = 7$
axes The two perpendicular lines of a coordinate plane that intersect at the origin. (p. 610)	**ejes** Las dos rectas numéricas perpendiculares del plano cartesiano que se intersecan en el origen.	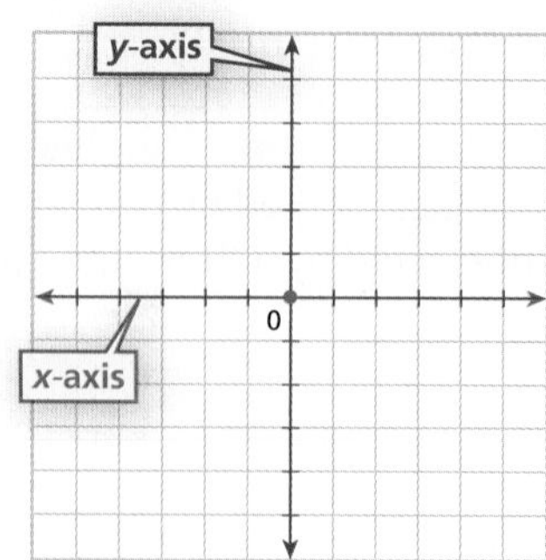

ENGLISH	SPANISH	EXAMPLES

B

bar graph A graph that uses vertical or horizontal bars to display data. (p. 308)

gráfica de barras Gráfica en la que se usan barras verticales u horizontales para presentar datos.

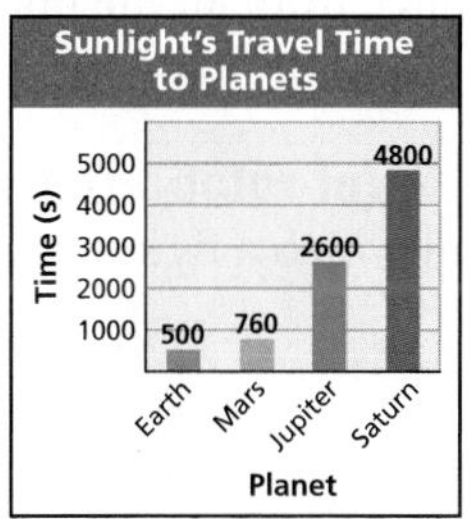

---

base (in numeration) When a number is raised to a power, the number that is used as a factor is the base. (p. 14)

base (en numeración) Cuando un número es elevado a una potencia, el número que se usa como factor es la base.

$3^5 = 3 \cdot 3 \cdot 3 \cdot 3 \cdot 3$; 3 is the base.

---

base (of a polygon or three-dimensional figure) A side of a polygon; a face of a three-dimensional figure by which the figure is measured or classified. (p. 566)

base (de un polígono o figura tridimensional) Lado de un polígono, la cara de una figura tridimensional, a partir del cual se mide o se clasifica una figura tridimensional.

Bases of a cylinder

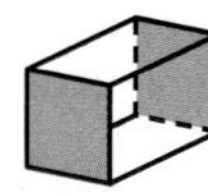

Bases of a prism

Base of a cone

Base of a pyramid

---

bisect To divide into two congruent parts.

trazar una bisectriz Dividir en dos partes congruentes.

---

box-and-whisker plot A graph that displays the highest and lowest quarters of data as whiskers, the middle two quarters of the data as a box, and the median.

gráfica de mediana y rango Gráfica que muestra los valores máximo y mínimo, los cuartiles superior e inferior, así como la mediana de los datos.

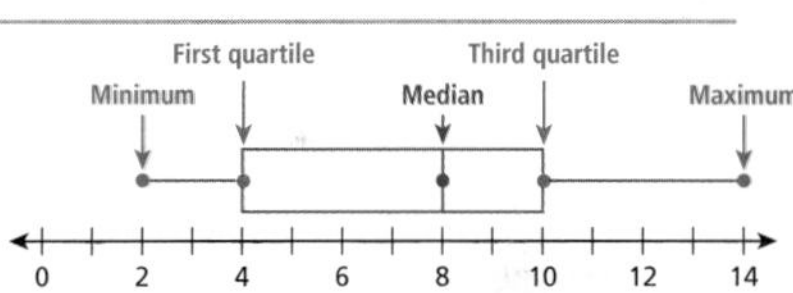

---

break (graph) A zigzag on a horizontal or vertical scale of a graph that indicates that some of the numbers on the scale have been omitted. (p. 309)

discontinuidad (gráfica) Zig-zag en la escala horizontal o vertical de una gráfica que indica la omisión de algunos de los números de la escala.

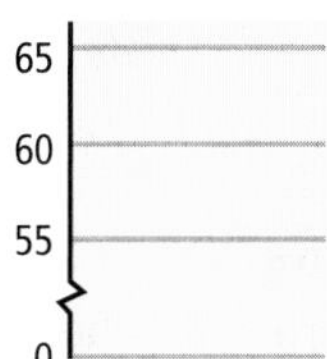

C

capacity The amount a container can hold when filled.

capacidad Cantidad que cabe en un recipiente cuando se llena.

Celsius A metric scale for measuring temperature in which 0°C is the freezing point of water and 100°C is the boiling point of water; also called *centigrade.*

Celsio Escala métrica para medir temperatura, en la que 0° C es el punto de congelación del agua y 100° C es el punto de ebullición. También se le llama *centígrado.*

ENGLISH	SPANISH	EXAMPLES
center (of a circle) The point inside a circle that is the same distance from all the points on the circle. (p. 520)	**centro (de un círculo)** Punto interior de un círculo que se encuentra a la misma distancia de todos los puntos de la circunferencia.	A
center (of rotation) The point about which a figure is rotated.	**centro (de rotación)** Punto alrededor del cual se hace girar una figura.	90° 90° Center 90° 90°
certain (probability) Sure to happen; having a probability of 1. (p. 668)	**seguro (probabilidad)** Que con seguridad sucederá. Representa una probabilidad de 1.	
circle The set of all points in a plane that are the same distance from a given point called the center. (p. 520)	**círculo** Conjunto de puntos en un plano que se encuentran a la misma distancia de un punto llamado centro.	
circle graph A graph that uses sections of a circle to compare parts to the whole and parts to other parts. (p. 524)	**gráfica circular** Gráfica que usa secciones de un círculo para comparar partes con el todo y con otras partes.	Residents of Mesa, AZ 65+ 13%; Under 18 27%; 18–24 11%; 25–44 30%; 45–64 19%
circumference The distance around a circle. (p. 520)	**circunferencia** Distancia alrededor de círculo.	Circumference
clockwise A circular movement in the direction shown.	**en sentido de las manecillas del reloj** Movimiento circular en la dirección que se indica.	
clustering A method used to estimate a sum when all addends are close to the same value. (p. 112)	**aproximación** Método que se usa para estimar una suma cuando todos los sumandos se aproximan al mismo valor.	27, 29, 24, and 23 all cluster around 25.
combination An arrangement of items or events in which order does not matter.	**combinación** Agrupación de objetos o sucesos en la cual el orden no es importante.	For objects *A, B, C,* and *D,* there are 6 different combinations of 2 objects: *AB, AC, AD, BC, BD, CD.*
common denominator A denominator that is the same in two or more fractions. (p. 199)	**común denominador** Denominador que es común a dos o más fracciones.	The common denominator of $\frac{5}{8}$ and $\frac{2}{8}$ is 8.
common factor A number that is a factor of two or more numbers.	**factor común** Número que es factor de dos o más números.	8 is a common factor of 16 and 40.

ENGLISH	SPANISH	EXAMPLES
common multiple A number that is a multiple of each of two or more numbers.	**común multiplo** Un número que es múltiplo de dos o más números.	15 is a common multiple of 3 and 5.
Commutative Property of Addition The property that states that two or more numbers can be added in any order without changing the sum. (p. 26)	**Propiedad conmutativa de la suma** Establece que sumar dos o más números en cualquier orden no altera la suma.	$8 + 20 = 20 + 8$
Commutative Property of Multiplication The property that states that two or more numbers can be multiplied in any order without changing the product. (p. 26)	**Propiedad conmutativa de la multiplicación** Establece que multiplicar dos o más números en cualquier orden no altera el producto.	$6 \cdot 12 = 12 \cdot 6$
compatible numbers Numbers that are close to the given numbers that make estimation or mental calculation easier. (p. 10)	**números compatibles** Números que pueden reemplazar a otros en un problema por ser más fáciles de usar para hacer estimaciones o cálculos mentales.	To estimate 7,957 + 5,009, use the compatible numbers 8,000 and 5,000: 8,000 + 5,000 = 13,000
compensation When a number in a problem is close to another number that is easier to calculate with, the easier number is used to find the answer. Then the answer is adjusted by adding to it or subtracting from it. (p. 30)	**compensación** Cuando un número de un problema está cercano a otro con el que es más fácil hacer cálculos, se usa el número más fácil para hallar la respuesta. Luego, se ajusta la respuesta sumando o restando.	
complement All the ways that an event can not happen. (p. 683)	**complemento** Todas las maneras en que no puede ocurrir un suceso.	When rolling a number cube, the complement of rolling a 3 is rolling a 1, 2, 4, 5, or 6.
complementary angles Two angles whose measures add to 90°. (p. 425)	**ángulos complementarios** Dos ángulos cuyas medidas suman 90°.	37° B 53° A The complement of a 53° angle is a 37° angle.
composite number A number greater than 1 that has more than two whole-number factors. (p. 165)	**número compuesto** Número mayor que 1 que tiene más de dos factores que son números cabales.	4, 6, 8, and 9 are composite numbers.
compound event An event made up of two or more simple events. (p. 688)	**suceso compuesto** Suceso que consta de dos o más sucesos simples.	When tossing a coin and rolling a number cube, the event of the coin landing heads up and the number cube landing on 3 is a compound event.
cone A three-dimensional figure with one vertex and one circular base. (p. 567)	**cono** Figura tridimensional con un vértice y una base circular.	

ENGLISH	SPANISH	EXAMPLES
congruent Having the same size and shape. (p. 424)	**congruentes** Que tienen la misma forma y tamaño.	
congruent angles Angles that have the same measure. (p. 424)	**ángulos congruentes** Ángulos que tienen la misma medida.	m $\angle ABC$ = m $\angle DEF$
constant A value that does not change. (p. 54)	**constante** Valor que no cambia.	3, 0, π
coordinates The numbers of an ordered pair that locate a point on a coordinate graph. (p. 610)	**coordenada** Uno de los números de un par ordenado que localiza un punto en un plano cartesiano.	The coordinates of *B* are (−2, 3).
coordinate grid See *coordinate plane.*	**cuadrícula de coordenadas** Ver plano cartesiano.	
coordinate plane A plane formed by the intersection of a horizontal number line called the *x*-axis and a vertical number line called the *y*-axis. (p. 610)	**plano cartesiano** Plano formado por la intersección de una línea numérica horizontal llamada eje de las *x* y otra vertical llamada eje de las *y*.	
correspondence The relationship between two or more objects that are matched.	**correspondencia** Manera de relacionar dos o más conjuntos de objetos.	
corresponding angles (for lines) A pair of angles formed by two lines intersected by a third line.	**ángulos correspondientes (en líneas)** Par de ángulos formados por dos líneas intersecadas por una tercera.	$\angle 1$ and $\angle 3$ are corresponding angles.
corresponding angles (in polygons) Matching angles of two or more polygons. (p. 366)	**ángulos correspondientes (en polígonos)** Ángulos que se localizan en la misma posición relativa en dos o más polígonos.	$\angle A$ and $\angle D$ are corresponding angles.
corresponding sides Matching sides of two or more polygons. (p. 366)	**lados correspondientes** Lados que se localizan en la misma posición relativa en dos o más polígonos.	$\overline{AB}$ and $\overline{DE}$ are corresponding sides.

ENGLISH	SPANISH	EXAMPLES
counterclockwise A circular movement in the direction shown.	**en sentido contrario a las manecillas del reloj** Movimiento circular en la dirección que se indica.	
cross product The product of numbers on the diagonal when comparing two ratios. (p. 363)	**producto cruzado** El producto de los números multiplicados en diagonal cuando se comparan dos razones.	$\frac{2}{3} = \frac{4}{6}$ For the proportion $\frac{2}{3} = \frac{4}{6}$, the cross products are $2 \cdot 6 = 12$ and $3 \cdot 4 = 12$.
cube (geometric figure) A rectangular prism with six congruent square faces.	**cubo (figura geométrica)** Prisma rectangular con seis caras cuadradas congruentes.	
cube (in numeration) A number raised to the third power.	**cubo (en numeración)** Número elevado a la tercera potencia.	$5^3 = 5 \cdot 5 \cdot 5 = 125$
cumulative frequency The sum of successive data items. (p. 290)	**frecuencia acumulativa** Es la suma de las sucesiones de los datos.	
customary system The measurement system often used in the United States. (p. 488)	**sistema usual de medidas** El sistema de medidas que se usa en Estados Unidos.	inches, feet, miles, ounces, pounds, tons, cups, quarts, gallons
cylinder A three-dimensional figure with two parallel, congruent circular bases connected by a curved lateral surface. (p. 566)	**cilindro** Figura tridimensional con dos bases circulares paralelas y congruentes, unidas por una superficie lateral curva.	

D

ENGLISH	SPANISH	EXAMPLES
decagon A polygon with ten sides.	**decágono** Polígono de diez lados.	
degree The unit of measure for angles or temperature.	**grado** Unidad de medida para ángulos y temperaturas.	
denominator The bottom number of a fraction that tells how many equal parts are in the whole.	**denominador** El número de abajo en una fracción que indica las partes en que se divide el entero.	$\frac{3}{4}$ ← denominator
dependent events Events for which the outcome of one event affects the probability of the other. (p. 700)	**sucesos dependientes** Sucesos en los que el resultado del primero no afecta la probabilidad del segundo.	A bag contains 3 red marbles and 2 blue marbles. Drawing a red marble and then drawing a blue marble without replacing the first marble is an example of dependent events.
diagonal A line segment that connects two non-adjacent vertices of a polygon.	**diagonal** Segmento de recta que une dos vértices no adyacentes de un polígono.	

ENGLISH	SPANISH	EXAMPLES
diameter A line segment that passes through the center of a circle and has endpoints on the circle, or the length of that segment. (p. 520)	**diámetro** Segmento de recta que pasa por el centro de un círculo y tiene sus extremos en la circunferencia, o bien la longitud de ese segmento.	
difference The result when one number is subtracted from another.	**diferencia** El resultado de restar un número de otro.	
dimension The length, width, or height of a figure.	**dimensión** Longitud, anchura o altura de una figura.	
discount The amount by which the original price is reduced. (p. 394)	**descuento** Cantidad que se resta del precio original de un artículo.	
Distributive Property The property that states if you multiply a sum by a number, you will get the same result if you multiply each addend by that number and then add the products. (p. 27)	**Propiedad distributiva** Propiedad que establece que si multiplicas una suma por un número, obtendrás el mismo resultado que si multiplicas cada sumando por ese número y luego sumas los productos.	$5(20 + 1) = 5 \cdot 20 + 5 \cdot 1$
dividend The number to be divided in a division problem.	**dividendo** Número que se divide en un problema de división.	In $8 \div 4 = 2$, 8 is the dividend.
divisible Can be divided by a number without leaving a remainder. (p. 164)	**divisible** Que se puede dividir entre un número sin dejar residuo.	18 is divisible by 3.
divisor The number you are dividing by in a division problem.	**divisor** El número entre el que se divide en un problema de división.	In $8 \div 4 = 2$, 4 is the divisor.
dodecahedron A polyhedron with 12 faces.	**dodecaedro** Poliedro de 12 caras.	
double-bar graph A bar graph that compares two related sets of data. (p. 309)	**gráfica de doble barra** Gráfica de barra que compara dos conjuntos de datos relacionados.	
double-line graph A graph that shows how two related sets of data change over time. (p. 323)	**gráfica de doble línea** Gráfica lineal que muestra cómo cambian con el tiempo dos conjuntos de datos relacionados.	

ENGLISH	SPANISH	EXAMPLES

E

ENGLISH	SPANISH	EXAMPLES
edge The line segment along which two faces of a polyhedron intersect. (p. 566)	**arista** Segmento de recta donde dos caras de un poliedro se intersecan.	Edge
elements The words, numbers, or objects in a set. (p. 212)	**elementos** Palabras, números u objetos que forman un conjunto.	Elements of A: 1, 2, 3, 4
empty set A set that has no elements. (p. 212)	**conjunto vacío** Un conjunto que no tiene elementos.	
endpoint A point at the end of a line segment or ray.	**extremo** Un punto ubicado al final de un segmento de recta o rayo.	A B D
equally likely Outcomes that have the same probability. (p. 682)	**resultados igualmente probables** Resultados que tienen la misma probabilidad de ocurrir. (pág. 564)	When you toss a coin, the outcomes "heads" and "tails" are equally likely.
equation A mathematical sentence that shows that two expressions are equivalent. (p. 70)	**ecuación** Enunciado matemático que indica que dos expresiones son equivalentes.	$x + 4 = 7$ $6 + 1 = 10 - 3$
equilateral triangle A triangle with three congruent sides. (p. 438)	**triángulo equilátero** Triángulo con tres lados congruentes.	
equivalent Having the same value.	**equivalentes** Que tienen el mismo valor.	
equivalent fractions Fractions that name the same amount or part. (p. 186)	**fracciones equivalentes** Fracciones que representan el mismo valor o parte.	$\frac{1}{2}$ and $\frac{2}{4}$ are equivalent fractions.
equivalent ratios Ratios that name the same comparison. (p. 352)	**razones equivalentes** Razones que representan la misma comparación.	$\frac{1}{2}$ and $\frac{2}{4}$ are equivalent ratios.
estimate (n) An answer that is close to the exact answer and is found by rounding or other methods.	**aproximación** Método empleado para estimar una suma cuando todos los sumandos están cercanos al mismo valor.	
estimate (v) To find an answer close to the exact answer by rounding or other methods.	**estimar** Hallar una solución aproximada a la respuesta exacta mediante el redondeo u otros métodos.	
evaluate To find the value of a numerical or algebraic expression. (p. 22)	**evaluar** Hallar el valor de una expresión numérica o algebraica.	Evaluate $2x + 7$ for $x = 3$. $2x + 7$ $2(3) + 7$ $6 + 7$ 13
even number A whole number that is divisible by two.	**número par** Un número cabal que es divisible entre dos.	

ENGLISH	SPANISH	EXAMPLES
event An outcome or set of outcomes of an experiment or situation.	**suceso** Un resultado o una serie de resultados de un experimento o una situación.	
expanded form A number written as the sum of the values of its digits.	**forma desarrollada** Número escrito como suma de los valores de sus dígitos.	236,536 written in expanded form is 200,000 + 30,000 + 6,000 + 500 + 30 + 6.
experiment In probability, any activity based on chance. (p. 672)	**experimento** En probabilidad, cualquier actividad basada en la posibilidad, como lanzar una moneda.	Tossing a coin 10 times and noting the number of "heads."
experimental probability The ratio of the number of times an event occurs to the total number of trials, or times that the activity is performed. (p. 672)	**probabilidad experimental** Razón del número de veces que ocurre un suceso al número total de pruebas o a las veces que se realiza el experimento.	Kendra attempted 27 free throws and made 16 of them. Her experimental probability of making a free throw is $\frac{\text{number made}}{\text{number attempted}} = \frac{16}{27} \approx 0.59$.
exponent The number that indicates how many times the base is used as a factor. (p. 14)	**exponente** Número que indica cuántas veces se usa la base como factor.	$2^3 = 2 \cdot 2 \cdot 2 = 8$; 3 is the exponent.
exponential form A number is in exponential form when it is written with a base and an exponent. (p. 14)	**forma exponencial** Cuando se escribe un número con una base y un exponente, está en forma exponencial.	4^2 is the exponential form for $4 \cdot 4$.
expression A mathematical phrase that contains operations, numbers, and/or variables.	**expresión** Enunciado matemático que contiene operaciones, numeros y(o) variables.	$6x + 1$

F

ENGLISH	SPANISH	EXAMPLES
face A flat surface of a polyhedron. (p. 566)	**cara** Lados planos de un poliedro.	Face
factor A number that is multiplied by another number to get a product. (p. 169)	**factor** Número que se multiplica por otro para hallar un producto.	7 is a factor of 21 since $7 \cdot 3 = 21$.
factor tree A diagram showing how a whole number breaks down into its prime factors. (p. 170)	**árbol de factores** Diagrama que muestra cómo se descompone un número cabal en sus factores primos.	12 / \ 3 · 4 / \ 2 · 2 $12 = 3 \cdot 2 \cdot 2$
Fahrenheit A temperature scale in which 32°F is the freezing point of water and 212°F is the boiling point of water.	**Fahrenheit** Escala de temperatura en la que 32° F es el punto de congelación del agua y 212° F es el punto de ebullición.	

ENGLISH	SPANISH	EXAMPLES
fair When all outcomes of an experiment are equally likely, the experiment is said to be fair. (p. 682)	**justo** Se dice de un experimento donde todos los resultados posibles son igualmente probables.	When tossing a fair coin, heads and tails are equally likely. Each has a probability of $\frac{1}{2}$.
formula A rule showing relationships among quantities.	**fórmula** Regla que muestra relaciones entre cantidades.	$A = \ell w$ is the formula for the area of a rectangle.
fraction A number in the form $\frac{a}{b}$, where $b \neq 0$.	**fracción** Número escrito en la forma $\frac{a}{b}$, donde $b \neq 0$.	
frequency table A table that lists items together according to the number of times, or frequency, that the items occur. (p. 314)	**tabla de frecuencia** Manera de organizar los datos de acuerdo con el número de veces (o la frecuencia) que aparece cada valor.	Data set: 1, 1, 2, 2, 3, 4, 5, 5, 5, 6, 6 Frequency table: (see below)
front-end estimation An estimating technique in which the front digits of the addends are added and then the sum is adjusted for a closer estimate. (p. 113)	**estimación por partes** Técnica en la que se suman sólo los números enteros de los sumandos y luego se ajusta la suma para tener una estimación más exacta.	Estimate 25.05 + 14.671 with the sum 25 + 14 = 39. The actual value is 39 or greater.
function An input-output relationship that has exactly one output for each input. (p. 640)	**función** Regla que relaciona dos cantidades de forma que a cada valor de entrada corresponda exactamente un valor de salida.	6 → −1, 5 → 0, 2 → −4, 1 → 0
function table A table of ordered pairs that represent solutions of a function. (p. 640)	**tabla de función** Tabla de pares ordenados que representan soluciones de una función.	(see below)

Frequency table:

Data	Frequency
1	2
2	2
3	1
4	1
5	3
6	2

Function table:

x	3	4	5	6
y	7	9	11	13

G

ENGLISH	SPANISH	EXAMPLES
graph of an equation A graph of the set of ordered pairs that are solutions of the equation.	**gráfica de una ecuación** Gráfica del conjunto de pares ordenados que son soluciones de la ecuación.	
greatest common factor (GCF) The largest common factor of two or more given numbers. (p. 173)	**máximo común divisor (MCD)** El mayor de los factores comunes compartidos por dos o más números cabales.	The GCF of 27 and 45 is 9.

ENGLISH	SPANISH	EXAMPLES

H

height In a triangle or quadrilateral, the perpendicular distance from the base to the opposite vertex or side. (p. 543) In a prism or cylinder, the perpendicular distance between the bases. (pp. 572, 583)	**altura** En un triángulo o cuadrilátero, longitud de un segmento de recta perpendicular que va de la base de la figura al vértice o lado opuesto. En un prisma o cilindro, la distancia perpendicular entre las bases.	h, b
heptagon A seven-sided polygon.	**heptágono** Polígono de siete lados.	
hexagon A six-sided polygon.	**hexágono** Polígono de seis lados.	
histogram A bar graph that shows the frequency of data within equal intervals. (p. 315)	**histograma** Gráfica de barras que muestra la frecuencia de los datos en intervalos iguales.	Starting Salaries; Frequency: 0, 10, 20, 30, 40; 20–29, 30–39, 40–49, 50–59; Salary range (thousand $)
hypotenuse In a right triangle, the side opposite the right angle.	**hipotenusa** En un triángulo rectángulo, el lado opuesto al ángulo recto.	hypotenuse

I

Identity Property of One The property that states that the product of 1 and any number is that number.	**Propiedad de identidad del uno** Propiedad que establece que el producto de 1 y cualquier número es ese número.	$5 \times 1 = 5$ $-8 \times 1 = -8$
Identity Property of Zero The property that states the sum of zero and any number is that number.	**Propiedad de identidad del cero** Propiedad que establece que la suma de cero y cualquier número es ese número.	$7 + 0 = 7$ $-9 + 0 = -9$
image A figure resulting from a transformation.	**imagen** Figura que resulta de una transformación.	
impossible (probability) Can never happen; having a probability of 0. (p. 668)	**imposible (en probabilidad)** Que no puede currir. Suceso cuya probabilidad de ocurrir es 0.	

ENGLISH	SPANISH	EXAMPLES
improper fraction A fraction in which the numerator is greater than or equal to the denominator. (p. 192)	**fracción impropia** Fracción cuyo numerador es mayor o igual al denominador.	$\frac{5}{5}$ $\frac{7}{3}$
independent events Events for which the outcome of one event does not affect the probability of the other. (p. 700)	**sucesos independientes** Sucesos en los que el resultado del primero no afecta la probabilidad del segundo.	A bag contains 3 red marbles and 2 blue marbles. Drawing a red marble, replacing it, and then drawing a blue marble is an example of independent events.
indirect measurement The technique of using similar figures and proportions to find a measure. (p. 370)	**medición indirecta** Técnica que usa figuras semejantes y proporciones para hallar una medida.	
inequality A mathematical sentence that shows the relationship between quantities that are not equal. (p. 90)	**desigualdad** Enunciado matemático que muestra una relación entre cantidades que no son equivalentes.	$5 < 8$ $5x + 2 \geq 12$
input The value substituted into an expression or function. (p. 640)	**valor de entrada** Valor que se usa para sustituir una variable en una expresión o función.	For the rule $y = 6x$, the input 4 produces an output of 24.
integer A member of the set of whole numbers and their opposites. (p. 602)	**enteros** Conjunto de todos los números cabales y sus opuestos.	$\ldots -3, -2, -1, 0, 1, 2, 3, \ldots$
interest The amount of money charged for borrowing or using money, or the amount of money earned by saving money. (p. 400)	**interés** Cantidad de dinero que se cobra por el préstamo o uso del dinero, o la cantidad que se gana al ahorrar dinero.	
interior angles Angles on the inner sides of two lines intersected by a third line. In the diagram, $\angle c$, $\angle d$, $\angle e$, and $\angle f$ are interior angles. (p. 341)	**ángulos internos** Ángulos en los lados internos de dos líneas intersecadas por una tercera. En el diagrama, $\angle c$, $\angle d$, $\angle e$, y $\angle f$ son ángulos internos.	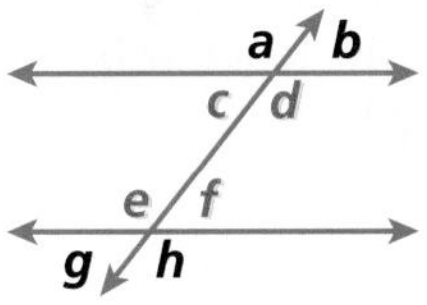
intersecting lines Lines that cross at exactly one point. (p. 428)	**líneas secantes** Líneas que se cruzan en un solo punto.	
intersection (sets) The set of elements common to two or more sets. (p. 212)	**intersección (de conjuntos)** Conjunto de elementos comunes a dos o más conjuntos.	
interval The space between marked values on a number line or the scale of a graph.	**intervalo** El espacio entre los valores marcados en una recta numérica o en la escala de una gráfica.	
inverse operations Operations that undo each other: addition and subtraction, or multiplication and division.	**operaciones inversas** Operaciones que se anulan mutuamente: suma y resta, o multiplicación y división.	

ENGLISH	SPANISH	EXAMPLES
isosceles triangle A triangle with at least two congruent sides. (p. 438)	**triángulo isósceles** Triángulo que tiene al menos dos lados congruentes.	

ENGLISH	SPANISH	EXAMPLES
lateral surface In a cylinder, the curved surface connecting the circular bases; in a cone, the curved surface that is not a base.	**superficie lateral** En un cilindro, superficie curva que une las bases circulares y forma los lados del cilindro; en un cono, la superficie curva que no es la base.	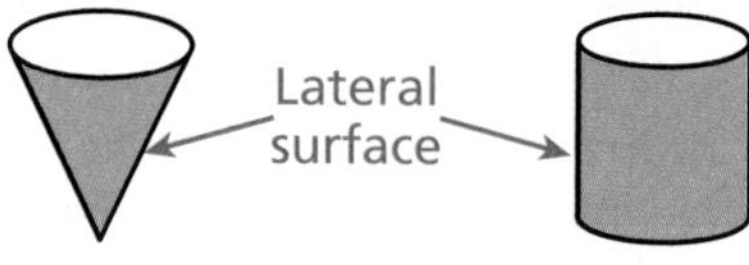
least common denominator (LCD) The least common multiple of two or more denominators. (p. 234)	**mínimo común denominador (mcd)** El múltiplo común más pequeño de dos o más denominadores.	The LCD of $\frac{3}{4}$ and $\frac{5}{6}$ is 12.
least common multiple (LCM) The smallest number, other than zero, that is a multiple of two or more given numbers. (p. 228)	**mínimo común múltiplo (mcm)** El menor de los múltiplos (diferente de cero) de dos o más números.	The LCM of 10 and 18 is 90.
like fractions Fractions that have the same denominator. (p. 198)	**fracciones semejantes** Fracciones que el mismo denominador.	$\frac{5}{12}$ and $\frac{3}{12}$ are like fractions.
line A straight path that extends without end in opposite directions. (p. 416)	**línea** Trayectoria que se extiende de manera indefinida en direcciones opuestas.	
line graph A graph that uses line segments to show how data changes. (p. 322)	**gráfica lineal** Gráfica que muestra cambios en los datos mediante segmentos de recta.	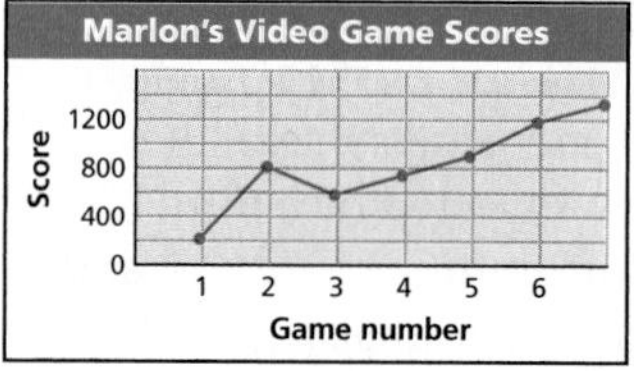
line plot A number line with marks or dots that show frequency. (p. 314)	**diagrama de acumulación** Recta numérica con marcas o puntos que indican frecuencia.	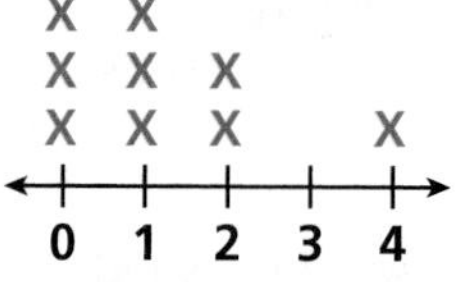
line of reflection A line that a figure is flipped across to create a mirror image of the original figure. (p. 459)	**línea de reflexión** Línea sobre la cual se voltea una figura para crear una imagen de espejo de la figura original.	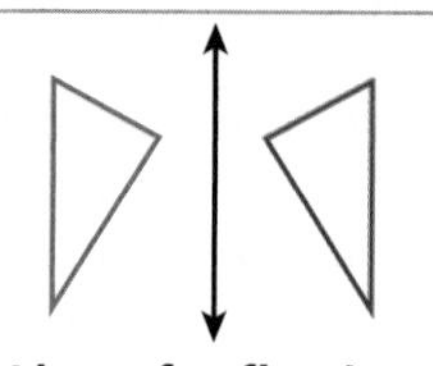
line of symmetry The imaginary "mirror" in line symmetry. (p. 464)	**simetría axial** Una figura tiene simetría axial si una mitad es imagen de espejo de la otra mitad.	

ENGLISH	SPANISH	EXAMPLES
line segment A part of a line between two endpoints. (p. 417)	**segmento de recta** Parte de una línea con dos extremos.	A B
line symmetry A figure has line symmetry if one half is a mirror-image of the other half. (p. 464)	**eje de simetría** Una figura tiene eje de simetría si una de sus mitades es la imagen reflejada de la otra.	
linear equation An equation whose solutions form a straight line on a coordinate plane. (p. 646)	**ecuación lineal** Ecuación en la que las soluciones forman una línea recta en un plano cartesiano.	$y = 2x + 1$
lower extreme The least number in a set of data.	**extremo inferior** El número menor en un conjunto de datos.	Data set: 18, 23, 28, 29, 6, 42 Lower extreme: 18

M

ENGLISH	SPANISH	EXAMPLES
mean The sum of the items in a set of data divided by the number of items in the set; also called *average.* (p. 298)	**media** La suma de todos los elementos, dividida entre el número total de elementos en el conjunto de datos. También se llama *promedio.*	Data set: 4, 6, 7, 8, 10 Mean: $\frac{4\ 1\ 6\ 1\ 7\ 1\ 8\ 1\ 10}{5} = \frac{35}{5} = 7$
median The middle number or the mean (average) of the two middle numbers in an ordered set of data. (p. 299)	**mediana** Valor intermedio o la media (el promedio) de los dos valores intermedios en un conjunto de datos ordenados de menor a mayor.	Data set: 4, 6, 7, 8, 10 Median: 7
metric system A decimal system of weights and measures that is used universally in science and commonly throughout the world. (p. 492)	**sistema métrico** Sistema decimal de pesos y medidas empleado universalmente en las ciencias y por lo general en todo el mundo.	centimeters, meters, kilometers, grams, kilograms, milliliters, liters
midpoint The point that divides a line segment into two congruent line segments.	**punto medio** El punto que divide un segmento de recta en dos segmentos de recta congruentes.	A B C B is the midpoint of $\overline{AC}$
mixed number A number made up of a whole number that is not zero and a fraction. (p. 181)	**número mixto** Número que contiene un número cabal que no sea cero y una fracción.	$5\frac{1}{8}$
mode The number or numbers that occur most frequently in a set of data; when all numbers occur with the same frequency, we say there is no mode. (p. 299)	**moda** Número o números más frecuentes en un conjunto de datos; si todos los números aparecen con la misma frecuencia, no hay moda.	Data set: 3, 5, 8, 8, 10 Mode: 8
multiple A multiple of a number is the product of the number and any nonzero whole number.	**múltiplo** El producto de cualquier número y un número cabal es múltiplo de ese número.	
Multiplication Property of Zero The property that states that the product of any number and 0 is 0.	**Propiedad de multiplicación del cero** Propiedad que establece que el producto de cualquier número y 0 es 0.	$6 \times 0 = 0$ $-5 \times 0 = 0$

ENGLISH	SPANISH	EXAMPLES

N

negative number A number less than zero. (p. 602)	**número negativo** Número menor que cero.	−2 is a negative number. −4 −3 −2 −1 0 1 2 3 4
net An arrangement of two-dimensional figures that can be folded to form a polyhedron. (p. 582)	**plantilla** Arreglo de figuras bidimensionales que se doblan para formar un poliedro.	10 m 6 m 10 m 6 m
numerator The top number of a fraction that tells how many parts of a whole are being considered.	**numerador** El número de arriba de una fracción; indica cuántas partes de un todo se están considerando.	$\frac{3}{4}$ ← numerator
numerical expression An expression that contains only numbers and operations. (p. 22)	**expresión numérica** Expresión matemática que incluye sólo números y operacions.	$(2 \cdot 3) + 1$

O

obtuse angle An angle whose measure is greater than 90° but less than 180°. (p. 421)	**ángulo obtuso** Ángulo cuya medida es mayor de 90° pero menor de 180°. (pág. 326)	
obtuse triangle A triangle containing one obtuse angle. (p. 437)	**triángulo obtusángulo** Triángulo que tiene un ángulo obtuso.	
octagon An eight-sided polygon.	**octágono** Polígono de ocho lados.	
odd number A whole number that is not divisible by two.	**número impar** Un número cabal que no es divisible entre dos.	
opposites Two numbers that are an equal distance from zero on a number line. (p. 602)	**opuestos** Dos números que están a la misma distancia de cero en una recta numérica.	5 and −5 are opposites. 5 units 5 units −6 −5 −4 −3 −2 −1 0 1 2 3 4 5 6
order of operations A rule for evaluating expressions: first perform the operations in parentheses, then compute powers and roots, then perform all multiplication and division from left to right, and then perform all addition and subtraction from left to right. (p. 22)	**orden de las operaciones** Regla para evaluar expresiones: primero se resuelven las operaciones entre paréntesis, luego se hallan las potencias y raíces, después todas las multiplicaciones y divisiones de izquierda a derecha y, por último, todas las sumas y restas de izquierda a derecha.	$3^2 - 12 \div 4$ $9 - 12 \div 4$ Evaluate the power. $9 - 3$ Divide. 6 Subtract.

ENGLISH	SPANISH	EXAMPLES
ordered pair A pair of numbers that can be used to locate a point on a coordinate plane. (p. 319)	**par ordenado** Par de números que sirven para localizar un punto en un plano cartesiano.	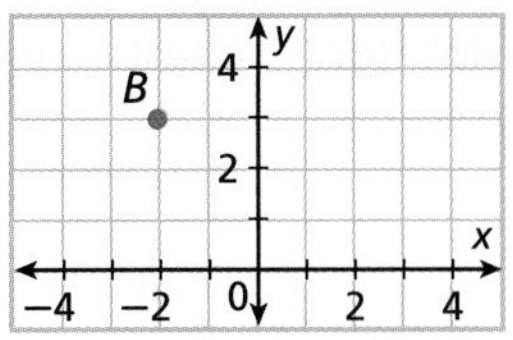 The coordinates of *B* are (−2, 3)
origin The point where the x-axis and y-axis intersect on the coordinate plane; (0, 0). (p. 610)	**origen** Punto de intersección entre el eje de las x y el eje de las y en un plano cartesiano: (0, 0).	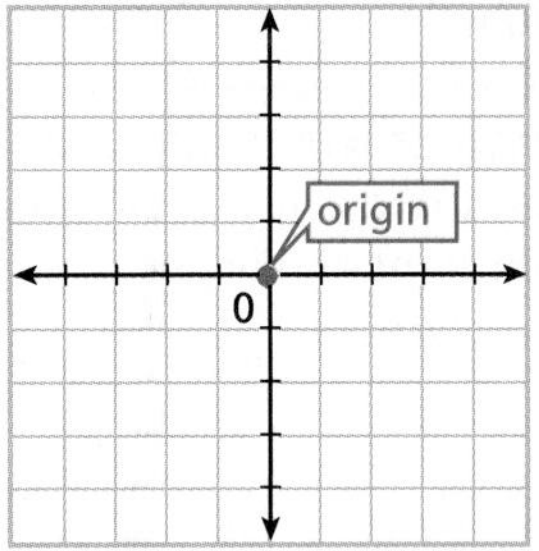
outcome A possible result of a probability experiment. (p. 672)	**resultado** Un posible resultado de un experimento de probabilidad.	When rolling a number cube, the possible outcomes are 1, 2, 3, 4, 5, and 6.
outlier A value much greater or much less than the others in a data set. (p. 302)	**valor extremo** Un valor mucho mayor o menor que los demás valores de un conjunto de datos.	Most of data Mean Outlier
output The value that results from the substitution of a given input into an expression or function. (p. 640)	**valor de salida** Valor que resulta luego de sustituir un valor de entrada determinado en una expresión o función.	For the rule $y = 6x$, the input 4 produces an output of 24.
overestimate An estimate that is greater than the exact answer. (p. 10)	**estimación alta** Estimación mayor que la respuesta exacta.	100 is an overestimate for the sum 23 + 24 + 21 + 22.

P

ENGLISH	SPANISH	EXAMPLES
parallel lines Lines in a plane that do not intersect. (p. 428)	**líneas paralelas** Líneas que se encuentran en el mismo plano pero que nunca se intersecan.	r s
parallelogram A quadrilateral with two pairs of parallel sides. (p. 442)	**paralelogramo** Cuadrilátero con dos pares lados paralelos.	
pentagon A five-sided polygon.	**pentágono** Polígono de cinco lados.	
percent A ratio comparing a number to 100. (p. 381)	**porcentaje** Razón que compara un número con el número 100.	$45\% = \frac{45}{100}$
perfect square A square of a whole number.	**cuadrado perfecto** El cuadrado de un número cabal.	$5^2 = 25$, so 25 is a perfect square.

Glossary/Glosario

ENGLISH	SPANISH	EXAMPLES
perimeter The distance around a polygon. (p. 514)	**perímetro** Distancia alrededor de un polígono.	18 ft 6 ft
permutation An arrangement of items or events in which order is important.	**permutación** Arreglo de objetos o sucesos en el que el orden es importante.	For objects *A*, *B*, and *C*, there are 6 different permutations: *ABC*, *ACB*, *BAC*, *BCA*, *CAB*, *CBA*.
perpendicular bisector A line that intersects a segment at its midpoint and is perpendicular to the segment.	**mediatriz** Línea que cruza un segmento en su punto medio y es perpendicular al segmento.	ℓ A B ℓ is the perpendicular bisector of $\overline{AB}$.
perpendicular lines Lines that intersect to form right angles. (p. 428)	**líneas perpendiculares** Líneas que al intersecarse forman ángulos rectos.	n m
pi (π) The ratio of the circumference of a circle to the length of its diameter; $\pi \approx 3.14$ or $\frac{22}{7}$. (p. 520)	**pi (π)** Razón de la circunferencia de un círculo a la longitud de su diámetro; $\pi \approx 3.14$ ó $\frac{22}{7}$	
plane A flat surface that extends forever. (p. 416)	**plano** Superficie plana que se extiende de manera indefinida en todas direcciones.	A C $\mathcal{R}$ B plane *R* or plane *ABC*
point An exact location in space. (p. 416)	**punto** Ubicación exacta en un plano.	*P* point *P*
polygon A closed plane figure formed by three or more line segments that intersect only at their endpoints. (p. 446)	**polígono** Figura plana cerrada, formada por tres o más segmentos de recta que se intersecan sólo en sus extremos.	
polyhedron A three-dimensional figure in which all the surfaces or faces are polygons. (p. 566)	**poliedro** Figura tridimensional cuyas superficies o caras tienen forma de polígonos.	
population The whole group being surveyed. (p. 694)	**población** El grupo completo que es objeto de estudio.	In a survey about eating habits of middle school students, the population is all middle school students.
positive number A number greater than zero. (p. 602)	**número positivo** Número mayor que cero.	2 is a positive number. −4 −3 −2 −1 0 1 2 3 4
power A number produced by raising a base to an exponent.	**potencia** Número que resulta al elevar una base a un exponente.	$2^3 = 8$, so 2 to the 3rd power is 8.
prediction A guess about something that will happen in the future. (p. 694)	**predicción** Pronóstico sobre algo que puede ocurrir en el futuro.	

ENGLISH	SPANISH	EXAMPLES
prime factorization A number written as the product of its prime factors. (p. 169)	**factorización prima** Proceso de escritura de unnúmero como el producto de sus factores primos.	$10 = 2 \cdot 5$ $24 = 2^3 \cdot 3$
prime number A whole number greater than 1 that has exactly two factors, itself and 1. (p. 165)	**número primo** Número cabal mayor que 1 que sólo es divisible entre 1 y entre él mismo.	5 is prime because its only factors are 5 and 1.
principal The initial amount of money borrowed or saved. (p. 400)	**capital** Cantidad inicial de dinero depositada o recibida en préstamo.	
prism A polyhedron that has two congruent, polygon-shaped bases and other faces that are all rectangles. (p. 566)	**prisma** Poliedro con dos bases congruentes con forma de polígono y caras con forma de rectángulos.	
probability A number from 0 to 1 (or 0% to 100%) that describes how likely an event is to occur. (p. 668)	**probabilidad** Un número entre 0 y 1 (ó 0% y 100%) que describe qué tan probable es un suceso.	A bag contains 3 red marbles and 4 blue marbles. The probability of randomly choosing a red marble is $\frac{3}{7}$.
product The result when two or more numbers are multiplied.	**producto** Resultado de multiplicar dos o más números.	The product of 4 and 8 is 32.
proper fraction A fraction in which the numerator is less than the denominator. (p. 192)	**fracción propia** Fracción en la que el numerador es menor que el denominador.	$\frac{3}{4}, \frac{1}{13}, \frac{7}{8}$
proportion An equation that states that two ratios are equivalent. (p. 362)	**proporción** Ecuación que establece que dos razones son equivalentes.	$\frac{2}{3} = \frac{4}{6}$
protractor A tool for measuring angles.	**transportador** Instrumento para medir ángulos.	
pyramid A polyhedron with a polygon base and triangular sides that all meet at a common vertex. (p. 567)	**pirámide** Poliedro cuya base es un polígono y tiene caras triangulares que se juntan en un vértice común.	

Q

ENGLISH	SPANISH	EXAMPLES
quadrant The x- and y-axes divide the coordinate plane into four regions. Each region is called a quadrant. (p. 610)	**cuadrante** El eje de las x y el eje de las y dividen el plano cartesiano en cuatro regiones. Cada región recibe el nombre de cuadrante.	Quadrant II, Quadrant I, 0, Quadrant III, Quadrant IV
quadrilateral A four-sided polygon. (p. 442)	**cuadrilátero** Polígono de cuatro lados.	

ENGLISH	SPANISH	EXAMPLES
quotient The result when one number is divided by another.	**cociente** Resultado de dividir un número entre otro.	In 8 ÷ 4 = 2, 2 is the quotient.

R

ENGLISH	SPANISH	EXAMPLES
radius A line segment with one endpoint at the center of a circle and the other endpoint on the circle, or the length of that segment. (p. 520)	**radio** Segmento de recta con un extremo en el centro de un círculo y el otro en la circunferencia. También se llama radio a la longitud de ese segmento.	
range (in statistics) The difference between the greatest and least values in a data set. (p. 299)	**rango (en estadística)** Diferencia entre los valores máximo y mínimo de un conjunto de datos.	Data set: 3, 5, 7, 7, 12 Range: 12 − 3 = 9
rate A ratio that compares two quantities measured in different units. (p. 353)	**tasa** Una relación que compara dos cantidades medidas en diferentes unidades.	The speed limit is 55 miles per hour or 55 mi/h.
rate of interest The percent charged or earned on an amount of money; see *simple interest.* (p. 400)	**tasa de interés** Porcentaje que se cobra por una cantidad de dinero prestada o que se gana por una cantidad de dinero ahorrada; ver *interés simple.*	
ratio A comparison of two quantities by division. (p. 352)	**razón** Comparación de dos cantidades mediante una división.	12 to 25, 12:25, $\frac{12}{25}$
ray A part of a line that starts at one endpoint and extends forever. (p. 417)	**rayo** Parte de una línea que inicia en un extremo y se extiende de manera indefinida.	D
reciprocal One of two numbers whose product is 1. (p. 270)	**recíproco** Uno de dos números cuyo producto es igual a 1.	The reciprocal of $\frac{2}{3}$ is $\frac{3}{2}$.
rectangle A parallelogram with four right angles. (p. 442)	**rectángulo** Paralelogramo con cuatro ángulos rectos.	
rectangular prism A polyhedron whose bases are rectangles and whose other faces are rectangles.	**prisma rectangular** Poliedro cuyas bases son rectángulos y sus caras tienen forma de rectángulos.	
reflection A transformation of a figure that flips the figure across a line. (p. 459)	**reflexión** Transformación que ocurre cuando se voltea una figura sobre la línea de reflexión.	
regular polygon A polygon with congruent sides and angles. (p. 446)	**polígono regular** Polígono con lados y ángulos congruentes.	

ENGLISH	SPANISH	EXAMPLES
repeating decimal A decimal in which one or more digits repeat infinitely. (p. 182)	**decimal periódico** Decimal en el que uno o más dígitos se repiten de manera indefinida.	$0.75757575... = 0.\overline{75}$
rhombus A parallelogram with all sides congruent. (p. 442)	**rombo** Paralelogramo en el que todos los lados son congruentes.	
right angle An angle that measures 90°. (p. 421)	**ángulo recto** Ángulo que mide exactamente 90°.	
right triangle A triangle containing a right angle. (p. 437)	**triángulo rectángulo** Triángulo que tiene un ángulo recto.	
rotation A transformation in which a figure is turned around a point. (p. 459)	**rotación** Transformación que ocurre cuando una figura gira alrededor de un punto.	
rounding Replacing a number with an estimate of that number to a given place value.	**redondear** Sustituir un número por una estimación de ese número hasta cierto valor posicional.	2,354 rounded to the nearest thousand is 2,000; 2,354 rounded to the nearest 100 is 2,400.

S

ENGLISH	SPANISH	EXAMPLES
sales tax A percent of the cost of an item, which is charged by governments to raise money. (p. 394)	**impuesto sobre la venta** Porcentaje del precio de un artículo que los gobiernos cobran para recaudar fondos.	
sample A part of a group being surveyed. (p. 694)	**muestra** Parte de un grupo que es objeto de estudio.	In a survey about eating habits of middle school math students, a sample is a survey of 100 randomly-chosen students.
sample space All possible outcomes of an experiment. (p. 678)	**espacio muestral** Conjunto de todos los resultados posibles de un experimento.	When rolling a number cube, the sample space is 1, 2, 3, 4, 5, 6.
scale The ratio between two sets of measurements. (p. 374)	**escala** La razón entre dos conjuntos de medidas.	1 cm: 5 mi
scale drawing A drawing that uses a scale to make an object proportionally smaller than or larger than the real object. (p. 374)	**dibujo a escala** Dibujo que usa una escala para que un objeto se vea proporcionalmente mayor o menor que el objeto real al que representa.	A blueprint is an example of a scale drawing. (E, A, F, D, B, C, H, G)
scale model A proportional model of a three-dimensional object.	**modelo a escala** Modelo proporcional de un objeto tridimensional.	

ENGLISH	SPANISH	EXAMPLES
scalene triangle A triangle with no congruent sides. (p. 438)	**triángulo escaleno** Triángulo que no tiene lados congruentes.	
scientific notation A method of writing very large or very small numbers by using powers of 10. (p. 124)	**notación científica** Método que se usa para escribir números muy largos o muy pequeños mediante potencias de 10.	$12{,}560{,}000{,}000{,}000 = 1.256 \times 10^{13}$
segment A part of a line between two endpoints.	**segmento** Parte de una línea entre dos extremos.	*A* *B*
sequence An ordered list of numbers. (p. 33)	**sucesíon** Lista ordenada de números.	2, 4, 6, 8, 10, . . .
set A group of items. (p. 212)	**conjunto** Un grupo de elementos.	
side A line bounding a geometric figure; one of the faces forming the outside of an object.	**lado** Segmento de recta que delimita las figuras geométricas; una de las caras que forman la parte exterior de un objeto.	A B C D E Side
significant figures The figures used to express the precision of a measurement.	**dígitos significativos** Dígitos usados para expresar la exactitud de una medida.	
similar Figures with the same shape but not necessarily the same size are similar. (p. 366)	**semejantes** Figuras que tienen la misma forma, pero no necesariamente el mismo tamaño.	
simple interest A fixed percent of the principal. It is found using the formula $I = Prt$, where P represents the principal, r the rate of interest, and t the time. (p. 400)	**interés simple** Un porcentaje fijo del capital. Se calcula con la fórmula $I\ Crt$, donde C representa el capital, r, la tasa de interés, y t, el tiempo.	
simplest form (of a fraction) A fraction is in simplest form when the numerator and denominator have no common factors other than 1. (p. 187)	**mínima expresión (de una fracción)** Una fracción está en su mínima expresión cuando el numerador y el denominador no tienen más factor común que 1.	Fraction: $\frac{8}{12}$ Simplest form: $\frac{2}{3}$
simplify To write a fraction or expression in simplest form.	**simplificar** Escribir una fracción o expresión numérica en su mínima expresión.	
simulation A model of an experiment, often one that would be too difficult or too time-consuming to actually perform. (p. 562)	**simulación** Representación de un experimento, por lo regular de uno cuya realización sería demasiado difícil o llevaría mucho tiempo.	

ENGLISH	SPANISH	EXAMPLES

skew lines Lines that lie in different planes that are neither parallel nor intersecting. (p. 428)

líneas oblicuas Líneas que se encuentran en planos distintos, por eso no se intersecan ni son paralelas.

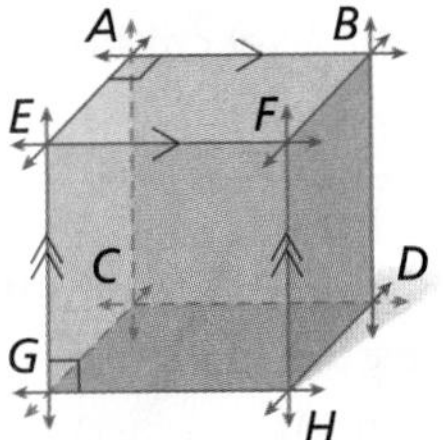

$\overleftrightarrow{AE}$ and $\overleftrightarrow{CD}$ are skew lines.

---

solid figure A three-dimensional figure.

figura sólida Figura tridimensional.

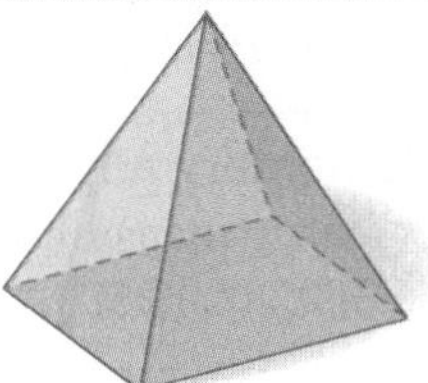

---

solution of an equation A value or values that make an equation true. (p. 70)

solución de una ecuación Valor o valores que hacen verdadera una ecuación.

Equation: $x + 2 = 6$
Solution: $x = 4$

---

solution of an inequality A value or values that make an inequality true. (p. 90)

solución de una desigualdad Valor o valores que hacen correcta una desigualdad.

Inequality: $x + 3 \geq 10$
Solution: $x \geq 7$

---

solve To find an answer or a solution.

resolver Hallar una respuesta o solución.

---

square (geometry) A rectangle with four congruent sides. (p. 442)

cuadrado (en geometría) Rectángulo con cuatro lados congruentes.

---

square (numeration) A number raised to the second power. (p. 14)

cuadrado (en numeración) Número elevado a la segunda potencia.

In 5^2, the number 5 is squared.

---

square number A number that is the product of a whole number and itself.

cuadrado de un número El producto de un número multiplicado por sí mismo.

25 is a square number since $5^2 = 25$.

---

square root One of the two equal factors of a number. (p. 645)

raíz cuadrada (en numeración) Uno de los dos factores iguales de un número.

$16 = 4 \cdot 4$ and $16 = 24 \cdot 24$, so 4 and -4 are square roots of 16.

---

standard form (in numeration) A number written using digits.

forma estándar (en numeración) Una forma de escribir números por medio de dígitos.

Five thousand, two hundred ten in standard form is 5,210.

---

stem-and-leaf plot A graph used to organize and display data so that the frequencies can be compared. (p. 330)

diagrama de tallo y hojas Gráfica que muestra y ordena los datos, y que sirve para comparar las frecuencias.

Stem	Leaves
3	2 3 4 4 7 9
4	0 1 5 7 7 7 8
5	1 2 2 3

Key: 3|2 means 3.2

---

straight angle An angle that measures 180°. (p. 421)

ángulo llano Ángulo que mide exactamente 180°.

ENGLISH	SPANISH	EXAMPLES
subset A set contained within another set. (p. 212)	**subconjunto** Conjunto que pertenece a otro conjunto.	
substitute To replace a variable with a number or another expression in an algebraic expression.	**sustituir** Reemplazar una variable por un número u otra expresión en una expresión algebraica.	
sum The result when two or more numbers are added.	**suma** Resultado de sumar dos o más números.	
supplementary angles Two angles whose measures have a sum of 180°. (p. 425)	**ángulos suplementarios** Dos ángulos cuyas medidas suman 180°.	30° 150°
surface area The sum of the areas of the faces, or surfaces, of a three-dimensional figure. (p. 582)	**área total** Suma de las áreas de las caras, o superficies, de una figura tridimensional.	12 cm, 6 cm, 8 cm Surface area = 2(8)(12) + 2(8)(6) + 2(12)(6) = 432 cm^2

T

ENGLISH	SPANISH	EXAMPLES
term (in a sequence) An element or number in a sequence. (p. 33)	**término (de una sucesión)** Elemento o número de una sucesión.	5 is the third term in the sequence 1, 3, 5, 7, 9, . . .
terminating decimal A decimal number that ends or terminates. (p. 182)	**decimal cerrado** Decimal con un número determinado de posiciones decimales.	6.75
tessellation A repeating pattern of plane figures that completely cover a plane with no gaps or overlaps. (p. 468)	**teselado** Patrón repetido de figuras planas que cubren totalmente un plano sin traslaparse ni dejar huecos.	
theoretical probability The ratio of the number of equally likely outcomes in an event to the total number of possible outcomes. (p. 682)	**probabilidad teórica** Razón del número de resultados igualmente probables en que puede ocurrir un suceso al número de resultados posibles.	When rolling a number cube, the theoretical probability of rolling a 4 is $\frac{1}{6}$.
tip The amount of money added to a bill for service; usually a percent of the bill. (p. 394)	**propina** Cantidad que se agrega al total de una factura por servicio. Por lo general, es un porcentaje del total de la factura.	
transformation A change in the size or position of a figure. (p. 459)	**transformación** Cambio en el tamaño o la posición de una figura.	Preimage, Image $\triangle ABC \rightarrow \triangle A'B'C'$

ENGLISH	SPANISH	EXAMPLES
translation A movement (slide) of a figure along a straight line. (p. 459)	**traslación** Desplazamiento de una figura a lo largo de una línea recta.	
trapezoid A quadrilateral with exactly one pair of parallel sides. (p. 442)	**trapecio** Cuadrilátero con un par de lados paralelos.	B C A D
tree diagram A branching diagram that shows all possible combinations or outcomes of an event. (p. 678)	**diagrama de árbol** Diagrama ramificado que muestra todas las posibles combinaciones o resultados de un suceso.	
triangle A three-sided polygon.	**triángulo** Polígono de tres lados.	
Triangle Sum Theorem The theorem that states that the measures of the angles in a triangle add to 180°.	**Teorema de la suma del triángulo** Teorema que establece que los ángulos de un triángulo suman 180°.	
triangular prism A polyhedron whose bases are triangles and whose other faces are rectangles.	**prisma triangular** Poliedro cuyas bases son triángulos y sus demás caras tienen forma de rectángulos.	

U

ENGLISH	SPANISH	EXAMPLES
underestimate An estimate that is less than the exact answer. (p. 10)	**estimación baja** Estimación menor que la respuesta exacta.	100 is an underestimate for the sum 26 + 29 + 31 + 27.
union The set of all elements that belong to two or more sets. (p. 212)	**unión** El conjunto de todos los elementos que pertenecen a dos o más conjuntos.	
unit conversion The process of changing one unit of measure to another.	**conversión de unidades** Proceso que consiste en cambiar una unidad de medición en otra.	
unit rate A rate in which the second quantity in the comparison is one unit. (p. 353)	**tasa unitaria** Una relación en donde la segunda cantidad de comparación es una unidad.	10 cm per minute
unlike fractions Fractions with different denominators. (p. 198)	**fracción distintas** Fracción con denominadores distintos.	$\frac{3}{4}$ and $\frac{1}{2}$ are unlike fractions.

ENGLISH	SPANISH	EXAMPLES

ENGLISH	SPANISH	EXAMPLES
variable A symbol used to represent a quantity that can change. (p. 54)	**variable** Letra o símbolo que representa una cantidad que puede cambiar.	In the expression $2x + 3$, x is the variable.
Venn diagram A diagram that is used to show relationships between sets. (p. 212)	**diagrama de Venn** Diagrama que sirve para ilustrar las relaciones entre conjuntos.	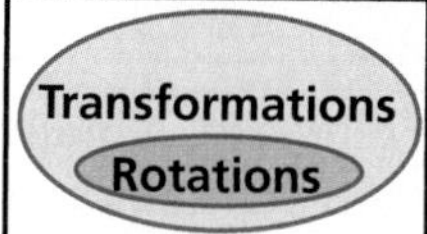
vertex On an angle or polygon, the point where two sides intersect. (p. 566)	**vértice** En un ángulo o polígono, el punto de intersección de dos lados	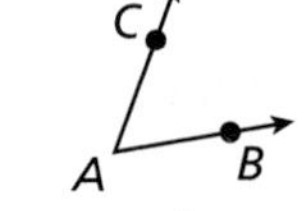 A is the vertex of $\angle CAB$.
vertical angles A pair of opposite congruent angles formed by intersecting lines. (p. 424)	**ángulos opuestos por el vértice** Par de ángulos opuestos congruentes formados por líneas secantes.	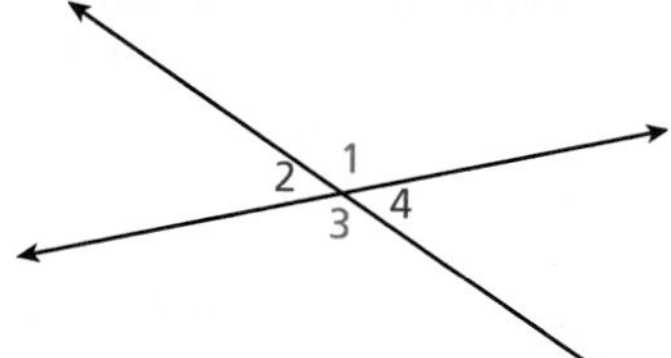 $\angle 1$ and $\angle 3$ are vertical angles. $\angle 2$ and $\angle 4$ are vertical angles.
volume The number of cubic units needed to fill a given space. (p. 572)	**volumen** Número de unidades cúbicas que se necesitan para llenar un espacio.	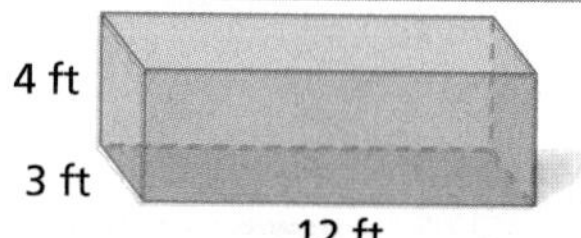 Volume $= 3 \cdot 4 \cdot 12 = 144$ ft^3

ENGLISH	SPANISH	EXAMPLES
***x*-axis** The horizontal axis on a coordinate plane. (p. 610)	**eje de las *x*** El eje horizontal del plano cartesiano.	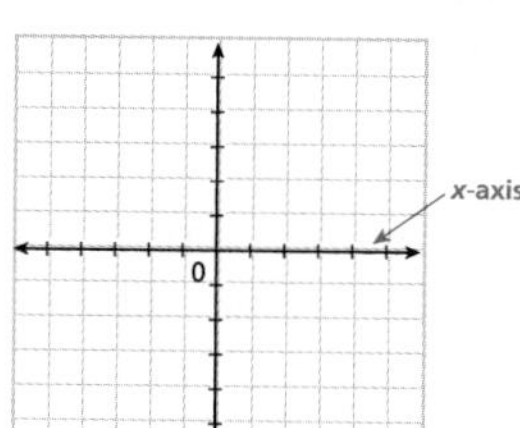
***x*-coordinate** The first number in an ordered pair; it tells the distance to move right or left from the origin, (0, 0). (p. 610)	**coordenada *x*** El primer número en un par ordenado; indica la distancia que debes avanzar hacia la izquierda o la derecha desde el origen, (0, 0).	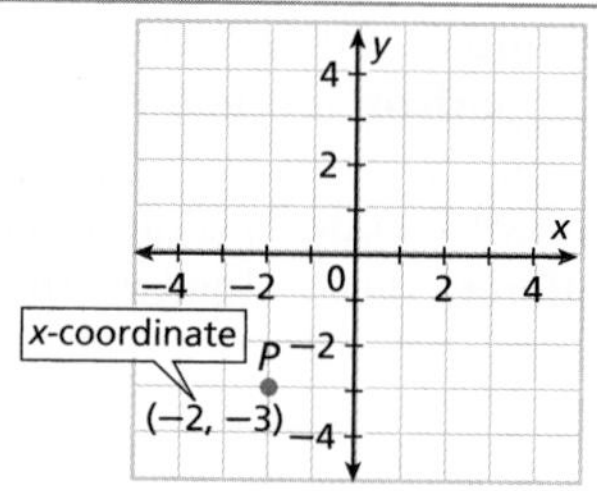

ENGLISH	SPANISH	EXAMPLES

y-axis The vertical axis on a coordinate plane. (p. 610)

eje de las y El eje vertical del plano cartesiano.

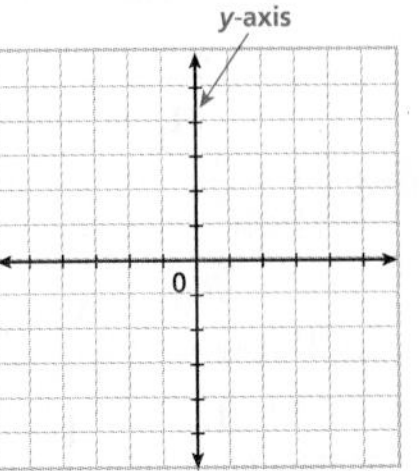

y-coordinate The second number in an ordered pair; it tells the distance to move up or down from the origin, (0, 0). (p. 610)

coordenada y El segundo número en un par ordenado; indica la distancia que debes avanzar hacia arriba o hacia abajo desde el origen, (0, 0).

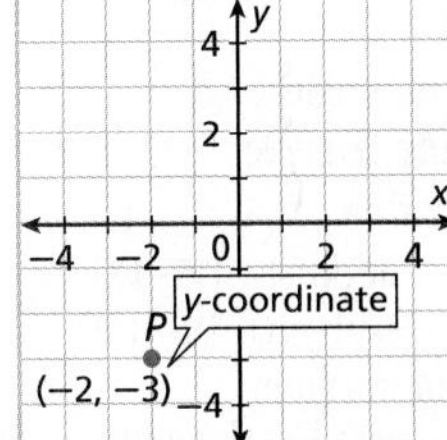

Z

zero pair A number and its opposite, which add to 0.

par nulo Un número y su opuesto, que sumados dan 0.

18 and −18

Index

Index

D

E

F

G

Index

H

I

Index

Index

N

Credits

Staff Credits

Bruce Albrecht, David Alvarado, Kimberley Cammerata, Henry Clark, Justin Collins, Lorraine Cooper, Marc Cooper, Jennifer Craycraft, Martize Cross, Grant Davidson, Nina Degollado, Sam Dudgeon, Kelli R. Flanagan, Ronald Fowler, Mary Fraser, Stephanie Friedman, Jeff Galvez, José Garza, Diannia Green, Jennifer Gribble, Liz Huckestein, Jevara Jackson, Cathy Kuhles, Jill M. Lawson, Jenifer Limb, Christine MacInnis, Jessika Maier, Jonathan Martindill, Virginia Messler, Susan Mussey, Kim Nguyen, Manda Reid, Patrick Ricci, Michael Rinella, Michelle Rumpf-Dike, Annette Saunders, John Saxe, Katie Seawell, Kay Selke, Robyn Setzen, Patricia Sinnott, Victoria Smith, Jeannie Taylor, Sherri Whitmarsh, Aimee F. Wiley, Alison Wohlman

Photo

Abbreviations used: (t) top, (c) center, (b) bottom, (l) left, (r) right, (bkgd) background

Master icons: teens (all), Sam Dudgeon/HRW; flowers (all), Georgia Department of Economic Development.

Author photos by Sam Dudgeon/HRW; Jan Scheer photo by Ron Shipper

Front Matter: Cover and ii, Arcaid/Alamy; Front Matter Borders Georgia Department of Economic Development; GA2 (t) Stamp Designs: ©2002, United Postal Service. Displayed with permission. All rights reserved. Written authorization from the Postal Service is required to use, reproduce, post, transmit, distribute, or publicly display these images; GA2 (tl) Georgia Department of Economic Development; vi Gary Randall/Getty Images/FPG International; vii Christian Michaels/Getty Images/FPG International; viii AP/Wide World Photos; ix Peter Van Steen/HRW; x Peter Van Steen/HRW; xi Charles W. Campbell/CORBIS; xii Ralph A. Clevenger/CORBIS; xiii Art by Jane Dixon/HRW; xiv Sam Dudgeon/HRW; xv Florian Monheim/age footstock; xvi Ernest Manewal/SuperStock; xvii SuperStock; xviii CORBIS/Brandon D. Cole; xix (t) Anna Clopet/CORBIS; xix (tr) corbisimages.com; xix (bl) Frank Siteman/Getty Images/Stone; xix (bc) Royalty-Free/Corbis; xix (br) Lloyd Sutton/Masterfile; xxii (tr) John Greim/Index Stock Imagery/PictureQuest; xxii (bl) Sam Dudgeon/HRW. **Chapter One:** 2 (br) Jeff Greenberg/MR/Photo Researchers, Inc.; 6 Steve Ewert Photography; 9 Image Source/elektraVision/PictureQuest; 11 (cr) Iowa State Fair; 11 (l) Georgia State Fair; 13 National Geographic Image 14 CORBIS/Bettmann; 17 CORBIS/Lester V. Bergman; 19 Michael Dunning/Getty Images/FPG International; 23 Sam Dudgeon/HRW; 25 National Geographic Image Collection/Kenneth Garrett; 26 (cr) © DINODIA/Art Directors & TRIP Photo Library; 26 (tr) Getty Images; 29 (c) Sam Dudgeon/HRW; 29 (r) PhotoDisc-Digital Image copyright © 2004 PhotoDisc; 29 (tl) C.K. Lorenz/Photo Researchers; 30 NASA; 31 Norm Lehrman; 33 Victoria Smith/HRW; 39 (tl) AP Photo/Amy Sancetta; 39 (b) Getty Images; 40 Jenny Thomas/HRW; 41 HRW **Chapter Two:** 50 (br) Peter Yang/HRW Photo; 50-51 (bkgd) ©Christian Michaels/Getty Images/FPG International; 57 United States Mint/Photo by Sam Dudgeon/HRW; 61 (tr) AP Photo/NASA; 61 (all patches) NASA; 65 Adam Woolfitt/CORBIS; 69 David A. Northcott/CORBIS; 71 CORBIS/Brandon D. Cole; 74 Franklin Jay Viola/Viola's Photo Visions; 77 Peter Yang/HRW; 78 (tl) Library of Congress; 78 (tr) AP Photo; 78 (bkgd) Corbis Images; 80 Rab Harling/Alamy; 81 ©National Geographic Image Collection/Bianca Lavies; 84 Darwin Dale/Photo Researchers, Inc.; 85 (c) Eric Kamp/Index Stock Imagery/PictureQuest; 85 (tr) Takeshi Takahara/Photo Researchers, Inc.; 89 NorthWind/NorthWind Picture Archives; 93 HRW; 100 (cr) George Hall/CORBIS; 100 (b) DoD/Roger-Viollet/The Image Works; 101 (c & b) Copyright 2005 by Phil Han; 101 (t) HAWKINS KEN/CORBIS SYGMA **Chapter Three:** 102 (br) Peter Yang/HRW Photo; 102-3 (bkgd) AP/Wide World Photos; 109 Jerry Schad/Photo Researchers, Inc.; 112 Cheryl Maeder/Getty Images/Stone; 115 Mark Tomalty/Masterfile; 118 AP Photo/John Russell; 121 AP Photo/Anderson Independent-Mail, Sarah Bates; 123 Peter Van Steen/HRW; 127 George Hall/Check Six; 130 NASA/Photo Researchers, Inc.; 131 Bettmann/CORBIS; 133 (tr) CORBIS; 133 (br) Bettmann/CORBIS; 134 HRW; 136 Victoria Smith/HRW; 137 Mark Gibson/Gibson Stock Photography; 140 Larry Stevens/Nawrocki Stock Photo; 141 Peter Yang/HRW; 144 CORBIS/Richard Hamilton Smith; 147 SuperStock; 149 Stockbyte Platinum/Alamy; 150 Jenny Thomas/HRW; 151 HRW **Chapter Four**: 160 (br) Digital Image copyright (c) 2004 PhotoDisc; 160-61 (bkgd) Peter Van Steen/HRW; 164 Darren Carroll/HRW; 167 Mike Norton/Animals Animals/Earth Scenes; 172 Frans Lanting/Minden Pictures; 174 PhotoEdit; 176 Frans Lanting/Minden Pictures; 179 Digital Image copyright © 2004 PhotoDisc; 181 Getty Images; 184 (cr) Pat Lanza/FIELD/Bruce Coleman, Inc.; 184 (tl) Getty I mages; 189 (tr) Bob Krist/CORBIS; 189 (cr) Wendell Metzen/Bruce Coleman, Inc.; 190 (t) Peter Van Steen/HRW; 191 (egg, shamrock, acorn, shell & rock) PhotoDisc-Digital Image copyright © 2004 PhotoDisc; 191 (key & penny) EyeWire-Digital Image copyright © 2005 EyeWire; 191 (cicada) Artville-Digital Image copyright © 2005 Artville; 192 Peter French/Bruce Coleman, Inc.; 195 (tl) Science Photo Library/Photo Researchers, Inc.; 195 (tr) Sam Dudgeon/HRW Photo; 197 Tom Brakefield/CORBIS; 198 Sam Dudgeon/HRW; 201 Peter Van Steen/HRW; 202 (tr) Mike Norton/Animals Animals/Earth Scenes; 202 (tc) Peter Van Steen/HRW; 205 Nora Good/Master File; 206 Daryl Benson; 207 SuperStock; 209 (tl) SuperStock; 209 (tr) Raymond A. Mendez/Animals Animals/Earth Scenes; 209 (tc) Mark Moffett/Minden Pictures; 214 Randall Hyman/HRW; 215 HRW; 222 Mark Gibson/Lonely Planet Images; 223 (t) Wild Adventures Theme Park,; Valdosta, Ga; 223 (cr) Winfred Wisniewski; Frank Lane Picture Agency/CORBIS; 223 (b) The Georgia Department of Economic Development **Chapter Five** 224-5 (bkgd) Peter Van Steen/HRW; 224 (br) Digital Image copyright (c) 2004 PhotoDisc; 228 (tr) Carl Yarbrough; 228 (c & b) Beverly Barrett/HRW; 231 Getty Images; 237 (tr) SuperStock; 237 (br) Gerry Ellis/Minden Pictures; 237 (cr) National Geographic Image Collection/Paul Chesley; 237 (cl) Eric Hosking/CORBIS; 238 Frans Lanting/Minden Pictures; 239 Frans Lanting/Minden Pictures; 241 Gerry Ellis/Minden Pictures; 248 Private Collection/Edmond Von Hoorick/SuperStock; 249 Alan Pitcairn/Grant Heilman Photography; 253 Maximilian Stock Ltd./FoodPix; 257 David Ryan/Photo 20-20/PictureQuest; 263 ©Merlin D. Tuttle/Bat Conservation International; 264 Ken Karp/HRW; 265 Beverly Barrett/HRW; 270 Victoria Smith/HRW; 273 Allen Blake Sheldon/Animals Animals/Earth Scenes; 274 Lori Grinker/Contact Press Images/PictureQuest; 275 (tr) Beverly Barrett/HRW; 275 (cl) © Royalty-Free/Corbis; 277 Frans Lanting/Minden Pictures; 279 Jell Kelly; 280 Ken Karp/HRW; 281 HRW **Chapter Six:** 290 (br) CORBIS; 290-91 (bkgd) Charles W. Campbell/CORBIS; 294 (tr) Reuters NewMedia Inc./CORBIS; 294 (bl) Carl and Ann Purcell/Index Stock Imagery, Inc.; 298 Jenny Thomas Photography/HRW; 301 Stockdisc Classic/Alamy; 302 (tr) Trent Nelson/The Salt Lake Tribune/CORBIS Sygma; 302 (cl) AFP PHOTO/George FREY/Corbis; 305 (tr) NASA/Science Photo Library/Photo Researchers, Inc.; 307 (bc) Victoria & Albert Museum/Art Resource, NY; 307 (br) U.S. Department of the Interior, National Park Service, Edison National Historic Site; 307 (bl) Index Stock/Alamy Photos; 307 (l) Pintail Pictures/Alamy Photos; 308 (cr) Tim Davis/Photo Researchers, Inc.; 308 (tr) Dr. Eckart Pott/Bruce Coleman, Inc.; 308 (t) SuperStock; 308 (l) Sharon Smith/Bruce Coleman, Inc.; 314 (l) Leonard Lessin/Peter Arnold; 314 (c) Federal Bureau of Investigation; 314 (r) Archive Photos; 317 Roland Seitre/Peter Arnold, Inc.; 319 Lloyd Sutton/Master File; 322 ©Bettmann/CORBIS; 325 GK Hart/Vikki Hart/Getty Images; 326 (cr) Shane Young/AP/Wide World Photos; 326 (c) BrandX Pictures; 326 (tr) David Madison/Bruce Coleman, Inc.; 329 John Bavosi/Science Photo Library/Photo Researchers, Inc.; 330 Bryan Berg; 335 Getty Images; 337 Travel Line/Alamy; 338 Randall Hyman/HRW; 339 HRW; 346 (br) DAVID NOBLE PHOTOGRAPHY/Alamy; 346 (bl) Dennis MacDonald\PhotoEdit, Inc.; 347 (t) James L. Amos/CORBIS; 347 (br) Terrance Klassen/Alamy; 347 (cr) New York Public Library **Chapter Seven:** 348 (br) Beth Davidow; 348 (bkgd) Ralph A. Clevenger/CORBIS; 352 Reuters NewMedia Inc./CORBIS; 356 AP Photo/Big Lots, Rene Macura; 359 Bettmann/CORBIS; 365 (tr) Ronald Zak/AP/Wide World Photos; 365 (tl) Imapress/Jean Claude N'Diaye/The Image Works; 365 (cr) AFP/CORBIS; 365 (cl) Jon Bower/Alamy Photos; 367 Mary Cassatt, The Boating Party, Chester Dale Collection, Photograph © 2002 Board of Trustees, National Gallery of Art, Washington. 1893/1894, oil on canvas; 368 Jenny Thomas/HRW; 370 Sharon McNeill/Bethel Area Chamber of Commerce; 371 Pat & Chuck Blackley; 374 (l) National Geographic Image Collection; 374 (tr) Kerrick James/Getty Images/Stone; 374 (cr) W. Perry Conway/CORBIS; 376 (b) E. R. Degginger/Bruce Coleman, Inc.; 381 Jenny Thomas/HRW Photo; 384 Michelle Bridwell/PhotoEdit/PictureQuest; 388 Bettman/CORBIS; 390 Sam Dudgeon/HRW; 393 Philip Gould/CORBIS; 394 (t) Peter Van Steen/HRW; 394 (tl) J. & P. Wegner/Animals Animals/Earth Scenes; 397 Sam Dudgeon/HRW; 399 Foodfolio/Alamy; 402 (br) Ken Karp/HRW; 402 (c) Mimmo Jodice/CORBIS; 402 (cl) Massimo Listri/CORBIS; 402 (cr) Gianni Dagli Orti/CORBIS; 403 HRW **Chapter Eight:** 412 (br) ©Zhi Xiong China Tourism Press/Getty Images/The Image Bank; 412-13 (bkgd) Art by Jane Dixon/HRW; 420 Courtesy of Icon Health Fitness; 423 Robin Nelson/PhotoEdit, Inc.; 424 (c) Michael Kelley/Getty Images/Stone; 424 (b) TempSport/CORBIS; 426 (tl) Peter Van Steen/HRW; 426 (tr) Peter Van Steen/HRW; 426 (cl) Werner Forman Archive/Piers Morris Collection/Art Resource, NY; 426 (cr) P. W. Grace/Photo Researchers, Inc.; 426 (tc) Peter Van Steen/HRW; 428 Walter Bibikow/Index Stock Imagery/PictureQuest; 429 (tl) Emmanuel Faure/SuperStock; 429 (tr) Peter Van Steen/HRW;

All teacher-to-teacher photos courtesy of the teachers.

429 (cl) ImageState/Alamy Photos; 429 (cr) Peter Van Steen/HRW; 437 (br) Bob Krist/CORBIS; 437 (cr) Peter Van Steen/HRW; 437 (r) Peter Van Steen/HRW; 442 Digital Image (c) The Museum of Modern Art/Licensed by SCALA/Art Resource, NY; 445 (tl) David Forbert/SuperStock; 446 (cl & bl) PhotoDisc-Digital Image copyright © 2004 PhotoDisc; 446 (t) Index Stock/Alamy; 447 PhotoDisc-Digital Image copyright © 2004 PhotoDisc; 448 (tl) Beverly Barrett/HRW; 448 (tc) Peter Van Steen/HRW; 448 (tr) Peter Van Steen/HRW; 448 (bl) Eric Grave/Science Source/Photo Researchers, Inc.; 448 (bc) M. Abbey/Photo Researchers, Inc.; 448 (br) Kim Taylor/Bruce Coleman/PictureQuest; 450 Lowe Art Museum, The University of Miami/SuperStock; 451 Peter Van Steen/HRW; 452 Peter Van Steen/HRW; 453 Steve Vidler/SuperStock; 455 Michael Boys/CORBIS; 456 Ken Karp/HRW Photo; 458 Original Artwork © "Sunflowers" by Mary Backer/Sam Dudgeon/HRW Photo; 462 Sam Dudgeon/HRW; 464 John Greim/Index Stock Imagery/PictureQuest; 467 (cr) corbisimages.com; 467 (t) Anna Clopet/CORBIS; (tl) Victoria Smith/HRW; 471 (b) Digital Vision/Getty Images; 473 HRW; 480 Wesleyan College; 481 (b) Jerry Driendl Photography/Panoramic Images; 481 (tr) BRUCE COLEMAN INC./Alamy; 481 (br) Chris Schluter/Emporis **Chapter Nine:** 482 (bkgd) Sam Dudgeon/HRW; 482 (br) V. C. L./Getty Images/FPG International; 489 (b) HRW; 490 HRW; 491 Winchester Cathedral, Hampshire, UK,/Bridgeman Art Library; 493 HRW; 494 (t) Photonica/Getty Images; 494 (b) Siede Preis/Getty Images; 495 Ron Sherman.com-All Rights Reserved; 496 Michael Steele/Getty Images; 499 Pierre Gleizes/Still Pictures; 500 AP Photo/Alessandro Trovati; 503 (tr) Robert Harding Picture Library Ltd/Alamy; 503 (tc) Taxi/Getty Images; 504 Alan Copson City Pictures/Alamy; 507 (cr) Alan Schein Photography/CORBIS; 507 (tr) Michael S. Yamashita/CORBIS; 507 (br) Lonely Planet Images/Getty Images; 507 (t) Travel-Shots/Alamy; 509 Nic Hamilton/Alamy; 510 Royalty-Free/Corbis; 513 AP Photo/Fabio Muzzi; 514 (tr) Courtesy of Sigma Tau Pharmaceuticals, Inc.; 514 (b) Victoria Smith/HRW; 516 (tr) Barry L. Runk/Grant Heilman Photography; 516 (br) PhotoDisc-Digital Image copyright © 2004 PhotoDisc; 520 Masterfile; 523 Mark McKeown/The Paris News/AP/Wide World Photos; 527 (tl) Stone/Getty Images; 527 (b) Jean Carter/AGE FotoStock; 528 Tim Davis/HRW Photo; 529 HRW **Chapter Ten:** 538 (bl) Sam Dudgeon/HRW Photo; 538-9 (bkgd) Florian Monheim/age fotostock; 541 HRW; 542 Larry Lefever/Grant Heilman Photography; 545 (tr) William Hamilton/SuperStock; 545 (c) NASA/Science Source/Photo Researchers, Inc.; 546 Raymond Patrick/Taxi/Getty Images; 549 Shirley Richards/SuperStock; 554 Kwame Zikomo/SuperStock; 558 Getty Images; 561 (r) William Sallez/Duomo/CORBIS; 561 (l) Getty Images; 563 Omni Photo Communications Inc./Index Stock Imagery/PictureQuest; 566 With permission from the Isamu Noguchi Foundation Inc., NY © Michael S. Yamashita/CORBIS; 567 (c) Sam Dudgeon/HRW; 567 (b) Peter Van Steen/HRW; 568 (cl) Barry L. Runk/Grant Heilman Photography; 568 (c & cr) Charles D. Winters/Photo Researchers, Inc.; 569 (cl) Richard Cummins/CORBIS; 569 (c) Joseph Sohm; ChromoSohm Inc./CORBIS; 569 (cr) Hisham Ibrahim/CORBIS; 572 HRW; 573 Sam Dudgeon/HRW; 575 (tr) TEK Image/Science Photo Library/Photo Researchers, Inc.; 575 (c) Runk/Schoenberger/Grant Heilman Photography; 575 (br) Charles D. Winters/Photo Researchers, Inc.; 576 (r) U.S. Department of the Interior, National Park Service, Edison National Historic Site; 576 (tr) LOC/Science Source/Photo Researchers, Inc.; 579 Andrew Lambert Photography/Photo Researchers, Inc; 585 (tl) Mark C. Burnett/Photo Researchers, Inc.; 585 (r) Peter Van Steen/HRW; 587 (l) NASA; 587 (r) CORBIS; 588 Tim Davis/HRW Photo; 589 HRW; 596 (cr) James Randklev/CORBIS; 596 (br) Flip Schulke/CORBIS; 597 (t & cr) Andre Jenny/Alamy; 597 (b) Gary W. Carter/CORBIS **Chapter Eleven:** 598 (br) Peter Yang/HRW; 598-9 (bkgd) Ernest Manewal/SuperStock; 602 (tl) CORBIS/Bill Ross; 602 (tr) Patrick J. Endres/AlaskaPhotographics.com; 605 National Geographic Image Collection/Emory Kristof; 606 CORBIS/AFP; 607 Chris Trotman/Duomo Photography; 615 AFP/CORBIS; 617 CORBIS/Douglas Peebles; 620 Getty Images; 625 Dennis Degnan/CORBIS; 627 Taxi/Getty Images; 628 AP/Wide World Photos; 631 (cr) Francisco Marquez; 631 (tr) Jacana/Photo Researchers, Inc; 633 Garry Black/Masterfile; 639 Stephen Frink/CORBIS; 646 Ken Karp/HRW; 649 Simon Fraser/MRC Unit, Newcastle General Hospital/Science Photo Library/Photo Researchers, Inc.; 651 (tl) Dorling Kindersley; 651 (b) The Image Bank/Getty Images; 652 AP Photo/The Norwich Bulletin, John Shishmanian; 654 Jenny Thomas/HRW; 655 HRW **Chapter Twelve:** 664 (br) Bill Varie/CORBIS; 664-5 (bkgd) SuperStock; 671 TEK Image/Science Photo Library/Photo Researchers, Inc.; 672 EyeWire-Digital Image copyright © 2004 EyeWire; 674 (cl & c) EyeWire-Digital Image copyright © 2004 EyeWire; 674 (cr & l) Sam Dudgeon/HRW; 683 Peter Van Steen/HRW; 685 CORBIS; 687 Jason Hawkes/Getty Images/Stone; 688 Dynamic Graphics Group/i2i/Alamy; 689 Digital Image copyright © 2004 EyeWire; 691 (r) Pat Doyle/CORBIS; 694 The Old Farmer's Almanac* and Design Mark* are used with permission of Yankee Publishing Inc., Dublin, New Hampshire; 691 (l) Terry W. Eggers/CORBIS; 697 (tr) Jeff Curtes/CORBIS; 697 (tl) Yvette Cardozo/Index Stock Imagery/PictureQuest; 697 (t) Richard T. Nowitz/CORBIS; 697 (r) Reuters NewMedia Inc./CORBIS; 699 (t) Stockdisc/Superstock; 699 (b) Gail Mooney/Masterfile; 702 Ken Karp/HRW; 703 HRW; 706 Digital Image copyright © 2004 EyeWire; 707 Stockbyte-four food images; frame-Victoria Smith/HRW; 710 (t) NGCSU University Relations; 710 (b, bl & br) Gold Rush Gallery; 711 (t) James Randklev/CORBIS; 711 (cr) Dale C. Spartas/CORBIS; 711 (c) PhotoDisc/Getty Images **Back Matter:** 712 John Langford/HRW; 713 Sam Dudgeon/HRW; 739 © Pictor/Alamy Photos; 740 (c) Victoria Smith/HRW; 740 (br) Sam Dudgeon/HRW; 740 (bl) Sam Dudgeon/HRW; 741 (tr) © Charles Gupton/CORBIS; 742 (tr) Victoria Smith/HRW; 743 (tr) Victoria Smith/HRW; 743 (tr) Victoria Smith/HRW; 743 (tr) Victoria Smith/HRW; 745 Cleo Freelance Photography/Painet Inc.; 746 (tr) Sam Dudgeon/HRW; 746 (cl) Victoria Smith/HRW; 746 (bl) Victoria Smith/HRW.

Table of Measures

METRIC

Length

1 kilometer (km) = 1,000 meters (m)
1 meter = 10 decimeters (dm)
1 meter = 100 centimeters (cm)
1 meter = 1,000 millimeters (mm)
1 centimeter = 10 millimeters

Capacity

1 liter (L) = 1,000 milliliters (mL)

Mass and Weight

1 kilogram (kg) = 1,000 grams (g)
1 gram = 1,000 milligrams (mg)

CUSTOMARY

Length

1 mile (mi) = 1,760 yards (yd)
1 mile = 5,280 feet (ft)
1 yard = 3 feet
1 yard = 36 inches (in.)
1 foot = 12 inches

Capacity

1 gallon (gal) = 4 quarts (qt)
1 gallon = 16 cups (c)
1 gallon = 128 fluid ounces (fl oz)
1 quart = 2 pints (pt)
1 quart = 4 cups
1 pint = 2 cups
1 cup = 8 fluid ounces

Mass and Weight

1 ton (T) = 2,000 pounds (lb)
1 pound = 16 ounces (oz)

TIME

1 year (yr) = 365 days
1 year = 12 months (mo)
1 year = 52 weeks (wk)
1 leap year = 366 days

1 week = 7 days
1 day = 24 hours (hr)
1 hour = 60 minutes (min)
1 minute = 60 seconds (s)